HANDBOOK OF
ORGANOMETALLIC COMPOUNDS

HANDBOOK OF
ORGANOMETALLIC COMPOUNDS

Editors-in-Chief

NOBUE HAGIHARA
Osaka University

MAKOTO KUMADA
Kyoto University

ROKURO OKAWARA
Osaka University

*Translated from the Japanese Edition published by
the Asakura Publishing Company, Ltd., Tokyo, Japan*

W. A. Benjamin, Inc.

New York   1968   Amsterdam

HANDBOOK OF ORGANOMETALLIC COMPOUNDS

Library of Congress Catalog Card Number 68-31355
Manufactured in the United States of America
12345K321098

W. A. Benjamin, Inc.
New York, New York 10016

PREFACE

In recent years the chemistry of organometallic compounds has been one of the most rapidly expanding of all the branches of chemistry. During the past decade organometallic chemistry has advanced into every corner of the field and has become important to researchers in a number of areas. In 1962 The Division of Organometallics of Kinki Society of Chemical Industry published "Organo-metallic Chemistry and Its Applications," which introduced recent advances in the field, and in the past few years many excellent monographs have appeared.

There remained, however, a need for a general handbook which could be used for reference in both academic and industrial laboratories. The present volume, laboriously compiled by the contributors and editors, and with the particular assistance of the Asakura Publishing Company, is an attempt to satisfy that need.

The principal part of this book consists of data and includes the organic compounds of both nontransition and transition metals. Preceding each section of tables is a short descriptive section on general properties of the group of metals under discussion, to aid the reader in understanding the nature of the individual compounds. Part II is a glossary of terms frequently encountered in organometallic chemistry.

Although some arbitrariness was unavoidable in the selection of compounds, selection was based on the two criteria of fundamental importance and frequency of use. It was anticipated from the beginning that the section on organosilicon compounds would occupy an unusally large proportion of the volume. The number of compounds included has been restricted to 1700 for balance. Dr. Post provided a large number of tables for the silicon compounds, but many had to be excluded for this reason.

Five years have passed since the beginning of this project, and in that time organometallic chemistry has seen still further advances, most particularly in the field of transition metal chemistry. We have taken advantage of the publication of this English edition to supplement and up-date the original material in order to remain abreast of recent developments.

S. Murahashi

EDITORIAL STAFFS

AUTHORS

Saburo Fuji   Faculty of Science, Osaka Univ. (Present: Mitsui Pertrochemical Ind.),

Masaoki Furue   Faculty of Science, Osaka Univ., M. Sci.

Kazuko Hayashi   Government Industrial Research Institute, Osaka

Masaru Hojo   Faculty of Engineering, Kyoto Univ., Associate Prof., Dr. Eng.

Shohei Inoue   Faculty of Engineering, Univ. of Tokyo, Associate Prof., Dr. Eng.

Mitsuo Ishikawa   Faculty of Engineering, Kyoto Univ., Instructor, Dr. Eng.

Michihiro Ishimori   Fuculty of Engineering, Univ. of Tokyo, Research Associate, Dr. Eng.

Osamu Itoh   Faculty of Engineering, Kyoto Univ., Research Associate

Jun Iyoda   Government Industrial Research Institute, Osaka

Nariyoshi Kawabata   Faculty of Engineering, Kyoto Univ., Research Associate Dr. Eng.

Katsuhiko Kawakami   Faculty of Engineering, Osaka Univ.

Yoshikane Kawasaki   Faculty of Engineering, Osaka Univ., Instructor, Dr. Eng

Michihiro Komura   Faculty of Engineering, Osaka Univ.

Hideo Kurosawa   Faculty of Engineering, Osaka Univ.

Yutaka Maeda   Mitsubishi Rayon Co. Ltd., M. Sci.

Gen'etsu MATSUBAYASHI Faculty of Engineering, Osaka Univ.

Yoshio MATSUMURA Faculty of Engineering, Osaka Univ.

Koji MIMURA Faculty of Engineering, Kyoto Univ., M. Eng.

Tadashi NARITA Faculty of Engineering, Univ. of Tokyo, M. Eng.

Koji NODA Nitto Electric Industrial Co. Ltd.

Mitsuaki OHARA Faculty of Engineering, Osaka Univ.

Howard W. POST State Univ. of New York, Prof., Ph. D.

Hideki SAKURAI Faculty of Engineering, Kyoto Univ., Associate Prof., Dr. Sci.

Mizuo SHINDO Faculty of Engineering, Osaka Univ.

Kenkichi SONOGASHIRA Institute of Scientific and Industrial Research, Osaka Univ., Research Associate, Dr. Sci.

Masakazu SUAMA Faculty of Engineering, Kyoto Univ., Research Associate

Shigetoshi TAKAHASHI Institute of Scientific and Industrial Research. Osaka Univ., M. Sci.

Ryuichiro TSUMURA Central Research Laboratory, Toyo Koatsu Industries Inc.

Akira UMEHARA Faculty of Science, Osaka Univ., Research Associate

Masanori WADA Faculty of Engineering, Osaka Univ., Instructor, Dr. Eng.

Haruyuki WATANABE Shionogi Research Laboratory, Shionogi & Co. Ltd., Section Head, Dr. Sci.

Keiji YAMAMOTO Faculty of Engineering, Kyoto Univ., Instructor, Dr. Eng.

Hiroshi YAMAZAKI Institute of Scientific and Industrial Research, Osaka Univ., Associate Prof., Dr. Sci.

Kiyoshi YASUDA Takeda Chemical Institute, Dr. Eng.

Yoshiro YASUDA Faculty of Engineering, Univ. of Tokyo, M. Eng.

Michio YONEYAMA Faculty of Engineering, Univ. of Tokyo, M. Eng.

EXPLANATORY NOTES

(1) Compounds are listed by groups of the periodic table.

The typical metals appear first, followed by the pseudotransition metals and then transition metals. Individual compounds are listed by formula, in the order of increasing numbers of metal, carbon, hydrogen, and other elements (the last mentioned are in alphabetical order).

(2) Tables of compounds contain the following items in this order.

Formula (printed in Gothic letters)

1 : Name

Rational or structural formula

2 : Methods of preparation

3 : Properties

Appearance. (Boiling point). [Melting point]. Refractive index. Density. Solubility. Stability. Other physical data.

4 : Reactivity

5 : Uses

6 : References

(3) Abbreviations of periodicals and books.

Special abbreviations used in this book are as follows. Others are abbreviated as in *Chemical Abstracts*.

Angew.	Angewandte Chemie
BCSJ	Bulletin of the Chemical Society of Japan
CA	Chemical Abstracts
Dokl.	Doklady Akademii Nauk S. S. S. R.
Izv. OKhN	Izvestiya Akademii Nauk S. S. S. R., Otdelenie Khimicheskikh Nauk
Izv. SKh	Izvestiya Akademii Nauk S. S. S. R., Ser. Khim.
JACS	The Journal of American Chemical Society
JCS	Journal of Chemical Society
JINC	Journal of Inorganic and Nuclear Chemistry
JOC	The Journal of Organic Chemistry
JOM	Journal of Organometallic Chemistry
Zhur.	Zhurnal Obshchei Khimii
Brauer	G. Brauer, "Handbuch der präparative anorganische Chemie" (1954)
Coates	G. E. Coates, "Organometallic Compounds", Methuen,

London (1960)

Eaborn	C. Eaborn, "Organosilicon Compounds", Butterworths (1960)
Kaufman	H. C. Kaufman, "Handbook of Organometallic Chemistry" (1961)
Kharasch, Reinmuth	M. S. Kharasch and O. Reinmuth, "Grignard Reactions of Nonmetallic Substances", Constable & Co. (1954)
Kosolapoff	G. M. Kosolapoff, "Organophosphorus Compounds", John Wiley, New York (1958)
Krause, Grosse	E. Krause and A. V. Grosse, "Die Chemie der Metall-organischen Verbindungen", Borntraeger (1937)
Post	H. Post, "Silicones and Other Organic Silicon Compounds", Reinhold Publ. Co., New York (1949)
Sidgwick	H. V. Sidgwick, "The Chemical Elements and Their Compounds", Oxford (1950)
Whitmore	F. C. Whitmore, "Organic Compounds of Mercury", The Chemical Catalog Co. (1921)

CONTENTS

I.

Tables of Organometallic Compounds

1. Organic Compounds of Alkali Metals
(Li, Na, K, Rb, Cs)

1.1. Introduction

Alkali metals (Li, Na, K, Rb, Ca, Fr) are group Ia elements of the periodic table and have just one s electron outside the rare gas structures. The closed shell effectively screens influence of the nucleus permitting the valence electron to be released easily; therefore alkali metals are apt to combine with electronegative elements (for example, C, N, O, Cl) to form compounds having ionic bonds(M^+C^-, M^+Cl^-, etc.). Typical properties of alkali metals are given in Table 1.1.

Table 1.1 *Properties of the Alkali Metals.*

Property	Li	Na	K	Rb	Cs
Atomic number	3	11	19	37	55
Electronic configuration	$1s^2\,2s^1$	$2s^2\,2p^6\,3s^1$	$3s^2\,3p^6\,4s^1$	$4s^2\,4p^6\,5s^1$	$5s^2\,5p^6\,6s^1$
Atomic weight	6.939	22.9898	39.102	85.47	132.905
Atomic radius (Å)	1.33	1.57	2.03	2.16	2.35
Ionic radius (Å)	0.78	0.98	1.33	1.48	1.69
Electronegativity	1.0	0.9	0.8	0.8	0.7
Ionization potential (eV)	5.390	5.138	4.339	4.176	3.893
Heat of hydration of gaseous ion (kcal/mole)	123	97	77	70	63
Electrode potential (volts)	−3.02	−2.71	−2.92	−2.99	−3.02
Bond energy for gas molecules M_2 (kcal/mole)	27.2	17.5	11.8	11.3	10.4
Bond distance for gas molecules M_2 (Å)	2.67	3.08	3.91	——	4.55

As is expected from Table 1.1, simple alkyl and aryl derivatives of sodium, potassium, rubidium, and cesium have a highly ionic metal-carbon bond, M^+-C^-, and are very reactive. They are colorless solid compounds, insoluble in most organic solvents, and on heating decompose without melting. For lithium compounds, however, considerable covalent character can be anticipated from the bond energy of the gaseous molecule Li_2(Table 1.1), which means that lithium is more like magnesium (diagonal similarities) than it is like the other alkali metals. In fact, simple alkyllithiums have highly covalent character and are liquids, which are readily soluble in ether and hydrocarbons and can be distilled without any decomposition.

Although organoalkali compounds had long been known as intermediates of Wurtz and some other related reactions, the first successful synthesis was reported in 1930 on alkyllithiums from alkyl halides and lithium metal. Alkylsodiums were first prepared by the reaction of dialkylmercuries or dialkylzincs and sodium, and, later by Gilman, directly from alkyl halides and sodium.

At present, direct use of these organoalkali compounds is limited to catalysts for polymerization of olefins, among which alkyl-lithiums, -sodiums and -potassiums are of practical value. Potential importance of these compounds can be found, however, in their use as intermediates for the synthesis of various kinds of organometallic compounds involving, for example, B, Mg, Al, Si, Ge, Pb, Sn, Sb, and Bi. Derivatives of rubidium and cesium are interesting only from the academic point of view and have no practical use.

1.2. Classification and Nomenclature

On the basis of covalent or ionic character of the carbon–metal bond, organo-alkali compounds may be conveniently classified as follows: (1) Compounds having almost-covalent M–C bonds, for example, alkyllithiums, alkenyllithiums, and aryl-lithiums; (2) Intermediary compounds between (1) and (3), for example, ben-zyllithium and triphenylmethyllithium; (3) Compounds having almost-ionic M–C bonds, for example, potassium cyclopentadienide. This classification is, of course, based on convenience. The boundaries are not so clear and the same compound may be sometimes classified differently. Acetylides of alkali metals and aromatic anion–radicals will be mentioned in Section 1.1.5 (related compounds).

Compounds which belong to (1) and (2) are called, for example, butyllithium, vinyllithium, benzylsodium, etc., on the basis of the reasoning that the metal-carbon bond is covalent. Compounds classified in (3) are called, for instance, lithium cyclopentadienide, suitable to the ionic bonds involved and to their salt-like character. However these names are again used somewhat arbitrarily, the boun-daries being not definite theoretically. In the case of alkali salts of active methylene compounds, they are named, as an example, sodiomalonate. The addition compound of sodium to naphthalene (radical anion) is usually called sodium naphthalenide, without any distinction from the substitution products such as cyclopentadienides.

1.3. Methods of Synthesis

Organoalkali compounds are very sensitive towards moisture in the air, oxygen, and carbon dioxide. At elevated temperatures, they react even with nitrogen and decompose spontaneously. Much attention should be paid to these points when one wishes to prepare these compounds. Most of the organoalkali compounds, especially in cases other than lithium compounds, are not ordinarily submitted to isolation but are used at once. Frequently they are not identified and used simply as reaction intermediates.

Synthesis of organoalkali compounds may be divided into two methods according to the source of the metals, that is, (1) methods in which relevant metals are used directly for the synthesis, and (2) indirect methods ·in which the desired organoalkali compounds are made by the use of other organoalkali compounds which are more readily available. Since method (2) makes use of the products of method (1), it is suitable for synthesis on a laboratory scale, and, of course, should be mentioned in the section on chemical properties of the organoalkali compounds. Hence, explanation given here will center on the direct method (1), and the indirect method (2) shall be treated only briefly.

1.3.1. Direct Methods Using Alkali Metals

(i) *Addition of Alkali Metals to Unsaturated Bonds.* Alkali metals add to carbon–carbon double bonds, for example

$$PhCH=CHPh + 2\,Li \longrightarrow PhCHLiCHLiPh$$

This reaction occurs in the order K < Na < Li and proceeds the more readily, the more strongly conjugated is the double bond. This process finds its industrial application in the sequence of reactions, butadiene $\longrightarrow$ disodiobutadiene $\longrightarrow$ isosebacic acid. Additions to C=O and C=N double bonds are also well-known.

(ii) *Metal–Hydrogen Exchange.* In those compounds which contain active hydrogen, RH (those which can produce a stable anion R^- by loss of a proton), metal–hydrogen exchange occurs very easily and hydrogen gas is evolved. For example, alkali compounds of ethyl malonate and triphenylmethane are prepared in this manner. The reaction takes place conveniently in such solvents as tetrahydrofuran and dimethylformamide; alkali compounds of cyclopentadiene, indene, fluorene, etc., are prepared in these solvents. This reaction proceeds much more easily in liquid ammonia. Acetylides are made using this solvent, the only exception being lithium acetylides to which metalation with *n*-butyllithium must be applied.

(iii) *Metal–Metal Exchange.* Although organoalkali compounds are ordinarily used without isolation (as in the case of the Grignard reaction), if one wishes to use them in the absence of any other materials, if one is obliged to isolate them in a pure state, or if one wants to get organo-potassium, -rubidium, or -cesium compounds which are not obtainable by the reaction (iv) of alkyl halides with the corresponding alkali metals, then the metal–metal exchange reaction becomes a useful method. For example,

$$R_2Hg + 2\,M(\text{excess}) \longrightarrow 2\,RM + Hg(\text{amalgam})$$

It is practical to use an excess of alkali metals and to carry out the reaction in a hydrocarbon as solvent, in order to bring the reaction to completion and to minimize the unreacted materials. The reaction proceeds just by shaking. Start and progress of the reaction can be easily recognized by the precipitation of alkali metal amalgams. Technically some devices are used; glass fragments are added to the reaction mixture in order to keep the metal surface in good contact with the solution. Mercury compounds are most frequently used for this purpose, but other organometallic compounds can also be used, for example,

$$C_6H_5CH_2MgCl + 2\,Li \longrightarrow C_6H_5CH_2Li + Mg$$

(iv) *Metal–Halogen Exchange.* This reaction is of the same type as used for

$$RX + 2M \longrightarrow RM + MX$$

the preparation of the Grignard reagent, and can be carried out almost in the same manner. Nowadays this reaction is the commonest method of access to the organoalkali compounds. Petroleum ether, cyclohexane, benzene, and ether are used as solvents. Finely divided particles of alkali metals are suitable for this reaction, and at present finely dispersed sodium ($0.5 \sim 20$ microns) is available and in frequent use. The drawback of this method of preparation is contamination of the product with the alkali halides. In the case of the preparation of sodium or potassium compounds, which are ordinarily very reactive, the products are susceptible to further reaction with the starting materials and often give Wurtz–Fittig reaction products as follows:

$$RNa + RX \longrightarrow R-R + NaX$$

Trityl derivatives of potassium, rubidium and cesium are made according to this method.

（ⅴ）*Fission of Carbon–Carbon Bonds.*   Weak carbon–carbon single bonds are easily cleaved by alkali metals to afford organoalkali compounds. Potassium–sodium alloy can best be used for this purpose, for example,

$$Ph_2CHCHPh_2 + Na \cdot K(alloy) \longrightarrow 2Ph_2CK$$

（ⅵ）*Reactions with Free Radicals.*   On addition of alkali metals a stable free radical, triphenylmethyl radical as an example, reacts at once and gives corresponding organoalkali compounds.

（ⅶ）*Cleavage of Ether Bonds.*   Benzylic ethers, including benzhydryl and trityl derivatives, are susceptible to the attack of alkali metals, the etheric linkages being cleaved to give benzylic compounds of the metals:

$$PhCH_2OR + 2Li \longrightarrow PhCH_2Li + ROLi$$

1.3.2. Indirect Methods Starting with Other Organoalkali Compounds

（ⅰ）*Addition to Carbon–Carbon Double Bonds.*

$$\mathrm{>C=C<} + RLi \longrightarrow \mathrm{>CLi-LiC<}$$

（ⅱ）*Metal–Hydrogen Exchange Reaction.*   This reaction is well known by its customary name, metalation. For example,

$$PhLi + \underset{O}{\bigcirc} \longrightarrow PhH + \underset{Li\ O}{\bigcirc}$$

It is common practice to use butyllithium or phenyllithium as metalation reagents and the reaction is carried out at low temperatures in tetrahydrofuran.

（ⅲ）*Metal–Metal Exchange.*

$$R_2Hg + 2R'Li \longrightarrow 2RLi + R'_2Hg$$

This reaction is also widely used and has its special use for the preparation of optically active organolithium compounds (see Section 1.1.4, b.).

Besides organomercury derivatives, organotin and organomagnesium compounds are also used.

(iv) *Metal–Halogen Exchange.* For example,

$$C_2H_5Li + CH_3I \longrightarrow CH_3Li + C_2H_5I$$

This process can be conveniently applied to those cases in which desired organo-lithium compounds cannot be synthesized directly from the corresponding alkyl halides and metallic lithium. Butyllithium is widely used for this purpose.

(v) *Disproportionation.* For example,

$$2\,LiCH_3 \longrightarrow CH_2Li_2 + CH_4$$

$$2\,C_5H_{11}Na \longrightarrow C_5H_{10}Na_2 + C_5H_{12}$$

(vi) *Reaction with Alkali Salts.* For example,

$$RNa + LiCl \longrightarrow RLi + NaCl$$

1.4. General Properties

1.4.1. Physical Properties and Structures

With a few exceptions alkyllithiums are colorless, somewhat viscous liquids which are readily soluble in ether, benzene, and paraffinic hydrocarbons. They are very sensitive toward moisture, carbon dioxide, and oxygen. Pure compounds of high lithium content ignite spontaneously in air. At elevated temperatures they react even with nitrogen to produce nitrides.

Methyllithium and ethyllithium are both solid. Although X-ray data reveals that solid methyllithium has almost a salt structure, the fact that it is very soluble in paraffinic hydrocarbons and that it is much less reactive in solution than butyllithium (which is considered to have a highly covalent carbon–metal bond), suggests that, at least in solution, methyl anion does not exist. This reasoning is supported by the further observation that ethyllithium and some other simple alkyllithiums do not conduct electricity either in melt or in solution. Thus it may be safely deduced that simple alkyllithiums do not have a salt-like structure in solution. On the other hand, as can be anticipated from the ebulio-scopic data, vapor pressure data, and the high latent heat of vaporization, alkyllithiums are highly associated in solution, which is hardly accomodated with the view that these compounds have a simple covalent bond. There is an abun-dance of information at present concerning the degree of association and the structure of the associated alkyllithiums. For instance, *n*-butyllithium exists as a dimer in ether solutions, for which a structure coordinated with one molecule of ether is proposed. In hydrocarbon solutions it is believed that ethyllithium exists as a hexamer and *tert*-butyllithium is a tetramer. In both benzene and ether as solvents, rapid exchange of alkyl groups among these associated species is reported to occur. However, these polymeric structures seem to be surprisingly stable; for instance, the hexameric structure of *n*-butyllithium in benzene cannot be destroyed on addition of a small amount of triethylamine.

Many reports are now available regarding the infrared spectra of alkyllithiums, their characteristic absorption band being found in the range of 350 to 570 cm^{-1}. For the nuclear magnetic resonance spectra and ultraviolet spectra of alkyllithiums, the reader should refer to the literature.   The dipole moment of *n*-butyllithium is rather small; 0.97 D in benzene.

When the group R in R$^-$·Li$^+$ involves a conjugated system and therefore the induced negative charge can be delocalized over the whole conjugated system, the molecule increases in ionic character, becomes solid, and finally exhibits color.   For example, butyllithium is a colorless liquid, phenyllithium is a white solid, benzyllithium is a yellow solid and triphenylmetyllithium is a red solid, while 1-lithiotriptycene, which is an analog of triphenylmethyllithium although its anion is structurally inhibited to have a planar structure, is colorless.

Because of the highly covalent character of the carbon-metal bonds, alkyllithiums are in general capable of being optically active at ordinary temperatures. Of course they are unstable at higher temperatures and racemize with extreme ease.   Quite reasonably this tendency increases with the increased ionic character of the carbon-metal bonds, and alkylsodium or alkylpotassium can barely exist as optically active compounds.   Lithium compounds in which the metal is bonded directly to vinyl or cyclopropyl groups exhibit extra optical stability (see Section 1.1.4, b.).

On heating, alkyllithiums decompose into olefins and lithium hydride.   For example, *n*-butyllithium rapidly decomposes at 150° to yield butene and lithium hydride, the activation energy for this reaction being 21 kcal/mole at 60~110°C.

Simple alkyl and phenyl derivatives of sodium, potassium, rubidium, and cesium are all colorless (benzylsodium is bright red), amorphous, nonvolatile solids, and are insoluble in petroleum ether and benzene.   They decompose without melting upon heating, and they ignite spontaneously in air.   They react much more easily with ethers than do the corresponding lithium compounds.   All these observations strongly suggest that they have salt-like structures.

Organoalkali compounds dissolve in diethylzinc and triethylaluminum with the formation of complexes.   Electrical conductivities of these complexes are low, implying existence as ion pairs.

$$C_2H_5Na + (C_2H_5)_2Zn \longrightarrow Na^+Zn(C_2H_5)_3{}^-$$

1.4.2. Chemical Properties

Since reactions of organoalkali compounds are supposed in general to be reactions of carbanions, the reactivity of these compounds will increase with an increase in their ionic character.   For instance, the rate of reaction of phenylalkalis with gaseous hydrogen to form benzene increases in the following order: Na < K < Rb < Cs.   On the other hand, if the negative charge can be dispersed over the conjugated system, the more ionic compounds (those which can produce the more stabilized anions) would exhibit the more reduced reactivities.   In fact the following reaction

$$RNa + R'H \longrightarrow RH + R'Na$$

proceeds in such a direction as to yield the more stable carbanions; butylsodium can be converted into phenylsodium, phenylsodium can be converted with high yield into benzylsodium, which in turn can be used for the synthesis of benzhydrylsodium and triphenylmethylsodium.

(i) *Substitution Reactions.*

(1) Metalation of Compounds Having Active Hydrogen.   Organoalkali compounds react violently with the active hydrogens of water, alcohols, amines, and acetylenes to form hydrocarbons:

$$RM + R'OH \longrightarrow RH + R'OM$$

Similarly, C–H bonds activated by adjacent $C\equiv C-$, $C=C-$, hetero rings, aryl groups, $>N-$, and $RO-$ groups are readily metalated to form C–M bonds.   This tendency increases in the order $Li < Na < K$.   This is why solvents other than hydrocarbons cannot be used for the reactions of alkylsodiums and alkylpotassiums although ethers are used safely in the case of alkyllithiums.

Relative reactivity of various alkyllithiums toward triphenylmethane is reported to decrease in the following order (numbers in parentheses are relative reactivities); benzyl (250) > allyl (51) > *n*-butyl (13) > phenyl (5.5) > vinyl (2.5) > methyl (1).

Alkylsodiums are so reactive that they are often used as reagents for proton abstraction.   Susceptibility of this abstraction varies with the change of the substrate as follows:

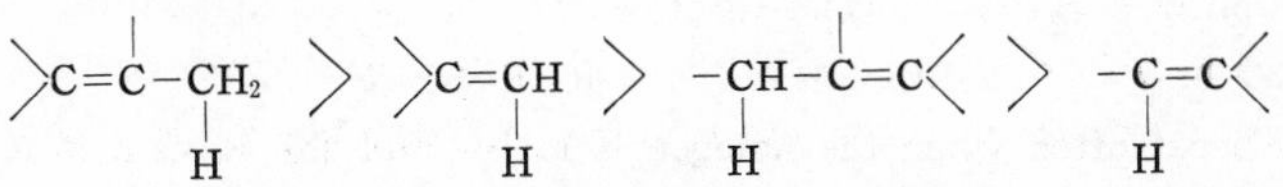

$$\underset{\overset{|}{H}}{>\!C\!=\!C}\!-\!CH_2 \;>\; \underset{\overset{|}{H}}{>\!C\!=\!CH} \;>\; -\!\underset{\overset{|}{H}}{CH}\!-\!C\!=\!C\!<\;>\; -\!\underset{\overset{|}{H}}{C}\!=\!C\!<$$

At present there is abundant data for the metalation of aromatic compounds. particular interest are anisole, the dimethyl ether of resorcinol, benzofuran, nzofuran, and thiophene, which are all metalated at *ortho* positions.   How-, metalation occurs at *meta* positions of triphenylamine and triphenylphos- ne, and in the case of methylphenyl sulfide the methyl group is metalated. alation of cumene and ethylbenzene takes place at *meta* and *para* positions , followed by a rapid rearrangement of the metal to the side chains.

his reaction can be successfully applied to the synthesis of various germyllithiums.

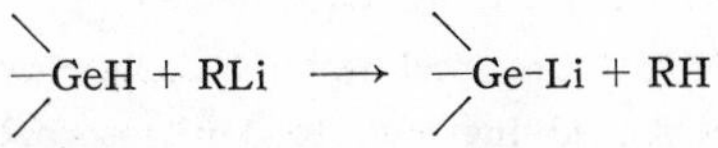

$$\underset{/}{\overset{\backslash}{-}}GeH + RLi \longrightarrow \underset{/}{\overset{\backslash}{-}}Ge\!-\!Li + RH$$

(2) Reaction with Metal Halides.

$$MCl_x + x\,RLi \longrightarrow R_xM + x\,LiCl$$

This reaction is often used to prepare various kinds of organometallic compounds containing Tl, Au, Ge, Si, Sn, Pb, Ti, As, P, B. etc.   According to the equation

$$RCl \xrightarrow{Na} RNa \xrightarrow{MgCl_2} RMgCl$$

this reaction can also be applied to the synthesis of those Grignard reagents which cannot be obtained by usual methods.   Another merit of this method is that alkyl chlorides can be used instead of bromides or iodides.

(3)   Metal–Metal Exchange Reaction with Other Organometallic Compounds. For example,

$$Ph_4Sn + 4\,n\text{-BuLi} \longrightarrow (n\text{-Bu})_4Sn + 4\,PhLi$$

(4)   Halogen–Metal Exchange Reaction with Alkyl Halides.

$$n\text{-BuLi} + RX \rightleftharpoons n\text{-BuX} + RLi \quad (X=Br,\ I)$$

This is the reaction most widely used for the preparation of organolithium compounds.   Generally speaking, this reaction proceeds in such a direction as to result in a combination of lithium with the more electronegative organic group. The rate of this reaction is slowed down by the solvents in the following order : $Bu_2O > Et_2O > EtNMe_2 > PhH >$ cyclohexane $>$ petroleum ether.   The reaction is fastest in tetrahydrofuran but accompanied with unfavorable side reactions. When R is aliphatic, reactivity increases in the order $RCl < RBr < RI$.   Because RI is susceptible to coupling reactions and RBr is still too fast, RCl is most suitable for the purpose of synthesis.   When R is aromatic the reactivity is much too low and therefore either RBr or RI is used for the preparation.   For vinyl derivatives bromides are the best choice.

(5)   Coupling Reaction.   The reaction

$$RLi + RX \longrightarrow R-R + LiX$$

is observed most often when the halogen is iodine and the solvent is tetrahydrofuran.   When R is benzyl or allyl the reaction occurs with extreme ease; this is the basis of Gilman's method for the quantitative determination of organolithium compounds.   This reaction occurs more easily for sodium or potassium compounds.

(6)   Alkylation.   Under forced conditions aromatic alkylation can be carried out with the use of alkyllithiums.   This reaction takes place with increasing order of facility when the alkyl groups are primary $<$ secondary $<$ tertiary.   For example, when naphthalene is heated with *tert*-butyllithium in decaline at 165° for 41 hours, $\alpha\text{-}tert$-butylnaphthalene is obtained in $30\sim45\%$ yield, with $30\sim50\%$ concurrent dialkylation.

(7)   Reactions with NOCl, Br_2, and I_2.   1-Carboranyllithium is reported to react with nitrosyl chloride, giving rise to 1-nitrosocarborane.   Bromine and iodine also react in the following manner to give bromides and iodides, respectively :

$$RLi + X_2 \longrightarrow RX + LiX \quad (X=I,\ Br)$$

(ii) *Addition Reactions.*

(1) Addition to C=C and C≡C Bonds.   Organoalkali compounds readily add to carbon-carbon double bonds.   Addition to ethylene, butadiene, and diphenylethylene are examples.

$$Ph_2C=CH_2 + n\text{-}BuLi \longrightarrow Ph_2CLi-CH_2Bu$$

Although addition to carbon-carbon triple bonds is generally impossible, the following exception is known.

$$Ph-C\equiv C-Ph \xrightarrow[\text{24 hrs., 30°}]{\text{RLi, in Et}_2\text{O}} \underset{R}{\overset{Ph}{>}}C=C\underset{Ph}{\overset{Li}{<}}$$

(R=n-Bu and Ph, Yield: 40%)

(2) Addition to C=N and C≡N Bonds.   In the case of azomethine linkages, addition can still occur to dormant bonds such as that of pyridine.   Addition to the nitrile group is much easier, as illustrated by the following example:

$$p\text{-}CH_3OC_6H_4C\equiv N \xrightarrow{PhLi} p\text{-}CH_3OC_6H_4C(=NLi)Ph \xrightarrow{H_3^+O} p\text{-}CH_3OC_6H_4COPh$$

(3) Addition to C=O Bond.   This is a typical reaction of organoalkali compounds.   The organoalkali reagents are more reactive and less susceptible to the

$$>\!C=O \xrightarrow{RLi} >\!CR-OLi \xrightarrow{H_2O} >\!CR-OH$$

influence of steric hindrance than Grignard reagent.   Another important difference is that the organoalkali reagents add to the carbonyl group almost invariably in a 1,2-fashion, in contrast to the case of Grignard reagents where predominance of conjugate addition (1,4- and 1,6-addition) is well known.   Organoalkali reagents react similarly toward epoxy compounds and cyclic ethers. When one descends from lithio- to sodio- to potassio-compounds the amount of enolization increases gradually and finally exceeds that of addition.

(4) Addition to Inorganic Compounds.   Reaction with carbon dioxide is widely used in laboratories, and corresponding carboxylic acids are obtained in high yields at low temperatures.   At higher than room temperatures, however, the alkali salts of the carboxylic acids produced react further with organoalkali compounds to yield ketones.   They react with nitrogen suboxide in a following manner.

$$PhLi + N_2O \longrightarrow PhN=NOLi \longrightarrow PhH + Ph-Ph + PhN=NPh \text{ etc.}$$

(iii) *Other Reactions.*

(1) Reactions with H_2 and O_2.   Gaseous hydrogen reacts with phenylalkalis and liberates benzene.   The reactivity increases in the following order: Li < Na < K < Rb < Cs.   Aromatic lithium compounds combine with oxygen to form phenols:

$$ArLi \xrightarrow{O_2} ArOLi \xrightarrow{H_2O} ArOH$$

(2) Elimination of LiH.   1,4-Dihydronaphthalene is metalated by phenyllithium, followed by elimination of lithium hydride to yield naphthalene.   Thus, phenyllithium is a useful dehydrogenating reagent.   Isoindole was first prepared according to this method.

(3) Elimination of Alkali Halides.   When halides of onium salts are submitted to metalation with organoalkali compounds, alkali halides are eliminated at once and ylid is produced.   For example,

$$Me_4N^+Cl^- \xrightarrow{\text{PhLi}} LiCH_2N^+Me_3Cl^- \xrightarrow{-LiCl} Me_3N^+ - CH_2^-$$

If alkyl halides $\underset{}{>}C\underset{H}{\overset{X}{<}}$ are metalated with alkyllithium or phenylsodium, the

product $\underset{}{>}C\underset{Li}{\overset{X}{<}}$ will on loss of LiX yield carbenes $>C:$.   Eventually, the

alkenyllithium reacts with methylene chloride and gives an alkylcyclopropene as a final product.   Presumably this reaction proceeds by way of an expected intermediate, that is, an alkenylcarbene, as is shown by the equations below:

$$CH_2Cl_2 + RLi \longrightarrow RH + CHLiCl_2 \longrightarrow :CHCl + LiCl$$

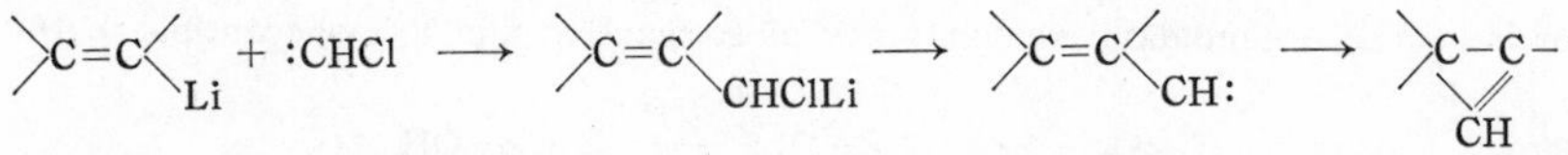

$$>C=C\underset{Li}{<} + :CHCl \longrightarrow >C=C\underset{CHClLi}{<} \longrightarrow >C=C\underset{CH:}{<} \longrightarrow \underset{CH}{>C-C-}$$

Benzal chloride behaves likewise, giving the expected chlorophenylcarbene, whereas benzal bromide yields phenylcarbene because metal–halogen exchange occurs first in the latter case.

In the case of the reaction of fluorobenzene and phenyllithium, the initially formed *o*-lithiofluorobenzene is accompanied by a loss of lithium fluoride and gives benzyne.

(4) Besides those reactions mentioned above, some others have been reported, including rearrangements, disproportionations, fission of sulfide linkages, and reactions with sulfoxides.

(iv) *Stereochemistry*.   Reactions of organoalkali compounds which are carried out at asymmetric centers are particularly interesting.   It is important to know how and to what extent the stereospecificity of these reactions is influenced by a change of conditions, since information of this kind is essential for elucidating the mechanisms of reactions of organoalkali compounds.   Optical stability of those compounds in which alkali metals are directly bonded to the asymmetric center is closely related to the nature of the carbon–metal bonds concerned and sheds more insight into the nature of carbanions.   In line with this view there have been many investigations in this field.

(1) Coupling Reaction.   If this reaction is a bimolecular nucleophilic substitution of alkyl halides by organoalkali compounds, it should be reasonable to expect Walden inversion.   In fact the following reaction gives inversion product in 69% yield, racemization being as low as 26%.

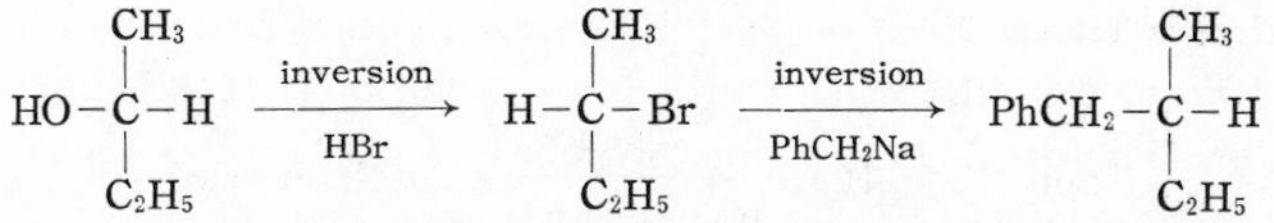

$$\underset{C_2H_5}{\overset{CH_3}{HO-C-H}} \xrightarrow[\text{HBr}]{\text{inversion}} \underset{C_2H_5}{\overset{CH_3}{H-C-Br}} \xrightarrow[\text{PhCH}_2\text{Na}]{\text{inversion}} \underset{C_2H_5}{\overset{CH_3}{PhCH_2-C-H}}$$

Analogously allylsodium reacts with ($-$)-2-bromooctane to give inverted coupling product in 83% yield, racemization again being less than 20%. However, complete racemization is reported for coupling reactions of *n*-butyllithium with ($-$)-2-bromobutane and of ethylsodium or butylsodium with ($-$)-2-bromooctane. Likewise both α-methylallyl chloride and γ-methylallyl chloride are known to give the same products when they react with phenyllithium.

On the basis of these findings it may be deduced that in general the coupling reaction proceeds by an S_N2 mechanism. However, in some cases in which reactants are apt to become carbonium ions, or when the attacking reagent is difficult to make a carbanion because of the influence of counter cation, the reaction presumably proceeds by way of a carbonium ion with the loss of stereospecificity.

(2) Metal-Halogen Exchange. Metal-halogen exchange reaction proceeds with retention of configuration. For example, about 20% retention is claimed for the product of the following reaction.

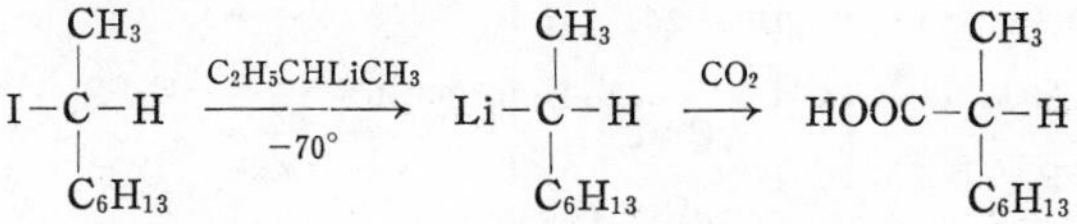

$$\underset{C_6H_{13}}{\overset{CH_3}{I-C-H}} \xrightarrow[-70°]{C_2H_5CHLiCH_3} \underset{C_6H_{13}}{\overset{CH_3}{Li-C-H}} \xrightarrow{CO_2} \underset{C_6H_{13}}{\overset{CH_3}{HOOC-C-H}}$$

Probably this reaction involves S_Ni mechanism as follows:

$$\text{>C*}-I + Li-C< \longrightarrow \text{>C*} \underset{Li}{\overset{I}{<}} C< \longrightarrow \text{>C*}-Li + I-C<$$

In contrast to the case of the coupling reaction, this exchange yields optically active lithium compounds as products, and hence much care should be taken with regard to racemization before and during work-up of the products.

(3) Metal-Metal Exchange. Retention of configuration is also exhibited in this case. For example,

$$2\underset{C_6H_{13}}{\overset{CH_3}{>}}CHLi + \left(\underset{C_2H_5}{\overset{CH_3}{>}}CH^*-\right)_2-Hg \rightleftharpoons 2\underset{C_2H_5}{\overset{CH_3}{>}}C^*HLi + \left(\underset{C_6H_{13}}{\overset{CH_3}{>}}CH-\right)_2-Hg$$

(*ca.* 50% retention)

Attention should also be paid to the optical stability of the product; complete racemization is recorded for the reaction in solvents containing some ether. Since, in general, organomercury compounds are optically stable and therefore easily resolved, this may be the most covenient route to the optically active lithium compounds.

(4) Metal-Hydrogen Exchange. Although this reaction is somewhat special, configuration is retained:

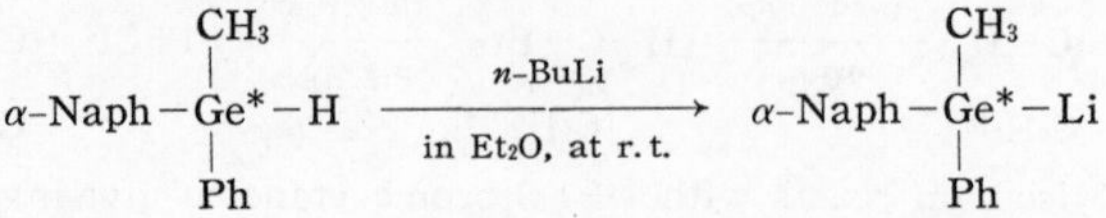

$$\alpha\text{-Naph}-\underset{\underset{Ph}{|}}{\overset{\overset{CH_3}{|}}{Ge^*}}-H \quad\xrightarrow[\text{in Et}_2O,\text{ at r. t.}]{n\text{-BuLi}}\quad \alpha\text{-Naph}-\underset{\underset{Ph}{|}}{\overset{\overset{CH_3}{|}}{Ge^*}}-Li$$

(5) Unsaturated Organolithium Compounds.   While amines $\left(\gt N:\right)$ are in general optically inactive, oximes $\left(\gt C=N\cdot^{\overset{OH}{\diagup}}\right)$ can exist as stable *cis-* and *trans-*isomers.   On the basis of analogy, it may be anticipated that although saturated lithium compounds $\left(\gt C:Li\right)$ are optically not so stable, unsaturated lithium compounds $\left(\gt C=C:_{Li}^{\diagup}\right)$ might have some extra stability.   This is really the case; for example, the lithium compounds below are stable enough under conditions of refluxing in ether for three hours, *cis-trans* interconversion being recorded as negligible.

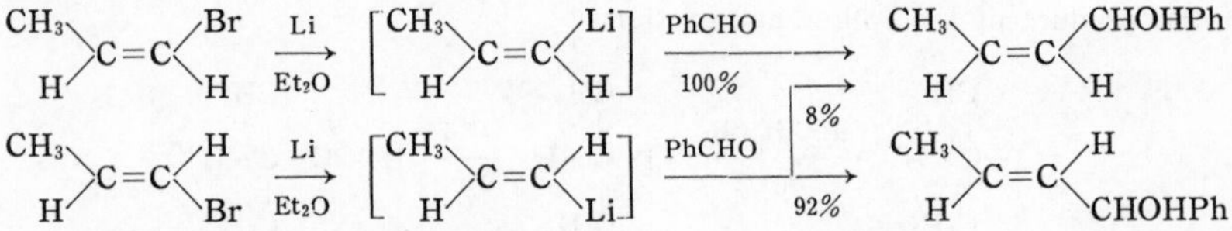

$$\underset{H}{\overset{CH_3}{\diagdown}}C=C\underset{H}{\overset{Br}{\diagup}}\quad\xrightarrow[\text{Et}_2O]{Li}\quad\left[\underset{H}{\overset{CH_3}{\diagdown}}C=C\underset{H}{\overset{Li}{\diagup}}\right]\quad\xrightarrow[100\%]{PhCHO}\quad\underset{H}{\overset{CH_3}{\diagdown}}C=C\underset{H}{\overset{CHOHPh}{\diagup}}$$

$$\underset{H}{\overset{CH_3}{\diagdown}}C=C\underset{Br}{\overset{H}{\diagup}}\quad\xrightarrow[\text{Et}_2O]{Li}\quad\left[\underset{H}{\overset{CH_3}{\diagdown}}C=C\underset{Li}{\overset{H}{\diagup}}\right]\quad\xrightarrow[92\%]{PhCHO}\quad\underset{H}{\overset{CH_3}{\diagdown}}C=C\underset{CHOHPh}{\overset{H}{\diagup}}$$

(8% shown between the two PhCHO arrows)

A similar stereospecific process is also reported for Sn–Li exchange between organotin and organolithium compounds as shown below:

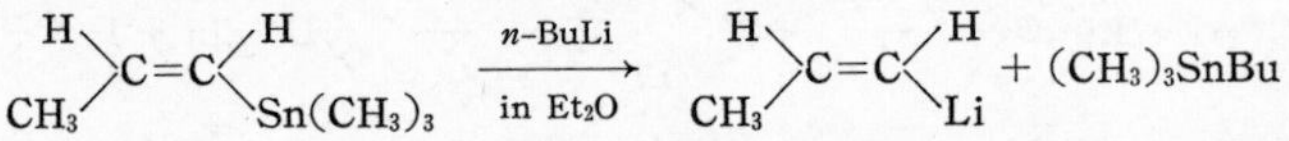

$$\underset{CH_3}{\overset{H}{\diagdown}}C=C\underset{Sn(CH_3)_3}{\overset{H}{\diagup}}\quad\xrightarrow[\text{in Et}_2O]{n\text{-BuLi}}\quad\underset{CH_3}{\overset{H}{\diagdown}}C=C\underset{Li}{\overset{H}{\diagup}}+(CH_3)_3SnBu$$

It should be noted here that this was the first instance in which configuration of the lithium compound was confirmed directly by means of nuclear magnetic resonance spectroscopy.   This result is quite important; it established unequivocally that reactions of various kinds of unsaturated lithium compounds with carbon dioxide, methanol, formaldehyde, methyl iodide, benzaldehyde, and trimethylchlorosilane proceeded in a stereospecific fashion, which had been assumed to be the case without any direct evidence.

Expectedly, cyclopropyllithiums appear to have intermediate stability between saturated and unsaturated compounds.   For example,

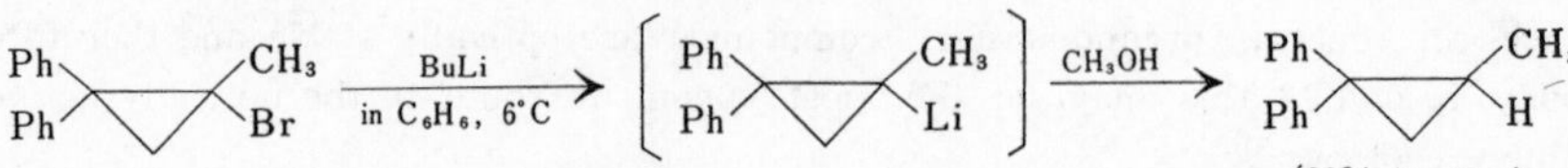

$$\underset{Ph}{\overset{Ph}{\diagdown}}\triangleleft\overset{CH_3}{\underset{Br}{}}\quad\xrightarrow[\text{in C}_6H_6,\,6°C]{BuLi}\quad\left[\underset{Ph}{\overset{Ph}{\diagdown}}\triangleleft\overset{CH_3}{\underset{Li}{}}\right]\quad\xrightarrow{CH_3OH}\quad\underset{Ph}{\overset{Ph}{\diagdown}}\triangleleft\overset{CH_3}{\underset{H}{}}$$

(80%retention)

1.4.3. Methods of Detection

Gilman's color test is most widely used to detect organolithium compounds and is particularly useful when one wishes to measure completion of reactions. There are three methods, as follows:

(1) About 1 ml of the sample solution is poured into about 1 ml of solution of Michler's ketone in benzene, and the resulting material is decomposed with water. Oxidation of the product with a 0.2% solution of iodine in acetic acid imparts color to the solution (formation of triphenylmethane dyes).

$$(p\text{-}Me_2NC_6H_4)_2CO \xrightarrow{PhLi} (p\text{-}Me_2NC_6H_4)_2PhCOLi \xrightarrow{H_2O}$$

$$(p\text{-}Me_2NC_6H_4)_2PhCOH \xrightarrow{I_2} [(p\text{-}Me_2NC_6H_4)_2PhC]^+I^-$$

This test can also be applied to Grignard reagents.

(2) About 1 ml of the sample solution is added to an equivolume solution of p-bromodimethylaniline (15%) in dry benzene. To this solution is added about 1 ml of a 15% solution of benzophenone in benzene, and the product is decomposed with water and acidified with concentrated hydrochloric acid.   Red color in the aqueous layer indicates the presence of active organolithium compounds.

$$p\text{-}BrC_6H_4NMe_2 \xrightarrow{BuLi} p\text{-}LiC_6H_4NMe_2$$

$$\xrightarrow[\substack{2)\ H_2O \\ 3)\ HCl}]{1)\ Ph_2CO} \left[Ph_2C=\!\!\!\left\langle\!\!\!\bigcirc\!\!\!\right\rangle\!\!\!=NMe_2 \right]^+ Cl^-$$

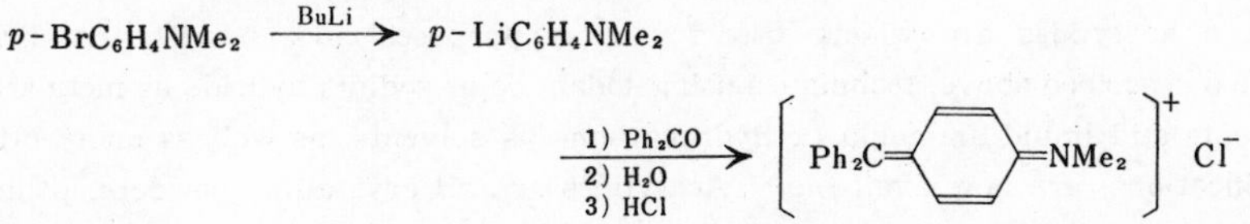

This reaction is positive only for active alkyllithiums, and negative for less active compounds such as CH_3Li or PhLi.

(3) One ml of the sample solution is introduced to an equivolume solution of 1% triphenylbismuth dichloride in dry benzene.   If aromatic lithium or magnesium compounds are present the solution becomes deep purple.   This test is negative for aliphatic lithium or magnesium compounds. The color is thought to be due to the formation of purple pentaarylbismuth.

1.4.4. Methods of Determination

The most frequently used technique is Gilman's double titration method.   To definite amounts (usually 1~2 ml) of the sample solution is added an ethereal solution (about 10 ml) of excess dry benzyl chloride (about 1 ml).   The following reactions occur at once (the solution becomes temporarily yellow) and all lithium in the sample as RLi is completely converted into LiCl.

$$RLi + RhCH_2Cl \longrightarrow RCl + PhCH_2Li$$
$$PhCH_2Li + PhCH_2Cl \longrightarrow PhCH_2CH_2Ph + LiCl$$
$$RLi + PhCH_2Cl \longrightarrow PhCH_2R + LiCl$$

On adding water to this solution, the lithium which initially existed in a form other than RLi (for example, as alkoxides) is changed into LiOH, which can be determined easily by titration with any acid. On the other hand, a definite amount of the sample solution is hydrolyzed directly and titrated with acid, giving the total amount of lithium in the original sample. Therefore the difference of the two titration values gives the amount of RLi in the sample. Allyl chloride can be used equally well in place of benzyl chloride. This method of determination, however, cannot be applied to a methyllithium or phenyllithium which does not react easily with benzyl chloride. Another method based on the rapid addition of alkyllithiums to benzophenone can also be used.

1.5. Related Compounds
1.5.1. Acetylides

Acetylides of sodium, potassium, rubidium, and cesium are all prepared by direct reaction of the metals and acetylenes.

$$PhC \equiv CH + M \longrightarrow PhC \equiv CM$$

However, lithium acetylides are not obtainable by this method and it is usual to apply metalation with butyllithium.

$$PhC \equiv CH + n\text{-}BuLi \longrightarrow PhC \equiv CLi + n\text{-}BuH$$

Sodium acetylides are widely used for many purposes, and, besides the direct method described above, techniques using sodamide or sodium hydride as metalating reagents and liquid ammonia or hydrocarbons as solvents, as well as many other modifications, are now available. Acetylides are all crystalline powders, lithium and sodium acetylides being colorless, potassium light brown, and rubidium and cesium dark brown. These compounds are preserved as dispersions in mineral oils. They ignite spontaneously when exposed to air. Typical reactions of the acetylides are as follows:

(1) Addition to Aldehydes and Ketones.

$$HC \equiv CNa + R_2CO \longrightarrow \overset{\displaystyle ONa}{\underset{\displaystyle |}{R_2C}}-C \equiv CH \longrightarrow \overset{\displaystyle OH}{\underset{\displaystyle |}{R_2C}}-C \equiv CH$$

This reaction is used in industry for the synthesis of unsaturated alcohols, preparation of Vitamin A being an example.

(2) Alkylation by Dimethyl Sulfate.

$$HC \equiv CNa + (CH_3)_2SO_4 \longrightarrow HC \equiv C-CH_3 + CH_3OSO_2ONa$$

(3) Reaction with Carbon Dioxide.

$$HC \equiv CNa + CO_2 \longrightarrow HC \equiv C-COONa$$

1.5.2. Aromatic Ion-radicals

When equimolar amounts of metallic sodium and naphthalene are dissolved in tetrahydrofuran or diglime a green solution is obtained, which on further addition of sodium does not change color. However, if sodium or lithium is added to a solution of naphthalene in liquid ammonia at $-65°$ to $-70°$, a green solution is obtained, which by dissolving additional amounts of sodium becomes orange red and finally turns to red. The green color is presumably due to the radical anion which can be formed by addition of one electron from sodium to naphtalene, and the red color may be ascribed to the existence of the dianion of naphthalene which is produced by addition of another electron to the radical anion.

$$C_{10}H_8 \xrightarrow{\text{Na}} [C_{10}H_8]^{\cdot-}Na^+ \xrightarrow{\text{Na}} [C_{10}H_8]^{--}2\,Na^+ \xrightarrow{2\,H^+} C_{10}H_{10}$$

(naphthalene)   radical anion (green)   dianion (red)   (dihydronaphthalene)

All results of the measurements, including electron spin resonance absorption, ultraviolet absorption, potentiometric titration, etc., leads to the conclusion that these radical anions are capable of existence with considerable stabilily, that there is a mobile equilibrium of electrons between naphthalene molecules, and that the addition of two electrons occurs stepwise in the case of polynuclear aromatic compounds. Phenanthrene is said to be able to produce dianion even in tetrahydrofuran, whereas in benzene it is difficult even to form radical anion in the same solvent.

1.5.3. Complex Salts

Organoalkali compounds can combine with other organoalkali compounds to form complex salts such as $Na^+[Me_2Li]^-$, $Na^+[n\text{-}Bu_2Li]^-$, $K^+[Ph_2Li]^-$, $Cs^+[Ph_2Li]^-$, etc. These compounds can also form complex salts with Lewis acids, examples of which are diethylzinc and triethylaluminum:

$$RLi + Et_2Zn \rightleftharpoons [RZnEt_2]^-Li^+$$

REFERENCES

1) G. E. Coates, "Organometallic Compounds", Methuen, London (1960).
2) M. Kumada, "Daiyukikagaku", Vol. 18, p. 19, Asakura, Tokyo (1962).
3) H. V. Sidgwick, "The Chemical Elements and Their Compounds", Vol. I, Oxford (1950).
4) T. Hoshino, I. Ichikizaki, "Jikkenkagaku Koza", Vol. 20, p. 139, Maruzen, Tokyo (1956),
5) G. Wittig, "Newer Methods of Preparative Organic Chemistry", Interscience (1948).
6) F. Runge, "Organometalverbindungen", Stuttgart (1944).
7) H. Gilman, J. W. Moore, "Organic Reactions", Vol. Ⅷ, p. 258, John Wiley (1954).
8) R. A. Benkeser, D. J. Forster, D. M. Sauve, *Chem. Revs.*, **57**, 867 (1957).
9) J. F. Nobis, L. F. Moormeier, R. E. Robinson, "Metal-Organic Compounds", Advances in Chemistry Series, p. 63, Am. Chem. Soc. (1959).
10) E. G. Rochow, D. T. Hurd, R. N. Lewis, "The Chemistry of Organometallic Compounds", John Wiley (1957).
11) J. Eisch, H. Oilman, "Organometallic Compounds", Advances in Inorganic Chemistry and Radiochemistry, Vol. 2, p. 61, Academic Press (1960).

【Li】

④ **General reactions**

RLi + H₂O ⟶ RH

RLi + R'OH ⟶ RH

RLi + CO₂ $\underset{H_2O}{\longrightarrow}$ RCOOH

RLi + R'I ⟶ RR'

RLi + R'H ⟶ R'Li + RH

RLi + R'X ⟶ R'Li + RX

(X : Cl or Br)

RLi + R'COR″ $\underset{H_2O}{\longrightarrow}$ RR'R″COH

RLi + O₂ ⟶

RLi + R'COOR″ $\underset{H_2O}{\longrightarrow}$ R₂R'COH

RLi + $\rangle$C=C$\langle$ $\underset{H_2O}{\longrightarrow}$ R$-$C$-$CH

⑤ Organic synthesis, initiator for polymerization, etc.

LiCH₃

① Methyllithium
CH₃Li

② CH₃I + Li ⟶ 82%

CH₃Cl + Li ⟶

CH₃I + C₂H₅Li ⟶

③ White powder.

IR, UV, NMR : JACS **79**, 1859(1957) ; **83**, 3580 (1961). Dokl. **123**, 113(1958). Izv. SFi **22**, 1110 (1958).

⑥ Z. anorg. allg. Chem. **141**, 161 (1924). JACS **55**, 1252 (1933) ; **79**, 1859 (1957). Ber. **50**, 262 (1917). JOC **22**, 1165(1957).

LiC₂F₃

① Trifluorovinyllithium
CF₂=CFLi

② C₄H₉Sn(CF=CF₂)₃ + C₄H₉Li ⟶ 46~50%

⑥ Tetrahedron Letters 20 (1960).

LiC₂H₃

① Vinyllithium

CH₂=CHLi

② (CH₂=CH)₄Sn + C₆H₅Li ⟶ 50~75%

(CH₂=CH)₄Pb + Li ⟶ 90%

③ Pale white solid.

Violently pyrophoric in air.

IR, UV, NMR : JOC **26**, 563 (1961) ; JACS **85**, 1651 (1963).

④ + H₂O ⟶ CH₂=CH₂

⑥ Z. Naturf. **14b**, 809 (1959). Chem. & Ind. **1959**, 402. JOC **26**, 563 (1961). E. A. Brande "Progress in Organic Chemistry" **3**, 172 (1955).

LiC₂H₄ClO

① Chloromethoxymethyllithium
ClCH₂OCH₂Li

② CH₃OCH₂Cl + t-C₄H₉Li ⟶ 50%

⑥ Tetrahedron Letters 241 (1962).

LiC₂H₅

① Ethyllithium
C₂H₅Li

② C₂H₅Br + Li ⟶ 50~65%

③ Colorless crystals. [95°].

Sol. 7g/100g in C₆H₆(16°) ; 6g in hexane (18°) ; 1g in pentane(18°) ; 3g in isopentane (16°).

IR, UV, NMR : JACS **84**, 1371(1962) ; **79**, 1859 (1957) ; **85**, 1651 (1963) ; **83**, 3580 (1961). Dokl. **124**, 873 (1959) ; **123**, 113 (1958) ; **125**, 562 (1959). Izv. SFi **22**, 1110 (1958).

⑥ Z. anorg. Chem. **141**, 161 (1924). Ber. **50**, 262(1917). JACS **63**, 2479(1941) ; **48**, 2689(1926). Ann. **567**, 179(1950). CA **45**, 10192 (1951). Z. phys. Chem. **A 151**, 234 (1930). Zhur. **23**, 392 (1953).

LiC₃H₂SN

① 2-Thiazolyllithium

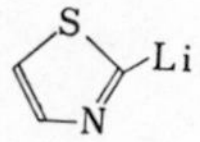

② [thiazole structure] + C_6H_5Li ⟶ 40%

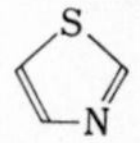

⑥ Bull. soc. chim. France **1953**, 708.

LiC₃H₅
① Propenyllithium
$CH_3CH=CHCi$
② $CH_3CH=CHBr + Li$ ⟶
⑥ JCS **1951**, 2078.   Nature **166**, 58 (1950).

LiC₃H₅
① Isopropenyllithium
$CH_2=C\begin{smallmatrix}Li\\CH_3\end{smallmatrix}$
② $CH_2=\underset{\underset{CH_3}{|}}{C}-Br + Li$ ⟶
② Dokl. **96**, 289 (1954).

LiC₃H₇
① *n*-Propyllithium
$n\text{-}C_3H_7Li$
② $n\text{-}C_3H_7Cl + Li$ ⟶ 85%
$n\text{-}C_3H_7Br + Li$ ⟶ 60~78%
③ IR, UV, NMR: Dokl. **125**, 562 (1959).
⑥ Ber. **50**, 262 (1917).   JACS **63**, 2479 (1941); **71**, 1499 (1949). Ann. **567**, 179 (1950).

LiC₃H₇
① Isopropyllithium
$i\text{-}C_3H_7Li$
② $i\text{-}C_3H_7Cl + Li$ ⟶ 75%
$i\text{-}C_3H_7Br + Li$ ⟶ 15%
⑥ JACS **63**, 2479 (1941).   Ber. **64 B**, 448 (1931).

LiC₃H₇
① Cyclopropyllithium

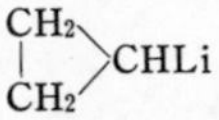

$\begin{smallmatrix}CH_2\\|\\CH_2\end{smallmatrix}\!\!\searrow CHLi$

② $\begin{smallmatrix}CH_2\\|\\CH_2\end{smallmatrix}\!\!\searrow CHCl + Li$ ⟶ 70%

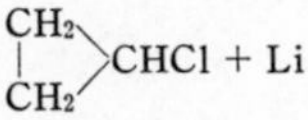

⑥ Chem. & Ind. **1956**, 1014.   JACS **85**, 743 (1963).

LiC₃H₇
① Heptafluoropropyllithium
C_3F_7Li
② $C_3F_7I + Li$ ⟶ 77%
⑥ JACS **76**, 474 (1954); **77**, 6387 (1955).

LiC₄H₃S
① α-Thienyllithium

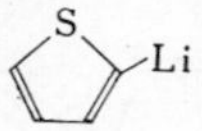

② [thiophene] + *n*-C_4H_9Li ⟶ 46%

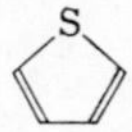

⑥ JACS **70**, 2809 (1948).

LiC₄H₇
① 1-Methylpropenyllithium
$CH_3CH=C\begin{smallmatrix}Li\\CH_3\end{smallmatrix}$
② $CH_3CH=C\begin{smallmatrix}Br\\CH_3\end{smallmatrix} + Li$ ⟶
⑥ JACS **76**, 1902 (1954).

LiC₄H₇
① Isobutenyllithium
$(CH_3)_2C=CHLi$
② $(CH_3)_2C=C\begin{smallmatrix}Br\\H\end{smallmatrix} + Li$ ⟶
④ $(CH_3)_2C=C\begin{smallmatrix}Li\\H\end{smallmatrix} + (CH_3)_2NCHO$
       ⟶ $(CH_3)_2C=CH-CHO$
⑥ JCS **1950**, 2007, 2012; **1952**, 1425; **1953**, 3131; **1955**, 3324.

LiC₄H₉

① *n*-Butyllithium
　n-C₄H₉Li

② n-C₄H₉Cl + Li ⟶ 75〜100%
　n-C₄H₉Br + Li ⟶ 60〜90%

③ IR, UV, NMR: JACS **85**, 1651 (1963).
　Compt. rend. **252**, 1616(1961). Dokl.
　123, 113 (1958); **125**, 562 (1959).

⑥ JACS **55**, 1252(1933); **63**, 2479(1941);
　48, 2689(1926); **54**, 1957(1932); **59**,
　1896(1937); **62**, 3206(1940); **71**, 1499
　(1949). Ann. **567**, 179 (1950); **479**,
　135 (1930).

LiC₄H₉

① Isobutyllithium
　i-C₄H₉Li

② i-C₄H₉Cl + Li ⟶ 85%

⑥ JACS **63**, 2479 (1941).

LiC₄H₉

① *sec*-Butyllithium
　s-C₄H₉Li

② s-C₄H₉Cl + Li ⟶ 85%

③ IR, UV, NMR: JACS **85**, 1651 (1963).

⑥ JACS **63**, 2479 (1941).

LiC₄H₉

① *tert*-Butyllithium
　t-C₄H₉Li

② t-C₄H₉Cl + Li ⟶ 50%

③ IR, UV, NMR: JACS **85**, 1651 (1963).

⑥ JACS **63**, 2479(1941); **70**, 2876(1948);
　75, 1771 (1953); **77**, 2804 (1955).

LiC₅H₅

① Cyclopentadienyllithium

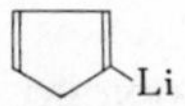

② + C₂H₅Li ⟶ 72%

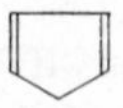

⑥ CA **51**, 14711 (1957). JACS **79**, 4970
　(1959).

LiC₅H₉

① Trimethylvinyllithium

$$(CH_3)_2C=C\diagup^{Li}_{\diagdown CH_3}$$

② $(CH_3)_2C=C\diagup^{Br}_{\diagdown CH_3}$ + Li

⑥ JACS **76**, 1902 (1954).

LiC₅H₁₁

① *n*-Amyllithium
　n-C₅H₁₁Li

② n-C₅H₁₁Cl + Li ⟶ 85%
　n-C₅H₁₁Br + Li ⟶ 81%

③ IR, UV, NMR: Dokl. **125**, 562(1959).

⑥ JACS **63**, 2479 (1941); **71**, 1499 (1949).

LiC₅H₁₁

① 2-Methylbutyllithium
　C₂H₅CH(CH₃)CH₂Li

② C₂H₅CH(CH₃)CH₂Cl + LiAlH₄ ⟶ 73%

⑥ Gazz. chim. ital. **91**, 441 (1961). Ann.
　chim. (Rome) **51**, 823 (1961).

LiC₅H₉

① 4-Pentenyllithium
　CH₂=CH(CH₂)₃Li

② CH₂=CH(CH₂)₃Br + Li ⟶ 63%

⑥ JOC **20**, 763 (1955).

LiC₆H₄Cl

① *p*-Chlorophenyllithium

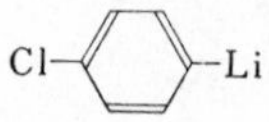

② p-ClC₆H₄Br + n-C₄H₉Li ⟶ 89%
　(p-ClC₆H₄)₃Sb + C₂H₅Li ⟶ 46%

③ Solid.
　IR, UV, NMR: Dokl. **128**, 728 (1959).

⑥ CA **45**, 10192(1951). Izv. OKhN **1953**,
　126.

LiC₆H₄N

① 2-Pyridyllithium

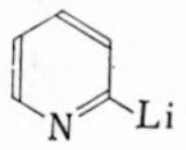

②   + n-C₄H₉Li ⟶ 69%

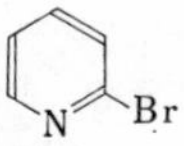

⑥ JOC 16, 1485 (1951).

LiC₆H₅

① Phenyllithium
   C₆H₅Li

② C₆H₅Cl + Li ⟶ 49%
   C₆H₅Br + Li ⟶ 98%
   C₆H₅I + Li ⟶ 83%
   (C₆H₅)₄Sb + C₄H₉Li ⟶ 50%
   C₆H₅Br + C₂H₅Li ⟶ 78%
   C₆H₅I + C₂H₅Li ⟶ 52%

③ Solid.
   IR, UV, NMR : JACS 85, 1651(1963);
      83, 3580 (1961).   Dokl. 128, 728
      (1959); 123, 113 (1958).

⑥ JACS 62, 1514(1940); 55, 1252 (1939).
   Z. anorg. allg. Chem. 141, 161 (1924).
   Ber. 50, 262 (1917); 72 B, 273 (1933).
   Ann. 479, 135 (1930).   CA 45, 10192
   (1951).   Izv. OKhN 1953, 126.

LiC₇H₄SN

① 2-Benzothiazolyllithium

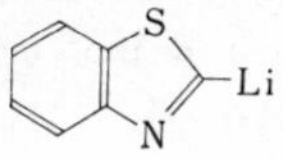

② 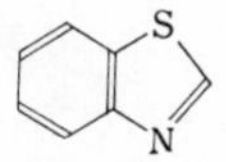   + n-C₄H₉Li ⟶ 90%

⑥ JACS 71, 2328 (1949).

LiC₇H₆Cl

① p-Chlorobenzyllithium
   p-ClC₆H₄CH₂Li

② p-ClC₆H₄CH₂OR + Li ⟶ 51%

⑥ JOC 26, 3723 (1961).

LiC₇H₇

① Tolyllithium
   o-, m-, p-CH₃C₆H₄Li

② CH₃C₆H₄Br + Li ⟶ 86~99%
   (CH₃C₆H₄)₃Sb + RLi ⟶ 48~82%
   CH₃C₆H₄I + C₂H₅Li ⟶ 30~66%

③ Solid.
   IR, UV, NMR : Dokl. 128, 728(1959);
      123, 113 (1958). Izv. SFi 22, 1110
      (1958).

⑥ Z. anorg. allg. Chem. 141, 161 (1924).
   JACS 55, 1252 (1933); 54, 1957
   (1932).   CA 45, 10192 (1951). Ber.
   72 B, 273 (1939).   Izv. OKhN 1953,
   126.   Compt. rend. 233, 1290 (1951).

LiC₇H₇

① Benzyllithium
   C₆H₅CH₂Li

② C₆H₅CH₂MgCl + Li ⟶ 40%
   (C₆H₅CH₂)₃Sb + C₂H₅Li ⟶ 65%,
      35%
   C₆H₅CH₂OR + Li ⟶ 75~83%

③ Crystals.
   IR, UV, NMR : JACS 85, 1651(1963).
      Dokl. 150, 1051 (1963).   J. Phys.
      Chem. 67, 148 (1963).

⑥ Ber. 64, 448 (1931).   CA 48, 3285,
   6389 (1954).   JOC 23, 2044 (1958).

LiC₇H₇O

① p-Anicyllithium
   p-CH₃OC₆H₄Li

② p-CH₃OC₆H₄Br + Li ⟶ 66%

⑥ JACS 54, 1957 (1932).

LiC₇H₁₁

① 1-Cycloheptenyllithium

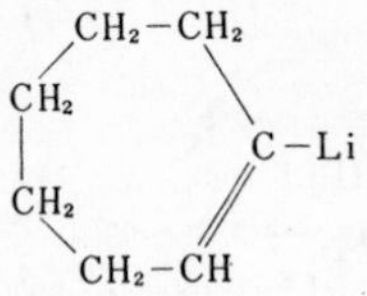

② CCl + Li ⟶ 90%

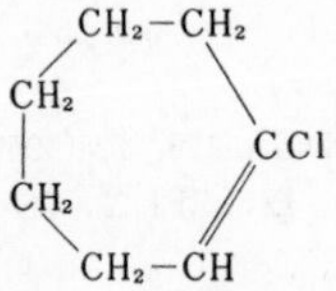

⑥ Nature **168**, 874 (1951).   JCS **1953**, 2202 ; **1955**, 3334 ; **1951**, 1755.

LiC₈H₅
① Phenylethynyllithium
C₆H₅C≡CLi
② C₆H₅C≡CH + C₆H₅Li ⟶ 100%
⑥ JACS **69**, 1181 (1947).   JOC **3**, 108 (1938) ; **1**, 315 (1936).   Ber. **72 B**, 273 (1939).   CA **45**, 10192 (1951) ; **48**, 6389 (1954).

LiC₈H₅O
① 2-Benzofuryllithium

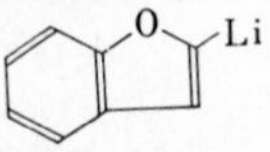

② 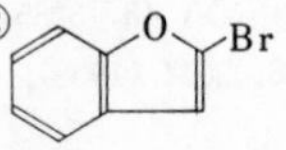 + n-C₄H₉Li ⟶ 62%

⑥ JACS **70**, 1655 (1948).

LiC₈H₅S
① 2-Thianaphthenyllithium

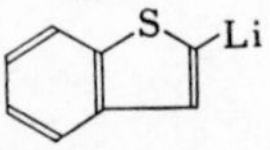

② 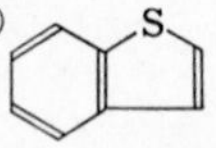 + n-C₄H₉Li ⟶ 70~74%

⑥ JACS **72**, 2788 (1950).

LiC₈H₇
① Styryllithium
C₆H₅CH=CHLi
② C₆H₅CH=CHBr + Li ⟶ 25%
⑥ JOC **1**, 457 (1936).   JACS **49**, 2323 (1927).

LiC₈H₇
① Cyclooctatetraenyllithium

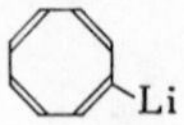

② 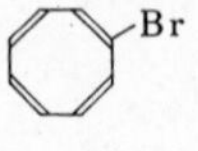 + n-C₄H₉Li ⟶ 59%

⑥ JACS **74**, 1730 (1952).

LiC₈H₈
① 1-Phenylvinyllithium

CH₂=C⟨Li⟨C₆H₅

② CH₂=C⟨Br⟨C₆H₅ + Li ⟶

⑥ JACS **73**, 4519 (1951).

LiC₈H₉
① α-Methylbenzyllithium
C₆H₅CH(CH₃)Li
② (C₆H₅CH(CH₃))₂O + Li ⟶ 68%
③ IR, UV, NMR : J. Phys. Chem. **67**, 148 (1963).   Chem. & Ind. **1962**, 1290.
⑥ JOC **26**, 3723 (1961).

LiC₈H₁₀N
① p-Dimethylaminophenyllithium
p-(CH₃)₂NC₆H₄Li
② p-(CH₃)₂NC₆H₄Br + Li ⟶ 96%
⑥ JACS **55**, 1252 (1933).

LiC₉H₆N
① γ-Quinolyllithium

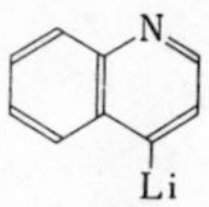

② + n-C₄H₉Li ⟶ 80%

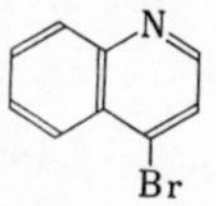

⑥ JOC **23**, 1584 (1958).

LiC₉H₇N₂

① 1-Phenyl-5-pyrazolyllithium

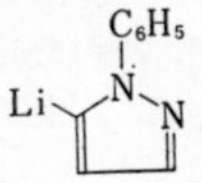

② C₆H₅— + n-C₄H₉Li ⟶ 80%

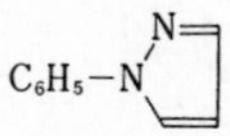

⑥ JACS **80**, 6271 (1958).

LiC₉H₈N

① 1-Methyl-2-indolyllithium

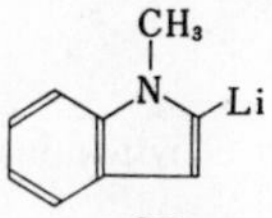

② 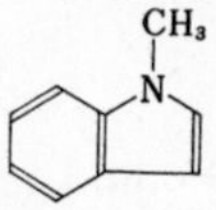 + n-C₄H₉Li ⟶ 78%

⑥ JACS **75**, 375 (1953).

LiC₉H₁₁

① 2,4,6-Trimethylphenyllithium

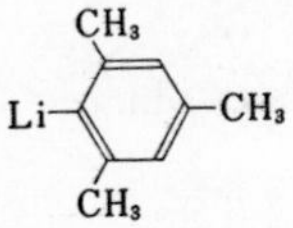

② (CH₃)₃C₆H₂Br + C₆H₅Li ⟶ 90%
   (CH₃)₃C₆H₂Br + C₂H₅Li ⟶ 40%
③ IR, UV, NMR: Dokl. **128**, 728 (1959).
⑥ CA **36**, 4475 (1942); **49**, 8162 (1955).
   JACS **75**, 20 (1953); **76**, 4389 (1954).

JOC **15**, 1155 (1950).

LiC₁₀H₇

① α-Naphthyllithium

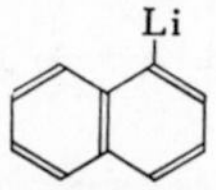

② α-C₁₀H₇Br + Li ⟶ 96%
   (α-C₁₀H₇)₃Sb + C₂H₅Li ⟶ 56%
③ Crystals.
   IR, UV, NMR: Dokl. **128**, 728(1959);
       123, 113 (1958).   Izv. SFi. **22**, 1110
       (1958).
⑥ JACS **55**, 1252 (1933).   CA **48**, 3286
   (1954).

LiC₁₂H₇N

① 2-Carbazolyllithium

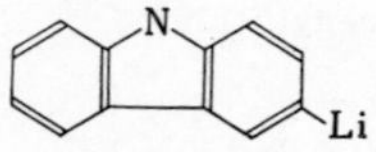

② 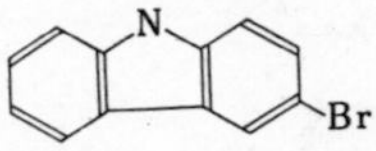 + n-C₄H₉Li
       ⟶ 58%

⑥ Iowa State Coll. J. Sci. **17**, 129(1942);
   CA **37**, 3434 (1943).

LiC₁₂H₁₀Na

① Diphenyllithium sodium
   (C₆H₅)₂LiNa
② PhLi + Ph₂Hg + Na ⟶
   Ph₂Hg + Li·Na alloy ⟶
③ Colorless crystals.
   Relatively inert to Et₂O.
④ + Ph₂CO ⟶ Ph₃CONa
   + Ph₂CH₂ ⟶ Ph₂CHNa
⑥ Ber. **88**, 294 (1955); **91**, 865, 873
   (1958).

LiC₁₃H₉

① 9-Fluorenyllithium

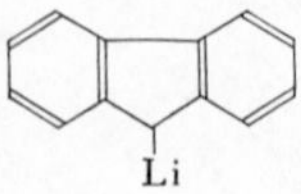

② 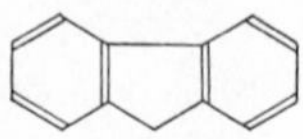 + C_2H_5Li ⟶ 100%

③ IR, UV, NMR: JACS **85**, 2633 (1963).
⑥ Dokl. **77**, 621 (1951).   Zhur. **25**, 2280
　(1955).

LiC₁₃H₁₁
① Diphenylmethyllithium
　$(C_6H_5)_2CHLi$
② $(C_6H_5)_2CHCl + Li$ ⟶ 80%
⑥ Compt. rend. **254**, 1054 (1962).　Chem.
　& Ind. **1962**, 696.

LiC₁₅H₁₀N
① *p*-2-Quinolylphenyllithium

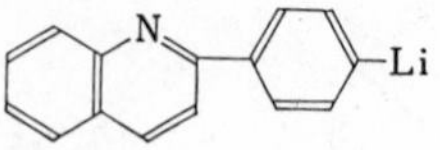

②

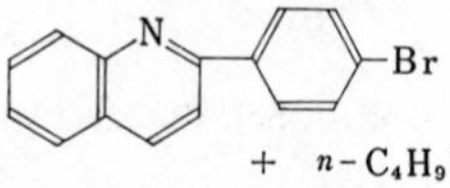

　　　 + *n*-C_4H_9Li ⟶ 75%
⑥ CA **47**, 7173 (1953).

LiC₁₆H₉
① 1-Pyrenyllithium

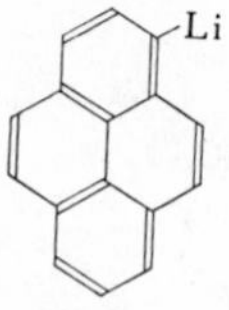

② 1-Br-$C_{16}H_9$ + C_6H_5Li ⟶ 72%
⑥ Acta Chem. Scand. **3**, 655 (1949).
　Zhur. **25**, 2280 (1955).

LiC₁₆H₃₃
① Hexadecyllithium

$C_{16}H_{33}Li$
② $C_{16}H_{33}Br + Li$ ⟶ 60%
③ IR, UV, NMR: Dokl. **125**, 562 (1959).
⑥ JACS **76**, 5798 (1954).　　JOC **9**, 211
　(1944).

LiC₁₉H₁₅
① Triphenylmethyllithium
　$(C_6H_5)_3CLi$
② $(C_6H_5)_3CCl + Li$ ⟶ 70%
③ IR, UV, NMR: JACS **85**, 1651, 2633
　(1963).　Dokl. **150**, 1051 (1963).
⑥ JOC **20**, 1531 (1955); **24**, 229 (1959).
　JACS **76**, 5833 (1954).

LiC₂₀H₁₅
① Triphenylvinyllithium

$$(C_6H_5)_2C=C\begin{matrix}Li\\C_6H_5\end{matrix}$$

② $(C_6H_5)_2C=C\begin{matrix}Br\\C_6H_5\end{matrix}$ + Li ⟶

⑥ JACS **77**, 4566 (1955).

LiC₂₂H₁₇SSi
① 5-Triphenylsilyl-2-thienyllithium

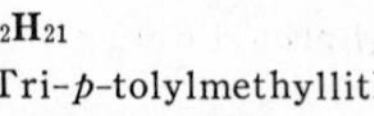

② 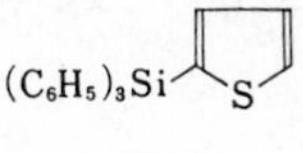 + *n*-C_4H_9Li
　　　　　⟶ 80%

⑥ JACS **71**, 1117 (1949).

LiC₂₂H₂₁
① Tri-*p*-tolylmethyllithium
　$(p\text{-}CH_3C_6H_4)_3CLi$
② $(p\text{-}CH_3C_6H_4)_3CH + n\text{-}C_3H_7Li$ ⟶ 70%
⑥ CA **48**, 144 (1954).

【Na】

NaCH₃
① Methylsodium
　CH_3Na

② $Hg(CH_3)_2 + Na \longrightarrow$
③ Colorless amorhpous solid.
   Thermally unstable. Decomp. without melting. Violently inflammable in air. Insol. in Et$_2$O and hydrocarbon solvents.
④ $+ CH_3COCH_2COOC_2H_5 \longrightarrow$
   $CH_3CO(Na)CH_2COOC_2H_5$
   $+ Me_3PtI \longrightarrow Me_4Pt$
   $+ CO_2 \longrightarrow CH_3COOH$
⑥ Ber. **50**, 262 (1917).   JACS **52**, 1254, 2998 (1930) ; **60**, 3085 (1938).

NaC₂H
① Ethynylsodium
   $HC \equiv CNa$
② $HC \equiv CH + Na \longrightarrow$
   $HC \equiv CH + NaNH_2 \longrightarrow$
   $HC \equiv CH + NaH \longrightarrow$
③ IR : Z. anorg. allg. Chem. **325**, 62 (1963).
④ $+ C_4H_9Br \longrightarrow C_4H_9C \equiv CH + NaBr$
   $+ (CH_3)_2SO_4 \longrightarrow CH_3C \equiv CH$
   $+ NH_4Cl \longrightarrow HC \equiv CH + NH_3$
   $+ NaCl$
   $+ CO_2 \longrightarrow HC \equiv CCO_2H$
   $+ R_2CO \longrightarrow R_2C(OH)C \equiv CH$
⑥ Z. anorg. allg. Chem. **325**, 62 (1963).
   Org. Syn. Coll. Vol. Ⅲ, 416 (1955).
   JOC **2**, 1 (1938).   JACS **60**, 2882 (1938).

NaC₂H₃
① Vinylsodium
   $CH_2 = CHNa$
② $CH_2 = CHBr + Na \longrightarrow$
   $(CH_2 = CH)_2Hg + Na \longrightarrow$
   $CH_2 = CH_2 + C_5H_{11}Na \longrightarrow$
④ $+ PhH \longrightarrow PhNa$
   $+ fluorene \longrightarrow fluorenylsodium$
   $+ CO_2 \longrightarrow CH_2 = CHCOOH$
⑥ Z. Naturf. **146**, 809 (1959).   JACS **72**, 3785 (1950).

NaC₂H₅
① Ethylsodium
   CH_3CH_2Na
② $Hg(C_2H_5)_2 + Na \longrightarrow$
   $C_2H_5Cl + Na \longrightarrow$
③ Colorless amorphous solid.
   Insol. in Et$_2$O, hydrocarbon solvents.
   Thermally unstable; inflammable in air.
④ $+ C_2H_5OC_2H_5 \longrightarrow C_2H_5ONa$
   $+ C_2H_6 + CH_2 = CH_2$
   $+ PhH \longrightarrow PhNa, C_6H_4Na_2$
   $+ C_6H_{13}Cl \longrightarrow C_8H_{18} + C_6H_{12} + C_2H_6$
   $+ NaCl$
   $+ CO_2 \longrightarrow C_2H_5COOH$
⑥ Ber. **50**, 262 (1917).   JACS **64**, 1783 (1942).   JCS **1953**, 861 ; **1963**, 5983.

NaC₃H₅
① Allylsodium
   $CH_2 = CH - CH_2Na$
② $AmNa + CH_3 - CH = CH_2 \xrightarrow{Na(OCH_3-i)}$
③ Colorless solid.
   IR : JACS **79**, 5578 (1957).
④ $+ (C_2H_5)_2O \longrightarrow C_2H_5ONa$
   $+ CO_2 \longrightarrow C_3H_5CO_2H$
⑤ A component of Alfin catalyst.
⑥ Ind. Eng. Chem. **42**, 1488 (1950).
   JACS **69**, 1675 (1947) ; **70**, 3342 (1948) ; **79**, 5578 (1957).

NaC₃H₇
① *n*-Propylsodium
   $CH_3(CH_2)_2Na$
② $C_3H_7Cl + Na \longrightarrow$
   $Hg(C_3H_7)_2 + Na \longrightarrow$
③ Colorless amorphous solid.
   Thermally unstable; inflammable in air. Insol. in Et$_2$O.
④ $+ CO_2 \longrightarrow C_3H_7COOH$

   $+ (CH_3)_3CCH_2Cl \longrightarrow CH_3-\underset{\underset{CH_2}{|}}{\overset{\overset{CH_3}{|}}{C}}-CH_2$

+ C$_3$H$_8$ + NaCl

⑥ JACS **63**, 327 (1941) ; **64**, 1783 (1942).

NaC$_4$H$_2$ClS

① 5–Chloro-2-thienylsodium

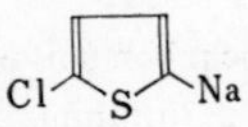

② 2-chlorothiophene + Na ⟶
③ Brown amorphous.
   Slightly sol. in Et$_2$O. Oxidized in air
   with evolution of light and heat.
④ + CO$_2$ ⟶ 5-Cl-2-C$_4$H$_2$S·CO$_2$H
⑥ JACS **70**, 286 (1948).

NaC$_4$H$_3$O(or Na$_2$C$_4$H$_2$O)

① 2,(5)-Furyl(di)sodium

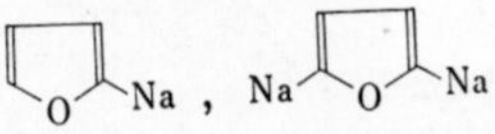

② furan + PhNa(or AmNa or PhCH$_2$Na)
   ⟶
③ Insol. in Et$_2$O.
④ + CO$_2$ ⟶ C$_4$H$_3$O·CO$_2$H or
   C$_4$H$_2$O(CO$_2$H)$_2$
⑥ JACS **56**, 1123 (1934) ; **68**, 93 (1946).

NaC$_4$H$_3$S

① 2-Thienylsodium

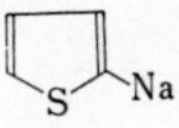

② 2-chlorothiophene + Na ⟶
   thiophene + EtCl(or PhCl) + Na
   ⟶
   thiophene + HgEt$_2$ + Na ⟶
④ + CO$_2$ ⟶ 2-C$_4$H$_3$S·CO$_2$H
⑥ JACS **70**, 286 (1948) ; **56**, 1123 (1934).

NaC$_4$H$_4$N$_2$

① Sodium pyrazine

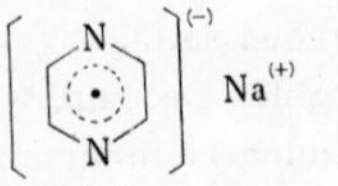

② Pyrazine + Na $\xrightarrow{\text{in glyme}}$
③ Colored soln.
   Sol. in dimethoxyethane or THF.
   Yields radical anions.
⑥ Proc. Chem. Soc. **1962**, 60.

NaC$_4$H$_9$

① *n*-Butylsodium
   CH$_3$(CH$_2$)$_3$Na
② (C$_4$H$_9$)$_2$Hg + Na ⟶
   C$_4$H$_9$Cl + Na ⟶
③ Colorless amorphous solid. Decomp.
④ + CO$_2$ ⟶ C$_4$H$_9$CO$_2$H
   + AlCl$_3$ ⟶ (C$_4$H$_9$)$_2$AlCl
⑥ JACS **63**, 327 (1941) ; **64**, 2240 (1942) ;
   59, 2387 (1937).   JOC **29**, 2689
   (1963).

NaC$_5$H$_5$

① Cyclopentadienylsodium

   C$_5$H$_5$Na,

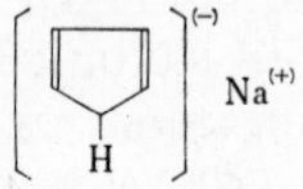

② C$_5$H$_6$ + Na ⟶
   C$_5$H$_6$ + Na dispersion ⟶
   C$_5$H$_6$ + indenyl (or fluorenyl) sodium
   ⟶
③ Colorless crystals.
   NMR : Can. J. Chem. **41**, 1231 (1963).
④ + CO$_2$ ⟶ C$_5$H$_5$CO$_2$H
   + RuCl$_3$ + Ru ⟶ C$_5$H$_5$·Ru·C$_5$H$_5$
   + TiCl$_4$ ⟶ (C$_5$H$_5$)$_2$TiCl$_2$
⑥ Ber. **89**, 434 (1956).   JINC **2**, 95
   (1956).   Org. Syn. **36**, 31 (1956).
   Can. J. Chem. **41**, 1231 (1963).

NaC₅H₅O

① 2-Methylfurylsodium

② 2-CH₃C₄H₃O + EtNa (or PhNa, or PhCH₂Na) $\longrightarrow$

④ + CO₂ $\longrightarrow$ 2,5-CH₃C₄H₂O·CO₂H

⑥ JACS **56**, 1123 (1934).

NaC₅H₅S

① 5-Methyl-2-thienylsodium

② 2-methylthiophene + (PhCH₂)₂Hg + Na $\longrightarrow$

④ + CO₂ $\longrightarrow$ 5-CH₃-2-C₄H₂S·CO₂H

⑥ JACS **56**, 1123 (1934).

NaC₅H₁₁

① Amylsodium
CH₃(CH₂)₄Na

② C₅H₁₁Cl + Na $\longrightarrow$
(C₅H₁₁)₂Hg + Na $\longrightarrow$

③ Colorless amorphous solid. Decomp.

④ + CO₂ $\longrightarrow$ C₅H₁₁CO₂H
+ C₂H₅OC₂H₅ $\longrightarrow$ C₂H₅ONa + C₅H₁₂
+ CH₂=CH₂
+ PhH $\longrightarrow$ PhNa
+ Ph₃CCH₂Cl $\longrightarrow$ Ph₃CCH₂Na
+ Ph₂C(Na)CH₂Ph
CH₃I $\longrightarrow$ C₅H₁₁·C₅H₁₁ + CH₃·CH₃
+ CH₄ + NaI
+ CH₂=CHCH=CH₂ $\longrightarrow$
CH₂=CHCH(Na)−CH₂C₅H₁₁

⑥ JACS **85**, 3984 (1963) ; **68**, 93 (1946) ; **59**, 2387 (1937) ; **79**, 1716, 5455 (1957).

NaC₆H₅

① Phenylsodium
C₆H₅Na

② PhCl + Na $\longrightarrow$

PhH + C₅H₁₁Na(or *n*-BuNa) $\longrightarrow$
Ph₂Hg + Na $\longrightarrow$

③ Colorless amorphous solid.
Thermally unstable. Insol. in Et₂O.
Inflammable in air.
IR : JOC 21, 830 (1956).

④ + CO₂ $\longrightarrow$ PhCO₂H
+ PhCH₃ $\longrightarrow$ PhCH₂Na
+ BCl₃ $\longrightarrow$ Ph₃B
+ I₂ $\longrightarrow$ Ph·Ph + PhI
+ N₂O $\longrightarrow$ Ph₃C−N=N−ONa
+ MgBr₂ $\longrightarrow$ Ph·MgBr

⑥ Ber. **97**, 1994 (1964). JCS **1953**, 861.
JACS **60**, 2336 (1938). JOC 21, 830 (1956).

NaC₆H₁₃

① *n*-Hexylsodium
CH₃(CH₂)₅Na

② C₆H₁₃Cl + Na $\longrightarrow$

③ Colorless amorphous solid. Decomp.

④ + CO₂ $\longrightarrow$ C₆H₁₃CO₂H
+ C₈H₁₇Cl $\longrightarrow$ C₆H₁₃·C₈H₇ + NaCl
$\longmapsto$ C₆H₁₄ + C₈H₁₆ + NaCl
$\longrightarrow$ polymer
$\longrightarrow$ C₆H₁₃Cl + C₈H₁₇Na $\longrightarrow$
C₆H₁₃·C₆H₁₃ + C₈H₁₇·C₈H₁₇
+ C₆H₁₂ + C₈H₁₈

⑥ JACS **64**, 2242 (1942).

NaC₇H₇

① Tolylsodium
CH₃C₆H₄Na

② CH₃C₆H₄Cl + Na $\longrightarrow$
(CH₃·C₆H₄)₂Hg + Na $\longrightarrow$
Ph·CH₃ + EtNa $\longrightarrow$

④ + CO₂ $\longrightarrow$ C₆H₄CO₂H
$\overset{\text{heat}}{\longrightarrow}$ PhCH₂Na

⑥ JACS **62**, 1514 (1940). Angew.
49, 455 (1936). Ber. 41, 2723 (1908).

NaC₇H₇

① Benzylsodium
C₆H₅CH₂Na

② (PhCH₂)₂Hg + Na $\longrightarrow$
PhCH₃ + PhNa(or C₅H₁₁Na) $\longrightarrow$

③ Red crystals. Decomp.
Sol. in Et₂O.

④ + (C₂H₅)₂O $\longrightarrow$ PhCH₃ + C₂H₅ONa
+ C₂H₄
+ CO₂ $\longrightarrow$
PhCH₂CO₂H, PhCH(CO₂H)₂
+ PCl₃ $\longrightarrow$ (PhCH₂)₃P
+ NH₃ $\longrightarrow$ PhCH₃ + NaNH₂

⑥ Ind. Eng. Chem. **46**, 539 (1954).
JACS **62**, 1514 (1940). Ann. **473**, 1
(1929). Ber. **64**, 448 (1931). Mol.
Phys. **6**, 206 (1963).

NaC₈H₅

① Phenylethynylsodium
C₆H₅C≡CNa

② PhC≡CH + Na $\longrightarrow$
PhC≡CH + indenylsodium $\longrightarrow$

③ Colorless solid.
Inflammable in air. Sol. in Et₂O.

④ + CO₂ $\longrightarrow$ PhC≡CCO₂H
+ (PhC≡C)₂CO $\longrightarrow$ (PhC≡C)₃COH

$$+ \begin{array}{c} CH-C=O \\ \| \quad\; O \\ CH-C=O \end{array} \longrightarrow \begin{array}{c} CH-CO\cdot C\equiv CPh \\ \| \\ CH-CO_2H \end{array}$$

⑥ JACS **69**, 1181 (1947) ; **54**, 1212 (1932) ;
83, 4027 (1961). JOC **1**, 315 (1936).

NaC₈H₈

① Sodium naphthaleneide

$$\left[\bigcirc\hspace{-0.5em}\bigcirc \right]^{(-)} Na^{(+)}$$

② Na + C₈H₈ $\xrightarrow{\text{Et}_2\text{O}}$

③ Sol. in Et₂O.

④ + CO₂ $\longrightarrow$ C₈H₈(CO₂H)₂

+ ROH $\longrightarrow$ C₈H₁₀
+ RCl $\longrightarrow$ C₈H₈R₂ (R=alkyl)
+ anthracene $\longrightarrow$ Disodium anthracene
+ Ph₃CH $\longrightarrow$ C₈H₁₀ + Ph₃CNa

⑤ Used as an anionic polymn. catalyst.

⑥ JACS **60**, 951 (1938) ; **65**, 2020 (1943) ;
78, 2656 (1956). Trans. Faraday
Soc. **58**, 953 (1962).

NaC₉H₇

① Indenylsodium

$$\left[\bigcirc\hspace{-0.5em}\bigcirc_{H} \right]^{(-)} Na^{(+)}$$

② indene + NaNH₂ $\longrightarrow$
indene + Ph₃CNa $\longrightarrow$

③ Yellow solid.
Sol. in Et₂O. Oxidized but not inflammable in air. Thermally unstable.

④ + CO₂ $\longrightarrow$ C₉H₇·CO₂H

⑥ JACS **54**, 1212 (1932) ; **42**, 569 (1909).
US 2171867 (1939).

NaC₉H₉

① β-Naphthylmethylsodium

$$\bigcirc\hspace{-0.5em}\bigcirc\text{—CH}_2\text{Na}$$

② β-CH₃C₈H₇ + C₆H₅Cl + Na $\longrightarrow$
β-CH₃C₈H₇ + (n-C₄H₉)₂Hg + Na $\longrightarrow$

③ Purple solid.

④ + CO₂ $\longrightarrow$ β-C₈H₇CO₂H

⑥ JACS **62**, 1514 (1940).

NaC₉H₁₁

① Phenylisopropylsodium
(CH₃)₂C(Na)C₆H₅

② PhCH(CH₃)₂ + HgEt₂ + Na

③ Purple solid.
Sol. in Et₂O.

④ + CO₂ ⟶ PhC(CO₂H)(CH₃)₂

⑥ JACS **62**, 1514 (1940).

NaC₉H₁₁

① 3,5-Dimethylbenzylsodium

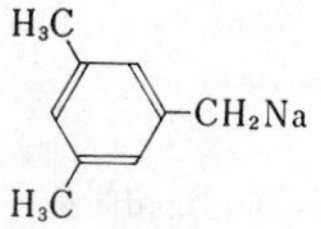

② 1,3,5-C₆H₃(CH₃)₃ + PhCl + Na ⟶

③ Sol. in Et₂O.

④ + CO₂ ⟶ C₆H₃(CH₃)₂CH₂CO₂H

⑥ JACS **62**, 1514 (1940).

NaC₁₀H₈N₂

① Sodium 2,2'-dipyridyl

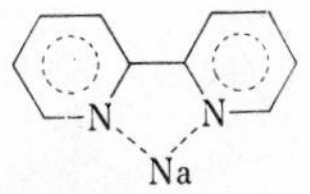

② 2,2'-dipyridyl + Na ⟶

③ Reddish brown soln.
    Sol. in dimethoxyethane.

⑥ J. Chem. Phys. **37**, 683 (1962).

NaC₁₃H₉

① Fluorenylsodium

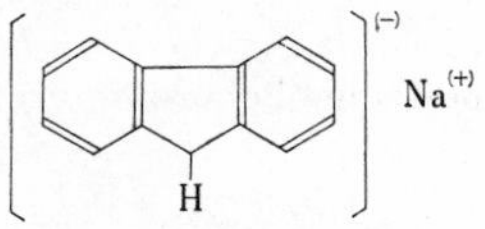

② C₁₃H₁₀ + Na ⟶
    C₁₃H₁₀ + NaNH₂ ⟶
    C₁₃H₁₀ + C₅H₁₁Na(or Ph₃CNa) ⟶

③ Yellow solid.
    Sol. in Et₂O.

④ + CO₂ ⟶ C₁₃H₁₀CO₂H
    + H₂O ⟶ C₁₃H₁₀
    + CH₃I ⟶ 9-CH₃C₁₃H₉
    + (CH₃)₂SO₄ ⟶ 9-CH₃C₁₃H₉

⑥ JCS **1951**, 2848. Ber. **41**, 2913 (1908) ;
    96, 627 (1963).

NaC₁₃H₁₀O

① Sodiumdiphenylketyl

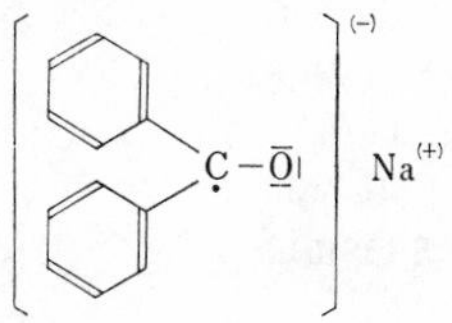

(C₆H₅)₂CO·Na

② Ph₂CO + Na ⟶

③ Blue soln. (in Et₂O).
    Very sensitive to O₂ and H₂O.
    UV: Trans. Faraday Soc. **58**, 948
    (1962).

⑤ Used in the purification of Et₂O.

⑥ Chem. Revs. **11**, 37 (1932).   Proc.
    Chem. Soc. **1962**, 229.   Trans.
    Faraday Soc. **58**, 948 (1962).

NaC₁₃H₁₁

① Diphenylmethylsodium
    (C₆H₅)₂CHNa

② Ph₂CH₂ + NaNH₂ ⟶ Ph₂CHNa

③ Red solid.
    Sol. in liq. NH₃.

④ + PhCH₂Cl ⟶ Ph₂CHCH₂Ph
    + Cl(CH₂)ₙCl ⟶
    Ph₂CH(CH₂)ₙCHPh₂
    + Ph₂CO ⇌ Ph₂CHC(ONa)Ph₂
    + PhCHO ⟶ Ph₂CHC(ONa)Ph

⑥ JOC **24**, 397 (1959).   JACS **81**, 2096
    (1959).

NaC₁₉H₁₅

① Triphenylmethylsodium
    (C₆H₅)₃CNa

② Ph₃CCl + Na
    Ph₃CH + NaNH₂ ⟶
    Ph₃CH + *n*-C₄H₉Na (or C₅H₁₁Na) ⟶

③ Red crystals.
    Sol. in Et₂O.

④ + CO₂ ⟶ Ph₃C·CO₂H
    + PhCHO ⟶ PhCH(OH)CPh₃

+ Ph₂CO $\rightleftharpoons$ Ph₃C· + Ph₂CO·Na

+ N₂O $\longrightarrow$ Ph₃C·N₂O·Na

+ H₂O $\longrightarrow$ Ph₃CH

+ O₂ $\longrightarrow$ Ph₃COONa $\longrightarrow$
    Ph₃COOCPh₃ + Na₂O₂

⑥ JACS **54**, 2419 (1932)；**81**, 2787 (1959).
    Org. Syn. Coll. Vol. 2, 607 (1943).
    Ber. **49**, 608 (1916).

Na₂C₁₂H₆O

① 4,6-Dibenzofuryldisodium

② Dibenzofuran + EtNa $\longrightarrow$
    (or AmNa)
    (or PhCH₂Na)

③ Sol. in Et₂O.

④ + CO₂ $\longrightarrow$ 4,6-C₁₂H₆O(CO₂H)₂
    + (CH₃)₂SO₄ $\longrightarrow$ 4,6-(CH₃)₂C₁₂H₆O

⑥ JOC 1, 315 (1937).   JACS **57**, 1121
    (1935).

Na₂C₁₄H₁₂

① Diphenylethylenedisodium
    C₆H₅CH(Na)·CH(Na)·C₆H₅

② PhCH=CHPh + Na $\longrightarrow$

④ + CO₂ $\longrightarrow$
    PhCH(CO₂H)·CH(CO₂H)Ph
    + S $\longrightarrow$ PhCH=CHPh
    + AsCl₃ $\longrightarrow$ PhCH=CHPh
    + (CH₃)₂SO₄ $\longrightarrow$
    CH₃·CH(Ph)·CH(Ph)·CH₃

⑥ JACS **69**, 710 (1947).

Na₂C₂₆H₂₀

① Tetraphenylethylenedisodium
    (C₆H₅)₂C(Na)C(Na)(C₆H₅)₂

② Ph₂C=CPh₂ + Na $\longrightarrow$

③ Dark red soln.

④ + CO₂ $\longrightarrow$
    Ph₂C(CO₂H)CHCH(CO₂H)Ph₂

+ H₂O $\longrightarrow$ Ph₂CHCHPh₂

+ PhCH₂Cl $\longrightarrow$ Ph₂C=CPh₂
    + PhCH₂CH₂Ph

⑥ Ber. **90**, 543 (1957)；**91**, 1106 (1958).
    Ann. **479**, 42, 58, 78 (1930).   Proc.
    Chem. Soc. 1962, 226.

Na₂C₂₈H₂₄

① 1,4-Tetraphenylbutanedisodium
    (C₆H₅)₂C(Na)CH₂CH₂C(Na)(C₆H₅)₂

② Ph₂C=CH₂ + Na $\longrightarrow$

④ + CO₂ $\longrightarrow$
    Ph₂C(CO₂H)CH₂CH₂C(CO₂H)Ph₂
    + CH₃I $\longrightarrow$
    Ph₂C(CH₃)CH₂CH₂C(CH₃)Ph₂
    + PhCHO $\longrightarrow$
    [Ph₂C(PhCHOH)CH₂]₂
    + Hg $\longrightarrow$ Ph₂C=CH₂

⑥ Ann. **479**, 78 (1930)；**463**, 1 (1928).

【K】

KCH₃

① Methylpotassium
    CH₃K

② (CH₃)₂Hg + K $\longrightarrow$

⑥ JACS **52**, 1254, 29?8 (1930).

KC₂H

① Ethynylpotassium (Potassium acety-
    lide)
    CH≡CK

② CH≡CH + K $\xrightarrow{\text{in liq. NH}_3}$

③ White crystals.

④ + (C₂H₅)₂SO₄ $\xrightarrow{\text{in liq. NH}_3}$ C₂H₅−C≡CH

⑥ JOC 2, 1 (1937)；1, 315 (1936).

KC₂H₃

① Vinylpotassium
    CH₂=CHK

② CH₂=CHCl + K $\longrightarrow$ 32%

⑥ JOC **23**, 750 (1958).

KC$_2$H$_5$

① Ethylpotassium
C$_2$H$_5$K

② (C$_2$H$_5$)$_2$Hg + K ⟶

④ C$_6$H$_6$ + C$_2$H$_5$K ⟶ C$_6$H$_5$K + C$_2$H$_6$

⑥ JACS **51**, 588 (1929) ; **58**, 2074 (1936).
JOC **1**, 315 (1937).

KC$_4$H$_3$O

① 3-Furylpotassium

$$\overline{O-CH=CK-CH=CH}$$

② $\overline{O-CH=CI-CH=CH}$ + K ⟶

⑥ JACS **55**, 2893 (1933).

KC$_5$H$_5$

① Cyclopentadienylpotassium

$$\overline{CHK-CH=CH-CH=CH}$$

② $\overline{CH_2-CH=CH-CH=CH}$ + K ⟶

⑥ Ber. **42**, 569 (1909) ; **44**, 1436 (1911).

KC$_5$H$_{11}$

① Amylpotassium
C$_5$H$_{11}$K

② AmCl + K ⟶
Am$_2$Hg + K ⟶

④ C$_6$H$_5$CH(CH$_3$)$_2$ + AmK ⟶
KC$_6$H$_4$CH(CH$_3$)$_2$ + C$_6$H$_5$CK(CH$_3$)$_2$

⑥ JACS **69**, 167, 172 (1947) ; **85**, 3984
(1963) ; **72**, 3785 (1950). J. Polymer
Sci. 52 (1961).

KC$_6$H$_5$

① Phenylpotassium
C$_6$H$_5$K

② C$_6$H$_5$OCH$_3$ + K ⟶
C$_6$H$_5$Cl + K ⟶
(*n*-Bu)$_2$Hg + K + C$_6$H$_6$ ⟶

③ White powder.

⑥ JACS **60**, 2336 (1938) ; **58**, 2074 (1936).
JCS **1953**, 861.   JOC **23**, 1638 (1958).

KC$_7$H$_7$

① *p*-Tolylpotassium
p-CH$_3$C$_6$H$_4$K

② *p*-ClC$_6$H$_4$CH$_3$ + K ⟶

⑥ Iowa State Coll. J. Sci. **16**, 117(1941).

KC$_7$H$_7$

① Benzylpotassium
C$_6$H$_5$CH$_2$K

② (*p*-CH$_3$C$_6$H$_4$)$_2$Hg $\xrightarrow{K}$ *p*-CH$_3$C$_6$H$_4$K
$\xrightarrow{heat}$ C$_6$H$_5$CH$_2$K
C$_6$H$_5$CH$_3$ + C$_6$H$_5$K ⟶ C$_6$H$_5$CH$_2$K
+ C$_6$H$_6$
C$_6$H$_5$CH$_3$ + K + C$_6$H$_5$Cl ⟶

③ Brick-red solid.

④ + Ph$_2$CO ⟶ Ph$_2$C(CH$_2$Ph)OH 59%

⑥ CA **56**, 10381 (1962).   JACS **62**, 1514
(1940).   Iowa State Coll. J. Sci.
16, 117 (1941).

KC$_8$H$_5$

① Phenylethynylpotassium
(Potassiumphenylacetylide)
C$_6$H$_5$C≡CK

② C$_6$H$_5$C≡CH + K ⟶

③ Light tan powder.

⑥ JACS **69**, 1181 (1947).   JOC **1**, 315
(1937).

KC$_8$H$_9$

① α-Phenylethylpotassium
C$_6$H$_5$CH$_2$CH$_2$K

② C$_6$H$_5$CH$_2$CH$_3$ + AmK
⟶ *m*- and *p*-KC$_6$H$_4$CH$_2$CH$_3$
⟶ C$_6$H$_5$CHKCH$_3$

⑥ JACS **84**, 4971 (1962).

KC$_9$H$_{11}$

① Cumylpotassium

C$_6$H$_5$C(CH$_3$)$_2$K

② C$_6$H$_5$CH(CH$_3$)$_2$ + AmK $\longrightarrow$

C$_6$H$_5$C(CH$_3$)$_2$OCH$_3$ + K-Na alloy $\longrightarrow$

③ Sol. in Et$_2$O (red soln.).

⑥ Ann. **473**, 1 (1921).   Compt. rend.
254, 674 (1962); **251**, 2356 (1960).
Iowa State Coll. J. Sci. **16**, 117
(1941). JACS **86**, 646 (1964).

KC$_9$H$_{11}$

① 3,5-Dimethylbenzylpotassium
3,5-(CH$_3$)$_2$C$_6$H$_3$CH$_2$K

② 1,3,5-(CH$_3$)$_3$C$_6$H$_3$ + K $\longrightarrow$

③ Brick-red solid.

⑥ JACS **62**, 1514 (1940).

KC$_{10}$H$_8$

① Potassium naphthalenide
C$_{10}$H$_8$K

② C$_{10}$H$_8$ + K $\xrightarrow{\text{in THF}}$

⑥ JACS **85**, 4052 (1963).

KC$_{12}$H$_7$O

① Dibenzofuranylpotassium
C$_{12}$H$_7$O·K

② C$_{12}$H$_8$O + C$_2$H$_5$K $\longrightarrow$

⑥ US 2146730 (1939).   JOC 1, 315
(1937).

KC$_{12}$H$_{23}$

① Dodecylpotassium
C$_{12}$H$_{23}$K

② C$_{12}$H$_{23}$Cl + K $\longrightarrow$

⑥ JOC **9**, 211 (1944).

KC$_{13}$H$_9$

① 9-Fluorenylpotassium

② Fluorene + K $\xrightarrow{\text{reflux in dioxane}}$

③ Reddish browm solid.

⑥ Ber. **34**, 1659 (1901); **41**, 2913 (1908).
Can. J. Chem. **38**, 697 (1960).

KC$_{13}$H$_{11}$

① Benzhydrylpotassium
(C$_6$H$_5$)$_2$CHK

② (C$_6$H$_5$)$_2$CHOCH$_3$ + K-Na alloy $\longrightarrow$

③ Sol. in Et$_2$O (red soln.).

⑥ Compt. rend. **251**, 2356 (1960).   JOC
1, 351 (1937).

KC$_{16}$H$_{33}$

① Hexadecylpotassium
C$_{16}$H$_{33}$K

② C$_{16}$H$_{33}$Cl + K $\longrightarrow$

⑥ J. Polymer Sci. 52 (1961).

KC$_{19}$H$_{15}$

① Triphenylmethylpotassium
(C$_6$H$_5$)$_3$CK

② (C$_6$H$_5$)$_3$CCl + K-Hg $\longrightarrow$
(C$_6$H$_5$)$_3$COC$_2$H$_5$ + K-Na alloy $\longrightarrow$

③ Dark red powder.
Slightly sol. in Et$_2$O.

⑥ Ber. **59**, 2646 (1926).

【Rb】

RbC$_2$H

① Ethynylrubidium
(Rubidium acetylide)
CH≡CRb

② CH≡CH + Rb $\longrightarrow$

③ Dark brown solid.

⑥ JOC 1, 315 (1936)

RbC$_2$H$_5$

① Ethylrubidium
C$_2$H$_5$Rb

② (C$_2$H$_5$)$_2$Zn + Rb $\longrightarrow$ isolated as an
addn. compd. with (C$_2$H$_5$)$_2$Zn

⑥ Ber. **59**, 2646 (1926).

RbC₆H₅
① Phenylrubidium
   C₆H₅Rb
② (n-Bu)₂Hg + Rb + C₆H₆ ⟶
⑥ JACS **60**, 2336 (1938) ; **58**, 2074 (1936).
   JCS 1953, 861.

RbC₇H₇
① Benzylrubidium
   C₆H₅CH₂Rb
② (C₆H₅CH₂)₂Hg + Rb ⟶
⑥ BCSJ **33**, 1091 (1960).

RbC₈H₅
① Phenylethynylrubidium
   (Rubidiumphenylacetylide)
   C₆H₅C≡CRb
② C₆H₅C≡CH + Rb ⟶
③ Dark tan solid.
⑥ JOC **1**, 315 (1937).

RbC₁₃H₁₁
① Benzhydrylrubidium
   (C₆H₅)₂CHRb
② (C₆H₅)₂CHCl + Rb ⟶
⑥ Ber. **59**, 2646 (1926).

RbC₁₉H₁₅
① Triphenylmethylrubidium
   (C₆H₅)₃CRb
② (C₆H₅)₃CCl + Rb amalgam ⟶
③ Dark red powder.
   Slightly sol. in Et₂O.
⑥ Ber. **59**, 2646 (1926).

【Cs】

CsC₂H
① Ethynylcesium
   (Cesium acetylide)
   CH≡CCs

② CH≡CH + Cs ⟶
③ Dark brown solid.
⑥ JOC **1**, 315 (1936).

CsC₂H₅
① Ethylcesium
   C₂H₅Cs
② (C₂H₅)₂Zn + Cs ⟶ isolated as an
   addn. compd. with (C₂H₅)₂Zn
⑥ Compt. rend. **223**, 1006 (1946). Ber.
   59, 2646 (1926).

CsC₆H₅
① Phenylcesium
   C₆H₅Cs
② (n-Bu)₂Hg + Cs + C₆H₆ ⟶
⑥ JACS **60**, 2336 (1938) ; **58**, 2074(1936).
   JCS 861 (1953).

CsC₇H₇
① Benzylcesium
   C₆H₅CH₂Cs
② (C₆H₅CH₂)₂Hg + Cs ⟶
⑥ BCSJ **33**, 1091 (1960). Compt. rend.
   222, 398 (1946).

CsC₈H₅
① Phenylethynylcessium
   (Cesium phenylacetylide)
   C₆H₅C≡CCs
② C₆H₅C≡CH + Cs ⟶
③ Dark tan solid.
⑥ JOC **1**, 315 (1937).

CsC₁₃H₉
① Fluorenylcesium

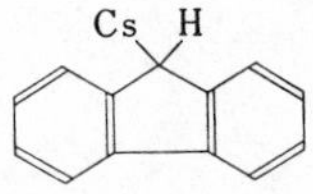

② fluorene + Cs-cyclohexylamide ⟶
③ UV: λ_{max} 447 (ε 678), 472 (835), 504
   (598) mμ. (in cyclohexylamine).
⑥ JACS **85**, 2633 (1963).

CsC₁₉H₁₅

① Triphenylmethylcesium
   $(C_6H_5)_3CCs$

② $(C_6H_5)_3CCl$ + Cs amalgam ⟶

③ Dark red powder.
   Slightly sol. in Et₂O.

⑥ Ber. **59**, 2646 (1926).

2. Organic Compounds of Alkaline-Earth Metals

(Be, Mg, Ca, Sr, Ba)

2.1. Introduction

Organic compounds of beryllium, calcium strontium, and barium belong to this family. Organoradium compounds have not yet been positively identified. Compounds of the most electropositive metals (barium, strontium, and calcium) have been very little studied, being not very well known. Not only does it appear nearly impossible to prepare these compounds, but there seems to be little advantage in making the attempt, because other more readily accessible organometallic compounds are equally useful for synthetic purposes.

On the other hand, organoberyllium and organomagnesium compounds have been investigated extensively, especially as Grignard reagents; organomagnesium compounds have been among the more widely studied organometallic compounds since their discovery by Victor Grignard in 1900.

Grignard reagents have the advantage over other active organometallic compounds in synthetic applications, especially in laboratory processes. Organic compounds of metals which are more electronegative than magnesium, for instance, mercury, thallium, or tin are less reactive and therefore less useful as reagents in syntheses. Metals of comparable electronegativity with magnesium (for instance, aluminum or zinc) afford relatively reactive organic compounds, which are particularly useful in industrial processes. However, for laboratory purposes these metals are less useful than magnesium because of the relative unreactivity of the metals themselves.

Alkyls of beryllium and magnesium have electron-deficient structures. In solution, therefore, interactions with solvents such as ether are an important factor in the structures and reactivities of these alkyls.

2.2. Classification and Nomenclature

There are three possible types of organic compounds of alkaline-earth metals: symmetric R_2M, asymmetric RMR', and mixed form RMX. For examples,

R_2Be (dialkylberyllium); $(CH_3)_2Be$; $(i-C_3H_7)_2Be$.

$RBeX$ (alkylberyllium halide); CH_3BeI.

R_2Mg (dialkylmagnesium); $(C_2H_5)_2Mg$; $(C_3H_7)_2Mg$.

$RMgX$ (alkylmagnesium halide); CH_3MgBr; C_2H_5MgI.

R_2Ca, $RCaX$, R_2Ba, R_2BaX, R_2Sr, and $RSrX$ are named in the same way.

In general, these compounds are in equilibrium in solution,

$$R_2M \cdot MX_2 \rightleftharpoons R_2X + MX_2 \rightleftharpoons 2RMX$$

Acordingly, structures based on the above nomenclature do not necessarily correspond strictly to the actual structures.

2.3. Methods of Synthesis

2.3.1. Reactions of Organic Halides with Metals

Compounds corresponding to the general formula RMX can be prepared by this method:

$$CH_3I + Be \longrightarrow CH_3BeI$$
$$C_2H_5Br + Mg \longrightarrow C_2H_5MgBr$$
$$CH_3I + Ca \longrightarrow CH_3CaI$$
$$CH_3I + Ba \longrightarrow CH_3BaI$$
$$CH_3I + Sr \longrightarrow CH_3SrI$$

Diethyl ether and, less commonly, higher ethers such as diisopropyl ether or di-*n*-butyl ether are used as solvents.   Tetrahydrofuran as well as some poly-ethers (dimethoxyethane, diglyme, etc.) can effectively be used as solvents.   In tetrahydrofuran, Grignard reagents from alkenyl halides and chlorobenzenes which did not react with magnesium in ethyl ether can be easily obtained:

$$CH_2{=}CHCl + Mg \xrightarrow{\text{THF}} CH_2{=}CHMgCl$$

Di-Grignard reagents of *p*-dibromobenzene have considerable synthetic value, but are not very easy to prepare in diethyl ether.   In tetrahydrofuran, however, they are readily prepared.   Yields as well as rates of formation of Grignard reagents are often improved considerably by using these new solvents.   Very recently, hexamethylphosphoramide has been introduced as a new and useful solvent in organomagnesium synthesis and reactions.   Of some importance as a special Grignard reaction is an *in situ* Grignard method in which formation of unstable Grignard reagent and coupling with a quencher such as chlorosilanes occurs concurrently.

$$HCBr_3 + 3Mg + 3(CH_3)_3SiCl \xrightarrow{\text{THF}} HC[Si(CH_2)_3]_3$$

Tertiary amines, such as dimethylaniline or pyridine, and some hydrocarbons are also used as solvents for Grignard reactions.   In toluene, methylcyclohexane, and kerosene, it was reported that the formation of Grignard reagent can be achieved smoothly in the presence of some alkali metal alkoxides ($0.5 \sim 1.0$ mole % to magnesium) or tetrahydrofuran of an equivalent amount as magnesium.

Mechanisms of Grignard formation from organic halides and magnesium have not been established convincingly, but the fact that considerable racemization occurs in the usual Grignard reactions of compound (I) whereas complete retention of configuration was observed in the reaction through organolithium reagent, may suggest the involvement of a free-radical intermediate in Grignard formation.

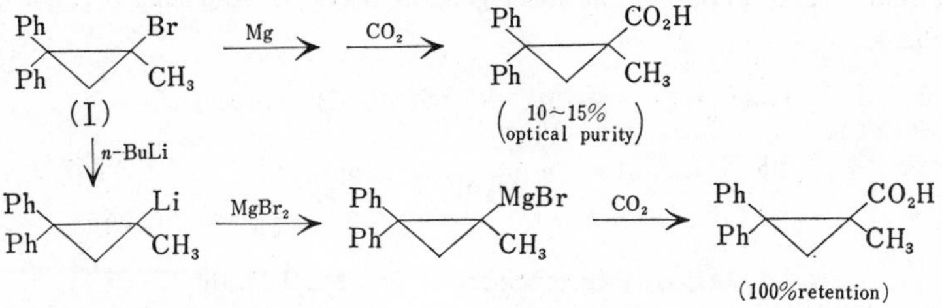

$$\text{(I)} \xrightarrow{\text{Mg}} \xrightarrow{\text{CO}_2} \quad \begin{pmatrix} 10\sim15\% \\ \text{optical purity} \end{pmatrix}$$

$$\text{(I)} \xrightarrow{n\text{-BuLi}} \cdots \xrightarrow{\text{MgBr}_2} \cdots \xrightarrow{\text{CO}_2} \quad (100\% \text{ retention})$$

In some cases, however, *cis-* and *trans-*2-bromobutene-2 also gave products with retention:

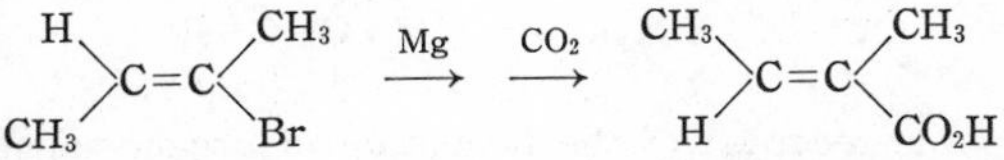

$$\xrightarrow{\text{Mg}} \xrightarrow{\text{CO}_2} \quad \text{(complete retention)}$$

Barium, strontium, and calcium also give Grignard-like reagents in ether but no detailed study has been reported.

2.3.2. Metal–Metal Exchange Reactions

$$(C_6H_5)_2Hg + Mg \xrightarrow{\text{ether}} (C_6H_5)_2Mg + Hg-Mg$$

$$2\,C_6H_5Li + Mg \rightleftharpoons (C_6H_5)_2Mg + 2\,Li$$

$$(CH_3)_2Hg + Be \rightleftharpoons (CH_3)_2Be + Hg$$

$$2\,(C_2H_5)_2Zn + Ca \rightleftharpoons (C_2H_5)_2Ca \cdot (C_2H_5)_2Zn + Zn$$

This is one of the most generally applicable methods, very suitable to obtaining these organometallic reagents in a pure state. Organomercury compounds are used conveniently for this purpose.

2.3.3. Reactions of Metals with Free Radicals

Free radicals, such as a methyl free radical, react with some metals to give corresponding organometallic compounds, although there is little synthetic significance. An example is

$$Ph_3C \cdot + Mg \xrightarrow{\text{trace MgX}_2} (Ph_3C)_2Mg$$

2.3.4. Direct Metalation of Hydrocarbons with Metals

Hydrocarbons with active hydrogen, such as acetylene and cyclopentadiene, react with alkali metals, magnesium, or calcium to give organometallic compounds:

$$HC\equiv CH + Ca \xrightarrow{\text{liq. NH}_3} (HC\equiv C)_2Ca$$

$$2\,C_5H_6 + Mg \xrightarrow{500\sim600^\circ} (C_5H_5)_2Mg$$

2.3.5. Reactions of Metal Salts with Organometallic Compounds

Organolithium compounds or Grignard reagents afford other organometallic compounds by reaction with salts of more electronegative metals than lithium or magnesium.   This is one of the most general ways of preparing organoberyllium compounds.

$$2\,C_2H_5MgBr + BeCl_2 \longrightarrow (C_2H_5)_2Be + 2\,MgBrCl$$

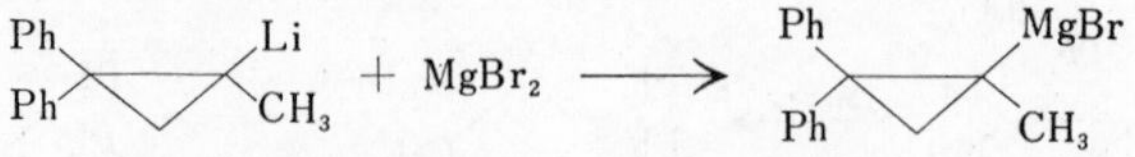

$$(C_2H_5)_2Mg + MgBr_2 \rightleftharpoons 2\,C_2H_5MgBr$$

The last example is a so-called Schlenk equilibrium.

2.3.6. Addition of Metal Hydrides to a Carbon–Carbon Double Bond

$$\begin{array}{c}\rangle C{=}C\langle + MH \rightleftharpoons M{-}\overset{|}{C}{-}\overset{|}{C}{-}H\end{array}$$

Only one example is recorded of the formation of organomagnesium compound (by this type of reaction):

$$2\,CH_3CH{=}CH_2 + MgH_2 \longrightarrow (n{-}C_3H_7)_2Mg$$

2.3.7. Metal–Metal Exchange between Organometallic Compounds

$$RM + R'M' \rightleftharpoons R'M + RM'$$

In these reactions, the more electropositive metal has a tendency to combine with the more electronegative organic group.

$$2\,C_6H_5MgBr + (4{-}CH_3C_6H_4)_2Hg \rightleftharpoons 2\,(4{-}CH_3C_6H_4)MgBr + (C_6H_5)_2Hg$$

2.3.8. Hydrogen–Metal Exchange (Metalation)

Hydrogen–metal exchange reactions offer a useful approach to certain organometallic compounds.   However, Grignard reagents are not sufficiently reactive to undergo such metalation reactions except for active-hydrogen compounds:

$$HC{\equiv}CH + C_2H_5MgBr \longrightarrow HC{\equiv}CMgBr + C_2H_6$$
$$C_5H_6 + C_2H_5MgBr \longrightarrow C_5H_5MgBr + C_2H_6$$

Phenylcalcium iodide has been reported to metalate as in the following example.

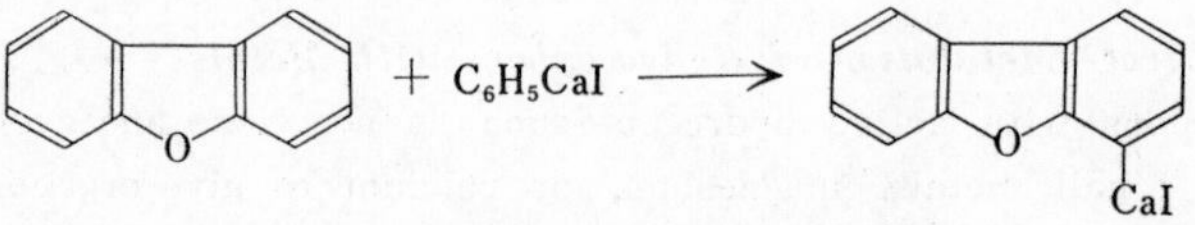

Interestingly, *n*-butyllithium and diethylstrontium metalate to different positions of phenyl methyl sulfide.

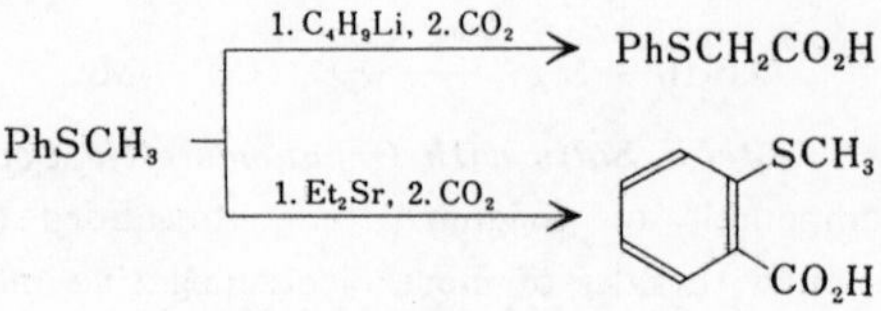

2.3.9. Halogen–Metal Exchange

Halogen-metal exchange reactions, which are commonly used for organolithium compounds, are not suitable for Grignard reagents.   Some examples, however, are known:

$$C_6H_5C \equiv CBr + CH_3MgBr \longrightarrow C_6H_5C \equiv CMgBr + CH_3Br$$

2.3.10. Synthesis of R₂M by Disproportionation of RMX

This is a microscopic reverse process of 2.3.5.   Addition of dioxane to ether solutions of Grignard reagents results in the precipitation of a dioxane complex of the magnesium halide, dialkylmagnesium being left in solution.

$$2\,RMgX \rightleftharpoons R_2Mg + MgX_2$$

This reaction has been most useful as a preparation of the dialkyls and diaryls of magnesium.

Thermal disproportionation of alkylberyllium halide affords dialkyls of beryllium:

$$2\,CH_3BeCl \xrightarrow{190°} (CH_3)_2Be + BeCl_2$$

2.3.11. Reaction of Grignard Reagents with α–Olefins

It has been recently reported that exchange of alkyl groups takes place between C_3H_7MgBr and α-olefins in the presence of a catalytic amount of $TiCl_4$:

$$CH_3CH_2CH_2MgBr + RCH = CH_2 \xrightarrow{TiCl_4} RCH_2CH_2MgBr + CH_3CH = CH_2$$

2.4. General Properties

2.4.1. Physical Properties

The organic compounds of the alkaline-earth metals show a striking gradation of properties and reactivities depending on the electronegativity of the metals. Some of these compounds are actually ionic infusible salts, while others are volatile and essentially covalent substances.   Reactivities also vary strikingly, changing in a manner parallel to the physical properties.   These differences in physical and chemical properties are mainly due to the degree of ionic character of the metal–carbon bonds.   The organic derivatives of the most electropositive metals, calcium, strontium, and barium, disclose salt or salt-like properties, and this fact is in accord with the enhanced ionic character of these compounds. These compounds, however, resemble organolithium more than organosodium compounds, in the sense that these are soluble in ether.

Table 2.1. *Electronegativities and Ionic Characters of C–M Bonds for Alkaline-Earth Metals.*

	Electronegativity	% Ionic Character of C–M Bond
Ba	0.9	35
Sr	1.0	32
Ca	1.0	32
Mg	1.2	27
Be	1.5	20

On the other hand, organic compounds of magnesium and beryllium show the properties associated with more covalent substances.   Thus the dialkylberyllium, BeR_2 ($R = C_2H_5$, C_3H_7), is volatile and can be distilled under reduced pressure. Except for dimethylberyllium, alkyls of beryllium are liquid substances.

Organic compounds of beryllium and magnesium have electron-deficient structures.   Therefore the lower dialkyls of magnesium are nonvolatile, crystalline solids.   These compounds undergo the typical reaction of electron-deficient molecules, that is, coordination with donor molecules such as ethers, amines, and phosphines, so that these compounds are soluble in ether.   Dimethylmagnesium– ether complex dissolves in ether to a concentration of 0.8 mole/liter.   Higher dialkyls dissolve more readily in ether.   Although diphenylmagnesium itself is insoluble in benzene, its ether complex is soluble.

2.4.2. Structures

There has been no detailed investigation of the structures of organic derivatives of calcium, strontium, and barium, hence this discussion will be limited to organic compounds of beryllium and magnesium.

From studies of vapor pressure and vapor densities, it has been concluded that dimethylberyllium forms a long chain polymer.   The following structure was established by X-ray analysis.   The Be–C distances are greater than the calculated value for a single bond, the bond order being 0.48~0.5.

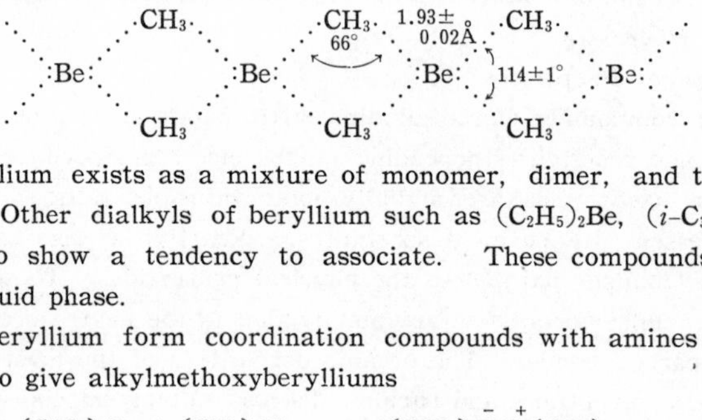

Dimethylberyllium exists as a mixture of monomer, dimer, and trimer in the vapor phase.   Other dialkyls of beryllium such as $(C_2H_5)_2Be$, $(i\text{-}C_3H_7)_2Be$, and $(n\text{-}C_4H_9)_2Be$ also show a tendency to associate.   These compounds are mostly dimer in the liquid phase.

Dialkyls of beryllium form coordination compounds with amines which react with methanol to give alkylmethoxyberylliums

$$(C_3H_7)_2Be + (CH_3)_3N \longrightarrow (C_3H_7)_2\overset{-}{Be}\overset{+}{N}(CH_3)_3$$

Some organoberyllium inner complexes of the spiran type have been prepared.

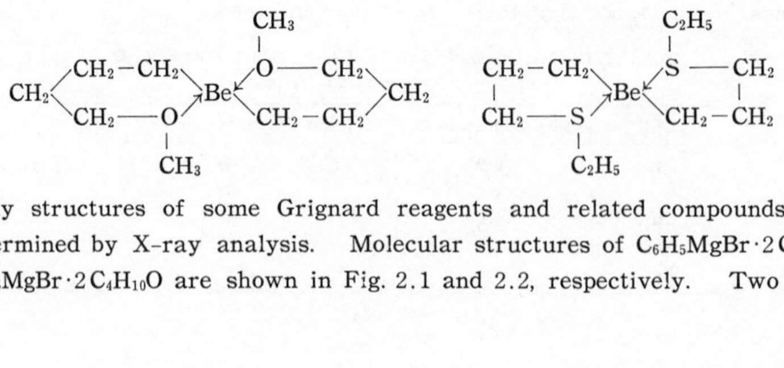

Recently structures of some Grignard reagents and related compounds have been determined by X-ray analysis.   Molecular structures of $C_6H_5MgBr \cdot 2C_4H_{10}O$ and $C_2H_5MgBr \cdot 2C_4H_{10}O$ are shown in Fig. 2.1 and 2.2, respectively.   Two molecules of ether, C_6H_5 (or C_2H_5) and Br are tetrahedrally bonded to a magnesium atom. Bond angles of ether to oxygen are very close to tetrahedral, showing the Mg-O bond nearly covalent.

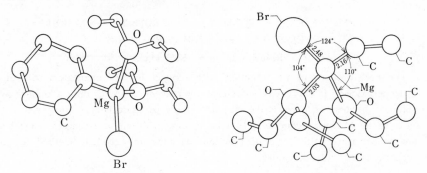

Eig. 2.1. *Molecular structure of* $C_6H_5MgBr \cdot 2\,C_4H_{10}O.$

Fig. 2.2. *Molecular structure of* $C_2H_5MgBr \cdot 2\,C_4H_{10}O.$

One of the most interesting problems in organometallic chemistry is the constitution of the Grignard reagent in solution. An equilibrium has been suggested between "Grignard reagent, RMgX" and the corresponding dialkylmagnesium in ether solution (the Schlenk equilibrium).

$$2\,RMgX \;\rightleftharpoons\; R_2Mg + MgX_2 \;\rightleftharpoons\; R_2Mg\underset{X}{\overset{X}{\diagdown\diagup}}Mg$$

Dessy and coworkers have cast doubt on the existence of the RMgX structure and concluded that the bridged structure, a 1 : 1 complex between dialkylmagnesium and magnesium halide, may be a more proper representation. This has reopened the question of the structure of the Grignard reagent. At present further studies are undoubtedly required to resolve the question, but recent evidence favors the structure of monomeric "alkylmagnesium halide", especially in THF, in dilute diethylether, and in the solid state as dietherate (*vide supra*).

2.4.3. Chemical Properties

Grignard reagents have many advantages over other organometallics for laboratory processes in their moderate reactivity (stable in ether solution) and in their accessibility from readily available starting materials.

(i) *Reactions with Active Hydrogen Compounds.* Grignard reagents afford parent hydrocarbons by reaction with active hydrogen compounds including acids (even very weak acids such as alcohols), acetylenes, and primary and secondary amines. Formally, these reactions may be regarded as the neutralization of a strong base (R:⁻).

$$CH_3MgI + CH_3CH_2OH \;\longrightarrow\; CH_4 + CH_3CH_2OMgI$$

These reactions are used to determine the number of active hydrogens in a compound (Zerewitinoff determination).

(ii) *Reactions with Oxygen, Sulfur, and the Halogens.*   Molecular oxygen, sulfur, and the halogens react with Grignard reagents:

$$RMgX + O_2 \xrightarrow{} ROOMgX \xrightarrow{RMgX} 2\,ROMgX \xrightarrow{H_2O, H^+} 2\,ROH$$

$$RMgX + S_x \xrightarrow{} RSH + (RS)_2 + R_2S$$

$$RMgX + I_2 \xrightarrow{} RI + MgXI$$

The first product in the reaction with oxygen is the magnesium salt of a hydroperoxide.   If an excess of Grignard reagent is used, only alkoxides are obtained because of a reductive cleavage of the peroxide bond.   However, with care to avoid such reduction (that is, inverse addition of Grignard reagent at low temperature), this type of reaction provides an excellent method for the preparation of hydroperoxides.

$$t\text{-}C_4H_9MgCl + O_2 \xrightarrow{-74°} t\text{-}C_4H_9OOMgCl \xrightarrow{H^+} t\text{-}C_4H_9OOH \text{ (91.4\%)}$$

Neopentyl chloride can be converted to neopentyl iodide.   This is the only way to exchange halogens when direct halide exchange is not feasible because of the low reactivity in S_N2 reactions and/or the tendency toward rearrangement in S_N1 reactions.

$$\underset{\underset{CH_3}{|}}{\overset{\overset{CH_3}{|}}{CH_3-C-CH_2Cl}} \xrightarrow{Mg} \underset{\underset{CH_3}{|}}{\overset{\overset{CH_3}{|}}{CH_3-C-CH_2MgCl}} \xrightarrow{I_2} \underset{\underset{CH_3}{|}}{\overset{\overset{CH_3}{|}}{CH_3-C-CH_2I}}$$

(iii) *Addition to Carbonyl Groups.*   One of the most important Grignard reactions is the formation of a new carbon–carbon bond by addition to multiple bonds. From a mechanistic point of view, these reactions involve nucleophilic attack on an electrophilic carbon multiply bonded to either oxygen or nitrogen.   Additions to form a new carbon–carbon bond also occur at a sufficiently positive carbon by virtue of its strongly electronegative substituents.   There seem to be some similarities between these two types of reactions.   In the present text, however, emphasis is placed on synthetic applications rather than on mechanistic considerations.

[*Reaction with formaldehyde*]

$$RMgX + H_2CO \xrightarrow{} RCH_2OMgX \xrightarrow{} RCH_2OH$$

Primary alcohols are obtained, and the yields are generally excellent.

[*Reaction with aldehydes*]

$$RMgX + R'CHO \xrightarrow{} RR'CHOMgX \xrightarrow{} RR'CHOH$$

Secondary alcohols are obtained with high yield.

[*Reaction with ketones*]

$$RMgX + R'R''CO \xrightarrow{} RR'R''COMgX \xrightarrow{} RR'R''COH$$

Tertiary alcohols are obtaind.   The yields as well as types of side reactions depend on the structures of the ketones and Grignard reagents (*vide infra*).

[*Reaction with carboxylic esters*]

$$2\,RMgX + R'COOR'' \longrightarrow RRR'COMgX \longrightarrow R_2R'COH$$

This is an important method of preparing tertiary alcohols with two identical alkyl (or aryl) groups.

[*Reaction with carboxylic acid chloride*]

$$RMgX + R'COCl \longrightarrow R-\underset{\underset{R'}{|}}{\overset{\overset{Cl}{|}}{C}}-OMgX \longrightarrow RR'CO + MgXCl$$

$$RR'CO + RMgX \longrightarrow R_2R'COMgX \longrightarrow R_2R'COH$$

Ketones may be obtaind, but this is not a practical method for the synthesis of ketones since excess Grignard reagent adds rapidly to the ketone as it is formed.

However, ketones may be obtained in good yields when the reaction is carried out at sufficiently low temperature, or if the Grignard reagent is first converted to an organocadmium chloride. Acid anhydrides can also be used for ketone synthesis.

[*Reaction with N, N-dimethylcarboxylamides*]

$$RMgX + R'-CON(CH_3)_2 \longrightarrow R-\underset{\underset{OMgX}{|}}{\overset{\overset{R'}{|}}{C}}-N(CH_3)_2$$

$$\overset{H_2O}{\longrightarrow} RR'CO + MgXOH + HN(CH_3)_2$$

N, N-Disubstituted amides usually react with 1 mole of Grignard reagent to give stable adducts, which afford carbonyl compounds on hydrolysis, with good yields.

[*Reaction with carbon dioxide*]

$$RMgX + CO_2 \longrightarrow RCO_2MgX \longrightarrow RCO_2H$$

Initial products of the reaction of carbon dioxide with Grignard reagents are salts of carboxylic acids, RCO_2MgX, which react with another molecule of Grignard reagent only slowly even at room temperature. Thus, this reaction provides a good method for the synthesis of carboxylic acids.

(iv) *Side Reactions in Addition Reactions to Carbonyl Groups.* Generally, addition of Grignard reagents to carbonyl compounds proceeds with excellent yields, but side reactions sometimes occur with sterically hindered ketones as well as in the reaction of sterically hindered Grignard reagents. Enolization and reduction are two of the most important side reactions. Mechanisms of these side reactions are not necessarily clear but coordination of magnesium metal is undoubtedly involved in both reactions.

[*Addition*]

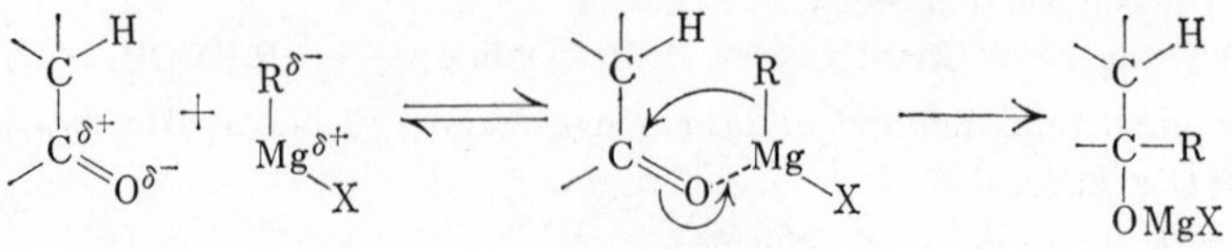

[*Enolization*]

If R in RMgX is bulky, addition to carbonyl group is hidered and enolization can compete successfully.   Ketones with no hydrogens on the β-carbons do not undergo this type of reaction, of course.

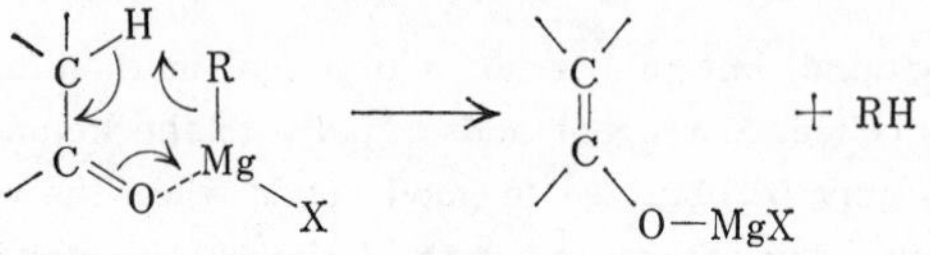

[*Reduction*]

Reduction may occur when R in RMgX has at least one β-hydrogen, which is transfered as a hydride ion to the carbonyl carbon.

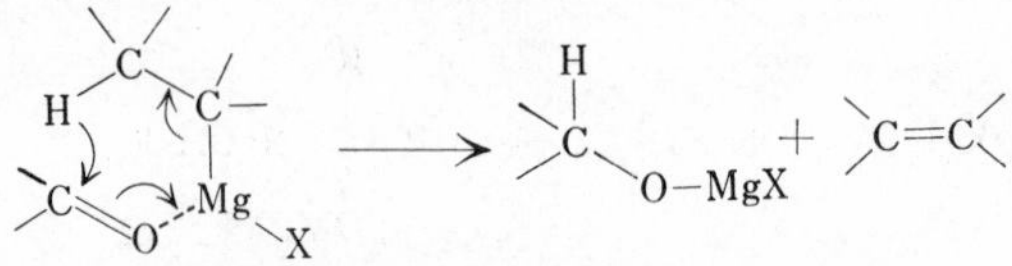

Grignard reagents with an asymmetric carbon at the β-position afford an optically active alcohol on reduction.   This fact indicates that the steric requirement governs the course of the reaction.

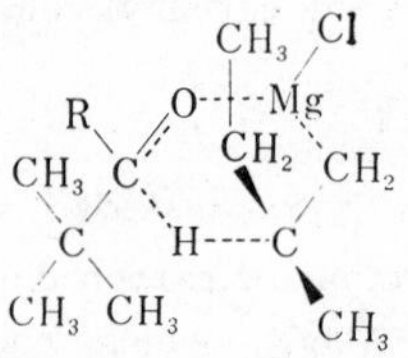

Table 2.2 shows the results of competition of these reactions in the reaction of diisopropyl ketone with various Grignard reagents.

(v)   *Addition to Carbon-Carbon Double Bonds.*   Alkenes are not attacked by Grignard reagents since R^- and ^+MgX in RMgX are not sufficiently nucleophilic and electrophilic, respectively, to add to a carbon-carbon double bond.   However, additions to a double bond occur if the double bond is activated by an electron-withdrawing substituent such as a carbonyl group.

Table 2.2. *Reaction Products of (i-C_3H_7)$_2$CO with RMgX.*

R	Addition (%)	Enolization (%)	Reduction (%)	Number and kind of β-hydrogens
CH_3	95	0	0	0
CH_3CH_2-	77	2	21	3-*prim*
$CH_3CH_2CH_2-$	36	2	60	2-*sec*
$(CH_3)_2CH-$	0	29	65	6-*prim*
$(CH_3)_2CHCH_2-$	8	11	78	1-*tert*
$(CH_3)_3C-$	0	35	65	9-*prim*
$(CH_3)_3CCH_2-$	4	90	0	0

$$CH_3CH=CH-\underset{\underset{O}{\|}}{C}-CH_3 \quad \xrightarrow{\begin{array}{l}1.\ C_2H_5MgX\\2.\ H^+,\ H_2O\end{array}}$$

$$CH_3-\underset{\underset{C_2H_5}{|}}{CH}-CH_2-\underset{\underset{O}{\|}}{C}-CH_3 + CH_3-CH=CH-\underset{\underset{C_2H_5}{|}}{\overset{\overset{OH}{|}}{C}}-CH_3$$

$$75\% \qquad\qquad\qquad 25\%$$

Steric requirements determine the balance between 1,2- and 1,4-addition to α, β-unsaturated carbonyl groups.

(vi) *Addition to Carbon-Nitrogen Triple Bonds.* Grignard reagents add to carbon-nitrogen triple bonds as well as to carbonyl groups. The reaction proceeds through an intermediate ketimine which affords a ketone on hydrolysis, usually in good yields.

$$RMgX + R'C\equiv N \longrightarrow RR'C=N-MgX \xrightarrow{H^+,\ H_2O}$$

$$[RR'C=NH] \xrightarrow{H_2O} RR'CO + NH_3$$

(vii) *Substitution.* In some cases, R^- in RMgX can function as a nucleophile in S_N2 reactions. However, this reaction is only important for a substrate with high S_N2 reactivity.

$$R'X + RMgX \longrightarrow RR' + MgX_2$$

This type of reaction often provides a useful way of preparing some organometallics, especially compounds with electronegative metals.

$$C_6H_5MgX + (CH_3)_3SiCl \longrightarrow (CH_3)_3SiC_6H_5 + MgXCl$$

$$2\,i\text{-}C_3H_7MgBr + BeCl_2 \longrightarrow (i\text{-}C_3H_7)_2Be + MgCl_2 + MgBr_2$$

However, for halides of cobalt or silver, intermediate organometallic compounds are usually unstable, so that decomposition of the intermediates followed by free-radical reactions takes place.

Grignard reagents also react with small cyclic ethers such as epoxides and oxacyclobutanes by an S_N2 mechanism.

$$RMgX + \underset{O}{CH_2-CH_2} \longrightarrow RCH_2CH_2OMgX$$

2.5. Related Compounds

All of the hydrides of Be, Mg, Ca, Sr, and Ba are known. BeH$_2$ is a white solid, synthesized by the following reactions:

$$BeCl_2 + 2\,LiH \xrightarrow{\text{20°, ether}} BeH_2 + 2\,LiCl$$

$$2\,BeR_2 + LiAlH_4 \xrightarrow{\text{20°, ether}} 2\,BeH_2 + LiAlR_4$$

MgH$_2$ can be prepared from diethylmagnesium by pyrolysis or by reaction with hydrogen under pressure.

$$(C_2H_5)_2Mg \xrightarrow{175°} MgH_2 + C_2H_4$$

$$(C_2H_5)_2Mg \xrightarrow{\text{H}_2,\ 75°,\ 68\,atm} MgH_2$$

CaH$_2$, SrH$_2$, and BaH$_2$ are prepared from the parent metals by heating under a stream of hydrogen. MgH$_2$ and CaH$_2$ have come into use as a source of hydrogen gas or a desiccant.

REFERENCES

1) G. E. Coates, "Organo-Metallic Compounds", Methuen (1960).
2) M. S. Kharasch, O. Reinmuth, "Grignard Reactions of Non-metallic Substances", Constable & Co. (1954).
3) S. T. Yoffé, A. N. Nesmeyanov, "Handbook of Magnesium-Organic Compounds", Vol. 3, Pergamon Press (1957).
4) G. A. Baltsecha, S. T. Yoffé, *Uspeki Khim.*, **31**, 940 (1962).
5) Ed. by Kinki Society of the Chemical Industry, "Organometallic Chemistry and Its Applications", Asakura, Tokyo (1962).

【Be】

BeCH₃I

① Methylberyllium iodide
CH₃BeI

② Be + CH₃I $\xrightarrow[\text{Et}_2\text{O, }80\sim98°]{\text{HgCl}_2, \text{ sealed tube}}$

④ + H₂O $\longrightarrow$ CH₄
+ O₂ $\longrightarrow$ BeO
+ C₆H₅N=C=O $\longrightarrow$
C₆H₅NHCOCH₃

⑥ JACS **49**, 2904 (1927).

BeC₂

① Beryllium acetylide
Be(C≡C)₂

② Be + CH≡CH $\xrightarrow{450°}$

④ + H₂O $\longrightarrow$ CH≡CH

⑥ Bull. soc. chim. France [4] **35**, 1141 (1924).

BeC₂Cl₆

① Bis(trichloromethyl)beryllium
(CCl₃)₂Be

② BeCl₂+CHCl₃

⑥ Ann. chim. (Paris) **7**, 182 (1952).

BeC₂H₅Cl

① Ethylberyllium chloride
C₂H₅BeCl

② BeCl₂ + (C₂H₅)₂Be $\longrightarrow$

⑥ JCS **1927**, 2663.

BeC₂H₅I

① Ethylberyllium iodide
C₂H₅BeI

② Be + C₂H₅I $\xrightarrow[12\sim60\,\text{hr.}]{130°}$ C₂H₅BeI

Be + C₂H₅I $\xrightarrow[80\sim90°, \text{ Et}_2\text{O}]{\text{HgCl}_2, \text{ sealed tube}}$

④ + H₂O $\longrightarrow$ C₂H₆
+ O₂ $\longrightarrow$ BeO

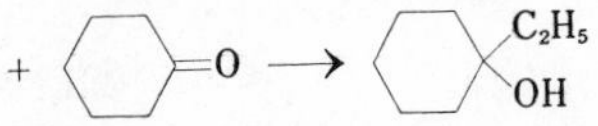

+ ⑥ Izv. OKhN **1961**, 2254.   JACS **49**, 2904 (1927).

BeC₂H₆

① Dimethylberyllium
(CH₃)₂Be

② (CH₃)₂Hg + Be $\longrightarrow$
CH₃MgX + BeCl₂ $\longrightarrow$

③ [217° sublime].
Sol. in hot Et₂O.
Cryst. structure: see text.
Spont. inflam.

④ + (CH₃)₃N $\longrightarrow$ (CH₃)₂Be·N(CH₃)₃
+ (CH₃)OH $\longrightarrow$ (CH₃Be·OCH₃)₂
+ (CH₃)₃P $\longrightarrow$ (CH₃)₂Be[P(CH₃)₃]₂

⑤ Catalysts from Ti or V compds. for polymn. of C₂H₄.

⑥ JCS **1927**, 2663 ; **1952**, 4496.

BeC₃H₈

① Isopropylberyllium hydride
i-C₃H₇BeH

② (*i*-C₃H₇)₂Be $\xrightarrow[8\,\text{hr.}]{200°}$
(*i*-C₃H₇BeH)ₙ + C₃H₆

③ Colorless, non-volatile, viscous oil.

④ + H₂O $\longrightarrow$ BeO + C₃H₈ + H₂
$\xrightarrow{220\sim250°}$ Be + H₂ + C₃H₆ + C₃H₈
+ orange-colored residue
+ (CH₃)₂NH $\longrightarrow$ [(CH₃)₂N·BeH]ₙ

⑥ JCS **1954**, 22.

BeC₄H₉I

① Butylberyllium iodide
C₄H₉BeI

② Be + C₄H₉I $\xrightarrow[12\sim60\,\text{hr.}]{130°}$
Be + C₄H₉I $\xrightarrow[\text{Et}_2\text{O, HgCl}_2 \text{ or Br}_2]{80\sim90°}$

④ + H₂O $\longrightarrow$ C₄H₁₀

$+ O_2 \longrightarrow$ BeO

$+$ $\longrightarrow$

⑥ Izv. OKhN 1961, 2254.   JACS **49**, 2904 (1927).

BeC₄H₉Br

① Butylberyllium bromide
   C_4H_9BeBr

② Be $+ C_4H_9Br \xrightarrow[12\sim60\,\text{hr.}]{130°} C_4H_9BeBr$

④ $+ H_2O \longrightarrow C_4H_{10}$
   $+ O_2 \longrightarrow$ BeO

$+$ $\longrightarrow$

⑥ Izv. OKhN 1961, 2254.

BeC₄H₁₀

① Diethylberyllium
   $(C_2H_5)_2Be$

② $(C_2H_5)_2Hg +$ Be $\longrightarrow$
   $C_2H_5MgX + BeCl_2 \longrightarrow$

③ Colorless liq. (194° extraporated).
   [$-13\sim-11°$]. Sol. in org. solvents.
   Assocn. to form polymer. Polymeric
   in cyclohexane.

④ Spont. 'inflam.
   $+ (C_6H_5)_2NH \longrightarrow Be[N(C_6H_5)_2]_2$
   $+ BeCl_2 \rightleftharpoons 2 C_2H_5BeCl$

$+$

$\longrightarrow$

$+ I_2 \longrightarrow C_2H_5BeI$

⑤ Catalyst from TiCl₃ for polymn. of α-
   olefins to isotactic polymers.

⑥ JCS **1954**, 22.   J. Polymer Sci. **43**,
   445 (1960).   Gazz. chim. ital. **90**,
   180 (1960).

BeC₄H₁₀O

① Isopropylberyllium methoxide
   $(CH_3)_2CHBeOCH_3$

② $[(CH_3)_2CH]_2Be + CH_3OH$
   $\xrightarrow{\text{cooling with liq. } N_2}$

③ Transparent plates. [133°].
   Unaffected by short exposure to air.

④ Vigorously hydrolysed by water.

⑥ JCS **1954**, 22.

BeC₅H₁₁I

① Pentylberyllium iodide
   $C_5H_{11}BeI$

② $C_5H_{11}I +$ Be $\xrightarrow[12\sim60\,\text{hr.}]{130°}$

④ $+$ $\longrightarrow$

⑥ Izv. OKhN 1961, 2254.

BeC₅H₁₂N₂

① Cyanomethyl trimethylamine
   beryllium
   (Methylberyllium cyanide trimethylamine complex)
   $[(CH_3)_3N \cdot CH_3BeCN]_n$

② $(CH_3)_2Be \cdot N(CH_3)_3 + HCN \xrightarrow{C_6H_6}$

③ Colorless amorphous solid. [$>300°$].
   Sensitive to air.

⑥ JCS **1963**, 229.

BeC₆H₅I

① Phenylberyllium iodide
   C_6H_5BeI

② $C_6H_5I +$ Be $\xrightarrow[Et_2O,\ 15\,\text{hr.}\ HgCl_2]{150\sim175°}$

⑥ JACS **49**, 2904 (1927).

BeC₆H₁₄

① Diisopropylberyllium
   $(i\text{-}C_3H_7)_2Be$

② $BeCl_2 + i\text{-}C_3H_7MgBr \xrightarrow{Et_2O}$

③ Clear liq. (280° extraporated).
  [-9.5°].
  Dimeric in C_6H_6 at 25°.

④ $\xrightarrow{200°}$ $(i\text{-}C_3H_7BeH)_n + C_3H_6$
  $+ (CH_3)_3N \longrightarrow (i\text{-}C_3H_7)_2Be\text{-}N(CH_3)_3$
  Fumes violently on exposure to air.
  Reacn. with H_2O is explosive.
  $+ CH_3OH \longrightarrow (i\text{-}C_3H_7Be\cdot OCH_3)_n$

⑥ JCS 1954, 22.

BeC₈H₁₆

① Di-1-butenylberyllium
  $(C_2H_5CH=CH_2)_2Be$

② $2 C_2H_5CH=CH_2MgX + BeCl_2 \xrightarrow{THF}$

⑥ Brit. 824944 ; CA 54, 17238 (1960).

BeC₈H₁₈

① Dibutylberyllium
  $(C_4H_9)_2Be$

② $C_4H_9MgX + BeCl_2 \longrightarrow$

③ Colorless liq. disagreeable odor.
  (170°/25 mm).
  Sol. in org. solvents.

④ $+ O_2 \longrightarrow Be(OC_4H_9)_2$

⑤ Catalyst in polymn. of vinyl chloride
  Activation reagent of Al for prepn.
  of triisobutylaluminum.

⑥ JCS 1954, 22 ; 1927, 2663.

BeC₈H₁₈

① Di-*t*-butylberyllium
  $[(CH_3)_3C]_2Be$

② $t\text{-}C_4H_9MgCl + BeCl_2 \xrightarrow{Et_2O}$
  $(t\text{-}C_4H_9)_2Be\cdot O(C_2H_5)_2$ (51~52%)
  $\xrightarrow[]{+BeCl_2} 40\%$

③ Colorless liq. (100° decomp.).
  [-16°]. d 0.65 g/cc.

④ $\xrightarrow{pyrolysis} BeH_2$

⑤ Catalyst in polymn. of vinyl chloride.

⑥ JCS 1954, 2526. JACS 79, 3787 (1957).

BeC₈H₁₇I

① Octylberyllium iodide
  $C_8H_{17}BeI$

② $C_8H_{17}I + Be \xrightarrow[12\sim60\,hr.]{130°}$

④

⑥ Izv. OKhN 1961, 2254.

BeC₁₀H₁₀

① Dicyclopentadienylberyllium
  $(C_5H_5)_2Be$

② $C_5H_5Na + BeCl_2 \xrightarrow{Et_2O\ (or\ C_6H_6)}$

③ Colorless. Dipole moment : 2.46±0.06
  (C_6H_6), 2.24±0.09(C_6H_{12}).
  IR : Ber. 92, 780 (1959).
  Sensitive towards hydrolysis.

④ $+ FeCl_2 \longrightarrow (C_5H_5)_2Fe$

⑥ Ber. 92, 482 (1959).

BeC₁₀H₂₂

① Ethyl(2-ethyl-2-methylpentyl)beryl-
  lium
  $(C_3H_7)(CH_3)(C_2H_5)CCH_2BeC_2H_5$

② $Be(C_2H_5)_2 + C_3H_7(CH_3)C=CH_2 \xrightarrow[82\,hr.]{100°}$

⑥ Brit. 763824 ; CA 52, 1203 (1958).

BeC₁₀H₂₂O₂

① Bis(4-methoxybutyl)beryllium

② $CH_3O(CH_2)_4Cl + Mg + BeCl_2 \xrightarrow{Et_2O}$

③ Colorless liq. (108°/4).
  Forms internal complex.

④ $+ H_2O \longrightarrow CH_3OC_4H_9$

⑥ Ber. 90, 1578 (1957).

BeC₁₀H₂₂S₂

① Bis[3-(ethylthio)propyl]beryllium

② $C_2H_5S(CH_2)_3Cl + Mg + BeCl_2 \xrightarrow{Et_2O}$

③ $(122 \sim 123°/2)$.

Forms internal complex.

④ $+ H_2O \longrightarrow C_3H_7SC_2H_5$

⑥ Ber. **90**, 1978 (1957).

BeC₁₂H₁₀

① Diphenylberyllium

$(C_6H_5)_2Be$

② $(C_6H_5)_2Hg + Be \xrightarrow[Et_2O\ 172°,\ 72\,hr.]{HgCl_2,\ BeBr_2}$

③ White crystals. sol. in org. solvents.

④ $+ {}^7BeBr_2 \xrightarrow{\ \ } C_6H_5BeBr + C_6H_5{}^7BeBr$

⑤ Catalyst in dimerization of olefins.

⑥ JACS **82**, 1580 (1960).   Ann. **571**, 167
   (1951) ; **577**, 11 (1952).

BeC₁₄H₁₄

① Di-*m*-tolylberyllium

$$\left(\text{CH}_3 \overline{} \right)_2 Be$$

② $2(m\text{-}CH_3C_6H_4MgX) + BeCl_2 \xrightarrow{THF}$

⑥ Brit. 824944 ; CA **54**, 17238 (1960).

BeC₂₄H₁₈

① Bisbiphenylylberyllium

$(C_6H_5C_6H_4)_2Be$

② $2 C_6H_5C_6H_4MgX + BeCl_2 \xrightarrow{THF}$

⑥ Brit. 824944 ; CA **54**, 17238 (1960).

Be₂C

① Beryllium carbide

Be₂C

② $C + Be \xrightarrow{1300°}$

   $BeO + C \xrightarrow{1930°}$

③ Brick-red, regular octahedra.
   [210° decomp.]. d 1.95.

④ React. slowly with H_2O, mineral acid.
   Rapidly decomp. by alkalies evolving
   CH_4.

⑥ Bull. soc. chim. France [4] **43**, 49
   (1928).
   Handbook of Chemistry and physics (1958).

【Mg】

MgCH₂

① Methylenemagnesium
   $(CH_2Mg)_n$

② $(CH_3)_2Mg \xrightarrow{250°}$

③ Amorphous brown solid.
   Decomp. with H_2O.   Insol. in org.
   solvents.

④ Spontaneously inflammable.
   $+ H_2O \longrightarrow CH_4$
   $+ CH_3CHCl_2 \longrightarrow CH_3CH=CH_2$

⑥ Z. anorg. allg. Chem. **282**, 345 (1955).
   Brit. 852933 ; CA **55**, 10314 (1961).

MgCH₃Br

① Methylmagnesium bromide
   CH₃MgBr

② $CH_3Br + Mg \xrightarrow{Et_2O}$ 98.9%

④ $+ CHCl_2CHO \longrightarrow$
   $CHCl_2(CH_3)CHOH(57.4\%)$
   $+ (C_6H_5)_2CO \longrightarrow$
   $CH_3(C_6H_5)_2COH(95\%)$
   $+ n\text{-}C_5H_{11}CO_2C_2H_5 \longrightarrow$
   $n\text{-}C_5H_{11}(CH_3)_2COH$ (80~85%)
   $+ ClCH_2(CH_3)_2SiCl \longrightarrow$
   $ClCH_2(CH_3)_3Si$ (90%)
   $+ H_2C=CBrCH_2Br \longrightarrow$
   $H_2C=CBrC_2H_5$

⑥ Kharasch and Reinmuth.

MgCH₃Cl

① Methylmagnesium chloride
CH₃MgCl

② CH₃Cl + Mg $\xrightarrow{Et_2O}$ 87~99.7%

④ + 2-BrC₆H₄CHO ⟶
2-BrC₆H₄CH(CH₃)OH (87%)
+ C₆H₅COC₆H₅ ⟶
CH₃(C₆H₅)₂COH (98%)
+ (+)CH₃(C₂H₅O)CHCO₂C₂H₅ ⟶
(−)CH₃(C₂H₅O)CHC(CH₃)OH (85%)
+ 2,4,6-Cl₃C₆H₂COCl ⟶
2,4,6-Cl₃C₆H₂COCH₃ (50%)
+ *t*-C₄H₉Cl ⟶ C(CH₃)₄ (42~50%)

⑥ Kharasch and Reinmuth.

MgCH₃I

① Methylmagnesium iodide
CH₃MgI

② CH₃I + Mg $\xrightarrow{Et_2O}$ 100.0%

④ + C₆H₅CHO ⟶
CH₃(C₆H₅)CHOH (93%)
+ CH₃COCH₃ ⟶
(CH₃)₃COH (70%)
+ CH₃CO₂CH₃ ⟶
(CH₃)₃COH (82%)
+ ¹⁴CO₂ ⟶ CH₃¹⁴CO₂H (94%)
+ styrene oxide ⟶
CH₃(C₆H₅CH₂)CHOH (51~53%)

⑥ Kharasch and Reinmuth.

Mg₂C₂Br₂

① Ethynylenemagnesium dibromide
BrMgC≡CMgBr

② CH≡CH + C₂H₅MgBr $\xrightarrow{Et_2O}$

④ + CH₃CHO ⟶
[≡CCH(CH₃)OH]₂ (<70%)
+ CH₃COCH₃ ⟶
[≡CC(CH₃)₂OH]₂ (80%)
+ CO₂ ⟶ (≡CCO₂H)₂ (5%)
+ C₂H₅Br ⟶ (≡CC₂H₅)₂ (20%)
+ I₂ ⟶ (≡CI)₂

⑥ Kharasch and Reinmuth.

MgC₂H₃Br

① Vinylmagnesium bromide
CH₂=CHMgBr

② CH₂=CHBr + Mg $\xrightarrow{THF}$

④ + (C₂H₅)₃SnBr ⟶
(C₂H₅)₃SnCH=CH₂ (85%)
+ *n*-C₄H₉OCH₂Cl ⟶
CH₂=CHCH₂OC₄H₉ (67%)
+ C₂H₅OCHClCH₂Cl ⟶
CH₂=CHCH(OC₂H₅)CH₂Cl (65%)
+ CH₂–CH₂ (with O bridge) ⟶
CH₂=CHCH₂·CH₂OH (65%)
+ C₆H₅CHO ⟶
CH₂=CHCH(OH)C₆H₅ (67%)
+ CH₃COCH₃ ⟶
(CH₃)₂C(OH)CH=CH₂ (74%)
+ CH₃CO₂C₂H₅ ⟶
CH₃C(OH)(CH=CH₂)₂ (85%)

⑥ Compt. rend. **239**, 1510, 1811 (1954);
240, 314, 440, 631, 1111, 1435 (1955).

MgC₂H₃Cl

① Vinylmagnesium chloride
CH₂=CHMgCl

② CH₂=CHCl + Mg $\xrightarrow{THF}$

④ + SiCl₄ ⟶ Si(CH=CH₂)₄ (87.5%)
+ *n*-C₃H₇CO₂C₂H₅ ⟶
n-C₃H₇C(OH)(CH=CH₂)₂ (66%)
+ (C₂H₅CO₂)O ⟶
CH₂=CHCOC₂H₅ (60%)
+ ClSi(CH₃)₂Si(CH₃)₃ ⟶
CH₂=CHSi(CH₃)₂Si(CH₃)₃ (63%)
+ (C₆H₅)₃SnCl ⟶
(C₆H₅)₃SnCH=CH₂ (79%)
+ CH₃COCH₃ ⟶
(CH₃)₂C(OH)CH=CH₂ (74%)
+ CH₃CO₂C₂H₅ ⟶
CH₃C(OH)(CH=CH₂)₂ (44%)

⑥ JOC **22**, 1200 (1957). Advances in
Organic Chemistry, Vol. Ⅱ, Inters-

cience (1960).

MgC$_2$H$_5$Br

① Ethylmagnesium bromide
CH$_3$CH$_2$MgBr

② CH$_3$CH$_2$Br + Mg $\xrightarrow{\text{Et}_2\text{O}}$ 97.0%

④ + C$_6$H$_5$CHO $\longrightarrow$
C$_2$H$_5$(C$_6$H$_5$)CHOH (78%)
+ (C$_6$H$_5$)$_2$CO $\longrightarrow$
C$_2$H$_5$(C$_6$H$_5$)$_2$COH (80%)
+ CH$_3$CO$_2$C$_2$H$_5$ $\longrightarrow$
CH$_3$(C$_2$H$_5$)$_2$COH (67%)
+ CO$_2$ $\longrightarrow$ C$_2$H$_5$CO$_2$H (72%)
(CH$_2$)$_2$O $\longrightarrow$ *n*-C$_4$H$_9$OH (79%)
+ BrCH$_2$CH$_2$OH
+ (*i*-C$_3$H$_7$)$_2$CO $\longrightarrow$ C$_2$H$_5$(*i*-C$_3$H$_7$)$_2$COH
(77%) + (*i*-C$_3$H$_7$)$_2$CHOH (21%)

⑥ Kharasch and Reinmuth.

MgC$_2$H$_5$I

① Ethylmagnesium iodide
C$_2$H$_5$MgI

② C$_2$H$_5$I + Mg $\xrightarrow{\text{Et}_2\text{O}}$ (96.4%)

④ + CuI $\longrightarrow$ C$_2$H$_4$ + C$_2$H$_6$ + Cu
+ C$_6$H$_5$CHO $\longrightarrow$ C$_2$H$_5$(C$_6$H$_5$)CHOH
+ C$_6$H$_5$CH$_2$OH + other products
+ 3-methylcyclohexanone $\longrightarrow$
1-ethyl-3-methylcyclohexanol
(good yield)
+ (−CH$_2$CH$_2$CO$_2$C$_2$H$_5$)$_2$ $\longrightarrow$
[−CH$_2$CH$_2$C(C$_2$H$_5$)$_2$OH]$_2$ (70%)

⑥ Kharasch and Reinmuth.

MgC$_2$H$_6$

① Dimethylmagnesium
(CH$_3$)$_2$Mg

② CH$_3$MgCl $\xrightarrow{190° \text{ distiln.}}$
(CH$_3$)$_2$Hg + Mg $\xrightarrow{\text{in sealed tube}}$

③ Sol. in Et$_2$O.

④ + AgX $\longrightarrow$ C$_2$H$_6$ (X=Br, I)
+ ZrCl$_4$(or TaCl$_5$, CrCl$_3$) $\longrightarrow$ CH$_4$
+ cyclohexene oxide $\longrightarrow$ *trans*-2-

methylcyclohexanol
+ isobutylene oxide $\longrightarrow$
C$_2$H$_5$(CH$_3$)$_2$COH
+ C$_6$H$_5$CHOHCOC$_6$H$_5$ $\longrightarrow$
C$_6$H$_5$−CH−C(CH$_3$)C$_6$H$_5$
          | |
         OH   OH
(92%) + C$_6$H$_5$CO$_2$H (8.5%)

⑤ Catalysts from TiCl$_4$ for polymn. of C$_2$H$_4$.

⑥ Rec. trav. chim. **48**, 1134 (1929); **49**, 724 (1930). JACS **76**, 3615 (1954). Can. J. Chem. **35**, 873 (1957).

MgC$_3$H$_5$Br

① Allylmagnesium chloride
CH$_2$=CHCH$_2$MgCl

② CH$_2$=CHCH$_2$Cl + Mg $\xrightarrow{\text{Et}_2\text{O}}$

③ White cryst. solid.

④ + ClCH$_2$CH$_2$N(C$_2$H$_5$)$_2$ $\longrightarrow$
CH$_2$=CHCH$_2$CH$_2$CH$_2$N(C$_2$H$_5$)$_2$
(85%)
+ CH$_3$CHO $\longrightarrow$
CH$_3$(H$_2$C=CHCH$_2$)CHOH (57%)
+ CH$_3$COC$_2$H$_5$ $\longrightarrow$
CH$_3$(C$_2$H$_5$)(H$_2$C=CHCH$_2$)COH (52%)
+ CH$_3$CH=CHCH$_2$Cl $\longrightarrow$
(H$_2$C=CHCH$_2$)$_2$CH$_2$ (>50.8%)
+ H$_2$C=CHCH(CH$_3$)CH$_2$CH=CH$_2$
(<3.2%)
+ SiCl$_4$ $\longrightarrow$ (CH$_2$=CHCH$_2$)$_4$Si (90%)

⑥ Kharasch and Reinmuth.

MeC$_3$H$_5$Br

① Propenylmagnesium bromide
CH$_3$CH=CHMgBr

② CH$_3$CH=CHBr + Mg $\longrightarrow$

④ + BrCH$_2$CH=CH$_2$ $\longrightarrow$
CH$_3$CH=CHCH$_2$CH=CH$_2$ (80%)
                O
               / \
+ CH$_3$CHCH$_2$ $\longrightarrow$
CH$_3$CH=CHCH$_2$CH(OH)CH$_3$ (60%)
+ *n*-C$_3$H$_7$CHO $\longrightarrow$
CH$_3$CH=CHCH(OH)(*n*-C$_3$H$_7$) (60%)

+ CH₃COCH₃ $\longrightarrow$

  (CH₃)₂C(OH)CH=CHCH₃ (75%)

+ C₂H₅CO₂C₂H₅ $\longrightarrow$

  C₂H₅C(OH)(CH=CH−CH₃)₂ (84%)

+ CH₃CH=CHCO₂C₂H₅ $\longrightarrow$

  (CH₃CH=CH)₃COH (30%)

+ (CH₃CO)₂O $\longrightarrow$

  CH₃CH=CHCOCH₃ (80%)

⑥ Compt. rend. **239**, 1811 (1954) ; **240**,
   314, 440, 1111 (1955).   Bull. soc.
   chim. France **1956**, 951.

MgC₃H₅Br

① Isopropenylmagnesium bromide

  CH₂=C(CH₂)MgBr

② CH₂=C(CH₃)Br + Mg $\overset{\text{THF}}{\longrightarrow}$

④ + C₂H₅OCHBrCH₂Br $\longrightarrow$

   CH₂=C(CH₃)CH(OC₂H₅)CH₂Br (70%)

  + CH₃CHO $\longrightarrow$

   CH₂=C(CH₃)CH(OH)CH₃ (83%)

  + CH₃COCH₃ $\longrightarrow$

   (CH₃)₂C(OH)C(CH₃)=CH₂ (56%)

  + CH₃CO₂C₂H₅ $\longrightarrow$

   CH₃C(OH)[C(CH₃)=CH₂]₂ (77%)

  + (CH₃CO)₂O $\longrightarrow$

   CH₂=C(CH₃)COCH₃ (50%)

  + (CH₃)₃SiCl $\longrightarrow$

   (CH₃)₃SiC(CH₃)=CH₂

⑥ Bull. soc. chim. France **1957**, 429.
   Ann. chim. (Paris) **13**, 541 (1959).

MgC₃H₇Br

① n-Propylmagnesium bromide

  CH₃CH₂CH₂MgBr

② n-C₃H₇Br + Mg $\longrightarrow$

④ + CH₃CHO $\longrightarrow$

   CH₃(n-C₃H₇)CHOH (50%)

  + (i-C₃H₇)₂CO $\longrightarrow$

   n-C₃H₇(i-C₃H₇)₂COH (35.8%) +
   (i-C₃H₇)₂CHOH (60.3%)

  + CO₂ $\longrightarrow$ n-C₃H₇CO₂H (77%)

  + (CH₂)₂O $\longrightarrow$ n-C₅H₁₁ (76%)

   + BrCH₂CH₂OH

+ t-C₄H₉Cl + CuI $\longrightarrow$ t-C₄H₉−C₃H₇

  (21%)

+ C₂H₅(C₆H₅CH₂)SiCl₂ $\longrightarrow$

  C₂H₅(n-C₃H₇)C₆H₅CH₂SiCl (50~60%)

+ C₂H₅(C₆H₅CH₂)(n-C₃H₇)₂Si

⑥ Kharasch and Reinmuth.

MgC₃H₇Br

① Isopropylmagnesium bromide

  (CH₃)₂CHMgBr

② (CH₃)₃CHBr + Mg $\longrightarrow$

④ + CH₃CHO $\longrightarrow$ CH₃(i-C₃H₇)CHOH

  + ClCN $\longrightarrow$ i-C₃H₇CN (9%)

   + i-C₃H₇Cl (67%)

  + (CH₃CO)₂O $\overset{-70°}{\longrightarrow}$ CH₃CO-i-C₃H₇

   (74~78%)

  + (CH₂)₂O $\longrightarrow$ i-C₅H₁₁OH (74%)

   + BrCH₂CH₂OH

  + 4-CH₃OC₆H₄CH₂Br $\longrightarrow$

   4-CH₃OC₆H₄-i-C₄H₉ (29.8%)

   + (4-CH₃OC₆H₄CH₂)₂

   + 4-CH₃OC₆H₄CH₃

  + C₂H₅(n-C₃H₇)(C₆H₅CH₂)SiCl $\longrightarrow$

   C₂H₅(n-C₃H₇)(i-C₃H₇)(C₆H₅CH₂)Si

   (60%)

⑥ Kharasch and Reinmuth.

MgC₃F₇I

① Heptafluoro-n-propyl magnesium
   iodide

  C₃F₇MgI

② C₃F₇I + Mg $\longrightarrow$

④ $\longrightarrow$ C₃F₆ + MgIF

  + H₂O $\longrightarrow$ CF₃CF₂CF₂H

  + CO₂ $\longrightarrow$ CF₃CF₂CF₂CO₂H

⑥ Nature **167**, 139 (1951). JCS **1953**, 1748.

MgC₄H₃SBr

① 2-Thienylmagnesium bromide

② Br + Mg $\longrightarrow$

④　+ CH₃CHClCCl₂CHO ⟶
　　CH₃CHClCCl₂(2-C₄H₃S)CHOH (74%)
　　+ (C₆H₅)₂CO ⟶ 2-C₄H₃S(C₆H₅)₂COH
　　+ (CH₂)₂O ⟶ 2-thiopheneëthanol
　　(53%)
　　+ HCO₂C₂H₅ ⟶ 2-thiophene-
　　carboxaldehyde (15%)
　　+ C₇H₇SO₃(CH₂)₂Cl ⟶
　　(2-C₄H₃S)–(CH₂)₂Cl (71%)
⑥　Kharasch and Reinmuth.

MgC₄H₆

①　Divinylmagnesium
　　(CH₂=CH)₂Mg

②　(CH₂=CH)₂Hg + Mg $\xrightarrow[3\,hr.]{Et_2O}$

③　Infusible solid.
⑥　US 2999889 ; CA **56**, 1477 (1962).

MgC₄H₇Br

①　1-Methylpropenylmagnesium
　　bromide

②　*cis*(or *trans*)-CH₃CH=CBrCH₃ + Mg
　　$\xrightarrow{THF}$

④　+ CO₂ ⟶ *cis*(or *trans*)-CH₃CH
　　=C(CH₃)CO₂H (retention of con-
　　figuration)
　　+ CCl₃CHO ⟶
　　CH₃CH=C(CH₃)CH(OH)CCl₃ (73%)
　　+ (CH₃CO)₂O ⟶
　　CH₃CH=C(CH₃)COCH₃ (70%)
⑥　Bull. soc. chim. France **1956**, 1439.

Mg₂C₄H₈Br₂

①　Tetramethylenemagnesium
　　dibromide
　　BrMg(CH₂)₄MgBr

②　Br(CH₂)₄Br + 2 Mg ⟶

④　+ C₆H₅SbCl₂ ⟶ $\begin{matrix} CH_2-CH_2 \\ | \quad\quad \\ CH_2-CH_2 \end{matrix}\!\!\Big\rangle SbC_6H_5$

　　+ C₆H₅PCl₂ ⟶ $\begin{matrix} CH_2-CH_2 \\ | \quad\quad \\ CH_2-CH_2 \end{matrix}\!\!\Big\rangle PC_6H_5$

　　+ CO₂ ⟶ $\begin{matrix} CH_2-CH_2 \\ | \quad\quad \\ CH_2-CH_2 \end{matrix}\!\!\Big\rangle CO$

　　+ ClSi(CH₃)₂Si(CH₃)Cl

　　⟶ $\begin{matrix} (CH_3)_2Si \diagdown \\ (CH_3)_2Si \diagup \end{matrix}\begin{matrix} CH_2 \\ \diagup \quad \diagdown CH_2 \\ \diagdown \quad \diagup CH_2 \\ CH_2 \end{matrix}$

⑥　Ber. **49**, 437 (1916). Quart. Revs. **11**,
　　109 (1957).

MgC₄H₉Cl

①　*t*-Butylmagnesium chloride
　　(CH₃)₃CMgCl
②　(CH₃)₃CCl + Mg ⟶
④　+ AgBr ⟶ C₈H₁₈ (19.4%)
　　+ *i*-C₃H₇CHO ⟶
　　i-C₃H₇(*t*-C₄H₉)CHOH (25%)
　　+ *i*-C₃H₇CH(OH)C(CH₃)₂CHO (25%)
　　+ *i*-C₄H₉OH (50%)
　　+ (C₆H₅)₂CO ⟶ (C₆H₅)₂CHOH
　　(38%)
　　+ (CH₃CO)₂O ⟶ CH₃CO-*t*-C₄H₉
　　(77%)
　　+ CO₂ ⟶ *t*-C₄H₉CO₂H (69~70%)
⑥　Kharasch and Reinmuth.

MgC₄H₁₀

①　Diethylmagnesium
　　(C₂H₅)₂Mg
②　Hg + 2 C₂H₅Na + Mg ⟶
　　(C₂H₅)₂Hg + Mg ⟶
　　2 C₂H₅MgX $\xrightarrow{dioxane}$ (C₂H₅)₂Mg
　　+ MgX₂
③　White soild.
　　Sol. in Et₂O (165 g/*l*, 2.0 mole/*l*).
　　Decomp. readily between 175° and
　　200° with evolution of olefin.
④　Spontaneously inflamable.
　　+ H₂O ⟶ Mg(OH)₂ + 2 C₂H₆
　　+ ROH ⟶ Mg(OH)₂ + 2 C₂H₆
　　+ NH₃ ⟶ Mg(NH₂)₂ + 2 C₂H₆
　　3 (C₂H₅)₂Mg + B₂H₆ ⟶ 3 MgH₂
　　+ 2 (C₂H₅)₃B

3 $(C_2H_5)_2Mg + 4 B_2H_6 \longrightarrow 3 Mg(BH_4)_2$
$+ 2 (C_2H_5)_3B$

⑤ Catalysts in polymn. of olefin and olefin oxide. Coating of glass and metals with Mg by decompn.

⑥ Ann. **140**, 353 (1866).   Rec. trav. chim. **49**, 724 (1930).   Compt. rend. **213**, 179 (1941).

MgC4H10SO4

① Diethylmagnesium sulfate
$C_2H_5Mg(C_2H_5)SO_4$

② $(C_2H_5)_2SO_4 + Mg \xrightarrow{\text{Et}_2\text{O}}$

④ $+ C_6H_5CHO \longrightarrow C_6H_5(C_2H_5)CHOH$
(good yield)

⑥ JACS **55**, 3496 (1933).

MgC4H11SiCl

① Trimethylsilylmethylmagnesium chloride
$(CH_3)_3SiCH_2MgCl$

② $(CH_3)_3SiCH_2Cl + Mg \longrightarrow$

④ $+ CH_3CHO \longrightarrow$
$CH_3[(CH_3)_3SiCH_2]CHOH$
$+ CH_3COCl \longrightarrow (CH_3)_2CO$
$+$ unidentified products
$+ CO_2 \longrightarrow (CH_3)_3SiCH_2CO_2H$ (88%)
$+ CH_2CH_2 \longrightarrow$

$$\underset{O}{\overset{}{}}$$

$(CH_3)_3Si(CH_2)_3OH$ (71.4%)
$+ (CH_3)_2SiCl_2 \longrightarrow$
$(CH_3)_2Si[CH_2Si(CH_3)_3]_2$ (65%)
$+ (CH_3)_3SiCl \longrightarrow [(CH_3)_3Si]_2CH_2$
(63%)
$+ CoCl_2 \dashrightarrow (CH_3)_3SiCH_2CH_2Si(CH_3)_3$

⑥ Kharasch and Reinmuth.

MgC5H5Br

① Cyclopentadienylmagnesium bromide

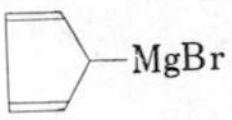

C5H5MgBr

② $C_5H_6 + C_2H_5MgBr \longrightarrow$

④ $+ FeCl_2 \longrightarrow (C_5H_5)_2Fe$ (ferrocene)
$+ ClCN \longrightarrow (C_5H_5CN)_2$

⑥ Kharasch and Reinmuth.

MgC5H12

① Ethylisopropylmagnesium
$CH_3CH_2-Mg-CH(CH_3)_2$

② $MgH_2 + CH_2=CH_2 + CH_3CH=CH_2 \longrightarrow$

⑥ US 2985692 ; CA **55**, 22133 (1961).

MgC5H15Al

① Methylmagnesium tetramethylaluminum complex
$CH_3MgAl(CH_3)_4$

② $CH_3MgCl + Al(CH_3)_3$

③ [88.5°]

⑥ Ann. **605**, 93 (1957).

Mg2C6H4Br2

① p-Phenylenemagnesium dibromide

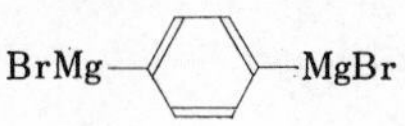

②

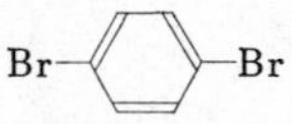

④ $+ B(OC_4H_9)_3 \longrightarrow$
$(C_4H_9O)_2BC_6H_4B(OC_4H_9)_2$

⑥ JACS **79**, 3081 (1957).

MgC6H5Br

① Phenylmagnesium bromide
C_6H_5MgBr

② $C_6H_5Br + Mg \longrightarrow$

④ $\xrightarrow{\text{electrolysis}} C_6H_5C_6H_5 + MgBr_2 + Mg$
$+ H_2S \longrightarrow C_6H_6 + MgBrSH$
$+ PCl_5 \longrightarrow (C_6H_5)_3P$ (76%)
$+ CH_2O \longrightarrow C_6H_5CH_2OH$ (70%)
$+ CO_2 \longrightarrow C_6H_5CO_2H$

⑥ Kharasch and Reinmuth.

MgC6H14

① Dipropylmagnesium

$(C_3H_7)_2Mg$

② C_3H_7MgBr + dioxane $\longrightarrow$

$(C_3H_7)_2Mg \cdot$ dioxane $\xrightarrow{120°}$

$MgH_2 + CH_3CH=CH_2$
$\xrightarrow{\text{Me}_2\text{SO, 66 atm, 100°}}$

③ Soly.: 1.3 g/*l* (benzene, 20°), 0.35 g/*l*
(heptane, 20°)

④ + $(Br-CH_2CH_2O-)_2Mg$ $\longrightarrow$
$(C_3H_7CH_2CH_2O-)_2Mg$
+ $CH_2\overset{\displaystyle CH_2}{\underset{O}{\diagdown\diagup}}$ $\longrightarrow$ $(C_3H_7CH_2CH_2O-)_2Mg$

⑥ JOC **6**, 123(1941). Ber. **94**, 2356(1961).
US 2985692 ; CA **55**, 22133 (1961).

MgC₆H₁₄

① Diisopropylmagnesium
$(i\text{-}C_3H_7)_2Mg$

② $i\text{-}C_3H_7MgBr$ $\xrightarrow{\text{dioxane}}$

③ Soly : 2.7 g/*l* (benzene, 20°), 0.37 g/*l*
(heptane, 20°).

⑥ Ber. **94**, 2356 (1961).

MgC₈H₇Br

① Styrylmagnesium bromide
$C_6H_5CH=CHMgBr$

② $C_6H_5CH=CHBr + Mg$ $\xrightarrow{\text{Et}_2\text{O}}$ 90%

④ + $(C_6H_5)CO$ $\longrightarrow$
$C_6H_5CH=CH(C_6H_5)_2COH$ (14%)
+ CO_2 $\longrightarrow$ $C_6H_5CH=CHCO_2H$
+ $1\text{-}C_{10}H_7NCO$ $\longrightarrow$
$1\text{-}C_{10}H_7NHCOCH=CHC_6H_5$
+ $C_6H_5SO_2Cl$ $\longrightarrow$ $C_6H_5CH=CHCl$
(40.4%) + $C_6H_5SO_2H$ (39.6%)

⑥ Rec. trav. chim. **54**, 584 (1935). JACS
50, 1214 (1928).

MgC₈H₁₄

① Dibutenylmagnesium
$(CH_3CH=CHCH_2)_2Mg$

② $CH_3CH=CHCH_2MgBr$ $\xrightarrow{\text{dioxane}}$

③ Pasty mass.

④ + CO_2 $\longrightarrow$ $CH_2=CHCH(CH_3)CO_2H$
(37%)
+ H_2O $\longrightarrow$ $CH_2=CHCH_2CH_3$
(55%) + $CH_3CH=CHCH_3$ (*cis*) (28%)
+ $CH_3CH=CHCH_3$ (*trans*) (17%)

⑥ JACS **67**, 148 (1945). JOC **17**, 233 (1942).

MgC₈H₁₈

① Dibutylmagnesium
$(n\text{-}C_4H_9)_2Mg$

② $n\text{-}C_4H_9MgBr$ $\xrightarrow{\text{dioxane}}$

③ Soly.: 3.3 g/*l* (benzene, 20°), 0.42 g/
l (heptane, 20°).

④ $\xrightarrow{\text{heat}}$ $MgH_2 + C_2H_5CH=CH_2 + C_4H_{10}$
+ C_8H_{18}
+ $ClCN$ $\longrightarrow$ $n\text{-}C_4H_9CN + n\text{-}C_4H_9Cl$
+ $(CH_2)_2O$ $\longrightarrow$ $n\text{-}C_6H_{13}OH$ (43.5%)
+ $CH_3(n\text{-}C_4H_9)CHOH$

⑤ Catalysts in polymn. of acrylonitrile.

⑥ JOC **12**, 510 (1947). J. Polymer Sci.
43, 445 (1960). Ber. **94**, 2356 (1961).

MgC₈H₁₈

① Di-*t*-butylmagnesium
$(t\text{-}C_4H_9)_2Mg$

② $t\text{-}C_4H_9MgCl$ $\xrightarrow{\text{dioxane}}$

④ + isobutylene oxide $\longrightarrow$
$t\text{-}C_4H_9CH_2(CH_3)_2COH$ (6.0%)

⑤ Catalysts in polymn. of vinylchlo-
ride, unsatd. ether and nitrile.

⑥ JOC **15**, 1211 (1950). Brit. 843611 ;
CA **55**, 4044 (1961). Brit. 847676 ;
CA **55**, 7919 (1961).

MgC₉H₁₃SiCl

① Phenyldimethylsilylmethyl
magnesium chloride
$C_6H_5(CH_3)_2SiCH_2MgCl$

② $C_6H_5(CH_3)_2SiCH_2Cl + Mg$ $\longrightarrow$

④ $+ CO_2 \longrightarrow C_6H_5(CH_3)_2SiCH_2CO_2H$
   (69%)

⑥   JOC **17**, 1509 (1949).

$MgC_{10}H_{10}$

①   Dicyclopentadienylmagnesium
   $(C_5H_5)_2Mg$

② $C_5H_5MgBr \xrightarrow{\text{ignition}}$

   $C_5H_6(\text{vapor}) + Mg \xrightarrow{500\sim600°} 80\%$

③   Colorless crystals. (300° decomp.).
   [176~178°].
   Sol. in Et_2O, liq. NH_3 and THF.
   React violently with H_2O, CS_2, CCl_4,
   CO_2 and air.
   IR, mass spectrum, NMR : JINC **2**, 95
   (1956).
   Dipole moment : 0.7D (benzene).

④   Decomp. in H_2O, alc. and air.

⑥   JINC **4**, 373 (1957). Inorg. Syn. **6**, 11
   (1960). Z. anorg. allg. Chem. **278**,
   219 (1955).

$MgC_{10}H_{22}$

①   Bis[(+)S-2-methylbutyl]magnesium
   $[CH_3CH_2CH(CH_3)CH_2]_2Mg$

② $(+)CH_3CH_2CH(CH_3)CH_2MgCl \xrightarrow{\text{dioxane}}$
   (80%)
   $(+)[CH_3CH_2CH(CH_3)CH_2]_2Hg + Mg$
   $\xrightarrow{130°,\ 10\,hrs.}$

③ $[\alpha]^D{}_{20}\,2.9)$

④ $+ (CH_3)_3CCOCH_3 \xrightarrow{Et_2O}$
   $(CH_3)_3CCH(OH)CH_3([\alpha]_D{}^{20}\,0.26)$
   $+ AlCl_3 \xrightarrow{Et_2O} (+)$
   $[CH_3CH_2CH(CH_3)CH_2-]_3Al\cdot O(C_2H_5)_2$

⑥   JACS **78**, 4959 (1956). Ann. chim. **48**,
   1426 (1958).

$MgC_{10}H_{22}$

①   Bis[1-methylbutyl]magnesium
   $[CH_3CH_2CH_2CH(CH_3)]_2Mg$

② $CH_3CH_2CH_2CH=CH_2 + MgH_2 \longrightarrow$

⑥   US 2985692 ; CA **55**, 22133 (1961).

$MgC_{10}H_{25}Al$

①   Ethylmagnesium tetraethylaluminum complex
   $C_2H_5MgAl(C_2H_5)_4$

② $C_2H_5MgCl + Al(C_2H_5)_3$
   $\xrightarrow{C_6H_{14},\ 100°,\ 6\,hr.} Mg(AlC_2H_5)_2$
   $\xrightarrow[\text{from Et}_2O\ \text{soln.}]{\text{dist. } 60°} C_2H_5Al\cdot C_2H_5O$
   $+ C_2H_5MgAl\ (C_2H_5)_4$ (as residue)

③   Colorless oil.

④ $+ H_2O \longrightarrow C_2H_6$ (90%)

⑥   Ann. **605**, 93 (1957).

$MgC_{12}H_{10}$

①   Diphenylmagnesium
   $(C_6H_5)_2Mg$

② $(C_6H_5)_2Hg + Mg \xrightarrow{N_2,\ Et_2O}$
   $(C_6H_5)MgX + \text{dioxane} \longrightarrow$

③   Colorless bulky solid.
   Soly. : 0.0001 g/*l* (heptane) ; 0.11 g/*l*,
   0.0006 mole/*l* (benzene) ; 42.9 g/*l*,
   0.24 mole/*l* (dioxane) ; ∞(Et_2O).
   X-ray analysis : JACS **86**, 4825 (1964).

④   Decomp. at 280° to give biphenyl.
   $+ O_2 \longrightarrow (C_6H_5O)_2Mg$
   $+ C_2H_5OC_2H_5 \longrightarrow (C_6H_5)_2Mg(OC_2H_5)_2$
   $+ C_6H_5Li \longrightarrow Li[Mg(C_6H_5)_3]$
   $+ C_6H_5CH(OH)COC_6H_5 \longrightarrow$
   $(C_6H_5)_2C(OH)CH(OH)C_6H_5$ (20%)
   $+ C_6H_5CO_2H$ (6.5%)
   $+ l$-menthyl-$O_2CCO_2C_2H_5 \longrightarrow$
   $HO_2C\cdot C(OH)C_2H_5C_6H_5$
   (α_D : −3.1, asym. proportion 6%)

⑤   Catalysts in polymn. of olefins.
   Coating with Mg by decompn.

⑥   Ber. **64**, 736 (1931). Ann. **606**, 15 (1957).
   JACS **86**, 4825 (1964) ; **85**, 1002 (1963).

MgC₁₂H₁₄

① Bis(methylcyclopentadienyl)mag-
   nesium
   $(C_6H_7)_2Mg$

② $C_6H_8 + Mg \xrightarrow{500°}$
   $C_2H_5MgBr + C_6H_8 \longrightarrow$

③ [29~30°].
   Air sensitive.
   Dipole moment : 0.5 D (heptane), 0.5
   D (benzene), 5.0 D (dioxane).

⑤ Oxygen scavenger and synthetic
   intermediates.

⑥ Z. anorg. allg. Chem. **307**, 120 (1960).
   Z. Elektrochem. **66**, 312 (1962) ; **64**,
   945 (1960).   US 2933537 ; CA **54**,
   18392 (1960).

MgC₁₂H₁₈

① Dihexynylmagnesium
   $(C_4H_9C{\equiv}C)_2Mg$

② $(C_2H_5)_2Mg + C_4H_9C{\equiv}CH \xrightarrow{\text{dioxane-Et}_2O}$

④ $+ CO_2 \xrightarrow{H^+} C_4H_9C{\equiv}CCO_2H$

⑥ JACS **78**, 1221 (1956).

MgC₁₂H₂₂

① Dicyclohexylmagnesium
   $(C_6H_{11})_2Mg$

② $(C_6H_{11})MgBr \xrightarrow{\text{dioxane}}$

⑤ Catalyst in polymn. of $CH_2{=}CMe{-}$
   CO_2Me

⑥ Kogyo Kagaku Zasshi **65**, 976 (1962).

MgC₁₄H₁₄

① Dibenzylmagnesium
   $(C_6H_5CH_2)_2Mg$

② $C_6H_5CH_2MgCl \xrightarrow{\text{dioxane}}$

④

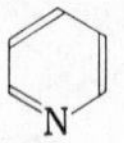

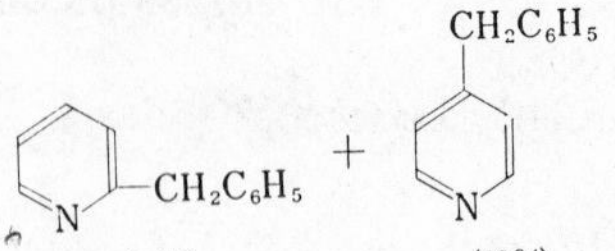

(20%)   (80%)

⑤ Catalyst in polymn. of olefins.

⑥ JACS **73**, 5861 (1951).   Ger. 889229 ;
   CA **52**, 12457 (1958).

MgC₁₆H₁₀

① Bis(phenylethynyl)magnesium
   $(C_6H_5C{\equiv}C)_2Mg$

② $C_6H_5C{\equiv}CH + (C_2H_5)_2Mg \longrightarrow$

④ $+ CO_2 \xrightarrow{20.6\%}$
   $C_6H_5C{\equiv}CCO_2MgCO_2C{\equiv}CC_6H_5$
   $+ C_6H_5CN \xrightarrow{H_2O} C_6H_5C{\equiv}CCOC_6H_5$
   $+ CH_2{=}CH{-}CH_2Br \xrightarrow{THF}$
   $C_6H_5C{\equiv}C{-}CH_2{-}CH{=}CH_2$ (60%)
   $+ CH{\equiv}C{-}CH_2Br \xrightarrow{THF}$
   $C_6H_5C{\equiv}C{-}CH_2{-}C{\equiv}CH$ (22%)

⑥ JACS **67**, 520 (1945).   Ann. chim. **6**,
   1071 (1961). Tetrahedron Letters
   1963, 729.

MgC₁₆H₁₅Br

① 1-methyl-2,2-diphenylcyclopropyl
   magnesium bromide

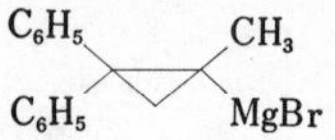

②

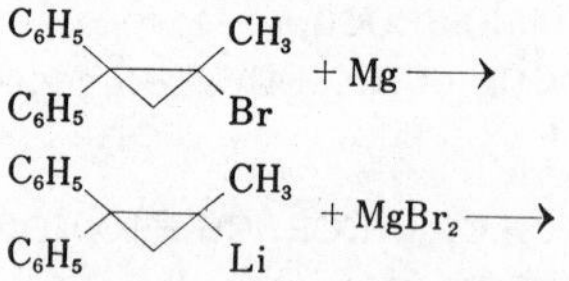

$+ Mg \longrightarrow$

$+ MgBr_2 \longrightarrow$

④ $+ CO_2 \longrightarrow$
   (100% retention)

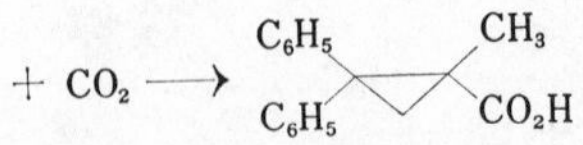

⑥ JACS **86**, 3288 (1964).

MgC₁₈H₁₅Li

① Triphenylmagnesiumlithium
   $Li[Mg(C_6H_5)_3]$

② $C_6H_5Li + (C_6H_5)_2Mg \xrightarrow{\text{xylene}}$
   $Li[Mg(C_6H_5)_3]$

③ Cryst, colorless leaflets.
   [212° decompn.].

⑥ Ann. **571**, 167 (1951).

MgC₁₈H₁₈

① Dicinnamylmagnesium
   $(C_6H_5CH=CHCH_2)_2Mg$

② $C_6H_5CH=CHCH_2MgBr + \text{dioxane} \longrightarrow$

③ UV: λ_{max} 252 mμ (ε 20000).

④ $+ CO_2 \longrightarrow CH_3CH=C(C_6H_5)CO_2H$

⑥ JACS **79**, 4795 (1957).

MgC₃₈H₃₀

① Bis(triphenylmethyl)magnesium
   $[(C_6H_5)_3C]_2Mg$

② $(C_6H_5)_3CH + Mg \xrightarrow[\text{Et}_2O\text{-}C_6H_6]{\text{trace MgBr}_2}$

⑥ JACS **52**, 4412 (1930).

【Ca】

CaC₂

① Calcium carbide
   $Ca(C\equiv C)$

② $CaO + C \longrightarrow$

③ Tetragonal white. [450° decompn.].
   d 2.22.
   Insol. in most org. solvents.

④ $+ H_2O \longrightarrow CH\equiv CH$

⑤ For C_2H_2 formation.
   Catalyze the polymn. of C_2H_4.

⑥ US 2710854 ; CA **49**, 1287 (1955).

CaC₂H₅I

① Ethylcalcium iodide
   C_2H_5CaI

② $C_2H_5I + Ca \xrightarrow{\text{Et}_2O}$

③ Amorphous powder.
   Slightly sol. in Et₂O.

④ $+ H_2O \longrightarrow C_2H_6$

⑥ Bull. soc. chim. France [5] **5**, 895
   (1938).   JACS **48**, 2463 (1926).

CaC₂H₆

① Dimethylcalcium
   $Ca(CH_3)_2$

② $CH_3\cdot + Ca \longrightarrow$

   $Ca + 2 CH_3I + \text{pyridine} \xrightarrow{\text{under He}}$
   $Ca(CH_3)_2\cdot\text{pyridine complex}$
   $\xrightarrow{\text{vacuum}} Ca(CH_3)_2$

③ White solid or pale in color.
   Stable to 400℃.

④ Hydrolyzed very rapidly. Reacts with
   O₂ or CO₂.

⑥ JACS **80**, 5324 (1958).

CaC₄H₂

① Calcium acetylide
   $Ca(C\equiv CH)_2$

② $Ca + CH\equiv CH \xrightarrow{\text{NH}_3}$

④ $+ (C_2H_5)_2SO_4 \longrightarrow CH_2CH_2C\equiv CH$
   $+ C_5H_{11}Cl \longrightarrow C_5H_{11}C\equiv CH$
   $+ C_5H_{11}Br \longrightarrow C_5H_{11}C\equiv CH$
   $+ C_4H_9Br \longrightarrow C_4H_9C\equiv CH$

⑥ Proc. Ind. Scand. Sci. **44**, 144 (1934) ;
   CA **30**, 429 (1936).

CaC₄H₉I

① n-Butylcalcium iodide
   n-C_4H_9CaI

② n-$C_4H_9I + Ca \longrightarrow$

④ $+ HCl \longrightarrow C_8H_{18} + n$-$C_4H_9OH$

⑥ Bull. soc. chim. France [5] **5**, 895
   (1938).   JACS **48**, 2463 (1926).

CaC₆H₅I

① Phenylcalcium iodide
   C_6H_5CaI

② $C_6H_5I + Ca \xrightarrow{\text{I}_2, \text{Et}_2O}$

③ Dark brown powder.
Slightly sol. in Et_2O.

④ $+ CO_2 \longrightarrow C_6H_5CO_2H$

$+ C_6H_5CHO \longrightarrow \xrightarrow{H_2O} (C_6H_5)_2CHOH$

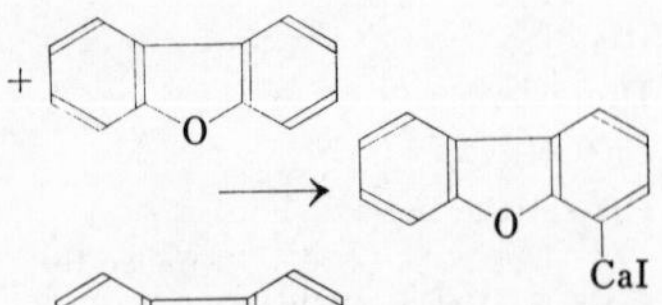

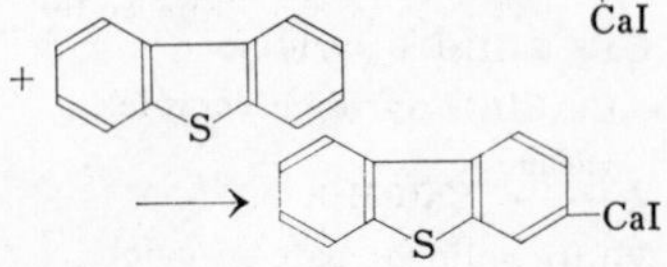

⑥ Ber. **38**, 904 (1905). Rec. trav. chim. **55**, 79 (1936). JOC **3**, 108, 120 (1938).

$CaC_8H_2F_4$

① Bis(4,4-difluoro-3-buten-1-ynyl) calcium
$(CF_2{=}CHC{\equiv}C)_2Ca$

② $2CF_2{=}CHC{\equiv}CH + \text{Ca salts} \xrightarrow{EtOH-H_2O}$

⑤ Useful as bactericides. For improving the combustion characteristics of motor fuels.

⑥ Brit. 809319; CA **53**, 15973 (1959).

$CaC_{10}H_{10}$

① Dicyclopentadienylcalcium

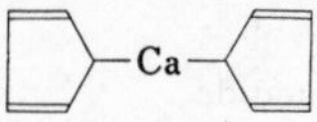

② 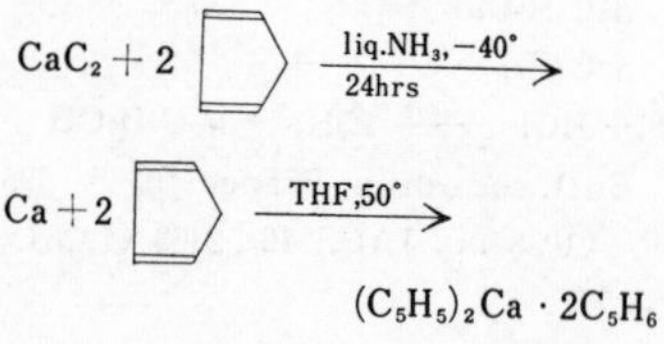
CaC₂ + 2
liq.NH₃, −40°
24hrs
Ca + 2
THF, 50°
(C₅H₅)₂Ca · 2C₅H₆

$(C_5H_5)_2Ca \cdot C_5H_6 \longrightarrow$

③ Faint yellowish powder. (265° sublime).
IR: $\nu_{C=C}$ 1433, γ_{CH} 750 cm^{-1}.

④ Glows in air.

$+2CO_2 \xrightarrow{\text{under pressure}}$

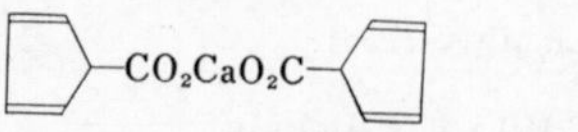

⑥ US 2835712; CA **52**, 17138 (1958). Ber. **89**, 434 (1956); **93**, 1171 (1960); **94**, 2187 (1961).

$CaC_{12}H_7OI$

① 1-Dibenzofuranylcalcium iodide

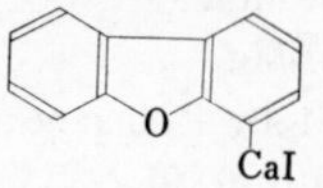

② 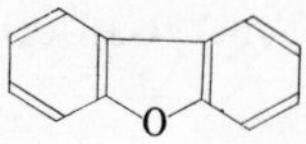 $+ C_6H_5CaI \longrightarrow$

④ $+ CO_2 \longrightarrow$ 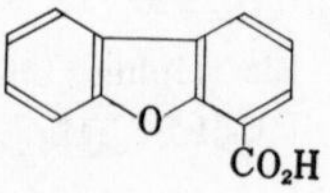

⑥ Rec. trav. chim. **55** 79 (1936).

$CaC_{12}H_7SI$

① 2-Dibenzothiophenylcalcium iodide

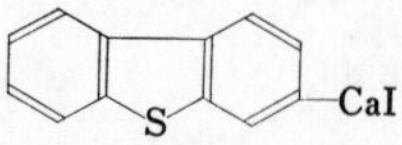

② 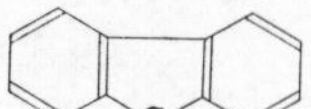 $+ C_6H_5CaI \longrightarrow$

④ $+ CO_2 \longrightarrow$ 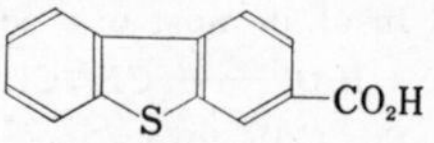

⑥ JOC **3**, 108, 120 (1938).

【Sr】

SrC_2H_5I

① Ethylstrontium iodide
C_2H_5SrI

② $SrHg + C_2H_5I \longrightarrow$

⑥ Krause and Grosse, 123.

SrC₂H₆

① Dimethyl strontium
$(CH_3)_2Sr$

② $Sr + 2\,CH_3I + C_5H_5N \xrightarrow{\text{under He}}$

$(CH_3)_2Sr \cdot C_5H_5N \xrightarrow{\text{vacuum}}$

③ White solid or pale in color.
Stable to 400°.

④ Hydrolyzed very rapidly. Reacts
with O_2 or CO_2

⑥ JACS **80**, 5324 (1958).

SrC₈H₂₀Zn

① Diethylstrontium-diethylzinc
complex
$(C_2H_5)_2Sr \cdot (C_2H_5)_2Zn$

② $Sr + 2\,(C_2H_5)_2Zn \longrightarrow$

③ Reddish brown soln.
Decomp. at 170°.

④ $+ (C_6H_5)_2C = CH_2 \longrightarrow$

$(C_6H_5)_2C - CH_2C_2H_5 \xrightarrow{1.CO_2, \ 2.H_2O}$
$\quad\quad |$
$\quad 1/2\,Sr$

$(C_6H_5)_2CCH_2CH_2CH_3$
$\quad\quad\quad |$
$\quad\quad\quad CO_2H$

$+ \ CH_3O\!\!-\!\!\bigcirc\!\!-\!\! \longrightarrow$

$\xrightarrow{CO_2, H^+} \ CH_3O\!\!-\!\!\bigcirc\!\!-\!\!CO_2H$

$+ \ \alpha\text{-}C_{10}H_7Br \longrightarrow (\alpha\text{-}C_{10}H_7)_2Sr$
$+ \ 2\,C_2H_5Br$

⑤ Catalyst for polymn.

⑥ JACS **65**, 268 (1943); **67**, 520 (1945).

SrC₁₀H₁₀

① Dicyclopentadienylstrontium
$(C_5H_5)_2Sr$

② $Sr + 2\,C_5H_6 \xrightarrow{\text{HCONMe}_2, \ 50°, \ 3\text{hr.}}$

$SrH_2 + 2\,C_5H_6 \xrightarrow{\text{HCONMe}_2}$

③ IR : $\nu_{C=C}$ 1433, γ_{CH} 744 cm⁻¹.

⑥ Ber. **94**, 2187 (1961); **93**, 1171 (1960).

【Ba】

BaC₂

① Barium carbide
BaC_2

② $Ba(C_2H)_2 \cdot 4\,NH_3 \xrightarrow{\text{heat}} BaC_2$

③ White solid. [130° decomp. *in vacuo*].

④ Decompd. by H_2O, alc.
Catalyze the polymn. of C_2H_4.

⑥ Compt. rend. 78 th Congr. socs. savan-
tes Paris et dépts., Sect. Sci. **1953**,
369; CA **49**, 13809 (1955).
US 2710854; CA **49**, 12877 (1955).

BaC₂H₅I

① Ethyl barium iodide
C_2H_5BaI

② $Ba + C_2H_5I \longrightarrow C_2H_5BaI$

⑥ Bull. soc. chim. France **41**, 1336
(1927).

BaC₂H₆

① Dimethyl barium
$(CH_3)_2Ba$

② $Ba + 2\,CH_3I + C_5H_5N \xrightarrow{\text{under He}}$
$Ba(CH_3)_2 \cdot C_5H_5N$

$Ba(CH_3)_2 \cdot C_5H_5N \xrightarrow{\text{vacuum}}$

③ White solid or pale in color.
Stable to 400 °C.

④ Hydrolyzed very rapidly. Reacts with
O_2 or CO_2.

⑥ JACS **80**, 5324 (1958).

BaC₄H₄O₄Ce

① Cerous α-barioacetate
$Ce(O_2CCH_2)_2Ba$

② $Ce(OAc)_2 + Ba(NH_2)_2 \longrightarrow$

③ Stable at elevated temp. Can be
handled in air.

⑥ US 2850528 ; CA **53**, 4135 (1959).

BaC₆H₅I

① Phenylbarium iodide

C_6H_5BaI

② $Ba + C_6H_5I \longrightarrow C_6H_5BaI$

⑥ Bull. soc. chim. France 41, 1336 (1927).

BaC₈H₂F₄

① Bis(4,4-difluoro-3-buten-1-ynyl) barium

$(CF_2=CHC\equiv C)_2Ba$

② $2 CF_2=CHC\equiv CH + Ba$ salts

$\xrightarrow{\text{1.EtOH 2.H}_2\text{O}}$

⑤ Useful as bactericides. For improving the combustion characteristics of motor fuels.

⑥ Brit. 809319 ; CA **53**, 15973 (1959).

BaC₈H₂₀Zn

① Diethylbarium–diethylzinc complex

$(C_2H_5)_2Ba \cdot (C_2H_5)_2Zn$

② $Ba + (C_2H_5)_2Zn \xrightarrow{C_6H_6, \ 65\sim70°}$

④ Catalyzes the stereospecific polymn. of isoprene with TiCl₄.

⑥ JACS **67**, 520 (1945). Belg. 617914 ; CA **58**, 9311 (1963).

BaC₁₀H₁₀

① Dicyclopentadienylbarium

$(C_5H_5)_2Ba$

② 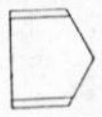 $+ BaH_2 \xrightarrow[\text{1.5hrs}]{400°} (C_5H_5)_2Ba$

③ gray powder. (420~460°sublime).

$\nu_{C=C}$ 1435, γ_{CH} 736, 662, 652, 625 cm⁻¹.

⑥ Ber. **94**, 2187 (1961) ; **93**, 1171 (1960).

BaC₁₆H₃₆Zn

① Dibutylbarium–dibutylzinc complex

$(n\text{-}C_4H_9)_2Ba \cdot (n\text{-}C_4H_9)_2Zn$

② $Ba + (n\text{-}C_4H_9)_2Zn \xrightarrow[C_6H_6, \ 10 \text{ hrs}]{\text{reflux}}$

③ jet-black mixture.

④ After carbonation it gives valeric acid.

Catalyzes the polymn. of lactone.

⑥ JACS **67**, 922 (1945).   US 3021310 ; CA **57**, 12719 (1962).

BaC₃₈H₃₀

① Bistriphenylmethylbarium

$[(C_6H_5)_3C]_2Ba$

② $Ba + (C_6H_5)_3CH \xrightarrow{\text{liq. NH}_3}$

③ Red solution.

④ $+ 2 CO_2 \xrightarrow{H^+} (C_6H_5)_3CCO_2H$

⑥ JACS **65**, 267 (1943).

3. Organic Compounds of Boron
(B)

3.1. Introduction

The first report on organoboron compounds dates back to 1859, in which was described the preparation of trimethylborane from dimethylzinc and boron trichloride. After the subsequent dormant decades, Stock and his co-workers developed the well-known vacuum technique to give an impetus to boron chemistry, and prepared various boron hydrides, trialkylboranes, and borazines. Despite their elegant techniques, the study of organoboron chemistry was pursued at a slower pace until about 1950, mainly due to the difficulties in handling many of the organoboron compounds.

In the 1940 s, the bridge-type structure of diborane was confirmed by various physical methods, and many attempts were made to interpret the structure in terms of classical valence theory to open a door for understanding the electronic structure of the electron-defficient molecules. The process designated "hydroboration" was found in 1948 by Hurd and then extended dy Brown to an unlimited field for the hydrogenation of unsaturated molecules. Metal tetrahydroborates also began to receive much attention as powerful reducing reagents, and amineboranes were the molecules of special interest in the B- and F-strain theory to account for disorderliness in basic and acid strength sequences. The most active researches are now progressing in the field of carboranes, boron-nitrogen compounds, and hydroboration.

Although progress has been limited so far, marked interest is being taken in actual and potential applications of various areas in addition to the above-mentioned uses. Numerous other instances might here be quoted: use of sodium tetraphenylborate(1-) as a reagent for the quantitative determination of potassium, the search for inorganic and organometallic polymers applicable for high-temperature duty, the potentialities of alkylboranes as catalysts in organic chemistry, the possible biological activities of alkyl- and arylboronic acids particularly with reference to the neutron capture therapy, the potential use of trimethoxyborane to extinguish some metal fires, and so on.

The chemical behavior of organoboron compounds may be ascribed to the following three origins. First, in the majority of cases, the boron atom in a molecule is strongly electrophilic by virtue of its tendency to fill the vacant $2p$ orbital to complete the octet. Second, the boron-carbon bond has less ionic character than the other metal–carbon bonds. The small ionic character may illustrate the increased stability of B–C bonds toward water and carbon dioxide.

Third, the covalent bond radius of boron is relatively small compared with those of other metals, which leads to the enhanced steric effect on the chemical behavior exerted by the substituents attached to the boron.

3.2. Classification and Nomenclature

The rapid growth of boron chemistry has occasioned confusion about the nomenclature of organoboron compounds. "Advisory Comittee on the Nomenclature of Organic Boron Compounds" was organized by the American Chemical Society in 1958 to prepare a report, "The Nomenclature of Boron", in order to meet the need for an elaborate system of nomenclature. In the following sections the reader will first find the outline of the system, and then some other systems along with customary names adopted in Chemical Abstracts.

3.2.1. Outline of "The Nomenclature of Boron"

Compounds which may be conceived as derived from a boron hydride by substitution of an atom of a group for a hydrogen are named as substitution derivatives. The parent boron hydride is named by analogy to the following examples:

Parent Boron Hydrides:

BH_3	borane(3)	B_5H_9	pentaborane(9)
B_2H_4	diborane(4)	B_5H_{11}	pentaborane(11)
B_2H_6	diborane(6)	$B_{10}H_{14}$	decaborane(14)

Derivatives:

$IBCl_2$	dichloroiodoborane	$CH_3BH_2BH_3$	1-methyldiborane(6)
$C_6H_5B(OH)_2$	dihydroxyphenylborane		
$(C_4H_9)_2BOC_2H_5$	dibutylethoxyborane		
$(CH_3)_2BN(CH_3)_2$	B-dimethyldimethylaminoborane		

Radicals:

H_2B- boryl H_3BBH_2- 1-diboran(6)yl H_9B_4- tetraboran(10)yl

Ring Systems: Names for four, five, and six membered rings, particularly in the lower stages of hydrogenation, are most conveniently given "Widmann" type names and the practices established in the Ring Index can be followed without modification. (A. M. Patterson and L. T. Capell, "The Ring Index", Reinhold Publishing Corporation, New York, 1940.) In larger rings, especially when these are in the highest stage of hydrogenation and contain isolated boron atoms, names based on those of the saturated cyclic hydrocarbons utilizing the "-a" nomenclature may be used.

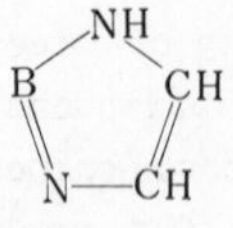

1,3,2-diazaborol 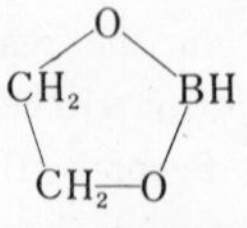   1,3,2-dioxaborolane 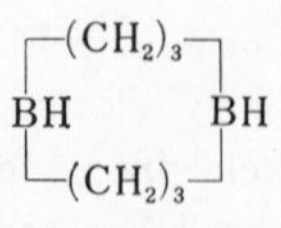   1,5-diboracyclooctane

Coordination Compounds: In addition compounds, both molecules are given their proper names and the title of the addition compound is formed by indicating the donor molecule first, and then joining this to the name of the acceptor by a hyphen.

$(CH_3)_3N \cdot BH_3$ trimethylamine-borane

$OC \cdot BH_3$ carbon monoxide(C-B)borane

3.2.2. *Existing Rules*

The practices of nomenclature can be classified into three main groups according to the choice of the name of parent as follows:

(i) BH_3 borane

(ii) BH_3 borine

(iii) $-\overset{|}{B}-$ boron

The practices of (ii) and (iii) appear to have nearly died out in recent papers, whereas that of (i) is becoming prevalent, especially in Chemical Abstracts. In this section reference will be mainly to system (i), which is fairly consistent with that in 3.2.1, and to some trivial names for compounds possessing particular features. These are ilustrated by the examples which follow. Some trivial names and the names based on system (ii) and system (iii) are enclosed in parentheses.

$(C_2H_5)_3B$ triethylborane (triethylborine, triethylboron)

CH_3BBr_2 dibromomethylborane (dibromomethylborine, methylboron dibromide)

$(C_6H_5)_2BOCH_2CH_2NH_2$ 2-aminoethyl ester of diphenylborinic acid (2-amino-ethoxydiphenylborane, 2-aminoethyl diphenylborinate, or -boronite, or -boronate)

$C_6H_5B(OH)_2$ benzeneboronic acid (phenylboronic acid)

$C_4H_9B(OC_2H_5)_2$ diethyl ester of butaneboronic acid (butyldiethoxyborane, diethyl butyl- or butane-boronate)

$CH_3B[N(CH_3)_2]_2$ bis(dimetylamino)methylborane, (bis(dimethylamino)-methylborine)

The compounds having B-OH groups are usually named as acids, and those having B-OR groups as esters. However, for the sake of overall simplicity and conformity, the "alkoxyborane" nomenclature will be used throughout this boron section in accordance with IUPAC rule 48.

R_2BOH dialkylborinic acid

$RB(OH)_2$ alkylboronic acid

The compounds involving B-O-B groupings are named as -borinic anhydride, -boronic anhydride, boron oxide, or -boroxane.

Some Other Illustrative Examples:

BCl_3 boron trichloride

ClB(OCH₃)₂   chlorodimethoxyborane (dimethyl chloroboronate)
LiBH₄   lithium tetrahydroborate (lithium borohydride)
Na[B(OCH₃)(C₆H₅)₃]   sodium methoxytriphenylborate(1-) (sodium triphenyl-
                     methoxyborohydride)
(CH₃)₃B·N(CH₃)₃   trimethylamine-trimethylborane

Ring Compounds:

Ring compounds are named as derivatives of the rings involved, and the parent
ring is named according to the rule accepted by IUPAC.

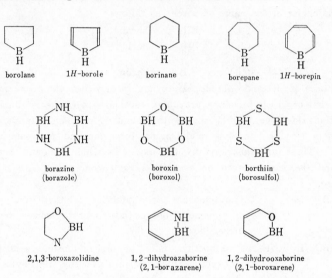

Examples:

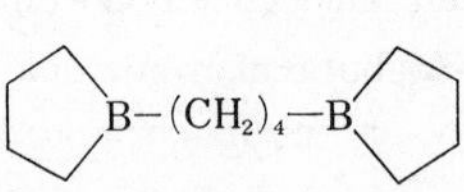

1,1′-tetramethylene-bis-
borolane

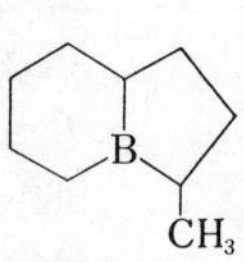

9-methylborabicyclo
[4,3,0] nonane

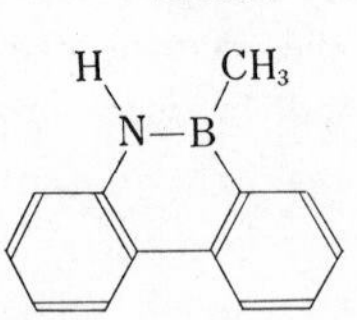

6-methyl-5,6-dihydro-dibenz-
[c,e] [1,2] azaborine
(10-methyl-10,9-borazaro-
  phenanthrene)

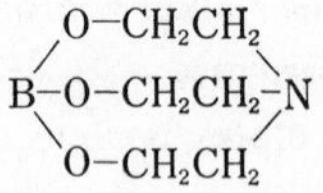

4,6,11,1,5-trioxazabora-
bicyclo[3,3,3]undecane
(triethanolamine borate)

Carboranes:

The cage-type polyboranes are taken as the parent compounds of carboranes, and in consistency with the numbering in the lower boranes, an apex atom is first numbered, then the belt or girdle atoms, and at last the opposite apex. As in the above-mentioned borane, the numerical suffix in parentheses indicates the number of hydrogen atoms in the parent compound. The prefix "clovo" from the Greek word for cage, "$\kappa\lambda\omega\beta o$" should be used only to supplement or replace the numerical suffix.

Examples :

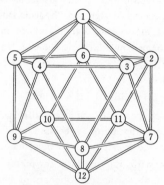

The skeletal network of 1,7-
dicarbaclovododecaborane(12)
(metacarborane)

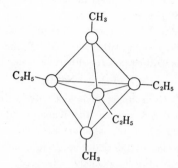

1,5-dimethyl-2,3,4-triethyl-1,5-di-
carbaclovopentaborane(5)

3.2.3. *Classification Based upon Structural Types*

Organoboron compounds may be divided into the following classes:

(1) Trialkyl- and triarylboranes R_3B
(2) Diborane derivatives $R_nB_2H_{6-n}$ ($n=1\sim4$)
(3) Higher borane derivatives and carboranes
(4) Organohalogenoboranes R_nBX_{3-n} ($n=1, 2$)
(5) Borinic acids R_2BOH and its esters R_2BOR'
(6) Boronic acids $RB(OH)_2$ and its esters $RB(OR')_2$
(7) Boroxin derivatives $R_3B_3O_3$
(8) Organoaminoboranes $R_nB(NR'R'')_{3-n}$ ($n=0, 1, 2$)
(9) Borazine derivatives $R_3B_3N_3R'_3$
(10) Heteroaromatic boron compounds
(11) Amine-borane derivatives $R_3NBR'_3$ and metal borate(1-) derivatives $M^+[BR_4]^-$

3.3. *Methods of Synthesis*

3.3.1. *Synthesis by the Use of Organometallic Compounds*

One of the most general procedures for attaching an alkyl or aryl group to boron is by interaction of a Grignard reagent and a boron trihalide or a trialkoxyborane.

$$>B-X + M-R \longrightarrow >B-R + M-X$$
$$>B-X + R-X + 2M \longrightarrow >B-R + 2M-X$$

For instance: $B(OC_4H_9)_3 + 3C_4H_9MgCl \longrightarrow B(C_4H_9)_3 + 3MgCl(OC_4H_9)$

Other organometallic compounds, for example, alkyllithiums can be used in place of the Grignard reagent, and offer advantages in certain circumstances.

3.3.2. Addition of Boron Hydrides to Unsaturated Compounds

Diborane reacts easily with all types of aliphatic and aromatic olefins to give various organoboranes in good yield. This process, designated "hydroboration", readily proceeds in tetrahydrofuran, diethyl ether and diglyme at room temperature. The reactant diborane may be formed by reactions such as $NaBH_4 + BF_3 \cdot O(C_2H_5)_2$, $LiAlH_4 + BF_3 \cdot O(C_2H_5)_2$, and $NaBH_4 + AlCl_3$. Amine-boranes, $R_3N \cdot BH_3$, may be substituted for diborane in some cases.

$$12RCH=CH_2 + 3NaBH_4 + 4BF_3 \longrightarrow 4(RCH_2CH_2)_3B + 3NaBF_4$$

The B-H grouping adds exclusively in the *cis* position, preferentially from the less-hindered side of the double bond, placing the boron predominantly in the position where the addition gives rise to less steric strain. In most cases, the orientation of the addition is in conformity with the anti-Markownikoff rule. Hydroboration is strongly influenced by the large steric requirements of both the boranes and the olefins. Utilizing a dialkylborane involving bulky substituents may lead to an increase in selectivity of addition and may affect stereospecific reactions. Interesting and useful results have been realized in the hydroboration of allenes, alicyclic olefins, dienes, and acetylenes, as well as terpenes and steroids.

3.3.3. Other Methods

$$BCl_3 + C_6H_6 \xrightarrow{\text{catalyst } Al + AlCl_3} C_6H_5BCl_2$$

$$BCl_3 + HC \equiv CH \xrightarrow{\text{catalyst } Hg(OAc)_2} ClCH = CHBCl_2$$

$$BF_3 + CH_2N_2 \longrightarrow FCH_2BF_2$$

3.3.4. Redistribution Reactions

Trialkylboranes undergo mutual exchange reactions with boranes, alkoxyboranes, aminoboranes, halogenoboranes, etc., at high temperatures or under the influence of catalyst.

$$R_3B + BX_3 \rightleftharpoons R_2BX + RBX_2$$
$$(X = \text{hydrogen, halogen, alkoxy, amino})$$

For instance, $2(C_2H_5)_3B + 2B_2H_6 \longrightarrow 3(C_2H_5)_2B_2H_4$

3.4. General Properties

3.4.1. Structures

Most of the lower trialkylboranes are liquids at room temperature, and higher trialkylboranes are low-melting solids. The aliphatic organoboranes are typical nonpolar substances resembling in physical properties the corresponding hydrocarbons which can be obtained by substituting a CH grouping for a B atom. It has been clarified by the structural analyses on some trialkyl-, triaryl- and alkylhalogenoboranes that trialkylboranes are monomeric and take trigonal-planar stuctures in contrast to the corresponding organoaluminum compounds. The boron atom has a vacant $2p$ orbital of low energy and most of the organoboron compounds are electron deficient in the sense of the Lewis octet theory. Much of recorded organoboron chemistry is related to the resulting electrophilic nature of the boron atom, that is, to the boron p orbital interaction with nucleophiles.

3.4.2. Redistribution and Exchange Reactions

It has long been recognized that mixed trialkylboranes, $RR'R''B$ or RR'_2B, are rarely isolated because of an easy redistribution of the groups to give homogeneous trialkylboranes. This reaction is supposed to occur through a dimer-structured intermediate stabilized by the participation of the vacant $2p$ orbital.

$$BR_3 + BR'_3 \rightleftharpoons {>}B{<}^R_{R'}{>}B{<} \rightleftharpoons BR_2R' + BRR'_2$$

In this connection, it should be mentioned that a small amount of triethylaluminum catalyzes the redistribution reaction among trialkylboranes, which may be accounted for by postulating an intermediate of alkyl-bridge structure to facilitate the exchange of alkyl groups.

Trialkyl- and triarylboranes exchange their organic substituents with alkylmagnesium and alkylaluminum.

$$(C_6H_5)_3B + (C_2H_5)_3Al \xrightarrow{140°} (C_2H_5)_3B + (C_6H_5)_3Al$$

The alkylboranes involving B–O, B–N, B–halogen, or B–H groupings show considerable stability at room temperature, but undergo redistribution reactions at elevated temperatures.

3.4.3. Thermal Behavior

Lower alkylboranes exhibit considerable thermal stability, whereas medium or higher alkylboranes undergo ready displacement of boron atoms. When a boron atom is placed in the interior of an alkane chain, the isomerization occurs at about 150°, shifting the boron atom to a terminal carbon.

Preference for terminal position may be ascribed to a tendency to place the boron atom at the least hindered position. The migration of the boron atom almost certainly proceeds through a succession of dehydroboration and hydroboration equilibria.

$$R' - \overset{\overset{\displaystyle H}{|}}{\underset{\underset{\displaystyle R_2B\cdots H}{|}}{C}} - \overset{\overset{\displaystyle H}{|}}{\underset{\underset{\displaystyle H}{|}}{C}} - H \;\; \rightleftharpoons \;\; R' - \overset{\overset{\displaystyle H}{|}}{\underset{\underset{\displaystyle R_2B - H}{|}}{C}} = \overset{\overset{\displaystyle H}{|}}{\underset{\underset{\displaystyle H}{|}}{C}} - H \;\; \rightleftharpoons \;\; R' - \overset{\overset{\displaystyle H}{|}}{\underset{\underset{\displaystyle H\cdots BR_2}{|}}{C}} - \overset{\overset{\displaystyle H}{|}}{\underset{\underset{\displaystyle H}{|}}{C}} - H$$

This mechanism also accounts for the fact that the boron atom can move past a single alkyl branch with ease but past a double branch only with difficulty, and that the existence of excess olefin represses the migration. The thermal isomerization can be utilized to achieve the conversion of internal olefins into the corresponding terminal olefins and alcohols. If the mechanism is correct, the equilibrium point must be shifted toward completion by adding a large excess of reactant olefin, or by distilling off one of the product olefins. This has been demonstrated by many experiments.

$$R'CH_2CH_2BR_2 \;\rightleftharpoons\; [R'CH=CH_2 + HBR_2] \xrightarrow{R''CH=CH_2} R''CH_2CH_2BR_2 + R'CH=CH_2$$

Example:

$$(i\text{-}C_4H_9)_3B \;+\; 3\;\bigcirc \xrightarrow{160\sim170^\circ} (cyclo\text{-}C_6H_{11})_3B \;+\; 3\,i\text{-}C_4H_8$$

The process provides a convenient synthetic route for the thermodynamically unstable terminal olefins.

The extension of the reaction time results in evolution of hydrogen to afford the related cyclic borane, when the hydrocarbon chain is long enough for cyclization. With lower trialkylboranes, irreversible C–C bond cleavages occur at higher temperatures.

$$(C_4H_9)_3B \xrightarrow{200\sim300^\circ} trans\text{-}2\text{-butene} \;+\; (C_4H_9)_2BH \longrightarrow C_4H_9B\!\!\bigcirc + H_2$$

$$(i\text{-}C_4H_9)_3B \xrightarrow{200^\circ} i\text{-}C_4H_8 + (i\text{-}C_4H_9)_2BH \xrightarrow{300^\circ} i\text{-}C_4H_9B(CH_3)(C_3H_7)$$

3.4.4. Oxidation

Alkylboron compounds are readily converted into alkoxyboranes by oxidizing agents such as hydrogen peroxide, oxygen, and potassium permanganate. The subsequent hydrolysis leads to the corresponding alcohols. Autooxidation of the trialkylborane with oxygen or air proceeds successively through an initial addition compound of the trialkylborane and oxygen termed a "borine peroxide", and rapidly to the monoalkoxy or dialkoxy stage. The lower alkylboranes and aryl boranes are especially sensitive to air, and in this connection, it has been reported that the trialkylboranes are effective catalysts for vinyl polymerization in the presence of minor amounts of oxygen. Hydrogen peroxide is a mild reagent and is used in alkaline solutions of tetrahydrofuran and diglyme at room temperature. The oxidation with this reagent retains the configuration of the alkyl group attached to the boron atom.

$$RCH{=}CH_2 \xrightarrow{B_2H_6} (RCH_2CH_2)_3B \xrightarrow[NaOH]{H_2O_2} RCH_2CH_2OH + H_3BO_3$$

The use of chromic acid makes possible the direct oxidation of alkylboranes to ketones.

3.4.5. Halogenation

Halogens react with trialkylboranes to break the B–C bonds one by one. The lower trialkylboranes are inflammable in chlorine gas.

Example: $(C_3H_7)_3B + I_2 \longrightarrow (C_3H_7)_2BI + C_3H_7I$

3.4.6. Protolysis

Trialkylboranes are remarkably stable toward water, but undergo protolyses under vigorous conditions, such as application of super-heated steam or hydrogen halide or carboxylic acid, to give hydrocarbons. The trialkylboranes react with carboxylic acids under relatively mild conditions to remove two of the three alkyl groups, and on refluxing in diglyme solution to remove all three. The protolyses have been proved to proceed with retention of configuration of the alkyl moieties. Hydroboration of olefins followed by protolysis provides a convenient noncatalytic procedure for the hydrogenation of double bonds.

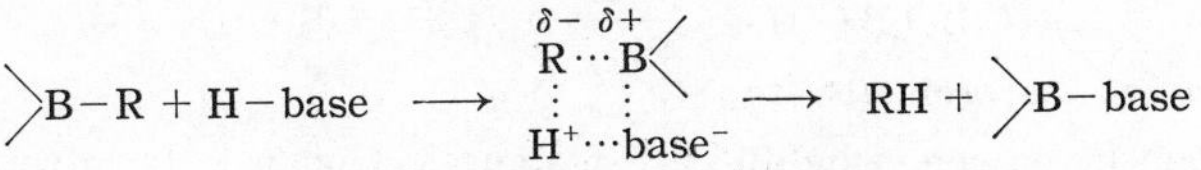

$$\diagdown{B}{-}R + H{-}base \longrightarrow \begin{array}{c} \overset{\delta-}{R}\cdots\overset{\delta+}{B}\diagup \\ \vdots \quad \vdots \\ H^+\cdots base^- \end{array} \longrightarrow RH + \diagdown{B}{-}base$$

3.4.7. Reaction with Carbonyl Compounds and Carbon Monoxide

Trialkylboranes react with aldehyde groups attached to some electrophilic group to reduce them to the corresponding alcohols, though the reaction is somewhat milder than those of Grignard reagents, trialkylaluminums, and borate ion.

$$CCl_3CHO + (C_2H_5)_3B \longrightarrow C_2H_4 + CCl_3CH_2OB(C_2H_5)_2 \xrightarrow{H_2O} CCl_3CH_2OH$$

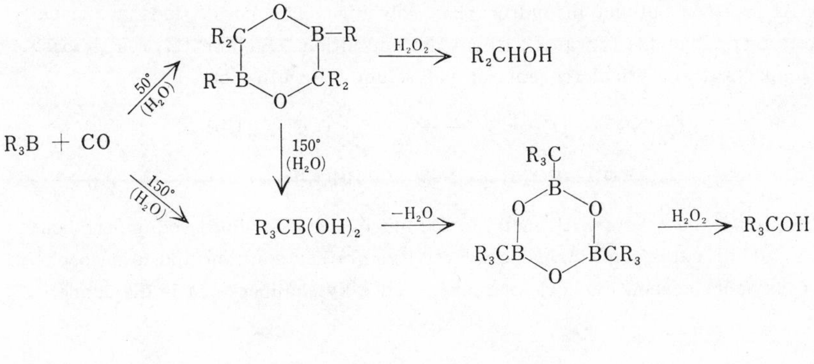

The reaction of trialkylborane with carbon monoxide under high pressure proceeds initially by the nucleophilic attack of CO onto the boron atom, followed by a migration of alkyl groups from boron to carbon. The final products vary depending on the species of solvent employed, temperature, and added reagents. In a water-alcohol solution, subsequent oxidation of the reaction mixture at a low temperature gives a secondary alcohol, R_2CHOH, and a similar procedure at a higher temperature $(140 \sim 170°)$ gives a tertiary alcohol, R_3COH.

No reaction with carbon dioxide has been reported.

3.4.8. Reactions with Salts

On treating a mixture of triethylborane and mercuric chloride in aqueous suspension with sodium hydroxide, one can isolate diethylmercury in a 95% yield. Mercuric oxide may be substituted for the chloride, and a similar reaction proceeds in the case of lead oxide to give tetraalkyllead.

$$(C_2H_5)_3B + HgCl_2 + 4\,NaOH \longrightarrow (C_2H_5)_2Hg + C_2H_5B(ONa)_2 + 2\,NaCl + H_2O$$

Silver and platinum salts seem to react with trialkylboranes in a similar way, but the intermediate organometallics are unstable and immediately decompose into radicals which couple with each other.

$$R_3B \xrightarrow{AgNO_3} R-R + B(OH)_3$$

In contrast to the results with trialkylboranes, the treatment of triarylboranes with various salts of silver, copper, and zinc produce apparent hydrolysis products.

$$(C_6H_5)_3B + H_2O \xrightarrow{AgNO_3} C_6H_6 + B(OH)_3$$

3.4.9. Donor–Acceptor Bonding

The trivalent boron compound BR_3 accepts an electron pair from a suitable electron donor, such as an amine, phosphine, carbanion, etc., to form a coordination bond. In such a compound, boron assumes tetrahedral sp^3 hybridization and its electron deficiency is reduced, thereby increasing its stability toward oxidation and hydrolysis.

Brown and his coworkers made extensive investigations to explain the relative strength of the B-N coordinate bond in terms of electronic and steric factors. Pyrolysis of an amine-borane usually gives a borazine derivative.

$$(CH_3)_3B + NH_3 \longrightarrow (CH_3)_3B \cdot NH_3 \xrightarrow{200°} (CH_3)_2BNH_2 \xrightarrow{330°} B_3(CH_3)_3N_3H_3$$

Organoalkali compounds and alkali metal hydrides are strong electron donors and form stable borate ions $(BR_4)^-$ by coordinating to boranes. The borates can be prepared in ether but not in hydrocarbon solvents. The borate ions are usually stable to air and soluble in water without decomposition. Sodium tetraphenylborate is an important analytical reagent for potassium determination.

$$Li(C_2H_5) + (CH_3)_3B \xrightarrow[(C_2H_5)_2O]{} Li[B(CH_3)_3(C_2H_5)]$$

$$LiH + B(C_6H_5)_3 \longrightarrow Li[BH(C_6H_5)_3]$$

Triphenylborane reacts with metallic sodium in ether to afford sodium-triphenylborane, which exhibits electrical conductivity in ether solution and is susceptible toward oxygen, carbon dioxide, mercury, and alkyl halides. It is diamagnetic, suggesting the dimeric structure $[Ph_3B \cdot BPh_3]Na_2$.

$$Na/Hg + (C_6H_5)_3B \xrightarrow[(C_2H_5)_2O]{} NaB(C_6H_5)_3$$

3.5. Boroxine and Its Derivatives

Boroxines are prepared from the corresponding boronic acid, $RB(OH)_2$, by desiccation at room temperature over phosphorus pentoxide.

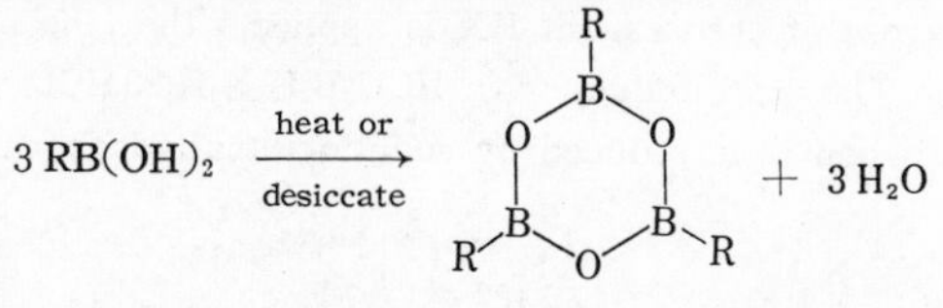

$$3\ RB(OH)_2 \xrightarrow[\text{desiccate}]{\text{heat or}}$$

$+ 3\ H_2O$

Boroxines are stable to air oxidation, but are readily cleaved by hydrogen peroxide. Some lower alkyl derivatives undergo disproportionation reactions into boric oxide and trialkylboranes, and react with trialkylaluminum to afford trialkylboranes.

$$B_2O_3 \xrightarrow{R_3B} (RBO)_3 \xrightarrow{AlR_3} R_3B + Al_2O_3$$

Ammonia reacts with boroxines to afford a 1 : 1 and a 1 : 2 adduct. The reaction with aluminum chloride has been reported to cleave the B–O bonds of alkylboroxines, but to cleave the B–C bonds of arylboroxines,

$$[C_4H_9BO]_3 + AlCl_3 \longrightarrow C_4H_9BCl_2 + Al_2O_3$$

$$[C_6H_5BO]_3 + AlCl_3 \xrightarrow{200°} C_6H_6,\ B_2O_3,\ tar$$

3.6. Borazine and Its Derivatives

The parent compound, $(HBNH)_3$, was first prepared by the thermal decomposition of the adduct of ammonia with diborane, diborane diammoniate. The most convenient method for the preparation of borazine is the reduction of B–trichloroborazine with tetrahydroborates. B–Trichloroborazine can be easily prepared by a simple large-scale procedure, that is, by the reaction of ammonium chloride with boron trichloride. N–Substituents may be introduced by utilizing properly substituted amines instead of ammonium chloride, while B–substituents may be introduced by the reaction of the appropriate Grignard reagent and B–trichloroborazine derivatives.

$$3\ BCl_3 + 3\ NH_4Cl \xrightarrow[C_6H_5Cl]{110°} B_3Cl_3N_3H_3 + 9\ HCl$$

$$3\ C_6H_5BCl_2 + 9\ C_2H_5NH_2 \longrightarrow B_3(C_6H_5)_3N_3(C_2H_5)_3 + 6\ C_2H_5NH_3Cl$$

$$B_3Cl_3N_3R_3 + 3\ R'MgX \longrightarrow B_3R_3'N_3R_3 + 3\ MgXCl$$

$$B_3Cl_3N_3H_3 + 3\ NaBH_4 \xrightarrow{\text{diglyme}} B_3H_3N_3H_3 + 3\ NaCl + 1.5\ B_2H_6$$

Bonding in the borazine ring has been the subject of many physicochemical investigations; borazine is discussed with benzene, with which it is isoelectronic. Borazine decomposes slowly at room temperature, but some hexa-substituted borazines have exceptional thermal stability compared to most boron-nitrogen compounds.   One of the most characteristic reactions of the borazine ring system is the facile addition of compounds of the type HX (X=halogen, OH, OR) to give 1 : 3 adducts of cyclohexane structure, which on pyrolysis afford borazine derivatives.   When an excess of the reagent HX is applied, the ring structure is completely decomposed. The 1 : 3 adduct with HCl, $B_3H_3N_3H_3 \cdot 3HCl$, yields its parent compound $B_3H_6N_3H_6$ when it is reduced by sodium tetrahydroborate.

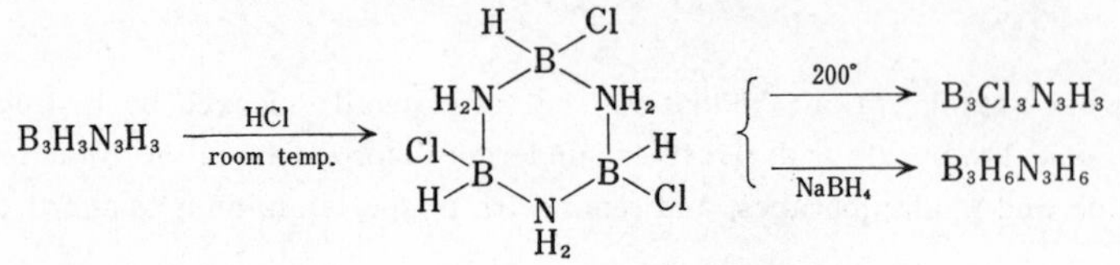

3.7. Aminoboranes

Aminoborane is isoelectronic with ethylene and has received much attention from theoretical chemists.   The tendency of monoaminoboranes to form dimers makes it difficult to measure the physical properties of pure samples of monomer. The parent compound of aminoborane, H_2NBH_2, is not yet known in monomeric form, the trimer having been refered to in Section 3.6 as a derivative of borazine.   N-Dimethylaminoborane is prepared through pyrolysis of the adduct of dimethylamine and diborane.

$$(CH_3)_2NH + B_2H_6 \xrightarrow{-42°} 2(CH_3)_2NH \cdot B_2H_6 \xrightarrow{130\sim160°} 2(CH_3)_2NBH_2 + H_2$$

The most important derivatives of aminoborane are heterocyclic boron-nitrogen compounds, on which Dewar and his coworkers have made extensive investigations.   Some representatives are listed below.

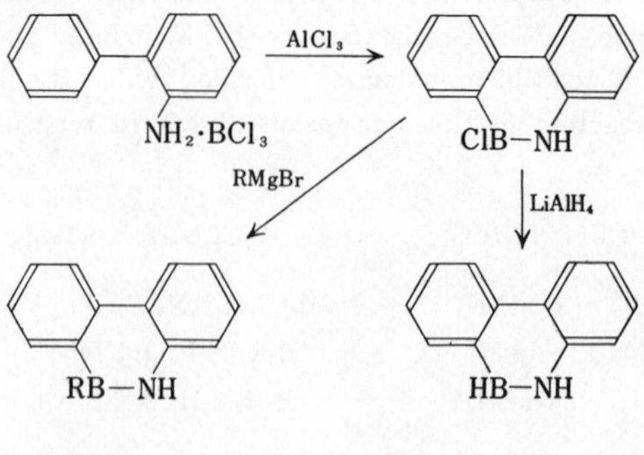

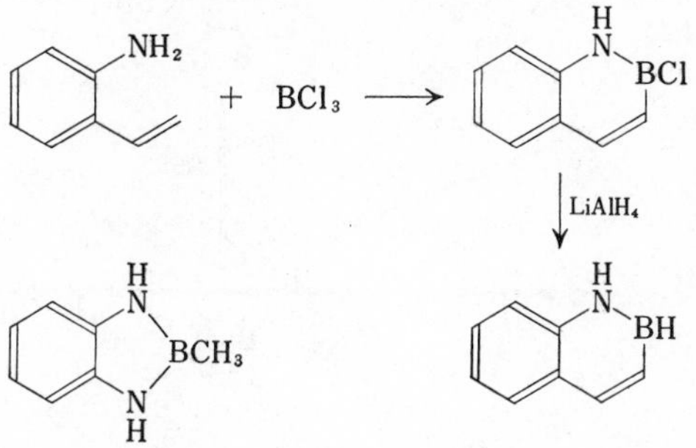

3.8. Carboranes

3.8.1. Small Carboranes

The term carborane designates a carbon–boron–hydrogen system in which both the carbon and boron atoms are incorporated into a skeletal network. Molecular orbital calculations predict increased stabilities for various carboranes as compared to those of boron hydrides. Small carboranes, $C_2B_3H_5$, $1,2\text{-}C_2B_4H_6$, $1,6\text{-}C_2B_4H_6$ and $C_2B_5H_7$, have been isolated from the product mixtures of the electric discharge in acetylene-diborane or acetylene-pentaborane mixtures. Recently a monocarbaclovodecaborate(10) ion was reported as a decomposition product of dicarbaclovododecaborane(12). These carboranes can remain in contact with acetone, trimethylamine, ammonia, air, and water at room temperature without noticeable reaction. The structure of an alkyl derivative of $C_2B_3H_5$ was depicted in the section on nomenclature.

3.8.2. Carboranes

The reaction of decaborane with acetylene in the presence of Lewis base affords 1,2-dicarbaclovododecaborane(12), which has nearly icosahedral geometry with two carbon atoms adjacent to each other. The cage structure is usually abbreviated

as .

$$B_{10}H_{14} + HC\equiv CH \xrightarrow{\text{Lewis base}} 1,2\text{-}C_2B_{10}H_{12} + 2\,H_2$$

The other two possible isomers, 1,7- and $1,12\text{-}C_2B_{10}H_{12}$, have been prepared by the pyrolysis of 1,2- and $1,7\text{-}C_2B_{10}H_{12}$, respectively. These carboranes are comparatively stable toward hydrolysis, air oxidation, and pyrolysis. C-Substituted and C, C'-disubstituted carborane derivatives can be prepared via two paths: from the corresponding substituted acetylenes, $RC\equiv CR'$, and by metallation of C–hydrogen followed by the reactions with appropriate reagents. Much of the chemical work on carboranes has been based on the facile metallation with n-butyllithium of $1,2\text{-}C_2B_{10}H_{12}$ and its mono substituted derivatives.

$$\text{HC} \overset{}{\underset{B_{10}H_{10}}{\diagdown\diagup}} \text{CR} \qquad \text{HC} \overset{}{\underset{B_{10}H_{10}}{\diagdown\diagup}} \text{CI} \qquad \text{HC} \overset{}{\underset{B_{10}H_{10}}{\diagdown\diagup}} \text{CSiR}_3 \qquad \text{HC} \overset{}{\underset{B_{10}H_{10}}{\diagdown\diagup}} \text{CCOOLi}$$

$$\text{RBr} \qquad\qquad \text{I}_2 \qquad\qquad \text{R}_3\text{SiCl} \qquad \text{CO}_2$$

$$\text{HC} \overset{}{\underset{B_{10}H_{10}}{\diagdown\diagup}} \text{CH} \;+\; n\text{-C}_4\text{H}_9\text{Li} \;\longrightarrow\; \text{HC} \overset{}{\underset{B_{10}H_{10}}{\diagdown\diagup}} \text{CLi} \;+\; \text{C}_4\text{H}_{10}$$

$$+$$

$$2\,n\text{-C}_4\text{H}_9\text{Li} \;\longrightarrow\; \text{LiC} \overset{}{\underset{B_{10}H_{10}}{\diagdown\diagup}} \text{CLi} \;+\; 2\,\text{C}_4\text{H}_{10}$$

$$2\,\text{H}_2\text{C}\overset{}{\underset{O}{\diagdown\diagup}}\text{CH}_2 \qquad\qquad 2\,\text{CH}_3\text{CHO}$$

$$\text{HO(CH}_2)_2\text{C} \overset{}{\underset{B_{10}H_{10}}{\diagdown\diagup}} \text{C(CH}_2)_2\text{OH} \qquad\qquad \overset{\text{OH}}{\text{CH}_3\text{CHC}} \overset{}{\underset{B_{10}H_{10}}{\diagdown\diagup}} \overset{\text{OH}}{\text{CCHCH}_3}$$

3.9. Related Compounds

3.9.1. Boron Hydrides

The simplest of the conceivable boron hydrides, BH_3, has not been isolated, although it is believed to play important roles in many of the reaction mechanisms involving the higher boranes. It exists as a dimer. The well-known hydrides are diborane(6), tetraborane(10), pentaborane(9), pentaborane(11), hexaborane(10), and decaborane(14). Lipscomb and his coworkers extended the theory of chemical bonding to include these electron-deficient compounds and proposed the concept of three-center orbitals and a basis of the extended Hückel MO theory.

Two of the most convenient methods for the preparation of diborane are (1) the reduction of boron halides with lithium aluminum hydride, and (2) the reaction of BF_3 etherate with lithium or sodium tetrahydroborate.

(1) $3\,\text{LiAlH}_4 + 4\,\text{BCl}_3 \longrightarrow 3\,\text{LiCl} + 3\,\text{AlCl}_3 + 2\,\text{B}_2\text{H}_6$

(2) $3\,\text{NaBH}_4 + 4\,\text{BF}_3 \longrightarrow 2\,\text{B}_2\text{H}_6 + 3\,\text{NaBF}_4$

Diborane is sensitive to hydrolysis and oxydation with air, and forms coordination compounds with Lewis bases. Higher boranes can be prepared by the pyrolysis of diborane with or without hydrogen under high pressure.

3.9.2. Alkali Metal Tetrahydroborate

The most convenient method for the preparation of sodium tetrahydroborate is effected by slowly adding trimethoxyborane onto an excess of powdered sodium hydride at $250°C$.

$$4\,\text{NaH} + \text{B(OCH}_3)_3 \longrightarrow 3\,\text{NaOCH}_3 + \text{NaBH}_4$$

Lithium tetrahydroborate may be prepared by interaction of lithium chloride and sodium tetrahydroborate in ethylamine. Sodium tetrahydroborate is stable in dry air up to $300°C$, insoluble in ether, soluble in water and alcohol with slow evolution of hydrogen, and soluble in diglyme without decomposition. The reducing power of tetrahydroborate varies with the solvent, the species of cation, etc. Thus the selectivity of reduction can be achieved by employing tetrahydroborate in conjunction with a particular solvent and a selected metal ion. The selectivities are tabulated in Table 3.1.

Table 3.1. *Reduction with Tetrahydroborates*.*

Functional Group	Product	NaBH₄	LiBH₄	NaBH(OCH₃)₃	NaBH₄ + AlCl₃	B₂H₆
RCHO	RCH₂OH	+	+	+	+	+
RCOR'	RCHOHR'	+	+	+	+	+
RCOCl	RCH₂OH	+	+	+	+	−
RCOOH	RCH₂OH	−	+	+	+	+
RCOONa	RCH₂OH	−	−	−	−	
RCOOR	RCH₂OH		+	+	+	−
RC≡N	RCH₂NH₂	−	−	+	+	+
RCONR'₂	RCH₂NR'₂	−	−		+	
$\rangle$C=C$\langle$	(−CH₂CH₂)₃B	−	−	−	+	+
$\rangle$C—C$\langle$ (epoxide O)	$\rangle$CH−C−OH	−	+		+	+
$\rangle$C=C$\langle$	$\rangle$CH−CH$\langle$	−	−	−		+
−C≡C−	$\rangle$C=C$\langle$					+
$\rangle$C=N−	$\rangle$CH−NH−	+	+		+	

* The sign + stands for "effective" and that − for "noneffective".

3.9.3. Trialkoxyboranes

The most convenient method of preparation is the esterification of boric acid with three moles of an alcohol or phenol.

$$B(OH)_3 + 3\,ROH \rightleftharpoons B(OR)_3 + 3\,H_2O$$

Since the reaction is reversible, in order to complete the esterification one component water has to be removed as azeotrope with the excess alcohol or with added hydrocarbons. Most of the trialkoxy- or triphenoxy-boranes are susceptible to hydrolysis. However, some sterically hindered esters and those coordinated to amines possess remarkable hydrolytic stability. It is difficult to obtain asymmetrically substituted trialkoxyboranes, but it is easy to prepare them with polyhydric alcohols and phenols. For instance, *vic–cis*-diol gives a stable complex ion having a tetrahedral boron. Thus, the boric ester of three-substituted catechol may be separated into optically active stereoisomers, and mannitol effects an enhancement of acidity of boric acid to allow an accurate titration.

$$2 \begin{array}{c} -CHOH \\ | \\ -CHOH \end{array} + B(OH)_3 \longrightarrow H^+ \left[\begin{array}{c} -CH-O \\ | \\ -CH-O \end{array} \right. B \left. \begin{array}{c} O-CH- \\ | \\ O-CH- \end{array} \right]^- + 3\,H_2O$$

Trialkoxyboranes are important starting materials for various organoboron compounds.

REFERENCES

1) A. Stock, "Hydrides of Boron and Silicon", University Press, Ithaca (1933).
2) E. Krause, A. v. Grosse, "Die Chemie der Metall-Organischen Verbindungen", Borntraeger (1937).
3) G. E. Coates, *Quart. Revs.*, **4**, 217~235 (1950).
4) M. F. Lappert, *Chem. Revs.*, **56**, 959~1064 (1956).
5) N. G. Gaylord, "Reduction with Complex Metal Hydrides", Interscience (1956).
6) G. Wittig, *Angew. Chem.*, **70**, 65~92 (1958).
7) "Metal Organic Compounds" (Advances in Chemistry Series, No. 23), Am. Chem. Soc. (1959).
8) A. V. Topchiev, S. V. Zavgorodnii, Ya. M. Paushkin, "Boron Fluoride and its Compounds as catalyst in Organic Chemistry", Pergamon Press (1959).
9) J. C. Sheldon, B. C. Smith, *Quart. Revs.*, **14**, 200~219 (1960).
10) B. M. Mikhailov, *Uspekhi Khim.*, **29**, 972 (1960).
11) B. M. Mikhailov, *Uspekhi Khim.*, **31**, 417 (1960).
12) W. Gerrard, "The Organic Chemistry of Boron", Academic Press (1961).
13) "Borax to Boranes" (Advances in Chemistry Series, No. 32), Am. Chem. Soc. (1961).
14) H. C. Brown, "Hydroboration", W. A. Benjamin (1962).
15) P. M. Maitlis, *Chem. Revs.*, **62**, 223~245 (1962).
16) R. Köster, *Angew. Chem.*, **75**, 1079~1090 (1963).
17) W. N. Lipscomb, "Boron Hydrides", W. A. Benjamin (1963).
18) H. Steinberg, A. L. McCloskey, "Progess in Boron Chemistry", Pergamon Press (1964).
19) R. Köster, "Advances in Organometallic Chemistry", Vol. 2, p. 257, Academic Press (1964).
20) "Boron-Nitrogen Chemistry" (Advances in Chemistry Series, No. 42), Am. Chem. Soc. (1964).
21) H. Steinberg, "Organoboron Chemistry", Vol. 1, Interscience (1964).
22) Roy M. Adams, "Boron, Metallo-Boron Compounds and Boranes", Interscience (1964).
23) T. Onak, "Advances in Organometallic Chemistry", Vol. 3, p. 263, Academic Press (1965).
24) D. Seyferth, R. B. King, "Annual Survey of Organometallic Chemistry", Elsevier Publishing Co. (1965).
25) K. Niedenzu, J. W. Dawson, "Boron-Nitrogen Compounds", Springer-Verlag (1965).
26) H. Steinberg, R. J. Brotherton, "Organoboron Chemistry", Vol. 2, Inter-

science (1966).

27) A. N. Nesmeyanov, R. A. Sokolik, "The Organic Compounds of Boron, Alminum, Gallium, Indium, and Thallium" (Series: Methods of Elemento-Organic Chemistry, Vol. 1), North-Holland Pub. Co. (1967).

28) E. L. Mutterties, "The Chemistry of Boron and Its Compounds", John Wiley & Sons (1967).

【B】

BCH₃Br₂

① Dibromomethylborane
   CH_3BBr_2

② $BBr_3 + AlMe_3 \longrightarrow$

   $BBr_3 + Me_3B \xrightarrow{390°}$

③ Liq. (60.0°). [−110.6°].
   Heat of vaporn. 7.3 kcal/mol.

④ $+ Si(OMe)_4 \longrightarrow MeB(OMe)_2$
   $+ (MeO)_2SiBr_2$
   $+ Et_3SiONa \longrightarrow MeB(OSiEt_3)_2$
   $+ NaBr$
   $+ Me_2PH + NEt_3 \longrightarrow (Me_2BPMe_2)_3$
   $+ MeBNMe_2 \longrightarrow MeBBrNMe_2$
   (80%)

⑥ Z. anorg. allg. Chem. **294**, 183 (1958).

BCH₃Cl₂

① Dichloromethylborane
   CH_3BCl_2

② $BCl_3 + ZnMe_2 \longrightarrow$

   $(MeO)_3 + BCl_3 \xrightarrow{heat}$

   $BCl_3 + HCl + AlC \xrightarrow{400°} 87\%$

   $BF_3 + MeAlCl_2 \longrightarrow$

③ Gas. (11.1°). [−127°].

④ $+ H_2NR \longrightarrow (MeBCl_2 \cdot NH_2R) \longrightarrow$
   $MeBClHNR \xrightarrow{heat} (MeBNR)_3$
   $+ ROH \longrightarrow MeB(OR)_2$
   $+ H_2O \longrightarrow (MeBO)_3$

⑥ Ber. **70 b**, 1583 (1937).   Z. anorg.
   allg. Chem. **322**, 103 (1963).

BCH₃F₂

① Difluoromethylborane
   CH_3BF_2

② $BF_3 + (CH_3BO)_3 \longrightarrow 60\sim80\%$

   $BF_3 + Me_4Sn \xrightarrow{100°} MeBF_2$
   $+ Me_3SnBF_4$

③ Gas. (−63°). [−130.4°].
   Heat of vaporn. 5.0 kcal/mol.
   Planar (electron diffraction); B-F
   1.30 Å, B-C 1.60 Å. ∠F-B-F −120°.
   $\log P = -1204.0/T + 1.75 \log T$
   $-0.00684\, T + 5.9680.$

④ $+ NMe_3 \longrightarrow MeBF_2 \cdot NMe_3$ (at 230°,
   90% dissociate)
   $+ KF \longrightarrow K(MeBF_3)$
   $+ CH_2N_2 \longrightarrow$ polymethylene

⑤ Polymn. promotor.

⑥ JACS **62**, 2228 (1940); **64**, 2686 (1942).

BCH₅O₂

① Methylboronic acid
   $CH_3B(OH)_2$

② $(MeBO)_3 + H_2O \longrightarrow$
   $sym\text{-}Me_2B_2H_4 + H_2O \longrightarrow$
   $(MeBNH)_3 + H_2O \longrightarrow$

③ Plates. (110° extrapd., 25°/2.5). [73∼
   77°].
   $\log P = 11.813 - 3404/T.$

④ Distn. $\longrightarrow (MeBO)_3$
   $+ CaSO_4 \xrightarrow{-H_2O} (MeBO)_3$

⑥ JACS **62**, 2228 (1940).

BC₂F₃Cl₂

① Dichloro(1,2,2-trifluorovinyl)borane
   $(CF_2=CF)BCl_2$

② $BCl_3 + (CF_2=CF)_2SnMe_2$
   $\longrightarrow 93\%$

③ (48.0° extrapd.). [−108°].
   $\log P = 8.008 - 1645/T.$
   IR: 1698 (s), 1351 (s), 1294 (s), 1158
   (w), 1129 (m), 1022 (m), 981 (s),
   864 (b. vs) cm⁻¹ (gas phase).

④ $+ H_2O \xrightarrow{heat} CF_2=CFH$

⑥ JACS **82**, 6238 (1960).

BC₂H₂Cl₃

① Dichloro(2-chlorovinyl)borane
   $CHCl=CHBCl_2$ (*trans*)

② $BCl_3 + (ClCH=CH)_2Hg$ $\xrightarrow{\text{r.t. 12 hr}}$

$BCl_3 + HC\equiv CH$ $\xrightarrow[\text{HgCl}_2/\text{C}]{150\sim300°}$

$BCl_3 + (ClCH=CH)_3Sb$ $\xrightarrow{\text{C}_6\text{H}_6}$

③ Yellow liq. (99°, 28°/50).

    d 1.3045 (20°).

④ $+ C_8H_{17}SH$ $\xrightarrow{100°}$

    $C_8H_{17}S(ClCH=CH)BCl + HCl$

    $+ H_2O$ $\longrightarrow$ $ClCH=CHB(OH)_2$

    $+ MeOH$ $\longrightarrow$ $ClCH=CHB(OMe)_2$

⑥ Izv. OKhN 1951, 402.

BC₂H₃Cl₂

① Dichlorovinylborane

    $(CH_2=CH)BCl_2$

② $BCl_3 + (CH_2=CH)_4Sn$ $\xrightarrow{\text{r.t. 128 days}}$

    65%

    $3 CH_2=CHBF_2 + 2 BCl_3 \rightleftharpoons 2 BF_3$

    $+ 3 CH_2=CHBCl_2$

    $(CH_2=CHBO)_3 + BCl_3$ $\longrightarrow$ 67%

③ Liq. (45.1°). [−111.1°].

    $\log P = 7.434 - 1449/T$. Slowly polym-

    erize in liq. state.

    IR : 3095 (w), 3060 (w), 3025, 2985

    (w), 1980 (vw), 1610 (m), 1424 (s),

    1379 (m), 1290 (w), 1149 (s), 1125,

    1116 (vs), 1032 (m), 1007 (vs), 987

    (m), 913 (vvs), 640 (m) cm⁻¹.

④ $+ Ag_2O + NH_4OH$ $\longrightarrow$ $CH_2=CH_2$

⑥ JACS 82, 6218 (1960). Rec. trav.

    chim. 82, 355 (1963).

BC₂H₃F₂

① Difluorovinylborane

    $CH_2=CHBF_2$

② $BF_3 + (CH_2=CH)_2Zn$ $\xrightarrow{\text{r.t.}}$ 27%

    $BF_3 + (CH_2=CH)_4Sn$ $\xrightarrow{60°, 24 hr}$ 52%

    $BF_3 + (CH_2=CH)_2Mg$ $\longrightarrow$ 19%

③ Gas. (−38.8° extrapd.). [−133.4°].

    $\log P = 7.915 - 1180/T$.

    Fairly stable to heat and dispropor-

tionation.

    IR : 3095 (w), 3040 (sh), 2995 (w),

    1980, 1640, 1629, 1620 (m), 1431 (s),

    1383, 1369 (s), 1327, 1319, 1309 (s),

    1256, 1248, 1241 (s), 1023 (w), 1013

    (m), 988 (m), 730(m), 728(m) cm⁻¹.

④ $+ NMe_3$ $\longrightarrow$ $CH_2=CHBF_2\cdot NMe_3$

    $+ H_2O$ $\xrightarrow{120°}$ $CH_2=CH_2$

    $+ Me_3Al$ $\xrightarrow{0°}$ Me_3B 71%

    $+ KF$ $\xrightarrow{250°}$ $K(CH_2=CHBF_3)$ 55%

⑥ JACS 82, 6223 (1960).

BC₂H₄ClO₂

① 2-Chlorovinylboronic acid

    $ClCH=CHB(OH)_2$

② $ClCH=CHBCl_2 + H_2O$ $\longrightarrow$

③ Crystals. [129°].

    Sol. in H_2O (6.8% at 25°, 15% at 65°),

    EtOH, Et_2O, C_6H_6 and $CHCl_3$.

④ $\xrightarrow[\text{H}_2\text{SO}_4]{-\text{H}_2\text{O}}$ $(ClCH=CHBO)_3$

    $+ HgCl_2$ $\longrightarrow$ $ClCH=CHHgCl$ 90%

⑤ Fungicide. Modifier for vinyl poly-

    mers.

⑥ Izv. OKhN 1951, 402. CA 40, 5769

    (1946).

BC₂H₅Cl₂

① Dichloroethylborane

    $C_2H_5BCl_2$

② $(EtBO)_3 + BCl_3$ $\longrightarrow$

    $BCl_3 + H_2 + C_2H_4$ $\longrightarrow$

    $BF_3 + EtAlCl_2$ $\longrightarrow$

③ Liq. (51.5°/750)

④ $+ HC\equiv CH$ $\xrightarrow{\text{active C}}$

    $Et(ClCH=CH)BCl$ 75%

⑥ Z. anorg. allg. Chem. 322, 103 (1961).

BC₂H₅F₂

① Ethyldifluoroborane

    $C_2H_5BF_2$

② [EtBO]₃ + BF₃ ⟶

Et₃B + BF₃ ⟶

EtB(OR)₂ + BF₃ ⟶

$$\underset{Me_2N}{\overset{Et}{\diagdown}}B-B\underset{NMe_2}{\overset{Et}{\diagdown}} + 2\,BF_3 \longrightarrow$$

③ Gas. (−25°). [−101°].

⑥ Chem. & Ind. **1955**, 1181.

BC₂H₆Br

① Bromodimethylborane
(CH₃)₂BBr

② Me₃B + HBr ⟶

③ Liq. (31.6°). [−129°].
Heat of vaporn. 6.3 kcal/mol.

④ + CH₂=CHNa ⟶ Me₂BCH=CH₂

+ Me₃SiOSiMe₃ ⟶ Me₃SiOBMe₂
+ Me₃SiBr

+ PH₃ $\xrightarrow{Et_3N}$ Me₂BPH₂ + Et₃N·HBr

+ (H₃Si)₃N ⟶ H₃SiBr, SiH₄, Me₃B,
Me₂BN(SiH₂Br)₂

⑥ JACS **76**, 1710 (1954). Z. Naturf. **8b**,
608 (1953).

BC₂H₆Cl

① Chlorodimethylborane
(CH₃)₂BCl

② BCl₃ + Me₂Zn ⟶

Me₃B + BCl₃ ⟶

Me₃B + HCl $\xrightarrow{150\sim180°}$

Me₂BNHMe + HCl (excess) ⟶

③ Gas. (4.9°).
Heat of vaporn. 5.7 kcal/mol.

④ $\xrightarrow{heat}$ BMe₃ + BCl₃

+ MeNH₂HCl ⟶ Me₂BCl·MeNH₂
+ HCl

+ HCl + AlCl₃ ⟶ MeBCl₂ + CH₄

+ CH₂N₂ $\xrightarrow{low\ temp.}$ Me₂BCH₂Cl

+ CH₂N₂ ⟶ polymethylene

⑥ Ber. **70b**,1583 (1937). Z. phys. Chem.
(Frankfurt) **2**, 276 (1954).

BC₂H₆F

① Fluorodimethylborane
(CH₃)₂BF

② BF₃ + Me₂Zn (excess) ⟶

3 Me₂BOBMe₂ + 2 BF₃ ⟶

Me₂BNMe₂ + BF₃ ⟶

③ Gas. (−42° extrapd., −112°/6).
[−147.3°].
Heat of vaporn. 5.1 kcal/mol. Planar
(electron diffraction): B-F 1.29 Å,
B-C 1.55 Å, ∠CBC 121.5°. log *P*=
7.7370−1121.4/*T*.

④ + MeNH₂ ⟶ 1:1 complex $\xrightarrow{heat}$

Me(MeNH)BF $\xrightarrow{heat}$ [MeNBF]₃

+ Me₂NH ⟶ Me₂BF·HNMe₂ $\xrightarrow{heat}$
Me(Me₂N)BF

+ NaSnMe₃ ⟶ Sn₂Me₆ + solid

⑥ JACS **62**, 2228 (1940). Z. Naturf. **6b**,
338 (1951).

BC₂H₆I

① Iododimethylborane
(CH₃)₂BI

② Me₃B + HI $\xrightarrow{150\sim180°}$

③ Liq. (68.8°). [−107.5°].
Heat of vaporn. 6.6 kcal/mol.

⑥ Brit. 124518 (1951)

BC₂H₇Na₂

① Disodium dimethylhydroborane
Na₂HB(CH₃)₂

② Me₄B₂H₂ + Na + liq.NH₃ $\xrightarrow{-78°}$ quant.

③ White solid. [110°].
Sol. in liq.NH₃ and the soln. have
yellow color, diamagnetic properties, and well ionized. Stable to
disproportionation.

④ + H₂O ⟶ Me₂BOH + H₂

+ BMe₃ $\xrightarrow{liq.NH_3}$ Na₂HBMe₂·BMe₃
(probably B-B bond is present)

+ BMe₃ $\xrightarrow{\text{Me}_2\text{O}}$ NaHBMe₃

⑥ JACS **74**, 3744 (1952).

BC₂H₇O

① Dimethylborinic acid
(CH₃)₂BOH

② Me₄B₂H₂ + H₂O $\longrightarrow$

③ Liq. (0°/36).
Sol. in H₂O and polar org. solvents.

④ + P₂O₅ $\longrightarrow$ Me₂BOBMe₂

⑥ JACS **62**, 2228 (1940) ; **57**, 621 (1935).

BC₂H₇O₂

① Ethylboronic acid
C₂H₅B(OH)₂

② EtB(OEt)₂ + H₂O $\longrightarrow$
EtB₂H₅ + H₂O $\longrightarrow$
(EtBO)₃ + H₂O $\longrightarrow$

③ Leaflets. (166~167° extrapd.). [40°, sublime].

⑥ Ann. **124**, 129 (1862).

BC₂H₈N

① Aminodimethylborane
(CH₃)₂BNH₂

② Me₃B + NH₃ $\xrightarrow{280°,\ 20\,\text{atm.}}$ quant.
Me₂BCl + NH₃ $\longrightarrow$
Me₄B₂H₂ + NH₃ $\xrightarrow{200°}$ 97%

③ Gas. (4°). [−55°].
Dimeric, but monomeric above 30°.

④ + HCl $\xrightarrow{20°}$ Me₂BCl·NH₃
$\xrightarrow{320\sim340°}$ (MeBNH)₃ + CH₄

⑥ Z. anorg. allg. Chem. **268**, 133 (1952) ;
256, 177 (1948). JACS **58**, 409
(1936).

BC₃H₆NO

① Dimethylboron isocyanate
(CH₃)₂BNCO

② Me₂BBr + AgOCN $\longrightarrow$

③ Gas. (−74°/0.7, −31°/21). *d* 1.174

(−78°).
Easily polymerizes.

④ + MeOH $\longrightarrow$ Me₂BOH, H₂NCO₂Me,
HOCN
+ MeNH₂ $\longrightarrow$ H₂NCONHMe,
Me₂BNHMe
+ Et₂NH $\longrightarrow$ Et₂NCONH₂,
Me₂BNEt₂
+ NEt₃ $\longrightarrow$ Me₂BNCO·Et₃N

⑥ Ber. **93**, 1379 (1960).

BC₃H₉

① Trimethylborane
(CH₃)₃B

② Me₂Zn + BF₃ $\longrightarrow$

BX₃ + MeMgBr $\xrightarrow{n\text{-Bu}_2\text{O}}$
(X=F, Cl, Br)

B₂O₃ + Me₃Al₂Cl₃ $\longrightarrow$

CH₃Cl + BCl₃ + Al $\xrightarrow{350°}$

③ Gas. (−21°, −50°/80, −80°/31).
[−161.5°].
d 0.63 (−100°), 1.9108 g/*l*(gas).
Not decomp. in H₂O at room temp.
Heat of vaporn. 5.7 kcal/mol ; heat
of combustion 23000 Btu/lb. Planar
(electron diffraction).
Spont. inflammable in air and in Cl₂ ;
explodes in O₂.

④ + RNH₂ $\xrightarrow{\text{heat, pressure}}$
RNHBMe₂ + CH₄
BCl₃ $\longrightarrow$ Me₂BCl, MeBCl₂
+ B₂O₃ $\xrightarrow{300°}$ [MeBO]₃
+ LiAlH₄ $\longrightarrow$
LiBH₃Me + Me₂AlH
+ HX $\xrightarrow{150\sim180°}$ Me₂BX + MeX
(X=Cl, Br, I)
+ LiEt $\xrightarrow[\text{Et}_2\text{O}]{}$ LiBMe₃Et
+ H₂ $\xrightarrow[210°,\ 12\,\text{hr}]{\text{Pd catalyst, 2200 psi}}$
B₂H₆ + CH₄

+ 1,2-diol or diamine $\xrightarrow{\text{high temp.}}$

or Me₃B

$+ O_2 \xrightarrow{77°K} [Me_3B\cdot O_2] \xrightarrow{77°K}$
Me₂BOOMe

$+ t\text{-BuNC} \xrightarrow[Et_2O]{-190 \sim -60°} t\text{-BuNC}\overset{+}{\text{B}}\overset{-}{\text{Me}}_3$

$\xrightarrow{\text{slowly}} t\text{-BuN}=\text{CBMe}_2$
           |
          Me

$\xrightarrow{600°}$ 25% Me- and Et- diboranes

⑥ Ber. **70 b**, 1583 (1937).   Z. anorg.
    allg. Chem. **268**, 1 (1952).

BC₃H₉ClN

① Chloro(dimethylamino)methylborane
   CH₃BClN(CH₃)₂

② Me₂BNMe₂ + Me₂NBCl₂ $\xrightarrow{160\sim170°}$
   60~70%

③ Liq. (90° extrapd., 0°/11.8, 18.2°/33.7).
   d(g/ml)0.9518−0.001082 t (°C)
   Slowly forms solid dimer [100~102°].
   Sol. in C₆H₆, CCl₄ and CHCl₃;
     sparingly sol. in aliph. hydro-
     carbons.
   Monomer, log Pmm=8.377−1995/T
     (°K); dimer, log P=15.261−4218/T.

⑥ Inorg. Chem. 1, 349 (1962).

BC₃H₉N₂

① 2-Methyl-1,3,2-diazaborolidine

② H₂NCH₂CH₂NHB(CH₃)₂ $\xrightarrow{370°,\ 6hr.}$

③ Solid. (106° extrapd.). [43.5°].
   d (solid) 0.9466 (19.8°); d (liq.)
   0.8718 (49.5°).

⑥ Z. anorg. allg. Chem. **279**, 38 (1955).

BC₃H₉O

① Methoxydimethylborane
   (CH₃)₂BOCH₃

② Me₂BNMe₂·CH₃OH + HCl $\longrightarrow$
   Me₂BPH₂ + CH₃OH $\longrightarrow$

③ Gas. (21.5°). [51~52°].

④ + Me₂NH $\longrightarrow$ Me₂BOMe·NHMe₂

⑥ JCS **1950**, 3481. JACS 75, 3872 (1953).

BC₃H₉O₂

① Dimethoxymethylborane
   CH₃B(OCH₃)₂

② Me₃BBr₂ + Si(OMe)₄ $\longrightarrow$
   MeB(OMe)₂ + (MeO)₂SiBr₂
   Me₃B + O₂ $\longrightarrow$
   (MeBO)₃ + MeOH $\longrightarrow$

③ Liq. (53.5°).

⑥ Z. Naturf. **8 b**, 608 (1953).

BC₃H₉O₂

① Propylboronic acid
   C₃H₇B(OH)₂

② PrB₂H₅ + H₂O $\longrightarrow$
   Pr₂BOH + O₂ + H₂O $\longrightarrow$

③ Plates. [107°].
   Sol. in H₂O and org. solvents.

④ Inert to strong base, 40% HBr and
   40% HI.
   + HgCl₂ $\xrightarrow{H_2O,\ 140\sim150°}$ PrHgCl + HCl
   + B(OH)₃

⑥ Ber. **42**, 3090 (1909).

BC₃H₉S

① Dimethyl(methylthio)borane
   (CH₃)₂BSCH₃

② Me₄B₂H₂ + 2 MeSH $\xrightarrow{-78°}$

   Me₂BH·HSMe $\xrightarrow{0°}$ 60%

③ Liq. (70.8°). [−84°].
   Slightly unstable.
   $\log P = 7.677 − 1651/T$

④ + H₂O $\longrightarrow$ Me₂BOH + MeSH
   $\xrightarrow{\text{slowly}}$ BMe₃ + MeB(SMe)₂

⑥ JACS **76**, 3307 (1954).

BC₃H₉S₂

① Methyldi(methylthio)borane
   CH₃B(SCH₃)₂

② Me₂BSMe + B(SMe)₃ $\xrightarrow{\text{B}_2\text{H}_6 \text{ catalyst}}$

③ Liq. (155°). [−59°].
   $\log P = −2553/T + 1.75 \log T − 0.004911$
   $T + 6.3425.$

④ $\longrightarrow$ Me₂BSMe + B(SMe)₃

⑥ JACS **78**, 1523 (1956).

BC₃H₁₀N

① Dimethyl(methylamino)borane
   (CH₃)₂BNHCH₃

② BMe₃·H₂NMe $\xrightarrow{310°,\ 20\sim30\ \text{atm.}}$ quant.

③ Liq. (38.3° extrapd.).
   Heat of vaporn.: 6.2 kcal/mol; $\log P$
   $= 7.2663 − 1366.1/T$; dimeric at low
   temp.

④ + HCl $\xrightarrow{20°}$ Me₂BCl·MeNH₂
   + HCl $\xrightarrow{100°}$ Me₂BCl + MeNH₂·HCl
   $\xrightarrow{450°}$ (MeBNMe)₃ + CH₄

⑥ Z. anorg. allg. Chem. **255**, 141 (1947);
   268, 133 (1952).

BC₃H₁₀N

① (Dimethylamino)methylborane
   (CH₃)₂NB(H)CH₃

② MeBH₂BH₂Me + Me₂NH $\xrightarrow{-78°}$

③ Liq. (dimer, white solid). (40∼43°).
   [−136.4°].
   Sol. in org. solvents; decompd. in
   H₂O.
   Heat of vaporn.: 6.1 kcal/mol; $\log P$
   $= −1947/T + 1.75 \log T − 0.009815\ T$
   $+ 7.771$; monomeric in vapor, dimeric in liq.

④ $\xrightarrow{\text{r.t.}}$ Me₂NBMe₂ + Me₂NBH₂ (40%
   disproportionation)

⑥ JACS **78**, 1521 (1956).

BC₃H₁₂N

① Ammine-trimethylborane
   (CH₃)₃B·NH₃

② Me₃B + NH₃ $\xrightarrow{\text{low temp.}}$

③ White solid. (101°, 0°/1). [56°].
   Stable in air. Heat of dissocn.
   −7.26±0.21 kcal/mol; dissocn.
   const.: $K_{0°} = 5.2 × 10^{-3}$, $K_{100°} = 4.6$.

⑥ Proc. Roy. Soc. **12**, 123 (1863). JACS
   67, 374, 378 (1945).

BC₄H₄Cl₃

① Chlorobis(2-chlorovinyl)borane
   (ClCH=CH)₂BCl

② BCl₃ + (*trans*-ClCH=CH)₂Hg $\xrightarrow{\text{C}_6\text{H}_6}$
   40%

③ Liq. (80∼82°/25). n_D 1.5452 (20°).
   d 1.2759 (20°/4°).

④ + EtOH $\longrightarrow$ (ClCH=CH)₂BOEt
   61%
   + NaOH $\longrightarrow$ CH≡CH

⑥ Izv. OKhN **1951**, 402.

BC₄H₅Cl₂O

① Bis(2-chlorovinyl)borinic acid
   (ClCH=CH)₂BOH

② (ClCH=CH)₂BCl + H₂O

③ Liq. (66∼68°/3). n_D 1.5832 (20°).
   d 1.2822 (20°/4°).

④   + OH$^-$ $\longrightarrow$ CH≡CH

⑥   Izv. OKhN 1951, 402.

BC$_4$H$_5$O$_2$S

① 2-Thienylboronic acid

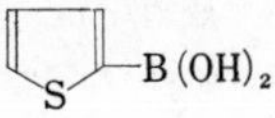

② B(OR)$_3$ + —MgI $\longrightarrow$ 95%

(R=Me, Et)

BF$_3$ + —MgBr $\longrightarrow$

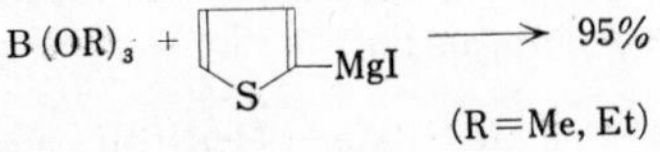

③ Crystals. [134~135°].
Stable in air.

④   + I$_2$ $\longrightarrow$ B(OH)$_3$ + HI + —I

+ CuBr$_2$ + H$_2$O
$\longrightarrow$ B(OH)$_3$ + —Br

+ AgNO$_3$ + NH$_4$OH
$\longrightarrow$ + B(OH)$_3$

+ HgCl$_2$ $\xrightarrow{\text{H}_2\text{O}}$ —HgCl
+ HCl + B(OH)$_3$

+ H$_2$O (6N HCl or 20% NaOH)
$\longrightarrow$ + B(OH)$_3$

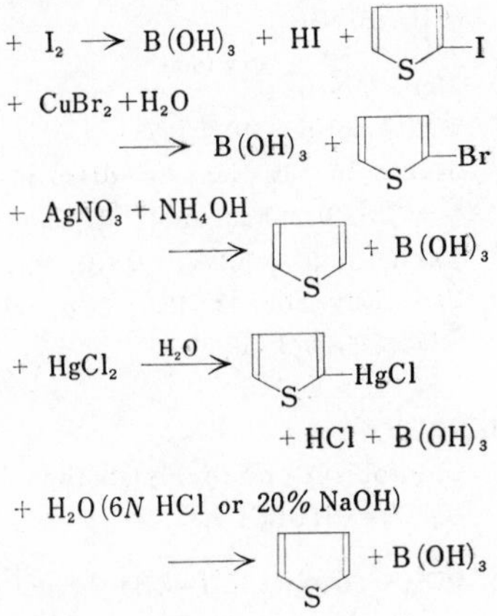

⑥ JACS **60**, 111 (1938).   Arch. Pharm.
297, 513 (1964).

BC$_4$H$_5$O$_3$

① 2-Furylboronic acid

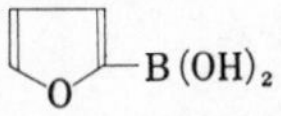

② B(OBu)$_3$ + —MgI $\longrightarrow$ 78%

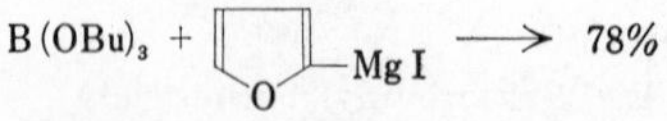

③ Dimorphic crystals. [110°] (from
H$_2$O), [121~122°] (from toluene).
Fairly stable in air; slightly sol. in
ligroin; very sol. in Me$_2$CO, EtOH

and Et$_2$O.

④   + I$_2$ $\longrightarrow$ B(OH)$_3$ + HI + —I

+ CuCl$_2$ (or CuBr$_2$) + H$_2$O
$\longrightarrow$ B(OH)$_3$ + —Cl

+ AgNO$_3$ + NH$_3$ + H$_2$O
$\longrightarrow$ + B(OH)$_3$ + Ag
80%

+ HgCl$_2$ $\xrightarrow{\text{H}_2\text{O}}$ —HgCl
+ HCl + B(OH)$_3$

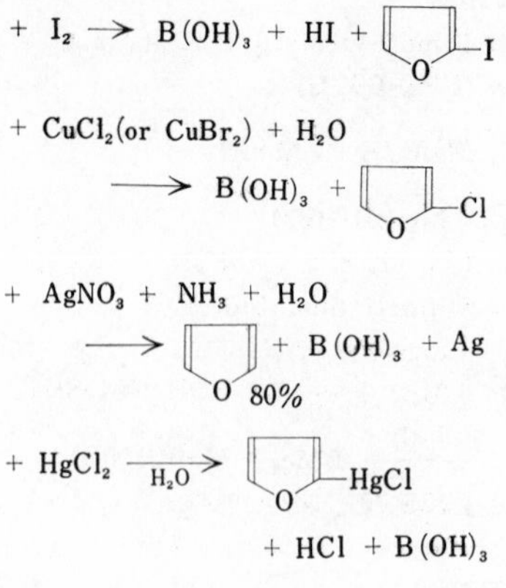

⑥ JACS **60**, 111 (1938).

BC$_4$H$_6$Cl$_2$O$_2$

① 2-(2-Chlorovinyl)-1,3,2-dioxaborolane

ClCH=CHB<$\begin{array}{c}\text{O}-\text{CH}_2 \\ | \\ \text{O}-\text{CH}_2\end{array}$

② ClCH=CHB(OH)$_2$ + HOCH$_2$CH$_2$OH
· 130~160°

③ Liq. (200°).
Sol. in CHCl$_3$, H$_2$O and oxygenated
org. solvents. Slowly hydrolyzed.

⑤ Fungicide, plasticizer, polymer
modifier.

⑥ CA **40**, 5769 (1946).

BC$_4$H$_8$ClO$_2$

① 2-Chlorovinyldimethoxyborane
ClCH=CHB(OCH$_3$)$_2$

② ClCH=CHBCl$_2$ + MeOH $\xrightarrow{-20°}$ 87%

③ Straw liq. (132°, 53°/42). n_D 1.4328
(20°). d 1.0753 (20°).

⑥ CA **40**, 5769 (1946).

BC$_4$H$_9$

① Dimethylvinylborane
(CH$_3$)$_2$BCH=CH$_2$

② (CH$_3$)$_2$BBr + CH$_2$=CHNa $\xrightarrow{\text{low temp.}}$

③ Liq. (43°, −38.4°/15, 0°/126, 16.7°/
   259). Heat of vaporn. 7.2 kcal/mol.
   r. t.
④ ——→(CH$_3$)$_3$B + (CH$_2$=CH)$_3$B +
   CH$_3$(CH$_2$=CH)$_2$B
⑥ JACS **79**, 5091 (1957) ; **76**, 1710 (1954).

BC$_4$H$_9$Br$_2$

① Dibromobutylborane
   C$_4$H$_9$BBr$_2$
② Bu$_3$B + Br$_2$ ——→
   BuB(OBu)$_2$ + BBr$_3$ ——→
③ Liq. (65°/23).
⑥ JACS **74**, 1415 (1952).

BC$_4$H$_9$Cl$_2$

① Butyldichloroborane
   C$_4$H$_9$BCl$_2$
② (BuBO)$_3$ + BCl$_3$ ——→
   Bu$_2$BCl + HCl + AlCl$_3$

   Bu$_3$B + HCl + AlCl$_3$ $\xrightarrow{110°}$
   BCl$_3$ + H$_2$ + 1-C$_4$H$_8$ ——→
   BHCl$_2$ + 1-C$_4$H$_8$ ——→
③ Liq. (106~8°).
   Fumes in air.
④ + Et$_3$N ——→ BuBCl$_2$·NEt$_3$ $\xrightarrow{PH_3}$
   n-BuB(PH$_2$)$_2$
   + 2 NaH$_2$P $\xrightarrow{\text{liq. SO}_2}$ BuB(PH$_2$)$_2$
   + NaCl
   + Na $\xrightarrow{\text{liq. NH}_3}$ BuB=NH + H$_2$
   + NH$_3$ ——→ BuB(NH$_2$)$_2$ (polymeric)
⑥ JACS **74**, 1415 (1952).

BC$_4$H$_9$Cl$_2$

① *s*-Butyldichloroborane
   CH$_3$CH$_2$CHBCl$_2$
          |
         CH$_3$
② (*s*-BuBO)$_3$ + BCl$_3$ ——→ 58%
③ Liq. (99.0°/748).
⑥ JACS **79**, 5182 (1957).

BC$_4$H$_9$Cl$_2$

① Dichloroisobutylborane
   i-C$_4$H$_9$BCl$_2$
② (*i*-BuBO)$_3$ + BCl$_3$ ——→
   t-Bu$_2$BCl $\xrightarrow{\text{4-day}}$ *i*-BuBCl$_2$ + *i*-Bu$_3$B
   BCl$_3$ + H$_2$ + *i*-C$_4$H$_8$ $\xrightarrow{440°,\ \text{Pt}}$
   BHCl$_2$ + *i*-C$_4$H$_8$ ——→
③ Liq. (97°/754).
④ + H$_2$O ——→ *i*-BuB(OH)$_2$ ——→
   (*i*-BuBO)$_3$
⑥ JACS **77**, 5182 (1957).

BC$_4$H$_9$Cl$_2$

① *t*-Butyldichloroborane
   t-C$_4$H$_9$BCl$_2$
② (*t*-BuBO)$_3$ + BCl$_3$ ——→
③ Liq. (88°/744).
⑥ JACS **77**, 5182 (1957).

BC$_4$H$_9$F$_2$

① Butyldifluoroborane
   C$_4$H$_9$BF$_2$
② BuB(OBu)$_2$ + BF$_3$ ——→ 81%
   (BuBO)$_3$ + BF$_3$ ——→
③ Liq. (37°). n_D 1.3290 (20°). *d* 0.8510
   (25°).
④ + BuB(OBu)$_2$ ⇌ BuB(OBu)F
⑥ JCS **1956**, 824.

BC$_4$H$_9$O$_2$

① 2-Methyl-1-propenylboronic acid
   (CH$_3$)$_2$C=CHB(OH)$_2$
② B(OMe) + Me$_2$C=CHLi ——→ 22%
③ Crystals. [84~86°].
   UV : λ_{max} 223 mμ (ε=1000).
④ + H$_2$ $\xrightarrow{\text{Pt}}$ *i*-BuB(OH)$_2$
   + H$_2$O$_2$——→ Me$_2$CHCHO
   + Ag$_2$O + NH$_4$OH ——→
   (CH$_3$)$_2$C=CH$_2$+Ag
⑥ JOC **18**, 895 (1953).

BC₄H₁₀Br

① Bromodiethylborane
  (C₂H₅)₂BBr

② Et₃B + HBr $\longrightarrow$

  BF₃·Bu₂O + EtMgBr $\longrightarrow$

③ Liq. (101°). [−81°]. n_D 1.4332 (20°).
  d 1.2092 (20°).
  Heat of vaporn. 8.4 kcal/mol.

⑤ Polymn. catalyst.

⑥ Ital. 631928; CA **58**, 7973 (1963).

BC₄H₁₀Cl

① Chlorodiethylborane
  (C₂H₅)₂BCl

② Et₃B + HCl $\xrightarrow{150\sim180°}$

  BCl₃ + C₂H₆ $\xrightarrow{150°,\ \text{electric discharge}}$

  Et₃B + BCl₃ $\longrightarrow$

③ Liq. (78.5°, 25°/100). [−84.6°].
  Heat of vaporn. 7.9 kcal/mol.

④

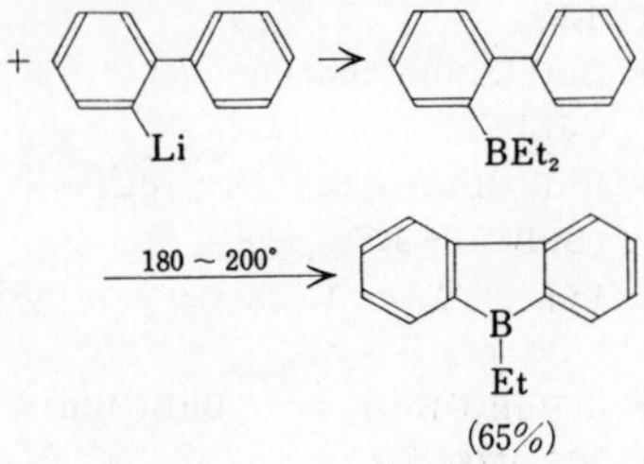

  (65%)

  + Li $\xrightarrow{\text{THF}}$ C₁₄H₃₁B₅ (I) +

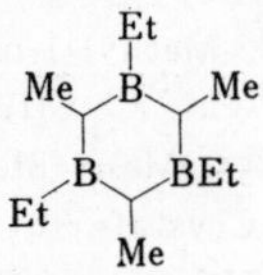

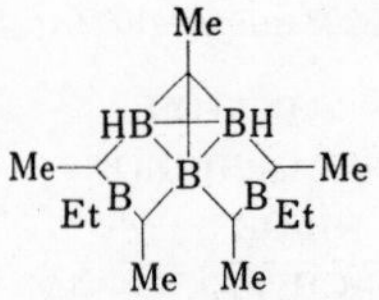

⑥ JACS **79**, 337 (1957).

BC₄H₁₁BrN

① Bromo(dimethylamino)ethylborane
  (C₂H₅)BrBN(CH₃)₂

② EtBBr₂ + EtB(NMe₂)₂ $\xrightarrow{0°}$ 80%

③ Liq. (116~118°/720). n_D 1.4319 (20°).
  d 0.924 (20°).
  Slowly dimerize in liq. phase.

⑥ Z. anorg. allg. Chem. **324**, 270 (1963).

BC₄H₁₁N₂

① 2-Methyl-1,3,2-diazaborinane

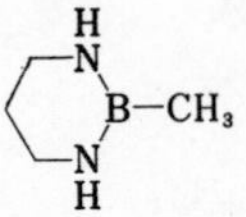

② Me₃B + H₂NCH₂CH₂CH₂NH₂ $\xrightarrow{220°}$

  Me₂BNHCH₂CH₂CH₂NH₂ $\xrightarrow{370°}$

③ Liq. (132°).
  Becomes brown accompanied by
  polymn. in air.

④ + 2HCl $\longrightarrow$

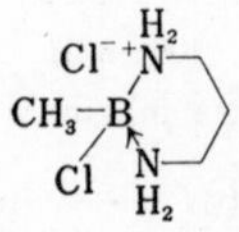

⑥ Z. anorg. allg. Chem. **279**, 38 (1955).

BC₄H₁₁O

① Diethylborinic acid
  (C₂H₅)₂BOH

② + H₂O

  $\longrightarrow$ 89%

  Et₄B₂H₂ + H₂O $\longrightarrow$

③ Liq. (35~37°/75). [−51~−48°].
  d 0.7921 (20°/4°).

④ $\xrightarrow{\text{heat}}$ Et₂BOBEt₂
  + HOAc $\longrightarrow$ Et₂BOAc

⑥ J. prakt. Chem. **147**, 251 (1937).

BC$_4$H$_{11}$O$_2$

① Butylboronic acid
  $C_4H_9B(OH)_2$

② $B(OMe)_3 + BuMgBr \xrightarrow{-70°} \xrightarrow{H_2O(H^+)}$
  $60{\sim}70\%$
  $B(OBu)_3 + BuMgBr \longrightarrow 30\%$

③ Crystals. [92~94°].
  Readily sol. in Et$_2$O, EtOH, CHCl$_3$,
  Me$_2$CO, AcOEt, HOAc, 40% HFaq.
  and 10% NaOHaq ; less. sol. in H$_2$O,
  C$_6$H$_6$, toluene, CCl$_4$ and petr.
  ether.

④ $+ \begin{matrix} CH_2OH \\ | \\ CH_2OH \end{matrix} \longrightarrow BuB\begin{matrix} O-CH_2 \\ | \\ O-CH_2 \end{matrix}$

  $+$ concd. NaOH $\longrightarrow$

  $BuB(ONa)_2 \cdot nH_2O \xrightarrow{heat} BuH$

  $+ H_2O_2 \longrightarrow BuOH$

  $+ Ag_2O + H_2O \xrightarrow{NH_4OH} Bu \cdot Bu +$
  $Ag + B(OH)_3$

  $+ \begin{matrix} H_2NCN=CNH_2 \\ \quad\ \| \quad\quad | \\ \quad\ NH \quad\ NH_2 \end{matrix} \xrightarrow{H_2O}$

  $H_2N\overset{N}{\diagdown}\diagup NH_2$ ... [structure]

  $\overset{+NH}{}\underset{B}{}\overset{NH}{}$
  $\underset{Bu}{}\quad\underset{OH}{}$
  [192~218°]
  (68%)

  $+ NaOH \longrightarrow BuB(OH)(ONa) \cdot$

  $1/2\ H_2O \xrightarrow{on\ P_2O_5} Na_2[(BuBO)_2O]$
  $\xrightarrow{distn.} [BuBO]_3$

⑥ JACS **60**, 105 (1938) ; **57**, 1476 (1935).

BC$_4$H$_{11}$O$_2$

① Isobutylboronic acid
  i-C$_4$H$_9$B(OH)$_2$

② $(MeO)_3B + i\text{-BuMgBr} \longrightarrow \xrightarrow{H_2O} 57\%$

③ Solid. [106~112°].
  Easily oxidized ; stable towards
  H$_2$O, OH$^-$ and 40% HBr.

④ $+ H_2O_2 \longrightarrow i\text{-BuOH}$

⑥ JACS **60**, 105 (1938).   Ber. **54**, 2784
  (1921).

BC$_4$H$_{11}$O$_2$

① t-Butylboronic acid
  t-C$_4$H$_9$B(OH)$_2$

② $B(OBu)_3 + t\text{-BuMgCl} \xrightarrow{-70°} \xrightarrow{H_2O}$
  $50{-}60\%$
  $t\text{-Bu}_3B + O_2 \longrightarrow (?)$

③ Crystals. [103~105° decomp.].
  Most easily oxidized of Bu derivs.

④ $+$ air $+ H_2O \longrightarrow t\text{-C}_4H_9OH +$
  H_3BO_3
  $+ Ag_2O + H_2O \longrightarrow t\text{-BuOH} + Ag$
  $+ H_3BO_3$
  $+ SOCl_2 \longrightarrow [t\text{-BuBO}]_3$

⑥ JACS **60**, 111 (1938).   Ber. **64**, 2112
  (1931).

BC$_4$H$_{12}$N

① Dimethyl(dimethylamino)borane
  (CH$_3$)$_2$BN(CH$_3$)$_2$

② $Me_3B + Me_2NH \xrightarrow{heat,\ pressure}$
  $Me_2BBr + Me_2NH \longrightarrow$
  $Me_4B_2H_2 + Me_2NH \longrightarrow$
  $Me_2NBCl_2 + MeMgX \longrightarrow$

③ Liq. (0°/53, 63°). [−92°].
  Monomeric in vapor.

④ $+ MeOH \longrightarrow Me_2BNMe_2 \cdot MeOH$
  [51~52°]
  $+ BF_3 \longrightarrow Me_2BF + (Me_2N)_2BF$

⑥ JACS **76**, 3903 (1954).   JOC **24**, 1161
  (1959).

BC$_4$H$_{13}$N$_2$

① (2-Aminoethylamino)dimethylborane
  (CH$_3$)$_2$BNHCH$_2$CH$_2$NH$_2$

② $BMe_3 + NH_2CH_2CH_2NH_2 \xrightarrow{250°} 75\%$

③ Liq. (125° extrapd.). [−35~−30°].
  Monomeric at 75~100°.

④ $+ HCl \xrightarrow{140°} Me_2BCl$

$$\xrightarrow{440°} \begin{array}{c} CH_2-CH_2 \\ | \qquad | \\ NH \quad NH \\ \backslash \quad / \\ B \\ | \\ Me \end{array}$$

⑥ Z. anorg. allg. Chem. **279**, 38 (1955).

BC₄H₁₄N

① Methylamine-trimethylborane
   $(CH_3)_3B \cdot NH_2CH_3$

② $Me_3B + H_2NMe \longrightarrow$

③ Solid. (147°, 0°/0.16). [27°].
   Heat of dissocn. -7.26 ± 0.21 kcal/
   mol; dissocn. const.: $K_{0°} = 5.8 \times$
   10^{-6}, $K_{100°} = 0.0350$. Stable in air.

④ + Dil. mineral acid $\longrightarrow$ Me_3B

⑤ Intermediate for purification or storage of Me_3B.

⑥ JACS **67**, 378 (1945); **75**, 4231 (1953).
   Z. anorg. allg. Chem. **255**, 141
   (1947).

BC₄H₁₄N

① Trimethylamine-methylborane
   $CH_3BH_2 \cdot N(CH_3)_3$

② $sym\text{-}Me_2B_2H_4 + NMe_3 \longrightarrow$
   $Me_2BH \cdot NMe_3 \xrightarrow{100°} MeBH_2 \cdot NMe_3$
   $+ Me_3B \cdot NMe_3$

③ Liq. (176°). [0.8°].
   Not dissociates at 100°. Trouton
   const. 21.9; $\log P = 7.676 - 2155/T$.
   Stable at 100°.

④ + HCl $\xrightarrow{-80°}$ $MeBHCl \cdot NMe_3$,
   $MeBCl_2 \cdot NMe_3$, H_2
   $\xrightarrow{200°}$ $BH_3 \cdot NMe_3 + Me_3B \cdot NMe_3$

⑥ JACS **61**, 1078 (1939).

BC₅H₉

① Methyldivinylborane
   $CH_3B(CH=CH_2)_2$

② $Me_2BBr + CH_2=CHNa \xrightarrow{\text{low temp.}}$

③ Colorless liq. (49°, $-49°/8.5$, $-17.5°/$
   44, 0°/110, 18.5°/246).

$\log P = -1574/T + 7.816$;
Heat of vaporn. 7.04 kcal/mol.

⑥ PB Report 123089 (1955). JACS **79**,
   5091 (1957).

BC₅H₁₁

① Dimethylpropenylborane
   $(CH_3)_2BCH=CHCH_3$

② $(CH_3)_2BBr + LiCH=CHCH_3 \xrightarrow{\text{low temp.}}$

③ Colorless liq. (55°, $-29°/14.5$, 0°/
   76.5, 17.5°/178).
   Heat of vaporn. 7.51 kcal/mol.

④ + $AgNO_3 + NH_4OH \longrightarrow$ CH_4,
   C_2H_6, H_2, 2,4-hexadiene, H_3BO_3

⑥ JACS **76**, 1710 (1954); **79**, 5091 (1957).
   PB Report 123089 (1955).

BC₅H₁₁F₂

① Difluoropentylborane
   $C_5H_{11}BF_2$

② $(C_5H_{11}BO)_3 + BF_3 \longrightarrow$

③ Liq. (64.5°/743). n_D 1.3409 (25°).
   d 0.8550 (25°).
   s- and t-isomers, spont. inflammable
   in air.

④ + $Et_2O \longrightarrow$ exothermic,
   but recovered unchanged on
   distn.

⑥ JACS **77**, 4253 (1955).

BC₅H₁₁F₂

① Difluoro-t-pentylborane
   $t\text{-}C_5H_{11}BF_2$

② $(t\text{-}C_5H_{11}BO)_3 + BF_3 \longrightarrow$

③ Liq. (47.7~47.9°/748). d 0.8448 (25°).

⑥ JACS **77**, 4253 (1955).

BC₅H₁₁O₂

① Allyldimethoxyborane
   $CH_2=CHCH_2B(OCH_3)_2$

② $(CH_2=CHCH_2)_3B + 2 B(OMe)_3 \xrightarrow{70~100°}$
   78%

③ Liq. (104~108°). n_D 1.4023 (20°).

④ + $\xrightarrow{195\sim200°}$

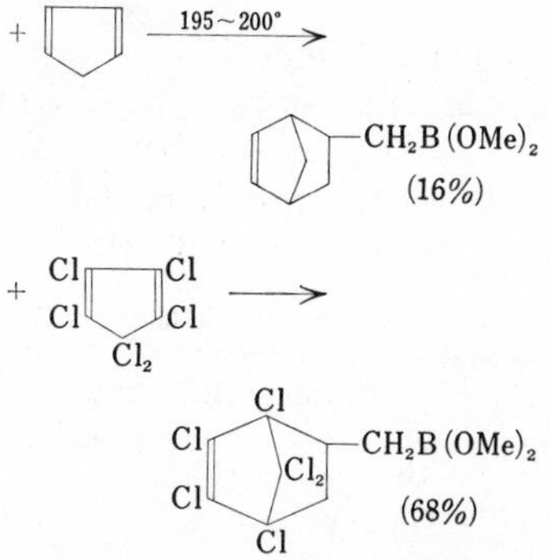

—CH₂B(OMe)₂
(16%)

+ ⟶

—CH₂B(OMe)₂
(68%)

+ B₂H₆ ⟶ B[CH₂CH₂CH₂B(OMe)₂]₃

$\xrightarrow{\text{EtSH, in MeOH}}$ MeOB[CH₂CH₂CH₂B-
(OMe)₂]₂ + n-PrB(OMe)₂

⑥ Izv. OKhN **1962**, 1698. Dokl. **151**, 577 (1963).

BC₅H₁₃O₂

① Pentylboronic acid
C₅H₁₁B(OH)₂

② B(OMe)₃ + n-C₅H₁₁MgBr $\xrightarrow{-75° \text{ H}_2\text{O}}$
70%

③ Flakes. [93~94°].
Stable towards H₂O, OH⁻ and H⁺.
Decomp. on distn.

④ H₂O₂ ⟶ n-C₅H₁₁OH

⑥ JACS **60**, 352 (1938); **57**, 1476 (1935).

BC₅H₁₃O₂

① Isopentylboronic acid
i-C₅H₁₁B(OH)₂

② B(OR)₃ + i-C₅H₁₁MgBr $\xrightarrow{\text{H}_2\text{O}}$

③ Solid. [101°].

⑥ Ber. **54**, 2784 (1921); **42**, 3090 (1909).
JACS **76**, 4174(1954).

BC₅H₁₄N

① t-Butyl(methylamino)borane
[CH₃NHB(H)(C₄H₉-t)]₂

② t-BuBH₂·NMe₃ + MeNH₂
$\xrightarrow{\text{MeNH}_2\cdot\text{HCl, catalyst}}$ 68%

③ Liq. (42°/110).
Dimeric in C₆H₆.
IR: $\nu_{\text{B-H}}$ 2400 cm⁻¹. ¹¹B-NMR: doublet, $\delta \times 10^6 = +9.7, +18.0$.

⑥ JACS **83**, 2671 (1961).

BC₅H₁₄N

① 1,2-Dihydro-1,1-dimethyl-1,2-azaborolidine
[3-Dimethylaminopropylborane (N-B)]

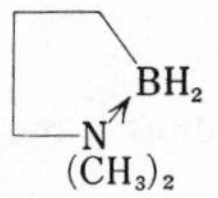

② BH₃·NMe₃ + Me₂NCH₂CH=CH₂
$\xrightarrow{\text{toluene}}$ 25%

③ Colorless liq. (185°/745, 85°/25).
n_D 1.4538 (25°). d 0.8161 (25°).
Heat of vaporn. 112 cal/g. Sol. in
Et₂O and toluene; insol. in H₂O.

⑥ Inorg. Chem. **2**, 640 (1963).

BC₅H₁₅N₂

① Bis(dimethylamino)methylborane
CH₃B[N(CH₃)₂]₂

② (Me₂N)₂BCl + Me₂Zn ⟶

③ Liq. (45°/30). [−85°].

④ + MeNHNHMe

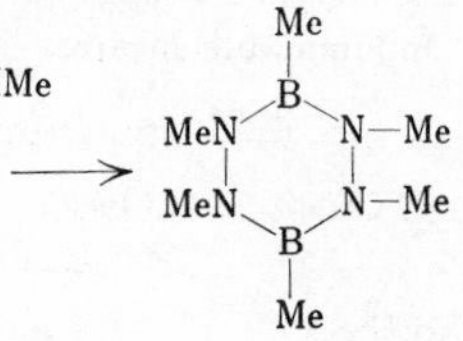

$\xrightarrow{\text{heat}}$ Me₂BNMe₂ + B(NMe₂)₃

⑥ Z. Naturf. **18 b**, 1138 (1963). JCS **1950**, 3481.

BC₅H₁₆N

① Dimethylamine-trimethylborane
(CH₃)₃B·NH(CH₃)₂

② Me₃B + Me₂NH ⟶

③ Solid. (143°, 0°/0.20). [35°].

Sol. in org. solvents. Dissocn. const. :
$K_{0°}=1.5\times10^{-6}$, $K_{100°}=0.0214$.

⑥ JACS **67**, 378 (1945).

BC₅H₁₆N

① Trimethylamine-dimethylborane
$(CH_3)_2BH\cdot N(CH_3)_3$

② $Me_4B_2H_2 + Me_3N \longrightarrow$

③ Liq. (172° decomp.). [−18°].
Not decomp. at 68°. Heat of vaporn.
9614 cal/mol ; Trouton const. 21.6 ;
$\log P=7.610-2102/T$.

④ $\xrightarrow{200°}$ $MeH_2B\cdot NMe_3 + Me_3B\cdot NMe_3$

⑥ JACS **61**, 1078 (1939).

BC₆F₉

① Tris(1,2,2-trifluorovinyl)borane
$(CF_2=CF)_3B$

② $BCl_3 + (CF_2=CF)_2SnMe_2 \longrightarrow$
$(CF_2=CF)_2BCl + (CF_2=CF)_2SnMe_2$
$\xrightarrow{50°}$ quant.

③ Liq. (104.9° extrapd., 41~42.5°/45).
[−107°].
$\log P=8.559-2147/T$.
IR : 1678 (vs), 1363 (s), 1313 (s), 1209
(m), 1137 (m), 1112 (m), 877 (m),
856 (s), 836 (m) cm⁻¹ (gas).
Inflammable in air.

④ $+ H_2O \xrightarrow{heat} CF_2=CFH$ (90%)

⑥ JACS **82**, 6238 (1960).

BC₆H₅Cl₂

① Dichlorophenylborane
$C_6H_5BCl_2$

② $(PhBO)_3 + BCl_3 \longrightarrow$

$BCl_3 + Ph_2Hg \xrightarrow{180\sim200°}$

$BCl_3 + C_6H_6 \xrightarrow{500\sim600°} PhBCl_2 + HCl$
70%

$PhB(OR)_2 + BCl_3 \xrightarrow{FeCl_3}$

$BCl_3 + Ph_4Sn \longrightarrow$ 85~90%

$(PhBO)_3 + PCl_5 \xrightarrow{120\sim130°}$ 60%

③ Liq. (175°, 57°/8). [7°]. n_D 1.5385
(25°). d 1.194 (20°/4°).
Planar (electron diffraction).

④ $+ HI + I_2 \longrightarrow PhBI_2\cdot 2HI$

$+ Me_2NH \xrightarrow{0°} PhBCl_2\cdot HNMe_2$
$\xrightarrow{Et_3N} Ph(Me_2N)BCl$ 72%

$+ PhN-NPh \longrightarrow$
    | |
    Li Li

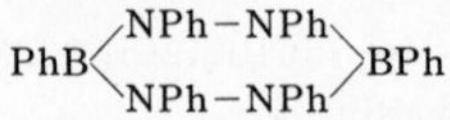

$+ Bu_2O \longrightarrow PhBCl(OBu) + BuCl$

$+ LiAlH_4 \longrightarrow [PhBH_2] \longrightarrow Ph_3B$
30% $+ C_6H_6$

$+ Na \xrightarrow{toluene} (PhB)_n + NaCl$

$+ PhPH_2 \xrightarrow{C_6H_6} (PhH\overset{+}{P}\overset{-}{B}ClPh)_3$ 15%

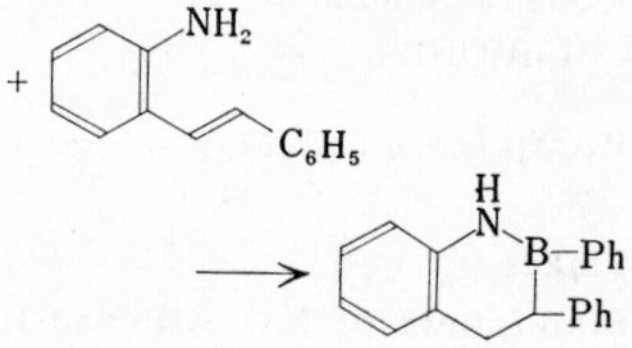

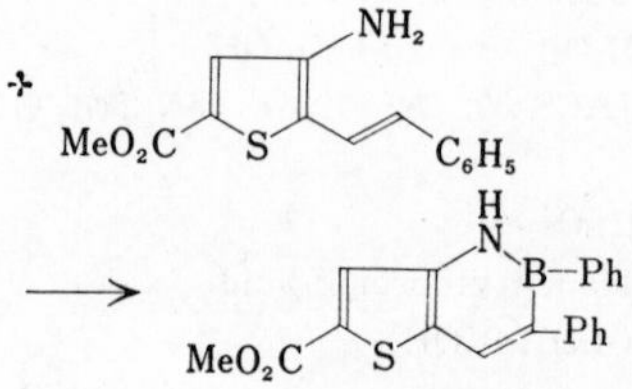

$+ H_2S_2 + H_2S \longrightarrow$

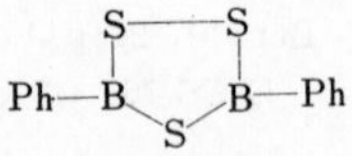

$+ R_2NSiMe_3 \longrightarrow Me_3SiCl$
$+ PhB(NR_2)_2$

⑥ Ber. **13**, 58 (1880).

BC₆H₅Br₂

① Dibromophenylborane

C6H5BBr2

② $BBr_3 + Ph_2Hg \longrightarrow$

$BBr_3 + C_6H_6 + AlCl_3 \longrightarrow$

$BBr_3 + C_6H_6 \xrightarrow{h\nu} 25\sim48\%$

③ Crystals. (100°/20). [34°].

⑥ Ann. **315**, 26 (1901).

BC6H5F2

① Difluorophenylborane
C6H5BF2

② $BF_3 + PhMgBr \longrightarrow 20\%$
$BF_3 + Ph_2Zn \longrightarrow 68\% + PhZnF$
$(PhBO)_3 + BF_3 \longrightarrow$

③ Liq. (82~5°/730).

④ $+ Li(CH_2)_nLi \longrightarrow PhB(CH_2)_n$ (n= 4,5)
$+ o\text{-}CH_3C_6H_4MgBr$(or Zn) $\longrightarrow$
$Ph(o\text{-}MeC_6H_4)_2B$

⑥ Acta Chem. Scand. **9**, 239 (1955).

BC6H6BrO2

① *p*-Bromophenylboronic acid

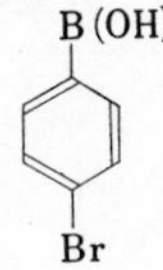

② $n\text{-}BuOB$ with O—CH2 / O—CH2 $+ Br$—⬡—$MgBr$

$\xrightarrow{-60°}$ Br—⬡—B with O—CH2 / O—CH2

$\xrightarrow{\text{1. NaOH 2. H}^+} 58\%$

$B(OBu\text{-}i)_3 + Br$—⬡—$MgBr \longrightarrow$

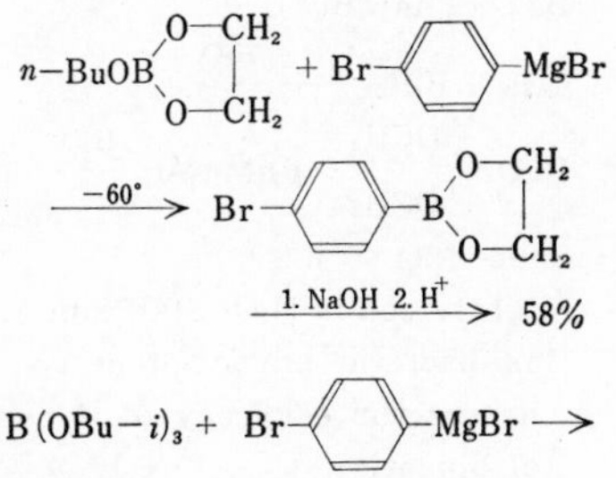

③ Solid. [255~256°].
$K_a = 7.26 \times 10^{-10}$ (25°, in 25%EtOH).

④ $+ H_2O \xrightarrow{130\sim150°, 6hr}$ Br—⬡— $+ B(OH)_3$

$+ HgO \xrightarrow{H_2O}$ (Br—⬡—)2Hg

$+ HNO_3$ (fuming) $\longrightarrow$

Br—⬡—B(OH)2 / O2N   (45~50%)

$+ 3HOBr \longrightarrow$ Br—⬡—OH with Br, Br

$+ H_2NCH_2CH_2OH \longrightarrow$

Br—⬡—$B(OCH_2CH_2NH_2)_2$
(58%)

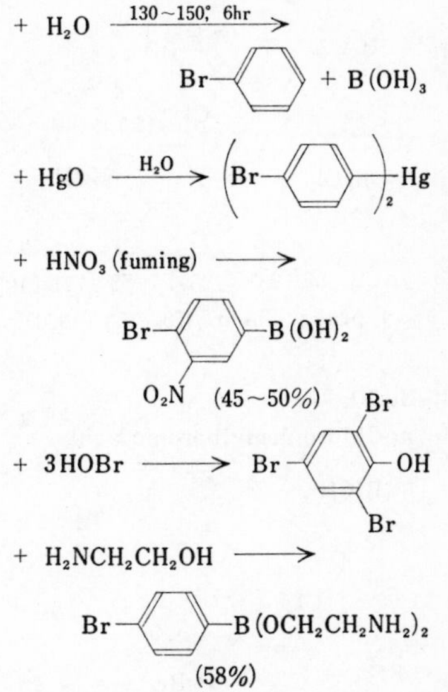

⑥ JACS **77**, 2491(1955); **79**, 3681(1957);
44, 4415 (1932).

BC6H6ClO2

① *o*-Chlorophenylboronic acid

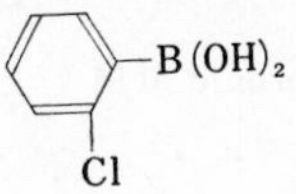

② $B(OBu)_3 +$ ⬡—MgBr $\xrightarrow{-75°}$
with Cl

$B(OBu\text{-}i)_3 +$ ⬡—MgBr $\longrightarrow$
with Cl

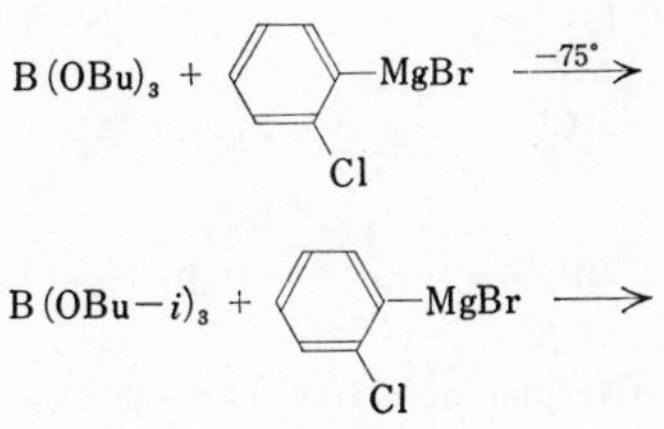

③ Needles. [97~98°].
Dissocn. const. $K_a = 14.0 \times 10^{-10}$
(25°, in 25% EtOH).

④ $\xrightarrow{\text{heat}}$ $\left[\text{(benzene ring)}{-}\text{BO} \right]_3$ with Cl

+ HgCl$_2$ $\longrightarrow$ (benzene ring)—HgCl with Cl

⑥ JACS **56**, 937 (1934); **53**, 711 (1931).
    J. prakt. Chem. **128**, 153 (1930).

BC$_6$H$_6$ClO$_2$

① *m*-Chlorophenylboronic acid

B(OH)$_2$ (benzene ring with Cl)

② BF$_3$ + (benzene ring)—HgBr with Cl $\longrightarrow$

③ Plates. [189~190°].
    Dissocn. const. $K_a = 14.5 \times 10^{-10}$
    (25°, in 25% EtOH).
⑥ JACS **56**, 937 (1934).

BC$_6$H$_6$ClO$_2$

① *p*-Chlorophenylboronic acid

B(OH)$_2$ (benzene ring with Cl)

② BF$_3$ + Cl—(benzene ring)—MgBr $\longrightarrow$

③ Needles or plates. [306~307°].
    Dissocn. const. $K_a = 6.23 \times 10^{-10}$ (25°,
    in 25% EtOH).
⑥ JACS **56**, 937 (1934).

BC$_6$H$_6$Cl$_3$

① Tris(2-chlorovinyl)borane
   (ClCH=CH)$_3$B
② (ClCH=CH)$_2$BCl + HC≡CH
    $\xrightarrow{140\sim180°,\ \text{HgCl}_2/\text{C}}$

    (ClCH=CH)$_2$BCl $\xrightarrow{140°}$ 63%
③ Liq. (55°/0.05, 226° extrapd.). n_D
    1.5570 (20°). d 1.2520 (20°/20°).
    $\log P = 8.539 - 3876/T$.
④ $\xrightarrow{185°}$ HCl + CH≡CH +
    (ClCH=CH)$_2$BCl (64%)
⑥ JOC **26**, 2947 (1961).

BC$_6$H$_6$NO$_4$

① *p*-Nitrophenylboronic acid

O$_2$N—(benzene ring)—B(OH)$_2$

② (benzene ring)—B(OH)$_2$ + HNO$_3$ $\longrightarrow$
    (mainly *o*-isomer)

③ Solid. [309°]
    $K_a = 9.8 \times 10^{-9}$ (25°, in 25% EtOH)
⑥ JACS **56**, 1865 (1934); **53**, 711 (1931).

BC$_6$H$_7$O$_2$

① Phenylboronic acid
   C$_6$H$_5$B(OH)$_2$
② B(OMe)$_3$ + PhMgBr $\longrightarrow$ 86%
    BX$_3$ + PhMgBr $\longrightarrow$
    C$_6$H$_6$ + B$_2$H$_6$ $\longrightarrow$ $\xrightarrow{\text{H}_2\text{O}}$
    BuOB$\underset{\text{OCH}_2}{\overset{\text{OCH}_2}{\big\langle}}$ + PhMgMr $\xrightarrow{\text{H}_2\text{O}}$ 85%
③ Solid. [214~6°].
    Slightly sol. in H$_2$O. Stable in air.
    Has bacterio static property; en-
    hances the efficiency of a number
    of hipnotics.
    $K_a = 19.7 \times 10^{-11}$ (25°, 25% EtOH).
④ + ROH $\longrightarrow$ PhB(OR)$_2$
    + H$_2$O $\xrightarrow{(\text{H}^+,\ \text{OH}^-)}$ C$_6$H$_6$ + H$_3$BO$_3$
    (when heated with 50% NaOH,

concd. HCl, ZnBr₂, CdBr₂,
Ag(NH₃)₂⁺ or AcOH)

+ CuCl₂ + H₂O $\longrightarrow$ PhCl + Cu₂Cl₂
+ HCl + B(OH)₃

+ HgCl₂ + H₂O $\longrightarrow$ PhHgCl + HCl
+ B(OH)₃

+ TlCl₃ $\xrightarrow{H_2O}$ Ph₂TlCl, PhTlCl₂

+ NH(CH₂CH₂SH)₂ + Et₃N

$\longrightarrow$

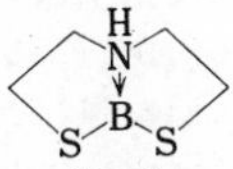

(47%)

+ HNO₃ $\longrightarrow$

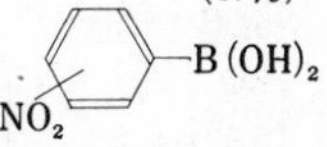

HNO₃+H₂SO₄, −20°, o- 15% m- 85%
HNO₃, Me₂O, −15°, o- 95% p- 5%

+ X₂ + H₂O $\longrightarrow$

PhX + HX + B(OH)₃

+ HOBr $\longrightarrow$

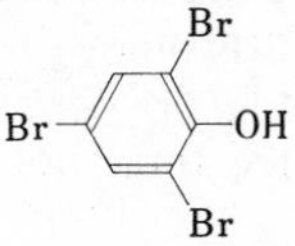

+ HOCl $\longrightarrow$

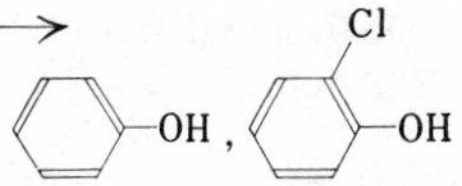

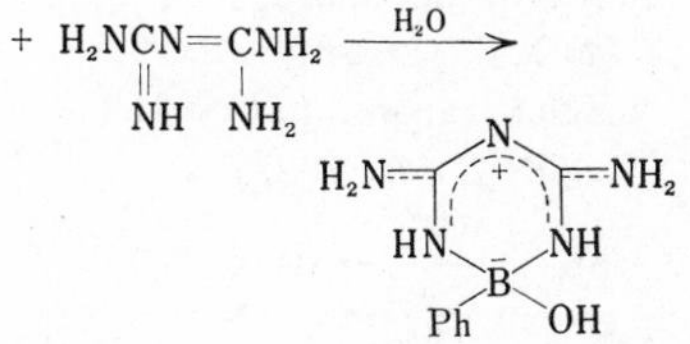

+ H₂NCN=CNH₂ $\xrightarrow{H_2O}$
∥   ∣
NH NH₂

+ R₃N $\longrightarrow$

PhB(OH)₂·R₃N $\xrightarrow{PhB(OH)_2}$

HO−B−O−B−O−B−OH
    ∣   ↑   ∣
    Ph   NR₃   Ph

(R₃N=Et₂NH, Me₃N, C₅H₅N)

⑤ Fungicide, intermediate, herbicide.

⑥ JACS **48**, 1063 (1926). Ber. **55**, 1261

(1922).

BC₆H₉

① Trivinylborane
(CH₂=CH)₃B

② Me₂BCH=CH₂ $\xrightarrow{disproportionation}$

CH₂=CHMgBr + BCl₃ $\longrightarrow$ 70%

③ Liq. (54°, 17°/160, 10°/116, 0°/67).
Heat of vaporn. 8.07 kcal/mol; log
$P = -1848/T + 8.570$.

④ + AgOH + NH₄OH $\longrightarrow$ C₂H₄,
CH₂=CHCH=CH₂

+ HSiMe₂OSiMe₃ $\xrightarrow{100°, H_2PtCl_6}$

(Me₃SiOSiMe₂CH₂CH₂)₃B

⑥ JACS **76**, 1710 (1954); **79**, 5091 (1957).
Dokl. **129**, 598 (1960).

BC₆H₁₁F₂

① Cyclohexyldifluoroborane
cyclo-C₆H₁₁BF₂

② [(*cyclo*-C₆H₁₁)BO]₃ + BF₃ $\longrightarrow$

③ Liq. (96.0°/743). *d* 0.9734 (25°).

⑥ JACS **77**, 4253 (1955).

BC₆H₁₂Br₃O

① Diethyl(2,2,2-tribromoethoxy)-
borane
(C₂H₅)₂BOCH₂CBr₃

② BEt₃ + Br₃CCHO $\xrightarrow{35\sim40°}$ 75%

③ Liq. (117~119°/12).

⑥ J. prakt. Chem. **147**, 226 (1936).

BC₆H₁₂Cl

① 1-Chloroborepane

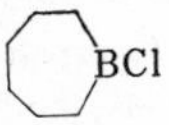

② ClBH₂ + (CH₂=CHCH₂)₂ $\xrightarrow{Et_2O}$

③ Liq. (54~60°/35). *d* 0.9664 (20°).

④ + H₂O₂ $\longrightarrow$ 1,6-hexanediol

⑥ Izv. SKh **1964**, 365.

BC$_6$H$_{12}$Cl$_3$O

① Diethyl(2,2,2-trichloroethoxy)borane
(C$_2$H$_5$)$_2$BOCH$_2$CCl$_3$

② Et$_3$B + Cl$_3$CCHO $\longrightarrow$ 90%

Et$_3$B + Cl$_3$CH$_2$OH $\overset{150°}{\longrightarrow}$

③ Liq. (78~79°/12).

④ + H$_2$O $\longrightarrow$ Cl$_3$CCH$_2$OH + Et$_2$BOH

⑥ J. prakt. Chem. **147**, 226 (1936).

BC$_6$H$_{13}$F$_2$

① Difluorohexylborane
C$_6$H$_{13}$BF$_2$

② (C$_6$H$_{13}$BO)$_3$+BF$_3$ $\longrightarrow$ 47.5%

③ Liq. (91.9~92.0°/744). *d* 0.8591 (25°).

⑥ JACS **77**, 4253 (1955).

BC$_6$H$_{13}$O$_2$

① 2-Butyl-1,3,2-dioxaborolane

$$C_4H_9-B\diagup\!\!\!\diagdown \begin{matrix} O-CH_2 \\ | \\ O-CH_2 \end{matrix}$$

② $BuOB\diagup\!\!\!\diagdown \begin{matrix} O-CH_2 \\ | \\ O-CH_2 \end{matrix}$ + BuMgBr $\longrightarrow$

B(OMe)$_3$ + BuMgBr $\longrightarrow$

[BuB(OH)$_2$] $\overset{HOCH_2CH_2OH}{\longrightarrow}$ 46%

③ Liq. (78~79°/66). n_D 1.4129 (25°).
d 0.9141 (25°/4°).

④ + H$_2$O $\longrightarrow$ BuB(OH)$_2$

⑥ JACS **76**, 4174 (1954).

BC$_6$H$_{13}$O$_2$

① Acetoxydiethylborane
(C$_2$H$_5$)$_2$BOCOCH$_3$

② (C$_2$H$_5$)$_3$B + AcOH $\longrightarrow$

③ Needles. [86~87°]
Decomp. in air. Sublime *in vacuo*.

⑥ J. prakt. Chem. **147**, 251 (1937).

BC$_6$H$_{14}$Br

① Bromodipropylborane
(C$_3$H$_7$)$_2$BBr

② Pr$_2$BI + SbBr$_3$ $\overset{100°}{\longrightarrow}$

③ Liq. (145°). [−94°]. *d* 1.095 (20°).
log P=−2120/T + 7.9549.
Fumes in air.
Decomp. by H$_2$O and O$_2$.

④ + H$_2$O $\longrightarrow$ Pr$_2$BOH

⑥ JCS **1953**, 3906.

BC$_6$H$_{14}$Cl

① Chlorodipropylborane
(C$_3$H$_7$)$_2$BCl

② Pr$_2$BI + SbCl$_3$ $\longrightarrow$

③ Liq. (127°). [<−125°]. *d* 0.848 (20°).
Spont. inflammable in air.
log P=−2056/T + 8.0146.

④ + H$_2$O $\longrightarrow$ Pr$_2$BOH
+ LiAlH$_4$ $\longrightarrow$ Pr$_4$B$_2$H$_2$

⑥ JCS **1953**, 3906.

BC$_6$H$_{14}$ClO

① Butoxychloroethylborane
C$_2$H$_5$B(OC$_4$H$_9$)Cl

② EtB(OBu)$_2$ + PCl$_5$ $\longrightarrow$ 78%

③ Liq. (49~52°/30). *d* 0.9030 (20°).

⑥ Izv. OKhN **1957**, 1080.

BC$_6$H$_{14}$I

① Iododipropylborane
(C$_3$H$_7$)$_2$BI

② (C$_3$H$_7$)$_3$B + I$_2$ $\overset{160°}{\longrightarrow}$ 69%

③ Liq. (174° decomp.). [−87°]. *d* 1.521
(20°).
Heat of vaporn. 10.03 kcal/mol.
log P=7.7791−2191/T.

④ + SbX$_3$ $\overset{100°}{\longrightarrow}$ Pr$_2$BX + SbI$_3$
(X=Cl, Br)
+ AgF $\longrightarrow$ Pr$_2$BF, Pr$_3$B
+ SbF$_3$ $\longrightarrow$ Pr$_3$B
+ H$_2$O $\longrightarrow$ Pr$_2$BOH

⑥ JCS **1953**, 3902.

BC$_6$H$_{15}$

① Triethylborane
(C$_2$H$_5$)$_3$B

② BX$_3$ + EtMgBr ⟶
  (X=Cl, F,alkoxy)
 BX$_3$ + Et-Metal ⟶
  (Metal=Li, Al, Zn)
 EtCl + BCl$_3$ + Al (or Zn) $\xrightarrow{350°}$
 C$_2$H$_4$ + B$_2$H$_6$ ⟶
 (ClBNH)$_3$ + AlEt$_3$ ⟶ 81%
 BCl$_3$ + SiH$_4$ + CH$_2$=CH$_2$ $\xrightarrow{\text{active C, 140°}}$
  91%
 (MeOBO)$_3$ + Et$_3$Al ⟶

③ Liq. (95.2~95.5°/758, 0°/12.5).
 [−93°]. n_D 1.397 (20°), 1.3920 (30°).
 d 0.6850 (20°/4°).
 Insol. in cold H$_2$O; decomp. in
 boiling H$_2$O; decomp. slowly on
 heating (4% in 60 hrs at 100°).
 Heat of combustion 21900 Btu/lb.
 Dielec. const.: 1.974 (20°).
 Spont. inflammable.

④ + O$_2$ ⟶ EtB(OEt)$_2$,B(OEt)$_3$
 + RCH$_2$OH ⟶ Et$_2$BOCH$_2$R + C$_2$H$_6$
  (R=CCl$_3$, Cl-⟨⟩-, Ph)
 + RCOOH ⟶ Et$_2$BOCOR + C$_2$H$_6$
  (R=Me, Cl-⟨⟩-)
 + RCHO ⟶ Et$_2$BOCH$_2$R + C$_2$H$_4$
  (R=Ph, Cl-⟨⟩-, CCl$_3$)
 + HBr $\xrightarrow{150\sim180°}$ Et$_2$BBr + EtBr
 + H$_2$ + Et$_3$N $\xrightarrow[220\,\text{atm.}]{200°}$ Et$_3$NBH$_3$(92%)
 + NaH ⟶ NaHBEt$_3$
 + CO + HOCH$_2$CH$_2$OH $\xrightarrow[650\,\text{atm., 2 hr.}]{150°}$
 Et$_3$CB$\underset{O-CH_2}{\overset{O-CH_2}{<}}|$ 94%
 + NaCl + NaH + SiCl$_4$ ⟶ Et$_3$SiH
  85%
 + EtNC $\xrightarrow{\frac{20°}{EtO_2}}$

+ HgCl$_2$ + NaOH $\xrightarrow{H_2O}$ Et$_2$Hg +
 EtB(ONa)$_2$ + NaCl + H$_2$O
 + CH$_2$=CHC$_8$H$_{17}$ ⟶
 B[CH$_2$CH(Et)C$_8$H$_{17}$]$_3$
⑤ Polymn. catalyst. Rocket fuel.
⑥ JACS 67, 374 (1945).   Ber. 54, 531
 (1921).

BC$_6$H$_{15}$O
① Dipropylborinic acid
 (C$_3$H$_7$)$_2$BOH
② Pr$_2$BI + H$_2$O ⟶
 Pr$_4$B$_2$H$_2$ + H$_2$O ⟶
③ Liq.
⑥ JCS 1953, 3902. JACS 58, 407 (1936).

BC$_6$H$_{15}$O$_2$
① Butyldimethoxyborane
 C$_4$H$_9$B(OCH$_3$)$_2$
② BuB(NHEt)$_2$ + MeOH ⟶ 73.4%
 Bu$_3$B + (MeO)$_3$B $\xrightarrow{\text{Bu}_4\text{B}_2\text{H}_2 \text{ catalyst}}$
  73−90%
③ Liq. (37~8°/21, 43~5°/25). n_D 1.3933
  (20°). d 0.8372 (20°/4°).
⑥ Izv. OKhN 1958, 777.

BC$_6$H$_{15}$O$_2$
① Hexylboronic acid
 C$_6$H$_{13}$B(OH)$_2$
② B(OMe)$_3$ + C$_6$H$_{13}$MgBr $\xrightarrow{-75°\ \text{H}_2\text{O}}$
  70%
③ Solid. (156°). [89°].
 Sparingly sol. in H$_2$O.
④ + H$_2$O$_2$ ⟶ n-C$_6$H$_{13}$OH + B(OH)$_3$
 + Ag$_2$O + NH$_4$OH ⟶ n-dodecane
  + B(OH)$_3$ + Ag
 $\xrightarrow{\text{H}_2\text{SO}_4,\ \text{P}_2\text{O}_5 \text{ or SOCl}_2}$ (n-C$_6$H$_{13}$BO)$_3$
  (149~151°/4)
⑥ JACS 60, 105 (1938).

BC$_6$H$_{16}$N
① (Diethylamino)dimethylborane

$(CH_3)_2BN(C_2H_5)_2$

② Me₃B + Et₂NH $\xrightarrow{\text{heat, pressure}}$

   Me₂BBr + Et₂NH $\longrightarrow$

③ Liq. (98° extrapd.).

   Heat of vaporn.: 8.8 kcal/mol.

⑥ PB Report 124518 (1951). Ber. **93**, 1379 (1960).

BC₆H₁₆N

① Diethyl(dimethylamino)borane

   $(C_2H_5)_2BN(CH_3)_2$

② Et₃B + Me₂NH $\xrightarrow{\text{heat}}$

   Me₂NBBr₂ + EtMgBr $\longrightarrow$ 58%

③ Liq. (123° extrapd.).

   Heat of vaporn.: 9.0 kcal/mol.

⑥ JOC **24**, 1161 (1959).

BC₆H₁₆N

① *t*-Butyl(dimethylamino)borane

   $(CH_3)_2NB(H)C_4H_9\text{-}t$

② *t*-BuBH₂·NMe₃ + Me₂NH

   $\xrightarrow[\text{}]{\text{Me₂NH · HCl catalyst, 100∼150°}}$ 46%

   t-BuBH₂·NMe₃ + Al(NMe₂)₃ $\longrightarrow$ 70%

③ Liq. (48∼40°/80).

   IR: ν_{B-H} 2450 cm⁻¹, ¹¹B-NMR.:

   $\delta = -25.5$ ppm, $+13.7$ ppm, from B(OMe)₃. MW shows monomer.

⑥ JACS **83**, 2671 (1961).   JOC **27**, 1020 (1962).

BC₆H₁₈N

① Ammine-triethylborane

   $(C_2H_5)_3B\cdot NH_3$

② Et₃B + NH₃ $\longrightarrow$

③ Liq. (57°/14, 131° extrapd.). [−11∼ −10°].

   $\log P = -3094/T + 10.538$.

④ + H₂ $\xrightarrow{\text{180∼210°, 220 atm, 36 hr.}}$

   Et₂BNH₂ + C₂H₆,

   byproduct (EtBNH)₃

⑥ JACS **67**, 374 (1945).   Ann. **644**, 1

(1961).

BC₆H₁₈N

① Trimethylamine-trimethylborane

   $(CH_3)_3B\cdot N(CH_3)_3$

② Me₃B + NMe₃ $\longrightarrow$

③ Solid. (110° sublime). [128°].

   Dissocn. const.: $K_{0°} = 7.8 \times 10^{-5}$, $K_{100°} = 0.472$.

④ + C₅H₅N $\longrightarrow$ Me₃B·C₅H₅N + NMe₃

⑥ JACS **61**, 1078 (1939); **67**, 374, 378 (1945).

BC₇H₇Br₂

① Dibromo-*p*-tolylborane

② BBr₃ + $\left(CH_3-\!\!\!\!\!\bigcirc\!\!\!\!\!-\right)_2$ Hg $\longrightarrow$

   MgB(C₆H₄CH₃-*p*)₄Br + BBr₃ $\longrightarrow$

③ Solid. (145°/25, 98∼110°/10). [39∼41°].

⑥ Ann. **315**, 26 (1901).   US 3096370; CA **60**, 546 (1964)).

BC₇H₇Cl₂

① Dichloro-*p*-tolylborane

② BCl₃ + (*p*-MeC₆H₄)₂Hg $\longrightarrow$

   (*p*-MeC₆H₄BO)₃ + BCl₃ $\longrightarrow$

③ Liq. (207°). [17°].

⑥ Ber. **15**, 180 (1882).

BC₇H₇Cl₂

① Dichloro-*o*-tolylborane

② BCl₃ + $\left(\underset{CH_3}{}\right)_2$ Hg $\xrightarrow{150\sim180°}$

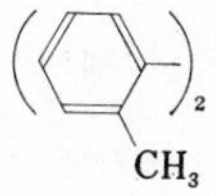

③ Liq. (193°). [6°].

④ + H₂O ⟶ o-MeC₆H₄B(OH)₂

⑥ Ber. **27**, 244 (1894).

BC₇H₇F₂

① Difluoro-p-tolylborane

CH₃—⟨ ⟩—BF₂

② BF₃ + CH₃—⟨ ⟩—MgBr ⟶

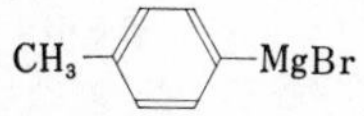

③ Liq. (96°).

⑥ Chem. Zentr. **1923**, Ⅱ, 1089.

BC₇H₇O₂

① 1,3-Dihydro-1-hydroxy-2,1-benz[d]-
oxaborole (called as "boronophtha-
lide")

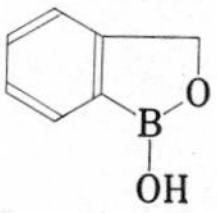

②

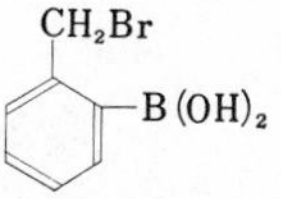

$\xrightarrow{}$ 70%

③ Crystals. (sublime 50°/0.05).
[97~98°].
Very stable to hydrolysis.
IR: ν_{O-H} 3300, ν_{C-O} 970 cm⁻¹.

④ + NH₃, C₆H₅CH₂NH₂, or

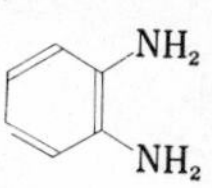

—×→

+ SeO₂ —×→

+ HNO₃ (fuming) $\xrightarrow{-35\sim-40°}$

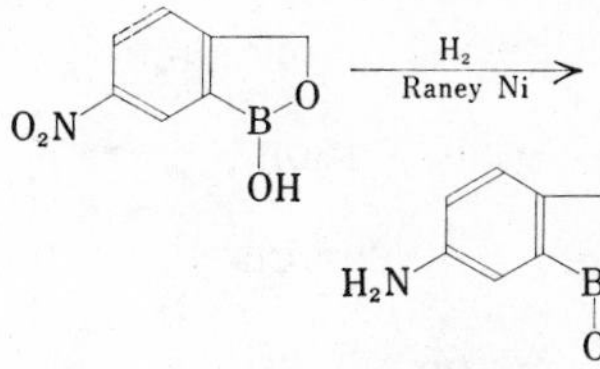

$\xrightarrow{H_2}{Raney\ Ni}$

+ AgNO₃ aq. ⟶ PhCH₂OH

+ ROH ⟶

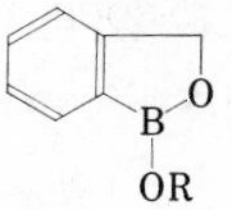

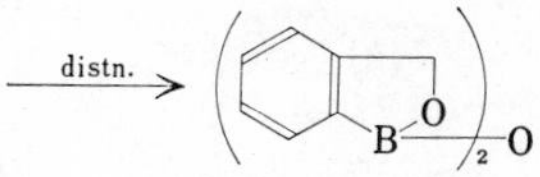

$\xrightarrow{distn.}$

+ PCl₅ ⟶

byproduct $\left(\underset{CH_2Cl}{}B{-}O\right)_3$

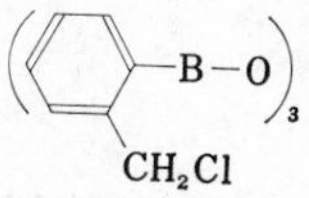

+ PhMgBr (excess)

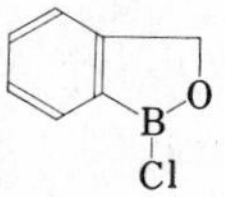

⟶

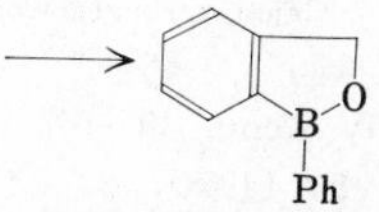

⑥ JACS **80**, 835 (1958); **82**, 2172 (1960).
Arkiv. Kemi. **10**, 507 (1957).   JOC
29, 3229 (1964).

BC₇H₇O₃

① p-Formylphenylboronic acid

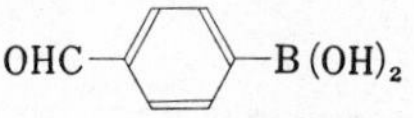

OHC—⟨ ⟩—B(OH)₂

② CH₃—⟨ ⟩—B(OH)₂

$\xrightarrow[\text{2. hexamethylene-tetramine}]{}$ 27%

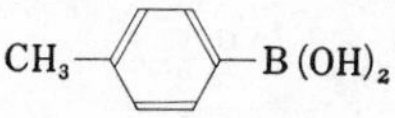

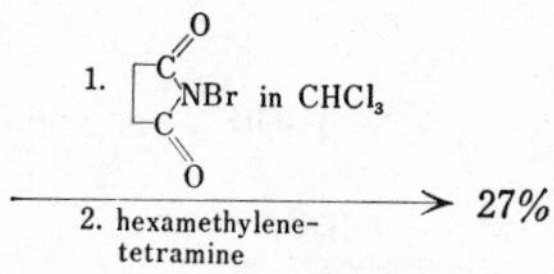

③ Solid. [240°].

④ $\xrightarrow{\text{heat}}$ $(p-\text{OHCC}_6\text{H}_4\text{BO})_3$

+ MeNO₂ + NaOH $\longrightarrow$

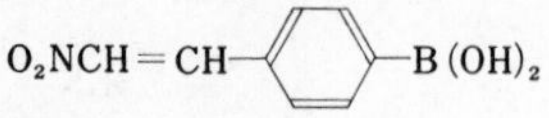

$O_2NCH=CH-$⟨benzene ring⟩$-B(OH)_2$

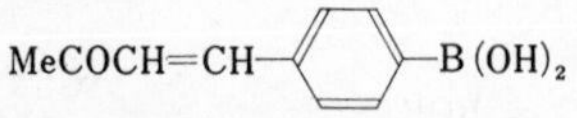

+ CH₃COCH₃ $\xrightarrow{\text{OH}^-}$

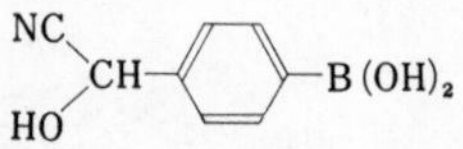

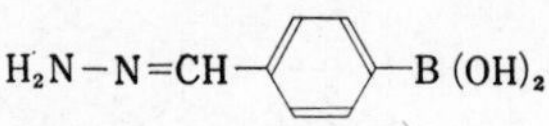

$MeCOCH=CH-$⟨benzene ring⟩$-B(OH)_2$

+ KCN $\longrightarrow$

+ H₂NNH₂ $\longrightarrow$

$H_2N-N=CH-$⟨benzene ring⟩$-B(OH)_2$

+ KMnO₄ $\longrightarrow$

HO_2C-⟨benzene ring⟩$-B(OH)_2$
(86%)

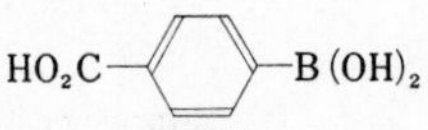

Benzoin condensation,
Cannizzaro reaction $\longrightarrow\!\!\!\times\!\!\!\longrightarrow$

⑥ Arkiv. Kemi. **10**, 507 (1957). JACS **80**, 835 (1958).

BC₇H₇O₃

① o-Formylphenylboronic acid

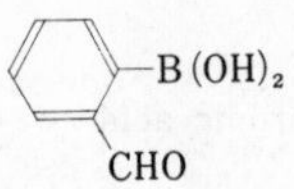

②

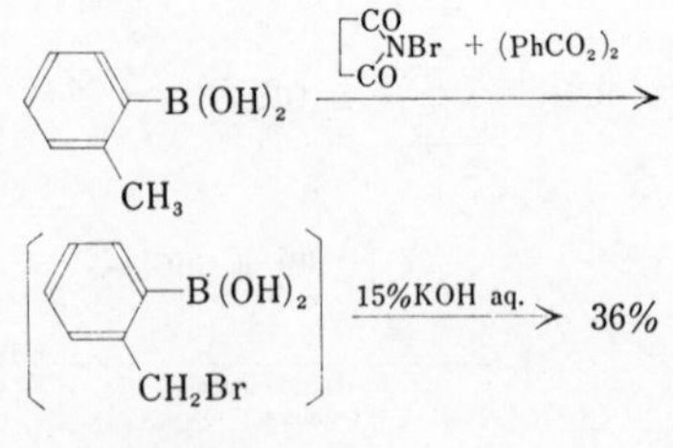

③ Crystals. [118~120°].

④ + NaOH $\longrightarrow$ PhCO₂H

+ NH₂OH $\longrightarrow$

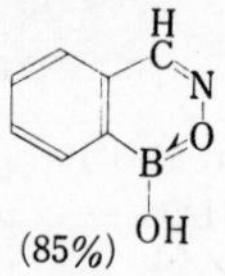

(85%)

+ MeNO₂, or MeCOMe $\longrightarrow\!\!\!\times\!\!\!\longrightarrow$

+ H₂NNH₂ $\longrightarrow$

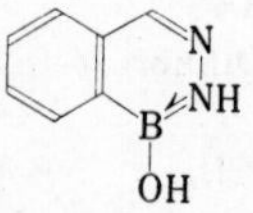

+ CH₂(CN)₂ $\longrightarrow$

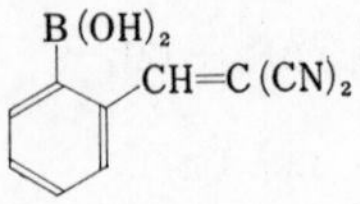

+ H₂NNHCONH₂ $\longrightarrow$

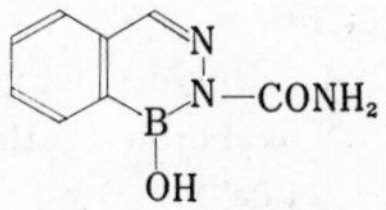

⑥ Arkiv. Kemi. **10**, 507 (1957). JACS **80**, 835 (1958).

BC₇H₉O

① Methylphenylborinic acid
   (CH₃)(C₆H₅)BOH

② MePhB(OPr) + H₂O $\longrightarrow$

③ Solid. [20°].

⑥ Acta Chem. Scand. **9**, 239 (1955).

BC₇H₉O₂

① o-Tolylboronic acid

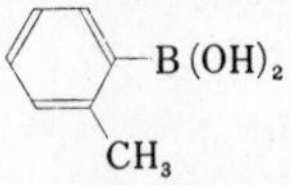

② $B(OBu-i)_3$ + ⟨benzene ring⟩$-MgBr$ $\longrightarrow$
   (Me substituent)

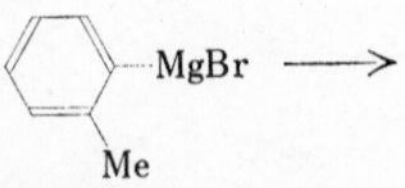

③ Plates. [150° decomp.].
   $K_a = 2.61 \times 10^{-10}$ (25°, in 25% EtOH).

④ + ROH $\longrightarrow$ o-MeC₆H₄B(OR)₂

+ AgNO₃ + NH₃ ⟶ MePh
+ B(OH)₃
+ HgCl₂ ⟶ o-MeC₆H₄HgCl
+ B(OH)₃

+ KMnO₄ ⟶

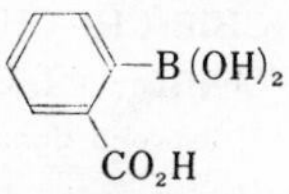

⑥ J. prakt. Chem. **128**, 153 (1930).
Acta Chem. Scand. **8**, 1779 (1954).

BC₇H₉O₂
① m-Tolylboronic acid

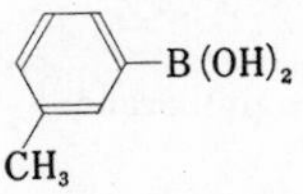

② B(OR)₃ +

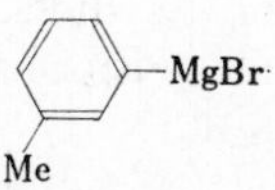

③ Solid. [140°].
$K_a = 14.0 \times 10^{-11}$ (25°, in 25% EtOH).
④ + ROH ⟶ m-MeC₆H₄B(OR)₂
(R = Me, Et, Pr, Bu)

+ KMnO₄ ⟶

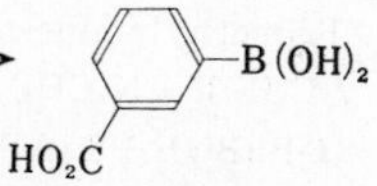

⑥ Acta Chem. Scand. **8**, 1779 (1954).
Ber. **42**, 3090 (1909).

BC₇H₉O₂
① p-Tolylboronic acid

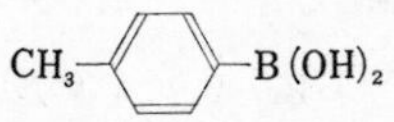

② B(OMe)₃ + p-MeC₆H₄MgBr ⟶
B(OBu-i) + p-MeC₆H₄MgBr ⟶
③ Needles. [240°].
$K_a = 1.00 \times 10^{-10}$ (25°, in 25% EtOH).
④ + ROH ⟶ p-MeC₆H₄B(OR)₂

+ H₂O $\xrightarrow{130\sim150°}$ MePh + H₃BO₃

+ HgO $\xrightarrow{\text{in H}_2\text{O}}$ (p-MeC₆H₄)₂Hg

+ KMnO₄ ⟶ p-HO₂CC₆H₄B(OH)₂

+ HNO₃ (fuming) $\xrightarrow{-28\sim-30°}$

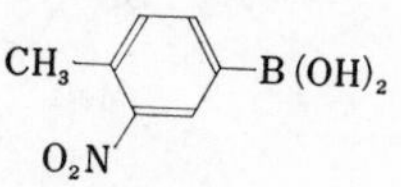

75%

⑥ JACS **54**, 4415 (1932). J. prakt. Chem.
128, 153 (1930).

BC₇H₉O₂
① Benzylboronic acid
C₆H₅CH₂B(OH)₂

② B(OMe)₃ + PhCH₂MgCl $\xrightarrow{-70°}$ $\xrightarrow{\text{H}_2\text{O}}$
50%
③ Solid. [104° decomp.].
$K_a = 14.9 \times 10^{-11}$ (25°, in 25% EtOH).
④ + 5% NaOH ⟶ MePh + B(OH)₃
+ HgCl₂ + H₂O ⟶ PhCH₂HgCl
+ HCl + B(OH)₃
+ O₂ + H₂O ⟶ PhCH₂OH
+ Ag₂O + NH₄OH ⟶ PhCH₂CH₂Ph
+ Ag
⑥ JACS **60**, 111 (1938); **56**, 1850 (1934).

BC₇H₉O₃
① m-Methoxyphenylboronic acid

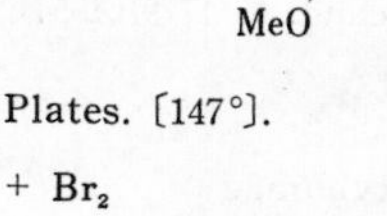

② B(OBu-i)₃ +

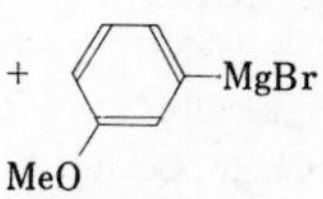

③ Plates. [147°].
④ + Br₂

$\xrightarrow{\text{in 20% AcOH}}$

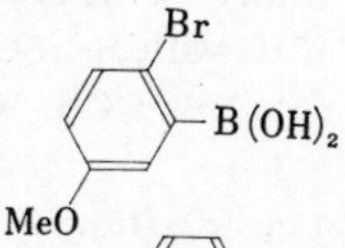

$\xrightarrow{\text{ZnCl}_2 \text{ in H}_2\text{O}}$

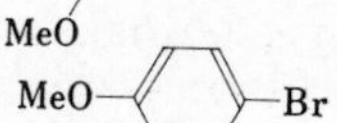

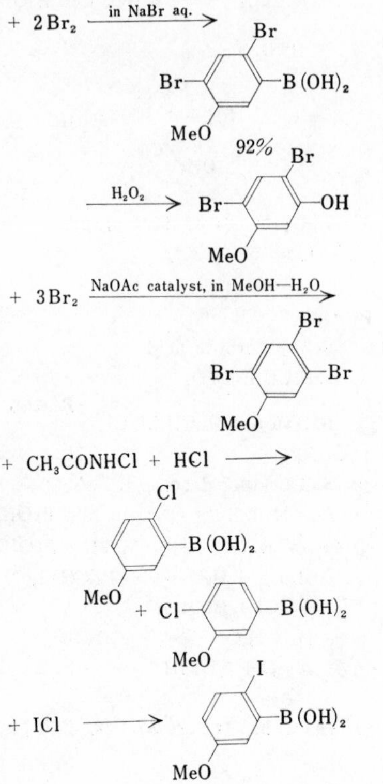

+ 2 Br₂ $\xrightarrow{\text{in NaBr aq.}}$

Br
Br ⟶ B(OH)₂
MeO

92%

$\xrightarrow{\text{H₂O₂}}$

Br ⟶ OH
MeO

+ 3 Br₂ $\xrightarrow{\text{NaOAc catalyst, in MeOH—H₂O}}$

Br
Br — Br
MeO

+ CH₃CONHCl + HCl ⟶

Cl
B(OH)₂
MeO

+ Cl — B(OH)₂
MeO

I

+ ICl ⟶

I
B(OH)₂
MeO

⑥ JOC **27**, 825 (1962).   J. prakt. Chem. **128**, 153 (1930).

BC₇H₁₀F₂N

① Methylamine-difluorophenylborane
C₆H₅BF₂·NH₂CH₃

② PhBF₂ + MeNH₂ ⟶

③ Solid. [98~101°].

⑥ Acta Chem. Scand. **8**, 1779 (1954).

BC₇H₁₃O

① Diallylmethoxyborane
(CH₂=CHCH₂)₂BOCH₃

② (MeO)₃B + CH₂=CHCH₂MgBr ⟶ 31%

③ Liq. (82°/15).

④ + H₂O ⟶
(CH₂=CHCH₂)₂BOB(CH₂CH=CH₂)₂

⑥ JCS **1952**, 2987

BC₇H₁₈

① Methyldipropenylborane
CH₃B(CH=CHCH₃)₂

② Me₂BBr₂ + LiCH=CHCH₃
$\xrightarrow{\text{disproportionation}}$

③ Colorless liq. (95° extrapd., 0°/12.5). Decomp. in air.

④ + AgOH ⟶ CH₄, H₂, C₂H₄, 2,4-hexadiene

⑥ JACS **76**, 1710 (1954).

BC₇H₁₉N₂

① Bis(ethylamino)propylborane
C₃H₇B(NHC₂H₅)₂

② PrBCl(OBu) + 2 NH₂Et ⟶
PrB(NHEt)₂ (46%) + PrB(OBu)₂
+ EtNH₂·HCl

③ Liq. (50~51°/7). n_D 1.4230 (20°). d 0.9727 (20°).

⑥ Izv. OKhN **1958**, 777.

BC₇H₂₀N

① Trimethylamine-*t*-butylborane
t-C₄H₉BH₂·N(CH₃)₃

② (*t*-BuBO)₃ + LiAlH₄ + Me₃N ⟶ 64%

③ (60°/3.5).

④ thermal dissociation ⇌ *t*-C₄H₉BH₂ + NMe₃

+ CH₃CH=CH₂ ⟶ *t*-BuBPr₂ 88%

+ CH₂=CH—CH=CH₂ ⟶

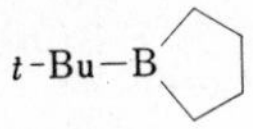

t-Bu—B◯ (66%)

+ (CH₂=CH)₂O ⟶

t-Bu—B◯O (70%)

+ (CH₂=CH)₂SiMe₂ ⟶

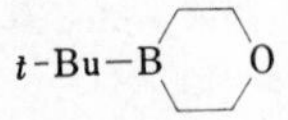

t-Bu—B◯SiMe₂

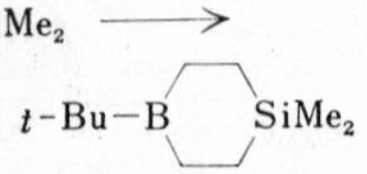

+ 1-hexyne ⟶

t-Bu-di-1-hexenylborane （70%）

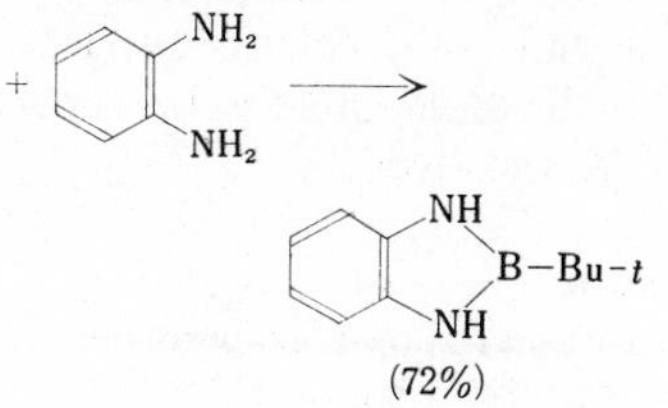

+ NH₃ $\xrightarrow{100\sim150°}$ (*t*-BuBNH)

⑥ JACS **83**, 831, 2541 (1961).

BC₈H₇ClN

① 2-Chloro-2,1-borazaronaphthalene
    (2-Chloro-1,2-dihydro-benz[*e*]-
    [1,2] azaborine)

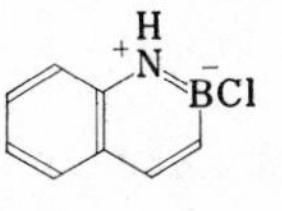

②

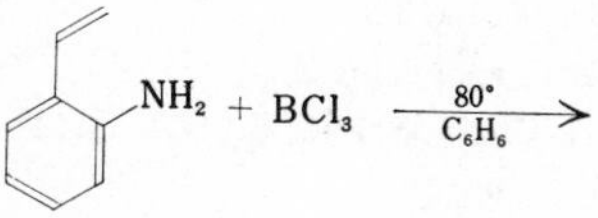

③ Solid. [72～74°].
⑥ JCS **1958**, 2728.

BC₈H₈BrO₂

① 2-(*p*-Bromophenyl)-1,3,2-dioxabo-
    rolane

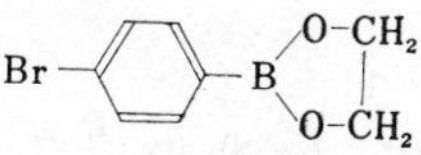

②

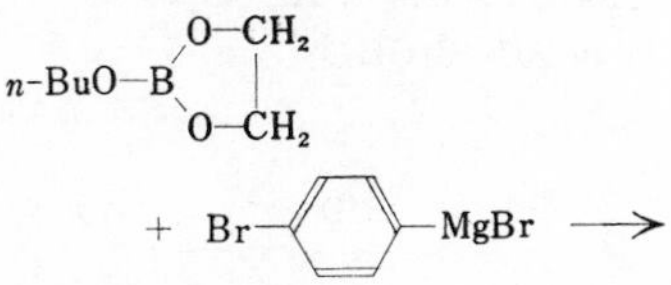

③ Crystals. (150～153°/15). [72～80°].
⑥ JACS **77**, 2491 (1955).

BC₈H₈N

① 8 *a*, 4 *a*-Borazaronaphthalene
    ([1,2]azaborino[1,2-*a*][1,2]aza-

borine)

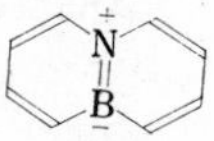

② NH(CH₂CH₂CH=CH₂)₂ + BH₃·NMe₃

$\xrightarrow[\text{Pd-C, }300\sim350°]{}$

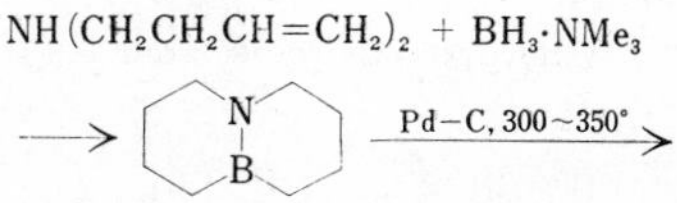

③ Plates. [41～43°].
    Resembles to naphthalene in odor and
    appearance.
    NMR : τ 2.28, 3.36.
⑥ JACS **86**, 5698 (1964).

BC₈H₈N

① 2,1-Borazaronaphthalene
    (1,2-Dihydrobenz[*e*][1,2]zaborine)

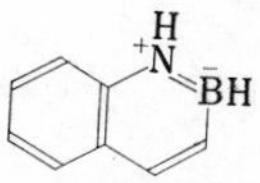

②

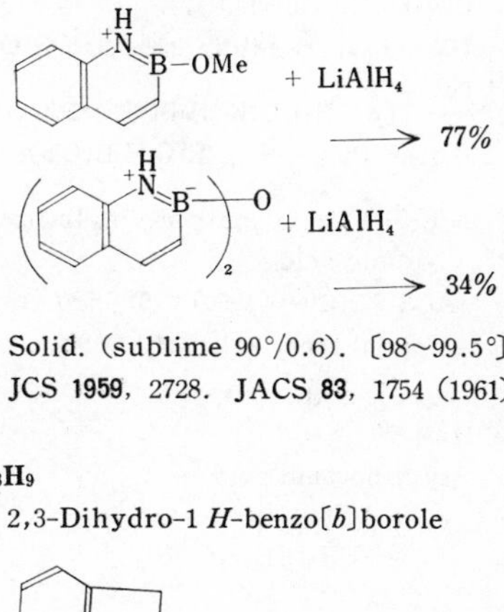

$\longrightarrow$ 77%

$\longrightarrow$ 34%

③ Solid. (sublime 90°/0.6). [98～99.5°].
⑥ JCS **1959**, 2728. JACS **83**, 1754 (1961).

BC₈H₉

① 2,3-Dihydro-1 *H*-benzo[*b*]borole

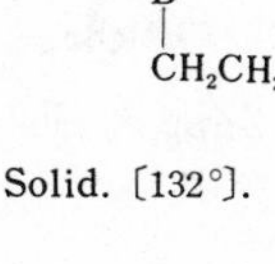

②

+ H₂ $\xrightarrow[\text{pressure}]{160°}$

③ Solid. [132°].

Dimeric at room temp.
⑥ Angew. **71**, 521 (1959).   Ann. **644**, 1
   (1961).

BC$_8$H$_9$O$_2$

① *p*-Vinylphenylboronic acid

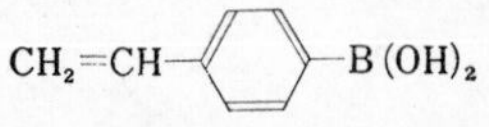

CH$_2$=CH—⟨ ⟩—B(OH)$_2$

② (MeO)$_3$B + CH$_2$=CH—⟨ ⟩—MgCl

$\xrightarrow{-50°}$ 80%

Et—⟨ ⟩—B(OH)$_2$ $\xrightarrow{\begin{smallmatrix}CO\\NBr\\CO\end{smallmatrix}}$

CH$_3$CH—⟨ ⟩—B(OH)$_2$
  |
  Br

$\xrightarrow{\text{quinoline}}$ CH$_2$=CH—⟨ ⟩—B(OH)$_2$

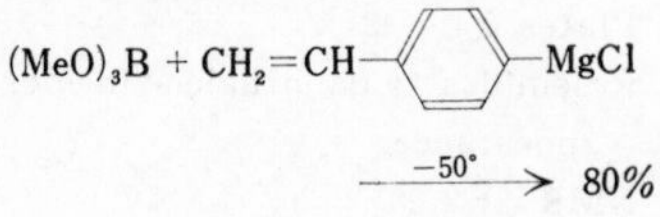

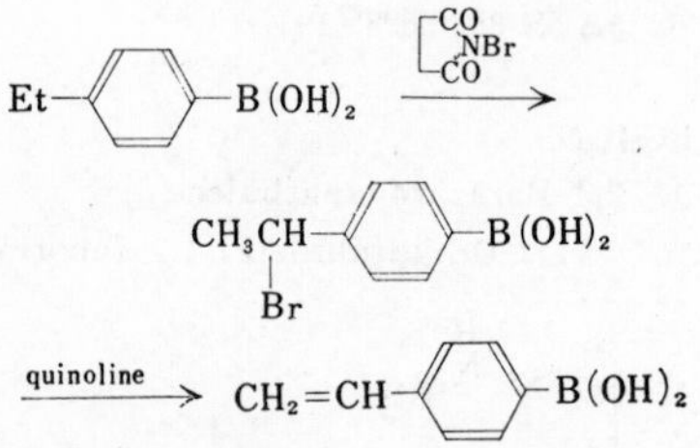

③ Crystals. [176~180°].
   UV: λ_{max} 257 mμ (ε 23850)(in EtOH)

④ $\xrightarrow{\text{P}_2\text{O}_5}$ [*p*-CH$_2$=CHC$_6$H$_4$BO]$_3$ 95%
   + H$_2$ + Pt $\longrightarrow$ *p*-EtC$_6$H$_4$B(OH)$_2$
   + K$_2$S$_2$O$_8$ $\xrightarrow{80°}$ poly-*p*-vinylbenzene
   boronic acid

⑥ JACS **82**, 2169 (1960); **81**, 580 (1959).
   Compt. rend. **248**, 828 (1959).

BC$_8$H$_9$O$_2$

① Styrylboronic acid

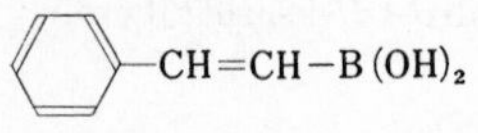

⟨ ⟩—CH=CH—B(OH)$_2$

② B(OR)$_3$ +

   BrMgCH=CH—⟨ ⟩ $\longrightarrow$

   KBF$_4$ + ⟨ ⟩—CH=CHMgBr

   $\longrightarrow$ [KB(CH=CHPh)$_4$] $\xrightarrow{\text{H}_2\text{O}}$

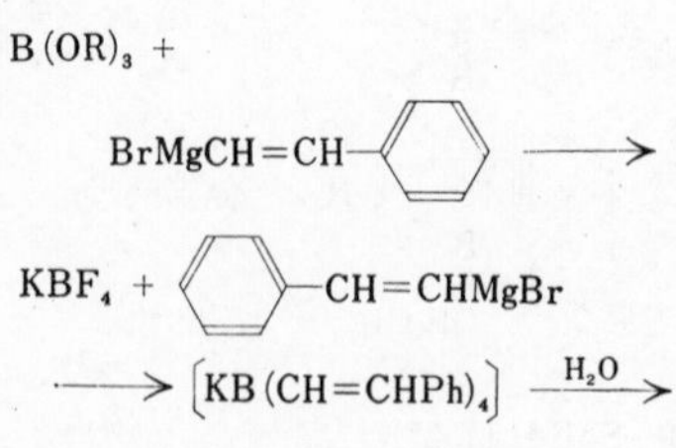

③ Solid. [138~141°].
   + HgCl$_2$ $\longrightarrow$ PhCH=CHHgCl
   + TlCl$_3$ $\longrightarrow$ (PhCH=CH)$_2$TlCl

⑥ J. Gen. Chem. USSR **6**, 636 (1936);
   8, 1768 (1938).

BC$_8$H$_9$O$_2$

① 2-Phenyl-1,3,2-dioxaborolane

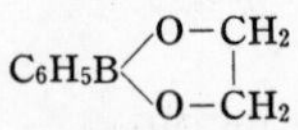

C$_6$H$_5$B⟨$\begin{smallmatrix}O-CH_2\\O-CH_2\end{smallmatrix}$

② PhB(OH)$_2$ + HOCH$_2$CH$_2$OH $\longrightarrow$
③ Liq. (84~91°/5).
⑥ JACS **77**, 2491 (1955).

BC$_8$H$_{11}$O$_2$

① Dimethoxyphenylborane
   C$_6$H$_5$B(OCH$_3$)$_2$

② PhB(OH)$_2$ + MeOH + CuSO$_4$ $\longrightarrow$
   PhBCl$_2$ + MeOH $\longrightarrow$

③ Liq. (74~75°/11). n_D 1.4926 (25°).
   d 1.0024 (25°).

⑤ Useful as herbicide.
⑥ Acta Chem. Scand. **8**, 1779 (1954).

BC$_8$H$_{11}$O$_3$

① *p*-Ethoxyphenylboronic acid

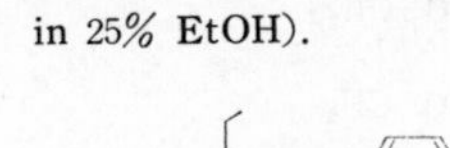

C$_2$H$_5$O—⟨ ⟩—B(OH)$_2$

② EtO—⟨ ⟩—MgBr + B(OBu)$_2$ $\longrightarrow$

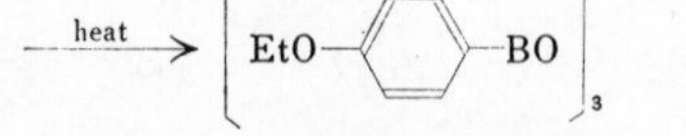

③ Needles. [150°].
   Dissocn. const.: K_a=0.608×10^{-10} (25°,
   in 25% EtOH).

④ $\xrightarrow{\text{heat}}$ [EtO—⟨ ⟩—BO]$_3$

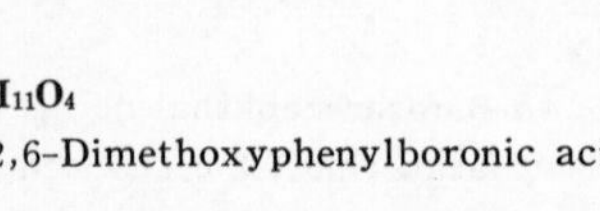

⑥ Ber. **27**, 244 (1894).   JACS **56**, 937
   (1934).

BC$_8$H$_{11}$O$_4$

① 2,6-Dimethoxyphenylboronic acid

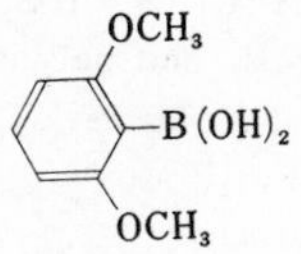

OCH₃

—B(OH)₂

OCH₃

② [structure: OMe, OMe benzene] + BuLi → [structure: OMe, OMe, Li benzene]

$\xrightarrow{B(OMe)_3, -60°}$ $\xrightarrow{H_2O}$ 31%

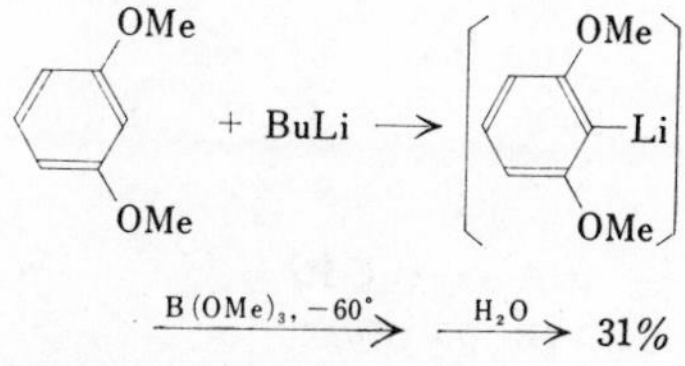

③ Crystals. [100~115°].
   Slowly develops the odor of *m*-(Me-O)₂C₆H₄ on standing at room temp.
⑥ JACS **83**, 2159 (1961).

BC₈H₁₄N
① Pyridine-trimethylamine

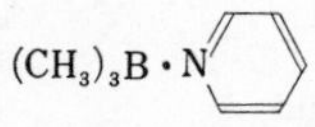

   (CH₃)₃B · N⟨ ⟩

② Me₃B + C₅H₅N ⟶
③ Solid. (0°/0.03 mm). [53.8~55.1°].
⑥ JACS **64**, 325 (1942); **69**, 1137 (1947).

BC₈H₁₆N
① Anilinodiethylborane
   (C₂H₅)₂BNHC₆H₅
② Et₂BCl + H₂NPh ⟶ 83%
   Et₄B₂H₂ + H₂NPh ⟶
③ Liq. (95°/15).

④ + Et₃B + Et₄B₂H₂ $\xrightarrow{180~200°, 9hr}$

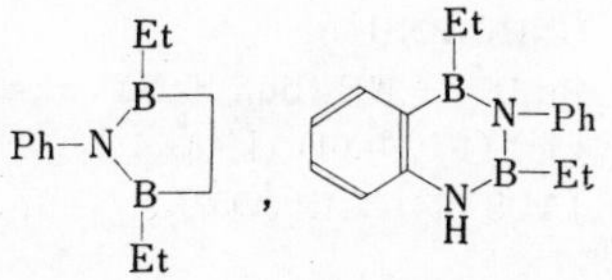

   [structure: Et
   Ph—N   B
           B
           Et], [structure: Et
                 B—N—Ph
                 B—Et
                 N
                 H]

⑥ Köster, Iwasaki, "Boron-Nitrogen Chemistry" p.148 (1964).

BC₈H₁₆NO
① (2-Dimethylaminoethoxy)divinyl-borane

(CH₂=CH)₂BOCH₂CH₂N(CH₃)₂

② Vin B(OBu)₂ + Vin MgBr $\xrightarrow{-60°}$
   $\xrightarrow{HOCH_2CH_2NMe_2}$ 64~66%
③ Liq. (71~72°/0.1). [3~6°]
   IR: 1610, 1630, 940, 950, 1875 cm⁻¹.
   UV: λₘₐₓ 189 mμ (ε 13000).
④ + BuOH ⟶ Vin₂BOBu

    + H₂S + azobisisobutyronitrile

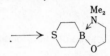

⑥ JOC **27**, 275 (1962).

BC₈H₁₈Br
① Bromodibutylborane
   (C₄H₉)₂BBr
② Bu₃B + HBr ⟶
   Bu₃B + Br₂ ⟶
③ Liq. (65°/4).
   log P=8.682−2643/T.
④ + H₂O ⟶ Bu₂BOH
⑥ JACS **60**, 115 (1933).   JCS **1953**, 3378.

BC₈H₁₈Cl
① Dibutylchloroborane
   (C₄H₉)₂BCl
② Bu₃B + HCl $\xrightarrow{110°}$
   Bu₂BOBBu₂ + PCl₅(or BCl₃) ⟶
   Bu₂BOBu + PCl₅ ⟶
   Bu₃B + BCl₃ $\xrightarrow{150~170°}$ 90%
③ Liq. (173°, 25°/1, 70°/13). d 0.8792 (20°/4°).
   log P=8.592−2518/T.
④ + Me₂NNH₂ ⟶ Bu₂BNHNMe₂ (77%)
    + EtNH₂ ⟶ Bu₂BNHEt
    + EtNH₂·HCl
    + Et₃N ⟶ Bu₂BCl·NEt₃ $\xrightarrow{PH_3}$
   Bu₂BPH₂ + Et₃N·HCl
    + NaH₂P $\xrightarrow{in\ liq.\ SO_2}$ Bu₂BPH₂

+ NaCl

+ Na(or K) $\xrightarrow{\text{in Et}_2O}$ Bu_2BNa $\xrightarrow{MeI}$

$MeBu_2B$

+ C_5H_5N $\xrightarrow{20°, \text{ in pentane}}$

$[Bu_2BPy]^+Cl^-$

+ HCl + AlCl$_3$ $\xrightarrow{110°}$ $BuBCl_2$

⑥ JACS **74**, 1415 (1952). Bull. soc. chim. France **1963**, 558.

$BC_8H_{18}Cl$

① Chlorodiisobutylborane
$(i\text{-}C_4H_9)_2BCl$

② $i\text{-}Bu_3B + BCl_3$ $\xrightarrow{160°}$

$t\text{-}BuMgCl + BCl_3$ $\longrightarrow$ $i\text{-}Bu_3B$ $\xrightarrow{BCl_3}$

③ Liq. (33°/7). n_D 1.4160 (25°). d 0.8251 (25°).

④ +$C_5H_{13}MgBr$ $\longrightarrow$ $i\text{-}Bu_3B + (C_5H_{11})_3B$
+ $C_6H_{13}MgCl$ $\longrightarrow$ $i\text{-}Bu_3B + (C_6H_{13})_3B$

⑥ JACS **79**, 5192 (1957).

$BC_8H_{18}FO$

① Butoxybutylfluoroborane
$C_4H_9B(OC_4H_9)F$

② $3\,BuB(OBu)_2 + BF_3$ $\xrightarrow{0°}$
$3\,BuB(OBu)F + B(OBu)_3$
$2\,BuB(OBu)_2 + BuBF_2$ $\longrightarrow$
$BuB(OBu)F + B(OBu)_3$

③ Liq. (volatile at 0.01 mm). n_D 1.3900 (20°). d 0.888 (20°/4°).

④ + H_2O(excess) $\longrightarrow$ HF + $B(OH)_3$
+ BuOH
Heat, or addn. of C_5H_5N $\longrightarrow$
$BuBF_2 + BuB(OBu)_2$

⑥ JCS **1956**, 824, 1540.

$BC_8H_{18}NOS$

① 4-(2-Dimethylaminoethoxy)-1,4-thiaborinane

$(CH_3)_2NCH_2CH_2OB$⟨⟩S

② $Me_2NCH_2CH_2OB(CH=CH_2)_2 + H_2S$
+ AIBN $\longrightarrow$ 34% and polymer

③ Solid. (123~125°/0.1). [40~51°].

④ + BuOH + H$^+$ $\longrightarrow$
$C_2H_5SCH_2CH_2B(OBu)_2$

+ BuOH $\longrightarrow$ BuOB⟨⟩S

+ KOH $\longrightarrow$ C_2H_4

⑥ JOC **27**, 275 (1962).

BC_8H_{19}

① Diethyl-t-butylborane
$(C_2H_5)_2BC_4H_9\text{-}t$

② $t\text{-}BuBH_2\cdot NMe_3 + C_2H_4$ $\longrightarrow$ 35%

③ Liq. (60°/70).

⑥ JACS **83**, 2541 (1961).

$BC_8H_{19}O$

① Dibutylborinic acid
$(C_4H_9)_2BOH$

② $BF_3 + BuMgBr$ $\xrightarrow{-70° \text{ in Et}_2O}$
$\xrightarrow{\text{HCl aq.}}$ 56%
$Bu_2BOBu + H_2O$ $\longrightarrow$ 66%

③ Liq. (55~65°). n_D 1.4269 (20°). d 7906 (20°/4°).

④ $\xrightarrow{20°, \ 0.2\,\text{mm. 6 hr.}}$ Bu_2BOBBu_2 100%

⑥ JCS **1957**, 3828.

$BC_8H_{20}N$

① Aminodibutylborane
$(C_4H_9)_2BNH_2$

② $Bu_2BCl + NH_3(\text{liq.}) + Na$ $\longrightarrow$

③ Liq. (100°/0.01). [−33.4°].

⑥ JACS **74**, 1415 (1952).

$BC_8H_{20}Na$

① Sodium tetraethylborate
$NaB(C_2H_5)_4$

② $NaH + BEt_3$ $\longrightarrow$ $NaBHEt_3$
$\xrightarrow{\text{disproportionation}}$

$NaH + BEt_3 + C_2H_4 \xrightarrow{150°,\ 1000\,psi,\ in\ diglyme}$ 90%

$BEt_3 + NaEt \xrightarrow{in\ petroleum}$

$BEt_3 + Na + HgEt_2 \xrightarrow{in\ Et_2O}$ 70%

③ Solid. (sublime 160−170°/1−2).
Stable in H_2O but decomp. by mineral acids. Forms etherate. Specific electric conductivity of saturated soln. in Et_2O: 5.3×10^{-3} (at 0°), $9.1\times10^{-3}\ \Omega^{-1}cm^{-1}$ (at 22°).

④ $+ HgCl_2 \xrightarrow{H_2O} HgEt_2 + BEt_3 + NaCl$

$+ Pb \xrightarrow{electrolysis} PbEt_4$

$+ Bi \xrightarrow{electrolysis} BiEt_3$ (94%)

$+ Hg \xrightarrow{electrolysis} HgEt_2$ (81%)

$+ Pb(OAc)_2$(or PbO, $PbCl_2$) $\longrightarrow$ $PbEt_4$ 96%

$+ K\text{-}Hg \xrightarrow{160°} KBEt_4$

$+ SnCl_2 \longrightarrow Sn(BEt_4)_2$ 39%

⑤ Useful as electrolyte component, ethylating agent and intermediate in metal plating.

⑥ Ann. **652**, 1 (1962). JACS **83**, 369 (1961).

$BC_8H_{21}N_2$

① Butylbis(ethylamino)borane
$C_4H_9B(NHC_2H_5)_2$

② $BuBCl(OBu) + NH_2Et \longrightarrow$
$BuB(NHEt)_2$ (50%) $+ BuB(OBu)_2$
$+ H_2NEt\cdot HCl$

③ Liq. (55~6°/4). n_D 1.4283 (20°).
d 0.7965 (20°).

④ $+ BuOH \longrightarrow BuB(NHEt)(OBu)$
$\xrightarrow{BuOH} BuB(OBu)_2 + EtNH_2$

⑥ Izv. OKhN **1958**, 777.

$BC_9H_8NO_2$

① 8-Quinolinylboronic acid

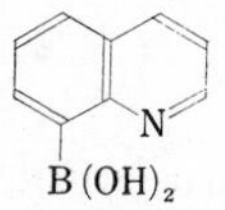
N
B(OH)2

②
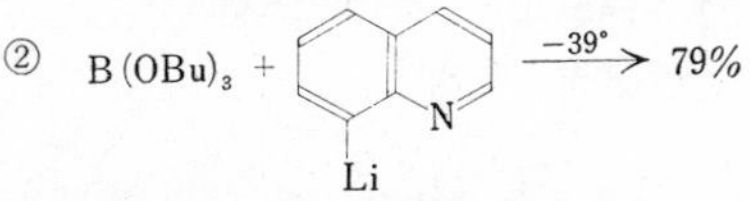
B(OBu)3 +
N
Li
−39°
79%

③ Solid. [>300°].
Sol. in acidic and alk. H_2O.
IR: 3.0, 6.3, 6.7, 7.3, 8.0, 8.6, 8.9, 10.5, 11.9 and 12.7 μ.

④
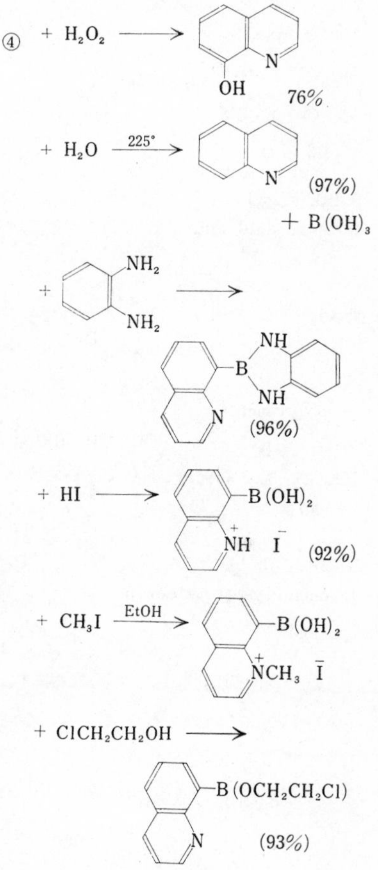
+ H2O2
N
OH
76%
+ H2O
225°
N
(97%)
+ B(OH)3
+
NH2
NH2
NH
B
NH
N
(96%)
+ HI
B(OH)2
NH
I
(92%)
+ CH3I
EtOH
B(OH)2
NCH3
I
+ ClCH2CH2OH
B(OCH2CH2Cl)
N
(93%)

⑤ Catalyze the solvolysis reaction of chlorohydrins.

⑥ JACS **81**, 498 (1959).

BC₉H₁₀N

① 2-Methyl-2,1-borazaronaphthalene
(1,2-Dihydro-2-methyl-benz [*e*]-
[1,2] azaborine)

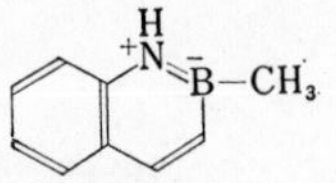

② + MeMgI ⟶

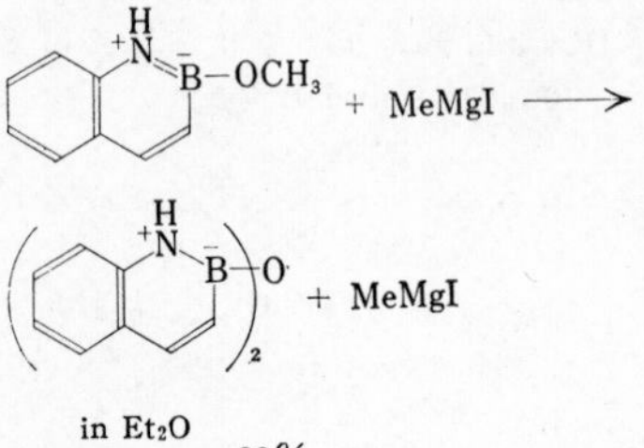

+ MeMgI

in Et₂O
⟶ 93%

③ Solid. [73~74°].
Inert to acid and alk.

④ + Br₂ ⟶

+ (byproduct)

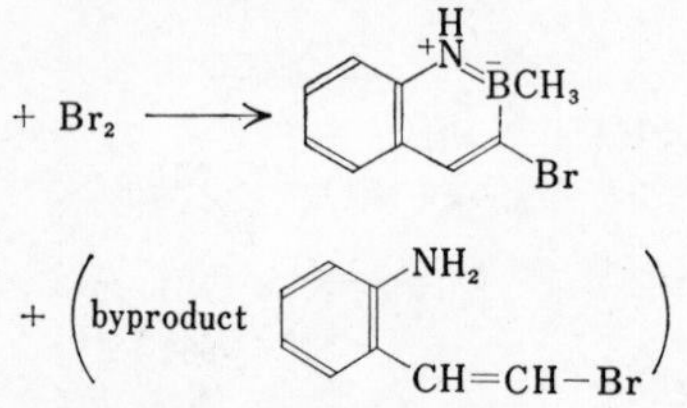

⑥ JOC **26**, 3253 (1961).   JACS **83**, 1754
(1961).

BC₉H₁₃O₂

① Dimethoxy-*o*-tolylborane

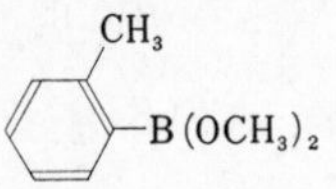

② + CH₃OH

+ CuSO₄ $\xrightarrow{-H_2O}$

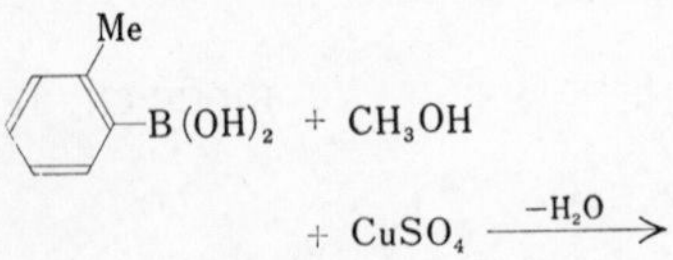

③ Liq. (74~75°/9). n_D 1.4870 (25°).
d 0.9798 (25°).

⑥ Acta Chem. Scand. **8**, 1779 (1954).

BC₉H₁₃O₂

① Mesitylboronic acid

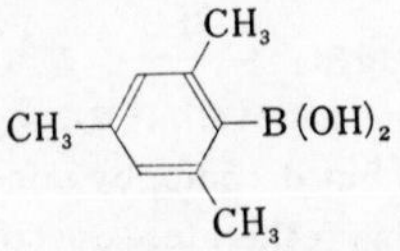

② (MeO)₃B + 2,4,6-Me₃C₆H₂MgBr $\xrightarrow[Et_2O]{-78°}$

72%

③ Solid. [143~145°].
Forms dimer. [220~222°] (sublime
170°/1~2).

④ + ⟶

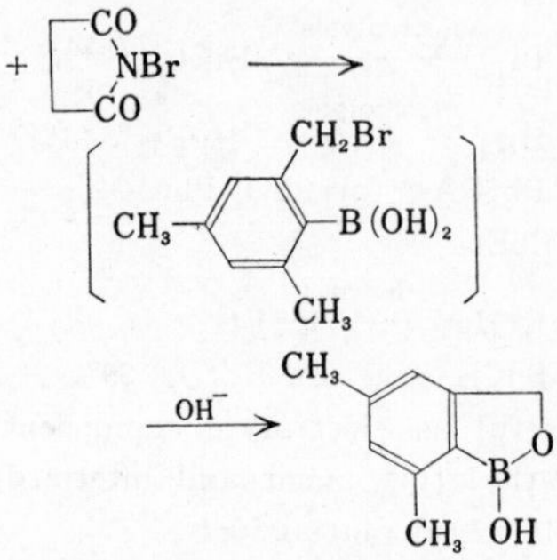

[ ]

$\xrightarrow{OH^-}$

heat
⟶ (2,4,6-Me₃C₆H₂BO)₃
+ BuOH ⟶
2,4,6-Me₃C₆H₂B(OBu)₂

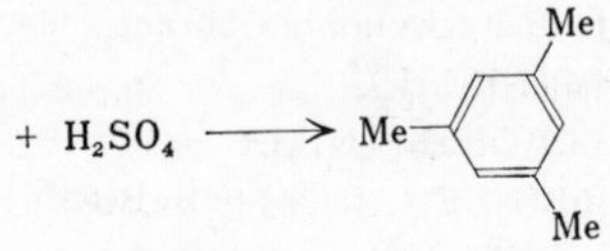

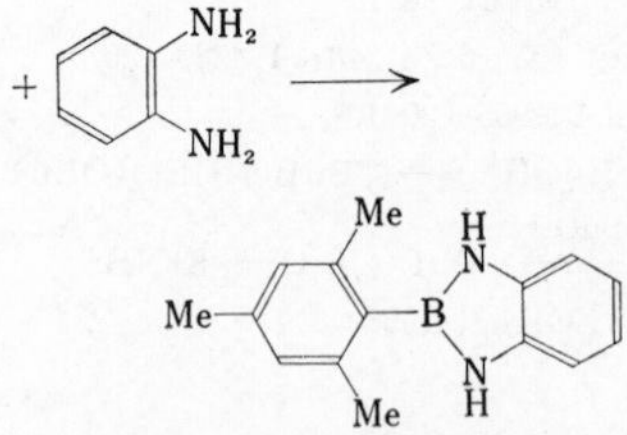

+ H₂SO₄ ⟶

+ ⟶

(46.4%)

⑥ JACS **82**, 3053 (1960).   JOC **23**, 1579
(1958).

BC₉H₁₅

① Triallylborane
B(CH₂CH=CH₂)₃

② B(OBu)₃ + (CH₂=CHCH₂)₃Al₂Br₃
$\xrightarrow{55\sim60°}$ 80.5%
BF₃·OEt₂ + (CH₂=CHCH₂)₃Al₂Br₃
$\xrightarrow{45\sim50°}$ 78%
B(OEt)₃ + CH₂=CHCH₂MgBr ⟶
33%
BF₃·Et₂O + CH₂=CHCH₂MgBr ⟶
47%

③ Liq. (153.5~154°/720, 52.5~53°/18).
n_D 1.4512 (20°). d 0.7745 (20°).
Decomp. in air.

④ + 2 EtSH ⟶ CH₂=CHCH₂B(SEt)₂
+ CH₃CH=CH₂
+ H₂O ⟶ (CH₂=CHCH₂BO)₃
+ CH₃CH=CH₂
+ Bu(OBu)₃ $\xrightarrow{160\sim170°,\ 16\ hr.}$
CH₂=CHCH₂B(OBu)₂
+ Br₂ $\xrightarrow{-30\sim-35°}$ BrCH₂CHBrCH₂Br
+ H₂ $\xrightarrow{Pt}$ Pr₃B
+ HgCl₂ $\xrightarrow{in\ EtOH}$ CH₂=CHCHHgCl
+ B₂H₆ ⟶ forms polymer

+ B₂H₆ ⟶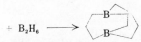

⑥ Izv. OKhN **1960**, 1896. Japan 7019
(1954); CA **50**, 4197 (1956). US
3109029; CA **60**, 3005 (1964).

BC₉H₁₅

① Tricyclopropylborane
(*cyclo*-C₃H₅)₃B

② (R₂B)₂CHCH₂CH₂Cl + NaBHR₃ ⟶
2 B(Pr-*cyclo*)₃ + 10 BR₃ + 3 B₂H₂R₄
+6 NaCl
(Et₂B)₂CHCH₂CH₂Cl + NaBEt₄ $\xrightarrow{120\sim130°}$
2 B(Pr-*cyclo*)₃ + Et₂B-◁ + NaCl
Et₂B-◁ + >BH $\xrightarrow{disproportionation}$

③ Liq. (65~66°/10, 75~76°/150).
④ + AlEt₃ ⟶ BEt₃ + Al(-◁)₃
⑥ Angew. **74**, 652 (1962).

BC₉H₁₆N

① Aniline-trimethylborane

(CH₃)₃B·H₂N—⬡

② Me₃B + H₂NPh $\xrightarrow{low\ temp.}$
③ Solid. [21°].
④ $\xrightarrow{300°}$ Me₂BNH⬡
$\xrightarrow{300°}$ (MeBNPh)₃
⑥ Z. anorg. allg. Chem. **257**, 138 (1948).

BC₉H₁₈Cl₉Si₃

① Tris(3-trichlorosilylpropyl)borane
(Cl₃SiCH₂CH₂CH₂)₃B

② *i*-Bu₃B + CH₂=CHCH₂SiCl₃ $\xrightarrow{170\sim230°}$
69% + *i*-C₄H₈

③ Liq. (157~159°/0.1). n_D 1.4870(20°). d
1.3487(20°/4°).

⑥ Izv. OKhN **1959**, 546.

BC₉H₂₁

① Tripropylborane
(C₃H₇)₃B

② BF₃ + PrMgX ⟶ 50~60%
BF₃·OEt₂ + PrMgX ⟶

③ Liq. (156°, 60°/20, 52°/13). [−65.5°].
n_D 1.4135(20°). d 0.7250(20°).

④ Decomp. in air. Michler ketone test
positive, but weak.
+ I₂ ⟶ (C₃H₇)₂BI 69%
+ H₂ $\xrightarrow{170\sim190°,\ 145\ atm.}$ Pr₄B₂H₂ + C₃H₈
+ Al(NMe₂)₃ $\xrightarrow{110°}$ Pr₂BNMe₂ +
PrAl(NMe₂)₂
$\xrightarrow{160°}$ *i*-PrBPr₂(16%) + *i*-Pr₂BPr(1%)
(by gaschromatograȥn)

+ PrMeC=CH₂ $\xrightarrow{250°, \ 3.2\,\text{atm.,\ 1sec.}}$

(PrMeCHCH₂)₃B

+ (MeO)₃B $\xrightarrow{Pr_4B_2H_2 \ \text{catalyst}}$ PrB(OMe)₂

62.3%

⑥ JCS **1953**, 3902.   Ber. **54**, 2784 (1921).

BC₉H₂₁

① Triisopropylborane

(*i*-C₃H₇)₃B

② BF₃ + *i*-PrMgX $\longrightarrow$

③ Liq. (151°, 34°/12). [−52.5°].

④ + PhMgBr $\xrightarrow{Et_2O}$ *i*-Pr₂BPh 65%

(150~152°/10). n_D 1.4930 (20°).

d 0.9562 (20°).

⑥ Ber. **64**, 2112 (1931).   JACS **67**, 374

(1945).

BC₉H₂₄N

① Triethylamine-trimethylborane

(CH₃)₃B·N(C₂H₅)₃

② Me₃B + NEt₃ $\longrightarrow$

③ Liq. (0°/238). [−18~−14°].

⑥ JACS **69**, 1332 (1947).

BC₉H₂₄N

① Trimethylamine-triethylborane

(C₂H₅)₃B·N(CH₃)₃

② Et₃B + NMe₃ $\longrightarrow$

③ Liq. (86° extrapd.). [−46~−45°].

$\log P = -3164/T + 11.698$.

⑥ JACS **67**, 374 (1945).

BC₁₀H₇Cl₂

① Dichloro-1-naphthylborane

C₁₀H₇BCl₂

② BCl₃ + (1-C₁₀H₇)₂Hg $\xrightarrow[12\,\text{hr.}]{120~150°}$

③ Liq. (164°/25).

⑥ Ber. **27**, 244 (1894).

BC₁₀H₇Cl₂

① Dichloro-2-naphthylborane

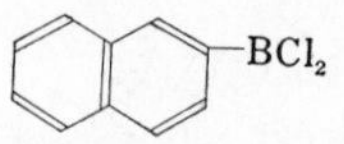

② BCl₃ + $\left(\vphantom{\bigg|}\text{naphthyl}\right)_2$Hg $\longrightarrow$

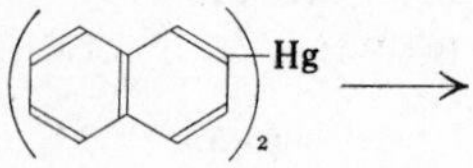

③ Solid. [116°].

④ + NaOMe $\longrightarrow$

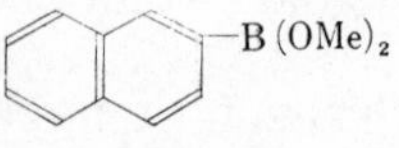

⑥ Ber. **27**, 244 (1894).

BC₁₀H₉Cl₆O₂

① Phenylbis(2,2,2-trichloroethoxy)-

borane

C₆H₅B(OCH₂CCl₃)₂

② C₆H₅B(OH)₂ + Cl₃CCH₂OH $\longrightarrow$

③ Liq. (118°/0.1). n_D 1.5333(20°).

④ + C₅H₅N $\longrightarrow$

PhB(OCH₂CCl₃)₂·C₅H₅N

⑥ JCS **1955**, 2956 ; **1956**, 1540.

BC₁₀H₉O₂

① 1-Naphthylboronic acid

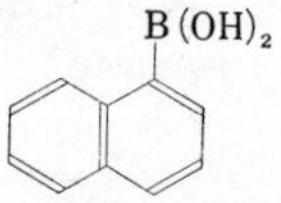

②

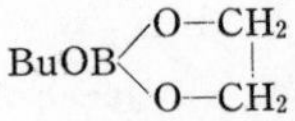

BuOB$\big\langle$$\substack{O-CH_2 \\ | \\ O-CH_2}$ + 1-C₁₀H₇MgBr $\longrightarrow$

B(OBu-*i*)₃ + 1-C₁₀H₇MgBr $\longrightarrow$

③ Crystals(dimorphic). [248°] (plates,

ordinary form). [266°] (needles).

$K_a = 8.88 \times 10^{-11}$(25°, in 25% EtOH).

④ HOCH₂CH₂NH₂ $\longrightarrow$

1-C₁₀H₇B(OCH₂CH₂NH)₂ (88%)

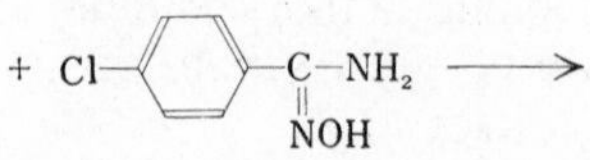

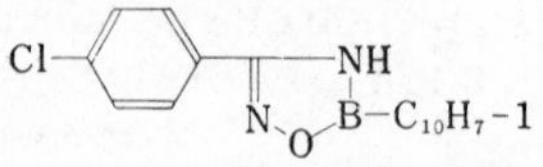

⑥ J. prakt. Chem. **128**, 153 (1930).
  JACS **77**, 2489 (1955).

BC₁₀H₁₀N

① 2-Phenyl-2,1-borazarene
  (1,2-Dihydro-2-phenyl-1,2-azaborine)

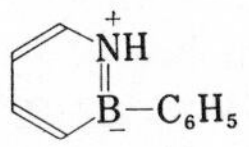

②

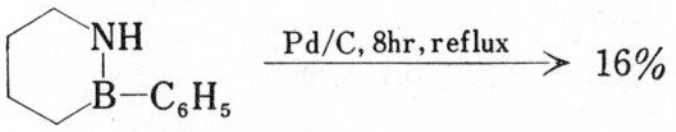

$\xrightarrow{\text{Pd/C, 8hr, reflux}}$ 16%

③ Solid. (60°/0.5 sublime). [117~118.5°].
  Stable in air and in boiling EtOH;
  attacked in H₂O, strongly basic or
  acidic EtOH-H₂O;
  IR: 1546, 1601, 1615, 3010~3075, 3375,
  3419 cm⁻¹.
  UV: λ_{max} 244 (ε 10.030), 289 (ε 10.860)
  mμ.
  NMR: τ=2.2~3.7 (CDCl)₃.

⑥ JACS **85**, 3634 (1963).

BC₁₀H₁₃

① 1-Phenylborolane

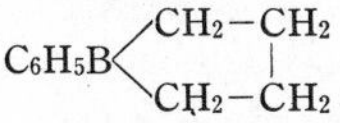

  $C_6H_5B\begin{matrix}CH_2-CH_2\\ | \\ CH_2-CH_2\end{matrix}$

② C₆H₅BF₂ + Li(CH₂)₄Li ⟶
  PhBH₂·Et₃N + CH₂=CHCH=CH₂ ⟶

③ Liq. (85~87/11°, 50~51°/1). n_D 1.5298
  (20°). d 0.9239(20°).
  Spont. inflammable, thermally stable.

⑥ Acta Chem. Scand. **8**, 1779 (1954).
  JCS **1965**, 448.

BC₁₀H₁₃O₂

① 2-Phenyl-1,3,2-dioxaborepane

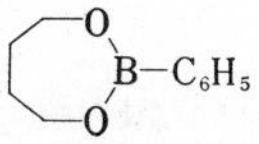

② PhB(OH)₂ + HOCH₂CH₂CH₂CH₂OH
  $\xrightarrow{\text{reflux in Me}_2\text{CO}}$ 88%

③ Liq. (90~95°/1).

⑥ JACS **80**, 2443 (1958).

BC₁₀H₁₄ClO

① Butoxychlorophenylborane
  C₆H₅B(OC₄H₉)Cl

② PhB(OBu)₂ + BCl₃ ⟶
  PhBCl₂ + BuOH ⟶
  PhBCl₂ + PhB(OBu)₂ ⟶
  PhBCl₂ + Bu₂O ⟶ 80%

③ Liq. (65°/0.4). [−32°]. n_D 1.4996(20°).
  d 1.021 (20°/4°).

④ Excess C₅H₅N ⟶
  PhB(OBu)Cl·2C₅H₅N
  ⟶ PhB(OBu)₂ + PhBCl₂

⑥ JCS **1956**, 824, 1540; **1957**, 2983.

BC₁₀H₁₄N

① 1-Methyl-2-phenyl-1,2-azaborolidine

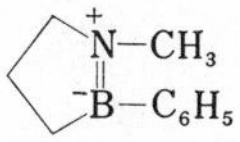

② PhBCl₂ + MeNHCH₂CH=CH₂ ⟶
  CH₂=CHCH₂NMe $\xrightarrow{\text{LiAlH}_4}$ 36%
      |
      Cl−BPh
      (70%)
  PhBH₂·NMe₂ + CH₂=CHCH₂NHMe
  $\xrightarrow{\text{130~135° in diglyme}}$ 39%

③ (74~75°/2.35).
  IR: No ν_{B-H}, $\nu_{B=N}$ at 1512 cm⁻¹.

⑥ JACS **85**, 3634 (1963).

BC₁₀H₁₄N

① 2-Phenyl-1,2-azaborolidine

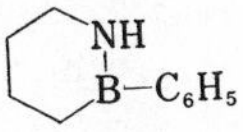

② PhBH₂·NMe₃ + CH₂=CHCH₂CH₂NH₂
  $\xrightarrow{\text{120~133° in diglyme}}$ 58%

③ (64~68°/0.4).
  Stable to reflux (ca. 230°) under N₂.
  IR: $\nu_{B=N}$ 1512 cm⁻¹.

④ + Pd/C ⟶

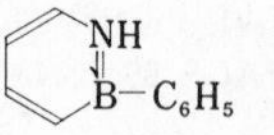

⑥ JACS **85**, 3634 (1963).

BC$_{10}$H$_{14}$NO$_2$

① Perhydro-2-phenyl-1,3,6,2-dioxaza-
borocine

$$C_6H_5B\begin{cases} OCH_2CH_2 \\ OCH_2CH_2 \end{cases}NH$$

② PhB(OH)$_2$ + (HOCH$_2$CH$_2$)$_2$NH $\xrightarrow{\text{in } C_6H_6}$

③ Needles. (180°/0.04 sublime). [209~
210°].

IR data shows transannular cycli-

zation, as Ar—B$\overset{O}{\underset{O}{<}}$NH ; stable to

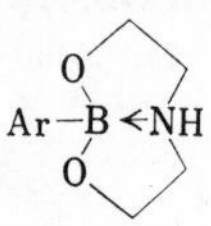

hydrolysis.

⑥ Chem. & Ind. **1955**, 1552.

BC$_{10}$H$_{15}$O

① Methylphenylpropoxyborane
(CH$_3$)(C$_6$H$_5$)BOC$_3$H$_7$

② PhB(OPr)$_2$ + MeMgBr $\xrightarrow{-60°}$ 58%

③ Liq. (87~9°/9). n_D 1.4880 (25°).
d 0.8985 (25°).

④ + H$_2$O ⟶ PhMeBOH
+ MeMgBr ⟶ Ph$_3$B + Me$_3$B

⑥ Acta Chem. Scand. **9**, 242 (1955).

BC$_{10}$H$_{15}$O$_2$

① Diethoxyphenylborane
C$_6$H$_5$B(OC$_2$H$_5$)$_2$

② PhBCl$_2$ + EtOH ⟶
PhB(OH)$_2$ + EtOH ⟶ 73%

③ Liq. (176°, 90~1°/11). n_D 1.4760 (25°).
d 0.9480 (25°).

④ + H$_2$O ⟶ PhB(OH)$_2$ + EtOH
+ ROH ⟶ PhB(OR)$_2$ + EtOH
+ Al(NMe$_2$)$_3$ $\xrightarrow{85\sim90°}$ PhB(NMe$_2$)$_2$
+ (EtO)$_2$AlNMe$_2$

⑥ Ber. **15**, 180 (1882).   Acta Chem.

Scand. **8**, 1779 (1954).

BC$_{10}$H$_{16}$BrN$_2$O$_2$

① Bis(2-aminoethoxy)-*p*-bromophenyl-
borane

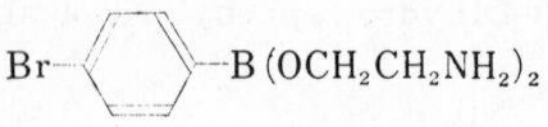

Br—⟨ ⟩—B(OCH$_2$CH$_2$NH$_2$)$_2$

② *p*-BrC$_6$H$_4$B(OH)$_2$ + HOCH$_2$CH$_2$NH$_2$ ⟶

③ Solid. [255~256°].

⑥ JACS **77**, 2491 (1955).

BC$_{10}$H$_{17}$N$_2$

① Bis(dimethylamino)phenylborane
C$_6$H$_5$B[N(CH$_3$)$_2$]$_2$

② PhBCl$_2$ + Me$_2$NH ⟶ 87.5%
(Me$_2$N)$_2$BCl + PhCl + Na ⟶ 70%

③ Liq. (59°/3).

④ + Me$_2$NNH$_2$ ⟶ PhB(NHNMe$_2$)$_2$
76%

+ PhNHNH$_2$ $\xrightarrow{110°}$

$$PhB\begin{cases} NH-N(Ph) \\ N(Ph)-NH \end{cases}BPh + Me_2NH$$

+ NH$_2$NH$_2$ ⟶ $PhB\begin{cases} NHNH \\ NHNH \end{cases}BPh$

+ Me$_2$NH

+ MeC$_6$H$_3$(NCO)$_2$ ⟶

$$\left[\begin{array}{c} Ph \\ | \\ -B-NCONC_6H_3MeNCON- \\ |\quad\quad\quad\quad\quad | \\ Me\ Me\quad\quad Me\ Me \end{array} \right]_x$$

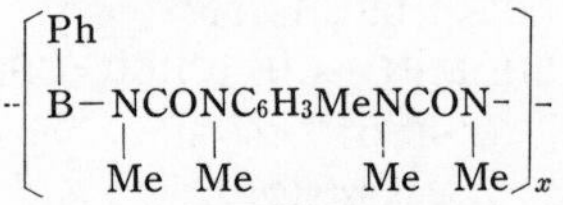

+ SO$_2$ ⟶ (PhBO)$_3$ + (Me$_2$N)$_2$SO

⑤ Additive in fuel and hydraulic fluids.
Stabilizer for lubricating oil. Epoxy
resin curing agent.

⑥ Inorg. Chem. **1**, 738 (1962).   US
3079432 ; CA **59**, 2857 (1963).

BC$_{10}$H$_{17}$N$_2$O$_2$

① Bis(2-aminoethoxy)phenylborane

⟨ ⟩—B(OCH$_2$CH$_2$NH$_2$)$_2$

② PhB(OH)$_2$ + HOCH$_2$CH$_2$NH$_2$ $\xrightarrow{\text{PhMe}}$
   85%

③ Solid. [214~215°].
   Dipole moment : 8.5 D.

⑥ JACS **77**, 2491 (1955).

BC$_{10}$H$_{19}$O$_2$

① Dibutoxyethynylborane
   HC≡CB(OC$_4$H$_9$)$_2$

② B(OBu)$_3$ + HC≡CNa $\longrightarrow$

   B(OMe)$_3$ + HC≡CMgBr $\xrightarrow{-68°}$ $\xrightarrow{\text{BuOH}}$
   58~63%

③ Liq. (34°/0.1). n_D 1.4180 (26°).
   Rapidly decomp. by alk. Stable on
   storage at 5° under N$_2$.
   IR : $\nu_{C≡C-H}$ 3.10, 4.84 μ.

④ + NaHCO$_3$ aq(or Mg(OH)$_2$, NH$_3$,
   NaOH) $\longrightarrow$ C$_2$H$_2$ + B(OH)$_3$
   + BrCCl$_3$ + azobisisobutyronitrile
   $\xrightarrow{95°}$ CCl$_3$CH=CBrB(OBu)$_2$ (90%)

   + HBr $\xrightarrow{h\nu}$ BrCH=CHB(OBu)$_2$
   (58%)

   + Br$_2$ $\xrightarrow{h\nu,\ \text{in CH}_2\text{Cl}_2}$
   BrCH=CBrB(OBu)$_2$ (88%)

   + RSH + azobisisobutyronitrile $\longrightarrow$
   RSCH=CHB(OBu)$_2$ (R=C$_6$H$_{13}$, C$_6$H$_5$)

   $\xrightarrow{130°}$

   —B(OBu)$_2$ (25%)

   + H$_2$O $\longrightarrow$ HC≡CB(OH)$_2$ 54%
   + ArMgBr $\longrightarrow$ (Ar)(HC≡C)BOBu
   (Ar=o-MeC$_6$H$_4$-, Ph-)
   + RMgBr $\longrightarrow$ RB(OBu)$_2$
   (R=Et, CH$_2$=CH-)

⑤ Starting material for insecticide,
   bactericide and fungicide.

⑥ US 3036111 (1962).   JOC **28**, 366, 369
   (1963).

BC$_{10}$H$_{21}$O$_2$

① Dibutoxyvinylborane
   CH$_2$=CHB(OC$_4$H$_9$)$_2$

② B(OMe)$_3$ + CH$_2$=CHMgBr $\xrightarrow[\text{2. HCl}]{\text{1. THF}}$

   [CH$_2$=CHB(OH)$_2$] $\xrightarrow{\text{BuOH}}$ 68.5%

③ Liq. (76~77°/10). n_D 1.4187 (20°).
   d 0.8372 (20°/4°).

④ + Br$_2$ $\xrightarrow{-70°}$ BrCH$_2$CHBrB(OBu)$_2$ 90%

   (83%)
   (exo 61~66%, endo 39~34%)

   + B$_2$H$_6$ $\xrightarrow{0°,\ \text{THF}}$ $\xrightarrow{\text{BuOH}}$
   CH$_3$CH[B(OBu)$_2$]$_2$ $\xrightarrow{\text{H}_2\text{O}}$
   CH$_3$CH[B(OH)$_2$]$_2$

   + HBr $\xrightarrow{\text{UV}}$ BrCH$_2$CH$_2$B(OBu)$_2$ $\xrightarrow{\text{H}_2\text{O}}$
   C$_2$H$_4$ + HBr + B(OH)$_3$

   + BrCCl$_3$ $\xrightarrow{\text{radical}}$
   Cl$_3$CCH$_2$CHBrB(OBu)$_2$
   + PCl$_5$ $\longrightarrow$ CH$_2$=CHB(OBu)Cl,
   BuCl, POCl$_3$
   + HSiCl$_3$ $\xrightarrow{\text{H}_2\text{PtCl}_6}$
   Cl$_3$SiCH$_2$CH$_2$B(OBu)$_2$

⑤ Starting material for insecticide,

bactericide and fungicide.

⑥ JOC **28**, 269, 366 (1963). JACS **82**, 4228 (1960). Izv. Akad. Nauk SSSR **1959**, 1865.

BC₁₀H₂₃

① *t*-Butyldipropylborane
t-C₄H₉B(C₃H₇)₂

② n-PrMgBr + t-BuBCl₂ ⟶ 75%
t-BuBH₂·NMe₃ + CH₃CH=CH₂ ⟶ 88%

③ Liq. (44.5~45°/6.2, 67°/22). n_D 1.4187 (25°). d 0.7285 (25°).
Recovered in 82% yield after 6 months standing in diffuse daylight.

④ + H₂O₂ ⟶ t-BuOH + n-PrOH

⑥ JACS **83**, 1924, 2541 (1961).

BC₁₀H₂₃Si

① 4-*t*-Butyl-1,1-dimethyl-1,4-sila-borinane

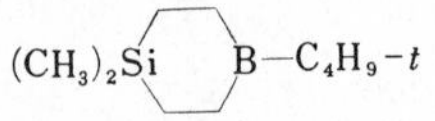

$$(CH_3)_2Si \quad B{-}C_4H_9{-}t$$

② Me₂Si(CH=CH₂)₂ + t-BuBH₂·NMe₃ ⟶ 58%

③ Liq. (44°/2).
NMR: τ+5.75, +5.38, +6.70 ppm.

⑥ JACS **82**, 748 (1960); **83**, 2541 (1961).

BC₁₀H₂₃O

① Dibutylethoxyborane
(C₄H₉)₂BOC₂H₅

② Bu₃B + EtOH ⟶

③ Liq. (71°/13). n_D 1.4138 (20°). d 0.7768 (20°/4°).

⑥ Bull. soc. chim. France **1963**, 558.

BC₁₀H₂₄N

① Dibutyl(ethylamino)borane
(C₄H₉)₂BNHC₂H₅

② Bu₂BCl + 2 EtNH₂ ⟶ Bu₂BNHEt + EtNH₂·HCl

③ Liq. (100°/0.02).

⑥ JACS **74**, 1415 (1952)

BC₁₁H₈N

① Pyridine-Triethynylborane
(HC≡C)₃B·NC₅H₅

② HC≡CNa + BF₃·C₅H₅N $\xrightarrow{-60°}$

③ Crystals.
Stable in air and to the shock; free borane is unstable above −30°.

⑥ JOC **29**, 3225 (1964).

BC₁₁H₁₁N₄O

① 2-Phenyl-6-hydroxy-7-methyl-2-bora-1,2-dihydropurin

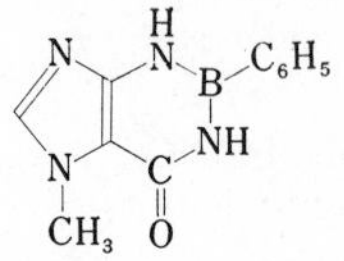

②

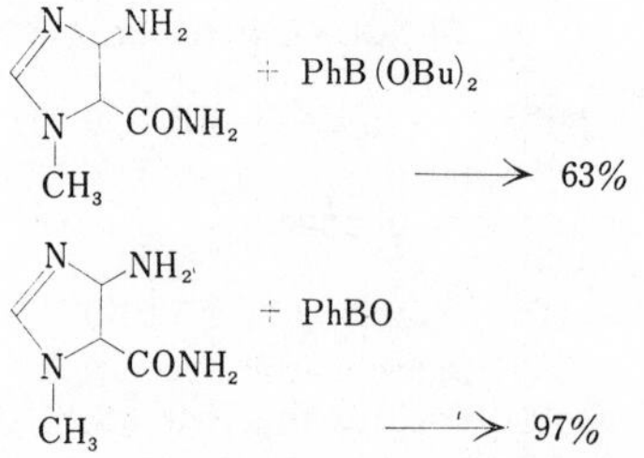

③ Solid. Sublime slowly above 300°, not fused.
Readily solvolyzed; shows no aromatic character.

⑥ Tetrahedron Letters **1960**, No. 23, 8. Angew. **72**, 188 (1960). JACS **83**, 2708 (1961).

BC₁₁H₁₅

① 1-Phenylborinane

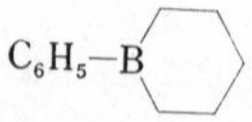

② PhBF₂ + LiCH₂CH₂CH₂CH₂CH₂Li ⟶

③ Liq. (105~107°/11).
⑥ Acta Chem. Scand. **8**, 1779 (1954).

BC$_{11}$H$_{16}$ClO

① Chloroisobutoxy-*o*-tolylborane

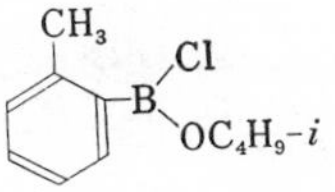

② *o*-MeC$_6$H$_4$B(OBu-*i*)$_2$ + PCl$_5$ ⟶ 86%
③ Liq. (110~1°/8). *d* 0.9918 (21°).
⑥ Izv. OKhN **1956**, 376.

BC$_{11}$H$_{17}$O

① Benzyloxydiethylborane
 (C$_2$H$_5$)$_2$BOCH$_2$C$_6$H$_5$
② Et$_3$B + PhCHO ⟶
 Et$_3$B + PhCH$_2$OH ⟶
③ Liq. (114°/16).
⑥ J. prakt. Chem. **147**, 226 (1937).

BC$_{11}$H$_{19}$N$_2$O$_3$

① Bis(2-aminoethoxy)-*p*-methoxy-
 phenylborane

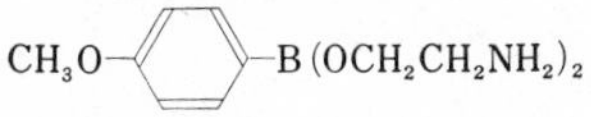

② *p*-MeOC$_6$H$_4$B(OH)$_2$ + HOCH$_2$CH$_2$NH$_2$
 ⟶
③ Solid. [216~218°].
⑥ JACS **77**, 2491 (1955).

BC$_{11}$H$_{25}$O$_2$

① Dibutoxypropylborane
 C$_3$H$_7$B(OC$_4$H$_9$)$_2$
② PrB(OH)$_2$ + BuOH ⟶
 PrBCl(OBu) + NHEt$_2$ ⟶
 PrB(OBu)$_2$ (74%) + PrB(NHEt)$_2$
 + NHEt$_2$HCl
③ Liq. (65~68°/2). n_D 1.4120 (20°).
⑥ Izv. OKhN **1958**, 777.

BC$_{12}$H$_9$ClN

① 10-Chloro-10,9-borazarophenanthrene

(6-Chloro-5,6-dihydrodibenz[*c, e*]-
 [1,2]azaborine)

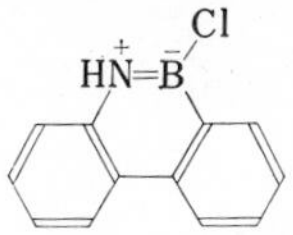

②

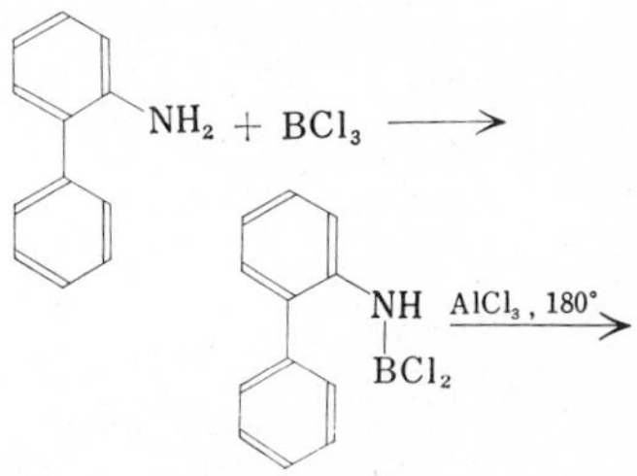

③ Solid. [93~94°].

④ + H$_2$O ⟶

 + LiAlH$_4$ ⟶

 + RMgX ⟶

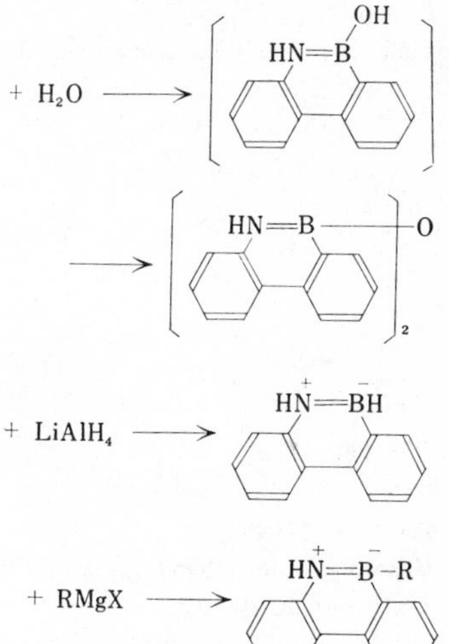

⑥ JCS **1958**, 3073.

BC$_{21}$H$_{20}$N

① 3,6,9-Trimethyl-10-phenyl-10,9-
 borazaroanthracene
 (5,10-Dihydro-2,5,8-triphenyl-10-
 phenyl-dibenzo-[*b, e*][1,4]
 azaborine)

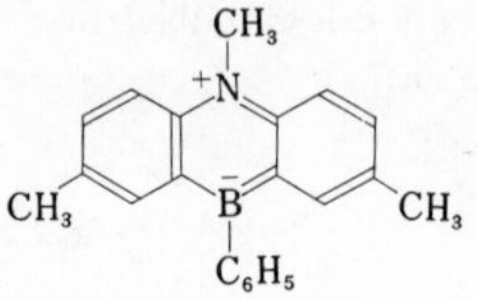

② PhB(OBu)$_2$ + MeN

$\longrightarrow$ 10%

+ PhMgBr $\longrightarrow$ 77%

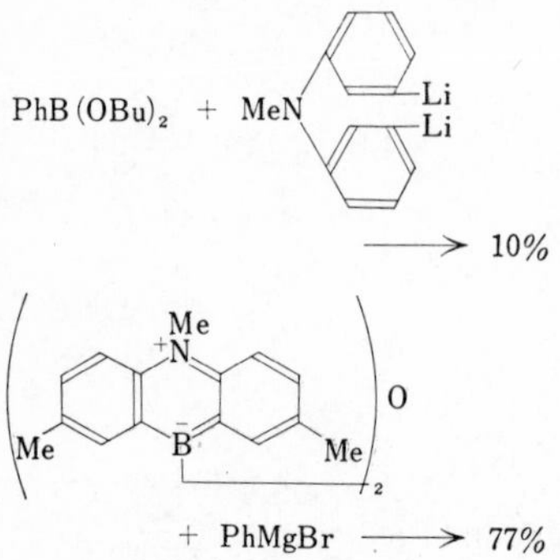

③ Crystals. [114~115°].
Undergoes rapid hydrolytic oxidn. in solution.

④ $\underset{H^+}{\overset{OH^-}{\rightleftharpoons}}$

$\xrightarrow[AcOH]{+Br_2}$

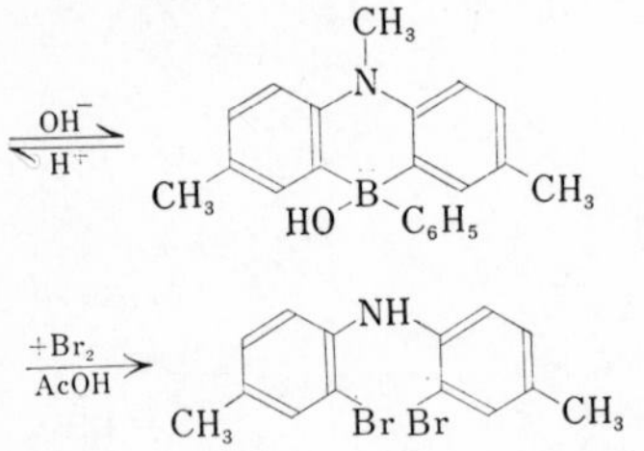

⑥ JCS **1961**, 425.

BC$_{12}$H$_9$Cl$_2$

① Chloro(*p*-chlorophenyl)phenylborane
(C$_6$H$_5$)(*p*-ClC$_6$H$_4$)BCl

② PhBCl(OBu-*i*) + *p*-ClC$_6$H$_4$MgBr $\longrightarrow$
Ph(*p*-ClC$_6$H$_4$)B(OBu-*i*) $\xrightarrow{PCl_5}$ 47.2%

③ Liq. (135~40°/7). *d* 1.145 (20°/4°).

④ + H$_2$O $\longrightarrow$ $\underset{p\text{-ClC}_6\text{H}_4}{\overset{OH}{Ph-B\leftarrow OH_2}}$

+ *o*-MeC$_6$H$_4$MgBr $\longrightarrow$
Ph(*o*-MeC$_6$H$_4$)(*p*-ClC$_6$H$_4$)B (49%)

⑥ Izv. OKhN **1957**, 589.

BC$_{12}$H$_9$Cl$_2$O

① Bis(*p*-chlorophenyl)borinic acid.

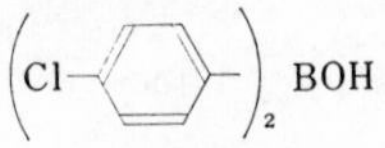

② (*p*-ClC$_6$H$_4$)$_2$BOBu-*i* + Ba(OH)$_2$ $\longrightarrow$
(*p*-ClC$_6$H$_4$)$_2$B(OH)$_2$Ba $\xrightarrow{HCl}$

③ Crystals. [76~78°].

④ $\xrightarrow{\text{heat } in\ vacuo}$ *p*-ClC$_6$H$_4$B(OH)$_2$ + PhCl

⑥ J. Gen. Chem. USSR **8**, 1768 (1938).
Izv. OKhN **1956**, 451.

BC$_{12}$H$_9$O$_2$

① 2-Phenyl-1,3,2-benzodioxaborole

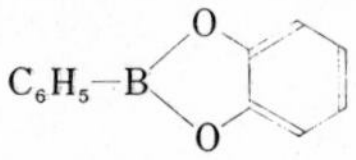

② PhB(OH)$_2$ +

$\longrightarrow$ 57%

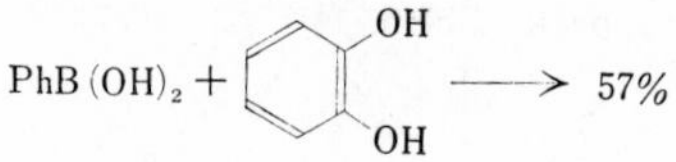

③ Solid. [111~112°].

⑥ JOC **19**, 780 (1954).

BC$_{12}$H$_9$O$_2$

① 10-Hydroxy-10,9-boroxarophenan-
threne
(6-Hydroxydibenz-[*c, e*][1,2]-
oxaborine

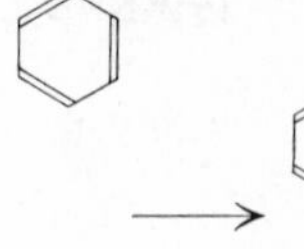

②

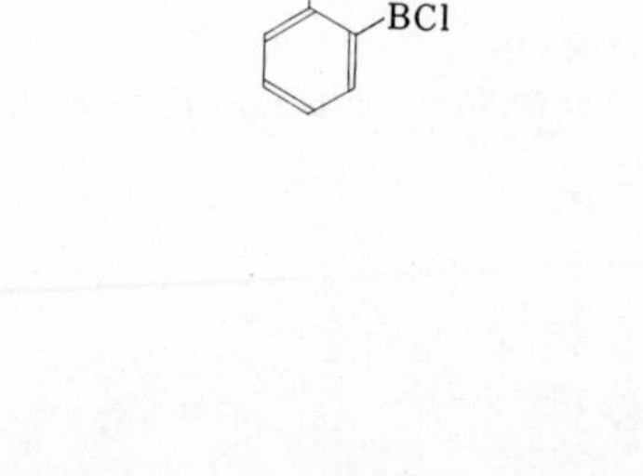

+ BCl$_3$ $\longrightarrow$

$\xrightarrow{H_2O}$

③ Solid. [205~206°].

Stable in aq. acids and alk.; unaffected in air.

④ + ROH ⟶

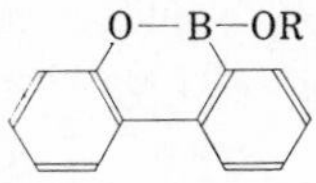

+ KOH $\xrightarrow{\text{fusion}}$

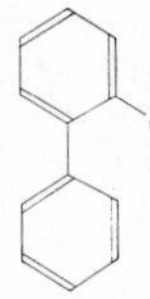

+ H₂O₂ ⟶

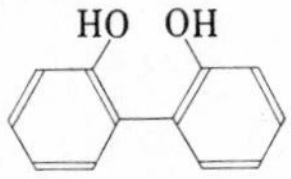

+ Br₂ $\xrightarrow{\text{HOAc}}$

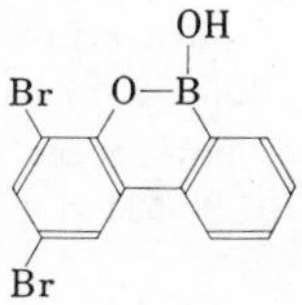

⑥ Tetrahedron **15**, 26 (1961). JCS **1960**, 344.

BC₁₂H₁₀Br

① Bromodiphenylborane
  (C₆H₅)₂BBr

② BBr₃ + Ph₂Hg ⟶

③ Crystals. (155°/8). [25°].
  Decomp. in H₂O.

⑥ Ann. **315**, 26 (1901).

BC₁₂H₁₀Cl

① Chlorodiphenylborane
  (C₆H₅)₂BCl

② BCl₃ + HgPh₂ ⟶
  Ph₂BOBu + PCl₅ ⟶
  Ph₃B + PhBCl₂ ⟶ 77%

③ Liq. (271°, 119~20°/3). n_D 1.6075
  (20°). d 1.1091 (20°).

④ + NH₂NH₂ $\xrightarrow{25°}$ [Ph₂B(N₂H₄)₂]Cl
  + Me₂NNH₂ ⟶ Ph₂BNHNMe₂

+ Me₂NNH₃Cl

+ 2 Et₂NH $\xrightarrow{0°}$ Ph₂BNEt₂
+ Et₂NH·HCl

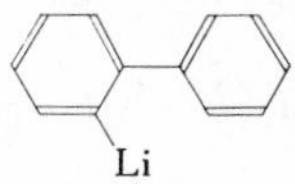

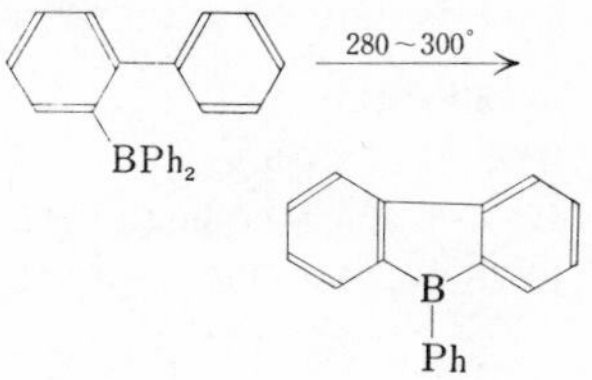

$\xrightarrow{280~300°}$

+ NaMn(CO)₅ ⟶ (Ph₂BMn)₂
+ NaMn(CO)₄PPh₃ ⟶
  Ph₂B·Mn(CO)₄PPh₃
+ Na[FeCp(CO)₂] ⟶
  Ph₂BFeCp(CO)₂
+ LiN₃ $\xrightarrow{\text{reflux in C₆H₆}}$ Ph₂BN₃ 52%
  $\xrightarrow{>100°}$ Ph₄B₂N₂
+ Me₂NCHO ⟶ 1:1 adduct
+ RLi ⟶ Ph₂BR $\xrightarrow{\text{RLi}}$ Li(Ph₂BR₂)
  (R=o-tolyl, etc.)

+ AgClO₄ + CH₃NO₂ + α,α′-dipyridyl

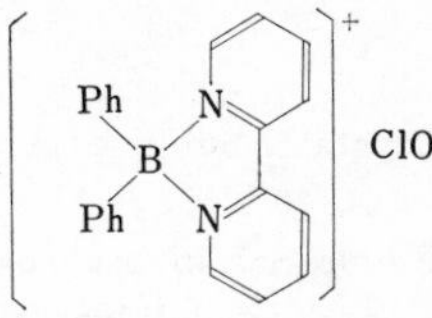

⑥ Ann. **315**, 19 (1901).   Izv. SKh **1964**, 1838.

BC₁₂H₁₀N

① 10a,4a-Borazarophenanthrene
  ([1,2]-Azaborino[1,2-a]benz[e][1,2]-azaborine)

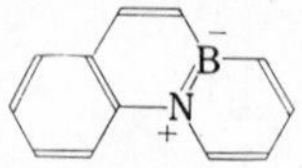

② + Pd/C + 1-hexene

$$\xrightarrow{290\sim300°}$$

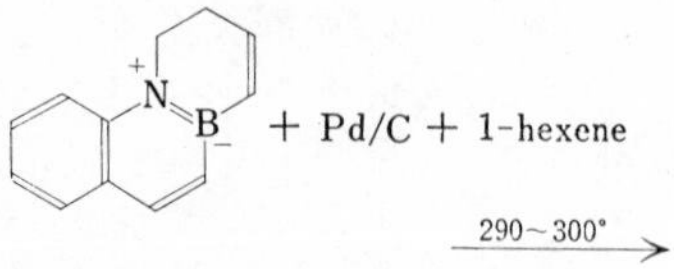

③ Needles. [75~77°].
UV: λ_{max} 320 mμ.
Stable; shows aromatic character.
⑥ JACS **84**, 4884 (1962).

BC$_{12}$H$_{10}$N

① 10,9-Borazarophenanthrene
(5,6-Dihydrodibenz [c, e][1,2]
azaborine)

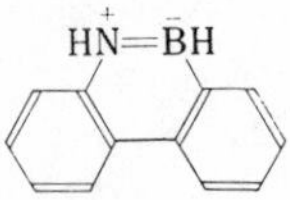

② + LiAlH$_4$ $\longrightarrow$

+ LiAlH$_4$ + AlCl$_3$

$$\longrightarrow 75\%$$

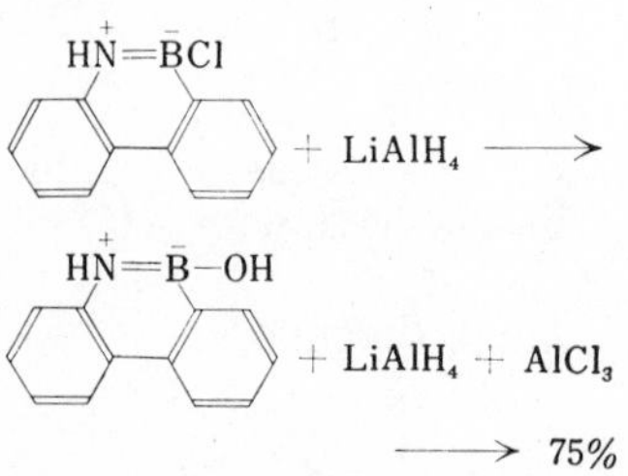

③ Crystals. Sublime at 65~70°/0.5°.
[69~70°].
Stable. Sol. in org. solvents. Acid
and base catalyze the hydrolytic
oxidation in soln.

④ + conc. H$_2$SO$_4$ $\longrightarrow$

+ 9 N HCl $\longrightarrow$

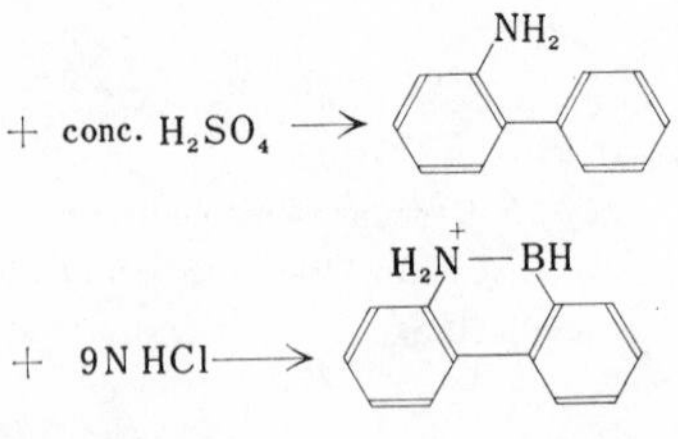

⑥ JCS **1958**, 3073.   JACS **83**, 1754(1961).

BC$_{12}$H$_{10}$NO

① 10-Hydroxy-10,9-borazaroanthracene
(5,10-Dihydro-10-hydroxydibenzo-
[b, e][1,4]azaborine)

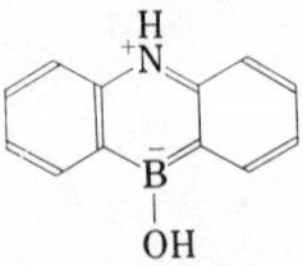

② + BuOBO $\xrightarrow{H_2O}$

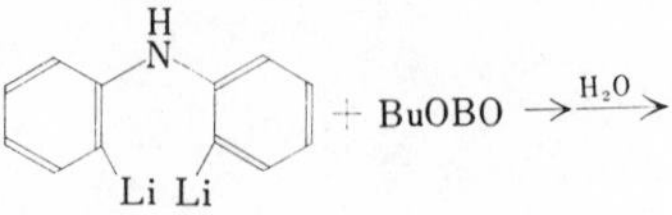

③ Solid. [285°].
Less stable than 10,9-borazaro-
phenanthrene derivs.
Similar to xanthone, acridine and
anthracene in UV.
⑥ JCS **1960**, 191.

BC$_{12}$H$_{11}$N$_2$

① 2,3-Dihydro-2-phenyl-1 H-1,3,2-
benzo-[d]diazaborole

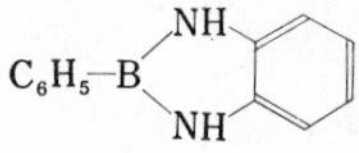

② + BCl$_3$ $\longrightarrow$

$\xrightarrow{PhMgBr}$

+ PhBCl$_2$
(or Ph(OH)$_2$) $\longrightarrow$

+ PhB(NMe$_2$)$_2$
$\longrightarrow 65\%$

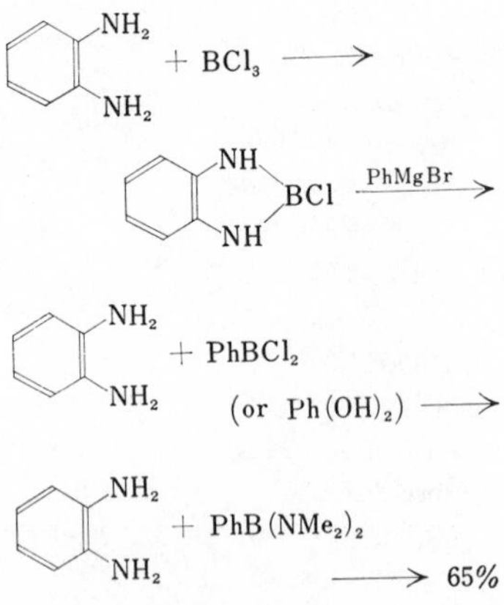

③ Solid. [215~216°].
Stable in air but slowly autoxidized.

④ + HCl $\longrightarrow$ PhB$\underset{NH}{\overset{NH}{<}}$⟨benzene⟩ · 2HCl

Readily solvolyzed, especially in the presence of acids.

⑥ JACS 80, 5411 (1958).

BC$_{12}$H$_{11}$O

① Diphenylborinic acid
(C$_6$H$_5$)$_2$BOH

② Ph$_2$BCl + H$_2$O $\longrightarrow$
B(OBu-i) + PhMgBr $\longrightarrow$ + H$_2$O
$\longrightarrow$

③ Solid. (215°, 150°/20). [57.5°].
IR : ν_{B-O} 1325 cm^{-1}.

④ + X$_2$ + H$_2$O $\longrightarrow$ PhB(OH)$_2$ + PhX
+ HX (X=Cl, Br)
Forms no salt with alk.

+ NH$_2$OH $\xrightarrow{EtOH}$
$\underset{Ph_2}{\overset{Ph_2}{\underset{B}{\overset{B}{\underset{O \diagdown \diagup NH_2}{NH_2 \diagup \diagdown O}}}}}$

+ CH$_3$COCH$_2$CO$_2$Et $\longrightarrow$ chelate
compd. [74~75°].

⑥ J. Gen. Chem. USSR 6, 636 (1936).
J. prakt. Chem. 128, 153 (1930).

BC$_{12}$H$_{12}$F$_2$N

① Aniline-difluorophenylborane
C$_6$H$_5$BF$_2$·H$_2$NC$_6$H$_5$

② PhBF$_2$ + H$_2$NPh $\longrightarrow$

③ Crystals. [178~179°].

⑥ Acta Chem. Scand. 8, 1779 (1954).

BC$_{12}$H$_{13}$O$_2$

① Dimethoxy-2-naphthylborane

⟨naphthyl⟩—B(OCH$_3$)$_2$

② ⟨naphthyl⟩—BCl$_2$ + 2NaOCH$_3$ $\longrightarrow$

③ Liq. (160~180°/5).

④ + H$_2$O $\longrightarrow$ (2-C$_{10}$H$_7$BO)$_3$ + MeOH

⑥ Ber. 27, 244 (1894).

BC$_{12}$H$_{19}$O

① Butoxyethylphenylborane
(C$_2$H$_5$)(C$_6$H$_5$)BOC$_4$H$_9$

② PhB(OBu)$_2$ + EtMgBr $\longrightarrow$ 58%

③ Liq. (110~111°/9). n_D 1.4864 (25°).
d 0.8940 (25°).

⑥ Acta Chem. Scand. 9, 242 (1955).

BC$_{12}$H$_{20}$NO

① Ethylaminoisobutoxyphenylborane
C$_6$H$_5$(i-C$_4$H$_9$O)BNHC$_2$H$_5$

② PhBCl(OBu-i) + H$_2$NEt $\longrightarrow$
PhB(NHEt)(OBu-i) + EtNH$_2$·HCl

③ Liq. (86~7°/2). n_D 1.4831 (20°).
d 0.9057 (20°).

④ + i-BuOH $\longrightarrow$ PhB(OBu) + EtNH
$\xrightarrow{heat}$ PhB(NHEt)$_2$ + PhB(OBu-i)$_2$

⑥ Izv. OKhN 1957, 646.

BC$_{12}$H$_{21}$

① Perhydro-9 b-boraphenalene

all $cis-($I$)$
$cis, cis, tr($II$)$

② $tr, tr, tr-$ ⟨cyclododecatriene⟩ + BH$_3$·NEt$_3$
$\longrightarrow$

$tr, tr, tr-$cyclododecatriene (1,5,9)
+ Et$_2$B$_2$H$_4$ $\longrightarrow$

$\xrightarrow{200~220°}$

+ H$_2$ + C$_{12}$H$_{22}$

70~80% (R= $cyclo$-C$_{12}$H$_{23}$)

③ I : Liq. Ⅱ: Solid. (131°/6, I : 115°/
10, Ⅱ : 113.5°/10). [Ⅱ: +31°]. I :
n_D 1.5100 (35°). Ⅱ: n_D 1.5029 (35°).
I : d 0.9357 (35°/4°), Ⅱ : d 0.9220
(35°/4°).

Have two isomers (I all *cis* and Ⅱ
cis, *cis*, *tr*); spontaneously inflammable; thermally stable. Could not
be hydrogenated. Does not react
with olefin.

④ + H$_2$O$_2$ ⟶ cyclododecanetriol-
(1,5,9)
+ NH$_3$ or piperidine ⟶ 1 : 1
adduct.
+ THF or NEt$_3$ ⟶×⟶

I + Et$_3$N + H$_2$ $\xrightarrow{200°}$ Ⅱ

+ O$_2$ $\xrightarrow[25\%]{0° \text{ (in dil. soln.)}}$ C$_{12}$H$_{23}$B(OOH)$_2$

⑥ Angew. **69**, 684 (1957); **74**, 329 (1962).

BC$_{12}$H$_{23}$

① Di(1-butenyl)-*t*-butylborane
t-C$_4$H$_9$B(CH=CHCH$_2$CH$_3$)$_2$

② *t*-BuBH$_2$·NMe$_3$ + CH$_3$CHC≡CH $\xrightarrow[65\%]{60°}$

③ Liq. (40°/0.3).

⑥ JACS **83**, 2541 (1961)

BC$_{12}$H$_{26}$Cl

① Chlorodihexylborane
(C$_6$H$_{13}$)$_2$BCl

② (C$_6$H$_{13}$)$_3$B + BCl$_3$ $\xrightarrow{150\sim170°}$ 93%
(C$_6$H$_{13}$)$_2$BOB(C$_6$H$_{13}$)$_2$ + BCl$_3$ ⟶ 80%

③ Liq. (75°/0.1). d 0.9006 (20°/4°)

⑥ Bull. soc. chim. France **1963**, 558.

BC$_{12}$H$_{27}$

① Dibutyl-*t*-butylborane
(*n*-C$_4$H$_9$)$_2$BC$_4$H$_9$-*t*

② *t*-BuBH$_2$ + CH$_2$=CHCH$_2$CH$_3$ $\xrightarrow{60°}$ 90%

③ Liq. (74°/6).
^{1}H-NMR: + 5.92, + 0.50 ppm (C$_6$H$_6$);
^{11}B-NMR: −40 ppm (B(OMe)$_3$)

④ + H$_2$O$_2$ ⟶ *n*-Bu aldehyde (as 2,4-
dinitrophenylhydrazone)

⑥ JACS **83**, 2541 (1961).

BC$_{12}$H$_{27}$

① Tributylborane
(*n*-C$_4$H$_9$)$_3$B

② BX$_3$ + *n*-BuMgX ⟶
(X=F, Cl, alkoxy, phenoxy)
BF$_3$ + BuMgCl $\xrightarrow{\text{in Et}_2\text{O}}$ 70%

③ Liq. (209°, 109°/20, 90∼91°/9). n_D
1.4260 (20°). d 0.7556 (20°).
log P=8.797−2857/T.

④ $\xrightarrow{160°}$ *i*-BuBBu$_2$ (by gaschromato-
graph)
+ dry air ⟶ BuB(OBu)$_2$
+ H$_2$O$_2$ (or benzoylperoxide) ⟶
B(OBu)$_3$
+ HCl + AlCl$_3$ ⟶ BuBCl$_2$ + 2 C$_4$H$_{10}$
+ Br$_2$ ⟶ Bu$_2$BBr + BuBr
+ RM ⟶ [Metal]$^+$[RBBu$_3$]$^-$
R=butyl, phenyl
M=Li, MgBr, etc.
+ H$_2$ $\xrightarrow[260\,\text{atm}]{140\sim150°}$ B$_2$H$_6$ + C$_4$H$_{10}$ 75% up.
(Pd has catalytic activity)

$\xrightarrow{300°}$ (*n*- and *s*-) Bu ⎯⟨cyclopentyl⟩

+ CH$_3$CH=CHCH$_3$ + H$_2$

+ AlMe$_3$ $\xrightarrow{145\sim200°}$ Me$_3$B + AlBu$_3$

+ Al(NMe$_2$)$_3$ $\xrightarrow[1\,\text{hr.}]{100\sim120°}$ Bu$_2$BNMe$_2$
+ Bu$_2$AlNMe$_2$

+ CO + Cl$_3$CCHO·H$_2$O + EtOH
$\xrightarrow{50°,\,60\,\text{atm.}}$ $\begin{matrix} \text{Bu}-\text{B}-\text{O} \\ | \\ \text{Bu}-\text{B}-\text{O} \end{matrix}$CHCCl$_3$

$+$ PhNC $\xrightarrow[\text{in Et}_2\text{O}]{25°}$

$$
\begin{array}{c}
\text{Ph} \\
\text{N} \\
\text{BuC}^+\!\!\diagup\!\!\searrow\!\!\text{BBu}_2 \\
\text{Bu}_2\text{B}^-\diagdown\!\!\nearrow\text{CBu} \\
\text{N} \\
\text{Ph}
\end{array}
$$

58%

$\longrightarrow$

$$
\begin{array}{c}
\text{Ph} \\
\text{N} \\
\text{Bu}_2\text{C}\diagup\diagdown\text{BBu} \\
\text{BuB}\diagdown\diagup\text{CBu}_2 \\
\text{N} \\
\text{Ph}
\end{array}
$$

Bu₃B + 0.8 NO $\longrightarrow$

0.13 Bu₂BN—N=O
       |
       OBu

+ 0.15 Bu₂BONBu₂ + 0.3 Bu₂BNBBu₂
                              |
                             OBu

+ 1-decene $\xrightarrow{150°}$ *n*-C₄H₈ + (decyl)₃B

catalyst : (Me₂N)₂CO, (Me₂N)₃PO,
Me₂SO

+ (MeO)₃B $\xrightarrow{\text{Bu}_4\text{B}_2\text{H}_2,\,\text{catalyst}}$

BuB(OMe)₂ (73~90%)

⑥ JACS **60**, 121, 352 (1938).

BC₁₂H₂₇

① Tri-*s*-butylborane
   (*s*-C₄H₉)₃B

② BF₃ + CH₃CH₂CH(Me)MgBr $\longrightarrow$

③ Liq. (60°/2.5). n_D 1.4349 (25°). *d*
   0.7658 (25°).
   Heat of combustion. 2130 kcal/mol.

④ $\xrightarrow{\text{reflux 20 hr.}}$ *n*-Bu₃B

   + BCl₃ $\xrightarrow{160°}$ *s*-Bu₂BCl (82%)

   + O₂ $\longrightarrow$ *s*-BuB(OOBu)₂

   + (MeOBO)₃ $\longrightarrow$ (*s*-BuBO)₃

   + B(OMe)₃

⑥ JACS **79**, 5192 (1957).

BC₁₂H₂₇

① Triisobutylborane

(*i*-C₄H₉)₃B

② BF₃ + *t*-BuMgCl $\xrightarrow{\text{heat}}$

   BF₃ + *i*-BuMgX $\longrightarrow$ 60~70%

   B₂H₆ + *i*-butene $\longrightarrow$

   (*i*-PrO)₃B + (*i*-Bu)₂AlH $\xrightarrow{\text{Et}_3\text{N catalyst}}$

   BH₃·NH₃ + *i*-C₄H₈ $\xrightarrow{200°}$ 80%

③ Liq. (188°/750, 86°/20, 68°/7). n_D
   1.4203 (25°). *d* 0.7352 (25°).

④ + H₂O₂ $\longrightarrow$ *i*-BuOH

   + HCHO + CO $\xrightarrow{50°,\ 700\,\text{atm. 1 hr.}}$

$$
\begin{array}{c}
i\text{-Bu}-\text{B}-\text{O} \\
\phantom{i\text{-Bu}-}|\phantom{-\text{B}-}\diagdown\!\!\text{CH}_2 \\
(i\text{-Bu})_2\text{C}-\text{O}\diagup
\end{array}
$$

   + H₂ $\xrightarrow{250\,\text{atm, }150\sim160°,\ 24\,\text{hr}}$

   (*i*-Bu)₂B₂H₄ + *i*-butene

   + CH₂=CHCH₂SiMe₃ $\longrightarrow$

   B(CH₂CH₂CH₂SiMe₃)₃ + *i*-butene

   $\xrightarrow{200°}$ *i*-C₄H₈, (*i*-Bu₂BH)₂

   $\xrightarrow{350°,\ 20\,\text{min}}$ *i*-BuPrMeB, *i*-BuBPr₂,

   i-BuBMe₂, *i*-C₄H₈, C₃H₆

   + cyclohexene $\xrightarrow{160\sim170°}$

   (*cycro*-C₆H₁₁)₃B + 3 *i*-C₄H₈

⑥ Ber. **54**, 2784 (1921).   Nature **189**, 1005
   (1961).

BC₁₂H₂₇

① Butyldi-*t*-butylborane
   (*n*-C₄H₉)(*t*-C₄H₉)₂B

② BF₃ + *t*-BuMgCl + CH₃CH₂CH=CH₂
   $\longrightarrow$ 55%

③ Liq. (47.5°/1.7). n_D 1.4373 (25°).
   d 0.7608 (25°).

④ + H₂O₂ $\longrightarrow$ 2 *t*-BuOH + *n*-BuOH

   + *i*-BuMgBr $\xrightarrow{\text{reflux 6 hr. in Et}_2\text{O}}$

   recovered in 81% yield

⑥ JACS **83**, 1924 (1961).

BC₁₂H₂₇

① *t*-Butyldiisobutylborane
   (*t*-C₄H₉)(*i*-C₄H₉)₂B

② BF₃ + *t*-BuMgCl +
　(CH₃)₂C=CH₂(excess) ⟶ 54%
　t-BuBH₂·NMe₃ + (CH₃)₂C=CH₂ ⟶
　85%
③ Liq. (62°/7.5).
④ $\xrightarrow{130°}$ *i*-Bu₃B
⑥ JACS **80**, 617 (1958) ; **83**, 2541 (1961).

BC₁₂H₂₇O
① Butoxydibutylborane
　(C₄H₉)₂BOC₄H₉
② Bu₂BOBBu₂ + BuOH ⟶ 90%
　Bu₃B + O₂ + H₂O ⟶
③ Liq. (114°/20). n_D 1.4210 (20°).
　d 0.8060 (20°).
④ + PCl₅ ⟶ Bu₂BCl
　+ H₂O ⟶ Bu₂BOH
　+ BCl₃ ⟶ Bu₂BCl
　+ HX ⟶ Bu₂BOH + BuX
　+ HOAc ⟶ [Bu(AcO)B]₂O
⑥ JACS **60**, 115, 121 (1938).

BC₁₂H₂₇O₂
① Dibutoxybutylborane
　C₄H₉B(OC₄H₉)₂
② B(OBu)₃ + LiBu, or BuMgCl ⟶
③ Liq. (105°/10). n_D 1.4169 (20°).
　d 0.8300 (20°).
④ + H₂O ⟶ BuB(OH)₂
　+ HCl $\xrightarrow[\quad]{120°,\ 7\,hr}\!\!\!\!\!\times$
　+ HBr ⟶ BuBBr₂ (slowly)
　+ BF₃, or BuBF₂ ⟶ Bu(BuO)BF
　$\xrightarrow{BF_3}$ BuBF₂
　+ C₅H₅N ⟶ no complex
⑥ JCS **1955**, 2956.

BC₁₂H₂₇O₃
① Tris(2-ethoxyethyl)borane
　(C₂H₅OCH₂CH₂)₃B
② B₂H₆ + CH₂=CHOC₂H₅ ⟶ 89%
③ Liq. (77~9°/2). n_D 1.4145 (20°).
　d 0.8757 (20°/4°).
⑥ Izv. OKhN **1959**, 546.　US 3115526 ;

CA **60**, 6866 (1964).

BC₁₂H₂₇S
① Dibutyl(butylthio)borane
　(C₄H₉)₂BSC₄H₉
② Bu₃B + C₄H₉SH ⟶
③ Liq. (68°/0.1). n_D 1.4554 (20°).
　d 0.8324 (20°/4°).
⑥ Bull. soc. chim. France **1963**, 558.

BC₁₂H₂₉N₂
① Butylbis(diethylamino)borane
　C₄H₉B[N(C₂H₅)₂]₂
② BuBH₂·NMe₃ + Et₂NH
　$\xrightarrow{Et_2NH·HCl\ cat.\ 100\sim150°}$ 42%
③ (77°/0.3).
　¹¹B-NMR : $\delta = -21.2$ ppm
⑥ JACS **83**, 2671 (1961).

BC₁₃H₁₁N₂O
① 2-Phenyl-2-boradihydro-4-quinazolone

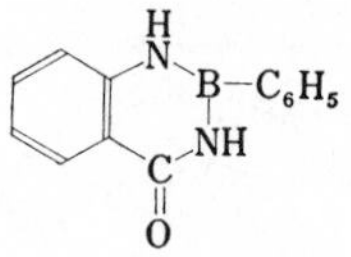

②

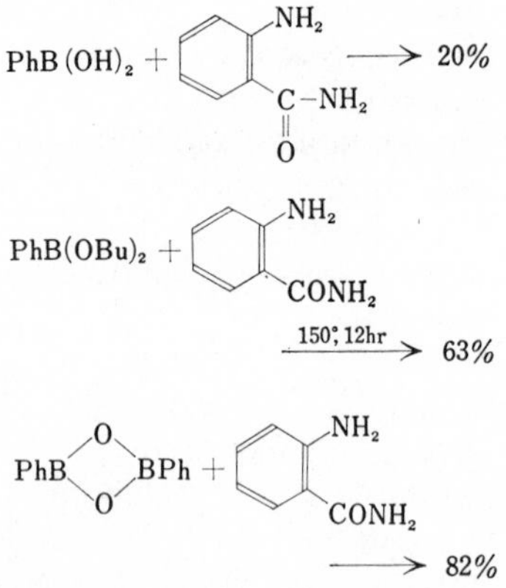

③ Solid. [210~211°].
　Stable in air and moisture. Solvolyzed in 95% EtOH.

④ + OH⁻ ⟶

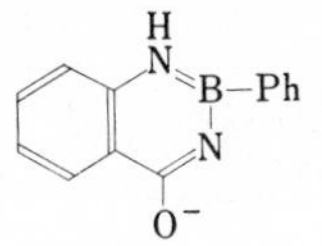

bathochromic shift occured

+ CH_2N_2 ⟶

slow decomp. to polymer

+ $POCl_3$ ⟶

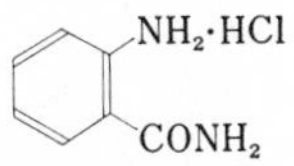

⑥ JACS **83**, 2708 (1961).

$BC_{13}H_{11}N_2O_2$

① 2-(2'-Dihydroxyborylphenyl)benz-
imidazole

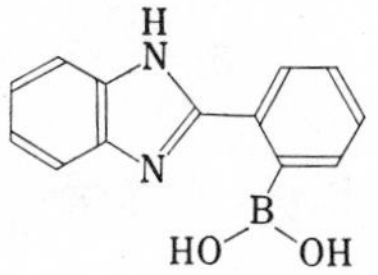

②

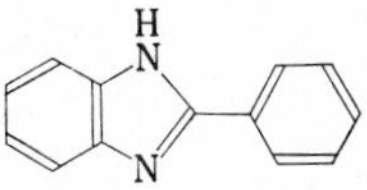

 + BCl_3

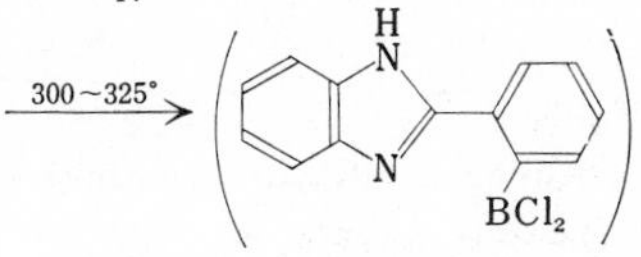

$\xrightarrow{300\sim325°}$

$\xrightarrow{H_2O}$ 47%

③ Solid. [>330°].
UV: 329 (sh), 318, 296, 252, 244 mμ.

④ + H_2O_2 ⟶

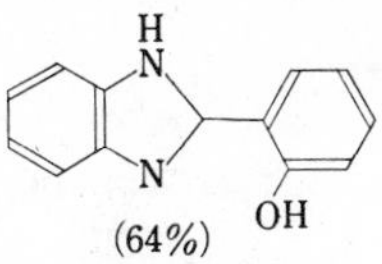

(64%)

+ 10%NaOH $\xrightarrow{\text{reflux 2hr}}$

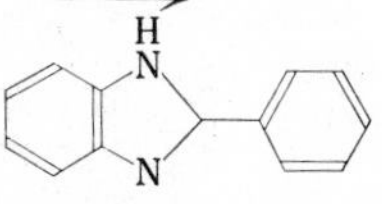

(78%)

+ Me_2SO_4 ⟶

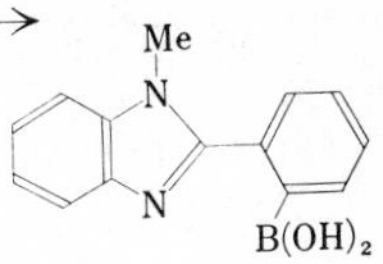

⑤ Catalyst of solvolysis of halogenoal-
cohol.

⑥ JACS **85**, 2230 (1963).

$BC_{13}H_{12}Cl$

① Chlorophenyl(o-tolyl)borane
$(C_6H_5)(o\text{-}CH_3C_6H_4)BCl$

② $PhB(OBu\text{-}i)_2$ $\xrightarrow{PCl_5}$ $PhBCl(OBu\text{-}i)$

$\xrightarrow{o\text{-}MeC_6H_4MgBr}$ $Ph(o\text{-}MeC_6H_4)BOBu\text{-}i$

$\xrightarrow{PCl_5}$ 67%

③ Liq. (143~146°/7). d 1.090 (20°/4°).

④ + H_2O ⟶

+ $p\text{-}MeC_6H_4MgBr$ ⟶
$Ph(o\text{-}MeC_6H_4)(p\text{-}MeC_6H_4)B$
$\xrightarrow{Li(1\text{-}C_{10}H_7)}$ $Li[BPh(o\text{-}MeC_6H_4)\text{-}$
$(p\text{-}MeC_6H_4)(1\text{-}C_{10}H_7)]$

⑥ Izv. OKhN **1957**, 589.

$BC_{13}H_{12}F$

① Fluorophenyl(o-tolyl)borane
$(C_6H_5)(o\text{-}CH_3C_6H_4)BF$

② $PhBF_2 + o\text{-}MeC_6H_4MgBr$ $\xrightarrow{-60°}$

③ Liq. (140°/12).

⑥ Acta Chem. Scand. **8**, 1779 (1954).

$BC_{13}H_{12}N$

① 10-Methyl-10,9-borazarophenanthrene
(5,6-Dihydro-6-methyldibenz[c, e]-
[1,2]azaborine)

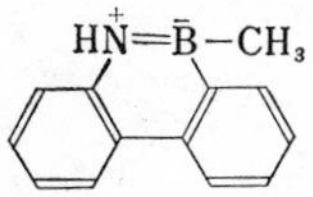

② + MeMgI ⟶

+ MeMgI ⟶

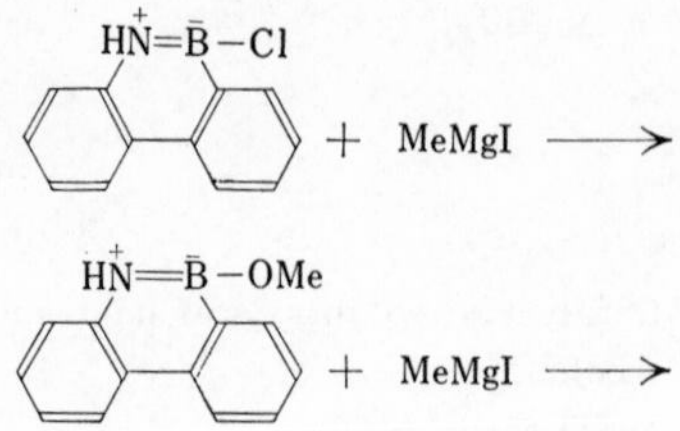

③ Crystals. [103~104°].
Sol. in common org. solvent.
UV: 297 (log ε 3.7), 312 (3.92), 325 (3.98) mμ.

④ + D₂O $\xrightarrow{\text{NaOD}}$

+ Cl₂ $\xrightarrow{\text{25° in AcOH}}$
58%

+ CH₃COCl + AlCl₃ $\xrightarrow{\text{20° in CS₂}}$

,
CH₃CO 42.4%

CH₃CO 19.4%

+ HNO₃ $\xrightarrow{\text{0° in Ac₂O}}$

,
O₂N 33%

O₂N 63%

+ RLi ⟶

$\xrightarrow{\text{Me₂SO₄}}$

+ 2RLi ⟶ ( ) (A)

(A) $\xrightarrow{\text{H₂O}}$

(A) ⟶
$\xrightarrow{\text{Me₂SO₄}}$

(R=Ph)

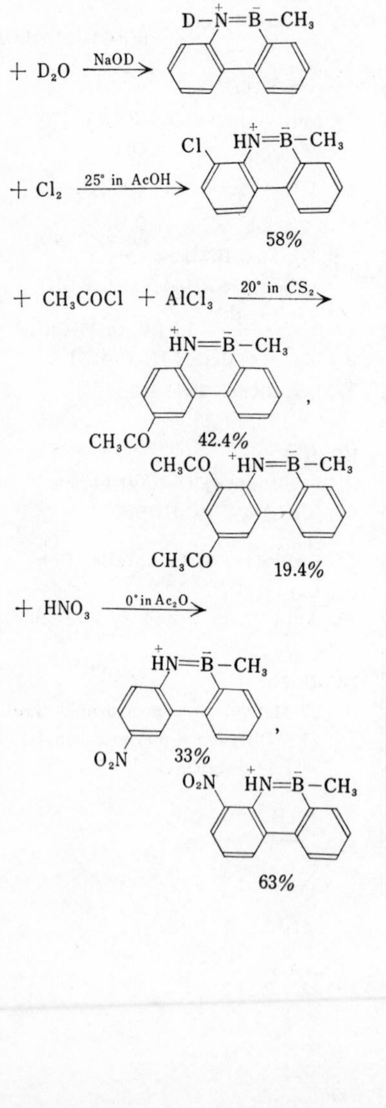

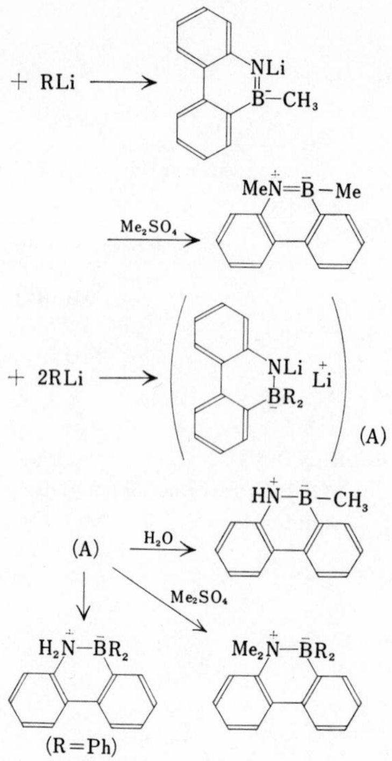

⑥ JCS **1958**, 3073.

BCH₁₃₁₂N₃

① 4-Amino-1,2-dihydro-2-phenyl-1,4,2-benzo[e]diazaborine

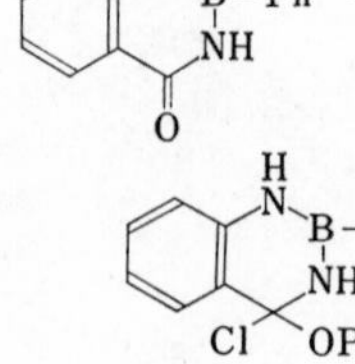

② $\xrightarrow{\text{POCl₃}}$

$\xrightarrow{\text{EtOH}}$

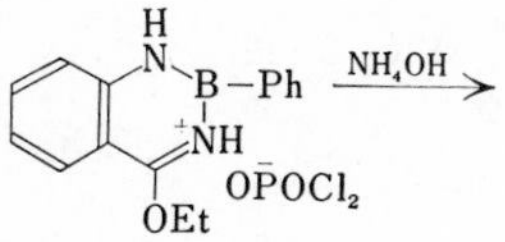

③ Solid. [260~263° decomp.]

Stable in boiling H_2O; forms trihydrate from H_2O, and free at 110° *in
vacuo*.

UV: λ_{max}^{EtOH} 378 mμ(ε 4.350).

IR: 3.0, 6.1, 6.25, 6.55 μ (in Nujol).

⑥ JACS **84**, 688 (1962).

BC₁₃H₂₉

① Di-*t*-butylpentylborane
    $(C_5H_{11})(t\text{-}C_4H_9)_2B$

② $BF_3 \cdot Et_2O$ + *t*-BuMgCl + 1-pentene
    $\xrightarrow{20\,hr}$ 39%

③ Liq. (44.8~45.0°/0.57). n_D 1.4397
    (25°). d 0.7668 (25°).

④ + H_2O_2 ⟶ 2 *t*-BuOH + *n*-$C_5H_{11}OH$
    heat (205°, 15 min) ⟶
    n-$(C_5H_{11})_3B$ + *i*-Bu_3B

⑥ JACS **83**, 1924 (1961).

BC₁₃H₂₉

① Isobutyl-*t*-butyl-*n*-pentylborane
    $(i\text{-}C_4H_9)(t\text{-}C_4H_9)(n\text{-}C_5H_{11})B$

② $n\text{-}C_5H_{11}BF_2$ + *t*-BuMgCl $\xrightarrow{<30°}$ 49%
    $(t\text{-}Bu)(n\text{-}C_5H_{11})_2B$ + *i*-BuMgBr
    $\xrightarrow{reflux,\ 4hr.\ in\ Et_2O}$ 12%

③ Liq. (44°/0.6). n_D 1.4296 (25°).
    d 0.7506 (25°).

④ + H_2O_2 ⟶ *t*-BuOH, *i*-BuOH,
    n-$C_5H_{11}OH$
    heat (205°, 20 min) ⟶ $(n\text{-}C_5H_{11})_3B$
    + *i*-Bu_3B

⑥ JACS **83**, 1924 (1961).

BC₁₄H₁₃O

① 5-Hydroxy-10,11-dihdypro-5 *H*-

dibenzo[*b*, *f*]borepin

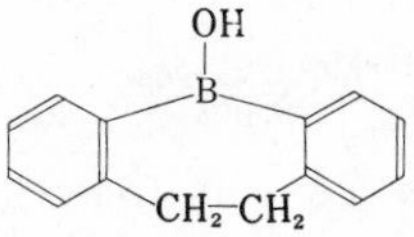

② + BF_3

    $\xrightarrow{-70°}$ (after hydrolysis)

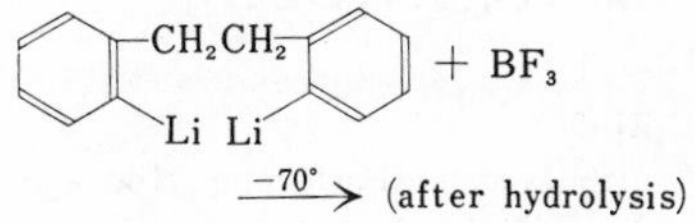

③ Crystals. [145~146°].

④

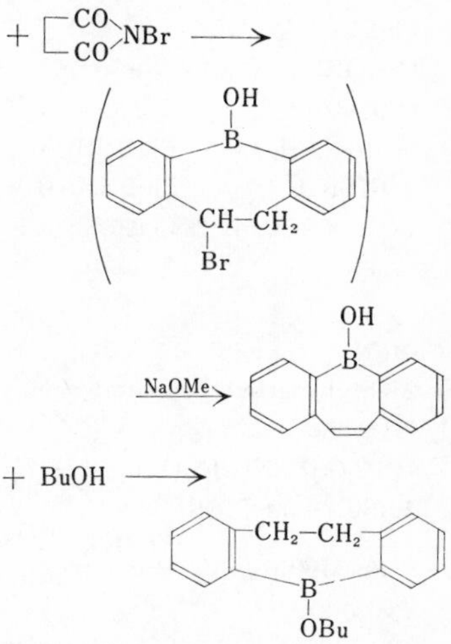

⑥ JACS **77**, 5176 (1955).   Fr. 1336364·~
    CA **60**, 1793 (1964).

BC₁₄H₁₄N

① 1,2,3,4-Tetrahydro-10 *a*, 4 *a*-borazaro
    phenanthrene
    (1,2,3,4-Tetrahydro-[1,2]azaborino
    [1,2-*a*]benz[*e*]-[1,2]azaborine)

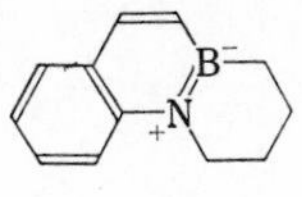

② $\xrightarrow[\text{2. Br(CH}_2)_4\text{Br}]{\text{1. MeLi (Et}_2\text{O)}}$

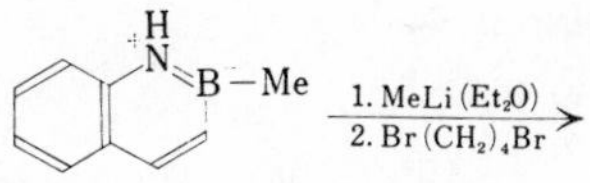

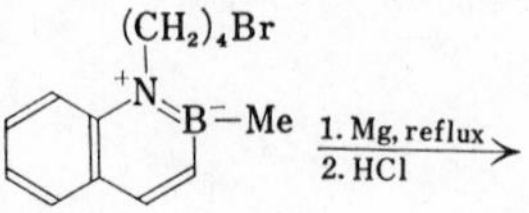

③ Needles. (150~155°/0.5). [26~28°].
⑥ JACS **84**, 4884 (1962).

BC$_{14}$H$_{16}$N
① (Dimethylamino)diphenylborane
(C$_6$H$_5$)$_2$BN(CH$_3$)$_2$
② Ph$_2$BCl + Me$_2$NH ⟶ 81%
Ph$_2$BCl + Me$_2$NLi ⟶
Me$_2$NBCl$_2$ + PhCl + Na ⟶
③ (104°/2).
④ + Me$_2$NNH$_2$ ⟶ Ph$_2$BNHNMe$_2$ 89%
+ NH$_2$NH$_2$ ⟶ (Ph$_2$BNHNH$_2$)$_2$ 94%
⑥ Inorg. Chem. **1**, 738 (1962). JCS **1961**,
1000.

BC$_{14}$H$_{16}$N
① Methyl(methylphenylamino)phenyl-
borane
(CH$_3$)C$_6$H$_5$BN(CH$_3$)C$_6$H$_5$
② PhBCl$_2$ + MePhNH ⟶

Ph(MePhN)BCl $\xrightarrow{\text{MeMgX}}$

③ (98°/0.3).
Cis and *trans* isomers are recognized.
⑥ JACS **82**, 4223 (1960).

BC$_{14}$H$_{16}$N
① 10,10-Dimethyl-9,10-dihydro-10,9-
borazarophenanthrene
(5,5,6,6-Tetrahydro-6,6-dimethyl-
dibenz[*c*, *e*][1,2]azaborine)

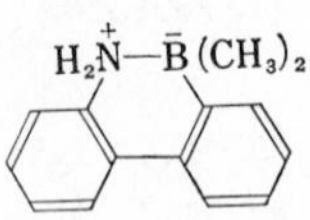

② +2 MeLi
$\xrightarrow{-10°}$ $\xrightarrow{CO_2}$ 29%

+ 2 MeLi

$\xrightarrow{CO_2}$

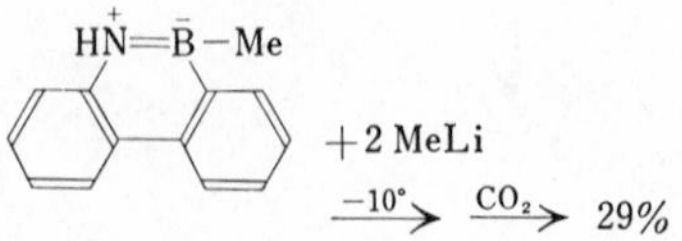

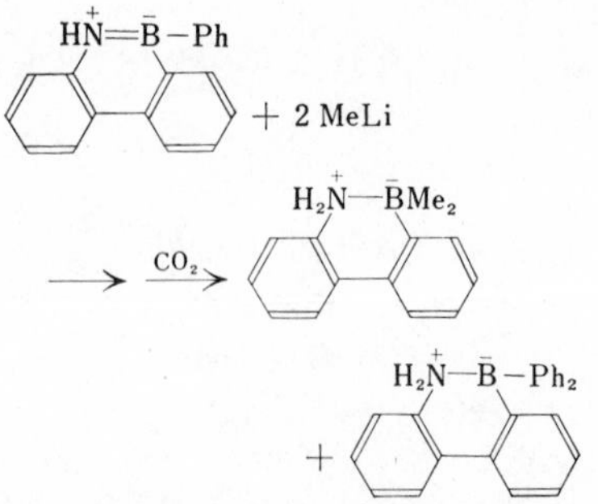

+

③ Solid. [136°].
Thermally stable; does not undergo
autoxidation or disproportionation.

④ + RLi ⟶

$\xrightarrow{+H_2O}$

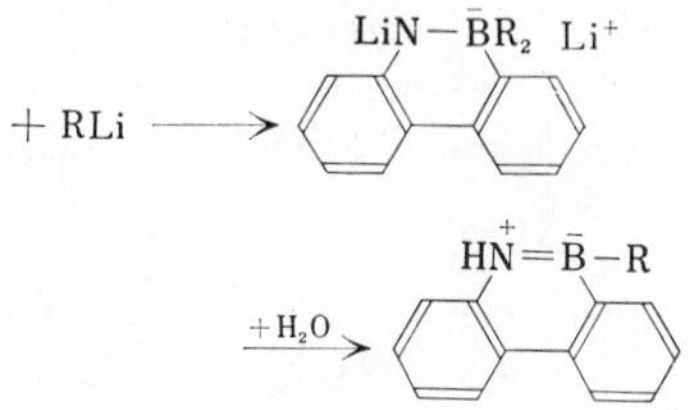

⑥ JACS **83**, 187 (1961).

BC$_{14}$H$_{16}$NO
① 2-Aminoethoxydiphenylborane
(C$_6$H$_5$)$_2$BOCH$_2$CH$_2$NH$_2$
② (C$_6$H$_5$)$_3$B + NH$_2$CH$_2$CH$_2$OH ⟶
(C$_6$H$_5$)$_2$BOC$_4$H$_9$-*i*·NH$_3$ + NH$_2$CH$_2$CH$_2$OH
⟶
③ Needles. [190~192°].
Stable to alcoholysis; fairly stable
to oxidn. and hydrolysis.
Dipole moment: 8.7 D.
④ + Ni^{2+} + C$_5$H$_{11}$OH + dimethylglyoxime

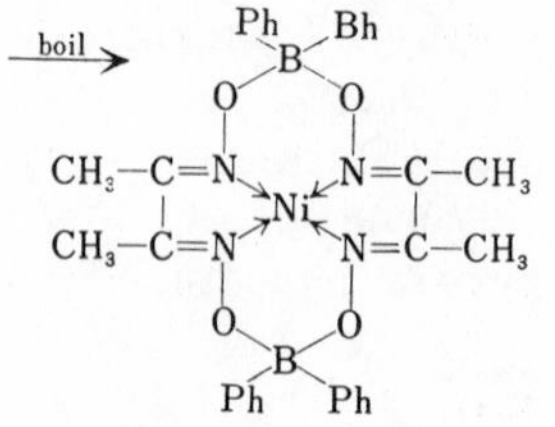

$\xrightarrow{\text{boil}}$

(Pd, Cu^{2+}, Fe^{2+} forms similar

complex)

⑥ JACS **77**, 2491 (1955).   JOC **20**, 9 (1955).

BC$_{14}$H$_{19}$N$_2$O$_2$

① Bis(2-aminoethoxy)-1-naphthyl-borane

$$B(OCH_2CH_2NH_2)_2$$

② 1-C$_{10}$H$_7$B(OH)$_2$ + HOCH$_2$CH$_2$NH$_2$ $\longrightarrow$

③ Solid. [242~243°].

⑥ JACS **77**, 2491 (1955).

BC$_{14}$H$_{23}$O$_2$

① Diisobutoxyphenylborane
C$_6$H$_5$B(OC$_4$H$_9$-i)$_2$

② PhBCl$_2$ + i-BuOH $\longrightarrow$
PhB(OEt)$_2$ + i-BuOH
PhB(OH)$_2$ + i-BuOH $\longrightarrow$ 96%

③ Liq. (116~117°/5, 55°/0.2). n_D 1.4711 (20°). d 0.9163 (20°).

⑥ JCS **1956**, 1540.

BC$_{14}$H$_{23}$O$_2$

① Di-t-butoxyphenylborane
C$_6$H$_5$B(OC$_4$H$_9$-t)$_2$

② C$_6$H$_5$BCl$_2$ + t-BuOH $\longrightarrow$
PhBCl$_2$ + t-BuOH + C$_5$H$_5$N $\longrightarrow$

③ Liq. (42/0.1). n_D 1.4635 (20°). d 0.9053 (20°).

④ + HCl $\xrightarrow{20°}$ PhB(OH)$_2$ + t-BuCl

⑥ JCS **1955**, 2956.

BC$_{14}$H$_{23}$O$_2$

① Dibutoxyphenylborane
C$_6$H$_5$B(OC$_4$H$_9$)$_2$

② PhBCl$_2$ + BuOH $\longrightarrow$
PhB(OH)$_2$ + BuOH $\longrightarrow$ 83%
PhB(OEt$_2$) + BuOH $\longrightarrow$

③ Liq. (103°/2). n_D 1.4718 (25°). d 0.9166 (25°).

④ + HBr $\longrightarrow$ C$_4$H$_9$Br

+ BF$_3$(or BCl$_3$) $\longrightarrow$ PhBF(OBu)
+ BuOBF$_2$

⑥ JCS **1956**, 1540.   Acta Chem. Scand. **8**, 1779 (1954).

BC$_{14}$H$_{24}$NO

① Butoxy(diethylamino)phenylborane
C$_6$H$_5$B(OC$_4$H$_9$)N(C$_2$H$_5$)$_2$

② PhB(OBu-i)Cl + HNEt$_2$ $\xrightarrow{-30°}$ 57%

③ Liq. (92~94°/3). n_D 1.4822 (20°). d 0.8931 (20°).

⑥ Izv. OKhN **1957**, 646.

BC$_{14}$H$_{31}$

① t-Butyldipentylborane
(t-C$_4$H$_9$)(n-C$_5$H$_{11}$)$_2$B

② t-BuBCl$_2$ + n-C$_5$H$_{11}$MgBr $\longrightarrow$ 72%

③ Liq. (47.5°/0.14 mm). n_D 1.4333 (25°). d 0.7585 (25°).

④ + i-BuMgBr $\xrightarrow{\text{reflux 4 hr. in Et}_2\text{O}}$
(t-Bu)(i-Bu)(n-C$_5$H$_{11}$)B 12%

⑥ JACS **83**, 1924 (1961).

BC$_{14}$H$_{31}$O$_2$

① Tetradecylboronic acid
C$_{14}$H$_{29}$B(OH)$_2$

② B(OBu)$_3$ + C$_{14}$H$_{29}$MgBr $\longrightarrow$

③ Waxy solid.

④ + H$_2$O$_2$ $\longrightarrow$ C$_{14}$H$_{29}$OH

⑥ JACS **60**, 107 (1938).

BC$_{15}$H$_{17}$N$_2$O

① 2-Hydroxy-1,3-dimethyl-2-phenyl-2-bora-1,3-diazaazulene

②

+ PhB(OH)$_2$

$\xrightarrow{\text{heat in toluene}}$ 80% (as hydrochloride)

③ Yellow solid. [163~164°](CH$_2$Cl$_2$-petr.
    ether), [96~98°].

    Stable to hydrolysis. Has fluores-
    cence in soln.

    High mp. form obtained when
    recrystalized without use of char-
    coal, and low mp. form obtained
    with its use.

④ + H$_2$O ———>

⑥ JACS **84**, 4720 (1962).

BC$_{15}$H$_{19}$N$_2$

① Dianilinopropylborane
    C$_3$H$_7$B(NHC$_6$H$_5$)$_2$

② PrB(OBu)Cl + H$_2$NPh ——>
    PrB(NHPh)$_2$ (58%) + PrB(OBu)$_2$
    + NH$_2$Ph·HCl

③ Liq. (122~125°/0.1). n_D 1.5820 (20°).
    d 1.0187 (20°).

⑥ Izv. OKhN **1958**, 777.

BC$_{15}$H$_{25}$O$_2$

① Dibutoxy-*p*-tolylborane

② *p*-MeC$_6$H$_4$B(OH)$_2$ + BuOH ——>

③ Liq. (159~160°/13). n_D 1.4758 (25°).
    d 0.9127 (25°).

⑥ Acta Chem. Scand. **8**, 1779 (1954).

BC$_{15}$H$_{25}$O$_2$

① Dibutoxy-*o*-tolylborane

② *o*-MeC$_6$H$_4$B(OH)$_2$ + BuOH ——>

③ Liq. (139~140°/9). n_D 1.4706 (25°).
    d 0.9099 (25°).

⑥ Acta Chem. Scand. **8**, 1779 (1954).

BC$_{15}$H$_{25}$O$_2$

① Dibutoxy-*m*-tolylborane

② *m*-MeC$_6$H$_4$B(OH)$_2$ + BuOH ——>

③ Liq. (146~147°/8). n_D 1.4744 (25°).
    d 0.9126 (25°).

⑥ Acta Chem. Scand. **8**, 1779 (1954).

BC$_{15}$H$_{26}$NO

① (Diethylamino)isobutoxy-*o*-tolyl-
    borane

② *o*-CH$_3$C$_6$H$_4$B(OBu-*i*)Cl + Et$_2$NH $\xrightarrow{-30°}$
    57.4%

③ Liq. (122.5~123.0°/8). n_D 1.4808(20°).
    d 0.8877 (20°).

⑥ Izv. OKhN **1957**, 646.

BC$_{15}$H$_{33}$

① Tripentylborane
    (*n*-C$_5$H$_{11}$)$_3$B

② BF$_3$·Et$_2$O + *n*-C$_5$H$_{11}$MgBr ——>

③ Liq. (140°/14). n_D 1.4167 (20°).
    d 0.7449 (20°/4°).

⑥ Bull. soc. chim. France **1963**, 558.

BC$_{15}$H$_{33}$

① Triisopentylborane
    (*i*-C$_5$H$_{11}$)$_3$B

② BF$_3$ + *i*-C$_5$H$_{11}$MgX ——>

③ Liq. (119°/14). n_D 1.432 (20°). d 0.7607
    (22.6°).

⑥ Ber. **54**, 2784 (1921).

BC$_{15}$H$_{33}$

① Tris(2-methyl-1-butyl)borane
    [CH$_3$CH$_2$CH(CH$_3$)CH$_2$]$_3$B

② B₂H₆ + H₂C=C−CH₂CH₃ ⟶
         |
         CH₃

③ Liq. (80°/1.3). n_D 1.4350 (23°). d 0.807
   (22°).

④ + H₂O₂ + OH⁻ ⟶
   CH₃CH₂CH(CH₃)CH₂OH
   $\xrightarrow{150°}$ [(CH₃)₂CHCH₂CH₂]₃B, and other
   isomers
   + B₂H₆ ⟶
   [CH₃CH₂CH(CH₃)CH₂]₂BH

⑥ US 3161686 ; CA **62**, 7795 (1965).

BC₁₅H₃₃

① (+)Tris[(R)-2-methylbutyl]borane
   [C₂H₅CH(CH₃)CH₂]₃B

② (−)(S)-EtCHMeCH₂OH $\xrightarrow{SOCl_2}$
   (+)(S)-EtCHMeCH₂Cl $\xrightarrow{Mg, BF_3·Et_2O}$

③ Liq. (68°/0.5). n_D 1.4360 (20°). d 0.773
   (20°/4°). [α]$_D^{20}$ 39.8°.

④ $\xrightarrow{120°, \ 9hr}$ 43% racemize
   + H₂O₂ ⟶ (−)(S)-EtCHMe-
   CH₂OH and minor amount of
   (+)(3 S : 6 S)(EtCHMeCH₂)₂

⑥ Ann. chim. (Rome) **62**, 456 (1962).

BC₁₆H₁₂N

① 2-Phenyl-1-aza-2-bora-acenaphthy-
   lene

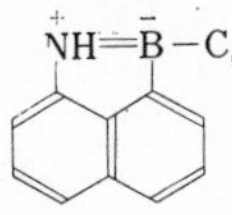

② PhBCl₂ +

   $\xrightarrow[\text{in toluene}]{\text{reflux 48hr}}$ 85%

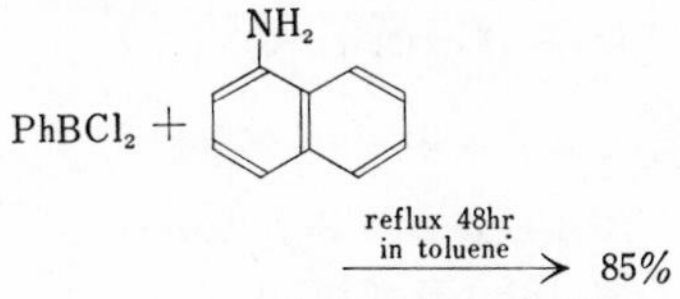

③ Solid. (220~225°/0.001). [243~246°
   decomp.]

⑥ Monatsh. **95**, 373 (1964).

BC₁₆H₁₃N₂

① 2-Phenyl-2-boradihydroperimidine

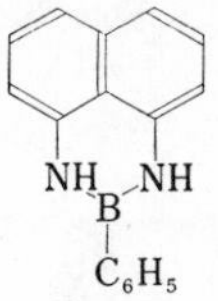

② + PhBCl₂ ⟶

+ PhBO $\xrightarrow{100°, 1hr}$ 71%

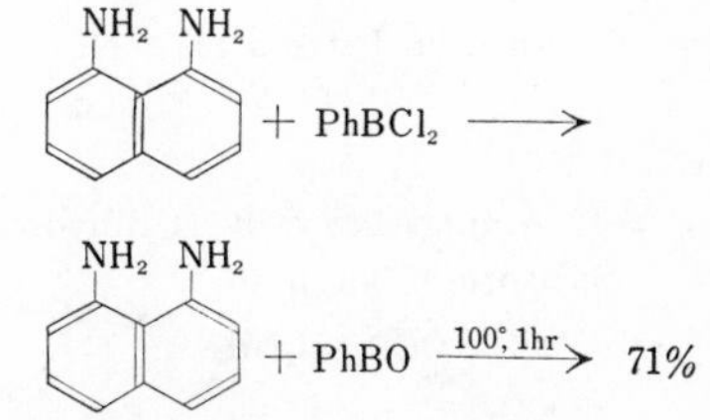

③ Pale yellow needles. (sublime at 180°/
   1). [95~96°].
   Readily autoxidized ; shows strong
   stability to solvolysis.

⑥ Tetrahedron Letters **1960**, No. 23, 8.
   JOC **26**, 2157 (1961).

BC₁₆H₁₆NO

① 5-(2-Aminoethoxy)dibenzo[*b*, *f*]-
   borepin

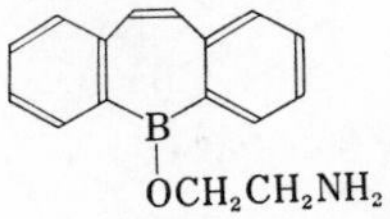

   OCH₂CH₂NH₂

②
   OH
   $\xrightarrow[\substack{1.\ \text{CO-CO-NBr} \\ 2.\ \text{NaOMe/MeOH} \\ 3.\ \text{HOCH}_2\text{CH}_2\text{NH}_2}]{}$

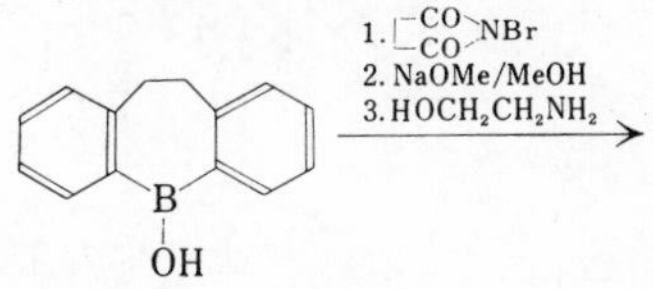

③ Solid. [222~226°].
   UV spectra rerembles to that of *cis*-
   stilbene.

④ + AgNO₃ + NH₄OH
   ⟶
   (*cis*)

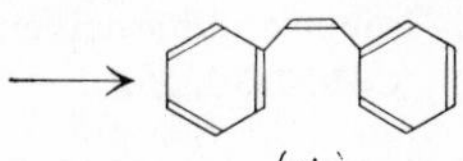

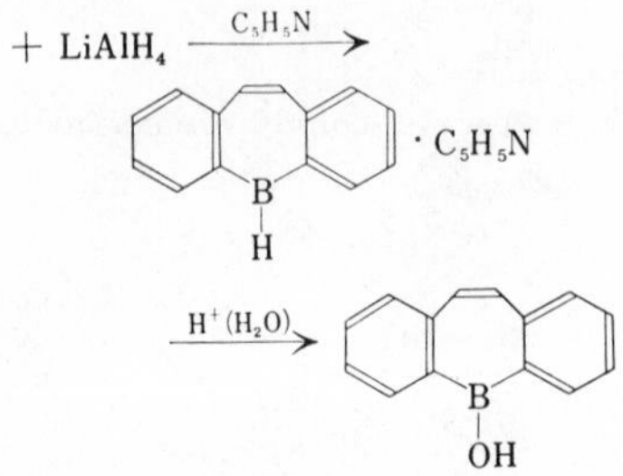

+ LiAlH$_4$ $\xrightarrow{\text{C}_5\text{H}_5\text{N}}$

· C$_5$H$_5$N

$\xrightarrow{\text{H}^+ \text{(H}_2\text{O)}}$

⑥ Tetrahedron Letters **1960**, No. 8, 14.

BC$_{16}$H$_{18}$NO

① 5-(2-Aminoethoxy)-10,11-dihydrodi-
benzo[*b*, *f*]borepin

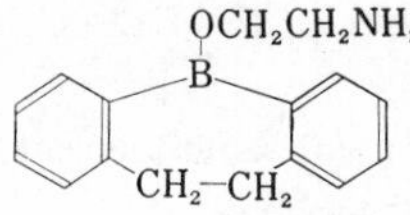

② + B(OBu)$_3$

$\xrightarrow{\text{HOCH}_2\text{CH}_2\text{NH}_2}$

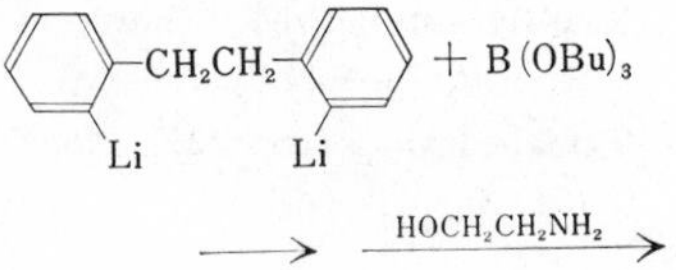

③ Crystals. [195~196°].

④ + Br$_2$ $\xrightarrow{\text{in AcOH}}$

+ H$_2$O$_2$ $\longrightarrow$

+ H$_2$O $\longrightarrow$ $\left(\underset{}{\text{}} \right)_2$O

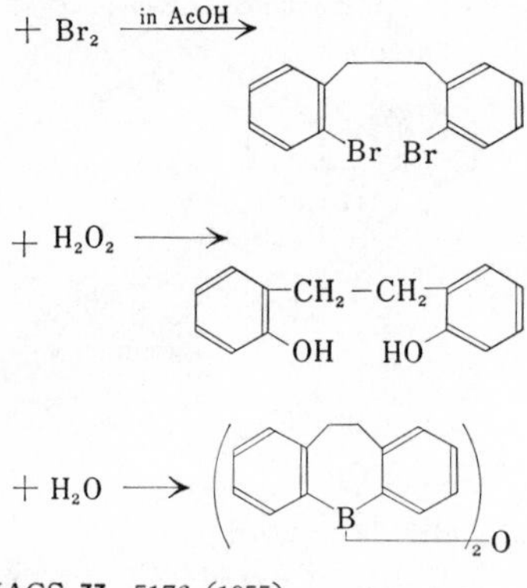

⑥ JACS **77**, 5176 (1955).

BC$_{16}$H$_{19}$O

① Isobutoxydiphenylborane
(C$_6$H$_5$)$_2$BOC$_4$H$_9$-*i*

② B(OC$_4$H$_9$-*i*)$_3$ + PhMgBr $\xrightarrow{-60°}$ 57%

③ Liq. (142~145°/6, 152~155°/8). n_D
1.5393 (20°). *d* 0.9767 (20°).

④ + NH$_3$ $\longrightarrow$ Ph$_2$BOBu-*i*·NH$_3$
[64~67°]

+ HX $\longrightarrow$ Ph$_2$BOH + RX

+ BX$_3$ $\longrightarrow$ Ph$_2$BX + ROBX$_2$
(X=Cl, Br)

+ H$_2$O $\longrightarrow$ Ph$_2$BOBPh$_2$

+ H$_2$NCH$_2$CO$_2$H $\longrightarrow$
Ph$_2$BOCOCH$_2$NH$_2$

+ PCl$_5$ $\longrightarrow$ Ph$_2$BCl

⑥ JACS **77**, 2489 (1955). Izv. SKh **1964**,
1838.

BC$_{16}$H$_{21}$N$_2$

① Dianilinobutylborane
C$_4$H$_9$B(NHC$_6$H$_5$)$_2$

② BuBCl(OBu) + H$_2$NPh $\longrightarrow$
BuB(NHPh)$_2$(70%) + BuB(OBu)$_2$
+ PhNH$_2$·HCl

③ Liq. (136~138°/0.2). n_D 1.5757 (20°).
d 1.0078 (20°).

⑥ Izv. OKhN **1958**, 777.

BC$_{16}$H$_{22}$NO

① Ammine-butoxydiphenylborane
(C$_6$H$_5$)$_2$BOC$_4$H$_9$·NH$_3$

② B(OBu)$_3$ + PhMgBr $\xrightarrow{-60°}$ (Ph$_2$BOBu)
$\xrightarrow{\text{NH}_3}$ 49%

③ Crystals. [64~67° decomp.]
Slightly sol. in H$_2$O.

④ + HOCH$_2$CH$_2$NH$_2$ $\longrightarrow$
Ph$_2$BOCH$_2$CH$_2$NH$_2$ (89%)

⑥ JACS **77**, 2491 (1955).

BC$_{16}$H$_{31}$

① Di-1-hexenyl-*t*-butylborane
t-C$_4$H$_9$B(CH=CHC$_4$H$_9$)$_2$

② *t*-BuBH$_2$·NMe$_3$ + 1-hexyne
$\longrightarrow$ 70%

③ (72°/0.1).

⑥ JACS **83**, 2541 (1961).

BC₁₇H₁₄N

① 6-Methyl-6,5-borazarobenz[a]an-
thracene

(5,6-Dihydro-6-methyl-benzo[e]-
naphtho[2,3-c][1,2]azaborine)

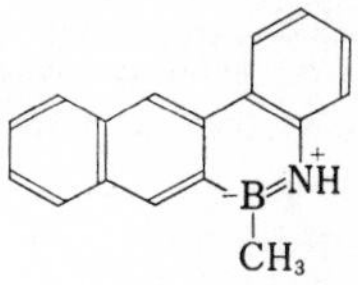

②

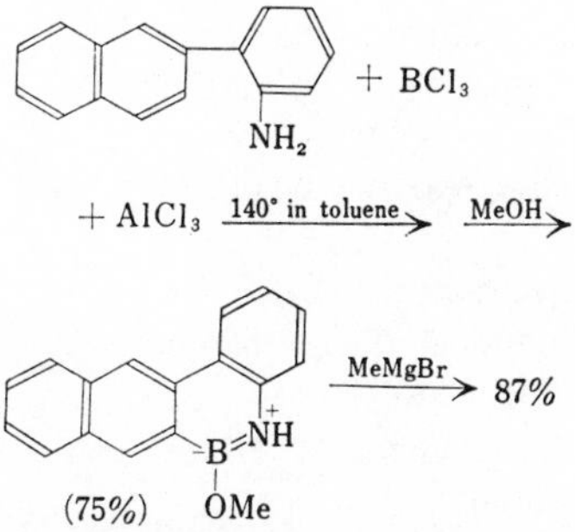

+ BCl₃

+ AlCl₃ $\xrightarrow{140° \text{ in toluene}}$ $\xrightarrow{MeOH}$

$\xrightarrow{MeMgBr}$ 87%

(75%)   OMe

③ Solid. (sublime 120°/0.1). [141~143°].
UV: 364 (log ε 3.37), 349 (3.95), 334
(3.94), 301 (3.75), 289 (4.36), 268
(4.78) mμ.

④ + (NC)₂C=C(CN)₂ ⟶ complex

⑥ JACS **85**, 2253 (1963).

BC₁₇H₁₄N

① 5-Methyl-5,6-borazarobenz[a]anth-
racene

(5,6-Dihydro-5-methylbenzo[c]
naphtho[2,3-e][1,2]azaborine)

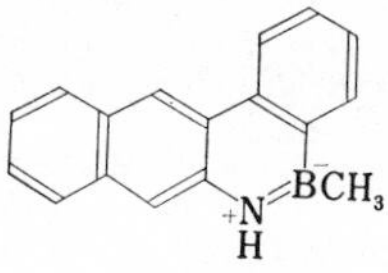

②

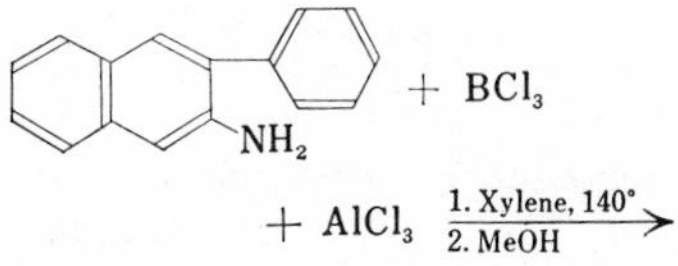

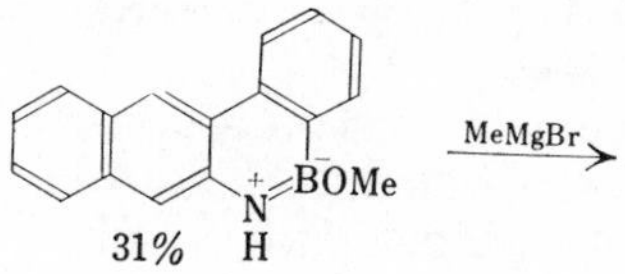

+ BCl₃

+ AlCl₃ $\xrightarrow[\text{2. MeOH}]{\text{1. Xylene, 140°}}$

$\xrightarrow{MeMgBr}$

31% H

③ Needles. (sublime 150°/0.005). [160~
161.3°].
UV: 373 (log ε 3.68), 354 (3.58), 328
(4.01), 274 (4.80), 265 (4.70), 247
(4.50) mμ.

④ Forms complex with(NC)₂C=C(CN)₂.

⑥ JACS **85**, 2253 (1963).

BC₁₈H₁₃O

① 10-Phenyl-10,9-boroxarophenanthrene

(6-phenyldibenz[c,e][1,2]oxaborine)

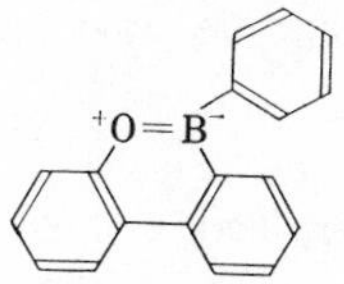

②

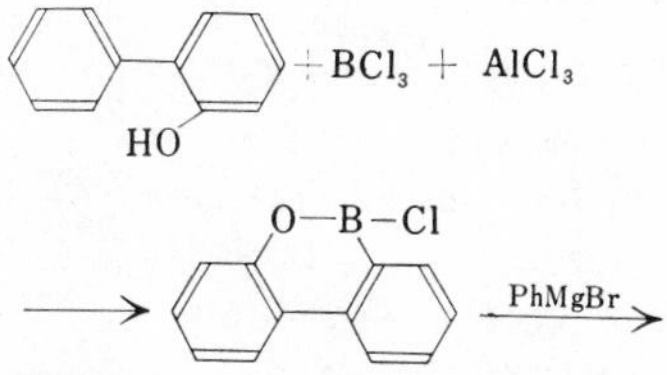

+ BCl₃ + AlCl₃

⟶

$\xrightarrow{PhMgBr}$

③ Crystals. [82~83°].
Readily undergoes hydrolytic oxidn.
in soln.

⑥ JCS **1960**, 1344.

BC₁₈H₁₅

① Triphenylborane
(C₆H₅)₃B

② BX₃(X=F, Cl, alkoxy) + PhMgBr
(or PhLi) ⟶
(MeOBO)₃ + Ph₃Al ⟶

③ White, hexagonal crystals. (347°,
205~210°/14). [147~148°].
Fumes in air, and easily oxidized.

Michler ketone test positive, but weak.

④ + H₂O₂ $\longrightarrow$ PhOH + B(OH)₃

  + NH₂CH₂CH₂OH $\longrightarrow$

   + Ph₂BOCH₂CH₂NH₂ + C₆H₆

  + LiR $\longrightarrow$ Li(BRPh₃)

  (R=H, Me, Et, alkoxy etc.)

  + Na $\xrightarrow{\text{in Et}_2\text{O}}$ Ph₃B·Na

  Na−Hg $\xrightarrow{\text{in THF}}$ Ph₃B·2 Na

  Ph₃$\overset{+}{\text{P}}$=$\overset{-}{\text{CH}_2}$ $\longrightarrow$ Ph₃$\overset{+}{\text{P}}$CH₂$\overset{-}{\text{B}}$Ph₃

  + H₂ $\xrightarrow{170\sim180°,\ 100\ \text{atm.}}$ Ph₂B₂H₄ + C₆H₆

  + AlEt₃ $\xrightarrow{140°}$ BEt₃ + AlPh₃

  + Ph₃P=NMe $\longrightarrow$

   (Ph₃$\overset{+}{\text{P}}$=$\overset{-}{\text{NMe}}$)BPh₃ 93%

⑤ Neutron detector.

⑥ Ann. **629**, 89 (1960); **563**, 110 (1949).

BC₁₈H₁₅K

① Potassium triphenylborane

  KB(C₆H₅)₃

② BPh₃ + K $\xrightarrow{\text{in Et}_2\text{O}}$

③ Yellow solid.

  Slightly sol. in Et₂O; etherate is unstable.

④ + CH₃OH $\longrightarrow$ K(HBPh₃)

   + K(CH₃OBPh₃)

⑥ Ber. **59**, 777 (1926).

BC₁₈H₁₅Li

① Lithium triphenylborane

  LiB(C₆H₅)₃

② (C₆H₅)₃B + Li $\xrightarrow{\text{in Et}_2\text{O}}$

③ Greenish yellow solid (pyramid).

  Sol. in polar org. solvents; forms etherate; much more sol. in Et₂O than the salts of the other metal.

④ + CH₃OH $\longrightarrow$ Li[HB(C₆H₅)₃]

   + Li[(CH₃O)B(C₆H₅)₃]

   + I₂ $\longrightarrow$ LiI + Ph₃B

⑥ Ber. **59**, 777 (1926).

BC₁₈H₁₅Na

① Sodium triphenylborane

  NaB(C₆H₅)₃

② Ph₃B + Na $\longrightarrow$

  Ph₃B + Na−Hg $\longrightarrow$

③ Orange-yellow solid.

  Sol. in Et₂O; forms etherate. Has electric conductivity; perhaps dimerization occurs in soln.

④ + Hg $\longrightarrow$ Na-Hg + BPh₃

  + CH₃OH $\longrightarrow$ Na(HBPh₃)

   + Na(CH₃OBPh₃)

  + Na−Hg $\longrightarrow$ Na₂BPh₃

  + I₂ $\longrightarrow$ Ph₃B + NaI

⑥ Ann. **563**, 110 (1949).

BC₁₈H₁₆Li

① Lithium triphenylborate

  LiHB(C₆H₅)₃

② LiH + BPh₃ $\longrightarrow$

③ Solid.

  Cryst. from dioxane assocd. with 5 moles of solvent.

④ + C₆H₅COCl $\longrightarrow$ C₆H₅CH₂OH

⑥ Ann. **566**, 101 (1950).

BC₁₈H₁₈N

① Ammine-triphenylborane

  (C₆H₅)₃B·NH₃

② Ph₃B + NH₃ $\longrightarrow$

③ Solid. [212°].

⑥ Ber. **57**, 813 (1924).

BC₁₈H₁₈ON

① 2-Aminoethoxy-1-naphthylphenyl-borane

② PhB(OBu)₂ + 1-C₁₀H₇MgBr $\xrightarrow{-60°}$

  Ph(1-C₁₀H₇)BOH $\xrightarrow{\text{NH}_2\text{CH}_2\text{CH}_2\text{OH}}$

75%

③ Solid. [228~229°].

④ + 6N HCl/Et₂O

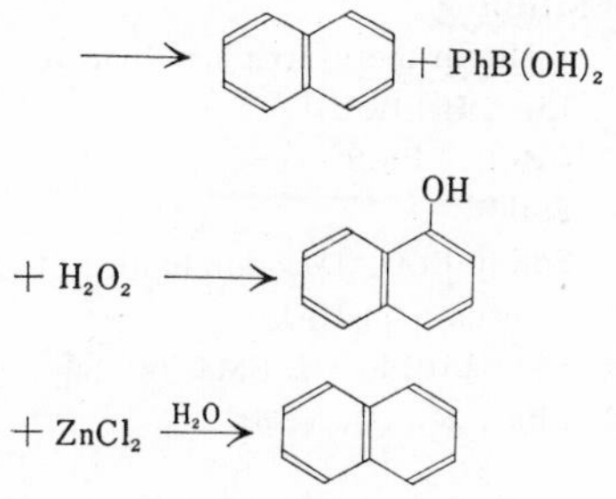

$$\longrightarrow \quad \text{(naphthalene)} \quad + \text{PhB(OH)}_2$$

$$+ H_2O_2 \longrightarrow \text{(1-naphthol, OH)}$$

$$+ ZnCl_2 \xrightarrow{H_2O} \text{(naphthalene)}$$

$$+ Br_2 \longrightarrow PhBr + C_{10}H_7Br$$

⑥ JACS **77**, 2489 (1955); **76**, 4047(1954).

BC₁₈H₂₅O₂

① Dibutoxy-1-naphthylborane

B(OC₄H₉)₂

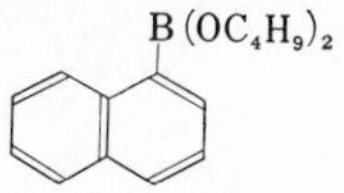

② 1-C₁₀H₇B(OH)₂ + BuOH ⟶

③ Liq. (170~174°/1). n_D 1.5322 (27°).
   d 0.9777 (20°).

④ + PhMgBr ⟶ $\xrightarrow{NH_2CH_2CH_2OH}$
   (1-C₁₀H₇)PhBOCH₂CH₂NH₂ (90%)

⑥ JACS **77**, 2489 (1955).

BC₁₈H₂₆NO

① (Diethylamino)isobutoxy-1-naphthyl_
   borane

   i-C₄H₉O—B—N(C₂H₅)₂

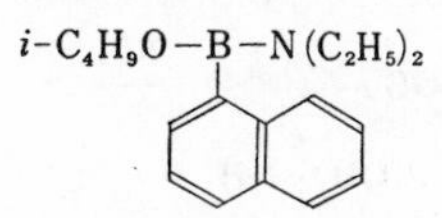

② 1-C₁₀H₇BCl(OBu-i) + Et₂NH $\xrightarrow{-30°}$
   57.2%

③ Liq. (127~128°/2). n_D 1.5378 (20°).
   d 0.9502 (20°).

⑥ Izv. OKhN **1957**, 646.

BC₁₈H₃₂LiO₃

① Lithium triisobutoxyphenylborate
   Li[C₆H₅B(OCH₂CH(CH₃)₂)₃]

② PhLi + B(OBu-i)₃ $\xrightarrow{-40°}$ 45%
   PhB(OBu-i)₂ + LiOBu-i ⟶

③ Solid. [200°]. (in sealed tube).
   Sparingly sol. in Et₂O and C₆H₆.

⑥ Dokl. **98**, 791 (1954).

BC₁₈H₃₃

① Tricyclohexylborane
   (*cyclo*-C₆H₁₁)₃B

② B₂H₆ + (hexene) ⟶ 90%

   BF₃ + (cyclohexyl)—MgX ⟶

   i-Bu₃B + (cyclohexene) $\xrightarrow{160~170°}$

   NaH + (cyclohexene) + Et₃B + BCl₃

   $\longrightarrow$ 87%

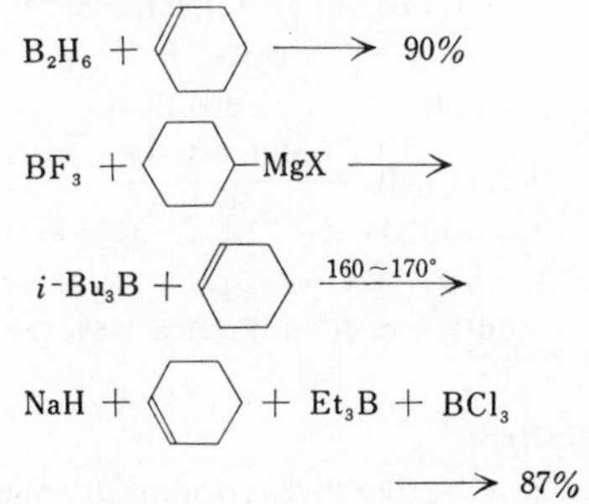

③ Crystals. (194°/15, 140°/0.5). [118°].

④ pyrolysis (250°) ⟶

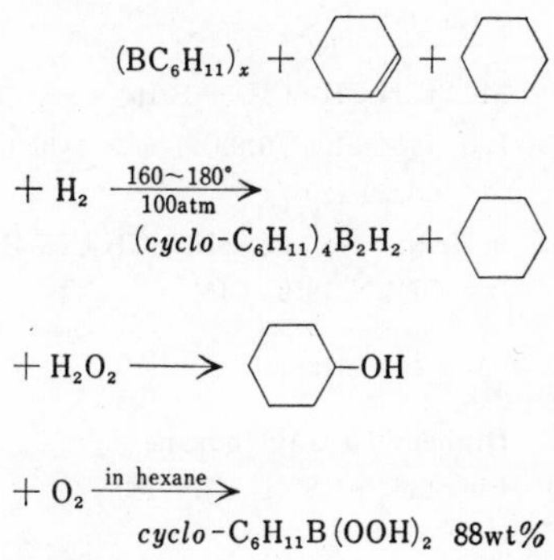

   (BC₆H₁₁)ₓ + (cyclohexene) + (cyclohexane)

   + H₂ $\xrightarrow[100atm]{160~180°}$
   (*cyclo*-C₆H₁₁)₄B₂H₂ + (cyclohexane)

   + H₂O₂ ⟶ (cyclohexyl)—OH

   + O₂ $\xrightarrow{\text{in hexane}}$
   cyclo-C₆H₁₁B(OOH)₂ 88wt%

⑥ Ber. **61**, 271 (1928).   Ann. **618**, 31
   (1958).

BC₁₈H₃₆N

① Ammine-tricyclohexyborane
   (*cyclo*-C₆H₁₁)₃B·NH₃

② (*cyclo*-C₆H₁₁)₃B + NH₃ ⟶
③ Solid. [105～106°]
   Oxidized in air. Loses NH₃ at 100° *in vacuo*.
⑥ JACS **64**, 325 (1942).

BC₁₈H₃₉

① Trihexylborane
   (*n*-C₆H₁₃)₃B
② BF₃ + *n*-C₆H₁₃MgX ⟶
   BH₃·NH₃ + 2-C₆H₁₂ ⟶ 94.3%
   B₂H₆ + 1-C₆H₁₂ ⟶ 90%
③ Liq. (97°/0.02, 101°/0.1, 120°/0.4).
   n_D 1.4200 (20°). *d* 0.7612 (20°/4°).
④ + H₂O₂ --⟶ *n*-C₆H₁₃OH
   + BuOH ⟶ (C₆H₁₃)₂BOBu
   + (MeO)₃B $\xrightarrow{Bu_4B_2H_2\ catalyst}$
   C₆H₁₃B(OMe)₂ (72.2%) (59～61°/10).
⑥ JACS **77**, 4253 (1955) ; **81**, 4791 (1959).
   Bull. soc. chim. France **1963**, 558.

BC₁₈H₄₅Si₃

① Tris(3-trimethylsilylpropyl)borane
   [(CH₃)₃SiCH₂CH₂CH₂]₃B
② B(*i*-Bu)₃ + CH₂=CHCH₂SiMe₃
   $\xrightarrow[130～180°]{}$ 62%
   Me₃SiCH₂CH=CH₂ + B₂H₆ ⟶ 70%
③ Liq. (104～106°/0.09). n_D 1.4410 (20°).
   d 0.8222 (20°/4°).
④ + H₂O₂ ⟶ Me₃SiCH₂CH₂CH₂OH
⑥ Izv. OKhN **1959**, 546.

BC₁₉H₁₇

① Diphenyl(*o*-tolyl)borane
③ Liq. (167～169°/1, 177～180°/4).

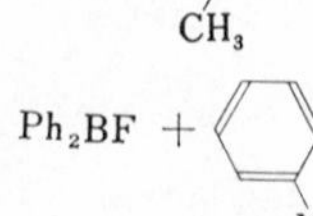

(C₆H₅)₂B—[structure]
   CH₃

② Ph₂BF + [structure]—MgBr ⟶
   Me

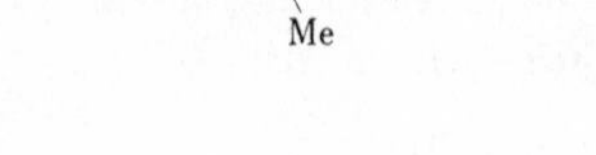

⑥ Acta Chem. Scand. **8**, 1779 (1954).
   Izv. OKhN **1957**, 589.

BC₁₉H₁₈Li

① Lithium methyltriphenylborate
   Li[(C₆H₅)₃BCH₃]
② CH₃Li + Ph₃B ⟶
③ Solid.
   Sol. in Et₂O. Decomp. in air ; slightly decomp. in H₂O.
④ ⟶ LiBPh₄ + LiBMe₄ (slowly)
⑥ Zhur. **24**, 1415 (1954).

BC₂₀H₁₄Cl

① Chlorodi-1-naphthylborane
   (1-C₁₀H₇)₂BCl
② (1-C₁₀H₇)₂BOBu-*i* + PCl₅ $\xrightarrow{12 hr}$
   70%
③ Liq. (213～215°/1.5).
⑥ Izv. OKhN **1956**, 375.

BC₂₀H₁₅O

① Di-1-naphthylborinic acid
   (1-C₁₀H₇)₂BOH

② 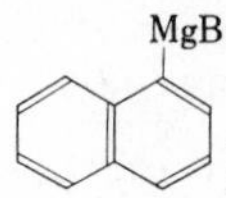
MgBr
+ B(OBu)₃

$\xrightarrow[-60°]{NH_2CH_2CH_2OH}$

(1 - C₁₀H₇)₂BOCH₂CH₂NH₂ (58%)

$\xrightarrow{H_2O}$

1-C₁₀H₇MgBr + B(OBu-*i*)₃ ⟶

(C₁₀H₇)₂BOBu-*i* (63%) $\xrightarrow{NH_3}$

(1-C₁₀H₇)₂B(OH)₂·NH₄ (97.5%) $\xrightarrow{H^+}$
71.7%

③ Solid. [114～115°].
④ + H₂NCH₂CH₂OH ⟶
   (1-C₁₀H₇)₂BOCH₂CH₂NH₂ (74%)

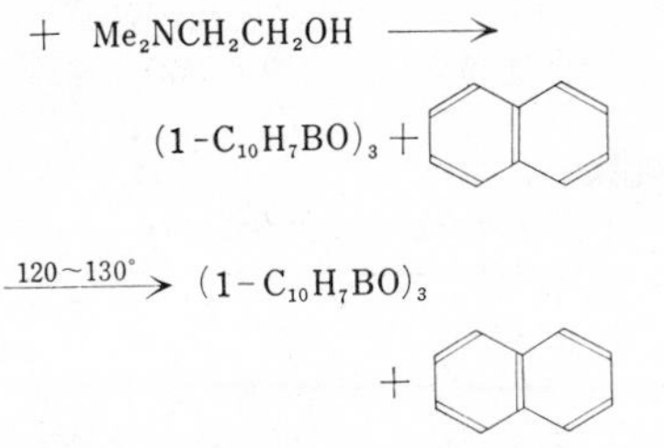

+ Me$_2$NCH$_2$CH$_2$OH ⟶

(1-C$_{10}$H$_7$BO)$_3$ +

$\xrightarrow{120\sim130°}$ (1-C$_{10}$H$_7$BO)$_3$

+

+ SOCl$_2$ ⟶ [(1-C$_{10}$H$_7$)$_2$B]$_2$O 98%

⑥ JACS **77**, 2489 (1955). Izv. OKhN
1956, 451.

BC$_{20}$H$_{15}$O$_2$

① 2,4,5-Triphenyl-1,3,2-dioxaborole

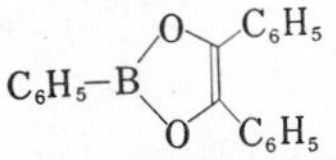

② PhB(OH)$_2$ + PhCCH(OH)Ph
$\quad\quad\quad\quad\quad\quad\quad\overset{\|}{O}$

$\underline{\text{reflux in toluene}}$

③ Solid. [112~113°].
Fairly stable to hydrolysis.

④ + PhNH$_2$, or ⟶×⟶

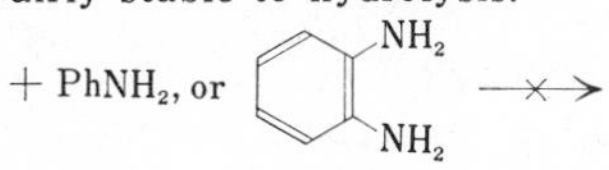

+ O$_2$ ⟶ PhCOCOPh

⑥ JOC **25**, 592 (1960).

BC$_{20}$H$_{16}$NO$_2$S

① 2-Methoxycarbonyl-5,6-diphenyl-5,4-
borazarobenzothiophene
(4,5-Dihydro-2-methoxycarbonyl-5,6-
diphenyl-thieno[2,3-*e*][1,2]aza-
borine)

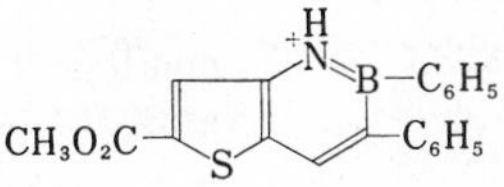

②

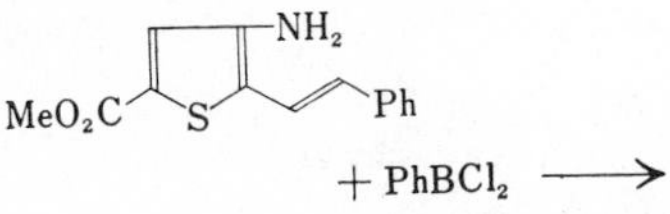

+ PhBCl$_2$ ⟶

③ Pale yellow needles. [200~201°].
$\lambda_{\text{max}}^{\text{EtOH}}$ 222 (ε 20100), 240 (17780), 286
(14930), 310 (10310), 355 (25500) mμ.

④ + NaOH ⟶

$\xrightarrow{\text{+Raney-Ni}}$

(80~85%)

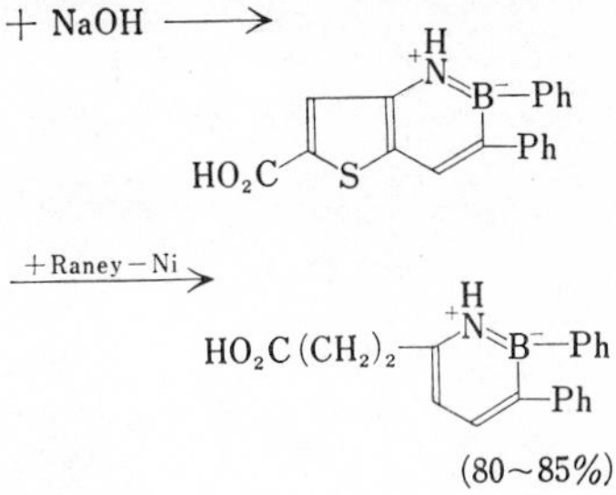

⑥ JACS **84**, 3782 (1963).

BC$_{20}$H$_{43}$O

① Butoxydioctylborane
(C$_8$H$_{17}$)$_2$BOC$_4$H$_9$

② (BuO)$_3$B + LiOctyl ⟶
(BuO)$_3$B + Oct MgBr ⟶

③ Liq. (84°/0.005). n_D 1.4312 (20°).
d 0.8036 (20°/4°).

⑥ JCS **1955**, 2956.

BC$_{21}$H$_{21}$

① Tri-*o*-tolylborane

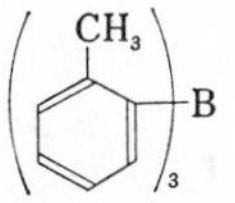

② BF$_3$ + ⟶ 74%

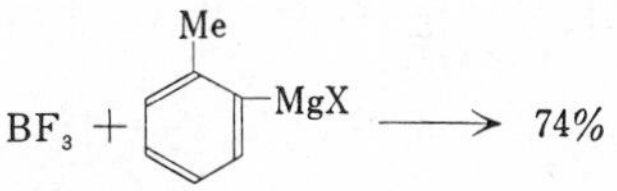

③ Crystals. (208°/12). [67~69°].

④ + HgCl$_2$ ⟶ *o*-MeC$_6$H$_4$HgCl
+ NaCN ⟶ Na[(*o*-MeC$_6$H$_4$)$_3$BCN]

⑥ Ber. **88**, 962 (1955) ; **63**, 2347 (1930).

BC$_{21}$H$_{21}$

① Tri-*m*-tolylborane

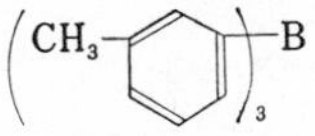

② BF$_3$ + (Me—C$_6$H$_4$)—MgX $\longrightarrow$ 78%

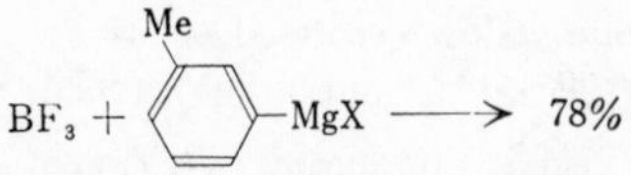

③ Crystals. (218~222°/12). [59~60°].

④ + HgCl$_2$ $\longrightarrow$ *m*-MeC$_6$H$_4$HgCl
   + NaCN $\longrightarrow$ Na[(*m*-MeC$_6$H$_4$)$_3$BCN]

⑥ Ber. **88**, 962 (1955).

BC$_{21}$H$_{21}$

① Tri-*p*-tolylborane

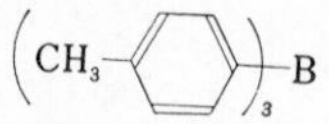

$$\left(CH_3-\bigcirc-\right)_3 B$$

② BF$_3$ + Me—$\bigcirc$—MgX $\longrightarrow$ 54%

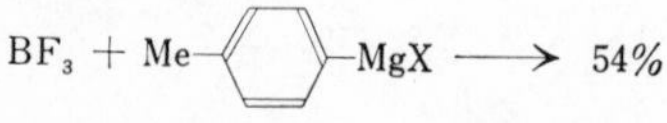

③ Solid. (233~234°/12). [142~144°].
   Fumes in air and easily oxidized.

④ + Na $\longrightarrow$ $\left(Me-\bigcirc-\right)_3 B\cdot Na$

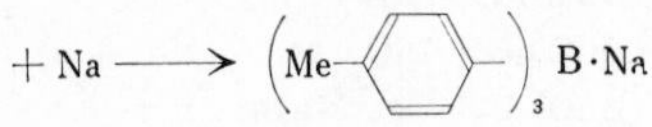

   + HgCl$_2$ $\longrightarrow$ *p*-MeC$_6$H$_4$HgCl
   + NaCN $\longrightarrow$ [(*p*-MeC$_6$H$_4$)BCN]Na
   (45%)

⑥ Ber. **59**, 777 (1926); **88**, 962 (1955).

BC$_{21}$H$_{21}$

① Tribenzylborane
   (C$_6$H$_5$CH$_2$)$_3$B

② BF$_3$ + $\bigcirc$—CH$_2$MgCl $\longrightarrow$

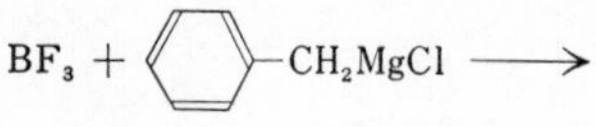

③ Needles. (160°/0.1, 229~232°/13).
   [47°].
   Insol. in Et$_2$O, petr. ether; sol. in org.
   solvents.

④ + Na $\longrightarrow$ (C$_6$H$_5$CH$_2$)$_3$B·Na (violet
   color)

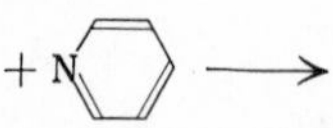

   + N$\bigcirc$ $\longrightarrow$

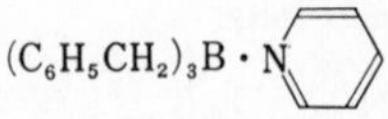

   (C$_6$H$_5$CH$_2$)$_3$B · N$\bigcirc$

+ NH$_3$ $\longrightarrow$ (C$_6$H$_5$CH$_2$)$_3$B·NH$_3$

⑥ Ber. **63**, 934 (1930). Ann. **629**, 89 (1960).

BC$_{21}$H$_{21}$O$_3$

① Tris(*p*-methoxyphenyl)borane

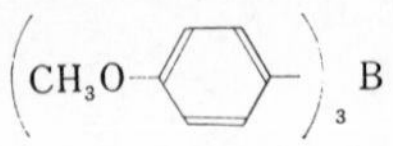

$$\left(CH_3O-\bigcirc-\right)_3 B$$

② BF$_3$ + CH$_3$O—$\bigcirc$—MgX $\longrightarrow$

③ Needles. [128°].
   Fumes in air and easily oxidized.

④ + Na $\xrightarrow{\text{in Et}_2\text{O}}$

$$\left(CH_3O-\bigcirc-\right)_3 B\cdot Na$$

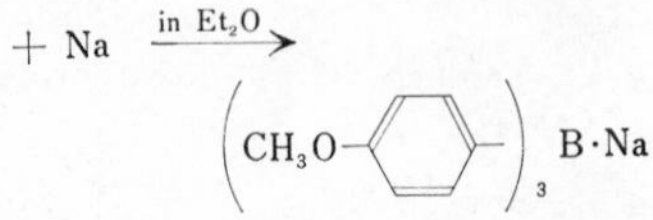

⑥ Ber. **64**, 2112 (1931); **88**, 962 (1955).

BC$_{21}$H$_{24}$N

① Trimethylamine-triphenylborane
   (C$_6$H$_5$)$_3$B·N(CH$_3$)$_3$

② Ph$_3$B + NMe$_3$ $\longrightarrow$

③ Solid. [135~137°].
   Sparingly sol. in Et$_2$O.

⑥ Ber. **57**, 813 (1924).

BC$_{22}$H$_{20}$NO

① 2-Aminoethoxydi-1-naphthylborane

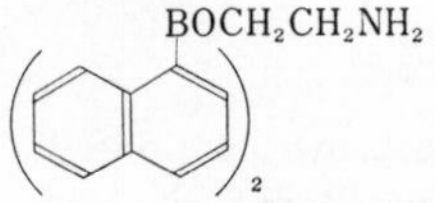

BOCH$_2$CH$_2$NH$_2$

② (1-C$_{10}$H$_7$)$_3$B + H$_2$NCH$_2$CH$_2$OH $\longrightarrow$

   B(OBu)$_3$ + 1-C$_{10}$H$_7$MgBr $\xrightarrow{-60°}$
   NH$_2$CH$_2$CH$_2$OH
   $\longrightarrow$

③ White solid. [205° decomp.].

⑥ JOC **20**, 9 (1955).   JACS **77**, 2489
   (1955).

BC$_{24}$H$_{15}$

① Tris(phenylethynyl)borane
   (C$_6$H$_5$C≡C)$_3$B

② BCl$_3$ + PhC≡CNa ⟶   20%
Na(PhC≡C)$_4$B + BCl$_3$ ⟶
④ + PhC≡CNa ⟶ Na[B(C≡CPh)$_4$]
⑥ Z. Naturf. 11 **b**, 364 (1956).

BC$_{24}$H$_{16}$Li

① Lithium bis(2,2′-biphenylylene)
   borate(-1)

② + BF$_3$ ⟶

③ Solid.
   Very stable in soln.
④ + H$^+$(H$_2$O) ⟶

⑥ Ber. **88**, 962 (1955).

BC$_{24}$H$_{20}$Cu

① Cuprous tetraphenylborate
   CuB(C$_6$H$_5$)$_4$
② Ph$_4$BLi + CuBr$_2$ $\xrightarrow{\text{in Et}_2\text{O}}$ CuBPh$_4$
   + Ph$_2$ + Ph$_3$B
   Ph$_4$BK + Et cuproacetate + C$_5$H$_5$N
   ⟶ Ph$_4$BCu·4 C$_5$H$_5$N $\xrightarrow{\text{H}_2\text{SO}_4}$
③ Solid. [72∼73° decomp.]
   Relatively unstable.
④ $\xrightarrow{\text{in air}}$ Ph$_2$
⑥ Izv. OKhN **1955**, 48.   Ann. **573**, 195
   (1951).

BC$_{24}$H$_{20}$K

① Potassium tetraphenylborate
   KB(C$_6$H$_5$)$_4$
② KBF$_4$ + PhMgBr ⟶
③ White solid.
   Sol. in CHCl$_3$; insol. in H$_2$O, C$_6$H$_6$ and
   cyclohexane. Specific electric conductivity; 3.3×10^{-8} Ω^{-1}cm^{-1} (25°).
④ + Hg ⟶ HgPh$_2$ + Ph$_3$B
   + H$_2$O(+cellosolve) $\xrightarrow{\text{heat}}$ C$_6$H$_6$,
   PhOH, Ph$_2$BOH

   + Br$_2$ $\xrightarrow{\text{MeOH}}$ PhBr ,

   PhB(OH)$_2$,

   + FeCl$_3$ $\xrightarrow{\text{H}_2\text{O, heat}}$ PhB(OH)$_2$,

   , C$_6$H$_6$

   $\xrightarrow[]{h\nu \text{ in CHCl}_3}$ C$_6$H$_6$, Ph$_2$, PhOH
⑥ Izv. OKhN **1955**, 48.   Zhur. **24**, 1415
   (1954).

BC$_{24}$H$_{20}$Li

① Lithium tetraphenylborate
   LiB(C$_6$H$_5$)$_4$
② LiPh + BPh$_3$ ⟶
③ Solid.
   Sol. in Et$_2$O and H$_2$O.
④ + KCl ⟶ KBPh$_4$ + LiCl
   + Me$_3$N·HCl ⟶ [Me$_3$NH]$^+$[BPh$_4$]$^-$
   $\xrightarrow{200°}$ BPh$_3$ + Me$_3$N + C$_6$H$_6$
⑤ Precipitating agent for K$^+$, Rb$^+$, Cs$^+$,
   NH$_4^+$.
⑥ Naturwiss. **34**, 216 (1947).   Ann. **571**,
   167 (1951).

BC$_{24}$H$_{20}$Na

① Sodium tetraphenylborate
   NaB(C$_6$H$_5$)$_4$
② NH$_4$B(C$_6$H$_5$)$_4$ + NaOCH$_3$ $\xrightarrow{\text{in CH}_3\text{OH}}$

BF$_3$·Et$_2$O + PhMgBr (excess) + NaCl
$\longrightarrow$ 62~68%
NaBF$_4$ + PhMgBr $\longrightarrow$
③ White solid.
④ + BF$_3$·Et$_2$O $\xrightarrow{130\sim135°}$
BPh$_3$ + NaF
+ HgCl$_2$ $\longrightarrow$ PhHgCl + B(OH)$_3$
+ NaCl
+ BBr$_3$ $\longrightarrow$ PhBBr$_2$ 54%
⑤ Analytical reagent for K$^+$, NH$_4^+$, etc.
⑥ Brit. 705719 (1954).   Bull. acad. sci.
USSR. Classe sci. chim. **1955**, 187.
Ann. **573**, 195 (1951).

BC$_{24}$H$_{20}$NO

① 2,3-Dihydro-2,3,4,5-tetraphenyl-
1,3,2-oxaazaborole

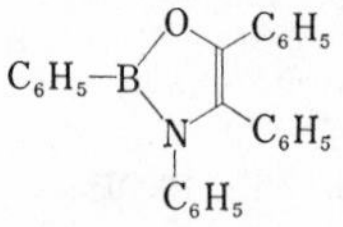

② PhB(OH)$_2$ + PhCOCHOHPh + PhNH$_2$
$\longrightarrow$
③ Crystals. [183~185°].
④ + O$_2$ $\longrightarrow$ PhB(OH)$_2$, PhC–CPh
O NPh (with ‖ ‖)
⑥ JOC **25**, 592 (1960).

BC$_{24}$H$_{21}$

① Tristyrylborane

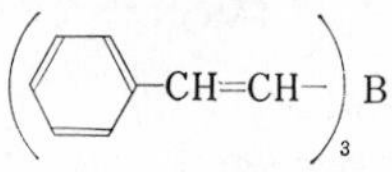

② BF$_3$·OEt$_2$ + [phenyl]–CH=CHBr
+ Mg $\longrightarrow$ 76%
③ Solid. [64~65°].
Sol. in C$_6$H$_6$, THF ; insol. in CHCl$_3$
and petr. ether.
④ + C$_5$H$_5$N $\longrightarrow$

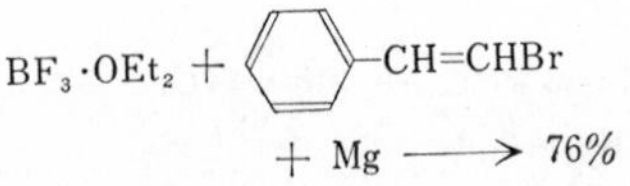

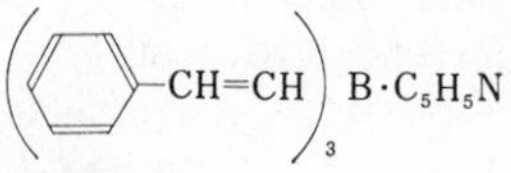

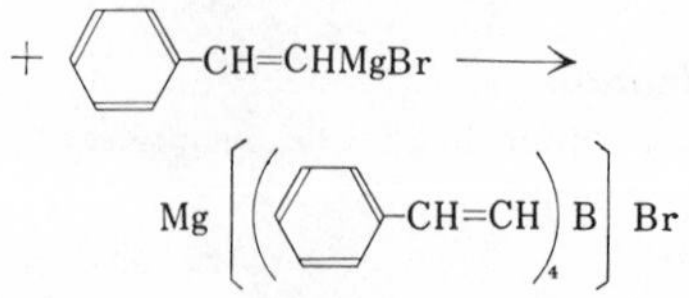

+ [phenyl]–CH=CHMgBr $\longrightarrow$

⑥ Dokl. **141**, 1386 (1961).

BC$_{24}$H$_{24}$N

① Ammonium tetraphenylborate
NH$_4$B(C$_6$H$_5$)$_4$
② LiBPh$_4$ + NH$_4^+$ $\longrightarrow$
③ Solid.
Insol. in H$_2$O, C$_6$H$_6$ and cyclohexane ;
sol. in CHCl$_3$.
④ + Hg $\longrightarrow$ HgPh$_2$ + Ph$_3$B
+ NaOMe $\xrightarrow{\text{in MeOH}}$ NaBPh$_4$ 59%
$\xrightarrow{110\sim120°,\ 5\sim7\,hr}$ C$_6$H$_6$, BPh$_3$·NH$_3$
+ MeOH $\xrightarrow{100°,\ 5\,hr}$ NH$_3$, Ph$_3$B·NH$_3$
⑥ Zhur. **24**, 1415 (1954).   Dokl. **85**, 815
(1952).   Ann. **573**, 195 (1951).

BC$_{24}$H$_{27}$

① Tris(2,5-dimethylphenyl)borane

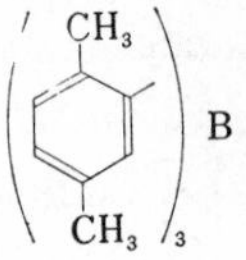

② BF$_3$ +

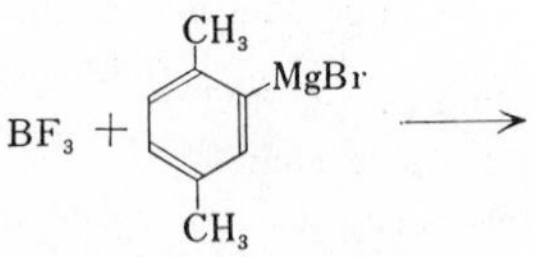

③ Needles. (221°/12). [147°].
⑥ Ber. **63**, 934, 2347 (1930).

BC$_{24}$H$_{27}$

① Tri(2-phenylethyl)borane

(C₆H₅CH₂CH₂)₃B

② BF₃·Et₂O + PhCH₂CH₂MgBr ⟶

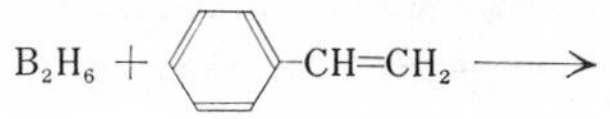

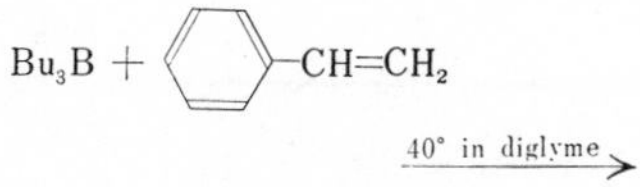

B₂H₆ + ⟨benzene⟩–CH=CH₂ ⟶

Bu₃B + ⟨benzene⟩–CH=CH₂

$\xrightarrow{\text{40° in diglyme}}$

④ + O₂ $\xrightarrow{\text{in hexane}}$

PhCH₂CH₂B(OOCH₂CH₂Ph)₂ ⟶

B(OCH₂CH₂Ph)₃

pyrolisis (250°) ⟶

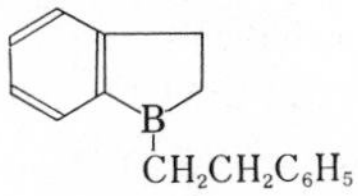

CH₂CH₂C₆H₅

+ C₆H₅CH=CH₂ + H₂

⑥ Ann. **644**, 1 (1961).

BC₂₄H₃₀N₃

① Tris(*p*-dimethylaminophenyl)borane

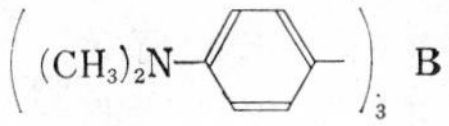

$\left((CH_3)_2N-\text{⟨benzene⟩}- \right)_3 B$

② BF₃ + (CH₃)₂N–⟨benzene⟩–Li ⟶

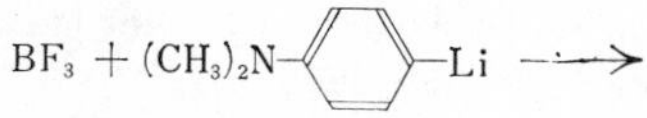

③ Leaflets. [219~222°].

⑥ Ber. **88**, 962 (1955).

BC₂₄H₄₅

① Tricyclooctylborane
(*cyclo*-C₈H₁₅)₃B

② BH₃·NEt₃ + cyclooctene ⟶

③ Needles. [100~108°].

④ $\xrightarrow{\text{>150°}}$ (*cyclo*-C₈H₁₅)₂BH +

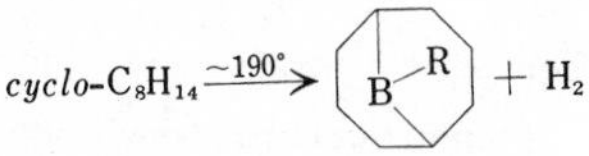

cyclo-C₈H₁₄ $\xrightarrow{\text{~190°}}$ + H₂

R=C₈H₁₅

+ O₂ $\xrightarrow{\text{in hexane}}$ [RB(OOR)₂] ⟶
cyclo-C₈H₁₅B(OOH)₂

⑥ Angew. **69**, 684 (1957).

BC₂₄H₅₁

① Trioctylborane
(*n*-C₈H₁₇)₃B

② B₂H₆ + 1-C₈H₁₆ ⟶ >80%

octene-1 + BF₃ + NaBH₄ $\xrightarrow{\text{THF}}$

Et₃B + octene-1 $\xrightarrow{\text{140° in diglyme}}$

(MeOBO)₃ + (octyl)₃Al $\xrightarrow{50°}$

BH₃·NH₃ + octene-1
(or *trans*-octene-2) ⟶

③ Liq. (169°/0.2).

④ + O₂ $\xrightarrow{\text{in hexane}}$ C₈H₁₇B(OOC₈H₁₇)₂
88%

pyrolisis (350°) ⟶

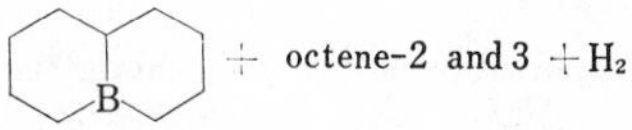

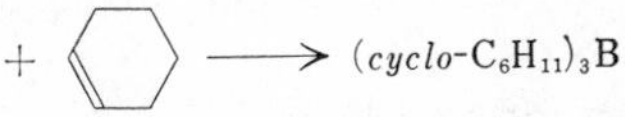

÷ octene-2 and 3 + H₂

+ ⟨cyclohexene⟩ ⟶ (*cyclo*-C₆H₁₁)₃B

⑥ Angew. **72**, 563 (1960). Ger. 1125923 ;
CA **57**, 9880 (1962).

BC₂₄H₅₁O₂

① Dioctoxyoctylborane
C₈H₁₇B(OC₈H₁₇)₂

② B(OBu)₃ + *n*-C₈H₁₇MgBr $\xrightarrow{-60°}$
C₈H₁₇B(OC₈H₁₇)₂ + (C₈H₁₇)₂BOBu
(C₈H₁₇)₃B + O₂ ⟶

③ Straw liq. (125~132°/0.005). n_D 1.4409
(20°). *d* 0.842 (20°).

⑥ JCS **1955**, 2956.

BC₂₆H₅₂ClS₂

① 2-Chlorovinyldidodecylthioborane
ClCH=CHB(SC₁₂H₂₅)₂

② ClCH=CHB(OMe)₂ + 2 C₁₂H₂₅SH $\xrightarrow{100°}$
ClCH=CHBCl₂ + C₁₂H₂₅SH ⟶

③ Straw liq.

⑤ Plasticizer, polymer modifier,

fungicide.

⑥ CA **40**, 5769 (1946).

BC₂₈H₂₂K

① Potassium 1-naphthyltriphenylborate
$KB(C_6H_5)_3(1-C_{10}H_7)$

② $LiB(Ph)_3(1-C_{10}H_7) + KCl \longrightarrow$

③ Solid.

④ $+ HgCl_2 \longrightarrow 3 PhHgCl +$
$1-C_{10}H_7HgCl + KCl + HCl + B(OH)_3$

⑥ Dokl. **91**, 861 (1953).   Zhur. **24**, 1415
(1954).

BC₂₈H₂₈K

① Potassium tetra(*p*-tolyl)borate
$KB(C_6H_4CH_3-p)_4$

② $KBF_4 + p\text{-}MeC_6H_4MgBr \xrightarrow{\text{in Et}_2O} 32\%$

③ Solid.
Sparingly sol. in org. solvents.

④ $+ HgCl_2 \longrightarrow p\text{-}MeC_6H_4HgCl$
$+ Br_2 \longrightarrow p\text{-}MeC_6H_4C_6H_4Me\text{-}p$
(95%)

⑥ Izv. OKhN **1955**, 48.

BC₃₀H₂₁

① Tri-1-naphthylborane

(*sym.* and *unsym.* form exist)

③ Needles. [206~207°].
Stable in air; crystalize accompanying with benzene (1:1 or 1:2) and
have two rotational isomers.
Solubility per 100ml solvents at
25°C : 1.7 g/Et₂O, 0.2 g/EtOH, 6.4
g/C₆H₆, 5.0 g/CCl₄, at −80° : 1.4
g/Et₂O.

④ $+ Me_3N \nrightarrow$
$+ Na \longrightarrow NaB(C_{10}H_7)_3$
$+ Na\text{-}Hg \longrightarrow Na_2B(C_{10}H_7)_3$
(free energy : −11.2 kcal/mol)

$+ CH_3OH \longrightarrow$

$+ B(OMe)_3$

$+ NH_2CH_2CH_2OH \longrightarrow$
$(1-C_{10}H_7)_2BOCH_2CH_2NH_2$

$+ AlEt_3 \xrightarrow{110\sim150°} BEt_3 \; 88\%$
$+ Al(1-C_{10}H_7)_3 \; 82\%$

$+ NaOEt \longrightarrow Na^+[(1-C_{10}H_7)_3BOEt]^-$
[titrated with NaOEt (phenolph-
thalein indicator)]

⑥ Ber. **63**, 934 (1930).   JACS **70**, 2793
(1948).

BC₃₀H₂₁Na

① Sodium tri-1-naphthylborane
$NaB(1-C_{10}H_7)_3$

② $(1-C_{10}H_7)_3B + Na \longrightarrow$

③ Yellow solid.
Decomp. in H₂O ; sol. in Et₂O. Diamagnetic dimer form in Et₂O and
also diamagnetic at solid state.

⑥ JACS **81**, 2638 (1959).

BC₃₀H₂₁Na₂

① Disodium tri-1-naphthylborane
$Na_2B(1-C_{10}H_7)_3$

② $(1-C_{10}H_7)_3B + 40\% \; Na\text{-}Hg \longrightarrow$

③ Violet solid.
Have one molecule of ether of crystn.,
and free at 175° *in vacuo*.   Diamagnetic in Et₂O and THF solns.

⑥ JACS **54**, 2132 (1932) ; **57**, 1259 (1935).

BC₃₂H₂₀Na

① Sodium tetrakis(phenylethynyl)-
borate
$NaB(C \equiv CC_6H_5)_4$

② BCl$_3$ + NaC≡CPh

$\xrightarrow{\text{1. in Et}_2\text{O}}$ $\xrightarrow{\text{2. THF}}$

NaB(C≡CPh)$_4$·3 $\xrightarrow{\text{heat}}$

③ Crystals. (80°/0.05 decomp.).

Forms 1 : 3 complex with THF and THF free at 80°C under high vacuum. Sol. in H$_2$O and THF; insol. in CHCl$_3$ and C$_6$H$_6$.

④ + H$_2$O $\xrightarrow{\text{H}^+}$ PhC≡CH + B(OH)$_3$

Fe^{2+}, Al^{3+}, Ca^{2+}, Li$^+$, K$^+$, NH$_4^+$ ⟶ complex salt, insol. in H$_2$O and stable at 300°.

⑥ Z. Naturf. **11 b**, 364 (1956).

BC$_{30}$H$_{24}$N

① Ammine-tri-1-naphthylborane
(1-C$_{10}$H$_7$)$_3$B·NH$_3$

② (1-C$_{10}$H$_7$)$_3$B + NH$_3$ ⟶

③ Solid. [193~194°].

Exists in two polymorphic modification resulted from restricted rotation of 1-naphthyl groups.

④ Unstable form *unsym*-(1-C$_{10}$H$_7$)$_3$B·NH$_3$
$\xrightarrow{100~140°}$ stable form $\underset{140°}{\rightleftharpoons}$
sym-(1-C$_{10}$H$_7$)$_3$B + NH$_3$

⑥ JACS **70**, 2793 (1948). Proc. Roy. Soc. (London) **12**, 123 (1863).

BC$_{32}$H$_{26}$Li

① Lithium ethyltri-1-naphthylborate
Li(C$_2$H$_5$)B(1-C$_{10}$H$_7$)$_3$

② LiEt + (1-C$_{10}$H$_7$)$_3$B ⟶

③ Solid.
Unstable in air.

④ + K$^+$ ⟶ KBEt(C$_{10}$H$_7$)$_3$
(NH$_4^+$ reacts similarly)

⑥ Zhur. **24**, 1415 (1954).

BC$_{36}$H$_{27}$

① Tris(2-biphenylyl)borane

② BF$_3$ + ⟶ 55%

③ Solid. [201.5~203°].

④ + HgCl$_2$/MeOH

⟶

⑥ Ber. **88**, 962 (1955).

BC$_{36}$H$_{69}$

① Tricyclododecylborane
(*cyclo*-C$_{12}$H$_{23}$)$_3$B

② BH$_3$·NEt$_3$ + cyclododecene ⟶

③ Needles. [127~132°].

④ $\xrightarrow{\text{heat}}$ (*cyclo*-C$_{12}$H$_{23}$)$_2$BH + C$_{12}$H$_{22}$-*cyclo*
(28% *cis*, 64% *trans*, 8% cyclododecane)

⟶ + H$_2$ $\xrightarrow{>200°}$

+ H$_2$ + C$_{12}$H$_{22}$

(70~80%)

+ B(OMe)$_3$ $\xrightarrow{250°, \text{ 3 hr}}$
cyclo-C$_{12}$H$_{23}$B(OMe)$_2$ 81.5%

+ O$_2$ $\xrightarrow[\text{in hexane}]{}$ $\xrightarrow{\text{NaHCO}_3}$
cyclo-C$_{12}$H$_{23}$B(OOH)$_2$ (24%)
+ *cyclo*-C$_{12}$H$_{23}$OH

⑥ Angew. **69**, 684 (1957) ; **74**, 252(1962).

BC$_{40}$H$_{32}$N

① Ammonium tetra(1-naphthyl)borate

NH$_4$B(1-C$_{10}$H$_7$)$_4$

② LiB(1-C$_{10}$H$_7$)$_4$ + NH$_4$Cl ⟶

③ Solid.

⑥ Zhur. **24**, 1415 (1954).

BC$_{42}$H$_{33}$

① Tri-1-naphthylborane dibenzene
(1-C$_{10}$H$_7$)$_3$B·2 C$_6$H$_6$

② (1-C$_{10}$H$_7$)$_3$B + C$_6$H$_6$ ⟶

③ Solid. [170°].

Unsym- and *sym*-(1-C$_{10}$H$_7$)$_2$B form 1 : 1
and 1 : 2 complexes with benzene,
respectively ; free from benzene at
150~160°/1 mm.

⑥ Zhur. **24**, 1415 (1954).   Ber. **63**, 934
(1930). JACS **70**, 2793 (1948).

BC$_{46}$H$_{44}$N

① Tetramethylammonium tris(2-biphe-
nylyl)phenylborate
(CH$_3$)$_4$NB(C$_6$H$_5$)(*o*-C$_6$H$_5$C$_6$H$_4$)$_3$

② (*o*-PhC$_6$H$_4$)$_3$B + PhLi ⟶

[Li(*o*-PhC$_6$H$_4$)$_3$BPh] $\xrightarrow{\text{Me}_4\text{NCl}}$

③ Solid.

④ 1. + H$_2$SO$_4$ (in Me$_2$CO) ⎫
    2. + HgCl$_2$ ⎬ ⟶

HgCl

⑥ Ber. **88**, 962 (1955).

B$_2$CH$_8$

① Methyldiborane
CH$_3$BH$_2$BH$_3$

② Me$_3$B + B$_2$H$_6$ ⟶

Me$_3$B + H$_2$ $\xrightarrow{190°,\ 55\,\text{atm.}}$ 83%

③ Gas. (−15° extrapd., −78.5°/55).
Rapidly disproportionates to B$_2$H$_6$ and
BMe$_3$.

④ + Me$_2$O (or THF) ⟶ BH$_3$·OMe$_2$
+ MeBH$_2$BH$_2$Me
+ H$_2$O ⟶ MeB(OH)$_2$ + B(OH)$_3$
+ H$_2$

⑥ JACS **57**, 621 (1935).

B$_2$C$_2$H$_2$Cl$_4$

① Vinylenebis(dichloroborane)
Cl$_2$BCH=CHBCl$_2$

② BHCl$_2$ + CH≡CH ⟶

③ Liq. (24°/9~11).

⑥ Brit. 853379 ; CA **55**, 18553 (1961).

B$_2$C$_2$H$_4$Cl$_4$

① Ethylenebis(dichloroborane)
Cl$_2$BCH$_2$CH$_2$BCl$_2$

② B$_2$Cl$_4$ + C$_2$H$_4$ $\xrightarrow{-80°,\ 4\,\text{hr}}$ 95%

B$_2$H$_6$ + HC≡CH $\xrightarrow{\text{Et}_2\text{O or THF}}$

(B$_2$C$_2$H$_4$)$_x$ $\xrightarrow{\text{BCl}_3,\ 180\sim200°}$

Cl$_2$BCH$_2$CH$_2$BCl$_2$ and MeCH(BCl$_2$)$_2$

③ Straw liq. (142° extrapd., 26.3°/6.9,
48.4°/21.4, 91.8°/134). [−28.5°].
Fumes in air.
Heat of vaporization 10.14 kcal/mol ;
log *P*=8.230−2220/*T*.

④ + MeOH ⟶
(MeO)$_2$BCH$_2$CH$_2$B(OMe)$_2$
+ MeMgCl ⟶Me$_2$BCH$_2$CH$_2$BMe$_2$
+ H$_2$O ⟶ (HO)$_2$BCH$_2$CH$_2$B(OH)$_2$

⑥ JACS **76**, 5299 (1954).   Izv. OKhN
1964, 398.

B$_2$C$_2$H$_{10}$

① Ethyldiborane
C$_2$H$_5$BH$_2$BH$_3$

② 5 Et$_3$B + B$_2$H$_6$ $\xrightarrow{\text{r. t.}}$ EtB$_2$H$_5$ + Et$_2$B$_2$H$_4$

③ Gas. (−30° decomp., −78.5/7).
Decomp. at −30°.

④ + B$_5$H$_{11}$ $\underset{}{\overset{25°}{\rightleftarrows}}$ B$_2$H$_6$, C$_2$H$_5$B$_2$H$_5$,
sym-Et$_2$B$_2$H$_4$, EtB$_5$H$_{10}$

+ H$_2$C=C—C=CH$_2$ ⟶
      | |
      CH$_3$ CH$_3$

Et—⬠ (*cis*)
      CH$_3$
      CH$_3$

+ H$_2$O ⟶ B(OH)$_3$ + EtB(OH)$_2$ + H$_2$

$\rightleftharpoons$ B₂H₆ + EtBH₂BH₂Et
(equilibrium const. 0.039 (25°)).

+ Et₂BNHPh $\longrightarrow$ Ph–N⟨ structure: Et, B–CH₂, B–CH₂, Et ⟩

+ HC≡CH $\xrightarrow{200°}$

Et₃B, Et₂BCH₂CH₂BEt₂,

EtB⟨ring⟩BEt, structure with Me, B, Me, EtB, BEt, Me

⑥ JACS **58**, 407 (1936) ; **80**, 4520 (1958).

B₂C₂H₁₀

① 1,1-Dimethyldiborane
(CH₃)₂BHBH₃

② B₂H₆ + Me₃B $\longrightarrow$
3 LiBH₄ + BCl₃ + 2 BMe₃ $\longrightarrow$
B₂H₄Me₂ + 3 LiCl

③ Gas. (−2.6°, −78.5°/10). [−150°].
Decomp. in air and H₂O. Heat of
vaporization : 5.5 kcal/mol ; log P
$= −1212/T + 7.363$.

④ + H₂O $\longrightarrow$ Me₂BOH + B(OH)₃ + H₂

⑥ JACS **57**, 621 (1935) ; **82**, 4163 (1960).

B₂C₂H₁₀

① 1,2-Dimethyldiborane
CH₃BH₂BH₂CH₃

② MeBH₂BH₃ + Me₂O (or THF) $\xrightarrow{−80°}$
MeBH₂BH₂Me + BH₃·Me₂O
B₂H₆ + Me₃B $\longrightarrow$

③ Gas. (4.9° extrapd., −78.5°/7.6).
[−124.9°].
Sol. in org. solvents ; Decomp. in air
and H₂O. Changes spontaneously
into Me₂BHBH₃.
log $P = 7.523 − 1290/T$.

④ + H₂O $\longrightarrow$ CH₃B(OH)₂ + H₂

+ NMe₃ $\longrightarrow$ MeBH₂·NMe₃
⑥ JACS **61**, 1078 (1939).

B₂C₃H₁₂

① 1,1,2-Trimethyldiborane
(CH₃)₂BHBH₂(CH₃)

② B₂H₆ + Me₃B $\longrightarrow$

③ Liq. (45.5°, 0°/123). [−122.9°].
Heat of vaporization 7.0 kcal/mol.
Disproportionates to Me₄B₂H₂ and
unsym. Me₂B₂H₄.
log $P = −1527/T + 7.673$.

④ + H₂O $\longrightarrow$ Me₂B(OH) + MeB(OH)₂
+ H₂

⑥ JACS **57**, 621 (1935).

B₂C₃H₁₂

① Propyldiborane
C₃H₇BH₂BH₃

② Pr₃B + excess B₂H₆ $\longrightarrow$

③ Liq. (−60°/6.2).

④ + H₂O $\longrightarrow$ H₂ + PrB(OH)₂ + B(OH)₃

⑥ JACS **58**, 407 (1936).

B₂C₄H₈Cl₄

① Tetramethylenebis(dichloroborane)
Cl₂BCH₂CH₂CH₂CH₂BCl₂

② BHCl₂ + H₂C=CHCH=CH₂ $\longrightarrow$

③ Liq. (130°/110).

⑥ Brit. 853379 ; CA **55**, 18553 (1960).

B₂C₄H₁₂O

① Tetramethyldiboroxane
(CH₃)₂BOB(CH₃)₂

② Me₂BOH + P₂O₅

③ Liq. (43°). [−37°].

④ + BF₃ $\longrightarrow$ Me₂BF

⑥ JACS **62**, 2228 (1940) ; **57**, 625 (1935).

B₂C₄H₁₄

① 1,1-Diethyldiborane
(C₂H₅)₂BHBH₃

② Et₃B + B₂H₆ $\longrightarrow$

③ Liq. (67° extrapd., 0°/42).
  Heat of vaporization, 8.1 kcal/mol ;
  log $P=1760/T + 8.055$.
④ + H_2O ⟶ $Et_2B(OH) + H_2 + B(OH)_3$
⑥ JACS **58**, 407 (1936).

$B_2C_4H_{14}$
① 1,1,2,2-Tetramethyldiborane
  $(CH_3)_2BHBH(CH_3)_2$
② $B_2H_6 + Me_3B$ ⟶
  $NaBH_4 + HCl + 3 BMe_3 + (AlCl_3$
  catalyst) $\xrightarrow{40\sim200\ atm.,\ 150\sim175°}$
  $2 Me_4B_2H_2 + NaCl + MeH$
  $2 LiBH_4 + 2 HCl + 4 BMe_3 \xrightarrow{100\sim140°}$
  $3 Me_4B_2H_2 + 2 LiCl + 2 H_2$ 100%
  $3 LiBH_4 + BCl_3 + 2 BMe_3$ ⟶
  $Me_3B + H_2 \xrightarrow{electric\ discharge}$
③ Liq. (68.6~72.0°, 0°/48). [−72.5°].
  Sol. in org. solvents ; Decomp. in air
  and H_2O.
  Heat of vaporization: 7.3 kcal/mol ;
  log $P=-1643/T + 7.687$.
  IR : ν_{B-H}(bridge) 1987, 2137 cm^{-1}.
④ + CH_3SH ⟶ $(CH_3)_2BSCH_3 + 2 H_2$
  + H_2O ⟶ $Me_2BOH + H_2$
  + Me_2PH ⟶ $Me_2BH·HPMe_2$
  + Me_3N ⟶ $Me_2BH·NMe_3$
  + $MeCN$ ⟶ $(Me_2BN=CHMe)_2$
⑥ JACS **57**, 621 (1935).   Chem. & Ind.
  1959, 295.   JINC **5**, 250 (1958).

$B_2C_4H_{14}$
① 1,2-Diethyldiborane
  $C_2H_5BH_2BH_2C_2H_5$
② $2 C_2H_5BH_2BH_3 + B_2H_6$ ⇌
  $C_2H_5BH_2BH_2C_2H_5 + 2 B_2H_6$
  $NaBH_4 + CH_2=CHBr \xrightarrow{in\ tetraglyme}$
  72%
③ Liq. (0°/36, −23.2°/10.4).
⑥ JINC **5**, 250 (1958).   JACS **80**, 4520
  (1958).

$B_2C_6H_4Cl_4$
① *m*-Phenylenebis(dichloroborane)

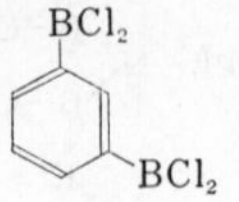

② $B(OMe)_3$ + + Li ⟶

$\xrightarrow{PCl_5}$ 58%

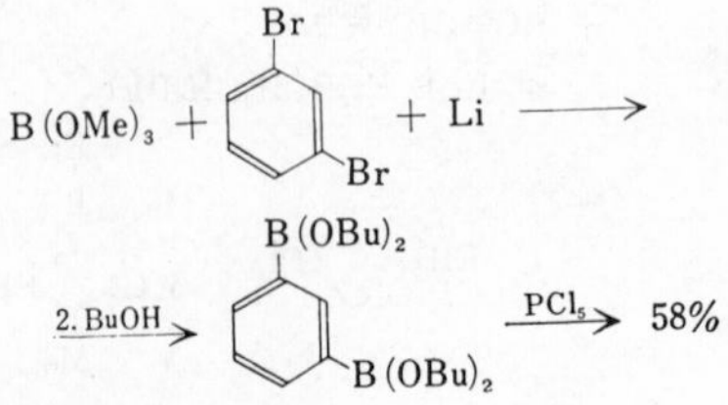

③ Liq. (82~84°/1.2).
⑥ JACS **79**, 3081 (1957).

$B_2C_6H_4Cl_4$
① *p*-Phenylenebis(dichloroborane)

②
  + $PCl_5 \xrightarrow{reflux,\ 7hr\ in\ CCl_4}$ 84%

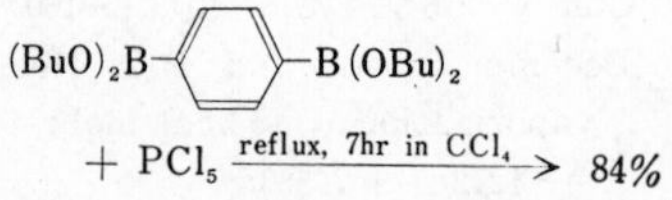

③ Crystals. (104°/5). [93~96°].
⑥ JACS **79**, 3081 (1957).

$B_2C_6H_8O_4$
① *p*-Phenylenebisboronic acid

② $B(OMe)_3 + $
  + Li ⟶

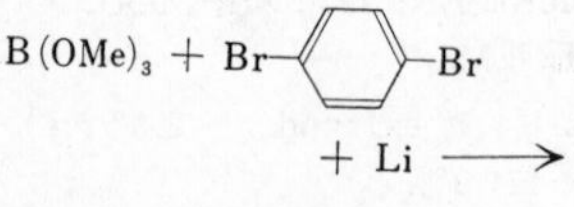

③ Crystals. [>420°].
  Very slightly sol. in polar org.
  solvents.
⑥ JACS **79**, 3081 (1957).

B₂C₆H₁₄
① Vinylenebis(dimethylborane)
   (CH₃)₂BCH=CHB(CH₃)₂
② Me₂BBr + CH₂=CHNa ⟶
   as by-product.
③ Liq. (0°/21).
⑥ JACS **76**, 1710 (1954); **79**, 5091 (1957).

B₂C₆H₁₆
① Ethylenebis(dimethylborane)
   (CH₃)₂BC₂H₄B(CH₃)₂
② Cl₂BCH₂CH₂BCl₂ + ZnMe₂

   $\xrightarrow[\text{in pentane or Me}_3\text{B}]{}$ 88%

   CH₂=CHBMe₂ + Me₄B₂H₂ $\xrightarrow{0°}$

   Me₄B₂H₂ + CH≡CH $\xrightarrow{0°}$
③ Liq. (98° extrapd., −23°/8, 5.1°/16,
   23.7°/41.5 decomp.). [−114.9°].
   Heat of vaporization: 8.54 kcal/mol,
   log P=7.916−1869/T.
④ + NMe₃ ⟶
   Me₂BCH₂CH₂BMe₂·2 Me₃N
⑤ High energy fuels.
⑥ JACS **76**, 5299 (1954).

B₂C₆H₁₆O₄
① Ethylenebis(dimethoxyborane)
   (CH₃O)₂BCH₂CH₂B(OCH₃)₂
② Cl₂BCH₂CH₂BCl₂ + MeOH ⟶
③ Liq. (28.3°/1.4, 44.1°/4, 93.3°/50.2).
   [−21.4°].
   Heat of vaporization: 8.54 kcal/mol,
   log P=8.933−2647/T.
⑥ JACS **76**, 5299 (1954). Dokl. **100**, 1103
   (1955).

B₂C₆H₁₈
① Dipropyldiborane
   (C₃H₇)₂B₂H₄
② Pr₃B + B₂H₆ ⟶

   PrB₂H₅ + Pr₃B + H₂ $\xrightarrow{180\sim185°,\ 245\,\text{atm.}}$
③ Liq. (0°/2.8).

IR: $\nu_{\text{B–H}}$ 2580, 2500, 1565 cm⁻¹.
④ + H₂O ⟶ C₃H₇B(OH)₂
⑥ JACS **58**, 407 (1936).

B₂C₆H₁₈
① 1,1,2-Triethyldiborane
   (C₂H₅)₂BHBH₂C₂H₅
② B₂H₆ + 8 Et₃B ⟶ Et₃B₂H₃ + Et₄B₂H₂

   Et₃B + H₂ $\xrightarrow{150°,\ 300\,\text{atm.}}$
③ Liq. (0°/4).
   Spontaneously inflammable.
④ + H₂O ⟶ EtB(OH)₂ +
   Et₂BOH + H₂
⑥ JACS **58**, 407 (1936).

B₂C₆H₁₈N₂
① (1,2-Ethylenediamino)bis(dimethylborane)
   (CH₃)₂BNHCH₂CH₂NHB(CH₃)₂
② 2 Me₃B·H₂NCH₂CH₂NH₂ $\xrightarrow{250°}$
   Me₂BNHCH₂CH₂NHBMe₂ + 2 CH₄
③ Liq. (149° extrapd.).
⑥ Z. anorg. allg. Chem. **279**, 38 (1955).

B₂C₈H₁₈
① Bisborolane

② BH₃·NEt₃ + CH₂=CHCH=CH₂ ⟶
   B₂H₆ + CH₂=CHCH=CH₂ ⟶
③ Liq. (76~77°/10). n_D 1.4894 (20°).
   d 0.8541 (20°/4°).
   Stable to H₂O, ROH and olefins at
   room temp.
   IR: $\nu_{\text{B–H}}$(bridge) 1612 cm⁻¹.
④ + olefin $\xrightarrow{100°}$ R₃B
   + H₂O₂ ⟶ HOCH₂CH₂CH₂CH₂OH

   + Et₂NH $\xrightarrow{100°,\ 3hr}$ ⬡BNEt₂ 84%
⑥ Angew. **72**, 626 (1960).   JACS **84**,

1831 (1962).

B₂C₈H₂₀O

① Tetraethyldiboroxane
$(C_2H_5)_2BOB(C_2H_5)_2$

② $Et_2BOH \xrightarrow{distn.}$

③ Liq. (143°).

⑥ J. prakt. Chem. **147**, 251 (1937).

B₂C₈H₂₂

① 1,1,2,2-Tetraethyldiborane
$(C_2H_5)_2BHBH(C_2H_5)_2$

② $Et_3B + B_2H_6 \longrightarrow$
$Et_3B + H_2 \xrightarrow{150°, \ 300 \ atm.}$
$Et_3B_2H_3 + Et_3B \longrightarrow$
$B(OMe)_3(or \ BF_3 \cdot Et_2O) + Et_2AlH \longrightarrow$
44%

③ Liq. (0°/5, 112°). [−56.3°].
IR : ν_{B-H} 2500, 1567 cm⁻¹.

④ $+ HC{\equiv}CCH_2Cl \longrightarrow$
$Et_2BCH{=}CHCH_2Cl \xrightarrow{Et_4B_2H_2}$
$(Et_2B)_2CHCH_2CH_2Cl$

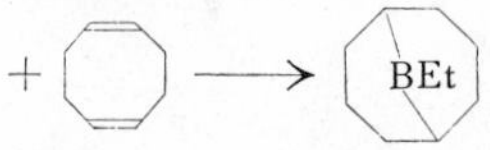

$+ H_2O \longrightarrow Et_2BOH + H_2$

$+ MeCH{=}CH_2 \xrightarrow{0°} BEt_3 \ (37\%),$
$BEt_2Pr \ (41\%), BEtPr_2 \ (20\%), BPr_3$
2% (by gaschromatograph)

$+ MeCN \longrightarrow (MeCH{=}NBEt_2)_2$

⑥ JACS **58**, 407 (1936). Angew. **74**, 652
(1962).   US 2953603 ; CA **55**, 3434
(1961).

B₂C₁₂H₁₀O

① Tetraallyldiboroxane
$(CH_2{=}CHCH_2)_2BOB(CH_2CH{=}CH_2)_2$

② $BF_3 + CH_2{=}CHCH_2MgBr \xrightarrow{H_2O}$
32%

③ Liq. (118~120°/12).

⑥ JCS **1952**, 2987.

B₂C₁₂H₁₄

① 1,2-Diphenyldiborane
$(C_6H_5)_2B_2H_4$

② $Ph_3B + H_2 \xrightarrow{170\sim180°, \ 100 \ atm. \ H_2}$
$PhBCl_2 + LiBH_4 \longrightarrow$
$Ph_2BOBu + B_2H_6 \xrightarrow{in \ Et_2O} 71\%$

③ Needles. [81~83°].
Sol. in aromatic hydrocarbons, Et₂O,
THF and C₅H₅N.

④ $+ CH_3CH{=}CH_2 \xrightarrow{-20°} Ph_3B + Pr_3B$
$+ CH_2{=}CHCH{=}CH_2 \longrightarrow$

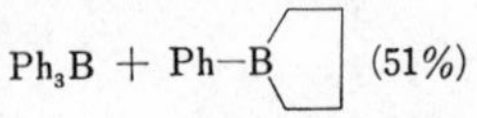

$+ CH_2{=}CHCH_2SH \longrightarrow$

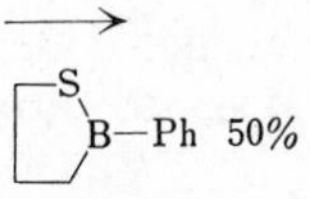

⑥ Z. Naturf. **13 b** 263 (1958).   Dokl. **133**,
119 (1960) ; **130**, 782 (1960).

B₂C₁₂H₂₄

① 1,1'-Tetramethylenebis(borolane)

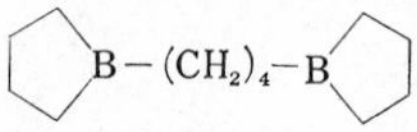

② $B_2H_6 + CH_2{=}CHCH{=}CH_2$

③ Liq. (55°/0.1).

④ $+ BCl_3 \xrightarrow{120\sim140°}$

B—Cl 90%

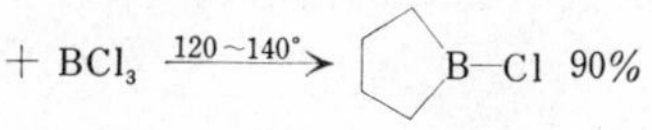

$+ B_2H_6 \longrightarrow$

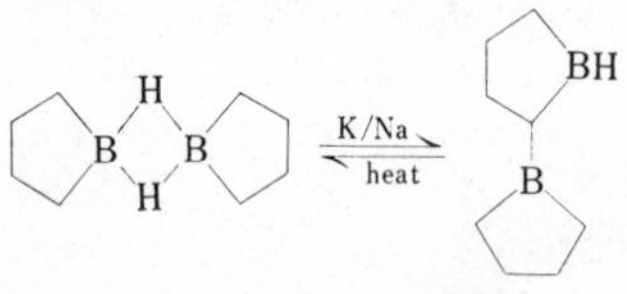

$+ Bu_4B_2H_2 + BCl_3 \xrightarrow{100\sim140°}$

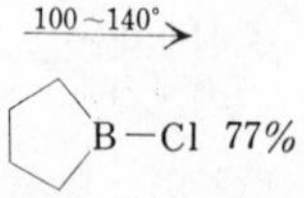

B—Cl 77%

⑥ Angew. **71**, 520 (1959) ; **75**, 346(1963).

B₂C₁₂H₃₀

① 1,2-Bis(1,1,2-trimethylpropyl)-
  diborane (ordinarily called as *sym*-
  dithexylborane)
  [(CH₃)₂CHC(CH₃)₂]₂B₂H₄

② B₂H₆ + (CH₃)₂C=C(CH₃)₂ $\xrightarrow{0°}$ 96%

③ Liq. (0°/0.5). [−34.7～−32.3°].
  IR: ν_{B-H} 1565, 2540 cm⁻¹.

④ + B₂H₆ $\xrightarrow{0°}$ C₆H₁₃B₂H₅

  + NMe₃ $\xrightarrow{0°}$ C₆H₁₃BH₂·NMe₂

  + MeOH $\xrightarrow{0°}$ C₆H₁₃B(OMe)₂ + 4H₂

  + RCH=CHR′ $\xrightarrow{fast}$
  C₆H₁₃BH(CHRCH₂R′) $\xrightarrow{RCH=CHR' \text{ slow}}$
  C₆H₁₃B(CHRCH₂R′)₂
  (olefin=hexene, styrene, hexyne,
  etc.)

⑤ Hydroborating reagent.

⑥ Inorg. Chem. 1, 204 (1962). JACS 85,
  2066 (1963).

B₂C₁₄H₁₂O₄

① 2,2′-Dihydroxyboryltolan

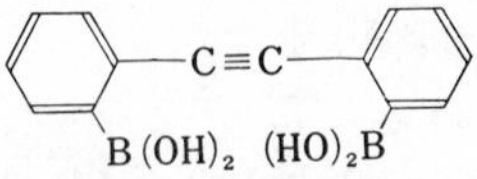

② 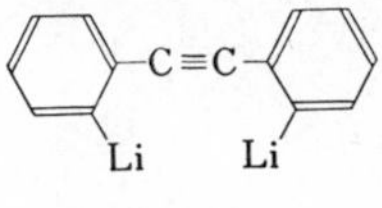 + B(OBu)₃

  $\xrightarrow{}$ $\xrightarrow{H_2O}$ 86%

③ Solid. [233～234°].

④ + H₂O₂ $\longrightarrow$

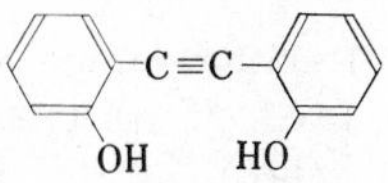

  + $\longrightarrow$

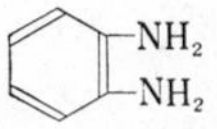

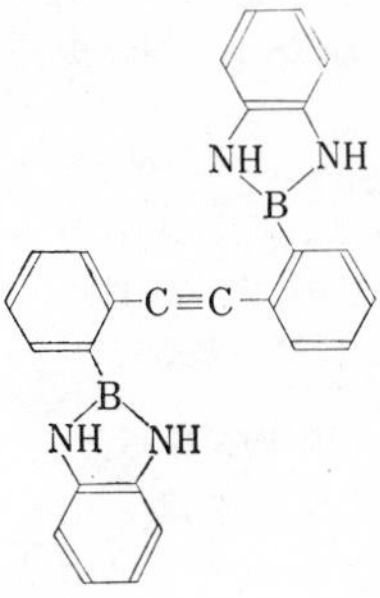

+ $\xrightarrow{Na-tartarate \text{ in EtOH}}$

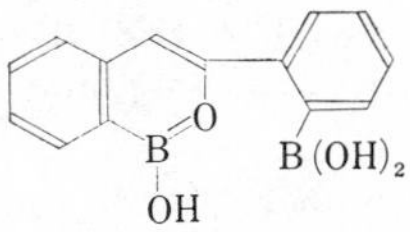

89.5%

⑥ JACS 81, 3013 (1959).

B₂C₁₄H₃₀O₂

① 1,5-Dibutoxy-1,5-diborocane

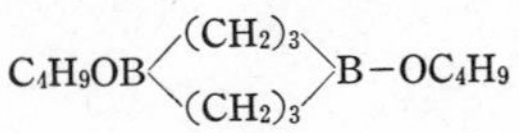

② B(CH₂CH=CH₂)₃ + B(Bu-*i*)₃ $\xrightarrow{130～140°}$
  polymer $\xrightarrow{BuOH}$

③ Liq. (106～107°/2). n_D 1.4510 (20°).
  Spont. inflammable.

④ + PCl₅ $\longrightarrow$

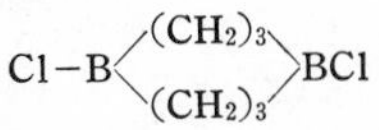

⑥ Izv. OKhN 1959, 1127.

B₂C₁₆H₃₆O

① Tetrabutyldiboroxane
  (C₄H₉)₂BOB(C₄H₉)₂

② Bu₃B + HBr aq $\longrightarrow$
  Bu₂BOCH₂CH₂OBBu₂ + H₂O $\longrightarrow$ 95%

  Bu₂BNMe₂ + SO₂ $\xrightarrow{180～200°}$ (Bu₂B)₂O
  + (Me₂N)₂SO

③ Liq. (102°/1, 136°/12, 110～112°/10).
  n_D 1.4258 (25°). d 0.7933 (25°).

④ + BuOH $\longrightarrow$ Bu₂BOBu + H₂O
  + BBr₃ $\longrightarrow$ Bu₂BBr

+ PCl$_5$ ⟶ Bu$_2$BCl

⑥ JACS 60, 115 (1938); 76, 4174 (1954).

$B_2C_{16}H_{38}$

① Tetrabutyldiborane
　[(n-C$_4$H$_9$)$_2$BH]$_2$

② Bu$_3$B + B$_2$H$_6$ ⟶ 86.8%

　CH$_3$CH$_2$CH=CH$_2$ + B$_2$H$_6$ $\xrightarrow{-30°}$ 45%

③ Liq. (40～41°/0.25). n_D 1.4375 (20°).
　d 0.7647 (20°/4°).

④ + HOCH$_2$CH$_2$OH ⟶
　Bu$_2$BOCH$_2$CH$_2$BOBBu$_2$ + H$_2$
　+ NH$_2$Ph ⟶ Bu$_2$BNHPh 76%
　+ BuSH ⟶ Bu$_2$BSBu 75%

　$\xrightarrow{heat}$ BuB⟨ ⟩ + H$_2$

　+ CH$_2$=CHCH$_2$NH$_2$ ⟶
　CH$_2$=CHCH$_2$NHBBu$_2$ (52%)
　+ H$_2$NCH$_2$CH$_2$CH$_2$BBu$_2$ (28%)

⑥ Dokl. 136, 828 (1961).

$B_2C_{18}H_{40}O_2$

① Ethylenedioxybis(dibutylborane)
　(C$_4$H$_9$)$_2$BOCH$_2$CH$_2$OB(C$_4$H$_9$)$_2$

② BuOB⟨O-CH$_2$ / O-CH$_2$⟩ + 2 BuMgBr $\xrightarrow{-60°}$
　47.4%

③ Liq. (144°/1. n_D 1.4340 (27°). d 0.8266
　(25°/4°).
　Spont. inflammable in air.

④ + H$_2$O $\xrightarrow{distiln.}$ Bu$_2$BOBBu$_2$

⑥ JACS 76, 4174 (1954).

$B_2C_{20}H_{18}$

① 1,2-Di(1-naphthyl)diborane
　(1-C$_{10}$H$_7$BH$_2$)$_2$

② (1-C$_{10}$H$_7$)$_2$BOBu-i + B$_2$H$_6$ ⟶ 81%
　(1-C$_{10}$H$_7$)$_2$BOBu-i + H$_2$BOBu ⟶

③ Solid. [117～119°].

⑥ Dokl. 130, 782 (1960).

$B_2C_{20}H_{46}$

① Tetrakis(1,2-dimethylpropyl)-
　diborane (ordinarily called as tetra-
　siamylborane)
　[(CH$_3$)$_2$CHCH(CH$_3$)]$_4$B$_2$H$_2$

② B$_2$H$_6$ + CH$_3$CH=C(CH$_3$)$_2$ $\xrightarrow{0°, \ 12 \ hr}$
　99%

③ Solid. (0°/0.1). [40.6～44.5°].
　IR: ν_{B-H} 1565 (in cyclohexane), 1551
　(in THF) cm^{-1}.
　Heat of dissocn.: 6.7 kcal/mol.

④ + B$_2$H$_6$ ⟶ (C$_5$H$_{11}$)$_2$B$_2$H$_4$
　+ Me$_3$N ⟶ (C$_5$H$_{11}$)$_2$BH·NMe$_3$
　+ MeOH ⟶ (C$_5$H$_{11}$)$_2$BOMe
　+ olefin (⟩C=C⟨) ⟶

　(C$_5$H$_{11}$)$_2$B-C-CH⟨ $\xrightarrow{H_2O_2}$

　HC-C-OH

⑤ Hydroborating reagent.

⑥ Inorg. Chem. 1, 204 (1962).

$B_2C_{24}H_{20}O$

① Tetraphenyldiboroxane
　(C$_6$H$_5$)$_2$BOB(C$_6$H$_5$)$_2$

② B(OBu)$_3$ + PhMgBr ⟶
　NaBPh$_4$ + H$_2$O $\xrightarrow{heat}$
　Ph$_2$BOCH$_2$CH$_2$NH$_2$ + HCl + H$_2$O ⟶

③ Solid. (210～213°/1). [116～118°].

④ +

　⟶

⑤ Used for various analytical purpose.

⑥ JACS 77, 2491 (1955). Ber. 88, 1761
　(1955).

$B_2C_{24}H_{46}$

① Tetracyclohexyldiborane

(cyclo-C₆H₁₁)₄B₂H₂

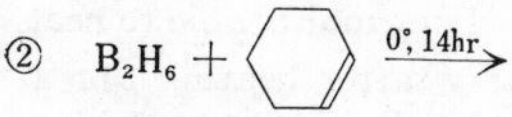

② $B_2H_6 +$ $\xrightarrow{0°,\ 14hr}$

③ Solid. (sublime 80°/high vacuum).
[103~105°].
Slightly sol. in Et₂O and THF at 0°;
sol. in cyclohexane, THF at 40~50°.

④ $+$ >C=C< $\longrightarrow$

(cyclo-C₆H₁₁)₂BC–CH

⑥ Inorg. Chem. 1, 204 (1962).

B₂C₄₀H₇₀

① Tetra(isopinocampheyl)diborane

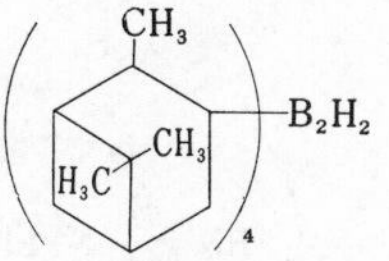

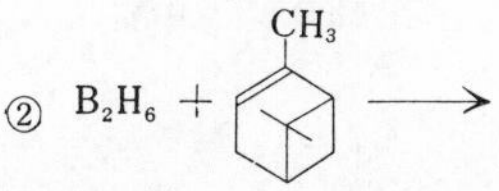

② $B_2H_6 +$ $\longrightarrow$

③ Solid. [74.5~79°].
Opticaly active derivative ($[\alpha]_D^{20}$
$=-37.1°$, $[M]_D^{20}=-212.7°$). obtained
from d-α-pinene $[\alpha]_D^{20} 47.5°$.

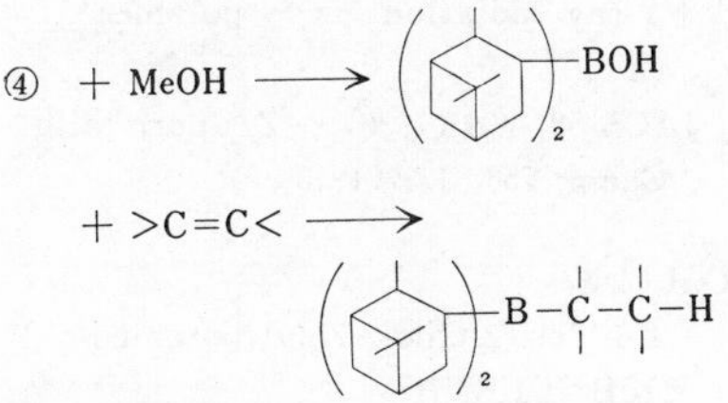

④ $+$ MeOH $\longrightarrow$

$+$ >C=C< $\longrightarrow$

⑤ Stereoselective hydroborating
reagent.

⑥ Inorg. Chem. 1, 204 (1962).

B₃CH₈N₃

① 2-Methylborazine

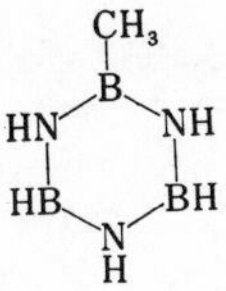

② $MeB_2H_5 + NH_3 \xrightarrow{200°,\ 2\sim5\,atm.}$

③ Liq. (87°). [−59°].
$\log P = 7.880 - 1800/T$; heat of vaporization: 9.0 kcal/mol.

⑥ JACS **58**, 407 (1936).

B₃C₂H₁₀N₃

① 2,4-Dimethylborazine

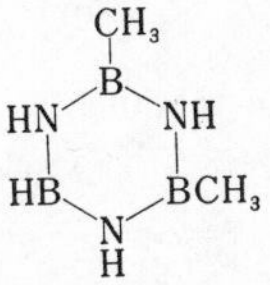

② $Me_2B_2H_4 + NH_3 \xrightarrow{190°,\ 6\,atm.}$

③ Liq. (109°). [−48°].
$\log P = 8.200 - 2019/T$; heat of vaporization: 9.23 kcal/mol.

⑥ JACS **58**, 409 (1936).

B₃C₃H₉O₃

① Trimethylboroxin

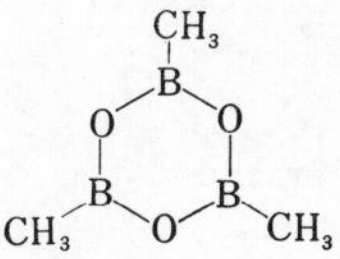

② $BMe_3 + B_2O_3 \xrightarrow{300\sim350°,\ 6\,hr.}$
(MeBNH)₃ + H₂O $\longrightarrow$

③ Liq. (79°, 25°/80). [−38°].
Planar (electron diffraction), B−O
1.39 Å, B−C 1.57 Å, ∠B−O−B 112°,
∠O−B−O 128°.
$\log P = 8.307 - 1909/T$.

④ $+$ H₂O $\longrightarrow$ MeB(OH)₂
$+$ BF₃ $\xrightarrow{-45°}$ MeBF₂ + B₂O₃
$+$ NH₃ $\longrightarrow$ (MeBO)₃·NH₃,

$(MeBO)_3 \cdot 2\,NH_3$

$+\, NMe_3 \longrightarrow (MeBO)_3 \cdot NMe_3$
 (85% dissociate at 100°)

$$\underset{H_2SO_4}{\overset{C_5H_5N}{\rightleftharpoons}} (MeBO)_3 \cdot C_5H_5N$$

$+\, t\text{-BuOCl} \xrightarrow[C_6H_6]{h\nu\ 15°} (t\text{-BuOBO})_3,\ MeCl$

⑥ JACS **62**, 2228 (1940). Z. anorg. allg. Chem. **267**, 1 (1951) ; **272**, 303 (1953).

B₃C₃H₉S₃

① Trimethylborthiin
 (CH₃BS)₃

② $BMe_3 + B(SH)S \xrightarrow{r.\,t.,5\sim6\,hr} (MeBS)_3$
 $+\, H_2S$

③ Crystals. [60°].
 Unstable ; changes to tetramer
 (CH₃BS)₄.

④ $\xrightarrow{\text{heat in CHCl}_3} (MeBS)_4\ [62°]$

$+\, O_2 \longrightarrow$

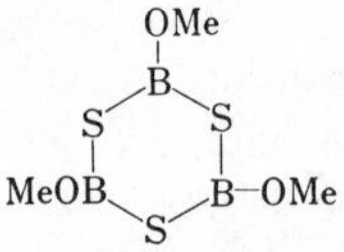

$\xrightarrow{170°} B_2S_3 + B(OMe)_3$

$+\, H_2O \longrightarrow MeB(OH)_2 + H_2S$

$\xrightarrow{\text{heat in vacuum}} BMe_3 + B_2S_3$

⑥ Z. Naturf. **10 b**, 112 (1955).

B₃C₃H₁₂N₃

① 2,4,6-Trimethylborazine

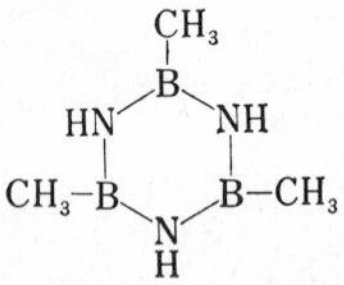

② $BMe_3 + NH_3 \xrightarrow{330°,\ 20\,atm.} (MeBNH)_3$
 $+\, CH_4$

$Me_2B_2H_4 + NH_3 \xrightarrow{300°} (MeBNH)_3 + H_2$

$Me_2BNH_2 \xrightarrow{330°,\ 20\,atm.}$

$(MeBO)_3 + NH_3 \longrightarrow$

③ Crystals. (129°). [32°]. *d* 0.84 (35°).
 $\log P = 7.992 - 2054/T$; heat of vaporization : 9.8 kcal/mol. Stable to heat, 97% recovery after heating 3 hr at 450°. Electron diffraction : B−N 1.42 Å, C−N 1.48 Å.

④ $+\, RNCO \longrightarrow$

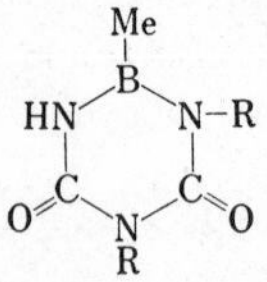

$+\, MeNHCONHMe$

$\longrightarrow$

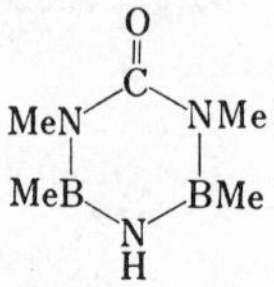

$+\, LiMe \longrightarrow$

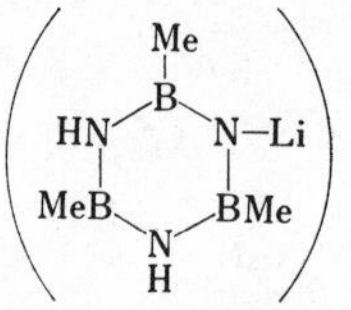

$\xrightarrow{MeI}$

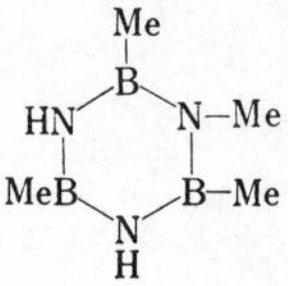

(40.6%)

$+\, \gamma\text{-ray radiation} \longrightarrow$ polymer
 (n≒9)

⑥ JACS **58**, 409 (1936). Z. anorg. allg. Chem. **256**, 177 (1948).

B₃C₆H₉Cl₃N₃

① 2,4,6-Tris(2-chlorovinyl)borazine
 (ClCH=CHBNH)₃

② $ClCH=CHBCl_2 + NH_3 \longrightarrow$

③ Solid. [127~128.5°].
 Stable to hot H₂O

④ $+\, H_2O \xrightarrow{OH^-} NH_3$

$\xrightarrow{\text{reflux in Me}_2CO}$ (linear) polymer as

glassy solid

⑥ CA **54**, 10914 (1960).

B₃C₆H₁₅O₃

① Triethylboroxin

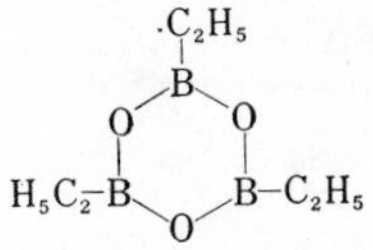

C_2H_5

② B(OMe)₃ + EtMgBr $\longrightarrow$

Et₃B + B₂O₃ $\xrightarrow{\text{heat}}$

Et₃B + BBr₃ + Na₂B₄O₇ $\xrightarrow{250°}$ 79%

③ Liq. (153°/736). n_D 1.3958 (25°).
d 0.8963 (25°).
IR : B–O ring 1350 cm⁻¹.

④ + H₂O $\longrightarrow$ EtB(OH)₂
+ BCl₃ $\longrightarrow$ EtBCl₂
+ Et₃Al $\longrightarrow$ Et₃B 96%
+ Ac₂O $\xrightarrow{\text{reflux}}$ EtB(OAc)₂ 83.8%

⑥ JACS **79**, 5179 (1957).

B₃C₆H₁₈N₃

① Hexamethylborazine

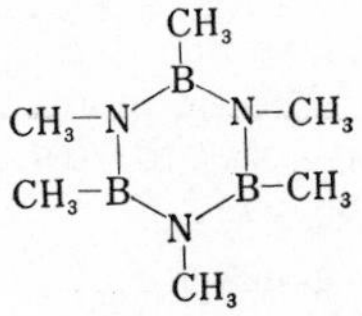

② Me₂BNHMe $\xrightarrow{450°}$

Me₃B + NH₂Me $\xrightarrow{450°}$

(HBNMe)₃ + MeLi $\longrightarrow$

③ Needles. (221°, 20°/0.5). (sublime
100°/1 mm). [97°].
Heat of vaporization : 11.5 kcal/mol;
stable at 400°.
IR : B–N ring 1402 cm⁻¹.
Dipole moment : 0.72 D.

④ + 3 HCl $\xrightarrow{\text{r. t.}}$ (MeClBNHMe)₃
$\xrightarrow[\text{HCl}]{150°}$ MeBCl₂·MeNH₂

+ HCl $\xrightarrow{450°}$ (ClBNMe)₃

+ (ClBNMe)₃ $\xrightarrow{250\sim300°}$
(MeₙCl₃₋ₙB₃N₃Me₃)

+ BuNH₂ $\xrightarrow{\text{reflux}}$ MeB(NHBu)₂ 41%
+ Et₃Al $\longrightarrow$ Et₃B + (MeAlNH)ₓ
+ (HBNMe)₃ $\xrightarrow{250\sim350°}$ H₂MeB₃N₃Me₃,
(53%). HMe₂B₃N₃Me₃ (23%)

⑥ Z. anorg. allg. Chem. **255**, 141 (1947).
JACS **81**, 582 (1959).

B₃C₆H₁₈N₃

① 2,4,6-Triethylborazine
(C₂H₅BNH)₃

② BEt₃·NH₃ $\xrightarrow{440\sim450°,\ 50\ \text{atm.}}$ 80%

③ Liq. (66～67°/7～8). [−54°]. d 0.866
(20°/4°).
Decomp. at 100°.

⑥ Dokl. **111**, 1029 (1956).

B₃C₉H₂₄N₃

① 2,4,6-Tripropylborazine
(C₃H₇BNH)₃

② PrBH₂·NMe₃ + NH₃ $\xrightarrow{100\sim150°,\ \text{NH₄Cl cat.}}$
88%

③ Liq. (108°/9).

⑥ JACS **81**, 5836 (1959).

B₃C₁₂H₂₇O₃

① Tributylboroxin

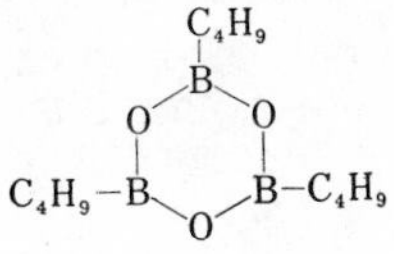

C_4H_9

② BuB(OH)₂ $\xrightarrow{\text{(distillation or SOCl₂)}}$ 80%

Bu₃B + O₂ $\xrightarrow{\text{(controled oxidn.)}}$

Bu₃B + B₂O₃ $\longrightarrow$

③ Liq. (138°/18, 154°/30). n_D 1.4175
(25°). d 0.8718 (25°).

④ + dry air $\longrightarrow$ (BuOBO)₃

+ H_2O $\longrightarrow$ $BuB(OH)_2$

+ HCl, $SOCl_2$, PCl_3, $SiCl_4$ $\longrightarrow\!\!\!\times\!\!\!\longrightarrow$

+ $AlCl_3$ $\longrightarrow$ Bu_2BCl, $BuBCl_2$

+ $Al(NMe_2)_3$ $\xrightarrow[\text{1 hr}]{100°}$ $BuB(NMe_2)_2$

+ Me_2NAlO

+ *cis*-cycloalkane diol $\longrightarrow$ volatile cyclic ester

+ *trans*-cycloalkane diol $\longrightarrow$ non volatile polymeric ester

+ BX_3 $\longrightarrow$ $BuBX_2$ (X=F,Cl)

+ $LiAlH_4$ + NR_3 $\longrightarrow$ $BuBH_2NR_3$ $\longrightarrow$ $(BuBNH)_3$

⑥ JACS **60**, 105 (1938) ; **79**, 5194 (1957).

$B_3C_{12}H_{27}O_3$

① Triisobutylboroxin

$$i\text{-}C_4H_9$$

⟨structure: boroxine ring with three $i\text{-}C_4H_9$ groups⟩

② $B(OMe)_3$ + i-BuMgBr $\longrightarrow$

i-BuB(OH)$_2$ $\xrightarrow{-H_2O}$

i-Bu$_3$B + B_2O_3 $\longrightarrow$

③ Liq. (96°/5). n_D 1.4127 (25°). d 0.8540 (25°).

$\log P = 13.98 - 5250/T$.

IR : B−O ring 1450, 1350 cm^{-1}.

④ + BCl_3 $\longrightarrow$ i-BuBCl$_2$

+ $AlCl_3$ $\longrightarrow$ BCl_3, $CHMe_3$, trace of unsatd. material

⑥ Ber. **54**, 2784 (1921).   JACS **79**, 5179 (1957).

$B_3C_{12}H_{27}O_3$

① Tri-t-butylboroxin

$$t\text{-}C_4H_9$$

⟨structure: boroxine ring with three $t\text{-}C_4H_9$ groups⟩

② t-BuB(OH)$_2$ + $SOCl_2$

③ Solid. (66~68°/5, 89°/17). [30°].

④ + Ag_2O + NH_4OH $\xrightarrow{0°}$ t-BuOH

+ i-C$_4$H$_{10}$ + i-C$_4$H$_8$ + Ag

+ BX_3 $\longrightarrow$ t-BuBX$_2$ (X=F, Cl)

+ $LiAlH_4$ + NEt_3 $\longrightarrow$ t-BuBH$_2$·NEt$_3$

⑥ JACS **60**, 115 (1938).

$B_3C_{12}H_{30}N_3$

① 2,4,6-Tributylborazine ($C_4H_9BNH)_3$

② $3\,BuBCl_2$ + $9\,NH_3$ $\longrightarrow$ $(BuBNH)_3$ + $6\,NH_4Cl$

$BuBH_2$·NMe_2 + NH_3 $\xrightarrow{\text{NH}_4\text{Cl catalyst,100~150°}}$ 91%

③ (110°/0.6).

⑥ JACS **81**, 5836 (1959).

$B_3C_{12}H_{36}P_3$

① Dodecahydrododecamethyl-*sym*-triphosphatriborin [$(CH_3)_2BP(CH_3)_2]_3$

② Me_2PH + Me_2BBr + NEt_3 $\longrightarrow$ 30%

③ Solid. [334°].

$\log P = 9.883 - 4184/T$; inert to air.

IR : Trans. Faraday Soc. **59**, 806 (1963).

Mass Spectra : J. Research NBS **63 A**, 63 (1959).

④ HClaq $\xrightarrow{325°. \ 7\,\text{days}}$ H_2, CH_4, $B(OH)_3$, Me_2POOH

⑥ JACS **75**, 3872 (1953).

$B_3C_{15}H_{42}N_3Si_3$

① 1,3,5-Trimethyl-2,4,6-tris(trimethylsilylmethyl)borazine [$(CH_3)_3SiCH_2BNCH_3]_3$

② $(ClBNCH_3)_3$ + Me_3SiCH_2MgCl $\longrightarrow$

③ Solid. [59~60°].

Stable toward air oxidn. and toward hydrolysis under neutral or mild alk. conditions.

⑥ JINC **15**, 99 (1960).

$B_3C_{18}H_{12}Cl_3O_3$

① Tris(*p*-chlorophenyl)boroxin

$$\left(Cl-\!\!\left\langle\bigcirc\right\rangle\!\!-BO \right)_3$$

② $Cl-\!\!\left\langle\bigcirc\right\rangle\!\!-B(OH)_2 \xrightarrow{-H_2O \text{ on } H_2SO_4}$

③ Solid. [261~262.5°].

⑥ JACS **74**, 5068 (1952).

$B_3C_{18}H_{12}N_3O_9$

① Tris(*m*-nitrophenyl)boroxin

$$\left(\begin{array}{c} O_2N \end{array}\!\!\left\langle\bigcirc\right\rangle\!\!-BO \right)_3$$

② $\left\langle\bigcirc\right\rangle\!\!-B(OH)_2 \xrightarrow{-H_2O \ (\text{on } H_2SO_4)}$
O_2N

③ Solid. [280~281°].

⑥ JACS **74**, 5068 (1952) ; **53**, 711 (1931).

$B_3C_{18}H_{15}O_3$

① Triphenylboroxin

$$\begin{array}{c} C_6H_5 \\ B \\ O \diagup \ \diagdown O \\ C_6H_5-B \ \ \ B-C_6H_5 \\ \diagdown O \diagup \end{array}$$

② $PhB(OH)_2 \xrightarrow{-H_2O}$

$B(OBu)_3 + Mg + PhBr$
$\xrightarrow[230°, \ 2\sim3 \, hr]{} 33\sim44\%$

$PhB(NMe)_2 + SO_2 \longrightarrow$

$Ph_3B + BBr_3 + Na_2B_4O_7 \xrightarrow{250°}$

③ Solid. [214~216°].

④ $+ ROH \rightleftharpoons PhB(OR)_2 + H_2O$

$+ BX_3 \longrightarrow PhBX_2 \ (X=F, \ Cl)$

$+ LiAlH_4 + NEt_3 \longrightarrow PhBH_2 \cdot NEt_3$

$+ PCl_5 \xrightarrow{120\sim130°} PhBCl_2 \ 60\%$

⑤ Pesticide.

⑥ Ber. **64**, 2112 (1930).   Org. Syn. **39**, 3 (1959).

$B_3C_{18}H_{15}S_3$

① Triphenylborthiin

$$\begin{array}{c} C_6H_5 \\ B \\ S \diagup \ \diagdown S \\ C_6H_5-B \ \ \ B-C_6H_5 \\ \diagdown S \diagup \end{array}$$

② $PhBBr_2 + H_2S$

③ Needles. [232~233°]. (in sealed tube)
Stable in air ; sol. in C_6H_6, CS_2,
$CHCl_3$ and CCl_4 ; insol. in Et_2O.

④ $+ H_2O \longrightarrow PhB(OH)_2 + H_2S$

⑥ Z. Naturf. **10 b**, 113 (1955).

$B_3C_{18}H_{18}N_3$

① 2,4,6-Triphenylborazine
$(C_6H_5BNH)_3$

② $(ClBNH)_3 + PhMgBr \longrightarrow$

$6 \, PhBCl(OBu-i) + 9 \, NH_3 \xrightarrow{heat}$
$(PhBNH)_3 \ (79\%) + 3 \, PhB(OBu-i)_2$
$+ 6 \, NH_4Cl$

$PhBCl_2 + NH_3 \longrightarrow PhBCl_2 \cdot NH_3$
$\xrightarrow{heat} (PhBNH)_3 + NH_4Cl$

③ Crystals. [181~182.5°].
IR : B–N ring 1479 cm^{-1}.

④ $+ Et_3Al \xrightarrow{r.t.} Et_3B + (PhAlNH)_x$
$+ ROH \longrightarrow PhB(OR)_2$
$+ \gamma$-ray $\longrightarrow$ polymer

⑥ Angew. **1**, 651 (1959).   Z. anorg.
allg. Chem. **295**, 83 (1958).   Izv.
OKhN **1957**, 1125.

$B_3C_{18}H_{33}O_3$

① Tricyclohexylboroxin

② B(OMe)₃ + *cyclo*-C₆H₁₁MgBr ⟶
   (*cyclo*-C₆H₁₁)₃B + B₂O₃ ⟶
④ + BF₃ ⟶ *cyclo*-C₆H₁₁BF₂
⑥ JACS **77**, 4253 (1955).

B₃C₁₈H₃₉O₃
① Trihexylboroxin

② B(OMe)₃ + C₆H₁₃MgBr ⟶ 70%
③ Liq. (150°/4, 180°/24, 211°/23).
   n_D 1.4323 (20°). *d* 0.8876 (20°/4°).
④ + BF₃ ⟶ C₆H₁₃BF₂
⑥ JACS **77**, 4253 (1955); **60**, 105 (1938).

B₃C₂₁H₂₁O₃
① Tri-*p*-tolylboroxin

② Me—⟨benzene⟩—B(OH)₂ $\xrightarrow{\text{(on } H_2SO_4)}$
③ Solid. [246~248°].
④ + H₂O $\xrightarrow{H^+}$ MePh + B(OH)₃
⑥ JACS **74**, 5068(1952). J. prakt. Chem.
   128, 153 (1930).

B₃C₂₁H₂₁O₃
① Tribenzylboroxin

② C₆H₅CH₂B(OH)₂ $\xrightarrow{\text{heat}}$
③ Solid. [140°].
④ + LiAlH₄ + Et₃N ⟶
   PhCH₂BH₂·NEt₃
⑥ JACS **56**, 1850 (1934).

B₃C₂₁H₂₁O₆
① Tris(*p*-methoxyphenyl)boroxin

② BF₃ + *p*-MeOC₆H₄MgBr ⟶
   B(OMe)₃ + *p*-MeOC₆H₄MgBr ⟶
   p-MeOC₆H₄B(OH)₂ $\xrightarrow{\text{heat}}$
③ Solid. [204~207°].
⑥ JACS **74**, 5068 (1952). J. prakt.
   Chem. **128**, 153 (1930).

B₃C₂₁H₂₄N₃
① 2,4,6-Trimethyl-1,3,5-Triphenylbora-
   zine
   (CH₃BNC₆H₅)₃
② BCl₃ + PhMH₂ ⟶ (ClBNPh)₃
   + MeMgX ⟶ 77%
   Me₃B + NH₂Ph $\xrightarrow{375°, \ 15\,hr, \ on \ BaCO_3}$
③ Solid. [267~269°].
   Phenyl group and borazine ring don't
   present in a same plane.
   IR : B-N ring 1376 cm⁻¹.
   Dipole moment : 0.18 D.
④ $\xrightarrow{440°, \ 3\,hr}$ 37% recovery
⑥ JACS **80**, 1357 (1958). Z. anorg. allg.
   Chem. **295**, 83 (1958).

B₃C₂₁H₂₄N₃
① 1,3,5-Trimethyl-2,4,6-Triphenylbora-
   zine
   (C₆H₅BNCH₃)₃
② (HBNMe)₃ + PhMgBr ⟶ 61%
   (49% by PhLi)
   (ClBNMe)₃ + PhMgBr
③ Solid. [270°].

Sol. 1 mg/100 ml H_2O at 25°.

IR : B-N ring 1413 cm^{-1}.

④ + H_2O $\xrightarrow{100°,\ 2\,hr}$ $PhB(OH)_2$ + $MeNH_2$

(86.8% consumed)

+ MeOH $\longrightarrow$ $PhB(OMe)_2$ + $MeNH_2$

⑥ JACS **81**, 582 (1959). Z. anorg.
allg. Chem. **295**, 83 (1958).

B₃C₂₄H₂₄N₃

① 1,3,5-Triphenyl-2,4,6-Trivinylbora-
zine
$(CH_2=CHBNC_6H_5)_3$

② $CH_2=CHMgX$ + $(ClBNPh)_3$ $\longrightarrow$
40~45%

③ Solid. [187~189°].

④ Vinylpolymerization ocurrs by peroxide, $BF_3 \cdot Et_2O$ or Na catalyst.

+ Me_2HSiCl $\xrightarrow{H_2PtCl_6\ catalyst}$
$(Me_2ClSiCH_2CH_2BNC_6H_5)_3$ 81%

+ Et_3SnH $\xrightarrow{ABIN,\ 100°,\ 5\,hr}$
$(Et_3SnCH_2CH_2BNPh)_3$ 84%

+ Ph_3SnH $\longrightarrow$
$(Ph_3SnCH_2CH_2BNPh)_3$ 74%

+ H_2 $\xrightarrow{Pd}$ $(EtBNPh)_3$

+ vinyl monomer (styrene, vinyl
acetale, methyl methacrylate) +
catalyst $\longrightarrow$ copolymer

+ Ph_2PH + t-BuOOH $\longrightarrow$

$(Ph_2PCH_2CH_2BNPh)_3$ $\xrightarrow{\quad S\quad}$
$(Ph_2PCH_2CH_2BNPh)_3$
$\overset{\parallel}{S}$

+ PhSH $\xrightarrow{radical}$ $(PhSCH_2CH_2BNPh)_3$

+ CBr_4 $\xrightarrow{radical}$ $(CBr_3CH_2CHBrBNPh)_3$

+ HBr (gas) $\longrightarrow$ $PhNH_2 \cdot HBr$

+ HBr + $(PhCOO)_2$ $\longrightarrow$
$(BrCH_2CH_2BNC_6H_5)_3$

⑥ CA **55**, 4043 (1961). J. Polymer Sci.
55, 153 (1961). Inorg. Chem. **2**, 731
(1963).

B₃C₂₄H₃₀N₃

① 2,4,6-Triethyl-1,3,5-triphenylborazine
$(C_2H_5BNC_6H_5)_3$

② Et_2BNPh + $BH_3 \cdot NEt_3$ $\xrightarrow{110~130°,\ 3\,hr}$
71%
$(ClBNPh)_3$ + EtMgCl $\longrightarrow$ 68%

③ Solid. [169~170°].
Dipole moment : 0.47 D.

⑥ JACS **80**, 1357 (1958).

B₃C₃₀H₂₁O₃

① Tri-1-naphthylboroxin
$(1\text{-}C_{10}H_7BO)_3$

②

$\xrightarrow{H_2O}$

$1\text{-}C_{10}H_7B\,(OH)_2$ $\xrightarrow{on\ H_2SO_4}$

③ Plates. [205°].

⑥ JACS **58**, 197 (1936). J. prakt. Chem.
128, 153 (1930). Ber. **27**, 244 (1894).

B₃C₃₀H₂₁O₃

① Tri-2-naphthylboroxin
$(2\text{-}C_{10}H_7BO)_3$

② $2\text{-}C_{10}H_7B(OH)_2$ $\xrightarrow{on\ H_2SO_4}$
$2\text{-}C_{10}H_7BCl_2$ + NaOEt $\longrightarrow$
$(2\text{-}C_{10}H_7BO)_3$ + NaCl + Et_2O

③ Solid. [248°].
Sol. in EtOH ; sparingly sol. in Et_2O ;
insol. in petr. ether.

⑥ Ber. **27**, 244 (1894). J. prakt. Chem.
128, 153 (1930).

B₃C₃₆H₃₀N₃

① Hexaphenylborazine
$(C_6H_5BNC_6H_5)_3$

② $PhB(OBu)_2$ + H_2NPh + BuLi
$\xrightarrow{in\ ligroin}$ 5.3%
$(ClBNPh)_3$ + PhMgBr $\longrightarrow$ 65%
(18% by PhLi)

PhBCl(OBu-*i*) + PhNH₂ ⟶

PhB(OBu-*i*)(NHPh) $\xrightarrow{\text{heat}}$ 30%

PhB(NHPh)₂ $\xrightarrow{260\sim270°}$ 36%

③ Solid [413~415°].
    IR: B-N ring 1368 cm⁻¹.

⑥ Izv. OKhN 1957, 1123. JACS 80, 1357
    (1958). Zhur. 29, 1477 (1959).

B₅CH₁₁

① 1-Methylpentaborane(9)

1-CH₃B₅H₈,

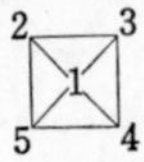

② B₅H₉ + CH₃Cl + AlCl₃ $\xrightarrow[3\,hr]{100°}$ 80%

B₅H₉ + CH₃I + AlCl₃ $\xrightarrow[24\,hr]{100°}$

③ Liq, (0°/34).

④ $\xrightarrow{190\sim200°,\ 18\,hr}$ 2-Methylpentaborane
    (9) 90%

+ 2,6-dimethylpyridine $\xrightarrow{\text{heat}}$
    2-Methylpentaborane(9)

+ MeCl + AlCl₃ $\xrightarrow{\text{heat}}$ 1,2-dimethyl-
    pentaborane(9)

⑤ High energy fuel.

⑥ US 3038012 ; CA 57,15152 (1962). JCS
    1960, 430. Inorg. Chem. 1, 742(1962).

B₅CH₁₁

① 2-Methylpentaborane(9)

2-CH₃B₅H₈,

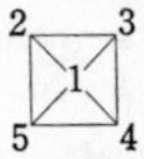

② 1-MeC₅H₈ $\xrightarrow{190\sim200°,\ 18\,hr}$
    B₅H₉ + MeCl + AlCl₃
    $\xrightarrow{100°,\ 20\,hr.\ and\ 190\sim200°,\ 10\,hr.}$ 85%

③ Liq.

⑥ Inorg. Chem. 1, 742 (1962).   JACS
    83, 2584 (1961).

B₁₀CH₁₆

① 2-Methyldecaborane(14)

B₁₀H₁₃CH₃,

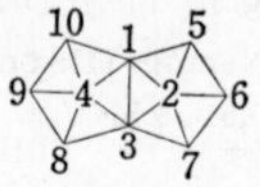

② B₁₀H₁₄ + CH₃Br + AlCl₃ $\xrightarrow{80°,\ 6\,hr.\ in\ CS_2}$
    55.8%

B₁₀H₁₄ + MeCl + FeCl₃ $\xrightarrow{70°}$

③ Liq. (223°, 45~55°/0.5). [4~6°].

⑥ JCS 1960, 5006.   US 3109030 ; CA 60,
    3005 (1965).

B₁₀CH₁₆

① 5-Methyldecaborane(14)

B₁₀H₁₃CH₃,

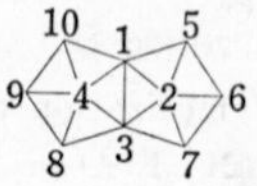

② B₁₀H₁₄ + MeMgI ⟶ (B₁₀H₁₃MgI)
    $\xrightarrow{Me_2SO_4}$ 17.7% (and 6-Me-derivative)

③ Solid. [19~21°].

⑥ JCS 1960, 5016.

B₁₀CH₁₆

① 6-Methyldecaborane(14)

B₁₀H₁₃CH₃,

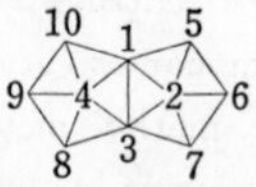

② B₁₀H₁₄ + LiMe ⟶ 45.4%

③ Solid. [27~28°].

⑥ JCS 1960, 5012.

B₁₀CH₁₈

① 1,1′-Methylene-bis (pentaborane(9))
    1,1′-(B₅H₈)₂CH₂

② B₅H₉ + CH₂Cl₂ + AlCl₃ $\xrightarrow{85\sim92°,\ 3\,hr.}$

③ Solid. (88°/14). [50.8~51.8°].
    Ignites in air.
    IR: 2600, 1800, 1400, 1100 cm⁻¹ (B₅H₉
    derivative).

⑤ High energy fuel.

⑥ Inorg. Chem. 3'454(1964). US 3118936
    (1964) ; CA 60, 9311 (1965).

$B_{10}C_2H_{12}$

① 1,2-Dicarbaclovodecaborane-(12)

$$HC\underset{B_{10}H_{10}}{\overset{\frown}{\underset{\smile}{\bigcirc}}}CH$$

② $B_{10}H_{14}$ + Lewis base $\longrightarrow$

$B_{10}H_{12}$ (base)$_2$ $\xrightarrow{HC\equiv CH}$

Lewis base = Et_2S, CH_3CN, etc.

$B_{10}H_{14}$ + $HC\equiv CH$ + Lewis base $\xrightarrow{heat}$

③ Crystals. [287~288°].

Have cage structure. Stable to heat; inert to alc., nitrile, sulfide, weakly basic amine and mineral acid; slowly isomerize to neocarborane

$$HC\underset{B_{10}H_{10}}{\overset{\frown}{\underset{\smile}{\bigcirc}}}CH \quad [263\sim265°].$$ at 465~500°;

NMR data show that neocarborane is *meta* C configuration and carborane is *ortho* C configuration.

IR: 1212, 1149, 1034, 1015, 985, 716 cm^{-1}.

④ + Cl_2 $\xrightarrow{h\nu \ in \ CCl_4}$

$$HC\underset{B_{10}H_8Cl_2}{\overset{\frown}{\underset{\smile}{\bigcirc}}}CH \ , \quad HC\underset{B_{10}H_7Cl_3}{\overset{\frown}{\underset{\smile}{\bigcirc}}}CH \ , \quad \cdots\cdots$$

$$\cdots\cdots HC\underset{B_{10}Cl_{10}}{\overset{\frown}{\underset{\smile}{\bigcirc}}}CH \ , \quad HC\underset{B_{10}Cl_{10}}{\overset{\frown}{\underset{\smile}{\bigcirc}}}CCl$$

$$+ \ BuLi \ \xrightarrow{0°} \left(HC\underset{B_{10}H_{10}}{\overset{\frown}{\underset{\smile}{\bigcirc}}}CLi \right)$$

$$\xrightarrow{RX} \quad HC\underset{B_{10}H_{10}}{\overset{\frown}{\underset{\smile}{\bigcirc}}}CR$$

$R = Bu, H_2C=CCH_2-, Me_3Si-$

$$+ \ 2 \ BuLi \ \xrightarrow{0°} \left(LiC\underset{B_{10}H_{10}}{\overset{\frown}{\underset{\smile}{\bigcirc}}}CLi \right)$$

$$\xrightarrow{CO_2} \quad HO_2CC\underset{B_{10}H_{10}}{\overset{\frown}{\underset{\smile}{\bigcirc}}}CCO_2H$$

(R_2SiCl_2, PCl_3, etc, reacted

similarly)

$+ \ CH_2Cl_2 + AlCl_3 \xrightarrow{135°}$

$$HC\underset{B_{10}H_9}{\overset{\frown}{\underset{\smile}{\bigcirc}}}CH \quad HC\underset{H_9B_{10}}{\overset{\frown}{\underset{\smile}{\bigcirc}}}CH \quad + \ 2HCl$$
$$\qquad\qquad -CH_2-$$

Carborane $\overset{465\sim500°}{\underset{24\sim48 \ hr}{\rightleftarrows}}$ neocarborane

$\qquad\qquad\qquad\qquad\downarrow \ Na$
$\qquad\qquad\qquad\qquad \ Liq. \ NH_3$

$\qquad\qquad \xrightarrow{H_2O} Na(B_{10}H_{12}C_2)\cdot xNH_3$

$+ \ PrNH_2 \ \longrightarrow$

$$HC\underset{B_{10}H_{10}}{\overset{\frown}{\underset{\smile}{\bigcirc}}}CH\cdot PrNH_2$$

$+ \ N_2H_4\cdot H_2O \ \xrightarrow{heat} \ N_2H_5C_2B_9H_{12} + H_2$
$+ \ B(OH)_3$

$+ \ piperidene \ \xrightarrow[in \ C_6H_6]{20°} \ (piperidino)_2BH$

$+ \ C_2B_9H_{12}\cdot C_5H_{10}NH_2 \ [169\sim170°]$

⑥ Inorg. Chem. **2**, 1089, 1111, 1128 (1963).
J. Chem. Phys. **86**, 3489 (1962).
Izv. OKhN **1963**, 2236.

$B_nC_{6n}H_{5n}$

① Poly(phenylboron)
$(C_6H_5B)_n$ $n=9\sim12$

② $PhBCl_2 + Na \xrightarrow{reflux \ in \ toluene}$

③ Yellow-brown amorphous solid.
Sol. in C_6H_6, toluene and dioxane; slightly sol. in Et_2O; insol. in ligroin. Decomp. without melting above 200° *in vacuo*.

④ moist air $\longrightarrow$ H_2, oxidized product
$+ \ O_2 \ \longrightarrow \ (PhBO)_n$ (higher degree of polymerization than the original material)
$+ \ NH_3 \ \longrightarrow \ [(PhB)_2NH_3]_n$
$\xrightarrow{heat, \ in \ vacuo} \ Ph_3B$
$+ \ H_2O \ \longrightarrow \ PhB(OH)_2, \ H_2$

⑥ Z. anorg. allg. Chem. **325**, 225 (1963).

4. Organic Compounds of Aluminum

(Al)

4.1. Introduction

The first reported preparation of an organoaluminum compound dates back to 1859, when Hallwachs prepared ethylaluminum sesquiiodide. This was only a few years after Wöhler first isolated metallic aluminum from aluminum chloride and metallic potassium (1845). In the other hand, the organomagnesium halides called Grignard reagents, initially appeared in 1900, proved even more useful than the organoaluminum compounds, although both aluminum and magnesium were later classified among the modern light metals. These Grignard reagents played a major role in the fields of organic and organometallic chemistry for more than half a century. The reason for the slow development of organoaluminum chemistry is found mainly in the difficulties of preparing and handling these unstable compounds.

Since the 1950's organoaluminum chemistry has entered into a third wave of research (properly named by K. Ziegler). Evidence of this new surge of interest is found in the relative numbers of published reports in the field; from 1950 to the present, 450 papers have appeared on the subject, while only 80 are recorded for the entire prriod peeceding 1950. Most of the papers were written in Germany, and one can easily understand the influence of these German researchers.

One more fact will serve to point up the 50-year gap between the major research achievements regarding these two organometallic groups: V. Grignard received a Nobel prize in 1912 for his work on organomagnesiums, and K. Ziegler received one in 1963 for his work on organoaluminums.

Until about 1950, most research efforts were focused on synthesis and separation of organometallic compounds. Even though some physical properties were determined, they were not defined so precisely as for other organic compounds because of the difficulties encountered in handling of this organometallics. This situation altered radically after the discovery of the addition reaction of alminum hydride or alkylaluminum to the unsaturated carbon-carbon bonds of olefins and acetylenes. This was followed very shortly by the discovery of the Ziegler catalyst (which made possible a low-pressure method for ethylene polymerization), by the discovery of the Natta catalyst (which brought isotactic polypropylene), and by important developments in processes involving tetraethyllead, all of which arose from organoaluminum chemistry. These applications were all closely connected to the petrochemical industry, and the demands of mass production in this field has made organoaluminum compounds among the most important of the organometallics. The production of organoaluminums in Japan currently amounts to several hundred tons a year, and in the United States, to several thousands tons a year.   If high-purity aluminum production, and direct production of aluminum metal from bauxite without electric power can be realized through the use of organoaluminum compounds, the use of these compounds will expand greatly in view of the present rapid increase in the late production of aluminum itself. (In 1962, total world production was 5.5 million tons a year, and Japanese production was 187,000 tons a year.)

4.2. Classification and Nomenclature

Three types of organoaluminums can be classified according to the number of carbon atoms connecting directly to the aluminum atom, as indicated by the following general formulas:

$$RAlX_2, \quad R_2AlK, \quad R_3Al$$

X may be hydrogen, a halogen, or any of the following groups: OR', SR', NH$_2$, NHR' or NR'$_2$ (R' represents an alkyl group). R is usually an alkyl group, but may in certain cases be aryl or acyl; and $-NR'_2$ indicates a linear or cycloamide group.

As to the nomenclature of these compounds, IUPAC rule 48 touches lightly upon the subject in the general statements about organometallics, but particular or elaborate rules are not given.   Usually the name of the organogroup is prefixed to the name of the metal; sometimes alumine, which designates AlH$_3$ as the parent compound of the derivative is used with the name of the oragano group.   In this handbook, we have adopted the former nomenclature, as used in Chemical Abstracts.   For example, $(C_2H_5)_3Al$ is triethylaluminum, $(C_2H_5)_2AlCl$ is diethylaluminum chloride, and $(C_2H_5)_2Al_2Cl_3$ is ethylaluminum sesquichloride. These are also called by other names, such as triethylalumine, diethylmonochloroalumine, and triethyltrichlorodialumine.   Other examples are $(C_2H_5)AlH_2$, named ethylaluminum dihydride, $(C_6H_5)_3Al\cdot(C_2H_5)_2O$, named triphenylaluminum diethylether complex and $LiAl(C_2H_5)_4$, named lithium aluminum tetraethyl, but no structure too complicated to name this way is known at present.

Several recently discovered types of compounds are shown below.   The five-membered cyclic compound containing aluminum atom (1) has been prepared and

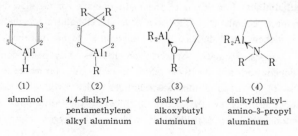

(1)	(2)	(3)	(4)
aluminol	4,4–dialkyl–pentamethylene alkyl aluminum	dialkyl–4–alkoxybutyl aluminum	dialkyldialkyl–amino–3–propyl aluminum

is called aluminol. The six-membered cyclic compound (2) is known as a cyclo-alkylene aluminum, and the intramolecular complexes (3) and (4) have been known for some years.

4.3. Methods of Synthesis

There are four common methods for making carbon–aluminum bonds: by intro-duction from other organometallics; by the reaction of organohalide and metallic aluminum; by the reaction of aluminum trichloride and a diazoalkane; and by direct synthesis of a trialkylaluminum compound.

4.3.1. Introduction from other Organometallics

Metallic aluminum reacts with organomercury compounds, affording triorgano-aluminum by the following formula:

$$3\,HgR_2 + 2\,Al \rightleftharpoons 2\,AlR_3 + 3\,Hg$$

This method is a good way to prepare organoaluminum compounds having no ether as a complex component. However, the reaction is reversible to some degree, and alkymercury compounds are always dangerous to handle, so this method is not always to be preferred. Even though mercury compounds contain-ing branched chain alkyl groups are unstable and difficult to prepare, this method is the only known way to prepare triisopropyl aluminum, $Al(i\text{-}Pr)_3$. The prepa-ration from aluminum trihalide and Grignard reagent is the classical one, and the ether used as a solvent enters into the complex of the organoaluminum, causing a decrease in reactivity.

$$AlCl_3 + RMgX \xrightarrow{Et_2O} R_3Al\cdot Et_2O + MgXCl$$

Pino and Nozakura prepared the optically active organoaluminum compound tris-2-methylbutylaluminum ether complex.

$$(+)\text{-}(CH_3CH_2CHCH)_3Al\cdot(C_2H_5)_2O$$
$$|$$
$$CH_3$$

From this the Ziegler catalyst was derived, which in turn made possible the asymmetric polymerization of α–olefins.

4.3.2. Reaction of an Organohalide and Metallic Aluminum

Even though this method is similar to Grignard reagent preparation, its appli-cation is still limited; this is one of the main reasons for the slow development of oraganoaluminum chemistry. The available alkyl halides are methyl and ethyl halides, the higher alkyl halides being impossible to use because they readily decompose. Among aromatic hydrocarbon halides only iodo compounds (for example, iodobenzene) are effective; chlorobenzene and bromobenzene cannot be used to prepare phenylauminum sesquihalides. However, by using vibromill as a reactor and forming the active surface of the aluminum metal in the reaction system, and by expelling all water and oxygen from the reagents used, the reaction can be made to proceed smoothly.   The product can be obtained as a sesquihalide as follows:

$$2\,Al + 3\,RX \longrightarrow R_3Al_2X_3$$

Besides aluminum metal, Al-Mg or Al-Cu systems as alloys or mixtures can be used.   When Al-Mg is used, the main product is diorganoaluminum halide, $R_4Al_2X_2$.   The reaction is generally carried out in the liquid phase, but reaction in the vapor phase is possible and convenient for preparing methylaluminum sesquichloride from methychloride.

4.3.3. Reaction of Aluminum Chloride and a Diazoalkane

As an example, trichloromethylaluminum, $Al(CH_2Cl)_3$, can be obtained as follows:

$$AlCl_3 + CH_2N_2 \xrightarrow{-50°} Al(CH_2Cl)_3 + N_2$$

In the same manner, lithium aluminum tetraethyl can be prepared by the reaction of diazomethane and lithium aluminum hydride, $LiAlH_4$.

4.3.4. Direct Synthesis of Trialkylaluminum Compounds

This new method is the most reasonable and effective preparation for organoaluminum compounds, and K. Zieglers successful efforts in its perfection were directly responsible for the recent connections between organoaluminum chemistry and the petroleum chemistry.   Triethyl- and triisobutylaluminum are especially important for this process.   The principle is shown by the following formula:

$$AlH_3 + 3\,C_nH_{2n} = Al(C_nH_{2n+1})_3$$

Best yields can be obtained by separating the reaction into two stages to avoid the side reaction.

$$Al + 2\,Al(C_2H_5)_3 + 1.5\,H_2 \xrightarrow[100\sim120°C]{100\sim200\,atm} 3\,Al(C_2H_5)_2H \qquad (1)$$

$$3\,Al(C_2H_5)_2H + 3\,C_2H_4 \xrightarrow[60\sim80°C]{20\sim30\,atm} 3\,Al(C_2H_5)_3 \qquad (2)$$

$$Al + 3\,C_2H_4 + 1.5\,H_2 \longrightarrow Al(C_2H_5)_3$$

In short, by the combination of processes (1) and (2), the liquid product R_3Al can be obtained from aluminum, hydrogen, and olefin alone.   This can be an excellent method for mass production without any side-reaction products.   By this new method, dialkylaluminum hydride can be prepared with the same facility as trialkylaluminum, and these two oraganoaluminum compounds can be made available to the same degree and in equally large quantities.   The value of the direct method has increased with recent developments in the petrochemical industry which have given access to many kinds of α-olefines, and which have expanded the variety of organoaluminum compounds that can be produced easily and at low cost.

4.4. General Properties

4.4.1. Physical Properties and Structure

Aluminum metal has an electronegativity of 1.5, with three electrons in the outer shell which contribute to the six electrons in molecular orbitals of AlX_3 compounds; the resulting tendency to complete the octet causes a large electron deficiency in organoaluminum compounds. When combined with other molecules having free electrons, they easily form Al-complexes, and in organoaluminum compounds containing small alkyl groups such as methyl, ethyl, and hydrogen, the molecules associate into two or three molecular compounds, all of which are affected by an electron deficiency.

The structure of trimethylaluminum has been studied extensively; it is known to form dimer in solution and vapor phases, and X-ray analysis of a single crystal shows that the molecule has a bridged form. From electron-diffraction analysis data alone, it cannot be determined whether the structure is a bridged form or an ethane form, but it is most probably the bridged form:

$$CH_3 \diagdown \qquad \diagup CH_3 \diagdown \qquad \diagup CH_3$$
$$Al \qquad Al$$
$$CH_3 \diagup \qquad CH_3 \qquad CH_3$$

Four methy groups project out to the ends and the two alminum atoms form one plane, with the two bridged methyls placed symmetrically above and below them in the same plane and at equal distances from the two aluminum atoms. The Al-C-Al angle in the bridge is nearly 70°. The C-Al bond distance at the ends is 1.99Å and in the bridge is 2.24Å. Dissociation to monomer occurs in the vapor phase over 160°, and the dissociation energy is measured as 20.2 kcal/mole. The methyl group exchange between the bridge and the outside part of the dimer was recognized by the measurement of NMR, and its activation energy was calculated as 6~14 kcal/mole.

The usual organoaluminum compounds may be distilled under atmospheric pressure or vacuum unless the organo group is too large. Many are liquids but some are crystalline, and several compounds have been investigated with regard to physical properties such as (1) specific gravity, boiling point, and refractive index; (2) viscosity; (3) vapor pressure, heat of eveporation, and Trouton's constant; (4) heat of combustion; (5) magnetic susceptibility; (6) electron diffraction; and (7) dielectric values.

4.4.2. Chemical Properties

To facilitate understanding of the reactivity of organoaluminums, the general chemical properties will be discussed first, and then specific properties.

(1) The strongest reactivity is seen when the three bonds in the aluminum atom are all connected to carbons or hydrogens, and if one or two of them are replaced by oxygen, nitrogen, or halogen, reactivity decreases considerably. The

reactivity of R_2AlX may be increased by adding a small amount of R_3Al, but for $RAlX_2$ no increase occurs and its reactivity in fact becomes a minimum.

（2） The reason for the large reactivity arises mostly from the electron-deficient nature of $AlR_{3-n}X_n(n=0, 1, 2)$, but if this electron deficiency is saturated by complexing with ether or amine, then the reactivity decreases considerably compared to the original compound.

（3） Between Al−C and Al−H bonds, there is reversibility as follows;

$$(C_nH_{2n+1})_2AlH + C_nH_{2n} \rightleftharpoons Al(C_nH_{2n+1})_3$$

This reaction is an equilibrium, and in thermal decomposition the reverse reaction predominates.

（4） Both Al−C and Al−H bonds can add to C=C or C≡C, and these reactions afford the valuable new method for preparing organoaluminum compounds which was discussed in Section 4.3.4.

（5） In organoaluminum compounds, carbon can be removed from the aluminum, just as with many other metal alkyls, by means of alkylation reactions with

$$-\overset{H}{C}=O, \quad \underset{}{\overset{}{>}}C=O, \quad -C\overset{O}{\underset{OR}{\diagup}}, \quad \overset{}{>}C=N-, \quad -C≡N, \text{ or by other halogenation or oxidation}$$

reactions.

（6） A new and interesting field has opened up through the use of organo-aluminum double complexes such as $NaF \cdot 2\,AlR_3$ or $NaAlR_4$, which are especially useful as dissolving agents in the bath when aluminum metal is electrically dissolved in alkylaluminum. Following are some more concrete examples.

（i） *Relation Between Association and Reactivity.* This relates to (1) and (2) above, the molecular weight of organoaluminum compounds measured in benzene by cryoscopy agrees well with theoretical values only in the case of the general formula $Al(-CH_2-CHRR')_3$, for example, triisopropyl, triisobutyl-aluminum. Most other organoaluminum compounds associate into the dimer or trimer forms, and sometimes into larger forms. The hydride of the type R_2AlH takes the form of the trimer in benzene solution at 5°C. When R is methyl, ethyl, or isopropyl, it always appears in a cyclic trimer form with hydrogen bonds, irrespective of the alternation of the alkyl groups:

$$
\begin{array}{c}
\overset{H}{R_2Al{\diagup}\quad{\diagdown}AlR_2} \\
H{\diagdown}\quad{\diagup}H \\
\underset{R_2}{Al}
\end{array}
$$

In the mixed trialkylauminum, the following equilibra are possible:

$$R_3Al + AlR_3' \rightleftharpoons R_2Al\overset{R}{\underset{R'}{\diagup\diagdown}}AlR_2' \rightleftharpoons R_2AlR' + RAlR_2'$$

Because the reaction velocity between these molecules is very large, two different trialkylaluminum mixtures can exchange their alkyl groups very rapidly, but the mixed alkylaluminums having the different alkyls connected to aluminum cannot be separated as constant boilng point fractions. $R_2Al(OR)$ and R_2AlNR_2 compounds have the structures below owing to these associations.

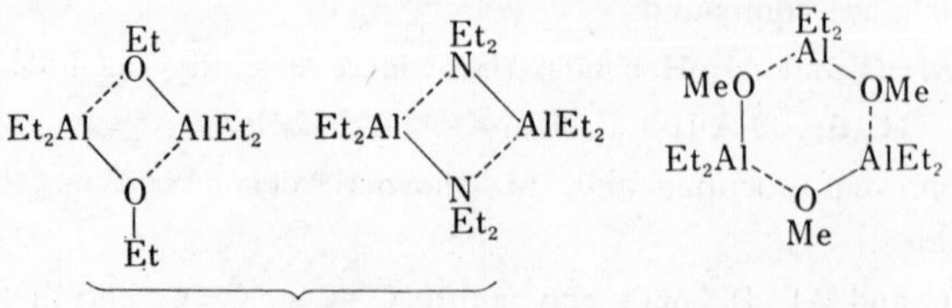

Dimer   Trimer

The reason for the decrease in alkylating ability of these associated compounds stems from the cyclic structures.   However, alkyl exchange between molecules is possible, the bridging by alkyl groups probably occurring as follows:

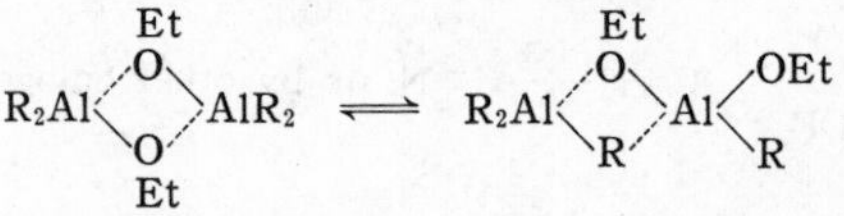

Organoaluminum compounds can form stable complexes with ether or Lewis bases as tertiary amine.   The ether complex can even be distilled, and it is generally hard to remove the ether.   In these complexes, no polymer forms exist and the types $R_3Al \leftarrow OR_2$ and $R_2Al \leftarrow NR_3$ are seen.   Fluorine-containing compounds such as

R_2AlF, or alkoxy compounds of the type R_2AlOR are not able to form the additive complex.   Alkylaluminum can also form a complex of the type $M^I(AlR_4)$ with several organometallic compounds such as sodium, lithium, and magnesium.   This type is also obtained by reaction of $LiAlH_4$ with olefin, and is decomposed by aluminum trichloride to give the original trialkylaluminum.

$$3 LiAl(C_2H_5)_4 + AlCl_3 \longrightarrow 4 Al(C_2H_5)_3 + 3 LiCl$$

Alkali metal halides can form the same type of complex.   Sodium fluoride complex can be decomposed by heating in excess sodium fluoride and separating cryolite and trialkylaluminum.

(ii) *Thermal Cracking.*   This relates to part (3) of the section above on general properties of organoaluminum.   When trialkylaluminum is heated under the proper conditions, dialkylaluminum hydride is formed, and on further heating this hydride decomposes completely to metallic aluminum.   For example, diiso-butylaluminum hydride decomposes evenly at 250° by the following reaction:

$$(i\text{-}Bu)_2AlH = Al + 1\frac{1}{2} H_2 + 2\,i\text{-}C_4H_8$$

This reaction can be used to purify crude aluminum metal by reacting it with isobutylene and hydrogen, and then subjecting the triisobutylaluminum thus produced to thermal cracking. There is one difficulty, however, in that this process always produces a small amount of aluminum carbide. Especially in a sealed or pressurized system, this side reaction proceeds easily as triisobutylaluminum decomposes first to trimethylaluminum and propylene, and then the trimethylaluminum undergoes thermal cracking at $200 \sim 250°$:

$$4\, AlMe_3 = Al_4C_3 + 9\, CH_4$$

(iii) *Reaction with Unsaturated Bonds.* This relates to the part (4) of the general properties of organoaluminum compounds described above. Organoaluminums react with olefins in two different ways: addition or "growing" reactions (see Eq. 1); and replacement reactions (see Eq. 2).

$$Al-C_nH_{2n+1} + C_mH_{2m} \longrightarrow Al-C_{n+m}H_{2(n+m)+1} \tag{1}$$

$$Al-C_nH_{2n+1} + C_mH_{2m} \longrightarrow \left[\underset{R}{\overset{H}{\underset{\diagdown}{\diagup}}} Al \underset{R}{\overset{H}{\diagup\diagdown}} Al \diagdown + C_nH_{2n} + C_mH_{2m} \right]$$

$$\longrightarrow Al-C_mH_{2m+1} + C_nH_{2n} \tag{2}$$

The additive reactivities of $Al-R$ or $Al-H$ decrease in the order $CH_2{=}CH_2 > R-CH{=}CH_2 > R_2C{=}CH_2$. $Al-H$ can add to ethylene easily at $60 \sim 80°$, forming AlC_2H_5. This AlC_2H_5 can further add to ethylene at $100 \sim 120°C$ and thus can grow to higher alkylaluminums. By hydrolyzing, polymers having molecular weights about 3000 can be obtained, but no higher polymer than this can be obtained by the use of alkylaluminums alone. Trimethylaluminum cannot undergo the ethylene growing reaction, and moreover, if this is admixed to another trialkylaluminum which can, the reactivity of the latter is greatly decreased. The reason is probably that the mixed methylethylaluminum produced by alkyl exchange has a stronger association tendency than the original. The existence of a trace of colloidal nickel accelerates the replacement reaction. By polymerizing ethylene with triethylaluminum and nickel, the growing reaction stops at the dimer stage and gives mostly butene-1. Ethylene is the only olefin which can grow by this reaction; in other α-olefins the replacement reaction predominates and the reaction stops at the dimer stage. As with Grignard reagents, reaction of R_3Al or R_2AlH with acetylene is dificult to do; the substitution reaction usually gives $1:1$ and $1:2$ adducts to acetylene, or acetylene derivatives mainly by *cis*-addition.

$$Al-C_2H_5 \xrightarrow[40 \sim 60°C]{HC{\equiv}CH} Al-CH{=}CHC_2H_5 \xrightarrow[120°C]{Al-C_2H_5} Al-\underset{\underset{Al}{|}}{CH}CH(C_2H_5)_2$$

But the substitution reaction has recently been found.

(iv) *Reaction with Carbonyl Compounds.* This relates to part (5) of the general properties of organoaluminum compounds. R_2AlH can reduce ketones, aldehydes, esters, nitriles, and quinoline in the same way as $LiAlH_4$. Trialkylaluminum can reduce ketones and aldehydes in the same way as $Al-H$, by liberating olefins in most cases, but the addition of $Al-R$ to these groups is also known. Usually only one alkyl is available among the three of trialkylaluminum. R_3Al can also react with acid chloride, which is a good preparation for ketones.

$$C_6H_5COCl + CH_3AlCl_2 \xrightarrow[\text{C}_6\text{H}_6]{\text{room temp.}} C_6H_5COCH_3 + AlCl_3$$

(v) *Reaction with Compounds Having Active Hydrogen.* This also relates to part (5). Organoaluminums are decomposed by alcohol, thiol, and amine, and the organo groups liberate as hydrocarbon. In particular, they react explosively (and dangerously) with water. A safe treatment of the waste organo-aluminum compounds in the vessel is to dilute them with abundant quantities of hydrocarbons and then to decompose them with alcohol. One application of this reaction is the pretreatment of Ziegler catalyst by hydrogen chloride gas in which the molecular weight adjustment of the formed polyethylene is realized.

(vi) *Reaction with Halogen.* This is similar to reaction (v). The $Al-C$ bond is cleaved by halogens.

$$(CH_3)_2AlCl \xrightarrow[\text{C}_6\text{H}_6,\ 0°C]{Cl_2} CH_3AlCl_2 + CH_3Cl$$

The quantitative analysis of alkylaluminum by iodimetry is one application of this reaction.

(vii) *Oxidation.* This belongs to the same type as the reaction with halo-gens. The lower alkylaluminums react with oxygen vigorously and ignite spontaneously, so these compounds must be maintained in nitrogen, argon, or other inactive gas atmospheres. When they are mixed very slowly with oxygen, they form aluminum alcoholate and on further hydrolysis, alcohol.

$$R_3Al \xrightarrow{O_2} (RO)_3Al \xrightarrow{H_2O} ROH + Al(OH)_3$$

The first two oxygen atoms are absorbed rapidly, but the third one only slowly. Peroxide is formed as an intermediate which soon disappears by reacting with the unreacted organoaluminum.

$$Al-R \xrightarrow{O_2} Al-O-O-R \xrightarrow{Al-R} 2\,AlOR$$

Primary alcohol may be obtained in one course by combining direct synthesis of alkylaluminum and its auto-oxidation with hydrolysis of the aluminum alcoholate intermediate. This course plays a very important role in the petrochemical industry.

(viii) *Reaction with Carbon Dioxide.* This relates to part (5) of the general properties of organoaluminum compounds described above. These compounds react with carbon dioxide to give carboxylic acid or tertiary alcohol:

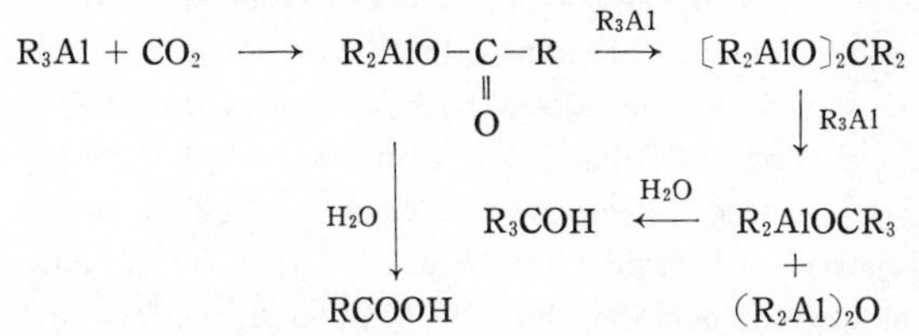

$$R_3Al + CO_2 \longrightarrow R_2AlO-\underset{\underset{O}{\|}}{C}-R \overset{R_3Al}{\longrightarrow} [R_2AlO]_2CR_2$$

$$\downarrow R_3Al$$

$$H_2O \downarrow \qquad R_3COH \overset{H_2O}{\longleftarrow} R_2AlOCR_3$$

$$+$$

$$RCOOH \qquad (R_2Al)_2O$$

In order to stop at the stage of carboxylic acid, R_3Al must be added slowly to excess CO_2 dissolved in hydrocarbon. Among the three organo groups, only one reacts at $100°C$, and even under pressure only two are reactive. Sulfur dioxide on the other hand, reacts with all three organo groups and on hydrolyzing gives sulfinic acid.

$$AlR_3 + 3SO_2 \longrightarrow Al|O-\underset{\underset{O}{\|}}{S}-R|_3 \overset{H_2O}{\longrightarrow} RS-OH + Al(OH)_3$$
$$\underset{O}{\|}$$

(ix) *Synthesis of Other Organometallics.* This relates to parts (1) and (5) of the general properties of organoaluminum compounds. It has recently become possible to obtain organoaluminums abundantly and inexpensively, and the preparation of other organometallics has been extensively studied. These can react with halides and oxides of many kinds of metals and metalloids to obtain many types of products. If the other metals are alkylmetals, the only possible reaction is the exchange of alkyl groups. The exchange reactions between trialkylaluminum and boron proceed very rapidly even without catalyst. Alkyl groups with the same structure, ethyl and *n*-butyl, for example, can distribute evenly between the two metals. In this case, the metal alkyls have a tendency to associats each other and make it possible to exchange alkyls. If higher alkyls are involved, aluminum atoms bond selectively with the lower alkyls to yield the higher association state of AlR_3. However, the exchange reaction shown below has the reverse result, because the boiling point of BEt_3 is $100°C$, which is lower than that of $AlEt_3$. This affords a preparative method for organoaluminums which are difficult to obtain by any other route.

$$B(CH_2Ph)_3 + AlEt_3 \longrightarrow BEt_3 + Al(CH_2Ph)_3$$

The separation of the products is very clear. The alkylation of oxides and halides by organoaluminum componuds is broadly described by the following general formula:

$$alR + elX \longrightarrow alX + elR$$

here, al is 1/3 Al, el is one equivalent of another optional element, X is a negative atom or the equivalent in radicals. In this case, the possible reaction of the first alR in AlR_3 does not neccessarily arise from the alR in AlR_2X. This reaction has been studied for lead, mercury, boron, silicon, tin, galium, titanium, phosphorus, antimony, bismuth, and many other elements, including the improved method of tetraethyl lead preparation.   In the exchange reaction between alkyl-aluminum hydrides and silicones, $(R_2SiO)_n$, hydrogen exceeds alkyl.   This reduction is also attained by using $Na(AlR_3H)$, $Na(AlR_2H_2)$, and NaH activated with AlR_3.

(x) *Electrolysis of Organoaluminum Compounds.*   This relates to part (6) of the general properties of organoaluminums.   Organoaluminums cannot conduct electricity as single components, but the compound of the type $M(AlR_4)$, when complexed with organo alkali metal or sodium fluoride, can conduct because of the ionic charactor.   By electrolysis of these compounds, or by using the ethyl radical generated on the cathode the purification of aluminum is achieved, or the ethylated compound of the metal comprising the cathode can be obtainable. By this route, the preparation of tetraethyl lead and other organometallics, such as those of tin. antimony, zinc, and magnesium, have been studied.

4.5. Related Compounds

The most essential material for synthesis is aluminum metal, but the shape of this material varies from lump, granule, or foil (this means the thickness of the film is under 1 mm), to sheet and powder.   Generally the higher the purity of aluminum, the softer it becomes, making cutting difficult, even though the pre-treatment affects the softness.   Commercial aluminum foil and powder for painting are not preferable because of their impurity.   Especially, the use of stearic acid as a lubricant in milling is common, and the stearic acid must be removed by washing prior to using.   The purest aluminum available at the present time is the sheet or foil for condenser use.   In the Japanese Industrial Standard (JIS), reagent-grade aluminum is specified by K 8069, aluminum powder by K 8070, aluminum ingots by H 2102, and high-purified by three consecutive electrolyses by H 2103, the latter two are classified into five and three grades.

In anhydrous aluminum trichloride. H 8115, the yellow color is generally proportional to the content of iron, and the white lumps are preferable for use. When the compound absorb moisture, it becomes a white powder which cannot be returned to the original anhydrous state by any ordinary method.   Contrary to this, anhydrous aiuminum tribromide may be prepared or purified by distil-lation in the laboratory.

Another related material, aluminum triisopropoxide, can be prepared from isopropanol and aluminum, and a transparent, colorless liquid is obtained by vacuum distillation which solidifies after several days.   This phenomenon is produced not only by oxidation or hydration, but also by the further complexing action around the aluminum atom by which it polymerizes and the liquid state can be recovered by vacuum distillation.   Finally, of the aluminum hydrides, lithium aluminum hydride, $LiAlH_4$, is most widely used.

REFERENCES

1) H. Zeiss, "Organometallic Chemistry", p. 194~269, K. Ziegler, "Organo-aluminum Compounds", Reihold (1960).
2) "Reaktsii i Metody Issledovaniya Organicheskikh Soedinenii", 10. A. F. Zhigach, D. S. Stasinevich, "Metody Sinteza Aliuminiiorganicheskikh Soedinenii", p. 209~374.
3) A. N. Nesmeyanov, K. A. Kocheshkov, "Metody Element-Organicheskoi Khimii", Nauka, Moscow (1964); English edition, "Methods of Elemento-Organic Chemistry", North-Holland Publishing Company, Amsterdam (1967).

【Al】

AlCH₃Br₂
① Methylaluminum dibromide
   CH₃AlBr₂
② Al + MeBr

   in autoclave, distn. by Podbielniak
   →

③ Solid. (124~139°/50). [79°].
   Sol. in org. solvents. Decomp. with
   H₂O. Dimer in liq. phase.
⑥ JOC **5**, 106 (1940).

AlCH₃Cl₂
① Methylaluminum dichloride
   CH₃AlCl₂
② Me₃Al₂Cl₃ + AlCl₃

   distn. 97~101°/100 mmHg.
   →

   Me₃Al₂Cl₃ + Cl₂ $\xrightarrow{0\sim5° \text{ in benzen}}$ 86%
③ White crystals. (100°/100). [72.7°].
   Sol. in org. solvents. Flammable in
   air ; explode in H₂O.
   Dimer in liq. and vap. phases.
⑤ Chemical intermediate such as for
   the use of Lewis acid and methylating agent.
⑥ Ann. **589**, 91 (1954).   JOC **5**, 106
   (1940).

AlCH₃N₆
① Methyldiazidoaluminum
   CH₃Al(N₃)₂
② Al(CH₃)₃ + 2 HN₃ ⟶ CH₃Al(N₃)₂
   2 CH₄
③ White solid.
   Sol. in THF ; decomp. with acid, air
   and H₂O.
④ + 3 H⁺ ⟶ CH₄ + Al³⁺ + 2 HN₃
   + O₂ ⟶ 2 CH₃OAl(N₃)₂
⑥ Z. Naturf. **9 b**, 495 (1954).

AlC₂H₅Cl₂
① Ethylaluminum dichloride

C₂H₅AlCl₂
② Et₃Al₂Cl₃ + AlCl₃

   180~190° with EtI catalyst
   →

   EtCl + Al + AlCl₃ $\xrightarrow{30\sim80°, \text{ 10 hr}}$
③ Yellow liq. (194°, extrapd.). [22°].
   Vap. press 8°/12, 100°/30, 120°/69,
   160°/280. *d* 1.232 (25°/0°).
   Sol. in org. solvent. Viscosity 3.18 cp
   (23.3°). Decomp. with air and
   H₂O.
   Dimer in liq. phase.
⑤ Catalyst for· polymn. of olefins and
   hydrogenation of aromatics. Chemical intermediate.
⑥ JOC **5**, 106 (1940).   Ethyl Corp.
   Bulletins - Aluminum alkyls (Dec.
   1958).   Fr. 1044081 (1958).

AlC₂H₅I₂
① Ethylaluminum diiodide
   C₂H₅AlI₂
② Et₃Al₂I₃ $\xrightarrow[\text{distn. in Vigreau column}]{158\sim160°/4\sim5 \text{ mmHg}}$

   Et₃Al + I₂ $\xrightarrow{\text{heat in Ether}}$
③ Crystals. (158~160°/4).´ [35~37°].
   Decomp. with H₂O. Sol. in org.
   solvents.
⑥ Izv. OKhN **1959**, 166.   Compt. rend.
   179, 89 (1924).   JOC **5**, 106 (1940).

AlC₂H₆Br
① Dimethylaluminum bromide
   (CH₃)₂AlBr
② Al + MeBr $\xrightarrow[\text{distn. by Podbielniak}]{\text{in autoclave}}$
③ Colorless liq. (150°), (29°/5), (74~
   77°/50).
   Sol. in org. solvents. Decomp. with
   H₂O. Spont. flammable in air.
   Associate in dimer form.
⑥ JOC **5**, 106 (1940).

AlC₂H₆Cl

① Dimethylaluminum chloride
(CH₃)₂AlCl

② Me₃Al₂Cl₃ $\xrightarrow[\text{distn. in Podbielniak}]{70\sim76°/100\text{ mmHg.}}$

Me₃Al₂Cl₃ + NaCl ⟶

③ Colorless liq. (119.4°), (84~4°/200),
(25°/14). [−45°].
Decomp. with H₂O. Sol. in org.
solvents.
Dimer in liq. and vap. phases.

⑤ Catalyst for polymn. of olefins, and
methylating agent.

⑥ Ann. **589**, 91 (1954).   JACS **60**, 2276
(1938).   JOC **5**, 106 (1940).

AlC₂H₇

① Dimethylaluminum hydride
(CH₃)₂AlH

② LiAlH₄ + Me₃Al $\xrightarrow{\text{heat over 24 hr.}}$

Al + H₂ + Me₃Al $\xrightarrow[250\text{ atm.(initial pressure),}120\sim130\text{(final)}]{210\sim130°,\,24\text{ hr}}$ 85%

Me₃Al + H₂ $\xrightarrow[300\text{ atm., }200\text{ hr}]{150\sim160°\text{ in hexane}}$ 50%

③ Colorless liq. (154°), (25°/2).
Decomp. at 160°. log $P = -2575/T$
+ 8.92.
Decomp. with H₂O. Sol. in org. solvents.
Mixt. of equal amounts of dimer and
trimer in the lowest temp., whereas
the dimer is predominant at higher
temp.

④ Me₂AlH + RCH=CH₂ ⟶
Me₂AlCH₂CH₂R

⑤ Hydrogenating agent and chemical
intermediate.

⑥ Ber. **75 B** 2003 (1942).   JACS **75**, 835
(1953) ; **72**, 3237 (1950).   Ger. 16850
(1959).

AlC₃H₆Br₃

① Tris(bromomethyl)aluminum
Al(CH₂Br)₃

② AlBr₃ + CH₂N₂ $\xrightarrow{-50°}$

③ Solid. (119~120°/0.7), (128~129°/4.5).
[47~48°].

⑥ Dokl. **118**, 1121 (1958).

AlC₃H₆Cl₃

① Tris(chloromethyl)aluminum
Al(CH₂Cl)₃

② AlCl₃ + CH₂N₂ $\xrightarrow{-50°}$

③ (108~109°/1.5), (128~129°/4.5). [32~
33°].

⑥ Dokl. **118**, 1121 (1958).

AlC₃H₉

① Trimethylaluminum
(CH₃)₃Al

② Me₂AlCl + NaF $\xrightarrow{180°,\,5\text{ hr. in benzene}}$
80~90%

Me₂Hg + Al $\xrightarrow{\text{heat}}$

③ Colorless liq. Decomp. above 70°.
(20°/8.4). (60°/68.5). [15.4°]. n_D
1.432 (12°). d 0.752 (20°/0°).
Specific heat 0.53 (33°).
Decomp. with H₂O and air. Sol. in
org. solvenets.
Heat of combustion : 10.5 kcal/mol.
Dimer in liq. and vapour forms ;
dissociation energy 20.0 kcal/mol.

④ Spont. flammable.

⑤ Catalyst for polymerization of
olefins. Pyrophoric fuel.

⑥ Ethyl Corp. Bulletins-Alminum
Alkyls (Dec. 1958).   Ann. **589**, 91
(1954).   Ger. 13368 (1958).

AlC₃H₉O

① Dimethylaluminum methoxide

(CH₃)₂AlOCH₃

② Me₃Al + Al(OMe)₃ ⟶

③ White crystals. [35°].
Doesn't dissociate by ethers.
Stable trimer.

⑥ JACS **64**, 316 (1942).

AlC₄H₉Cl₂

① *n*-Butylaluminum dichloride
n-C₄H₉AlCl₂

② AlCl₃ + BuMgCl $\xrightarrow{\text{in Et}_2\text{O}}$

③ Liq. (118°/10), (105°/5), (77°/1).
[−29.8°]. n_D 1.4604 (20°). d 1.1218
(20°/20°), 1.1116 (30°/20°).
Decomp. with H₂O. Sol. in org. solvents.

⑥ Ber. **92**, 2714 (1959).

AlC₄H₉Cl₂

① Isobutylaluminum dichloride
(i-C₄H₉)AlCl₂

② (i-Bu)₃Al + AlCl₃ $\xrightarrow{140°}$

③ Colorless liq. (105°/5), (41~43°/0.03).
[−29.8°]. d 1.1218 (20°/20°).
Decomp. with H₂O. Sol. in org.
solvents.

⑤ Catalyst for polymn. of olefins.
Chemical intermediate.

⑥ J. Polymer Sci. **38**, 51 (1959). Stauffer
Chem. Co. Bulletins.

AlC₄H₁₀Cl

① Diethylaluminum chloride
(C₂H₅)₂AlCl

② Al-Mg (powder mixture or alloy)
+ EtCl $\xrightarrow{70°}$
Et₃Al₂Cl₃ + Na−Hg (1%) $\xrightarrow{118°}$ 95%
Et₃Al₂Cl₃ $\xrightarrow{110°, 1\,hr.}$

③ Colorless liq. (208°, extrapd.). (40°/1,
90°/12, 110°/29, 130°/65, 150°/134,
170°/256, 190°/465). [−74°]. d 0.958

(25°/4°).
Spont. flammable; explode in H₂O.
Dimer in liq. form. Decomp. with
air and H₂O. Sol. in org. solvents.

④ + O₂ ⟶ (EtO)₂AlCl
+ H₂O ⟶ Cl(Et)AlOAl(Et)Cl
+ CO₂ ⟶ EtCO₂H

⑤ A component of Ziegler-Natta catalysts. Ethylating agent.

⑥ Z. Elektrochem. **64**, 616 (1960). Ma-
kromol. Chem. **18**, 186(1956). Ethyl
Corp. Bulletins-Aluminum Alkyls
(Dec. 1958).

AlC₄H₁₀ClO

① Ethylethoxyaluminum chloride
(C₂H₅)(C₂H₅O)AlCl

② Al + AlX₃ + R₂O $\xrightarrow{170°,\ 8\,hr.\ 100\,atm.}$
(Coarse powder)
Et(EtO)AlCl

③ Colorless liq. (85°/1).
Decomp. with air and H₂O. Sol. in
org. solvents.

⑥ Brit. 804059 (1958).

AlC₄H₁₀I

① Diethylaluminum iodide
(C₂H₅)₂AlI

② Et₃Al₂I₃ $\xrightarrow{118~120°/4~5\,mmHg}$
Et₃Al + AlI₃ $\xrightarrow{\text{distn. in vacuum}}$

③ Liq. (118~120°/4). d 1.6091 (27°/4°).
Sol. in org. solvents.

⑥ Ann. **566**, 113 (1950). JOC **5**, 106
(1940). Compt. rend. **179**, 89(1924).

AlC₄H₁₁

① Diethylaluminum hydride
(C₂H₅)₂AlH

② Et₂AlCl + NaH ⟶ Et₂AlH
+ NaCl
Et₂AlCl + 2 LiH ⟶ Li(AlEt₂H₂)
Et₂AlCl $\xrightarrow{}$ 2 Et₂AlH

$$2\,Et_3Al + AlH_3 \longrightarrow 3\,Et_2AlH$$

③ Colorless liq. (55~56°/0.001~0.0001 decomp.) n_D 1.47396 (20°). d 0.808 (20°), 0.8081 (22°).

Decomp. with H_2O and air. Flammable.

Associates as more than dimer.

④ $Et_2AlH + RCH=CH_2 \longrightarrow$

$$Et_2AlCH_2CH_2R$$

$$+ \; \begin{matrix} Et \\ n\text{-Bu} \end{matrix}\!\!>\!\!C=CH_2 \longrightarrow$$

$$\begin{matrix} Et \\ n\text{-Bu} \end{matrix}\!\!>\!\!CH-CH_2AlEt_3$$

⑤ Hydrogenating agent and chemical intermediate.

⑥ Angew. **64**, 323 (1952). Ann. **589**, 91 (1954).

AlC₄H₁₂N

① Dimethylaminodimethylaluminum
$(CH_3)_2AlN(CH_3)_2$

② $Me_3Al \cdot NHMe_2 \xrightarrow{110°}$

$Me_2AlH + Me_2NH \xrightarrow{\text{boil in pentene}}$

③ Crystals. [154~156°].
Decomp. with H_2O. Sol. in org. solvents.
Dimer form.

④ $Me_2AlNMe_2 + 4\,HCl \longrightarrow 2\,CH_4$
$+ Me_2NH_2Cl : AlCl_3$

⑥ JACS **64**, 316 (1942).

AlC₄H₁₂ClO

① Dimethylaluminum chloride-dimethylether complex
$(CH_3)_2AlCl \cdot (CH_3)_2O$

② $Me_2AlCl + Me_2O \xrightarrow{\text{distn.}}$

③ Colorless liq. (224°).
Sol. in org. solvents.

⑥ JACS **64**, 316 (1942).

AlC₅H₁₅ClN

① Dimethylaluminum chloride-

trimethylamine complex
$(CH_3)_2AlCl \cdot N(CH_3)_3$

② $Me_2AlCl + NMe_3 \longrightarrow$

③ Solid. [124°].

⑥ JACS **64**, 316 (1942).

AlC₅H₁₅O

① Trimethylaluminum-dimethylether complex
$(CH_3)_3Al \cdot (CH_3)_2O$

② $Me_3Al + Me_2O \longrightarrow$

$AlCl_3 + MeMgBr \xrightarrow{\text{in Me}_2O} 100\%$

③ Colorless liq. (159°). [−30°].
Decomp. with H_2O. Sol. in org. solvents. Spont. inflammable.

⑥ JACS **64**, 316 (1942). Ber. **56**, 446 (1923). JOC **13**, 711 (1948).

AlC₅H₁₆N

① Trimethylaluminum-dimethylamine complex
$(CH_3)_3Al \cdot NH(CH_3)_2$

② $Me_3Al + NHMe_2 \longrightarrow$

③ Solid. [49°].

⑥ JACS **64**, 316 (1942).

AlC₆H₅Br₂

① Phenylaluminum dibromide
$C_6H_5AlBr_2$

② $Ph_3Al + AlBr_3 \longrightarrow$

③ Crystals. [77~78°].
Decomp. with H_2O. Sol. in org. solvents.

⑥ JOC **5**, 106 (1940).

AlC₆H₅Cl₂

① Phenylaluminum chloride
$C_6H_5AlCl_2$

② $2\,Ph_3Al + AlCl_3 \longrightarrow \frac{3}{2}(Ph_2AlCl)_2$

③ Solid. [94~95°].
Decomp. with H_2O. Sol. in org. solvents.

⑥ JACS **49**, 830 (1927).   JOC **4**, 162 (1939).

AlC₆H₁₅
① Triethylalminum
(C₂H₅)₃Al
② Al + 3 C₂H₄ + 1.5 H₂ $\longrightarrow$ Al(C₂H₅)₃
Et₃Al₂Cl₃ + Na $\longrightarrow$ Et₃Al + NaCl + Al

Al + Et₂Zn $\xrightarrow{110°}$

③ Colorless liq. (194° decomp.). (207° extrapd.). [−46°]. n_D 1.480 (6.5°). d 0.8324 (25°/0°).
Spont. flammable. Explode in H₂O and air. Sol. in org. solvents. 2.58 cp (25°). Specific heat 0.527 (33°).
④ 3 Cl₃CCHO + AlEt₃ $\longrightarrow$
(Cl₃CCHO)₃Al + 3 C₂H₄
(Cl₃CCHO)₃Al + 3 H₂O $\longrightarrow$
3 Cl₃CCHOH + Al(OH)₃
⑤ A component of Ziegler-Natta catalysts. Ethylating agent.
⑥ Z. Elektrochem. **64**, 616(1960).   Ann. (Rome) **48**, 193 (1958).   Ethyl Co. Bulletins-Alminum Alkyls (Dec. 1958).

AlC₆H₁₅FNa
① Sodium triethylfluoroaluminum
Na[(C₂H₅)₃AlF]
② NaF + Et₃Al $\xrightarrow{\text{extd. by hexane}}$
③ Solid. [72∼74°].
Stable in ether; decomp. by Me₃N.
⑥ Ann. **629**, 33 (1960).

AlC₆H₁₅FK
① Potassium triethylfluoroaluminum
K[(C₂H₅)₃AlF]
② KF + Et₃Al $\xrightarrow{\text{vibration reactor in hexane}}$
③ Solid. [56∼58°].
⑥ Ann. **629**, 33 (1960).

AlC₆H₁₈N
① Trimethylaluminum-trimethylamine complex
(CH₃)₃Al·N(CH₃)₃
② Me₃Al + NMe₃ $\longrightarrow$
③ Solid. [105°].
⑥ JACS **64**, 316 (1942).

AlC₆H₁₈P
① Trimethylaluminum-trimethylphosphine complex
(CH₃)₃Al·P(CH₃)₃
② Me₃Al + PMe₃ $\longrightarrow$
③ [62.5°].
⑥ JACS **64**, 316 (1942).

AlC₇H₁₇O
① Diethylaluminum propoxide
(C₂H₅)₂AlOC₃H₇
② Et₃Al + C₃H₇OC₃H₇ $\xrightarrow{130∼145°}$
⑥ Izv. OKhN **1959**, 444.

AlC₇H₁₉O
① Trimethylaluminum-diethylether complex
(CH₃)₃Al·O(C₂H₅)₂
② Me₃Al + Et₂O $\longrightarrow$
AlCl₃ + MeMgBr $\xrightarrow{\text{in Et₂O}}$ 100%
③ Liq. (68°/15).
Spont. flammable.
⑥ Ann. **589**, 91 (1954).   JOC **13**, 711 (1848).

AlC₈H₁₈Cl
① Diisobutylaluminum chloride
(i-C₄H₉)₂AlCl
② (i-Bu)₃Al + AlCl₃ $\longrightarrow$
③ Colorless liq. (152°/10, 138°/5, 108°/1). [−39.5]. n_D 1.4506 (20°). d 0.9088 (20°/20°), 0.9013 (30°/20°), 0.914 (25°/4°).

Decomp. with H_2O. Sol. in org. solvents.

⑤ Compoment of the Ziegler's catalyst. Chemical intermediate.

⑥ J. Polymer Sci. **38**, 51 (1959). Ber. **88**, 742 (1955).

AlC₈H₁₉

① Diisobutylaluminum hydride $(i\text{-}C_4H_9)_2AlH$

② $Al + (i\text{-}Bu)_3Al + H_2$

$$\xrightarrow[110\sim115°,\ 100\,atm.,\ 4\sim6\,hr]{} 89\%$$

$$(i\text{-}Bu)_3Al \xrightarrow{100\sim120°} 100\%$$

⑤ Hydrogenating agent. Chemical intermediate.

⑥ Stauffer Chem. Co. Bulletins.   J. Polymer Sci. **38**, 51 (1959).   Ger. 14808 (1958).

AlC₈H₂₀Li

① Lithium aluminum tetraethyl $LiAl(C_2H_5)_4$

② $LiAlH_4 + 4 C_2H_4$

$$\xrightarrow{Et_2O\ in\ autoclave,\ 80\,atm.}$$

$$Et_3Al + Li \xrightarrow{60\sim100°}$$

$LiAlH_4 + C_2H_4$

$$\xrightarrow{120°,\ 42\,atm.\ 3\,hr,\ AlCl_3\ or\ ZnCl_2\ in\ decalin}$$

$99\sim100\%$

③ Crystals. [160°].

⑥ Ann. **589**, 91 (1954).   Brit. 757524 (1957).

AlC₈H₂₀N

① Diethylaminodiethylaluminum $(C_2H_5)_2AlN(C_2H_5)_2$

② $Et_3Al + Et_2NC_3H_5 \longrightarrow$

③ Liq. (141~145°/14). Sol. in org. solvents. Decomp. with H_2O.

⑥ Izv. OKhN **1959**, 444.

AlC₈H₂₀Na

① Tetraethylaluminum sodium $NaAl(C_2H_5)_4$

② $NaEt + AlEt_3 \cdot Et_2O \xrightarrow[on\ cooling]{in\ petr.\ ether}$

$$Na + AlEt_3 \xrightarrow{130°} NaAlEt_4 + Al$$

③ Colorless crystals. [125°]. Sol. in Et_2O, less sol. in C_6H_6.

⑤ Dehydration agent of org. solvents.

⑥ JACS **75**, 5193 (1953). Z. anorg. allg. Chem. **141**, 161(1924). Angew. **72**, 565 (1960).   J. Phys. Chem. **68**, 2595 (1964).

AlC₈H₂₀OCl

① Diethylaluminum chloride-diethyl-ether complex $(C_2H_5)_2AlCl \cdot (C_2H_5)_2O$

② $Et_2AlCl + Et_2O \longrightarrow$

③ Liq. Decomp. with H_2O. Sol. in org. solvents.

⑥ Ann. **589**, 91 (1954).

AlC₉H₂₁

① Tri-*n*-propylaluminum $(n\text{-}C_3H_7)_3Al$

② $LiAlPr_4 + AlCl_4 \xrightarrow[ball\ mill\ reactor]{in\ hexane\ by}$

75%

③ Colorless liq. (248~252°, 65°/15). [−107°]. d 0.823 (20°), 0.827 (17°). Decomp. with H_2O. Sol in. org. solvents.

⑥ Ann. **589**, 91 (1954).   JACS **68**, 2204 (1946).

AlC₉H₂₁

① Triisopropylaluminum $Al(i\text{-}C_3H_7)_3$

② $(i\text{-}Pr)_2Hg + Al \xrightarrow{100\sim120°}$

③ Colorless liq. [2°].

Decomp. with H₂O. Sol. in org.
  solvents.
⑥ JACS **68**, 2204 (1946).   Izv. OKhN
  1958, 1279.

AlC₁₀H₂₃
① Diethylisohexylaluminum
  $(i\text{-}C_6H_{13})Al(C_2H_5)_2$
② EtAlH + hexene-2
  $\xrightarrow{\text{65°, 48 hr. in sealed tube}}$ 86%
③ Colorless liq. (42.5~44.0°/10).
  Decomp. with H₂O. Sol. in org.
  solvents.
⑥ Ann. **589**, 91 (1954).

AlC₁₀H₂₃O
① Diethyl-4-ethoxybutylaluminum

$(C_2H_5)_2Al\left\langle\begin{array}{c}CH_2-CH_2\\ \diagdown CH_2\\ O-CH_2\\ |\\ C_2H_5\end{array}\right.$

② $\left.\begin{array}{l}Et_2AlCl\\ \text{or}\\ Et_2AlI\end{array}\right\}$ + ClMg(CH₂)₄OEt $\xrightarrow{Et_2O}$
③ Colorless liq. (99.5°/5.5).
  Spont. flammable.
  Decomp. with air. Sol. in org.
  solvents.
⑥ Ber. **88**, 251, 1765 (1955).

AlC₁₀H₂₅O
① Triethylaluminum–diethylether
  complex
  $Al(C_2H_5)_3 \cdot (C_2H_5)_2O$
② Et₃Al·anisolate + Et₂O
  $\xrightarrow[\text{standing in r. t.}]{\text{smooth reaction by}}$ 100%
  AlCl₃ + EtMgBr $\xrightarrow{\text{in Et}_2O}$ 100%
③ Colorless liq. (216~218°, 112°/16).
  n_D 1.4370 (17.4°). d 0.8200 (17°/4°).
  Spont. flammable.
⑥ Ber. **56**, 466 (1923); **91**, 2446 (1958).

AlC₁₁H₂₆N
① Diethyl[(diethylamino)-3-propyl]-
  aluminum

$(C_2H_5)_2Al\left\langle\begin{array}{c}CH_2-CH_2\\ \\ N-CH_2\\ C_2H_5\ \ C_2H_5\end{array}\right.$

② Et₂AlI + ClMg(CH₂)₃NEt₂ $\longrightarrow$
③ Straw liq. (97°/2). [−2°].
  Spont. flammable.
  Decomp. with air. Sol. in org.
  solvents.
⑥ Ber. **88**, 251 (1954).   Izv. OKhN **1959**,
  444.

AlC₁₂H₂₇
① Tri-*n*-butylaluminum
  $(n\text{-}C_4H_9)_3Al$
② $(n\text{-Bu})_2Hg$ + Al $\xrightarrow[\text{in xylene}]{135\sim140°, 38\,hr.}$ 90%
  $(s\text{-Bu})_3Al$ $\xrightarrow{110\sim130°, 30\,hr.}$ 100%
③ Colorless liq. (120°/2). [20°]. d 0.823
  (20°/20°).
  Spont. flammable.
  Explode in H₂O and decomp. in air.
⑥ Izv. OKhN **1958**, 1279.

AlC₁₂H₂₇
① Triisobutylaluminum
  $(i\text{-}C_4H_9)_3Al$
② Al + H₂ + isobutylene + $(i\text{-Bu})_3Al$
  $\xrightarrow[\text{200 atm.(initial), 60 atm. (final)}]{110\sim120°,\ 4\sim5\,hr.}$ 66.5%
③ Colorless liq. (86°/10, 73°/5, 33~35°/
  0.10), (114°/30, 130°/58, 30°/0.06).
  [1.0~4.3°]. n_D 1.4494 (20°). d 0.7859
  (20°/20°), 0.7738 (30°/20°).
  Decomp. with air ; explode in H₂O.
  Sol. in org. solvents.
  Viscosity 2.39 cp (20°).
④ $(i\text{-Bu})_3Al \xrightarrow{200°} (i\text{-Bu})_2AlH$

$+ (CH_3)_2C=CH_2$

⑤ Catalyst for polymn. of olefins.
   Chemical intermediate.

⑥ J. Polymer Sci. **38**, 5106 (1959). Ber.
   88, 742 (1955).

AlC₁₂H₂₈Li

① Lithium aluminum tetrapropyl
   $LiAl(C_3H_7)_4$

② $LiAlH_4$ + propylene $\xrightarrow{\text{137~170° in vacuum}}$

   $LiAlH_4$ + propylene $\xrightarrow[\text{120°, AlCl}_3]{}$ 96%

③ Crystals.

⑥ Ann. **589**, 91 (1954).   Fr. 956956
   (1957).

AlC₁₃H₃₁O

① Tripropylaluminum–diethylether
   complex
   $Al(C_3H_7)_3 \cdot (C_2H_5)_2O$

② $AlH_3 + 3C_3H_6 \xrightarrow[\text{in autoclave}]{\text{in Et}_2\text{O, 127°, 6 hr.}}$

③ Colorless liq. (76°/0.4, 135°/18).
   Sol. in org. solvents. Decomp. with
   H_2O and air.

⑥ Ann. **589**, 91 (1959) ; **566**, 113 (1950).

AlC₁₄H₂₇

① Ethyldicyclohexylaluminum
   $C_2H_5Al(C_6H_{11})_2$

③ Decomp. with H_2O. Sol. in org. solvents.

⑥ Ann. **589**, 91 (1954).

AlC₁₄H₃₁O

① Diisobutyl(3-propoxypropyl)-
   aluminum
   $(i\text{-}C_4H_9)_2Al(CH_2)_3OC_3H_7$

③ Colorless liq. (103~104°/2).
   Sol. in. org. solvent. Decomp. with
   H_2O.

⑥ Izv. OKhN **1959**, 444.

AlC₁₅H₂₂N

① Triethylaluminum-quinolin complex
   $(C_2H_5)_3Al \cdot C_9H_7N$

③ Yellow crystals.
   Sol. in org. solvents.

⑥ Ber. **88**, 251 (1955).

AlC₁₅H₂₇

① Triisoprenylaluminum
   $(C_5H_9)_3Al$

③ Straw color viscous liq.   *d* 0.810
   (23°).
   The structure is not yet determined.

⑤ Catalyst for polymn. of olefins.

⑥ Ann. **14**, 460 (1888).

AlCl₁₅H₂₈Li

① Tricyclopentylhydrolithium
   aluminum
   $LiAlH(C_5H_9\text{-}cyclo)_3$

② $LiAlH_4$ + cyclopentene
   $\xrightarrow[\text{65 hr. in autoclave}]{\text{110~123°}}$

③ [72°].

⑥ Ann. **589**, 91 (1954).

AlC₁₅H₃₄N

① (3-Diethylaminopropy)ldiisobutyl-
   aluminum
   $(i\text{-}C_4H_9)_2Al(CH_2)_3N(C_2H_5)_2$

② $(i\text{-}Bu)_2AlH + Et_2NC_3H_5 \xrightarrow[\text{4 hr.}]{\text{90~100°}}$

③ Colorless liq. (115~116°/1.5).
   Sol. in org. solvents. Decomp. with
   H_2O.

⑥ Izv. OKhN **1959**, 444.

AlC₁₆H₃₇O

① Triisobutylalminum-diethylether
   complex
   $(i\text{-}C_4H_9)_3Al \cdot (C_2H_5)_2O$

②
$$AlH_3 + 3 \begin{array}{c} CH_3 \\ \diagdown \\ CH_3 \diagup \end{array} C=CH_2$$

with Et₂O in autoclave

$\xrightarrow{\text{60~65°, 6~8 hr.}}$

③ Colorless liq. (58~59°/0.001). [0°].
Sol. in org. solvents. Decomp. with
H₂O.

⑥ Ann. **589**, 91 (1954).

AlC₁₈H₁₅

① Triphenylaluminum
(C₆H₅)₃Al

② Ph₂Hg + Al $\xrightarrow{\text{in xylene}}$

PhLi + AlCl₃ $\xrightarrow{\text{decomp. of etherate}}$

NaAlPh₄ + CH₃COCl $\xrightarrow{\text{in vacuum}}$

③ White solid. [230°].
Sensiteve to O₂, H₂O and I₂. Sol. in
org. solvents.

⑤ Phenylating agent, and the other
chemical intermediate.

⑥ Ber. **90**, 2339 (1957).   Ann. **606**, 1
(1957).   Izv. OKhN 1957, 181.

AlC₁₈H₁₆Li

① Triphenylhydrolithium aluminum
LiAl(C₆H₅)₃H

② Ph₃Al + LiH ⟶

③ Colorless crystals.
Hexagonal plates.
Sol. in Et₂O.

⑥ Ann. **566**, 113 (1950).

AlC₁₈H₁₈N

① Triphenylaluminum ammonium
complex
(C₆H₅)₃Al·NH₃

③ Crystals. [114°].
Sol. in org. solvents. Decomp. with air.

⑥ Ann. **566**, 113 (1950).

AlC₁₈H₃₉

① Tri-2-methylpentylaluminum

$$(CH_3CH_2CH_2CHCH_2)_3Al$$
$$\qquad\qquad\quad |$$
$$\qquad\qquad\quad CH_3$$

③ Colorless liq. (120°/high *vacuo*),
(150°/0.01). *d* 0.798 (22°).

⑥ Stauffer Chem. Co. Bulletin.

AlC₁₈H₃₉

① Tri-*n*-hexylaluminum
(*n*-C₆H₁₃)₃Al

② (*i*-Bu)₃Al + hexene-1 $\xrightarrow{\text{110~120°}}$

AlH₃ + hexene-1 $\xrightarrow[\text{amount of Et}_2\text{O}]{\text{105° with small}}$

LiAlH₄ + hexene-1 + AlCl₃

110° forming complex first

$\xrightarrow{\text{then decomp. with AlCl}_3\text{ by heat}}$

③ Colorless liq. (105°/0.001, 150°/0.01).
d 0.826 (23°).
Sol. in org. solvents. Decomp. with
H₂O.

⑥ Ann. **589**, 91 (1954).

AlC₁₉H₄₃O

① Tris(2-methylbutyl)aluminum
diethylether complex (Optically
active)

$$(+) (CH_3CH_2CH_2CHCH_2)_3Al·(C_2H_5)_2O$$
$$\qquad\qquad\qquad\quad |$$
$$\qquad\qquad\qquad\quad CH_3$$

② AlCl₃ + (+)-2-methylbutyl-MgCl
$\xrightarrow{\text{in Et}_2\text{O}}$

⎰ HgCl₂ + 2 (+)-2-methylbuthyl-MgCl
⎱ ⟶ Hg(C₅H₁₁)₂

2 Al + 3 Hg(C₅H₁₁)₂ $\xrightarrow{\text{100~110°}}$
2 Al(C₅H₁₁)₃ (50%)

③ Colorless liq. (87~89°/0.6, 102~103°/
1.5). [α]$_D^{18.5}$=23.66, [α]$_D^{23}$=21.78.
d 0.824 (18°).

④ + O₂ ⟶ Al(OC₅H₁₁)₃
+ HCl aq. ⟶ AlCl₃ aq. + C₅H₁₁OH
Optical purity 27%.

⑤ Component of the optically active
Ziegler catalyst.

⑥ Angew. **70**, 599 (1958). BCSJ **33**, 658
(1960).

AlC₂₁H₂₁
① Tri-*p*-tolylaluminum
(p-CH₃C₆H₄)₃Al

② (p-CH₃C₆H₄)₂Hg + Al $\xrightarrow{\text{boiling in xylene}}$
③ White crystals. [262°].
Sol. in org. solvents. Decomp. in air.
④ (p-CH₃C₆H₄)₃Al + Et₂O ⟶ ether
complex [125°].
⑥ Ann. **14**, (6) 460 (1888).   Rec. trav.
chim. **55**, 133 (1936).

AlC₂₁H₄₀Li
① Tricycloheptylhydrolithium
aluminum
LiAlH(C₇H₁₃-*cyclo*)₃

② LiAlH₄ + cycloheptene $\xrightarrow[\text{several days}]{105°}$
③ White crystals.
⑥ Ann. **589**, 91 (1954).

AlC₂₂H₂₅N₂
① Diethylaluminum hydride diquino-
line complex
(C₂H₅)₂AlH·2 C₉H₇N
② Et₂AlH + 2 C₉H₇N ⟶
③ Red crystals.
Sol. in org. solvents. Decomp. with air
and H₂O.
⑥ Ber. **88**, 251 (1955).

AlC₂₂H₂₅O
① Triphenylaluminum-diethylether
complex
(C₆H₅)₃Al·(C₂H₅)₂O

② Ph₃Al + Et₂O + Ph₂Hg + Al $\xrightarrow{\text{in Et}_2\text{O}}$
PhLi + AlCl₃ $\xrightarrow{\text{in Et}_2\text{O}}$
③ White-needles. [112~113°].
Sol. in org. solvents.
⑥ Ber. **45**, 2828 (1912).   Ann. **606**, 1

(1957).

AlC₂₄H₂₀Li
① Tetraphenylaluminum lithium
LiAl(C₆H₅)₄
② Ph₃Al + PhLi ⟶
③ Needle crystals.
Sol. in ether and THF.
④ + 4 H₂O ⟶ Al(OH)₃ + LiOH
+ 4 C₆H₆
⑥ Ann. **566**, 113 (1950).

AlC₂₄H₂₇
① Tri-2-phenylethylaluminum
Al(CH₂CH₂C₆H₅)₃
② (*i*-Bu)₃Al + CH₂=CHC₆H₅ $\xrightarrow[\text{in hexan}]{\text{colloidal Ni}}$ 76~78%
Al + (*i*-Bu)₃Al + CH₂=CHC₆H₅ + H₂ $\xrightarrow{\text{Na, 182°, 125 atm.}}$

④ $\xrightarrow[\text{catalyst 3.9\%, 100 hr. in 80°}]{\substack{\text{isomerization reaction}\\ \text{by Ni acetylacetonate}}}$ Al(CHC₆H₅)₃
|
CH₃
$\xrightarrow{\text{O}_2,\ \text{H}_2\text{O}}$ Al(OCH₂CH₂C₆H₅)₃ $\xrightarrow{\text{H}_2\text{O}}$
C₆H₅CH₂CH₂OH
⑥ JACS **81**, 2561 (1959).   Fr. 1179056
(1959).

AlC₂₄H₅₁
① Tri(2-ethylhexyl)aluminum
(C₈H₁₇)₃Al

② (*i*-Bu)₃Al + 2-ethylhexene-1 $\xrightarrow{\text{heat at bp}}$

AlH₃ + 2-ethylhexene-1 $\xrightarrow{80~115°}$
Al + (*i*-Bu)₃Al + 2-ethylhexene
+ H₂ $\xrightarrow{\text{Na, 180°, 140 atm.}}$
③ Colorless liq (115°/0.01).
Sol. in org. solvents. Decomp. with
H₂O.
⑥ Ann. **589**, 91 (1954).

AlC$_{25}$H$_{31}$O
① Tri-p-tolylaluminum-diethylether
   complex
   $(p\text{-}CH_3C_6H_4)_3Al\cdot(C_2H_5)_2O$
② $(p\text{-}CH_3C_6H_4)_2Hg + Al \xrightarrow[\text{sealed tube}]{120\sim130° \text{ in Et}_2O}$
③ (275° decomp.). [127°].
⑥ Ber. **63**, 2401 (1930).

AlC$_{24}$H$_{46}$Li
① Tricyclooctylhydrolithium aluminum
   $LiAlH(C_8H_{15})_3$
② $LiAlH_4 + cyclooctene \longrightarrow$
③ Liq. (147°). [7°]. n_D 1.4588 (20°).
   Sol. in org. solvents. Decomp. in
   H$_2$O.
⑥ Ann. **589**, 91 (1954).

AlC$_{24}$H$_{51}$
① Tri-n-octylaluminum
   $(n\text{-}C_8H_{17})_3Al$
② $(n\text{-}C_8H_{17})_2Hg + Al \xrightarrow{\text{heat}}$
③ Colorless liq. d 0.810 (25°).
⑥ Fr. 1179056 (1959).

Al$_2$C$_3$H$_9$Br$_3$
① Methylaluminum sesquibromide
   $(CH_3)_3Al_2Br_3$
② $Me_3Al + AlBr_3 \xrightarrow{\text{admix. by cooling}}$
③ Yellow liq. (166° extrapd.). (60°/15),
   (100°/89). [4°]. n_D 1.514 (25°).
   Viscosity 2.76 cp (23.3°).
   Sol. in org. solvents. Decomp. with
   H$_2$O. Spont. flammable.
⑥ JOC **5**, 106 (1940).

Al$_2$C$_3$H$_9$Cl$_3$
① Methylaluminum sesquichloride
   $(CH_3)_3Al_2Cl_3$

② $3 CH_3Cl + Al \xrightarrow[\text{vap. phase}]{\text{Cu powder catalyst}}$
③ (50°/22.6). [22.8°]. d 1.1629 (25°).
   Spont. flammable: explode violently
   in H$_2$O.
④ $+ Me_2SiCl_2 \xrightarrow{TiCl_3} Me_3SiCl$
   $+ Me_3SiOSiMe_3 \longrightarrow Me_4Si$
   $+ Me_3SiOAlMeCl$
   $+ B_2O_3 \longrightarrow Me_3B$
⑥ Ethyl Co. Bulletins-Aluminum
   Alkyls (Dec. 1958). J. Chem. Soc.
   Japan (Ind. Chem. Sect.) **62**, 1106
   (1959).

Al$_2$C$_3$H$_{12}$
① Methylaluminum sesquihydride
   $(CH_3)_3Al_2H_3$
③ Decomp. with air and H$_2$O; spont.
   flammable.
⑥ Sidgewick.

Al$_2$C$_6$H$_{15}$Cl$_3$
① Ethylaluminum sesquichloride
   $(C_2H_5)_3Al_2Cl_3$
② $Et_3Al + AlCl_3 \xrightarrow[\text{distn. in vacuum}]{\text{admix. by cooling}}$
③ Yellow liq. (204° extrapd., 90°/14,
   110°/34, 130°/76, 150°/302, 170°/294,
   190°/525). [−20°]. d 1.092 (25°).
   Viscosity 1.91 cp.
   Sol. in org. solvent. Decomp. with
   H$_2$O. Spont. flammable.
⑤ Catalyst for polymn. of olefins.
   Catalyst for hydrogenation of aromatics.
   Chemical intermediate.
⑥ Stauffer Chem. Co. Bulletins. Ethyl
   Co. Bulletins-Aluminum Alkyls
   (Dec. 1958).

Al$_2$C$_{12}$H$_{30}$FK
① Bis(triethylaluminum) potassium
   fluoride

[$(C_2H_5)_3Al]_2KF$

② $KF + 2\,Et_3Al \xrightarrow[\text{hot benzene}]{\text{extd. by}}$

③ Solid. [127~129°].
   Stable in ether. Decomp. to 1:1
   complex by Me₃N.

⑥ Ann. **629**, 33 (1960).

$Al_2C_{12}H_{30}FNa$

① Bis(triethylaluminum) sodium
flouoride

[$(C_2H_5)_3Al]_2NaF$

② $NaF + 2\,Et_3Al \longrightarrow$ extracted by
   pentane from the liq. phase.

③ Liq. [35°].
   Decomp. to 1:1 complex by ether.
   Complete decomp. by Me₃N.

⑥ Ann. **629**, 33 (1960).

5. Organic Compounds of Gallium, Indium, and Thallium
(Ga, In, Tl)

5.1. Introduction

Triethylgallium was first prepared in 1932 and relatively few organic compounds of gallium have been described, but studies in this area are gradually increasing. Two years after the first preparation of triethylgallium, trimethylindium was prepared. Organic derivatives of indium have not yet been studied extensively.

On the other hand, diethylthallium chloride was first prepared in 1870 and the organothallium compounds of the type R_2TlX have long been recognized as among the most stable and least reactive organometallic compounds. Most of the recent studies on organothallium compounds include useful NMR techniques.

The elements of Group Ⅲ have a strong tendency to expand their covalency to four, or even more in some instances. This is achieved by the formation of coordination compounds with donor molecules, and by reactions with electron donating compounds. This tendency is at a maximum for the organic derivatives of aluminum, and is somewhat less for those of gallium and indium. The organic compounds of thallium differ from those of the other elements in their general character.

Major developments on these compounds published up to the end of 1966 have been reviewed.

5.2. Classification and Nomenclature

The organic compounds of Ga(Ⅲ), In(Ⅲ), and Tl(Ⅲ) include three types: R_3M, R_2MX, RMX_2 and their coordination compounds. The nomenclature of these compounds corresponds to that of organoaluminum compounds. There are also a few compounds of the type RM in In(I) and Tl(I).

5.3. Methods of Synthesis
5.3.1. R₃M

Gallium and indium compounds of this type were prepared by heating organo-mercury compounds with the corresponding metal. The presence of a slight amount of mercury or organomercury halide accelerated the reaction. Indium metal reacted with magnesium and alkyl halide in ether to give trialkylindium.

Gallium or indium halides reacted with Grignard reagents, organolithium, -zinc or -aluminum giving triorgano-compounds. Thallium compounds were obtained by Grignard reactions in THF or by the following reaction:

$$TlI + 2RLi + RI \longrightarrow R_3Tl + 2LiI$$

5.3.2. R_2MX

A great number of compounds of this type were prepared by the reaction of triorganometals with the compounds containing active hydrogen. The Grignard reaction with metal trihalides yielded most thallium and a few indium compounds. Organolithium, -mercury, -lead, and -bismuth were also used.

5.3.3. RMX_2

Gallium halides were found to react with tetraorganometal compounds of group IV or organosiloxanes to give monoorganogallium dihalides with good yields. Dichlorogallane, $HGaCl_2$, was found to add to olefins as follows:

$$HGaCl_2 + H_2C=CHR \longrightarrow RCH_2CH_2GaCl_2$$

Thallic acetate also added to olefins:

$$Tl(OAc)_3 + R-CH=CH-R' \longrightarrow \begin{array}{c} R-CH-CH-R' \\ | \quad\quad | \\ AcO \quad Tl(OAc)_2 \end{array}$$

Monoarylthallium(III) compounds were prepared by the reaction of thallic halides with arylboric acid. Thallic carboxylate reacts with aromatic hydrocarbons, giving arylthallium dicarboxylate. Monoalkylthallium dicarboxylates were prepared from dialkylthallium carboxylate and mercuric acetate. Disproportion reactions between triphenylmetal compounds and metal trihalides gave monophenylgallium or -thallium dihalides.

5.3.4. $M(C_5H_5)_n$

Thallous salts reacted with cyclopentadiene in the presence of alkaline to give cyclopentadienyl thallium(I). Cyclopentadienyl indium(I) was prepared by the reaction of indium trichloride with cyclopentadienyl sodium.

5.4. Properties and Reactions

5.4.1. Reactivity of Triorganogallium, -indium, and -thallium

The lower trialkyls of gallium, indium, and thallium are spontaneously flammable.

From the results of the reactions of triphenylmetal compounds with aldehydes, ketones, and acyl halides, the reactivity has been suggested to decrease in the order $Ph_3In > Ph_3Ga > Ph_3Tl$.

The result of the calculation of the net charge on a methyl group in trimethyl compounds was as follows: Al, -0.170; B, -0.067; In, -0.065; Ga, -0.031; Tl, -0.002. The order of decreasing negative charge on the methyl group is equivalent to the order of decreasing polarity and hence the reactivity of the metal-carbon bond.

5.4.2. Reactions with Compounds Containing Active Hydrogen

Trialkylmetal compounds are highly reactive, being violently hydrolyzed by cold water to lose one to three alkyl groups in the case of gallium and indium. In thallium, however, owing to the particular stability of dialkylthallium compounds, hydrolysis does not proceed further than the R_2TlOH stage.

Trimethylmetal compounds reacted with RDH (D: Group VI elements) to give methane even at low temperature. R_2DH (D: Group V elements), however, formed 1: 1 complexes at low temperature; these evolved methane above room temperature.   The order of temperatures at which the formation of Me_2MDR_2 takes place was $D=N > P > As$ for gallium and indium, while the reverse order was observed for aluminum.

5.4.3.   Reactions with Alkenes and Alkynes

Branched alkylgalliums reacted with 1-alkenes as follows:

$$i\text{-}Bu_3Ga + 3\,CH_2{=}CH{-}R \xrightarrow{\;150\sim160^\circ\;} (RCH_2CH_2)_3Ga + i\text{-}C_4H_8$$

At higher pressure a growth reaction occured:

$$Et_3Ga + 3n\,CH_2{=}CH_2 \xrightarrow[170^\circ]{100\sim125\,atm} Ga[(C_2H_4)_nEt]_3$$

With 1-alkynes, triethylgallium reacted with acetylenic protons

$$Et_3Ga + HC{\equiv}CR \longrightarrow Et_2Ga(C{\equiv}CR) + EtH$$

while triethylaluminum added to acetylene.

5.4.4.   Stability of Monoorganothallium(III) Compounds

Monoalkylthallium dihalides have not been prepared, in spite of various trials. Recently, monomethylthallium diacetate was first prepared by the reaction of dimethylthallium acetate and mercuric acetate.   Several monoalkylthallium diacetates, in which the β-hydrogen of the alkyl group was substituted by a negative group, also were prepared.   The compounds of the type $RTlX_2$ are thermally unstable and decompose to RX and TlX.

5.4.5.   Alkyl and Aryl Group Exchange

From the PMR spectra of trimethylthallium it was shown that the inter-molecular exchange of methyl groups follows second order kinetics and has an activation energy of 6.3 ± 0.5 kcal/mole in toluene and 6 ± 1 kcal/mole in dichloro-methane.   Donor solvents such as trimethylamine or dimethylether retarded the exchange.   No alkyl exchange has been observed in dialkylthallium compounds.

Exchange of methyl groups between trimethylaluminum and trimethylgallium or indium has been observed in cyclopentane and toluene.

5.4.6.   PMR Spectra of Organothallium Compounds

Thallium has two isotopes, ^{203}Tl (29.5% abundant) and ^{205}Tl (70.5%), both with nuclear spin 1/2, and with very similar magnetic moments.   These isotopes of thallium produce large spin-spin splittings in the proton resonance spectra of organothallium compounds.   The studies on J_{Tl-H} coupling constants have suggested that they may involve Fermi contact involving the $6s$ orbitals of the thallium atom.   The ratio of the J_{Tl-H} coupling constants in R_3Tl, R_2Tl^+, and RTl^{2+} are approximately $1:1.7:4.0$.

5.5. Addition Compounds

Trimethylgallium forms an ammonia adduct which can be distilled at room temperature at reduced pressure, while the adducts of trimethylthallium are dissociated in the vapor. The order of acceptor properties of trimethylmetal compounds of Group III is B < Al > Ga > In > Tl (Table 5.1). To trimethylgallium, indium, and thallium the heat of coordination, measured in the gas phase, of the trimethyls of the Group Vb elements falls steadily from nitrogen to antimony; trimethylbismuth does not react.

Table 5.1. *The heats of coordination of trimethylmetals with trimethyls of the group Vb elements.*

Adducts	$-\Delta H$ (kcal/mole)	Adducts	$-\Delta H$	Adducts	$-\Delta H$	Adducts	$-\Delta H$
$Me_3B \cdot NMe_3$	17.62						
$Me_3Al \cdot NMe_3$	very large						
$Me_3Ga \cdot NMe_3$	21	$Me_3Ga \cdot PMe_3$	18	$Me_2Ga \cdot AsMe_3$	10	$Me_3Ga \cdot SbMe_3$	very small
$Me_3In \cdot NMe_3$	19.9	$Me_3In \cdot PMe_3$	17.1	$Me_3In \cdot AsMe_3$	very small		
$Me_3Tl \cdot NMe_3$	very small	$Me_3Tl \cdot PMe_3$	very small	$Me_3Tl \cdot AsMe_3$	very small		

Compounds of the type R_2MX form strong adducts, for example, $Me_2GaCl \cdot NH_3$, $Me_2GaX \cdot L$ (X=Cl, Br; L=NMe₃, PMe₃). Dimeric dimethylgallium methylmercaptide has been found to combine reversibly with trimethylamine.

$$(Me_2GaSMe)_2 + 2 NMe_3 \rightleftharpoons 2 Me_2GaSMe \cdot NMe_3$$

Measurement of the dissociation pressures of the trimethylamine adducts of many such compounds has shown that the order of donor character is O > S > Se in dimethylgallium compounds. The dimeric methoxide did not react with trimethylamine.

The solubility of otherwise rather insoluble dialkylthallium salts in pyridine has been interpreted in terms of the formation of the coordination compounds. Recently, stable adducts of dimethylthallium perchlorate with pyridine and 1,10-phenanthroline were isolated.

The compounds of the type RMX_2 form the following adducts: $MeGaCl_2 \cdot NH_3$, $PhTlX_2 \cdot pyridine$, $[Me_4N][PhTlCl_3]$, and $[Me_4N]_2[PhTlCl_4]$.

5.6. Degree of Association and Structural Studies
5.6.1. R₃M

The compounds of the type R_3M are monomeric in solution and in vapor, except for trivinylgallium, which has been reported to be dimeric. Trimethylindium, which had been reported to be tetrameric in benzene, has been shown to be monomeric in solution.

An electron diffraction study has shown that gaseous trimethylindium is planar, with the indium–carbon distance being 2.16 Å. The X-ray diffraction study has revealed a most unusual structure (Fig. 5.1 and 5.2). Trimethylindium is a tetramer of symmetry $\bar{4}$ in the crystal, with methyl bridges of a new type. The tetramers appear to interact, though more weakly, through additional methyl

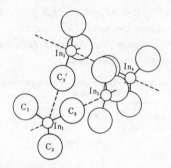

Fig 5.1. *The trimethylindium tetramer. Weak bridge bonds to neighboring tetra mers are indicated by dashed lines.*

bridges. There are then five methyl groups about each indium, forming a somewhat distorted trigonal bipyramid, with three short, 2.1 Å, bonds in the trigonal plane, and two much longer bonds, 3.1 Å, within the tetramer, 3.6 Å, to the next tetramer, on either side of the plane.

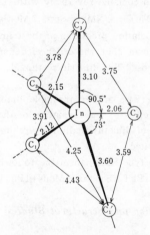

Fig 5.2. *Configuration about indium. C_1, C_2 and C_3 are in a plane, with ∠C–In–C nearly 120°. C_3 is a carbon with in the tetramer, while C_1 is a carbon in a neighboring tetramer.*

5.6.2. R_2MX

Halides of dimethyl- and diphenylgallium, dimethyl- and bis(perfluorophenyl) indium, and bis(perfluorophenyl)thallium are dimeric in the vapor state or in solution (as are the aluminum halides). Crystalline dimethylthallium halides have an essentially ionic lattice consisting of layers where dimethylthallium cations are surrounded by four halogen anions, and each halogen anion is surrounded by four dimethylthallium cations.

Most of the compounds of Me_2MX are associated in solution as follows:

$(Me_2MX)_2$

   M=Ga, X=OOCH, OMe, OOSPh, etc.

   M=In, X=SMe, NPh_2, OBu^t, etc.

   M=Tl, X=SMe, NMe_2, OEt, etc.

$(Me_2MX)_3$

   M=Ga, X=PMe_2, $AsMe_2$, OH

   M=In, X=PMe_2, $AsMe_2$, OMe

$(Me_2MX)_4$

   M=Ga, In, X=CN

$(Me_2M)^+X^-$

   M=Tl, X=CN, CNO, $SPMe_2$

The factors affecting the degree of association of these organometallic compounds have been considered as follows: (i) steric interference, (ii) valence angle strain, (iii) entropy effect, and (iv) the nature of the intermediates involved in their formation.

There have been prepared many chelate compounds of the type R_2MX (X= β-diketones, oxine, etc.).

5.6.3. RMX_2

Methyl, ethyl, and phenylgallium dihalides are dimeric in benzene or in the vapor phase. Thallium is believed to be 5-coordinated in phenylthallium bis-oxinate.

5.6.4. C_5H_5M

Gaseous cyclopentadienylindium (I) is an "open-faced half-sandwich" a symmetry closely approximately C_{5v}. The crystal structure of this compound is composed of a chain disposition of the indium atoms and of the rings enclosed between them at the same distance between beth metals.

The same structure was suggested for thallium analogs.

5.7. Applications

   (a) Polymerization catalysis of olefins

   (b) Production of metal carbonyls

   (c) Antiknock reagent

   (d) Production of metal cyclopentadienyls

   (e) Lubricant

   (f) Production of ultrapure metals

The electrolysis of liquid complex quaternary ammonium or phosphonium salts of organogallium or indium gave high purity metal.

REFERENCES

K. Yasuda, R. Okawara, *Organometallic Chem. Revs.*, **2**, 255 (1967).

【Ga】

GaCH₃O

① Methyloxygallium

CH_3GaO

③ White glass.

Insol. in H_2O and org. solvents.

Polymeric.

⑥ JACS **76**, 4839 (1954).

GaCH₃Cl₂

① Methyldichlorogallium

CH_3GaCl_2

② $Me_3Ga \cdot NH_3 \xrightarrow{2\,HCl}$

$Me_3Ga \cdot OEt_2 \xrightarrow{2\,HCl}$

③ White amorphous solid. [46～47°].

Sol. in ether.

Dimeric in vapor.

⑥ Proc. Nat. Acad. Sci. **19**, 298 (1933).

Coates (1960).

GaCH₆Cl₂N

① Methyldichlorogallium ammine adduct

$CH_3GaCl_2 \cdot NH_3$

③ White crystals. [>80°].

Insol. in ether, decomp. in H_2O.

⑥ Proc. Nat. Acad. Sci. **19**, 298 (1933).

GaCH₁₈Cl₂N₅

① Methyldichlorogallium pentaammine adduct

$CH_3GaCl_2 \cdot 5\,NH_3$

③ White crystals. [80° decomp.].

Insol. in NH_3 ; decomp. in H_2O, NH_3 readily removed *in vacuo* at 80°.

⑥ Proc. Nat. Acad. Sci. **19**, 298 (1933).

GaC₂H₆Cl

① Dimethylchlorogallium

$(CH_3)_2GaCl$

② $Me_3Ga + GaCl_3 \longrightarrow$

$Me_3Ga \cdot OEt_2 + HCl \xrightarrow{ether}$

③ Crystals. (154° extrapd.). [45.3～45.6°].

Dimeric in vapor.

④ $+ Na \xrightarrow{liq.\ NH_3} [Me_2GaNH_3] \cdot \longrightarrow$

$Me_2GaNH_2 + \frac{1}{2}H_2$

⑥ Proc. Nat. Acad. Sci. **19**, 298 (1933).

JACS **55**, 3547 (1933).

GaC₂H₆Br

① Dimethylbromogallium

$(CH_3)_2GaBr$

② $Me_3Ga \cdot OEt_2 + HBr \xrightarrow{ether}$

③ Crystals. [58.5～59.0°].

Dimeric in vapor.

⑥ Coates 151 (1960).

GaC₂H₇

① Dimethylgallium hydride

$(CH_3)_2GaH$

② $Me_3Ga + H_2 \xrightarrow{discharge} \xrightarrow{cooling}$

③ (132° decomp.).

Violently hydrolyzed by cold water.

Dimeric in vapor.

④ $+ R_3N \longrightarrow Ga_2H_6 + Me_3Ga \cdot NR_3$

(R=Me, Et)

⑥ Angew. **55**, 38 (1942).

GaC₂H₇O

① Dimethylhydroxygallium

$(CH_3)_2GaOH$

② $Me_3Ga \cdot OEt_2 + H_2O \longrightarrow$

③ White solid. [87.0～88.5°]. d 1.75 (25° /4°).

Sol. in org. solvents ; slightly sol. in H_2O.

Decomp. in acids.

IR : JACS **76**, 4839 (1954).

Trimeric in benzene, tetrameric in the crystals.

④ $\xrightarrow{150°}$ (MeGaO)$_x$

⑥ JACS 81, 3907 (1959).

GaC₂H₈N

① Dimethylaminogallium
   (CH₃)₂GaNH₂

② Me₃Ga·NH₃ $\xrightarrow{70°}$

③ White crystals. (60° sublime in
   vacuum). [97°].

⑥ JCS 1951, 2003.

GaC₂H₉ClN

① Dimethylchlorogallium ammine
   adduct
   (CH₃)₂GaCl·NH₃

② Me₃Ga·NH₃ + HCl $\xrightarrow{Et_2O}$ NH₄Cl
   + Me₃Ga $\longrightarrow$

③ White crystals. [54°].
   Sol. in NH₃, ether. Decomp. in H₂O.

④ + Na $\xrightarrow{liq. NH_3}$ Me₂GaNH₃· $\longrightarrow$
   Me₂GaNH₂ + $\frac{1}{2}$H₂

⑥ Proc. Nat. Acad. Sci. 19, 298 (1933).
   JACS 55, 3547 (1933).

GaC₂H₁₀B

① Dimethyl(tetrahydroborino)gallium
   (CH₃)₂GaBH₄

③ Colorless liq. (92°). [1.5°].

⑥ Kaufman (1961).

GaC₂H₁₂ClN₂

① Dimethylchlorogallium diammine
   adduct
   (CH₃)₂GaCl·2 NH₃

② Me₃Ga + HCl $\longrightarrow$ Me₂GaCl $\xrightarrow{NH_3}$

③ White crystals. [112°].
   Sol. in NH₃; insol. in org. solvents.
   Loses ammonia *in vacuo* at 60°.
   Stable in air. Decomp. in H₂O.
   IR, X-ray powder pattern: Inorg.

Chem. 1, 835 (1962).
Composed of ion pairs
   [Me₂Ga(NH₃)₂]Cl.

④ $\xrightarrow{r. t.}$ [Me₂GaNH₂]₂
   + KBH₄ $\xrightarrow{liq. NH_3}$ [Me₂Ga(NH₃)₂]BH₄

⑥ Proc. Nat. Acad. Sci. 19, 292 (1933).

GaC₃H₆N

① Dimethylcyanogallium
   (CH₃)₂GaCN

② Me₃Ga + HCN $\xrightarrow{benzene}$

③ (90°/10⁻². sublime). [79°].
   IR: ν_{C-N} 2178 cm⁻¹ in CCl₄ soln.
   Tetrameric in benzene.

⑥ JCS 1953, 229.

GaC₃H₇O₂

① Formoxydimethylgallium
   (CH₃)₂GaOOCH

② Me₃Ga + HCOOH $\longrightarrow$

③ (60/0.01 sublime). [97~98°].
   Dimeric in benzene

⑥ JCS 1964, 1295.

GaC₃H₉

① Trimethylgallium
   (CH₃)₃Ga

② Ga + Me₂Hg $\xrightarrow{MeHgCl}$
   GaCl₃ + Me₂Zn $\xrightarrow{80~120°}$
   GaCl₃ + Me₃Al $\xrightarrow{80°}$ 64.5%

③ Colorless liquid. (55.7°/760). [−15.7~
   −15.9°].
   Sol. in ether, NH₃. Spont. inflammable
   in air. Decomp. in H₂O.
   IR, Raman: Spectrochim. Acta 20,
   1249 (1964).
   Monomeric in vapor.

④ + H₂O $\xrightarrow[cool]{ether}$ [(Me₂Ga)₂O]$_n$
   + I₂ $\longrightarrow$ GaI₃ + MeI
   + HI $\longrightarrow$ GaI₃ + CH₄

+ Ph₂PH $\longrightarrow$ (Me₂GaPPh₂)₂
+ Ph₂AsH $\longrightarrow$ (Me₂GaAsPh₂)₂
+ LiAlH₄ $\longrightarrow$ Me₂AlH
⑤ Catalyst for the polymn. of ethylene
   with Ti⁴⁺, V⁴⁺.
⑥ JCS 1963, 233 ; 1951, 2003 ; 1953,
   2519.

GaC₃H₁₂N

① Trimethylgallium ammonia adduct
   (CH₃)₃Ga·NH₃
② Me₃Ga·OEt₂ $\xrightarrow{\text{liq. NH}_3}$
③ White crystals. (70° sublime in
   vacuum). [31°].
   Sol. in ether, NH₃; insol. in org.
   solvents.
   Decomp. in H₂O.
④ + KOH $\longrightarrow$ Me₂GaOK + CH₄ + NH₃
   + HCl $\xrightarrow{\text{Et}_2\text{O}}$ Me₃Ga·OEt₂ + NH₄Cl
   $\longrightarrow$ Me₂GaCl·NH₃ + CH₄ + Et₂O
   + Na $\xrightarrow{\text{liq. NH}_3}$ Na[Me₃GaNH₂GaMe₃]
   (60~100%) + (Me₃Ga)₂Na₂ (30~0%)
   + NaNH₂ $\longrightarrow$ Na[Me₃GaNH₂GaMe₃]
   + 2 HCl $\longrightarrow$ MeGaCl₂
   + HCl $\xrightarrow{160°}$ NH₄GaCl₄ + CH₄
⑥ Proc. Nat. Acad. Sci. 19, 292, 298
   (1933). JACS 55, 3547 (1933).

GaC₃H₉O

① Dimethylmethoxygallium
   (CH₃)₂GaOCH₃
② Me₃Ga + MeOH $\longrightarrow$
③ (128°). [24.5~24.7°].
   Stable in dry air, does not react with
   an excess of methanol.
   Not detectably dissociated in the
   vapor up to 170°.
⑥ JCS 1953, 2519.

GaC₃H₉S

① Dimethyl(methylthio)gallium

(CH₃)₂GaSCH₃
② Me₃Ga + MeSH $\longrightarrow$
③ Colorless solid. [113.3~113.7°].
   Dimeric in vapor.
⑥ JCS 1953, 2519.

GaC₃H₉Se

① Dimethyl(methylseleno)gallium
   (CH₃)₂GaSeCH₃
② Me₃Ga + MeSeH $\longrightarrow$
③ Non-volatile solid. [119~120°].
   Dimeric in vapor.
④ + NMe₃ $\longrightarrow$ Me₂GaSeMe·NMe₃
⑥ JCS 1953, 2519.

GaC₃H₉O₃S

① Dimethylgallium methanesulphonate
   (CH₃)₂GaO₃SCH₃
② Me₃Ga + MeSO₃H $\longrightarrow$
③ (100°/0.01 sublime). [79~80°].
   Trimeric in benzen.
⑥ JCS 1964, 1295.

GaC₄H₉O₂

① Dimethylacetoxygallium
   (CH₃)₂GaOOCCH₃
② Me₃Ga + CH₃COOH $\longrightarrow$
③ Colorless crystals. (90~95°/0.01
   sublime). [162.0~162.3°].
   Sublimable.
   IR : JCS 1964, 1295.
   Dimeric in acetone.
⑥ JCS 1953, 2519.

GaC₄H₁₀F

① Diethylfluorogallium
   (C₂H₅)₂GaF
② Et₂GaCl + KF $\xrightarrow{100~105°}$ 70%
③ Colorless viscous liq. (80~81°/1).
⑥ JACS 84, 3820 (1962).

GaC₄H₁₀Cl

① Diethylchlorogallium

(C₂H₅)₂GaCl

② GaCl₃ + Et₃Ga $\xrightarrow{100°}$ 98%

③ Colorless liq. (60~62°/2). *d* 1.35 (20°/20°).
Does not ignite in air or reacts vigo-lously with water.

④ + KF $\xrightarrow{100\sim105°}$ Et₂GaF

⑥ JACS **84**, 3830 (1962).

GaC₄H₁₁

① Diethylgallium hydride
(C₂H₅)₂GaH

② Et₂GaCl + KCN + Et₂AlH ⟶ 24%

③ Colorless liq. (40~42°/10⁻⁴).
Ignites spontaneously in air and reacts violently with water.

④ + C₂H₅C≡CC₂H₅ $\xrightarrow{65°}$ diethyl-3-hexenylgallium

⑥ JACS **84**, 3830 (1962).

GaC₄H₁₂O₂P

① Dimethylgallium dimethylphosphi-nate
(CH₃)₂GaO₂P(CH₃)₂

② Me₃Ga + Me₂PO₂H ⟶

③ (80°/0.01 sublime). [54°].
Dimeric in benzene.

⑥ JCS **1964**, 1295.

GaC₄H₁₂PS₂

① Dimethylgallium dimethyldithio-phosphinate
(CH₃)₂GaS₂P(CH₃)₂

② Me₃Ga + Me₂PS₂H ⟶

③ (100°/0.01 sublime). [153~154°].
Monomeric in benzene.

⑥ JCS **1964**, 1295.

GaC₄H₁₂AsO₂

① Dimethylgallium dimethylarsinate
(CH₃)₂GaO₂As(CH₃)₂

② Me₃Ga + Me₂AsO₂H ⟶

③ (110°/0.01 sublime). [144~145°].
Dimeric in benzene.

⑥ JCS **1964**, 1295.

GaC₄H₁₄ClN₂

① Dimethylchlorogallium ethylene-diamine adduct
(CH₃)₂GaCl·H₂NCH₂CH₂NH₂

② [Me₂Ga(NH₃)₂]Cl + en ⟶ 98%
Me₂GaCl + en $\xrightarrow{Me₂O}$

③ White solid. [>130°].
Insol. in ether; sol. in ethylene-diamine, H₂O and alcohol.
Composed of ion pairs [Me₂Gaen]Cl

④ + Ag₂SO₄ $\xrightarrow{H₂O-EtOH}$ [Me₂Gaen]₂SO₄ + AgCl

⑥ Inorg. Chem. **1**, 835 (1962).

GaC₅H₁₅ClN

① Dimethylchlorogallium trimethyl-amine adduct
(CH₃)₂GaCl·N(CH₃)₃

③ Solid. [111.5~112.5°].

⑥ Kaufman (1961).

GaC₅H₁₅BrN

① Dimethylbromogallium trimethyl-amine adduct
(CH₃)₂GaBr·N(CH₃)₃

③ Solid. [133.5~136.0°].
Sol. in org. solvents.

⑥ Kaufman (1961).

GaC₅H₁₅IN

① Dimethyliodogallium trimethylamine adduct
(CH₃)₂GaI·N(CH₃)₃

③ Solid. [127.5~128.0°].
Sol. in org. solvents.

⑥ Kaufman (1961).

GaC₅H₁₅ClP

① Dimethylchlorogallium trimethyl-

phosphine adduct
(CH₃)₂GaCl·P(CH₃)₃
③ Solid. [93.0～93.5°].
Sol. in org. solvents.
⑥ Kaufman (1961).

GaC₆H₅Cl₂

① Phenyldichlorogallium
(C₆H₅)GaCl₂

② Ph₃Ga + 2 HCl ⟶

Ph₃Ga + 2 GaCl₃ $\xrightarrow{160°}$

③ White crystals. [122.4～123.4°].
Readily hydrolyzed and turns brown
even on short exposure to air.
Dimeric in benzene.

⑥ JCS **1965**, 1038.

GaC₆H₅Br₂

① Phenyldibromogallium
C₆H₅GaBr₂

② Ph₃Ga + 2 GaBr₃ $\xrightarrow{170°}$

③ White solid. [129～130°].
Readily hydrolyzed in air.
Dimeric in benzene.

⑥ JCS **1965**, 1038.

GaC₆H₉

① Trivinylgallium
(CH₂=CH)₃Ga

② Ga + (CH₂=CH)₂Hg ⟶ 87%

③ [−7～−9°].
IR: JINC **24**, 953 (1962).
Dimeric in soln.

④ $\xrightarrow{70°}$ polymer + CH₄
+ O₂ ⟶ C₂H₄ + stable white
crystals contg. OH and vinyl group

⑥ JINC **19**, 378 (1961); **11**, 24 (1959).

GaC₆H₁₅

① Triethylgallium
(C₂H₅)₃Ga

② Ga + Et₂Hg $\xrightarrow{160°}$

GaCl₃ + Et₃Al $\xrightarrow{70°,\ n\text{-hexane}}$ 82%

GaBr₃ + Et₂Zn $\xrightarrow{pentane}$ 66%

③ Colorless viscous liq. (143°/760),
(46～48°/18), (43～44°/16). [−82.3°].
d 1.0586 (30°/4°).
Sol. in org. solvents. Inflammable in
the air. Decomp. in H₂O.
Monomeric in vapor; dimeric in
benzene, cyclohexane.

④ + O₂ $\xrightarrow{50～60°}$ Et₂GaOEt

+ H₂O $\xrightarrow{cooling}$ Et₂GaOH

+ EtOH $\xrightarrow[reflux]{pentane}$ Et₂GaOEt

+ HC≡CC₄H₉ $\xrightarrow{50～55°}$ Et₂GaC≡CC₄H₉

$\xrightarrow[\text{Et}_2\text{O, THF, Dioxane}]{\text{UV}}$ High purity Ga

⑤ Catalysis for stereospesific polymn.
of olefins.

⑥ JCS **1953**, 2519. JACS **54**, 182 (1932);
84, 3605, 3830 (1962).

GaC₆H₁₅O

① Diethylethoxygallium
(C₂H₅)₂GaOC₂H₅

② Et₃Ga + O₂ ⟶

Et₃Ga + EtOH ⟶ 87%

③ Colorless liq. (86～87°/3). n_D 1.448
(20°). *d* 1.158 (20°/4°).
Slowly changes into a white solid by
moisture.

⑥ JACS **84**, 3830 (1962).

GaC₆H₁₆ON

① Dimethyl(dimethylaminoethoxy)
gallium
(CH₃)₂GaOC₂H₄N(CH₃)₂

② Me₃Ga + Me₂NC₂H₄OH ⟶

③ Colorless crystals. [81.4°].
Dimeric in benzene.

④ + MeI $\xrightarrow{\text{C}_6\text{H}_6 \text{ acetone-H}_2\text{O}}$

HOC₂H₄Me₃NI

⑥ JCS **1953**, 2519.

GaC₆H₁₈NSe

① Dimethyl(methylseleno)gallium
   trimethylamine adduct
   (CH₃)₂GaSeCH₃·N(CH₃)₃

② Me₂GaSeMe + NMe₃ ⟶

③ [29.8~30.0°].

⑥ JCS **1953**, 2519.

GaC₆H₁₈NS

① Dimethyl(methylthio)gallium
   trimethylamine adduct
   (CH₃)₂GaSCH₃·N(CH₃)₃

② Me₂GaSCH₃ + NMe₃ ⟶

③ Long needles. [26.0~26.2°].

⑥ JCS **1953**, 2519.

GaC₇H₁₃O₂

① Dimethyl(acetylacetonyl)gallium
   (CH₃)₂GaO₂C₅H₇

② Me₃Ga + acetylacetone ⟶

③ Colorless prisms. (166°). [21.8~
   22.0°].
   Monomeric in vapor.

⑥ JCS **1953**, 2519.

GaC₇H₁₉O

① Trimethylgallium diethylether
   adduct
   (CH₃)₃Ga·O(C₂H₅)₂

② Me₃Ga + Et₂O ⟶

   GaCl₃ + MeMgI $\xrightarrow{\text{ether}}$ 90%

③ Colorless liq. (98.3°). [<−76°].
   Sol. in NH₃, ether. Decomp. in H₂O.
   Slowly oxidized by atm. oxygen.
   The vapor is 70% dissociated at 25°.

④ + H₂O ⟶ (Me₂GaOH)₄ + Et₂O
   + CH₄

   + KOH $\xrightarrow{35°}$ Me₂GaOK + CH₄

$\xrightarrow{100°}$ MeGa(OK)₂ + 2 CH₄

+ HCl $\xrightarrow{\text{ether}}$ Me₂GaCl + CH₄

+ 3 HCl ⟶ MeGaCl₂

⑥ Proc. Nat. Acad. Sci. **19**, 298 (1933).
   JACS **76**, 4839 (1954). Ber. **65**, 1308
   (1932).

GaC₈H₁₀ClO

① Dimethyl(*p*-chlorophenoxy)gallium
   (CH₃)₂GaOC₆H₄Cl-*p*

② Me₃Ga + *p*-ClC₆H₄OH ⟶

③ Colorless needles. [147°].
   Dimeric in C₆H₆.

⑥ JCS **1953**, 2519.

GaC₈H₁₀ClS

① Dimethyl(*p*-chlorophenylthio)-
   gallium
   (CH₃)₂GaSC₆H₄Cl-*p*

② Me₃Ga + *p*-ClC₆H₄SH ⟶

③ Colorless needles. [187~188°].
   Dimeric in C₆H₆.

⑥ JCS **1953**, 2519.

GaC₈H₁₁O

① Dimethylphenoxygallium
   (CH₃)₂GaOC₆H₅

② Me₃Ga + C₆H₅OH ⟶

③ Colorless plates. [132°].
   Very sol. in most org. solvents,
   dissolves in cold water with hydrolysis.
   Dimeric in C₆H₆.

⑥ JCS **1953**, 2519.

GaC₈H₁₁S

① Dimethyl(phenylthio)gallium
   (CH₃)₂GaSC₆H₅

② Me₃Ga + PhSH ⟶

③ Colorless crystals. [143~145°].
   Dimeric in C₆H₆.

⑥ JCS **1953**, 2519.

GaC₈H₁₁Se

① Dimethyl(selenophenyl)gallium
   $(CH_3)_2GaSeC_6H_5$
② $Me_3Ga + PhSeH \longrightarrow$
③ Colorless crystals. [136°].
   Decomp. on exposure to air.
   Dimeric in C_6H_6.
⑥ JCS **1953**, 2519.

GaC₈H₁₁O₂S

① Dimethylgallium benzenesulfinate
   $(CH_3)_2GaO_2SC_6H_5$
② $Me_3Ga + PhSO_2H \longrightarrow$
③ (120°/0.01 sublime). [56~57°].
   Dimeric in C_6H_6.
⑥ JCS **1964**, 1295.

GaC₉H₁₁O₂

① Dimethyl(salicylformyl)gallium
   $(CH_3)_2GaOC_6H_4$-o-CHO
② $Me_3Ga + C_6H_4(CHO)(OH) \longrightarrow$
③ Bright yellow needles. [79°].
   Sol. in org. solvents.
   Monomeric in C_6H_6.
⑥ JCS **1953**, 2519.

GaC₉H₁₅

① Triallylgallium
   $(CH_2=CHCH_2)_3Ga$
② $Ga + (CH_2=CHCH_2)_2Hg \longrightarrow$
   $GaCl_3 + CH_2=CHCH_2MgCl \longrightarrow$
③ [−72°].
⑥ JINC **24**, 953 (1962).

GaC₉H₂₁

① Tri-n-propylgallium
   $(n-C_3H_7)_3Ga$
② $GaCl_3 + (n-Pr)_3Al \longrightarrow 80\%$
   $Ga + (n-Pr)_2Hg \xrightarrow{150°} 80\%$
   $GaCl_3 + n-PrMgCl$
   $\xrightarrow{ether} (n-Pr)_3Ga \cdot OEt_2 \xrightarrow{vacuo}$

③ Colorless liquid. (184°/760), (74°/14).
   [−85.2°].
   Sol. in org. solvents. Very sensitive
   to air, light and H_2O. Thermodynamic data.
   IR : JINC **24**, 953 (1962).
   Monomeric in the vapor.
⑥ Naturwiss. **49**, 182 (1962) ; **48**, 601
   (1961).   Ger. 1158977 (1963).

GaC₉H₂₁

① Tri-isopropylgallium
   $(iso-C_3H_7)_3Ga$
② $GaCl_3 + (iso-Pr)_3Al \longrightarrow 84.5\%$
   $Ga + (iso-Pr)_2Hg \xrightarrow{150°} 75\%$
   $GaCl_3 + iso-PrMgCl \longrightarrow$
③ Yellow liquid. (175°/760), (95~98°/
   60). [<−100°].
   Sol. in org. solvents. Sensitive to air,
   light and H_2O.   Thermodynamic
   data.
   IR : JINC **24**, 953 (1962).
   Monomeric in vapor.
⑥ Naturwiss. **49**, 182 (1962).   Ger.
   1158977 (1963).

GaC₁₁H₂₀ON

① Dimethylphenoxygallium trimethylamine adduct
   $(CH_3)_2GaOC_6H_5 \cdot N(CH_3)_3$
② $Me_2GaOPh + NMe_3 \longrightarrow$
③ Colorless needles. [39~40°].
   Sol. in org. solvents. Dissociates
   slowly by pumping at r. t.
⑥ JCS **1953**, 2519.

GaC₁₁H₂₀NS

① Dimethyl(phenylthio)gallium
   trimethylamine adduct
   $(CH_3)_2GaSC_6H_5 \cdot N(CH_3)_3$
② $Me_2GaSPh + Me_3N \longrightarrow$
③ Crystals. [51°].

Sol. in org. solvents.

⑥ JCS **1953**, 2519.

GaC₁₁H₂₀NSe

① Dimethyl(selenophenyl)gallium
trimethylamine adduct
$(CH_3)_2GaSeC_6H_5 \cdot N(CH_3)_3$

② Me₂GaSePh + NMe₃ $\longrightarrow$

③ Crystals. [48~50°].

⑥ JCS **1953**, 2519.

GaC₁₂H₁₀Cl

① Diphenylchlorogallium
$(C_6H_5)_2GaCl$

② Ph₃Ga + HCl $\longrightarrow$

③ White crystals. [197°].
Dimeric in C₆H₆.

⑥ JCS **1965**, 1038.

GaC₁₂H₁₀Br

① Diphenylbromogallium
$(C_6H_5)_2GaBr$

② Ph₃Ga + Br₂ $\longrightarrow$

2 Ph₃Ga + GaBr₃ $\xrightarrow{200°}$

③ [212~214°].
Dimeric in C₆H₆.

⑥ JCS **1965**, 1038.

GaC₁₂H₁₉O

① Dimethyl-*p-t*-butylphenoxy-
gallium
$(CH_3)_2GaOC_6H_4$-*p-t*-C_4H_9

② Me₃Ga + *p-t*-BuC₆H₄OH $\longrightarrow$

③ Needles. [92°].
Dimeric in C₆H₆.

⑥ JCS **1953**, 2519.

GaC₁₂H₂₄N

① Tri-*trans*-propenylgallium trimethyl-
ammine adduct
$(trans\text{-}CH_3CH=CH)_3Ga \cdot N(CH_3)_3$

② $(trans\text{-}CH_3CH=CH)_2Hg$ + Ga $\xrightarrow{CCl_4}$

$(trans\text{-}CH_3CH=CH)_3Ga \xrightarrow{N(CH_3)_3}$

③ White solid. (35~40° sublime in
vacuo), [40°].

⑥ JACS **86**, 371 (1964).

GaC₁₂H₂₇

① Tri-*n*-butylgallium
$(n\text{-}C_4H_9)_3Ga$

② GaCl₃ + *n*-BuMgCl $\longrightarrow$

③ Colorless liq. (113.5°/12).
Sol. in org. solvents. Very sensitive
to air, light and H₂O. Thermodynamic data.

⑥ Naturwiss. **49**, 182 (1962).

GaC₁₂H₂₇

① Tri-isobutylgallium
$(i\text{-}C_4H_9)_3Ga$

② GaCl₃ + $(i\text{-}Bu)_3Al$ $\xrightarrow{\text{pentane KCN}}$ 92%
GaCl₃ + *i*-BuMgCl $\longrightarrow$

③ (94°/12), (88~90°/10), (67~69°/3).
d 0.94 (20°/20°).
Sol. in org. solvents. Very sensitive
to air, light and H₂O. Thermodynamic data.

④ + O₂ $\longrightarrow$ $(i\text{-}Bu)_2Ga(OBu\text{-}i)$

+ CH₂=CHC₈H₁₇ $\xrightarrow{155°}$ $(n\text{-}C_{10}H_{21})_3Ga$

⑥ Naturwiss. **49**, 182 (1962). JACS **84**,
3830 (1962). Ger. 1158977 (1963).

GaC₁₂H₂₇O

① Di-isobutyl-isobutoxygallium
$(i\text{-}C_4H_9)_2GaOC_4H_9\text{-}i$

② $(i\text{-}Bu)_3Ga$ + O₂ $\longrightarrow$

③ Liquid. Apricot-like odor. (161~163°/
3). n_D 1.458 (20°).

⑥ JACS **84**, 3830 (1962).

GaC₁₄H₁₆N₃

① 1,3-Diphenyltriazenodimethylgallium

$(CH_3)_2GaNC_6H_5NNC_6H_5$

② $Me_3Ga + PhN_3PhH \longrightarrow$

③ Brown-yellow solid. (100°/0.01 sublime). [53~55°].
Monomeric in C_6H_6.

⑥ JCS **1964**, 1295.

GaC₁₄H₁₆P

① Dimethyl(diphenylphosphino)-gallium
$(CH_3)_2GaP(C_6H_5)_2$

② $Me_3Ga + Ph_2PH \xrightarrow{90~110°} 96\%$

$Me_2GaCl + Ph_2PNa \xrightarrow{THF, ether} 87\%$

③ [194°].
Sol. in C_6H_6 and hexane. Easily hydrolyzed by moisture.
Dimeric in C_6H_6.

④ $+ H_2O \longrightarrow Me_2GaOH$

⑥ JCS **1963**, 233.

GaC₁₄H₁₆As

① Dimethyl(diphenylarsino)gallium
$(CH_3)_2GaAs(C_6H_5)_2$

② $Me_3Ga + Ph_2AsH \longrightarrow$

③ [160~170°].
Less sensitive to moisture than its phosphorous analogue.
Dimeric in C_6H_6.

⑥ JCS **1963**, 233.

GaC₁₄H₁₆OPS

① Dimethylgallium diphenylthiophosphinate
$(CH_3)_2GaSOP(C_6H_5)_2$

② $Me_3Ga + Ph_2POSH \longrightarrow$

③ (160~180°/<0.01 sublime). [203~204°].

⑥ JCS **1964**, 1295.

GaC₁₄H₁₆O₂P

① Dimethylgallium diphenylphosphinate
$(CH_3)_2GaO_2P(C_6H_5)_2$

② $Me_3Ga + Ph_2POOH \longrightarrow$

③ (160°/<0.01 subl.). [164°].
Decomp. in hot concd. HCl.
Dimeric in C_6H_6.

⑥ JCS **1964**, 1295.

GaC₁₈H₁₅

① Triphenylgallium
$(C_6H_5)_3Ga$

② $Ga + Ph_2Hg \xrightarrow{130°} 82\%$

③ White crystals. [166°].
Hydrolyzed by moisture. Decomp. in acid.

④ $+ PhCHO \xrightarrow{2 N HCl} Ph_2CHOH$
$+ PhC_2H_2COPh \longrightarrow CH_3CPh_2COPh$
$+ PhCOCl \longrightarrow Ph_2CO + GaCl_3$

⑤ Catalyst for the polymn. of olefins.

⑥ JACS **62**, 980 (1940). Brit. 775384 (1957)

Ga₂C₄H₁₂

① Tetramethyldigallium
$(CH_3)_2GaGa(CH_3)_2$

③ Colorless liq. (172° extrapd.).
Spont. inflammable. Decomp. in H_2O.

⑥ Kaufman (1961).

【In】

InC₂H₈N

① Aminodimethylindium
$(CH_3)_2InNH_2$

② $Me_3In \cdot NH_3 \xrightarrow{70~80°}$

③ [120~124°].
Not appreciably volatile.

⑥ JCS **1956**, 3351.

InC₃H₆N

① Dimethylcyanoindium
$(CH_3)_2InCN$

② $Me_3In + HCN \xrightarrow{ether}$

③ (120°/0.05 sublime). [147°].

Sol. in C_6H_6, 2-methoxymethanol.

IR: ν_{CN} 2178 cm^{-1} in CCl$_4$.

Tetrameric in C_6H_6.

⑥ JCS **1963**, 229.

InC₃H₉

① Trimethylindium

(CH₃)₃In

② InCl₃ + MeMgCl $\xrightarrow{\text{ether}}$ Me₃In·OEt₂

$\xrightarrow{\text{heat in vacuo}}$

In + Me₂Hg $\xrightarrow{100°,\ HgCl_2}$

In−Mg + MeBr $\xrightarrow{\text{ether}\ \text{benzene}}$

③ Colorless liq. (135.8°). [88.4°].

d 1.568 (19°/19°).

Sol. in polar org. solvents.

Spont. inflmmable in air; decomp. in H₂O.

IR, Raman: Spectrochim. Acta **20**, 1249 (1964).

NMR: Inorg. Chem. **2**, 1075 (1963).

Structure detn.: JACS **80**, 4141 (1958).

Monomeric in vapor; tetrameric in C₆H₆.

④ + O₂ $\xrightarrow{-78°}$ (Me₂In)₂O + C₂H₆

+ H₂O $\longrightarrow$ MeIn(OH)₂ + 2 CH₄

+ Ph₂AsH $\longrightarrow$ Me₂InPPh₂

+ PH₃ $\longrightarrow$ -(-MeIn-PH-)ₙ-

⑤ Catalyst for dimerization of olefins.

⑥ JACS **80**, 4141 (1958). Z. anorg. allg. Chem. **267**, 39 (1951).

InC₃H₉O

① Dimethylmethoxyindium

(CH₃)₂InOCH₃

② Me₃In + MeOH $\xrightarrow{-98°}$

③ Colorless viscous liq.

Sensitive to H₂O.

Trimeric in C₆H₆.

⑥ JCS **1956**, 3351.

InC₃H₉S

① Dimethyl(methylthio)indium

(CH₃)₂InSCH₃

② Me₃In + MeSH $\xrightarrow{\text{ether}}$

③ Colorless crystals. [122∼124° decomp.].

Sol. in C₆H₆. Less sensitive to hydrolysis than the methoxy compd.

Decomp. in dil. acids.

Dimeric in benzene.

⑥ JCS **1956**, 3351.

InC₃H₁₂N

① Trimethylindium ammonia adduct

(CH₃)₃In·NH₃

② Me₃In + NH₃ $\longrightarrow$

③ Colorless acicular crystals. [28.5∼ 29.5°].

④ $\xrightarrow{70∼80°}$ (Me₂In·NH₂)ₓ + CH₄

⑥ JCS **1956**, 3351.

InC₄H₁₂N

① Dimethyl(dimethylamino)indium

(CH₃)₂InN(CH₃)₂

② Me₃In·NHMe₂ $\xrightarrow{160°}$

③ Crystals. Dimorphic.

Dimeric in vapor.

⑥ JCS **1956**, 3351.

InC₅H₅

① Cyclopentadienylindium(I)

C₅H₅In

② InCl₃ + NaC₅H₅ $\xrightarrow{150°}$ 65%

③ Pale yellow needles.

Stable to H₂O, decomp. by dil. H₂SO₄, O₂.

Structure detn.

⑥ Nature **199**, 1087 (1963). J. Chem. Phys. **41**, 717 (1964). Angew. **69**, 639 (1957).

InC$_5$H$_{15}$S

① Trimethylindium dimethylsulfide
   adduct
   (CH$_3$)$_3$In·S(CH$_3$)$_2$

③ (185° extrapd.). [19.0~19.5°].
   Almost wholly dissociated in vapor.

⑥ JCS **1956**, 3351.

InC$_5$H$_{16}$N

① Trimethylindium dimethylamine
   adduct
   (CH$_3$)$_3$In·NH(CH$_3$)$_2$

② Me$_3$In + NHMe$_2$ ⟶

③ Liq.

④ $\xrightarrow{140\sim160°}$ Me$_2$InNMe$_2$ + CH$_4$

⑥ JCS **1956**, 3351.

InC$_6$H$_5$Br$_2$

① Phenyldibromoindium
   C$_6$H$_5$InBr$_2$

② Ph$_3$In + Br$_2$ $\xrightarrow{\text{benzene}}$

③ [>300°].
   Resembles diphenylbromoindium.

⑥ JACS **60**, 306 (1938).

InC$_6$H$_5$I$_2$

① Phenyldiiodoindium
   C$_6$H$_5$InI$_2$

② Ph$_3$In + I$_2$ $\xrightarrow{\text{benzene}}$

③ Resembles diphenylbromoindium.

⑥ JACS **60**, 306 (1938).

InC$_6$H$_{15}$

① Triethylindium
   (C$_2$H$_5$)$_3$In

② InCl$_3$ + EtMgCl $\xrightarrow{\text{ether}}$ 70%

   InCl$_3$ + Et$_3$Al + KCl $\xrightarrow{\text{pentane}}$ 67%

   In−Mg + EtBr $\xrightarrow{\text{ether}}$ 95%

③ Colorless liq. (144°/760, 118°/38, 92°/

18, 51~54°/3). [−32°]. n_D 1.538
(20°). d 1.260 (20°/4°).
Sol. in org. solvents. Spont. inflam-
mable in air; decomp. in H$_2$O.
IR: Z. anal. Chem. **197**, 309 (1963).
Monomeric in C$_6$H$_6$.

④ + H$_2$O $\xrightarrow{15°}$ C$_2$H$_6$

   + H$_2$O $\xrightarrow{90°}$ 3 C$_2$H$_6$

   + EtOH $\xrightarrow{70°}$ Et$_2$InOEt + C$_2$H$_6$

⑤ Catalyst for the polymn. of vinyl
   chloride.

⑥ Z. anorg. allg. Chem. **267**, 39 (1951).
   JACS **84**, 3605, 3830 (1962).

InC$_6$H$_{18}$As

① Trimethylindium trimethylarsine
   adduct
   (CH$_3$)$_3$In·As(CH$_3$)$_3$

③ (155° extrapd.). [28.2~28.8°].
   Sol. in polar org. solvents. Decomp.
   in H$_2$O.

⑥ Kaufman (1961).

InC$_6$H$_{18}$N

① Trimethylindium trimethylamine
   adduct
   (CH$_3$)$_3$In·N(CH$_3$)$_3$

③ Crystals. [66.2~66.4°].
   Decomp. in H$_2$O.

⑥ Kaufman (1961).

InC$_6$H$_{18}$P

① Trimethylindium trimethylphosphine adduct
   (CH$_3$)$_3$In·P(CH$_3$)$_3$

③ Crystals. (189° extrapd.). [46.5°].
   Sol. in org. solvents. Decomp in H$_2$O.

⑥ Kaufman (1961).

InC$_7$H$_{13}$O$_2$

① Dimethyl(acetylacetonato)indium
   (CH$_3$)$_2$In(C$_5$H$_7$O$_2$)

② $Me_3In + C_5H_8O_2 \longrightarrow$

③ [118° decomp.].

⑥ JCS **1956**, 3351.

InC₉H₂₁

① Tri-*n*-propylindium
$(n\text{-}C_3H_7)_3In$

② $InCl_3 + n\text{-}PrMgCl \longrightarrow 70\%$

$In-Mg + n\text{-}PrBr \xrightarrow{\text{ether}} 95\%$

③ Colorless liq. (178°/760, 121°/70, 103°/
12). [−51°]. n_D 1.501 (20°). *d* 1.187
(20°/4°).
Sol. in org. solvents. Spont. inflammable in air; decomp. in H_2O.
IR : Z. anal. Chem. **197**, 309 (1963).
Monomeric in C_6H_6.

⑥ Z. anorg. allg. Chem. **267**, 39 (1951);
321, 120 (1963).

InC₉H₂₁

① Tri-isopropylindium
$(i\text{-}C_3H_7)_3In$

② $In-Mg + i\text{-}PrBr \xrightarrow{\text{ether}} 50\%, 70\%$

③ (88°/12).
IR : Z. anal. Chem. **197**, 309 (1967).

⑥ Z. anorg. allg. Chem. **321**, 120 (1963).

InC₁₂H₁₀Br

① Diphenylbromoindium
$(C_6H_5)_2InBr$

② $InBr_3 + PhMgBr \xrightarrow{\text{ether, benzene}} 28\%$

$Ph_3In + Br_2 \xrightarrow{\text{benzene}} 80\%$

③ Colorless rhombic crystals. [315°].
n_D 1.562 (20°).
Sol. in C_6H_6, ether and pyridine;
insol. in petr. ether. Decomp. in
air, H_2O.

⑥ Z. anorg. allg. Chem. **267**, 39 (1951).
JACS **60**, 306 (1938).

InC₁₂H₁₀I

① Diphenyliodoindium

$(C_6H_5)_2InI$

② $Ph_3In + I_2 \xrightarrow{\text{benzene}}$

③ Resembles diphenylindium bromide.

⑥ JACS **60**, 306 (1938).

InC₁₂H₂₇

① Tri-*n*-butylindium
$(n\text{-}C_4H_9)_3In$

② $In-Mg + n\text{-}BuBr \longrightarrow 71\%$

③ (85~86°/0.1).
IR : Z. anal. Chem. **197**, 309 (1963).

⑥ Z. anorg. allg. Chem. **321**, 120 (1963).

InC₁₂H₂₇

① Tri-isobutylindium
$(i\text{-}C_4H_9)_3In$

② $In-Mg + i\text{-}BuBr \longrightarrow 85\%$

③ (71~72°/0.05).
IR : Z. anal. Chem. **197**, 309 (1963).

⑥ Z. anorg. allg. Chem. **321**, 120 (1963).

InC₁₂H₂₇

① Tri-*s*-butylindium
$(s\text{-}C_4H_9)_3In$

② $In-Mg + s\text{-}BuBr \longrightarrow 79\%$

③ Yellow liq. (70~72°/0.1).
IR : Z. anal. Chem. **197**, 309 (1963).

⑥ Z. anorg. allg. Chem. **321**, 120 (1963).

InC₁₄H₁₆As

① Dimethyl(diphenylarsino)indium
$(CH_3)_2InAs(C_6H_5)_2$

② $Me_3In + Ph_2AsH \longrightarrow$

③ [192~195° decomp.].
Dimeric in C_6H_6.

⑥ JCS **1963**, 233.

InC₁₅H₁₅

① Tricyclopentadienylindium(Ⅲ)
$(C_5H_5)_3In$

② $InCl_3 + NaC_5H_5 \xrightarrow{\text{ether}} 0.2\%$

③ Golden-yellow crystals. [160°

decomp.].

④ $\xrightarrow{160°}$ C₅H₅In

⑥ Angew. **69**, 639 (1957).

InC₁₈H₁₅

① Triphenylindium
   (C₆H₅)₃In

② In + Ph₂Hg ⟶ 65～81%

③ Colorless needles. [208°].
   Slightly sol. in org. solventes.
   Decompd. by CO₂.

④ + CO₂ $\xrightarrow{\text{xylene}}$ PhCOOH

   + O₂ $\xrightarrow{\text{air}}$ phenylindium oxides

   + O₂ $\xrightarrow{\text{benzene}}$ Ph−Ph + PhOH

   + RCOR′ ⟶ JACS **62**, 2353 (1940)

   + Br₂ $\xrightarrow{\text{benzene}}$ Ph₂InBr, PhInBr₂

⑤ Catalyst for dimerization of olefins.

⑥ JACS **60**, 306 (1938).

InC₂₀H₁₄Br

① Di-α-naphthylbromoindium
   (α-C₁₀H₇)₂InBr

② α-C₁₀H₇MgBr + InBr₃ ⟶

③ Colorless crystals.
   Sol. in org. solvents except petr.
   ether and cyclohexane.
   Monomeric in C₆H₆.

⑥ Z. anorg. allg. Chem. **267**, 39 (1951).

InC₂₇H₅₇

① Tri-n-nonylindium
   (n-C₉H₁₉)₃In

② InCl₃ + C₉H₁₉MgCl ⟶ 60%

③ (>150° decomp.). n 1.4632 (20°).
   Sol. in org. solvents.

⑥ Z. anorg. allg. Chem. **267**, 39 (1951).

In₂C₁₀H₂₈O

① Trimethylindium ethylether adduct
   2(CH₃)₃In·O(C₂H₅)₂

② InCl₃ + MeMgCl $\xrightarrow{\text{ether}}$ 50%

③ (139°/760, 73°/70, 56°/15). [−15°].
   n_D 1.480 (20°). d 1.241 (20°/4°).
   Sol. in inert org. solvents.
   Decomp. in air.
   Dissociate in dioxane.

⑥ Z. anorg. allg. Chem. **267**, 39 (1951).

【Tl】

TlCH₃O

① Methoxythallium
   TlOCH₃

② TlOEt + excess CH₃OH ⟶
   Recyst. from benzene.

③ White microcrystalline solid. [120°
   decomp.].
   Decomp. by water. Sol. in MeOH and
   benzene.
   Structure detn. by X-ray.

⑥ JINC **24**, 357 (1962).

TlCH₃Br₂

① Methyl dibromothallium
   CH₃TlBr₂

③ Crystals. [140～160° decomp.].
   Sol. in water.

⑥ J. Gen. Chem. USSR **5**, 1786 (1935).

TlC₂H₃Br₂

① Vinyldibromothallium
   (CH₂=CH)TlBr₂

② (CH₂=CH)₂TlBr + TlBr₃ ⟶

③ [152～155° decomp.].

⑥ Izv. OKhN **1958**, 1490.

TlC₂H₅Cl₂

① Ethyl dichlorothallium
   C₂H₅TlCl₂

③ Crystals. [180° decomp.].

⑥ Krause (1937).

TlC₂H₅O

① Ethoxythallium
   TlOC₂H₅

② Tl + O₂ + EtOH ⟶

③ Colorless oil. (80° decomp.)

Decomp. by water, CO_2, miscible with benzene, partially with EtOH.

⑥ JCS **1930**, 1461.

TlC₂H₆I

① Dimethyl iodothallium

(CH₃)₂TlI

② Me₂TlBr + KI ⟶

③ White-silvery plates. [265° decomp.].

d 3.909 (25°/4°).

Sol. in liq. NH₃.

NMR. Structure detn. by X-ray.

⑥ J. Chem. Phys. **40**, 933 (1964). Z. Krist. **87**, 370 (1934). Ber. **37**, 2051 (1904).

TlC₂H₆F

① Dimethyl fluorothallium

(CH₃)₂TlF

② (CH₃)₂TlCl + AgF ⟶

③ Crystals.

Sol. in water and MeOH; insol. in ether and C₆H₆.

⑥ J. Chem. Phys. **40**, 933 (1964).

TlC₂H₆Br

① Dimethyl bromothallium

(CH₃)₂TlBr

② CH₃MgBr + TlCl₃ ⟶

③ White silvery plates. [275° decomp.].

n 1.785. d 3.790 (25°/4°).

Sol. in liq. NH₃; slightly sol. in water.

Structure detn. by X-ray.

⑥ Z. Krist. **87**, 370 (1934). Ber. **37**, 2051 (1904).

TlC₂H₆Cl

① Dimethyl chlorothallium

(CH₃)₂TlCl

② MeMgCl + TlCl₃ $\xrightarrow[-15\sim20°]{\text{ether}}$

③ White solid. [280° decomp.]. d 3.445 (25°/4°).

Sol. in aq. ammonia; slightly sol. in water; insol. in org. solvents.

Structure detn. by X-ray.

⑥ Z. Krist. **87**, 370 (1934). Ber. **37**, 2051 (1904).

TlC₂H₆N₃

① Dimethyl azidothallium

(CH₃)₂TlN₃

③ Solid.

Slightly sol. in water.

⑥ Krause (1937).

TlC₂H₆O₄Cl

① Dimethyl perchloratothallium

(CH₃)₂TlClO₄

② Me₂TlCl + AgClO₄ ⟶

③ Crystals. [105° explodes.].

Sol. in water.

⑥ Trans. Faraday Soc. **56**, 1591 (1960). J. Chem. Phys. **40**, 933 (1964).

TlC₂H₆NO₃

① Dimethyl nitratothallium

(CH₃)₂TlNO₃

② Me₂TlCl + AgNO₃ ⟶

③ White plates. [300°].

Sol. in water or polar org. solvents.

⑥ J. Chem. Phys. **40**, 933 (1964). Trans. Faraday Soc. **56**, 1591 (1960). Krause (1937).

TlC₂H₇S

① Dimethyl mercaptothallium

(CH₃)₂TlSH

③ White solid.

④ + HCl ⟶ Me₂TlCl

⑥ Ber. **37**, 2051 (1904).

TlC₂H₇O

① Dimethyl hydroxythallium

(CH₃)₂TlOH

② Me₂TlBr + Ag₂O $\xrightarrow{\text{water}}$

③ Very sol. in water and alc.

④ + CO₂ $\longrightarrow$ (Me₂Tl)₂CO₃ (easily)

⑥ J. Chem. Phys. 40, 933 (1964).

TlC₃H₆N

① Dimethyl cyanothallium
   (CH₃)₂TlCN

② (CH₃)₃Tl + HCN $\longrightarrow$
   (CH₃)₂TlF + KCN $\longrightarrow$

③ Solid. [275° decomp.].
   Sol. in water.

⑥ J. Chem. Phys. 40, 933 (1964).   JCS
   1963, 229.

TlC₃H₉

① Trimethylthallium
   (CH₃)₃Tl

② Me₂TlCl + MeLi $\longrightarrow$
   TlI + 2 MeLi + MeI $\longrightarrow$

③ Colorless needles. (147° extrapd.).
   [38.5°].
   Sol. in benzene and ether.
   Stable in the dark, darkens on
     exposure to light.
   Decomp. with explosion at 90°.
   Monomeric in benzene (cryoscopic).

④ + Hg $\xrightarrow{\text{r.t.}}$ Me₂Hg + Tl
   + HX $\longrightarrow$ Me₂TlX

⑥ Discussions Faraday Soc. No. 34, 147
     (1962).   JACS 68, 517 (1946); 72,
     1760 (1950).

TlC₃H₉Se

① Dimethyl(methylseleno)thallium
   (CH₃)₂TlSeCH₃

② Me₂TlF + MeSeNa $\longrightarrow$

③ Colorless crystals. [210°].
   Decomp. at 170°. Sol. in benzene.
   Dimeric in benzene.

⑥ JCS 1956, 3351.

TlC₃H₉S

① Dimethyl(methythio)thallium
   (CH₃)₂TlSCH₃

② Me₂TlF + MeSNa $\xrightarrow{\text{MeOH}}$

③ Colorless crystals. [207~208°].
   Decomp. at 190°. Sublimes under
     vacuum.
   Dimeric in benzene.

⑥ JCS 1956, 3351.

TlC₃H₉O

① Dimethyl methoxy thallium
   (CH₃)₂TlOCH₃

② Me₂TlBr + TlOMe $\longrightarrow$

③ White-solid. [177~181°].
   Easily decomp. by water, CO₂.
   Sparingly sol. in light petr.
   Dimer.

⑥ JCS 1934, 1131.

TlC₄H₉O₂

① Dimethyl acetoxythallium
   (CH₃)₂TlOCOCH₃

② Me₂TlOH + AcOH $\longrightarrow$

③ Long plates. [293°].
   Very sol. in water, alc. and acetone.
   Less sol. in ether or petr. ether.

⑥ JCS 1922, 36, 256, 482.

TlC₄H₁₀Br

① Diethyl bromothallium
   (C₂H₅)₂TlBr

② EtMgBr + TlCl₃ $\longrightarrow$

③ Crystals. [>270° decomp.].
   Sol. in pyridine; slightly sol. in
     water.

⑥ Ber. 37, 2051 (1904)

TlC₄H₁₀Cl

① Diethyl chlorothallium
   (C₂H₅)₂TlCl

② EtMgCl + TlCl₃ $\longrightarrow$

③ Crystals. [200° decomp.].
Slightly sol. in water. Sol. in pyridine.
⑥ Ber. **37**, 2051 (1904).

TlC₄H₁₀I
① Diethyl iodothallium
$(C_2H_5)_2TlI$
② $Et_2TlCl + KI \longrightarrow$
③ Solid. [185~187° decomp.].
Sol. in pyridine ; slightly sol. in
water and alc.
⑥ J. Chem. Phys. **40**, 933 (1964).   Ber.
37, 2051 (1904).

TlC₄H₁₀O₂N
① Diethyl nitritothallium
$(C_2H_5)_2TlNO_2$
② $Et_2TlI + AgNO_2 \longrightarrow$
③ Solid-plates. [>290° decomp.].
Sol. in pyridine ; insol. in other org.
solvents.
⑥ JCS **1922**, 36.   Krause (1937).

TlC₄H₁₁S
① Diethyl mercaptothallium
$(C_2H_5)_2TlSH$
② $Et_2TlBr + (NH_4)_2S \xrightarrow{H_2O}$
③ White solid.
⑥ Ber. **37**, 2051 (1904).

TlC₄H₁₁O
① Dimethyl ethoxythallium
$(CH_3)_2TlOC_2H_5$
② $TlOEt + Me_2TlBr \longrightarrow$
③ Colorless liq. (110~120°/15).
Decomp. by water, CO₂. Miscible
with MeOH, ether, *n*-hexane.
Rapidly becomes cloudy on exposure
to air. Dimeric.
⑥ JCS **1930**, 1571.   Coates (1960).

TlC₄H₁₁O
① Diethyl hydroxythallium
$(C_2H_5)_2TlOH$
② $Et_2TlBr + Ag_2O \xrightarrow{water}$
③ [127~128°].
Very sol. in water and alc.
④ Soln. is basic. Easily react with CO₂.
⑥ Ber. **37**, 2051 (1904).

TlC₄H₁₂N
① Dimethyl(dimethylamino)thallium
$(CH_3)_2TlN(CH_3)_2$
② $Me_2TlBr + Me_2NLi \longrightarrow$
③ Solid. (Sublimable). [120~130°
decomp.].
Very sensitive to hydrolysis.
Dimeric in benzene.
⑥ JCS **1956**, 3351.

TlC₅H₇O₂
① Acetylacetonylthallium
$TlO_2C_5H_7$
② $TlOH + acacH \longrightarrow$
$TlOEt + acacH \longrightarrow$
③ Crystals. [159°].
Sol. in water and warm alc.
④ $+ R_2TlX \longrightarrow TlX + R_2Tlacac$
⑥ JINC **5**, 295 (1958).

TlC₅H₅
① Cyclopentadienylthallium
C_5H_5Tl
② $TlOH + C_5H_6 \xrightarrow{alkali}$
③ Colorless to pale yellow needles.
[100° sublimes].
Sol. in org. solvents. Hydrolysed by
warm acids.
⑥ JACS **80**, 269 (1958).   Angew. **69**, 533
(1957).   Nature **199**, 1087 (1963).

TlC₅H₁₀SN
① Diethyl thiocyanothallium
$(C_2H_5)_2TlCNS$
② $Et_2TlBr + AgCNS \longrightarrow$

③ Plates. [300°].

Slightly sol. in polar org. solvents.

⑥ J. Chem. Phys. **40**, 933 (1964).

Krause (1937).

TlC$_5$H$_{11}$O$_3$

① Diethyl bicarbonatothallium

(C$_2$H$_5$)$_2$TlHCO$_3$

② Et$_2$TlOH + CO$_2$ $\longrightarrow$

③ Crystals.

⑥ Ber. **37**, 2051 (1904).   Coates (1960).

TlC$_6$H$_4$Cl$_2$Br

① *p*-Bromophenyl dichlorothallium

BrC$_6$H$_4$TlCl$_2$

② (*i*-PrCOO)$_2$TlC$_6$H$_4$Br + MeOH $-$ HCl

$\longrightarrow$

Recryst. from pyridine.

③ [261°].

⑥ JCS **1934**, 405.

TlC$_8$H$_5$Br$_2$

① Phenyl dibromothallium

C$_6$H$_5$TlBr$_2$

② PhB(OH)$_2$ + TlBr$_3$ $\longrightarrow$

③ Crystals. [149°].

Sol. in water. Slowly disproportionates at room temp. Decomp. on
heating.

④ + KI $\longrightarrow$ C$_6$H$_5$I

⑥ JCS **1931**, 1462.

TlC$_6$H$_5$Cl$_2$

① Phenyl dichlorothallium

C$_6$H$_5$TlCl$_2$

② PhB(OH)$_2$ + TlCl$_3$ + H$_2$O $\longrightarrow$

Ph$_2$Hg + (*i*-PrCOO)$_3$Tl $\longrightarrow$

PhTl(*i*-PrCOO)$_2$ $\overset{\text{HCl}}{\longrightarrow}$

Ph$_2$Tl(*i*-PrCOO) + (*i*-PrCOO)$_3$Tl

$\longrightarrow$ PhTl(*i*-PrCOO)$_2$ $\overset{\text{HCl}}{\longrightarrow}$

③ Solid. [235° decomp.].

Sol. in water and org. solvents.

Slightly decomp. in boiling water.

④ + KCN $\longrightarrow$ K[PhTl(CN)$_3$] $\longrightarrow$

Ph$_2$TlCN

+ HgCl$_2$ $\longrightarrow$ PhHgCl + TlCl$_3$

+ KI $\longrightarrow$ C$_6$H$_5$I ·

⑥ JCS **1931**, 1462 ; **1934**, 405.   Dokl.

116, 233 (1957) ; CA **52**, 6236 (1958).

TlC$_6$H$_7$

① Methyl cyclopentadienylthallium

CH$_3$C$_5$H$_4$Tl

② TlOH + CH$_3$C$_5$H$_5$ $\longrightarrow$

③ [88~89°].

Sensitive to atmospheric oxidn.

⑥ JINC **9**, 86 (1959).

TlC$_6$H$_7$O$_2$

① Phenyl dihydroxythallium

C$_6$H$_5$Tl(OH)$_2$

② PhTlCl$_2$ + NaOH $\longrightarrow$

③ [280° decomp.].

Slightly sol. in hot pyridine ; insol.
in most org. solvents.

⑥ JCS **1934**, 405.   Krause (1937).

TlC$_6$H$_{10}$Br

① Di-isopropenyl bromothallium

[CH$_2$=C(CH$_3$)]$_2$TlBr

② (CH$_2$=CMe)$_2$Hg + TlBr$_3$ $\longrightarrow$

③ [190~194° decomp.].

⑥ Izv. OKhN **1959**, 259.

TlC$_6$H$_{10}$Cl

① Dipropenyl chlorothallium

(CH$_3$CH=CH-)$_2$-TlCl

② (MeCH=CH-)$_2$-Hg + TlCl$_3$ $\longrightarrow$

③ [340° decomp.].

⑥ Izv. OKhN **1961**, 1036.

TlC$_6$H$_{13}$O$_2$

① Diethyl acetoxythallium

(C$_2$H$_5$)$_2$TlO·CO·CH$_3$

② Et$_2$TlOH + AcOH $\longrightarrow$

③ White needles. [232~233°].

Very sol. in water and alc. Slightly
sol. in ether.

⑥ JCS **1922**, 36, 256, 482.

TlC₆H₁₄I

① Di-*n*-propyl iodothallium
   (n-C₃H₇)₂TlI

② Pr₂TlBr + KI ⟶

③ Solid. [183° decomp.].

⑥ Krause (1937).

TlC₆H₁₄Cl

① Di-isopropyl chlorothallium
   (i-C₃H₇)₂TlCl

② i-C₃H₇MgCl + TlCl₃ ⟶

③ Solid. [150° explodes].
   Much less stable than the *n*-propyl
   compd.
   Hydrolysed by boiling water.

⑥ Coates (1960).

TlC₆H₁₄Cl

① Di-*n*-propyl chlorothallium
   (n-C₃H₇)₂TlCl

② n-C₃H₇MgCl + TlCl₃ ⟶

③ Solid. [198° decomp.].
   Sol. in aq. NH₃.

⑥ Ber. **37**, 2051 (1904).   Krause (1937).

TlC₆H₁₅

① Triethylthallium
   (C₂H₅)₃Tl

② Et₂TlCl + EtLi $\xrightarrow{\text{r. t.}}$
   TlCl + EtLi + EtBr ⟶

③ Bright yellow liq. (192° extrapd.).
   [−63°]. *d* 1.957 (23°/23°).
   Sol. in ether.   Darkens on heating.
   Decomp. above 125°.   Decomp. in air
   and in water.

④ + H₂O $\xrightarrow{\text{fast}}$ Et₂TlOH
   + HX ⟶ Et₂TlX

⑥ JACS **83**, 4473 (1961); **57**, 486 (1935).
   Proc. Chem. Soc. **1961**, 208.

JCS **1934**, 1132.

TlC₆H₁₈N

① Trimethylthallium trimethylamine
   adduct
   (CH₃)₃Tl·N(CH₃)₃

② Me₃Tl + NMe₃ ⟶

③ Crystals. (15° decomp.). [0°].
   Sol. in polar org. solvents.
   Extensively dissociated in vapor.

⑥ Coates (1960).

TlC₆H₁₈P

① Trimethylthallium trimethylphosphine adduct
   (CH₃)₃Tl·P(CH₃)₃

③ Crystals. (50° decomp.). [27∼28°].
   Sol. in polar org. solvents.
   Extensively dissociated in vapor.

⑥ Coates (1960).

TlC₇H₇Cl₂

① *p*-Tolyl dichlorothallium
   p-CH₃C₆H₄TlCl₂

③ [223∼224°].
   Sol. in water

④ $\xrightarrow{\text{boiling water}}$ (*p*-tolyl)₂TlCl + TlCl₃

⑥ JCS **1931**, 1462; **1934**, 405.

TlC₇H₁₃O₂

① Dimethyl acetylacetonyl thallium
   (CH₃)₂TlO₂C₅H₇

② Me₂TlI + Tl·acac. ⟶
   (Me₂Tl)₂CO₃ + acacH ⟶

③ Crystals. [214∼215°].
   Sol. in water, alc. and benzene.
   Sublimes under diminished pressure.

⑥ JCS **1928**, 1288

TlC₈H₅N₂

① Phenyl dicyanothallium
   C₆H₅Tl(CN)₂

② PhTlCl₂ + KCN ⟶

③ Colorless needles. [228° decomp.].

⑥ JCS **1934**, 405.   Krause (1937).

TlC₈H₅S₂N₂

① Phenyl dithiocyanothallium
   C₆H₅Tl(SCN)₂

② PhTlCl₂ + KSCN ⟶

③ Needles. [100~120° liberates Ph-SCN].
   Insol. in cold water; readily sol. in
   KSCN soln.
   Turns red at 100°C.

⑥ JCS **1934**, 405.   Krause (1937).

TlC₈H₁₈O₃N

① Dibutyl nitratothallium
   (C₄H₉)₂TlNO₃

③ [280~290° decomp.].
   Insol. in water.

⑥ Krause (1937).

TlC₈H₁₅O₃

① Thallium dimethylethylacetoacetate

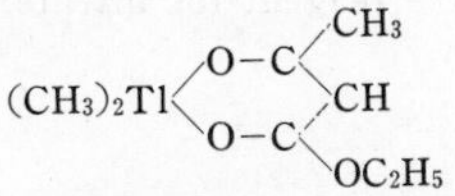

$$(CH_3)_2Tl \left\langle \begin{matrix} O-C \\ O-C \end{matrix} \right. \begin{matrix} CH_3 \\ CH \\ OC_2H_5 \end{matrix}$$

② Me₂TlOH + ethyl acetoacetate ⟶

③ Thick, colourless prisms. [128~130°].
   Sol. in *n*-hexane, benzene and
   toluene.

⑥ JCS **1928**, 1288.

TlC₈H₁₈F

① Di-*n*-butyl fluorothallium
   (*n*-C₄H₉)₂TlF

② (*n*-C₄H₉)₂TlCl + AgF ⟶

③ Needles. [220~240° explodes].
   Slightly sol. in water or pyridine.

⑥ Krause (1937).

TlC₈H₁₈Cl

① Di-*n*-butyl chlorothallium
   (*n*-C₄H₉)₂TlCl

② *n*-C₄H₉MgCl + TlCl₃ ⟶

③ Solid. [240~250° explodes].
   Sol. in water, ether, pyridine or alc.

⑥ Krause (1937).

TlC₉H₁₁O₂

① Dimethylthalliumsalicylaldehyde

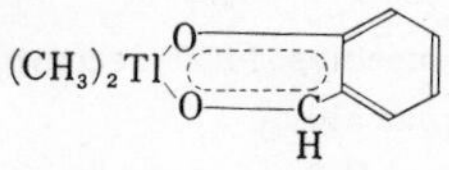

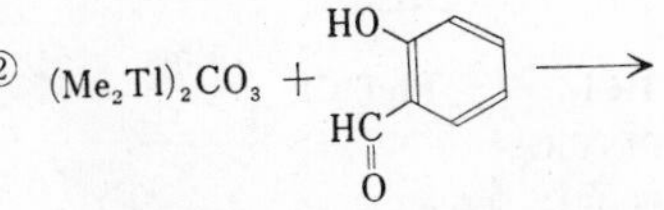

$$(CH_3)_2Tl \genfrac{}{}{0pt}{}{O}{O} \cdots C_6H_4 \cdots \genfrac{}{}{0pt}{}{}{CH}$$

② (Me₂Tl)₂CO₃ + [salicylaldehyde] ⟶

③ Yellow crystals. (160~170/20 sublime).
   [200° decomp.].
   Easily sol. in benzene; slowly sol.
   in water.

⑥ JCS **1928**, 1288.

TlC₁₀H₂₂Cl

① Diisoamyl chlorothallium
   (*i*-C₅H₁₁)₂TlCl

③ Needles. [253° decomp.].
   Sol. in polar org. solvents.

⑥ Krause (1937).

TlC₁₀H₂₂F

① Diisoamyl fluorothallium
   (*i*-C₅H₁₁)₂TlF

③ Prisms. [216° decomp.].
   Sol. in water; slightly sol. in alc. or
   pyridine.

⑥ Krause (1937).

TlC₁₁H₁₀NBr₂

① Phenyl dibromothallium pyridine
   complex
   C₆H₅TlBr₂·C₅H₅N

② C₆H₅TlBr₂ + pyridine ⟶
   Recryst. from warm alc.

③ Glistening leaflets. [85°].

④ + HBr ⟶ Ph₂TlBr

⑥ JCS **1934**, 405.

TlC₁₁H₁₀NCl₂

① Phenyl dichlorothallium pyridine comlpex
$C_6H_5TlCl_2·C_5H_5N$

② $PhTlCl_2$ + pyridine $\xrightarrow[\text{petr.}]{}$

③ Colourless needles. [172° decomp.].
Recryst. from alc.

④ + KI $\longrightarrow$ C_6H_5I

+ HCl $\longrightarrow$ $PhTlCl_2$ $\xrightarrow{\text{boiling}}$
Ph_2TlCl.

⑥ JCS **1934**, 405.

TlC₁₂H₁₀F

① Diphenyl fluorothallium
$(C_6H_5)_2TlF$

② Ph_2TlCl + AgF $\dashrightarrow$

③ Crystals. [310°].
Sol. in water.

⑥ Ber. **58**, 272 (1925).   Krause (1937).
Coates (1960).

TlC₁₂H₁₀Br

① Diphenyl bromothallium
$(C_6H_5)_2TlBr$

② $PhMgBr$ + $TlCl_3$ $\longrightarrow$
Recryst. from alcoholic ammonia or pyridine.

③ White needles. [>290° decomp.].
Slightly sol. in water.

④ + Hg $\longrightarrow$ Ph_2Hg + $TlBr$

+ Na $\xrightarrow{\text{in liq. NH}_3}$ Tl + Ph_3Tl

⑥ Ber. **37**, 2051 (1904).   JCS **1922**, 36,
256, 482.   JACS **61**, 1513 (1939);
62, 2357 (1940).

TlC₁₂H₁₀Cl

① Diphenyl chlorothallium
$(C_6H_5)_2TlCl$

② $2Ph_2Hg$ + $TlCl_3$ $\longrightarrow$
$PhMgCl$ + $TlCl_3$ $\longrightarrow$

③ Colorless microscopic needles.

[>288°].
Sol. in pyridine; slightly sol. in boiling acetic acid, alc and chloroform; insol. in water and ether.

⑥ Ber. **37**, 2051 (1904).   JCS **1922**,
36, 256, 482.

TlC₁₂H₁₅O₂

① Dimethyl benzoylacetonylthallium
$(CH_3)_2TlO_2C_{10}H_9$

② Me_2TlBr + $TlO_2C_{10}H_9$ $\longrightarrow$

③ Crystals. (120°/20 sublime). [128~
129°].
Sol. in polar org. solvents; slightly sol. in non-polar org. solvents.

⑥ JCS **1928**, 1288.

TlC₁₂H₂₂Cl

① Dicyclohexyl chlorothallium
$(C_6H_{11})_2TlCl$

③ Needles. [210~230° decomp.].
Sol. in pyridine and water.

⑤ Quantitative reagent for nitrate.

⑥ Krause (1937).

TlC₁₂H₂₆Br

① Di-*n*-hexyl bromothallium
$(n\text{-}C_6H_{13})_2TlBr$

② $(n\text{-}C_6H_{13})_2TlF$ + HBr $\longrightarrow$
Recryst. from hot alc.

③ White rhombic crystals. [216°
decomp.].
Begins to darken at 205°.

⑥ Ber. **63**, 1953 (1930).

TlC₁₂H₂₆Cl

① Di-*n*-hexyl chlorothalliu*m*
$(n\text{-}C_6H_{13})_2TlCl$

② $(n\text{-}C_6H_{13})MgCl$ + $TlCl_3$ $\longrightarrow$
Recryst. from pyridine.

③ Colorless plates. [198° decomp.].
Slightly sol. in water.

⑥ Ber. **63**, 1953 (1930).

TlC₁₂H₂₆F
① Di-*n*-hexyl fluorothallium
   (*n*-C₆H₁₃)₂TlF
② (*n*-C₆H₁₃)₂TlCl + AgF ⟶
③ White crystals. [240° decomp.].
   Sol. in org. solvents; slightly sol. in
   water.
   Forms ionaggregates in benzene.
⑥ Ber. **63**, 1953 (1930).

TlC₁₂H₂₆O₃N
① Dihexyl nitratothallium
   (C₆H₁₃)₂TlNO₃
③ Needles. [270° decomp.].
   Sol. in water or alc.
⑥ Krause (1937).

TlC₁₂H₂₇
① Tri-isobutylthallium
   (*i*-C₄H₉)₃Tl
② *i*-Bu₂TlBr + *i*-BuLi ⟶
③ (74~76°/1.6).
   Sol. in org. solvents.   Decomp. by
   light and water.
⑥ JCS **1934**, 1132.

Tl₃C₁₂H₃₀O₄P
① Tris(diethylthallyl)phosphate
   [(C₂H₅)₂Tl]₃PO₄
③ Needles. [189° decomp.].
   Slightly sol. in water
⑥ Krause (1937).

TlC₁₃H₁₀N
① Diphenyl cyano thallium
   (C₆H₅)₂TlCN
② PhTlCl₂ + KCN ⟶
   2 K[PhTl(CN)₃] $\xrightarrow{\text{boil.}}$
③ Solid. [318° decomp.].
   Sparingly sol. in water, with slight
   hydrolysis.
⑥ JCS **1934**, 405.

TlC₁₃H₂₅O₂
① Dibutyl acetylacetonylthallium
   (C₄H₉)₂TlO₂C₅H₇
③ Crystals. (138~139°).
⑥ Krause (1937)

TlC₁₄H₁₃O₂
① Diphenyl acetoxythallium
   (C₆H₅)₂Tl·O·COCH₃
② Ph₂TlOH + AcOH ⟶
③ Needles. [262° with gas evolution].
   Completely sol. in hot pyridine,
   chloroform, toluene and alc.; sol.
   in water; slightly sol. in ether
   and acetone.
⑥ JCS **1922**, 482.

TlC₁₄H₁₄O₂Cl
① Bis(*o*-methoxyphenyl)chlorothallium
   (CH₃OC₆H₄)₂TlCl
② 2-MeOC₆H₄HgC₁₀H₇-α + TlCl₃ ⟶
   2-MeOC₆H₄HgBu + TlCl₃ ⟶
③ [269° decomp.].
⑥ Izv. OKhN **1961**, 1036, 1039.

TlC₁₄H₁₉O₂
① Diethyl benzoylacetonylthallium

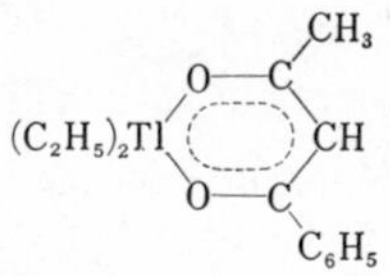

② Et₂TlOH

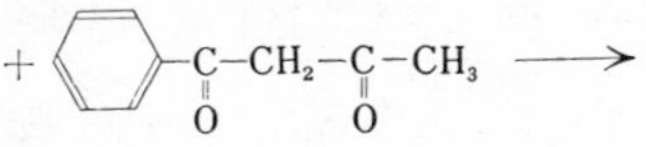

③ Crystals. [116~118°].
   Sol. in methyl iodide; very sol. in
   dry ether.
⑥ JCS **1928**, 1288.

TlC₁₄H₁₉O₄
① Phenyl di-isobutyryloxythallium
  C₆H₅Tl(i-C₃H₇COO)₂
② (i-PrCOO)₃Tl + Ph₂Hg ⟶
③ [221〜222°].
④ React with dicarboxylic acid.
  + HCl ⟶ PhTlCl₂
⑥ Dokl. 1957, 233 ; CA 52, 6236 (1958).

TlC₁₆H₁₄Cl
① Distyryl chlorothallium
  (C₆H₅CH=CH)₂TlCl
② 2 PhCH=CHB(OH)₂ + TlCl₃ ⟶
③ Solid. [254° decomp.].
⑥ Zhur. 26, 1876 (1956) ; CA 51, 4980 (1957).

TlC₁₈H₁₅
① Triphenylthallium
  (C₆H₅)₃Tl
② Ph₂TlBr + PhLi ⟶
③ Colorless needles. [169〜170°].
  Sol. in org. solvents. Decomp. above
  m. p.
④ + Hg ⟶ Ph₂Hg + Tl
  + PhCOCl ⟶ Ph₂TlCl + PhCOPh
  + CO₂ $\xrightarrow{\text{in boling xylene}}$ PhCOOTl
  + Ph-Ph
  + n-BuLi ⟶ PhLi + n-Bu₃Tl
  + O₂ $\xrightarrow{\text{in } C_6H_6}$ PhOH + Ph-Ph
  + (Ph₂Tl)₂O
⑥ Proc. Chem. Soc. 1963, 176. JCS 1934, 1132. JACS 61, 1513 (1939) ; 62, 2357 (1940).

TlC₂₀H₁₄Cl
① Di-α-naphthyl chlorothallium

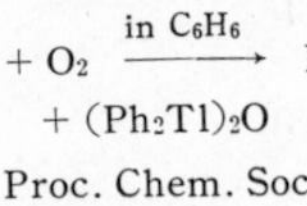

 TlCl

② (α-naphthyl)HgEt + TlCl₃ ⟶
③ Solid. [>310°].
⑥ Izv. OKhN 1961, 1036, 1039.

TlC₂₀H₁₄Br
① Di-α-naphthyl bromothallium
  (C₁₀H₇)₂TlBr
③ Solid. [272°].
  Completely sol. in cold pylidine ; sol.
    in ethyl acetate ; slightly sol. in
    alc. and CCl₄ ; insol. in toluene
⑥ JCS 1922, 36, 256, 482.

Tl₂C₂₄H₂₀O₄Cr
① Bis(diphenylthallyl)chromate
  [(C₆H₅)₂Tl]₂CrO₄
② Ph₂TlBr + Ag₂CrO₄ ⟶
③ Pale yellow needles. [>290°].
  Completely sol. in pyridine and
    boiling acetic acid ; slightly sol. in
    acetone ; insol. in water. Burns
    with slight explosion.
⑥ JCS 1922, 482.

Tl₂C₄H₁₂O₄Cr
① Bis(dimethylthallyl)chromate
  [(CH₃)₂Tl]₂CrO₄
② Me₂TlBr + Ag₂CrO₄ ⟶
③ Yellow plates.
  Slightly sol. in water and polar org.
    solvents.
⑥ J. Chem. Phys. 40, 933 (1964).

Tl₂C₅H₁₂O₃
① Bis(dimethylthallyl)carbonate
  [(CH₃)₂Tl]₂CO₃
② Me₂TlOH + CO₂ ⟶
③ Plates. [255° decomp.].
  Sol. in water and alc.
④ + acacH ⟶ Me₂Tlacac
⑥ J. Chem. Phys. 40, 933 (1964). Krause (1937).

Tl₂C₉H₂₀O₃

① Bis(diethylthallyl)carbonate
   [(C₂H₅)₂Tl]₂CO₃

② Et₂TlOH + CO₂ ⟶

③ Needles. [204° decomp.].
   Sol. in water and alc.

⑥ J. Chem. Phys. **40**, 933 (1964). Krause
   (1937).

Tl₂C₁₆H₃₆O₄S

① Bis(dibutylthallyl)sulfate
   [(C₄H₉)₂Tl]₂SO₄

③ Needles. [158~159°].
   Sol. in water and alc.

⑥ Krauss (1937).

Tl₂C₂₄H₂₀O

① Tetraphenyl dithalloxane
   (C₆H₅)₂TlOTl(C₆H₅)₂

③ Solid.
   Sol. in pyridine. Insol. in water.

⑥ JCS **1922**, 482.

6. Organic Compounds of Silicon

(Si)

6.1. Introduction

6.1.1. Chemical Behavior of Silicon

Silicon forms stable organic derivatives. The bonds are directed to the corners of a tetrahedron resulting from sp^3 orbital hybridization as in carbon. In fact, a number of optically active organosilicon compounds having a center of asymmetry at the silicon atom have recently been resolved; a pair of enantiomers of α-naphthylphenylmethylsilane (*1*) and (*2*) represent a typical example.

$$
\begin{array}{cc}
C_6H_5 & C_6H_5 \\
\vdots & \vdots \\
\alpha\text{-}C_{10}H_7-Si-CH_3 & CH_3-Si-C_{10}H_7\text{-}\alpha \\
\vdots & \vdots \\
H & H \\
[\alpha]_D+33° & [\alpha]_D-33° \\
(1) & (2)
\end{array}
$$

Silicon is known not to form $p_\pi-p_\pi$ multiple bonds, such as occur in olefins or ketones. Instead, polymeric structures are formed. However, since $3d$-orbitals are available for bond formation under the proper circumstances, partial multiple bonding due to $d_\pi-p_\pi$ conjugation can occur.

In general, peralkylated and perarylated derivatives are both thermally and chemically inert, but silicon-functional derivatives such as organosilicon halides, alkoxides, and acylates are highly reactive, especially in comparison with the carbon compounds.

6.1.2. Nomenclature

The nomenclature of silicon compounds recommended by the Commission of Nomenclature of Organic Chemistry of the IUPAC has been widely adopted.

The compound SiH_4 is called silane. Compounds of the general formula $H_3Si-(SiH_2)_nSiH_3$ are called disilane, trisilane, etc. Compounds substituted with alkyl, alkoxy, or halogen groups are named as substituted silanes. Compounds with the formula $H_3Si(OSiH_2)_nOSiH_3$ are siloxanes, and with the formula $H_3Si(NHSiH_2)_n-NHSiH_3$, silazanes. Hydroxyl groups attached to silicon are named by adding the suffixes ol, diol, triol, etc. Compounds containing carbon as well as silicon and in which there is a "reactive group" in the carbon-containing portion of the molecule not shared by a silicon atom, such as $(CH_3)_3SiCH_2CONHPh$, can be named in terms of the organic parent compound, that is, α-trimethylsilylacetanilide.

6.1.3. History

The first organosilicon compound with Si–C bonds, tetraethylsilane, was prepared in 1863 by C. Friedel and J. M. Crafts, but the foundations of organosilicon chemistry were laid by F. S. Kipping in the peroid 1899 to 1944, during which he published 51 papers on the preparation and properties of organosilicon compounds.

In the period 1931 to 1940 research on organopolysiloxanes was commenced by J. F. Hyde with the object of utilizing them for electrical insulating materials capable of withstanding high temperatures, and commercial production was first accomplished by the Grignard method. In 1944, E. G. Rochow discovered the "direct synthesis" of organohalosilanes, which not only brought about considerable development in commercial production of "silicones" but also prompted today's remarkable progress in the chemistry of organosilicon compounds.

6.2. *Classification*

Numerous types of organosilicon compounds are now known. The present description briefly summarizes the important types of compounds. Some typical preparation methods for silicon-functional compounds are also described.

6.2.1. R_4Si

Compounds containing a silicon atom attached to four organic groups through carbon-silicon bonds are represented by the general formula R_4Si, where R stands for the same or different kinds of organic radicals of various types, such as simple or heteroatom-substituted alkyl, alkenyl, alkynyl, aryl, and aralkyl, and heterocyclic systems like pyridyl, furyl, and thienyl.

Silicon-containing heterocyclic compounds, such as 1,1-dimethyl-1-silacyclobutane (*3*), 10,10-diphenylphenoxasiline (*4*) and 5,5'-spirobis(dibenzosilole) (*5*) also can be represented by the general formula R_4Si.

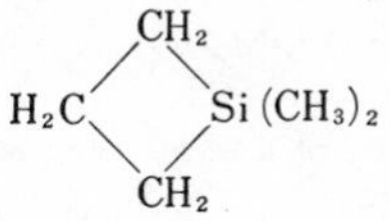

(*3*) 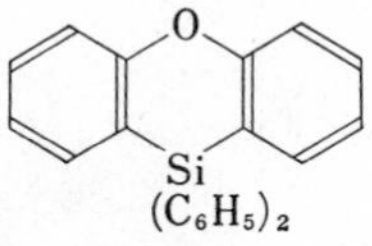   (*4*) 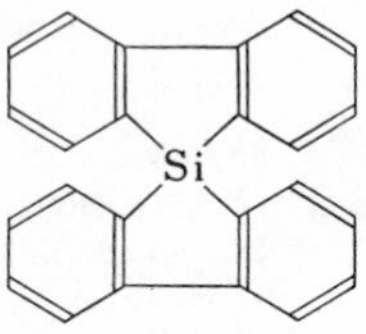   (*5*)

Some compounds in which four bulky organic groups are bonded to a silicon atom are known, whereas the analogous carbon compounds are not. Tetraisopropylsilane, tetracyclohexylsilane, and tetra(*o*-tolyl)silane are examples.

6.2.2. R_nSiX_{4-n}

A large number of organosilicon compounds are represented by the general formula R_nSiX_{4-n} ($n=1,2,3$), where X stands for a monovalent atom or group (other than an organic group) which is more or less negative relative to silicon. The most important types of compounds, together with their prepatative methods, are listed in Table 6.1.

Table 6.1. R_nSiX_{4-n} ($n=1, 2$ *and* 3)

X	Name	Preparation
H	Silane	(1) Reduction of halo (or alkoxy) silanes with a metal hydride or its complex; (2) "direct synthesis" (See 6.3.2).
Hal	Halosilane	(1) "Direct synthesis" (See 6.3.2); (2) halogenation of Si-H bonds; (3) from acyl chlorides or 47 % aq. HF and alkoxysilanes.
OH	Silanol	Controlled hydrolysis of halo-, alkoxy-, or acyloxylsilanes.
OR'	Alkoxy (or aryloxy)-silane	(1) Alcoholylis of halosilanes; (2) partial alkylation of alkyl orthosilicates by Grignard reagents.
OCOR'	Acyloxysilane	Action of carboxylic acids, their metal salts, or anhydrides on halosilanes.
OOR'	Silylalkyl peroxide	From alkyl hydroperoxides and chlorosilanes in the presence of pyridine.
OM	Metal silanolate	(1) Action of an active metal, for example, sodium, on silanols; (2) reaction of conc. caustic alkali with siloxanes.
SH	Silanethiol	From (1) H_2S and aminosilanes; (2) metal hydrosulfides and halosilanes.
SR'	Mercaptosilanes	(1) From aminosilanes and mercaptans; (2) reaction of halosilanes with metal mercaptides.
NH₂ NHR' NR₂'	Aminosilane *N*-Alkylaminosilane *N,N*-Dialkylaminosilane	Ammonolysis or aminolysis of halosilanes.
(CN)	(Iso)cyanosilane	From AgCN and bromo- or iodosilanes.
NCO	Isocyanatosilane	From AgNCO or Pb(NCO)₂ and halosilanes.
NCS	Isothiocyanatosilane	From AgNCS or NH₄NCS and halosilanes.
N₃	Silyl azide	From metal azides and halosilanes.
PH₂ PHR PR₂	Silylphosphine (*P*-Alkyl)silylphosphine (*P, P*-Dialkyl)silyl-phosphine	Action of alkali metal phosphide, for example, LiPH₂, on chlorosilanes.

6.2.3. $(R_3Si-)_nY$

Two, three, or even four organosilyl groups R_3Si (where R stands for alkyl or aryl groups; R may often be also any group X in Table 6.1) can be linked, respectively, to a bi-, tri-, or tetravalent atom or group to form a compound of the general formula $(R_3Si-)_nY$, n being 2, 3, or 4.   Some important types of this class are listed in Table 6.2, together with their typical preparative methods. Silylmetaloxanes such as $(CH_3)_3Si(OSnR_2)_2OSi(CH_3)_3$ and $(CH_3)_3SiOTi(OC_4H_9)_2O-Si(CH_3)_3$ also belong to this class.

6.2.4. $R_3Si(-Y-SiR_2-)_nR$

Linear polymers having the framework of $-Y-SiR_2-$ and end-groups of R_3Si are

Table 6.2. $(R_3Si-)_nY$ $(n=2, 3$ and $4)$

Y	Name	Preparation
$-O-$	Disiloxane	(1) Condensation of silanols; (2) hydrolysis or cohydrolysis, followed by condensation of any silicon-functional compounds R_3SiX.
$-S-$	Disilthiane	From (1) $R_3SiCl+H_2S$ (in presence of pyridine); (2) $R_3SiI+Ag_2S$ by heating.
$-NH-$	Disilazane	Ammonolysis of R_3SiCl.
$-NR'-$	N-Alkyldisilazane	(1) Aminolysis of R_3SiCl; (2) transamination between an aminosilane or a silazane and an amine.
$-\overset{\mid}{N}-$	Trisilylamine	From $[(CH_3)_3Si]_2NNa$ and $(CH_3)_3SiCl$.
$-PH-$	Disilylphosphine	
$-PR-$	P-Alkyldisilylphosphine	From chlorosilanes and lithium phosphides.
$-\overset{\mid}{P}-$	Trisilylphosphine	
$-CH_2-$	Disilylmethane (Silmethylene)	(1) Action of Grignard (or organolithium) reagents on $Cl_3SiCH_2SiCl_3$; (2) from $R_3SiCH_2-MgCl+R_3SiCl$.
$-\overset{\mid}{C}H-$	Trisilylmethane	(1) "Direct synthesis" using $CHCl_3$ and CCl_4 giving $(Cl_3Si)_3CH$ and $(Cl_3Si)_4C$, respectively; (2) Reaction of CHX_3 or CX_4 with R_3SiCl in the presence of Li or Mg in tetrahydrofuran.
$-\overset{\mid}{\underset{\mid}{C}}-$	Tetrasilylmethane	
$-(CH_2)_2-$	1,2-Disilylethane	(1) Action of metal alkyls on $Cl_3CH_2CH_2Cl_3$; (2) hydrosilation (See 6.3.3) of vinylsilanes.
$-CH(CH_3)-$	1,1-Disilylethane	(1) Hydrosilation (See 6.3.3) of acetylene; (2) intramolecular rearrangement of $(CH_3)_3SiSi(CH_3)_2-CHCl_2$ with $AlCl_3$.
$-CH=CH-$	1,2-Disilylethylene	$Cl_3SiCHClCH_2SiCl_3 \xrightarrow{\text{quinoline}}$
$>C=CH_2$	1,1-Disilylethylene	$AlCl_3 \begin{cases} \rightarrow Cl_3SiCH=CHSiCl_3 \\ \rightarrow (Cl_3Si)_2C=CH_2 \end{cases}$
$-C\equiv C-$	1,2-Disilylacetylene	From $BrMgC\equiv CMgBr$ and R_3SiCl.
$-(CH_2)_3-$	1,3-Disilylpropane	(1) Hydrosilation (See 6.3.3) of allylsilanes; (2) $R_3Si(CH_2)_3MgBr+R_3SiCl$.
$-(CH_2)_x-$	α, ω-Disilylalkane	From R_3SiCl and $M(CH_2)_xM$, where M is MgHal or Li.
$-C_6H_4-$	o-, m-, or p-Disilylbenzene	(1) o-, m-, or p-$R_3SiC_6H_4MgBr+R_3SiCl$; (2) p-$BrMgC_6H_4MgBr+R_3SiCl$.

listed in Table 6.3. In general, R stands for an alkyl or aryl group, but sometimes R may, in part, be a fuctional group such as hydrogen, halogen, or alkoxyl. The most important compounds of these are dimethylpolysiloxanes ($R=CH_3$ and $Y=O$), which are produced and used commercially ("silicone"). So-called modified silicones of various types are known which contain a variety of bridging groups

Table 6.3. $R_3Si(-Y-SiR_2-)_nR$ $(n \geqslant 2)$

Y	Name	Preparation
$-O-$	Polysiloxane	(1) Hydrolysis of R_2SiCl_2 or cohydrolysis with R_3SiCl; (2) generally, from polycondensation between R_2SiX_2 and $R_2SiX'_2$; (3) acid- or base-catalyzed ring-opening polymerization of cyclopolysiloxanes $[R_2SiO]_n$ ("equilibration").
$-S-$	Polysilthiane	From R_2SiCl_2 and H_2S in the presence of pyridine, with a large amount of cyclopolysilthianes being produced concurrently.
$-NH-$	Polysilazane	(1) From R_2SiCl_2 and NH_3, with a large amount of cyclopolysilazanes being produced concurrently; (2) ring-opening polymerization of cyclopolysilazanes.
$-CH_2-$	Polysilmethylene	(1) Alkali metal condensation of $ClSiR_2CH_2Cl$; (2) from $R_3SiCH_2SiR_2CH_2Li$ and R_2SiCl_2 or R_3SiCl; catalytic ring-opening polymerization of $\overline{\left[R_2SiCH_2\right]_2}$.
$-(CH_2)_x-$	Polysilpolymethylene	Platinum-catalyzed polyaddition of hydrosilanes to olefins or acetylenes (See 6.3.3)
$-C_6H_4-$	Polysilphenylene	Alkali metal-condensation of $p\text{-}ClSi(CH_3)_2C_6H_4Cl$.

as well as the siloxane bonds in the main chain of the molecule.   A few examples are given as follows:

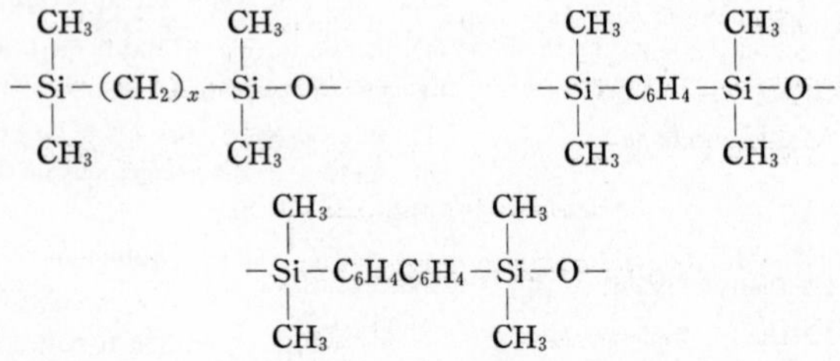

$$-\underset{\underset{CH_3}{|}}{\overset{\overset{CH_3}{|}}{Si}}-(CH_2)_x-\underset{\underset{CH_3}{|}}{\overset{\overset{CH_3}{|}}{Si}}-O-\qquad\qquad -\underset{\underset{CH_3}{|}}{\overset{\overset{CH_3}{|}}{Si}}-C_6H_4-\underset{\underset{CH_3}{|}}{\overset{\overset{CH_3}{|}}{Si}}-O-$$

$$-\underset{\underset{CH_3}{|}}{\overset{\overset{CH_3}{|}}{Si}}-C_6H_4C_6H_4-\underset{\underset{CH_3}{|}}{\overset{\overset{CH_3}{|}}{Si}}-O-$$

6.2.5. $\overline{-(Y-SiR_2-)_n-}$

Cyclic polymers having the framework of $-Y-SiR_2-$ are listed in Table 6.4. Cyclopolysiloxanes (especially methyl derivatives) are most important, and are produced and converted commertially to linear polysiloxanes as intermediates for

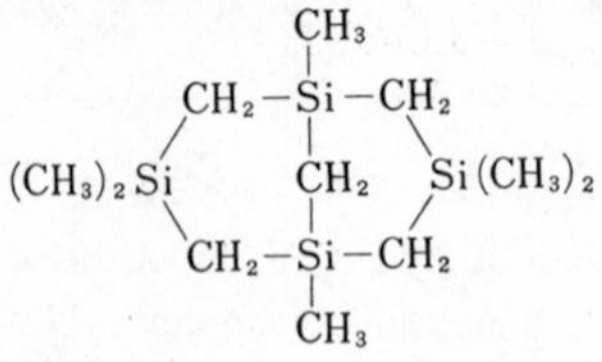

(6)

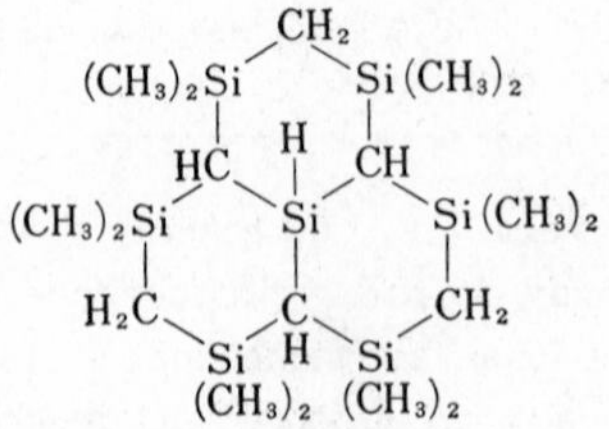

(7)

silicone oil and rubber.   Many cyclopolycarbosilanes composed of condensed rings are also known.   For example, 1,3,3,5,7,7-hexamethyl-1,3,5,7-tetrasila-bicyclo-[3.3.1]nonane (*6*) and *Si*-dodecamethyltricyclocarbosilane (*7*) are produced in the pyrolysis of tetramethylsilane at 750°.

Table 6.4. $-(Y-R_2Si)_n-$ $(n \geqslant 3)$

Y	Name	Preparation
$-O-$	Cyclopolysiloxane	Hydrolysis of R_2SiX_2.
$-S-$	Cyclopolysilthiane	From R_2SiCl_2 and H_2S in the presence of pyridine.
$-NH-$	Cyclopolysilazane	From R_2SiCl_2 and NH_3.
$-CH_2-$	Cyclopolycarbosilane	(1) "Direct synthesis" using CH_2Cl_2 to produce $[-CH_2SiCl_2-]_3$; (2) pyrolysis of $(CH_3)_xSiCl_{4-x}$.

6.2.6. $[-O_{1.5}-SiR-]_n$ and $[-O-SiR-Y_{0.5}-]_n$

Dehydration condensation of, for example, $RSi(OH)_3$ and $(HO)_2SiR-CH_2-Si-R(OH)_2$ often gives insoluble polymers with cage-like structures as well as three-dimensional high polymers.   Hexaorganohexasilsesquioxane (*8*) and octaorgano-octasilsesquioxane (*9*) are examples.   A ladder-like polymer with high-molecular weight (*10*) has been obtained by base-catalyzed polymerization ("equilibration") of phenylsilsesquioxanes.

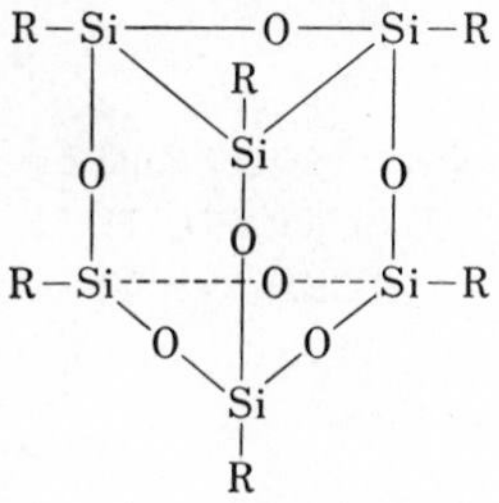

(*8*) 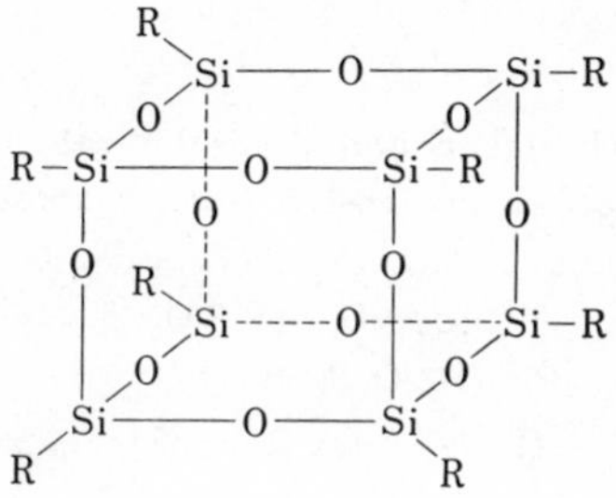   (*9*)

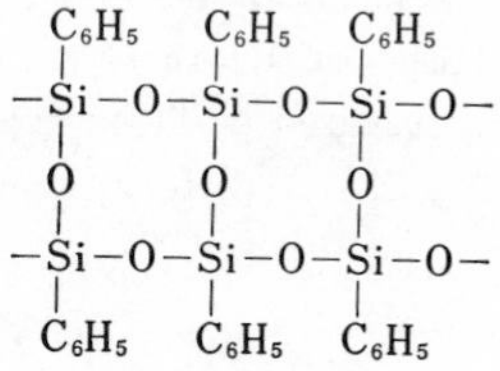

(*10*)

Acid hydrolysis of *sym*-dimethyltetraethoxydisilmethylene gives a cage-like polymer (*11*).

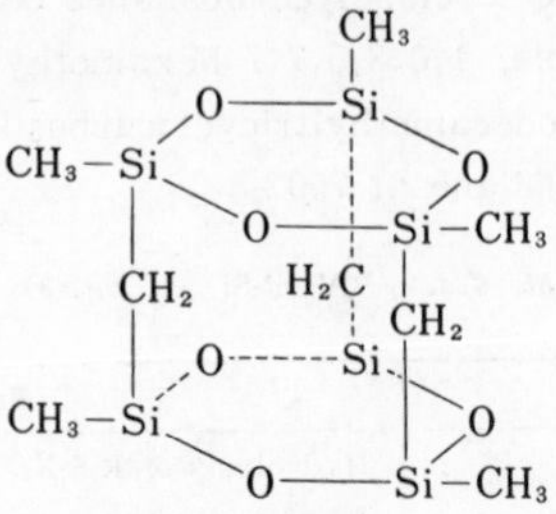

$$(11)$$

Cohydrolysis of chloro (or alkoxy) silanes produces various types of siloxanes, the structures of which cannot be expressed in terms of general formulas. Octamethylbicyclo[5.3.1]pentasiloxane (*12*) and decamethylspiro-5,7-hexasiloxane (*13*) are examples;

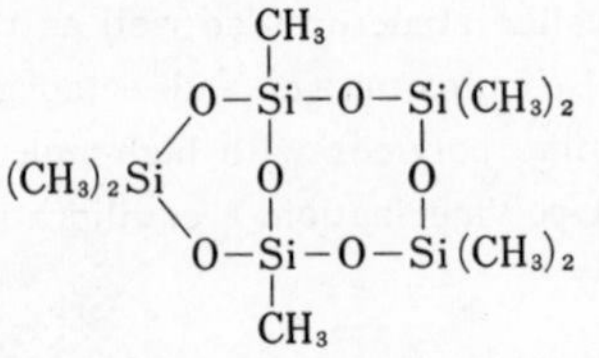

$$(12) \qquad\qquad (13)$$

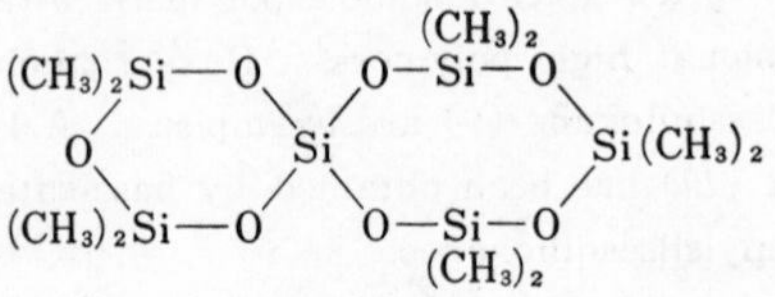

6.2.7. $(R_3SiY)_nE$ *and* $EO(-R_2Si-O-)_nE$

A number of organosilyl and organosilylene esters of inorganic oxyacids are known; for example, $(R_3SiO)_3B$, $(R_3SiO)_3Al$, $(R_3SiO)_4Si$, $(R_3SiO)_4Ti$, $(R_3SiO)_4Zr$, $(R_3SiO)_5Ta$, $(R_3SiO)_3VO$, $(R_3SiO)_3P$, $(R_3SiO)_3PO$, $(R_3SiO)_3As$, $(R_3SiO)_3AsO$, $(R_3SiO)_3Sb$, $(R_3SiO)_2SO_2$, and

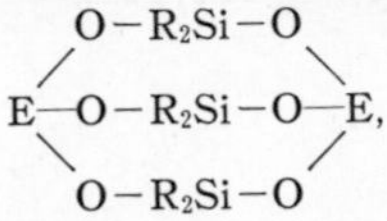

$$E \underset{\diagdown O-R_2Si-O}{\overset{\diagup O-R_2Si-O\diagdown}{-O-R_2Si-O-}} E, \quad \text{where } E=P, \quad As, \quad Sb.$$

Many compounds that have a metal or metalloid atom in the organic portion of the molecule, such as $[(CH_3)_3SiCH_2]_nM$ (M=Li, MgCl, Si, Sn, etc.) and $[(CH_3)_3SiC_6H_4]_4Ge$, have been prepared. These compounds correspond to the formula $(R_3SiY)_nE$ with Y being CH_2 or C_6H_4, although they can also be regarded as compounds of the type R_4Si.

6.2.8. $R(SiR_2)_nR$ *and* $\boxed{-(SiR_2)_n-}$

Over four hundred derivatives (peralkylated or arylated, silicon-functional, and carbon-functional) of di- and polysilanes have been prepared and characterized. Most of them are of the linear type, but a few are cyclic and branched-chain compounds.   Some examples are given below.

$CH_3-[Si(CH_3)_2]_n-CH_3$ Permethylpolysilanes

$n=2\sim12$

$-[Si(C_6H_5)_2]_n-$ Perphenylcyclopolysilanes

$n=4,\ 5,\ 6$

$[(CH_3)_3Si]_4Si$ Tetrakis(trimethylsilyl)silane

$ClCH_2(CH_3)_2SiSi(CH_3)_2Cl$ 1-Chloromethyl-2-chlorotetramethyldisilane

6.2.9. $(R_3Si-)_nE$

Organosilyl groups can be attached to a metallic or metalloidal atom.   Triphenylsilyllithium, $(C_6H_5)_3SiLi$, and related compounds have been most extensively investigated.   Other familiar examples are as follows:

$[(CH_3)_3Si]_2Hg$ $R_3SiGe(C_6H_5)_3$

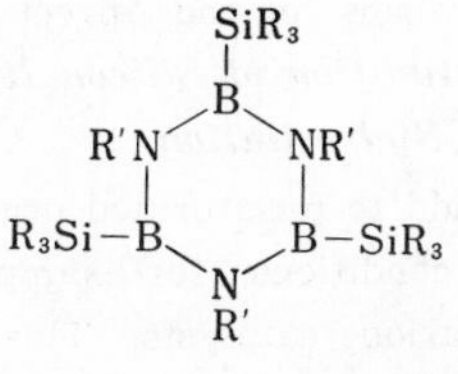

6.3. Synthesis of Carbon–Silicon Bond

The methods by which a carbon–silicon bond can be synthesized may be divided into five main categories, which will be described below.

6.3.1. Reaction of Organometallic Compounds with Silicon Halides, Alkoxides, or Hydrides

Organosilanes are most frequently synthesized from a silicon halide and an alkoxide, or sometimes from a silicon hydride by reaction with a metal alkyl, usually a Grignard reagent or a lithium alkyl, but sometimes an aluminum alkyl. The reaction proceeds stepwise so that it is possible to obtain partially alkylated silanes under the proper conditions.

$$n\,RM + SiX_4 \longrightarrow R_nSiX_{4-n} + n\,MX$$

Partial alkylation is, in some cases, effected most successfully by using less reactive organometallic reagents.   Thus $(\beta\text{-cyanoethyl})$methyldichlorosilane, $(NCCH_2CH_2)CH_3SiCl_2$, can be obtained in 90% yield from the reaction of dimethylcadmium with $NCCH_2CH_2SiCl_3$.

One of the most interesting syntheses involves the use of an alkylalminum sesquichloride, which reacts with SiO_2 to produce a tetraalkylsilane as the main product.

$$4\,R_3Al_2Cl_3 + 3\,SiO_2 \longrightarrow 3\,R_4Si + 2\,Al_2O_3 + 4\,AlCl_3$$

6.3.2. Reaction of Organic Halides with Elementary Silicon (the "Direct Synthesis")

An alkyl (or aryl) halide reacts at high temperatures $(250\sim500°)$ with elementary silicon, in the presence of copper as catalyst, to produce a mixture of alkyl (or aryl) halosilanes, that is, R_2SiX_2 (major product), $RSiX_3$, R_3SiX, and $RSiHX_2$. This process is usually called the "direct synthesis" after E. G. Rochow, the discover of it.   Methyl- and phenylchlorosilanes are prepared industrially by this method.   Although a variety of organic halides can be employed in this synthesis, products are more complex from reaction with higher alkyl halides.   Allylchlorosilanes are successfully prepared by the "direct synthesis", whereas vinylchlorosilanes are not.   Copper is the most effective catalyst, but several other metals may be used, for example, Ag, Ni, Sn.   In the industrial production of phenylchlorosilanes, small amounts of zinc or tin are added as a promotor for the copper catalyst.   For the reaction of methyl chloride with silicon-copper, the formation of methylcopper as an intermediate was suggested.   However, the reaction mechanisms for the "direct synthesis" appear to be much more involved.

6.3.3. Addition of Silicon Hydrides to Olefins and Acetylenes (Hydrosilation)

Silanes add to unsaturated organic compounds (olefins and acetylenes) under a variety of conditions, for example, under free radical conditions and in the presence of various catalysts.   This process is usually called "hydrosilation".

To an olefin of the type $YCH=CH_2$ adds a silane $HSiX_3$ to produce either a Markownikoff adduct (α-adduct) or an anti-Markownikoff adduct (β-adduct), or a mixture of both, depending upon the nature of olefins and catalysts.

$$YCH=CH_2 + HSiX_3 \longrightarrow \begin{cases} \overset{\displaystyle YCH-CH_3}{\underset{\displaystyle SiX_3}{|}} \\ YCH_2CH_2SiX_3 \end{cases}$$

The substituents X and Y can be varied widely, for example, alkyl, aryl, hydrogen, halogen, alkoxy, acyloxy, and cyano for either X or Y.

Thus, *n*-octyltrichlorosilane is obtained quantitatively from trichlorosilane and 1-octene in the presence of acetyl peroxide.   A free radical mechanism involving the $Cl_3Si\cdot$ radical has been suggested for the reaction.   With polymerizable olefins such as styrene and methyl methacrylate, telomerization occurs to produce the telomers, $H[YCHCH_2]_xSiCl_3$.

The metals of Periodic Group VIII, particularly platinum, and their derivatives, such as $H_2PtCl_6\cdot6H_2O$, are very useful as hydrosilation catalysts.   Using such catalysts, together with free-radical inhibitors, only hydrosilation products are obtainable in high yields even from polymerizable olefins without being accompanied by the formation of telomers.

Although the mechanism for platinum- or chloroplatinic acid-catalysed hydrosilation is not yet fully understood, it seems probable that a platinum-olefin complex is formed, with which the silane and hydrogen may also be complexed.

The addition of trichlorosilane to acrylonitrile gives the α-adduct, $NCCH(CH_3)$-

SiCl$_3$, almost exclusively under uncatalyzed thermal conditions, or in the presence of catalysts such as NiCl$_2 \cdot 4$ C$_5$H$_5$N. On the other hand, the β–isomer alone can be produced by change to basic catalysts such as organic tertiary amines and phosphines. Platinum catalysts are not effective for the hydrosilation with acrylonitrile. A special catalyst system composed of $(n$–C$_4$H$_9)_3$N·(CH$_3)_2$NCH$_2$CH$_2$N–(CH$_3)_2$·CuCl (in 17 : 7 : 20 molar ratio) is of particular interest because it enables one to obtain (β–cyanoethyl)methyldichlorosilane in 79% yield from methyldichlorosilane, CH$_3$SiHCl$_2$, and acrylonitrile, whereas any other catalysts are ineffective.

Peroxide-induced addition of trichlorosilane to acetylenes is largely *trans* addition to give *cis* adducts, whereas platinum or chloroplatinic acid induced one is *cis* addition to give *trans* products:

$$\text{RC}\equiv\text{CH} + \text{HSiCl}_3 \quad \begin{cases} \xrightarrow{\text{Peroxide}} & \underset{(cis\ 80\%)}{\overset{R}{\underset{H}{\diagdown}}\text{C}=\text{C}\overset{\diagup SiCl_3}{\diagdown H}} \\[2em] \xrightarrow{\text{Pt–catalyst}} & \underset{(trans)}{\overset{R}{\underset{H}{\diagdown}}\text{C}=\text{C}\overset{\diagup H}{\diagdown SiCl_3}} \end{cases}$$

6.3.4. *Interaction of Unsaturated or Aromatic Hydrocarbons or their Chloro Derivatives with Silicon Hydrides*

Olefins and chloroolefins, such as vinyl chloride, trichloroethylene, 1,2–dichloroethylene, and allyl chloride, react with trichlorosilane and methyldichlorosilane at about 600°C with elimination of hydrogen or hydrogen chloride to give unsaturated organosilicon compounds.

$$\text{R}'\text{CH}=\text{CH}_2 + \text{RSiHCl}_2 \xrightarrow{600°} \underset{(10\sim20\%\ \text{yield})}{\text{R}'\text{CH}=\text{CHSiRCl}_2 + \text{H}_2}$$

$$\text{CH}_2=\text{CHCl} + \text{RSiHCl}_2 \xrightarrow{600°} \underset{(50\sim60\%\ \text{yield})}{\text{CH}_2=\text{CHSiRCl}_2 + \text{HCl}}$$

$$(\text{R}=\text{Cl or CH}_3)$$

Aromatic hydrocarbons undergo condensation with RSiHCl$_2$ (R=Cl or CH$_3$) in the presence of aluminum chloride or boron chloride catalyst at 230°C in an autoclave, or at 400°C in the absence of catalysts, to give arylchlorosilanes.

$$\text{ArH} + \text{RSiHCl}_2 \longrightarrow \text{ArSiRCl}_2 + \text{H}_2$$

Arylchlorosilanes are also prepared in good yields by passing a mixed vapor of chlorobenzene or chloronaphthalene and RSiHCl$_2$ (R=Cl or CH$_3$) through an empty quartz tube heated to 600°C.

$$\text{ArCl} + \text{RSiHCl}_2 \xrightarrow{600°} \text{ArSiRCl}_2 + \text{HCl}$$

6.3.5. Methylenation of Silicon Halides with Diazomethane

Silicon halides with higher halogen content, such as silicon tetrachloride and tetrabromide, react with diazomethane in ether solution at $-50°C$ to give the (halomethyl)silane derivatives.   A small amount of copper powder is used as the catalyst.

$$SiX_4 + n\,CH_2N_2 \longrightarrow (XCH_2)_nSiX_{4-n} + N_2$$
$$(X=Cl \text{ or } Br; \quad n=1, 2, 3)$$

By means of this method, it is possible to prepare (chloromethyl) dichlorosilane, $ClCH_2SiHCl_2$, in 70% yield from trichlorosilane, the product being otherwise obtainable only with considerable difficulty.

6.4. Some Chemical Properties of Organosilicon Compounds

Among a variety of reactions which organosilicon compounds undergo, we briefly discuss here only some problems on nucleophilic substitution reactions at a silicon atom, electrophilic substitution reactions at a carbon atom directly attached to silicon, and reactions at the organic portion focusing our attention on the effects of the organosilyl group upon the reactivity.

6.4.1. Nucleophilic Substitution at Silicon

Organosilicon halides, alkoxides, acylates, and other compounds with functional groups bonded to silicon are much more reactive than the analogous carbon compounds, especially toward nucleophilic reagents.   Extensive studies recently done on kinetics and stereochemistry (using optically active compounds with asymmetric silicon such as $(\alpha\text{-}C_{10}H_7)(C_6H_5)(CH_3)Si^*X$) of S_N reactions at silicon argue for the methanisms involving a pentacovalent silicon intermediate, the geometry of which would be that of a trigonal bipyramid or a square pyramid.

6.4.2. Electrophilic Substitution at Carbon

The carbon-silicon bond sometimes undergoes cleavage by the attack of electrophilic reagents.

$$\overset{\delta-}{\underset{}{C}} - \overset{\delta+}{\underset{}{Si}} + Y^-Z^+ \longrightarrow -C-Z + Y-Si-$$

In general, alkyl groups attached to silicon are quite resistant to electrophilic cleavage.   However, under proper conditions concentrated sulfuric acid is capable of cleaving one methyl group from certain trimethylsilyl organic structures. This demethylation can be applied extensively to synthesis of various types of organopolysiloxanes.

$$(CH_3)_3Si(CH_2)_2CO_2H + H_2SO_4 \longrightarrow HSO_4Si(CH_3)_2(CH_2)_2CO_2H + CH_4$$
$$\downarrow H_2O$$
$$O\text{-}[-Si(CH_3)_2CH_2CH_2CO_2H]_2 + H_2SO_4$$

A 1 : 1 mixture of acetyl chloride and anhydrous aluminum chloride also serves as an effective chlorodealkylating reagent for peralkylated silanes.

The unsaturated groups, for example, vinyl, allyl, and alkynyl, and aromatic groups attached to silicon are cleaved very easily by many electrophilic reagents; this is probably because of either the increased s-character and hence electronegativity of the attached carbon, or of the ability of these unsaturated groups to stabilize bonding to the incoming hydrogen atom or other cations *via* "onium" ion formation.

6.4.3. *Reactions at the Organic Portion. Electronic Effects of Organosilyl Groups*

Since silicon is more electropositive than carbon (electronegativities on the Pauling scale are 1.8 for silicon and 2.5 for carbon), it may be reasonably expected that an organosilyl group exerts an electron-donating ($+I$) effect. Evidence that this is so is afforded by the fact that trimethylsilyl substituted aliphatic amines, $(CH_3)_3Si(CH_2)_nNH_2$, have markedly higher basicities than the carbon analogs, $CH_3(CH_2)_{n-1}NH_2$, on the one hand, and trimethylsilyl aliphatic and aromatic carboxylic acids ($(CH_3)_3Si(CH_2)_nCO_2H$ and $(CH_3)_3SiCH_2C_6H_4CO_2H$) are more acidic than the analogous carbon compounds ($CH_3(CH_2)_{n-1}CO_2H$ and $CH_3C_6H_4CO_2H$) on the other. However, with progressive substitution of more electronegative groups for the methyl groups in $(CH_3)_3Si$, the $+I$ effect of the silyl group becomes weaker; on the contrary, groups such as Cl_3Si and $(C_2H_5O)_3Si$ show an electron-accepting effect.

If a silyl group, even trimethylsilyl is bonded to an atom having at least one pair of nonbonding electrons, such as nitrogen, oxygen and halogens, or to a π-electron system, such as a vinyl or phenyl group, $(p \rightarrow d)_\pi$ bonding can occur ($-T$ effect of the silyl groups). Thus, the addition of hydrogen halides to trialkylvinylsilanes to give the anti-Markownikoff adducts can be interpreted in terms of the entry of the π-electrons of the vinyl group into the d-orbitals of silicon.

$$R_3SiCH=CH_2 + X_2 \longrightarrow R_3SiCH_2CH_2X$$
$$(R=CH_3 \text{ or } C_2H_5; \ X=I \text{ or } Br)$$

The reactivities toward nitronium ion of the o-, m- and p-positions of trimethylsilylbenzene relative to a single position in benzene (partial rate factors) are shown below, with those for toluene and chlorobenzene given for comparison.

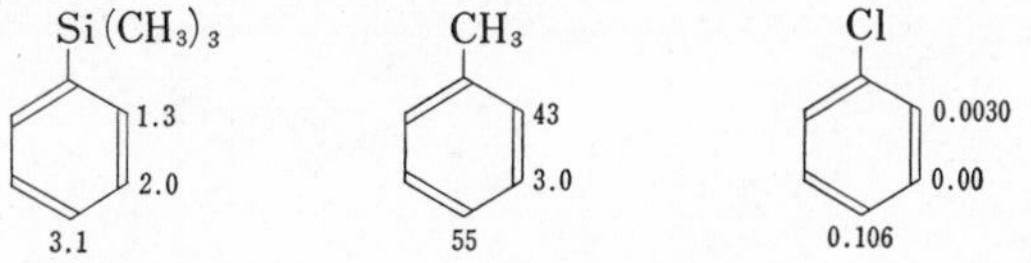

It will be seen that the $(CH_3)_3Si$ group activates the p-position only about 3.1/55 times as effectively as a CH_3 group, whereas the m-position 2/3 times as effectively. These results may be understood by considering contributions from structures such as (14) and (15).

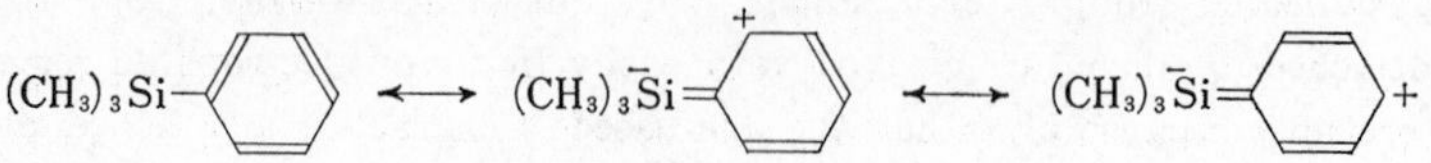

$$(CH_3)_3Si-\hexagon \longleftrightarrow (CH_3)_3Si=\hexagon^+ \longleftrightarrow (CH_3)_3\bar{S}i=\hexagon+$$

(*14*)   (*15*)

REFERENCES

1) E. G. Rochow, "An Introduction to the Chemistry of the Silicones", John Wiley, New York (1951).

2) M. Kumada, R. Okawara, "Organosilicon Chemistry" (in Japanese). Maki. Tokyo (1959).

3) R. N. Meals, F. M. Lewis, "Silicones", Reinhold, New York (1959).

4) S. Fordham (ed.), "Silicones", George Newnes, London (1960).

5) C. Eaborn, "Organosilicon Compounds", Butterworths, London (1960).

6) W. Noll, "Chemie und Technologie der Silicone", Verlag Chemie, Weinheim (1960).

7) F. G. A. Stone, W. A. G. Graham (ed.), "Inorganic Polymers", Academic Press, New York (1962).

8) M. F. Lappert, G. J. Leich (ed.), "Developments in Inorganic Polymer Chemistry", Elsevier, Amsterdam (1962).

9) A. D. Petrov, B. F. Mironov, V. A. Ponomarenko, E. A. Chernyshev, "Synthesis of Organosilicon Monomers", Consultants Bureau, New York (1964).

10) V. Bazant, V. Chvalovsky, J. Rathousky, "Organosilicon Compounds", 3 volumes, Czechoslovak. Acad. Sci., Prague (1965).

11) L. H. Sommer, "Stereochemistry, Mechanism and Silicon", McGraw-Hill, New York (1965).

(1955).   Zhur. **22**, 1783 (1952) ; CA **47**, 9256 (1953).

【Si】

It is estimated that nearly twenty thousand organosilicon compounds are to be found in chemical literature. On picking up 10% out of the total, attention was concentrated on relatively new compounds.

SiCCl₆

① (Trichloromethyl)trichlorosilane
CCl₃SiCl₃

② MeSiCl₃ + Cl₂ $\xrightarrow{h\nu}$ 95%

③ White solid. [121°].
Sol. in org. solvents. Decomp. in H₂O.

④ +4H₂O $\longrightarrow$ Si(OH)₄ + MeCl + 3HCl
+3MeOH $\longrightarrow$ (MeO)₃SiCCl₃ + 3HCl
48%

⑥ Ber. **87**, 282, 887 (1954).

SiCF₆

① (Trifluoromethyl)trifluorosilane
CF₃SiF₃

② Cu–Si + CBrF₃ $\xrightarrow{400°}$

③ Gas. (−42°).

⑥ US 2651651 (1953) ; CA **48**, 10056 (1954).

SiCH₂Cl₄

① (Chloromethyl)trichlorosilane
ClCH₂SiCl₃

② SiCl₄ $\xrightarrow{CH_2N_2}$ ClCH₂SiCl₃

MeSiCl₃ $\xrightarrow{Cl_2 \cdot h\nu}$ ClCH₂SiCl₃ (53%)

MeSiCl₃ $\xrightarrow{SO_2Cl_2}$ ClCH₂SiCl₃

③ Colorless liq.   (111~112°).   d 1.4776 (20°/20°).
Sol. in org. solvents. Decomp. in H₂O and alcohol.

⑥ Dokl. **94**, 485 (1954).   JACS **77**, 907

SiCH₃Br₃

① Methyltribromosilane
CH₃SiBr₃

② SiCl₄ + MeMgBr $\longrightarrow$

③ Colorless liq.(131.2~131.3°). [−28.4~ −28.1]. n_D 1.5152 (25°). d 2.2130 (25°).

⑥ JACS **75**, 1583 (1953).

SiCH₃Cl₃

① Methyltrichlorosilane
CH₃SiCl₃

② Cl₂ + PhSiCl₂Me $\longrightarrow$
Cl₂ + p-MeC₆H₄SiCl₂Me $\longrightarrow$
SiCl₄ + MeMgBr $\longrightarrow$
Si–Cu + MeCl $\longrightarrow$

③ Colorless liq. (65.4°). [−77.8]. n_D 1.4170 (20°). d 1.2811 (20°/20°).

④ +(Me₂SiO)₃ $\longrightarrow$ oils
+ p-MeC₆H₄MgBr $\longrightarrow$
p-MeC₆H₄SiCl₂Me

⑥ Inorg. Chem. **2**, 825 (1963).   Izv. OKhN **1963**, 282.   Zhur. **32**, 3737 (1962) ; English page 3654.   Zhur. **33**, 1299 (1963).

SiCH₃FCl₂

① Methylfluorodichlorosilane
CH₃SiFCl₂

② MeSiCl₃ + SbF₃ + SbCl₅ $\xrightarrow{600~650mmHg}$

③ Colorless liq. (29.5°). [−98.7°].
Sol. in org. solvents. Decomp. in H₂O and alcohol.

⑥ JACS **68**, 2655 (1946).

SiCH₃F₂Cl

① Methyldifluorochlorosilane
CH₃SiF₂Cl

② MeSiCl₃ + SbF₃ + SbCl₅ $\longrightarrow$

③ Colorless gas. (−0.5°). [−110°].

⑥ US 2258220 (1941) ; CA **36**, 858 (1942).
JACS **68**, 2655 (1946).

SiCH₃F₃

① Methyltrifluorosilane
CH_3SiF_3

② $MeSiCl_3 \xrightarrow{HF} MeSiF_3$

$SiF_4 \xrightarrow[CuCl]{MeCl, Si} MeSiF_3$

$MeSiCl_3 \xrightarrow[SbCl_5]{BzF} MeSiF_3$

③ Gas. (−30.2°). [−72.8°].

⑥ Ber. **68**, 2736 (1946).   JACS **68**, 2736
(1946) ; **67**, 1769 (1945).   JINC **6**,
303 (1958).

SiCH₃I₃

① Methyltriiodosilane
CH_3SiI_3

② $MeSiCl_3 + 6PhNH_2 \longrightarrow MeSi(HNPh)_3$
$+ 3PhNH_3Cl$

$MeSi(HNPh)_3 + 6HI \longrightarrow MeSiI_3 +$
$3PhNH_3I$

③ (228∼230°). *d* 2.946 (20°).

⑥ JACS **73**, 2351, 5804 (1951).

SiCH₄Cl₂

① Methyldichlorosilane
$CH_3Si(H)Cl_2$

② $MeCl + Cu-Si \longrightarrow 11.8\%$

③ Colorless liq. (41.5°). [−93°]. *d* 1.110
(25°).
NMR : JCS **1960**, 5132.

④ $+ PhC\equiv CH \xrightarrow{H_2PtCl_6 \cdot 6H_2O}$
$PhCH=CHSiMeCl_2$ (58%)

$+ \text{1-hexyne} \xrightarrow{H_2PtCl_6 \cdot 6H_2O}$
$BuCH=CHSiMeCl_2$ (28%)

$+ \text{3-heptene} \xrightarrow{H_2PtCl_6 \cdot 6H_2O}$
$n\text{-}C_7H_{15}SiMeCl_2$

$+ C_6H_6 \xrightarrow{Ni, 300°} MePhSiCl_2$

⑥ JACS **67**, 963 (1945) ; **80**, 4104 (1958).

Izv. OKhN **1960**, 1419 ; **1956**, 630.

SiCH₄F₂

① Methyldifluorosilane
$CH_3Si(H)F_2$

② $MeSi(H)Cl_2 \xrightarrow{SbCl_5}$

③ (−35.6°). [−110.1°].

⑥ JACS **71**, 971 (1949).

SiCH₄I₂

① Methyldiiodosilane
$CH_3Si(H)I_2$

② $MeSiH_3 + HI \xrightarrow{AlI_3} MeSiH_2I + MeSiHI_2$

③ Colorless liq. (159°). [−80.5°].
Sol. in org. solvents.
IR : 817∼803 (s) cm⁻¹.

⑥ Z. anorg. allg. Chem. **283**, 74(1956).

SiCH₅Cl

① Methylchlorosilane
$CH_3(H_2)SiCl$

② $SiH_4 \xrightarrow{HCl, AlCl_3, 100°} H_3SiCl \xrightarrow{Me_2Zn, 0°}$

$MeSiH_3 \xrightarrow{HCl}$

③ Colorless gas. (7°). [−134.1°]. *d* 0.935
(−80°).

④ $\xrightarrow{Me_2Zn} Me_2SiH_2$

⑥ Ber. **52 B**, 695 (1919).

SiCH₅F

① Methylfluorosilane
$CH_3(F)SiH_2$

② $(MeSiH_2)_2O + BF_3 \xrightarrow{-78°}$

③ Colorless gas. (−44°). [−125°].

⑥ JCS **1958**, 604.

SiCH₆

① Methylsilane
CH_3SiH_3

② $CH_3SiCl_3 \xrightarrow{LiH}$

③ Gas. (−57.5°). [−156.81°]. *d* 0.6277
    (−57.5).
    IR : Spectrochim. Acta **18**, 115 (1962),
    CA **57**, 5481 (1963).

④ $MeSiH_3 \xrightarrow[r.t.]{HCl \ or \ HI} MeSiH_2X$

⑥ Zhur. **32**, 2982 (1962). JACS **75**, 3753
    (1953) ; **69**, 2692 (1947). Ber. **52 B**,
    695 (1919) ; **52**, 724 (1919).

SiC₂Cl₈

① (Pentachloethyl)trichlorosilane
    $C_2Cl_5SiCl_3$

② $HSiCl_3 \xrightarrow{C_2Cl_4, \ 570° \sim 595°} CCl_2 = CClSiCl_3$

    $\xrightarrow{Cl, \ h\nu.}$

    $EtSiCl_3 + Cl \xrightarrow{h\nu \ 30 \sim 40°, \ then \ 60 \sim 70°}$

③ Solid. (98°/1). [62°].
    Sol. in org. solvents. Decomp. in H₂O
    and alc.

④ $+ Cu \xrightarrow{130 \sim 140°} Cl_3SiCCl = CCl_2$

⑥ JACS **79**, 2326 (1957). Ber. **92**, 1957
    (1959).

SiC₂HCl₃

① Ethynyltrichlorosilane
    $CH \equiv CSiCl_3$

② $CH_2BrCHBrSiCl_3 \xrightarrow{620°} CHBr = CHSiCl_3$
    $+ CH_2 = CBrSiCl_3 + HC \equiv CSiCl_3$

⑥ JACS **74**, 3899 (1952) ; **71**, 755 (1949).

SiC₂H₂Cl₄

① 1-Chlorovinyltrichlorosilane
    $CH_2 = CClSiCl_3$

② $ClCH_2CHClSiCl_3 + Me_2NPh,$

    Et_2NPh or

③ Liq. (125°). n_D 1.4648 (20°). *d* 1.4243
    (20°).
    Sol. in org. solvents. Decomp. in
    H₂O.

⑥ Izv. OKhN **1956**, 461 ; CA, **50**, 16663
    (1956).

SiC₂HCl₄F₃

① 1,1,2-Trifluoro-2-chloroethyltrichlo-
    rosilane
    $CHFClCF_2SiCl_3$

② $Cl_2 + CHF_2CF_2SiCl_3 \longrightarrow$
    $SiHCl_3 + CF_2 = CFCl \longrightarrow$

③ (120～121°)

④ $+ NaOH \longrightarrow CHFClCHF_2$
    $+ H_2O \longrightarrow CHFClCHF_2$
    $+ Cl_2 \longrightarrow CFCl_2CF_2SiCl_3$

⑥ JCS **1960**, 4503 ; **1956**, 962.

SiC₂H₂GeCl₈

① 1,2-Dichloro-1-trichlorosilyl-2-tri-
    chlorogermylethane
    $Cl_3SiCHClCHClGeCl_3$

② $CHCl = CClSiCl_3 + H_2PtCl_6$

    $+ GeHCl_3 \xrightarrow{60 \sim 70°}$

③ (137°/13). n_D 1.5345 (20°). *d* 1.8609
    (20°/4°).

⑥ Izv. OKhN **1963**, 75.

SiC₂H₃Cl₃

① Vinyltrichlorosilane
    $CH_2 = CHSiCl_3$

② $ClCH_2CH_2SiCl_3 +$

    $\longrightarrow 46.4\%$

    $HSiCl_3 + CH_2 = CHCl \xrightarrow{500°} 65\%$

    $HSiCl_3 + CH_2 = CCl_2 \xrightarrow{650°} 16\%$

③ Colorless liq. (91～3°). n_D 1.4365
    (20°). *d* 1.2650 (20°).
    Sol. in org. solvents. Decomp. in
    H₂O.
    NMR : JINC **6**, 303 (1958).

④ $+ HSiCl_3 \xrightarrow{600°} SiCl_4 +$

aromatic compds. + (Cl₃Si)₂C=CH₂
+ Cl₃SiCH=CHSiCl₃

+ m-BrMgC₆H₄CF₃ $\xrightarrow{10\sim15°}$
m-F₃CC₆H₄Si(CH=CH₂)Cl₂

+ HSiCl₃ $\xrightarrow{180\sim5°}$ (CHSiCl₃)₂ (55%)

⑥ Ber. **92**, 1012 (1959).   BCSJ **29**, 660
(1956).   JOC **22**, 596 (1957).   Izv.
OKhN 1957, 310.

SiC₂H₃F₂Cl₃

① 2,2-Difluoroethyltrichlorosilane
F₂CHCH₂SiCl₃

② HSiCl₃ + F₂C=CH₂
$\xrightarrow{\text{Pt}-\text{C},100\sim300°,\ 30\sim100\ \text{psi}}$

③ Colorless liq. (104.0~105.5°). n_D
1.4050 (25°). d 1.43 (25°)
Sol. in polar org. solvents. Decomp.
in H₂O

⑥ US 2637738 (1953); CA **48**, 8254(1954).

SiC₂H₄

① Ethynylsilane
CH≡CSiH₃

② SiH₃I + CH≡CMgBr ⟶
CH≡CSi(OEt)₃ + LiAlH₄ ⟶

③ (−22.5° ± 0.5°). [−90.7° ± 0.5°].

⑥ JCS 1963, 661.

SiC₂H₄Cl₂

① Vinyldichlorosilane
CH₂=CHSiHCl₂

② MeCHCl₂ + Si–Cu $\xrightarrow{280°,\ 16\ \text{hrs}}$ 6.4%

CH₂=CHCl + Si–Cu $\xrightarrow{220°}$ 45.5%

CH₂=CHCl + H₂SiCl₂ $\xrightarrow{450\sim545°}$ 20%

③ Colorless liq. (73°). n_D 1.4160 (20°).
d 1.1222 (20°).
Sol. in org. solvents. Decomp. in
H₂O.

④ + MeSiHCl₂ $\xrightarrow{\text{Me}_2\text{NCN}}$ MeSiH₂Cl +

CH₂=CHSiH₂Cl

⑥ Dokl. **107**, 99 (1956); CA **50**, 13728
(1956).   Zhur. **27**, 2475 (1957); CA
52, 7131 (1958).   Dokl. **126**, 1009
(1959); CA **53**, 21747 (1959).   US
2732280; CA **50**, 12097 (1956).

SiC₂H₄Cl₄

① 1-Chloroethyltrichlorosilane
CH₃CHClSiCl₃

② EtSiCl₃ + Cl₂ $\xrightarrow[\text{final temp. }140°]{h\nu,\ 50\ \text{hrs}}$
EtSiCl₃ + MeCHClSiCl₃ +
ClCH₂CH₂SiCl₃ + ClCHClSiHCl₃

③ Colorless liq. (136.4°). d 1.377 (24°).
Sol. in org. solvents. Decomp. in
H₂O.

④ + LiH ⟶ H₃SiCHClMe (39%)
+ MeMgI ⟶ Me₃SiCHClMe
(74%)

⑥ Dokl. **97**, 687 (1954); **100**, 1107 (1955).
CA **49**, 10166 (1955).

SiC₂H₄Cl₄

① 2-Chloroethyltrichlorosilane
ClCH₂CH₂SiCl₃

② Cl₂ + EtSiCl₃ $\xrightarrow{17\text{hrs, final temp. }135.5°}$
EtSiCl₃ + MeCHClSiCl₃ + ClCH₂CH₂-
SiCl₃

Cl₂ + EtSiHCl₂ $\xrightarrow{50\text{hrs, final temp. }140°}$
EtSiCl₃ + MeCHClSiCl₃ +
ClCH₂CH₂SiCl₃

③ Colorless liq. (152°).
Sol. in org. solvents. Decomp. in
H₂O.

⑥ Dokl. **97**, 687 (1954); **100**, 1107 (1955);
CA **49**, 10166 (1955).

SiC₂H₅Br₃

① Ethyltribromosilane
C₂H₅SiBr₃

② Si–Cu(80 : 20) + EtBr + H₂ $\xrightarrow{290\sim300°}$
   EtSiHBr₂(5%) + EtSiBr₃(36.6%)
   SiCl₄ + EtMgBr ⟶

③ Straw liq. (160.1~160.3°). [−43.2].
   n_D 1.5155 (25°). d 2.0671 (25°).
   Sol. in org. solvents. Decomp. in
   H₂O.

④ + EtMgBr ⟶ Et₂SiBr₂
   + EtSiCl₃ $\xrightarrow{\text{AlCl}_3,\ 190°}$ EtSiCl₃ +
   EtSiCl₂Br + EtSiClBr₂ + EtSiCl₃
   (mole ratio 1 : 3.0 : 2.5 : 0.8)

⑥ JACS **75**, 1583 (1953). J. Inst.
   Polytech. Osaka city Univ., Ser. C,
   2, 131 (1952) ; CA **48**, 11303 (1954).

SiC₂H₅Cl₃

① Ethyltrichlorosilane
   C₂H₅SiCl₃

② SiCl₄ + EtMgBr
   $\xrightarrow{\text{reflux in benzene, 3}\sim\text{4 hrs}}$
   ClCH₂CH₂SiEtCl₂ + AlCl₃ ⟶ 95%
   SiHCl₃ + C₂H₄ $\xrightarrow{285°,\ 200\,\text{atm.}}$ 20.1%

③ Colorless liq. (98.8°). [−105.6°].
   n_D 1.4253 (20°). d 1.2393 (20°).
   Sol. in org. solvents. Decomp. in
   H₂O.
   NMR : JINC **6**, 303 (1958)

④ + $\overset{\text{CH}_2-\text{CH}_2}{\underset{\text{O}}{\diagdown\!\diagup}}$ ⟶ ClCH₂CH₂OSiEtCl₂

⑥ J. Gen. Chem. USSR **16**, 487 (1946) ;
   CA **41**, 701 (1947). Zhur. **27**, 267
   (1957). Dokl. **114**, 128 (1957) ; **113**,
   120 (1957).

SiC₂H₅Cl₃

① Methyl(chloromethyl)dichlorosilane
   CH₃(CH₂Cl)SiCl₂

② Me₂SiCl₂ + Cl₂ $\xrightarrow{h\nu}$ 80%

③ Colorless liq. (121.3°). n_D 1.4495 (20°).
   d 1.2842 (20°).

Sol. in org. solvent.

④ + EtMgJ ⟶ Et₂SiMeCH₂I (81%)

⑥ Dokl. **94**, 485 (1954). CA **49**, 3795
   (1955). Dokl. **94**, 873 (1954) ; CA
   49, 3000 (1955). Dokl. **100**, 81
   (1955) ; CA **50**, 1573 (1956).

SiC₂H₅FCl₂

① Ethylfluorodichlorosilane
   C₂H₅(F)SiCl₂

② EtSiCl₃ + SbF₃ ⟶

③ Colorless liq. (62.2°).
   Sol. in org. solvents.

⑥ Post 53 (1949). JACS **68**, 2650 (1946).

SiC₂H₅F₃

① Ethyltrifluorosilane
   C₂H₅SiF₃

② C₂H₅SiCl₃ + SbF₃ ⟶ 39%
   C₂H₅SiCl₃ + HF ⟶ 88~90%

③ Gas. (−4.4°). [−113.3°]. d 1.227
   (20°).

④ + Cl₂ ⟶ MeCHClSiF₃ (7.4%) +
   ClCH₂CH₂SiF₃ (32.4%) + Cl₂C₂H₃SiF₃

⑥ Zhur. **27**, 2067 (1957). CA **52**, 6147
   (1957). US 2436777 (1948) ; CA **42**,
   4199 (1948). JCS **1944**, 454.

SiC₂H₅N

① Methylisocyanosilane
   CH₃(H₂)SiNC

② MeSiH₂I + Ag(NC)₂ ⟶

③ Colorless liq. [−23.1°].
   Sol. in org. solvents.
   IR : 953~940 (m), 711, 706 (s) cm⁻¹.

④ + H₂O ⟶ MeSi(H₂)OH + HNC
   + BF₃ ⟶ unaffected

⑥ Z. anorg. allg. Chem. **283**, 74 (1956).

SiC₂H₆

① Vinylsilane
   CH₂=CHSiH₃

② CH₂=CHSiCl₃ $\xrightarrow{\text{LiAlH}_4\ \text{in dioxane}}$

③ Colorless gas.(−22.8°), (α)[−179.08°],
(β)[−171.61°]. d0.6664 (−22.8°).

⑥ JACS **75**, 3753 (1953).   JINC **11**, 24
(1959)；CA **53**, 21353 (1958).

SiC₂H₆Br₂

① Dimethyldibromosilane
(CH₃)₂SiBr₂

② CH₃Br + Si $\xrightarrow{\text{Cu}}$
Me₂SiCl₂ + MgBr₂ ⟶
Me₂SiBr₂ + Me₂SiBrCl

③ Colorless liq. (110.3~112.3°). [−58.5
~58.0°]. n_D 1.4696 (25). d 1.6952
(25°).
Sol. in org. solvents.

⑥ JACS **75**, 1583 (1953).   Post (1949).

SiC₂H₆Br₂

① Ethyldibromosilane
C₂H₅SiHBr₂

② Si-Cu(80 : 20) + EtBr + H₂ $\xrightarrow{290\sim300°}$
EtSiHBr₂(5%) + EtSiBr₂(36.6%)

③ Liq. (119.5~120.0°). d 1.728 (20°).
Sol. in org. solvents.

⑥ J. Inst. Polytech. Osaka City Univ.
Ser. C, **2**, 131 (1952)；CA, **48**, 11303
(1954).

SiC₂H₆Cl₂

① Dimethyldichlorosilane
(CH₃)₂SiCl₂

② SiCl₄ + MeMgCl ⟶
Si + MeCl ⟶
Si-Cu + MeCl $\xrightarrow{280°}$ 50%

③ Colorless liq. (70.5°). [−76°].
Sol. in org. solvents. Decomp. in
H₂O.
NMR : JINC **6**, 303 (1958).
IR : Spectroscopiya **10**, 69 (1961).

④ + 2HO−$\overset{\text{CCl}_3}{\underset{|}{\text{CH}}}$−NH₂ ⟶

$\overset{\text{CCl}_3}{\underset{|}{\text{Me}_2\text{Si}(\text{O}-\text{CH}}}$−NH₂)₂ + 2HCl

⑥ JACS **63**, 801 (1941).   Zhur. **27**, 2648
(1957). Makromol. Chem. **26**, 236
(1958).

SiC₂H₆Cl₂

① Ethyldichlorosilane
C₂H₅SiHCl₂

② SiHCl₃ + C₂H₅MgBr ⟶
Si-Cu + EtCl $\xrightarrow{190°}$ 51%
H₂SiCl₂ + CH₂=CH₂ $\xrightarrow{\text{H}_2\text{PtCl}_6}$ 42%

③ Colorless liq. (75.5°). n_D1.4162 (20°).
d 1.0892 (20°).

④ + CH₂=CHCH₂Cl $\xrightarrow[160°]{\text{Pt}-\text{C}}$
EtSiCl₂(CH₂CH₂CH₂Cl)

⑥ JACS **72**, 2032 (1950).   Zhur. **27**, 2648
(1957). Dokl. **126**, 1009 (1959).
Izv. OKhN **1957**, 1206.

SiC₂H₆F₂

① Dimethyldifluorosilane
(CH₃)₂SiF₂

② Me₂Si(OEt)₂ $\xrightarrow{\text{HF}}$

③ Gas. (2~3°). [−87.5°].
NMR : JINC **6**, 303 (1958).

⑥ US 2519879.   JACS **68**, 2736 (1946).

SiC₂H₆N₆

① Dimethyldiazidosilane
(CH₃)₂Si(N₃)₂

② Me₂SiCl₂ + NaN₃ ⟶ 61.5%
Me₃SiN₃ + Me₂SiCl₂ ⟶ 73%

③ (144.3°).

④ + HOH ⟶ HN₃ + (Me₂SiO)ₓ

⑥ Angew. **74**, 717 (1962).   Ber. **96**, 1293
(1963).

SiC₂H₇Cl

① Dimethylchlorosilane

(CH₃)₂SiHCl

② (Me₂SiH)₂O + BCl₃ ⟶

Me₃SiSiMe₂Cl + HCl ⟶

Si + MeCl $\xrightarrow{Cu}$

③ Colorless liq. (34.7~36.0°). [−111°].
IR, NMR : JCS 1960, 5132.

④ + 2 H₂O ⟶

H(Me)₂SiOSi(Me)₂OSi(Me)₂H +
3 HCl + H₂

+ *n*-heptene-3 $\xrightarrow{HPtCl_6}$

n-heptylchlorosilane

⑥ JACS 80, 4104 (1958).   JCS 1958, 604.
Kogyo Kagaku Zasshi 60, 1357
(1957).   BCSJ 29, 236 (1956).

SiC₂H₇Cl

① Ethylchlorosilane
C₂H₅SiH₂Cl

② EtSiHCl₂ + Me₂NCN $\xrightarrow{<150°}$

EtSiHCl₂ + AlCl₃ $\xrightarrow{distn., heat}$

EtSiHCl₂ + EtSiH₂Cl + EtSiCl₃

Si-Cu(80/20) + EtCl $\xrightarrow{270~330°}$ 40%

EtSiHCl₂ + (CH₂)₄(CN)₂ $\xrightarrow{heat}$ 71%

③ Colorless liq. (43°). n_D 1.3975 (20°).
d 0.9013 (20°).
Sol. in org. solvents.

⑥ Zhur. 27, 709 (1957) ; CA 51, 16283
(1957).   US 2732281 ; CA 50, 12097
(1956).   Izv. OKhN 1957, 956 ; CA
52, 4472 (1958).   Izv. OKhN 1960,
519 ; CA 54, 22342 (1960).

SiC₂H₇Cl

① 1-Chloroethylsilane
CH₃CHClSiH₃

② MeCHClSiCl₃ + LiH ⟶ 39%

③ Colorless liq. (49.1°). n_D 1.4147 (20°).
d 0.8846 (20°) .
Sol. in org. solvents.

⑥ Dokl. 100, 1107 (1955) ; CA 49, 10166
(1955).

SiC₂H₇F

① Dimethylfluorosilane
(CH₃)₂SiHF

② (Me₂SiH)₂O + 2 BF₃ $\xrightarrow{-78°}$ 64%

③ Gas. (−9.0°). [−115°].

⑥ JCS 1958, 604.

SiC₂H₇I

① Dimethyliodosilane
(CH₃)₂SiHI

② 2Me₂SiH₂ + HI $\xrightarrow{AlI_3,\ 110°,\ 12\ hrs}$

③ Colorless liq. (92°). [−88°].
Sol. in org. solvents.

④ + Ag₂CO₃ ⟶ (Me₂SiH)₂O + 2 AgI
+ CO₂ 70%

+ HgS ⟶ (Me₂SiH)₂S + HgI₂
65~70%

⑥ JCS 1958, 609.

SiC₂H₈

① Dimethylsilane
(CH₃)₂SiH₂

② SiH₂Cl₂ + 2 CH₃MgBr ⟶
(CH₃)₂SiCl₂ + LiAlH₄ ⟶

③ Gas. (−19.6°). [−150.22°]. d 0.6377
(−19.6).
IR : JCS 1958, 1453

⑥ Ger. 936138 (1955).   JCS 1958, 1453.
JACS 75, 3753 (1953) ; 69, 2692
(1947).

SiC₂H₈

① Ethylsilane
C₂H₅SiH₃

② C₂H₅SiCl₃ $\xrightarrow{LiH}$

C₂H₅SiCl₃ $\xrightarrow[Dioxane]{LiAlH_4}$

SiH₄ + C₂H₄ $\xrightarrow{120°\ 24hr}$

③ Colorless gas. (−13.7°). [−179.7°].

⑥ JACS 75, 3853 (1953) ; 69, 2692 (1947).

SiC₂H₈O₂
① Dimethyldihydroxysilane
  $(CH_3)_2Si(OH)_2$
② $(CH_3)_2Si(OCH_3)_2 + 2H_2O \longrightarrow$
③ White flakes. [96~101°]. $d1.097(20°)$.
  Sol. in H_2O.
④ Sensitive to traces of acid or base
  and condenses to polysiloxanes.

$$\xrightarrow{\text{heat}} \underset{\underset{\text{OH}}{|}}{(CH_3)_2Si} - O - \underset{\underset{\text{OH}}{|}}{Si(CH_3)_2}$$

⑥ JACS **75**, 2712 (1953). J. Chem. Phys.
  21, 167 (1953).   Sci. & Ind. Japan
  28, 261 (1955) ; **31**, 85 (1957).

SiC₃H₃Cl₂F₃
① Methyltrifluorovinyldichlorosilane
  $(CF_2=CF)(CH_3)SiCl_2$
② $MeSiHCl_2 + CF_2=CF_2 \longrightarrow$
③ (84°/740).
⑥ US 2800494 ; CA **51**, 17982 (1957).

SiC₃H₅Cl₃
① Allyltrichlorosilane
  $CH_2=CHCH_2SiCl_3$
② Si-Cu alloy + $CH_2=CHCH_2Cl$
  $\xrightarrow{290\sim300°}$ low yield
  $SiCl_4 + CH_2=CHCH_2MgBr \longrightarrow$
③ Liq. (116.8~117.5°). $n_D1.4449$ (20°).
  $d1.215$ (25°).
  Sol. in org. solvents. Decomp. in
  H_2O.
⑥ Izv. OKhN **1954**, 497 ; CA **49**, 9495
  (1955).

SiC₃H₅Cl₃
① Isopropenyltrichlorosilane
  $CH_2=C(CH_3)SiCl_3$
② $SiCl_4 + i\text{-}C_3H_5MgCl \longrightarrow$
③ Colorless liq. (119°/736).
  Sol. in org. solvents. Decomp. in
  H_2O.
⑥ JACS **76**, 1186 (1954).

SiC₃H₆Cl₂
① Allyldichlorosilane
  $CH_2=CHCH_2SiHCl_2$
② Si-Cu + $CH_2=CHCH_2Cl \xrightarrow{230\sim300°}$
  $CH_2=CHCH_2SiHCl_2 +$
  $CH_2=CHCH_2SiCl_3$
③ Liq. (97.0~98.5°). $d1.086$ (27°/27°).
④ $\xrightarrow{\text{hydrolysis}}$ alkylene polysiloxane
⑥ Post 99 (1949). JACS **67**, 1813 (1945).
  US 2420912 (1947).

SiC₃H₆Cl₂
① Methylvinyldichlorosilane
  $CH_3SiCl_2CH=CH_2$
② $CH_2=CHSiCl_3 + MeMgI \longrightarrow$
③ (92.0~92.5°). $n_D1.4270$ (20°). $d1.104$
  (20°/4°).
④ + $KOP(O)(OH)_2 \longrightarrow$
  $CH_2=CHSiMe[OP(O)(OH)_2]_2$
  + $C_5H_5N + t\text{-}BuOOH \longrightarrow$
  $CH_2=CHSi(OOBu\text{-}t)_2Me$
  + $t\text{-}AmOOH \longrightarrow$
  $CH_2=CHSi(OOAm\text{-}t)_2Me$
  + $EtMgBr \longrightarrow CH_2=CHSiMeEtCl$
  + $AcONa \longrightarrow$
  $(AcO)_2Si(Me)CH=CH_2$
⑥ Zhur. **33**, 261 (1963) ; **34**, 2711 (1961).
  Dokl. **146**, 1117 (1962) ; English page
  2564.   Dokl. **142**, 1316 (1962) ; English page 140.

SiC₃H₇Br₃
① *n*-Propyltribromosilane
  $n\text{-}C_3H_7SiBr_3$
② $PrBr + Si + Cu \xrightarrow{340°} 82\sim78\%$
③ Liq. (179~180°/754).
  Decomp. in H_2O.
⑥ Dokl. **93**, 667 (1953) ; CA **50**, 3216
  (1956).

SiC₃H₇Cl₃

① *n*-Propyltrichlorosilane
n-C₃H₇SiCl₃

② $Si_2Cl_6 + n\text{-PrCl} \xrightarrow[\substack{\text{catalyst (CuCl,}\\ \text{SbCl}_3, \text{HgCl}_2, \text{etc.)}}]{100\sim450°,\,5\,\text{atm}}$
n-PrSiCl₃ + SiCl₄
$HSiCl_3 + n\text{-PrCl} \xrightarrow{312\sim316°\ \text{in Ni bomb}}$
n-PrSiCl₃ + SiCl₄
$HSiCl_3 + CH_2=CHMe \xrightarrow{H_2PtCl_6}$

③ Colorless liq. (122.7~125.0°). n_D 1.4309 (20°). *d* 1.2096 (20°/4°).
Sol. in org. solvents. Decomp. in H₂O.
Raman: Z. anorg. allg. Chem. **261**, 62 (1950).

④ + SbF₃ ⟶ PrSiF₃

⑥ JACS **68**, 2652 (1946). US 2474087 (1949). Brit. 636559 (1950). JACS **82**, 3601 (1960).

SiC₃H₇Cl₃

① Isopropyltrichlorosilane
i-C₃H₇SiCl₃

② SiCl₄ (excess) + *i*-C₃H₇MgCl ⟶ 46%

③ Colorless liq. (119.4°). [−87.7°].
Sol. in org. solvents. Decomp. in H₂O.

④ + SbF₃ ⟶ *i*-PrSiF₃ (75~70%) + *i*-PrSiF₂Cl(8~10%)+ *i*-PrSiFCl₂ (17~20%)
+ Cl₂ $\xrightarrow{148°,\,63\,\text{hrs}}$
Me₂CClSiCl₃ + ClCH₂CHMeSiCl₃

⑥ JACS **76**, 1186 (1954); **68**, 2660(1946); **71**, 755 (1949).

SiC₃H₇F₃

① *n*-Propyltrifluorosilane
n-C₃H₇SiF₃

② *n*-PrSiCl₃ + SbF₃ + SbCl₅
$\xrightarrow{460\sim480\,\text{mmHg}}$ 80%

③ Colorless liq. (24.9°).
Sol. in org. solvents. Decomp. in H₂O.

⑥ JACS **68**, 2652 (1946).

SiC₃H₈

① Allylsilane
CH₂=CHCH₂SiH₃

② SiCl₄ $\xrightarrow{CH_2=CHCH_2MgBr}$
CH₂=CHCH₂SiCl₃ $\xrightarrow{LiH}$

③ Straw liq. (16.9°). n_D 1.4050 (4°). *d* 0.6764 (4°).

⑥ Izv. OKhN **1954**, 497; CA **49**, 9495 (1955).

SiC₃H₈BrCl

① Dimethylbromomethylchlorosilane
(CH₃)₂Si(Cl)CH₂Br

② Me₃SiCl + Br₂ ⟶

③ (131.5~135.0°).

④ + Mg ⟶ (Me₂SiCH₂)ₓ
+ Me₃SiOSiMe₃ + (Me₂SiCH₂)₂

⑥ Ber. **95**, 3030 (1962).

SiC₃H₈Br₂

① Methylethyldibromosilane
CH₃(C₂H₅)SiBr₂

② Me₂SiCl₂ $\xrightarrow{EtSiCl_3,\,375°,\,NaOH}$
EtMeSiCl₂ $\xrightarrow{EtOH}$ EtMeSi(OEt)₂ $\xrightarrow{PBr_5}$

③ Colorless liq. (139~141°). Decomp. in H₂O.

⑥ US 2647136 (1953); CA **48**, 8252(1954).

SiC₃H₈ClF

① Dimethylchloromethylfluorosilane
(CH₃)₂Si(F)CH₂Cl

② BF₃ + (Me₂SiCH₂Cl)₂O ⟶
H₂SO₄ + NH₄HF₂
+ Me₂Si(CH₂Cl)CMe=CH₂ ⟶

③ (84°). n_D 1.4000 (25°). *d* 1.0234 (25°/4°).

④ + *p*-BrC₆H₄Li
⟶ Me₂Si(CH₂Cl)C₆H₄Br-*p*

⑥ JOC **27**, 1486 (1962). JOM **2**, 146(1964).

SiC₃H₈Cl₂

① *n*-Propyldichlorosilane
   n-C₃H₇SiHCl₂

② PrCl + Cu-Si(20/80) $\xrightarrow{350\sim360°}$ 32.5%

   PrCl + Cu-Si $\xrightarrow{170°}$ 82.5%

   C₃H₆ + H₂SiCl₂ $\xrightarrow{H_2PtCl_6}$

   Pr₂SiCl₂ + PrSiCl₂H 69%

③ IR : CA **53**, 19569 (1949).

④ + C₂H₂ $\xrightarrow{H_2PtCl_6}$

   Various addition products.

⑥ Zhur. **25**, 2332 (1955) ; CA **50**, 9280 (1956). Zhur. **27**, 2475 (1957) ; CA **52**, 7131. Izv. OKhN **1960**, 1610.

SiC₃H₈Cl₂

① Methylethyldichlorosilane
   CH₃(C₂H₅)SiCl₂

② MeSiHCl₂ + CH₂=CH₂
   $\xrightarrow{2\,hrs,\,260°,\,560\,atm}$ 23.6%

   MeSiHCl₂ + CH₂=CH₂
   $\xrightarrow{H_2PtCl_6}$ in good yield

   MeSiCl₃ + EtMgBr ⟶ 60%

③ (100°).

④ + NH₃ $\xrightarrow{below\ 25°\ in\ C_6H_6}$ (MeEtSiNH)₃

⑥ Dokl. **112**, 271 (1957) ; CA **51**, 11988 (1957). Izv. OKhN **1958**, 247 ; CA **52**, 12751 (1958). Izv. OKhN **1959**, 628. Kogyo Kagaku Zasshi **59**, 1445 (1956). CA **54**, 1268 (1958).

SiC₃H₈Cl₂

① Dimethylchloromethylchlorosilane
   (CH₃)₂(CH₂Cl)SiCl

② Me₃SiCl + Cl₂ $\xrightarrow{UV}$ 49%, 77.2%

③ Liq.(113.7∼115.2°). [<−75°]. n_D1.4369 (20°). d1.0789 (20°/4°).
   Sol. in org. solvents.

④ + 2 H₂O $\xrightarrow{OH^-}$ Me₂Si(OH)₂ + MeCl
   + HCl
   + EtMgI ⟶ EtMe₂SiCH₂I (63%)
   + Ac₂O ⟶ ClCH₂SiMe₂OAc
   and AcOCH₂SiMe₂OAc
   + H₂O ⟶ [Me₂(CH₂Cl)Si]₂O
   + EtOH ⟶ Me₂(CH₂Cl)SiOEt

⑥ Ber. **87**, 282, 887 (1954). Dokl. **94**, 485 (1954) ; **105**, 725 (1955) ; CA **49**, 3795 (1955) ; **50**, 11233 (1956).

SiC₃H₈Cl₂O

① Methylethoxydichlorosilane
   CH₃(C₂H₅O)SiCl₂

② MeSiCl₃ + MeSi(OEt)₃
   $\xrightarrow{30hrs,\,180°}$ MeSi(OEt)Cl₂ (41.1%)
   and MeSi(OEt)₂Cl (32.0%)

③ Colorless liq. (101.2°). n_D1.380 (20°). d1.098 (20°). Decomp. in H₂O.

⑥ J. Inst. Polytech. Osaka City Univ. Ser. C **2**, 139 (1952) ; CA **48**, 11303 (1954).

SiC₃H₉AlBr₂O

① Trimethylsilyloxyaluminium dibromide
   (CH₃)₃SiOAlBr₂

② [(CH₃)₃Si]₂O + AlBr₃ $\xrightarrow{heat}$

③ (127°/4). [111.5∼113°].
   Stable in dry air but reacts vigorously with H₂O.

④ (CH₃)₃SiOAlBr₂ $\xrightarrow{H_2O}$ [(CH₃)₃Si]₂O

⑥ Dokl. **114**, 1033 (1957) ; CA **52**, 2742 (1958).

SiC₃H₉Br

① Trimethylbromosilane
   (CH₃)₃SiBr

② (Me₃Si)₂NH + AlBr₃ ⟶
   Me₃SiBr + Me₃SiNHAlBr₂

③ Colorless liq. (77.3°). [−43.5°]. n_J 1.4211 (25°). d1.1727 (25°).

Sol. in org. solvents.
⑥ JACS **75**, 1583 (1953).   Izv. OKhN
   1962, 1852.

SiC₃H₉Cl

① Trimethylchlorosilane
   (CH₃)₃SiCl
② SiCl₄ + MeMgBr $\longrightarrow$
   SiCu + MeCl $\longrightarrow$
   AlCl₃ + Me₃SiNHSiMe₃ $\longrightarrow$ 73.7%
   Me₃SiSiMe₂Cl + SO₂Cl₂ + (BzO)₂ $\longrightarrow$
③ (57∼59°).
④ + (Me₃SiNHCH₂)₂ $\longrightarrow$
   (Me₃Si)₂NCH₂CH₂NHSiMe₃
   + (Me₃Si)₂NCH₂CH₂N(SiMe₃)₂
   + NH₂OH $\longrightarrow$ Me₃SiNH₂O
   + Me₃SiN(Li)CH₂CH₂NHSiMe₃
   $\longrightarrow$ (Me₃Si)₂NCH₂CH₂NHSiMe₃
   + Me₃SiN(Li)CH₂CH₂N(Li)SiMe₃
   $\longrightarrow$ (Me₃Si)₂NCH₂CH₂N(SiMe₃)₂
⑥ Monatsh. **94**, 141 (1963).   Izv. OKhN
   1962, 1852.   Z. anorg. allg. Chem.
   321, 21 (1963).

SiC₃H₉ClO

① Dimethylchloromethylsilanol
   (CH₃)₂Si(OH)CH₂Cl
② Me₂Si(Cl)CH₂Cl + NH₄OH $\longrightarrow$
   Me₂Si(CH₂Cl)NHSi(Me)₂CH₂Cl $\xrightarrow{H_2O}$
③ (47°/5). n_D 1.4402 (25°). d 1.071 (20°).
   IR : 3230, 2950, 1250, 1070, 845, 820
   cm⁻¹.
④ + Me₂Si(Cl)OSiMe₂Cl $\longrightarrow$
   Me₂Si(Cl)OSiMe₂OSiMe₂CH₂Cl
   + Me₂SiCl₂ + Et₃N $\longrightarrow$
   Me₂Si(OSiMe₂CH₂Cl)₂ 100%
   + Me₂GeCl₂ $\longrightarrow$
   Me₂Ge(OSiMe₂CH₂Cl)₂ 100%
   + Me₂SnCl₂
   $\longrightarrow$ Me₂SnO(SiMe₂CH₂Cl)₂
⑥ Angew. **74**, 903 (1963).   Makromol.
   Chem. **55**, 87 (1962).   Ber. **96**, 1016
   (1963).

SiC₃H₉ClO₃S

① Trimethylsilyl chlorosulfonate
   ClSO₂OSi(CH₃)₃
② PCl₅ + SO₂(OSiMe₃)₃ $\longrightarrow$ 73%
   Me₃SiCl + ClSO₂OH $\longrightarrow$ 85.0%
   Me₃SiCl + SO₃ $\longrightarrow$ 83%
③ (70°/16). [−26°]. d 1.220 (20°/4°).
④ + MeOH $\longrightarrow$ Me₃SiOSiMe₃
   + SO₂(OSiMe₃)₂
⑥ Angew. **70**, 657 (1958).   Ber. **95**, 47
   (1962).   Bull. soc. chim. France
   1963, 512.

SiC₃H₉Cl₂O₂P

① Trimethylsiloxyphosphonyl dichloride
   (CH₃)₃SiOPOCl₂
② [(CH₃)₃Si]₂O + POCl₃ $\longrightarrow$ 59.4%
③ [−20.5°]. (63∼64°/10). n_D 1.4290(20°).
   d 1.2105 (25°).
⑥ Ber. **93**, 326, 872 (1960).   JCS **1957**,
   1488.

SiC₃H₉Cl₃OTi

① Trichlorotitanyloxytrimethylsilane
   (CH₃)₃SiOTiCl₃
② Me₃SiONa + TiCl₄ $\xrightarrow{\text{in } C_6H_6}$ 27.3%
③ Crystals. (67°/9).
   Decomp. in H₂O. Sol. in org.
   solvents.
⑥ Izv. OKhN **1958**, 644 ; CA **52**, 19910
   (1958).

SiC₃H₉F

① Trimethylfluorosilane
   (CH₃)₃SiF
② Me₃SiCl + FSO₂OH $\longrightarrow$ 96.5%
   (Me₃Si)₂O + FSO₂OH $\longrightarrow$
   Me₃SiCl + SF₄, (BF₃ or SOF₂) $\longrightarrow$
   Me₃SiCl + PhSiMeF₂ + Ph₃N
   $\longrightarrow$ 88%
③ (16.4°).
⑥ Ber. **94**, 2496 (1961) ; **95**, 47 (1962).

Z. anorg. allg. Chem. **324**, 78, 86
(1963).   French. 1303018 (1962);
CA **58**, 9137 (1963).

SiC₃H₉I

① Trimethyliodosilane
$(CH_3)_3SiI$

② $(Me_3Si)_2O + I_2 \longrightarrow 93\%$
$Me_3SiCl + 1/2 MgI_2 \longrightarrow$

③ Liq. $(106.6 \sim 107.5°)$. Sol. in org.
solvents.

⑥ JCS **1950**, 3077. Dokl. **84**, 959 (1952);
CA **47**, 3228 (1953).   Izv. OKhN
1956, 713; CA **51**, 18 (1957).

SiC₃H₉I

① Iodomethyl dimethylsilane
$(CH_2I)(CH_3)_2SiH$

② $(ClCH_2)(CH_3)_2SiH + NaI \xrightarrow{(CH_3)_2CO}$
35%

③ $(128°/731)$. $n_D 1.5043(20°)$. $d 1.542(20°)$.

④ aq. $C_2H_5OH \xrightarrow{OH^-}$
$(CH_3)_3SiOH + (CH_3)_2(CH_2I)SiOH$
(89%) (11%)
(rearr.)   (solvolysis)

⑥ JACS **81**, 251 (1959).

SiC₃H₉N₃

① Trimethylazidosilane
$(CH_3)_3SiN_3$

② Pyrolysis of

$HN_3 + Me_3SiNHSiMe_3 \longrightarrow 62\%$
$NaN_3 + Me_3SiCl \longrightarrow 73\%$

③ $(96°)$. $[-95°]$.

④ $+ AlCl_3 + Me_2SiCl_2 \longrightarrow$
$\longrightarrow Me_3SiCl + Me_2Si(N_3)_2$
$+ AlCl_3 + PhSiCl_3 \longrightarrow PhSi(N_3)_3$
$+ Me_2SiCl_2 \longrightarrow Me_2Si(N_2)_2$ 61.5%
$+ AlCl_3 + Ph_3SiCl \longrightarrow Ph_3SiN_3$
$+ AlCl_3 + Ph_2SiCl_2 \longrightarrow Ph_2Si(N_3)_2$
$+ PPh_3 \longrightarrow Me_3SiNPPh_3$ 97%

$+ PhC \equiv CPh \longrightarrow$

$+ (\equiv CCOOMe)_2 \longrightarrow$

⑥ Ber. **96**, 1293, 2780 (1963).   Angew.
74, 717 (1962).

SiC₃H₉ONa

① Sodioxytrimethylsilane
$(CH_3)_3SiONa$

② $Me_3SiCl + H_2O \xrightarrow[0 \sim 53°]{Al_2(SO_4)_3 - BaCO_3 \text{ etc.}}$
$Me_3SiOH \xrightarrow{NaOH} 97\%$

③ White powder. [$147 \sim 151°$ decomp.].
Sol. in H_2O.

⑥ Sci. & Ind. (Japan) **29**, 70 (1955); CA
49, 13888 (1955).

SiC₃H₁₀

① Trimethylsilane
$(CH_3)_3SiH$

② $Me_3SiCl \xrightarrow{H_2, Na, 280°, 130 \text{ atm.}} Me_3SiH$
$Me_3SiSiMe_3 \xrightarrow{HCl, 660°} Me_3SiH$
$(Me_3Si)_2O \xrightarrow{H_2, Na, 195 \text{ atm}} Me_3SiH$
$Me_3SiCl \xrightarrow{NaH, 300°} Me_3SiH$
$(Me_3Si)_2O \xrightarrow{AlEt_3} Me_3SiH$ (93%)

③ Gas. $(6.7°)$. $[-135.89°]$. $d 0.6375$.
NMR: JCS **1960**, 5132.

⑤ Useful as additions for high powered
fuels, particularly rocket fuels.

⑥ JACS **75**, 3753 (1953). Kogyo Kagaku
Zasshi **60**, 1395 (1957). Phys. Revs.
62, 151 (1952).

SiC₃H₁₀

① n-Propylsilane
$(n-C_3H_7SiH_3)$

② $n\text{-}C_3H_7SiCl_3 \xrightarrow{\text{LiH}}$

$SiH_3Cl \xrightarrow{n\text{-}C_3H_7MgBr}$

③ Colorless liq. $n_D 1.3759$ (20°). $d\,0.6434$
   (20°/4°).

Sol. in org. solvents ; insol. in H_2O.

⑥ JACS **69**, 2692 (1947) ; **78**, 292 (1956).

SiC₃H₁₀O

① Trimethylhydroxysilane
   $(CH_3)_3SiOH$

② $[(CH_3)_2SiO]_x + CH_3MgI \longrightarrow$

   $(CH_3)_3SiOMgI \xrightarrow{H_2O}$

③ Colorless liq. (98.0~98.2°). [-4.5°].
   $n_D 1.3892$ (20°). $d\,0.8146$ (20°).

Sol. in org. solvents.

④ $+ NaOH \longrightarrow (CH_3)_3SiONa$

⑥ Dokl. **95**, 531 (1954) ; CA **49**, 6089(1955).
   Zhur. **24**, 2202 (1954). JACS **75**,
   2230 (1953).

SiC₃H₁₀O₂

① Trimethylsilyl hydroperoxide
   $(CH_3)_3SiOOH$

② $(CH_3)_3SiCl + HOOH + C_5H_5N \longrightarrow$

③ (<35° decomp.).

④ $2(CH_3)_3SiOOH$

   $\longrightarrow (CH_3)_3SiOOSi(CH_3)_3 + HOOH$

⑥ Makromol. Chem. **21**, 113 (1956).

SiC₃H₁₀S

① Trimethylmercaptosilane
   $(CH_3)_3SiSH$

② $(CH_3)_3SiCl + Li_2S \longrightarrow 48\%$

③ (77°).

⑥ Compt. rend. **234**, 1985 (1925) ; CA **46**,
   8559 (1952). Z. anorg. allg. Chem.
   294, 113 (1958).

SiC₃H₁₁NO

① Trimethylsilylamine oxide
   $(CH_3)_3SiNH_2{\to}O$

② $NH_2OH + Me_3SiCl \longrightarrow 67\%$

③ (99.6°/737). [-78°~-76°].

④ $+ PhNCO$
   $\longrightarrow PhNHCOON(SiMe_3)CONHPh$

⑥ Monatsh. **94**, 141 (1963).

SiC₄H₃N₃S₃

① Methylsilyl triisothiocyanate
   $CH_3Si(NCS)_3$

② $MeSiCl_3 + NH_4SCN$ or $KSCN$
   $\longrightarrow 85\%$

③ [73°].

⑥ JINC **22**, 205 (1961).

SiC₄H₃O₃N₃

① Methylsilyl triisocyanate
   $CH_3Si(NCO)_3$

② $Me_3SiCl + CO(NH_2)_2$
   $\xrightarrow{\text{24hr. in sealed tube, 160~170°, Cu}}$

$Me_3SiCl + AgNCO \longrightarrow 80\%$

$Me_3SiCl + Pb(NCO)_2$
   $\xrightarrow{\text{reflux in Et}_2O} 21\%$

$Me_3SiCl + KCNO + AcOH \longrightarrow 37\%$

③ (267.5°), [72°]. $n_D 1.5815$ (20°). $d\,1.304$
   (20°).

IR : Z. anorg. allg. Chem. **300**, 194
   (1959).

⑥ JACS **70**, 1222 (1948). Kogyo kagaku
   Zasshi **61**, 214 (1958). Ber. **93**, 1111
   (1960). CA **59**, 8715 (1963).

SiC₄H₄Cl₂

① 1,1-Dichloro-1-silacyclopentadiene

$$\begin{array}{c} CH\!-\!\!-\!CH \\ \| \qquad \| \\ CH \qquad CH \\ {}^{\backslash}SiCl_2{}^{/} \end{array}$$

② $(C_4H_6Cl_2)SiCl_2 \xrightarrow{\text{heat}}$

③ (128~130°).

⑥ JACS **83**, 3716 (1961) ; **84**, 4723 (1962).

SiC₄H₆Cl₂

① Divinyldichlorosilane
   $(CH_2{=}CH)_2SiCl_2$

② CH₂=CHCl + Cu-Si(powder)

$\xrightarrow{220°}$ 15%

ClCH₂CH₂SiCl₃ + quinoline

$\xrightarrow{heat}$ 50%

CH₂=CHCl + Ni-Si (20/80)

$\longrightarrow$ 3.2% (more effective than
Cu-Si (20/80) alloy)

③ Liq. (118~119°). d1.0813 (27°/27°).

⑥ Izv. OKhN **1954**, 174; CA **49**, 6090
(1955). JACS **69**, 1813 (1945). Zhur.
27, 2475 (1957); CA **52**, 7131 (1958).

SiC₄H₆N₂O₂

① Dimethylsilyl diisocyanate
(CH₃)₂Si(NCO)₂

② AgNCO + Me₂SiCl₂
Pb(NCO)₂ + Me₂SiCl₂
Cu + CO(NH₂)₂ + Me₂SiCl₂
HNCO + Me₂SiCl₂

③ (130°~132°). n_D 1.4266 (20°). d 1.072
(20°).
IR : 2994, 2933, 2381, 2273, 2000, 1445,
1414, 1266cm⁻¹.

⑥ JOC **28**, 586 (1963).   Kogyo Kagaku
Zasshi **61**, 214 (1958); CA **54**, 5434
(1960). Mitsubishi Denki Laboratory
Reports, **4**, 139 (1963).

SiC₄H₆N₂S₂

① Dimethylsilyl diisothiocyanate
(CH₃)₂Si(NCS)₂

② Me₂SiCl₂ + NH₄SCN or KSCN
$\longrightarrow$ 83%

③ (55°/0.8).

⑥ Chem. & Ind. **1960**, 1306.   JINC **22**,
205 (1961).

SiC₄H₇Cl₂N

① Methyldichloro-2-cyanoethylsilane
(CH₃)Si(Cl)₂CH₂CH₂CN

② MeSiHCl₂ + CH₂=CHCN
(with or without H₂PtCl₆) $\longrightarrow$
Me₂Cd + Cl₃SiCH₂CH₂CN $\longrightarrow$

MeMgCl + Cl₃SiCH₂CH₂CN $\longrightarrow$ 70%

③ (215°). n_D 1.4578 (20°). d 1.1959 (20°/4°).

④ + Ac₂O $\longrightarrow$ MeSi(OAc)₂CH₂CH₂CN
(82.5%)

+ BuOH $\longrightarrow$
MeSi(OBu-n)₂CH₂CH₂CN (93.4%)

+ i-BuOH $\longrightarrow$
MeSi(OBu-i)₂CH₂CH₂CN

⑥ Ger. 1140577 (1962); CA **58**, 9138
(1963).   US 2971970 (1961); CA
55, 12356 (1961).   Zhur. **32**, 1997
(1962); English page 1978.   Ger.
1122063 (1962); CA **57**, 3484 (1962).

SiC₄H₇Cl₃

① Crotonyltrichlorosilane
CH₃CH=CHCH₂SiCl₃

② SiHCl₃ + CH₂=CH-CH=CH₂ $\longrightarrow$

③ Liq. (143°). n_D 1.4548 (20°). d 1.19
(25°).

⑥ CA **49**, 11002 (1955); **48**, 8254 (1954).
US 2637738 (1953).

SiC₄H₇Cl₃

① Methallyltrichlorosilane
CH₂=C(CH₃)CH₂SiCl₃

② Si-Cu alloy + CH₂=CMeCH₂Cl
$\xrightarrow{300°}$ CH₂=CMeCH₂SiHCl₂,
CH₂=CMeCH₂SiCl₃ and
(CH₂=CMeCH₂)₂SiCl₂

Si + Al + CH₂=CMeCHCl $\xrightarrow{300°}$
SiCl₄ + C₄H₇Br + Mg $\longrightarrow$

③ Liq. (136.0~140.5°). n_D 1.4520 (20°).
d 1.2013 (20°).
Sol. in org. solvents. Decomp. in H₂O.

⑥ Japan 421 (1954); CA **49**, 11002 (1955).
Izv. OKhN **1954**, 504; CA **49**, 9494
(1955).   Izv. OKhN **1957**, 383; CA
51, 15457 (1957).

SiC₄H₇F₃Cl₂

① Methyl-3,3,3-trifluoropropyl-
dichlorosilane

CF₃C₂H₄Si(CH₃)Cl₂
② MeSiHCl₂ + H₂C=CHCF₃ ⟶
③ Colorless liq. (122°). n_D1.3817 (25°).
Sol. in org. solvents. Decomp. in
H₂O.
⑥ JACS **81**, 1983 (1959).

SiC₄H₈

① Divinylsilane
(CH₂=CH)₂SiH₂
② (CH₂=CH)₂SiCl₂ + LiAlH₄ ⟶
③ (55°). n_D1.4030 (25°).
④ + H(Pt) ⟶ (C₂H₅)₂SiH₂
⑥ JACS **84**, 4727 (1962).

SiC₄H₈Cl₂

① Ethylvinyldichlorosilane
C₂H₅(CH₂=CH)SiCl₂
② EtSiHCl₂ + C₂H₂ ⟶
③ Colorless liq. (123°). n_D 1.4405 (20°).
d 1.058 (25°).
Sol. in org. solvents.
⑥ US 2637738 (1953); CA **48**, 8254 (1954).

SiC₄H₈Cl₂

① Allylmethyldichlorosilane
CH₂=CHCH₂(CH₃)SiCl₂
③ Si-Cu $\xrightarrow{\text{CH}_2=\text{CHCH}_2\text{Cl, 230}\sim300°}$

CH₂=CHCH₂SiCl₃ $\xrightarrow{\text{MeMgBr}}$
③ Liq. (119~120°). d1.057 (27°/27°).
Sol. in org. solvents.
⑥ Post 99 (1949). JACS **68**, 1675 (1946).
US 2420912 (1947).

SiC₄H₈Cl₂

① Methallyldichlorosilane
CH₂=C(CH₃)CH₂SiHCl₂
② Si-Cu alloy + CH₂=CMeCH₂Cl
$\xrightarrow{300°}$ CH₂=CMeCH₂SiHCl₂,
CH₂=CMeCH₂SiCl₃ and
(CH₂=CMeCH₂)₂SiCl₂
③ Liq. (115~118°). n_D 1.4469 (20°).

d1.0673 (20°).
Sol. in org. solvents
⑥ Izv. OKhN **1957**, 383; CA **51**, 15457
(1957).

SiC₄H₈Cl₂

① Tetramethylenedichlorosilane
$\begin{array}{c} \text{CH}_2-\text{CH}_2 \\ | \qquad\qquad \text{SiCl}_2 \\ \text{CH}_2-\text{CH}_2 \end{array}$
② BrMgCH₂(CH₂)₂CH₂MgBr+SiCl₄
⟶ 51%
Cu-Si + (CH₂)₄Cl₂ $\xrightarrow{300°}$ 29.7%
③ Colorless liq. (140.5~143.0°). n_D
1.4630 (20°). d1.1854 (20°).
Sol. in org. solvents.
④ + (CH₂)₄SiH₂ + H₂S $\xrightarrow{\text{Al}_2\text{O}_3}$ thiophen
+ Cl₂ ⟶ Cl₂SiCH₂CH₂CHClCH₂
⑥ JACS **76**, 6012 (1954). Izv. OKhN
1958, 1468; **1959**, 1231; CA **54**, 1268
(1960).

SiC₄H₈Cl₄

① 4-Chlorobutyltrichlorosilane
Cl₃SiCH₂CH₂CH₂CH₂Cl
② (CH₂CH₂Cl)₂ + Mg + SiCl₄ ⟶
③ (205°). n_D1.4685 (25°). d1.3233 (20°
/4°).
④ + Fe(powder) or Cu(powder)
⟶ CH₃CH=CHCH₂SiCl₃
⑥ Ber. **92**, 1012 (1959). US 3053873
(1962); CA **58**, 3458 (1963).

SiC₄H₈O

① Dimethylhydroxysilylacetylene
CH≡CSi(CH₃)₂OH
② (Me₂SiO)$_x$ + CH≡CMgBr ⟶
③ (46°/20). n_D 1.1438 (20°). d0.8898 (20°
/4°).
⑥ Zhur. **32**, 320 (1962); English page
316. Izv. OKhN **1963**, 97.

SiC₄H₉Br₃

① *n*-Butyltribromosilane
   n-C₄H₉SiBr₃

③ Si-Cu + *n*-BuBr ⟶

③ Liq. (198~200°/749).
   Sol. in org. solvents. Decomp. in H₂O.

⑥ Dokl. **101**, 885 (1955); CA **50**, 3216 (1956).

SiC₄H₉Cl

① 1-Methyl-1-chloro-1-silacyclobutane

$$CH_2 \underset{CH_2}{\overset{CH_2}{\diagup}} Si(CH_3)Cl$$

② MeSi(Cl)₂CH₂CH₂CH₂Cl

$$+ \ Mg \begin{cases} \longrightarrow \ 68\% \\ \longrightarrow \ 65.0\% \end{cases}$$

③ (103.5~104.0°). n_D 1.4490 (20°). d 0.9858 (20°/4°).

④ + MeMgBr

$$\longrightarrow \ Me_2Si \underset{CH_2}{\overset{CH_2}{\diagdown}} CH_2 \ (65\%)$$

   + heat (230°) ⟶
   [-Si(Me)(Cl)CH₂CH₂CH₂-]$_x$
   (elastomeric)

⑥ Dokl. **141**, 843 (1961); English page 1203.   US 3046291 (1962); CA **57**, 16874 (1962).   Dokl. **150**, 799 (1963).

SiC₄H₉Cl

① Vinyldimethylchlorosilane
   (CH₃)₂Si(Cl)CH=CH₂

② MeMgCl + CH₂=CHSiCl₃ ⟶
   NH₄Cl + H₂SO₄
   + [Me₂Si(CH₂=CH₂)]₂O ⟶ 42.6%

③ (83~84°). n_D 1.4141 (20°). d 0.8744 (20°/4°).

④ + HCl + HOH
   ⟶ (Me₂SiCH=CH₂)₂O

⑥ Coll. Czech. Chem. Comm. **24**, 3758 (1959); CA **54**, 7607 (1960).   Dokl. **146**, 1117 (1962).   Zhur. **32**, 1126 (1962); English page 1102.

SiC₄H₉Cl₃

① Trimethyltrichloromethylsilane
   (CH₃)₃SiCCl₃

② ClCH₂SiMe₃ $\xrightarrow{Cl_2, \ h\nu}$ 1.3%

③ (146~156°). [60~66°].

⑥ JACS **73**, 824 (1951). Mem. Fac. Eng. Osaka City Univ. **2**, 28 (1960); CA **55**, 25732 (1961).

SiC₄H₉Cl₃

① Methyltris(chloromethyl)silane
   CH₃Si(CH₂Cl)₃

② ClCH₂SiMe₃ $\xrightarrow{Cl_2, \ h\nu}$ 2.1%

③ (205°/749). n_D 1.4857 (25°). d 1.24 (25°).

⑥ JACS **73**, 824 (1951).

SiC₄H₉Cl₃

① *n*-Butyltrichlorosilane
   n-C₄H₉SiCl₃

② *n*-BuMgBr + SiCl₄(excess) ⟶ 72%
   Si-Cu (80/20) + BuCl $\xrightarrow{350~360°}$ 18.2%
   SiHCl₃ + C₂H₄ $\xrightarrow{285°, \ 200 \, atm}$
   a series of Cl₃Si(CH₂CH₂)$_n$H,
   n=2; 25.3%.

③ Colorless liq. (148.9°). d 1.1487 (29.9°/4°).

④ + Et₃SiH $\xrightarrow{AlCl_3 \ (1~4 mole\%)}$
   BuSiH₃ (98%)

⑥ Dokl. **113**, 120 (1957); CA **51**, 14541 (1957).   Izv. OKhN **1959**, 1231; CA **54**, 1268 (1960).   Zhur. **25**, 2332 (1955); CA **50**, 9280 (1956).   Dokl. **114**, 93 (1957); CA **52**, 1057 (1958).

SiC₄H₉Cl₃

① Methyldichloro-3-chloropropylsilane
   CH₃Si(Cl)₂CH₂CH₂CH₂Cl

② MeSiHCl₂ + CH₂=CHCH₂Cl
   ⟶ 24%

③ (186°). n_D 1.4585 (20°). d 1.2040 (20°/4°).

④ + C₅H₁₁N ⟶
   MeSi(Cl)₂CH₂CH=CH₂ (84%)

⑥ Dokl. **150**, 1055(1963). Mem. Fac. Eng.
   Osaka City Univ. **1**, 1 (1959). US
   3046291(1962) ; CA **57**, 16, 874 (1962).
   Izv. OKhN **1960**, 2140 ; English page
   1983.

SiC₄H₉F₃

① *n*-Butyltrifluorosilane
   n-C₄H₉SiF₃

② *n*-BuSiCl₃ + SbF₃
   $\xrightarrow{\text{112~117°, 300~350 mmHg}}$ 40%
   n-BuSiCl₃ + HF (anhydrous)
   ⟶ 40%

③ Colorless liq. (52.4°). d 1.006 (26.5°).
   Sol. in polar org. solvents.

⑥ JACS **68**, 2662 (1946) ; **67**, 1769 (1945).

SiC₄H₉N

① Trimethylisocyanosilane
   (CH₃)₃SiCN

② Me₃SiCl + K₂Hg(CN)₄ $\xrightarrow{\text{in DMF}}$ 31%
   Me₃SiOMe + Me₃CCOCN $\xrightarrow{\text{AlCl₃}}$
   Me₃SiNHSiR₃+3 HCN ⟶ 46%
   R₃SiCl + R₃'SiCN ⟶
   Me₃SiBr (or I) + AgCN ⟶ 80%

③ (117.8°). [11~12°]. n_D 1.3891 (23°).
   d 0.7834 (30°).

④ + LiAlH₄ ⟶ Me₃SiH
   + Ph₃SiCl ⟶ Me₃SiCl + Ph₃SiCN
   + AgCl ⇌ Me₃SiCl + AgCN
   + H₂O ⟶ (Me₃Si)₂O
   + PhMgBr ⟶ Me₃SiPh
   + Br₂ ⟶ the bromine color
      disappeares
   + S ⟶ Me₃SiN=C=S
   + HgO ⟶ (Me₃Si)₂O
   + BX₃ ⟶ Me₃SiX + (BX₂CN)ₙ

⑥ JACS **80**, 4151 (1958) ; **74**, 5247 (1952).
   JCS **1950**, 3077. JINC **13**, 239(1960).

SiC₄H₉NO

① Trimethylsilyl isocyanate
   (CH₃)₃SiNCO

② Me₃SiCl + HNCO ⟶ 57%
   AgOCN
      + Me₃SiOCH₂CH₂CH₂CH₂Cl ⟶
   KOCN + Me₃SiCl ⟶ 95%

③ (90~91°). n_D 1.3948 (20°). d 0.9862
   (20°).
   IR : 2994, 2933, 2381, 2273, 1972~2000,
   1445, 1418, 1261 cm⁻¹.

⑥ Z. anorg. allg. Chem. **313**, 290 (1961).
   Ber. **95**, 426(1962). Mitsubishi Denki
   Laboratory Reports **4**, 139 (1963).
   JOC **28**, 586 (1963).

SiC₄H₉NS

① Trimethylsilyl isothiocyanate
   (CH₃)₃SiNCS

② Me₃SiCl + NH₄SCN or KSCN
   ⟶ 51%

③ (75~77°/80).

⑥ Chem. & Ind. **1960**, 1306. JINC **22**,
   205 (1961).

SiC₄H₁₀

① Dimethylvinylsilane
   (CH₃)₂(CH₂=CH)SiH

② Me₂(CH₂=CH)SiCl + LiAlH₄ $\xrightarrow{\text{in Bu₂O}}$

③ (36.7°/738). n_D 1.3855 (25°). d 0.6744
   (25°).

④ $+ K \longrightarrow -\left[\begin{array}{c} \text{Me} \\ | \\ -\text{Si}-\text{CH}_2-\text{CH}_2-\text{Si}- \\ | \\ \text{Me} \end{array}\right]_n -$

   $+ \begin{array}{c} \text{Me} \\ \diagdown \\ \diagup \\ \text{Me} \end{array} \text{Si} \begin{array}{c} \diagup \text{CH}_2-\text{CH}_2 \diagdown \\ \diagdown \text{CH}_2-\text{CH}_2 \diagup \end{array} \text{Si} \begin{array}{c} \diagup \text{Me} \\ \diagdown \\ \text{Me} \end{array}$

⑥ JACS **78**, 1686 (1956).

SiC₄H₁₀

① Ethylvinylsilane
   C₂H₅Si(H₂)CH=CH₂

② ClCH₂CH₂SiCl₂Et

$$\xrightarrow{\text{quinoline}} CH_2=CHSiEtCl_2$$

$$\xrightarrow{\text{LiH in Am}_2O} CH_2=CHSiEtH_2$$

③ (47°). n_D 1.4030 (20°). d 0.6940 (20°).

⑥ Izv. OKhN **1957**, 310 ; CA **51**, 14588 (1957).

SiC₄H₁₀

① Buten-2-ylsilane
$CH_3CH=CHCH_2SiH_3$

② $CH_2=CH-CH=CH_2 \xrightarrow{\text{HBr in AcOH}}$

$C_4H_7Br \xrightarrow{\text{Mg}} C_4H_7MgBr \xrightarrow{\text{SiCl}_4}$

$C_4H_7SiCl_3 \xrightarrow{\text{LiH in } i\text{-Am}_2O}$

$MeCH=CHCH_2SiH_3$

③ Liq. (56.0~57.5°). n_D 1.4178 (20°). d 0.7042 (20°).

Sol. in org. solvents.

⑥ Izv. OkhN **1954**, 504 ; CA **49**, 9494(1955).

SiC₄H₁₀

① 1-Methylallylsilane
$CH_2=CHCH(CH_3)SiH_3$

② butadiene $\xrightarrow{\text{HBr}}$ C₄H₇Br $\xrightarrow{\text{1. Mg, 2. SiCl}_4}$

$C_4H_7SiCl_3 \xrightarrow{\text{LiH}} MeCH=CHCH_2SiH_3$
and $CH_2=CHCHMeSiH_3$

③ Liq. (43°/750). n_D 1.4050 (20°). d 0.6846 (20°).

⑥ Izv. OKhN **1954**, 504 ; CA **49**, 9494 (1955).

SiC₄H₁₀

① Tetramethylenesilane

$\begin{matrix} CH_2-CH_2 \\ | \qquad\ \rangle SiH_2 \\ CH_2-CH_2 \end{matrix}$

② SiCl₄ $\xrightarrow[\text{LiAlH}_4, \text{ or LiH}]{\text{BrMg(CH}_2)_4\text{MgBr}}$ (CH₂)₄SiCl₂

③ Colorless liq. (70.7~70.8°/733.5). n_D 1.4458 (25°). d 0.8065 (20°).

Insol. in H₂O. Decomp. in acid.

⑥ Dokl. **97**, 847 (1954) ; CA **49**, 10169 (1955). JACS **76**, 6012 (1954).

SiC₄H₁₀Br₂

① Diethyldibromosilane
$(C_2H_5)_2SiBr_2$

② EtBr + Si $\xrightarrow{\text{catalyst, Cu}}$

③ (166.2~168.5°). [−73.0~−72.5]. n_D 1.4850 (25°). d 1.5767 (25°), 1.564 (20°).

⑥ US 2698334(1954). Sci. & Ind.(Japan) **27**, 200 (1953). Post (1949). JCS **1953**, 494.

SiC₄H₁₀Cl₂

① Diethyldichlorosilane
$(C_2H_5)_2SiCl_2$

② EtSiHCl₂ + C₂H₄ $\longrightarrow$ 86%
EtMgBr + SiCl₄ $\longrightarrow$

③ (128~129°). n_D 1.4302 (25°). d 1.0507 (20°/4°).

④ + KOP(O)(OH)₂
$\longrightarrow$ Et₂Si[OP(O)(OH)₂]₂

⑥ Zhur. **33**, 261 (1963). USSR 114156 (1958) ; CA **53**, 14003 (1959). Zhur. **29**, 1109 (1959) ; English page 1079. Dokl. **144**, 576 (1962) ; English page 463.

SiC₄H₁₀Cl₂

① Methyl-*n*-propyldichlorosilane
$CH_3(n\text{-}C_3H_7)SiCl_2$

② MeSiHCl₂ + CH₂=CHCH₂Cl

$\xrightarrow{\text{Pt}-\text{C, 160°, 10 atm}}$

$MeSiCl_2CH_2CH_2CH_2Cl$
and Me(*n*-Pr)SiCl₂

③ Colorless liq. (124.4°). n_D 1.4250 (20°). d 1.0383 (20°).

Sol. in org. solvents. Decomp. in H₂O.

⑥ Dokl. **106**, 76 (1956) ; CA **50**, 13726 (1956).

SiC₄H₁₀Cl₂

① *n*-Butyldichlorosilane
   (*n*-C₄H₉)SiHCl₂

② *n*-BuMgBr + HSiCl₃ ⟶

③ Colorless liq. (127~128°).
   Sol. in org. solvents.

④ hydrolysis ⟶ HO[BuSi(H)O]₄H

⑥ US 2698334 (1954) ; CA **49**, 4328 (1955).

SiC₄H₁₀Cl₂

① Dimethylbis(chloromethyl)silane
   (CH₃)₂Si(CH₂Cl)₂

② Me₂ClSiCH₂Cl $\xrightarrow{\text{Cl}_2,\ h\nu}$ 20%

③ (97°). n_D1.4180 (20°). d0.8791 (20°).

④ + Zn $\xrightarrow{\text{in aq. EtOH}}$ 55% ClCH₂SiMe₃

   + Mg $\xrightarrow{\text{in } n\text{-Bu}_2\text{O−xylene}}$ polymer

   + KOAc ⟶ Me₂Si(CH₂OCOCH₃)₂

⑤ This compd. is intermediates in the
   prepn. of resins useful as paint
   and varnish vehicles.

⑥ JACS **75**, 2821 (1953) ; **73**, 824, 1879
   (1951).   US 2607791 ; CA **48**, 13732
   (1954).

SiC₄H₁₀F₂

① Diethyldifluorosilane
   (C₂H₅)₂SiF₂

② Et₂Si(OEt)₂ $\xrightarrow{\text{HF}}$ Et₂SiF₂

   Et₃Al etherate + Na₂SiF₆ ⟶

③ Liq. (60.9°). [−78.7°].
   NMR : JINC **6**, 303 (1958).

④ + H₂O₂ + NH₃ $\xrightarrow{\text{Et}_2\text{O}}$
   (EtO)₂SiF₂ + (EtO)EtSiF₂

   + Cl₂ $\xrightarrow{\text{28 hr}}$

   ⎰MeCHClSiEtF₂ (30%)
   ⎱ClCH₂CH₂SiEtF₂ (35%)
   ⎩Cl₂C₂H₃SiEtF₂ (trace)

⑥ JCS **1954**, 2143.   JACS **73**, 5127 (1952).
   US 2477704 ; CA **44**, 3008 (1950).

Zhur. **27**, 2067 (1957) ; CA **52**, 6146
(1958).

SiC₄H₁₁Br

① Dimethylethylbromosilane
   (CH₃)₂C₂H₅SiBr

② Me₂EtSiSiMeEt₂ + Br₂
   ⟶ Me₂EtSiBr and MeEt₂SiBr

③ Colorless liq. (110~113°).
   Sol. in org. solvents. Decomp. in
   H₂O.

⑥ J. Chem. Soc. Japan. Ind. Chem. Sect.
   57, 175, 230 (1954) ; CA **49**, 11542
   (1955).

SiC₄H₁₁Br

① Trimethylbromomethylsilane
   (CH₃)₃SiCH₂Br

② Me₃SiCl + Cl₂ + Br₂
   ⟶ Me₂SiClCH₂Br $\xrightarrow{\text{MeMgBr}}$

③ Colorless liq. (115~117°). n_D1.4437
   (20°).
   Sol. in org. solvents ; insol. in H₂O.

④ + K⁺OCOCH₃⁻ $\xrightarrow{\text{CH}_3\text{COOH, 118}°}$
   Me₃SiCH₂OCOCH₃ + KBr

   + KCN $\xrightarrow{\text{in MeOH}}$
   Me₃SiOCH₃ + CH₃CN

⑥ Hua Hsüeh Hsüeh Pao. **23**, 291(1957).
   JACS **74**, 1361, 5091 (1952) ; **73**, 829
   (1951).

SiC₄H₁₁Cl

① Diethylchlorosilane
   (C₂H₅)₂SiHCl

② HSiCl₃ + 2EtMgBr ⟶
   EtSiHCl₂ + EtMgBr ⟶ 44.8%

③ Colorless liq. (99~100°/104~106).
   n_D1.4133 (25°). d0.8842 (20°).
   Sol. in org. solvents.

④ + CH₂=CHCH₂Cl $\xrightarrow{\text{Pt−C, 160}°}$
   Et₂Si(Cl)CH₂CH₂CH₂Cl (21%)
   + Et₂SiCl₂ + Et₂PrSiCl

Et₂SiHCl $\xrightarrow{\text{AlCl}_3,\ \text{distd.}}$ Et₂SiH₂

    +EtSiHCl + Et₂SiCl₂

⑥ JACS **72**, 2032 (1950).   Izv. OKhN
    1956, 1062 ; **1957**, 1206 ; CA **51**, 4983
    (1957) ; **52**, 6160 (1958).   Zhur. **27**,
    2062 (1957).

SiC₄H₁₁Cl

① Dimethylethylchlorosilane
    (CH₃)₂C₂H₅SiCl

② Me₂SiCl₂ + EtMgBr $\longrightarrow$ 44%

③ Colorless liq. (89.5∼90.5°). n_D 1.4105
    (20°). d 0.8657 (20°).
    Sol. in org. solvents.

⑥ Zhur. **25**, 622 (1955) ; CA **50**, 3270
    (1956).

SiC₄H₁₁Cl

① Trimethylchloromethylsilane
    (CH₃)₃SiCH₂Cl

② Me₂Si(Cl)CH₂Cl + MeMgBr $\longrightarrow$

③ (95∼97°). n_D 1.4179 (20°).

⑥ Dokl. **148**, 598 (1963).

SiC₄H₁₁ClO

① Dimethylethoxychlorosilane
    (CH₃)₂Si(OC₂H₅)Cl

② Me₂Si(OEt)₂ + Me₂SiCl₂
    $\xrightarrow{180°,\ 35\,\text{hrs}}$ 76.2%
    Me₂SiCl₂ + HC(OEt)₃
        + AlCl₃ $\longrightarrow$ 56%

③ Liq. (94∼95°/740.5). n_D 1.3898 (25°).
    d 0.934 (20°).
    Sol. in org. solvents.

⑥ JACS **76**, 1390 (1954).   US 2698661
    (1955).   J. Inst. Polytech. Osaka
    City Univ. Ser. C. **2**, 139 (1952) ; CA
    48, 11303 (1954).

SiC₄H₁₁I

① Trimethyliodomethylsilane
    (CH₃)₃SiCH₂I

② Me₃SiCH₂Cl + NaI $\xrightarrow{\text{in Me}_2\text{CO}}$ 70%

③ Liq. (139.5°/744). n_D 1.4800 (20°).

④ + AgCN $\xrightarrow{\text{in Ph}_2\text{O, 175°}}$ Me₃SiNC

⑥ JACS **68**, 481 (1946) ; **76**, 3943 (1954).
    Izv. OKhN **1954**, 504.   Dokl. **94**, 485
    (1954).

SiC₄H₁₁Li

① Trimethylsilylmethyllithium
    (CH₃)₃SiCH₂Li

② Li + Me₃SiCH₂Cl

③ [112°].

④ + SiCl₄ $\longrightarrow$ Si(CH₂SiMe₃)₄
    + MeOH $\longrightarrow$ Me₄Si
    + Me₃SiCH₂Cl
        $\longrightarrow$ Me₃SiCH₂CH₂SiMe₃ + Me₄Si
        + Me₃SiCH₂SiMe₂Et
    + CoCl₂ $\longrightarrow$ Me₄Si
        + Me₃SiCH₂CH₂SiMe₃

⑥ Inorg. Chem. **2**, 645 (1963).

SiC₄H₁₁N₃

① 1-Amino-3-trimethylsilylcyanamide
    (CH₃)₃SiN=C=NNH₂

② (NH₂)₂ + Me₃SiNCO $\longrightarrow$ 90%

③ [95°].

⑥ Monatsh. **94**, 63 (1963).

SiC₄H₁₂

① Tetramethylsilane
    (CH₃)₄Si

② AlBr₃ + p-C₆H₄(CH₂SiMe₃)₂ $\longrightarrow$
    Me₃Al₂Br₃ + SiO₂ $\xrightarrow{310°}$
    Me₃SiOSiMe₃ + Me₃Al₂Cl₃ $\longrightarrow$
    HSiO₁.₅ + Me₃Al₂Cl₃ $\longrightarrow$
    Si(OEt)₄ + Me₃Al₂Cl₃ $\longrightarrow$

③ (27.5∼28.0°).

⑥ Chem. & Ind. **1960**, 1335.   US 3004053
    (1961). Izv. OKhN **1963**, 822. Japan
    14617 (1961) ; CA **56**, 10190 (1962).

SiC₄H₁₂

① Diethylsilane

(C₂H₅)₂SiH₂
② NaH + Et₃Al + Et₂SiCl₂ ⟶ 92%
H + Pt + (CH₂=CH)₂SiH₂ ⟶
③ (56°∼57°). n_D 1.3924 (20°).
⑥ Izv. OKhN 1960, 2244; English page
2079.   JACS 84, 4727 (1962).

SiC₄H₁₂
① n-Butylsilane
n-C₄H₉SiH₃
② H₃SiCl $\xrightarrow{n\text{-BuMgBr}}$
n-BuSiCl₃ $\xrightarrow{\text{LiAlH}_4}$
BuSiCl₃ + Et₃SiH $\xrightarrow{\text{AlCl}_3}$ 98%
③ Colorless liq. (56.4°). [−138.2°].
n_D 1.3922 (20°). d 0.6786 (20°).
Sol. in org. solvents; insol. in H₂O.
④ C₄H₉SiH₃ $\xrightarrow{\text{HgCl}_2}$ C₄H₉SiH₂Cl
C₄H₉SiH₃ $\xrightarrow{\text{HgBr}_2}$ C₄H₉SiH₂Br
C₄H₉SiH₃ $\xrightarrow{\text{I, Cu}}$ C₄H₉SiH₂I
⑥ JACS 78, 292 (1956); 75, 3753 (1953);
69, 2692 (1947).

SiC₄H₁₂O
① Trimethylmethoxysilane
(CH₃)₃SiOCH₃
② MeOH + Me₃SiSBu ⟶
MeSi(OMe)₃ + O(SiMe₂OK)₂ ⟶
Na + Me₂Si(OMe)₂ ⟶
Na + (MeO)₂Si(Me)OSi(OMe)₂Me ⟶
③ (57.3°). n_D 1.3690 (20°). d 0.759 (20°).
④ + HOH ⟶ Me₃SiOH
+ P₂O₅ ⟶ OP(OSiMe₃)₃
⑥ Zhur. 32, 2190 (1962); English page
1960, 2155. JCS 1960, 4406. JACS
84, 4730(1962). Zhur. 32, 369 (1959);
English page 384.

SiC₄H₁₂O
① Dimethylethylhydroxysilane
(CH₃)₂C₂H₅SiOH

② Me₂SiCl₂ $\xrightarrow{\text{EtMgBr}}$ Me₂EtSiCl (44%)
$\xrightarrow{\text{NH}_3}$ (Me₂EtSi)₂NH (65%)
$\xrightarrow{\text{HCl, H}_2\text{O-Et}_2\text{O}}$ 70%
③ Colorless liq. (58°/50). n_D 1.4070 (20°).
d 0.8332 (20°).
Decomp. with acid. Sol. in alkali,
and org. solvents. Readily formed
the disiloxane on storage or
heating.
④ + a little HCl
$\xrightarrow{\text{2 hrs, reflux}}$ (Me₂EtSi₂)O
⑥ Zhur. 25, 622 (1955); CA 50, 3270
(1956).

SiC₄H₁₂O
① Dimethylethoxysilane
(CH₃)₂(H)SiOC₂H₅
② Si + MeCl $\xrightarrow{\text{EtOH}}$
③ Colorless liq. (54.4°).
Sol. in org. solvents.
④ + BzCl ⟶ Me₂SiHCl
⑥ Kogyo Kagaku Zasshi 58, 805 (1955);
CA 50, 11939 (1956).

SiC₄H₁₂O
① Trimethylhydroxymethylsilane
(CH₃)₃SiCH₂OH
② Me₃SiCH₂OAc + abs. MeOH
$\xrightarrow{\text{concd. H}_2\text{SO}_4,\ 2\,\text{days}}$
Me₃SiCH₂MgCl
$\xrightarrow[\text{dry O}_2\text{ at }0°]{\text{dil. H}_2\text{SO}_4}$ 48.1%
Me₃SiCH₂MgCl $\xrightarrow{\text{BF}_3\cdot\text{OEt}_2}$
(Me₃SiCH₂)₃B $\xrightarrow{\text{NaOH-H}_2\text{O}_2\text{ in EtOH}}$ 79%
③ Colorless liq. (120∼122°). n_D 1.4176
(20°).
Sol. in org. solvents.
④ 3,5-Dinitrobenzoate [70∼70.5°]
Phenylurethan [80∼80.5°]

+ CH₂=CHCN

$$\xrightarrow{\text{Triton B}} \quad Me_3SiCH_2OCH_2CH_2CN$$

+ H₂SO₄ $\xrightarrow{120\sim170°}$ (Me₃SiCH₂)₂SO₄
44.4%

⑥ Hua Hsüeh Hsüeh Pao. **23**, 291 (1957).
US 2687424 ; CA **49**, 11684 (1955).
JACS **70**, 1117 (1948) ; **81**, 1844
(1959).

SiC₄H₁₂O₂

① Diethylsilanediol
(C₂H₅)₂Si(OH)₂
② Na–Hg + HOH + CH₂=CHSi(OH)₂Et
③ [96°~97°].
④ + Me₃SiNEt₂ ⟶ polymer
⑥ J. Polymer. Sci. **50**, 151 (1961). Rocz.
Chem. **34**, 1667 (1960) ; CA **56**, 7344
(1962). Nippon Kagaku Zasshi, **83**,
188 (1962) ; CA **58**, 11392 (1963).

SiC₄H₁₂O₂

① Dimethyldimethoxysilane
(CH₃)₂Si(OCH₃)₂
② Si(OMe)₄ + MeMgX ⟶
Na + (MeO)₂Si(Me)Si(OMe)₂Me ⟶
MeSi(OMe)₃ + O[Si(Me)₂OMe]₂ ⟶
NaBH(OMe)₃ + MeOSi(Me)₂Cl
⟶ 36.8%
③ (80.2°). n_D 1.3699 (25°). d 0.8554
(25°/4°).
⑥ Rocz. Chem. **34**, 1667 (1960) ; CA **56**,
7344 (1962). JACS **84**, 4730 (1962).
Kogyo Kagaku Zasshi **62**, 1262(1963).
Coll. Czech. Chim. **26**, 1815 (1961).

SiC₄H₁₂O₂

① Dimethylbis (hydroxymethyl) silane
(CH₃)₂Si(CH₂OH)₂
② (CH₃)₂Si(CH₂OAc)₂ + MeOH $\xrightarrow{\text{HCl}}$
③ Viscous liq. (130°/27). n_D 1.4611
(20°). d0.993 (25°).
Sol. in H₂O.

⑥ US 2582569 ; CA **46**,7582(1952). JACS
70, 1400 (1948). US 2601646. Brit.
673148 (1952).

SiC₄H₁₂O₃

① Methyltrimethoxysilane
CH₃Si(OCH₃)₃
② MeONa
+ (MeO)₂Si(Me)OSi(OMe)₂Me ⟶
Na + MeSi(OMe)₂OSi(OMe)₂Me ⟶
③ (103°~104°). n_D1.3701 (20°). d0.9388
(25°/4°).
④ + MeONa + PhSi(OMe)₃
⟶ Si(OMe)₄ + PhSi(OMe)₂Me
+ MeONa + Ph₂Si(OMe)₂
⟶ PhSi(OMe)₂Me + PhSi(OMe)₃
+ [OSi(Me)₂OK]₂
⟶ Me₂Si(OMe)₂ + Me₃SiOMe
⑥ Kogyo Kagaku Zasshi **62**, 1262 (1959).
JACS **84**, 4730 (1962). Zhur. **29**, 907
(1959).

SiC₄H₁₂S

① Trimethylmercaptomethylsilane
(CH₃)₃SiCH₂SH
② Me₃SiCH₂Cl $\xrightarrow{\text{H}_2\text{S, KOH}}$ 42%

Me₃SiCH₂Cl $\xrightarrow{\text{NaSCN, EtOH}}$

Me₃SiCH₂SCN $\xrightarrow{\text{PrMgBr H}^+\text{-H}_2\text{O}}$

Me₃SiCH₂Cl $\xrightarrow{\text{NaSH}}$

③ Yellow liq. (116.9°/746). n_D 1.4502
(20°). d0.8430 (20°).
Sol. in org. solvents.
④ Me₃SiCH₂SH + Me₃SiCH₂Br
$\xrightarrow{\text{NaOH, EtOH}}$ (Me₃SiCH₂)₂S

Me₃SiCH₂SH
$\xrightarrow{\text{NaOH, EtOH H}_2\text{O}}$ (Me₃SiCH₂S)₂

⑥ JACS **76**, 2500 (1954). US 2719165
(1955). Izv. OKhN **1956**, 707 ; CA
51, 1819 (1957). Rec. trav. chim.
76, 187 (1957).

SiC$_4$H$_{13}$N

① Trimethylaminomethylsilane
(CH$_3$)$_3$SiCH$_2$NH$_2$

② Me$_3$SiCH$_2$Cl + NH$_3$ $\xrightarrow[640\,\text{psi}]{1.5\,\text{hrs, at}\,89°}$ 50%

③ Colorless liq. (90°/739). n_D1.3905
(25°). d0.7395 (25°).

⑤ This compd. is useful in resins,
as siloxane polymn. catalysts,
and emulsifying agents.

⑥ Brit. 686068 ; CA **48**, 3385 (1954). JACS
77, 3493(1955) ; **73**, 3781, 3867(1951) ;
71, 2746 (1949).

SiC$_5$H$_7$ClS

① Methyl-2-thienylchlorosilane
CH$_3$(C$_4$H$_3$S)SiHCl

② C$_4$H$_3$SMgBr + MeSiHCl $\longrightarrow$ 48%

③ Liq. (199~200°).
Sol. in org. solvents.

⑥ US 2640833 (1953) ; CA **48**, 5227 (1954).

SiC$_5$H$_9$Cl$_2$N

① 1-Methyldichlorosilyl-3-cyano-
propane
CH$_3$Si(Cl)$_2$CH$_2$CH$_2$CH$_2$CN

② MeSiHCl$_2$ +
CH$_2$=CHCH$_2$CN $\longrightarrow$ 88.6%

③ (242~244°). n_D 1.4568 (25°). d 1.14
(25°).

⑥ JOC **26**, 2008 (1961) ; Fr. 1303018
(1962) ; CA **58**, 9137 (1963). US
2823218 (1958) ; CA **53**, 16965 (1959).
Brit. 847802 (1960) ; CA **55**, 10318
(1961).

SiC$_5$H$_9$Cl$_3$

① 1-Pentenyltrichlorosilane
C$_3$H$_7$CH=CHSiCl$_3$

② HSiCl$_3$ + C$_3$H$_7$C≡CH + Bz$_2$O$_2$ $\xrightarrow{80°}$

HSiCl$_3$ + C$_3$H$_7$C≡CH $\xrightarrow{310°\sim325°}$

③ Liq. (168~171°).

Sol. in org. solvents ; insol. in H$_2$O.

⑥ JACS **72**, 1402 (1950). US 2413582 ;
CA **41**, 2069 (1947).   Brit. 684597
(1952) ; CA **48**, 2761 (1954).

SiC$_5$H$_9$Cl$_3$

① 4-Pentenyltrichlorosilane
CH$_2$=CH(CH$_2$)$_3$SiCl$_3$

② CH$_2$=CHSiCl$_3$ +

MeHC=CH$_2$ $\xrightarrow[\text{polymn. inhibitor}]{200\sim375°,\ 100\,\text{atm.}}$

③ Liq. (162~165°).
Sol. in H$_2$O with decompn.

⑥ US 2728725 (1955) ; CA **50**, 12098
(1956).

SiC$_5$H$_9$Cl$_3$

① 1-Trichlorosilyl-2-methylbutene-2
CH$_3$CH=CCH$_3$CH$_2$SiCl$_3$

② + SiHCl$_3$ + C$_5$H$_8$ $\xrightarrow{\text{H}_2\text{PtCl}_6\ \text{catalyst}}$
60~76%

③ (56°/15). d1.14 (25°/25°).

④ + MeMgCl $\longrightarrow$
MeCH=CMeCH$_2$SiMe$_3$

⑥ JOC **26**, 4000 (1961).

SiC$_5$H$_{10}$Cl$_2$

① Ethylallyldichlorosilane
C$_2$H$_5$(CH$_2$=CHCH$_2$)SiCl$_2$

② Et[Cl(CH$_2$)$_3$]SiCl$_2$ + AlCl$_3$
$\longrightarrow$ Et(MeCH=CH)SiCl$_2$
+ Et(CH$_2$=CHCH$_2$)SiCl$_2$ $\longrightarrow$
Cu−Si + Et[Cl(CH$_2$)$_3$]SiCl$_2$
$\overset{370\sim380°}{}$

Et[Cl(CH$_2$)$_3$]SiCl$_2$ + C$_5$H$_5$N $\longrightarrow$

③ Liq. (143.5°/745). n_D 1.4483 (20°). d
1.0529 (20°).
Decomp. with H$_2$O. Sol. in org.
solvents.

⑥ US 2752380 (1956). Brit. 743968(1956) ;
CA **51**, 2020 (1957).   Zhur. **27**, 2479
(1957) ; CA **52**, 7135 (1958).   Izv.

OKhN **1960**, 2140 ; CA **55**, 15331
(1961).

SiC$_5$H$_{10}$Cl$_2$

① Pentamethylenedichlorosilane

② SiCl$_4$ + BrCH$_2$(CH$_2$)$_3$CH$_2$Br + Mg
  $\longrightarrow$ 70%

③ Colorless liq. (170°). n_D 1.4679 (25°).
  d 1.156 (20°/4°).
  IR : JACS **79**, 2057 (1957).

⑥ JACS **76**, ,6012 (1954).

SiC$_5$H$_{10}$Cl$_2$

① 4-Pentenyldichlorosilane
  CH$_2$=CHCH$_2$CH$_2$CH$_2$SiHCl$_2$

② SiHCl$_3$ +
  CH$_2$=CHCH$_2$CH$_2$CH$_2$MgBr $\longrightarrow$

③ (65~66°/28).

⑥ JOC **28**, 1417 (1963).

SiC$_5$H$_{10}$O$_2$

① Vinylmethylethylenedioxysilane

CH$_2$=CH(CH$_3$)Si$\displaystyle\diagdown\!\!\!\diagup\begin{smallmatrix}O-CH_2\\O-CH_2\end{smallmatrix}$

② CH$_2$=CHSi(Cl)$_2$Me + (CH$_2$OH)$_2$ $\longrightarrow$

③ (88~90°/20).

⑥ US 3065254 (1962) ; CA **58**, 9138 (1963).

SiC$_5$H$_{11}$Br

① 1-Bromo-1-methyl-1-silacyclopen-
  tane

$\begin{matrix} CH_2CH_2 \\ | \\ CH_2CH_2 \end{matrix}\!\!\diagup\!\!\diagdown Si(CH_3)Br$

② Br$_2$ + (CH$_2$)$_4$Si(Me)Si(Me)(CH$_2$)$_4$
  $\longrightarrow$ 73%

③ (40°/13). n_D 1.4840 (20°). d 1.2818
  (20°/4°).

⑥ Unpublished work.

SiC$_5$H$_{11}$Cl

① Pentamethylenechlorosilane
  (CH$_2$)$_5$SiHCl

② HSiCl$_3$ + BrMg(CH$_2$)$_5$MgBr $\longrightarrow$

③ Colorless liq. (143°). n_D 1.467 (25°). d
  1.018 (25°/4°).
  Sol. in org. solvents.

⑥ JACS **76**, 6012 (1954).

SiC$_5$H$_{11}$Cl

① Allyldimethylchlorosilane
  (CH$_3$)$_2$(CH$_2$=CHCH$_2$)SiCl

② Si$-$Cu $\xrightarrow[\text{2 MeMgBr}]{\text{CH}_2=\text{CHCH}_2\text{Cl}}$ C$_3$H$_5$SiCl$_3$

③ Liq. (111~112°). d 1.022 (27°).
  Decomp. in H$_2$O. Sol. in org.
  solvents.

⑥ Post. 99 (1949).   JACS **67**, 1813
  (1945).

SiC$_5$H$_{11}$Cl

① Trimethyl-2-chlorovinylsilane
  (CH$_3$)$_3$SiCH=CHCl

② Cl$_2$CHCH$_2$SiCl$_3$ + Me$_2$NPh, Et$_2$NPh

  or $\longrightarrow$

  ClCH=CHSiCl$_3$ $\xrightarrow{\text{3 MeMgBr}}$

③ Colorless liq. (117°). n_D 1.4380 (20°).
  d 0.8924 (20°).
  Sol. in org. solvents ; insol. in H$_2$O.

⑥ Izv. OKhN **1956**, 461 ; CA **50**, 16663
  (1956).

SiC$_5$H$_{11}$Cl

① Tetramethylenemethylchlorosilane

$\begin{matrix} CH_2-CH_2 \\ | \\ CH_2-CH_2 \end{matrix}\!\!\diagup\!\!\diagdown Si\!\!\diagup\!\!\diagdown\begin{matrix} CH_3 \\ Cl \end{matrix}$

② (CH$_2$)$_4$SiCl$_2$ + MeMgBr $\longrightarrow$

③ Colorless liq. (132°). n_D 1.453 (25°).

$d\,0.981\ (30°/4°)$.

Sol. in org. solvents.

④ $+ \text{NaOH} \xrightarrow{0°} (\text{CH}_2)_4\text{Si(Me)OH}$

$\longrightarrow [(\text{CH}_2)_4\text{SiMe}]_2\text{O} + \text{H}_2\text{O}$

⑥ JACS **76**, 6012 (1954).

SiC₅H₁₁Cl₃

① *n*-Amyltrichlorosilane

$n\text{-C}_5\text{H}_{11}\text{SiCl}_3$

② $\text{SiCl}_4 + n\text{-C}_5\text{H}_{11}\text{MgBr} \longrightarrow 52\%$

$\text{C}_3\text{H}_7\text{CH}{=}\text{CH}_2 + \text{HSiCl}_3$

$$\underset{24\,\text{hr}}{\overset{\text{Ac}_2\text{O}_2,\ 70\sim100°}{\xrightarrow{\hspace{2cm}}}}\ 73\%$$

$$\underset{45\,\text{hr}}{\overset{h\nu,\ 42\sim52°}{\xrightarrow{\hspace{2cm}}}}\ 64\%$$

③ Colorless liq. (166~169°). $n_\text{D}\,1.4415$ (25°). $d\,1.137$ (25°).

Sol. in org. solvents. Decomp. in H₂O.

⑥ Post. 59, 72 (1949). JACS **68**, 475 (1946); **69**, 2687 (1947); **70**, 484 (1948).

SiC₅H₁₁N

① Trimethylcyanomethylsilane

$(\text{CH}_3)_3\text{SiCH}_2\text{CN}$

② $(\text{CN})_2 + \text{Me}_3\text{SiCH}_2\text{MgCl} \longrightarrow 30.6\%$

$\text{Me}_3\text{SiCH}_2\text{Cl} + \text{Mg} + (\text{CN})_2 \longrightarrow$

$\text{Me}_3\text{SiCH}_2\text{Cl} + \text{NaCN} \longrightarrow$

③ (83~85°/53). $n_\text{D}\,1.4203$ (20°). $d\,0.827$ (20°).

④ $+ \text{LiAlH}_4 \longrightarrow \text{Me}_3\text{SiCH}_2\text{CH}_2\text{NH}_2$ (46.1%)

⑥ Mem. Fac. Eng. Osaka City Univ. 3, 195 (1961); CA **58**, 3455 (1963). Rec. trav. chim. **81**, 430 (1962). JACS **77**, 3224 (1955); **78**, 2274 (1956).

SiC₅H₁₁NS

① Trimethylisothiocyanomethylsilane

$(\text{CH}_3)_3\text{SiCH}_2\text{NCS}$

② $\text{Me}_3\text{SiCH}_2\text{NH}_2 \xrightarrow{\text{CS}_2,\ \text{NaOH}-\text{EtOH}}$

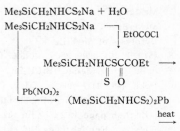

$\text{Me}_3\text{SiCH}_2\text{NHCS}_2\text{Na} + \text{H}_2\text{O}$

$\text{Me}_3\text{SiCH}_2\text{NHCS}_2\text{Na}$

$\downarrow \text{EtOCOCl}$

$\underset{\overset{\|}{\text{S}}\ \overset{\|}{\text{O}}}{\text{Me}_3\text{SiCH}_2\text{NHCSCCOEt}} \longrightarrow$

$\xrightarrow{\text{Pb(NO}_3)_2} (\text{Me}_3\text{SiCH}_2\text{NHCS}_2)_2\text{Pb}$

$\xrightarrow{\text{heat}}$

③ Colorless liq. (196~199°). $n_\text{D}\,1.4676$ (20°). $d\,0.9476$ (20°).

⑥ JACS **77**, 3149 (1955). US 2762826; CA **51**, 5827 (1957).

SiC₅H₁₁SN

① Trimethylthiocyanomethylsilane

$(\text{CH}_3)_3\text{SiCH}_2\text{SCN}$

② $\text{Me}_3\text{SiCH}_2\text{Cl} \xrightarrow{\text{NaSCN, EtOH}} 84\%$

$\text{Me}_3\text{SiCH}_2\text{Cl} + \text{KSCN} \xrightarrow{\text{Me}_2\text{CO}}$

③ (198.5°). $n_\text{D}\,1.4682$ (20°). $d\,0.9476$ (20°).

IR, Raman: Z. Physik Chem. **25**, 271 (1960).

⑥ JACS **76**, 2499 (1954); **77**, 3146 (1955). Dokl. **100**, 81 (1955). US 2719165 (1955). Izv. OKhN **1957**, 1199.

SiC₅H₁₂

① 1,1-Dimethyl-1-silacyclobutane

$(\text{CH}_3)_2\text{Si}\underset{\text{CH}_2}{\overset{\text{CH}_2}{\Big<}}\text{CH}_2$

② $\text{MeMgBr} + (\text{CH}_2)_3\text{SiMeCl} \longrightarrow 65\%$

$\text{MeMgCl} + (\text{CH}_2)_3\text{SiMeCl}$

$\longrightarrow 74.2\%$

③ (80.2°). $n_\text{D}\,1.4250$ (20°). $d\,0.7700$ (20°).

④ $\xrightarrow{\text{heat}} [-\text{Si(Me)}_2\text{CH}_2\text{CH}_2\text{CH}_2\text{-}]_x$

⑥ Dokl. **150**, 799 (1963); **141**, 843 (1961); English page 1203.

SiC₅H₁₂

① Vinyltrimethylsilane

$(\text{CH}_3)_3\text{SiCH}{=}\text{CH}_2$

② MeMgI + CH₂=CHSiCl₂Me ⟶
  MeMgBr + CH₂=CHSiCl₃ ⟶
  Pyrolysis of Me₃SiEt
③ (54.6°). n_D1.3910 (20°). d0.6903 (20°).
④ + Br₂ ⟶ Me₃SiCHBrCH₂Br
⑥ Dokl. **146**, 1117 (1962).   Izv. OKhN
  1963, 1111.   Zhur. **31**, 3738 (1961);
  English page 3492.   Zhur. **32**, 1126
  (1962); English page 1102.

SiC₅H₁₂
① Tetramethylenemethylsilane
  CH₂–CH₂   Me
  | ⟩Si⟨
  CH₂–CH₂   H
② MeSiHCl₂ + BrMg(CH₂)₄MgBr ⟶
③ Colorless liq. (91.5°). n_D1.4390 (25°).
  d0.798 (25°).
  Sol. in org. solvents; insol. in H₂O.
⑥ JACS **76**, 6012 (1954).

SiC₅H₁₂
① Trimethylenedimethylsilane
       CH₂
  H₂C⟨   ⟩Si(CH₃)₂
       CH₂
②   H₂SO₄   H₂O
  Me₃Si(CH₂)₃Br ⟶   ⟶
                        NH₄Cl
  [Br(CH₂)₃SiMe₂]₂O ⟶
                        H₂SO₄
                    Mg, Et₂O
  Br(CH₂)₃SiMe₂Cl ⟶ 66%
③ (81°). n_D1.4270 (20°). d0.7746 (20°).
  IR: JACS **76**, 5002 (1954).
⑥ JACS **76**, 5002 (1954).

SiC₅H₁₂Cl₂
① Methyl-*t*-butyldichlorosilane
  t-C₄H₉(CH₃)SiCl₂
② MeSiCl₃ + Me₃CLi ⟶
③ Liq. (136~138°/730).
  Sol. in org. solvents.
      hydrolysis
④ ⟶ *t*-BuMeSi(OH)₂
      liq. NH₃
   ⟶ *t*-BuMeSi(NH₂)₂

⑥ US 2626270 (1954); CA **49**, 4705 (1955).

SiC₅H₁₂Cl₂
① Ethyl-*n*-propyldichlorosilane
  C₂H₅(*n*-C₃H₇)SiCl₂
② EtSiHCl₂ + CH₂=CHCH₂Cl
      Pt–C
  ⟶ Et(*n*-Pr)SiCl₂
  + EtSiCl₂CH₂CH₂CH₂Cl
③ Liq. (151~154°). n_D 1.4370 (20°). d
  1.0532 (10°/4°).
  Sol. in org. solvents. Decomp. in
  H₂O.
⑥ Dokl. **106**, 76 (1956); CA **50**, 13726
  (1956).

SiC₅H₁₂Cl₂
① *n*-Amyldichlorosilane
  n-C₅H₁₁SiHCl₂
② *n*-C₅H₁₁MgBr + HSiCl₃ ⟶
③ Liq. (151~152°).
  Decomp. in H₂O. Sol. in org.
  solvents.
⑥ US 2698334 (1954); CA **49**, 4328 (1955).

SiC₅H₁₂Cl₃O
① Dimethylchloromethyl-2-chloro-
  ethoxysilane
  (CH₃)₂Si(CH₂Cl)OCH₂CH₂Cl
② KOH + (CH₂)₂O + Me₂Si(Cl)CH₂Cl
  ⟶ 47.1%
③ (115°/30). n_D 1.4677 (20°). d 1.2203
  (20°/4°).
⑥ Zhur. **33**, 905 (1963).

SiC₅H₁₂O₂
① Trimethylcarboxymethylsilane
  (CH₃)₃SiCH₂CO₂H
               Mg, Et₂O, CO₂
② Me₃SiCH₂Cl ⟶ 88%
③ [40°].
⑥ JACS **71**, 1509 (1949); **69**, 1551 (1947).

SiC₅H₁₂O₂

① Trimethylacetoxysilane
   (CH₃)₃SiOCOCH₃

② (CH₃)₃SiCl + NaOCOCH₃ $\longrightarrow$ 64.3%

③ (103.3~105°). n_D1.3860 (20°). d0.8742
   (20°).

⑥ Post. (1949). US 2573302 ; CA 46, 7582
   (1952). JACS 69, 2110 (1947).

SiC₅H₁₃Br

① Methyldiethylbromosilane
   CH₃(C₂H₅)₂SiBr

② Me₂EtSiSiMeEt₂ + Br₂
   in EtBr
   $\xrightarrow{\hspace{1cm}}$ Me₂EtSiBr and MeEt₂SiBr

③ Liq. (139~140°). d1.131 (20°).
   Sol. in org. solvents.

⑥ J. Chem. Soc. Japan, Ind. Chem. Sec.
   57, 175, 230 (1954) ; CA **49**, 11542
   (1955).

SiC₅H₁₃Br

① Trimethyl-2-bromoethylsilane
   BrCH₂CH₂Si(CH₃)₃

② Me₃SiCH=CH₂ + HBr $\xrightarrow{\text{peroxide}}$ 79%

③ (64~65°/39). n_D1.4575 (20°). d1.1499
   (20°).

⑥ JACS **76**, 1613 (1954). BCSJ **28**, 44
   (1955).

SiC₅H₁₃Br

① Trimethyl-1-bromoethylsilane
   CH₃CHBrSi(CH₃)₃

② CH₃CH(MgCl)SiMe₃ $\xrightarrow{\text{Br}_2}$

③ (134°/736). n_D 1.4509 (20°). d 1.1440
   (20°).

⑥ Izv. OKhN **1956**, 50 ; CA **50**, 8327
   (1956). JACS **76**, 1613 (1954).

SiC₅H₁₃BrO

① Ethoxydimethylbromomethylsilane
   (CH₃)₂Si(CH₂Br)OC₂H₅

② EtOH + Me₂Si(Cl)CH₂Br $\longrightarrow$ 85%

③ (55°/30). n_D1.4409 (20°).

⑥ Ber. **96**, 1495 (1963).

SiC₅H₁₃Cl

① Diethylmethylchlorosilane
   (C₂H₅)₂CH₃SiCl

② MeSiCl₃ + 2EtMgBr $\longrightarrow$ 34%

③ Colorless liq. (135~138°).
   Sol. in org. solvents.

⑥ Zhur. **25**, 622 (1955).

SiC₅H₁₃Cl

① n-Propyldimethylchlorosilane
   n-C₃H₇Si(CH₃)₂Cl

② n-PrMgBr + Me₂SiCl₂ $\longrightarrow$ 67%

③ (113~114°).

⑥ Izv. OKhN **1963**, 1333.

SiC₅H₁₃Cl

① 1-Chloroethyltrimethylsilane
   CH₃CHClSi(CH₃)₃

② CH₃CH₂SiCl₃ $\xrightarrow{\text{SO}_2\text{Cl}_2,\ \text{Bz}_2\text{O}_2}$
   CH₃CHClSiCl₃ + ClCH₂CH₂SiCl₃
   $\underset{\xrightarrow{\hspace{1cm}}}{|3\,\text{MeMgBr}}$ 53%

③ (118°). n_D1.4242 (20°). d0.8768 (20°).

④ + AlCl₃ $\longrightarrow$ Me₂CHSiMe₂C
   + Me₃SiCl + CH₂=CH₂

⑥ Dokl. **100**, 1107 (1955). JACS **76**, 801
   (1954) ; **68**, 485 (1946).

SiC₅H₁₃Cl

① Ethyldimethylchloromethylsilane
   C₂H₅Si(CH₃)₂CH₂Cl

② EtMgBr + Me₂Si(Cl)CH₂Cl $\longrightarrow$ 60%

③ (124.5~125.5°/739.5). n_D1.4277 (20°).
   d0.8899 (20°/4°).

⑥ Dokl. **143**, 840 (1962). Zhur. **33**, 1945
   (1963).

SiC₅H₁₃ClO

① Ethoxydimethylchloromethylsilane
   (CH₃)₂Si(CH₂Cl)OC₂H₅

② Me₂Si(Cl)CH₂Cl + EtOH ⟶

③ (131~132°). n_D 1.4190 (20°). d 0.9484
   (20°/4°).

④ + Et₂NH ⟶ EtOSi(Me)₂CH₂NEt₂
   + Na + EtOH + CH₂(COOEt)₂
   ⟶ EtOSi(Me)₂CH₂CH(COOEt)₂
   + P(OEt)₃ ⟶
   EtOSi(Me)₂CH₂P(O)(OEt)₂ (63%)

⑥ Dokl. **143**, 840 (1962).   Zhur. **33**, 258
   (1963).   JACS **83**, 761 (1961).   Izv.
   OKhN. **1962**, 454.

SiC₅H₁₃ClS₂

① 1-Mercapto-2-dimethylchlorosilyl-
   methylmercaptoethane
   (CH₃)₂Si(Cl)CH₂SCH₂CH₂SH

② HCl + Me₂Si⟨CH₂—S / S—CH₂⟩CH₂ ⟶ 74%

③ (124~126°/12). d 1.116 (20°/4°).

⑥ Ber. **96**, 1019 (1963).

SiC₅H₁₃F

① Methylfluoro-*n*-butylsilane
   CH₃(F)Si(H)C₄H₉-*n*

③ (83°/727). n_D 1.3770 (20°). d 0.8039
   (20°/4°).

④ + PhCH=CH₂
   ⟶ PhCHMeSiFMeBu-*n*
   + PhCH₂CH₂SiFMeBu-*n*

⑥ Zhur. **32**, 3882 (1962).

SiC₅H₁₃I

① α-Iodoethyltrimethylsilane
   CH₃CHISi(CH₃)₃

② CH₃CHClSiMe₃ —NaI, acetone→

③ (156°). n_D 1.4941 (20°). d 1.3862 (20°).

④ Relatively unreactive with dilute
   alk.

⑥ JACS **76**, 1613 (1954).

SiC₅H₁₃I

① 2-Iodoethyltrimethylsilane
   ICH₂CH₂Si(CH₃)₃

② Me₃SiCH=CH₂ —dry HI, −30°→

③ (76~76.5°/27). n_D 1.5008 (20°). d 1.3862
   (20°).

⑥ JACS **76**, 1613 (1954).   BCSJ **28**, 44
   (1955); CA **52**, 4556 (1958).

SiC₅H₁₃NO

① 1,1-Dimethyl-1-sila-2-oxa-5-nitra-
   cyclohexane

   (CH₃)₂Si⟨CH₂NH / O—CH₂⟩CH₂

② CH₂(NH₂)CH₂OH + Et₃N
   + Me₂Si(Cl)CH₂Br ⟶ 85%

③ (155°).

⑥ Ber. **96**, 349 (1963).

SiC₅H₁₄

① Ethyltrimethylsilane
   C₂H₅Si(CH₃)₃

② EtMgBr + SiCl₄ ⟶ EtSiCl₃
   —3 MeMgBr→ about 70%
   Me₃SiCH=CH₂ —H/PtO₂, AcOH→ 70%

③ Liq. (62°). n_D 1.3828 (20°). d 0.6849
   (20°).

   NMR: Trans. Faraday Soc. **59**, 630
   (1963).

   Raman: Izv. OKhN **1960**, 1553.

④ EtSiMe₃ —Cr−catalyst, 590~600°→
   Me₃SiCH=CH₂ + C₂H₄ + H
   11.4%   38%   26%
   EtSiMe₃ —Al₂Br₆→ Me₄Si + Me₂SiEt₂

⑥ Tetrahedron Letters **1961**, 421. Zhur.
   31, 3738 (1961).   Izv. OKhN **1960**,
   1553.

SiC$_5$H$_{14}$

① Diethylmethylsilane

CH$_3$(C$_2$H$_5$)$_2$SiH

② MeSiHCl$_2$ $\xrightarrow{\text{EtMgBr}}$

③ (77.4°). n_D 1.3984 (20°). d 0.7053 (20°).
NMR : Izv. OKhN, **1963**, 1130 ; CA **59**,
9485.

④ MeEt$_2$SiH $\xrightarrow{\text{AlCl}_3, \text{ heat}}$ Me$_2$EtSiH + Et$_4$Si

MeEt$_2$SiH

$\xrightarrow{\text{PhOH, GeCl}_4 \text{ or NiCl}_2}$ MeEt$_2$SiOPh

Catalytic addition to unsaturated
compd.

⑥ Post (1959). Izv. OKhN **1959**, 1238 ;
CA **54**, 1381 (1960). Izv. OKhN
1960, 1610 ; CA **55**, 9262 (1961).
Izv. OKhN **1963**, 1130 ; CA **59**, 9485
(1965).

SiC$_5$H$_{14}$

① n-Amylsilane

n-C$_5$H$_{11}$SiH$_3$

② H$_3$SiBr + n-C$_5$H$_{11}$MgBr $\longrightarrow$ 58%

③ Colorless liq. (86.0~87.5°). n_D 1.4042
(20°). d 0.7019 (20°).
Sol. in org. solvents.
IR : 938~917 cm^{-1}.

⑥ JACS **78**, 292 (1956).   Acta Chem.
Scand. **8**, 1830 (1954).

SiC$_5$H$_{14}$O

① Ethoxytrimethylsilane

(CH$_3$)$_3$SiOC$_2$H$_5$

② Me$_2$Si(OCH$_2$CH$_2$CH$_2$Si(OEt)$_3$)$_2$
+ Et$_2$Si(OCH$_2$CH$_2$Si(OMe)$_3$)$_2$ $\longrightarrow$

③ (75~76°). n_D 1.3737 (25°). d 0.755
(25°/4°).

⑥ Kogyo Kagaku Zasshi **62**, 1262 (1959).
JCS **1961**, 4933.   J. prakt. Chem.
12, 18 (1960) ; CA **55**, 776 (1961).
Dokl. **151**, 849 (1963).

SiC$_5$H$_{14}$O

① 1-Hydroxyethyltrimethysilane

(CH$_3$)$_3$SiCH(OH)CH$_3$

② (CH$_3$)$_3$SiCH=CH$_2$ $\xrightarrow{\text{B}_2\text{H}_6 \quad \text{aq. H}_2\text{O}_2}$
(CH$_3$)$_3$SiCH(OH)CH$_3$
+ (CH$_3$)$_3$SiCH$_2$CH$_2$OH   (total 88%)

(CH$_3$)$_3$SiCH(OCOCH$_3$)CH$_3$ $\xrightarrow{\text{OH}^-}$ 42%

③ (127.3°). n_D 1.4241 (20°). d 0.8303
(20°/4°).

⑥ JACS **81**, 1844 (1959).   Dokl. **100**,
1107 (955).   JINC **7**, 152 (1958).

SiC$_5$H$_{14}$O

① Methyldiethylsilanol

CH$_3$(C$_2$H$_5$)$_2$SiOH

② MeSiCl$_3$ $\xrightarrow{\text{2 EtMgBr}}$ MeEt$_2$SiCl (34%)
$\xrightarrow{\text{H}_2\text{O}}$ 62%

③ Colorless liq. (61~62°/30). n_D 1.4206
(20°). d 0.8458 (20°).
Sol. in org. solvents and alk. ;
readily formed the disiloxane on
storage or heating.

④ + a little HCl $\longrightarrow$ (Et$_2$MeSi)$_2$O
+ Me$_2$CHCH$_2$OCH=CH$_2$ $\xrightarrow{\text{a little HCl}}$
MeCH(OCH$_2$CHMe$_2$)OSiEt$_2$Me

⑥ Zhur. **25**, 622 (1955) ; CA **50**, 3270
(1956).

SiC$_5$H$_{14}$O

① n-Propyldimethylsilanol

n-C$_3$H$_7$Si(CH$_3$)$_2$OH

② HOH + HCl
+ n-PrSiMe$_2$NHSiMe$_2$Pr-n $\longrightarrow$

③ (41~42°/8). n_D 1.4112 (20°). d 0.8271
(20°/4°).

⑥ Izv. OKhN **1963**, 1333. JCS **1959**, 3404.

SiC$_5$H$_{14}$O

① Methoxymethyltrimethylsilane

CH$_3$OCH$_2$Si(CH$_3$)$_3$

② Me$_3$SiCH$_2$Cl + CH$_3$ONa
$\xrightarrow{\text{in MeOH, 24hrs.}}$ 64%

Me$_3$SiCl + ClCH$_2$OMe + Na $\longrightarrow$ 26%

③ (83°). n_D1.3878 (25°). d0.7576 (25°).

⑥ JACS 70, 4142 (1948).   US 2572402 ;
  CA 46, 4560 (1952).

SiC₅H₁₄O₂

① Methyldiethoxysilane
  $CH_3SiH(OC_2H_5)_2$

② $MeSiHCl_2 + 2\,EtOH \xrightarrow{reflux} 40\%$

  $MeSiHCl_2 + 2\,HC(OEt)_3 \xrightarrow{46°} 32\%$

  $MeSiHCl_2 + Me_3Si(OEt) + Si(OEt)_4$
  $\longrightarrow 70\%$

③ (94°/731.3). n_D1.3724 (20°). d0.829
  (20°).

⑥ JACS 76, 1390 (1954).   US 2698661
  (1955).   Zhur. 27, 2487 (1957) ; CA
  52, 7132 (1958).   US 2626273
  (1947/53).

SiC₅H₁₄O₂S

① Trimethyl(methylsulfonylmethyl)-
  silane
  $(CH_3)_3SiCH_2SO_2CH_3$

② $Me_3SiCH_2Cl \xrightarrow{NaSMe,\ EtOH}$

  $Me_3SiCH_2SMe \xrightarrow{H_2O_2,\ AcOH}$

③ (78~79°).

④ $Me_3SiCH_2SO_2Me \xrightarrow{OH^-}$
  $Me_3SiOSiMe_3 + MeSO_2Me$

⑥ JACS 76, 3713 (1954).   US 2719165
  (1955).

SiC₅H₁₄O₃

① Ethyltrimethoxysilane
  $C_2H_5Si(OCH_3)_3$

② $EtSiCl_3 + 3MeONa \longrightarrow 58\%$

③ (123~125°). n_D 1.3838 (20°). d 0.9488
  (20°/4°).

⑥ Ann. 173, 143 (1874).   Ber. 5, 1081
  (1872).   JCS 1647, 1592.

SiC₅H₁₄S

① 2-Trimethylsilylethylmercaptan

$(CH_3)_3SiCH_2CH_2SH$

② $(CH_3)_3SiCH=CH_2 + HSH \longrightarrow 21\%$
  $NaOH + AcSCH_2CH_2SiMe_3 \longrightarrow$

③ (143°). n_D1.4515 (25°). d0.8488 (20°/4°).

④ $+ CH_2=CHCN$
  $\longrightarrow Me_3SiCH_2CH_2SCH_2CH_2CN$

⑥ JOC 28, 3264 (1963).   Izv. OKhN 1959,
  85 ;   English page 76.

SiC₅H₁₄S

① Trimethylmethylthiomethylsilane
  $(CH_3)_3SiCH_2SCH_3$

② $Me_3SiCH_2Cl \xrightarrow{NaSMe,\ EtOH}$

  $Me_3SiCH_2SMe\ 67\%$

③ (70°/93). n_D 1.4505 (20°). d0.8399 (20°).

⑥ JACS 26, 3713 (1954).   US 2719165
  (1955).

SiC₅H₁₅N

① β-Aminoethyltrimethylsilane
  $(CH_3)_3SiCH_2CH_2NH_2$

② Me_3SiCH_2Cl
  1.$CH_2(COOEt)_2$, NaOEt 2.KOH 3.HCl, heat

  $Me_3SiCH_2CH_2COOH \xrightarrow{SOCl_2}$

  $Me_3SiCH_2CH_2COCl \xrightarrow{NH_3}$

  $Me_3SiCH_2CH_2CONH_2 \xrightarrow{NaOMe,\ Br_2}$

  $Me_3SiCH_2CH_2NHCOOMe$
  $\xrightarrow{KOH,\ MeOH\ HCl} Me_3SiCH_2CH_2NH_2 \cdot HCl$
  $\xrightarrow{KOH}$

  Me_3SiCH_2Cl
  $\xrightarrow{Mg,\ (CN)_2} Me_3SiCH_2CN \xrightarrow{H_2}$

③ (121°/735). n_D1.4244 (20°).

⑥ US 2557802 ; 2557803 ; 2607793.   Brit.
  684295 ; 684296 ; 709157.

SiC₅H₁₈N₄

① Bis(dimethylhydrazino)methylsilane
  $CH_3SiH[NHN(CH_3)_2]_2$

② $MeSiHCl_2 + Me_2NNH_2 \longrightarrow$

③　(44~45°/9~10).　n_D 1.4348 （20°）.
　　d 0.867 （20°/4°）.
⑥　Zhur. **33**, 1874 （1963）.

SiC₆Cl₈

① Pentachlorophenyltrichlorosilane
　Cl₅C₆SiCl₃
② PhSiCl₃ + Cl₂ $\xrightarrow{\text{FeCl}_3}$
③ （147~150°/10）. [59.5°].
⑥ Izv. OKhN **1956**, 457.　Zhur. **23**, 771
　　（1953）.

SiC₆H₄BrCl₃

① p-Bromophenyltrichlorosilane
　p-BrC₆H₄SiCl₃
② PhSiCl₃ $\xrightarrow{\text{Br}_2,\ \text{Fe}}$ p-BrC₆H₄SiCl₃
　（40%）
③ （264.5~265.5°）. d 1.6771 （20°）.
　Raman : CA **52**, 6237 （1959）.
⑥ Coll. Czech. Chem. Comm. **16**, 580
　　（1951）.　Dokl. **23**, 412 （1953）.　CA
　　49, 3050 （1955）; **48**, 3286 （1954）.
　　Zhur. **29**, 395 （1959）; CA **54**, 9806
　　（1959）.

SiC₆H₄Cl₃F

① p-Fluorophenyltrichlorosilane
　p-FC₆H₄SiCl₃
② SiCl₄ + p-FC₆H₄MgBr $\longrightarrow$ 88%
③ Colorless liq. （194.5~196.5°/738）.
　Sol. in org. solvents. Decomp. in
　H₂O.
⑥ Coll. Czech. Chem. Comm. **16**, 580
　　（1951）; CA **47**, 8030 （1953）.

SiC₆H₄Cl₄

① p-Chlorophenyltrichlorosilane
　p-ClC₆H₄SiCl₃
② SiCl₄ $\xrightarrow{p\text{-BrMgC}_6\text{H}_4\text{Cl}}$ 39.4%
　SiCl₄ $\xrightarrow{p\text{-ClC}_6\text{H}_4\text{MgCl}}$
　PhSiCl₃ $\xrightarrow{\text{Cl}_2,\ \text{FeCl}_3}$

Cl₃SiH $\xrightarrow{p\text{-Cl}_2\text{C}_6\text{H}_4,\ 640°}$ 30%
③ （240.5°）.
④ p-ClC₆H₄SiCl₃ $\xrightarrow{\text{hydrolysis}}$ polymn.
⑥ JOC **25**, 126 （1960）.　Coll. Czech.
　　Chem. Comm. **16**, 580 （1951）.　Ber.
　　50, 1559(1917）.　Dokl. **93**, 87(1953）;
　　CA **48**, 143 （1954）.

SiC₆H₅Br₃

① Phenyltribromosilane
　C₆H₅SiBr₃
② PhSiH₃ + 3 Br₂ （slightly excess)
　$\longrightarrow$ 82%
③ Liq. （178.3°/80）. [−21.0°~−20.8°].
　n_D 1.5970 （25°）. d 2.0228 （25°）.
　Decomp. at boiling point at atmo-
　spheric pressure.
⑥ JACS **75**, 1583 （1953）.

SiC₆H₅Cl₃

① Phenyltrichlorosilane
　C₆H₅SiCl₃
② C₆H₅Cl + SiHCl₃ $\xrightarrow{^{60}\text{Co}\ \gamma\text{-ray}}$
③ （198~200°）. n_D 1.5243 （20°）. d 1.3210
　（20°）.
④ + CH₂⟨CH₂/O⟩CHMe
　$\longrightarrow$ PhSi(Cl)₂OCH₂CH₂CHClMe
　+ PhSi(Cl)₂OCH(Me)CH₂CH₂Cl
　（with AlCl₃, TiCl₄ or HCl）
　+ (Me₂SiO)₃ or (Me₂SiO)₄
　$\longrightarrow$ polymer
⑥ Izv. OKhN **1963**, 282.　Fr. 1303018
　　（1962）; CA **58**, 9137 （1963）.　Dokl.
　　144, 576 （1962）; **141**, 649 （1961）.

SiC₆H₅F₃

① Phenytrifluorosilane
　C₆H₅SiF₃
② Electrolysis in liq. HF at −10° of
　PhSiCl₃.

PhSiCl₃ + HF $\xrightarrow{20°}$

PhSiCl₃ + SbF₃ $\longrightarrow$

③ (102.5~103.0°). n_D1.4110 (20°). d1.2169 (20°).

⑥ Ger. 1139498 (1962) ; CA **58**, 7975(1963). Tetrahedron Letters (No.5) 11

(1960). Izv. OKhN **1960**, 244 ; English page 222. Z. anorg. allg. Chem. **308**, 105 (1961).

SiC₆H₅N₃S₃

① Allylsilyl triisothiocyanate
CH₂=CHCH₂Si(NCS)₃

② NaSCN + CH₂=CHCH₂SiCl₃
$\longrightarrow$ 70%

③ (126~128°/2.5). n_D1.6140 (26°).
IR : 3080, 2090, 1995, 1635, 1055 cm⁻¹.

⑥ JOC **27**, 634 (1962).

SiC₆H₅N₉

① Phenylsilyl triazide
C₆H₅Si(N₃)₃

② PhSiCl₃ + Me₃SiN₃ + AlCl₃ $\longrightarrow$

③ (62.5~63.5°/0.01).

⑥ Angew. **74**, 875 (1962). Ber. **96**, 1293 (1963).

SiC₆H₆Br₂

① Phenyldibromosilane
C₆H₅SiHBr₂

② 2PhSiH₃ + 3Br₂ $\longrightarrow$ PhSiH₂Br
+PhSiHBr₂ (1 : 0.75) (60%)

③ Liq. (146.7~147.0°/58). [−51.0~50.6°].
n_D1.5778 (25°). d1.7293 (25°).
Sol. in org. solvents. Decomp. in H₂O.

⑥ JACS **75**, 1583 (1953).

SiC₆H₆Cl₂

① Phenyldichlorosilane
C₆H₅SiHCl₂

② PhMgBr + SiHCl₃ $\longrightarrow$ 26%

PhCl + Si−Ag $\longrightarrow$

③ (180~182°). n_D1.5246 (20°).
IR : Appl. Spectroscopy **14**, 85 (1960).

④ + CH₂=CHCF₃
$\longrightarrow$ PhSi(Cl)₂(CH₂)₂CF₃ (69.5%)
+ CH₂=CHCH₂Cl
$\xrightarrow{H_2PtCl_6}$ PhCl₂SiCH₂CH₂CH₂Cl

⑥ Dokl. **126**, 1009 (1959) ; CA **53**, 21747 (1959). JACS **82**, 3601 (1960).

SiC₆H₇Br

① Phenylbromosilane
C₆H₅SiH₂Br

② PhSiH₃ + C₂H₅Br $\longrightarrow$ 30%

③ (180°/70). [−29.9°]. n_D1.5555 (25°). d 1.3632 (25°).

⑥ JACS **76**, 4555 (1954) ; **75**, 1583 (1953) ; **79**, 5604 (1957).

SiC₆H₈

① Phenylsilane
C₆H₅SiH₃

② SiCl₄ $\xrightarrow{PhLi}$ PhSiCl₃
$\xrightarrow{LiAlH_4}$ PhSiH₃

③ (120°). n_D1.5125 (20°). d0.8681 (20°).

④ + 3RLi $\longrightarrow$ PhSiR₃
+ 3EtOH $\xrightarrow{LiOEt}$ PhSi(OEt)₃
+ CH₂N₂ $\longrightarrow$ PhSiMeH₂
+ PhSiMe₂H

⑥ Angew. **74**, 468 (1962) ; CA **57**, 9872 (1962).   Post (1949).   JACS **72**, 4702 (1950) ; **51**, 3067 (1929).

SiC₆H₈O₃

① Phenylsilanetriol
C₆H₅Si(OH)₃

② PhSi(OCH₃)₃ $\xrightarrow{AcOH\ aq.}$ 75%

③ [120~130°].
Decomp. on heating; sensitive to alk. and acid catalysts. Slightly sol. in H₂O, MeOH and Me₂CO;

insol. in PhMe and petr. ether;
very unstable in soln.

⑥ JACS **77**, 770 (1955).

SiC₆H₉Cl

① Vinyl(dimethylchlorosilyl)acetylene

$CH_2=CHC\equiv CSi(CH_3)_2Cl$

② $CH_2=CHC\equiv CSi(Me)_2OH + SOCl_2$

$\xrightarrow{C_5H_5N}$ 53.4%

$CH_2=CHC\equiv CMgBr + Me_2SiCl_2 \longrightarrow$

③ (52~54°/26). n_D 1.4694 (20°). d 0.9570 (20°).

⑥ Dokl. **139**, 913 (1961).   Izv. OKhN **1936**, 97.

SiC₆H₉Cl₃

① Cyclohexen-3-yltrichlorosilane

② $CH_2=CHSiCl_3 +$

$CH_2=CHCH=CH_2 \xrightarrow{160~180°}$

③ (87~88°/16). n_D 1.405 (20°). d 1.25 (25°).

⑥ Ind. Eng. Chem. **45**, 367 (1953).

SiC₆H₁₀

① Trivinylsilane

$(CH_2=CH)_3SiH$

② $HSiCl_3 + 3CH_2=CHMgCl \xrightarrow{THF}$

③ (92.5°). n_D 1.4498 (20°). d 0.7725 (25°).
NMR: CA **55**, 11089 (1961).

⑥ JOC **22**, 1200 (1957); CA **52**, 7134 (1958).   JCS **1960**, 5132.

SiC₆H₁₀Cl₂

① Diallyldichlorosilane

$(CH_2=CHCH_2)_2SiCl_2$

② $Si-Cu (80/20) + CH_2=CHCH_2Cl$

$\xrightarrow{300°}$ $(CH_2=CHCH_2)_2SiCl_2$,

$CH_2=CHCH_2SiHCl_2$

and $CH_2=CHCH_2SiCl_3$

$SiCl_4 + CH_2=CHCH_2MgBr \longrightarrow$

③ (116°).

⑥ Izv. OKhN **1954**, 497; CA **49**, 9495 (1955).   Izv. OKhN **1957**, 383; CA **51**, 15457 (1957).

SiC₆H₁₀N₂O₂

① Diethyldiisocyanatosilane

$(C_2H_5)_2Si(NCO)_2$

② $Et_2SiCl_2 + AgNCO \longrightarrow$

③ (176.7°). n_D 1.4348 (20°). d 1.0223 (20°).

⑥ JACS **72**, 196 (1950).

SiC₆H₁₀N₂S₂

① Diethyldiisothiocyanatosilane

$(C_2H_5)_2Si(NCS)_2$

② $Et_2SiCl_2 + 2NH_4NCS \longrightarrow 60~80\%$

③ Colorless liq. (245.5°).
Sol. in org. solvents.

⑥ Zhur. **24**, 1082 (1954); CA **49**, 8791 (1955).

SiC₆H₁₀N₂S₂

① Dimethylbis(thiocyanatomethyl)-silane

$(CH_3)_2Si(CH_2SCN)_2$

② $Me_2Si(CH_2Cl)_2 + NaSCN \xrightarrow{EtOH} 79\%$

③ (142.5°/2). n_D 1.5361 (20°). d 1.1513 (20°).

⑤ Useful as mold inhibitors and for modifying silicones.

⑥ Izv. OKhN **1956**, 707; CA **51**, 1819 (1957).   Brit. 778272; CA **52**, 429 (1958).

SiC₆H₁₀O

① Vinyl(dimethylhydroxysilyl)acetylene

$CH_2=CHC\equiv CSi(CH_3)_2OH$

② $CH_2=CHC\equiv CMgBr + (Me_2SiO)_x$

$\longrightarrow 45\%$

③ (56~57°/10). n_D 1.4800 (20°). d 0.8943 (20°).

④ $+ HCl + CH_2=CHOBu \longrightarrow$

CH₂=CHC≡CSi(Me)₂OCHMeOBu

(25.8%)

+ (BzO)₂ ⟶ colorless liq. polymer

+ K₂CO₃ ⟶

(CH₂=CC≡CSiMe₂)₂O

+ HCl + CH₂=CHOPr-*i* ⟶

CH₂=CHC≡CSiMe₂OCHMeOPr-*i*

⑥ Izv. OKhN **1963**, 97.   Dokl. **139**, 913
   (1961).

SiC₆H₁₀O

① Vinyl(ethylhydroxysilyl)acetylene
   CH₂=CHC≡CSiH(C₂H₅)OH

② CH₂=CHC≡CMgBr + (EtHSiO)$_x$ ⟶

③ (64°/22). n_D1.4715 (20°). d0.8960 (20°).

⑥ Dokl. **139**, 913 (1961); English page
   792.   Izv. OKhN **1963**, 91.

SiC₆H₁₁Cl₃

① Cyclohexyltrichlorosilane
   C₆H₁₁SiCl₃

② HSiCl₃ + C₆H₁₁MgBr ⟶

   C₆H₁₀ + HSiCl₃ $\xrightarrow[\text{(CH₃COO)₂, 70~100°}]{}$ 64%

③ Colorless liq. (199°).

   Sol. in org. solvents. Decomp. in
   water.

⑥ JCS **1930**, 1020.   JACS **69**, 2687 (1947).

SiC₆H₁₁F₂N

① 1-Cyano-2-methyl-4,4-difluoro-4-
   silapentane
   CH₃Si(F)₂CH₂CH(CH₃)CH₂CN

② NaCN + MeSi(F)₂CH₂CH(Me)CH₂Cl

③ (199.5~200.0°/750). n_D1.3932 (25°).

⑥ US 3053874 (1962); CA **58**, 3458 (1963).

SiC₆H₁₂

① Dimethyldivinylsilane
   (CH₂=CH)₂Si(CH₃)₂

② CH₂=CHMgCl + Me₂SiCl₂ ⟶66.1%

   CH₂=CHLi $\xrightarrow{\text{Me₂SiCl₂}}$ 39%

③ (80°). n_D1.4176 (20°). d0.7337 (20°).

④ Copolymerized with compd. such as
   PhCH=CH₂, MMA or vinyl acetate.

⑥ JACS **83**, 3583 (1961). JOC **22**, 1200
   (1957); **22**, 1200 (1957).

SiC₆H₁₂

① Diallylsilane
   (CH₂=CHCH₂)₂SiH₂

② (CH₂=CHCH₂)₂SiCl₂ + LiH ⟶

③ (103.7°). n_D 1.4420 (20°). d 0.7533
   (20°).

⑥ Izv. OKhN **1954**, 497;   CA **49**, 9495
   (1955).

SiC₆H₁₂

① Trimethylpropynylsilane
   CH₃C≡CSi(CH₃)₃

② MeC≡CMgBr + Me₃SiBr ⟶

③ (99~100°). n_D 1.4091 (20°). d 0.7581
   (20°).

④ + SiHCl₃ $\xrightarrow{\text{Bz₂O₂}}$ MeCH=C(SiMe₃)SiCl₃

⑥ Dokl. **93**, 293 (1953).   Zhur. **26**, 3338
   (1956).

SiC₆H₁₂ClF₃O

① 3,3,3-Trifluoropropylmethylchloro-
   ethoxysilane
   CF₃CH₂CH₂Si(Cl)(CH₃)OC₂H₅

③ (140.9~141.3°/76). n_D 1.3739 (20°). d
   1.1309 (20°).

④ + MeMgCl
   ⟶ CF₃CH₂CH₂SiMe₂OEt

⑥ Zhur. **33**, 704 (1963).

SiC₆H₁₂Cl₂O₂

① 3-Methyldichlorosilylpropyl acetate
   CH₃COOCH₂CH₂CH₂Si(Cl)₂CH₃

② AcOCH₂CH=CH₂+MeSiHCl₂ $\xrightarrow{\text{H₂PtCl₆}}$

③ (79~80°/4). n_D 1.4455 (20°). d 1.1618
   (20°).

⑥ Dokl. **150**, 1055 (1963).   Zhur. **32**,

2302 (1962) ; English page 2270. US
2922806 (1960) ; CA **54**, 16008 (1960).

SiC₆H₁₂O₄

① Dimethylsilyl diacetate
(CH₃COO)₂Si(CH₃)₂

② AcONa + Me₂SiCl₂ ⟶ 60%
Ac₂O + Me₂SiCl₂ ⟶
Ac₂O + (Me₂SiO)₄ ⟶ 19.9%

③ (155~162°). n_D 1.4020 (20°).

⑥ Vysokomol. Soed. **5**, 343 (1963). US
2866900 (1958) ; CA **53**, 9059 (1959).
Ger. 1039516 (1958) ; CA **54**, 17269
(1960). US 2910496 (1959).

SiC₆H₁₃BrO

① Dimethylbromomethylallyloxysilane
(CH₃)₂Si(CH₂Br)OCH₂CH=CH₂

② CH₂=CHCH₂OH
+ Me₂SiClCH₂Br ⟶

③ (160°). n_D 1.4580 (20°).

⑥ Ber. **96**, 1495 (1963).

SiC₆H₁₃Cl

① 1-Methyl-1-chloromethyl-1-sila-
cyclopentane

$$\begin{matrix} CH_2CH_2 \\ \quad \big\rangle Si(CH_3)CH_2Cl \\ CH_2CH_2 \end{matrix}$$

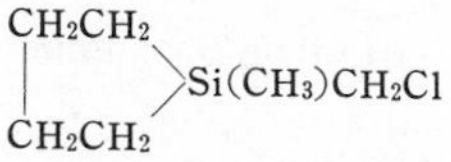

② (CH₂CH₂MgBr)₂+MeSi(Cl)₂CH₂Cl
⟶ 50%
Cl₂ + (CH₂)₄SiMe₂ ⟶63%

③ (168.0~168.6°). n_D 1.4738 (20°). d 0.9893
(20°).

④ + AlCl₃ ⟶ (CH₂)₅SiMeCl

⑥ Izv. OKhN **1963**, 274.   JOC **26**, 2003
(1961).   Izv. OKhN **1962**, 1127 ;
English page 1057.

SiC₆H₁₃Cl

① 1-Methyl-1-chloro-1-silacyclohexane

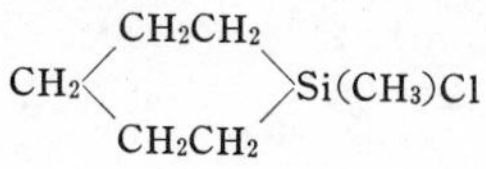

$$CH_2\big\langle \begin{matrix} CH_2CH_2 \\ \\ CH_2CH_2 \end{matrix} \big\rangle Si(CH_3)Cl$$

② AlCl₃ + (CH₂)₄Si(Me)CH₂Cl ⟶ 91%

③ (155.5~157.0°). n_D 1.4613 (20°). d
0.9847 (20°).

⑥ Izv. OKhN **1962**, 1127 ; English page
1057. Izv. OKhN **1968**, 274.

SiC₆H₁₃ClO

① 2-Trimethylsilylpropionyl chloride
ClOCCH₂CH₂Si(CH₃)₃

② Me₃SiCH₂CH₂CO₂H + SOCl₂ ⟶

③ (92/65°). n_D 1.4375 (20°). d 0.9609 (20°).

⑥ BCSJ **29**, 322 (1956).   JACS **73**, 5130
(1951).

SiC₆H₁₃Cl₃

① n-Hexyltrichlorosilane
n-C₆H₁₃SiCl₃

② SiCl₄ + n-C₆H₁₃MgBr ⟶
HSiCl₃ + hexene-(1) ⟶

③ Colorless liq. (188~191°).
Decomp. in H₂O. Sol. in org.
solvents.

④ + LiH $\xrightarrow{(i\text{-}Am)_2O}$ C₆H₁₃SiH₃ 65%

⑥ Izv. OKhN **1954**, 497 ;   CA **49**, 9495
(1955).

SiC₆H₁₃F₃

① 3,3,3-Trifluoropropyltrimethylsilane
CF₃CH₂CH₂Si(CH₃)₃

② CF₃CH=CH₂+SiHCl₃ $\xrightarrow{(Me_3CO)_2}$
CF₃(CH₂)₂SiCl₃ $\xrightarrow{MeMgX}$ 58%

③ (94.3~95.1°). n_D 1.3576 (20°). d 0.896
(20°).

⑥ JACS **79**, 2329 (1957).

SiC₆H₁₃I

① 1-Methyl-1-iodomethyl-1-silacyclo-
pentane

$$\begin{matrix} CH_2CH_2 \\ \quad \big\rangle Si(CH_3)CH_2I \\ CH_2CH_2 \end{matrix}$$

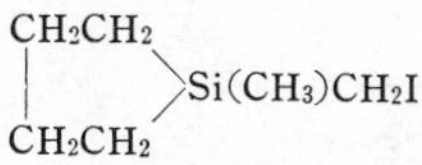

② KI + $\begin{array}{c}CH_2CH_2\\|\qquad\\CH_2CH_2\end{array}$ Si(CH₃)CH₂Cl

⟶ 89%

③ (93.5°/20). n_D 1.5383 (20°). d 1.4973
(20°/4°).

⑥ Izv. OKhN 1963, 274.

SiC₆H₁₃N

① Trimethyl-α-cyanoethylsilane
(CH₃)₃SiCH(CH₃)CN

② Cl₃SiH + CH₂=CHCN

$\xrightarrow{C_5H_5N}$ Cl₃SiCHMeCN $\xrightarrow{MeMgBr}$

MeSiHCl₂ + CH₂=CHCN $\xrightarrow{Fe(CO)_5 \sim NiCl^2}$

MeSiCl₂CHMeCN $\xrightarrow{MeMgBr}$

③ (91.5~92.5°/58). n_D 1.4232 (25°). d
0.8254 (25°).

⑥ BCSJ 29, 326 (1956). Dokl. 100, 711
(1955); CA 50, 1574 (1956). Dokl.
132, 149 (1960); CA 54, 20847 (1960).

SiC₆H₁₃NO

① Ethoxydimethylcyanomethylsilane
C₂H₅OSi(CH₃)₂CH₂CN

② NaCN + EtOSiMe₂CH₂Cl ⟶

③ (76~77°/40). n_D1.3903 (20°).

⑥ Mem. Fac. Eng. Osaka City Univ. 3,
195 (1961); CA 58, 3455 (1963).

SiC₆H₁₄

① Cyclohexylsilane
C₆H₁₁SiH₃

② H₃SiBr+C₆H₁₁MgBr $\xrightarrow{n-Bu_2O}$ 38%

③ Colorless liq. (120.2°). n_D1.4464 (25°).
d0.7958 (25°).
Sol. in org. solvents; insol. in H₂O.

⑥ JACS 78, 292 (1956).

SiC₆H₁₄

① Allyltrimethylsilane
(CH₃)₃SiCH₂CH=CH₂

② MeSi(Cl)₂CH₂CH=CH₂
+ MeMgBr ⟶

CH₂=CHCH₂SiCl₃ + MeMgBr ⟶

③ (85.4°/752). n_D 1.4075 (20°). d 0.5195
(20°/4°).

⑥ Coll. Czech. Chem. Comm. 28, 1384
(1963); 27, 1658 (1962). Dokl. 146,
1117 (1962). Izv. OKhN 1963, 572.

SiC₆H₁₄

① Trimethylpropenylsilane
CH₃CH=CHSi(CH₃)₃

② MeCl₂SiH + MeCH=CH₂

$\xrightarrow{Fe(CO)_5}$ MeCl₂SiCH=CHMe

$\xrightarrow{MeMgBr}$

MeCH=CHLi + Me₃SiCl ⟶ 30%

③ (86~86°). n_D 1.4086 (20°). d 0.7167
(20°).
Raman: Izv. OKhN 1960, 1553.

⑥ Zhur. 26, 1233 (1956). Izv. OKhN
1960, 1553; CA 50, 14515 (1956).
Zhur. 26, 1225 (1956); CA 50, 14515
(1956). Tetrahedron 17, 61 (1962).

SiC₆H₁₄

① 1,1-Dimethyl-1-silacyclopentane
$\begin{array}{c}CH_2-CH_2\\|\qquad\\CH_2-CH_2\end{array}$ Si(CH₃)₂

② Me₂SiCl₂ + (CH₂CH₂MgBr)₂ ⟶
Li + (CH₂CH₂Br)₂ + Me₂SiCl₂ ⟶

③ (103~105°). [−97.5°]. n_D1.4335 (20°).
d0.7935 (20°/4°).

④ + Pt−SiO₂ ⟶ $\begin{array}{c}CH_2-CH_2\\CH=CH\end{array}$ SiMe₂

+ $\begin{array}{c}CH=CH\\|\qquad\\CH=CH\end{array}$ SiMe₂ + C₁₀H₂₂Si₂

⑥ Dokl. 150, 562 (1963). Ann. 659, 39
(1962). JOC 26, 2530 (1961). Izv.
OKhN 1963, 274.

SiC$_6$H$_{14}$

① 1-Methyl-1-ethyl-1-silacyclobutane

CH$_2$
CH$_2$〈 〉Si(CH$_3$)C$_2$H$_5$
CH$_2$

② Mg + EtSi(Me)(Cl)CH$_2$CH$_2$CH$_2$Cl —→
Mg + EtBr
+ MeSi(Cl)$_2$CH$_2$CH$_2$CH$_2$Cl —→

③ (60~64°/168). n_D1.4392 (20°). d0.7920
(20°/4°).

⑥ Dokl. **150**, 799 (1963).   Izv. OKhN
1957, 1206; English page 1230.
Zhur. **27**, 2062 (1957).

SiC$_6$H$_{14}$

① Cyclopropyltrimethylsilane

CH$_2$
(CH$_3$)$_3$SiCH〈 |
CH$_2$

② CH$_2$I$_2$ + Cu(sintered) +
Me$_3$SiCH$_2$CH=CH$_2$ —→

③ (90°/745). n_D 1.4093 (20°). d 0.7523
(20°/4°).

⑥ Izv. OKhN **1963**, 1111.

SiC$_6$H$_{14}$ClF

① t-Butylmethylfluorochloromethyl-
silane
t-C$_4$H$_9$Si(F)(CH$_3$)CH$_2$Cl

② Me$_2$Si(CH$_2$Cl)CMe=CH$_2$ +
H$_2$SO$_4$ + NH$_4$HF$_2$ —→

③ (142~143°). n_D 1.4191 (25°). d 0.9745
(20°/4°).

⑥ "Studies in Organosilicon Compounds" Vol.1, Chap. 11 (1963).

SiC$_6$H$_{14}$Cl$_2$

① Di-n-propyldichlorosilane
(n-C$_3$H$_7$)$_2$SiCl$_2$

② Si−Cu (80/20) + PrCl $\xrightarrow{350\sim360°}$
PrSiHCl$_2$ (32.5%), PrSiCl$_3$ (19%),
and Pr$_2$SiCl$_2$ (10%)

H$_2$SiCl$_2$+C$_3$H$_6$ $\xrightarrow{H_2PtCl_6}$ 60~6□%

③ (173~175°). n_D 1.4330 (20°). d 1.025
(20°).

④ + 1-C$_{10}$H$_7$Li —→ (1-C$_{10}$H$_7$)$_2$SiPr$_2$

⑥ Dokl. **126**, 1009 (1959); CA **53**, 21748
(1959). Zhur. **25**, 2332 (1955).
Dokl. **85**, 345 (1952).

SiC$_6$H$_{14}$Cl$_2$

① Diisopropyldichlorosilane
(i-C$_3$H$_7$)$_2$SiCl$_2$

② Si−Cu (80/20) + i-PrCl
$\xrightarrow{350\sim360°}$ 11%

SiCl$_4$ (excess) + i-PrMgX $\xrightarrow{C_6H_6}$ 11%

③ (67~69°/11). d1.06 (20°).

⑥ JACS **71**, 755 (1949).   Zhur. **25**, 2332
(1955); CA **50**, 9280 (1956).

SiC$_6$H$_{14}$Cl$_2$

① n-Hexyldichlorosilane
n-C$_6$H$_{13}$SiHCl$_2$

② n-C$_6$H$_{13}$MgBr + HSiCl$_3$ —→

③ Liq. (172~175°).
Sol. in org. solvents. Decomp. in
H$_2$O.

⑥ US 2698334 (1954); CA **49**, 4328(1955).

SiC$_6$H$_{14}$Cl$_2$

① n-Pentylmethyldichlorosilane
n-C$_5$H$_{11}$(CH$_3$)SiCl$_2$

② C$_3$H$_7$CH=CH$_2$ + MeSiHCl$_2$
$\xrightarrow{(CH_3COO)_2}$ 37%

③ Liq. (164~168°).
Sol. in org. solvents. Decomp. in
H$_2$O.

⑥ Post 72 (1949). JACS **69**, 2687 (1947).

SiC$_6$H$_{14}$Cl$_2$

① 4-Chlorobutyldimethylchlorosilane
(CH$_3$)$_2$Si(Cl)CH$_2$CH$_2$CH$_2$CH$_2$Cl

② ClCH$_2$CH$_2$CH=CH$_2$

+ Me₂SiHCl $\xrightarrow{H_2PtCl_6}$

③ (100.0~101.5°/30). n_D 1.4503 (25°). d 1.0296 (25°).

⑥ Fr. 1318979 (1963); CA **59**, 3958 (1963).

SiC₆H₁₄O

① Trimethylallyloxysilane
(CH₃)₃SiOCH₂CH=CH₂

② (CH₃)₃SiCl + HOCH₂CH=CH₂ ⟶

③ (100.0~100.2°). n_D1.3904(30°). d0.7830 (30°).

⑥ Nippon Kagaku Zasshi **76**, 9 (1955); CA **51**, 17724 (1957).

SiC₆H₁₄O

① Trimethyl-2-formylethylsilane
(CH₃)₃SiC₂H₄CHO

② Me₃SiCH=CH₂ + CO + H₂ $\xrightarrow{Co(CO)_4}$
AcOCH₂CH=CH₂ + MeSiHCl₂
$\xrightarrow{Pt-C}$ MeSiCl₂CH₂CH₂CH₂OAc
$\xrightarrow{MeMgBr}$ Me₃Si(CH₂)₃OH $\xrightarrow[300°]{Cu}$

③ (63°/25). n_D1.4238(20°). d0.8347 (20°).

⑥ JOC **17**, 1107 (1952). US 2588083 (1952). Zhur. **32**, 2302, (1962); CA **58**, 7963, 9138 (1964).

SiC₆H₁₄O₂

① (2-Carboxyethyl)trimethylsilane
(CH₃)₃SiCH₂CH₂CO₂H

② Me₃SiCH₂Cl $\xrightarrow{\text{malonic ester synthesis}}$ 66%
Cl₃SiH + CH₂=CHCN ⟶
Cl₃SiCH₂CH₂CN $\xrightarrow{\text{MeMgBr, alc., NaOH}}$

③ (147°/65). [22°]. n_D 1.4278 (20°). d 0.9196 (20°).

⑥ BCSJ **29**, 322 (1956). Dokl. **100**, 711 (1955). JACS **76**, 1609 (1954); **72**, 1935 (1950).

SiC₆H₁₄S₂

① 1,1-Dimethyl-1-sila-2,6-disulfacyclo-

heptane
$$(CH_3)_2Si\begin{matrix}\diagup SCH_2CH_2 \\ \diagdown CH_2SCH_2\end{matrix}$$

② Me₂Si(Cl)CH₂Cl + CH₂(CH₂SH)₂ ⟶

③ (61~63°/1).

⑥ Ber. **96**, 1019 (1963).

SiC₆H₁₅Br

① Triethylbromosilane
(C₂H₅)₃SiBr

② Et₄Si + AlCl₃ + *i*-PrBr ⟶

③ (164.5°). n_D 1.4571 (20°). d 1.145 (20°/4°).

⑥ Zhur. **29**, 1534 (1959); **33**, 613 (1963); **31**, 4056 (1961); English page 3784. Coll. Czech. Chem. Comm. 24, 3816 (1959).

SiC₆H₁₅Br

① Trimethyl-3-bromopropylsilane
BrCH₂CH₂CH₂Si(CH₃)₃

② Me₃Si(CH₂)₃OH $\xrightarrow{PBr_3}$

③ (70°/25). n_D1.4541 (20°). d1.1173 (20°).

④ $\xrightarrow{H_2SO_4-NH_4Cl}$ Br(CH₂)₃SiMe₂Cl

⑥ US 2610198; 2610199; 2635109; CA **47**, 9346 (1953); **48**, 8252 (1954). Brit. 684293; 684294. JACS **76**, 5002(1954).

SiC₆H₁₅Cl

① Triethylchlorosilane
(C₂H₅)₃SiCl

② AlCl₃ + Et₄Si + *i*-PrCl ⟶ 92.2%
Et₃SiOSiEt₃ + AlCl₃
(NPCl₂)₃ + Et₃SiOH

③ (143~145°/758). n_D1.4300 (20°).

④ + EtCH=NOH ⟶ EtCH=NOSiEt₃
+ *n*-PrCH=NOH
⟶ *n*-PrCH=NOSiEt₃
+ *i*-PrCH=NOH
⟶ *i*-PrCH=NOSiEt₃

⑥ Zhur. **33**, 613 (1963); **30**, 3347 (1960);

English page 3314.   Zhur. **7**, 2192
(1962); **30**, 3352 (1960); English
page 3319.

SiC$_6$H$_{15}$Cl

① *n*-Butyldimethylchlorosilane
   n-C$_4$H$_9$(CH$_3$)$_2$SiCl
② Me$_2$SiCl$_2$ + *n*-BuMgBr $\longrightarrow$ 50%
③ Colorless liq. (138.5°). n_D1.4208 (20°).
   d 0.8766 (20°).
   Sol. in org. solvents. Decomp. with
   H$_2$O.
⑥ Dokl. **102**. 1131 (1955).

SiC$_6$H$_{15}$Cl

① 3-Chloropropyltrimethylsilane
   CH$_2$ClCH$_2$CH$_2$Si(CH$_3$)$_3$
② MeHSiCl$_2$+CH$_2$=CHCH$_2$Cl
   $\longrightarrow$ MeSiCl$_2$(CH$_2$)$_3$Cl $\xrightarrow{\text{MeMgI}}$ 80%
③ (148°). n_D1.4310 (20°). *d*0.8825 (20°).
④ + AlCl$_3$ $\xrightarrow{\text{HBr}}$
   Me$_3$SiBr + CH$_2$=CHCH$_3$
   + NaI $\xrightarrow{\text{Me}_2\text{CO}}$ Me$_3$Si(CH$_2$)$_3$I
⑥ US 2496419; CA **44**, 4926 (1950).
   JACS **79**, 2764 (1957).

SiC$_6$H$_{15}$Cl

① Trimethyl-1-chloroisopropylsilane
   (CH$_3$)$_2$CClSi(CH$_3$)$_3$
② Me$_3$SiCMe=CH$_2$ + HCl $\xrightarrow{50°}$ 35%
③ [95~97°].
⑥ JACS **76**, 1613 (1954).

SiC$_6$H$_{15}$ClO$_2$

① Methyldiethoxychloromethylsilane
   CH$_3$Si(OC$_2$H$_5$)$_2$CH$_2$Cl
③ (160~162°). n_D1.4163 (20°).
④ + CH$_2$=CMeCOOH + Et$_3$N
   + *p*-C$_6$H$_4$(OH)$_2$ $\longrightarrow$
   CH$_2$=CMeCOOSi(OEt)$_2$Me (53%)
⑥ Vysokomol. Soed. **5**, 343 (1963).

SiC$_6$H$_{15}$DO

① Triethyldeuteroxysilane
② (C$_2$H$_5$)$_3$SiOD
   Et$_3$SiOH + D$_2$O $\longrightarrow$
   Et$_3$SiCl + D$_2$O $\longrightarrow$
   Et$_3$SiOMe + D$_2$O $\longrightarrow$
③ (155.2°). n_D1.4320 (20°).
   IR: 1465, 1463, 1418, 1377, 1380~1370,
   824~138 cm^{-1}; Izv. OKhN **1959**, 1019.
⑥ Z. anorg. allg. Chem. **323**, 190 (1963).
   Coll. Czech. Chem. Coll. **24**, 3816
   (1959); CA **54**, 7340 (1960).   Izv.
   OKhN **1959**, 1019; English page
   983.

SiC$_6$H$_{15}$F

① Triethylfluorosilane
   (C$_2$H$_5$)$_3$SiF
② (Et$_3$Si)$_2$O $\xrightarrow{\text{KHF}_2-\text{H}_2\text{SO}_4}$ Et$_3$SiF
   Et$_3$SiX $\xrightarrow{\text{HF}-\text{EtOH}}$ Et$_3$SiF
   (X=Cl, Br)
③ (109°). n_D1.3900 (25°). *d*0.8354 (25°).
   NMR: J. Phys. Chem. **63**, 761 (1959).
⑥ Post (1949).   Izv. OKhN **1957**, 517;
   CA **51**, 12660 (1957).   JCS **1954**, 3169.
   JACS **73**, 5127 (1952).

SiC$_6$H$_{15}$I

① Triethyliodosilane
   (C$_2$H$_5$)$_3$SiI
② (Et$_3$Si)$_2$O + I$_2$ $\longrightarrow$ 88%
   Et$_3$SiH $\xrightarrow{\text{HI}}$
   Et$_3$SiCl $\xrightarrow{\text{liq. NH}_3}$ Et$_3$SiNH$_2$ $\xrightarrow{\text{HI}}$
③ (191.2°). n_D1.4948(20°). *d*1.3512(20°).
⑥ Izv. OKhN **1956**, 713, 805.   JACS **75**,
   2932 (1953); **73**, 2144 (1951).   JCS
   1949, 2755.

SiC$_6$H$_{15}$NO

① 1,1,3-Trimethyl-1-sila-3-aza-6-oxacyclohexane

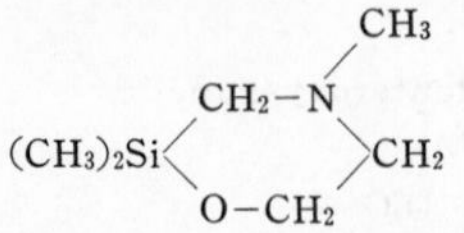

$$\begin{array}{c} CH_3 \\ CH_2-N \\ (CH_3)_2Si \diagdown \qquad CH_2 \\ O-CH_2 \end{array}$$

② EtOSi(Me)₂CH₂Br + Et₃N
+ MeNHCH₂CH₂OH ⟶

③ n_D 1.4349 (20°).

⑥ Ber. **96**, 349 (1963).

SiC₆H₁₆

① Triethylsilane
HSi(C₂H₅)₃

② Heating of SiEt₄ ⟶
TiCl₄ + Et₃SiCl + i-PrMgBr ⟶
SiHCl₃ + EtMgX ⟶

③ (107~108°). n_D 1.4120 (20°). d 0.7318
(20°).
IR : ν_{Si-H} 2099 cm⁻¹.

④ + TiCl₄ ⟶ TiHCl₃
+ OH⁻ ⟶ H₂

⑥ Zhur. **30**, 2988 (1960).   JOC **27**, 340
(1962).   JACS **83**, 1916 (1961).
BCSJ **35**, 364 (1962).

SiC₆H₁₆

① Di-n-propylsilane
(n-C₃H₇)₂SiH₂

② SiH₂Cl₂ + 2n-C₃H₇MgBr ⟶
(n-C₃H₇)₂SiCl₂ + LiH ⟶

③ (111°). n_D 1.4112 (20°). d 0.7194 (20°).

⑥ Izv. OKhN **1954**, 497. Dokl. **95**, 805
(1954). Acta. Chem. Scand. **8**, 1830
(1954).

SiC₆H₁₆

① Diisopropylsilane
(i-C₃H₇)₂SiH₂

② SiH₂Cl₂ + 2i-C₃H₇MgBr ⟶

③ (98.5°). n_D 1.4041 (25°). d 0.7085 (25°).

⑥ Izv. OKhN **1954**, 497 ; CA **49**, 9495
(1955).   JOC **18**, 303 (1953).

SiC₆H₁₆

① n-Hexylsilane
C₆H₁₃SiH₃

② SiCl₄ $\xrightarrow{C_6H_{13}MgBr}$ C₆H₁₃SiCl₃
C₆H₁₃SiCl₃ + LiH $\xrightarrow{i\text{-}Am_2O}$

③ (114~114.5°). n_D 1.4129 (20°). d 0.7182
(20°).

⑥ Izv. OKhN **1954**, 497 ; CA **49**, 9495
(1955).   Dokl. **95**, 805 (1954) ; CA **49**,
6089 (1955).   Acta. Chem. Scand.
8, 1830 (1954).

SiC₆H₁₆

① Diethyldimethylsilane
(CH₃)₂Si(C₂H₅)₂

② Et₂SiCl₂ + MeMgBr ⟶

③ (95.7~96.2°). n_D 1.3982 (20°). d 0.7168
(20°).
IR, NMR : Spectrochim. Acta **19**,
835 (1963).
Raman : Izv. OKhN **1960**, 1553.

④ + I₂ $\xrightarrow{AlI_3}$ MeI + EtI + Me₂EtSiI

SiC₆H₁₆

① Trimethyl-n-propylsilane
(CH₃)₃Si(n-C₃H₇)

② n-PrSiCl₃ + 3MeMgBr ⟶ 54%
MeHSiCl₂ + MeCH=CH₂
$\xrightarrow{Fe(CO)_5}$ $\xrightarrow{MeMgX}$ 25%

③ Liq. (90°). n_D 1.3929 (20°). d 0.7020
(20°).
Raman : Izv. OKhN **1960**, 1553.

④ 2Me₃SiPr $\xrightarrow{Al_2Br_6 \text{ in } C_6H_6}$
Me₄Si + Me₂SiPr₂
Me₃SiPr $\xrightarrow{HBr-Al_2Br_6 \text{ in } C_6H_6}$ cleavage
Me₃SiPr $\xrightarrow{Cr-catalyst, 500~600°}$
Me₃SiC₃H₅ + Me₄Si + H

⑥ Tetrahedron Letters, **1961**, 421.
Dokl. **132**, 374 (1960).   Izv. OKhN

1960, 1553.

SiC₆H₁₆O
① Triethylsilanol
   (C₂H₅)₃SiOH
② Et₃SiCl + NaOH ⟶
   Et₃SiH + H₂PtCl₆ + HOH ⟶
③ (153~155°). *n* 1.4330 (20°). *d* 0.8650
   (20°).
⑥ Zhur. **33**, 1945 (1963).   Dokl. **145**, 789,
   806 (1962); English page 652, 668.
   Z. anorg. allg. Chem. **323**, 190
   (1963).

SiC₆H₁₆O
① Dimethyl-*t*-butylsilanol
   (CH₃)₂(*t*-C₄H₉)SiOH
②   H₂SO₄ H₂O
   CH₂=CMeSiMe₃ ⟶
                    −H₂O, CaCl₂
   Me₂(*t*-Bu)SiOH·1/2 H₂O ⟶
③ Colorless liq. (141°). *n*D 1.4234 (20°).
   d 0.8397 (20°).
   Sol. in org. solvents.
⑥ JACS **76**, 1186 (1954).

SiC₆H₁₆O₂
① Methyl-*n*-propyldimethoxysilane
   n-C₃H₇Si(OCH₃)₂CH₃
②   MeMgBr, *n*-PrMgBr
   Si(OMe)₄ ⟶
③ (126°/750). *n*D 1.3931 (20°).   *d* 0.8689
   (20°).
④ + Na ⟶ *n*-PrSi(Me)₂OMe
   + MeSi(Pr-*n*)₂OMe
⑥ Rocz. Chem. **34**, 1667 (1960); CA **56**,
   7344 (1962). JACS **84**, 4730 (1962).

SiC₆H₁₆O
① *n*-Propyldimethylmethoxysilane
   n-C₃H₇Si(CH₃)₂OCH₃
② *n*-PrSi(OMe)₂Me + Na ⟶
③ (111.1~111.3°). *n*D 1.3927 (25°). *d* 0.7860
   (25°).
⑥ JACS **84**, 4730 (1962).

SiC₆H₁₆O
① Trimethylethoxymethylsilane
   C₂H₅OCH₂Si(CH₃)₃
② ClCH₂SiMe₃ + EtOH ⟶ 70%
③ (101~103°). *n*D 1.3935 (20°). *d* 0.7538
   (20°).
   IR : JACS **71**, 269 (1949).
⑥ JACS **70**, 4142 (1948). US 2572402;
   CA **46**, 4560 (1952).

SiC₆H₁₆O
① Trimethyl-2-methoxyethylsilane
   CH₃OCH₂CH₂Si(CH₃)₃
②   5hrs.
   MeOCH₂Cl + Me₃SiCH₂MgCl ⟶
③ (48~49°/70). *n*D 1.4030 (20°). *d* 0.7867
   (20°).
   IR : Compt. rend. **249**, 826 (1959); CA
   54, 2939 (1952).
⑥ Zhur. **26**, 1239; CA **50**, 14514 (1956).

SiC₆H₁₆O
① Trimethyl-3-hydroxypropylsilane
   (CH₃)₃SiCH₂CH₂CH₂OH
② Me₃SiCH₂MgCl + (CH₂)₂O ⟶ 71%
③ (83°/27). *n*D 1.4290 (20°). *d* 0.8316 (20°).
④   0°   heat, 4hrs.
   + PBr₃ ⟶ ⟶
   BrCH₂CH₂CH₂SiMe₃ (84%)
                      HCl, 80°
   + BuOCH=CH₂ ⟶
   BuOCHMeO(CH₂)₃SiMe₃ (68.2%)
⑥ Izv. OKhN **1954**, 745.   US 2557802;
   2589446; 2610198.   Brit. 684295;
   685533; 684293.

SiC₆H₁₆O₂
① Diethoxydimethylsilane
   (CH₃)₂Si(OC₂H₅)₂
② Na + MeSi(OEt)₃ ⟶
   Me₂SiCl₂+EtOH ⟶
   Si(OEt)₄ + (Me₂SiO)₄ ⟶
③ (112.0~113.5°). *n*D 1.3840 (25°). *d* 0.827
   (25°).

④ + MePOOH
   ⟶ [-OPMe(O)OSiMe₂₋ₓ]
   + Cl₂ ⟶ MeSi(OEt)₂CH₂Cl
⑥ Zhur. **32**, 608 (1962). JACS **84**, 4730
   (1962). Vysokomol. Soed. **5**, 343
   (1963). Kogyo Kagaku Zasshi **62**,
   1262 (1959).

SiC₆H₁₆O₂
① Diethyldimethoxysilane
   (C₂H₅)₂Si(OCH₃)₂
② Et₂SiCl₂ + 2 MeONa ⟶ 70%
   Si(OMe)₄ + 2 EtMgBr ⟶
③ (130°).
④ + H₂O $\xrightarrow{\text{MeOH}}$ Et₂Si(OH)₂
   + cellulose nitrate $\xrightarrow{\text{in acetone}}$
   silicon-nitrocellulose
⑥ JCS **1947**, 1592. Roczniki Chem. **34**,
   1667 (1960). Technol. Repts. Osaka
   Univ. **7**, 447 (1957).

SiC₆H₁₆O₂
① Ethyldiethoxysilane
   C₂H₅SiH(OC₂H₅)₂
② Cl₃SiH $\xrightarrow{\text{EtOH}}$ SiHCl(OEt)₂
   $\xrightarrow{\text{EtMgBr}}$ EtSiH(OEt)₂
   EtSiHCl₂ + EtOH
   $\xrightarrow[\text{}]{\text{with PhNMe₂ in C₆H₆}}$ 51%
③ (119~121°). n_D 1.3869 (20°). d 0.8465
   (20°).
⑥ J. Inst. Polytech. Osaka City Univ.
   Ser. C. **2**, No.1, 11 (1951); CA **46**,
   6082 (1952).

SiC₆H₁₆O₂
① Di-*n*-propylsilanediol
   (*n*-C₃H₇)₂Si(OH)₂
② (*n*-C₃H₇)₂SiCl₂ $\xrightarrow{\text{NaOH aq.}}$ 74%
③ [99~100°].
④ This exhibits typical silanol
   reactions.

⑥ JACS **75**, 1585 (1953).

SiC₆H₁₆S
① Trimethylethylthiomethylsilane
   (CH₃)₃SiCH₂SC₂H₅
② Me₃SiCH₂Br + NaSEt $\xrightarrow{\text{EtOH}}$ 37.1%
③ (44°/9). n_D 1.4512 (25°). d 0.8402 (25°).
⑥ JOC **17**, 1393 (1952).

SiC₆H₁₆S
① 3-Trimethylsilylpropylmercaptan
   (CH₃)₃SiCH₂CH₂CH₂SH
② H₂S + Me₃SiCH₂CH=CH₂ ⟶ 74.4%
   Me₃SiCH₂CH₂CH₂SCN +
   RMgX ⟶ 63%
③ (164°). n_D 1.4538 (25°). d 0.8496 (20°).
④ + CH₂=CHCN
   ⟶ Me₃SiCH₂CH₂CH₂SCH₂CH₂CN
⑥ JOC **28**, 3264 (1963). Izv. OKhN **1959**,
   85, 707; English page 76, 719.

SiC₆H₁₆S
① Triethylmercaptosilane
   (C₂H₅)₃SiSH
② Et₃SiNH₂ + H₂S(g) ⟶
③ (160~167°).
⑥ Acta Chem. Scand. **5**, 964 (1951);
   CA **46**, 7518 (1952). Sweden 138357;
   CA **48**, 2761 (1954).

SiC₆H₁₇N
① Trimethyl-3-aminopropylsilane
   (CH₃)₃SiCH₂CH₂CH₂NH₂
② Me₃Si(CH₂)₂CO₂H $\xrightarrow{\text{SOCl₂}}$
   Me₃Si(CH₂)₂COCl $\xrightarrow{\text{liq. NH₃}}$
   Me₃Si(CH₂)₂CONH₂ $\xrightarrow{\text{P₂O₅}}$
   Me₃Si(CH₂)₂CN $\xrightarrow{\text{LiAlH₄}}$
   Me₃Si(CH₂)₂CN $\xrightarrow{\text{H₂, Pt-C, or Raney Ni}}$
③ (145°/726). n_D 1.430 (20). d 0.7886 (20°).
⑥ JACS **73**, 5130 (1951). US 2557802; CA
   46, 1026 (1952). Izv. OKhN **1960**,

1878; CA **55**, 15334 (1961).   Kogyo
Kagaku Zasshi **63**, 168 (1960).

SiC₆H₁₇N

① aminotriethylsilane
   $(C_2H_5)_3SiNH_2$
② Et₃SiCl + liq. NH₃ —→ 70%
③ (137.5°/748). n_D 1.4279 (20°). d 0.7990
   (20°).
   IR : JOC **25**, 2191 (1960).
④ + Et₃SiCl $\xrightarrow{160\sim170°}$ (Et₃Si)₂NH
                        (79~81%)
   + H₂O —→ Et₃SiOH (81%)
   + EtOH —→ Et₃SiOEt (80%)
   + (NH₄)₂SO₄ —→
        (Et₃Si)₂O (30%) + (Et₃Si)₂NH (70%)
   + PVA —→ polymer
   + HX —→ Et₃SiX
⑥ JACS **68**, 241 (1946).   Izv. OKhN
   1958, 47 ; CA **52**, 11734 (1958).   JOC
   25, 2191 (1960).   JCS **1963**, 1073.

SiC₆H₁₇NO

① Triethylsilylamine oxide
   $(C_2H_5)_3SiNH_2O$
② NH₂OH + Et₃SiCl —→ 76%
③ (53°/7). [−65~−64°].
④ + PhNCO —→
   PhNHCOON(SiEt₃)CONHPh
⑥ Monatsh. **94**, 141 (1963).

SiC₆H₁₈GeO

① Trimethyl(trimethylsiloxy)germane
   $(CH_3)_3SiOGe(CH_3)_3$
② THF + Me₃SiOLi + Me₃GeOGeMe₃
        —→
   (Me₃GeO)₂SO₂ + Me₃SiOLi —→
   Me₃SiONa + Me₃GeCl —→
③ (117°). [−68°]. n_D 1.4038 (18°). d 0.99
   (20°).
④ + PhLi —→ Me₃GePh (93.3~95.0%)
⑥ Ber. **94**, 237, 1138 (1961).   JACS **83**,
   2963 (1961).   Inorg. Chem. **2**, 418
   (1963).

SiC₆H₁₈OSn

① Trimethyl(trimethylsiloxy)stannane
   $(CH_3)_3SiOSn(CH_3)_3$
② THF + Me₃SiOLi + Me₃SnBr —→
③ (144°). [−59°].
④ + PhLi —→ Me₃SnPh
   + Me₃SiOSiMe₃ (64.2%~70.0%)
⑥ JACS **83**, 7963 (1961).   Inorg. Chem.
   2, 418 (1963).

SiC₇H₄Cl₆

① Tetrachlorophenylmethyldichloro-
   silane
   $(C_6HCl_4)Si(Cl)_2CH_3$
② Cl₂ + PhSiCl₂Me —→ 11.7%
③ (164~170°/8). n_D 1.5810 (20°). d 1.6026
   (20°).
⑥ Zhur. **32**, 3727 (1962).

SiC₇H₅Cl₅

① Trichlorophenylmethyldichloro-
   silane
   $(C_6H_2Cl_3)Si(Cl)_2CH_3$
② Cl₂ + PhSiCl₂Me —→ 15.9%
③ (154~158°/8). n_D 1.5711 (20°). d 1.5225
   (20°).
⑥ Zhur. **32**, 3727 (1962).

SiC₇H₆Cl₄

① Dichlorophenylmethyldichlorosilane
   $(C_6H_3Cl_2)Si(Cl)_2CH_3$
② Cl₂ + PhSiCl₂Me —→
③ (126~131°/10). n_D 1.5540 (20°). d 1.4218
   (20°).
⑥ Zhur. **32**, 377 (1962) ; **33**, 255 (1963).

SiC₇H₇Cl₃

① Phenylchloromethyldichlorosilane
   C₆H₅Si(Cl)₂CH₂Cl
② CH₂N₂ + PhSiCl₃ —→
   Cl₂ + PhSiCl₂Me —→
③ (68~70°/0.3). n_D 1.5365 (20°). d 1.3170
   (20°).
⑥ Ber. **96**, 1877 (1963).   Zhur. **30**, 3011

(1960).

SiC₇H₇Cl₃

① Benzyltrichlorosilane
$C_6H_5CH_2SiCl_3$

② $SiCl_4 + PhCH_2MgCl$ $\xrightarrow{\text{reflux in } C_6H_6}$

$Si-Cu\ (85/15) + PhCH_2Cl \xrightarrow{200°}$

$ClCH_2SiCl_3 + C_6H_6 + AlCl_3 \longrightarrow$

③ (213~214°). n_D 1.5252 (20°). d 1.2796 (20°).

④ $+ xCl_2 + SbCl_3$
$\xrightarrow{50~700°}$ p-ClC₆H₄CH₂SiCl₃,
2,4-Cl₂C₆H₃CH₂SiCl₃,
2,4,6-Cl₃C₆H₂CH₂SiCl₃,
2,3,4,6-Cl₄C₆HCH₂SiCl₃,
and Cl₅C₆CH₂SiCl₃

⑥ J. Gen. Chem. USSR **16**, 478 (1946);
CA **41**, 701(1947). Japan 3965(1951);
CA **47**, 8089 (1952).   Dokl. **97**, 687
(1954).   Zhur. **26**, 2622 (1956).

SiC₇H₇Cl₃

① *m*-Tolyltrichlorosilane
m-CH₃C₆H₄SiCl₃

② $SiCl_4 + m$-MeC₆H₄MgBr $\longrightarrow$ 61%

③ Yellow liq.
Sol. in org. solvents. Decomp. in H₂O.

⑥ Coll. Czech. Chem. Comm. **16**, 580
(1951); CA **47**, 8030 (1953).

SiC₇H₇Cl₃

① Methyl-*p*-chlorophenyldichlorosilane
CH₃(*p*-ClC₆H₄)SiCl₂

② MeSiCl₃ + *p*-ClC₆H₄MgBr $\longrightarrow$ 34%

③ Yellow liq. (161~164°/99~100).
Sol. in org. solvents.

⑥ JACS **74**, 6275 (1952).

SiC₇H₇Cl₃

① *p*-Tolyltrichlorosilane

p-CH₃C₆H₄SiCl₃

② $SiCl_4 + Hg(C_6H_4Me$-$p)_2$ $\xrightarrow{300~320°}$

$HSiCl_3 + p$-ClC₆H₄Me + Pd $\longrightarrow$

$Si_2Cl_6 + MePh + S_2Cl_2 \longrightarrow$

③ Liq. (210~215°).
Sol. in org. solvents. Decomp. in H₂O.

⑥ Ann. **173**, 143 (1874). Ber. **7**, 387
(1874).   JCS **123**, 2830 (1923).

SiC₇H₈Br₂

① Methylphenyldibromosilane
$C_6H_5Si(Br)_2CH_3$

② MeSiBr₃ + PhMgBr $\longrightarrow$

③ (140~144°/60). n_D 1.5537 (30°). d 1.599 (30°).

⑥ JOC **24**, 2029 (1959).   Fr. 1303018
(1962); CA **58**, 9137 (1963).

SiC₇H₈Cl₂

① Benzyldichlorosilane
$C_6H_5CH_2SiHCl_2$

② HSiCl₃ + C₆H₅CH₂MgBr $\longrightarrow$

③ Liq. (48°/2).
Sol. in org. solvents. Decomp. in H₂O.

⑥ Post. (1949).   JCS **1947**, 1592.

SiC₇H₈Cl₂

① Methylphenyldichlorosilane
$C_6H_5Si(Cl)_2CH_3$

② CH₃SiCl₃ + PhMgBr $\longrightarrow$

③ (71.0~71.2°/7). n_D 1.5200 (20°). d 1.1897 (20°).

④ + Me₂SiCl₂ $\longrightarrow$ elastomers

⑥ Plasticheskie Massy (No.5) 19
(1962); CA **58**, 4591 (1963).   Zhur.
33, 255 (1963); **32**, 909 (1962); English page 899.   Vysokomol. Soed.
4, 1507 (1962).

SiC₇H₈Cl₈

① 1,2,3,4,5,6-Hexachlorocyclohexyl-

methyldichlorosilane
C$_6$H$_5$Cl$_6$Si(Cl)$_2$CH$_3$

② Cl$_2$ + PhSiCl$_2$Me ⟶

③ (175～179°/5). n_D1.5717 (20°). d1.7028
   (20°).

④ + EtOH ⟶ (C$_6$H$_5$Cl$_6$)Si(OEt)$_2$Me

⑥ Zhur. **33**, 255 (1963); **32**, 909 (1962);
   English page 899. Dokl. **148**, 116
   (1963).

SiC$_7$H$_8$F$_2$

① Methylphenyldifluorosilane
   C$_6$H$_5$Si(F)$_2$CH$_3$

② BF$_3$ + PhSi(OEt)$_2$Me ⟶
   HF + PhSiCl$_2$Me ⟶
   Na$_2$SiF$_6$ + PhSiCl$_2$Me ⟶
   MeSiHF$_2$ + PhCl $\xrightarrow{640°}$

③ (135～145°). n_D 1.5250 (20°). d 1.2361
   (20°).

⑥ JOC **27**, 632 (1962). Fr. 1303018(1962);
   CA **58**, 9137 (1963). US 2730540
   (1956); CA **50**, 12108 (1956). Zhur.
   33, 1696 (1963).

SiC$_7$H$_{10}$

① Phenylmethylsilane
   C$_6$H$_5$Si(H$_2$)CH$_3$

② NaH + Et$_3$Al + PhSiCl$_2$Me ⟶ 71%
   LiAlH$_4$ + PhSiCl$_2$Me ⟶

③ (139.5～140.0°). n_D1.5058 (20°). d0.8895
   (20°).

⑥ Izv. OKhN **1960**, 2244; English page
   2079. Izv. OKhN **1962**, 2251.

SiC$_7$H$_{11}$Cl$_3$O$_2$

① 3-Trichlorosilylpropyl methacrylate
   CH$_2$=C(CH$_3$)COOCH$_2$CH$_2$CH$_2$SiCl$_3$

② SiHCl$_3$ +
   CH$_2$=CMeCOOCH$_2$CH=CH$_2$ ⟶

③ (100°/1).

⑥ Belg. 613466 (1962); CA **58**, 6861
   (1963).

SiC$_7$H$_{12}$O$_6$

① Methyltriacetoxysilane
   CH$_3$Si(OCOCH$_3$)$_3$

② CH$_3$SiCl$_3$ + NaOCOCH$_3$ ⟶

③ (100°/8). [41.4°]. n_D1.407 (25°). d
   1.1677 (25°).

⑥ Dokl. **94**, 697 (1954).   US 2573302;
   CA **46**, 7582 (1952).   JACS **69**, 2110
   (1947).

SiC$_7$H$_{13}$NS

① 1-Methyl-1-thiocyanatomethyl-1-
   silacyclopentane

   $$\begin{array}{l} CH_2CH_2 \\ \quad\bigg\rangle Si(CH_3)CH_2SCN \\ CH_2CH_2 \end{array}$$

② KSCN + (CH$_2$)$_4$Si(Me)CH$_2$Cl
   ⟶ 78%

③ (108～110°/7). n_D1.5116 (20°). d1.0295
   (20°).

⑥ Izv. OKhN **1963**, 274.

SiC$_7$H$_{14}$

① 1-Methyl-1-allyl-1-silacyclobutane

   $$CH_2\bigg\langle \begin{array}{c} CH_2 \\ \\ CH_2 \end{array} \bigg\rangle Si(CH_3)CH_2CH_2=CH_2$$

② CH$_2$=CHCH$_2$Cl + Mg
       + MeSi(Cl)$_2$CH$_2$CH$_2$CH$_2$Cl ⟶

③ (53°/50). n_D1.4571 (20°). d0.8150
   (20°).

⑥ Dokl. **150**, 799 (1963).

SiC$_7$H$_{14}$Cl$_2$

① 7,7-Dichloro-7-silaoctene-1
   CH$_3$Si(Cl)$_2$CH$_2$CH$_2$CH$_2$CH$_2$CH=CH$_2$

② MeSiHCl$_2$ + CH$_2$=CHCH$_2$CH$_2$CH=CH$_2$
   $\xrightarrow{H_2PtCl_6}$ 55%

③ (112～113°/75). n_D1.4523 (20°). d1.0067
   (20°).

④ + MeMgCl ⟶

CH₂=CHCH₂CH₂CH₂CH₂SiMe₃
+ MeCH₂CH=CHCH₂CH₂SiMe₃

⑥ Izv. OKhN 1960, 1419. "Studies in Organosilicon Compounds" Vol. 1, Chap. 11 (1963).

SiC₇H₁₄Cl₄

① 1,6,6-Trichloro-4-chloromethyl-6-silaheptane
CH₃Si(Cl)₂CH₂CH(CH₂Cl)CH₂-CH₂CH₂Cl

② CH₂=CHCH₂Cl + CH₃SiHCl₂
⟶ 9.2%
(with peroxides)

③ (69~70°/1). n_D 1.4790 (20°). d 1.1950 (20°).

⑥ Dokl. 150, 1055 (1963).

SiC₇H₁₄S

① 1,4,4-Trimethyl-1-mercapto-4-silapentyne-2
(CH₃)₃SiC≡CCH(CH₃)SH

② EtMgBr + Me₃SiC≡CCHMeSCN
⟶ 65%

③ (54~55°/8). n_D 1.4664 (20°). d 0.8650 (20°).

④ + HgCl₂ ⟶
Me₃SiC≡CCHMeSHgCl

⑥ Izv. OKhN 1963, 90.

SiC₇H₁₅ClO

① 3-Trimethylsilylbutyrylchloride
(CH₃)₃SiCH₂CH₂CH₂COCl

② Me₃Si(CH₂)₃CO₂H $\xrightarrow{SOCl_2}$

③ (105°/57). n_D 1.4381 (20°). d 0.9464 (20°).

⑥ US 2557802; 2610198; 2610199; CA 46, 1026 (1952); 47, 9346 (1953). Brit. 684295; 684294; 684293.

SiC₇H₁₅F₃O

① 3,3,3-Trifluoropropyldimethyl-ethoxysilane

CF₃CH₂CH₂Si(CH₃)₂OC₂H₅

② CF₃CH₂CH₂Si(Me)(Cl)OEt
+ MeMgCl ⟶ 62%

③ (126.8~127.2°/743). n_D 1.3635 (20°). d 0.9963 (20°).

⑥ Zhur. 33, 704 (1963).

SiC₇H₁₅N

① 3-Cyanopropyltrimethylsilane
(CH₃)₃SiCH₂CH₂CH₂CN

② MeMgBr + Cl₃SiCH₂CH₂CH₂CN
NaCN+Me₃SiCH₂CH₂CH₂Cl

③ (97~98°/30). n_D 1.4277 (20°). d 0.8249 (20°).

④ + H(Ni) ⟶ Me₃Si(CH₂)₄NH₂

⑥ Mem. Fac. Eng. Osaka City Univ. 3, 195 (1962); 1, 1 (1959). BCSJ 29, 784 (1956). Nippon Kagaku Zasshi 63, 168 (1960).

SiC₇H₁₅N

① 1-Trimethylsilyl-2-cyanopropane
(CH₃)₃SiCH₂CH(CH₃)CN

② MeMgBr + Cl₃SiCH₂CHMeCN ⟶

③ (68~71°/50). n_D 1.4244 (20°).

④ + HOH ⟶ Me₃SiCH₂CHMeCOOH

⑥ Mem. Fac. Eng Osaka City Univ. 3, 195 (1961); CA 58, 3455 (1963).

SiC₇H₁₅NS

① Triethylisothiocyanatosilane
(C₂H₅)₃SiNCS

② Et₃SiCl + NH₄NCS ⟶ 60~80%

③ Colorless liq (210.5°). n_D 1.4948 (20°). d 0.9385 (20°).
Sol. in org. solvents.

⑥ Zhur. 24, 1082 (1954); CA 49, 8791 (1955).

SiC₇H₁₆

① Trimethylbuten-3-ylsilane
(CH₃)₃SiC₂H₄CH=CH₂

② Me₃SiCH₂MgBr + CH₂=CHCH₂Br

   ⟶ 68%

③ Colorless liq. (112~113°). n_D 1.4102
(27°), d 0.7294 (27°).

Sol. in org. solvents.

⑥ JACS **74**, 5091 (1952).

SiC₇H₁₆

① Trimethylsilylmethylcyclopropane

             CH₂
(CH₃)₃SiCH₂CH⟨ |
             CH₂

② Cu (sintered) + Me₃SiCH₂CH=CH₂
+ CH₂I₂ ⟶ 38%

③ (113~114°/740). n_D1.4168 (20°). d0.7594
(20°).

⑥ Izv. OKhN **1963**, 1111.

SiC₇H₁₆

① 1-Methyl-1-ethyl-1-silacyclopentane

CH₂CH₂
| ⟩Si(CH₃)C₂H₅
CH₂CH₂

② (CH₂CH₂MgBr)₂ + MeSiCl₂Et ⟶

③ (133~134°). n_D 1.4451 (20°). d 0.810
(20°).

⑥ Izv. OKhN **1963**, 274.

SiC₇H₁₆

① 1,1-Dimethyl-1-silacyclohexane

      CH₂CH₂
CH₂⟨   ⟩Si(CH₃)₂
      CH₂CH₂

② (CH₂)₅SiCl₂ + MeLi ⟶
MeMgBr + (CH₂)₅SiClMe ⟶
CH₂(CH₂CH₂Br)₂ + Li
+ Me₂SiCl₂ ⟶

③ (131.0~131.2°). n_D1.4429 (20°). d0.8127
(20°).

IR: 153, 178, 210, 339, 375, 438, 588,
642, 698, 732, 798, 915, 1012, 1188,
1204, 1258, 1298, 1416, 1448, 2855,
2885, 2907, 2936, 2962, 3070 cm⁻¹.

⑥ Izv. OKhN **1963**, 274; **1962**, 1127;
English page 1057.   JOC **25**, 246
(1960); **26**, 2530 (1961).

SiC₇H₁₆ClF

① 3-Chloropropyldiethylfluorosilane
(C₂H₅)₂Si(F)CH₂CH₂CH₂Cl

② Et₂Si(Cl)CH₂CH₂CH₂Cl + CoF₂ ⟶

③ (180°/728). n_D 1.4298 (20°). d 0.9927
(20°).

⑥ Zhur. **32**, 3882 (1962).

SiC₇H₁₆O

① Diethylallyloxysilane
(C₂H₅)₂Si(H)OCH₂CH=CH₂

② Et₂SiHCl + CH₂=CHCH₂OH
    pyridine, 24 hrs.
  ⟶ 53%

③ Colorloss liq. n_D 1.4175 (20°). d0.8174
(20°).

Sol. in org. solvents.

⑥ Izv. OKhN **1957**, 383; CA **51**, 15457
(1957).

SiC₇H₁₆O

① 2,4,4-Trimethyl-4-silapentene-1-
epoxide
(CH₃)₃SiCH₂(CH₃)C——CH₂
                 O

② NaOH + Me₃SiCH₂CMe(OH)CH₂Cl
  ⟶ 52%

③ (154°). n_D 1.4243 (20°). d 0.8338 (20°).

⑥ Azerb. Khim. Zhur. No. 5, 105
(1962).   Dokl. **118**, 723 (1958).

SiC₇H₁₆O₂

① 2-Trimethylsilylethyl acetate
CH₃COOCH₂CH₂Si(CH₃)₃

② CH₂=CO + Me₃SiCH₂CH₂OH
  ⟶ 51%

③ (63°/8.5). n_D1.4141 (23°).
IR: 8.0, 5.76 μ.

⑥ Rec. trav. chim. **81**, 429 (1962).

SiC₇H₁₆O₂

① Ethyl trimethylsilylacetate
$(CH_3)_3SiCH_2CO_2C_2H_5$

② $Me_3SiCH_2Cl \xrightarrow{Mg, \ ClCO_2Et}$ 74.5%

$MeCOOEt \xrightarrow{NaCPh_3 \ Me_3SiCl}$

③ (157°). $n_D 1.4149$ (20°). $d 0.8762$ (20°).

④ $+ Me_3SiCH_2CO_2Et \xrightarrow{\text{dil. alk. or dil. acid}}$

$(Me_3Si)_2O + MeCO_2Et$

$+ HCl \longrightarrow Me_3SiCl + MeCO_2Et$

$+ Br_2 \longrightarrow Me_3SiBr + BrCH_2CO_2Et$

$+ EtOH \longrightarrow Me_3SiOEt + MeCO_2Et$

⑥ JACS **70**, 2874 (1948) ; **75**, 994 (1953).

SiC₇H₁₆O₂

① 1,1-Dimethoxy-1-silacyclopentane

$$\begin{array}{c} CH_2 - CH_2 \\ | \quad\quad | \\ CH_2 \quad Si(OCH_3)_2 \\ CH_2 \end{array}$$

② $(CH_2)_4SiCl_2 + MeONa \longrightarrow$

③ Colorless liq. (171~173°). $n_D 1.4309$
(25°). $d 0.958$ (25°).
Sol. in org. solvents.
Camphor-like odor.

⑥ JACS **76**, 6012 (1954).

SiC₇H₁₆O₂

① Diethoxyallylsilane
$(C_2H_5O)_2Si(H)CH_2CH=CH_2$

② $Si-Cu + CH_2=CHCH_2Cl$

$\longrightarrow CH_2=CHCH_2SiHCl_2$

$\xrightarrow{\text{EtOH, pyridine}}$ 70%

③ Colorless liq. (54°/22). $n_D 1.4063$ (20°).
$d 0.8607$ (20°).
Sol. in org. solvents.

⑥ Izv. OKhN **1957**, 383 ; CA **51**, 15457
(1957).

SiC₇H₁₆O₂

① Vinylmethyldiethoxysilane
$CH_2=CHSi(OC_2H_5)_2CH_3$

② $EtOH + CH_2=CHSi(Cl)_2Me$

$\longrightarrow$ 62.5%

$MeMgCl + CH_2=CHSi(OEt)_3 \longrightarrow$

③ (132~134°). $n_D 1.3982$ (20°). $d 0.8649$
(20°).

④ $+ HOH + EtOH \longrightarrow$

$CH_2=CHSi(OH)_2Me$

$+ HOH + HCl \longrightarrow$

$(CH_2=CHSiMeO)_x$

$+ MeMgI \longrightarrow CH_2=CHSi(Me)_2OEt$

⑥ Nippon Kagaku Zasshi **78**, 1324
(1957) ; CA **54**, 5434 (1960). Zhur.
32, 1126 (1962) ; English page 1102,
Zhur. **30**, 3615 (1960) ; English page
3583.

SiC₇H₁₆O₂

① Trimethyl-3-carboxypropylsilane
$(CH_3)_3Si(CH_2)_3CO_2H$

② $Me_3Si(CH_2)_3Br \xrightarrow{Mg, \ CO_2}$

$MeHSiCl_2 + CH_2=CHCH_2CN$

$\xrightarrow{Pt-C} MeSiCl_2(CH_2)_3CN$

$\xrightarrow{MeMgBr, \ NaOBr}$

③ (91°/5). [4°]. $n_D 1.4325$ (20°). $d 0.9098$
(20°).

⑥ US 2557802 ; 2589445 ; 2589446 ; 2610198 ;
CA **46**, 1026 (1952) ; **47**, 145, 9346
(1953). JACS **79**, 2764 (1957).

SiC₇H₁₇Br

① Trimethyl-4-bromobutylsilane
$(CH_3)_3Si(CH_2)_4Br$

② $Me_3Si(CH_2)_4OH + PBr_3 \dashrightarrow$ 94%

$Me_3SiCH_2CH_2CH=CH_2 \xrightarrow{HBr, \ Bz_2O_2}$

③ liq. (85°/26). $n_D 1.4551$ (20°). $d 1.0932$
(20°).
Sol. in org. solvents ; insol. in H_2O.

④ $\xrightarrow{\text{H}_2\text{SO}_4\ \text{H}_2\text{O}}$ [Me₂(C₄H₈Br)Si]₂O + 2CH₄
+ HSCH₂CO₂H + NaOH $\longrightarrow$
Me₃Si(CH₂)₄SCH₂CO₂H + NaBr
+ H₂O

⑥ Svensk. Kem. Tidskr. **65**, 216 (1953);
CA **49**, 1541 (1955).   JACS **77**, 2485
(1955).

SiC₇H₁₇Cl

① Triethylchloromethylsilane
(C₂H₅)₃SiCH₂Cl

② EtMgBr + Cl₃SiCH₂Cl $\longrightarrow$

③ (59~61°). n_D 1.4480 (20°). d 0.9097
(20°).

④ + P(OEt)₃ $\longrightarrow$ Et₃SiCH₂P(O)(OEt)₃
46.7%
+ KSH $\longrightarrow$ Et₃SiCH₂SH
+ (Et₃SiCH₂)₂S
+ Na₂S $\longrightarrow$ (Et₃SiCH₂)₂S

⑥ Dokl. **148**, 875 (1963); **94**, 485(1954).
JOC **25**, 249 (1960).

SiC₇H₁₇Cl

① t-Butyldimethylchloromethylsilane
t-C₄H₉Si(CH₃)₂CH₂Cl

② MeMgBr + t-BuSi(F)(Me)CH₂Cl
$\longrightarrow$ 75%

③ [50.0~51.5°].

⑥ "Studies in Organosilicon Compounds" Vol. 1, Chap. 11 (1963).

SiC₇H₁₈

① Triethylmethylsilane
CH₃Si(C₂H₅)₃

② EtMgBr + MeSiCl₃ $\longrightarrow$
Et₃SiH + MeLi $\longrightarrow$ 54%

③ (127°). n_D1.4160 (20°). d0.7434 (20°).
Raman: Izv. OKhN **1960**, 1553.

⑥ Izv. OkhN **1955**, 1031.   JACS **68**, 1128
(1946).

SiC₇H₁₈

① Methyldi-n-propylsilane
CH₃(n-C₃H₇)₂SiH

② MeSiHCl₂ + n-C₃H₇MgBr $\longrightarrow$

③ (127°). n_D1.4140 (20°). d0.7327
(20°).

④ Me(n-Pr)₂SiH + OH⁻ + R'OH
$\longrightarrow$ n-Pr₂MeSiOH + OR'⁻ + H₂

⑥ JACS **69**, 2600 (1947).   Acta Chem.
Scand. **9**, 947 (1955).

SiC₇H₁₈

① n-Butyltrimethylsilane
n-C₄H₉Si(CH₃)₃

② n-BuSiCl₃ + 3MeMgBr $\longrightarrow$ 64%

③ Colorless liq. (115.0~115.5°). d0.7353
(0°).
Sol. in org. solvents; insol. in
water.

⑥ Post. 36, 60 (1949).   Inaugural Diss.
Upsala, Sweden (1916); CA **14**, 1974
(1920).   JACS **68**, 475 (1946).   Z.
phys. Chem. **90**, 246 (1915).

SiC₇H₁₈BrN

① Diethylaminodimethylbromomethyl-
silane
(C₂H₅)₂NSi(CH₃)₂CH₂Br

② Et₂NH + Me₂Si(Cl)CH₂Br $\longrightarrow$

③ (76°/10). n_D1.4632 (20°).

④ + n-PrNH₂ $\longrightarrow$

$n\text{-PrN}\Big\langle \begin{array}{c} \text{SiMe}_2\text{CH}_2 \\ \\ \text{SiMe}_2\text{CH}_2 \end{array} \Big\rangle \text{NPr-}n$

⑥ Ber. **96**, 965 (1963).

SiC₇H₁₈N₂

① 1,2,2,4-Tetramethyl-2-sila-1,4-di-
azacyclohexane

$\text{CH}_3\text{N}\Big\langle \begin{array}{c} \text{CH}_2\text{---CH}_2 \\ \\ \text{Si(CH}_3)_2\text{CH}_2 \end{array} \Big\rangle \text{NCH}_3$

② Me₂Si(Cl)CH₂Cl + Et₃N

+ $MeNHCH_2CH_2NHMe \longrightarrow$ 99.5%
③ (64°/53). $n_D1.4508$ (20°).
⑥ Ber. **96**, 349 (1963).

$SiC_7H_{18}O$
① 5,5-Dimethyl-5-silahexanol-1
   $(CH_3)_3SiCH_2CH_2CH_2CH_2OH$
② $Mg + THF + Me_3SiCl$
   $+ CHBr_3 \longrightarrow$
③ (182°). $n_D1.4332$ (25°).
⑥ JACS **85**, 2243 (1963).

$SiC_7H_{18}O$
① 4,4-Dimethyl-4-silahexanol-1
   $C_2H_5Si(CH_3)_2CH_2CH_2CH_2OH$
② $EtSiMe_2CH_2MgCl + (CH_2)_2O \longrightarrow$
③ (92.5~94.0°/20). n_D 1.4389 (20°). d
   0.8478 (20°/4°).
⑥ Zhur. **33**, 1945 (1963).

$SiC_7H_{18}O$
① 2-Ethoxyethyltrimethylsilane
   $C_2H_5OCH_2CH_2Si(CH_3)_3$
② $CH_2=CHOEt + HSiCl_3$
   $\overset{reflux}{\longrightarrow} Cl_3Si(CH_2)_2OEt$
   $\overset{MeMgBr}{\longrightarrow}$ 85%
③ (131~132°). $n_D1.4054$ (20°). d 0.7810
   (20°).
⑥ Bull. soc. chim. France. **1955**, 790;
   CA **50**, 5536 (1956).

$SiC_7H_{18}O$
① Triethylmethoxysilane
   $(C_2H_5)_3SiOCH_3$
② $Et_3SiH + MeOH \overset{Na}{\longrightarrow}$ 92.7%
   $Et_3SiNHEt \overset{MeOH}{\longrightarrow}$
③ (141.5°). $n_D1.4129$ (20°). $d0.8203$ (20°).
   Raman : Coll. Czech. Chem. Commun
   24, 3816 (1959).
   IR : Zhur. **31**, 1321 (1957).
⑥ Zhur. **24**, 1178 (1954). Ttans. Chal-

mers Univ. Technol. Gothenburg
87, 29 (1949).

$SiC_7H_{18}O_2$
① Bis(ethoxymethyl)methylsilane
   $CH_3SiH(CH_2OC_2H_5)_2$
② $MeSiHCl_2 + Mg + EtOCH_2Cl \longrightarrow$
③ (205°). $n_D1.4227$ (20°). $d0.8865$ (20°).
⑥ Belg. 620518 (1963); CA **59**, 6440
   (1963).

$SiC_7H_{18}O_2$
① Trimethylsilyl *t*-butyl peroxide
   $(CH_3)_3SiOOC(CH_3)_3$
② $(CH_3)_3COOH + (CH_3)_3SiCl$
   $\overset{pyridine}{\longrightarrow} (CH_3)_3SiOOC(CH_3)_3 + HCl$
③ (41°/41). $n_D1.3933$ (20°). $d0.798$ (20°).
④ $(CH_3)_3SiOOC(CH_3)_3 + (C_6H_5)_3COH$
   $\overset{AcOH-H_2SO_4}{\longrightarrow} (C_6H_5)_3COOC(CH_3)_3$
   $(CH_3)_3SiOOC(CH_3)_3 + RNH_2$
   $\longrightarrow (CH_3)_3COOH + (CH_3)_3SiNHR$
⑤ Catalyst of the styrene-polym.
⑥ Chem. & Ind. **1956**, 1052; **1957**, 1294.
   Makromol. Chem. **21**, 113 (1956).

$SiC_7H_{18}O_3$
① Methyltriethoxysilane
   $CH_3Si(OC_2H_5)_3$
② $Si(OEt)_4 \overset{MeMgBr}{\longrightarrow}$ 78%
③ (143°). $n_D1.3835$ (20°). $d0.8923$ (20°).
④ $MeSi(OEt)_3 + Et_3SiOH$
   $\longrightarrow Et_3SiOSiMe(OEt)_2$
⑥ F. Sorm. Chem. Listy **48**, 1197
   (1954). JACS **76**, 1390 (1954). Kg.
   Fysiograph Salls kapi Lund. Hand
   (NF). **63**, No.12 (1952). Z. Lasocki
   Zeszyty Nauk Politech. tödz. No.6
   Chem. No. 273 (1955); CA **50**, 3992
   (1956).

$SiC_7H_{18}O_3$
① Trimethoxy-*n*-butylsilane

(CH₃O)₃SiC₄H₉-*n*

② Si(OMe)₄ + *n*-BuMgBr $\longrightarrow$ 18~20%

③ Colorless liq. (164.8°). n_D1.3979(20°).
   *d*0.9312 (20°).
   Sol. in org. solvents.

⑥ Zhur. **25**, 1124 (1955); CA **50**, 3217
   (1956).

SiC₇H₁₉N

① Trimethyldiethylaminosilane
   (CH₃)₃SiN(C₂H₅)₂

② Et₂NH + Me₃SiNHSiMe₃ $\longrightarrow$
   Et₂NH + Me₃SiCl $\longrightarrow$

③ (125~127°). n_D 1.4110 (25°). *d* 0.962
   (20°/4°).

④ + CH₂(NH₂)COOH
       $\longrightarrow$ Me₃SiNHCH₂COOSiMe₃
   + CH₃CH(NH₂)COOH
       $\longrightarrow$ Me₃SiNHCHMeCOOSiMe₃
   + *s*-BuCH(NH₂)COOH
       $\longrightarrow$ Me₃SiNHCH(Bu-*s*)COOSiMe₃
   + PhCH₂CH(NH₂)COOH
       $\longrightarrow$ Me₃SiNHCH(CH₂Ph)COOSiMe₃

⑥ US 2876209 (1959); CA **53**, 12321
   (1959).   JOC **26**, 4638 (1961).   J.
   prakt. Chem. **9**, 315 (1959); **27**, 2190
   (1962).

SiC₇H₁₉N

① Trimethyl-*n*-butylaminosilane
   (CH₃)₃SiNHC₄H₉-*n*

② *n*-BuNH₂ + Me₃SiCl $\longrightarrow$ 35.8%
   n-BuNH₂ + Me₃SiSiMe₃ $\longrightarrow$

③ (135°). n_D 1.4103 (20°). *d* 0.7616
   (20°/4°).

④ + CH₂(NH₂)COOH
       $\longrightarrow$ Me₃SiNHCH₂COOSiMe₃
   + MeCH(NH₂)COOH
       $\longrightarrow$ Me₃SiNHCHMeCOOSiMe₃
   + *s*-BuCH(NH₂)COOH
       $\longrightarrow$ Me₃SiNHCH(Bu-*s*)COOSiMe₃
   + PhCH₂CH(NH₂)COOH
       $\longrightarrow$ Me₃SiNHCH(CH₂Ph)COOSiMe₃

⑥ J. prakt. Chem. **16**, 172 (1962); **9**, 315
   (1959).   JCS **1961**, 4933. Rec. trav.
   chim. **81**, 430 (1962).

SiC₇H₁₉O₃P

① Triethylsilylmethylphosphonic acid
   (C₂H₅)₃SiCH₂P(O)(OH)₂

② HCl + HOH + Et₃SiCHP(O)(OEt)₂ $\longrightarrow$

③ [98.5~99.5°].

⑥ Dokl. **148**, 875 (1963).

SiC₇H₁₉O₃P

① Diethyl trimethylsilyl phosphite
   (C₂H₅O)₂POSi(CH₃)₃

② Me₃SiONa + (EtO)₂PCl $\longrightarrow$ 50~60%

③ (60~61°/11). n_D1.4116 (20°). *d*0.9485
   (20°/4°).

④ + S $\longrightarrow$ (EtO)₂P(S)OSiMe₃ 87%

⑥ Izv. OKhN **1963**, 769.

SiC₇H₁₉O₃PS

① Diethyl trimethylsilyl thioortho-
   phosphate
   (CH₃)₃SiOP(S)(OC₂H₅)₂

② S + (EtO)₂P(OSiMe₃) $\longrightarrow$ 87%

③ (56~57°/1.5). n_D1.4433 (20°). *d*1.0261
   (20°/4°).

⑥ Izv. OKhN **1963**, 769.

SiC₇H₂₁BN₂

① Trimethylsilylbis(dimethylamino)-
   boron
   (CH₃)₃SiB[N(CH₃)₂]₂

③ (65°/9).

⑥ Angew. **74**, 718 (1962).

SiC₈H₄Cl₈

① (*p*-Trichloromethylphenyl)trichloro-
   methyldichlorosilane
   p-CCl₃C₆H₄Si(Cl)₂CCl₃

② *p*-MeC₆H₄Si(Cl)₂Me + Cl₂ $\longrightarrow$

③ (168~170°/3). [60.5~61.5°]. n_D 1.5764
   (20°). *d*1.6360 (20°/4°).

④ + EtOH(dry)

    ⟶ p-CCl₃C₆H₄Si(OEt)₂CCl₃

    + KOH(40%) ⟶ CHCl₃ +

    + C₆H₅COOH + ?

⑥ Zhur. **33**, 1299 (1963).

SiC₈H₅Cl₃

① Phenylacetylenyltrichlorosilane

    C₆H₅C≡CSiCl₃

② HSiCl₃ + PhC≡CH

$\xrightarrow{\text{500° in a quartz tube}}$ PhC≡CSiCl₃

    + PhCH=CHSiCl₃

③ (132~135°/26). n_D1.5527 (20°). d1.2871

    (20°).

⑥ Izv. OKhN **1963**, 387.

SiC₈H₆Cl₄

① 1-Trichlorosilyl-1-phenyl-2-chloro-

    ethene

    C₆H₅C(=CHCl)SiCl₃

② AlCl₃ + PhCHClCHClSiCl₃ ⟶

③ (115°/5). n_D 1.5749 (20°). d 1.3929

    (20°/4°).

⑥ Izv. OKhN **1963**, 756.

SiC₈H₇Cl₃

① 2-Phenylvinyltrichlorosilane

    C₆H₅CH=CHSiCl₃

② SiHCl₃ + PhC≡CH + H₂PtCl₆ ⟶

    PhCH=CH₂ + SiHCl₃ ⟶ 89%

    SiHCl₃ + PhC≡CH + MeCN

    + Bu₃N ⟶

    PhCH=CHCl + SiHCl₃

$\xrightarrow{\text{620° or 640°}}$ 75%

③ (74°/1.0). n_D 1.5575 (20°). d 1.2862

    (20°/4°).

④ + Cl₂ ⟶PhCHClCHClSiCl₃ (92%)

    + MeMgCl ⟶ PhCH=CHSiMe₃

⑥ Izv. OKhN **1963**, 756 ; **1962**, 1223 ;

    1960, 1419.   JOC **27**, 2186 (1962).

SiC₈H₇Cl₃

① 1-Phenyl-1-trichlorosilylethene

    C₆H₅C(=CH₂)SiCl₃

② PhCCl=CH₂ + SiHCl₃

$\xrightarrow{620°}$ 56%, 28.5%, 65%

③ (100~104°/7). n_D1.5480 (20°). d1.2763

    (20°/4°).

④ + HF ⟶ PhCH=CHSiF₃ (74%)

⑥ Izv. OKhN **1962**, 1223 ; English page

    1147. Izv. OKhN **1963**, 756 ; **1963**,

    136 ; CA **59**, 11550 (1963).

SiC₈H₇Cl₅

① 1-Phenyl-1,2-dichloro-1-trichloro-

    silylethane

    C₆H₅C(Cl)(SiCl₃)CH₂Cl

② PhC(SiCl₃)=CH₂ + Cl₂ ⟶ 57.4%

③ (131~132°/7). n_D1.5612 (20°). d1. 4838

    (20°/4°).

⑥ Izv. OKhN **1963**, 756.

SiC₈H₇Cl₅

① 1-Phenyl-2-trichlorosilyl-1,2-di

    chloroethane

    C₆H₅CHClCHClSiCl₃

② Cl₂ + PhCH=CHSiCl₃ ⟶ 92%

③ (122~125°/5). n_D 1.5572. d 1.4730

    (20°/4°).

④ + AlCl₃ ⟶ PhC(=CHCl)SiCl₃

⑥ Izv. OKhN **1963**, 756.

SiC₈H₇F₃

① 1-Phenyl-2-trifluorosilylethene

    C₆H₅CH=CHSiF₃

② HF + PhCH=CHSiCl₃ ⟶ 74%

③ (41°/1). n_D1.4590 (20°). d1.2245 (20°).

⑥ Izv. OKhN **1963**, 136 ; CA **59**, 11550

    (1963).

SiC₈H₈Cl₄

① p-Dichloromethylphenylmethyl-

    dichlorosilane

p-CHCl$_2$C$_6$H$_4$SiCl$_2$CH$_3$

② p-MeC$_6$H$_4$SiCl$_2$Me + Cl$_2$ $\longrightarrow$

③ (131~133°/5). n_D1.5520 (20°). d1.3773
(20°/4°).

④ + KOH(40%) $\longrightarrow$ C$_6$H$_5$CO$_2$H
+ (MeSiO$_{1.5}$)$_x$

⑥ Zhur. 33, 1299 (1963).

SiC$_8$H$_9$Cl$_3$

① 1-Phenylethyltrichlorosilane
C$_6$H$_5$CH(CH$_3$)SiCl$_3$

② MeCHClSiCl$_3$ + AlCl$_3$ + C$_6$H$_6$

$\xrightarrow{\text{reflux 80~100 hrs}}$ 65%

③ Liq. (225~228°). n_D1.5210 (20°). d
1.2425 (20°).
Sol. in org. solvents. Decomp. in
H$_2$O.

⑥ Dokl. 97, 687 (1954); CA 49, 10166
(1955).

SiC$_8$H$_9$Cl$_3$

① 2-Phenylethyltrichlorosilane
C$_6$H$_5$(CH$_2$)$_2$SiCl$_3$

② ClCH$_2$CH$_2$SiCl$_3$ + Al + C$_6$H$_6$
$\xrightarrow{\text{AlCl}_3}$ 83%

ClCH$_2$CH$_2$SiCl$_3$ + C$_6$H$_6$ $\xrightarrow{\text{AlCl}_3}$ 32.5%

CH$_2$=CHSiCl$_3$ + C$_6$H$_6$ $\xrightarrow{\text{AlCl}_3}$

③ Liq. (242°). n_D1.5185 (20°). d1.2397
(20°).
Sol. in org. solvents. Decomp. in
H$_2$O.

⑥ Zhur. 27, 48 (1957). CA 51, 12045
(1957). Zhur. 25, 2469 (1955); CA
50, 9319 (1956). Ind. Eng. Chem.
45, 367 (1953).

SiC$_8$H$_{10}$Cl$_2$

① p-Chlorophenyldimethylchlorosilane
p-ClC$_6$H$_4$Si(CH$_3$)$_2$Cl

② p-ClC$_6$H$_4$MgBr + Me$_2$SiCl$_2$ $\longrightarrow$
Mg + Me$_2$SiCl$_2$ + p-C$_6$H$_4$Cl$_2$ $\longrightarrow$

③ (92~94°/5). n_D 1.5283 (20°). d 1.182
(20°/20°).

⑥ Nippon Kagaku Zasshi 81, 170 (1960).
US 3053872 (1962); CA 58, 3457
(1963).

SiC$_8$H$_{10}$Cl$_2$

① Phenylmethylchloromethylchloro-
silane
C$_6$H$_5$Si(CH$_3$)(Cl)CH$_2$Cl

③ (238~240°, 106~108°/8). n_D1.5370. d
1.1986 (20°).

④ + EtMgBr $\longrightarrow$ PhSi(Me)(Et)CH$_2$Cl
+ Ph$_2$Si(Me)CH$_2$Li $\longrightarrow$
Ph$_2$Si(Me)CH$_2$Si(Ph)(Me)CH$_2$Cl
+ KOH + (CH$_2$)$_2$O
$\longrightarrow$ MeSi(Ph)(CH$_2$Cl)OCH$_2$CH$_2$Cl

⑥ Z. anorg. allg. Chem. 322, 34 (1963).
Izv. OKhN 1958, 702. Zhur. 31,
3178 (1961); 33, 905 (1963).

SiC$_8$H$_{10}$Cl$_2$

① Ethylphenyldichlorosilane
C$_2$H$_5$(C$_6$H$_5$)SiCl$_2$

② PhSiHCl$_2$ + C$_2$H$_2$ $\xrightarrow{\text{250~410°, 100 psi}}$

EtSiHCl$_2$ + C$_6$H$_6$ $\xrightarrow{\text{H}_3\text{BO}_3, 250° \text{ in autoclave}}$

③ (227~230°). n_D 1.5321 (20°). d1.1837
(20°).

④ + NaOH (powder) + H$_2$O
$\xrightarrow{\text{in Et}_2\text{O}}$ EtPhSi(OH)$_2$
+ (EtPhSiH)$_2$O

⑥ US 2626268; CA 148, 3712 (1954).
Dokl. !17, 623 (1957); CA 52, 8996
(1958). Zhur. 26, 3344 (1956); CA
51, 9514 (1957).

SiC$_8$H$_{10}$Cl$_2$

① p-Tolylmethyldichlorosilane
p-CH$_3$C$_6$H$_4$SiCl$_2$CH$_3$

② MeSiCl$_3$ + p-MeC$_6$H$_4$MgBr $\longrightarrow$ 40%

MeHSiCl$_2$ + MeC$_6$H$_5$ + H$_3$BO$_3$ $\xrightarrow{290°}$

③ (57.0∼57.5°/2). n_D1.5170 (20°). d1.1619 (20°/4°).

④ + Cl₂ ⟶ *p*-ClCH₂C₆H₄SiCl₂CH₂Cl

⑥ Zhur. **32**, 24 (1962); **33**, 1299 (1963); CA **59**, 11548 (1955). US 2611775 (1952); CA **47**, 8092 (1953).

SiC₈H₁₀F₂

① Ethylphenyldifluorosilane
C₂H₅(C₆H₅)SiF₂

② Et₂SiCl₂ $\xrightarrow{\text{PhSiCl}_3,\ 350°,\ \text{NaOH}}$

EtPhSiCl₂ $\xrightarrow{\text{EtOH, HF}}$

③ Colorless liq. (163∼164°).
Sol. in. org. solvents.

⑥ US 2647136 (1953); CA **48**, 8252 (1954).

SiC₈H₁₁Br

① Dimethylphenylbromosilane
C₆H₅(CH₃)₂SiBr

② MeSiCl₂ + PhMgBr
⟶ PhMe₂SiCl (48.1%)
+ PhMe₂SiBr (17.2%)

③ yellow liq. (213∼216°).
Sol in org. solvents.

④ $\xrightarrow{\text{NH}_3}$ (PhMe₂Si)₂NH

⑥ Chem. Listy **49**, 894 (1955); CA **50**, 3276 (1956). Izv. OKhN **1956**, 811; CA **51**, 3486 (1957).

SiC₈H₁₁Cl

① Phenyldimethylchlorosilane
C₆H₅Si(CH₃)₂Cl

② PhMgBr + Me₂SiCl₂ ⟶63.3%

③ (196°/760, 97∼100°/33). n_D1.5184 (20°). d1.0646 (20°).

④ + AcOK ⟶ AcOSiMe₂Ph
+ NH₃ ⟶ PhSiMe₂NHSiMe₂Ph

⑥ Dokl. **122**, 393 (1958); CA **53**, 2133 (1959). Z. anorg. allg. Chem. **310**,100(1961). Plasticheskie Massy (No.5) 19 (1962). Zhur. **29**, 1534

(1959).

SiC₈H₁₁NaO

① Sodium dimethylphenylsilanolate
C₆H₅(CH₃)₂SiONa

② (PhMe₂Si)₂O + NaOH $\xrightarrow{\text{in EtOH or MeOH}}$
(PhMe₂Si)₂O + Na₂O + MeOH ⟶

③ Needles. [87∼94°].

⑥ JACS **75**, 5615 (1953). Brit. 631506 (1949); CA **44**, 4490 (1950). US 2472799(1949); CA **43**, 7500 (1949).

SiC₈H₁₂

① Dimethylphenylsilane
(CH₃)₂(C₆H₅)SiH

② Me₂SiCl₂ + PhMgBr
⟶ Me₂PhSiCl + LiAlH₄ ⟶
PhSiCl₃ + MeMgCl ⟶ SiPhMe₂Cl
+ LiAlH₄ $\xrightarrow{\text{in Et}_2\text{O}}$
PhSiH₃ + CH₂N₂
⟶ PhSiMeH₂ + PhSiMe₂H

③ (158°). n_D1.4992 (20°).
NMR: Sepectrochim. Acta **15**, 412 (1959).

④ PhMe₂SiH $\xrightarrow{t\text{-Bu}_2\text{O}_2\ 130°}$ Ph₂SiMe₂
+ Me₂SiH₂

⑥ JACS **76**, 6392 (1954). Angew. **74**, 468 (1962). JCS **1956**, 1436; **1960**, 5132.

SiC₈H₁₂

① Ethylphenylsilane
C₆H₅(H)₂SiC₂H₅

② PhSiH₂Br + EtMgBr ⟶

③ Colorless liq. (60∼61°/18). n_D 1.504 (25°).
Sol. in org. solvents; insol in H₂O.

⑥ JACS **76**, 4555 (1954).

SiC₈H₁₂

① Tetravinylsilane
(CH₂=CH)₄Si

② 4CH₂=CHMgCl + SiCl₄ ⟶ 87.5%

③ (130.2°). n_D1.4625 (20°). d0.7999 (20°).
NMR: Spectrochim. Acta **15**, 412
(1959).

④ + vinylmonomers

$\xrightarrow[5500\,atm]{t\text{-Bu}_2\text{O}_2,\ 130°}$ solid copolymers

⑥ Spectrochim. Acta **19**, 321 (1963).
Brit. 641268; CA **45**, 391 (1951).
JOC **22**, 1200 (1957).

SiC₈H₁₂O

① Phenyldimethylsilanol
C₆H₅Si(CH₃)₂OH

② (Me₂SiPh)₂O + NaOH ⟶
(Me₂PhSi)₂NH + H₂O $\xrightarrow{HCl}$

③ Colorless liq.(104°/15). n_D1.5110(20°).
d0.990 (25°).

④ + Na ⟶ PhSiMe₂ONa

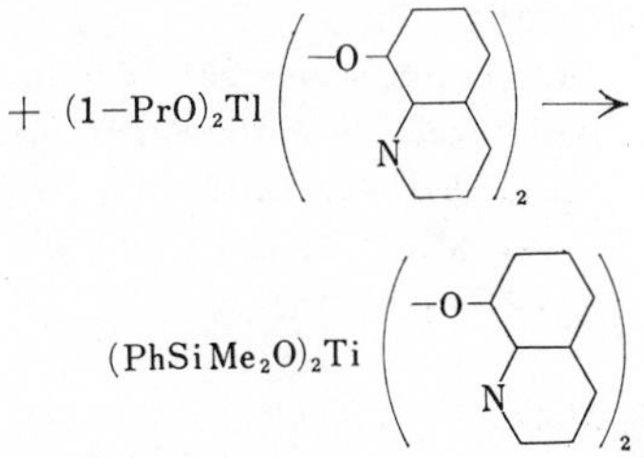

+ (1-PrO)₂Tl $\left(\begin{array}{c}-O-\\ \end{array}\right)_2$ ⟶

(PhSiMe₂O)₂Ti $\left(\begin{array}{c}-O-\\ \end{array}\right)_2$

$\xrightarrow{distn.}$ (Me₂PhSi)₂O 91.2%
+ ROCH=CH₂

$\xrightarrow{conc.\ HCl}$ ROCHMeOSiMe₂Ph
(R=Me, Et, i-Pr)

⑥ Z. anorg. allgem. Chem. **323**, 190
(1963). JOC **27**, 257 (1962). Izv.
OKhN **1956**, 811; CA **51**, 3486 (1957).

SiC₈H₁₂OS

① α-Trimethylsilyl-α'-thienaldehyde

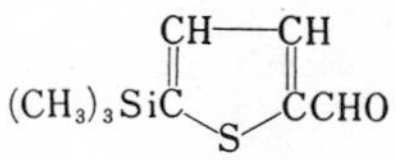

(CH₃)₃SiC⟨CH—CH, S, CCHO⟩

② LiC⟨CH—CH, S, CSiMe₃⟩ + HCONMe₂

⟶ 69%

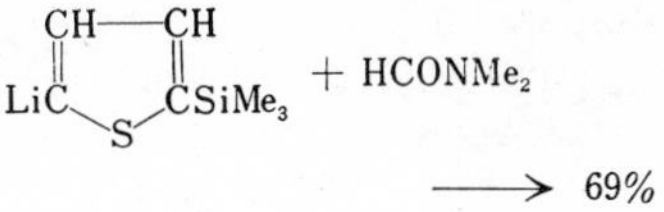

③ [33~34°].

④ + NH₂OH ⟶

Me₃SiC⟨CH—CH, S, CCH=NOH⟩

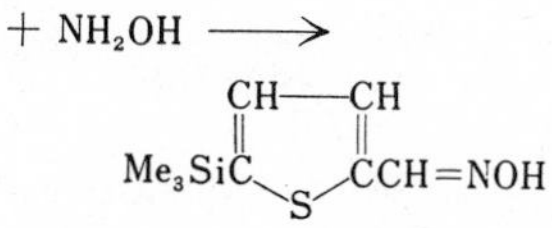

[131~132°]

⑥ Zhur. **33**, 1251 (1963).

SiC₈H₁₂O₂

① Phenylethylsilanediol
C₆H₅Si(OH)₂C₂H₅

② PhSiCl₂Et + HOH ⟶
CH₂=CHSi(OH)₂Ph + NaOH
+ Hg(Na) ⟶

③ [69~70°].

④ + HCl ⟶ (PhSiEtOH)₂O

⑥ Zhur. **26**, 3344 (1956); English page
3721. JCS **101**, 2156 (1912). Nippon
Kagaku Zasshi **83**, 188 (1962); CA
58, 11392 (1963).

SiC₈H₁₃Cl₃

① 5-Trichlorosilylcyclooctene
C₈H₁₃SiCl₃-5

② SiHCl₃ + C₈H₁₂(1,5) $\xrightarrow{in\ PhMe,\ 225°,\ 12hrs}$

③ (49~53°/0.2).

⑥ JCS **1963**, 2831.

SiC₈H₁₃N

① α-Trimethylsilylpyridine
(CH₃)₃Si(C₅H₄N-α)

② Me₃SiCl + 2-Cl·C₅H₄N + Mg
$\xrightarrow{in\ pyridine}$ 2-Me₃Si·C₅H₄N

Me₃SiCl + 2-BrC₅H₄N + Mg $\xrightarrow{in\ Et_2O}$

③ (88~90°/38). n_D1.4918 (20°).

⑤ Emulsifying and ion-exchange
agent.

⑥ Brit. 685186; CA **48**, 2783 (1954).

SiC₈H₁₃NS

① 2,2-Dimethyl-5-thiocyanato-2-sila-
hexyne-3
$(CH_3)_2SiC\equiv CCH(CH_3)SCN$

② $Me_3SiC\equiv CCHClMe + NaSCN$
$\longrightarrow$ 35%

③ (80°/2.5). n_D 1.4830 (20°). d 0.9285
(20°/4°).

④ $EtMgBr \longrightarrow Me_3SiC\equiv CCHMeSH$
65%

⑥ Izv. OKhN 1963, 90.

SiC₈H₁₄

① Cyclopentadienyltrimethylsilane
$C_5H_5Si(CH_3)_3$

② $C_5H_5MgBr + Me_3SiCl \xrightarrow{\text{in } C_6H_6}$

③ Liq. (43~44°/19).
Sol. in org. solvents ; insol. in H_2O.

⑥ JACS 75, 6050 (1953).

SiC₈H₁₄O

① Vinyldiethylhydroxysilylacetylene
$CH_2=CHC\equiv CSi(C_2H_5)_2OH$

② $(Et_2SiO)_x + CH_2=CHC\equiv CMgBr \longrightarrow$

③ (75~76°/4). n_D 1.4815 (20°). d 0.9075
(20°/4°).

④ $+ HCl + CH_2=CHOBu \longrightarrow$
$CH_2=CHC\equiv CSiEt_2OCHMeOBu$

⑥ Dokl. 139, 913 (1961) ; English page
792. Zhur. 32, 320 (1962) ; English
page 316. Izv. OKhN 1963, 97.

SiC₈H₁₆

① Diallylethylsilane
$C_2H_5(CH_2=CHCH_2)_2SiH$

② $EtHSiCl_2 + 2CH_2=CHCH_2MgI \longrightarrow$

③ (147.5°). n_D1.4510 (20°). d0.7808 (20°).

④ $(CH_2=CHCH_2)_2EtSiH$
$\xrightarrow{\text{60Co-}\gamma\text{ rays}}$ polymn.

⑥ Izv. OKhN 1954, 1123. Khim. Akad.
Nauk. SSSR Otd. Kh. Nauk.
Moscow 1960, 477 ; CA 58, 4659
(1964).

SiC₈H₁₆O

① 5,5-Dimethyl-2-hydroxy-5-sila-
heptyne-3
$C_2H_5Si(CH_3)_2C\equiv CCH(OH)CH_3$

② $EtMgBr + EtSiMe_2Cl + s\text{-BuOH}$
$\longrightarrow$ 64.5%

③ (92°/14). n_D 1.4520 (20°). d 0.8551
(20°/4°).

④ $+ C_5H_5N + SOCl_2 \longrightarrow$
$EtSiMe_2C\equiv CCHClMe$ (81.8%)

⑥ Izv. OKhN, 1963, 90.

SiC₈H₁₈

① Trimethylpenten-3-ylsilane
$(CH_3)_3SiC_2H_4CH=CHCH_3$

② $Me_3SiCl_3 \xrightarrow{Cl_2,\ h\nu} ClCH_2SiCl_3$ (39%)
$\xrightarrow{MeMgI} Me_3SiCH_2Cl$
$\xrightarrow{Mg} Me_3SiCH_2MgCl \xrightarrow{C_4H_9Br}$

③ Liq. (139.8°). n_D1.4235 (20°). d0.7466
(20°).
Sol. in org. solvents ; insol. in H_2O.

⑥ Bull. Acad. Sci. USSR Div. Chem.
Sci. 1955, 161 ; CA 50, 1574 (1956).
Izv. OKhN 1954, 504 ; CA 49, 9494
(1955).

SiC₈H₁₄O₂

① Ethyl trimethylsilylpropiolate
$(CH_3)_3SiC\equiv CCOOC_2H_5$

② $Me_3SiC\equiv CMgBr + ClCOOEt \longrightarrow$

③ (92~96°/28).

⑥ US 2887371.

SiC₈H₁₄S

① α-Methyl-α'-trimethylsilylthiophene

②

$+Me_3SiCl \longrightarrow$ 72%

③ (101~102°/50). n_D1.4949 (20°). d0.9274
　(20°/4°).
⑥ Zhur. **33**, 1251 (1963).

SiC$_8$H$_{15}$Cl$_3$

① 5-Trichlorosilylcyclooctene
　C$_8$H$_{15}$SiCl$_3$-5
② SiHCl$_3$ + C$_8$H$_{14}$(1,5)
$$\xrightarrow[\text{in PhMe,225°, 1hr. under N}_2]{} 35\%$$
③ (85~89°/1.25).
⑥ JCS **1963**, 2831.

SiC$_8$H$_{16}$

① Dimethyldiallylsilane
　(CH$_3$)$_2$Si(C$_3$H$_5$)$_2$
② Et$_2$SiCl$_2$ + 2CH$_2$=CHCH$_2$I + Mg
　$\longrightarrow$ 77.5%
③ Colorless liq. (135.5°). n_D 1.4420
　(20°). d0.7679 (20°).
　Sol. in org. solvents; insol. in H$_2$O.
⑥ Izv. OKhN **1954**, 1123; CA **49**, 7510
　(1955).

SiC$_8$H$_{16}$

① Triethylethynylsilane
　CH≡CSi(C$_2$H$_5$)$_3$
② C$_2$H$_2$ + MeMgI $\longrightarrow$ CH≡CMgI
　CH≡CMgI + Et$_3$SiCl
　+ HgCl$_2$ catalyst $\longrightarrow$ 10%
③ (59~61°/43). n_D1.4347 (20°). d 0.7918
　(20°).
⑥ Dokl. **93**, 293 (1953). Izv. OkhN **1958**,
　1011.

SiC$_8$H$_{16}$Cl$_4$

① 4-Chlorobutyl-3-chloro-2-methyl-
　propyldichlorosilane
　CH$_2$ClCH$_2$CH$_2$CH$_2$Si(Cl)$_2$CH$_2$CH-
　(CH$_3$)CH$_2$Cl
② CH$_2$ClCH$_2$CH$_2$CH$_2$MgCl
　+ Cl$_3$SiCH$_2$CHMeCH$_2$Cl $\longrightarrow$
③ (98~99°/0.4). n_D1.4856 (25°).
④ + EtOH $\longrightarrow$ CH$_2$ClCH$_2$CH$_2$CH$_2$Si-
　(OEt)$_2$CH$_2$CHMeCH$_2$Cl

⑥ US 3053873 (1962); CA **58**, 3458
　(1962).

SiC$_8$H$_{16}$Cl$_4$

① Bis(4-chlorobutyl)dichlorosilane
　Cl$_2$Si(CH$_2$CH$_2$CH$_2$CH$_2$Cl)$_2$
② SiCl$_4$ + Mg + (CH$_2$CH$_2$Cl)$_2$ $\longrightarrow$
③ (114°/0.8).
⑥ US 3053873 (1962); CA **58**, 3458
　(1963).

SiC$_8$H$_{16}$O$_2$

① Methacryloxymethyltrimethylsilane
　(CH$_3$)$_3$SiCH$_2$OC(O)C(CH$_3$)=CH$_2$
② Me$_3$SiCH$_2$Cl + NaOC(O)C(CH$_3$)
　$=$CH$_2$ $\xrightarrow[]{\text{HCONMe}_2}$ 62%
③ (98°/75). n_D1.4282 (25°). d0.883 (25°).
④ Me$_3$SiCH$_2$OC(O)C(CH$_3$)=CH$_2$
　$\xrightarrow[]{\text{BPO}}$ polymer
⑥ JOC 21, 1536 (1956). Izv. OKhN **1957**.
　459; CA **51**, 15457 (1957).

SiC$_8$H$_{16}$O$_2$

① Dimethyldiallyloxysilane
　(CH$_3$)$_2$Si(OCH$_2$CH=CH$_2$)$_2$
② Et$_2$SiCl$_2$ + 2CH$_2$=CHCH$_2$OH
　$\xrightarrow[]{\text{pyridine, 24hrs.}}$ 85%
③ Colorless liq. (156°). n_D1.4170 (20°).
　d0.8822 (20°).
　Sol. in org. solvents.
⑥ Izv. OKhN **1957**, 383; CA **51**, 15457
　(1957).

SiC$_8$H$_{16}$O$_4$

① Dimethyldipropionyloxysilane
　(CH$_3$)$_2$Si(OCOC$_2$H$_5$)$_2$
② (CH$_3$)$_2$SiCl$_2$ + AgOCOC$_2$H$_5$
　$\longrightarrow$ 80%
③ (83.5~84°/10). n_D1.4080 (20°). d1.0057
　(20°).
④ 2AgOCOCF$_3$ + Me$_2$Si(OCOC$_2$H$_5$)$_2$
　$\rightleftharpoons$ 2AgOCOC$_2$H$_5$

+ Me₂Si(OCOCF₃)₂

⑥ JOC. **19**, 1296 (1954). Bull. Acad. Sci.
   USSR, Div. Chem. Sci. **1955**, 465.

SiC₈H₁₆O₄

① Diethyldiacetoxysilane
   (C₂H₅)₂Si(OCOCH₃)₂
② Et₂SiCl₂ + 2CH₃C(O)ONa ⟶ 37%
③ Colorless liq. (70~72°/4). *d* 1.0190
   (25°/4°).
   Sol. in org. solvents. Decomp. in
   H₂O.
⑥ JACS **69**, 2110 (1947).

SiC₈H₁₇ClO₂

① Triethylsilyl chloroacetate
   CH₂ClCOOSi(C₂H₅)₃
② CH₂ClCOOH + Et₃SiH + Ni(colloidal)
   ⟶ 67.0%
   CH₂ClCOOH + MeCOOSiEt₃ ⟶
③ (211.0~212.5°). *d* 1.0183 (20°/4°).
④ + Et₃SiH + Ni(colloidal)
   ⟶ MeCOOSiEt₃
⑥ Zhur. **33**, 1934 (1963). JOC **18**, 1716
   (1953).

SiC₈H₁₇Cl₃

① *n*-Octyltrichlorosilane
   n-C₈H₁₇SiCl₃
② SiCl₄ + *n*-C₈H₁₇MgBr ⟶ 46%
③ Colorless liq. (231~232°/731). *n*ᴅ
   1.4480 (20°).
   Sol. in org. solvents. Decomp. in H₂O
   and EtOH.
⑥ Post 59, (1949). JACS **68**, 475(1946) ;
   68, 1881 (1946).

SiC₈H₁₇Cl₃

① 2-Methylheptyltrichlorosilane
   C₅H₁₁CH(CH₃)CH₂SiCl₃
② HSiCl₃ + C₅H₁₁CMe=CH₂ $\xrightarrow{\text{Ac}_2\text{O}_2,\ 49\sim58°}$
③ Colorless liq. (190~212°). *n*ᴅ 1.4500
   (20°).

Sol. in org. solvents. Decomp. in
H₂O.

⑥ JACS **70**, 445 (1948).

SiC₈H₁₇Cl₃

① 1,1,3,3-Tetramethylbutyl-
   trichlorosilane
   (CH₃)₃CCHCH(CH₃)₂SiCl₃
② HSiCl₃ + Me₃CCH=CMe₂
   $\xrightarrow{300\sim340°,\ 1500\ \text{psi}}$
③ Liq. (220~225°). *d* 1.237 (28°).
   Sol. in org. solvents. Decomp. in
   H₂O.
⑥ US 2642447 (1953) ; CA **48**, 5206 (1954).

SiC₈H₁₈

① Vinyltriethylsilane
   CH₂=CHSi(C₂H₅)₃
② CH₂=CHSiCl₃ + EtMgX ⟶ 76%
   CH₂=CHLi + Et₃SiBr ⟶
③ (146~147°). *n*ᴅ 1.4347. (20°). *d* 0.7729
   (20°/4°).
④ + HP(O)(OEt)₂ + (*t*-BuO)₂O
   ⟶ (EtO)₂P(O)CH₂CH₂SiEt₃
   (87.5%)

   + BzOOH ⟶ Et₃SiCHCH₂
   $\diagdown\diagup$
   O

⑥ Dokl. **143**, 840 (1962) ; **148**, 875 (1963).
   JOC **28**, 486 (1963).   JACS **84**, 361
   (1962).

SiC₈H₁₈

① Trimethylpenten-1-ylsilane
   CH₃CH₂CH₂CH=CHSi(CH₃)₃
② Me(CH₂)₂C≡CMgBr + Me₃SiCl
   ⟶ Me(CH₂)₂C≡CSiMe₃
   $\xrightarrow{\text{H}_2-\text{Pd}}$ Me(CH₂)₂CH=CHSiMe₃
   HSiCl₃ + PrC≡CH

   $\xrightarrow[\text{(2)MeMgBr}]{\text{(1)Bz}_2\text{O}}$ 77% (*cis*)

   $\xrightarrow{\text{Pt}-\text{C}}$ 65% (*trans*)

   $\xrightarrow{\text{H}_2\text{PtCl}_2\cdot6\text{H}_2\text{O}}$ 93% (*trans*)

③ (133~135°). n_D 1.4200 (28°). d 0.734 (28°).

⑥ US 2671795 (1954). JACS **74**, 4853 (1952); **83**, 4385 (1961).

SiC_8H_{18}

① 2-Methyl-1-trimethylsilylbutene-2
$CH_3CH=C(CH_3)CH_2Si(CH_3)_3$

③ $MeMgCl + MeCH=CMeCH_2SiCl_3$
⟶ 68.2%

③ (133~135°). n_D 1.4256 (25°). d 0.7518 (25°/25°).

④ $+ O_3$ ⟶ $Me_3SiOSiMe_3 + Me_2CO$
$+ AcOEt$

⑥ JOC **26**, 4000 (1961).

SiC_8H_{18}

① Trimethylenemethylbutylsilane

$CH_2\underset{CH_2}{\overset{CH_2}{\big<}}Si\underset{C_4H_9}{\overset{CH_3}{\big<}}$

② $BuMgCl + CH_2\underset{CH_2}{\overset{CH_2}{\big<}}Si(Cl)Me$
⟶ 55.6%
$BuMgCl + MeSi(Cl)_2CH_2CH_2CH_2MgCl$
⟶ 19.1%

③ (42.5~46.0°/18). n_D 1.4470 (20°). d 0.8025 (20°/4°).

⑥ Dokl. **150**, 799 (1963).

SiC_8H_{18}

① Tetramethylenediethylsilane
$\begin{matrix}CH_2-CH_2\\ \ \\ CH_2-CH_2\end{matrix}\Big>Si(C_2H_5)_2$

② $(CH_2)_4(MgCl)_2 + Et_2SiCl_2$
$\xrightarrow{\text{in Et}_2\text{O, 12hrs}}$ 23%
$(CH_2)_4(MgBr)_2 + SiCl_4$
⟶ $(CH_2)_4SiCl_2 + EtMgBr$
⟶ 42%

③ (160°). n_D 1.4471 (20°). d 0.8256 (20°).

④ $+ H_2SO_4$ ⟶ $(Et_2BuSi)_2O$ 80%

⑥ Dokl. **97**, 847 (1954). J. Inst.

Polytech. Osaka City Univ., Ser. C. **2**, No.1, 11 (1951); CA **46**, 6082 (1952).

$SiC_8H_{18}Cl_2$

① Di-n-butyldichlorosilane
$(n\text{-}C_4H_9)_2SiCl_2$

② $SiCl_4 + n\text{-}BuMgBr$ ⟶ 35%
$SiCl_4 + n\text{-}BuMgBr$ ⟶ 53.6%

③ (62~63.5°/4.5). n_D 1.4448 (20°). d 0.9915 (20°).

⑥ JACS **74**, 1361 (1952). Dokl. **86**, 737 (1952).

$SiC_8H_{18}F_2$

① Di-n-butyldifluorosilane
$(n\text{-}C_4H_9)_2SiF_2$

② $(n\text{-}Bu)_2SiCl_2 + HF$ ⟶

③ Colorless liq. (153.9~154.1°). d 0.9048 (26.5°/4°).
Sol. in org. solvents.

⑥ Post 53 (1949). JACS **69**, 488 (1947).

$SiC_8H_{18}O$

① Vinyltriethylsilane epoxide
$(C_2H_5)_3SiCH-CH_2$
$\diagdown O \diagup$

② $C_6H_5COOOH + Et_3SiCH=CH_2$ ⟶

③ (182~183°). n_D 1.4430 (20°). d 0.8656 (20°).

⑥ Hua Hsüeh Hsüeh Pao, **24**, 426 (1958); CA **54**, 471 (1960). Plaste und Kautschuk **8**, 301 (1961). JOC **28**, 487 (1963).

$SiC_8H_{18}O_2$

① Trimethyl-2-carboethoxyethylsilane
$(CH_3)_3SiCH_2CH_2CO_2C_2H_5$

② $Me_3SiCH_2Cl \xrightarrow{NaI} Me_3SiCH_2I$
$\xrightarrow{\text{MeCOCH}_2\text{CO}_2\text{Et or CH}_2(\text{CO}_2\text{Et})_2, \text{ excess Na}}$

$Me_3SiCH_2Cl \xrightarrow{\text{NaOEt, CH}_2(\text{CO}_2\text{Et})_2}$
$Me_3SiCH_2CH(CO_2Et)_2$ ⟶

③ (93°/40). n_D1.4198 (20°). d0.8763 (20°).

⑥ JACS 72, 1935 (1950); 76, 1606 (1954).
US 2589445; 2634282; 2635108;
2672474; CA 47, 145, 6700, 6697
(1953); 49, 3241 (1955).

SiC$_8$H$_{18}$O$_3$

① Vinyltriethoxysilane
CH$_2$=CHSi(OC$_2$H$_5$)$_3$

② CH$_2$=CHSiCl$_3$ + EtOH + C$_5$H$_5$N ⟶

③ (161°). n_D1.3967 (20°). d0.9050 (20°/4°).

④ + B(OH)$_3$ ⟶ (BO$_3$SiCH=CH$_2$)$_x$
+ P$_2$O$_5$ ⟶
[CH$_2$=CHSi(OEt)$_2$PO$_{2.5}$]$_x$

⑥ Coll. Czech. Chem. Comm. 28, 1384
(1963); 27, 2391 (1962). Zhur.
Priklad. Khim. 34, 2711 (1961);
English page 2564.

SiC$_8$H$_{19}$ClO$_2$

① Diisopropoxymethylchloromethyl-
silane
(i-C$_3$H$_7$O)$_2$Si(CH$_3$)CH$_2$Cl

③ (177~178°). n_D1.4151 (20°). d 0.955
(20°/4°).

④ + Et$_2$NH ⟶ MeSi(OPr-i)$_2$CH$_2$NEt$_2$

⑥ Dokl. 95, 269 (1954). Zhur. 33, 258
(1963).

SiC$_8$H$_{19}$ClO$_2$

① Ethyldiisopropoxychlorosilane
C$_2$H$_5$Si(OC$_3$H$_7$-i)$_2$Cl

② EtSiCl$_3$ + 2PrOH $\xrightarrow{3~5°}$ 50%

③ Colorless liq. n_D1.4018 (20°). d0.9361
(20°).
Sol. in org. solvents.

④ + (i-PrO)$_4$Si
⟶ pentaisopropoxyethyl-
disiloxane
+ hexaisoproxydisiloxane ⟶
heptaisopropoxy-1-ethyltrisiloxane

⑥ BCSJ 27, 582 (1954); CA 50, 162
(1956).

SiC$_8$H$_{20}$

① Tetraethylsilane
(C$_2$H$_5$)$_4$Si

② SiCl$_4$ + EtLi ⟶ 92%
SiCl$_4$ + EtMgBr ⟶ 30%
Et$_3$SiH + C$_2$H$_4$ $\xrightarrow{5\,atm}$ 73%

③ (153.8°). n_D1.4246 (20°). d0.7659 (20°).
Decomp. at 580°

④ Et$_4$Si + i-PrCl $\xrightarrow{AlCl_3}$
Et$_3$SiCl + C$_2$H$_6$ + C$_2$H$_4$ + C$_3$H$_8$
92.2%   1.8%   41.3% 44.4%
+ isopentane
17%
Et$_4$Si $\xrightarrow[\text{or AcO}_2\text{Bz}]{Bz_2O_2}$ [Et$_3$SiĊHMe]
⟶ (Et$_3$SiCHMe)$_2$
Et$_4$Si $\xrightarrow{CrO_3/Al_2O_3 \text{ under } H_2}$
↓ 530~600° higher temp. ↓
Et$_3$SiH   Si
+   +
C$_2$H$_4$ C$_2$H$_6$

⑥ Zhur. 33, 613 (1963); 32, 2161 (1962).

SiC$_8$H$_{20}$

① Amyltrimethylsilane
C$_5$H$_{11}$Si(CH$_3$)$_3$

② Me$_3$SiC$_5$H$_9$ + H$_2$ ⟶

Ni + MeOH + MeC$\overset{\displaystyle CH-CH}{\underset{\displaystyle S}{\big|\quad\big|}}$CSiMe$_3$

⟶ 72%

SiCl$_4$ $\xrightarrow{n\text{-AmMgBr}}$ n-AmSiCl$_3$ (52%)
$\xrightarrow{MeMgBr}$ 50%

③ Colorless liq. (137~139°). n_D1.4096
(20°). d0.7352 (20°/4°).
Sol. in org. solvents; insol. in H$_2$O.

⑥ Zhur. 33, 1251 (1963); 31, 1855
(1961); English page 1735. JACS
68, 475 (1946).

SiC$_8$H$_{20}$

① Dimethyldi-*n*-propylsilane
  (CH$_3$)$_2$Si(C$_3$H$_7$-*n*)$_2$

② *n*-PrMgBr + Me$_2$SiCl$_2$ $\longrightarrow$

③ (141~142°). n_D 1.4119 (20°). d 0.7396
  (20°).

⑥ JACS **75**, 3753 (1953) ; **56**, 195 (1934).
  Svensk. Kem. Tid. **64**, 283 (1952).

SiC$_8$H$_{20}$

① Di-*n*-butylsilane
  (*n*-C$_4$H$_9$)$_2$SiH$_2$

② *n*-BuMgBr + H$_2$SiCl$_2$ $\longrightarrow$

③ Colorless liq. (160°). n_D1.4241 (20°).
  d0.7458 (20°).
  Sol. in org. solvents ; insol. in H$_2$O.
  IR : Acta Chem. Scand. **8**, 1830
  (1954).

⑥ JOC **18**, 303 (1953).

SiC$_8$H$_{20}$Ge

① 1-Trimethylsilyl-2-trimethyl-
  germylethylene
  (CH$_3$)$_3$SiCH=CHGe(CH$_3$)$_3$

② Na + Me$_3$SiCl +
  Me$_3$GeCH=CHCl $\longrightarrow$

③ (158~160°/748). n_D1.4460 (20°). d0.9558
  (20°/4°).

⑥ Izv. OKhN **1963**, 75.

SiC$_8$H$_{20}$O

① Trimethyl-3-ethoxypropylsilane
  C$_2$H$_5$OCH$_2$CH$_2$CH$_2$Si(CH$_3$)$_3$

② CH$_2$=CHCH$_2$OEt + HSiCl$_3$
  $\xrightarrow{\text{reflux, 48hrs.}}$ 53% Cl$_3$Si(CH$_2$)$_3$OEt
  $\xrightarrow{\text{MeMgBr}}$

  Me$_3$Si(CH$_2$)$_3$Cl + EtONa-EtOH $\longrightarrow$
  71%

③ (155°), n_D1.4136 (20°), d0.7921 (20°).

⑥ Bull. soc. chim. France **1955**, 790.
  Izv. OKhN **1957**, 1199 ; CA **52**, 6162
  (1957).

SiC$_8$H$_{20}$O

① Triethylethoxysilane
  (C$_2$H$_5$)$_3$SiOC$_2$H$_5$

② Et$_3$SiH + Li $\xrightarrow{\text{abs. EtOH 3hrs}}$ 74%

  Et$_3$SiH $\xrightarrow{\text{in EtOH, NaOH}}$ 40%

  Et$_3$SiH $\xrightarrow{\text{EtOH, K}}$ 90.1%
  Si(OEt)$_4$ + ZnEt$_2$ + Na $\longrightarrow$

③ (154°). n_D1.4140 (20°). d0.8160 (20°).

⑥ Zhur. **24**, 1178 (1954).   JACS **68**, 1880
  (1946).   CA **41**, 89 (1946).

SiC$_8$H$_{20}$O

① Methyldi-*n*-propylmethoxysilane
  CH$_3$Si(*n*-C$_3$H$_7$)$_2$OCH$_3$

② *n*-PrSi(OMe)$_2$Me + Na $\longrightarrow$

③ (149°). n_D 1.4099 (25°). d 0.7962
  (25°/4°).

④ + B(OH)$_3$ $\longrightarrow$ B[OSi(Pr-*n*)$_2$Me]$_3$

⑥ Zhur. **57**, 1476 (1957).   JACS **84**,
  4730 (1962).

SiC$_8$H$_{20}$O

① 5-Trimethylsilylpentanol-1
  (CH$_3$)$_3$Si(CH$_2$)$_5$OH

② CH$_2$$\Big\langle$ $\begin{smallmatrix}\text{CH}_2\text{CH}_2\\ \\ \text{CH}_2\text{CH}_2\end{smallmatrix}$ $\Big\rangle$O + Mg
  + Me$_3$SiCl $\longrightarrow$

  Me$_3$Si$\underset{S}{\overset{\text{CH——CH}}{\diagup\diagdown}}$CCHO + Ni
  + MeOH $\longrightarrow$

  O$_2$ + H$_2$O + [Me$_3$Si(CH$_2$)$_5$]$_3$Al $\longrightarrow$

③ (198.0~198.5°). n_D1.4367 (20°).
  d0.8346 (20°/4°).

⑥ JACS **82**, 6129 (1960).   Izv. OKhN
  1962 253 ; English page 231. Zhur.
  33, 1251 (1963).

SiC₈H₂₀O

① *n*-Amyloxytrimethylsilane
   $(CH_3)_3SiOC_5H_{11}\text{-}n$

② $n\text{-AmOH} + Me_3SiCl + NH_3 \longrightarrow$
   $n\text{-AmOH} + Me_3SiCl \longrightarrow$
   $n\text{-AmOH} + Me_3SiCl + C_5H_5N \longrightarrow$

③ $(145\sim149°)$. $n_D 1.4020$. $d 0.7852$.
   IR : 1259, 1100, 841, 756 cm⁻¹.

⑥ J. Chin. Chem. Soc. (Ⅱ) **9**, 273(1962);
   8, 834 (1961); CA **58**, 12591 (1963).
   JOC **23**, 50 (1958).   Zhur. **29**, 1528
   (1959).

SiC₈H₂₀O

① Isoamyloxytrimethylsilane
   $(CH_3)_3SiOCH_2C_5H_{11}\text{-}i$

② $Me_3SiCl + i\text{-BuCH}_2OH \longrightarrow$

③ $(144°)$. $n_D 1.3977 (20°)$. $d 0.7806$
   $(20°/4°)$.

⑥ Zhur. **29**, 1528 (1959).   J. Chin.
   Chem. Soc. (Ⅱ) **8**, 834 (1961); CA
   58, 12, 591 (1963).

SiC₈H₂₀O₂

① Bis(ethoxymethyl)dimethylsilane
   $(CH_3)_2Si(CH_2OC_2H_5)_2$

② $EtOCH_2MgCl + Me_2SiCl_2 \longrightarrow$

③ $(54.0\sim54.5°/16)$. $n_D 1.4121 (20°)$.
   $d 0.835 (20°)$.

⑥ Fr. 1303195 (1962); CA **58**, 7975 (1963).

SiC₈H₂₀O₂

① Dimethyldi-*n*-propoxysilane
   $(CH_3)_2Si(OC_3H_7\text{-}n)_2$

② $Me_2SiCl_2 + n\text{-PrOH} \longrightarrow 48\%$
   $(Me_2SiNH)_4 + n\text{-PrOH} \longrightarrow 24.8\%$

③ $(149\sim150°)$. $n_D 1.3950 (20°)$. $d 0.8435$
   $(20°)$.

⑥ J. Ind. Chem. Soc. **39**, 65 (1962).
   Zhur. **29**, 907(1959); **32**, 2316(1962);
   English page 2284.

SiC₈H₂₀O₂

① Diethyldiethoxysilane
   $(C_2H_5)_2Si(OC_2H_5)_2$

② $SiCl_4 \xrightarrow{\text{EtOH}} SiCl_2(OEt)_2 \xrightarrow{\text{EtMgBr}}$
   $Et_2SiCl_2 + EtONa \xrightarrow{\text{in Et}_2O} 40\%$

③ $(157°)$. $n_D 1.4022 (20°)$. $d 0.8622 (20°)$.

⑥ J. Inst. Polytech. Osaka City Univ.
   Ser C. 2, No.1, 11 (1951).

SiC₈H₂₀O₂

① Di-*n*-propyldimethoxysilane
   $(n\text{-}C_3H_7)_2Si(OCH_3)_2$

② $n\text{-PrSi(OMe)}_3 + Na \longrightarrow$
   $Si(OMe)_4 + n\text{-PrMgX} \longrightarrow$

③ $(166\sim167°)$. $n_D 1.4071 (25°)$. $d 0.8634$
   $(25°/4°)$.

⑥ Zhur. **25**, 1124 (1955); English page
   1079. JACS **84**, 4730 (1962).

SiC₈H₂₀O₂

① Di-*n*-butylsilanediol
   $(n\text{-}C_4H_9)_2Si(OH)_2$

② $(n\text{-}C_4H_9)_2SiCl_2 \xrightarrow{\text{NaOH aq.}}$

③ $[95\sim97°]$.
   Insol. in H₂O; readily sol. in
   oxygenated org. solvents.

⑥ JACS **75**, 1585 (1953).

SiC₈H₂₀O₂

① Di-*t*-butylsilanediol
   $(t\text{-}C_4H_9)_2Si(OH)_2$

② $t\text{-BuSiCl}_3 \xrightarrow{t\text{-BuLi}} (t\text{-Bu})_2SiCl_2 \xrightarrow{\text{H}_2O}$

③ White solid. $(210°)$. $[151\sim153°]$.

⑥ US 2626270 (1953); CA **49**, 4705
   (1955).

SiC₈H₂₀O₃

① Ethyltriethoxysilane
   $C_2H_5Si(OC_2H_5)_3$

② $EtSiH(OEt)_2 + NaOEt$
   $\longrightarrow EtSiH_3 + EtSi(OEt)_3$

③ (159~161°). n_D 1.3939 (20°). *d* 0.8960 (20°).

⑥ Sci. & Ind. (Japan) **27**, 200 (1953). US 2637738 (1953). BCSJ **27**, 428, 582 (1954).

SiC₈H₂₀O₃

① *n*-Amyltrimethoxysilane
   n-C₅H₁₁Si(OCH₃)₃

② Si(OMe)₄ + *n*-C₅H₁₁MgBr ⟶ 26%

③ Colorless liq. (181.9°). n_D 1.4030 (20°). *d* 0.9199 (20°).
   Sol. in org. solvents.

⑥ Zhur. **25**, 1124 (1955) ; CA **50**, 3217 (1956).

SiC₈H₂₁NO

① *N*-Bis(trimethylsilyl)acetamide
   CH₃CON[Si(CH₃)₃]₂

② AcNH₂ + Et₃N + Me₃SiCl ⟶

③ (67.5°/30).

⑥ Angew. Int'l Ed. **2**, 96 (1963).

SiC₈H₂₂N₂

① Di-*t*-butyldiaminosilane
   (*t*-C₄H₉)₂Si(NH₂)₂

② (*t*-Bu)₂SiCl₂ $\xrightarrow{\text{liq. NH}_3}$

③ Colorless liq. (189~190°/737). n_D 1.4534 (20°). *d* 0.8608 (20°).
   Sol. in org. solvents.

⑥ CA **49**, 4705 (1955).

SiC₉H₅N₃S₃

① Phenyltriisothiocyanosilane
   C₆H₅Si(NCS)₃

② PhSiCl₃ + 3AgNCS (30% excess)
   $\xrightarrow{\text{in C}_6\text{H}_6}$ 72~90%

   PhSiCl₃ + NH₄NCS $\xrightarrow{\text{in C}_6\text{H}_6}$ 60~75%

③ (338.6~340.6, 151°/2). [51~53°]. *d* 1.291 (30°).
   Moderately hydrolyzed in H₂O.

⑥ Zhur. **24**, 1082 (1954).   JACS **70**,

1220 (1948).

SiC₉H₁₀ClF₃

① *p*-Trifluoromethylphenyldimethyl-chlorosilane
   p-CF₃C₆H₄Si(CH₃)₂Cl

② *p*-BrMgC₆H₄CF₃ + Me₂SiCl₂
   ⟶ 13.4%

③ (90~100°/15).

④ + *n*-BuLi + Fe(C₅H₅)₂ ⟶
   p-CF₃C₆H₄Si(Me)₂C₅H₄FeC₅H₅
   + [*p*-CF₃C₆H₄Si(Me)₂C₅H₄]₂Fe

⑥ Dokl. **151**, 1319 (1963).

SiC₉H₁₀O

① Propargyloxyphenylsilane
   C₆H₅Si(H)₂OCH₂C≡CH

② PhSiH₃ + Ag(Colloidal)
   + CH≡CCH₂OH ⟶ 15.6%

③ (109~110°/5).

⑥ Zhur. **33**, 2617 (1963).

SiC₉H₁₁NO₂

① Benzo-2,2-dimethyl-2-sila-1-aza-3-oxanon-(4)

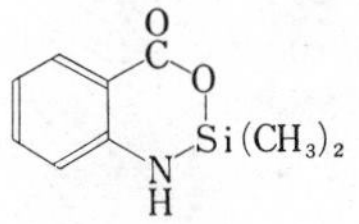

② *o*-H₂NC₆H₄COOH + Et₃N + Me₂SiCl₂
   ⟶ 89%

③ [126°].

⑥ Ber. **96**, 1561 (1963).

SiC₉H₁₀O₃

① Benzo-2,2-dimethyl-2-sila-1,3-dioxanon-(4)

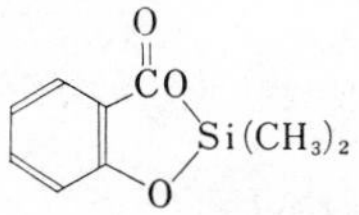

② *o*-HOC₆H₄COOH + Me₂SiCl₂ ⟶

③ (114°/1.5). [62°].

⑥ J. Ind. Chem. Soc. **40**, 623 (1963).
    Ber. **96**, 1561 (1963).

SiC$_9$H$_{12}$

① Methylphenylvinylsilane
    CH$_3$(C$_6$H$_5$)(CH$_2$=CH)SiH

② MePh(CH$_2$=CH)SiCl
    + LiAlH$_4$ $\longrightarrow$

③ (56~56.5°/6.5~6.8). n_D1.5115 (25°).
    d0.891 (25°).

④ + K $\longrightarrow$ $\left\{-\left(-\underset{\underset{Ph}{|}}{\overset{\overset{Me}{|}}{Si}}-CH_2CH_2-\underset{\underset{Ph}{|}}{\overset{\overset{Me}{|}}{Si}}-\right)-\right\}_n$
    $\underset{Me}{\overset{Ph}{>}}Si\underset{CH_2CH_2}{\overset{CH_2CH_2}{<}}Si\underset{Me}{\overset{Ph}{<}}$

⑥ JACS **78**, 1686 (1956).

SiC$_9$H$_{12}$ClF$_9$

① Tris(3,3,3-trifluoropropyl)-
    chlorosilane
    (CF$_3$CH$_2$CH$_2$)$_3$SiCl

② CF$_3$CH$_2$CH$_2$MgCl + SiCl$_4$ $\longrightarrow$ 12.9%

③ (80~120°/20).

④ + n-BuLi + Fe(C$_5$H$_5$)$_2$ $\longrightarrow$
    C$_5$H$_5$FeC$_5$H$_4$Si(CH$_2$CH$_2$CF$_3$)$_3$
    + Fe[C$_5$H$_4$Si(CH$_2$CH$_2$CF$_3$)$_3$]$_2$

⑥ Dokl. **151**, 1319 (1963).

SiC$_9$H$_{12}$Cl$_2$

① Benzylethyldichlorosilane
    C$_6$H$_5$CH$_2$(C$_2$H$_5$)SiCl$_2$

② EtSiCl$_3$ + Mg + PhCH$_2$Cl $\longrightarrow$ 60~70%

③ Liq. (169°/100).
    Sol. in org. solvenents. Decomp. in
    H$_2$O.

⑥ JCS **93**, 2004 (1908); **91** (1907).

SiC$_9$H$_{12}$Cl$_2$

① 1-Phenyl-2-methyldichlorosilyl-
    ethane
    C$_6$H$_5$CH$_2$CH$_2$Si(Cl)$_2$CH$_3$

② CH$_2$=CHSi(Cl)$_2$Me + Et$_3$N + AlCl$_3$
    + C$_6$H$_6$ $\longrightarrow$ 59.3%

PhCH=CH$_2$ + MeSiHCl$_2$ $\longrightarrow$ 53%

③ (90~92°/5). n_D 1.5120 (20°). d 1.1311
    (20°/4°).

④ + MeMgBr $\longrightarrow$ PhCH$_2$CH$_2$SiMe$_3$

⑤ Synthesis of elastomers.

⑥ Vysokomol. Soed. **4**, 1507 (1962).
    Zhur. **31**, 4033 (1961); English page
    3764. JOC 24, 2052 (1959). Zhur.
    32, 1126 (1962); English page 1102.

SiC$_9$H$_{12}$F$_2$

① 1-Phenyl-1-methyldifluorosilylethane
    C$_6$H$_5$CH(CH$_3$)Si(CH$_3$)F$_2$

② MeSiHF$_2$ + PhCH=CH$_2$ $\longrightarrow$

③ (178°/728). n_D 1.4620 (20°). d 1.0668
    (20°/4°).

⑥ Zhur. **32**, 3882 (1962).

SiC$_9$H$_{12}$F$_2$

① 1-Phenyl-2-methyldifluorosilyl-
    ethane
    C$_6$H$_5$CH$_2$CH$_2$SiCH$_3$F$_2$

② MeSiHF$_2$ + PhCH=CH$_2$ $\longrightarrow$

③ (184°/728). n_D 1.4600 (20°). d 1.0674
    (20°/4°).

⑥ Zhur. **32**, 3882 (1962).

SiC$_9$H$_{12}$O

① Phenylallyloxysilane
    C$_6$H$_5$Si(H)$_2$OCH$_2$CH=CH$_2$

② PhSiH$_3$ + Cu(powder)
    + CH$_2$=CHCH$_2$OH $\longrightarrow$ 16.5%

③ (69~70°/7). n_D 1.4997 (20°). d 0.9550
    (20°/4°).

⑥ Zhur. **33**, 2617 (1963).

SiC$_9$H$_{13}$Br

① m-Bromophenyltrimethylsilane
    m-BrC$_6$H$_4$Si(CH$_3$)$_3$

② m-BrC$_6$H$_4$Li + Me$_3$SiCl $\longrightarrow$

③ Liq. (96~97°/5). n_D 1.5290 (20°).
    Sol. in org. solvents; insol in H$_2$O.

⑥ JACS **76**, 599 (1954).

SiC₉H₁₃BrO

① Dimethylbromomethylphenoxysilane
   $C_6H_5OSi(CH_3)_2CH_2Br$

② $Me_2Si(Cl)CH_2Br + PhOH \longrightarrow 82\%$

③ $(113°/14)$. $n_D 1.5245 (20°)$.
   NMR : 6.9, 0.30, 2.42.

⑥ Ber. **96**, 1495 (1963).

SiC₉H₁₃Cl

① Phenylmethylethylchlorosilane
   $C_6H_5Si(Cl)CH_3(C_2H_5)$

② $PhSiHMeEt + Cl_2 \longrightarrow$

③ $[\alpha]_D + 2.0°$

⑥ JACS **85**, 3712 (1963).

SiC₉H₁₃ClO

① p-Chlorophenyl--n-propoxysilane
   p-$ClC_6H_4Si(H)OC_3H_7$-n

② n-PrOH + Cu(powder)
   $+ p$-$ClC_6H_4SiH_3 \longrightarrow 8.3\%$

③ $(105.0°/10)$. $n_D 1.5248 (20°)$.

⑥ Zhur. **33**, 2617 (1963).

SiC₉H₁₃F

① p-Fluorophenyltrimethylsilane
   p-$FC_6H_4Si(CH_3)_3$

② $SiCl_4 \xrightarrow[\text{3 MeMgBr}]{p\text{-}FC_6H_4MgBr} p$-$FC_6H_4SiCl_3$
   $\xrightarrow{} 87\%$

③ Liq. $(173°)$. $n_D 1.4751 (20°)$. $d 0.9656$
   $(20°)$.
   Sol in org. solvents ; insol. in H_2O.

④ $+ 71\%$ $HNO_3 + Ac_2O$
   $\xrightarrow{\text{reflux}} p$-$FC_6H_4NO_2 + (Me_3Si)_2O$

⑥ Coll. Czech. Chem. Comm. **16**, 580
   (1951) ; CA **47**, 8030 (1953).

SiC₉H₁₃NO₂

① Trimethyl-o-nitrophenylsilane
   $(CH_3)_3SiC_6H_4NO_2$-o

② $Me_3SiPh \xrightarrow{HNO_3 + Ac_2O} Me_3SiC_6H_4NO_2$

③ $(117°/10)$. $n_D 1.5321 (20°)$. $d 1.073 (20°)$.

⑥ JACS **75**, 2930 (1953) ; **73**, 4770, 5817
   (1951) ; **76**, 1252(1954). US 2582568 ;
   CA **46**, 7582 (1952).

SiC₉H₁₃NO₂

① Trimethyl-m-nitrophenylsilane
   $(CH_3)_3SiC_6H_4NO_2$-m

② $Me_3SiPh \xrightarrow{HNO_3 + Ac_2O}$

③ $(126°/10)$. $n_D 1.5329 (20°)$. $d 1.055 (20°)$.

⑥ Rec. trav. chim. **76**, 335 (1957).
   JACS. **75**, 2821, 2930 (1953) ; **73**,
   4770 (1951) ; **76**, 1252 (1954). US
   2582568 ; CA **46**, 7582 (1952).

SiC₉H₁₄

① Trimethylphenylsilane
   $(CH_3)_3SiC_6H_5$

② $\left.\begin{matrix} PhMgBr + Me_3SiCl \longrightarrow \\ PhSiCl_3 + 3MeMgBr \longrightarrow \end{matrix}\right\} 40{\sim}80\%$
   $Me_3SiOEt + PhLi \longrightarrow 72\%$

③ Liq. $(171.6°)$. $n_D 1.4901 (20°)$. $d 0.8687$
   $(20°)$.
   Mass : Colloq. Spectros. Intn'l. 9th
   Lyons, 1961, **3**, 556.
   IR : BCSJ 27, 441 (1954).

④ $+ Br_2 \longrightarrow Me_3SiBr + PhBr$
   $+ AlBr_3 \longrightarrow Me_4Si + Me_2SiPh_2$
   $+ HCl \longrightarrow C_6H_6$
   $+ H_2SO_4 \xrightarrow{AcOH + H_2O} HSO_3Ph$
   $+ Me_3SiOH$
   $+ HClO_4 \xrightarrow{MeOH}$ cleavage of the
   aryl-Si bond

⑥ JCS **1959**, 2299. Zhur. **31**, 3735
   (1961).

SiC₉H₁₄

① Phenylmethylethylsilane
   $C_6H_5SiH(CH_3)C_2H_5$

② $PhSiBrMeEt + LiAlH_4 \longrightarrow$
   $PhSiClMeEt + LiAlH_4 \longrightarrow$

③ $[\alpha]_D + 0.76°$ or $-0.75°$

④ + Cl₂ ⟶ PhSiClMeEt
⑥ JACS **85**, 3712 (1963).

SiC₉H₁₄BrN

① Phenylaminodimethylbromomethyl-
    silane
    C₆H₅NHSi(CH₃)₂CH₂Br
② PhNH₂ + Et₃N
    + Me₂Si(Cl)CH₂Br ⟶
③ (115°/2.5). n_D1.5572 (20°).
⑥ Ber. **96**, 965 (1963).

SiC₉H₁₄O

① *m*-Hydroxyphenyltrimethylsilane
    (CH₃)₃SiC₆H₄OH-*m*
② *m*-Me₃SiC₆H₄OSiMe₃ + H₂O
    + H⁺ ⟶
③ Colorless liq. (70°/1). n_D1.5190 (20°).
    *d*0.977 (20°/4°).
    Sol. in org. solvents.
⑥ JACS **75**, 2421 (1953).

SiC₉H₁₄O

① *p*-Hydroxyphenyltrimethylsilane
    (CH₃)₃SiC₆H₄OH-*p*
② *p*-Me₃SiC₆H₄OSiMe₃ + H₂O
    + H⁺ ⟶
③ White crystals. [74~76°].
    Sol. in org. solvents.
⑥ JACS **75**, 1249. 2421 (1953).

SiC₉H₁₄O

① *n*-Propoxyphenylsilane
    C₆H₅Si(H)₂OC₃H₇-*n*
② PhSiH₃ + *n*-PrOH + Cu(powder)
    ⟶ 14.2%
③ (46°/4). n_D 1.4852 (20°). *d* 0.9416
    (20°/4°).
⑥ Zhur. **33**, 2617 (1963).

SiC₉H₁₄O

① Trimethylphenoxysilane
    (CH₃)₃SiOC₆H₅
② (CH₃)₃SiCl + C₆H₅OH ⟶
③ (68~69°/13). n_D1.4787 (20°). *d*0.9265
    (20°).
⑥ JOC **23**, 50 (1958); **19**, 441 (1954).

SiC₉H₁₄O₂

① Dimethoxyphenylmethylsilane
    C₆H₅Si(OCH₃)₂CH₃
② MeONa + MeSi(OMe)₃
    + PhSi(OMe)₃ ⟶
③ (100°/25). n_D 1.4694 (20°). *d* 0.9934
    (20°).
⑥ Rocznicki Chem. **34**, 1667 (1960); CA
    56, 7344 (1962). Rocznicki Chem.
    32, 155 (1958); CA **52**, 16, 188 (1958).
    JACS **84**, 4730 (1962).

SiC₉H₁₄O₃

① Phenyltrimethoxysilane
    C₆H₅Si(OCH₃)₃
② PhSi(OMe)₂Me + Na ⟶
    MeONa + MeSi(OMe)₃
    + Ph₂Si(OMe)₂ ⟶
    Si(OMe)₄ + PhMgBr ⟶ 5%
    PhSiCl₃ + MeOH + Me₂NPh ⟶
③ Colorless liq. (120°/30). n_D 1.4710
    (25°). *d*1.064 (20°).
    Sol. in org. solvents.
④ + Na ⟶ Ph₂Si(OMe)₂
    + MeSi(OMe)₃ + MeONa
    ⟶ Si(OMe)₄ + PhSi(OMe)₂Me
    + H₂O ⟶ Phenyl-T-polymer
⑥ JACS **84**, 4730 (1962); **75**, 2712 (1953).
    Zhur. **25**, 1124; CA **50**, 3217
    (1956).

SiC₉H₁₄O₃S

① Trimethylsilyl benzenesulfonate
    C₆H₅SO₂OSi(CH₃)₃
② C₆H₆ + Me₃SiOSO₂Cl ⟶

③ (155°/18). n_D 1.4938 (20°). d 1.418
　　(20°/4°).
⑥ Bull. soc. chim. France **1963**, 512.

SiC₉H₁₅ClO₃

① Triallyloxychlorosilane
　　$(CH_2=CHCH_2O)_3SiCl$
② $SiCl_4 + NH_3 + CH_2=CHCH_2OH \longrightarrow$
③ (138~143°/1).
⑥ Z. anorg. allg. Chem. **319**, 244 (1963).

SiC₉H₁₅N

① Phenylaminotrimethylsilane
　　$(CH_3)_3SiNHC_6H_5$
② $PhNHN(Li)Ph + Me_3SiCl \longrightarrow$
　　$PhNH_2 + Me_3SiCl \longrightarrow$
　　$PhNH_2 + Me_3SiNHCH_2COOSiMe_3 \longrightarrow$
　　$PhNH_2 + Me_3SiSiMe_3 \longrightarrow$
③ [208°]. n_D 1.5222 (20°). d 0.9308 (20°/4°).
⑥ US 2876209(1959); CA **53**, 12, 321(1959).
　　JCS **1961**, 4933. J. prakt. Chem. **9**,
　　315 (1959). Z. anorg. allg. chem.
　　321, 198 (1963).

SiC₉H₁₅N

① Trimethyl-_m_-aminophenylsilane
　　$(CH_3)_3SiC_6H_4NH_2$-_m_
② $(CH_3)_3SiC_6H_4CONH_2$-_m_ $+ NaOCl$
　　$\longrightarrow$ 68%
③ Colorless liq. (94°/5). n_D 1.5362 (20°).
　　Sol. in org. solvents.
⑥ JACS. **75**, 2421 (1953).

SiC₉H₁₅N

① Trimethyl-_p_-aminophenylsilane
　　$(CH_3)_3SiC_6H_4NH_2$-_p_
② $PhSiMe_3 + HNO_3 + Ac_2O \longrightarrow$
　　$p\text{-}NO_2C_6H_4SiMe_3 \xrightarrow{H_2+Ni+EtOH}$
　　$p\text{-}Me_3SiC_6H_4SiMe_3 + HNO_3 + Ac_2O$
　　$\longrightarrow$ $p\text{-}NO_2C_6H_4SiMe_3$ (80%)
　　$\xrightarrow{H_2+EtOH}$
③ (113°/10). n_D 1.5393 (20°). d 0.947

(20°).
④ This amine is diazotized and coupled
　　with 2-naphthol to yield the azo
　　compound (red-orange).
⑥ JACS **74**, 253 (1952); **75**, 2421 (1953);
　　73, 5817 (1951). JCS **1959**, 2299.

SiC₉H₁₆

① Triallylsilane
　　$(CH_2=CHCH_2)_3SiH$
② $HSiCl_3 + CH_2=CHCH_2MgBr \longrightarrow$
③ (163°). n_D 1.4678 (25°). d 0.8705 (25°).
　　IR: Z. Chem. **1**, 346 (1961)
④ $(CH_2=CHCH_2)_3SiH + KOH$
　　$\xrightarrow{ROH}$ $H_2 + ROK$
　　$+ (CH_2=CHCH_2)_3SiOH$
　　$(CH_2=CHCH_2)_3SiH \xrightarrow{^{60}Co\ \gamma\text{-ray}}$
　　polymer
⑥ JOC **13**, 862 (1948). Izv. OKhN **1960**.
　　477; CA **58**, 4659 (1964).

SiC₉H₁₆F₆O

① Bis(3,3,3-trifluoropropyl)methyl-
　　ethoxysilane
　　$(CF_3CH_2CH_2)_2Si(CH_3)OC_2H_5$
② $CF_3CH_2CH_2Si(Me)(Cl)OEt$
　　$+ CF_3CH_2CH_2MgCl \longrightarrow$ 79%
③ (83.8°/27.5). n_D 1.3603 (20°). d 1.1560
　　(20°/4°).
⑥ Zhur. **33**, 704 (1963).

SiC₉H₁₇Cl₃O₃

① Allyltris(2-chloroethoxy)silane
　　$CH_2=CHCH_2Si(OCH_2CH_2Cl)_2$
② $CH_2=CHCH_2SiCl_3 + (CH_2)_2O + KOH$
　　$\longrightarrow$ 37.8%
③ (149°/5). n_D 1.4688 (20°). d 1.2308
　　(20°/4°).
⑥ Zhur. **33**, 905 (1963).

SiC₉H₁₈O₅

① 3-Trimethoxysilylpropyl acrylate

CH$_2$=CHCOOCH$_2$CH$_2$CH$_2$Si(OCH$_3$)$_3$

② CH$_2$=CHCOOCH$_2$CH=CH$_2$
+ HSi(OMe)$_3$ ⟶

③ (65~70°/0.1). n_D1.4155 (25°).

⑥ Belg. 613466 (1962); CA **58**, 6861 (1963).

SiC$_9$H$_{19}$ClO

① 3-Triethylsilylpropionyl chloride
(C$_2$H$_5$)$_3$SiCH$_2$CH$_2$COCl

② Et$_4$Si + Bz$_2$O$_2$ + (COCl)$_2$ ⟶
Et$_3$Si(CH$_2$)$_2$COCl + Et$_3$SiCl
+ EtSiCl$_3$ + BzCl

③ (86~87.5°/5). n_D1.4449 (20°). d0.9453 (20°).

⑥ Izv. OKhN **1957**, 8643; **1956**, 1445; CA **51**, 8675 (1957).

SiC$_9$H$_{19}$Cl$_3$

① 2-Methyloctyltrichlorosilane
CH$_3$(CH$_2$)$_5$CH(CH$_3$)CH$_2$SiCl$_3$

② SiHCl$_3$ + CH$_2$=C(CH$_3$)(CH$_2$)$_5$CH$_3$
$\xrightarrow{\text{(CH}_3\text{COO)}_2}$ 70%

③ Liq. (221~222°/736), n_D1.4500 (20°).
Sol. in org. solvents. Decomp. with
H$_2$O and alcohol.

⑥ Post (1949).   JACS **70**, 484 (1948).

SiC$_9$H$_{19}$F$_3$

① 3-Trifluoropropyltriethylsilane
CF$_3$CH$_2$CH$_2$Si(C$_2$H$_5$)$_3$

② CF$_3$CH=CH$_2$ + SiHCl$_3$
$\xrightarrow[\text{(Me}_3\text{CO)}_2]{\text{EtMgX}}$ CF$_3$(CH$_2$)$_2$SiCl$_3$ ⟶ 76.1%

③ (166.1~167.8°). n_D1.3962 (20°). d0.961 (20°).

⑥ JACS **79**, 2329 (1957).

SiC$_9$H$_{19}$N

① α-(Triethylsilyl)propionitrile
(C$_2$H$_5$)$_3$SiCH(CH$_3$)CN

② Et$_3$SiH + Ni(CO)$_4$ + CH$_2$=CHCN
⟶ 75%

Fe(CO)$_5$ + Et$_3$SiH + NiCl$_2$
+ CH$_2$=CHCN ⟶

③ (110~113°/12). n_D1.4520 (20°). d0.8687 (20°/4°).

⑥ Izv. OKhN **1963**, 761.   USSR 132222 (1960); CA **55**, 8292 (1961).   Tetrahedron **17**, 61 (1962).

SiC$_9$H$_{19}$NO$_2$

① 3-Cyanopropylmethyldiethoxysilane
CH$_3$Si(OC$_2$H$_5$)$_2$CH$_2$CH$_2$CH$_2$CN

② NaCN + MeSi(OEt)$_2$CH$_2$CH$_2$CH$_2$Cl
+ (Me$_2$SiO)$_x$ ⟶
EtOH + MeSi(Cl)$_2$CH$_2$CH$_2$CH$_2$CN ⟶

③ (83.5~85.0°/3.7). n_D1.4206(25°). d0.929 (25°).

④ + H(Ni)
⟶ MeSi(OEt)$_2$CH$_2$CH$_2$CH$_2$NH$_2$
also using PtNi, Cu chromate or
PtC.

⑥ Brit. 847802 (1960); CA **55**, 10318 (1961).   Mem. Fac. Eng. Osaka City Univ. **3**, 195 (1961); **1**, 1 (1959).   Izv. OKhN **1961**, 2007; English page 1872.

SiC$_9$H$_{20}$

① Cyclohexyltrimethylsilane
(CH$_3$)$_3$SiC$_6$H$_{11}$

② 3 MeLi + C$_6$H$_{11}$SiX$_3$ ⟶ 85%
Me$_3$SiPh + CH$_3$C$_6$H$_{11}$ $\xrightarrow{\text{H}_2}$ 67%

③ (84~85°/10). [−98.5°]. n_D1.4487 (20°). d0.8221 (20°).
IR: BCSJ **27**, 441 (1954).

④ Disproportionation in the presence
of AlBr$_3$ in C$_6$H$_6$.
Cleavage by HBr-AlBr$_3$ in C$_6$H$_6$.

⑥ Tetrahedron Letters **1961**, 421.   Dokl. **111**, 1260 (1956).

SiC₉H₂₀

① Allyltriethylsilane
$(C_2H_5)_3SiCH_2CH=CH_2$

② $EtMgBr + CH_2=CHCH_2SiCl_3 \longrightarrow$
$Et_3SiCl + CH_2=CHCH_2MgBr \longrightarrow$
$Et_3SiBr + CH_2=CHCH_2Li \longrightarrow$

③ $(170\sim172°/735). n_D1.4445 (20°). d0.7873$
$(20°/4°).$

④ $+ (BzO)_2 + SiHCl_3$
$\longrightarrow Et_3SiCH_2CH_2CH_2SiCl_3$

⑥ Izv. OKhN **1963**, 572. Dokl. **75**, 707
(1950) ; **80**, 761 (1951).   Trudy
Moskov Neft. Inst. imeni I. M.
Gubkina (No. 23) 22 (1958).

SiC₉H₂₀

① Triethylcyclopropylsilane
$(C_2H_5)_3SiCHCH_2CH_2$

② $Et_3SiCH=CH_2 + CH_2I_2 + Cu-Zn \longrightarrow$

③ $(173.3\sim174.0°/748). n_D 1.4444 (20°).$
$d0.8095 (20°/4°).$
IR : 295, 405, 492, 543, 632, 653, 718,
732, 790, 841, 901, 980, 1018, 1035,
1110, 1128, 1191, 1242, 1292, 1377,
1417, 1467, 2882, 2917, 2950, 2960,
3008, 3075 cm⁻¹.

⑥ Izv. OKhN **1963**, 1111 ; CA **59**, 7551
(1965).

SiC₉H₂₀

① Methyldiethylbuten-3-ylsilane
$CH_3(C_2H_5)_2SiCH_2CH_2CH=CH_2$

② $CH_3(C_2H_5)_2SiCH_2MgCl$
$+ CH_2=CHCH_2Br \longrightarrow 68\%$

③ Colorless liq. (166.3°/736). $n_D1.4364$
(20°). $d0.7743$ (20°).
Sol. in org. solvents ; insol. in H₂O.

⑥ Izv. OKhN **1955**, 182 ; CA **50**, 1574
(1956).

SiC₉H₂₀O

① 1-Triethylsilylpropionaldehyde
$(C_2H_5)_3SiCH_2CH_2CHO$

② $CH_2=CHCHO + Ni(CO)_4$
$+ Et_3SiH \longrightarrow$

③ $(73°/15). n_D 1.4330 (20°). d 0.8384$
$(20°/4°).$

⑥ Izv. OKhN **1963**, 761.

SiC₉H₂₀O₃

① Allyltriethoxysilane
$CH_2=CHCH_2Si(OC_2H_5)_3$

② $CH_2=CHCH_2MgCl + Si(OEt)_4 \longrightarrow$
$CH_2=CHCH_2SiCl_3 + EtOH \longrightarrow 84\%$

③ $(175.8°). n_D1.4063 (25°).$

⑥ US 3008975 (1958) ; CA **56**, 6001 (1962).
Periodica Polytech. **6**, 35 (1962) ;
CA **58**, 4593 (1963).

SiC₉H₂₁Br

① 3-Bromopropyltriethylsilane
$(C_2H_5)_3SiCH_2CH_2CH_2Br$

② $Et_3SiH + CH_2=CHCH_2Br \xrightarrow{h\nu} 24\%$

③ $(96°/2).$

⑥ J. prakt. Chem. **21**, 149 (1963).

SiC₉H₂₁Br

① Tri-n-propylbromosilane
$(n-C_3H_7)_3SiBr$

② $[(n-C_3H_7)_3Si]_2O + PBr_3 \longrightarrow 55.69\%$

③ Liq. (213°).
Sol. in org. solvents.

⑥ Dokl. **93**, 667 (1953) ; CA **49**, 1541a
(1954).

SiC₉H₂₁Cl

① Tri-n-propylchlorosilane
$(n-C_3H_7)_3SiCl$

② $Si(OEt)_4 + n-C_3H_7MgBr \longrightarrow$
$[(n-C_3H_7)_3Si]_2O \xrightarrow[NH_4Cl]{H_2SO_4} 32\%$
$(n-Pr)_3SiOEt + MeCOCl \longrightarrow$
$HSiCl_3 \xrightarrow{Me_2CO} i-PrOSiCl_3$
$\xrightarrow{n-PrMgBr} i-PrOSi(Pr-n)_3 \xrightarrow{BzCl}$

③ Colorless liq. (202.0°). n_D 1.4404
(20°). d 0.9074 (20°).
Sol. in org. solvents.

④ + H₂O $\xrightarrow{\text{slow}}$ Pr₃SiOSiPr₃
+ EtOH $\xrightarrow{\text{rapid}}$ Pr₃SiOEt

⑥ JACS **77**, 6647 (1955).   JCS **1949**,
2755. Compt. rend. **249**, 1769
(1959).

SiC9H21Cl

① Dibutylmethylchlorosilane
CH₃(C₄H₉)₂SiCl

② CH₃SiCl₃ + 2C₄H₉MgBr $\longrightarrow$

③ Colorless liq. (193~198°). n_D 1.4325
(20°). d 0.8656 (20°).
Sol. in org solvents.

④ Hydrolysis and dehydration
$\longrightarrow$ [CH₃(C₄H₉)₂Si]₂O

⑥ Izv. OKhN **1954**, 707 ; CA **49**, 10874
(1954).

SiC9H21F

① Tri-*n*-propylfluorosilane
(*n*-C₃H₇)₃SiF

② (*n*-C₃H₇)₃SiOC₂H₅ + HF $\longrightarrow$ 91.3%
(Pr₃Si)₂O + KHF₂ + H₂SO₄ $\longrightarrow$

③ Colorless liq. (175°). n_D 1.4107 (25°).
d 0.8339 (25°/4°).
Sol. in org. solvents.

⑥ Post (1949).   JACS **73**, 5127 (1952).
Izv. OKhN **1957**, 600 ; CA **51**, 12660
(1957).

SiC9H21N

① Cyclohexylaminotrimethylsilane
(CH₃)₃SiNHC₆H₁₁

② C₆H₁₁NH₂ + Me₃SiCl $\longrightarrow$
C₆H₁₁NH₂
+ Me₃SiNHCH₂COOSiMe₃ $\longrightarrow$
C₆H₁₁NH₂
+ Me₃SiNHCHMeCOOSiMe₃ $\longrightarrow$
C₆H₁₁NH₂

+ Me₃SiNHCH(Bu-*s*)COOSiMe₃ $\longrightarrow$
C₆H₁₁NH₂ + PrCOOSiMe₃ $\longrightarrow$

③ (47°/3). n_D 1.4453 (20°). d 0.8384
(20°/4°).

⑥ J. prakt. Chem. **9**, 315 (1959) ; **16**, 172
(1962).

SiC9H22

① Tri-*n*-propylsilane
(*n*-C₃H₇)₃SiH

② (*n*-C₃H₇)₃SiOC₂H₅ + LiAlH₄
$\longrightarrow$ 75~80%

③ Colorless liq. (171~173°). n_D 1.4492
(25°). d 0.7590 (20°).
Sol. in org. solvents : insol in H₂O.

⑥ Zhur. **24**, 1178 (1954) ; CA **49**, 12275
(1954).   Acta Chem. Scand. **8**, 1830
(1954).

SiC9H22

① *n*-Propyltriethylsilane
n-C₃H₇Si(C₂H₅)₃

② (C₂H₅)₃SiC≡CCH₃ + 2H₂ $\xrightarrow{\text{Pd}}$

③ Colorless liq. (172.4~172.8°). n_D 1.4308
(20°). d 0.7725 (20°).

⑥ Dokl. **93**, 293 (1953) ; CA **48**, 13616
(1953).   Post (1949).

SiC9H22O

① Tri-*n*-Propylsilanol
(*n*-C₃H₇)₃SiOH

② H₂O + (*n*-Pr)₃SiOC₆H₄Br-*p*
+ HCl $\longrightarrow$
n-Pr₃SiCl + NaOH $\longrightarrow$

③ (96.5~98.5°/13.5). n_D 1.4467 (20°).
d 0.8473 (20°/4°).

⑥ Z. anorg. allg. Chem. **323**, 190 (1963).
Zhur. **30**, 3352 (1960) ; English page
3319.

SiC9H22O3

① *n*-Propyltriethoxysilane

n-C$_3$H$_7$Si(OC$_2$H$_5$)$_3$

② n-C$_3$H$_7$SiCl$_3$ + EtOH ⟶
Si(OEt)$_4$ + n-C$_3$H$_7$MgBr ⟶

③ Colorless liq. (179~180°). n_D 1.3956
(20°). d 0.8916 (20°).
Sol. in org. solvents.

⑥ JOC 4, 363 (1939).

SiC$_9$H$_{22}$S

① Pentylthiomethyltrimethylsilane
C$_5$H$_{11}$SCH$_2$Si(CH$_3$)$_3$

② C$_5$H$_{11}$SNa + BrCH$_2$Si(CH$_3$)$_3$ ⟶ 95%

③ (89°/9). n_D 1.4542 (25°). d 0.8374
(25°/4°).

⑥ JOC 17, 1393 (1952).

SiC$_9$H$_{23}$NO

① Ethoxydimethyldiethylaminomethyl-
silane
C$_2$H$_5$OSi(CH$_3$)$_2$CH$_2$N(C$_2$H$_5$)$_2$

② EtOSi(Me)$_2$CH$_2$Cl + Et$_2$NH ⟶

③ (106°/20). n_D 1.4232 (20°). d 0.8277
(20°/4°).

⑥ Zhur. 33, 258 (1963).

SiC$_9$H$_{23}$O$_3$P

① 3-Triethylsilylpropylphosphonic
acid
(C$_2$H$_5$)$_3$SiCH$_2$CH$_2$CH$_2$P(O)(OH)$_2$

② Et$_3$SiCH$_2$CH$_2$CH$_2$P(O)(OEt)$_2$ + H$_2$O
+ HCl ⟶

③ [72.5~73.0°].

⑥ Dokl. 148, 875 (1963).

SiC$_9$H$_{24}$N$_2$

① Methylbis(diethylamino)silane
CH$_3$SiH[N(C$_2$H$_5$)$_2$]$_2$

② MeSiHCl$_2$ + Et$_2$NH ⟶

③ (80~81°/25°). n_D 1.4310 (20°). d 0.8204
(20°/4°).

④ + Et$_2$NNH$_2$ ⟶ MeSiH(NHNEt$_2$)$_2$
+ MeSi(NHNEt$_2$)$_3$

⑥ Zhur. 33, 1294 (1963); 32, 1987 (1962);

English page1 968.

SiC$_9$H$_{24}$OSn

① Triethyltrimethylsiloxystannane
(C$_2$H$_5$)$_3$SnOSi(CH$_3$)$_3$

② Et$_3$SnCl + HOH + Me$_3$SiCl ⟶

③ (99°/20).

⑥ JACS 83, 4480 (1963).

SiC$_9$H$_{24}$OSn

① Trimethyltriethylsiloxystannane
(CH$_3$)$_3$SnOSi(C$_2$H$_5$)$_3$

② Et$_3$SiCl + Me$_3$SnOLi ⟶

③ (48~49°/1.5).

⑥ Angew. Int'l. Ed. 2, 328 (1963).

SiC$_{10}$H$_7$Cl$_3$

① 1-Naphthyltrichlorosilane
(1-C$_{10}$H$_7$)SiCl$_3$

② SiCl$_4$ + 1-C$_{10}$H$_7$MgBr ⟶ 28%
SiCl$_4$ + 1-C$_{10}$H$_7$MgBr ⟶ 60%
1-C$_{10}$H$_7$Cl + SiHCl$_3$
  1 : 2
$\xrightarrow[\text{quartz tube 640°}]{}$ 60%

③ (181°/30). [183.5°]. n_D 1.6085 (20°).
d 1.355 (20°).

④ + Mg + CH$_2$=CHCH$_2$Br $\xrightarrow{\text{reflux in Et}_2\text{O}}$
(1-C$_{10}$H$_7$)Si(CH$_2$CH=CH$_2$)$_3$ (82.2%)

⑥ JACS 73, 4982 (1951). Coll. Czech.
Chem. Comm. 25, 2161 (1960).
Zhur. 27, 1286 (1957); CA 52, 3751
(1958).

SiC$_{10}$H$_7$N$_3$S$_3$

① Benzyltriisothiocyanosilane
C$_6$H$_5$CH$_2$Si(NCS)$_3$

② PhCH$_2$SiCl$_3$ + 3 NH$_4$NCS
$\xrightarrow{\text{C}_6\text{H}_6}$ 60~75%

☺ (169°/2). [36°]. d 1.28 (20°).

⑥ Zhur. 24, 1082 (1954).

SiC$_{10}$H$_{10}$

① 1-Naphthylsilane
   1-C$_{10}$H$_7$SiH$_3$

② SiH$_3$Br + 1-C$_{10}$H$_7$MgBr $\longrightarrow$ 25%

③ Colorless liq. (49.5°/0.025). n_D 1.6030
   (25°). d 1.0054 (25°).
   Sol. in org. solvents ; insol. in H$_2$O.

⑥ JACS **78**, 292 (1956).

SiC$_{10}$H$_{12}$Cl$_2$

① 1-Phenyl-2-ethyldichlorosilylethene
   C$_6$H$_5$CH=CHSi(Cl)$_2$C$_2$H$_5$

② EtSiHCl$_2$ + PhC≡CH + H$_2$PtCl$_6$
   $\longrightarrow$ 77%

③ (142°/16). n_D 1.5525 (20°). d 1.1398
   (20°).

④ + HF $\longrightarrow$ PhCH=CHSi(F)$_2$Et

⑥ Izv. OKhN **1963**, 136 ; CA **59**, 11550
   (1963).

SiC$_{10}$H$_{12}$F$_2$

① 1-Phenyl-2-ethyldifluorosilylethene
   C$_6$H$_5$CH=CHSi(F)$_2$C$_2$H$_5$

② HF + PhCH=CHSi(Cl)$_2$Et $\longrightarrow$ 85%

③ (85°/5). n_D 1.4920 (20°). d 1.0725 (20°).

⑥ Izv. OKhN **1963**, 136 ; CA **59**, 11550
   (1963).

SiC$_{10}$H$_{12}$O$_2$

① Phenyldiacetoxysilane
   (CH$_3$COO)$_2$Si(H)C$_6$H$_5$

② AcOH + C$_5$H$_5$N + PhSiH$_3$
   $\longrightarrow$ 26.2%

③ (130~134°/5). n_D 1.4807 (20°). d 1.1675
   (20°/4°).

⑥ Zhur. **33**, 2617 (1963).

SiC$_{10}$H$_{12}$S$_2$

① Dimethyldi-1-thienylsilane

① $\left(\begin{matrix} \text{CH---CH} \\ \text{CH} \quad \text{C---} \\ \quad \text{S} \end{matrix} \right)_2$ Si(CH$_3$)$_2$

② $\begin{matrix} \text{CH---CH} \\ \text{CH} \quad \text{CLi} \\ \quad \text{S} \end{matrix}$ + Me$_3$SiCl$_2$ $\longrightarrow$ 71%

③ (131~133°/8). n_D 1.5775 (20°). d 1.1184
   (20°/4°).

④ + Ni + MeOH $\longrightarrow$ Me$_2$SiBu$_2$

⑥ Zhur. **33**, 1251 (1963).

SiC$_{10}$H$_{13}$N

① p-Trimethylsilylbenzonitrile
   p-(CH$_3$)$_3$SiC$_6$H$_4$CN

② CuCN + p-BrC$_6$H$_4$SiMe$_3$ + C$_5$H$_5$N,
   then NH$_4$OH $\longrightarrow$

③ (133~139°/29).

⑥ Yakugaku Zasshi **82**, 931 (1962) ; CA
   59, 653 (1963).

SiC$_{10}$H$_{14}$

① Dimethylphenylvinylsilane
   (CH$_3$)$_2$C$_6$H$_5$SiCH=CH$_2$

② (CH$_3$)$_2$C$_6$H$_5$SiCl + CH$_2$=CHCl
   + Na $\longrightarrow$ 36%

③ Colorless liq. (84~85°/20). n_D 1.5048
   (20°). d 0.8919 (20°).
   Sol. in org. solvents ; insol. in H$_2$O.

⑥ BCSJ **26**, 493 (1953).

SiC$_{10}$H$_{14}$

① Allylmethylphenylsilane
   CH$_3$(C$_6$H$_5$)Si(H)CH$_2$CH=CH$_2$

③ Colorless liq. (76°/8). n_D 1.5137 (20°).
   d 0.8937 (20°).
   Sol. in org. solvents ; insol. in H$_2$O.

⑥ Izv. OKhN **1957**, 383 ; CA **51**, 15457
   (1955).

SiC$_{10}$H$_{14}$

① Trimethylenemethylphenylsilane

CH$_2$-CH$_2$-CH$_2$-Si(CH$_3$)C$_6$H$_5$

② Mg + CH$_2$CH$_2$CH$_2$Si(Cl)Me

  + C$_6$H$_5$X ⟶

③ (61.5~62.5°/18). n_D 1.5349 (20°).
  d 0.9511 (20°/4°).

⑥ Dokl. **150**, 799 (1963).

SiC$_{10}$H$_{14}$Cl$_2$

① β-Phenethylethyldichlorosilane
  C$_6$H$_5$C$_2$H$_4$(C$_2$H$_5$)SiCl$_2$

② ClCH$_2$CH$_2$Si(C$_2$H$_5$)Cl$_2$ + C$_6$H$_6$ + AlCl$_3$
  ⟶ 34%

③ Liq. (126~127°/4). n_D 1.5135 (20°).
  d 1.1109 (20°).
  Sol. in org. solvents. Decomp. in
  H$_2$O.

⑥ Zhur. **25**, 2469 (1955); CA **50**, 9319
  (1956).

SiC$_{10}$H$_{14}$Cl$_2$

① Methylphenylchloromethyl
  -β-chloroethylsilane
  CH$_3$Si(C$_6$H$_5$)(CH$_2$Cl)CH$_2$CH$_2$Cl

② MeSiPh(Cl)CH$_2$Cl + KOH
  + (CH$_2$)$_2$O ⟶ 58.3%

③ (145°/8). n_D 1.5262 (20°). d 1.1898
  (20°/4°).

⑥ Zhur. **33**, 905 (1963).

SiC$_{10}$H$_{14}$FeO$_2$

① (π-Cyclopentadienyl)dicarbonmono-
  oxidetrimethylsilyliron
  C$_5$H$_5$Fe(CO)$_2$Si(CH$_3$)$_3$

② π-C$_5$H$_5$Fe(CO)$_4$FeC$_5$H$_5$-π + Na-Hg
  ⟶ π-C$_5$H$_5$Fe(CO)$_2$Na
  (CH$_3$)$_3$SiCl
  ⟶ π-C$_5$H$_5$Fe(CO)$_2$Si(CH$_3$)$_3$

③ [70°].
  Thermally stable; attacked by atmospheric O$_2$; decompd. in a day
  in org. solvents; extensively decompd. by air oxidn. within an
  hour.

⑥ Naturwiss. **43**, 129 (1956).

SiC$_{10}$H$_{14}$O

① p-Trimethylsilylbenzaldehyde
  p-(CH$_3$)$_3$SiC$_6$H$_4$CHO

② SnCl$_2$ + HCl(gas)
  + p-Me$_3$SiC$_6$H$_4$CN ⟶
  CaCO$_3$ + HOH
  + p-Me$_3$SiC$_6$H$_4$CHBr$_2$ ⟶
  p-Me$_3$SiC$_6$H$_4$CH$_2$Br $\xrightarrow{(CH_2)_6N_4}$

③ (118~119°/15). n_D1.5245 (20°).

④ + KOH ⟶ p-Me$_3$SiC$_6$H$_4$COOH
  + p-Me$_3$SiC$_6$H$_4$CH$_2$OH
  + NaOH + MeCHO ⟶
  p-Me$_3$SiC$_6$H$_4$CH=CHCHO (82.4%)
  + NaOH + HCHO
  ⟶ p-Me$_3$SiC$_6$H$_4$CH$_2$OH (65.2%)
  + NaOH + C$_6$H$_{10}$O ⟶
  (p-Me$_3$SiC$_6$H$_2$CH=)$_2$C$_6$H$_6$O(2,6)
  + NaOH + MeCOPh ⟶
  p-Me$_3$SiC$_6$H$_4$CH=CHCOPh (67%)
  + Me$_2$CO + NaOH ⟶
  p-Me$_3$SiC$_6$H$_4$CH=CHCOMe (74%)
  + H$_2$NNHC$_6$H$_3$(NO$_2$)$_2$(2,4) ⟶
  p-Me$_3$SiC$_6$H$_4$CH=NNHC$_6$H$_3$(NO$_2$)$_2$

⑥ Izv. OKhN **1961**, 1069. Yakugaku
  Zasshi **82**, 929 (1962). Rec. trav.
  chim. **81**, 88 (1962). Hua Hsüeh
  Hsüeh Pao **26**, 7 (1960); CA **55**,
  18654 (1961).

SiC$_{10}$H$_{14}$O$_2$

① Trimethyl-p-carboxyphenylsilane
  (CH$_3$)$_3$Si(C$_6$H$_4$COOH-p)

② (CH$_3$)$_3$Si(C$_6$H$_4$C$_2$H$_5$-p) + O$_2$
  $\xrightarrow{CrO_3}$ 11.8%

③ White crystals. [116.5~118.0°].

⑥ JACS **76**, 4552 (1954); **75**, 1249 (1953);
  71, 1003 (1952).

SiC$_{10}$H$_{14}$O$_2$

① p-Trimethylsilylbenzoic acid
  p-(CH$_3$)$_3$SiC$_6$H$_4$COOH

② p-Me₃SiC₆H₄CHO + KOH ⟶
HCHO + p-Me₃SiC₆H₄CHO
+ KOH ⟶
③ Solid. [118~119°].
⑥ JCS 1959, 2299. Izv. OKhN 1961, 1069 ;
English page 989. Yakugaku Zasshi
82, 929 (1962) ; CA 59, 653 (1963).
Rec. trav. chim. 81, 88 (1962).

SiC₁₀H₁₄O₂
① Ethyl phenylsilylacetate
C₆H₅Si(H)₂CH₂COOC₂H₅
② PhSiH₃ + CH(N)₂COOEt ⟶ 27%
③ (116~118°/15).
⑥ JCS 1963, 3604.

SiC₁₀H₁₅Br
① p-Trimethylsilylbenzyl bromide
p-(CH₃)₃SiC₆H₄CH₂Br
② p-Me₃SiC₆H₄Me + (CH₂CO)₂NBr
+ BzOOH ⟶
③ (130~131°/12). n_D 1.5422 (25°). d 1.2244
(20°).
④ + MeCOCH(Na)COOEt ⟶
MeCOCH(COOEt)CH₂C₆H₄SiMe₃-p
+ CHNa(COOEt)₂ ⟶
Me₃SiC₆H₄CH₂CH(COOEt)₂
+ KCN ⟶ p-Me₃SiC₆H₄CH₂CN
+ (CH₂)₆N₄ ⟶ p-Me₃SiC₆H₄CHO
⑥ Hua Hsüeh Hsüeh Pao 26, 7 (1960) ;
CA 55, 18654 (1961).

SiC₁₀H₁₅Cl
① Diethylphenylchlorosilane
C₆H₅(C₂H₅)₂SiCl
② (C₂H₅)₂SiCl₂ + C₆H₅MgBr (or C₆H₅Li)
⟶ 60%
③ Colorless liq. (229°). n_D 1.5130 (20°).
d 1.0252 (20°).
Sol. in org. solvents ; Decomp. with
H₂O.
④ + NaOH ⟶ C₆H₅(C₂H₅)₂SiOH(91%)
⑥ Dokl. 95, 821 (1954) ; CA 49, 6159

(1953).

SiC₁₀H₁₅FO₂
① Diethoxyphenylfluorosilane
(C₂H₅O)₂C₆H₅SiF
② C₆H₅SiF₃ + HC(OC₂H₅)₃ $\xrightarrow{AlCl_3}$ 39.6%
③ Colorless liq. (110°/25). n_D 1.4487
(25°). d 1.029 (25°).
Sol. in org. solvents.
⑥ JACS 76, 1390 (1954). US 2698661
(1955).

SiC₁₀H₁₅N
① Benzaltrimethylsilylamine
C₆H₅CH＝NSi(CH₃)₃
② C₆H₅CHO + [(CH₃)₃Si]₂NNa ⟶
③ (100~102°/19). n_D 1.5232 (22°).
④ + H₂O ⟶ (PhCH＝N)₂CHPh
⑥ Ber. 96, 2132 (1963).

SiC₁₀H₁₅NO
① p-Trimethylsilylbenzamide
p-(CH₃)₃SiC₆H₄CONH₂
② p-Me₃SiC₆H₄CN + Na₂CO₃
+ Me₂CO ⟶
p-Me₃SiC₆H₄COOH + SOCl₂,
then NH₃ ⟶
③ [154~155°].
⑥ Hua Hsüeh Hsüeh Pao 26, 7 (1960) ;
CA 55, 18654 (1961). Yakugaku
Zasshi 82, 929 (1962) ; CA 59, 653
(1963).

SiC₁₀H₁₆
① Benzyltrimethylsilane
(CH₃)₃SiCH₂C₆H₅
② PhCH₂MgCl + Me₃SiCl ⟶ (91%)
ClCH₂SiCl₃ + C₆H₆
$\xrightarrow{AlCl_3}$ PhCH₂SiCl₃ $\xrightarrow{MeMgI}$
③ (84~85°/10). n_D 1.4487 (20°). d 0.8933
(20°).
④ + SO₂Cl₂ + Bz₂O₂ ⟶ Me₃SiCHClPh

$+$ NBS $\xrightarrow{\text{CCl}_4}$ Me$_3$SiCHBrPh

$+$ Me$_3$SiCBr$_2$Ph

$+$ HCHO $+$ HCl $\longrightarrow$

Me$_3$SiCH$_2$(C$_6$H$_4$)CH$_2$Cl

$\xrightarrow{\text{(1)OH}^-\text{/MeOH, (2)H}_2\text{O}}$ MePh

⑥ JCS **1963**, 2342. JACS **74**, 5091 (1952);
   73, 5846 (1951), Zhur. **25**, 2469
   (1955).

SiC$_{10}$H$_{15}$

① Butylphenylsilane
   C$_6$H$_5$(H$_2$)SiC$_4$H$_9$-n

② C$_6$H$_5$(H$_2$)SiBr $+$ n-C$_4$H$_9$MgBr
   $\longrightarrow$ 58%

③ Colorless liq. (50°/1.5). n_D 1.499
   (25°).
   Sol. in org. solvents; insol. in H$_2$O.

⑥ JACS **76**, 4555 (1954).

SiC$_{10}$H$_{16}$

① Trimethyl-o-tolylsilane
   (CH$_3$)$_3$SiC$_6$H$_4$CH$_3$-o

② ClC$_6$H$_4$CH$_3$-o $+$ (CH$_3$)$_3$SiCl $+$ Na
   $\longrightarrow$ 68%

③ Colorless liq. (196°/750).
   Sol. in org. solvents; insol. in H$_2$O.

④ $+$ KMnO$_4$ $\longrightarrow$ o-CH$_3$SiC$_6$H$_4$CO$_2$H
   (21.4%)

⑥ JACS **76**, 599 (1954).

SiC$_{10}$H$_{16}$

① p-Tolyltrimethylsilane
   p-CH$_3$C$_6$H$_4$Si(CH$_3$)$_3$

② p-MeC$_6$H$_4$Li $+$ Me$_3$SiCl $\longrightarrow$ 53%
   p-MeC$_6$H$_4$MgBr $+$ Me$_3$SiCl $\longrightarrow$
   p-MeC$_6$H$_4$Li $+$ Me$_3$SiOSiPh$_3$ $\longrightarrow$

③ (191.5°). n_D 1.4930 (20°).

④ Loses silicon in acid.

⑥ Rec. trav. chim. **81**, 88 (1962).   JACS
   80, 5289 (1958).   JCS **1959**, 2299;
   JOC **19**, 419 (1954).

SiC$_{10}$H$_{16}$N$_2$

① p-Trimethylsilylbenzamidine
   p-(CH$_3$)$_3$SiC$_6$H$_4$C($=$NH)NH$_2$

② NH$_3$ $+$ [p-Me$_3$SiC$_6$H$_4$C($=$NH)$_2$OEt]$^+$Cl$^-$
   $\longrightarrow$

③ [236~241°].

⑥ Yakugaku Zasshi **82**, 931 (1962); CA
   59, 653 (1963).

SiC$_{10}$H$_{16}$O

① p-Trimethylsilylbenzyl alcohol
   p-(CH$_3$)$_3$SiC$_6$H$_4$CH$_2$OH

② AcOCH$_2$C$_6$H$_4$SiMe$_3$ $+$ NaOH $\longrightarrow$
   HCHO $+$ p-Me$_3$SiC$_6$H$_4$CHO
   $+$ KOH $\longrightarrow$
   HCHO $+$ p-Me$_3$SiC$_6$H$_4$CHO
   $+$ NaOH $\longrightarrow$
   KOH $+$ p-Me$_3$SiC$_6$H$_4$CHO $\longrightarrow$

③ (120~140°/15). [117~118°]. n_D 1.5140
   (20°). d 0.9705 (20°/4°).

⑥ JACS **79**, 6540 (1957).   Yakugaku
   Zasshi **82**, 929 (1962); CA **59**, 653
   (1963).   Rec. trav. chim. **81**, 88
   (1962).   Izv. OKhN **1961**, 1069;
   English page 939.

SiC$_{10}$H$_{16}$O

① Diethylphenylhydroxysilane
   C$_6$H$_5$(C$_2$H$_5$)$_2$SiOH

② C$_6$H$_5$(C$_2$H$_5$)$_2$SiCl $+$ NaOH $\longrightarrow$ 92%

③ Colorless liq. (107.5~110°/9). n_D 1.5170
   (20°). d 0.9905 (20°).
   Sol. in org. solvents.

④ $+$ HCl $\longrightarrow$ [C$_6$H$_5$(C$_2$H$_5$)$_2$Si]$_2$O
   $+$ C$_4$H$_9$OCH$=$CH$_2$ $\longrightarrow$
   C$_6$H$_5$(C$_2$H$_5$)$_2$SiOCH(CH$_3$)OC$_4$H$_9$

⑥ Dokl. **95**, 821 (1954); CA **49**, 6159
   (1953).

SiC$_{10}$H$_{16}$O

① Phenylethoxydimethylsilane
   C$_6$H$_5$Si(CH$_3$)$_2$OC$_2$H$_5$

② (CH$_3$)$_2$Si(OC$_2$H$_5$)$_2$ $+$ C$_6$H$_5$MgCl $\longrightarrow$

③ (195~196°).

④ Hua Hsüeh Hsüeh Pao. 27, 38 (1961);
    CA 59, 11547 (1963).

$SiC_{10}H_{16}O$

① Trimethyl-*m*-methoxyphenylsilane
    $(CH_3)_3Si(C_6H_4OCH_3-m)$

② $(CH_3)_3SiCl + m\text{-}CH_3OC_6H_4MgBr$
    $\longrightarrow$ 36%

③ Colorless liq. (216°). n_D 1.5020 (20°).
    d 0.9383 (20°).
    Sol. in org. solvents.

④ + HCl $\longrightarrow$ $(CH_3)_3SiCl$
    $+ CH_3OC_6H_5$

⑥ JACS 75, 4528 (1953).

$SiC_{10}H_{16}O$

① Trimethyl-*p*-methoxyphenylsilane
    $(p\text{-}CH_3OC_6H_4)Si(CH_3)_3$

② $p\text{-}CH_3OC_6H_4Li + ClSi(CH_3)_3$
    in Et_2O
    $\longrightarrow$ 55%

③ (220°). n_D 1.5014 (20°). d 0.9398 (20°).

④ + HCl $\longrightarrow$ $CH_3OC_6H_5 + ClSi(CH_3)_3$

⑥ JACS 75, 4528 (1953); 72, 2629 (1950).
    JCS 1953, 3148.

$SiC_{10}H_{16}O$

① 2,2,7-Trimethyl-7-hydroxy-2-sila-
    3,5-octadiine
    $(CH_3)_2C(OH)C\equiv CC\equiv CSi(CH_3)_3$

② $BrMgOCMe_2C\equiv CC\equiv CMgBr$
    $+ Me_3SiCl \longrightarrow$ 68%

③ (85°/3). [67°].

⑥ Izv. OKhN 1962, 1694.

$SiC_{10}H_{16}O_2S$

① Trimethylphenylsulfonylmethyl-
    silane
    $(CH_3)_3SiCH_2SO_2C_6H_5$

② $Me_3SiCH_2Cl \xrightarrow{PhSH,\ NaOH}$
    $Me_3SiCH_2SPh \xrightarrow{C_6H_4(COOOH)_2\ in\ Et_2O}$

③ (160°/6). n_D 1.5250 (25°).

④ $Me_2SiCH_2SO_2Ph \xrightarrow{OH^-} (Me_3Si)_2O$

⑥ JACS 76, 3713 (1954).   US 2719165
    (1955).

$SiC_{10}H_{16}O_3$

① Benzyltrimethoxysilane
    $C_6H_5CH_2Si(OCH_3)_3$

② $(CH_3O)_4Si + C_6H_5CH_2MgBr \longrightarrow$ 10%

③ Colorless liq. (227.7°). n_D 1.4590 (20°).
    d 1.064 (20°).
    Sol. in org. solvents.

⑥ Zhur. 25, 1124 (1955); CA 50, 3217
    (1954).

$SiC_{10}H_{16}O_3S$

① Trimethylsilyl *p*-tolylsulfonate
    $p\text{-}CH_3C_6H_4SO_2OSi(CH_3)_3$

② $PhMe + Me_3SiOSO_2Cl \longrightarrow$

③ (164°/16). n_D 1.4960 (20°). d 1.120
    (20°).

⑥ Bull. soc. chim. France 1963, 512.

$SiC_{10}H_{16}S$

① Trimethylphenylthiomethylsilane
    $(CH_3)_3SiCH_2SC_6H_5$

② $Me_3SiCH_2Cl \xrightarrow{PhSH,\ NaOH}$ 67%
    $Me_3SiCH_2Cl \xrightarrow{PhSNa\ in\ EtOH}$ 74%

③ (158.5°/52). n_D 1.5380 (20°). d 0.9671
    (20°).

⑥ JACS 76, 3713 (1954).   US 2719165
    (1955).   Rec. trav. chim. 76, 187
    (1957).

$SiC_{10}H_{18}F_6O_2$

① Diethoxybis(3,3,3-trifluoropropyl)-
    silane
    $(CF_3CH_2CH_2)_2Si(OC_2H_5)_2$

② $(EtO)_2SiCl_2 + CF_3CH_2CH_2MgCl \longrightarrow$
    92%
    $CF_3CH_2CH_2MgBr$
    $+ CF_3CH_2CH_2Si(OEt)_2Cl \longrightarrow$

③ (88.7~89.0°/20). d 1.1595 (20°).

④ + HCl(5%), then KOH(200°~220°)

$\longrightarrow$ [(CF₃CH₂CH₂)₂SiO]₄

+ LiAlH₄ $\longrightarrow$ (CF₃CH₂CH₂)₂SiH₂

⑥ US 3070617 (1962); CA **58**, 12600
  (1963). Brit. 835523 (1960); CA **55**,
  1445 (1961). JACS **33**, 4932 (1961).
  Zhur. **33**, 704 (1963).

SiC₁₀H₁₈O

① Triallylmethoxysilane
  (CH₂=CHCH₂)₃SiOCH₃

② Si(OCH₃)₄ + 3CH₂=CHCH₂MgBr
  $\longrightarrow$ 11%

③ Colorless liq. (191.2°). n_D1.4480 (20°).
  d0.8316 (20°).
  Sol. in org. solvents.

⑥ Zhur. **25**, 1124 (1955); CA **50**, 3217
  (1954).

SiC₁₀H₁₈O

① Vinyl(trimethylsiloxydimethyl-
    methyl)acetylene
  CH₂=CHC≡CC(CH₃)₂OSi(CH₃)₃

② CH₂=CHC≡CCMe₂OMgBr
  + Me₃SiCl $\longrightarrow$ 73.6%

③ (36°/6). n_D 1.4403 (20°). d 0.8271
  (20°).

⑥ Izv. OKhN **1963**, 97.

SiC₁₀H₁₈O

① Vinyl diisopropylhydroxysilyl
    acetylene
  CH₂=CHC≡CSi(C₃H₇-i)₂OH

③ (86°). n_D1.4848. d0.8900 (20°).

⑥ Izv. OKhN **1963**, 97.

SiC₁₀H₁₈S₂N₂

① Dibutyldiisothiocyanosilane
  (C₄H₉)₂Si(NCS)₂

② (C₄H₉)₂SiCl₂ + NH₄NCS $\longrightarrow$ 60~75%

③ Colorless liq. (154.5°/6). n_D 1.5106
  (20°). d0.9950 (20°).
  Sol. in org. solvents.

⑥ Zhur. **24**, 1082 (1954); CA **49**, 8791
  (1953).

SiC₁₀H₂₀O₂

① Ethyl 2-trimethylsilylmethylcyclo-
    propanecarboxylate
  (CH₃)₃SiCH₂CH
      | >CHCOOC₂H₅
     CH₂

② CH(N)₂COOEt + Me₃SiCH₂CH=CH₂
  $\longrightarrow$ 66.5%

③ (86.5~87.5°/10.5). n_D1.4400 (20°). d
  0.9072 (20°/4°).

⑥ Izv. OKhN, **1963**, 572. Zhur. **33**, 2422
  (1963).

SiC₁₀H₂₀O₂

① Diallyldiethoxysilane
  (CH₂=CHCH₂)₂Si(OC₂H₅)₂

② CH₂=CHCH₂MgCl + Si(OEt)₄ $\longrightarrow$

③ (189.5°). n_D 1.4316 (25°). d 0.8846
  (20°).

⑤ Forms polymers.

⑥ Periodica Polytech. **6**, 35 (1962);
  CA **58**, 4593 (1963).   US 2595728
  (1952); CA **46**, 7820 (1952). Kungl.
  Fysiografiska Sallskarets I Lund
  Forhadlingar **25** (No.7) (1955).
  Brit. 663770 (1951); CA **46**, 11228
  (1952).

SiC₁₀H₂₀O₂

① Triethylsilyl crotonate
  CH₃CH=CHCOOSi(C₂H₅)₃

② MeCOOSiEt₃ + MeCH=CHCOOH
  $\longrightarrow$ 77.0%

③ (72.0~73.5°/2). n_D1.4458 (20°). d0.9054
  (20°).

⑥ Zhur. **33**, 1934 (1963).

SiC₁₀H₂₀O₂

① Diallyloxydiethylsilane
  (C₂H₅)₂Si(OCH₂CH=CH₂)₂

② CH₂=CHCH₂OH + (C₂H₅)₂SiCl₂
  $\longrightarrow$ 74%

③ Colorless liq. (72°/7). n_D1.4302 (20°).

d 0.8888 (20°).

Sol. in org. solvents.

⑥ Izv. OKhN **1957**, 383 ; CA **51**, 15457 (1955).

SiC$_{10}$H$_{20}$O$_4$

① Methyldiethoxysilylmethyl methacrylate

CH$_2$=C(CH$_3$)COOCH$_2$Si(OC$_2$H$_5$)$_2$CH$_3$

② *p*-C$_6$H$_4$(OH)$_2$ + MeSi(OEt)$_2$CH$_2$Cl
+ CH$_2$=C(Me)COOH + Et$_3$N
⟶ 53%

(EtO)$_2$Si(Me)CH$_2$Cl +
CH$_2$=C(Me)COOK + *p*-C$_6$H$_4$(OH)$_2$
+ Cu(powder) ⟶

③ (80~82°/5). n_D 1.4283 (20°). *d* 0.9753 (20°).

④ + Me$_2$Si(OEt)$_2$ + (AcO)$_2$Si(OEt)$_2$
⟶ linear polymers
+ AcOSiMe$_3$ ⟶

            OSiMe$_3$
            |
CH$_2$=CCOOCH$_2$SiMe   (71%)
     | |
     Me   OSiMe$_3$

+ AcOSiMe$_2$Ph ⟶

            OSiMe$_2$Ph
            |
CH$_2$=CCOOCH$_2$SiMe   (22%)
     | |
     Me   OSiMe$_2$Ph

⑥ Izv. OKhN **1956**, 1767 ; **1962**, 1572. Dokl. **119**, 1149 (1958), Vysokomol. Soed. **5**, 343 (1963).

SiC$_{10}$H$_{20}$O$_5$

① γ-Trimethoxysilylpropyl methacrylate

CH$_2$=C(CH$_3$)COO(CH$_2$)$_3$Si(OCH$_3$)$_3$

② HSi(OMe)$_3$ +
CH$_2$=C(Me)COOCH$_2$CH=CH$_2$
   $\xrightarrow{\text{H}_2\text{PtCl}_6}$

③ (94~96°/1), n_D 1.4305 (25°).

⑥ Belg. 613466 (1962) ; CA **58**, 6861 (1963).

SiC$_{10}$H$_{21}$Cl

① 1-Triethylsilyl-3-chlorobutene-2
(C$_2$H$_5$)$_3$SiCH$_2$CH=CClCH$_3$

② H$_2$PtCl$_6$ + Et$_3$SiH + CH$_2$=CClCH=CH$_2$
⟶ 30%

③ (218~220°). n_D 1.4650 (20°). *d* 0.9067 (20°).

⑥ Azerb. Khim. Zhur. (No.6) 9 (1962) ; CA **59**, 5189 (1963).

SiC$_{10}$H$_{22}$

① Buten-3-yltriethylsilane
(C$_2$H$_5$)$_3$SiCH$_2$CH$_2$CH=CH$_2$

② CH$_2$=CHCH$_2$CH$_2$SiCl$_3$
+ EtMgBr ⟶

Et$_3$SiCH$_2$Cl +
CH$_2$=CHCH$_2$MgBr ⟶

③ (64~65°/8). n_D 1.4439 (20°). *d* 0.7913 (20°).

④ + HP(O)(OEt)$_2$ + (*t*-BuO)$_2$ ⟶
Et$_3$Si(CH$_2$)$_4$P(O)(OEt)$_2$ (63%)

⑥ Izv. OKhN **1955**, 182 ; **1959**, 1231 ; English page 1188. Dokl. **148**, 875 (1963).

SiC$_{10}$H$_{22}$O

① 3-(Methyldi-*n*-propylsilyl)propanal
CH$_3$Si(C$_3$H$_7$-*n*)$_2$CH$_2$CH$_2$CHO

② MeSi(Pr-*n*)$_2$CH$_2$CH$_2$CH$_2$OH + Cu
⟶ 80.8%

③ (120~122°/4). n_D 1.4654 (20°).

④ + H$_2$NNHC$_6$H$_4$NO$_2$-*p* ⟶
MeSi(Pr-*n*)$_2$(CH$_2$)$_2$CH=
NNHC$_6$H$_4$NO$_2$-*p* (mp 209~210°)

⑥ Zhur. **33**, 3262 (1963).

SiC$_{10}$H$_{22}$O

① 2,6,6-Trimethyl-6-silaoctene-1 epoxide

C$_2$H$_5$Si(CH$_3$)$_2$CH$_2$CH$_2$CH$_2$C(CH$_3$)CH$_2$
                        \ /
                         O

② NaOH + EtSiMe$_2$CH$_2$CH$_2$CH$_2$CMe-

(OH)CH$_2$Cl $\longrightarrow$

③ (85.0 ~ 85.5°/1.0). n_D1.4382 (20°). d
0.8487 (20°).

④ + EtONa $\longrightarrow$
EtSiMe$_2$(CH$_2$)$_3$CMe(OH)CH$_2$OEt
+ EtSiHMe$_2$ $\longrightarrow$
EtSiMe$_2$(CH$_2$)$_3$CMe$_2$OSiMe$_2$Et
+ Ac$_2$O $\longrightarrow$
EtSiMe$_2$(CH$_2$)$_3$C(OAc)CH$_2$OAc
+ NH$_3$ $\longrightarrow$
EtSiMe$_2$(CH$_2$)$_3$CMe(OH)CH$_2$NH$_2$
+ [EtSiMe$_2$(CH$_2$)$_3$CMe(OH)CH$_2$]$_2$NH
+ Me$_2$NH $\longrightarrow$
EtSiMe$_2$(CH$_2$)$_2$CMe(OH)CH$_2$NMe$_2$

⑥ Azerb. Khim. Zhur. (No.5) 105 (1962) :
CA **59**, 2847 (1963).

SiC$_{10}$H$_{22}$O

① Methyldi-n-propylallyloxysilane
CH$_3$Si(C$_3$H$_7$-n)$_2$OCH$_2$CH=CH$_2$

② n-Pr$_2$SiHMe +

$$CH_2 = CHCH_2OH \xrightarrow[\text{ZnCl}_2 \text{ or SnCl}_2]{\text{catalyst Li, Na}}$$

③ (84.0~84.5°/15). n_D 1.4259 (20°). d
0.8225 (20°/4°).

⑥ Izv. OKhN **1963**, 1749.

SiC$_{10}$H$_{22}$O$_2$

① Triethylsilyl n-butyrate
n-C$_3$H$_7$COOSi(C$_2$H$_5$)$_3$

② Et$_3$SiH + n-PrCOOH + Ni(colloidal)
$\longrightarrow$ 93.9%
H$_2$PtCl$_6$ + Et$_3$SiH + n-PrCOOH $\longrightarrow$
NiCl$_2$ + Et$_3$SiH + n-PrCOOH $\longrightarrow$

③ (204°/778). n_D 1.4275 (20°). d 0.8862
(20°/4°).

⑥ Zhur. **33**, 1934 (1963) ; **32**, 2561 (1962).

SiC$_{10}$H$_{24}$

① Methyltri-n-propylsilane
CH$_3$Si(C$_3$H$_7$)$_3$

② n-PrMgBr + MeSiCl$_3$ $\longrightarrow$
n-Pr$_3$SiF + MeMgI $\longrightarrow$ 83%

③ (182.5~183.5°). n_D 1.4280 (20°). d

0.7660 (20°).

⑥ Izv. OKhN **1955**, 1031.

SiC$_{10}$H$_{24}$

① Dimethyldi-n-butylsilane
(CH$_3$)$_2$Si(C$_4$H$_9$-n)$_2$

② Ni + MeOH +

$$\left(\begin{array}{c} CH{=\!=\!=}CH \\ CH{}\underset{S}{}C- \end{array} \right)_2 SiMe_2 \longrightarrow$$

③ (180~182°). n_D1.4247. d0.7660 (20°/4°).

⑥ Naturwiss. **44**, 181 (1957).   Svensk
Kemisk Tidskrift **63**, 179 (1951).
Zhur. **33**, 1251 (1963).

SiC$_{10}$H$_{24}$O$_2$

① Dimethyldi-n-butoxysilane
(CH$_3$)$_2$Si(OC$_4$H$_9$-n)$_2$

② n-BuOH + (Me$_2$SiNH)$_3$ $\longrightarrow$ 80%
(Me$_2$SiO)$_4$ + Ti(OBu-n)$_4$ $\longrightarrow$ 18.4%
Me$_2$SiCl$_2$ + n-BuOH $\longrightarrow$ 76%

③ (187~188°). n_D 1.4058 (20°). d 0.8465
(20°).

④ + P$_2$O$_5$ $\longrightarrow$ [(Me$_2$Si)$_3$(PO$_4$)$_2$]$_7$ or $_8$

⑥ Izv. OKhN **1962**, 833, J. Ind. Chem.
Soc. **39**, 65 (1962) ; CA **57**, 4279
(1962). Zhur. Priklad. Khim. **32**,
369 (1959) ; CA **53**, 13989 (1959).
Zhur. **32**, 2316 (1962) ; English
page 2284.

SiC$_{10}$H$_{24}$O$_2$

① Dimethyldiisobutoxysilane
(CH$_3$)$_2$Si(OC$_4$H$_9$-i)$_2$

② i-BuOH + (Me$_2$SiNH)$_4$ $\longrightarrow$ 49.2%
Si(OBu-i)$_4$ + KOH + (Me$_2$SiO)$_x$ $\longrightarrow$

③ (172.0°). n_D 1.3999 (20°). d 0.8444
(20°/4°).

⑥ Zhur. **29**, 907 (1959) ; **32**, 2316 (1962) ;
English page 2284.

SiC$_{10}$H$_{24}$O$_2$

① Di-*n*-butyldimethoxysilane
(C$_4$H$_9$)$_2$Si(OCH$_3$)$_2$

② Si(OCH$_3$)$_4$ + 3C$_4$H$_9$MgBr $\longrightarrow$ 38%

③ Colorless liq. (205.4°). n_D1.4185 (20°).
d0.8710 (20°).
Sol. in org. solvents.

⑥ Zhur. **25**, 1124 (1955); CA **50**, 3217
(1956).

SiC$_{10}$H$_{24}$O$_3$

① Methyltri-*n*-propoxysilane
CH$_3$Si(OC$_3$H$_7$)$_3$

② CH$_3$SiCl$_3$ + *n*-C$_3$H$_7$OH $\longrightarrow$ 46.9%

③ Colorless liq. (192°/760, 90~91°/20).
n_D1.39917 (20°). d0.8831 (20°).
Sol. in org. solvents.

⑥ JOC 17, 1400 (1952). Chem. Listy **48**,
1197 (1954); CA **49**, 94951 (1955).

SiC$_{10}$H$_{24}$O$_3$

① *n*-Butyltriethoxysilane
n-C$_4$H$_9$Si(OC$_2$H$_5$)$_3$

② (C$_2$H$_5$O)$_4$Si + Mg + *n*-C$_4$H$_9$Cl $\longrightarrow$

③ Colorless liq. (197°). n_D1.4011 (20°).
d0.8883 (20°).
Sol. in org. solvents.

④ + HCOOH $\longrightarrow$ HCOOC$_2$H$_5$
+ *n*-C$_4$H$_9$Si(OH)$_3$
+ poly-*n*-butylsiloxane

⑥ Kg. Fysiograph Sallskapi Lund.
Hand (NF) **63**, No.12 (1952). US
2477704; CA **44**, 2010 (1950). US
2442053. Japan 2669 (1951); CA **42**,
7786 (1948).

SiC$_{10}$H$_{24}$O$_4$

① Dimethylbis(β-ethoxyethoxy)silane
(CH$_3$)$_2$Si(OCH$_2$CH$_2$OC$_2$H$_5$)$_2$

② Me$_2$SiCl$_2$ + EtOCH$_2$CH$_2$OH $\longrightarrow$ 88%

③ (177°/200). n_D1.411 (25°). d0.931
(25°).

⑥ Compt. rend. **256**, 4920 (1963). Ger.
936038 (1955); CA **52**, 19947 (1958).
JOC **15**, 106 (1950).

SiC$_{10}$H$_{25}$O$_3$P

① 4-Triethylsilylbutylphosphonic acid
(C$_2$H$_5$)$_3$SiCH$_2$CH$_2$CH$_2$CH$_2$P(O)(OH)$_2$

② HCl + HOH
+ Et$_3$SiCH$_2$CH$_2$CH$_2$CH$_2$P(O)(OEt)$_2$
$\longrightarrow$

③ [53~56°].

⑥ Dokl. **148**, 875 (1963).

SiC$_{10}$H$_{25}$O$_3$P

① Diethyl triethylsilyl phosphite
(C$_2$H$_5$O)$_2$POSi(C$_2$H$_5$)$_3$

② Et$_3$SiONa + (EtO)$_2$PCl $\longrightarrow$

③ (105~106°/10). n_D1.4332 (20°). d0.9340
(20°/4°).

⑥ Izv. OKhN 1963, 768.

SiC$_{10}$H$_{26}$N$_2$

① Dimethylbis(diethylamino)silane
(CH$_3$)$_2$Si[N(C$_2$H$_5$)$_2$]$_2$

② Me$_2$SiCl$_2$ + Et$_2$NH $\longrightarrow$

③ (84~85°/20). n_D 1.4350 (20°). d 0.826
(20°/4°).

④ + Et$_2$NNH$_2$ $\longrightarrow$ Me$_2$Si(NHNEt$_2$)$_2$
+ (C$_6$H$_4$NH$_2$-*p*)$_2$
$\longrightarrow$ (Me$_2$SiNHC$_6$H$_4$C$_6$H$_4$NH-*p*)$_x$
+ *p*-C$_6$H$_4$(NH$_2$)$_2$
$\longrightarrow$ (Me$_2$SiNHC$_6$H$_4$NH-*p*)$_x$

⑥ Rec. trav. chim. **80**, 819 (1961).
Zhur. **33**, 1294(1963); **32**, 1987(1962);
English page 1968. J. Polym. Sci.
50, 151 (1961).

SiC$_{10}$H$_{26}$N$_2$

① Ethylbis(diethylamino)silane
C$_2$H$_5$SiH[N(C$_2$H$_5$)$_2$]$_2$

② EtSiHCl$_2$ + Et$_2$NH $\longrightarrow$

③ (91~92°/20). n_D1.4391 (20°). d0.8267
(20°/4°).

④ + Et₂NNH₂ ⟶ EtSiH(NHNEt₂)₂
  + EtSi(NHNEt₂)₃
⑥ Zhur. **32**, 1987(1962) ; **33**, 1294 (1963) ;
  English page 1968.

SiC₁₀H₂₆O
① 1-Trimethylsiloxy-4-trimethylsilyl-
  butane
  (CH₃)₃SiO(CH₂)₄Si(CH₃)₃
② Me₃SiCl + Mg + THF ⟶
③ (134°/78). n_D1.4181 (20°).
⑥ US 3083219 (1963) ; CA **59**, 8789
  (1963).

SiC₁₀H₂₇N
① Bis(*n*-propyldimethylsilyl)amine
  [*n*-C₃H₇Si(CH₃)₂]₂NH
② NH₃ + *n*-PrSiMe₂Cl ⟶
③ (75.5~76.5°/8). n_D1.4270 (20°). d0.8152
  (20°/4°).
⑥ Izv. OKhN **1963**, 1333.

SiC₁₀H₃₀N₆
① *n*-Butyltris(β-aminoethylamino)-
  silane
  n-C₄H₉Si(NHCH₂CH₂NH₂)₃
② *n*-BuSiH₃ + (CH₂NH₂)₂ ⟶ 59%
③ [242~243°].
⑥ Zhur. **33**, 2617 (1963).

SiC₁₁H₈Cl₂
① 1,1-Dichloro-1-silaacenaphthene

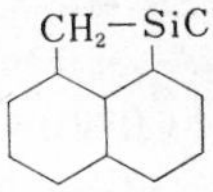

② + SiHCl₃ $\xrightarrow{(600°~700°)}$ 50%
③ Solid. (139~142°/4.5). [49°].

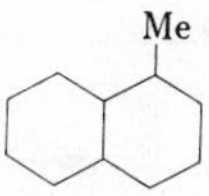

④ + HF ⟶

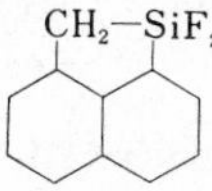

⑥ Izv. OKhN **1963**, 1146.

SiC₁₁H₈F₂
① 1,1-Difluoro-1-silaacenaphthene

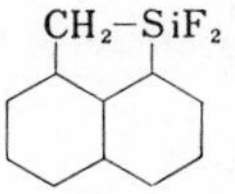

② HF +

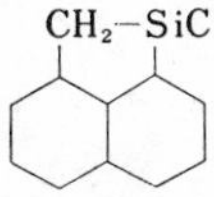

③ Solid. (112~113°/6.5). [39°].
⑥ Izv. OKhN **1963**, 1146.

SiC₁₁H₁₀Cl₂
① Methyl-α-naphthyldichlorosilane
  CH₃(C₁₀H₇-α)SiCl₂
② CH₃SiCl₃+α-C₁₀H₇Li ⟶ 33.2%
③ Liquid. (122°/1). n_D1.6025 (20°). d
  1.2333 (20°).
  Sol. in org. solvents. ; Decomp.
  with H₂O.
⑥ Izv. OKhN **1954**, 1123 ; CA **49**, 2510
  (1953).

SiC₁₁H₁₁Cl
① α-Naphthylmethylchlorosilane
  α-C₁₀H₇SiH(CH₃)Cl
② α-C₁₀H₇MgBr + MeSiHCl₂ ⟶
③ (175°/4).
⑥ Latvijas PSR Vestis, Khim. Ser.
  1962, (No.2) 315 ; CA **58**, 11394
  (1963).

SiC₁₁H₁₄
① Trimethylphenylethynylsilane
  (CH₃)₃SiC≡CC₆H₅
② (CH₃)₃SiBr + C₆H₅C≡CH
  + C₂H₅MgBr ⟶
③ Liquid. (87.5°/9). n_D1.5284 (20°). d
  0.8961 (20°).
  Sol. in org. solvents ; insol. in H₂O.

④ + Na ⟶ cyclic dimer
⑥ Dokl. **93**, 293 (1953) ; CA **46**, 13616
  (1954).

SiC₁₁H₁₄S
① 1-Sulfa-2-trimethylsilylindene

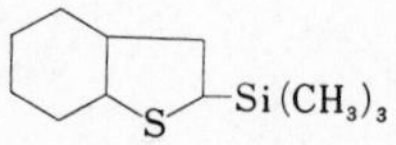

②

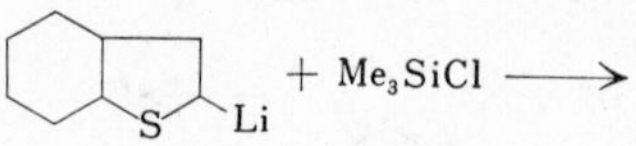

  + Me₃SiCl ⟶
③ (123°/7). n_D1.5759 (20°).
⑥ JCS **1961**, 4921.

SiC₁₁H₁₅Br
① Allyl-*p*-bromophenyldimethylsilane
  $(CH_3)_2Si(CH_2CH=CH_2)C_6H_4Br-p$
② p-BrC₆H₄Li + Me₂Si(Cl)CH₂CH=CH₂
  ⟶ 33%
③ (81~84°/0.3). n_D1.5304 (27°).
  IR : 3070, 2960, 1630, 1575, 1482, 1380,
    1255, 1160, 1070, 1015, 900, 850~800,
    725 cm⁻¹.
⑥ JOC **27**, 1486 (1962).

SiC₁₁H₁₅Cl
① 1-Phenyl-2-ethylmethylchloro-
  silylethene
  $C_6H_5CH=CHSi(CH_3)(C_2H_5)Cl$
② EtSi(H)(Cl)Me + PhC≡CH + H₂PtCl₆
  ⟶ 61%
③ (130°/7). n_D1.5292 (20°). d1.033(20°).
⑥ Izv. OKhN **1963**, 136 ; CA **59**, 11550
  (1963).

SiC₁₁H₁₅Cl
① (*p*-Vinylphenyl)dimethylchloro-
  methylsilane
  p-CH₂=CHC₆H₄Si(CH₃)₂CH₂Cl
② p-CH₂=CHC₆H₄MgBr
  + Me₂Si(Cl)CH₂Cl ⟶ 55%
③ (80°/5×10⁻³). n_D1.5488 (20°). d1.0559

(20°/4°).
⑥ Makromol. Chem. **67**, 98 (1963).

SiC₁₁H₁₅Cl₃O₂
① Methyldiethoxytrichlorophenylsilane
  $Cl_3C_6H_2Si(OC_2H_5)_2CH_3$
② $Cl_3C_6H_2Si(Cl)_2Me$ + EtOH
  ⟶ 78.4%
③ (135~137°/5). n_D1.5124 (20°). d1.2496
  (20°/20°).
⑥ Zhur. **32**, 3727 (1962).

SiC₁₁H₁₅N₃
① 4-Phenyl-1-trimethylsilyl-1,2,3-tria-
  zole

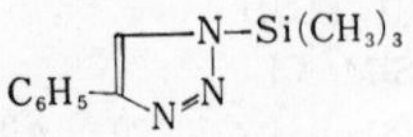

② PhC≡CH + Me₃SiN₃ ⟶ 64%
③ (98°/0.1).
⑥ Ber. **96**, 2750 (1963).

SiC₁₁H₁₆
① Trimethylstyrylsilane
  $C_6H_5CH=CHSi(CH_3)_3$
② PhCH=CHMgBr + Me₃SiCl
  ⟶ 53%
  PhCH=CHCl + HSiCl₃
  $\xrightarrow{640°}$ PhCH=CHSiCl₃ (75%)
  $\xrightarrow{MeMgBr}$ PhCH=CHSiMe₃
  PhC≡CH + HSiCl₃

  $\begin{array}{l}\xrightarrow{Pd-C} trans\text{-PhCH=CHSiCl}_3 \\ \qquad\qquad\qquad ⟶ trans\text{-} \\ \xrightarrow{Bz_2O_2} cis\text{-PhCH=CHSiCl}_3 \\ \qquad\qquad\qquad ⟶ cis\text{-}\end{array}$

③ (98°/10.5, *cis* 85°/7, *trans* 81°/5). n_D
  1.5270 (20°). *cis* 1.5096 (20°). *trans*
  1.5260 (20°). d0.888 (20°).
④ + H₂SO₄ ⟶ polystyrene
  + Me₃SiOSO₃H $\xrightarrow{H_2O}$ Me₃SiOSiMe₃
  + Br₂ ⟶ PhCH=CHBr + Me₃SiBr

$$+ H_2 \xrightarrow{\text{Raney Ni}} PhCH_2CH_2SiMe_3$$

⑥ Izv. OKhN 1961, 1886; 1962, 1223.
JACS 76, 1613 (1954); 80, 5294
(1958).

SiC₁₁H₁₆

① 1-Methyl-1-benzyl-1-silacyclobutane
$$CH_2-CH_2-CH_2-Si(CH_3)CH_2C_6H_5$$

② PhCH₂Cl + Mg + CH₂CH₂CH₂Si(Cl)Me
$$\longrightarrow 87.3\%$$

③ (73.5〜74.0°). n_D 1.5313 (20°). d 0.9400
(20°/4°).

⑥ Dokl. 150, 799 (1963).

SiC₁₁H₁₆F₂

① 1-Phenylethylpropyldifluorosilane
$$C_6H_5CH(CH_3)Si(F)_2C_3H_7$$

② PrSiHF₂ + PhCH=CH₂ $\longrightarrow$

③ (102°/13). n_D 1.4660 (20°). d 1.0326
(20°/4°).

⑥ Zhur. 32, 3882 (1962).

SiC₁₁H₁₆Cl₂O₂

① Methyldiethoxydichlorophenylsilane
$$Cl_2C_6H_3Si(OC_2H_5)_2CH_3$$

② EtOH + Cl₂C₆H₃Si(Cl)₂Me $\longrightarrow$ 82.1%

③ (124〜127°/5). n_D 1.4983 (20°). d 1.1580
(20°/20°).

⑥ Zhur. 32, 3727 (1962).

SiC₁₁H₁₆Cl₂O₂

① Methylphenylbis(2-chloroethoxy)-
silane
$$CH_3Si(OCH_2CH_2Cl)_2C_6H_5$$

② MeSi(Cl)₂Ph + KOH + (CH₂)₂O
$$\longrightarrow 62.2\%$$

③ (125〜130°/2). n_D 1.5075 (20°). d 1.1943
(20°).

⑥ Zhur. 33, 905 (1963).

SiC₁₁H₁₆O

① *p*-Trimethylsilylacetophenone

$$p\text{-}(CH_3)_3SiC_6H_4COCH_3$$

② MeMgX + *p*-Me₃SiC₆H₄CN $\longrightarrow$

③ (142〜144°/30).

④ + H₂NNHC₆H₃(NO₂)₂ (2,4) $\longrightarrow$
$$p\text{-}Me_3SiC_6H_4C(CH_3)=$$
$$NNHC_6H_3(NO_2)_2 \ (2,4) \ [203〜205°]$$

⑥ Yakugaku Zasshi 82, 929 (1962); CA
59, 653 (1963).

SiC₁₁H₁₇F₉O

① Tris(3,3,3-trifluoropropyl)ethoxy-
silane
$$(CF_3CH_2CH_2)_3SiOC_2H_5$$

③ (107.0°/16). n_D 1.3597 (20°). d 1.2706
(20°/4°).

⑥ Zhur. 33, 704 (1963).

SiC₁₁H₁₇NO₂

① Trimethylsilylmethyl phenylcarba-
mate
$$(CH_3)_3SiCH_2OCONHC_6H_5$$

② (CH₃)₃SiCH₂OH + C₆H₅NCO $\xrightarrow{C_6H_6}$

③ [80.5〜81.0°].

⑥ Hua Hsüeh Hsüeh Pao 23, 291 (1957).
JACS 70, 1117 (1948). Izv. OKhN
1960, 1998.

SiC₁₁H₁₈

① Trimethyl-2-phenethylsilane
$$(CH_3)_3SiCH_2CH_2C_6H_5$$

② ClCH₂CH₂SiCl₃ + C₆H₆
$$\xrightarrow{AlCl_3} PhCH_2CH_2SiCl_3 \xrightarrow{MeMgI}$$
$$PhCH=CH_2 + HSiCl_3 \xrightarrow{(C_5H_5N)_4NiCl_2}$$
$$PhCH_2CH_2SiCl_3 \xrightarrow{MeMgBr}$$

③ Liquid. (210〜211°). n_D 1.4874 (20°).
d 0.8650 (20°).
Raman and UV: Fiz. Sbornik Lvov
Univ. 1957, No.3, 390.

④ + Br₂ + Fe $\longrightarrow$
$$p\text{-}BrC_6H_4CH_2CH_2SiMe_3$$

⑥ JACS 79, 974 (1957). BCSJ 29, 784
(1956). Zhur. 25, 2469 (1955).

SiC₁₁H₁₈

① Trimethyl-1-phenylethylsilane

(CH₃)₃SiCH(CH₃)C₆H₅

② PhCH=CH₂ + HSiCl₃

$\xrightarrow{(C_5H_5N_4)NiCl_2}$

PhCHMeSiCl₃ + PhCH₂CH₂SiCl₃

$\underset{\big\downarrow\text{MeMgBr}}{\overset{\overbrace{}}{30\%}}$

$\longrightarrow$

③ Liq. (103~104.5°/32). n_D 1.4958 (25°).
d 0.8747 (25°).

⑥ BCSJ **29**, 784 (1956). JOC **24**, 2052 (1959).

SiC₁₁H₁₈

① *p*-Ethylphenyltrimethylsilane

(CH₃)₃Si(C₆H₄C₂H₅-*p*)

② (CH₃)₃SiOC₂H₅ + *p*-C₂H₅C₆H₄Li
$\longrightarrow$ 82%

③ Colorless liq. (207.0~208.5°). n_D 1.4930 (20°). d 0.8672 (20°).

Sol. in org. solvents ; insol. in H₂O.

⑥ JACS **76**, 4552 (1954).

SiC₁₁H₁₈Cl₆O₂

① 1,2,3,4,5,6-Hexachlorocyclohexyl-
methyldiethoxysilane

(C₆H₅Cl₆)Si(OC₂H₅)₂CH₃

② (C₆H₅Cl₆)Si(Cl)₂Me + EtOH $\longrightarrow$

③ (187~190°/5). n_D 1.5215 (20°). d 1.4378 (20°/20°).

⑥ Dokl. **148**, 116 (1963).   Zhur. **32**, 909 (1962) ; English page 899. Zhur. **33**, 255 (1963).

SiC₁₁H₁₈O

① 2,6-Dimethylphenoxytrimethylsilane

(CH₃)₃SiOC₆H₃(CH₃)₂ (2,6)

② Me₃SiCl + HOC₆H₃Me₂ (2,6)
$\longrightarrow$ 56.4%

③ (212°). [―44°]. n_D 1.4838(23°). d 0.9449 (23°/23°).

⑥ J. Chi. Chem. Soc. (Ⅱ) **10**, 66 (1963).

JOC **24**, 1717 (1959).

SiC₁₁H₁₈O

① 2,5-Dimethylphenoxytrimethylsilane

(CH₃)₃SiOC₆H₂(CH₃)₂ (2,5)

② Me₃SiCl + HOC₆H₂Me₂ $\longrightarrow$ 65.0%

③ (205~207°).

IR : 1510, 1250, 1000, 841 cm⁻¹.

⑥ J. Chi. Chem. Soc. (Ⅱ) **10**, 66 (1963) ;
(Ⅱ) **8**, 380 (1961) ; **9**, 273 (1962).

SiC₁₁H₁₈O

① 2,3-Dimethylphenoxytrimethylsilane

(CH₃)₃SiOC₆H₂(CH₃)₂ (2,3)

② Me₃SiCl + HOC₆H₂Me₂ (2,3)
$\longrightarrow$ 75.0%

③ (210~212°). n_D 1.4891 (21°). d 0.9127 (21°/21°).

⑥ J. Chi. Chem. Soc. (Ⅱ) **10**, 66 (1963).

SiC₁₁H₁₈O

① 3,4-Dimethylphenoxytrimethyl-
silane

(CH₃)₃SiOC₆H₂(CH₃)₂ (3,4)

② Me₃SiCl + HOC₆H₂Me₂ (3,4)
$\longrightarrow$ 58.0%

③ (213~215°).

⑥ J. Chi. Chem. Soc. (Ⅱ) **10**, 66 (1963).

SiC₁₁H₁₈O

① 3,5-Dimethylphenoxytrimethylsilane

(CH₃)₃SiOC₆H₂(CH₃)₂ (3,5)

② Me₃SiCl + HOC₆H₃Me₂ (3,5)
$\longrightarrow$ 47.0%

③ (207~208°). n_D 1.4775 (22°). d 0.9204 (21°/21°).

⑥ J. Chi. Chem. Soc. (Ⅱ) **10**, 66 (1963).

SiC₁₁H₁₈O

① Dimethylbenzylmethoxymethyl-
silane

(CH₃)₂Si(CH₂C₆H₅)CH₂OCH₃

② PhCH₂SiMe₂Cl + Mg
 + MeOCH₂Cl ⟶

③ (139°/1.4). n_D 1.5162 (20°). d 0.9706
 (20°).

⑥ Belg. 618520 (1963); CA **59**, 6440
 (1963).

SiC₁₁H₁₈O₂

① Phenyldiethoxymethylsilane
 C₆H₅Si(OC₂H₅)₂CH₃

② PhSi(OEt)₃ + MeMgBr ⟶

③ (75~78°/4). n_D1.4680. d0.9623 (20°).

④ Undergoes cohydrolysis with titanium compounds.

⑥ Hua Hsüeh Hsüeh Pao **27**, 38 (1961);
 CA **59**, 11547 (1963). Vysokomol.
 Soed. **4**, 839 (1962).

SiC₁₁H₁₈O₃

① Triethylsilyl furoate

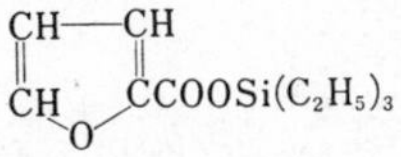

 CH——CH
 ‖ ‖
 CH CCOOSi(C₂H₅)₃
  O

② CH——CH
 ‖ ‖
 CH CCOOH + H₂PtCl₆
  O
    + Et₃SiH ⟶

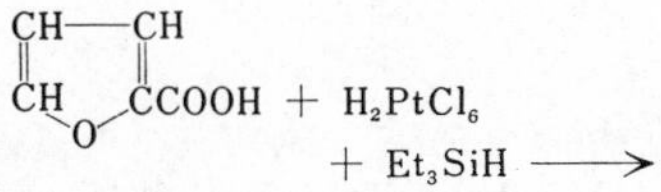

③ (109~110°/7). n_D1.4750 (20°). d1.0201
 (20°).

⑥ Latvijas PSR Zinatnu Akad. Vestis,
 Kem. Ser. 111 (1963); CA **59**,
 10102 (1963).

SiC₁₁H₂₀

① Trimethyl[α-(t-butylvinyl)ethynyl]-
 silane
 CH₂=C(t-C₄H₉)C≡CSi(CH₃)₃

② EtMgBr + CH₂=C(Bu-t)C≡CH
 + Me₃SiCl ⟶

③ (68~69°/20). n_D1.4488 (20°). d1.7871
 (20°/4°).
 IR: 3000, 2150, 1275, 1190, 1000, 900
 cm⁻¹.

④ Adds Br₂, H₂.

⑥ Zhur. **33**, 1421 (1963).

SiC₁₁H₂₀N₂

① N-Phenyl-N-ethyl-N′-trimethyl-
 silylhydrazine
 C₆H₅N(C₂H₅)NHSi(CH₃)₃

② PhNEtNH₂ + PhLi + Me₃SiCl
 ⟶ 64%

③ (94~95°). n_D1.5158 (20°).

④ Resistant to KOH.
 + HCl ⟶ PhNEtNH₃Cl
 + Me₃SiCl

⑥ Z. anorg. allg. Chem. **321**, 21 (1963).

SiC₁₁H₂₀O

① Triallylethoxysilane
 (CH₂=CHCH₂)₃SiOC₂H₅

② Si(OEt)₄ + CH₂=CHCH₂MgCl ⟶

③ (127~129°/84). n_D1.4564 (25°). d0.8543
 (25°).

⑤ Hydrolyzes and polymerizes to materials suitable for the coating
 of wires or laminated sheets.

⑥ Periodica Polytech. **6** (No.1) 35
 (1962); CA **58**, 4593 (1963). US
 2595728 (1952); CA **46**, 7820 (1952).
 Brit. 624362 (1949); CA **44**, 2287
 (1950).

SiC₁₁H₂₀OS

① Triethylfurfuroxysilane

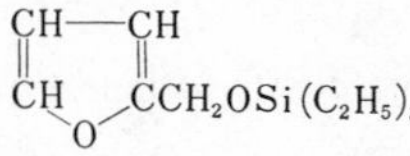

 CH——CH
 ‖ ‖
 CH CCH₂OSi(C₂H₅)₃
  O

② CH——CH
 ‖ ‖
 CH CCO + H₂PtCl₆
  O
    + Et₃SiH ⟶

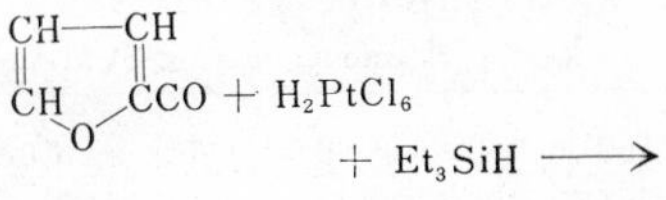

③ (90~91°/1.5). n_D1.4886 (20). d0.9788
 (20).

⑥ Latvijas PSR Zinatnu Akad. Vestis,
 Kem. Ser. 111 (1963); CA **59**, 10102

(1963).

SiC$_{11}$H$_{22}$O$_2$

① Ethyl 2-(2-trimethylsilyl)ethyl-
cyclopropylformate
(CH$_3$)$_3$SiCH$_2$CH$_2$CHCH$_2$
　　　　　　　　　　CHCOOC$_2$H$_5$
③ (80~82°/1). n_D 1.4406 (20°). d 0.8905
(20°/4°).
④ + HOH
⟶ Me$_3$SiCH$_2$CH$_2$CHCH$_2$
　　　　　　　　　　CHCOOH
⑥ Zhur. **33**, 2422 (1963).

SiC$_{11}$H$_{24}$

① Triethylpenten-4-ylsilane
CH$_2$=CHCH$_2$CH$_2$CH$_2$Si(C$_2$H$_5$)$_3$
② Et$_3$SiCH$_2$CH$_2$Br + CH$_2$=CHCH$_2$Br
　　Mg
　⟶ 24%
③ (207°). n_D1.4460 (20°). d0.7971 (20°).
⑥ Dokl. **80**, 761 (1951).

SiC$_{11}$H$_{24}$

① 1-Triethylsilyl-2-methylbutene-2
(C$_2$H$_5$)$_3$SiCH$_2$C(CH$_3$)=CHCH$_3$
② CH$_2$=CMeCH=CH$_2$ + Et$_3$SiH
+ H$_2$PtCl$_6$ ⟶ 79%
③ (64°/5). n_D1.4510 (25°). d0.8066 (25°).
⑥ Azerb. Khim. Zhur. (No.6) 9 (1962);
CA **59**, 5189 (1963).

SiC$_{11}$H$_{24}$Cl$_2$

① Methyl-n-decyldichlorosilane
CH$_3$Si(Cl)$_2$C$_{10}$H$_{21}$
② MeSiHCl$_2$ + C$_8$H$_{17}$CH=CH$_2$
(BzO$_2$) or dicyclohexylperoxydicarbonate
───────────────────────────────→
③ (90°/1). n_D 1.4488 (20°). d 0.9620
(20°/4°).
④ heat
　⟶ CH$_3$SiHCl$_2$.
　260°
⑥ Dokl. **150**, 1055 (1963); **112**, 271(1957);
115, 326 (1957). Tetrahedron 1,

248 (1957).

SiC$_{11}$H$_{24}$O

① Ethyldi-n-propylallyloxysilane
C$_2$H$_5$Si(n-C$_3$H$_7$)$_2$OCH$_2$CH=CH$_2$
② (Pr-n)$_2$SiHEt + CH$_2$=CHCH$_2$OH
Li, Na, ZnCl$_2$ or SnCl$_2$
③ (80.0°/6.0), n_D1.4324 (20°). d0.8334
(20°/4°).
⑥ Izv. OKhN **1963**, 1749.

SiC$_{11}$H$_{24}$O

① 2-Methyl-6,6-diethyl-6-sila-heptene-1
epoxide
CH$_3$Si(C$_2$H$_5$)$_2$CH$_2$CH$_2$CH$_2$C(CH$_3$)CH$_2$
　　　　　　　　　　　　　　　　O
② NaOH + MeSiEt$_2$CH$_2$CH$_2$CH$_2$CMe-
(OH)CH$_2$Cl ⟶
③ (85~86°/3). n_D1.4452 (20°). d0.8507
(20°).
⑥ Azerb. Khim. Zhur. (No.5) 105
(1962); CA **59**, 2847 (1963). Dokl.
118, 723 (1958).

SiC$_{11}$H$_{24}$O$_3$

① 1-Triethoxysilyl-2-methylbutene-2
(C$_2$H$_5$O)$_3$SiCH$_2$C(CH$_3$)=CHCH$_3$
② EtOH + Cl$_3$SiCH$_2$CMe=CHMe
⟶ 17%
③ (62.0~62.5°/1.5). n_D 1.4160 (20°). d
0.91069 (20°).
⑥ Azerb. Khim. Zhur. (No.6) 9 (1962);
CA **59**, 5189 (1963).

SiC$_{11}$H$_{25}$NO

① N-Propyl-N-triethylsilylacetamide
CH$_3$CON(n-C$_3$H$_7$)Si(C$_2$H$_5$)$_3$
② MeCONHPr-n + Et$_3$SiH + ZnCl$_2$
⟶ 66%
③ (109~110°/28). n_D1.4480 (20°). d0.895
(20°).
⑥ Compt. rend. **257**, 1304 (1963).

SiC₁₁H₂₈Sn

① Triethyl(ethyldimethylsilylmethyl)-
   stannane
   $C_2H_5Si(CH_3)_2CH_2Sn(C_2H_5)_3$

② $EtSiMe_2CH_2MgCl + Et_3SnCl \longrightarrow$

③ (99~100°/3.5). n_D 1.4790 (20°/4°). d
   1.1135 (20°/4°).

⑥ Zhur. **33**, 1945 (1963).

SiC₁₁H₂₉N₃O₃

① Tris(β-hydroxyethylamino)-
   isoamylsilane
   $i-C_5H_{11}Si(NHCH_2CH_2OH)_3$

② i-AmSiH₃ + CH₂(OH)CH₂NH₂
   $\longrightarrow$ 63.4%

③ (137~138°/1). n_D 1.4612 (20°). d 1.0149
   (20°/4°).

⑥ Zhur. **33**, 2617 (1963).

SiC₁₂H₈Cl₂Br₂

① Bis(p-bromophenyl)dichlorosilane
   $(p\text{-}BrC_6H_4)_2SiCl_2$

② $SiCl_4 + p\text{-}BrC_6H_4MgBr \longrightarrow$ 48%

③ Yellow solid. (389~397°/739), (241~
   244°/24). [87~88°].

④ + HNO₃ in Ac₂O $\xrightarrow{\text{reflux}}$ $p\text{-}BrC_6H_4NO_2$

⑥ Ber. **50**, 1559 (1917). Chem. Listy
   46, 158 (1952). Coll. Czech. Chem.
   Comm. **16**, 580 (1951); CA **47**, 8030
   (1953).

SiC₁₂H₈Cl₄

① Bis(p-chlorophenyl)dichlorosilane
   $(p\text{-}ClC_6H_4)_2SiCl_2$

② $SiCl_4 + p\text{-}ClC_6H_4MgBr \longrightarrow$ 47%

③ Solid. (364.5~367.5°/744). (234°/36).
   [71.2°].
   Sol. in org. solvents.

④ + HNO₃ in Ac₂O $\xrightarrow{\text{reflux}}$ $p\text{-}ClC_6H_4NO_2$
   + SbCl₅ $\longrightarrow$ SbCl₃ + $p\text{-}Cl_2C_6H_4$
   + $p\text{-}ClC_6H_4SiCl_3$

⑥ Chem. Listy **46**, 158 (1952). Coll.

Czech. Chem. Comm. **16**, 580(1951);
CA **47**, 8030 (1953). Zhur **23**, 1414
(1953); CA **47**, 12281 (1953).

SiC₁₂H₉Cl₃

① p-Biphenylyltrichlorosilane
   $p\text{-}C_6H_5C_6H_4SiCl_3$

② $C_6H_5\text{-}C_6H_5 + HSiCl_3 \xrightarrow{\text{BCl}_3\ 300°}$

③ Crystals. (205~207°/30mm). [43°].

⑥ US 2626266 (1953); CA **48**, 7636 (1954).

SiC₁₂H₉Cl₃O

① Phenyl-2,4,5-trichlorophenoxysilane
   $C_6H_5Si(H)_2OC_6H_2Cl_3$ (2,4,5)

② $HOC_6H_2Cl_3$ (2,4,5) + PhSiH₃
   + HCONMe₂ $\longrightarrow$ 23.7%

③ (222~225°/4). n_D 1.6042 (20°). d 1.3436
   (20°/4°).

⑥ Zhur. **33**, 2617 (1963).

SiC₁₂H₁₀Br₂

① Diphenyldibromosilane
   $(C_6H_5)_2SiBr_2$

② $(C_6H_5)_2SiH_2 + 2Br_2 \longrightarrow$

③ Yellow liq. (192.2°/1). [3.8~4.0]. n_D
   1.5869 (25°). d 1.6179 (25°).

⑥ JACS **75**, 1583 (1953).

SiC₁₂H₁₀Cl₂

① Diphenyldichlorosilane
   $(C_6H_5)_2SiCl_2$

② $Ph_2Si(OEt)_2 + PhCOCl + C_5H_5N \longrightarrow$
   PhSiH₂Cl + AlCl₃ $\xrightarrow{50°}$

③ (298~302°). d 1.1860 (20°).

④ + RNH₂ (R=Me, n-Pr, n-hexyl or
   benzyl) $\longrightarrow$ $Ph_2Si(NHR)_2$
   + NH₃ $\xrightarrow{\text{in dry benzene}}$ $(Ph_2SiNH)_3$
   + SbCl₃ + Cl₂ $\longrightarrow$ many products

⑥ JACS **75**, 995 (1953); **77**, 6395 (1955).
   Zhur. **26**, 1413 (1956); CA **50**, 14605
   (1956).

SiC₁₂H₁₀F₂

① Diphenyldifluorosilane
$(C_6H_5)_2SiF_2$

② Electrolysis of Ph_2SiCl_2 in liq. HF
$$\xrightarrow{-10°}$$

$HF + Ph_2Si(OEt)_2 \longrightarrow$

$HF + Ph_2SiCl_2 \longrightarrow$

③ $(246\sim247.5°)$.

④ $+ HNO_3 \longrightarrow F_2Si(C_6H_4NO_2)_2$

⑥ US 3020302 (1962).   German 1139498 (1962); CA **58**, 7975 (1963); German 957214 (1957); CA **53**, 15979 (1959). Tetrahedron Letters (No.5) 11 (1960).

SiC₁₂H₁₀N₆

① Diphenylsilyl diazide
$(C_6H_5)_2Si(N_3)_2$

② $Ph_2SiCl_2 + Me_3SiN_3 + AlCl_3 \longrightarrow$
$Ph_2SiCl_2 + NaN_3 \longrightarrow$

③ $(126°/0.01)$. $n_D 1.5887$ $(20°)$.

④ Stable but decomp. in sun.

⑥ Angew. **74**, 716 (1962).   Ber. **96**, 1293 (1963).

SiC₁₂H₁₀S₃

① Tris(2-thienyl)silane

$$\left(\begin{array}{c} CH-CH \\ CH \quad C- \\ S \end{array} \right)_3 SiH$$

② $(C_4H_3S)MgBr + SiHCl_3 \longrightarrow$

③ $(150\sim155°/0.5)$.

④ Ignites spontaneously with nitric acid.

⑥ US 3068241 (1962); CA **58**, 10239 (1963).

SiC₁₂H₁₁Cl

① Diphenylchlorosilane
$(C_6H_5)_2SiHCl$

② $HSiCl_3 + C_6H_5MgBr \longrightarrow$

③ Colorless liq. $(140\sim145°/7)$.
Sol. in org. solvents.

⑥ Brit. 622970; CA **44**, 653 (1950).   JCS **1947**, 1592.

SiC₁₂H₁₂

① Diphenylsilane
$(C_6H_5)_2SiH_2$

② $SiH_2Cl_2 + 2PhMgBr \longrightarrow$

③ $(95\sim97/13, 257°)$. $n_D 1.5795$ $(20°)$. d 0.9969 $(20°)$.
IR: Appl. Spectroscopy **16**, 12 (1962).

④ $Ph_2SiH_2 + $ diallylester $\xrightarrow{\text{polyaddition}}$
$+ HX \longrightarrow C_6H_6 + PhSiXH_2$
$+ CH_2N_2 \longrightarrow Ph_2SiMeH$

⑥ Angew. **74**, 468 (1962).   CA **57**, 9872 (1962).   Acta Chem. Scand. **8**, 1830 (1954).   JACS **80**, 2283 (1958). JOC **18**, 303 (1953).

SiC₁₂H₁₂O₂

① Diphenylsilanediol
$(C_6H_5)_2Si(OH)_2$

② $Ph_2SiCl_2 + (OH)^- \longrightarrow$

③ Solid. $[105\sim107°]$.

④ $+ HI \longrightarrow C_6H_6$
$+ Me_3SiNEt_2 \longrightarrow$ polymers
$+ Me_3SiHBu \longrightarrow$ polymers
$+ Me_2Si(NEt_2)_2 \longrightarrow$ polymers

⑥ J. Polymer Sci. **50**, 151 (1961).   Z. anorg. allg. Chem. **308**, 105 (1961). Chem. & Ind. 208 (1961).   Kogyo Kagaku Zasshi **63**, 1433 (1960); CA **57**, 11226 (1962)

SiC₁₂H₁₂O₂

① Phenyldipropynyloxysilane
$C_6H_5SiH(OCH_2C\equiv CH)_2$

② $Ag + PhSiH_3 + CH\equiv CCH_2OH$
$\longrightarrow 47\%$

③ $(132\sim134°/5)$.

⑥ Zhur. **33**, 2617 (1963).

SiC₁₂H₁₄Cl₆O₂

① *p*-Trichloromethylphenyldiethoxy-
trichloromethylsilane
p-CCl₃C₆H₄Si(OC₂H₅)₂CCl₃

② EtOH + *p*-CCl₃C₆H₄Si(Cl)₂CCl₃
⟶ 88.8%

③ (185~186°/3). n_D1.5355 (20°). d1.4144
(20°/4°).

⑥ Zhur. **33**, 1299 (1963).

SiC₁₂H₁₅Cl₅O₃

① Tris(2-chloroethoxy)dichloro-
phenylsilane
Cl₂C₆H₃Si(OCH₂CH₂Cl)₃

② KOH + (CH₂)₂O + Cl₂C₆H₃SiCl₃
⟶ 33.4%

③ (177°/1). n_D 1.5331 (20°). d 1.4187
(20°/4°).

⑥ Zhur. **33**, 905 (1963).

SiC₁₂H₁₆Cl₂

① Cyclohexylphenyldichlorosilane
(C₆H₁₁)(C₆H₅)SiCl₂

② C₆H₅SiCl₃ + cyclo-C₆H₁₁MgBr ⟶

③ Colorless liq. (123~125°/0.5).
Sol. in org. solvents; Decomp. with
water.

⑥ JCS **1932**, 2206.

SiC₁₂H₁₆Cl₂

① 1-Benzyldichlorosilyl-2-methyl-
butene-2
CH₃CH=C(CH₃)CH₂Si(Cl)₂CH₂C₆H₅

② isoprene + H₂PtCl₆ + PhCH₂SiHCl₂
⟶ 76%

③ (124~125°/5). n_D1.5429 (25°). d1.0950
(25°).

④ + EtMgBr ⟶
MeCH=CMeCH₂SiEt₂CH₂Ph ⟶
68.9%

⑥ JOC **26**, 4000 (1961).

SiC₁₂H₁₆Cl₄O₃

① Chlorophenyltris(2-chloroethoxy)-

silane
ClC₆H₄Si(OCH₂CH₂Cl)₃

② ClC₆H₄SiCl₃ + KOH + (CH₂)₂O
⟶ 22.4%

③ (182~185°/2). n_D1.5192 (20°). d1.3397
(20°/4°).

⑥ Zhur. **33**, 905 (1963).

SiC₁₂H₁₆O₄

① Phenylhydrosilyl dipropionate
(C₂H₅COO)₂SiHC₆H₅

② EtCOOH + C₅H₅N + PhSiH₃
⟶ 34%

③ (80~84°/3). n_D1.4711 (20°).

⑥ Zhur. **33**, 2617 (1963).

SiC₁₂H₁₆O₄

① Dimethyldifurfuroxysilane

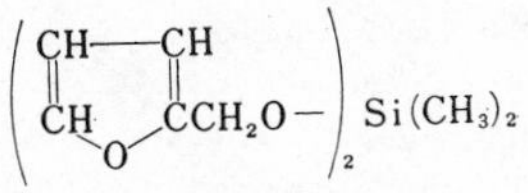

②

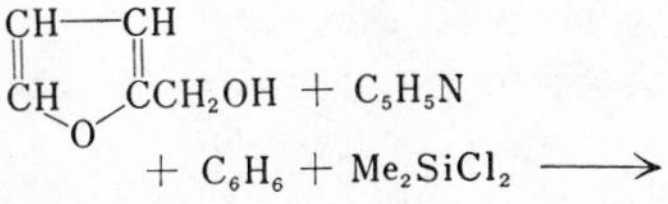

③ (102~103°/1). n_D1.4809 (20°). d1.1021
(20°).

⑥ Platicheskie Massy (No.3) 8 (1962).
PSR Zinatnu Vestis(No.7)59(1961);
CA **57**, 525 (1962).

SiC₁₂H₁₆S₂

① Diethylbis(2-thienyl)silane

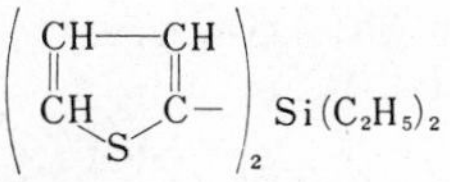

② (C₄H₃S)Li + Et₂SiCl₂ ⟶ 71%

③ (141~142°/6). n_D1.5740 (20°). d1.1000
(20°/4°).

⑥ Zhur. **33**, 1251 (1963).

SiC$_{12}$H$_{17}$NO$_2$

① m-Cyanophenylmethyldiethoxysilane
CH$_3$Si(OC$_2$H$_5$)$_2$C$_6$H$_4$CN-m

② m-BrC$_6$H$_4$Si(OEt)$_2$Me + NaCN
+ Cu$_2$(CN)$_2$ + C$_6$H$_5$CN ⟶

③ (111~112°/3). n_D1.4855 (25°). d1.2058
(20°/4°).

⑥ US 2975204 (1961).   Zhur. **33**, 316
(1963).

SiC$_{12}$H$_{17}$NO$_3$

① 2,2′,2″-Phenylsilyloxytriethylamine

$$\begin{array}{c} OCH_2CH_2 \\ \diagup \qquad \diagdown \\ C_6H_5Si-OCH_2CH_2-N \\ \diagdown \qquad \diagup \\ OCH_2CH_2 \end{array}$$

② PhSi(OEt)$_3$ + N(CH$_2$CH$_2$OH)$_3$ ⟶

③ Solid. [203.6~204.2°].

⑥ Ger. 1131681 (1962) ; CA **58**, 4598
(1963)

SiC$_{12}$H$_{17}$N$_5$

① 2,4-Diamino-6-(p-trimethylsilyl-
phenyl)triazine

$$p-(CH_3)_3SiC_6H_4-C \begin{array}{c} \diagup N \diagdown \\ \quad \quad C N \\ H_2NC \diagdown_{N} \diagup CNH_2 \end{array}$$

② NH$_3$ (dry) +

$$p-Me_3SiC_6H_4-C \begin{array}{c} \diagup N \diagdown \\ \quad \quad C N \\ ClC \diagdown_{N} \diagup CCl \end{array} \quad \longrightarrow$$

③ Solid. [166~167°].
IR : 3300, 3140, 2950, 1660, 1570, 1540,
1500, 1400, 1320, 1280, 1226, 1100,
1010, 840, 810, 730, 710 cm^{-1}.

⑥ JOC **27**, 1486 (1962).

SiC$_{12}$H$_{18}$Cl$_2$O$_3$

① Dichlorophenyltriethoxysilane
Cl$_2$C$_6$H$_3$Si(OC$_2$H$_5$)$_3$

② EtOH + Cl$_2$C$_6$H$_3$SiCl$_3$ ⟶

③ (137~139°/5). n_D1.4848 (20°). d1.1752
(20°/20°).

⑥ Zhur. **32**, 3727 (1962).

SiC$_{12}$H$_{18}$O

① p-Trimethylsilylpropiophenone
p-(CH$_3$)$_3$SiC$_6$H$_4$COC$_2$H$_5$

② (EtCO)$_2$O + p-Me$_3$SiC$_6$H$_4$MgBr
⟶   44%
EtMgX + p-Me$_3$SiC$_6$H$_4$CN ⟶

③ (169~171°/6). n_D1.5120 (25°). d0.9590
(25°/4°).

④ + H$_2$NNHC$_6$H$_3$(NO$_2$)$_2$ ⟶
p-Me$_3$SiC$_6$H$_4$CEt=NNHC$_6$H$_3$(NO$_2$)$_2$
mp 171°~175°
mp 190°~191.5°

⑥ Yakugaku Zasshi **82**, 929 (1962).
JOC **19**, 1757 (1954).

SiC$_{12}$H$_{18}$O$_2$

① Ethyl p-trimethylsilylbenzoate
p-(CH$_3$)$_3$SiC$_6$H$_4$COOC$_2$H$_5$

② K$_2$CO$_3$ + [p-Me$_3$SiC$_6$H$_4$C(=NH$_2$)OEt]$^+$
Cl$^-$ ⟶

③ (155~160°/30).

⑥ Yakugaku Zasshi **82**, 929 (1963).

SiC$_{12}$H$_{19}$Cl$_3$

① 1-Trichlorosilylcyclododecadiene-4,8

$$\begin{array}{l} CH_2CH_2CHSiCl_3 \\ CH \qquad\qquad CH_2 \\ CH \qquad\qquad CH_2 \\ CH_2 \qquad\qquad CH_2 \\ CH_2CH=CH \end{array}$$

② cyclo-C$_{12}$H$_{18}$ + SiHCl$_3$ $\xrightarrow{H_2PtCl_6}$ 77.0%

③ (148~150°/4). n_D1.5175 (20°).

④ + MeMgCl ⟶ cyclo-C$_{12}$H$_{19}$SiMe$_3$
+ HOH ⟶ cyclo-C$_{12}$H$_{19}$SiOOH

⑥ JOC **28**, 3353 (1963).

SiC$_{12}$H$_{19}$F

① 2-Phenethylmethylpropylfluoro-
silane
C$_6$H$_5$CH$_2$CH$_2$Si(F)(CH$_3$)n-C$_3$H$_7$

② H$_2$PtCl$_6$ + PhCH=CH$_2$

+ MeSi(H)(F)Pr-*n* ⟶

③ (103°/8). n_D 1.4812 (20°). d 0.9525
(20°/4°).

⑥ Zhur. **32**, 3882 (1962).

SiC₁₂H₁₉F

① Methylpropyl-1-phenylethylfluoro-
silane
$C_6H_5CH(CH_3)Si(F)(CH_3)n-C_3H_7$

② Pt + PhCH=CH₂
+ MeSi(H)(F)Pr-*n* ⟶

③ (99°/8). n_D1.4830(20°). d0.954(20°/4°).

⑥ Zhur. **32**, 3882 (1962).

SiC₁₂H₁₉F

① Methylisopropyl-1-phenylethylfluoro-
silane
$C_6H_5CH(CH)Si(F)(CH_3)i-C_3H_7$

② Pt + PhCH=CH₂
+ MeSi(H)(F)Pr-*i* ⟶

③ (87°~88°/6). n_D1.4828 (20°). d0.9559
(20°/4°).

⑥ Zhur. **32**, 3882 (1962).

SiC₁₂H₁₉F

① Methylisopropyl-2-phenylethylfluoro-
silane
$C_6H_5CH_2CH_2Si(F)(CH_3)i-C_3H_7$

② Pt + PhCH=CH₂
+ MeSi(H)(F)Pr-*i* ⟶

③ (90~91°/6). n_D 1.4809 (20°). d 0.9555
(20°/4°).

⑥ Zhur. **32**, 3882 (1962).

SiC₁₂H₁₉ClO₃

① Chlorophenyltriethoxysilane
$ClC_6H_4Si(OC_2H_5)_3$

② EtOH + ClC₆H₄SiCl₃ ⟶

③ (117~1120°/5). n_D1.4740 (20°). d1.0846
(20°/20°).

⑥ Zhur. **32**, 3727 (1962).

SiC₁₂H₁₉NO

① *N-p*-Trimethylsilylbenzylacetamide

p-(CH₃)₃SiC₆H₄CH₂NHCOCH₃

② LiAlH₄ + *p*-Me₃SiC₆H₄CN ⟶

③ Solid. [78°~80°].

⑥ Yakugaku Zasshi **82**, 929 (1962).

SiC₁₂H₂₀

① Triethylphenylsilane
$(C_2H_5)_3SiC_6H_5$

② PhMgBr + Et₃SiCl ⟶ ⎫
PhSiCl₃ + EtMgBr ⟶ ⎬ 40~80%
PhLi + Et₃SiCl ⟶ 31.2% ⎭

③ (238°). n_D1.5024 (20°). d0.891(20°).
Decomp. at 800°.

④ Et₃SiPh $\xrightarrow{\text{HCl-H}_2\text{O, in AcOH}}$ C₆H₆

⑥ JOC **18**, 1743 (1953). JACS **80**, 2279
(1958). Dokl. **118**, 73 (11958).

SiC₁₂H₂₀

① *n*-Hexylphenylsilane
$n-C_6H_{13}(C_6H_5)SiH_2$

② C₆H₅SiH₂Br + *n*-C₆H₁₃MgBr ⟶ 36%

③ Colorless liq. (56°/0.29). n_D1.486(25°).
Sol. in org. solvents; insol. in H₂O.

⑥ JACS **76**, 4555 (1954).

SiC₁₂H₂₀

① Tetraallylsilane
$(CH_2=CHCH_2)_4Si$

② SiCl₄ + CH₂=CHCH₂MgCl
$\xrightarrow[\text{(excess)}]{\text{in ether-benzene}}$ 90~95%

SiCl₄ + CH₂=CHCH₂I + Mg
$\xrightarrow{\text{in ether}}$ 37%

③ Liq. (90.5°/10). n_D1.4840 (20°). d0.8345
(20°/4°).
Sol. in org. solvents; insol. in H₂O.

④ $\xrightarrow{110~114°, \ (Me_3CC_6H_4)_2O_2}$ polymer 10%

$\xrightarrow[130°, \ 550 atm]{(Me_3CO)_2}$ solid polymer

⑥ Chem. zvesti **12**, 32 (1958). Dokl.
92, 15 (1953). US 2628246; CA **47**
5719 (1953). Izv. OKhN **1952**, 564;

CA **47**, 3792 (1953).

$SiC_{12}H_{20}$

① Diethylsilylcyclooctatriene-2,4,7
   $(C_2H_5)_2Si(H)$
   |
   $CH=CH-CH-CH_2-CH=CH-CH=CH$
   |_____|
② $Et_2SiH_2 + Pt-Al_2O_3 + cyclo-C_8H_8 \longrightarrow$
③ (51~56°/0.15). $n_D 1.5104$ (25°).
⑥ JCS **1963**, 4058.

$SiC_{12}H_{20}Cl_6O_3$

① 1,2,3,4,5,6-Hexachlorocyclo-
   hexyltriethoxysilane
   $(C_6H_5Cl_6)Si(OC_2H_5)_3$
② $(C_6H_5Cl_6)SiCl_3 + EtOH \longrightarrow$
③ (184~187°/3). $n_D 1.5065$ (20°). $d 1.4200$
   (20°/4°).
⑥ Dokl. **148**, 116 (1963).

$SiC_{12}H_{20}O$

① Triethylphenoxysilane
   $(C_2H_5)_3SiOC_6H_5$
② $(C_2H_5)_3SiH + C_6H_5OH \xrightarrow{Al+I_2} 80.3\%$
③ Colorless liq. (243.8°). $n_D 1.4880$ (20°).
   $d 0.9304$ (20°).
   Sol. in org. solvents.
⑥ Zhur. **24**, 1178 (1954); CA **49**, 12275
   (1955).

$SiC_{12}H_{20}O_2$

① Phenyldi-n-propoxysilane
   $C_6H_5SiH(O \ n-C_3H_7)_2$
② $PhSiH_3 + n-PrOH + Cu$ (powder)
   $\longrightarrow 25.1\%$
③ (80~81°/4). $n_D 1.4713$ (20°). $d 0.9497$
   (20°/4°).
⑥ Zhur. **33**, 2617 (1963).

$SiC_{12}H_{20}O_2$

① 2,5,5,8-Tetramethyl-2,8-dihydroxy-
   5-sila-nonadiyne-3,6
   $(CH_3)_2Si(C\equiv CC(CH_3)_2OH)_2$
② $Me_2CO + Me_2Si(C\equiv CMgBr)_2 \longrightarrow$

$EtMgBr + Me_2C(OH)C\equiv CH$
   $+ Me_2SiCl_2 \longrightarrow$
⑥ US 2887371 (1959); CA **53**, 19883(1959).
   Dokl. **109**, 344, 553 (1956); CA **51**,
   2534 (1957).

$SiC_{12}H_{20}O_3$

① Phenyltriethoxysilane
   $C_6H_5Si(OC_2H_5)_3$
② $Si(OEt)_4 + PhMgCl \longrightarrow 70\%$
   $EtOH + PhSiCl_3 \longrightarrow$
   $(EtO)_3SiCl + Na + PhCl \longrightarrow 40\%$
③ (122~124°/15). $n_D 1.4590$ (25°). $d 0.9904$
   (25°/4°).
⑥ Hua Hsüeh Hsüeh Pao **27**, 38 (1961);
   CA **59**, 11547 (1963).   Kogyo Kagaku Zasshi **62**, 1262 (1959).   JOC
   25, 435 (1960).

$SiC_{12}H_{20}O_3$

① Methyldi-n-propylsilylfuroate

   $\begin{array}{c} CH\text{——}CH \\ \| \quad\quad \| \\ CH \quad CCOOSi(n-C_3H_7)_2CH_3 \\ \diagdown O \diagup \end{array}$

② $\begin{array}{c} CH\text{——}CH \\ \| \quad\quad \| \\ CH \quad CCOOH + H_2PtCl_6 \\ \diagdown O \diagup \\ \quad + (n-Pr)_2SiHMe \longrightarrow \end{array}$

③ (102~104°/4). $n_D 1.4722$ (20°). $d 0.9994$
   (20°).
⑥ Latvijas PSR Zinatnu, Akad. Vestis, Khim. Ser. 111 (1963).

$SiC_{12}H_{21}N$

① Triethylphenylaminosilane
   $(C_2H_5)_3SiNHC_6H_5$
② $(C_2H_5)_3SiH + C_6H_5NH_2$
   $\xrightarrow{K}$ in good yield
③ Liq. (121°/6). $n_D 1.5210$ (20°). $d 0.9336$
   (20°).
   Sol. in org. solvents.
⑥ Zhur. **24**, 678 (1954); CA **49**, 5272
   (1955).

SiC₁₂H₂₂N₂

① Ethyl(diethylamino)(phenylamino)-
   silane
   $C_2H_5Si(H)[N(C_2H_5)_2]NHC_6H_5$
② $PhNH_2 + EtSiH(NEt_2)_2$ ⟶
③ (65~66°/3). $n_D1.4438$ (20°). $d0.8413$
   (20°/4°).
⑥ Zhur. **33**, 1294 (1963).

SiC₁₂H₂₂Cl₂

① Dicyclohexyldichlorosilane
   $(C_6H_{11})_2SiCl_2$
② $SiCl_4 + C_6H_{11}Li$ ⟶ 6%
③ Colorless liq.
   Sol. in org. solvents.
⑥ JCS **1952**, 2840.

SiC₁₂H₂₂F₂

① Dicyclohexyldifluorosilane
   $(C_6H_{11})_2SiF_2$
② $SiF_4 + C_6H_{11}MgBr$ ⟶
③ Solid. (248~260°).
④ $+ C_6H_{11}Cl + Li$
   ⟶ $(C_6H_{11})_4Si$ (11.3%)
   $+ H_2O$ ⟶ $(C_6H_{11})_2Si(OH)_2$
⑥ Zhur. **24**, 1189 (1954); CA **49**, 12276
   (1955). JCS **1952**, 2840.

SiC₁₂H₂₂N₂

① 1-Triethylsilyl-2-phenylhydrazine
   $(C_2H_5)_3SiNHNHC_6H_5$
② $2 C_6H_5NHNH_2 + (C_2H_5)_3SiCl$ ⟶
③ (129~130°/1). $n_D1.5210$ (20°).
⑥ Z. anorg. allg. Chem. **299**, 341 (1959).

SiC₁₂H₂₂O₂

① Di-*n*-propylmethyl-α-furfuroxysilane

   CH——CH
   ‖ $CH_2OSi(n-C_3H_7)_2CH_3$
   CH   CCH₂
      O

②
   CH——CH
   ‖   CCHO +
   CH
      O

SiC₁₂H₂₄ClNO₂

$n\text{-}Pr_2SiHMe \xrightarrow{H_2PtCl_6}$

③ (90~91°/4). $n_D1.4540$ (20°). $d0.9200$
   (20°).
⑥ Latvijas PSR, Zinatnu Akad. Vestis, Khim. Ser. 111 (1963).

SiC₁₂H₂₃N₃O₃

① Phenyltris(2-hydroxyethylamino)-
   silane
   $C_6H_5Si(NHCH_2CH_2OH)_3$
② $PhSiH_3 + CH_2(NH_2)CH_2OH$ ⟶ 28.2%
③ (182~183°/3). $n_D1.4976$ (20°).
⑥ Zhur. **33**, 2617 (1963).

SiC₁₂H₂₄

① Dibutyldivinylsilane
   $(C_4H_9)_2Si(CH=CH_2)_2$
② $(C_4H_9)_2SiCl_2 + 2 CH_2=CHMgCl \xrightarrow{THF}$
   81%
③ (59~61°/2). $n_D1.4528$ (25°). $d0.7916$
   (25°/4°).
⑥ JOC **22**, 1200 (1957).

SiC₁₂H₂₄

① Dicyclohexylsilane
   $(C_6H_{11})_2SiH_2$
② $SiH_2Cl_2 + 2C_6H_{11}MgBr$ ⟶ 79%
③ (140~141°/23). $n_D1.4854$ (25°). $d0.8890$
   (25)°.
   Led to flashing by being exposed to
   air at atmospheric pressure.
⑥ JOC **18**, 303 (1953).

SiC₁₂H₂₄ClNO₂

① 4-Chlorobutyl-3-cyanopropyldiethoxy-
   silane
   $(CH_2ClCH_2CH_2CH_2)(CH_2CNCH_2CH_2)\text{-}$
   $Si(OC_2H_5)_2$
② $CH_2ClCH_2CH_2CH_2MgCl$
   $+ Cl_3SiCH_2CH_2CH_2CN \xrightarrow[EtOH]{followed\ by}$
③ (122~124°/3). $n_D1.4492$ (25°).
⑥ US 3053873 (1962); CA **58**, 3458 (1963).

SiC$_{12}$H$_{24}$O
① (*n*-Propylmethylol)triethylsilyl-
 acetylene
 C$_3$H$_7$CH(OH)C≡CSi(C$_2$H$_5$)$_3$
② Et$_3$SiCl +
 PrCH(OMgBr)C≡CMgBr ⟶
③ (97~98°/2). n_D 1.4600 (20°). d 0.8708
 (20°/4°).
④ + HCl + BuOCH=CH$_2$
 ⟶ BuOCHMeOCHPrC≡CSiEt$_3$
⑥ Zhur. 33, 377 (1963).

SiC$_{12}$H$_{24}$O
① (*n*-Propylmethylol)(di-*n*-propylsilyl)-
 acetylene
 C$_3$H$_7$CH(OH)C≡CSiH(C$_3$H$_7$)$_2$
② Pr$_2$SiHCl +
 PrCH(OMgBr)C≡CMgBr ⟶
③ (104~105°/3). n_D1.4550 (20°). d0.8615
 (20°/4°).
④ + HCl + BuOCH=CH$_2$ ⟶
 BuOCHMeOCHPrC≡CSiHPr$_2$
⑥ Zhur. 33, 377 (1963).

SiC$_{12}$H$_{24}$O$_2$
① Dicyclohexyldihydroxysilane
 (C$_6$H$_{11}$)$_2$Si(OH)$_2$
② SiCl$_4$ + C$_6$H$_{11}$Li $\xrightarrow{\text{H}_2\text{O}}$ 6%
③ White solid. [164~165°].
⑥ JCS 1952, 2840.

SiC$_{12}$H$_{24}$O$_4$
① Dimethylditetrahydrofurfuryloxy-
 silane
$$\left(\begin{matrix} \text{CH}_2\text{---CH}_2 \\ \text{CH}_2 \diagdown \underset{\text{O}}{\diagup} \text{CHCH}_2\text{O}- \end{matrix} \right)_2 \text{Si(CH}_3)_2$$

②
$$\begin{matrix} \text{CH}_2\text{---CH}_2 \\ \text{CH}_2 \diagdown \underset{\text{O}}{\diagup} \text{CHCH}_2\text{OH} \end{matrix} + \text{Me}_2\text{SiCl}_2 \longrightarrow$$

③ (123~125°/1). n_D1.4505 (20°). d1.0324

(20°).
⑥ Plasticheskie Massy (No.3) 8 (1962);
 CA 59, 654 (1963).

SiC$_{12}$H$_{26}$
① Cyclooctyldiethylsilane
 cyclo-C$_8$H$_{15}$SiH(C$_2$H$_5$)$_2$
② Et$_2$SiH$_2$ + *cyclo*-C$_8$H$_{14}$ $\xrightarrow{250°,\ 2\,hr}$ 3.6%
③ (80~81°/0.05). n_D1.4742 (25°).
 IR: 2100, 1230 cm^{-1}.
⑥ JCS 1963, 2831.

SiC$_{12}$H$_{26}$Cl$_2$
① Di-*n*-hexyldichlorosilane
 (C$_6$H$_{13}$)$_2$SiCl$_2$
③ Colorless liq. (97~101°/0.5).
 Sol. in org. solvents. Decomp. with
 H$_2$O.
⑥ JOC 18, 1689 (1953).

SiC$_{12}$H$_{26}$O
① Methyldi-*n*-butylalloxysilane
 CH$_3$Si(*n*-C$_4$H$_9$)$_2$OCH$_2$CH=CH$_2$
② *n*-Bu$_2$SiHMe +
 CH$_2$=CHCH$_2$OH $\xrightarrow[\text{ZnCl}_2 \text{ or SnCl}_2]{\text{catalyst Li, Na,}}$
③ (87.0°/20). n_D 1.4315 (20°). d 0.825
 (20°/4°).
⑥ Izv. SKh 1963, 1749.

SiC$_{12}$H$_{26}$O
① Tri-*n*-propylalloxysilane
 (*n*-C$_3$H$_7$)$_3$SiOCH$_2$CH=CH$_2$
② (*n*-Pr)$_3$SiH +
 CH$_2$=CHCH$_2$OH $\xrightarrow{\text{Li, Na, ZnCl}_2 \text{ or SnCl}^2}$
③ (73.0~74.0°/1.0~2.0). n_D1.4331 (20°).
 d0.8303 (20°/4°).
⑥ Izv. SKh 1963, 1749.

SiC$_{12}$H$_{26}$O
① Methyldiisobutylalloxysilane
 CH$_3$Si(*i*-C$_4$H$_9$)$_2$OCH$_2$CH=CH$_2$
② *i*-Bu$_2$SiHMe + CH$_2$=CHCH$_2$OH

Li, Na ZnCl$_2$ or SnCl$_2$

③ (94.0°/10). n_D 1.4310 (20°). d 0.8245
(20°/4°).
⑥ Izv. **1963**, 1794.

SiC$_{12}$H$_{27}$Cl

① Tri-n-butylchlorosilane
(C_4H_9)$_3$SiCl
② [(n-C_4H_9)$_3$Si]$_2$O + AlCl$_3$ ⟶ 85%
③ Colorless liq. (242.5°/750.1). d0.879
(20°/4°).
Sol. in org. solvents.
⑥ JCS **1949**, 2755. JACS **75**, 1585 (1953).
Dokl. **84**, 959 (1952); CA **47**, 3228
(1953).

SiC$_{12}$H$_{28}$

① Tetra-n-propylsilane
(n-C_3H_7)$_4$Si
② 4n-PrMgBr + SiBr$_4$ ⟶ n-Pr$_4$Si
SiCl$_4$ + AcOH ⟶ Si(OAc)$_4$
$\xrightarrow{\text{PrMgBr}}$ 56%
③ (213~214°). n_D1.4384 (20°). d0.7845
(20°).
④ + Et$_4$Si $\xrightarrow{\text{AlCl}_3}$ PrSiEt$_3$ + Pr$_2$SiEt$_2$
+ Pr$_3$SiEt + Pr$_4$Si
⑥ Dokl. **93**, 667 (1953). JACS **77**, 1677
(1955).

SiC$_{12}$H$_{28}$

① Tri-n-butylsilane
(n-C_4H_9)$_3$SiH
② (n-C_4H_9)$_3$SiOC$_2$H$_5$ + AlCl$_3$ + LiAlH$_4$
⟶ 70%
③ Colorless liq. (88°/5). n_D1.4380 (20°).
d0.7795 (20°).
Sol. in org. solvents.
⑥ Zhur. **24**, 1178 (1954); CA **49**, 12275
(1955). Acta Chem. Scand. **8**, 1830
(1954).

SiC$_{12}$H$_{28}$

① Triisobutylsilane

(i-C_4H_9)$_3$SiH

② HSiCl$_3$ + i-C_4H_9MgBr ⟶ 70%
③ Colorless liq. (207.3°).
Sol. in org. solvents.
④ + I$_2$ ⟶ i-Bu$_3$SiI + HI
+ AgClO$_4$ ⟶ i-Bu$_3$SiClO$_4$ + AgH
⑥ JCS **1954**, 3169; **1955**, 2517.

SiC$_{12}$H$_{28}$O

① Tributylsilanol
(n-C_4H_9)$_3$SiOH
② n-Bu$_3$SiCl + NaOH ⟶
③ (109.5~110.5°/3.5). n_D1.4467 (20°/4°).
⑥ Z. anorg. allg. Chem. **323**, 190 (1963).

SiC$_{12}$H$_{28}$O$_2$

① Dimethyldi-n-amoxysilane
(CH$_3$)$_2$Si(OC$_5$H$_{11}$-n)$_2$
② Me$_2$SiCl$_2$ + C$_5$H$_5$N + n-AmOH ⟶
③ (142°~145°/65). n_D1.4135 (26°). d0.8521
(30°/30°).
IR: 3000, 1510, 1259, 1100 cm^{-1}.
⑥ J. Chi. Chem. Soc. (II) **8**, 237, 343
(1961); J. Ind. Chem. Soc. **39**, 65
(1962); **9**, 273 (1962).

SiC$_{12}$H$_{28}$O$_2$

① Dimethyldiisoamoxysilane
(CH$_3$)$_2$Si(OC$_5$H$_{11}$-i)$_2$
② Me$_2$SiCl$_2$ + i-AmOH ⟶ 72%
③ (122~125°/46). n_D1.4110 (20°). d0.8376
(30°/30°).
⑥ J. Chi. Chem. Soc. (II) **8**, 834
(1961); CA **58**, 12591 (1963).

SiC$_{12}$H$_{28}$O$_3$

① Tris(ethoxymethyl)-n-propylsilane
n-C_3H_7Si(CH$_2$OC$_2$H$_5$)$_3$
② n-PrSiCl$_3$ + Mg + EtOCH$_2$Cl ⟶
③ (67°/0.7). n_D 1.4295 (20°). d 0.8775
(20°).
⑥ Belg. 620518 (1963); CA **59**, 6440
(1963).

$SiC_{12}H_{29}N$

① Tri-*n*-butyl(amino)silane
$(C_4H_9)_3SiNH_2$
② $(n\text{-}C_4H_9)_3SiCl + NH_3 \longrightarrow$
③ Liq. (118~120°/14).
Sol. in org. solvents. Decomp. with H_2O.
④ $+ H_2O \longrightarrow (n\text{-}C_4H_9)_3SiOH$
⑥ Kgl. Fysiograf. Sallskap. Sallkap. Lund. Forh. **28**, 1 (1958); CA **53**, 21622 (1959).

$SiC_{12}H_{29}NO_2$

① Methyl(diethylaminomethyl)diisopropoxysilane
$CH_3Si(OC_3H_7\text{-}i)_2CH_2N(C_2H_5)_2$
② $MeSi(OPr\text{-}i)_2CH_2Cl + Et_2NH \longrightarrow$
③ (73.5°/5). n_D 1.4185 (20°). d 0.8686 (20°/4°).
⑥ Zhur. **33**, 258 (1963).

$SiC_{12}H_{30}OSn$

① Triethylsiloxytriethylstannane
$(C_2H_5)_3SiOSn(C_2H_5)_3$
② $Et_3SiOH + Et_3SnOSnEt_3 \longrightarrow$
③ (114~115°/4). n_D1.4635 (20°). d1.1149 (20°/4°).
⑥ Zhur. **33**, 1945 (1963).

$SiC_{13}H_{12}Cl_2$

① Diphenyldichloromethylsilane
$(C_6H_5)_2SiH(CHCl_2)$
② $PhHgCCl_2Br + Ph_2SiH_2 \longrightarrow$ 77%
③ (118~119°/0.4).
⑥ JACS **85**, 2667 (1963).

$SiC_{13}H_{13}Br$

① Phenylmethyl-*p*-bromophenylsilane
$p\text{-}BrC_6H_4Si(H)(CH_3)C_6H_5$
② $PhSi(H)(Cl)Me + p\text{-}BrC_6H_4MgBr \longrightarrow$
③ (138~140°/1). n_D1.5970 (20°). d1.284 (20°).
⑥ Neftekhimiya **2**, 632 (1962); CA **58**, 11392 (1963).

$SiC_{13}H_{14}$

① Methyldiphenylsilane
$(C_6H_5)_2SiHCH_3$
② $CH_2N_2 + Ph_2SiH_2 \longrightarrow$ 50%
③ (88~90°/0.3). n_D1.5731 (20°).
⑥ JCS **1963**, 3604. Z. für Chem. **1**, 346 (1961). JACS **81**, 5320 (1959).

$SiC_{13}H_{14}O$

① Methyldiphenylsilanol
$CH_3Si(C_6H_5)_2OH$
② $Ph_2SiCl_2 + MeMgCl \xrightarrow{\text{then NaOH}}$
$(MeSiPh_2)_2O + NaOH \longrightarrow$
③ (148~149°/3). [165~168°]. n_D1.5790 (20°).
⑥ Z. anorg. allg. Chem. **323**, 190 (1963). Nippon Kagaku Zasshi **81**, 1874 (1960); CA **56**, 2467 (1962).

$SiC_{13}H_{16}$

① Trimethyl-1-naphthylsilane
$(CH_3)_3Si(C_{10}H_7\text{-}1)$
② $Me_3SiCl + (1\text{-}C_{10}H_7)Li \longrightarrow$ 70%
$MeMgI + (1\text{-}C_{10}H_7)Si(OEt)_3 \longrightarrow$ 70%
$(1\text{-}C_{10}H_7)SiCl + MeMgBr \longrightarrow$ 80%
③ (115~116°/1), (102~103°/2.5).
n_D 1.5804 (20°). d0.981 (20°).
⑥ JCS **1959**, 3034. JACS **72**, 1689 (1950). Zhur. **27**, 1286 (1957).

$SiC_{13}H_{20}O_2$

① 1-Methyl-2-(phenyldihydroxysilyl)-cyclohexane
$1\text{-}CH_3C_6H_{10}Si(OH)_2C_6H_5\text{-}2$
② $PhMgBr + 1\text{-}MeC_6H_{10}SiCl_3\text{-}2 \xrightarrow{HOH}$
③ Solid [131~132°].
⑥ Fr. 73000 (1960); CA **59**, 663 (1963).

$SiC_{13}H_{20}O_2$

① Triethyl-*p*-carboxyphenysilane

$(C_2H_5)_3Si(C_6H_4CO_2H-p)$

② $Et_3SiC_6H_4Br \xrightarrow{\text{Mg, CO}_2} (71.5\%)$

③ (162°/2),   [49.5°～50°], n_D 1.5211
   (25°). d1.06263 (25°).

⑥ Rec. trav. chim. **24**, 77 (1955).

SiC13H21F

① Isobutylmethyl-α-phenylethylfluoro-
   silane
   $C_6H_5CH(CH_3)Si(F)(CH_3)(C_4H_9-i)$

② $H_2PtCl_6 + PhCH=CH_2$
   $+ MeSi(H)(F)Bu-i \longrightarrow$

③ (105～106°/8). n_D1.4811 (20°). d0.9487
   (20°/4°).

⑥ Zhur. **32**, 663 ; 3882 (1962).

SiC13H21F

① 1-Phenylethyl-n-butylmethylfluoro-
   silane
   $C_6H_5CH(CH_3)Si(F)(CH_3)(C_4H_9-n)$

② $H_2PtCl_6 + PhCH=CH_2$
   $+ MeSi(H)(F)Bu-n \longrightarrow$

③ (114～116°/9). n_D1.4815 (20°). d0.9509
   (20°/4°).

⑥ Zhur. **32**, 663, 3882 (1962).

SiC13H21F

① Isobutylmethyl-2-phenylethylfluoro-
   silane
   $C_6H_5CH_2CH_2Si(F)(CH_3)(C_4H_9-i)$

② $H_2PtCl_6 + i\text{-}PrOH + PhCH=CH_2$
   $+ MeSi(H)(F)(i\text{-}Bu) \longrightarrow$

③ (108～109°/8). n_D1.4791 (20°). d0.9443
   (20°/4°).

⑥ Zhur. **32**, 663, 3882 (1962).

SiC13H21F

① 2-Phenylethyl-n-butylmethylfluoro-
   silane
   $C_6H_5CH_2CH_2Si(F)(CH_3)n\text{-}C_4H_9$

② $H_2PtCl_6 + PhCH=CH_2$
   $+ MeSi(H)(F)Bu \longrightarrow$

③ (119°/9). n_D 1.4799 (20°). d 0.9468

(20°).

⑥ Zhur. **32**, 663, 3882 (1962).

SiC13H22

① Benzyltriethylsilane
   $(C_2H_5)_3SiCH_2C_6H_5$

② $Et_3SiCl + C_6H_5CH_2MgCl \longrightarrow 47\%$

③ Colorless liq. (250°～252°/735). n_D
   1.5030 (20°).
   Sol. in org. solvents ; insol. in H_2O.

⑥ JOC **18**, 1743 (1953).

SiC13H22

① Triethyl-p-tolylsilane
   $(C_2H_5)_3Si(C_6H_4CH_3-p)$

② $Et_3SiCl + p\text{-}CH_3C_6H_4Li \longrightarrow 65\%$

③ Colorless liquid. (68～69°/0.5). n_D
   1.5025 (20°). d0.888 (20°/4°).
   Sol. in org. solvents.

④ $+ Cu(NO_3)_2 + CH_3COOH \longrightarrow$

⑥ JACS **76**, 904 (1954).

SiC13H22Cl2

① (1-Methyldichlorosilyl)cyclododeca-
   diene-4,8

② $C_{12}H_{18} + MeSiHCl_2 + H_2PtCl_6 \longrightarrow$

③ (180～182°/15). n_D1.511 (20°).

④ $+ MeMgCl \longrightarrow C_{12}H_{19}SiMe_3$ (63%)
   $+ HOH \longrightarrow C_{12}H_{19}Si(OH)_2Me$

⑥ JOC **28**, 3353 (1963).

$SiC_{13}H_{22}O_2$
① 1-Furylmethyl-2-triethylsiloxyethene

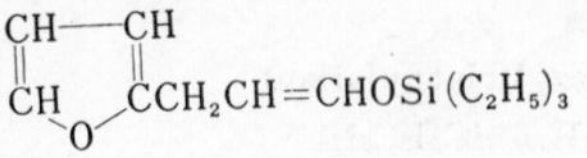

$$CH\!-\!CH$$
$$CH \quad CCH_2CH\!=\!CHOSi(C_2H_5)_3$$
$$\quad O$$

②
$$CH\!-\!CH$$
$$CH \quad CCH\!=\!CHCHO + Et_3SiH$$
$$\quad O$$
$$\qquad + H_2PtCl_6 \longrightarrow 46.7\%$$

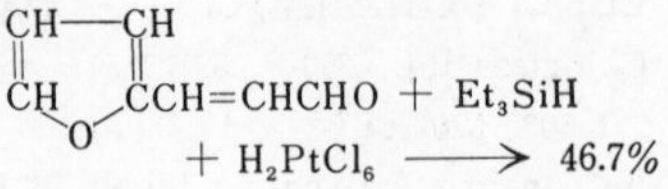

③ (113~115°/5). $n_D 1.4790$ (20°). $d 0.9623$ (20°).

⑥ Latvijas PRS Zinatnu Akad. Vestis, Kem. Ser. 111 (1963); CA **59**, 10102 (1963).

$SiC_{13}H_{22}O_3$
① Ethyldi-*n*-propylsilyl furoate

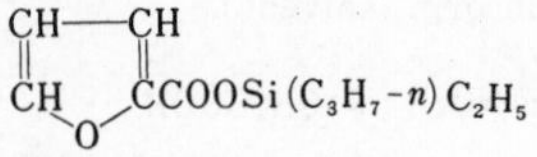

$$CH\!-\!CH$$
$$CH \quad CCOOSi(C_3H_7\text{-}n)C_2H_5$$
$$\quad O$$

②
$$CH\!-\!CH$$
$$CH \quad CCOOH +$$
$$\quad O$$
$$\qquad (n\text{-Pr})_2SiHEt \longrightarrow$$

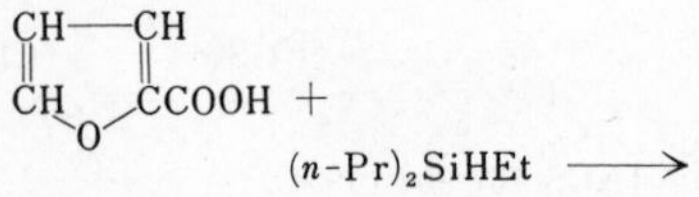

③ (122~124°/3). $n_D 1.4740$ (20°). $d 0.9930$ (20°).

⑥ Latvijas PSR Zinatnu, Akad. Vestis, Kem. Ser. 111 (1963); CA **59**, 10102 (1963).

$SiC_{13}H_{22}O_3$
① Benzyltriethoxsilane
$C_6H_5CH_2Si(OC_2H_5)_3$
② $PhCH_2SiCl_3 + EtOH \longrightarrow$
$PhCH_2MgCl + Si(OEt)_4 \longrightarrow$
③ (148°/26). $n_D 1.4628$ (25°). $d 0.9812$ (25°/4°).
⑥ Ber. **41**, 3390 (1908). JACS **84**, 4730 (1962).

$SiC_{13}H_{24}O_2$
① 2-Methyl-3-(3',3'-tetramethylene-3'-

silacyclohexyl)propanoic acid

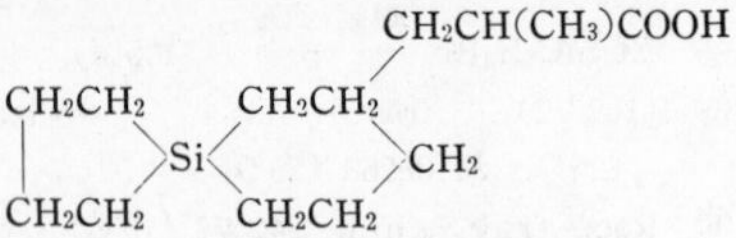

$$CH_2CH(CH_3)COOH$$
$$CH_2CH_2 \quad CH_2CH_2$$
$$\qquad Si \qquad CH_2$$
$$CH_2CH_2 \quad CH_2CH_2$$

② $(t\text{-BuO})_2 + EtCOOH$

$$CH_2CH_2$$
$$+ \quad Si(CH_2CH\!=\!CH_2)_2$$
$$CH_2CH_2$$
$$\longrightarrow 39.6\%$$

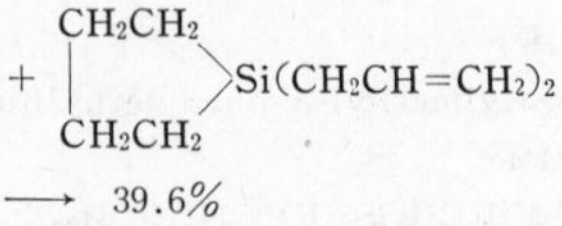

③ (153~155°/3.5). $n_D 1.4958(20°)$. $d 1.0208$ (20°/4°).

⑥ Izv. SKh 1963, 1816.

$SiC_{13}H_{26}O$
① Trimethylgeranioxysilane
$(CH_3)_3SiOC_{10}H_{17}$
② $Me_3SiCl + C_{10}H_{17}OH \longrightarrow$
③ (94~96°/4.5). $n_D 1.4515$ (22°). $d 0.8462$ (30°/30°).
IR: 3000, 1259, 841, 756, 1000 cm⁻¹.
⑥ J. Chi. Chem. Soc. (Ⅱ) **8**, 237, 384 (1961); (Ⅱ) **9**, 273 (1962).

$SiC_{13}H_{26}O_2$
① Ethyl 1-triethylsilylmethylcyclo-propyl-2-acetate
$(C_2H_5)_3SiCH_2CH$
$$\qquad\qquad CHCOOC_2H_5$$
$$CH_2$$
② $Et_3SiCH_2CH\!=\!CH_2$
$+ CH(N)_2COOC_2H_5 \longrightarrow 42\%$
③ (110°/11). $n_D 1.4543$ (20°). $d 0.9214$ (20°/4°).
⑥ Izv. OKhN, 1963, 572.

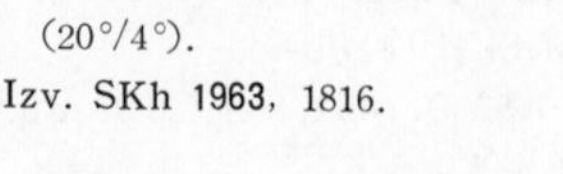

$SiC_{13}H_{27}N_3O_9$
① Methyl-tris-(3-nitrobutoxy-2)-silane
$CH_3Si(OCH(CH_3)CH(CH_3)NO_2)_3$
② $MeSiCl_3 +$
$MeCH(OH)CHMeNO_2 \longrightarrow$
③ (190~192°/2). $n_D 1.4500$ (20°). $d 1.1799$ (20°/4°).

⑥ Zhur. **33**, 1478 (1963).

SiC₁₃H₃₀
① Methyltributylsilane
   CH₃Si(C₄H₉)₃
② CH₃SiCl₃ + C₄H₉MgBr ⟶
③ Colorless liquid. (117~118/17). n_D
   1.4375 (20°). d 0.7818 (20°/0°).
   Sol. in org. solvents; insol. in
   H₂O.
⑥ Izv. OKhN **1955**, 1031; CA **50**, 6858
   (1956).

SiC₁₃H₃₀
① *n*-Decyltrimethylsilane
   n-C₁₀H₂₁Si(CH₃)₃
② (CH₃)₃SiCl + *n*-C₁₀H₂₁MgBr ⟶ 80%
③ Colorless liquid (240°/760). n_D 1.4310
   (20°). d 0.7705 (20°/4°).
   Sol. in org. solvents; insol. in
   H₂O.
⑥ JACS **68**, 475 (1946).

SiC₁₃H₃₁N
① Tri-*n*-butylmethylaminosilane
   (C₄H₉)₃SiNHCH₃
② (*n*-C₄H₉)₃SiCl + CH₃NH₂ ⟶
③ Colorless liquid. (117.5~118.5°/9).
   Sol. in org. solvents. Decomp. with
   H₂O.
④ + H₂O ⟶ (*n*-C₄H₉)₃SiOH
⑥ Kgl. Fysiograf. Sallskap. Lund.
   Forh. **28**, 1 (1958); CA **53**, 21622
   (1959).

SiC₁₃H₃₁O₃P
① Diethyl 3-triethylsilylpropylphospho-
   nate
   (C₂H₅)₃SiCH₂CH₂CH₂P(O)(OC₂H₅)₂
② Et₃SiCH₂CH₂CH₂Cl + P(OEt)₃
   ⟶ 43%
   Et₃SiH + (*t*-BuO)₂ +
   CH₂=CHCH₂P(O)(OEt)₂ ⟶ 20.7%

③ (118~120°/1.5). n_D 1.4498 (20°). d 0.9740
   (20°/4°).
⑥ Izv. OKhN **1962**, 1001; English page
   937. Dokl. **148**, 875 (1963).

SiC₁₃H₃₆N₆
① Methyltris(diethylaminoamino)-
   silane
   CH₃Si[NHN(C₂H₅)₂]₃
② MeSiCl₃ + Et₂NNH₂ ⟶
③ (127.8~128.3°/5). n_D 1.4533 (20°).
   d 0.8928 (20°/4°).
⑥ Zhur. **32**, 1987 (1962); **33**, 1874
   (1963).

SiC₁₄H₁₂Cl₄
① Diphenylbis(dichloromethyl)silane
   (C₆H₅)₂Si(CHCl₂)₂
② PhHgCCl₂Br + Ph₂SiH₂ ⟶ 83%
③ [100~102°].
⑥ JACS **85**, 2667 (1963).

SiC₁₄H₁₃Cl
① Vinyldiphenylchlorosilane
   (C₆H₅)₂Si(Cl)CH=CH₂
② PhSi(Cl)₂CH=CH₂ + PhMgCl
   ⟶ 47.6%
   PhMgCl + CH₂=CHSiCl₃ ⟶ 15%
   PhLi + CH₂=CHSiCl₃ ⟶ 42%
③ (125°/0.5). n_D 1.5793 (25°). d 1.1035
   (25°/4°).
⑥ JACS **78**, 1686 (1956). JOC **22**, 1606
   (1957); **28**, 487 (1963).

SiC₁₄H₁₄
① Diphenylvinylsilane
   (C₆H₅)₂Si(H)CH=CH₂
② Ph₂(CH₂=CH)SiCl + LiAlH₄ ⟶
③ (79.5~80.5°). n_D 1.5768 (25°). d 0.9979
   (25°).

④ + alkali metal ⟶

$$-\left(-\underset{\underset{Ph}{|}}{\overset{\overset{Ph}{|}}{Si}}CH_2CH_2\underset{\underset{Ph}{|}}{\overset{\overset{Ph}{|}}{Si}}-\right)-_n$$

$$\underset{Ph}{\overset{Ph}{>}}Si\underset{CH_2CH_2}{\overset{CH_2CH_2}{<}}Si\underset{Ph}{\overset{Rh}{<}}$$

⑥ JACS **78**, 1686 (1956).

SiC₁₄H₁₄Br₂

① Bis(*p*-bromophenyl)dimethylsilane
  $(CH_3)_2Si(C_6H_4Br-p)_2$
② $Me_2SiCl_2 + p\text{-}BrC_6H_4MgBr \longrightarrow$
③ Straw liquid. (155~170°/0.2).
  [72~73°].
  Sol. in org. solvents.
④ + CuCN $\xrightarrow{\text{pyridine}}$ $Me_2Si(C_6H_4CN-p)_2$
  (82%)
⑥ JOC **18**, 1689 (1953).

SiC₁₄H₁₄Cl₂

① Dibenzyldichlorosilane
  $(C_6H_5CH_2)_2SiCl_2$
③ White solid. (150~165°/0.5mm). [50~
  52°].
  Decomp. with H_2O.
⑥ JOC **18**, 1689 (1953).

SiC₁₄H₁₄Cl₂

① Di-*p*-tolyldichlorosilane
  $(p\text{-}CH_3C_6H_4)_2SiCl_2$
② $SiCl_4 + p\text{-}CH_3C_6H_4MgBr \longrightarrow$ 23%
③ Yellow liq. (168°/20).
  Sol. in org. solvents. Decomp. with
  H_2O.
④ + $H_2O \longrightarrow$ $(CH_3C_6H_4)_2Si(OH)_2$
⑥ Post (1949). JCS **1923**, 2830.

SiC₁₄H₁₄F₂

① Dibenzyldifluorosilane
  $(C_6H_5CH_2)_2SiF_2$
② $(PhCH_2)_2SiCl_2 \xrightarrow{\text{HF}}$

$SiF_4 \xrightarrow{PhCH_2MgBr}$

③ (140~150°/13).
⑥ Brit. 637739 ; CA **44**, 8362 (1950).

SiC₁₄H₁₄F₂

① Di-*p*-fluorophenyldimethylsilane
  $(p\text{-}FC_6H_4)_2Si(CH_3)_2$
② $(p\text{-}FC_6H_4)_2SiCl_2 + MeMgX$
  $\longrightarrow$ 79.9%
③ (184~185°/60). n_D1.5331 (20°). d1.1121
  (20°).
⑥ Chem. Listy **46**, 158 (1952) ; CA **47**,
  8030 (1953). Coll. Czech. Chem.
  Comm. **16**, 580 (1951).

SiC₁₄H₁₅Cl

① Methylchloromethyldiphenylsilane
  $CH_3Si(C_6H_5)_2CH_2Cl$
② $MeSi(Cl)_2CH_2Cl + PhMgBr \longrightarrow$ 66%
③ (121~122°).
④ + Mg $\longrightarrow$ $Ph_2SiMeCH_2MgCl$
⑥ Z. anorg. allg. Chem. **322**, 34 (1963).

SiC₁₄H₁₅ClO

① Dimethylchloro-*p*-phenoxyphenyl-
  silane
  $(CH_3)_2Si(Cl)C_6H_4OC_6H_5-p$
② $THF + Me_2SiCl_2$
  $+ p\text{-}PhOC_6H_4MgBr \longrightarrow$
③ (204~210°/40). n_D1.5722 (20°). d1.143
  (20°).
④ + $p\text{-}PhOC_6H_4SiMe_2ONa$
  $\longrightarrow$ $(p\text{-}PhOC_6H_5SiMe_2)_2O$
  + HOH + Na_2CO_3
  $\longrightarrow$ $(p\text{-}PhOC_6H_4SiMe_2)_2O$
  + Ph_3SiONa
  $\longrightarrow$ $Ph_3SiOSiMe_2C_6H_4OPh-p$
⑥ Fr. 1321436 (1963) ; CA **59**, 11561
  (1963). Izv. OKhN **1959**, 1341 ;
  English page 1294.

SiC₁₄H₁₆

① Dimethyldiphenylsilane
   $(CH_3)_2Si(C_6H_5)_2$

② $2\,PhBr + Me_2SiCl_2$
   $\xrightarrow[\text{or Mg}]{\text{Wurtz-Fittig}} Me_2SiPh_2$

③ (176~178°/45). n_D1.5593 (20°). d0.9877
   (20°).
   IR: BCSJ **27**, 441 (1954).

⑥ JCS **1950**, 3077.   Chem. Listy **16**, 580
   (1951).

SiC₁₄H₁₆

① Ethyldiphenylsilane
   $(C_6H_5)_2Si(H)C_2H_5$

② $C_2H_5SiHCl_2 + C_6H_5MgBr \longrightarrow 90\%$

③ Colorless liq.(119.8°/1). n_D1.5674(20°).
   d0.9900 (20°).
   Sol. in org. solvents; insol. in H_2O.

⑥ Izv. OKhN **1957**, 383 (1957); CA **51**,
   15457 (1957).

SiC₁₄H₁₆O

① Methyldiphenylmethoxysilane
   $CH_3Si(C_6H_5)_2OCH_3$

② $PhSi(OMe)_2Me + Na \longrightarrow$

③ n_D1.4410 (25°). d1.034 (25°/4°).

⑥ JACS **84**, 4730 (1962).

SiC₁₄H₁₆O₂

① Dimethyldiphenoxysilane
   $(CH_3)_2Si(OC_6H_5)_2$

② $PhOH + (Me_2SiNH)_3 \longrightarrow$
   $PhOH + Me_2SiCl_2 \longrightarrow$

③ (146~147°/10). [−23°]. n_D1.5303(20°).
   d1.0618 (20°/4°).

⑥ Izv. OKhN. **1963**, 950. JOC **24**, 1717
   (1959).   JACS **84**, 4730 (1962). US
   2837552 (1958); CA **52**, 17181 (1958).

SiC₁₄H₁₆O₂

① Diphenyldimethoxysilane
   $(C_6H_5)_2Si(OCH_3)_2$

② $PhCl + Na + NaNH_2$

$+ PhSi(OMe)_3 \longrightarrow$
$PhMgX + Si(OMe)_4 \longrightarrow$
$PhSi(OMe)_3 + Na \longrightarrow$
$MeONa + Ph_2Si(OMe)OCHPh_2 \longrightarrow$

③ (171°/18). n_D1.5404 (25°). d1.078
   (25°/4°).

⑥ JOC **25**, 1072(1960). Japan. 7172(1956);
   CA **52**, 8194 (1958).   Rocz. Chem.
   34, 1667 (1960); CA **56**, 7344 (1956).
   JACS **84**, 4730 (1962).

SiC₁₄H₁₆O₂

① Di-*p*-tolylsilanediol
   $(p\text{-}CH_3C_6H_4)_2Si(OH)_2$

② $p\text{-}MeC_6H_4MgBr + SiCl_4$, then HOH
   $\longrightarrow 90\%$

③ [201~202°].

⑥ Nippon Kagaku Zasshi **84**, 422 (1963).

SiC₁₄H₁₆O₄

① *p*-Bis(methoxyphenyl)silanediol
   $(p\text{-}CH_3OC_6H_4)_2Si(OH)_2$

② $p\text{-}MeOC_6H_4MgBr + SiCl_4$, then NaOH
   $\longrightarrow 86\%$

③ [124~125°].

⑥ Nippon Kagaku Zasshi **84**, 422 (1963).

SiC₁₄H₂₀

① Triethyl(phenylacetylenyl)silane
   $(C_2H_5)_3SiC\equiv CC_6H_5$

② $(C_2H_5)_3SiBr + C_6H_5C\equiv CH$
   $+ C_2H_5MgBr \longrightarrow$

③ Colorless liq. (132~133.5°/10). n_D
   1.5259 (20°). d0.8984 (20°).
   Sol. in org. solvents; insol. in H_2O.

④ $+ Na \longrightarrow$ cyclic dimer

⑥ Dokl. **93**, 283 (1953); CA **48**, 13616
   (1954).

SiC₁₄H₂₀

① 5-Phenylsilylcyclooctene-1

$$C_6H_5SiH_2\!-\!CH\!-\!CH_2$$
$$CH_2 \qquad CH_2$$
$$CH_2 \qquad CH_2$$
$$CH=CH$$

② (=CHCH₂CH₂CH=)₂ + PhSiH₃
 + (PhCOO)₂ ⟶ 25%

③ (67~69°/0.025). n_D1.5389(25°). d1.9818
 (26°).

⑥ JOC **28**, 1417 (1963).

SiC₁₄H₂₀O₄

① Diethyldifurfuryloxysilane

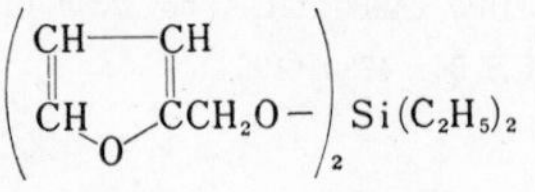

$$\left(\begin{array}{c} CH\!-\!\!-\!CH \\ \| \quad\quad \| \\ CH \quad CCH_2O- \\ \diagdown_O\diagup \end{array} \right)_2 Si(C_2H_5)_2$$

② Et₂Si(OEt)₂ +

$$\begin{array}{c} CH\!-\!\!-\!CH \\ \| \quad\quad \| \\ CH \quad CCH_2OH \\ \diagdown_O\diagup \end{array} \quad\longrightarrow$$

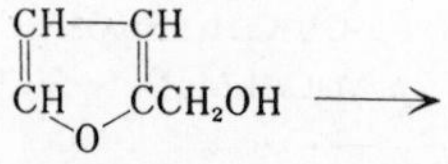

③ (138~139°/3). n_D1.4845 (20°). d1.0835
 (20°).

⑥ Plasticheskie Massy (No.3) 8 (1962);
 CA **59**, 654 (1963). Latvijas PSR
 Zinatnu Vestis (No.7) 59 (1961);
 CA **57**, 12525 (1962).

SiC₁₄H₂₁NO₃

① 1-Acetamino-2-(p-trimethylsilyl-
 phenyl)propanoic acid
 p-(CH₃)₃SiC₆H₄CH₂CH(COOH)-
 NHCOCH₃

② HCOOH or HCl
 + p-Me₃SiC₆H₄CH₂C(COONa)₂NHAc
 ⟶ 70%

③ [190°].

⑥ JCS **1963**, 5049.

SiC₁₄H₂₂

① 1-Phenyl-2-triethylsilylethene
 C₆H₅CH=CHSi(C₂H₅)₃

② Et₃SiH + PhC≡CH + H₂PtCl₆
 ⟶ 74%

③ (138°/10). n_D 1.5231 (20°). d 0.9035
 (20°).

⑥ Izv. SKh **1963**, 136; CA **59**, 11550
 (1963).

SiC₁₄H₂₃NO

① N-Phenyl-N-triethylsilylacetamide
 CH₃CON(C₆H₅)Si(C₂H₅)₃

② MeCONHPh + Et₃SiH + ZnCl₂
 ⟶ 55%

③ (128°/4). n_D1.5034 (20°). d0.96 (20°).

⑥ Compt. rend. **257**, 1304 (1963).

SiC₁₄H₂₄

① 1-Triethylsilylcyclooctatriene-2,4,6

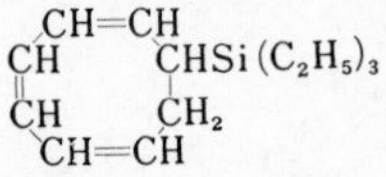

$$\begin{array}{c} CH=CH \\ CH \quad\quad CHSi(C_2H_5)_3 \\ | \quad\quad\quad | \\ CH \quad\quad CH_2 \\ CH=CH \end{array}$$

② EtMgBr + C₈H₉SiCl₃ ⟶

③ (70.4°/0.05). n_D 1.5019 (25°).

④ + H(PtO₂) ⟶ C₈H₁₅SiEt₃.

⑥ JCS **1963**, 4058.

SiC₁₄H₂₄O₂

① 1-Furylmethyl-2-methyl-2-triethyl-
 siloxyethene

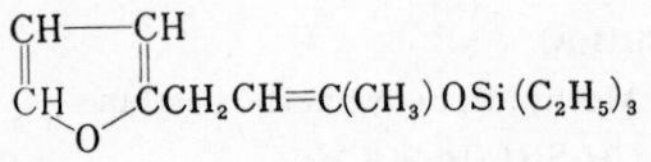

$$\begin{array}{c} CH\!-\!\!-\!CH \\ \| \quad\quad \| \\ CH \quad CCH_2CH=C(CH_3)\,OSi(C_2H_5)_3 \\ \diagdown_O\diagup \end{array}$$

②

$$\begin{array}{c} CH\!-\!\!-\!CH \\ \| \quad\quad \| \\ CH \quad CCH_2CH=CHCOMe\ + \\ \diagdown_O\diagup \end{array}$$
 Et₃SiH + H₂PtCl₆ ⟶

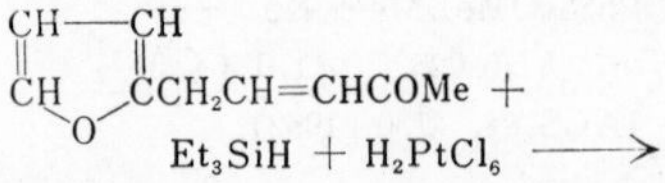

③ (120~123°/2.5). n_D1.4720(20°). d0.9291
 (20°).

⑥ Latvijas PSR Zinatnu Akad. Vestis,
 Kem. Ser. 111 (1963); CA **59**, 10102
 (1963).

SiC₁₄H₂₅O₃P

① 2-Triethoxysilylethylphenyl
 phosphine
 C₆H₅P(H)CH₂CH₂Si(OC₂H₅)₃

② PhPH₂ + CH₂=CHSi(OEt)₃
 + (t-BuO)₂ ⟶

③ (157~213°/2.5). n_D1.4844 (25°).

⑥ US 3067229 (1962); CA **58**, 10239
 (1963).

SiC₁₄H₂₈

① 1-Triethylsilylcyclooctene-4
   $C_8H_{13}Si(C_2H_5)_3$

② $cyclo$-$C_8H_{12}(1,5)$ + Et₃SiH ⟶

③ (80~85°/0.13). n_D1.4830 (25°).

④ + H(PtO₂) ⟶ C₈H₁₅SiEt₃

⑥ JCS 1963, 2831.

SiC₁₄H₂₈OS

① Ethyldimethyl(3-methyl-4-sulfa-7-
   oxaundecyn-1-yl)silane
   $C_2H_5(CH_3)_2SiC\equiv$
   $CCH(CH_3)SCH_2CH_2CH_2OC_4H_9$

② EtSiMe₂C≡CCHMeSH +
   BuOCH=CH₂ ⟶

③ (121°/2.5). n_D1.4700 (20°). d0.8839
   (20°/4°).

⑥ Izv. OKhN 1963, 90.

SiC₁₄H₃₀

① Cyclooctyltriethylsilane
   $cyclo$-$C_8H_{15}Si(C_2H_5)_3$

② H(PtO₂) + C₈H₉SiEt₃ ⟶
   C₈H₁₅SiCl₃ + EtMgBr ⟶ 26%

③ (82°/0.18). n_D1.4750 (26°).

⑥ JCS 1963, 2831, 4058.

SiC₁₄H₃₀N₂O₆

① Dimethylbis(1-nitro-4-methyl-
   pentoxy-2)silane
   $(CH_3)_2Si[OCH(C_4H_9\text{-}i)CH_2NO_2]_2$

② Me₂SiCl₂ + i-BuCH(OH)CH₂NO₂ ⟶

③ (158~160°/0.5). n_D1.4490(20°). d1.0551
   (20°/4°).

⑥ Trudy Kazansk. Khim. Tekhnol.
   Instituta (No.29), 16 (1960); CA 58,
   544 (1963). Zhur. 33, 1748 (1963).

SiC₁₄H₃₁IO₂

① α-Iodononylmethyldiethoxysilane
   $C_8H_{17}CHISi(OC_2H_5)_2CH_3$

② CH₂=CHSi(OEt)₂Me + C₇H₁₅I
   + Hg(lamp) ⟶

③ (150°/20). n_D1.3795 (25°).

⑥ JOC 27, 2261 (1962).

SiC₁₄H₃₂O

① Tri-n-butylethoxysilane
   $(C_4H_9)_3SiOC_2H_5$

② $(C_4H_9)_3SiCl$ + C₂H₂ + C₂H₅Br + Mg
   ⟶ 32%

③ Colorless liquid. (126~128°/13). n_D
   1.4340 (20°). d0.8228 (20°).
   Sol. in org. solvents.

⑥ Zhur. 25, 1128 (1955); CA 50, 3275
   (1956).

SiC₁₄H₃₂O₄

① Dimethylbis(β-n-butoxyethoxy)-
   silane
   $(CH_3)_2Si(OCH_2CH_2OC_4H_9\text{-}n)_2$

② Me₂SiCl₂ + n-BuOCH₂CH₂OH
   ⟶ 94%

③ (146°/10). n_D1.420 (25°). d0.910 (25°).

⑥ Compt. rend. 256, 4920 (1963).

SiC₁₄H₃₃O₃P

① Diethyl 4-triethylsilbutylphospho-
   nate
   $(C_2H_5)_3Si(CH_2)_4P(O)(OC_2H_5)_2$

② Et₃SiCH₂CH₂CH=CH₂ + (t-BuO)₂
   + HP(O)(OEt)₂ ⟶ 63%

③ (142~144°/2). n_D1.4489 (20°). d0.9722
   (20°/4°).

⑥ Dokl. 148, 875 (1963).

SiC₁₅H₁₆

① Allyldiphenylsilane
   $(C_6H_5)_2Si(H)CH_2CH=CH_2$

② CH₂=CHCH₂SiHCl₂ + C₆H₅MgBr ⟶

③ Colorless liquid. (155°/10). n_D1.5760
   (20°). d1.0000 (20°).
   Sol. in org. solvents; insol. in H₂O.

⑥ Izv. OKhN 1957, 383; CA 51, 15457
   (1957).

SiC₁₅H₁₆O

① 4-Trimethylsilyldibenzofurane

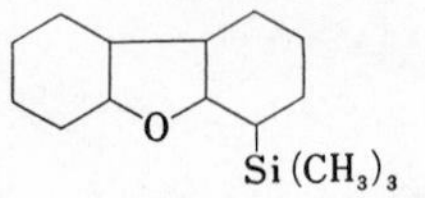

② + Me₃SiCl ⟶

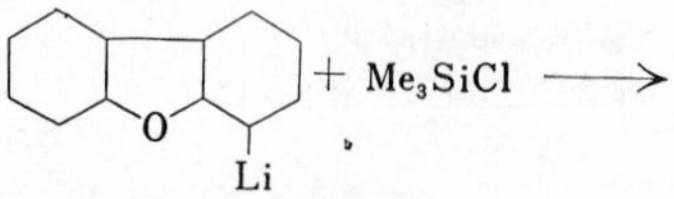

③ (163~164°/7). n_D1.6040 (20°).
⑥ JCS 1961, 4921. PB Report 145953
   (1959); CA 58, 4959 (1963).

SiC₁₅H₁₆O

① 2-Trimethylsilyldibenzofurane

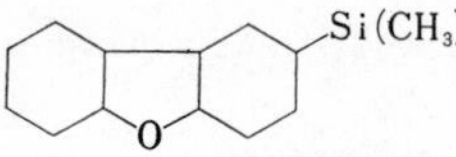

② + Me₃SiCl
   + Na ⟶

+ Me₃SiCl ⟶

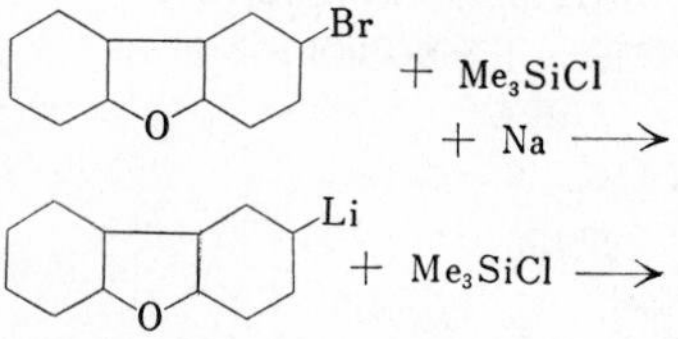

③ (140~148°/3~4). [49°].
⑥ JCS 1961, 4921. PB Report 145953
   (1959); CA 58, 4592 (1963).

SiC₁₅H₁₈

① 4-Biphenylyltrimethylsilane
   (CH₃)₃SiC₆H₄C₆H₅-*p*

② *p*-ClC₆H₄Ph + Me₃SiCl $\xrightarrow{Na}$ 86%
   p-LiC₆H₄Ph + Me₃SiCl ⟶ 65%
   HSiCl₃ + Ph₂
   $\xrightarrow[\text{(2)MeMgCl}]{\text{(1) BCl}_3}$ 28.5% (50% para)
③ (160~161°/6). [50~51°].
   IR: JACS 73, 3798 (1951).

④ Me₃Si— $\xrightarrow[\text{H}_2\text{O}]{\text{H}^+}$

   + (Me₃Si)₂O

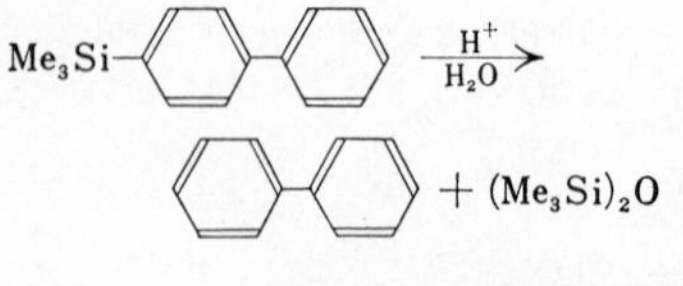

⑥ JACS 80, 2283 (1958); 73, 3798 (1951).

SiC₁₅H₁₈O

① Methyldiphenylethoxysilane
   CH₃Si(C₆H₅)₂OC₂H₅
② Ph₂Si(OEt)₂ + MeMgBr ⟶ 78%
③ (170~171°/10). n_D1.5430 (20°). d1.0172
   (20).
⑥ Hua Hsüeh Hsüeh Pao 27, 38 (1961);
   CA 59, 11547 (1963).

SiC₁₅H₁₈O

① Trimethyl-*o*-phenoxyphenylsilane
   o-C₆H₅OC₆H₄Si(CH₃)₃
② *o*-PhOC₆H₄Li + Me₃SiCl ⟶
③ (137~139°/6). n_D1.5525 (20°).
⑥ JCS 1961, 4921.

SiC₁₅H₁₈O

① Trimethyl-*p*-phenoxyphenylsilane
   p-C₆H₅OC₆H₄Si(CH₃)₃
② *p*-PhOC₆H₄Na + Me₃SiCl ⟶
③ (123~125°/1). n_D1.5505 (20°).
⑥ JCS 1961, 4921. PB Report 145953
   (1959); CA 58, 4592 (1963).

SiC₁₅H₁₈S

① Trimethyl-*o*-phenylmercaptophenyl-
   silane
   o-C₆H₅SC₆H₄Si(CH₃)₃
② *o*-PhSC₆H₄Na + Me₃SiCl ⟶
③ (132~136°/2). n_D1.5908 (20°).
⑥ PB Report 145953 (1959); CA 58, 4592
   (1963). JCS 1961, 4921.

SiC₁₅H₁₈S

① Trimethyl-*p*-phenylmercaptophenyl-
   silane
   p-C₆H₅SC₆H₄Si(CH₃)₃
② *p*-PhSC₆H₄MgBr + Me₃SiCl ⟶
③ (167~168°/3). n_D1.5903 (20°).
⑥ JCS 1961, 4921. PB Report 145953
   (1959); CA 58, 4592 (1963).

$SiC_{15}H_{20}FeO$

① (Trimethylsilylacetyl)ferrocene
$C_5H_5FeC_5H_4COCH_2Si(CH_3)_3$
② $C_5H_5FeC_5H_4COOMe + Me_3SiCH_2MgCl$
$\longrightarrow$ 66%
③ Solid. [66°].
⑥ Dokl. **148**, 598 (1963).

$SiC_{15}H_{20}N_2$

① N, N'-Diphenyl-N-trimethylsilyl-
hydrazine
$C_6H_5NHN(C_6H_5)Si(CH_3)_3$
② PhNHN(Li)Ph + Me₃SiCl $\longrightarrow$
③ Solid. (138°/1). [55°].
⑥ Z. anorg. allg. Chem. **321**, 198 (1963).

$SiC_{15}H_{20}N_2$

① (Phenylaminomethyl)phenylamino-
dimethylsilane
$C_6H_5NHCH_2Si(CH_3)_2NHC_6H_5$
② $PhNH_2 + Et_3N$
$+ Me_2Si(Cl)CH_2Br \longrightarrow$
③ (145°/0.4). $n_D 1.5831$ (20°).
⑥ Ber. **96**, 965 (1963).

$SiC_{15}H_{20}O_6$

① Phenylsilyl tripropionate
$(C_2H_5COO)_3SiC_6H_5$
② $EtCOOH + C_5H_5N + PhSiH_3 \longrightarrow$
③ $n_D 1.4772$ (20°). $d 1.1377$ (20°/4°).
⑥ Zhur. **33**, 2617 (1963).

$SiC_{15}H_{25}NO_2$

① 5-Trimethylsilylpentyl phenylcar-
bamate
$C_6H_5NHCOO(CH_2)_5Si(CH_3)_3$
② $PhNCO + Me_3Si(CH_2)_5OH \longrightarrow$
③ Solid. [53.5~54.0°].
⑥ Zhur. **33**, 1251 (1963).

$SiC_{15}H_{26}O_2$

① [β-(α-Furylmethyl)vinyloxy]ethyldi-
n-propylsilane

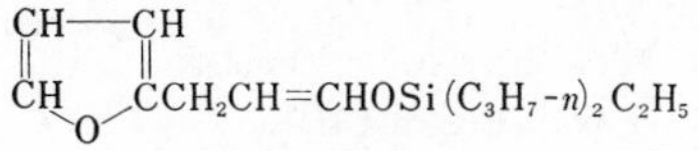

② 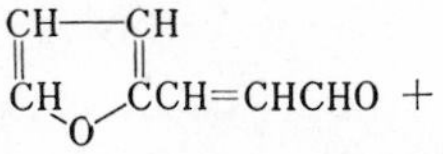
$n\text{-}Pr_2SiHEt + H_2PtCl_6 \longrightarrow$

③ (115~116°/3).
⑥ Latvijas PSR Zinatnu, Akad. Vestis
Kem. Ser. 111 (1963); CA **59**, 10102
(1963).

$SiC_{15}H_{28}$

① 1-Trimethylsilylcyclododecadiene-4,8

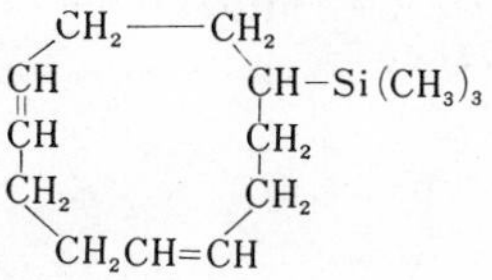

② $MeMgCl + C_{12}H_{19}SiCl_3 \longrightarrow$ 76.5%
$MeMgCl + C_{12}H_{19}SiCl_2Me \longrightarrow$ 63%
③ (122°/5). $n_D 1.4957$ (25°). $d 0.8946$
(25°/4°).
IR: 1243, 828~863, 747, 683, 965 cm⁻¹.
④ $+ H_2 + Pd\text{-}C \longrightarrow C_{12}H_{21}SiMe_3$
⑥ JOC **28**, 3353 (1963).

$SiC_{15}H_{28}O_2$

① α-Furfuryloxyethyldi-n-butylsilane

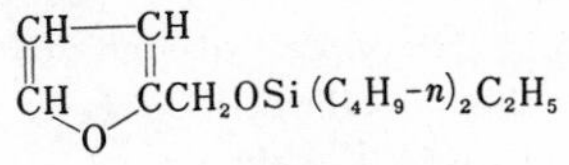

② 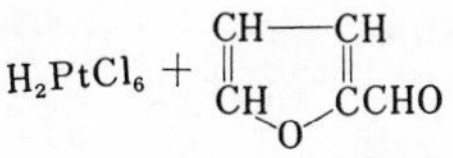
$H_2PtCl_6 +$
$+ n\text{-}Bu_2SiHEt \longrightarrow$

③ (109~112°/1). $n_D 1.4589$ (20°). $d 0.9143$
(20°).
⑥ Latvijas PSR Zunatnu Akad. Vestis,
Kem. Ser. 111 (1963); CA **56**, 10102
(1963).

SiC₁₅H₃₀

① Trimethylsilylcyclodecene
   cyclo-C₁₂H₂₁Si(CH₃)₃
② cyclo-C₁₂H₁₉SiMe₃ + H₂ + Pd-C ⟶
③ (98~100°/1). n_D1.4921 (25°). d0.8909
   (25°/4°).
⑥ JOC **28**, 3353 (1963).

SiC₁₅H₃₀O₂

① 3,8-Dimethyl-6-*n*-propyl-3-sila-7,9-
   dioxatridecyne-4
   C₄H₉OCH(CH₃)OCH(C₃H₇)C≡
   CSiH(CH₃)C₂H₅
② HCl + BuOCH=CH₂ +
   PrCH(OH)C≡CSiHMeEt ⟶
③ (137~138°/14). n_D1.4418 (20°). d0.8690
   (20°/4°).
⑥ Zhur. **33**, 377 (1963).

SiC₁₅H₃₂O

① Tri-*n*-butylallyloxysilane
   (*n*-C₄H₉)₃SiOCH₂CH=CH₂
② *n*-Bu₃SiH + CH₂=CHCH₂OH
   $\xrightarrow{\text{catalyst Li, Na,}}$
   $\overline{\phantom{\text{catalyst}}\text{ZnCl}_2\text{ or SnCl}_2\phantom{\text{cata}}}$
③ (112.5~113.0°/2.0). n_D1.4411 (20°). d
   0.8228 (20°/4°).
⑥ Izv. SKh. **1963**, 1749.

SiC₁₅H₃₂O₃

① Cyclohexyltris(ethoxymethyl)silane
   cyclo-C₆H₁₁Si(CH₂OC₂H₅)₃
② cyclo-C₆H₁₁SiCl₃ + Mg
   + EtOCH₂Cl ⟶
③ (154°/15.5). n_D 1.4562 (20°). d 0.9263
   (20°).
⑥ Belg. 618520 (1963); CA **59**, 6440 (1963).

SiC₁₅H₃₆Sn

① Dimethylsilylmethyltri-*n*-butyl-
   stannane
   (*n*-C₄H₉)₃SnCH₂SiH(CH₃)₂
② Bu₃SnCl + Me₂Si(H)CH₂MgCl ⟶
③ (133°/5). n_D 1.4764 (25°). d 1.047

(25°/4°).
⑥ JACS **81**, 975 (1959).   US 3043858
   (1962); CA **58**, 1489 (1963).

SiC₁₅H₃₆Sn

① Trimethylsilyltri-*n*-butylstannane
   (*n*-C₄H₉)₃SnSi(CH₃)₃
② Bu₃SnLi + Me₃SiCl ⟶
③ (88°/0.2). n_D1.4873 (20°).
⑥ JOC **28**, 237 (1963).

SiC₁₅H₃₆Sn

① Dimethylsilylmethyltri-*n*-butyl-
   stannane
   (CH₃)₂Si(H)CH₂Sn(C₄H₉-*n*)₃
② *n*-Bu₃SnCl
   + Me₂Si(H)CH₂MgCl ⟶
③ (133°/5). n_D1.4764 (25°). d1.047 (25°).
④ + Na + EtOH
   ⟶ Me₂Si(OEt)CH₂Sn(Bu-*n*)₃
⑥ Brit. 891087 (1962); CA **59**, 11560
   (1963).

SiC₁₆H₁₂

① Diphenyldiethynylsilane
   (C₆H₅)₂Si(C≡CH)₂
② BrMgC≡CMgBr + Ph₂SiCl₂ ⟶
③ Solid. [44~45°].
④ + H₂PtCl₆ + MeSi(H)₂Ph

$$\left(\text{Ph}_2\text{Si} \underset{\text{CH}_2\text{CH}_2}{\overset{\text{CH}_2\text{CH}_2}{\diagup\diagdown}} \text{SiMePh} \right)_{16}$$

⑥ Izv. OKhN **1962**, 2251.

SiC₁₆H₁₄

① 1,1-Diphenyl-1-silacyclopentadiene

$$\begin{array}{c} \text{CH——CH} \\ \| \quad\quad \| \\ \text{CH} \quad \text{CH} \\ \diagdown\text{Si(C}_6\text{H}_5)_2 \end{array}$$

② PhMgBr + $\begin{array}{c} \text{CH——CH} \\ \| \quad\quad \| \\ \text{CH} \quad \text{CH} \\ \diagdown\text{SiCl}_2 \end{array}$ ⟶

③ Solid. (128~130°/1). [54~56°].

④ $+$ H $\longrightarrow$

$$\begin{matrix} CH_2 \!\!-\!\! CH_2 \\ | \qquad | \\ CH_2 \quad CH_2 \\ \diagdown Si Ph_2 \diagup \end{matrix}$$

⑥ JACS **83**, 3716 (1961) ; **84**, 4723, 4727 (1962).

SiC$_{16}$H$_{16}$

① Diphenyldivinylsilane
  (C$_6$H$_5$)$_2$Si(CH=CH$_2$)$_2$

② 2 CH$_2$=CHMgCl + Ph$_2$SiCl$_2$
   $\longrightarrow$ 80%

③ (130~131°/0.05). n_D1.5350 (25°). *d* 1.0092 (25°).
  IR : JACS **82**, 555 (1960).

⑥ JOC **22**, 1200 (1957).   JACS **82**, 555 (1960).

SiC$_{16}$H$_{16}$Br$_4$

① Dimethylbis-(α, α-dibromobenzyl)-silane
  (CH$_3$)$_2$Si(CBr$_2$C$_6$H$_5$)$_2$

② Me$_2$Si(CH$_2$Ph)$_2$ + (CH$_2$CO)$_2$NBr
   + (BzO)$_2$ $\longrightarrow$ 94%

③ [122~125°].

⑥ Can. J. Chem. **41**, 2351 (1963).

SiC$_{16}$H$_{16}$O$_4$

① Diphenyldiacetoxysilane
  (C$_6$H$_5$)$_2$Si(OCOCH$_3$)$_2$

② (C$_6$H$_5$)$_2$SiCl$_2$ + Ag(CH$_3$COO)
   $\longrightarrow$ (C$_6$H$_5$)$_2$Si(OCOCH$_3$)$_2$

③ (176~178°/3).
  Quite viscous at 25° and completely fluid at 100°

⑥ JACS **74**, 2371 (1952).

SiC$_{16}$H$_{18}$

① Tetramethylenediphenylsilane

$$\begin{matrix} CH_2\!-\!CH_2 \\ | \qquad\quad \diagdown \\ \qquad\qquad Si(C_6H_5)_2 \\ | \qquad\quad \diagup \\ CH_2\!-\!CH_2 \end{matrix}$$

② Ph$_3$SiCl + Li(CH$_2$)$_4$Li $\longrightarrow$

③ (159~162°/5). n_D1.5853 (20°).

⑥ JACS **80**, 2677 (1958).

SiC$_{16}$H$_{18}$O

① 1,1-Diphenyl-1-sila-2-oxacyclo-hexane

$$(C_6H_5)_2Si \diagup \!\!\!\begin{matrix} CH_2CH_2 \\ \\ O\!-\!CH_2 \end{matrix}\!\!\! \diagdown CH_2$$

② THF + Mg + Ph$_2$SiCl$_2$ $\longrightarrow$

③ (215~216°/34~38). n_D1.5722 (20°).

⑥ US 3083219 (1963) ; CA **59**, 8789 (1963).

SiC$_{16}$H$_{18}$O

① Methyldiphenylallyloxysilane
  MeSi(C$_6$H$_5$)$_2$OCH$_2$CH=CH$_2$

② Ph$_2$SiHMe + CH$_2$=CHCH$_2$OH $\longrightarrow$
  (catalyst Li, Na, ZnCl$_2$ or SnCl$_2$)

③ (157.0°/3.0). n_D1.5459 (20°). *d*1.0233 (20°/4°).

⑥ Izv. SKh **1963**, 1749.

SiC$_{16}$H$_{18}$O$_2$

① Ethyl diphenylsilylacetate
  (C$_6$H$_5$)$_2$Si(H)CH$_2$COOC$_2$H$_5$

② CH(N)$_2$COOEt + Ph$_2$SiH$_2$ $\longrightarrow$ 20%

③ (110~115°/0.03).

⑥ JCS **1963**, 3604.

SiC$_{16}$H$_{18}$O$_6$

① Methyltrifurfuryloxysilane

$$\left(\begin{matrix} CH\!-\!CH \\ \| \quad\quad \| \\ CH \quad CCH_2O- \\ \diagdown O \diagup \end{matrix}\right)_3 \!\!\! SiCH_3$$

②

$$\begin{matrix} CH\!-\!CH \\ \| \quad\quad \| \\ CH \quad CCH_2OH \\ \diagdown O \diagup \end{matrix} + C_5H_5N$$
   + C$_6$H$_6$ + MeSiCl$_3$ $\longrightarrow$

③ (157~158°/1). n_D1.4992 (20°). *d*1.1801 (20°).

⑥ Plasticheskie Massy (No.3) 8 (1962).
  Latvijas PSR Zinatnu Vestis(No.7)

59 (1961) ; CA **57**, 12525 (1962).

SiC₁₆H₁₉N
① N-Trimethylsilyldiphenylmethylene-
   imine
   $(C_6H_5)_2C=NSi(CH_3)_3$
② Ph₂CO + (Me₃Si)₂NNa ⟶ 84%
③ (99~100°/1). n_D1.5563 (22°). d.0.9949
   (30°/4°).
⑥ Ber. **96**, 2132 (1963).

SiC₁₆H₂₀
① Diethyldiphenylsilane
   $(C_2H_5)_2Si(C_6H_5)_2$
② Ph₂SiCl₂ + 2EtMgBr ⟶ 98%
③ (297°). n_D1.5600 (20°). d0.9844 (20°).
⑥ Dokl. **118**, 731(1958). JCS **1935**, 1088.

SiC₁₆H₂₀
① Trimethyldiphenylmethylsilane
   $(C_6H_5)_2CHSi(CH_3)_3$
② Ph₂CCl₂ + Me₃SiCl + THF + Mg ⟶
   n-BuLi + Ph₂CH₂ + Me₃SiCl ⟶
③ [73~75°].
⑥ JACS **85**, 2243 (1963) ; **81**, 981 (1959).

SiC₁₆H₂₀
① Dimethyldibenzylsilane
   $(CH_3)_2Si(CH_2C_6H_5)_2$
② PhCH₂MgCl + Me₂SiCl₂ ⟶ 96%
③ [56~58°].
④ + (CH₂CO)₂NBr + (BzO)₂
   ⟶ Me₂Si(CBr₂Ph)₂
⑥ Can. J. Chem. **41**, 2351 (1963).

SiC₁₆H₂₀Cl₂
① 1-Dimethylchlorosilyl-2-diphenyl-
   chlorosilylethane
   $(CH_3)_2Si(Cl)CH_2CH_2Si(C_6H_5)_2Cl$
② H₂PtCl₆ + Ph₂SiHCl +
   Me₂Si(Cl)CH=CH₂ ⟶
③ (215°/10). n_D 1.5566 (25°). d 1.118
   (25°/4°).

④ + LiOH + HOH ⟶ 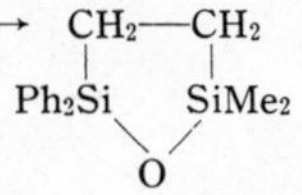
   $$CH_2\!-\!CH_2$$
   $$\underset{Ph_2Si\quad SiMe_2}{|\qquad\quad|}$$
   $$\underset{O}{\diagdown\;\diagup}$$
⑥ JACS **82**, 1883 (1960). US 3041362
   (1962) ; CA **58**, 1558 (1963).

SiC₁₆H₂₀N₂O,
① N,N'-Diphenyl-N-trimethylsilylurea
   $(CH_3)_3SiN(C_6H_5)CONHC_6H_5$
② PhNCO + Me₃SiNHPh ⟶ 98%
③ Solid. [67~69°].
   Readily hydrolyzed.
⑥ Z. anorg. allg. Chem. **321**, 208 (1963).

SiC₁₆H₂₀O
① Trimethyldiphenylhydroxymethyl-
   silane
   $(CH_3)_3SiC(OH)(C_6H_5)_2$
② Me₃SiCHPh₂ $\overset{NBS}{⟶}$ Me₃SiCBrPh₂ $\overset{AgOAc}{⟶}$
③ [158~159°].
⑥ JACS **80**, 1886 (1958) ; **81**, 981 (1959).

SiC₁₆H₂₀O₂
① Diphenyldiethoxysilane
   $(C_6H_5)_2Si(OC_2H_5)_2$
② Si(OEt)₄ + PhMgCl ⟶
   Ph₂Si(OEt)OCHPh₂ + EtONa
   ⟶ 8%
③ (130°/2). n_D1.5193 (20°).
④ + MeMgBr ⟶ MeSi(Ph)₂OEt
   + p-ClC₆H₄MgCl
   ⟶ p-ClC₆H₄Si(Ph₂)OEt
⑥ Hua Hsüeh Hsüeh Pao **27**, 38 (1961) ;
   CA **59**, 11547 (1963). JOC **25**, 1072
   (1960).

SiC₁₆H₂₂O₃
① α-Naphthyltriethoxysilane
   $\alpha\text{-}C_{10}H_7Si(OC_2H_5)_3$
② C₁₀H₇Li + Si(OC₂H₅)₄ ⟶
③ (291~293°). n_D1.5303 (20°). d1.0473
   (20°/20°).

⑥ JACS **73**, 4640 (1951). Dokl. **73**, 323
  (1950) ; CA **45**, 2921 (1951).

SiC₁₆H₂₄O₂

① Bis(vinylethynyldimethylmethoxy)-
  dimethylsilane
  [CH₂=CHC≡C-C(CH₃)₂O-]₂Si(CH₃)₂
② CH₂=CHC≡CCMe₂OH + Et₂NH
  + Me₂SiCl₂ ——→
③ (114~115°/9). n_D1.4702 (20°). d0.908
  (20°/4°).
④ + (BzO)₂ ——→ colorless liq. going
  to polymers
⑥ Izv. OKhN **1963**, 97.

SiC₁₆H₃₀O₆

① Methyltris(tetrahydrofurfuryloxy)-
  silane

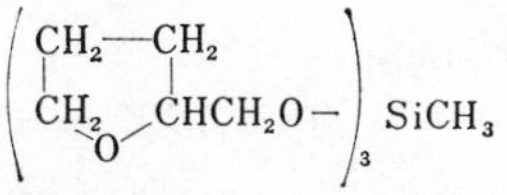

$$\left(\begin{array}{c} CH_2{-}CH_2 \\ CH_2 \quad CHCH_2O{-} \\ O \end{array}\right)_3 SiCH_3$$

②
$$\begin{array}{c} CH_2{-}CH_2 \\ CH_2 \quad CHCH_2OH \\ O \end{array} + MeSiCl_3$$
  ——→ 88~90%

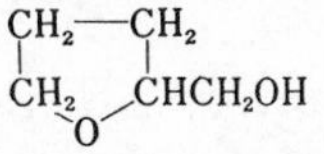

③ (179~181°/2). n_D1.4648 (20°). d1.1068
  (20°).
⑥ Plasticheskie Massy (No.3), 8 (1962) ;
  CA **59**, 654 (1963).

SiC₁₆H₃₂O₂

① 2,7-Dimethyl-2,7-dihydroxy-6-tri-
  ethylsilyloctadiene-3,5
  (CH₃)₂C(OH)C[Si(C₂H₅)₃]=CHCH
  =CHC(CH₃)₂OH
② H(Ni or Pd-CaCO₃) +
  + Me₂C(OH)C(SiEt₃)=CHC
  ≡CCMe₂OH ——→
③ (165°/3). n_D1.4850 (20°). d0.9238
  (20°/4°).
⑥ Dokl. **150**, 1043 (1963).

SiC₁₆H₃₆

① Tetra-*n*-butylsilane
  (C₄H₉)₄Si
② SiCl₄ + BuMgBr
  $\xrightarrow[\text{AcOH or no solvent}]{}$ 72%
  Si(OEt)₄ + *n*-BuMgBr ——→ 56%
  SiCl₄ or Si(OEt)₄ + *n*-BuLi ——→
  100%
③ (156~157°/22). n_D1.4465 (20°). d0.8008
  (20°).
  Raman : Izv. OKhN **1960**, 1553.
⑥ JACS **69**, 967 (1947).   Zhur **29**, 2960
  (1959).   Izv. OKhN **1960**, 1553.

SiC₁₆H₃₆

① Hexadecylsilane
  C₁₆H₃₃SiH₃
② C₁₄H₂₉CH=CH₂+SiH₄ + (*t*-BuO)₂ ——→
③ (158~160°/8). n_D1.4457 (25°).
⑤ For waterproofing masonry and
  brick.
⑥ US 3067051 (1962) ; CA **58**, 5896
  (1936).

SiC₁₆H₃₆O₃

① Methyltri-*n*-amyloxysilane
  CH₃Si(OC₅H₁₁-*n*)₃
② MeSiCl₃ + C₅H₅N + *n*-AmOH ——→
③ (142~145°/9). n_D1.4190 (25°). d0.8785
  (30°).
  IR : 3000, 1259, 1100 cm⁻¹.
⑥ J. Chi. Chem. Soc. (Ⅱ) **8**, 237, 384
  (1961) ; (Ⅱ) **9**, 273 (1962).   JOC **17**,
  1400 (1952).

SiC₁₆H₃₆O₃

① Methyltriisoamyloxysilane
  CH₃Si(OC₅H₁₁-*i*)₃
② MeSiCl₃ + C₅H₅N + *i*-AmOH ——→
③ (134~136°/10). n_D1.4160 (24°). d0.8725
  (30°/30°).
  IR : 3000, 1510, 1250, 1100 cm⁻¹.

⑥ J. Chi. Chem. Soc. (Ⅱ) **8**, 237, 384 (1961); **9**, 273 (1962). Zhur. **29**, 1528 (1959).

SiC₁₇H₁₅Cl

① Methylphenyl-1-naphthylchloro-silane

$1\text{-}C_{10}H_7Si(Cl)CH_3(C_6H_5)$

② $MeSiH(Ph)C_{10}H_7\text{-}1 + Cl_2 \longrightarrow$

③ $[\alpha]_D^{22} - 6.47°$.

④ $+ EtLi \longrightarrow MeSi(Et)(Ph)C_{10}H_7\text{-}1$

$+ BuLi \longrightarrow MeSi(Bu)(Ph)C_{10}H_7\text{-}1$

$+$ ⬡CHLi $\longrightarrow$

$MeSi(Ph)(C_{10}H_7\text{-}1)C_{13}H_9$

⑥ JACS **81**, 1013 (1959). Tetrahedron Letters **1962**, 815, 821.

SiC₁₇H₁₆

① Methylphenyl-1-naphthylsilane

$MeSiH(Ph)C_{10}H_7\text{-}1$

② $LiAlH_4 + MeSi(Br)(Ph)C_{10}H_7\text{-}1 \longrightarrow$

$LiAlH_4 +$

$MeSi(Ph)(C_{10}H_7\text{-}1)OC_{10}H_{19} \longrightarrow$

③ $[63\sim64°]$. $[\alpha]_D^{25} - 33.5°$. $[\alpha]_D^{25} + 33.2°$.

④ $+ Cl_2 \longrightarrow MeSi(Cl)(Ph)C_{10}H_7\text{-}1$

$+ t\text{-}BuOK$

$\longrightarrow 1\text{-}C_{10}H_7Si(Me)(Ph)OBu\text{-}t$

⑥ JACS **85**, 832 (1963). US 3024262 (1962); CA **57**, 2254 (1962). Tetrahedron Letters **1962**, 815. Proc. Chem. Soc. **59** (1963).

SiC₁₇H₂₀

① 1,1-Diphenyl-1-silacyclohexane

$CH_2 \begin{matrix} CH_2CH_2 \\ \\ CH_2CH_2 \end{matrix} Si(C_6H_5)_2$

② $(CH_2)_5SiCl_2 + PhLi \longrightarrow$

③ $(125\sim127°/0.1)$. $n_D 1.5820$ $(25°)$.

IR: 2640, 987 (strong), 908 (strong). cm⁻¹.

⑥ JOC **27**, 1422 (1962); **25**, 246 (1960).

SiC₁₇H₂₀O

① p-Trimethylsilylphenyl benzyl ketone

$p\text{-}[(CH_3)_3Si]C_6H_4COCH_2C_6H_5$

② $p\text{-}(Me_3Si)C_6H_4CN + PhCH_2MgX \longrightarrow$

③ Solid. $[75\sim77°]$.

⑥ Yakugaku Zasshi **82**, 929 (1962).

SiC₁₇H₂₀O₆

① Ethyltrifurfuryloxysilane

$\left(\begin{matrix} CH\!\!-\!\!CH \\ \| \quad \| \\ CH \quad CCH_2O- \\ \diagdown O \diagup \end{matrix} \right)_3 SiC_2H_5$

② $\begin{matrix} CH\!\!-\!\!CH \\ \| \quad \| \\ CH \quad CCH_2OH \\ \diagdown O \diagup \end{matrix} +$

$EtSi(OEt)_3 \longrightarrow$

③ $(159.5\sim160.0°/1.5)$. $n_D 1.4988$ $(20°)$. d 1.1743 $(20°)$.

⑥ Plasticheskie Massy (No.3) 8 (1962); CA **59**, 654 (1963). Latvijas PSR Zinatnu Vestis (No.7) 59 (1961); CA **57**, 12525 (1962).

SiC₁₇H₂₁N₃O₃

① α-Trimethylsilyl-α, β-bis-(phenyl-carbamyl)-hydroxylamine

$C_6H_5NHCOON[Si(CH_3)_3]CONHC_6H_5$

② $PhNCO + Me_3SiNH_2O \longrightarrow$

③ Solid. $[128\sim138°$ decomp.].

⑥ Monatsh. **94**, 141 (1963).

SiC₁₇H₂₂FeO₃

① Methyl 1-trimethylsilylacetylferrocene-1'-carboxylate

$(CH_3)_3SiCH_2COC_5H_4FeC_5H_4COOCH_3$

② $Me_3SiCH_2MgCl + Fe(C_5H_4COOMe)_2$

$\longrightarrow 57\%$

③ Solid. [106～108°].
⑥ Dokl. **148**, 598 (1963).

SiC₁₇H₂₅BN₂

① Trimethylsilylethylbis(phenylamino)-
   borane
   $(CH_3)_3SiCH_2CH_2B(NHC_6H_5)_2$
② $PhNH_2 + Me_3SiCH_2CH_2BCl_2 \longrightarrow$
③ [132～133°].
   IR: 1250, 832, 860, 740 cm⁻¹.
⑥ Inorg. Chem. **2**, 734 (1963).

SiC₁₇H₃₁O₃P

① Phenylethyl-3-triethoxysilylpropyl-
   phosphine
   $(C_6H_5)(C_2H_5)PCH_2CH_2CH_2Si(OC_2H_5)_3$
② $PhP(Et)CH_2CH=CH_2 + HSi(OEt)_3$
   $+ (t-BuO)_2 \longrightarrow$
   PhP(Na)Et
   $+ (EtO)_3SiCH_2CH_2CH_2Cl \longrightarrow$
③ (90～120°/0.2～0.3). n_D 1.4840 (25°).
⑥ US 2995594 (1961); CA **56**, 3516 (1962).
   US 3067229 (1962); CA **58**, 10239
   (1963).

SiC₁₇H₄₀OSn

① Ethoxydimethylsilylmethyl-
   tri-*n*-butylstannane
   $(CH_3)_2Si(OC_2H_5)CH_2Sn(C_4H_9-n)_3$
② $Me_2Si(H)CH_2Sn(Bu-n)_3 + Na$
   $+ EtOH \longrightarrow$
③ (147°/5). n_D 1.4682 (25°). d 1.053 (25°).
⑥ Brit. 891087(1962); CA **59**, 11560(1963).
   JACS **81**, 975 (1959).

SiC₁₈H₁₂BrCl₃

① Tris(*p*-chlorophenyl)bromosilane
   $(p-ClC_6H_4)_3SiBr$
② $CH_2=CHCH_2Br + (p-ClC_6H_4)_3SiH$
   $\longrightarrow$ 90%
③ [122°].
⑥ J. prakt. Chem. **21**, 149 (1963).   Ber.
   93, 2525 (1960).   Zhur. **32**, 698

(1962); English page 697.

SiC₁₈H₁₂BrF₃

① Tris(*p*-fluorophenyl)bromosilane
   $(p-FC_6H_4)_3SiBr$
② $CH_2=CHCH_2Br + (p-FC_6H_4)_3SiH$
   $\longrightarrow$ 87%
③ [117°].
⑥ J. prakt. Chem. **21**, 149 (1963).   Ber.
   93, 2525 (1960).

SiC₁₈H₁₂Br₄

① Tris(*p*-bromophenyl)bromosilane
   $(p-BrC_6H_4)_3SiBr$
② $Br_2 + (p-BrC_6H_4)_3SiH \longrightarrow$
③ [144～146°].
⑥ J. prakt. Chem. **21**, 149 (1963).

SiC₁₈H₁₃Br₃

① Tris(*p*-bromophenyl)silane
   $(p-BrC_6H_4)_3SiH$
② $SiHCl_3 + p-BrC_6H_4MgBr \longrightarrow$
③ [106°].
   IR: 2141 cm⁻¹
④ $+ Br_2 \longrightarrow (p-BrC_6H_4)_3SiBr$
⑥ J. prakt. Chem. **21**, 140 (1963).

SiC₁₈H₁₃F₃

① Tri-(*p*-fluorophenyl)silane
   $(p-FC_6H_4)_3SiH$
② $SiHCl_3 + p-FC_6H_4MgX \longrightarrow$
③ [47°].
   IR: 2134 cm⁻¹.
④ $+ CH_2=CHCH_2Br$
   $\longrightarrow (p-FC_6H_4)_3SiBr$
   Alkaline hydrolytic studies.
⑥ J. prakt. Chem. **21**, 149 (1963).   Z.
   anorg. allg. Chem. **306**, 180 (1960).

SiC₁₈H₁₄N₂O₆

① Phenylbis(*p*-nitrophenoxy)silane
   $C_6H_5SiH(OC_6H_4NO_2-p)_2$
② $p-HOC_6H_4NO_2 + PhSiH_3 + HCONMe_2$

③ n_D1.6101 (20°). d1.3848 (20°/4°).

⑥ Zhur. **33**, 2617 (1963).

SiC₁₈H₁₅Br

① Triphenylbromosilane

   $(C_6H_5)_3SiBr$

② $SiBr_4 + Ph_3SiOH \longrightarrow 46\%$

   $PhMgBr + Ph_2SiCl_2 \longrightarrow$

   $Ph_3SiCl + MgBr_2 \longrightarrow$

   $Br_2 + (MeNBSiMe_3)_3 \longrightarrow$

   $Br_2 + Ph_3SiOC(Pr)=C(Pr)OSiPh_3 \longrightarrow$

   $HSiPh_3 + CH_2=CHCH_2Br \longrightarrow$

   $HSiPh_3 + CH_2=CHBr \longrightarrow$

③ Solid. (242°/16). [120~122°].

⑥ Zhur. **32**, 698 (1962); English page
   697. JINC **15**, 99 (1960).   J. prakt.
   Chem. **12**, 18 (1960).   Monatsh. **93**,
   1363 (1962).

SiC₁₈H₁₅Cl

① Triphenylchlorosilane

   $(C_6H_5)_3SiCl$

② $Ph_4Si + AcCl \longrightarrow$

   $Ph_3SiH + CH_2=CHCH_2Cl \longrightarrow$

   $Ph_3SiH + PhCl \longrightarrow$

③ (378°). [90°].

④ $+ C_5H_5N + Ti[O(SiMePhO)_2\text{-}H]_4$
   $\longrightarrow Ti[O(SiMePhO)_2SiPh_3]_4$

   $+ C_5H_5N + Ti[O(SiMePhO)_3H]_4$
   $\longrightarrow Ti[O(SiMePhO)_3SiPh_3]_4$

   $+ NH_3 \longrightarrow Ph_3SiNH_2$

⑥ Zhur. **32**, 698 (1962); English page
   697. Rec. trav. chim. **81**, 28 (1962).
   Monatsh. **93**, 1363 (1962).   Izv.
   OKhN **1963**, 1672.

SiC₁₈H₁₅F

① Triphenylfluorosilane

   $(C_6H_5)_3SiF$

② $PhF + Ph_3SiH \longrightarrow 18\%$

   $SiF_4 \xrightarrow{PhMgBr}$

$Ph_3SiX \xrightarrow[EtOH]{HF} 50\%$ (X=Cl, Br)

③ (254~250/30°). [64°].

   IR: Appl. Spectroscopy **16**, 12 (1962).

⑥ Izv. OKhN **1955**, 181; **1953**, 860; CA
   49, 914 (1955).   JCS **1952**, 2846.

SiC₁₈H₁₆

① Triphenylsilane

   $(C_6H_5)_3SiH$

② $HSiCl_3 + PhMgBr \longrightarrow$

   $Ph_2SiH_2 + PhK \longrightarrow$

   $Ph_3SiSiPh_3 \xrightarrow[\text{2. 1 N HCl, } C_6H_6]{\text{1. LiAlH}_4} 19\%$

③ (95°/2). [202°].

   IR: Appl. Spectroscopy **16**, 12(1962).

④ $Ph_3SiH \begin{cases} \xrightarrow{K} Ph_3SiK \xrightarrow[H_2O]{H^+} \begin{cases} Ph_3SiOH \\ Ph_3SiH \end{cases} \\ \xrightarrow{PhK} Ph_4Si \end{cases}$

   $Ph_3SiH + CH_2N_2 \longrightarrow Ph_3SiMe$
   (trace)

⑥ JACS **74**, 4200 (1952); **71**, 4050 (1949);
   51, 3070 (1929).   JOC **23**, 501
   (1958).

SiC₁₈H₁₆

① Dimethylbis(phenylethynyl)silane

   $(CH_3)_2Si(C\equiv CC_6H_5)_2$

② $Me_2SiCl_2 + LiC\equiv CPh \longrightarrow 30\%$

   $Me_2SiCl_2 + NaC\equiv CPh \longrightarrow 85\%$

   $Me_2SiCl_2 + PhC\equiv CMgBr \longrightarrow 65\%$

③ [79~80°].

④ $+ Br_2 \longrightarrow$
   43% $Me_2Si(CHBr=CBrPh)_2$

   $+ H(Ni) \longrightarrow Me_2Si(CH_2CH_2Ph)_2$

⑤ Elastomeric properties.

⑥ Naturwiss. **50**, 373 (1963).   Izv.
   OKhN **1962**, 728.

SiC₁₈H₁₆Br₄

① Dimethylbis(1,2-dibromo-2-phenyl-
   vinyl)silane

   $(CH_3)_2Si(CBr=CBrC_6H_5)_2$

② $Br_2 + Me_2Si(C\equiv CPh)_2 \longrightarrow 43\%$

③ [158~159°].
⑥ Naturwiss. **50**, 373 (1963).

SiC$_{18}$H$_{16}$O
① Triphenylsilanol
  (C$_6$H$_5$)$_3$SiOH
② Ph$_3$SiCl + H$_2$O ⟶
  Ph$_3$SiCl + Ph$_3$SiBr + NH$_4$OH ⟶
③ [150~155°].
④ + H(Ni) ⇌ (*cyclo*-C$_6$H$_{11}$)$_3$SiOH
  + SiBr$_4$ ⟶ Ph$_3$SiBr 46%
⑥ BCSJ **35**, 1840 (1962). JCS **1962**, 3509.
  JOC **28**, 1651 (1963).   Monatsh. **93**,
  1363 (1962).   Z. anorg. allg. Chem.
  323, 190 (1963).

SiC$_{18}$H$_{16}$O$_2$
① Phenyldiphenoxysilane
  C$_6$H$_5$Si(H)(OC$_6$H$_5$)$_2$
② PhOH + HCONH$_2$ + PhSiH$_3$ ⟶ 35%
  PhOH + HCONMe$_2$ + PhSiH$_3$ ⟶ 16%
  PhOH + PhSiHCl$_2$ ⟶
③ (186~192°/6). n_D1.5850 (20°). d1.1526
  (20°/4°).
  Viscosity: 9.75 cs (25°).
⑥ Zhur. **33**, 2617 (1963).   J. Chem. Eng.
  Data **7**, 556 (1962).

SiC$_{18}$H$_{17}$N
① Triphenylaminosilane
  (C$_6$H$_5$)$_3$SiNH$_2$
② Ph$_3$SiCl + liq. NH$_3$ ⟶ Ph$_3$SiNH$_2$
  + NH$_4$Cl ⟶ 74%
③ [55~56°].
④ Ph$_3$SiNH$_2$ $\xrightarrow{\text{Ph}_3\text{SiCl}}$ (Ph$_3$Si)$_2$NH
⑥ JACS **47**, 2739 (1925).   Rec. trav.
  chim. **81**, 28 (1962).

SiC$_{18}$H$_{17}$NO
① Triphenylsilylamine oxide
  (C$_6$H$_5$)$_3$SiNH$_2$O
② NH$_2$OH + Ph$_3$SiCl ⟶

NH$_2$OH + Ph$_3$SiBr ⟶
③ Solid. [57~58°].
④ + PhNCO ⟶ PhNHCOON(SiPh$_3$)-
  CONHPh
⑥ Monatsh. **94**, 141 (1963).

SiC$_{18}$H$_{20}$O
① *p*-Trimethylsilyl(2-benzoylvinyl)-
  benzene
  p-(CH$_3$)$_3$SiC$_6$H$_4$CH=CHCOC$_6$H$_5$
② *p*-Me$_3$SiC$_6$H$_4$CHO + PhCOMe + NaOH
  + EtOH ⟶
③ Solid. [121~123°].
⑥ Yakugaku Zasshi **82**. 929 (1962).

SiC$_{18}$H$_{21}$
① 9-Phenylsilylcyclododecadiene-1,6

② PhSiH$_3$ + (=CHCH$_2$CH$_2$CH=)$_3$
  + (BzO)$_2$ ⟶
③ (114~127°/0.15).
⑥ JOC **28**, 1417 (1963).

SiC$_{18}$H$_{24}$
① Dimethylbis(2-phenylethyl)silane
  (CH$_3$)$_2$Si(CH$_2$CH$_2$C$_6$H$_5$)$_2$
② H(Ni) + Me$_2$Si(C≡CPh)$_2$ ⟶
③ (142°/2). n_D1.5353 (20°).
⑥ Naturwiss. **59**, 373 (1963).

SiC$_{18}$H$_{24}$O$_2$
① Diphenylbis(ethoxymethyl)silane
  (C$_6$H$_5$)$_2$Si(CH$_2$OC$_2$H$_5$)$_2$
② Ph$_2$SiCl$_2$ + Mg + EtOCH$_2$Cl ⟶
③ (154°/1.4). n_D1.5300 (20°). d1.0163
  (20°).
⑥ Belg. 620518 (1963); CA **59**, 6440 (1963).
  Fr. 1303195 (1962); CA **58**, 7975

(1963).

SiC18H24O2
① Dibenzyldiethoxysilane
   (C6H5CH2)2Si(OC2H5)2
② Na + PhCH2Si(OEt)3 ⟶
③ (203°/5). n_D1.5082 (25°). d1.0437
   (25°/4°).
④ For polymerization.
⑥ JACS **84**, 4730 (1962).   JOC **18**, 1689
   (1953).

SiC18H24O2
① Dimethylbis(2,5-dimethylphenoxy)-
   silane
   (CH3)2Si[OC6H3(CH3)(2,5)]2
② C5H5N + Me2SiCl2
   + (2,5)Me2C6H3OH ⟶
③ (177°/10). n_D1.5130 (31°). d1.0396
   (30°/30°).
   IR: 1510, 1259, 1130, 1150, 1010, 970,
   870, 800 cm^{-1}.
⑥ J. Chi. Chem. Soc. (II) **8**, 237, 380, 384
   (1961); **9**, 273 (1962).

SiC18H24O4
① Bis(β-methoxyethoxy)diphenylsilane
   (C6H5)2Si(OCH2CH2OCH3)2
② Ph2SiCl2 + MeOCH2CH2OH ⟶ 82%
③ (170°/2). n_D1.516 (25°). d1.085 (25°).
⑥ Compt. rend. **256**, 4920 (1963).

SiC18H31BrO
① p-Bromophenoxydi-n-amylethylsilane
   C2H5Si(C5H11)2OC6H4Br-p
② SnCl4 + EtSiHAm2
   + p-BrC6H4OH ⟶
③ (182~183°/3). n_D1.4850 (20°). d1.0412
   (20°/4°).
⑥ Zhur. **33**, 3265 (1963).

SiC18H33Cl
① Tricyclohexylchlorosilane

(cyclo-C6H11)3SiCl
② C6H11Li + SiCl4 ⟶
③ [101~102°].
④ + LiAlH4 ⟶ (C6H11)3SiH
   + H2O ⟶ (C6H11)3SiOH
⑥ JCS **1952**, 2840.   JACS **71**, 4022 (1949).

SiC18H33O3P
① Phenyl-n-butyl(2-triethoxysilylethyl)-
   phosphine
   C6H5P(C4H9)CH2CH2Si(OC2H5)3
② PhP(H)Bu + CH2=CHSi(OEt)3
   + (t-BuO)2 ⟶
③ n_D1.4912 (25°).
⑥ US 3067229(1962); CA **58**, 10239(1963).

SiC19H15Br2Cl
① α, α-Dibromobenzyldiphenylchloro-
   silane
   C6H5CBr2Si(C6H5)2Cl
② PhCH2SiPh2Cl + (CH2CO)2NBr
   + C5H5N ⟶ 52%
③ [79~81°].
④ + HOH + CF3COOAg
   ⟶ PhCOSiPh2OH (65%)
   + MeOH + C5H5N
   ⟶ PhCBr2SiPh2OMe (81%)
⑥ Can. J. Chem. **41**, 2351 (1963).

SiC19H15NS
① Triphenylisothiocyanosilane
   (C6H5)3SiNCS
② Ph3SiCl + (NH2)2CS ⟶ 68%
   Ph3SiCl + AgNCS,
   (PhNCS or NH4NCS)
   ⟶ 73%
   Ph3SiNC + S $\xrightarrow{\text{heat, 1 hr}}$
③ (394.5~397.5°). [99~100.5°].
④ + PhLi ⟶ Ph3SiOH + Ph4Si
   + PhCSNH2
   + PhMgBr ⟶ Ph3SiOH + H2S
   + Ph2CO

⑥ JACS **70**, 1220 (1948) ; **72**, 3045 (1950) ;
   80, 4151 (1958).

SiC$_{19}$H$_{19}$ON

① Triphenylisocyanatosilane
   (C$_6$H$_5$)$_3$SiNCO

② Ph$_3$SiCl + (NH$_2$)$_2$CO
   (or Na(NHCOOEt)]
   $\xrightarrow{\text{Cu-catalyst, 78\%}}$ 67% (or 48%)
   Ph$_3$SiCl + AgNCO $\longrightarrow$ 85%

③ (371~373°). [100~101°].

④ + PhLi $\longrightarrow$ Ph$_3$SiN=CPh−OLi $\longrightarrow$
   $\xrightarrow{+\text{H}_2\text{O}}$ Ph$_3$SiN=CPh−OH $\longrightarrow$
   Ph$_3$SiNHCPh=O $\xrightarrow{\text{H}_2\text{O}}$
   Ph$_3$SiOH + PhCONH$_2$
   + PhMgBr $\longrightarrow$ Ph$_3$SiOH +
   PhCONH$_2$

⑥ JACS **70**, 1043 (1948) ; **72**, 3045 (1950).

SiC$_{19}$H$_{16}$Br$_2$

① Triphenyldibromomethylsilane
   (C$_6$H$_5$)$_3$SiCHBr$_2$

② PhHgCBr$_3$ + Ph$_3$SiH $\longrightarrow$ 89%

③ [154~156°].

⑥ JACS **85**, 2667 (1963).

SiC$_{19}$H$_{16}$Cl$_2$

① Dichloromethyltriphenylsilane
   (C$_6$H$_5$)$_3$SiCHCl$_2$

② Ph$_3$SiH + PhHgCCl$_2$Br $\longrightarrow$ 90%

③ [151~152°].

⑥ JACS **85**, 2667 (1963).

SiC$_{19}$H$_{16}$O$_2$

① Triphenylcarboxysilane
   (C$_6$H$_5$)$_3$SiCO$_2$H

② Ph$_3$SiSiPh$_3$ $\left.\begin{array}{l} \\ \\ \end{array}\right\}\xrightarrow{\text{NaK}}$ Ph$_3$SiK $\xrightarrow{\text{CO}_2}$
   PhCMe$_2$SiPh$_3$
   Ph$_3$SiSiPh$_3$ $\xrightarrow{\text{Li}}$ Ph$_3$SiK $\xrightarrow{\text{CO}_2}$
   Ph$_3$SiCl + Ag(OCOH) $\longrightarrow$ 83%

③ [169°].

④ $\xrightarrow{\text{heat}}$ Ph$_3$SiOH + (Ph$_3$Si)$_2$O + CO
   $\xrightarrow{\text{[H}^+\text{]}}$ Ph$_3$SiOH + (Ph$_3$Si)$_2$O + CO

⑥ JACS **77**, 4827 (1955) ; **73**, 1424 (1951) ;
   76, 2333 (1954) ; **75**, 4759 (1953).

SiC$_{19}$H$_{16}$O$_2$

① Benzoyldiphenylsilanol
   C$_6$H$_5$COSi(C$_6$H$_5$)$_2$OH

② CF$_3$COOAg + H$_2$O
   + PhCBr$_2$SiPh$_2$Cl $\longrightarrow$ 65%

③ [97~99°].

⑥ Can. J. Chem. **41**, 2351 (1963) ; CA **59**,
   8565 (1963).

SiC$_{19}$H$_{17}$Cl

① Benzyldiphenylchlorosilane
   C$_6$H$_5$CH$_2$Si(C$_6$H$_5$)$_2$Cl

② Ph$_2$SiCl$_2$ + PhCH$_2$MgCl $\longrightarrow$ 67%

③ n_D1.6078 (25°).

④ + (BzO)$_2$ + (CH$_2$CO)$_2$NBr
   $\longrightarrow$ PhCBr$_2$SiPh$_2$Cl
   + MeOH + C$_5$H$_5$N
   $\longrightarrow$ PhCH$_2$SiPh$_2$OMe
   + NH$_4$OH $\longrightarrow$ PhCH$_2$SiPh$_2$OH

⑥ Can. J. Chem. **41**, 2351 (1963).

SiC$_{19}$H$_{17}$ClO

① Phenyl-*p*-phenoxyphenylmethyl-
   chlorosilane
   p-C$_6$H$_5$OC$_6$H$_4$Si(Cl)(CH$_3$)C$_6$H$_5$

② *p*-PhOC$_6$H$_4$MgBr + THF
   + PhSi(Cl)$_2$Me $\longrightarrow$

③ (198~219°/2).

④ + NaOH
   $\longrightarrow$ (*p*-PhOC$_6$H$_4$SiMePh)$_2$O

⑥ Fr. 1321436 (1963) ; CA **59**, 11561
   (1963).

SiC$_{19}$H$_{17}$ClO$_2$

① Phenylphenoxy-*o*-methoxyphenyl-

chlorosilane
$C_6H_5Si(Cl)(OC_6H_5)C_6H_4OCH_3$-*o*

② $PhSiCl_3 + o\text{-}MeOC_6H_4MgBr \longrightarrow$ 30%

③ Solid. [86°].

④ $+ H_2O \longrightarrow$
$PhSi(OH)(OPh)C_6H_4OMe$-*o*

⑥ Zhur. **33**, 1289 (1963).

SiC₁₉H₁₈

① Methyltriphenylsilane
$(C_6H_5)_3SiCH_3$

② $PhCOOEt + OP(OMe)_3 + Ph_3SiLi$
$\longrightarrow$ 40%
$Na + o\text{-}ClC_6H_4Si(H)MePh$
$\longrightarrow$ (by-product)
$Na + PhSi(OMe)_2Me \longrightarrow$
$OP(OMe)_3 + THF + Ph_3SiLi \longrightarrow$

③ [67~69°].

⑥ JOC **27**, 1414, 1836 (1962); **26**, 247
(1961).   JACS **84**, 4736 (1962).

SiC₁₉H₁₈O

① Methoxytriphenylsilane
$(C_6H_5)_3SiOCH_3$

② Ph_3SiCl (in ethyl ether)
$+ MeONa$ (in methanol) $\longrightarrow$ 71%
$Ph_3SiCO_2Me \xrightarrow[150\sim230°]{-CO}$ 98%

③ (164~165°/5). [54.5~55°].

④ $Ph_3SiOMe \xrightarrow[(2)Et_3SiCl]{(1)Na/K} Ph_3SiSiEt_3$

⑥ JOC **18**, 657 (1953).   JACS **74**, 648
(1952); **79**, 971 (1957).

SiC₁₉H₁₈O

① Benzyldiphenylsilanol
$C_6H_5CH_2Si(C_6H_5)_2OH$

② $NH_4OH + PhCH_2SiPh_2Cl \longrightarrow$

③ [51.5~53.0°].

⑥ Can. J. Chem. **41**, 2351 (1963).

SiC₁₉H₁₈O₃

① Methyltriphenoxysilane

$CH_3Si(OC_6H_5)_3$

② $PhOH + MeSiCl_3 \longrightarrow$

③ (179~183°).

⑥ Belg. 618142 (1962); CA **59**, 663 (1963).
Fr. 1311158 (1962); CA **59**, 1681
(1963).

SiC₁₉H₁₈O₃

① Phenylphenoxy-*o*-methoxyphenyl-
silanol
$C_6H_5Si(OH)(OC_6H_5)C_6H_4OCH_3$-*o*

② $HOH + PhSi(Cl)(OPh)C_6H_4OMe$-*o* $\longrightarrow$

③ Solid. [81°].

⑥ Zhur. **33**, 1289 (1963).

SiC₁₉H₁₉F₃Fe

① Dimethyl-*p*-trifluoromethylphenyl-
silylferrocene
$p\text{-}CF_3C_6H_4Si(CH_3)_2C_5H_4FeC_5H_5$

② $Me_2Si(Cl)C_6H_4CF_3$-*p* $+ Fe(C_5H_5)_2$
$+ n\text{-}BuLi \longrightarrow$

③ [50°].

⑥ Dokl. **151**, 1319 (1963).

SiC₁₉H₂₀

① 1-Naphthylphenylmethylethylsilane
$C_6H_5Si(CH_3)(C_2H_5)C_{10}H_7$-1

② $PhSi(Cl)(Me)C_{10}H_7$-1 $+ EtLi \longrightarrow$
$PhSi(Cl)(Me)Et + 1\text{-}C_{10}H_7Li \longrightarrow$
$PhSi(OMe)(Me)C_{10}H_7$-1
$+ EtMgBr \longrightarrow$
$PhSi(Me)(F)C_{10}H_7$-1 $+ EtLi \longrightarrow$

③ $[\alpha]_D - 18.6°$.

④ $+ Br_2 \longrightarrow PhSi(Br)(Me)Et$

⑥ JACS **85**, 3712 (1963).   Tetrahedron
Letters 821 (1962).

SiC₁₉H₂₁F₉Fe

① Tris-(3,3,3-trifluoropropyl)silyl-
ferrocene
$C_5H_5FeC_5H_4Si(CH_2CH_2CF_3)_3$

② $Fe(C_5H_5)_2 + n\text{-}BuLi$
$+ (CF_3CH_2CH_2)_3SiCl \longrightarrow$

③ [105°].

⑥ Dokl. **151**, 1319 (1963).

SiC$_{19}$H$_{23}$Cl

① 1,1-Dibenzylchlorosilyl-2-methyl-
butene-2
CH$_3$CH=C(CH$_3$)CH$_2$Si(CH$_2$C$_6$H$_5$)$_2$Cl

② C$_5$H$_8$ + H$_2$PtCl$_6$ + (PhCH$_2$)$_2$SiHCl
——→ 42%

③ (153°/2). n_D1.5607 (25°). d1.0489
(25°/25°).

④ + EtMgBr ——→
MeCH=CMeCH$_2$Si(CH$_2$Ph)$_2$Et

⑥ JOC **26**, 4000 (1961).

SiC$_{19}$H$_{24}$

① 9-Triethylsilylfluorene

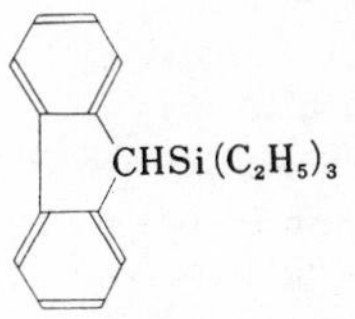

② Et$_3$SiCl + C$_{13}$H$_9$Li ——→

③ (151°/0.155). n_D1.5933 (20°). d1.018
(20°/4°).

⑥ Ber. **91**, 143 (1958). JCS **1963**, 2342.

SiC$_{19}$H$_{25}$NO

① N-Triethylsilylbenzanilide
C$_6$H$_5$CO
            ⟩N–Si(C$_2$H$_5$)$_3$
C$_6$H$_5$

② PhCONHPh + Et$_3$SiH + ZnCl$_2$
——→ 90%

③ (164°/2). n_D1.5523 (20°). d1.020
(20°).

⑥ Compt. rend. **257**, 1304 (1963).

SiC$_{19}$H$_{27}$N

① Phenylbenzyltriethylsilylamine
C$_6$H$_5$CH$_2$N(C$_6$H$_5$)Si(C$_2$H$_5$)$_3$

② PhC(OMe)=NPh + Et$_3$SiH + ZnCl$_2$
——→ 65%

③ (206°/25). n_D1.5631 (20°). d1.007
(20°).

⑥ Compt. rend. **257**, 1304 (1963).

SiC$_{19}$H$_{42}$O$_3$

① Bis(2-ethylbutoxy)-t-amoxyethyl-
silane
t-C$_5$H$_{11}$OSi(C$_2$H$_5$)[OCH$_2$CH(C$_2$H$_5$)$_2$]$_2$

② picoline + EtSi(Cl)(OCH$_2$CHEt$_2$)$_2$
+ t-AmOH ——→

③ (112~117°/1).

⑥ US 2995590 (1958) ; CA **56**, 3356 (1962).

SiC$_{20}$H$_{14}$Cl$_2$

① Di-α-naphthyldichlorosilane

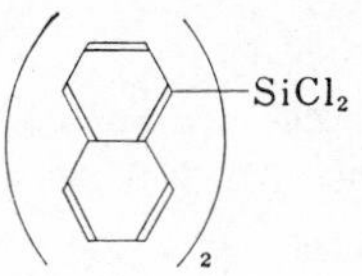

② SiCl$_4$ + 2 $\xrightarrow[\text{in C}_6\text{H}_6]{18\sim20°}$

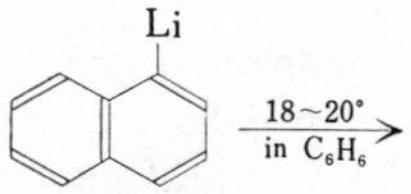

③ (230~235°/3). [151~152°].

④ + NaOH (powder) + H$_2$O
$\xrightarrow{\text{Et}_2\text{O}}$ (C$_{10}$H$_7$)$_2$Si(OH)$_2$

⑥ Zhur. **26**, 3344 (1956) ; CA **51**, 9514
(1957). Izv. OKhN **1957**, 319 ; CA
51, 14652 (1957).

SiC$_{20}$H$_{15}$F$_3$

① Vinyltris(p-fluorophenyl)silane
CH$_2$=CHSi(C$_6$H$_4$F-p)$_3$

② CH$_2$=CHSiCl$_3$ + p-FC$_6$H$_4$MgBr
——→ 65%

③ [71°].

④ + CF$_3$COOH + HOOH
                    O
——→ CH$_2$–CHSi(C$_6$H$_4$F-p)$_3$
(81%)

⑥ JOC **28**, 487 (1963).

SiC20H15F3O

① Epoxytris(*p*-fluorophenyl)silane

$$CH_2-CHSi(C_6H_4F-p)_3$$
(with O epoxide bridge above)

② $CH_2=CHSi(C_6H_4F-p)_3$ + HOOH
   + CF₃COOH ⟶ 81%

③ Solid. [72~73°].

⑥ JOC **28**, 487 (1963).

SiC20H15Cl3

① Vinyltris(*p*-chlorophenyl)silane
   $CH_2=CHSi(C_6H_4Cl-p)_3$

② *p*-ClC₆H₄MgBr + CH₂=CHSiCl₃
   ⟶ 40%
   CH₂=CHCl + HSi(C₆H₄Cl-*p*)₃
   ⟶ 36%

③ (220~225°/0.4). [72°].

④ + Ph₃SiH ⟶ 73% addition product

⑥ Zhur. **32**, 698 (1962). JCS **1963**, 797.

SiC20H16

① Di-1-naphthylsilane
   $(1-C_{10}H_7)_2SiH_2$

② SiH₂Cl₂ + C₁₀H₇MgBr ⟶

③ [98.5~99°].

⑥ JOC **18**, 303 (1953).

SiC20H16

① Triphenylsilylacetylene
   $(C_6H_5)_3SiC{\equiv}CH$

② Ph₃SiCl + CH≡CNa ⟶
   Ph₃SiC≡CCl + Ph₃SiLi ⟶ 15.8%
   Ph₃SiCl + LiC≡CLi ⟶

③ Solid. (146~149°/0.03). [45~46°].
   $n_D 1.6180$ (20°).
   IR: 3293, 2037 cm⁻¹.

⑥ US 2887371(1959); CA **53**, 19883(1959).
   Chem. & Ind. 1619 (1961). Inorg.
   Chem. 1, 967 (1962).

SiC20H16O2

① Di-1-naphtyldihydroxysilane
   $(1-C_{10}H_7)_2Si(OH)_2$

② SiCl₄ + 2(1-C₁₀H₇Li)

⟶ $(1-C_{10}H_7)_2SiCl_2$ $\xrightarrow{H_2O}$

③ [157~158°].

⑥ Zhur. **26**, 3344 (1956); CA **51**, 9514
   (1957).

SiC20H17F3O

① 2-Tris(*p*-fluorophenyl)silylethanol
   $(p-FC_6H_4)_3SiCH_2CH_2OH$

② $(p-FC_6H_4)_3SiCHCH_2$ + LiAlH₄
   (with O epoxide bridge)
   ⟶ 100%

③ [81~82°].

⑥ JOC **28**, 2870 (1963).

SiC20H18

① Vinyltriphenylsilane
   $CH_2=CHSi(C_6H_5)_3$

② $CH_2=CHCl$ + HSiPh₃ $\xrightarrow{600°}$
   CH₂=CHSiCl₃ + PhMgBr ⟶ 90%
   CH₂=CHMgCl + Ph₃SiCl ⟶ 87.1%
   CH₂=CHLi + Ph₃SiCl ⟶

③ Solid. [72°].

④ + HOOH + CF₃COOH
   ⟶ $CH_2-CHSiPh_3$ (80%)
   (with O epoxide bridge)

⑥ JOC **22**, 1200 (1957); **28**, 487 (1963).
   JACS **83**, 3583 (1961). Zhur. **32**,
   698 (1962).

SiC20H18

① 1,1-Diphenyl-1-silaindane
   $o-C_6H_4-CH_2-CH_2-Si(C_6H_5)_2$
   (ring closure bracket below)

② $o-ClC_6H_4CH_2CH_2MgBr$
   + Ph₂SiHCl ⟶

③ Solid. [62~63°].

⑥ Chem. & Ind. 208 (1961).

SiC20H18Br2O

① α, α-Dibromobenzyldiphenylmethoxy-
   silane
   $C_6H_5CBr_2Si(C_6H_5)_2OCH_3$

② PhCBr₂SiPh₂Cl + MeOH + C₅H₅N

──→   81%

③ [80~82°].

⑥ Can. J. Chem. **41**, 2351 (1963).

$SiC_{20}H_{18}N_2O_4$

① Dimethylbis(phthalimidomethyl)-
    silane

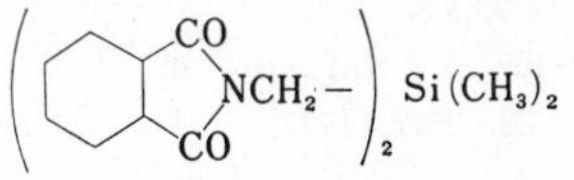

$$\left(\overset{CO}{\underset{CO}{\bigcirc\hspace{-1em}NCH_2-}} \right)_2 Si(CH_3)_2$$

② $\overset{CO}{\underset{CO}{\bigcirc\hspace{-1em}NK}}$ + $Me_2Si(CH_2Cl)_2$ ──→

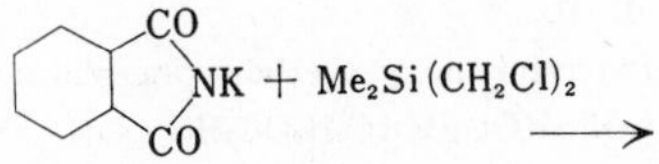

③ Solid. [146°].

④ + H_2O + HBr
    ──→ $Me_2Si(CH_2NH_3Br)_2$ (75~80%)
                mp 94~95°

⑥ Z. anorg. allg. Chem. **317**, 41 (1962).

$SiC_{20}H_{18}O$

① Triphenylsilylacetaldehyde
    $(C_6H_5)_3SiCH_2CHO$

② $Ph_3SiCHCH_2$ + $MgBr_2$ ──→
          $\underset{O}{\diagdown\!/}$

③ [115.5~116.0°].
    IR : 1700 cm^{-1}.

④ + $H_2NNHC_6H_4NO_2$-p
    ──→ $Ph_3SiCH_2CH=NNHC_6H_4NO_2$-$p$
                mp 228~229°

⑥ JOC **28**, 2870 (1963).

$SiC_{20}H_{18}O$

① Epoxyethyltriphenylsilane
    $\underset{O}{CH_2-CHSi(C_6H_5)_3}$
       $\diagdown\!/$

② $CH_2=CHSiPh_3$ + HOOH + CF_3COOH
    ──→ 84%

③ Solid. (85~86°).

⑥ JOC **28**, 487 (1963).

$SiC_{20}H_{18}O_2$

① Triphenylsilyl acetate
    $CH_3COOSi(C_6H_5)_3$

② Ph_3SiCl + Ac_2O ──→
    Ph_3SiOH + AcCl ──→

③ (230~240°/12°). [97°].

④ + HCl + HOH +
    $CH_2=C(Me)COOCH_2Si(Me)_2OEt$ ──→
    $CH_2=C(Me)COOCH_2Si(Me)OSiPh_3$
    (20%)

⑥ Izv. OKhN **1962**, 1572.   Dokl. **87**, 233
    (1952) ; CA **47**, 12281 (1953).

$SiC_{20}H_{19}ClO_2$

① *p*-Tolylphenoxy-*o*-methoxyphenyl-
    chlorosilane
    p-$CH_3C_6H_4Si(Cl)(OC_6H_5)C_6H_4OCH_3$-$o$

② p-$MeC_6H_4SiCl_3$ + o-$MeOC_6H_4MgBr$
    ──→ 28%

③ [98°].

④ + H_2O ──→ silanol

⑥ Zhur. **33**, 1289 (1963).

$SiC_{20}H_{19}ClO_2$

① Phenylphenoxy-*o*-ethoxyphenylchloro-
    silane
    $C_6H_5Si(Cl)(OC_6H_5)C_6H_4OC_2H_5$-$o$

② $PhSiCl_3$ + o-$EtOC_6H_4MgBr$ ──→ 26%

③ Solid. [82°].

④ + H_2O ──→ silanol

⑥ Zhur. **33**, 1289 (1963).

$SiC_{20}H_{19}ClO_2$

① *m*-Tolylphenoxy-*o*-methoxyphenyl-
    chlorosilane
    n-$CH_3C_6H_4Si(OC_6H_5)(C_6H_4OCH_3$-$o)Cl$

② m-$MeC_6H_4SiCl_3$ + o-$MeOC_6H_4MgBr$
    ──→ 22%

③ Solid. [88°].

④ + H_2O ──→ silanol

⑥ Zhur. **33**, 1289 (1963).

$SiC_{20}H_{20}$

① Ethyltriphenylsilane
    $C_2H_5Si(C_6H_5)_3$

② Ph_3SiCl + EtMgBr ──→ quantitative
    Ph_3SiH + C_2H_4 ──→

③ [76°].

⑥ J. Chem. Phys. **38**, 285 (1963).   Izb-rannye Trudy **2**, 688 (1959).

SiC$_{20}$H$_{20}$O

① Ethoxytriphenylsilane
  (C$_6$H$_5$)$_3$SiOC$_2$H$_5$

② EtOH + Ph$_3$SiNHBu $\longrightarrow$
  PhLi + Si(OEt)$_4$ $\longrightarrow$
  Ph$_3$SiCl + EtOH + C$_5$H$_{11}$N $\longrightarrow$

③ Solid. [65°].

④ + PhLi $\longrightarrow$ SiPh$_4$
  + Ph$_3$SiK $\longrightarrow$ Ph$_3$SiSiPh$_3$ +
  Ph$_3$SiOH

⑥ JACS **82**, 3319 (1960).   JOC **25**, 2251 (1960).   Dokl. **148**, 843 (1963).   Hua Hsüeh Hsüeh Pao. **27**, 38 (1961) ; CA **59**, 11547 (1963).

SiC$_{20}$H$_{20}$O

① 2-Triphenylsilylethanol
  (C$_6$H$_5$)$_3$SiCH$_2$CH$_2$OH

② Ph$_3$SiCHCH$_2$ + LiAlH$_4$ $\longrightarrow$ 85~100%
       \/
       O
  Ph$_3$SiLi + (CH$_2$)$_2$O $\longrightarrow$

③ [99~100°].
  IR : 925 cm^{-1}.

⑥ JOC **28**, 2870 (1963).   JACS **81**, 1107 (1959).

SiC$_{20}$H$_{20}$O

① 1-Triphenylsilylethanol
  (C$_6$H$_5$)$_3$SiCH(OH)CH$_3$

② Ph$_3$SiCHCH$_2$ + LiAlH$_4$ $\longrightarrow$
       \/
       O
  Ph$_3$SiCOCH$_3$ + LiAlH$_4$ $\longrightarrow$

③ [100~101°].

⑥ JOC **28**, 2870 (1963).

SiC$_{20}$H$_{20}$O

① Benzyldiphenylmethoxysilane
  C$_6$H$_5$CH$_2$Si(C$_6$H$_5$)$_2$OCH$_3$

② C$_5$H$_5$N + PhCH$_2$SiPh$_2$Cl + MeOH
    $\longrightarrow$ 70%

③ (159~161°/0.28). n_D1.5932 (25°).

⑥ Can. J. Chem. **41**, 2351 (1963).

SiC$_{20}$H$_{20}$O$_2$

① Dibenzyloxyphenylsilane
  C$_6$H$_5$SiH(OCH$_2$C$_6$H$_5$)$_2$

② PhSiH$_3$ + Cu (powder) + PhCH$_2$OH
    $\longrightarrow$ 53.7%

③ (180~183°/7). n_D1.5646 (20°).

⑥ Zhur. **33**, 2617 (1963).

SiC$_{20}$H$_{20}$O$_3$

① Phenylphenoxy-*o*-ethoxyphenylsilanol
  C$_6$H$_5$Si(OC$_6$H$_5$)(C$_6$H$_4$OC$_2$H$_5$-*o*)OH

② H$_2$O + PhSi(OPh)(C$_6$H$_4$OEt-*o*)Cl $\longrightarrow$

③ Solid. [78°].

⑥ Zhur. **33**, 1289 (1963).

SiC$_{20}$H$_{20}$O$_3$

① *o*-Tolylphenoxy-*o*-methoxyphenyl-silanol
  o-CH$_3$C$_6$H$_4$Si(OC$_6$H$_5$)(C$_6$H$_4$OCH$_3$-*o*)OH

② H$_2$O + *o*-MeC$_6$H$_4$Si(OPh)
    (C$_6$H$_4$OMe-*o*)Cl $\longrightarrow$

③ Solid. [140°].

⑥ Zhur. **33**, 1289 (1963).

SiC$_{20}$H$_{20}$O$_3$

① *m*-Tolylphenoxy-*o*-methoxyphenyl-silanol
  m-CH$_3$C$_6$H$_4$Si(OC$_6$H$_5$)(C$_6$H$_4$OCH$_3$-*o*)OH

② *m*-MeC$_6$H$_4$Si(OPh)(C$_6$H$_4$OMe-*o*)Cl
    + H$_2$O $\longrightarrow$

③ Solid. [80°].

⑥ Zhur. **33**, 1289 (1963).

SiC$_{20}$H$_{20}$O$_3$

① *m*-Tolylphenoxy-*o*-methoxyphenyl-silanol
  p-CH$_3$C$_6$H$_4$Si(OC$_6$H$_5$)(C$_6$H$_4$OCH$_3$-*o*)OH

② H$_2$O + *p*-MeC$_6$H$_4$Si(OPh)-
    (C$_6$H$_4$OCH$_3$-*o*)Cl $\longrightarrow$

③ Solid. [110°].

⑥ Zhur. **33**, 1289 (1963).

SiC20H21BClN

① Dimethylaminochlorotriphenylsilyl-
    boron
    $(C_6H_5)_3SiB(Cl)N(CH_3)_2$

② $Ph_3SiB(NMe_2) + HCl + Et_2O \longrightarrow$

③ Solid. (150~160°/vacuo.). [135°].

⑥ Angew. **74**, 718 (1962).

SiC20H27N3O3

① N-Triethylsilyl-N, O-bis(phenylcar-
    bamyl)hydroxylamine
    $C_6H_5NHCOON(CONHC_6H_5)Si(C_2H_5)_3$

② $Et_3SiNH_2O + PhNCO \longrightarrow$

③ Solid. [79~81°].

④ Very easily hydrolyzed.

⑥ Monatsh. **94**, 141 (1963).

SiC20H28

① Bis(cylooctatrienyl-2,4,7)diethyl-
    silane

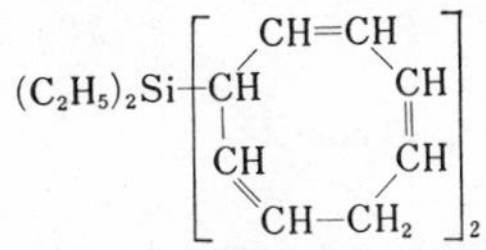

$$(C_2H_5)_2Si\left[CH\begin{array}{c}CH=CH\\ \\ CH\\ \| \\ CH\end{array}CH\right]_2 $$

② $Et_2SiH_2 + C_8H_8 + Pt-Al_2O_3 \longrightarrow$

③ (150~160°/0.15). $n_D1.5396$ (25°).

⑥ JCS **1963**, 4058.

SiC20H28O4

① Diphenylbis(β-ethoxyethoxy)silane
    $(C_6H_5)_2Si(OCH_2CH_2OC_2H_5)_2$

② $Ph_2SiCl_2 + EtOCH_2CH_2OH \longrightarrow 73\%$

③ (185°/3). $n_D1.510$ (25°). $d1.048$ (25°).

⑥ Compt. rend. **256**, 4920 (1963); CA
    59, 5188 (1963).

SiC20H29O3P

① (2-Diphenylphosphinoethyl)triethoxy-
    silane
    $(C_6H_5)_2PCH_2CH_2Si(OC_2H_5)_3$

② $Ph_2PH + (t-BuO)_2 +$
    $CH_2=CHSi(OEt)_3 \longrightarrow$

③ (136~151°/0.05). $n_D1.5510$ (25°).

⑥ US 3067229 (1962); CA **58**, 10239
    (1963).

SiC20H35BrO

① p-Bromophenoxydi-n-hexylethyl-
    silane
    $C_2H_5Si(C_6H_{13})_2OC_6H_4Br-p$

② $EtSiH(C_6H_{13})_2 + SnCl_4$
    $+ p-BrC_6H_4OH \longrightarrow$

③ (197~198°/4). $n_D1.4750$ (20°). $d0.9791$
    (20°).

⑥ Zhur. **33**, 3269 (1963).

SiC20H38O2

① 1,4-Di-t-butyl-2,5-bis(trimethyl-
    siloxy)benzene
    $(t-C_4H_9)_2C_6H_2[OSi(CH_3)_3]_2$

② $Me_3SiCl + t-Bu_2C_6H_2(OH)_2$
    (1,4,2,5) $\longrightarrow$

③ [129.1~130.1°].

⑥ Ric. Sci. Rend. Sez. A **3**, 329 (1963);
    CA **59**, 10105 (1963).

SiC21H13F9

① Tris(p-trifluoromethylphenyl)-
    silane
    $(p-CF_3C_6H_4)_3SiH$

② $SiHCl_3 + p-CF_3C_6H_4MgX \longrightarrow$

③ [83°].
    IR: 2159 cm⁻¹.

⑥ J. prakt. Chem. **21**, 149 (1963).

SiC21H17Cl3

① Tris(p-chlorophenyl)allylsilane
    $(p-ClC_6H_4)_3SiCH_2CH=CH_2$

② $(p-ClC_6H_4)_3SiH + CH_2=CHCH_2Br$
    or $CH_2=CHCH_2Cl \overset{580°}{\longrightarrow}$

③ [112°].

⑥ J. prakt. Chem. **21**, 149 (1963). Zhur.
    32, 698 (1962); English page 697.
    Dokl. **138**, 136 (1961).

SiC₂₁H₁₈

① Triphenylpropynylsilane
CH₃C≡CSi(C₆H₅)₃

② Ph₃SiF + MeC≡CMgBr ⟶ 55%

③ [113~114°].

④ The Si-C link in acetylenic silanes is cleaved under mild hydration conditions, but is quite stable to bromination, being able to add 2 or 4 Br atoms.

⑥ Zhur. **25**, 1128 (1955); CA **50**, 3275 (1956).

SiC₂₁H₂₀

① Allyltriphenylsilane
(C₆H₅)₃SiCH₂CH=CH₂

② CH₂=CHCH₂Li + Ph₃SiCl ⟶ 66%
CH₂=CHCH₂Cl + HSiPh₃ (600°) ⟶
CH₂=CHCH₂MgCl + THF
+ Ph₃SiH ⟶

③ [88~89°].

⑥ JOC **28**, 2145 (1963); **26**, 4797 (1961). JACS **81**, 5925 (1959). Zhur. **32**, 698 (1962); English page 697.

SiC₂₁H₂₀

① 1,1-Diphenyl-1-sila-1,2,3,4-tetahydronaphthalene

$$\text{(C}_6\text{H}_5\text{)}_2$$

(structure of 1,1-diphenyl-1-sila-tetrahydronaphthalene: benzene ring fused to Si(C₆H₅)₂–CH₂–CH₂–CH₂)

② Na + o-ClC₆H₄CH₂CH₂CH₂SiPh₂Cl ⟶
Ph₂SiCl₂ + o-BrMgC₆H₄CH₂CH₂CH₂-MgBr ⟶

③ Solid. (167~174°/0.006). [77.5~79.0°].

⑥ Chem. & Ind. 208 (1961).

SiC₂₁H₂₀O₂

① Ethyl triphenylsilanecarboxylate
(C₆H₅)₃SiCOOC₂H₅

② Ph₃Si−SiPh₃ $\xrightarrow[\text{Et}_2\text{O}]{\text{Na/K}}$ Ph₃SiK

$\xrightarrow{\text{CO}_2}$ Ph₃SiCO₂H $\xrightarrow[\text{Et}_2\text{O}]{\text{MeCHN}_2}$

③ [98.5~100°].

④ Ph₃SiCO₂Et $\xrightarrow[122~185°]{\text{heat}}$ Ph₃SiOEt + CO

⑥ JACS **80**, 1886 (1958); **79**, 971 (1957).

SiC₂₁H₂₀O₆

① Phenyltrifurfuroxysilane

$$\left(\begin{array}{c} \text{CH——CH} \\ \text{CH} \quad \text{CCH}_2\text{O—} \\ \text{O} \end{array} \right)_3 \text{SiC}_6\text{H}_5$$

②
$$\begin{array}{c} \text{CH——CH} \\ \text{CH} \quad \text{CCH}_2\text{OH} \\ \text{O} \end{array} + \text{C}_5\text{H}_5\text{N}$$

$$+ \text{C}_6\text{H}_6 + \text{C}_6\text{H}_5\text{SiCl}_3 \longrightarrow$$

③ (199.5~200.0°/1.5). n_D1.5358 (20°). d1.2040 (20°).

⑥ Plasticheskie Massy (No.3) 8 (1962); CA **59**, 654 (1963).

SiC₂₁H₂₁Br

① Tri-*p*-tolylbromosilane
(*p*-CH₃C₆H₄)₃SiBr

② CH₂=CHCH₂Br + (*p*-MeC₆H₄)₃SiH
⟶ 90%
Br₂ + (*p*-MeC₆H₄)₃SiH ⟶

③ [127°].

⑥ J. prakt. Chem. **21**, 149 (1963). Z. anorg. allg. Chem. **302**, 185 (1959). Ber. **93**, 2525 (1960). Zhur. **32**, 698 (1962); English page 697.

SiC₂₁H₂₁ClO₂

① (2,5-Dimethylphenyl)phenoxy(*o*-methoxyphenyl)chlorosilane
(2,5)(CH₃)₂C₆H₃Si(OC₆H₅)-(*o*-C₆H₄OCH₃)Cl

② o-MeOC₆H₄MgBr + (2,5)Me₂C₆H₃SiCl₃
⟶ 46%

③ Solid. [139°].

④ Hydrolyzed to silanol.

⑥ Zhur. **33**, 1289 (1963).

SiC$_{21}$H$_{21}$ClO$_2$

① *p*-Tolylphenoxy-*o*-ethoxyphenyl-
   chlorosilane
   p-CH$_3$C$_6$H$_4$Si(OC$_6$H$_5$)(C$_6$H$_4$OC$_2$H$_5$-*o*)Cl

② *p*-MeC$_6$H$_4$SiCl$_3$ + *o*-EtOC$_6$H$_4$MgBr
   $\longrightarrow$ 30%

③ Solid. [110°].

④ Hydrolyzes to the silanol.

⑥ Zhur. **33**, 1289 (1963).

SiC$_{21}$H$_{22}$

① *n*-Propyltriphenylsilane
   n-C$_3$H$_7$Si(C$_6$H$_5$)$_3$

② Ph$_3$SiCl + *n*-PrLi $\longrightarrow$ 89%

③ [84°].

⑥ JACS **75**, 3757 (1953).

SiC$_{21}$H$_{22}$

① Tri-*p*-tolylsilane
   (*p*-CH$_3$C$_6$H$_4$)$_3$SiH

② *p*-MeC$_6$H$_4$MgX + SiHCl$_3$ $\longrightarrow$

③ [71°].
   IR : 2135 cm^{-1}

④ + CH$_2$=CHCH$_2$Br
   $\longrightarrow$ (*p*-MeC$_6$H$_4$)$_3$SiBr (90%)
   + Br$_2$ $\longrightarrow$ (*p*-MeC$_6$H$_4$)$_3$SiBr
   Studies on alkaline hydrolysis.

⑥ J. prakt. Chem. **21**, 149 (1963).   Z.
   anorg. allg. Chem. **306**, 180 (1960) ;
   302, 185 (1959).

SiC$_{21}$H$_{22}$O

① Isopropoxytriphenylsilane
   (C$_6$H$_5$)$_3$SiOC$_3$H$_7$-*i*

② *i*-PrOH + Ph$_3$SiCl $\longrightarrow$

③ [87~89°].

⑥ JACS **85**, 3164 (1963).

SiC$_{21}$H$_{22}$O$_3$

① Tris(*p*-methoxyphenyl)silane
   (*p*-CH$_3$OC$_6$H$_4$)$_3$SiH

② SiHCl$_3$ + *p*-MeOC$_6$H$_4$MgX $\longrightarrow$

③ [77°].
   IR : 2121 cm^{-1}.

④ Studies on alkaline hydrolysis.

⑥ J. prakt. Chem. **21**, 149 (1963). Z.
   Chem. **1**, 346 (1961). Z. anorg. allg.
   Chem. **306**, 180 (1960).

SiC$_{21}$H$_{22}$O$_3$

① 2,5-Dimethylphenylphenoxy-*o*-
   methoxyphenylsilanol
   2,5-(CH$_3$)$_2$C$_6$H$_3$Si(OC$_6$H$_5$)
   (C$_6$H$_4$OCH$_3$-*o*)OH

② H$_2$O + (2,5)Me$_2$C$_6$H$_3$Si(OPh)-
   (C$_6$H$_4$OMe-*o*)Cl $\longrightarrow$

③ Solid. [126].

⑥ Zhur. **33**, 1289 (1963).

SiC$_{21}$H$_{22}$O$_3$

① *p*-Tolylphenoxy-*o*-ethoxyphenyl-
   silanol
   p-CH$_3$C$_6$H$_4$Si(OC$_6$H$_5$)(C$_6$H$_4$OC$_2$H$_5$-*o*)OH

② H$_2$O +
   p-MeC$_6$H$_4$Si(OPh)(C$_6$H$_4$OEt-*o*)Cl $\longrightarrow$

③ Solid. [105°].

⑥ Zhur. **33**, 1289 (1963).

SiC$_{21}$H$_{24}$NP

① Trimethylsilyltriphenylphosphino-
   amine
   (CH$_3$)$_3$SiNP(C$_6$H$_5$)$_3$

② PPh$_3$ + Me$_3$SiN$_3$ $\longrightarrow$ 97%

③ [76~77°].

⑥ Ber. **96**, 2750 (1963).

SiC$_{22}$H$_{24}$

① Triphenyl-*n*-butylsilane
   (C$_6$H$_5$)$_3$SiC$_4$H$_9$-*n*

② *n*-BuSiCl$_3$ + PhCl + Na $\longrightarrow$
   n-BuLi + Ph$_3$SiCl $\longrightarrow$

③ Solid. [87.8~88.5°].

④ + H(Ni) $\longrightarrow$ (C$_6$H$_{11}$)$_3$SiBu-*n* (20%)

⑥ BCSJ **36**, 284 (1963).   JOC **26**, 2471
   (1961).

SiC$_{22}$H$_{24}$

① Triphenylmethyltrimethylsilane
   (CH$_3$)$_3$SiC(C$_6$H$_5$)$_3$

② Ph$_3$CNa + Me$_3$SiCl $\longrightarrow$
③ Solid. [172.5~173.5°].
⑥ JCS **1963**, 2342.

SiC$_{22}$H$_{24}$O$_2$

① Triphenylsilyl-*t*-butylperoxide
(C$_6$H$_5$)$_3$SiOOC(CH$_3$)$_3$
② (CH$_3$)$_3$COOH + (C$_6$H$_5$)$_3$SiCl $\xrightarrow{\text{pyridine}}$
③ [50°].
⑥ Chem. & Ind. **1956**, 1052.

SiC$_{22}$H$_{27}$BN$_2$

① Triphenylsilylbis(dimethylamino)-
boron
(C$_6$H$_5$)$_3$SiB[N(CH$_3$)$_2$]$_2$
② Ph$_3$SiLi + (Me$_2$N)$_2$BCl $\longrightarrow$
Ph$_3$SiCl + K + (Me$_2$N)$_2$BCl $\longrightarrow$
③ Solid. (131.5~135.0°).
④ + H$_2$O $\longrightarrow$ Ph$_3$SiH
+ KOH $\longrightarrow$ H$_2$
Reduces Ag$^+$ to Ag.
+ HCl $\longrightarrow$ Ph$_3$SiB(Cl)NMe$_2$
⑥ Angew. **74**, 718 (1962).

SiC$_{22}$H$_{40}$O$_2$

① Dimethyldigeranioxysilane
Me$_2$Si(OC$_{10}$H$_{17}$)$_2$
② Me$_2$SiCl$_2$ + C$_{10}$H$_{17}$OH $\longrightarrow$
③ (169~172°/2). n_D1.4611 (22°). d0.8975
(30°).
IR: 3000, 1250, 1100, 841 cm^{-1}.
⑥ J. Chi. Chem. Soc. (Ⅱ) **8**, 237, 384
(1961); **9**, 273 (1962).

SiC$_{22}$H$_{42}$

① *n*-Butyltricyclohexylsilane
n-C$_4$H$_9$Si(C$_6$H$_{11}$-*cyclo*)$_3$
② H(Ni) + Ph$_3$SiBu $\longrightarrow$ 20%
BuLi + (C$_6$H$_{11}$)$_3$SiF $\longrightarrow$
③ Solid. [157~158°].
⑥ BCSJ **36**, 31, 284 (1963).

SiC$_{22}$H$_{42}$O

① Tricyclohexyl-*n*-butoxysilane

(*cyclo*-C$_6$H$_{11}$)$_3$SiOC$_4$H$_9$-*n*
② *n*-BuONa + (C$_6$H$_{11}$)$_3$SiCl $\longrightarrow$
③ Solid. [132.0~133.4°].
⑥ BCSJ **36**, 287 (1963).

SiC$_{22}$H$_{44}$O$_2$

① Dimethyldimenthoxysilane
(CH$_3$)$_2$Si(OC$_{10}$H$_{19}$)$_2$
② Me$_2$SiCl$_2$ + C$_{10}$H$_{19}$OH $\longrightarrow$
③ (195~200°/2). n_D1.4590 (20°). d0.9183
(30°).
IR: 3000, 1250, 1090, 870, 841 cm^{-1}.
⑥ J. Chi. Chem. Soc. (Ⅱ) **8**, 237, 384
(1961); **9**, 273 (1962).

SiC$_{23}$H$_{15}$F$_9$

① Tris(*p*-trifluoromethylphenyl) vinylsilane
CH$_2$=CHSi(C$_6$H$_4$CF$_3$-*p*)$_3$
② CH$_2$=CHSiCl$_3$ + *p*-CF$_3$C$_6$H$_4$MgBr
$\longrightarrow$ 49%
③ Solid. [100°].
④ Adds HOOH to form the epoxide.
⑥ JOC **28**, 487 (1963).

SiC$_{23}$H$_{15}$F$_9$O

① Epoxyethyltris(*p*-trifluoromethyl-
phenyl)silane
CH$_2$—CHSi(C$_6$H$_4$CF$_3$-*p*)$_3$
    _/
     O
② CF$_3$COOH + HOOH +
CH$_2$=CHSi(C$_6$H$_4$CF$_3$-*p*)$_3$ $\longrightarrow$ 80%
③ Solid. [98~99°].
⑥ JOC **28**, 487 (1663).

SiC$_{23}$H$_{17}$F$_9$O

① Tris(*p*-trifluoromethylphenyl)-
(2-hydroxyethyl)silane
[*p*-CF$_3$C$_6$H$_4$]$_3$SiCH$_2$CH$_2$OH
② LiAlH$_4$ + (*p*-CF$_3$C$_6$H$_4$)$_3$SiCHCH$_2$
                                    _/
                                     O
$\longrightarrow$ 90%
③ [120~121°].

IR : 2150 cm⁻¹
⑥ JOC **28**, 2870 (1963).

SiC₂₃H₁₉ClO₂
① 1-Naphthylphenoxy-*o*-methoxyphenyl-
chlorosilane
1-C₁₀H₇Si(OC₆H₅)(C₆H₄OCH₃-*o*)Cl
② 1-C₁₀H₇SiCl₃ + *o*-MeOC₆H₄MgBr
⟶ 30%
③ Solid. [180°].
④ + H₂O ⟶
1-C₁₀H₇Si(OPh)(C₆H₄OMe)OH
⑥ Zhur. **33**, 1289 (1963).

SiC₂₃H₁₉N
① α-Triphenylsilylpyridine
(C₆H₅)₃Si(C₅H₄N-α)
② 2-BrPy + BuLi
$\xrightarrow{Et_2O}$ 2-PyLi $\xrightarrow{Ph_3SiCl}$
③ [192~193°].
⑥ Chem. & Ind. **1958**, 390.

SiC₂₃H₂₀O₃
① 1-Naphthylphenoxy-*o*-methoxy-
phenylsilanol
1-C₁₀H₇Si(OC₆H₅)(C₆H₄OCH₃-*o*)OH
② H₂O +
1-C₁₀H₇Si(OPh)(C₆H₄OMe-*o*)Cl ⟶
③ Solid. [174°].
⑥ Zhur. **33**, 1289 (1963).

SiC₂₃H₂₄
① Vinyltribenzylsilane
CH₂=CHSi(CH₂Ph)₃
② CH₂=CHSiCl₃ + PhCH₂MgCl
⟶ 80%
③ Solid. [80°].
④ + HOOH ⟶ CH₂—CHSi(CH₂Ph)₃
                               \ /
                                O
⑥ JOC **28**, 487 (1963).

SiC₂₃H₂₄
① Tri-*p*-tolylvinylsilane

CH₂=CHSi(C₆H₄CH₃-*p*)₃
② CH₂=CHSiCl₃ + *p*-MeC₆H₄MgBr
⟶ 83%
③ Solid. (200~201°/1). [84°].
④ + Ph₂SiH₂ ⟶
Ph₂Si(H)CH₂CH₂Si(C₆H₄Me-*p*)₃
(29% but 35% with (PhCOO)₂)
+ HOOH ⟶ epoxide
⑥ JCS **1963**, 797. JOC **28**, 847 (1963).

SiC₂₃H₂₄O
① Epoxyethyltribenzylsilane
CH₂—CHSi(CH₂C₆H₅)₃
     \ /
      O
② CF₃COOH + HOOH +
CH₂=CHSi(CH₂Ph)₃ ⟶ 54%
③ Solid. [65°].
⑥ JOC **28**, 487 (1963).

SiC₂₃H₂₄O
① Epoxyethyltri-*p*-tolylsilane
CH₂—CHSi(C₆H₄CH₃-*p*)₃
     \ /
      O
② CF₃COOH + HOOH +
CH₂=CHSi(C₆H₄Me-*p*)₃ ⟶ 57%
③ Solid. [84~85°].
⑥ JOC **28**, 487 (1963).

SiC₂₃H₂₄O₃
① Vinyltri-*p*-methoxyphenylsiane
CH₂=CHSi(C₆H₄OCH₃-*p*)₃
② CH₂=CHSiCl₃ + *p*-MeOC₆H₄MgBr
⟶ 80%
③ Solid. [89.5~90.5°].
④ Adds oxygen from
o-HOOCC₆H₄COOOH to form the
epoxide.
⑥ JOC **28**, 487 (1963).

SiC₂₃H₂₄O₄
① Epoxyethyltri-*p*-methoxyphenylsilane
CH₂—CHSi(C₆H₄OCH₃-*p*)₃
     \ /
      O

② $CH_2=CHSi(C_6H_4OMe-p)_3$
  $+ o\text{-}HOOCC_6H_4COOOH \longrightarrow$
③ Solid. [94～95°].
⑥ JOC **28**, 487 (1963).

SiC₂₃H₂₆O
① 2-(Tribenzylsilyl)ethanol
  $(C_6H_5CH_2)_3SiCH_2CH_2OH$
② $(PhCH_2)_3SiCHCH_2 + LiAlH_4 \longrightarrow$
  $\underset{O}{\diagdown\diagup}$
③ [40～41°].
⑥ JOC **28**, 2870 (1963).

SiC₂₃H₂₆O
① 2-(Tri-*p*-tolylsilyl)ethanol
  $(p\text{-}CH_3C_6H_4)_3SiCH_2CH_2OH$
② $(p\text{-}MeC_6H_4)_3SiCHCH_2 + LiAlH_4$
  $\underset{O}{\diagdown\diagup}$
  $\longrightarrow 93\%$
③ [90～91°].
⑥ JOC **28**, 2870 (1963).

SiC₂₃H₂₆O
① 1-(Tri-*p*-tolylsilyl)ethanol
  $(p\text{-}CH_3C_6H_4)_3CH(OH)CH_3$
② $LiAlH_4 + (p\text{-}MeC_6H_4)_3SiCHCH_2$
  $\underset{O}{\diagdown\diagup}$
  $\longrightarrow 6\%$
③ [88.0～88.5°].
  IR: 880 cm⁻¹.
⑥ JOC **28**, 2870 (1963).

SiC₂₃H₂₆O₄
① 2-[Tris(*p*-methoxyphenyl)silyl]-
  ethanol
  $(p\text{-}CH_3OC_6H_4)_3SiCH_2CH_2OH$
② $LiAlH_4 + (p\text{-}MeOC_6H_4)_3SiCHCH_2$
  $\underset{O}{\diagdown\diagup}$
  $\longrightarrow 94\%$
③ [81～82°].
⑥ JOC **28**, 2870 (1963).

SiC₂₃H₄₂O₂
① 1-(*p*-Tri-*n*-amylsiloxyphenyl)ethanol

$(C_5H_{11})_3SiOC_6H_4CH(OH)CH_3-p$
② $Mg + Am_3SiOC_6H_4Br-p + Et_2O$
  $+ MeCHO \longrightarrow$
③ (208～216°/5). $n_D1.4885$ (20°). $d0.9589$
  (20°/4°).
⑥ Zhur. **31**, 3735 (1961), English page
  3489.

SiC₂₃H₄₄OSn
① Methylphenylisobutyltriisobutyl-
  stannoxysilane
  $i\text{-}C_4H_9Si(CH_3)(C_6H_5)OSn(C_4H_9-i)_3$
② $(i\text{-}Bu)_3SnOSn(Bu-i)_3$
  $+ MeSiPh(Bu-i)OH \longrightarrow 64.4\%$
③ (171.0～172.5°/2.2). $n_D1.4961$ (20°).
  $d1.0709$ (20°).
  IR: 740～700, 800～760, 600, 500 cm⁻¹.
⑥ Zhur. **32**, 4007 (1962).

SiC₂₃H₅₀O₃
① *t*-Amyloxydioctyloxyethylsilane
  $t\text{-}C_5H_{11}OSi(OC_8H_{17})_2C_2H_5$
② $EtSiCl_3 + t\text{-}AmOH + C_8H_{17}OH \longrightarrow$
③ (159～160°).
⑥ US 2995590 (1958); CA **56**, 3356 (1962).

SiC₂₄F₂₀
① $Si(C_6F_5)_4$
  Tetrakis(pentafluorophenyl)silane
② $SiCl_4 + C_6F_5MgBr \longrightarrow$
③ Solid. (208°/1 sublime). [248～220°].
⑥ JACS **82**, 2846 (1960).

SiC₂₄H₂₀
① Tetraphenylsilane
  $(C_6H_5)_4Si$
② $SiCl_4 + 4PhMgBr \longrightarrow$
  Ph_3SiCl
  $+ [(4\text{-}Me)(2\text{-}Li)C_6H_3]_2NMe \longrightarrow$
  $Ph_3SiCl + CH_2PPh_3 + PhLi$
  $+ Ph_2CO \longrightarrow$
  $Ph_2SiCl_2 + Li + PhBr \longrightarrow 58\%$
③ Solid. [234°].

④ + Br₂ ⟶ PhBr + Ph₃SiBr

⑥ Monatsh. **93**, 1363 (1962). JOC **27**, 2897, 3647 (1962). Ber. **40**, 2274 (1907).

SiC₂₄H₂₀Br₂

① α-Naphthylmethylphenyl-α, α-dibromobenzylsilane
α-C₁₀H₇Si(CH₃)(C₆H₅)CBr₂C₆H₅

② (CH₂CO)₂NBr + α-C₁₀H₇SiMePhCH₂Ph ⟶

③ Solid. [114.0~114.5°]. [α]²⁵_D12.90.

④ + H₂O ⟶
α-C₁₀H₇SiMePhCOPh 94%

⑥ JACS **85**, 832 (1963).

SiC₂₄H₂₀O

① Triphenylphenoxysilane
(C₆H₅)₃SiOC₆H₅

② PhONa + Ph₃SiCl ⟶

③ Solid. [103~105°].

⑥ BCSJ **36**, 284 (1963).

SiC₂₄H₂₀O

① 1-Naphthylmethylphenylbenzoylsilane
1-C₁₀H₇Si(CH₃)(C₆H₅)COC₆H₅

② H₂O + 1-C₁₀H₇SiMePhCBr₂Ph ⟶ 94%

③ Solid. [68~70°]. [α]²⁵_D6.72.

④ + MeMgBr ⟶
1-C₁₀H₇SiMePhCMePhOH

⑥ JACS **85**, 832 (1963).

SiC₂₄H₂₀O₃

① Triphenoxyphenylsilane
C₆H₅Si(OC₆H₅)₃

② PhOH + HCONMe₂ + PhSiH₃ ⟶ 13.2%

③ (241~245°/13). [61~62°]. n_D1.5880 (20°).

⑥ Zhur. **33**, 2617 (1963) ; **32**, 614 (1962).

SiC₂₄H₂₂

① 1-Naphthylmethylphenylbenzylsilane

1-C₁₀H₇Si(CH₃)(C₆H₅)CH₂C₆H₅

② PhCH₂Na + 1-C₁₀H₇SiHMePh ⟶

③ Solid. [69~70°]. [α]_D−6.68° (25°).

④ + (CH₂CO)₂NHBr
⟶ 1-C₁₀H₇SiMePhCBr₂Ph

⑥ JACS **85**, 832 (1963).

SiC₂₄H₂₂O

① Methylphenyl-1-naphthyl-p-methoxyphenylsilane
CH₃Si(C₆H₅)(C₁₀H₇-1)C₆H₄OCH₃-p

② p-MeOC₆H₄Li + MeSiPh(C₁₀H₇-1)OC₁₀H₁₉(menthyl) ⟶

③ [70~72°]. [α]_D−6.17°, −6.13° (20°), [α]_D−6.0° (19°).

⑥ Proc. Chem. Soc. **1963**, 59.

SiC₂₄H₂₃N₃

① Tris(phenylamino)phenylsilane
C₆H₅Si(NHC₆H₅)₃

② PhSiH₃ + PhNH₂ + C₅H₅N ⟶ 74.5%

③ [134~135°].

⑥ Zhur. **33**, 2617 (1963).

SiC₂₄H₂₄O₃

① Cyclohexenyltriphenoxysilane
cyclo-C₆H₉Si(OC₆H₅)₃

② C₆H₉SiCl₃ + PhOH ⟶

③ (210°/0.1).
Viscosity : 40.3 cs (25°).

⑥ J. Chem. Eng. Data **7**, 556 (1962).

SiC₂₄H₂₆

① Cyclohexyltriphenylsilane
C₆H₁₁Si(C₆H₅)₃

②

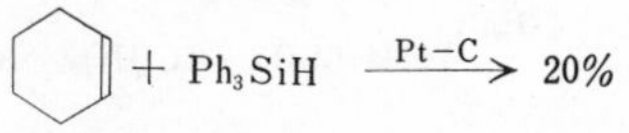

+ Ph₃SiH $\xrightarrow{Pt-C}$ 20%

③ (230°/3). [227°].

⑥ JACS **80**, 611 (1958). Dokl. **111**, 1260 (1956).

SiC$_{24}$H$_{26}$

① Allyltri(p-tolyl)silane
    (p-CH$_3$C$_6$H$_4$)$_3$SiCH$_2$CH=CH$_2$

② (p-MeC$_6$H$_4$)$_3$SiH +
    CH$_2$=CHCH$_2$Br or CH$_2$=CHCH$_2$Cl
    $\xrightarrow{580\sim640°}$ 5%

③ [114°].

⑥ J. prakt. Chem. **21**, 149 (1963).   Dokl.
    138, 136 (1961).

SiC$_{24}$H$_{28}$

① n-Hexyltriphenylsilane
    n-C$_6$H$_{13}$Si(C$_6$H$_5$)$_3$

② (C$_6$H$_5$)$_3$SiCH=CH$_2$ + n-C$_4$H$_9$Li
    $\xrightarrow{H_2O}$ 67%

③ White solid. [77~78°].
    Sol. in org. solvents; insol. in
    water.

⑥ JOC **19**, 1278 (1954).

SiC$_{24}$H$_{30}$BN

① Butyl(triphenylsilyl)(dimethylamino)-
    boron
    (C$_6$H$_5$)$_3$SiB(C$_4$H$_9$)N(CH$_3$)$_2$

② Ph$_3$SiLi + Me$_2$NB(Cl)Bu $\longrightarrow$

③ (155~165°).

④ + KOH $\longrightarrow$ H$_2$
    Reduces Ag$^+$ to Ag

⑥ Angew. **74**, 718 (1962).

SiC$_{24}$H$_{30}$Ge

① Triethyl(triphenylgermanyl)silane
    (C$_2$H$_5$)$_3$SiGe(C$_6$H$_5$)$_3$

② (C$_2$H$_5$)$_3$SiBr + (C$_6$H$_5$)$_3$GeNa $\longrightarrow$

③ [93.5°].

④ + C$_2$H$_5$NH$_2$ + Li
    $\xrightarrow{NH_4Br}$ (C$_2$H$_5$)$_3$SiH + (C$_6$H$_5$)$_3$GeH
    $\xrightarrow{C_2H_5Br}$ (C$_2$H$_5$)$_4$Si + (C$_6$H$_5$)$_3$Ge(C$_2$H$_5$)

⑥ WADC. TR 53-426, Part II (1955).
    Contrail No. AF 33 (616) 1994.
    JACS **56**, 195 (1934).

SiC$_{24}$H$_{36}$O$_4$

① Diphenyldi(β-butoxyethoxy)silane
    (C$_6$H$_5$)$_2$Si(OCH$_2$CH$_2$OC$_4$H$_9$-n)$_2$

② Ph$_2$SiCl$_2$ + n-BuOCH$_2$CH$_2$OH
    $\longrightarrow$ 97%

③ (195°/1). n_D1.500 (25°). d1.012 (25°).

⑥ Compt. rend. **256**, 4920 (1963); CA
    59, 5188 (1963).

SiC$_{24}$H$_{38}$

① Phenyltricyclohexylsilane
    C$_6$H$_5$Si(C$_6$H$_{11}$-$cyclo$)$_3$

② PhLi + (C$_6$H$_{11}$)$_3$SiF $\longrightarrow$

③ Solid. [207~208°].

⑥ BCSJ **36**, 31, 284 (1963).

SiC$_{24}$H$_{44}$

① Tetracyclohexylsilane
    Si(C$_6$H$_{11}$-$cyclo$)$_4$

② H(Ni) + PhSi(C$_6$H$_{11}$)$_3$ $\longrightarrow$
    H(Ni) + SiPh$_4$ $\longrightarrow$

③ Solid. [276~278°].

⑥ BCSJ **36**, 284 (1963); **27**, 441 (1954).

SiC$_{24}$H$_{44}$O

① Tricyclohexylcyclohexoxysilane
    ($cyclo$-C$_6$H$_{11}$)$_3$SiOC$_6$H$_{11}$-$cyclo$

② Li(under N$_2$) + C$_6$H$_{11}$Cl + SiCl$_4$ $\longrightarrow$
    Na + C$_6$H$_{11}$OH + (C$_6$H$_{11}$)$_3$SiCl
    $\longrightarrow$ 44%

③ Solid. [201~203.5°].

⑥ BCSJ **36**, 287 (1963).   JCS **1952**, 2840.

SiC$_{24}$H$_{48}$O$_2$

① Dimethyldicitronelloxysilane
    (CH$_3$)$_2$Si[OCH$_2$CH$_2$(CH$_3$)CHCH$_2$CH$_2$CH-
    =C(CH$_3$)$_2$]$_2$

② Me$_2$SiCl$_2$ + C$_{10}$H$_{19}$OH(citronellol) $\longrightarrow$

③ (177~178°/4). n_D1.4558 (15°). d0.8730
    (30°).
    IR: 3000, 1250, 1100, 841 cm^{-1}.

⑤ Water repellant.

⑥ J. Chi. Chem. Soc. (II) **8**, 237, 384
    (1961); **9**, 273 (1962).

SiC₂₅H₂₀Br₂

① Triphenyl-*m*-dibromomethyl-
   phenylsilane
   $(C_6H_5)_3SiC_6H_4CHBr_2-m$

② m-Ph₃SiC₆H₄Me + (CH₂CO)₂NBr
   + (BzO)₂ $\longrightarrow$ 66%

③ Solid. [119°].

④ + HOH $\longrightarrow$ m-Ph₃SiC₆H₄CHO

⑥ Rec. trav. chim. **81**, 88 (1962).

SiC₂₅H₂₀Cl₂

① Triphenyl-*m*, *p*-dichlorobenzylsilane
   $(C_6H_5)_3SiCH_2C_6H_3Cl_2(3,4)$

② Ph₃SiCl + (3,4)Cl₂C₆H₃CH₂MgCl $\longrightarrow$

③ Solid. [107~109°].

⑤ Possible high temperature stability.

⑥ JOC **26**, 3723 (1961).

SiC₂₅H₂₀O

① *m*-Triphenylsilylbenzaldehyde
   m-$(C_6H_5)_3SiC_6H_4CHO$

② HOH + m-Ph₃SiC₆H₄CHBr₂ $\longrightarrow$ 81%

③ Solid. [127~128°].

④ + H₂NNHC₆H₃(NO₂)₂(2,4) $\longrightarrow$
   m-Ph₃SiC₆H₄CH=NNHC₆H₃(NO₂)₂(2,4)
   mp 206~207°

⑥ Rec. trav. chim. **81**, 88 (1962).

SiC₂₅H₂₀O

① Triphenyl-*p*-formylphenylsilane
   $(C_6H_5)_3Si(C_6H_4CHO-p)$

② Ph₃SiCl $\xrightarrow[\text{NBS, CCl}_4]{\text{MeC}_6\text{H}_4\text{Li, Et}_2\text{O}}$ Ph₃SiC₆H₄Me

   $$Ph_3SiC_6H_4CHBr_2 \xrightarrow[\text{C}_6\text{H}_{12}\text{N}_4, \text{AcOH-H}_2\text{O}]{\text{AgNO}_3\text{-H}_2\text{O, HOCH}_2\text{CH}_2\text{OMe}}$$

③ (119°/15). [109~110°].

④ Ph₃SiC₆H₄CHO $\begin{array}{c}\xrightarrow[\text{CCl}_4]{\text{NBS, NH}_4\text{OH}} Ph_3SiC_6H_4CO_2H \\ \xrightarrow{\text{KOH}} (Ph_3Si)_2OPh_3SiC_6H_4CO_2H \end{array}$

⑥ Iowa State Coll. J. Sci. **26**, 170

(1952). JACS **78**, 1689 (1956). Rec. trav. chim. **81**, 88 (1962).

SiC₂₅H₂₀O₂

① Triphenyl-*p*-carboxyphenylsilane
   $(C_6H_5)_3Si(C_6H_4COOH-p)$

② p-MeC₆H₄Br + Li $\longrightarrow$ p-MeC₆H₄Li
   $\xrightarrow[\text{Ph}_3\text{SiCl } \text{C}_6\text{H}_6 \text{ H}^+\text{-H}_2\text{O}]{}$ p-MeC₆H₄SiPh₃
   $\xrightarrow[\text{CrO}_3 \text{ or KMnO}_4]{}$ 74%

③ [211~212°].

④ p-Ph₃SiC₆H₄CO₂H
   $\xrightarrow[\text{SOCl}_2 \text{ NH}_4\text{OH}]{}$ p-Ph₃SiC₆H₄CONH₂

⑥ JACS **78**, 682 (1956). Iowa State
   Coll. J. Sci. **26**, 170 (1952).

SiC₂₅H₂₀O

① Triphenylsilyl phenyl ketone
   $(C_6H_5)_3SiCOC_6H_5$

② Ph₃SiCH₂Ph $\xrightarrow[\text{AgOAc Me}_2\text{CO-EtOH-H}_2\text{O}]{\text{NBS, CCl}_4}$ Ph₃SiCBr₂Ph

③ [102~103°].

④ Ph₃SiCOPh $\xrightarrow{\text{OH}^-}$ Ph₃SiOH + PhCHO
   Ph₃SiCOPh
   $\xrightarrow[\text{PhH}]{\text{NaOEt H}^+\text{-H}_2\text{O}}$ EtOSiPh₂OCHPh₂
   (61%) + Ph₂Si(OEt)₂ + Ph₂CHOH
   EtOSiPh₂OCHPh₂ $\xrightarrow[\text{EtOH}]{\text{NaOH}}$ Ph₂Si(OH)₂
   + Ph₂CHOH
   Ph₃SiCOPh $\xrightarrow[\text{PhH}]{\text{NaOMe}}$ MeOSiPh₂−OCHPh₂

⑥ JACS **79**, 4373 (1957); **82**, 5102 (1960).
   JOC **27**, 2311 (1962).

SiC₂₅H₂₁Br

① α-Bromobenzyltriphenylsilane
   $C_6H_5CHBrSi(C_6H_5)_3$

② $(C_6H_5)_3SiCH_2C_6H_5$ $\xrightarrow{\text{NBS}}$ 52%

③ [145°].

⑥ JACS **74**, 5091 (1952).

SiC$_{25}$H$_{21}$Cl

① *p*-Chlorobenzyltriphenylsilane
   $(C_6H_5)_3SiCH_2C_6H_4Cl-p$
② $Ph_3SiCl + p-ClC_6H_4CH_2MgCl \longrightarrow$
③ Solid. [117~119°].
⑥ JOC **26**, 3723 (1961).

SiC$_{25}$H$_{21}$ClO$_2$

① *p*-Xenylchlorophenoxy-*o*-methoxy-
   phenylsilane
   $p-C_6H_5C_6H_4Si(Cl)(OC_6H_5)C_6H_4OCH_3-o$
② $p-PhC_6H_4SiCl_3 + o-MeOC_6H_4MgBr$
   $\longrightarrow 35\%$
③ Solid. [132°].
④ $+ H_2O \longrightarrow$
   $p-PhC_6H_4Si(OH)(OPh)C_6H_4OMe-o$
⑥ Zhur. **33**, 1289 (1963).

SiC$_{25}$H$_{22}$

① Triphenyl-*p*-tolylsilane
   $(C_6H_5)_3Si(C_6H_4CH_3-p)$
② $Ph_3SiCl + p-MeC_6H_4Li \longrightarrow 92\%$
   $Ph_3SiCl + p-BrC_6H_4Me \xrightarrow{Na} 30\%$
③ [141~143°].
⑥ JACS **77**, 3916 (1955); **78**, 682 (1956);
   68, 1675 (1946).

SiC$_{25}$H$_{22}$

① Benzyltriphenylsilane
   $C_6H_5CH_2Si(C_6H_5)_3$
② $Ph_3SiCl + C_6H_5CH_2MgCl \xrightarrow{ether} 80\%$
③ White crystals. [97~98°]. (438°).
   Slightly sol. in org. solvents.
④ $+$ aq. KOH $\xrightarrow{reflux} Ph_3SiOSiPh_3$
   $+ CH_3C_6H_5$
⑥ JACS **75**, 3757, 4531 (1953).

SiC$_{25}$H$_{22}$O$_3$

① *p*-Xenylphenoxy-*o*-methoxyphenyl-
   silanol
   $p-C_6H_5C_6H_4Si(OH)(OC_6H_5)C_6H_4OCH_3-o$

② $p-PhC_6H_4Si(Cl)(OPh)C_6H_4OMe-o +$
   $H_2O \longrightarrow 35\%$
③ Solid. [122°].
⑥ Zhur. **33**, 1289 (1963).

SiC$_{26}$H$_{20}$

① Triphenylphenylethynylsilane
   $(C_6H_5)_3SiC\equiv CC_6H_5$
② $Ph_3SiCl + PhC\equiv CLi \longrightarrow 72\%$
③ White crystals. (445~460° decomp.).
   [100~101°].
   Slightly. sol. in org. solvents.
⑥ JACS **75**, 3757 (1953).

SiC$_{26}$H$_{21}$Br$_3$

① α-Bromobenzyl-α, α-dibromobenzyl-
   diphenylsilane
   $(C_6H_5)_2Si(CHBrC_6H_5)CBr_2C_6H_5$
② $(PhCH_2)_2SiPh_2 + (CH_2CO)_2NBr$
   $+ (BzO)_2 \longrightarrow$
③ [145~149°].
④ $+ HOH + CH_3COOAg$
   $\longrightarrow Ph_2Si(CHBrPh)COPh$
   $+ SO_2Cl_2 + (BzO)_2$
   $\longrightarrow Ph_2Si(CClBrPh)CBr_2Ph$
⑥ Can. J. Chem. **41**, 2351 (1963).

SiC$_{26}$H$_{22}$

① Triphenylstyrylsilane
   $C_6H_5CH=CHSi(C_6H_5)_3$
② $Ph_3SiCl + PhCH=CHLi \longrightarrow cis\ 46\%$
   $PhC\equiv CH + SiHCl_3$
   $\xrightarrow{Pd-C} trans-PhCH=CHSiCl_3$
   $trans-PhCH=CHSiCl_3$
   $\xrightarrow{Ph-Li} trans\ 82\%$
③ *cis* isomer (83~85°/6). *trans* isomer
   [147~148.5°]. *cis* isomer $n_D 1.5300$
   (20°).
④ $PhCH=CHSiPh_3$
   $\xrightarrow[\text{in glacial } CH_3COOH]{\text{anhyd. HCl}} Ph_3SiOSiPh_3$
⑥ JACS **72**, 2629 (1950); **80**, 5298 (1958).

SiC26H24

① Diphenyldibenzylsilane
$(C_6H_5)_2Si(CH_2C_6H_5)_2$

② $PhCH_2MgCl + Ph_2SiCl_2 \longrightarrow$

③ [60.5~61.0°].

④ $+ (CH_2CO)_2NBr + (BzO)_2$
$\longrightarrow Ph_2Si(CHBrPh)CBr_2Ph$

⑥ Can. J. Chem. **41**, 2351 (1963). JACS
76, 6392 (1954).

SiC26H24

① Diphenyldi-*p*-tolylsilane
$(C_6H_5)_2Si(C_6H_4CH_3-p)_2$

② $SiCl_4 + 2PhLi \longrightarrow Ph_2SiCl_2$
$\xrightarrow{2p-MeC_6H_4Li} 78\%$

$PhSiCl_2 + p-BrC_6H_4Me \xrightarrow{Na} 59\%$

③ (190~240°/0.6). [119~120°].

⑥ JOC **18**, 1689 (1953). JACS **77**, 3916
(1955) ; **68**, 1675 (1946). Hua Hsüeh
Hsüeh Pao **24**, 170 (1958).

SiC26H24

① β-Phenethyltriphenylsilane
$C_6H_5CH_2CH_2Si(C_6H_5)_3$

② $Ph_3SiCH=CH_2 + PhLi$
$\longrightarrow [Ph_3SiCH(Li)CH_2Ph]$
$\xrightarrow{H_2O} 84\%$

③ [147°].

⑥ JOC **19**, 1278 (1954). Japan 1342
(1951).

SiC26H40

① Bis(pentamethylphenylmethyl)di-
methylsilane
$[(CH_3)_5C_6CH_2]_2Si(CH_3)_2$

② $Me_2SiCl_2 + K + Me_5C_6CH_2Cl \longrightarrow$

③ Solid. [134~135°].

⑥ Kogyo Kagaku Zasshi **61**, 1527 (1958).

SiC26H56O3

① *t*-Amoxybis(2-ethylhexoxy)amyl-
silane

$t-C_5H_{11}OSi[OCH_2CH(C_2H_5)(C_4H_9)]_2-$
(C_5H_{11})

② $AmSiCl_3 + t-AmOH$
$+ BuCH(Et)CH_2OH \longrightarrow$

③ Liq. (148~152°).

⑥ US 2995590 (1958) ; CA **56**, 3356 (1962).

SiC27H20O6

① Tribenzyloxyphenylsilane
$(C_6H_5COO)_3SiC_6H_5$

② $BzOH + C_5H_5N + PhSiH_3 \longrightarrow 71.2\%$

③ $n_D1.5767$ (20°). $d1.2390$ (20°/4°).

⑥ Zhur. **33**, 2617 (1963).

SiC28H26N2

① 5,5'-Diethyl-10,10'-spirobiphenyl-
phenazasiline

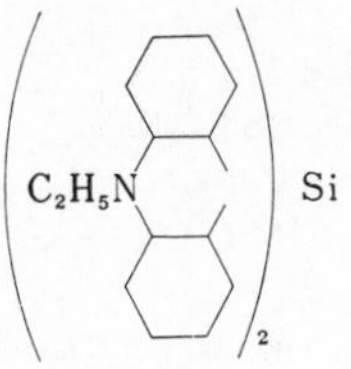

②

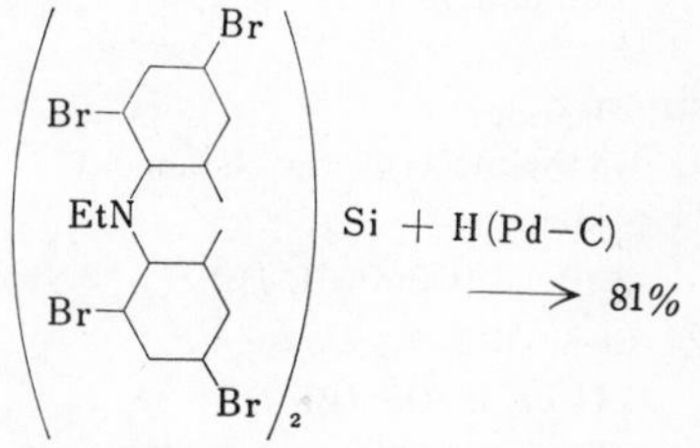

③ Solid. [214~215°].

⑤ Lubricant.

⑥ US 3069444 (1962); CA **58**, 13994
(1963). Fr. 1315605 (1963). Belg.
613915 (1962).

SiC28H28

① Tetra-*p*-tolylsilane
$(p-CH_3C_6H_4)_4Si$

② $Ph_3SiOSi(C_6H_4CH_3-p)_3 + p-CH_3C_6H_4Li$
$\longrightarrow 39\%$

③ Solid. (410°). [227~230°].
   Slightly sol. in org. solvents ; insol.
   in H$_2$O.
⑥ JOC **19**, 419 (1954).

SiC$_{28}$H$_{28}$O$_2$
① Bis(benzyloxymethyl) diphenylsilane
   (C$_6$H$_5$)$_2$Si(CH$_2$OCH$_2$C$_6$H$_5$)$_2$
② Ph$_2$SiCl$_2$ + Mg + PhCH$_2$OCH$_2$Cl $\longrightarrow$
③ (151°/0.65). n_D1.5289 (20°)$^.$ d1.017
   (20°).
⑥ Belg. 620518 (1963) ; CA **59**, 440 (1963).
   Fr. 1303195 (1962) ; CA **58**, 7975
   (1963).

SiC$_{28}$H$_{28}$Sn
① 1,1,4,4-Tetraphenyl-1-sila-4-stanna-
   cyclohexane

$$(C_6H_5)_2Si \underset{CH_2CH_2}{\overset{CH_2CH_2}{\diagup\diagdown}} Sn(C_6H_5)_2$$

② Ph$_2$SnH$_2$ + Ph$_2$Si(CH=CH$_2$)$_2$ $\longrightarrow$
③ Solid. [134°].
⑥ Rec. trav. chim. **82**, 561 (1960).
   Chimia **16**, 122 (1962).

SiC$_{28}$H$_{62}$O$_2$Sn$_2$
① Diethylbis(triisobutylstannoxy)-
   silane
   (C$_2$H$_5$)$_2$Si[OSn(C$_4$H$_9$-i)$_3$]$_2$
② Et$_2$Si(OH)$_2$ +
   (i-Bu)$_3$SnOSn(Bu-i)$_3$ $\longrightarrow$
③ (202.5~203.5°/3). n_D1.4800 (20°).
   d1.1443 (20°/4°).
   IR : Mostly 720~670, 620~600, 520~
   500 cm^{-1}.
⑥ Zhur. **32**, 4007 (1962).

SiC$_{30}$H$_{21}$F
① Tri-α-naphthylfluorosilane
   (C$_{10}$H$_7$)$_3$SiF

② Na$_2$SiF$_6$ $\longrightarrow$ SiF$_4$ $\xrightarrow{\text{C}_{10}\text{H}_7\text{MgBr}}$

   (C$_{10}$H$_7$)$_2$SiF$_2$ $\xrightarrow{\text{C}_{10}\text{H}_7\text{Li}}$

③ [226~227°].
⑥ Zhur. **24**, 1189 (1954) ; CA **49**, 12276
   (1955). Dokl. **84**, 515 (1952) ; **89**, 73
   (1953) ; CA **47**, 3288 (1953) ; **48**, 3916
   (1954).

SiC$_{30}$H$_{22}$O
① Tri-α-naphthylhydroxysilane
   (C$_{10}$H$_7$)$_3$SiOH

② SiCl$_4$ $\xrightarrow{\text{C}_{10}\text{H}_7\text{Li}}$

   (C$_{10}$H$_7$)$_3$SiCl $\xrightarrow{\text{H}_2\text{O, OH}^-}$

③ [208~208°].
⑥ JACS **72**, 1689 (1950) ; **13**, 4640 (1951).
   Izv. OKhN **1957**, 319.

SiC$_{30}$H$_{24}$
① Triphenyl-o-biphenylylsilane
   (C$_6$H$_5$)$_3$SiC$_6$H$_4$C$_6$H$_5$-o
② Ph$_3$SiCl + o-C$_6$H$_5$C$_6$H$_4$Li $\longrightarrow$ 12%
③ Yellow-crystals. (450°). [137~137.5°].
   Slightly sol. in org. solvents ; insol.
   in water.
⑥ JACS **77**, 3386 (1955). JOC **20**, 862
   (1955).

SiC$_{30}$H$_{24}$
① p-Biphenylyltriphenylsilane
   p-C$_6$H$_5$C$_6$H$_4$Si(C$_6$H$_5$)$_3$
② Ph$_3$SiCl + p-PhC$_6$H$_4$Br $\longrightarrow$ 84%
③ Luminescent property. (512°). [158.5
   ~159.5°].
⑥ JACS **77**, 6227 (1955). U. S. Dept.
   Com., Office Tech. Serv., AD 284019,
   194 (1962). Adv. in Chem. Ser.
   23, 212 (1959).

SiC$_{30}$H$_{24}$O
① Triphenyl-p-phenoxyphenylsilane
   C$_6$H$_5$OC$_6$H$_4$Si(C$_6$H$_5$)$_3$
② BuLi + 4-ClC$_6$H$_4$OPh
   $\xrightarrow[\text{in Et}_2\text{O, reflux}]{}$ 4-PhOC$_6$H$_4$Li

Ph₃SiCl
——→

③ [146~147°].

⑥ JACS 72, 2629 (1950).   JOC 21, 1009 (1956).

SiC₃₀H₂₄O₃

① m- and p-Xenyltriphenoxysilane
    C₆H₅C₆H₄Si(OC₆H₅)₃

② PhC₆H₄SiCl₃ + PhOH ——→

③ (190°/0.2). n_D1.6010 (25°).
    Viscosity: 350 csk (25°).

⑥ J. Chem. Eng. Data 7, 556 (1962).

SiC₃₀H₂₄O₄

① p-Phenoxyphenyltriphenoxysilane
    p-C₆H₅OC₆H₄Si(OC₆H₅)₃

② p-PhOC₆H₄SiCl₃ + PhOH ——→

③ (180°/0.2).
    Viscosity: 58.3 csk (25°).

⑥ J. Chem. Eng. Data 7, 556 (1962).

SiC₃₀H₃₀

① p-Cyclohexylphenyltriphenylsilane
    p-C₆H₁₁C₆H₄Si(C₆H₅)₃

② p-C₆H₁₁C₆H₄MgBr + Ph₃SiCl ——→

③ Solid. [150°].

⑥ Dokl. 51 (1961); CA 58, 543 (1963).

SiC₃₁H₂₆O

① Triphenyldiphenylhydroxymethyl-
    silane
    (C₆H₅)₃SiC(OH)(C₆H₅)₂

                NBS
② Ph₃SiCHPh₂ ——→ Ph₃SiCBrPh₂
    AgOAc in H₂O
    ——————→

③ [157~159°].

              in EtOH
④ + NaOH ——————→ Ph₃SiOH
    + Ph₂CHOH

⑥ JACS 80, 1886 (1958).

SiC₃₂H₂₀

① Tetraphenylethynylsilane

(C₆H₅C≡C)₄Si

② SiCl₄ + PhC≡CLi ——→

③ Solid. [198°].
    Slightly sol. in org. solvents.

⑥ JACS 76, 6392 (1954).   U. S. Atomic
    Energy Comm. BNL-2446 89 (1955);
    CA 50, 15992 (1956).

SiC₃₂H₆₈

① Dihexadecylsilane
    (C₁₆H₃₃)₂SiH₂

② (t-BuO)₂ + SiH₄ + C₁₄H₂₉CH=CH₂ ——→

③ Solid. [49~50°].

⑤ For water proofing masonry and
    brick.

⑥ US 3067051 (1962); CA 58, 5896(1963).

SiC₃₄H₄₅Cl₃

① Tri-p-chlorophenylhexadecylsilane
    C₁₆H₃₃Si(C₆H₄Cl-p)₃

② C₁₆H₃₃SiCl₃ + p-LiC₆H₄Cl ——→ 65.6%

③ (246~251°/0.03). n_D1.5530 (25°). d 1:071
    (25°).

⑥ JOC 27, 1023 (1962).

SiC₃₄H₄₅Cl₃

① Tri-m-chlorophenylhexadecyl-
    silane
    C₁₆H₃₃Si(C₆H₄Cl-m)₃

② C₁₆H₃₃SiCl₃ + o-LiC₆H₄Cl ——→ 65.8%

③ (240~241°/less than 0.001). n_D1.5579
    (25°). d 1.0751 (25°).

⑥ JOC 27, 1023 (1962).

SiC₃₄H₄₅F₃

① Tri(m-fluorophenyl)hexadecylsilane
    C₁₆H₃₃Si(C₆H₄F-m)₃

② m-LiC₆H₄F + C₁₆H₃₃SiCl₃ ——→ 71%

③ Solid. (214~217°/0.05). [36~38°].

⑥ JOC 27, 1023 (1962).

SiC₃₆H₂₆N₂

① 5,5'-Diphenyl-10,10'-spirobi-(5,10-

dihydrophenazasiline)

② SiCl$_4$ + PhN(C$_6$H$_4$Li-o)$_2$ ⟶ 24%
③ Solid. [313~314°].
　　Sol. in AcOEt.
⑥ JOC **26**, 2013 (1961).

SiC$_{36}$H$_{28}$

① Tri-o-biphenylylsilane
　　(o-C$_6$H$_5$C$_6$H$_4$)$_3$SiH
② (o-C$_6$H$_5$C$_6$H$_4$)$_3$SiCl + LiAlH$_4$
　　⟶ 71%
③ White solid. (470°). [169.5~170.5°].
　　Slightly sol. in org. solvents ; insol.
　　in water.
④ + KOH in piperidine + H$_2$O
　　⟶ (o-C$_6$H$_5$C$_6$H$_4$)$_3$SiOH
⑥ JOC **20**, 862 (1955).　JACS **77**, 3386
　　(1955).

SiC$_{36}$H$_{28}$O$_2$

① Bis(m-phenoxyphenyl)diphenyl-
　　silane
　　(m-C$_6$H$_5$OC$_6$H$_4$)$_2$Si(C$_6$H$_5$)$_2$
③ Amorphous solid. (256~257°/0.025).
　　[flow point 45°].
⑥ Chem. & Ind. 1091 (1959).

SiC$_{36}$H$_{28}$O$_2$

① m-Phenoxyphenoxy-m-triphenylsilyl-
　　benzene
　　m-C$_6$H$_5$OC$_6$H$_4$OC$_6$H$_4$Si(C$_6$H$_5$)$_3$-m
③ Amorphous solid.　(278~280°/0.07).

[flow point 45°].
⑤ Possible high temperature stability.
⑥ Chem. & Ind. 1091 (1959).

SiC$_{36}$H$_{28}$O$_2$

① p-Phenoxyphenyl-o-phenoxyphenyldi-
　　phenylsilane
　　p-C$_6$H$_5$OC$_6$H$_4$Si(C$_6$H$_5$)$_2$C$_6$H$_4$OC$_6$H$_4$-o
③ Amorphous solid. (238°/0.025). [flow
　　point 55°].
⑤ Possible stability at high tempera-
　　tures.
⑥ Chem. & Ind. 1091 (1959).

SiC$_{36}$H$_{28}$O$_3$

① o,o'-Terphenyltriphenoxysilane
　　(C$_6$H$_5$O)$_3$SiC$_6$H$_4$C$_6$H$_4$C$_6$H$_5$-o,o'
② PhOH + o,o'-PhC$_6$H$_4$C$_6$H$_4$SiCl$_3$ ⟶
③ (182~185°/0.5). n_D1.6130 (25°).
⑤ Moderate thermal stability.
⑥ J. Chem. Eng. Data **7**. 556 (1962).

SiC$_{36}$H$_{28}$O$_3$

① m,m'-Terphenyltriphenoxysilane
　　(C$_6$H$_5$O)$_3$SiC$_6$H$_4$C$_6$H$_4$C$_6$H$_5$-m,m'
② PhOH + m,m'-PhC$_6$H$_4$C$_6$H$_4$SiCl$_3$ ⟶
③ (200°/0.5).
⑤ Moderate thermal stability.
⑥ J. Chem. Eng. Data **7**, 556 (1962).

SiC$_{36}$H$_{28}$O$_3$

① p,p'-Terphenyltriphenoxysilane
　　(C$_6$H$_5$O$_3$)SiC$_6$H$_4$C$_6$H$_4$C$_6$H$_5$-p,p'
② PhOH + p,p'-PhC$_6$H$_4$C$_6$H$_4$SiCl$_3$ ⟶
③ Solid. (220°/0.5). [135~137°].
⑤ Shows moderate stability at high
　　temperatures.
⑥ J. Chem. Eng. Data **7**, 556 (1962).

SiC$_{36}$H$_{30}$Ge

① Triphenylsilyltriphenylgermane
　　(C$_6$H$_5$)$_3$SiGe(C$_6$H$_5$)$_3$
② Ph$_3$SiK + Ph$_3$GeCl ⟶

Ph$_3$SiK + Ph$_3$GeBr $\longrightarrow$

Ph$_3$SiLi + Ph$_3$GeCOOMe $\longrightarrow$

③ Solid. [351.5~353.0°].

④ Inert toward oxygen and iodine. Does not form free radicals.

  + NaK $\longrightarrow$ Ph$_3$GeK + Ph$_3$SiK.

⑥ JACS **78**, 5823 (1956); **77**, 4675 (1955).

SiC$_{36}$H$_{30}$NP

① Triphenyl(triphenylphosphoamino)-silane

  (C$_6$H$_5$)$_3$SiNP(C$_6$H$_5$)$_3$

② Ph$_3$P + Ph$_3$SiN$_3$ $\longrightarrow$

③ Solid. [215~216°].

⑥ Angew. **74**, 716 (1962).

SiC$_{36}$H$_{30}$Sn

① Triphenylsilyltriphenylstannane

  (C$_6$H$_5$)$_3$SiSn(C$_6$H$_5$)$_3$

② Ph$_3$SnLi + Ph$_3$SiCl $\longrightarrow$ 19.4%

③ Solid. [299~303°].

⑥ JOC **28**, 181 (1963).

SiC$_{36}$H$_{31}$O$_2$P

① Double compound: Triphenylsilanol and Triphenylphosphine oxide

  [(C$_6$H$_5$)$_3$SiOH](C$_6$H$_5$)$_3$PO

② CH$_2$PPh$_3$ + Ph$_3$SiCl, then PhLi and Ph$_2$CO $\longrightarrow$

③ Solid. [122~123°].

⑥ JOC **27**, 3647 (1962).

SiC$_{36}$H$_{36}$O$_8$

① Tetrakis(p-carboethoxyphenyl)-silane

  Si(C$_6$H$_4$COOC$_2$H$_5$-p)$_4$

② SOCl$_2$ + EtOH + Si(C$_6$H$_4$COOH-p)$_4$ $\longrightarrow$

③ Solid. [222.5~223.0°].

⑥ Hua Hsüeh Hsüeh Pao **25**, 289 (1959); CA **54**, 16412 (1960).

SiC$_{36}$H$_{38}$O$_3$

① Tri(5,6,7,8-tetralinoxy-2)phenyl-silane

② PhSiCl$_3$ +

③ (220~225°/0.5). n_D1.6014 (25°).

⑤ Moderate thermal stability.

⑥ J. Chem. Eng. Data **7**, 556 (1962).

SiC$_{36}$H$_{49}$Cl$_3$

① Tri-p-chlorophenyloctadecylsilane

  C$_{18}$H$_{37}$Si(C$_6$H$_4$Cl-p)$_3$

② C$_{18}$H$_{37}$SiCl$_3$ + p-ClC$_6$H$_4$Li $\longrightarrow$ 76.8%

③ (255~262°/0.001). n_D1.5558 (25°). d1.075 (25°).

⑥ JOC **27**, 1023 (1962).

SiC$_{36}$H$_{49}$Cl$_3$

① Tri-m-chlorophenyloctadecylsilane

  C$_{18}$H$_{37}$Si(C$_6$H$_4$Cl-m)$_2$

② m-LiC$_6$H$_4$Cl + C$_{18}$H$_{37}$SiCl$_3$ $\longrightarrow$ 87.4%

③ (250~255°/0.04). n_D1.5595 (25°). d1.085 (25°).

⑥ JOC **27**, 1023 (1962).

SiC$_{36}$H$_{49}$F$_3$

① Tri-(m-fluorophenyl)octadecylsilane

  C$_{18}$H$_{37}$Si(C$_6$H$_4$F-m)$_3$

② m-LiC$_6$H$_4$F + C$_{18}$H$_{37}$SiCl$_3$ $\longrightarrow$

③ Solid. (234~235°/0.08). [38~40°].

⑥ JOC **27**, 1023 (1962).

SiC$_{36}$H$_{60}$

① Diphenyldidodecylsilane

  (C$_6$H$_5$)$_2$Si(C$_{12}$H$_{25}$)$_2$

③ (237~243°/0.035). n_D1.5060 (25°).
   d0.905 (25°/4°).
⑥ J. Chem. Eng. Data **6**, 142 (1961).

SiC₃₆H₇₅Cl

① Tridodecylchlorosilane
   (C₁₂H₂₅)₃SiCl
② Cl₂ + HSi(C₁₂H₂₅)₃ ⟶ 93%
   C₁₂H₂₅SiCl₃ + C₁₂H₂₅MgBr ⟶
③ Liq. (228~238°/0.03). [4~5°]. n_D1.4647
   (20°).
⑤ Intermediate in the preparation of
   (C₁₂H₂₅)₃SiC₅H₅, etc.
⑥ JOC **27**, 616 (1962).

SiC₃₆H₇₅F

① Tridodecylfluorosilane
   (C₁₂H₂₅)₃SiF
② SiF₄ + C₁₂H₂₅MgBr ⟶ 68%
③ (290~295°/0.1). [−45°]. n_D1.4548
   (25°). d0.8605 (25°).
⑥ JOC **27**, 261 (1962).

SiC₃₇H₃₀

① Triphenyltriphenylmethylsilane
   (C₆H₅)₃SiC(C₆H₅)₃
② Ph₃CNa + Ph₃SiBr ⟶ 62%
   Ph₃CNa + Ph₃SiCl ⟶ 60%
③ [334~336°].
④ Ph₃CSiPh₃ —Na-K→ Ph₃CK + Ph₃SiK
   Ph₃SiK —(1) CO₂, (2) H₂O, H⁺→ Ph₃CCOOH
   + Ph₃SiCOOH
⑥ JACS **75**, 4759 (1953).

SiC₃₇H₅₄

① Methyltri(pentamethylphenylmethyl)-
   silane
   CH₃Si[CH₂C₆(CH₃)₅]₃
② MeSiCl₃ + K + Me₅C₆CH₂Cl ⟶
③ Solid. [223~250°].
⑥ Kogyo Kagaku Zasshi **61**, 1527 (1958).

SiC₃₇H₇₈S₃

① Methyltri(dodecylmercapto)silane
   CH₃Si(SC₁₂H₂₅)₃
② C₁₂H₂₅SNa + MeSiCl₃ ⟶ 85%
③ (220~224°/10~4). [33~34°].
⑤ Promotes the dropwise condensation
   of steam against cooled copper
   surfaces when applied in a monomolecular layer.
⑥ Brit. 839352 (1960); CA **55**, 1445
   (1961).

SiC₃₈H₃₂

① 1,1,2-Triphenyl-1-(triphenylsilyl)-
   ethane
   (C₆H₅)₃SiC(C₆H₅)₂CH₂C₆H₅
② Ph₃SiCPh₂Li + PhCH₂Cl ⟶ 25%
③ Solid. [198~200°].
⑥ JOC **25**, 506 (1960).

SiC₃₈H₃₂O

① 1,1,2-Triphenyl-1-triphenylsiloxy-
   ethane
   (C₆H₅)₃SiOC(C₆H₅)₂CH₂C₆H₅
② Ph₃SiOCPh₂K + Ph₂CO then
      Ph₃SiK ⟶
   Ph₃SiOCPh₂K + PhCH₂Cl ⟶
   Ph₃SiCl + PhCH₂CPh₂OH ⟶
③ Solid. [202~203°].
⑥ JACS **82**, 2435, 2439 (1960).

SiC₃₈H₃₄Sn

① 1-Triphenylsilyl-2-triphenylstannyl-
   ethane
   (C₆H₅)₃SiCH₂CH₂Sn(C₆H₅)₃
② Ph₃SiCH=CH₂ + Ph₃SnH ⟶ 54%
③ Solid. [207~208°].
   Sol. in HCONMe₂.
⑥ JACS **82**, 558 (1960).

SiC₃₈H₈₀O

① Ethoxytridodecylsilane

$C_2H_5OSi(C_{12}H_{25})_3$

② $Si(OEt)_4 + C_{12}H_{25}MgX \longrightarrow 11\%$

③ $(210°/11)$. $[15°]$. $n_D1.4575$ $(25°)$.
$d0.9062$ $(25°)$.

⑥ JOC **27**, 261 (1962).

$SiC_{40}H_{30}$

① Hexaphenyl-1-silacyclopentadiene-2,4

② $PhC(Li)=CPh-CPh=C(Li)Ph$
$+ Ph_2SiCl_2 \longrightarrow 1\%$

③ Solid. $[288\sim295°]$.

⑥ Chem. & Ind. 1250 (1959).   JACS **83**, 4406 (1961).

$SiC_{40}H_{34}N_2$

① 2,2′-Diphenyl-5,5′-diethyl-10,10′-spiro
(5,10-dihydrophenazasiline)

② $EtN(C_6H_4Li-o)[4-C_6H_3(C_6H_5)Li-2]$
$+ SiCl_4 \longrightarrow 41\%$

③ Solid. $[235\sim248°]$.

⑤ High temperature resistance.

⑥ JOC **26**, 2013 (1961).

$SiC_{42}H_{32}$

① Tri-*p*-biphenylylphenylsilane
$(p-C_6H_5C_6H_4)_3SiC_6H_5$

② $PhSiCl_3 + p-BrC_6H_4C_6H_5 + Na$
ether
$\longrightarrow 92\%$

③ Solid. $(580°$ decomp.$)$. $[155°$, $174°$ modifications$]$.
Slightly sol. in org. solvents.
IR: JACS **77**, 6227 (1955).

④ Recrystn. from *n*-BuOH
$\longrightarrow$ mp $172.5\sim174°$
Recrystn. from methylcyclohexane
$\longrightarrow$ mp $155.0\sim155.5°$

⑥ JOC **21**, 1307 (1956).

$SiC_{42}H_{32}O_3$

① Phenyltri(*o*-phenoxyphenyl)silane
$C_6H_5Si(C_6H_4OC_6H_5-o)_3$

② $PhOC_6H_4Li-o + PhSiCl_3 \longrightarrow$

③ Solid. $[192\sim193°]$.

⑤ High temperature stability.

⑥ JOC **21**, 1009 (1956).

$SiC_{42}H_{32}O_3$

① Tris(*m*-phenoxyphenyl)phenylsilane
$C_6H_5Si(C_6H_4OC_6H_5-m)_3$

② Synthesis not given.

③ Amorphous. $(272\sim304°/0.015)$.
Flow point 45°.

⑤ Molding material at flow point-only
partial crystn.

⑥ Chem. & Ind. 1091 (1959).

$SiC_{42}H_{32}O_3$

① Phenyltri(*p*-phenoxyphenyl)silane
$C_6H_5Si(C_6H_4OC_6H_5-p)_3$

② $PhSiCl_3 + PhOC_6H_4Li-p \longrightarrow$

③ Solid. $(530\sim533°)$. $[149\sim150°]$.

⑤ High temperature stability.

⑥ JOC **22**, 45 (1957).

$SiC_{42}H_{88}O_3$

① Tris(2-ethylhexoxy)octadecylsilane
$C_{18}H_{37}Si[OCH_2CH(C_2H_5)C_4H_9]_3$

② $C_{18}H_{37}SiCl_3 + BuCHEtCH_2OH \longrightarrow$

③ $(222°/0.03)$. $n_D1.4488$ $(25°)$. $d0.862$ $(25°)$.

⑥ US 2947772 (1960); CA **55**, 1443 (1961).

SiC₄₅H₄₅

① *p, p*-Terphenyltribenzylsilane
p-C₆H₅C₆H₄(p)C₆H₄Si(CH₂C₆H₅)₃

② HSi(CH₂Ph)₃ +
p-PhC₆H₄C₆H₄Li(p) ⟶

③ Solid. (510°). [125~127°].
Sol. in petr. ether.

⑤ Possible high temperature resistance.

⑥ JOC **25**, 1194 (1960).

SiC₄₅H₉₄

① Dodecyltriundecylsilane
C₁₂H₂₅Si(C₁₁H₂₃)₃

② C₁₂H₂₅SiCl₃ + C₁₁H₂₃Li ⟶

③ Liq. (268°/0.06). n_D1.4619 (25°).
d0.8268 (25°/4°).

⑤ High temperature stability.

⑥ JOC **25**, 243 (1960).

SiC₄₆H₉₆

① Didodecyldiundecylsilane
(C₁₂H₂₅)₂Si(C₁₁H₂₃)₂

② (C₁₂H₂₅)₂SiCl₂ + C₁₁H₂₃Li ⟶

③ Liq. (260°/0.04). [−2°]. n_D1.4619
(25°). d0.8266 (25°/4°).

⑤ High temperature stability.

⑥ JOC **25**, 243 (1960).

SiC₄₈H₃₆

① Tetra-p-biphenylylsilane
(C₆H₅C₆H₄)₄Si

② SiCl₄ + p-BrC₆H₄C₆H₅ + Na $\xrightarrow{\text{ether}}$ 90%

③ White needles. (600° decomp.). [283~
283.5°].
Slightly sol. in boiling xylene and
bromobenzene.

⑥ JACS **77**, 6227 (1955).

SiC₄₈H₄₀N₂P₂

① Diphenylbis(triphenylphosphino-
amino)silane
[(C₆H₅)₃PN]₂Si(C₆H₅)₂

② Ph₃P + Ph₃SiN₃ ⟶

③ Solid. [190~191°].

⑥ Angew. **74**, 716 (1962).

SiC₄₈H₅₂O₃

① Dodecyltri(p-phenoxyphenyl)silane
C₁₂H₂₅Si(C₆H₄OC₆H₅-p)₃

② Na + PhOC₆H₄Br-p + C₁₂H₂₅SiCl₃ ⟶
PhOC₆H₄Li-p + C₁₂H₂₅SiCl₃ ⟶

③ Liq. (365~395°/0.3). n_D1.5946 (25°).

⑤ High temperature stability.

⑥ JOC **22**, 45 (1957). US 2914548 (1959);
CA **54**, 7651 (1960).

SiC₄₈H₁₀₀

① Tetra-n-dodecylsilane
Si(C₁₂H₂₅)₄

② SiCl₄ + C₁₂H₂₅MgBr ⟶ 90%

③ Liq. (280°/0.13). [−15°]. n_D1.4630
(25°). d0.8304 (27°/27°).

⑥ JOC **24**, 219 (1959); **25**, 243 (1960).
J. Chem. Eng. Data **6**, 142 (1961).

SiC₄₈H₁₀₀

① Octadecyltrisdecylsilane
C₁₈H₃₇Si(C₁₀H₂₁)₃

② C₁₈H₃₇SiCl₂ + C₁₀H₂₁Li ⟶

③ Liq. (255°/0.06). n_D1.4649 (25°).
d0.8357 (25°/4°).
Viscosity: 689.1 cs (−18°), 0.69
(371°).

⑤ Possible heat stable lubricant.

⑥ JOC **25**, 243 (1960). J. Chem. Eng.
Data **6**, 142 (1961).

SiC₄₈H₁₀₀S₃

① Dodecyltri(dodecamercapto)silane
C₁₂H₂₅Si(SC₁₂H₂₅)₃

② C₁₂H₂₅SNa + C₁₂H₂₅SiCl₃ ⟶

③ Liq. (130~140°/10~3). [12~14°].
n_D1.4825 (20°).

⑤ Satisfactory in promoting the dropwise condensation of steam aga-

inst cooled copper surfaces when
applied in a monomolecular layer
⑥ JCS 1957, 169.   Brit. 839352 (1960);
CA 55, 1445 (1961).

SiC52H48Sn2

① Diphenylbis(2-triphenylstannyl-
ethyl)silane
$(C_6H_5)_2Si[CH_2CH_2Sn(C_6H_5)_3]_2$
② $Ph_2Si(CH=CH_2)_2$
$+ Ph_3SnH \xrightarrow{80°,\ 4.5hrs.,\ in\ vacuo.}$
③ [143~144°].
⑥ JACS 82, 558 (1960).

SiC52H108

① Didodecylditetradecylsilane
$(C_{12}H_{25})_2Si(C_{14}H_{29})_2$
② $(C_{12}H_{25})_2SiCl_2 + C_{14}H_{29}Li \longrightarrow 79\%$
③ (290°/0.05). [12°]. $n_D1.4635$ (25°).
$d0.8309$ (25°/4°).
⑥ JOC 25, 243 (1960).

SiC54H46Ge3

① Tris(triphenylgermyl)silane
$HSi[GeP(C_6H_5)_3]_3$
② $Ph_3GeNa + SiHCl_3 \longrightarrow$
③ Crystalline. [170~171°]. [187~188°]
(two forms).
Sol. in C_6H_6; slightly. sol. in EtOH.
Stable to 110° for long time.
No reaction with HCl in Et_2O.
⑥ JACS 72, 5297 (1959).   Quart. Revs.
18, 116 (1959).

SiC54H111F

① Trioctadecylfluorosilane
$(C_{18}H_{37})_3SiF$
② $SiF_4 + C_{18}H_{37}MgBr \longrightarrow 14\%$
③ (310~330°/3).   [64~66°].   [71~72°]
(two forms).
⑤ Lubricant.
⑥ Brit. 642139 (1950); CA 45, 3864 (1951).
JOC 27, 261 (1962).

SiC54H112

① Tridodecyloctadecylsilane
$C_{18}H_{37}Si(C_{12}H_{25})_3$
② $C_{18}H_{37}SiCl_3 + C_{12}H_{25}Li \longrightarrow 85\%$
③ (296°/0.05). $n_D1.4640$ (25°). $d0.8304$
(25°).
⑤ High temperature stability.
⑥ JOC 25, 243 (1960).

SiC56H56P4

① Tetrakis(2-diphenylphosphoethyl)-
silane
$Si[CH_2CH_2P(C_6H_5)_2]_4$
② $Ph_2PH + Si(CH=CH_2)_4 \longrightarrow 58\%$
③ [208~211°].
⑥ Ger. 1118781 (1959); CA 56, 11622
(1962).

SiC56H116

① Tetratetradecylsilane
$(C_{14}H_{29})_4Si$
② $C_{14}H_{29}MgBr + SiCl_4 \longrightarrow 40\%$
③ (253~255°/0.6). $n_D1.4590(27°)$. $d0.831$
(27°/27°).
⑥ JOC 24, 219 (1959).

SiC60H124

① Didodecyldioctadecylsilane
$(C_{12}H_{25})_2Si(C_{18}H_{37})_2$
② $(C_{12}H_{25})_2SiCl_2 + C_{18}H_{37}Li \longrightarrow 86.5\%$
③ (355°/0.10). [12°]. $n_D1.4648$ (25°).
$d0.8337$ (25°/4°).
⑤ High temperature stability.
⑥ JOC 25, 243 (1960).

SiC60H124

① Octadecyltriquadradecylsilane
$C_{18}H_{37}Si(C_{14}H_{29})_3$
② $C_{18}H_{37}SiCl_3 + C_{14}H_{29}Li \longrightarrow 81\%$
③ (323°/0.10). $n_D1.4648$ (25°). $d0.832$
(25°/4°).
⑤ High temperature stability.
⑥ JOC 25, 243 (1960).

SiC$_{72}$H$_{60}$Ge$_3$Sn

① Triphenylstannyltris(triphenylger-
　　myl)silane
　　[(C$_6$H$_5$)$_3$Ge]$_3$SiSn(C$_6$H$_5$)$_3$

② (Ph$_3$Ge)$_3$SiLi + Ph$_3$SnCl　──→

③ [340~342°].

⑥ Quart. Revs. **13**, 116 (1959).

Si$_2$CH$_2$Cl$_6$

① Hexachlorodisilylmethane
　　Cl$_3$SiCH$_2$SiCl$_3$

② CH$_2$Cl$_2$ + Si $\xrightarrow{\text{Cu-catalyst, 300~400°}}$

　　MeCl + Cl + Si−Cu　──→

　　MeSiCl$_3$ $\xrightarrow{\text{thermal docomp.}}$

③ (185°). n_D1.471 (22°). d1.545 (17°).
　　IR : Optika i Spektroscopiya **5**, 365
　　(1958).

④ Cl$_2$ $\xrightarrow{\text{17 hrs, 208°}}$ CHCl(SiCl$_3$)$_2$
　　+ CCl$_2$(SiCl$_3$)$_2$ + unreacted chloride
　　+ CH$_2$(SiCl$_3$)$_2$ + SO$_2$Cl$_2$ + Bz$_2$O$_2$
　　$\xrightarrow{\text{31 hrs gently reflux}}$ CHCl(SiCl$_3$)$_2$
　　+ CCl$_2$(SiCl$_3$)$_2$ + unreacted chloride

⑥ Ber. **91**, 22 (1958).　Dokl. **97**, 687
　　(1954); CA **49**, 10166 (1955).　J.
　　Inst. Polytech. Osaka City Univ.
　　Sec. No.9, **3**, 65 (1952). Z. anorg.
　　allg. chem. **302**, 60 (1959).

Si$_2$CH$_3$Cl$_5$

① Pentachlorodisilylmethane
　　Cl$_3$SiCH$_2$Si(H)Cl$_2$

② CH$_2$Cl$_2$ + Si−Cu(90/10) $\xrightarrow{\text{350~400°}}$ 3%

　　CHCl$_3$ + Si−Cu $\xrightarrow{\text{300°}}$ small amount

③ (167~168°). d1.464 (27.5°).

④ + LiH $\xrightarrow{\text{in } i\text{-AmOH}}$ CH$_2$(SiH$_3$)$_2$
　　+ BuBr + Mg　──→
　　Bu$_2$Si(H)CH$_2$SiBu$_2$OH
　　+ EtOH $\xrightarrow{\text{60~80°, petr. ether}}$
　　[Si(OEt)$_3$]$_2$CH$_2$

⑥ Can. J. Chem. **30**, 646 (1952).　Ber.
　　91, 22 (1958). Akad. **95**, 805 (1954);
　　CA **49**, 6089 (1955); **51**, 1826 (1957).
　　Dokl. **109**, 332 (1956).

Si$_2$CH$_8$

① Disilylmethane
　　H$_3$SiCH$_2$SiH$_3$

② Cl$_2$HSiCH$_2$SiCl$_3$ $\xrightarrow{\text{LiH + } i\text{-AmOH}}$

　　Cl$_3$SiCH$_2$SiCl$_3$ $\xrightarrow{\text{LiH + Bu}_2\text{O}}$

③ (26°). n_D1.4115 (4°). d0.6979 (4°).

⑥ Dokl. **95**, 805 (1954); CA **49**, 6089
　　(1955).　JACS **74**, 2927 (1952).
　　Can. J. Chem. **30**, 646 (1952).　US
　　2735861.

Si$_2$C$_2$Cl$_6$

① Bis(trichlorosilyl)acetylene
　　Cl$_3$SiC≡CSiCl$_3$

② CCl$_4$ + Si/Cu $\xrightarrow{\text{210°}}$ 10.5%
　　Yield depends reaction temp.,
　　increasing with temp.

③ (173~174°). [23~24°].

④ + (excess) NaOH ──→ HC≡CH
　　+ Na$_4$SiO$_4$
　　+ MeMgBr ──→ Me$_3$SiC≡CSiMe$_3$

⑥ Angew. **70**, 511 (1958). Ber. **92**, 1018,
　　1957 (1959).

Si$_2$C$_2$H$_2$Cl$_6$

① *cis*-Hexachlorodisilyl-1,2-ethylene
　　Cl$_3$SiCH=CHSiCl$_3$-*cis*

② Cl$_3$SiCHClCH$_2$SiCl$_3$

　　+ $\xrightarrow{\text{distn.}}$ 74%

　　Cl$_3$SiCHClCH$_2$SiCl$_3$ + Et$_2$NPh
　　$\xrightarrow{\text{distn.}}$ 56%
　　Cl$_3$SiCHClCH$_2$SiCl$_3$ + AlCl$_3$
　　$\xrightarrow{\text{180°, 740 mmHg}}$ *trans + cis*
　　HSiCl$_3$ + *cis*-ClCH=CHCl ──→ 72%

③ $(187°)$. $[-28°]$. $n_D 1.4939$ $(20°)$. $d 1.58$
  $(25°)$.
  IR: Izv. OKhN **1958**, 510.
⑥ Izv. OKhN **1956**, 1420; **1961**, 1795; CA
  56, 8736 (1962). Dokl. **104**, 865
  (1955).

$Si_2C_2H_2Cl_6$

① *trans*-Hexachlorodisilyl-1,2-ethylene
  Cl_3Si

  $\quad CH=CH$

  $\qquad SiCl_3$

② $Cl_3SiCHClCH_2SiCl_3$

  $+ \,$ [quinoline structure] $\longrightarrow$ 46%

  trans-ClCH=CHCl + $HSiCl_3$
  $\longrightarrow$ 37%

③ $(190\sim191°)$. $[36.1°]$.
  IR: CA **52**, 17093
⑥ Izv. OKhN **1956**, 550, 1420.   US
  2740802.

$Si_2C_2H_4Cl_6$

① Hexachlorodisilylmethylmethane
  $Cl_3SiCH(CH_3)SiCl_3$

② $Si-Cu(90/10) + MeCHCl_2 \xrightarrow{350\sim400°} 8\%$

  $Si-Cu + MeCHClSiCl_3 \xrightarrow{370°} 25\%$

  $CH_2{=}CHSiCl_3 + HSiCl_3$
  $\qquad\qquad + NiCl_2\cdot4C_5H_5N$
  $\xrightarrow[\text{7.5 hrs, 180}\sim\text{185° in sealed tube}]{} 55\%$

③ $(197.5°)$. $n_D 1.4820 (20°)$. $d 1.5059 (20°)$.
④ $+ MeMgBr \longrightarrow Me_3SiCHMeSiMe_3$
⑥ BCSJ **29**, 660 (1956). Dokl. **105**, 496
  (1955); **107**, 99 (1956).   Can. J.
  Chem. **30**, 646 (1952).

$Si_2C_2H_5Cl_5$

① 1,1,1,3,3-Pentachloro-1,3-disilabutane
  $CH_3Si(Cl)_2CH_2SiCl_3$
② $Me_3SiCl + Me_2SiCl_2$
  $\quad + MeSiCl_3 \xrightarrow{\text{pyrolysis}}$
③ $(138.7°)$.

⑥ Z. anorg. allg. Chem. **322**, 46 (1963).

$Si_2C_2H_6Cl_4O$

① 1,3-Dimethyltetrachlorodisiloxane
  $CH_3(Cl_2)SiOSi(CH_3)Cl_2$
② $(Cl_3Si)_2O + MeMgBr \longrightarrow$
③ Straw liq. $(200°)$.
  Sol. in org. solvents. Decomp. with
  water and alcohol.
④ $+ NH_4F \longrightarrow Me_3SiF_3$ (90%) and
  some polymer
⑥ JCS **1954**, 2143; **1947**, 1590.

$Si_2C_2H_{10}$

① 1,2-Disilylethane
  $H_3SiCH_2CH_2SiH_3$
② $(CH_2SiCl_3)_2 \xrightarrow{\text{LiH or LiAlH}_4}$
  $(EtO)_2SiHC_2H_4SiH(OEt)_2 \xrightarrow{\text{NaOEt, 6 hr}}$
③ $(67\sim68.5°)$. $[-14°]$. $n_D 1.4140$ $(20°)$.
  $d 0.6987$ $(20°)$.
⑥ Dokl. **95**, 805 (1954); **107**, 99 (1956).
  JACS **74**, 2927 (1952).

$Si_2C_2H_{10}O$

① 1,3-Dimethyldisiloxane
  $(H_2)CH_3SiOSi(H_2)CH_3$
② $(CH_3)H_2SiI + H_2O \longrightarrow$
③ $(34.5°)$. $[-138°]$. $d 0.748$ $(15.3°)$.
④ $+ BF_3 \longrightarrow MeSiH_2\cdot O\cdot BF_2 + MeSiH_2F$
  $\qquad\qquad\qquad\downarrow$
  $\qquad MeSiH_2F + BF_3 + B_2O_3$
⑥ Z. anorg. allg. Chem. **283**, 74 (1956).
  JCS **1958**, 604.

$Si_2C_3H_7Cl_5$

① 1-Trichlorosilyl-2-methyldichloro-
  silylethane
  $Cl_3SiCH_2CH_2Si(CH_3)Cl_2$
② $H_2PtCl_6 + CH_2{=}CHSiCl_3$
  $\quad + MeSiHCl_2 \longrightarrow$
  $Me_3SiCl_3 \xrightarrow{\text{silent discharge in H}_2}$
③ Liq. $(203°/741)$. $[5°]$. $d 1.3618 (20°/4°)$.
  Sol. in org. solvents. Decomp. in

H₂O.

⑥ Zhur. **33**, 2281 (1963).   Dokl. **100**, 697
(1955) ; CA **50**, 1575 (1956).   Izv.
OKhN **1957**, 818 ; English page 839 ;
CA **52**, 2741 (1958).

Si₂C₃H₈Cl₄

① 2,2,4,4-Tetrachloro-2,4-disilapentane
CH₃Si(Cl)₂CH₂SiCH₃Cl₂

② Me₃SiCl + Me₂SiCl₂

+ MeSiCl₃ $\xrightarrow{\text{pyrolysis}}$

③ (166.3°/750).

⑥ Z. anorg. allg. Chem. **322**, 46 (1963).

Si₂C₄H₁₀Cl₄O

① 1,3-Dimethyl-1,3-dichloro-1,3-
bis(chloromethyl)disiloxane
[CH₃Si(Cl)CH₂Cl]₂O

② HOH + MeSi(Cl)₂CH₂Cl ⟶ 37.9%

③ (66°/1.2). n_D1.4585(20°). d1.2903(20°)

④ + HOH ⟶ [MeSi(OH)CH₂Cl]₂O

⑥ Rocz. Chem. **36**, 1459 (1962) ; CA **59**,
6218 (1963).

Si₂C₄H₁₁Cl₃

① Trimethylsilyltrichlorosilylmethane
(CH₃)₃SiCH₂SiCl₃

② Pyrolysis of Me$_x$SiCl$_{4-x}$ ⟶

③ (173.0°/750). n_D1.4447 (20°).

⑥ Z. anorg. allg. Chem. **322**, 46 (1963).
Kogyo Kagaku Zasshi **60**, 1395
(1957) ; CA **53**, 17, 889 (1959).

Si₂C₄H₁₁Cl₃

① Methyldichlorosilyldimethylchloro-
silylmethane
CH₃Si(Cl)₂CH₂Si(CH₃)₂Cl

② In the silent discharge, from
Me₂SiCl₂ ⟶
Pyrolytic reactions ⟶

③ (159.0°/750). n_D1.4602 (20°). d1.1421
(20°/4°).

④ + MeMgBr ⟶ Me₃SiCH₂SiMe₃

⑥ Izv. OKhN **1960**, 231 ; English page

---

216.   Z. anorg. allg. Chem. **322**, 46
(1963).

Si₂C₄H₁₂Br₂

① 1,2-Dibromotetramethyldisilane
(CH₃)₂Si(Br)Si(CH₃)₂Br

② Na + Me₃SiCl
+ Me₂SiCl₂, then Br₂ ⟶

③ (79~82°/30). [ca. 40°].

④ + H₂O ⟶   Me₂Si—SiMe₂
| |
O   O
| |
Me₂Si—SiMe₂

⑥ Kogyo Kagaku Zasshi **66**, 637 (1963).

Si₂C₄H₁₂Cl₂

① 1,2-Dichlorotetramethyldisilane
(CH₃)₂Si(Cl)Si(CH₃)₂Cl

② Me₂Si(Cl)SiMe₂SiMe₂Cl + SO₂Cl₂
+ (BzO)₂ ⟶
Me₃SiSiMe₃ + NH₄Cl + H₂SO₄ ⟶
Me₃SiSiMe₂SiMe₃ + H₂SO₄
+ NH₄Cl ⟶

③ (49~50°/18). n_D1.4548 (20°). d1.010
(20°).

⑥ Japan 1073 (1959) ; CA **54**, 8634 (1960).
"Studies in Organosilicon Com-
pounds" Vol. 1, Chap. 5 and 7
(1963).   JOC **21**, 1264 (1956).

Si₂C₄H₁₂Cl₂O

① 1,3-Dichlorotetramethyldisiloxane
(CH₃)₂Si(Cl)OSi(CH₃)₂Cl

② Fe₂O₃ + Me₂SiCl₂ ⟶

③ (134~136°).

④ + Me₂SiCl₂ ⟶ Cl-(SiMe₂O)$_x$-
SiMe₂Cl (x 1 through 8)
(with or without FeCl₃)

⑥ Izv. OKhN **1962**, 2133.   Zhur. **32**,
3951 (1962).

Si₂C₄H₁₄

① Disilyltetramethylene
H₃Si(CH₂)₄SiH₃

② $Cl_3Si(CH_2)_4SiCl_3 \xrightarrow{\text{LiH}}$

③ $(0°/8)$.

⑥ JACS **74**, 2927 (1952). Can. J. Chem. **30**, 646 (1952).

$Si_2C_4H_{14}O$

① 1,1,3,3-Tetramethyldisiloxane
$(CH_3)_2Si(H)OSi(H)(CH_3)_2$

② $HOH + Et_2O + Me_2SiHCl \longrightarrow$
$LiAlH_4 + Me_2SiCl-(OSiMe_2)_xCl$
$\longrightarrow 56\%$
$Me_2SiHI + H_2O \longrightarrow$

③ $(70\sim71°)$. $n_D 1.3700$ $(20°)$. $d 0.7572$ $(20°)$.

④ $+ H_2SO_4 + (Me_2SiO)_4 \longrightarrow$
$Me_2Si(H)-(OSiMe_2)_x-OSiHMe_2$
$+ H_2PtCl_6 + C_nH_{2n} \longrightarrow$ polymers
$+ BF_3 \longrightarrow Me_2SiHF$
$+ BCl_3 \longrightarrow Me_2SiHCl$

⑥ Dokl. **128**, 960 (1959). Ger. 1085875 (1960); CA **55**, 27057 (1961). Ger. 1140348 (1962); CA **58**, 12600 (1963). JCS **1958**, 604.

$Si_2C_4H_{14}S$

① 1,1,3,3-Tetramethyldisilthiane
$[(CH_3)_2SiH_2]S$

② $2Me_2SiHI + HgS \longrightarrow 70\%$

③ Liq. $(145\pm1°$, extrapolated). $[-146°]$. Sol. in org. solvents.

④ $+ TiCl_4 \xrightarrow{0°} Me_2SiCl_2$
$+ PdCl_2 \longrightarrow H_2S + Me_2SiCl_2$

⑥ JCS **1958**, 609. Z. anorg. allg. Chem. **202**, 1 (1931).

$Si_2C_5H_{13}ClF_2$

① Bis(dimethylfluorosilyl)chloro-
methane
$(CH_3)_2Si(F)CHClSi(CH_3)_2F$

② $H_2SO_4 + NH_4HF_2 +$
$Me_3SiCHClSiMe_3 \longrightarrow$

③ $(53°/21)$. $n_D 1.4105$ $(20°)$. $d 1.0700$ $(20°/4°)$.

⑥ BCSJ **37**, 871 (1964).

$Si_2C_5H_{14}Cl_2$

① Bis(dimethylchlorosilyl)methane
$(CH_3)_2Si(Cl)CH_2Si(CH_3)_2Cl$

② $PhCl + Me_3SiSi(Me)_2Cl \xrightarrow{550°}$
$Me_2SiCl_2 + Me_2Si(Cl)CH_2MgCl \longrightarrow$
Pyrolytic reactions $\longrightarrow$

③ $(58°/10)$. $n_D 1.4483$ $(20°)$. $d 1.0139$ $(20°/4°)$.

⑥ Makromol. Chem. **52**, 174 (1962). Zhur. **32**, 369 (1962). Z. anorg. allg. Chem. **322**, 46 (1963).

$Si_2C_5H_{14}Cl_2$

① 1,1,1,3-Tetramethyldichlorodisilyl-
methane
$(CH_3)_3SiCH_2Si(CH_3)Cl_2$

② $Me_3SiCH_2MgCl + MeSiCl_3 \longrightarrow$
$Me_3SiCH_2Li + MeSiCl_3 \longrightarrow 25\%$

③ $(163°/742)$. $n_D 1.4400$ $(25°)$. $d 0.9942$ $(25°)$.

⑥ JOC **20**, 250 (1955). JACS **76**, 1619 (1954). US 2507520.

$Si_2C_5H_{14}Cl_2$

① 1-Chloro-2-chloromethyltetramethyl-
disilane
$(CH_3)_2Si(Cl)Si(CH_3)_2CH_2Cl$

② $Me_3SiSiMe_2Cl + SO_2Cl_2 + (BzO)_2$
$\longrightarrow 48\%$

③ $(65\sim66°/10)$. $[8\sim9°]$. $n_D 1.4745$ $(20°)$. $d 1.0213$ $(20°/4°)$.

⑥ "Studies in Organosilicon Compounds", Vol. 1, Chap. 7 (1963).

$Si_2C_5H_{14}F_2$

① Bis(dimethylfluorosilyl)methane
$(CH_3)_2Si(F)CH_2Si(CH_3)_2F$

② $H_2SO_4 + NH_4HF_2$
$+ Me_3SiCH_2SiMe_3 \longrightarrow$

③ $(115°)$. $n_D 1.3810$ $(20°)$. $d 0.9203$ $(20°/4°)$.

⑥ BCSJ **37**, 871 (1964).

Si₂C₅H₁₅Cl

① Pentamethylchlorodisilane
   $(CH_3)_3SiSi(CH_3)_2Cl$

② $H_2SO_4 + NH_4Cl + Me_3SiSiMe_3 \longrightarrow$

③ $(136 \sim 137°)$. $n_D 1.4336$ $(20°)$. $d 0.868$
   $(20°)$.

④ $+ SO_2Cl_2 + (BzO)_2 \longrightarrow Me_3SiCl$
   $+ Me_2Si(Cl)Si(Me)_2CH_2Cl$
   $+ (Me_2SiOSiMe_2SiMe_3)_2$
   $+ HOH \longrightarrow (Me_3SiSiMe_2)_2O$
   $+ AgCN \longrightarrow Me_3SiSi(Me)_2CN$

⑥ JCS **1962**, 548.   Japan 1073 (1959);
   CA **54**, 8634 (1960).   JOC **21**, 1264
   (1964).

Si₂C₅H₁₅F

① Pentamethylfluorodisilane
   $(CH_3)_3SiSi(CH_3)_2F$

② $NH_4F + Me_3SiSiMe_3 \longrightarrow$
   $BF_3 + (Me_3SiSiMe_2)_2O \longrightarrow$
   $BF_3 + (Me_3SiSiMe_2)_2NH \longrightarrow$

③ $(100.0 \sim 101.5°)$. $n_D 1.4031 (20°)$. $d 0.808$
   $(20°)$.

⑥ Japan 1073 (1959); CA **54**, 8634 (1960).
   JCS **1963**, 1091.

Si₂C₅H₁₆

① 1,1,3,3-Tetramethyldisilylmethane
   $[(CH_3)_2SiH]_2CH_2$

② $CH_2(SiHCl_2)_2 + MeMgI \longrightarrow 82.5\%$

③ $(103°)$. $n_D 1.4140 (20°)$. $d 0.7373 (20°)$.

⑥ Dokl. **109**, 332 (1956); CA **51**, 1826
   Makromol. Chem. **52**, 199 (1962).

Si₂C₆H₄Cl₆

① *p*-Hexachlorodisilylbenzene
   $Cl_3SiC_6H_4SiCl_3$

② $Cl_3SiSiCl_3 + C_6H_6 \xrightarrow{>200°, \; AlCl_3}$
   $HSiCl_3 + p\text{-}C_6H_4Cl_2 \longrightarrow$

③ Yellow crystals. $(168°/30)$. $[48°]$.
   Sol. in org. solvents. Decomp. with

water.

⑥ US 2626266. Brit. 682835; CA **47**, 3875
   (1953).   Brit. 635645; CA **44**, 6882
   (1950).

Si₂C₆H₁₂N₂O₃

① 1,3-Diisocyanatotetramethyldisilo-
   xane
   $(CH_3)_2Si(NCO)OSi(CH_3)_2NCO$

② $Me_2Si(Cl)OSiMe_2Cl + AgNCO$ or
   $Pb(NCO)_2 \longrightarrow$

③ $(91°/30)$. $n_D 1.4199$ $(20°)$. $d 1.033$
   $(20°)$.
   IR: 3003, 2941, 2381, 2273, 2000, 1445,
   1266, $1042 \sim 1111$ cm⁻¹.

⑥ Kogyo Kagaku Zasshi, **61**, 214
   (1958).   CA **54**, 5434 (1960).   Mitsubishi Denki, Laboratory Reports,
   4, 139 (1963).

Si₂C₆H₁₄O₂

① Bis(dimethylhydroxysilyl)acetylene
   $(CH_3)_2Si(OH)C \equiv CSi(CH_3)_2OH$

② $(Me_2SiO)_x + BrMgC \equiv CMgBr \longrightarrow$

③ $(119 \sim 120°)$.

⑥ Zhur. **32**, 320 (1962).   Izv. OKhN.
   1963, 97.

Si₂C₆H₁₅NO

① Pentamethylisocyanodisilane
   $(CH_3)_3SiSi(CH_3)_2NCO$

② $Me_3SiSiMe_2Cl + AgOCN \longrightarrow$

③ $(159.4 \sim 160.0°)$. $n_D 1.4337$ $(30°)$.
   $d 0.8537 (30°/4°)$.

⑥ JCS **1963**, 1091.

Si₂C₆H₁₆

① 1,1,3,3-Tetramethyl-1,3-disilacyclo-
   butane

$$(CH_3)_2Si \overset{\displaystyle CH_2}{\underset{\displaystyle CH_2}{\Big<\quad\Big>}} Si(CH_3)_2$$

② $Mg + Me_2Si(F)CH_2Si(Me)_2CH_2Cl \longrightarrow$
   $Mg + Me_2Si(Cl)CH_2Br \longrightarrow$

$Mg + Me_2Si(Cl)CH_2Si(Me)_2CH_2Cl \longrightarrow$
③ (120.6°). $n_D1.4380$ (27°). $d0.7985$(20°).
④ $+ AgNO_3 \longrightarrow$ Ag mirror
   $+$ heat(300°) $\longrightarrow$ viscous oil
   $+ HBr \longrightarrow Me_3SiCH_2SiMe_2Br$
⑥ JOC **23**, 1392 (1958). Ber **95**, 3030
   (1962). Makromol. Chem. **52**, 174
   (1962). US 2850514 (1958) ; CA **53**,
   4166 (1959).

$Si_2C_6H_{16}Cl_2$
① 1,2-Bis(dimethylchlorosilyl)ethane
   $(CH_3)_2Si(Cl)CH_2CH_2Si(CH_3)_2Cl$
② $Me_2SiHCl + CH_2{=}CHSiMe_2Cl$
   $+ H_2PtCl_6 \longrightarrow$
   $(Me_2SiClCH_2CH_2SiMe_2)_2O$
   $+ AlCl_3 \longrightarrow$
③ (198°/734). [36.4°].

④ $+ HOH \longrightarrow$ Me₂Si, SiMe₂ (cyclic O-bridged ring with CH₂–CH₂)

⑥ US 3041362 (1962) ; CA **58**, 1558(1963).
   Brit. 840402(1960) ; CA **55**, 381(1961).
   Izv. OKhN **1961**, 281; English page
   257.   JACS **82**, 1883 (1960).

$Si_2C_6H_{16}Cl_2$
① 1,1-Bis(dimethylchlorosilyl)ethane
   $CH_3CH[Si(CH_3)_2Cl]_2$
② $AlCl_3 + Me_3SiSi(Me)_2CHCl_2 \longrightarrow 68\%$
③ (77~78°/14). $n_D1.4607$ (20°). $d1.0390$
   (20°/4°).
⑥ JOM 1, 411 (1964).

$Si_2C_6H_{16}Cl_2$
① 2,4,4-Trimethyl-2,3-dichloro-2,4-
   disilapentane
   $(CH_3)_3SiCHClSi(CH_3)_2Cl$
② $AlCl_3 + Me_3SiSi(Me)_2CHCl_2 \longrightarrow$
③ (76°/12). $n_D1.4595$ (20°). $d1.0124$
   (20°/4°).
④ $+ MeMgBr \longrightarrow Me_3SiCHClSiMe_3$
⑥ JOM 1, 411 (1964).

$Si_2C_6H_{16}Cl_2$
① Pentamethyldichloromethyldisilane
   $(CH_3)_3SiSi(CH_3)_2CHCl_2$
② $(BzO)_2 + SO_2Cl_2 + Me_3SiSiMe_3 \longrightarrow$
③ (72°/10). [23~24°]. $n_D1.4740$ (30°).
   $d1.0004$ (30°/4°).
⑥ JOM 1, 411 (1964).

$Si_2C_6H_{16}Cl_2S_2$
① Dimethylchlorosilylmethyl disulfide
   $[(CH_3)_2Si(Cl)CH_2S]_2$
② $SO_2Cl_2 + Me_2Si(Cl)CH_2SH \longrightarrow$
③ (140°/1).
⑥ Angew. **74**, 902 (1962).

$Si_2C_6H_{16}F_2$
① 1,2-Bis(dimethylfluorosilyl)ethane
   $(CH_3)_2Si(F)CH_2CH_2Si(CH_3)_2F$
② $H_2SO_4 + NH_4HF_2$
   $+ Me_3SiCH_2CH_2SiMe_3 \longrightarrow$
③ (136~137°). $n_D1.3870$ (20°). $d0.9193$
   (20°/4°).
⑥ BCSJ **37**, 871 (1964).

$Si_2C_6H_{17}Br$
① Dimethyl(trimethylsilylmethyl)bromo-
   silane
   $(CH_3)_3SiCH_2Si(CH_3)_2Br$
② $HBr + Me_2Si$ (cyclic CH₂–CH₂ ring) $SiMe_2 \longrightarrow$
   $Br_2 + Me_3SiCH_2SiHMe_2 \longrightarrow$
③ (165~167°). $n_D1.4547$ (20°). $d1.0840$
   (20°).
⑥ Dokl. **109**, 787 (1956) ; English page
   477. Ber. **95**, 3030 (1962).

$Si_2C_6H_{17}Br_2N$
① 1,3-Bis(bromomethyl)tetramethyl-
   disilazane
   $(CH_3)_2Si(CH_2Br)NHSi(CH_3)_2CH_2Br$
② $NH_3 + Me_2Si(Cl)CH_2Br \longrightarrow$
③ [75~80°].

④ Cyclic compounds with $MeNH_2$,
   $PrNH_2$, $CH_2=CHCH_2NH_2$
⑥ Ber. **96**, 965 (1963).

$Si_2C_6H_{17}Cl$

① Pentamethylchloromethyldisilane
   $(CH_3)_3SiSi(CH_3)_2CH_2Cl$
② $(BzO)_2 + SO_2Cl_2 + Me_3SiSiMe_3 \longrightarrow$
   $Me_nSi_2Cl_{6-n} + Cl_2$
   $\xrightarrow{UV} Me_{n-1}(CH_2Cl)Si_2Cl_{6-n}$
③ $(52°/10)$. $[22.0\sim23.5°]$. $n_D1.4582(20°)$.
   $d0.8869$ $(20°/4°)$.
④ $+ Mg + CH_2=CHCH_2Cl$
   $\longrightarrow Me_3SiSiMe_2CH_2CH_2CH=CH_2$
   $+ AlCl_3 \longrightarrow Me_3SiCH_2SiMe_2Cl$
   $+ NaOEt \longrightarrow Me_3SiCH_2SiMe_2OEt$
   $+ I_2 \longrightarrow Me_3SiSiMe_2CH_2I$
   $+ Mg + HgCl_2$
   $\longrightarrow Me_3SiSiMe_2CH_2MgCl$
⑥ JOM **1**, 411 (1964).   Izv. OKhN **1963**,
   660.

$Si_2C_6H_{17}ClHg$

① 1-Chloromercuriomethylpentamethyl-
   disilane
   $(CH_3)_3SiSi(CH_3)_2CH_2HgCl$
② $Me_3SiSiMe_2CH_2MgCl + HgCl_2 \longrightarrow$
③ $[69\sim70°]$.
⑥ JOM **1**, 411 (1964).

$Si_2C_6H_{17}I$

① Pentamethyliodomethyldisilane
   $(CH_3)_3SiSi(CH_3)_2CH_2I$
② $NaI + Me_3SiSiMe_2CH_2Cl \longrightarrow$
③ $(96\sim97°/23)$. $n_D1.5110$ $(20°)$. $d1.2675$
   $(20°/4°)$.
④ $+ Mg \longrightarrow Me_3SiSiMe_2CH_2MgI$
⑥ JOM **1**, 411 (1964).

$Si_2C_6H_{17}NO$

① Pentamethylcyanomethyldisiloxane
   $(CH_3)_3SiOSi(CH_3)_2CH_2CN$
② $(CN)_2 + Me_3SiOSiMe_2CH_2MgCl$
   $\longrightarrow 38\%$

③ $(96°/28)$. $n_D1.4115$ $(20°)$. $d0.875$ $(20°)$.
④ $+ H_2SO_4 + Me_3SiOSiMe_3 \longrightarrow$
   $Me_3Si(CH_2CN)OSiMe_2CH_2CN$
⑥ JACS **77**, 3224 (1955).   Mem. Fac.
   Eng. Osaka City Univ. **3**, 195
   (1961); CA **58**, 3455 (1963).

$Si_2C_6H_{18}$

① Hexamethyldisilane
   $(CH_3)_3SiSi(CH_3)_3$
② $Na + Me_3SiCl \longrightarrow$
   $Na + AlCl_3 + Me_3SiCl \longrightarrow 79\%$
   (with K or NaK, 85%)
③ $(111\sim113°)$. $[13.0\sim13.5°]$. $n_D1.4230$
   $(20°)$. $d0.7266$ $(20°/4°)$.
⑥ JOM **1**, 153 (1963).   Coll. Czech. Chem.
   Comm. **28**, 1384 (1963).   Zhur. **32**,
   369 (1962).   Ger. 1127897; CA **57**,
   8618 (1962).

$Si_2C_6H_{18}NNaO_4$

① 1,3-Dimethyltetramethoxy-2-sodio-
   disilazane
   $CH_3Si(OCH_3)_2N(Na)Si(OCH_3)_2CH_3$
② $NaNH_2 +$
   $MeSi(OMe)_2NHSi(OMe)_2Me \longrightarrow$
③ $[171\sim172°]$.
④ $+ MeSiCl_3$
   $\longrightarrow MeSi(Cl)_2N[Si(OMe)_2Me]_2$
⑥ Angew. **75**, 95 (1963).

$Si_2C_6H_{18}N_2$

① 2,2,6,6-Tetramethyl-2,6-disila-1,4-
   dinitracyclohexane
   $$HN\underset{Si(CH_3)_2CH_2}{\overset{Si(CH_3)_2CH_2}{<\qquad>}}NH$$
② $Me_2Si(Cl)CH_2Br + NH_3 \longrightarrow 92\%$
③ $[270°$ decomp.$]$.
⑥ Ber. **96**, 965 (1963).

$Si_2C_6H_{18}O$

① Hexamethyldisiloxane
   $(CH_3)_3SiOSi(CH_3)_3$
② $SO_2(OSiMe_3)_2 + MeOH \longrightarrow$

Ph₃SiH + Me₃SiOSO₂Cl ⟶

Mg + Me₂Si(Cl)CH₂Br

⟶ by-product

SO₂(OSiMe₃)₃ + Et₃SiH ⟶

③ (100.5°). [−69.8°]. n_D1.3772 (20°).
d0.7632 (20°/4°).

④ + H₂SO₄ ⟶ SO₂(OSiMe₃)₂ (78%)

⑥ Zhur. **32**, 2302 (1962); English page
2270. Inorg. Chem. **2**, 825 (1963).
Ber. **95**, 3030 (1962). Bull. soc.
chim. France 512 (1963).

Si₂C₆H₁₈O₂

① Hexamethyldisilyl peroxide
(CH₃)₃SiOOSi(CH₃)₃

② 2(CH₃)₃SiCl + H₂O₂ + 2C₅H₅N ⟶
Me₃SiCl + Na₂O₂ ⟶

③ (38°/30). n_D1.3969 (20°). d0.842 (20°).
Decomp. at 135 °C

⑤ This peroxide initiates the polymerization of vinyl monomers.

⑥ Makromol. Chem. **21**, 113 (1956).
Chem. & Ind. **1957**, 1294.

Si₂C₆H₁₈Cl₂O₂Ti

① Bis(trimethylsiloxy)dichlorotitane
[(CH₃)₃SiO]₂TiCl₂

② Ti(OSi(CH₃)₃]₄ + TiCl₄ ⟶ 80.8%

③ Colorless liq. (72~73°/3).
Sol. in org. solvents. Decomp. with
water.
Crystals appeared after several days
standing.

⑥ Izv. OKhN **1958**, 644; CA **52**, 19910
(1958).

Si₂C₆H₁₈O₄S

① Bis(trimethylsilyl) sulfate
[(CH₃)₃SiO]₂SO₂

② ClSO₂OH + Me₃SiOSiMe₃ ⟶
H₂SO₄ + Me₃SiOSiMe₃ ⟶
H₂SO₄ + Me₃SiCl ⟶
H₂SO₄ + Me₃SiPh ⟶
Me₃SiOSO₂Cl + Et₃SiH ⟶

Me₃SiOSiMe₃ + MeOSO₂Cl ⟶

Me₃GeO−SO₂−OSiMe₃ $\xrightarrow{heat}$

③ (118°/18). [56~58°].

④ + HCl→Me₃SiCl + Me₃SiOSO₂OH
+ MeOH ⟶ Me₃SiOSiMe₃
+ Ph₃SiOH ⟶ SO₂(OSiPh₃)₂
+ Et₃SiH ⟶ Me₃SiOSiMe₃
+ Me₃SiOSiEt₃
+ PCl₅ ⟶ Me₃SiOSO₂Cl
+ Me₃SiCl

⑥ Bull. soc. chim. France 512 (1963).
Ber. **94**, 2137, 2446 (1961). Ger.
1106324; CA **56**, 2472 (1962).

Si₂C₆H₁₈O₅

① 1,3-Dimethyltetramethoxydisiloxane
CH₃Si(OCH₃)₂OSi(OCH₃)₂CH₃

② MeOH + MeSi(Cl)₂OSi(Cl)₂Me ⟶

③ (86.2~87.0°/30). n_D1.4166 (25°).
d0.9875 (25°/4°).

⑥ JACS **84**, 4730 (1962).

Si₂C₆H₁₈Se

① Bis(trimethylsilyl) selenide
(CH₃)₃SiSeSi(CH₃)₃

② Me₃SiCl + Na₂Se ⟶ 85%

③ (31°/2).

⑥ Angew. **73**, 64 (1961). Z. anorg. allg.
Chem. **321**, 270 (1963).

Si₂C₆H₁₉N

① Hexamethyldisilylamine
(CH₃)₃SiNHSi(CH₃)₃

② Me₃SiCl + NH₃ $\xrightarrow{petr. ether}$ 71.4%

Me₃SiCl + NH₄Cl $\xrightarrow{H₂O}$ 80%

④ + ROH + H⁺ ⟶ ROSiMe₃ + NH₃
+ RNH₂ + H⁺ ⟶ Me₃SiNHR + NH₃
+ SO₂(NH₂)₂ ⟶ (Me₃SiNH)₂SO₂
+ Na + PhCH=CH₂ + Me₃SiCl ⟶
(Me₃Si)₃N
+ TiCl₄ (or AlCl₃) ⟶ Me₃SiCl
+ Al + I₂ + C₆H₆ ⟶ Me₃SiI
+ AlBr₃ ⟶ Me₃SiBr

+ BCl$_3$ $\longrightarrow$ Me$_3$SiNHBCl$_2$

⑥ JOC **23**, 50 (1958). Angew. **74**, 468 (1962). Zhur. **31**, 3410 (1961); CA **57**, 852 (1963). Izv. OKhN **1962**, 1852; CA **58**, 9115 (1964).

Si$_2$C$_7$H$_{16}$O

① Trimethylsilyldimethylhydroxysilyl-acetylene
(CH$_3$)$_3$SiC≡CSi(CH$_3$)$_2$OH

③ (90°/10 sublimes). [112°].

⑥ Izv. OKhN **1963**, 97.

Si$_2$C$_7$H$_{18}$F$_2$

① 1,3-Bis(dimethylfluorosilyl)propane
(CH$_3$)$_2$Si(F)CH$_2$CH$_2$CH$_2$Si(CH$_3$)$_2$F

② Me$_2$Si(OMe)CH$_2$CH$_2$CH$_2$SiMe$_2$OMe
+ HF $\longrightarrow$
H$_2$SO$_4$ + NH$_4$HF$_2$
+ Me$_3$SiCH$_2$CH$_2$CH$_2$SiMe$_3$ $\longrightarrow$

③ (156°). d0.9137 (20°/4°).

④ + NaOH $\longrightarrow$ CH$_2$⟨$\begin{smallmatrix}\text{CH}_2\text{SiMe}_2\\ \\ \text{CH}_2\text{SiMe}_2\end{smallmatrix}$⟩O

⑥ BCSJ **37**, 871 (1964), J. Inst. Polytech. Osaka City Univ. **3** (Ser. C) 65 (1952).

Si$_2$C$_7$H$_{18}$F$_2$

① 2,3,3,4-Tetramethyl-2,4-disila-2,4-difluoropentane
(CH$_3$)$_2$Si(F)C(CH$_3$)$_2$Si(CH$_3$)$_2$F

② H$_2$SO$_4$ + NH$_4$HF$_2$ +
Me$_3$SiCMe$_2$SiMe$_3$ $\longrightarrow$

③ (57°/33). n_D1.4080 (20°). d0.9365 (20°).

④ + MeMgBr $\longrightarrow$ Me$_3$SiCMe$_2$SiMe$_3$

⑥ JOM **2**, 136 (1964).

Si$_2$C$_7$H$_{18}$O

① Vinylpentamethyldisiloxane
(CH$_3$)$_3$SiOSi(CH$_3$)$_2$CH=CH$_2$

② Me$_3$SiOSiHMe$_2$ + C$_2$H$_2$ $\longrightarrow$
Me$_3$SiOLi + Me$_2$Si(Cl)CH=CH$_2$
$\longrightarrow$ 80%

③ (122°). n_D1.3929 (25°).

⑥ US 2970150; CA **55**, 16423 (1961). Inorg. Chem. **2**, 418 (1963).

Si$_2$C$_7$H$_{18}$O$_2$

① Trimethylsilyldimethylsilylacetic acid
(CH$_3$)$_3$SiSi(CH$_3$)$_2$CH$_2$COOH

② Mg + Me$_3$SiSiMe$_2$Cl, then CO$_2$ and HCl $\longrightarrow$ 18%

③ [57°].

⑥ Izv. OKhN **1963**, 660.

Si$_2$C$_7$H$_{19}$Cl

① 1-Trimethylsilyl-1-dimethylchloro-silylethane
(CH$_3$)$_3$SiCH(CH$_3$)Si(CH$_3$)$_2$Cl

② AlCl$_3$ + Me$_3$SiCHClSiMe$_3$ $\xrightarrow{100\sim140°}$ 60%

③ (62°/12.5). n_D1.4462 (20°). d0.8930 (20°/4°).

⑥ JOM **1**, 411 (1964).

Si$_2$C$_7$H$_{19}$Cl

① Bis(trimethylsilyl)chloromethane
(CH$_3$)$_3$SiCHClSi(CH$_3$)$_3$

② MeMgBr + Me$_3$SiCHClSiMe$_2$Cl
$\longrightarrow$ 84%

③ (71°/21). n_D1.4491(20°). d0.9041 (20°).

④ + H$_2$SO$_4$ + NH$_4$HF$_2$
$\longrightarrow$ Me$_2$Si(F)CH$_2$Cl + Me$_3$SiF
+ Me$_2$Si(F)CHClSiMe$_2$F
+ AlCl$_3$ $\xrightarrow{100\sim140°}$
Me$_3$SiCHMeSiMe$_2$Cl

⑥ "Studies in Organosilicon Compounds" Vol. 1, Chap. 4, 12 (1963).

Si$_2$C$_7$H$_{19}$NO

① 1,3,3,5,5-Pentamethyl-3,5-disila-1-nitra-4-oxacyclohexane

$$\begin{array}{c}\text{CH}_3\\ |\\ \text{CH}_3-\text{Si}-\text{CH}_2\\ \text{O}⟨\qquad\qquad⟩\text{N}-\text{CH}_3\\ \text{CH}_3-\text{Si}-\text{CH}_2\\ |\\ \text{CH}_3\end{array}$$

② $Me_2Si(CH_2Br)OSiMe_2CH_2Br + MeNH_2$
   $\longrightarrow$ 86%
③ $(40\sim41°/10)$. $n_D 1.4295$ $(20°)$.
⑥ Ber. **96**, 965 (1963).

$Si_2C_7H_{20}$

① Bis(trimethylsilyl)methane
   $(CH_3)_3SiCH_2Si(CH_3)_3$
② MeMgBr
   + methylchlorosilylmethanes $\longrightarrow$
   $Mg + Me_3SiCl + CHBr_3 \xrightarrow{\text{THF}}$ 18.5%
③ $(132\sim134°)$. $n_D 1.4180$ $(20°)$. $d 0.7522$
   $(20°/4°)$.
④ $+ H_2SO_4 + NH_4HF_2 \longrightarrow Me_3SiF$
   $+ Me_2Si(F)CH_2SiMe_2F$
⑥ "Studies in Organosilicon Compounds" Vol. 1, Chap. 12(1963). Izv.
   OKhN. **1960**, 231; English page 216.
   Z. anorg. allg. Chem. **322** 46 (1963).
   JACS **85**, 2243 (1963).

$Si_2C_7H_{20}N_2$

① 3,3,4,5,5-Pentamethyl-1,4-dinitra-
   3,5-disilacyclohexane
   $$CH_3N\underset{Si(CH_3)_2CH_2}{\overset{Si(CH_3)_2CH_2}{\big<\ \big>}}NH$$
② $MeNH_2 + Me_2Si(CH_2Br)NHSi$-
   $Me_2CH_2Br \longrightarrow$
③ $(66°/15)$. $n_D 1.4503$ $(20°)$.
⑥ Ber. **96**, 965 (1963).

$Si_2C_7H_{20}O$

① Pentamethylethoxydisilane
   $(CH_3)_3SiSi(CH_3)_2OEt$
② $EtONa + Me_3SiSiMe_2CH_2Cl \longrightarrow$
   $MeSi(OEt)_2SiMe_2OEt$
   $+ MeMgBr \longrightarrow$
③ $(141°)$. $n_D 1.4250$ $(20°)$. $d 0.7993$
   $(20°/4°)$.
④ $+ AcCl \longrightarrow Me_3SiSiMe_2Cl$
   $+ HF \longrightarrow Me_3SiSiMe_2F$
⑥ Japan 7223; CA **50**, 10125 (1956).

JOC **21**, 1264 (1956).   US 2881197
(1959); CA **53**, 15979 (1959).   JOM
1, 411 (1964).

$Si_2C_7H_{20}O_6$

① Hexamethoxydisilylmethane
   $(CH_3O)_3SiCH_2Si(OCH_3)_3$
② $Cl_3SiCH_2SiCl_3 + CH_3OH \longrightarrow$ 87%
③ Colorless liq. $(125°/70)$.
   Sol. in org. solvents.
⑥ J. Inst. Polytech. Osaka City Univ.
   Ser. C **3**, 65 (1952).

$Si_2C_8H_8Cl_6$

① 1-Phenyl-2-bis(trichlorosilyl)ethane
   $C_6H_5CH_2CH(SiCl_3)_2$
② $H_2PtCl_6 + PhC{\equiv}CH + SiHCl_3$
   $\longrightarrow$ 74%
③ $(162°/8)$. $n_D 1.5288$ $(20°)$. $d 1.4187$
   $(20°)$.
⑥ CA **59**, 11550 (1963).

$Si_2C_8H_{10}Cl_4$

① o-Bis(methyldichlorosilyl)benzene
   o-$C_6H_4[Si(Cl)_2CH_3]_2$
② $MeSi(Cl)_2C_6H_4Cl$-$m + MeSiHCl_2 \longrightarrow$
③ $(105.3°/0.1)$. $[59\sim60°]$.
⑥ Zhur. **32**, 557 (1962).

$Si_2C_8H_{10}Cl_4$

① m-Bis(dichloromethylsilyl)benzene
   m-$C_6H_4[Si(Cl)_2CH_3]_2$
② m-$ClC_6H_4Si(Cl)_2Me + MeSiHCl_2 \xrightarrow{640°}$
   $MeSi(Cl)_2C_6H_4Cl$-$m + MeSiHCl_2 \longrightarrow$
③ $(95\sim96°/0.1)$. $n_D 1.5278$ $(20°)$. $d 1.2998$
   $(20°)$.
⑥ USSR 134688 (1961); CA **55**, 15918
   (1961).   Zhur. **32**, 557 (1962).

$Si_2C_8H_{10}Cl_4$

① p-Bis(methyldichlorosilyl)benzene
   p-$C_6H_4[Si(Cl)_2CH_3]_2$
② p-$C_6H_4Cl_2 + CH_3SiHCl_2 \xrightarrow{395°\sim410°}$

MeSi(Cl)₂C₆H₄Cl-*p* + MeSiHCl₂ $\xrightarrow{640°}$

③ Solid. (101~103°/1~2). [57~58°].

⑥ Zhur. **32**, 557 (1962).   USSR 134688 ;
   CA **55**, 15918 (1961).   US 2511820
   (1950) ;   CA **55**, 1490 (1961).

Si₂C₈H₁₄Cl₆

① 1,5-Bis(trichlorosilyl)cyclooctane
   C₈H₁₄(SiCl₃)₂(1,5)

② SiHCl₃ + C₈H₁₂(1,5) $\xrightarrow{\text{toluene, 225°, 12 hrs}}$

③ (115~127°/0.35~0.45).

⑥ JCS **1963**, 2831.

Si₂C₈H₁₈

① Bis(trimethylsilyl)acetylene
   (CH₃)₃SiC≡CSi(CH₃)₃

② CBr₂=CBr₂ + THF + Mg
   + Me₃SiCl $\longrightarrow$
   Cl₃SiCH=CHSiCl₃ + MeMgCl
   $\longrightarrow$ (by-product)

③ (133~135°). [21.8~22.0°]. n_D1.4255
   (25°). d1.7601 (25°/4°).

⑥ JACS **85**, 2243 (1963).   Izv. OKhN,
   1961, 1795 ; English page 1673.

Si₂C₈H₁₈N₄

① Bis(trimethylsilyl)azidoamine
   [(CH₃)₃Si]₂NN₃

② (Me₃Si)₂NCl + NaN₃ $\longrightarrow$

③ (40~42°/11).

⑥ Angew. **74**, 942 (1962).

Si₂C₈H₁₈O

① 1,3-Divinyltetramethyldisiloxane
   (CH₂=CH)(CH₃)₂SiOSi(CH₃)₂-
   (CH=CH₂)

② (CH₂=CH)(CH₃)₂Si(OC₂H₅)
   $\xrightarrow{\text{aq. HCl}}$ 64%

③ (139°). [−99.7°]. n_D1.4123 (20°).
   d0.811 (20°).

⑥ JACS **77**, 1685 (1955).

Si₂C₈H₁₈O₄

① Bis(trimethylsilyl) oxalate
   [COOSi(CH₃)₃]₂

② (COOH)₂ + Me₃SiCl $\longrightarrow$

③ (77.5~79.0°/0.5). [55.7°].

⑥ Z. anorg. allg. Chem. **323**, 228 (1963).

Si₂C₈H₁₉NO₄

① Bis(vinyldimethoxysilyl)amine
   [CH₂=CHSi(OCH₃)₂]₂NH

③ (109°/15~16). n_D1.4355 (25°). d1.0477
   (25°/4°).

⑥ Z. anorg. allg. Chem. **319**, 244 (1963).

Si₂C₈H₂₀

① Hexamethyldisilyl-1,2-ethylene
   (CH₃)₃SiCH=CHSi(CH₃)₃

② Cl₃SiCH=CHSiCl₃ + CH₃MgI
   $\longrightarrow$ 89.5%

③ Liq. (145.5°/750). n_D1.4310 (20°).
   d0.7589 (20°).

   Sol. in org. solvents ; insol. in water.

⑥ Dokl. **105**, 865 (1955) ; CA **50**, 11234
   (1956).

Si₂C₈H₂₀

① Allylpentamethyldisilane
   (CH₃)₃SiSi(CH₃)₂CH₂CH=CH₂

② CH₂=CHCH₂MgBr + Me₃SiSiMe₂Cl
   $\longrightarrow$ 24%

③ [155°]. n_D1.4505 (20°). d0.7782
   (20°/4°).

⑥ Izv. OKhN, **1963**, 660.

Si₂C₈H₂₀

① 1,1,4,4-Tetramethyl-1,4-disilacyclo-
   hexane

$$(CH_3)_2Si{<}^{CH_2CH_2}_{CH_2CH_2}{>}Si(CH_3)_2$$

② AlBr₃ + Me₃SiCH₂CH₂SiMe₃ $\longrightarrow$

③ (172.2~173.0°). n_D1.4530 (20°). d
   0.8298 (20/°4°).

⑥ JACS **78**, 1686 (1956).   Izv. OKhN

1963, 822; 1961, 281; English page 257.

Si₂C₈H₂₀

① Isopropenylpentamethyldisilane
$(CH_3)_3SiSi(CH_3)_2C(CH_3)=CH_2$

② $CH_2=CMeMgBr$
$+ Me_3SiSiMe_2Cl \longrightarrow$

③ (152°). $n_D 1.4517$ (20°). $d 0.7720$
(20°/4°).

⑥ JOM **2**, 136 (1964).

Si₂C₈H₂₀

① 1,1,2,2-Tetramethyl-1,2-disilacyclo-
hexane

$$
\begin{array}{c}
CH_2 \\
CH_2 \qquad Si(CH_3)_2 \\
| \qquad\qquad | \\
CH_2 \qquad Si(CH_3)_2 \\
CH_2
\end{array}
$$

② $(CH_2CH_2MgCl)_2 + THF$
$+ Me_2Si(Cl)SiMe_2Cl \longrightarrow 75\%$

③ (175°). $n_D 1.4647$ (25°). $d 0.8272$
(25°/4°).

⑥ Unpublished work.

Si₂C₈H₂₀F₂

① 1,4-Bis(dimethylfluorosilyl)butane
$(CH_3)_2Si(F)(CH_2)_4Si(CH_3)_2F$

② $Me_3Si(CH_2)_4SiMe_3 + H_2SO_4$
$+ NH_4HF_2 \longrightarrow$

③ (176°). $n_D 1.7990$ (20°). $d 0.9664$
(20°/4°).

⑥ BCSJ **37**, 871 (1964).

Si₂C₈H₂₁F

① 2-Trimethylsilyl-2-dimethylfluoro-
silylpropane
$(CH_3)_2Si(F)C(CH_3)_2Si(CH_3)_3$

② $Me_3SiSi(Me)_2C(Me)=CH_2 + H_2SO_4$
$+ NH_4HF_2 \longrightarrow 83\%$

③ (160°). $n_D 1.4256$ (20°). $d 0.8690$
(20°/4°).

⑥ JOM **2**, 136 (1964).

Si₂C₈H₂₂

① 1,2-Bis(trimethylsilyl)ethane
$(CH_3)_3SiCH_2CH_2Si(CH_3)_3$

② $MeCH(SiCl_3)_2 + MeMgCl$
$\longrightarrow \begin{cases} Me_3SiCH_2CH_2SiMe_3 & 18\% \\ (Me_3Si)_2CHMe_3 & 82\% \end{cases}$

③ (151~153°). $n_D 1.4200$ (20°). $d 0.7538$
(20°/4°).

④ $+ H_2SO_4 + NH_4HF_2 \longrightarrow Me_3SiF$
$+ Me_2Si(F)CH_2CH_2SiMe_2F$

⑥ Izv. OKhN **1960**, 231; English page
216. BCSJ **37**, 871 (1964). Z. anorg.
allg. Chem. **322**, 41 (1963).

Si₂C₈H₂₂

① 1,1-Bis(trimethylsilyl)ethane
$CH_3CH[Si(CH_3)_3]_2$

② $Me_3CH(SiCl_3)_2 + MeMgCl$
$\longrightarrow \begin{cases} (Me_3Si)_2CHMe & 82\% \\ Me_3SiCH_2CH_2SiMe_3 & 18\% \end{cases}$

$ClMe_2SiCHMeSiMe_2Cl$
$+ MeMgBr \longrightarrow 77\%$

③ (160~161°). $n_D 1.4331$ (20°).

④ $+ H_2SO_4 + NH_4HF_2 \longrightarrow Me_3SiF$
$+ MeCH(SiMe_2F)_2$

⑥ JOM **1**, 411 (1964). Z. anorg. allg.
Chem. **322**, 41 (1963).

Si₂C₈H₂₂N₂

① 1,1,3,5,5,6-Hexamethyl-1,5-disila-
3,6-dinitracyclohexane

$$
CH_3N \underset{Si(CH_3)_2CH_2}{\overset{Si(CH_3)_2CH_2}{\big\langle \qquad\quad \big\rangle}} NCH_3
$$

② $Me_2Si(Cl)CH_2Br + MeNH_2 \longrightarrow 71\%$

③ (74°/18). $n_D 1.4516$ (20°). $d 0.8687$
(20°/4°).

⑥ Ber. **96**, 965 (1963).

Si₂C₈H₂₂O

① (Trimethylsilylmethyl)dimethyl-
ethoxysilane

$(CH_3)_3SiCH_2Si(CH_3)_2OCH_2CH_3$

② $Me_3SiSi(Me)_2CH_2Cl + EtONa + EtOH$
$\longrightarrow$ 72%

$Me_3SiCH_2SiHMe_2 + EtONa$
$+ EtOH \longrightarrow$

③ (159~160°). $n_D1.4183$ (20°). $d0.8102$
(20°/4°).

⑥ JOC 23, 139 (1958).   Dokl. 97, 99
(1954).   CA 49, 8792 (1955).   JOM
1, 411 (1964).

Si₂C₈H₂₂O

① 1,1,3,3-Tetraethyldisiloxane
$H(C_2H_5)_2SiOSi(C_2H_5)_2H$

② $H(C_2H_5)_2SiCl + H_2O \longrightarrow$ 80.1%

③ (91~92.5°/5). $n_D1.4154$ (20°). $d0.8153$
(20°).

⑥ Zhur. 26, 3344 (1956); CA 51, 9514
(1957).   Izv. OKhN 1956, 1062.

Si₂C₈H₂₂O₂

① 1,2-Diethoxytetramethyldisilane
$(CH_3)_2(C_2H_5O)SiSi(CH_3)_2(OC_2H_5)$

② $Me_3Si-SiMe_3 \xrightarrow[\text{2. NH}_4\text{Cl}]{\text{1. H}_2\text{SO}_4}$

$ClMe_2SiSiMe_2Cl \xrightarrow[\text{2. NH}_3]{\text{1. C}_2\text{H}_5\text{OH}}$

③ (167~168°). $n_D1.4182$ (20°). $d0.8439$
(20°).

④ $+ PhMgBr \longrightarrow$
$PhMe_2SiSiMe_2(OC_2H_5)$

⑥ Kogyo Kagaku Zasshi 60, 201 (1957).
JOC 21, 1264 (1956).   JOM 1, 411
(1964).

Si₂C₈H₂₂S

① Hexamethyldisilylmethyl sulfide
$[(CH_3)_3SiCH_2]_2S$

② $Me_3SiCH_2Cl \xrightarrow{\text{Na}_2\text{S}}$ 71%

③ (71~73°/0.5). $n_D1.4906$ (20°). $d0.9203$
(20°).

④ $+ H_2O_2 + AcOH \longrightarrow$
$(Me_3SiCH_2)_2SO_2$ 59%

$+ MeI \longrightarrow [(Me_3SiCH_2)_2SMe]^+I^-$
$+ HgI_2 \longrightarrow (Me_3SiCH_2)_2S\cdot HgI_2$

⑥ US 2719165.   JACS 75, 3760 (1953);
76, 3713 (1954).   JOC 25, 249 (1960).

Si₂C₈H₂₃N

① Bis(trimethylsilylmethyl)amine
$[(CH_3)_3SiCH_2]_2NH$

② $Me_3SiCH_2I \xrightarrow[\text{KOH}]{\text{NH}_3} (Me_3SiCH_2)_2NH\cdot HI$

③ (87°/50). $n_D1.4252$ (20°). $d0.7864$
(20°).

④ $(Me_3SiCH_2)_2NH \xrightarrow[-CH_4]{\text{H}_2\text{SO}_4} \xrightarrow[\text{heat}]{\text{NaOH}}$

$\underset{\displaystyle Si(Me_2)CH_2NHCH_2Si(Me)_2}{\overset{\displaystyle Si(Me_2)CH_2NHCH_2Si(Me)_2}{O{<}{>}O}}$

⑥ JACS 77, 3493 (1955); 73, 3867, 5130
(1951).

Si₂C₈H₂₃NS

① Ethylmercaptobis(trimethylsilyl)-
amine
$[(CH_3)_3Si]_2NSC_2H_5$

② $(EtS)_2 + (Me_3Si)_2NNa \longrightarrow$

③ (32~37°).

⑥ Angew. 75, 139 (1963).

Si₂C₈H₂₄Sn

① Bis(dimethylsilylmethyl)dimethyl-
stannane
$[(CH_3)_2SiHCH_2]_2Sn(CH_3)_2$

② $Me_2SiHCH_2MgCl + Me_2SnCl_2 \longrightarrow$

③ (101°/20). $n_D1.4742$ (25°). $d1.108$
(25°).

⑥ Brit. 891087; CA 59, 11560 (1963).
JACS 81, 975 (1959).   US 3043858;
CA 58, 1489 (1963).

Si₄C₈H₂₆N₂

① 1,1,2,2,4,4,5,5-Octamethyl-1,2,4,5-
tetrasila-3,6-diazacyclohexane

$$\begin{array}{c} \text{Si(CH}_3\text{)}_2\text{Si(CH}_3\text{)}_2 \\ \text{HN}\!\!\diagdown\qquad\qquad\diagup\!\!\text{NH} \\ \text{Si(CH}_3\text{)}_2\text{Si(CH}_3\text{)}_2 \end{array}$$

② Me₂Si(Cl)SiMe₂Cl + NH₃ ⟶

③ (61°/2). [1°]. n_D1.4760 (20°).

④ + (Me₃Si)₂NNa
⟶ Me₃SiSi(Me)₂NHSiMe₃

⑥ Angew. **75**, 345 (1963). Angew. English Ed. **2**, 263 (1963).

Si₂C₉H₂₁NO

① N,N-Bis(trimethylsilyl)acrylamide
CH₂=CHCON[Si(CH₃)₃]₂

② CH₂=CHCONH₂ + Et₃N
+ Me₃SiCl ⟶

③ (73.5°/22).

⑥ Angew. English Ed. **2**, 96 (1963).

Si₂C₉H₂₂

① 3-Butenyl-1-pentamethyldisilane
(CH₃)₃SiSi(CH₃)₂CH₂CH₂CH=CH₂

② CH₂=CHCH₂Br
+ Me₃SiSiMe₂CH₂MgBr ⟶ 70%

③ (171°). n_D1.4517 (20°). d0.7839
(20°/4°).

⑥ Izv. OKhN **1963**, 660.

Si₂C₉H₂₂F₂

① 1,5-Bis(dimethylfluorosilyl)pentane
(CH₃)₂Si(F)(CH₂)₅Si(CH₃)₂F

② H₂SO₄ + NH₄HF₂
+ Me₃Si(CH₂)₅SiMe₃ ⟶

③ (93°/26). n_D1.4050 (20°). d0.9113
(20°/4°).

⑥ BCSJ **37**, 871 (1964).

Si₂C₉H₂₃Cl

① 1-Trimethylsilyl-4-dimethylchloro-
silylbutane
(CH₃)₃SiCH₂CH₂CH₂CH₂Si(CH₃)₂Cl

② Mg + Me₂Si(Cl)CH₂Cl
+ Me₃SiCH₂CH₂CH₂Br ⟶ 30%

③ (82.5~83.9°/9). n_D1.4470 (20°).
d0.8795 (20°/4°).

④ + AlCl₃ ⟶ Me₃SiCl

$$\begin{array}{c} \text{CH}_2\text{CH}_2 \\ +\;\; |\qquad\qquad\rangle\text{SiMe}_2 \\ \text{CH}_2\text{CH}_2 \end{array}$$

⑥ Dokl. **150**, 562 (1963).

Si₂C₉H₂₃ClO

① 1,1,1-Triethyl-2,2-dimethyl-2-chlo-
romethyldisiloxane
(C₂H₅)₃SiOSi(CH₃)₂CH₂Cl

② H₂O + Me₃Si(Cl)CH₂Cl
+ Et₃SiCl ⟶

③ (100~102°/10). n_D 1.4340 (20). d 0.9173
(20°/4°).

⑥ Izv. OKhN **1963**, 500.

Si₂C₉H₂₄

① 1,1,3,3-Tetraethyldisilylmethane
[(C₂H₅)₂SiH]₂CH₂

② CH₂(SiCl₂H)₂ + EtMgBr ⟶ 75.6%

③ (55°/3). n_D1.4473 (20°). d0.7978 (20°).

⑥ Dokl. **110**, 97 (1956).

Si₂C₉H₂₄

① Hexamethyldisilyl-1,3-propane
(CH₃)₃Si(CH₂)₃Si(CH₃)₃

② CH₂=CHCH₂SiCl₃ + SiHCl₃

$$\xrightarrow[\text{18 hrs. at }40\sim60°]{\text{Bz}_2\text{O}_2} 62.2\%\ \ \text{C}_3\text{H}_6\text{(SiCl}_3\text{)}_2$$

+ MeLi $\xrightarrow{\text{in Et}_2\text{O}}$ 85%

③ (172~173°). n_D1.4235 (20°). d0.7580
(20°).
IR

④ + H₂SO₄ $\xrightarrow{\text{NH}_4\text{FHF}}$
FMe₂Si(CH₂)₃SiMe₂F

⑥ Zhur. **30**, 2600 (1960). J. Inst.
Polytech. Osaka City Univ. Sec.
No. C **3**, 65 (1952). Dokl. **110**, 97
(1956). Izv. OKhN **1958**, 123.

Si₂C₉H₂₄

① 2,2-Bis(trimethylsilyl)propane
(CH₃)₂C[Si(CH₃)₃]₂

② MeLi + SiCl₃CCl₂SiCl₃ $\longrightarrow$
   Me₂C(SiMe₂F)₂ + MeMgBr $\longrightarrow$
③ (50~60°/14, 178°). n_D1.4459 (20°).
④ + H₂SO₄ + NH₄HF₂
   $\longrightarrow$ *i*-PrSiMe₂F +
   Me₂Si(F)CMe₂SiMe₂F
⑥ Z. anorg. allg. Chem. **309**, 77 (1961).
   JOM **2**, 136 (1964).

Si₂C₉H₂₄O
① 1,1,1-Trimethyl-3,3,3-triethyldisilo-
   xane
   (CH₃)₃SiOSi(C₂H₅)₃
② Et₃SiOH + C₅H₅N + Me₃SiCl
   $\longrightarrow$ 80%
   Et₃SiH + SO₂(OSiMe₃)₂ $\longrightarrow$
③ (46~47°/7, 71°/15, 171~172°).
   n_D1.4105, 1.4108 (20°). d0.8110,
   0.8105 (20°/4°).
⑥ Svensk Kemisk Tidskrift **65**, 101
   (1953).   JACS **70**, 434 (1948). Bull.
   soc. chim. France. 512 (1963).
   Zhur. **29**, 1534 (1959).

Si₂C₉H₂₇GeN
① Bis(trimethylsilyl)trimethyl-
   germylamine
   [(CH₃)₃Si]₂NGe(CH₃)₃
② Me₃SiN(Na)SiMe₃ + Me₃GeCl $\longrightarrow$
③ [29~32°]. (54~56°/1).
④ Resistant to water hydrolysis.
⑥ Angew. **2**, 478 (1963) (English Ed.).
   Angew. **75**, 642 (1963).

Si₂C₉H₂₇NSn
① Bis(trimethylsilyl)trimethylstannyl-
   amine
   [(CH₃)₃Si]₂NSn(CH₃)₃
② Me₃SiN(Na)SiMe₃ + Me₃SnCl $\longrightarrow$
③ (58~59°/1). [20~22°].
⑥ Angew. **2**, 478 (1963) (English Ed.).
   Angew. **75**, 642 (1963).

Si₂C₁₀H₁₆Cl₂
① *p*-Bis(dimethylchlorosilyl)benzene
   p-C₆H₄[Si(CH₃)₂Cl]₂
③ (110°/1.6). [87°]. n_D1.5800 (20°).
   d1.2259 (20°).
④ + NH₄OH $\longrightarrow$ *p*-C₆H₄(SiMe₂OH)₂
   + HOH $\longrightarrow$ *p*-C₆H₄(SiMe₂OH)₂
⑥ US 2561429 (1951); 3067230 (1962);
   CA **46**, 1814 (1952); **58**, 3457, 10238
   (1963). Izv. OKhN **1960**, 942,
   English page 880. US 3053872
   (1962).

Si₂C₁₀H₁₇N₂
① 1-Trimethylsilyl-2-methyl-2-chloro-
   1,3-dinitra-2-silaindane

② MeSiCl₃ + *o*-C₆H₄(NHSiMe₃)₂ $\longrightarrow$
③ Decomp. point +99°.
⑥ Angew. **2**, 152 (1963).

Si₂C₁₀H₁₈
① *p*-Bis(dimethylsilyl)benzene
   p-C₆H₄[SiH(CH₃)₂]₂
② LiAlH₄ + *p*-C₆H₄(SiMe₂Cl)₂ $\longrightarrow$ 95%
   p-C₆H₄(MgBr)₂ + Me₂SiHCl $\longrightarrow$
③ (118°/35, 94°/12). n_D1.5005 (20°),
   1.4995 (25°). d0.8730 (20°), 0.8718
   (25°/4°).
⑥ CA **58**, 4708 (1963). Mem. Fac. Eng.
   Osaka City Univ. **4**, 177 (1962).
   Brit. 916135 (1963); CA **59**, 10120
   (1963).

Si₂C₁₀H₁₈O₂
① *p*-Bis(dimethylhydroxysilyl)benzene
   p-C₆H₄(Si(CH₃)₂OH)₂
② HOH + *p*-C₆H₄(SiMe₂Cl)₂ $\longrightarrow$
   NH₄OH + *p*-C₆H₄(SiMe₂Cl)₂ $\longrightarrow$

③ [135°, 139°].
⑥ US 2561429 (1951); CA **46**, 1814 (1952).
　 US 3053872 (1962); CA **58**, 3457
　 (1963).

$Si_2C_{10}H_{20}F_6O$

① 1,2-Bis(3,3,3-trifluoropropyl)tetra-
　 methyldisiloxane
　 $[CF_3CH_2CH_2Si(CH_3)_2]_2O$
② $CF_3CH_2CH_2SiMe_2OEt + HOH + HCl$
　 $+ EtOH \longrightarrow$ 70%
③ (74.8~75.0°/10). n_D1.3656 (20°).
　 d1.0860 (20°/4°).
⑥ Zhur. **33**, 704 (1963).

$Si_2C_{10}H_{20}O_4$

① Bis(trimethylsilyl) fumarate
　 $[HCCOOSi(CH_3)_3]_2$
② $(HCCOOH)_2 + Me_3SiNHSiMe_3$
　 $\longrightarrow$ 95%
③ (123°/14). [64°].
④

$$+ PhC \underset{N=N}{\overset{N-NSiMe_3}{\diagup\!\!\!\diagdown}} \longrightarrow$$

$$PhC \underset{N\text{---}NSiMe_3}{\overset{COOSiMe_3}{\diagup\!\!\diagup CH-CHCOOSiMe_3}}$$

⑥ Ber. **96**, 2750 (1963).

$Si_2C_{10}H_{20}S$

① α,α'-Bis(trimethylsilyl)thiophene

$$(CH_3)_3SiC \underset{S}{\overset{CH\text{---}CH}{\diagup\!\!\!\diagdown}} CSi(CH_3)_3$$

② $LiC \underset{S}{\overset{CH\text{---}CH}{\diagup\!\!\!\diagdown}} CLi + Me_3SiCl \longrightarrow$ 65%

③ [31~32°].
④ $+ Ni + NaOH$
　 $\longrightarrow Me_3Si-(CH_2)_4-SiMe_3$
⑥ Zhur. **33**, 1251 (1963).

$Si_2C_{10}H_{22}$

① 1,3-Bis(1-methylvinyl)tetramethyl-
　 disilane
　 $[(CH_3)_2SiC(CH_3)=CH_2]_2$
② $CH_2=CMeMgBr$
　 $+ Me_2Si(Cl)SiMe_2Cl \longrightarrow$
③ (97~98°/32). n_D1.4750 (20°). d0.8081
　 (20°/4°).
⑥ JOM **2**, 136 (1964).

$Si_2C_{10}H_{22}$

① Dimethyl-1,2-bis(tetramethylene)
　 disilane

$$\left[\underset{CH_2CH_2}{\overset{CH_2CH_2}{\diagup\!\!\!\diagdown}} SiCH_3 \right]_2$$

② $(CH_2CH_2MgCl)_2 +$
　 $(EtO)_2Si(Me)Si(OEt)_2Me \longrightarrow$ 27%
③ (98°/10). n_D1.5049 (20°). d0.8950
　 (20°/4°).
⑥ Unpublished work.

$Si_2C_{10}H_{24}F_2$

① 1,6-Bis(dimethylfluorosilyl)hexane
　 $(CH_3)_2Si(F)(CH_2)_6Si(CH_3)_2F$
② $Me_3Si(CH_2)_6SiMe_3 + H_2SO_4$
　 $+ NH_4HF_2 \longrightarrow$
③ (95°/14). n_D1.4087 (20°). d0.9037
　 (20°/4°).
⑥ BCSJ **37**, 871 (1964).

$Si_2C_{10}H_{24}O_2$

① 1,2-Dimethyl-1,2-bis-(trimethyl-
　 siloxy)ethene
　 $(CH_3)_3SiOC(CH_3)=C(CH_3)OSi(CH_3)_3$
② $Na + Me_3SiCl + AcOEt \longrightarrow$ 75.5%
③ (69.0~70.5°/12). n_D1.4191 (20°).
　 d0.8580 (20°/4°).
④ $+ KOH \longrightarrow Me_3SiOSiMe_3$
⑥ Ber. **96**, 2780 (1963). J. prakt. Chem.
　 12, 18 (1960).

$Si_2C_{10}H_{24}O_6$

① 1,6-Tetramethoxy-1,6-disila-2,7-

dioxacyclodecane

$$(CH_3O)_2Si\!\!<^{\displaystyle CH_2CH_2CH_2O}_{\displaystyle OCH_2CH_2CH_2}\!\!>Si(OCH_3)_2$$

② $H_2PtCl_6 + MeSi(OCH_2CH=CH_2)_2$
   $+ HSi(OMe)_3 \longrightarrow$

③ $(90\sim93°/1)$. $n_D1.4171$ $(20°)$. $d1.0383$
   $(20°/4°)$.

⑥ Dokl. 151, 849 (1963).

$Si_2C_{10}H_{25}Br$

① Pentaethylbromodisilane
   $(C_2H_5)_3SiSi(C_2H_5)_2Br$

② $i\text{-}PrBr + AlCl_3 + Et_3SiSiEt_3$
   $\longrightarrow$ 72.2%

③ $(88°/2)$. $n_D1.4860$ $(20°)$.

④ $+ Na \longrightarrow Et_3SiSi(Et)_2Si(Et)_2SiEt_3$
   (20.2%)

⑥ Zhur. 31, 4056 (1961); English page
   3784. Zhur. 33, 613 (1963).

$Si_2C_{10}H_{26}$

① 1,4-Bis(trimethylsilyl)butane
   $(CH_3)_3Si(CH_2)_4Si(CH_3)_3$

② $Ni + MeOH + CH\!\!=\!\!=\!\!CH \longrightarrow$
     $Me_3SiC\!-\!S\!-\!CSiMe_3$
   $Me_3SiCl + (CH_2CH_2MgBr)_2 \longrightarrow$
   $Li + (CH_2CH_2Br)_2 + Me_3SiCl \longrightarrow$
   $MeMgCl + (CH_2CH_2SiCl_3)_2 \longrightarrow$

③ $(188\sim190°)$. $n_D1.4265$ $(20°)$, 1.4244
   $(25°)$. $d0.7660$ $(20°/4°)$, 0.763
   $(25°/25°)$.

④ $+ H_2SO_4 + BF_3 \longrightarrow$
   $Me_3SiF + (CH_2CH_2SiMe_2F)_2$
   $+ AlCl_3 \longrightarrow$

$$Me_4Si + \!\!\!\begin{array}{c}CH_2CH_2\\ |\qquad\quad\\ CH_2CH_2\end{array}\!\!\!\!>SiMe_2$$

⑥ JACS 77, 2482 (1955).   JOC 18, 1739
   (1953).   Izv. OKhN 1958, 1468.
   Zhur. 33, 1251 (1963).

$Si_2C_{10}H_{26}$

① 1,4-Bis(trimethylsilyl)-2-methyl-
propane
   $(CH_3)_3SiCH_2CH(CH_3)CH_2Si(CH_3)_3$

② $MeMgCl + Cl_3SiCH_2CHMeCH_2SiMeCl_2$
   $\longrightarrow$ 89.4%

③ $(182\sim183°)$. $n_D1.4283$ $(20°)$. $d0.7693$
   $(20°/4°)$.

⑥ Izv. OKhN 1963, 822.

$Si_2C_{10}H_{26}O_3$

① 8,8-Dimethyl-3,3-dimethoxy-3,8-
   disila-7-oxanonane
   $(CH_3)_3SiOCH_2CH_2CH_2Si(OCH_3)_2CH_2CH_3$

③ $(83\sim85°/1\sim2)$. $n_D1.4190$ $(20°)$. $d0.9007$
   $(20°/4°)$.

④ $+ H_2SO_4 \longrightarrow$

$$\begin{array}{c}MeO\qquad CH_2CH_2\\ \quad >Si<\qquad |\\ Et\qquad O\!-\!CH_2\end{array}$$

⑥ Dokl. 151, 849 (1963).

$Si_2C_{10}H_{26}O_4$

① Dimethyl-1,1,2,2-tetraethoxydisilane
   $CH_3Si(OC_2H_5)_2Si(OC_2H_5)_2CH_3$

② $Me_nSi_2Cl_{6-n} + EtOH + NH_3 \longrightarrow$

③ $(99°/19,\ 101.5\sim102.0°/22,\ 104°/24)$.
   $n_D1.4200$ $(20°)$. $d0.9282$ $(20°/4°)$.

④ $+ HCl \longrightarrow [MeSi(O)Si(O)Me]_4$
   $+ HCl \longrightarrow EtOSi(Me)_2Si(Me)_2OEt$
   $\longrightarrow$ polycyclic compounds

⑥ JOC 21, 1264 (1956).   Kogyo Kagaku
   Zasshi 60, 201 (1957); CA 53, 6065
   (1959).   Kogyo Kagaku Zasshi 66,
   637 (1963).

$Si_2C_{10}H_{26}S$

① Bis(β-trimethylsilylethyl) sulfide
   $[(CH_3)_3SiCH_2CH_2]_2S$

③ $(39°/0.05)$. $n_D1.4620$ $(25°)$.

④ $+ HOOH \longrightarrow$
   $(Me_3SiCH_2CH_2)_2SO_2 \longrightarrow$

⑥ JOC 28, 3264 (1963).

$Si_2C_{10}H_{26}SO_2$

① Bis(β-trimethylsilylethyl)sulfone
   $[(CH_3)_3SiCH_2CH_2]_2SO_2$

② HOOH + (Me₃SiCH₂CH₂)₂S ⟶

③ [123°].

⑥ JOC **28**, 3264 (1963).

Si₂C₁₀H₂₇NS

① *n*-Butylmercaptobis(trimethylsilyl)-
amine
[(CH₃)₃Si]₂NSC₄H₉-*n*

② (*n*-BuS)₂ + (Me₃Si)₂NNa ⟶

③ (71~72°/1).

⑥ Angew. **75**, 139 (1963).

Si₂C₁₁H₁₈Cl₂

① 2,4-Bis(dimethylchlorosilyl)toluene
(CH₃)C₆H₃[Si(CH₃)₂Cl]₂(2,4)

② Mg + Me₂SiCl₂ + MeC₆H₃Br₂(2,4) ⟶

③ (105~107°/1.5).

④ + Me₃SiCl, 86% H₂SO₄, then Na₂CO₃
⟶ liquid "asymmetric" polymers
with an improved low temperature
flow.

⑥ Ger. 1139648 (1962); CA **58**, 14151
(1963)

Si₂C₁₁H₁₈O

① 2,5,5-Trimethyl-2-phenyl-2,5-disila-
1-oxacyclopentane

CH₂———CH₂

(CH₃)₂Si   Si(CH₃)C₆H₅
          O

② LiOH + H₂O
+ Me₂Si(Cl)CH₂CH₂SiMePhCl ⟶

③ (146°/50). n_D 1.4962 (25°). d 0.9742
(25°/4°).

⑥ US 3041362 (1962); CA **58**, 1558 (1963).
JACS **82**, 1883 (1960).

Si₂C₁₁H₂₀

① Phenylpentamethyldisilane
(CH₃)₃SiSi(CH₃)₂C₆H₅

② Me₃SiCl + Me₃Si(Li)Ph ⟶
PhMgBr + Me₃SiSiMe₂Cl ⟶ 50%

③ (100~102°/19,   113.0~114.5°/25).
n_D 1.5056 (20°), 1.5078 (25°). d 0.8738

(20°/20°), 0.8760 (20°/4°).

⑥ JACS **80**, 608 (1958).   Izv. OKhN
1963, 660.

Si₂C₁₁H₂₀N₂

① *Si*-Phenylpentamethylcyclodisilazane

              N(CH₃)
(CH₃)₂Si   Si(CH₃)C₆H₅
              N(CH₃)

② PhSi(Cl)₂Me + Me₂Si[N(Li)Me]₂ ⟶

③ (69.5~71.0°/3).

⑥ Angew. **75**, 638 (1963).

Si₂C₁₁H₂₇Cl

① 1-Triethylsilyl-2-ethylmethylchloro-
silylethane
(C₂H₅)₃SiCH₂CH₂Si(CH₃)(C₂H₅)Cl

② H₂PtCl₆ + Et₃SiCH=CH₂
+ MeSiH(Cl)Et ⟶ 52%

③ (91°/2). n_D 1.4564 (20°). d 0.8828
(20°/4°).

④ + Me₂C(OMgBr)C≡CMgBr ⟶
Et₃Si(CH₂)₂SiMeEtC≡CCMe₂OH

⑥ Zhur. **33**, 2123, 2281 (1963).

Si₂C₁₁H₂₈

① 1,5-Bis(trimethylsilyl)pentane
(CH₃)₃Si(CH₂)₅Si(CH₃)₃

② Li + Me₃SiCl + Br(CH₂)₅Br ⟶
BrMg(CH₂)₅MgBr + Me₃SiCl ⟶

③ (88°/12,   216°/760). n_D 1.4335 (20°),
1.4310 (25°). d 0.763 (25°/4°), 0.7775
(20°/4°).

④ + H₂SO₄ + NH₄HF₂
⟶ Me₂Si(F)(CH₂)₅SiMe₂F

⑥ BCSJ **37**, 871 (1964).   J. Inst. Polytech. Osaka City Univ. **3** (Ser. C) 65
(1952).   JOC **18**, 1739 (1953).

Si₂C₁₂H₁₄O

① 1,2-Diphenyldisiloxane
C₆H₅Si(H)₂OSiH₂C₆H₅

② PhSiH₃ + Cu(powder) ⟶
+ CH₂=CHCH₂OH ⟶ 8.1%
(by-product)

$$PhSiCl_3 \xrightarrow{LiAlH_4} PhSiH_3 \ (67\%) \xrightarrow{HBr}$$
$$PhSiH_2Br \ (95\%) \xrightarrow{H_2O, \ distill} 78\%$$

③ (121~122°/7). n_D 1.5290 (20°).

⑥ Zhur. **33**, 2617 (1963).   JACS **79**, 1437 (1957).

Si₂C₁₂H₁₈Cl₄

① 1-Phenyl-2,2-bis-(ethyldichlorosilyl)-ethane
   $C_6H_5CH_2CH(SiCl_2C_2H_5)_2$

② $PhC\equiv CH + H_2PtCl_6 + EtSiHCl_2$
   $\longrightarrow$ 65%

③ (170°/10). n_D 1.5315 (20°). d 1.2153 (20°).

④ + HF $\longrightarrow$ $PhCH_2CH(SiF_2Et)_2$

⑥ CA **59**, 11550 (1963).

Si₂C₁₂H₁₈F₄

① 1-Phenyl-2,2-bis-(ethyldifluorosilyl)-ethane
   $C_6H_5CH_2CH(SiF_2C_2H_5)_2$

② $HF + PhCH_2CH(SiCl_2Et)_2 \longrightarrow$ 48%

③ (110°/5). n_D 1.4500 (20°). d 1.1428 (20°).

⑥ CA **59**, 11550 (1963).

Si₂C₁₂H₁₈O

① 1,3-Bis-(vinylethynyl)tetramethyl-disiloxane
   $[CH_2=CHC\equiv CSi(CH_3)_2-]_2O$

② $CH_2=CHC\equiv CSiMe_2OH + FeCl_3$
   $\longrightarrow$ 94.1%
   $CH_2=CHC\equiv CSiMe_2OMgBr + HCl$
   $\longrightarrow$ 51.5%

③ (74°/1). n_D 1.4730 (20°). d 0.8911 (20°/4°).

④ + $(C_6H_5COO)_2 \longrightarrow$ polymers

⑥ Izv. OKhN **1963**, 97.

Si₂C₁₂H₂₀O₈

① Dimeric diethylsilyl oxalate
   $[(COO)_2Si(C_2H_5)_2]_2$

② $Et_2SiCl_2 + (COOH)_2 \longrightarrow$

③ (53.5~54.5°/10~3). [38°].

⑥ Z. anorg. allg. Chem. **323**, 228 (1963).

Si₂C₁₂H₂₂

① p-Bis(trimethylsilyl)benzene
   $p\text{-}C_6H_4[Si(CH_3)_3]_2$

② $p\text{-}C_6H_4(MgBr)_2 + Me_3SiCl \longrightarrow$
   $C_6H_6 + Li + Me_3SiCl \longrightarrow$
   (by-product)

③ (194°/742). [95~96°].   Sublimes at 80~81°.

⑥ Rec. trav. chim. **81**, 565 (1962).
   JACS **84**, 2843 (1962). Zhur. **33**, 641 (1963).   Ber. **95**, 473 (1962).

Si₂C₁₂H₂₂N₂

① Bis-(N, N'-trimethylsilyl)-quinone-p-diimide

$$(CH_3)_3SiN=C\underset{CH=CH}{\overset{CH=CH}{\diagdown\diagup}}C=SiN(CH_3)_3$$

② $C_6H_4O_2 + (Me_3Si)_2NNa \longrightarrow$

③ [95~97°].

⑥ Ber. **96**, 2132 (1963).

Si₂C₁₂H₂₂O₂

① p-Bis(trimethylsiloxy)benzene
   $p\text{-}C_6H_4[OSi(CH_3)_3]_2$

② $p\text{-}C_6H_4(OK)_2 + Me_3SiCl \longrightarrow$

③ [48.9~49.3°].

⑥ CA **59**, 10105 (1963).   Ber. **92**, 2585 (1959).

Si₂C₁₂H₂₄

① 1,4-Bis(trimethylsilyl)cyclohexa-diene-2,5

$$(CH_3)_3SiHC\underset{CH=CH}{\overset{CH=CH}{\diagup\diagdown}}CHSi(CH_3)_3$$

② $Li + C_6H_6 + Me_3SiCl \longrightarrow$ 90%

③ (87~90°/4.5). [50~51°]. n_D 1.473~1.474 (22.5°).

⑥ JACS **84**, 2843 (1962).   Brit. 917770 (1963); CA **58**, 13994 (1963).

$Si_2C_{12}H_{26}O_5$

① Bis(vinyldiethoxy)disiloxane
   $[(CH_2=CH)(C_2H_5O)_2Si]_2O$

② $(CH_2=CH)SiCl_3 +$
   $2C_2H_5OH$ $\xrightarrow{\text{without pyridine}}$

③ (119°/19). $n_D1.4100$ (25°). $d0.9618$
   (25°).

⑥ JOC **16**, 1768 (1951).

$Si_2C_{12}H_{28}Cl_2O$

① 1,3-Dibutyl-1,3-dimethyl-1,3-bis-
   (chloromethyl)disiloxane
   $[n\text{-}C_4H_9Si(CH_3)CH_2Cl]_2O$

② $\begin{matrix} CH_2CH_2 \\ | \end{matrix} \!\! \Big\rangle Si(Me)CH_2Cl + H_2SO_4 \longrightarrow$
   CH_2CH_2

③ (130.0~130.5°/5). $n_D1.4530$ (20°).
   $d0.9909$ (20°/4°).

⑥ Izv. OKhN **1963**, 274.

$Si_2C_{12}H_{28}Cl_2O$

① 1,3-Diethyl-1,3-dimethyl-1,3-(3-
   chloropropyl)disiloxane
   $[C_2H_5Si(CH_3)CH_2CH_2CH_2Cl]_2O$

② $MeSiCl_2CH_2CH_2CH_2Cl$
   $+ EtMgBr \longrightarrow$

③ (134~140°/5).

⑥ Dokl. **150**, 799 (1963).

$Si_2C_{12}H_{28}O_2$

① 1,2-Diethyl-1,2-bis(trimethylsiloxy)-
   ethene
   $(CH_3)_3SiO(C_2H_5)C=C(C_2H_5)OSi(CH_3)_3$

② $Na + Me_3SiCl + EtCOCEt$
   $\longrightarrow$ 69.1%
   $Na + Me_3SiCl + EtCOCl \longrightarrow$

③ (85~88°/12~13). $n_D1.4279$ (20°).
   $d0.8597$ (20°/4°).

⑥ Ber. **96**, 2780 (1963).   J. prakt.
   Chem. **12**, 18 (1960).

$Si_2C_{12}H_{28}O_4$

① 1,6-Diethyl-1,6-dimethoxy-1,6-disila-

2,7-dioxacyclodecane

$$\begin{matrix} C_2H_5 & & CH_2CH_2CH_2O & & C_2H_5 \\ & \!\!\Big\rangle Si\!\Big\langle & & \!\!\Big\rangle Si\!\Big\langle & \\ CH_3O & & OCH_2CH_2CH_2 & & OCH_3 \end{matrix}$$

② $H_2PtCl_6 + Me_2Si(OCH_2CH=CH_2)_2$
   $+ (MeO)_2SiHEt \longrightarrow$

③ (94~95°/1). $n_D1.4184$ (20°). $d0.9500$
   (20°/4°).

⑥ Dokl. **151**, 849 (1963).

$Si_2C_{12}H_{29}Cl$

① 1-Triethylsilyl-2-methyl-*n*-propyl-
   chlorosilylethane
   $(C_2H_5)_3SiCH_2CH_2Si(Cl)(CH_3)(n\text{-}C_3H_7)$

② $H_2PtCl_6 + Et_3SiCH=CH_2$
   $+ MeSi(Cl)(H)Pr\text{-}n \longrightarrow$

③ (112.5°/5). $n_D1.4570$ (20°). $d0.893$
   (20°/4°).

④ $+ BrMgOCMe_2C\equiv CMgBr \longrightarrow$
   $Et_3Si(CH_2)_2Si(Me)(Pr\text{-}n)C\text{-}$
   $\equiv CCMe_2OH$

⑥ Zhur. **33**, 2281 (1963).

$Si_2C_{12}H_{30}$

① Hexaethyldisilane
   $(C_2H_5)_3SiSi(C_2H_5)_3$

② $Et_3SiI + Na$ (molten) $\longrightarrow$ 79.6%

③ (251.7°). $n_D1.4790$ (20°). $d0.8351$
   (20°).

⑥ Zhur. **26**, 584 (1956); CA **50**, 13729
   (1956).

$Si_2C_{12}H_{30}$

① 1,6-Bis(trimethylsilyl)hexane
   $(CH_3)_3Si(CH_2)_6Si(CH_3)_3$

② $Li + Me_3SiCl + (CH_2CH_2CH_2Br)_2 \longrightarrow$
   $MeMgCl +$
   $MeSi(Cl)_2(CH_2)_6SiMeCl_2 \longrightarrow$

③ (101°/7, 109.5°/16, 107~108°/14).
   $n_D1.4310$ (20°), 1.4322 (25°). $d0.773$
   (25°/4°).
   IR: 1160, 1195 cm⁻¹.

④ $+ H_2SO_4 + NH_4HF_2 \longrightarrow Me_3SiF +$
   $C_6H_{13}SiMe_2F + Me_2SiF(CH_2)_6SiMe_2F$

⑥ JOC **18**, 1739 (1953).   Izv. OKhN
   1993, 822.   BCSJ **37**, 871 (1964).

Si$_2$C$_{12}$H$_{30}$N$_2$

① 1,4-Di-*n*-propyl-3,3,5,5-tetramethyl-
   1,4-dinitra-3,5-disilacyclohexane

   n-C$_3$H$_7$N$\underset{\diagdown \text{Si(CH}_3)_2\text{CH}_2 \diagup}{\overset{\diagup \text{Si(CH}_3)_2\text{CH}_2 \diagdown}{}}NC_3H_7$-$n$

② Me$_2$Si(CH$_2$Br)NHSiMe$_2$CH$_2$Br
   + PrNH$_2$ $\longrightarrow$
   Et$_2$NSiMe$_2$CH$_2$Br + PrNH$_2$ $\longrightarrow$
   Me$_2$SiClCH$_2$Br + PrNH$_2$ $\longrightarrow$

③ (118°/13). n_D1.4572 (20°).

⑥ Ber. **96**, 965 (1963).

Si$_2$C$_{12}$H$_{30}$O

① Hexaethyldisiloxane
   (C$_2$H$_5$)$_3$SiOSi(C$_2$H$_5$)$_3$

② (C$_2$H$_5$)$_3$SiCl + H$_2$O $\longrightarrow$

③ (231°). n_D1.4340 (20°). d0.8590 (20°).

⑥ Dokl. **99**, 551 (1954).   Zhur. **25**, 437
   (1955).

Si$_2$C$_{12}$H$_{30}$O$_2$

① 1,6-Bis(trimethylsiloxy)hexane
   (CH$_2$CH$_2$CH$_2$OSiCH$_3$)$_2$

② (CH$_2$CH$_2$CH$_2$OH)$_2$ + Me$_3$SiCl $\longrightarrow$ 85%

③ (123.5~124.0°/17.5, 126~128°/20~22).
   n_D1.4200 (18°), 1.4185 (20°). d0.845
   (20°/4°).

⑥ CA **59**, 10105 (1963).   JOC **20**, 1750
   (1955).

Si$_2$C$_{12}$H$_{30}$O$_4$

① 1-Trimethylsiloxy-3-triethoxysilyl-
   propane
   (CH$_3$)$_3$SiOCH$_2$CH$_2$CH$_2$Si(OC$_2$H$_5$)$_3$

② H$_2$PtCl$_6$ + Me$_3$SiOCH$_2$CH=CH$_2$
   + HSi(OEt)$_3$ $\longrightarrow$

③ (81~85°/1). n_D1.411 (20°). d0.918
   (20°/4°).

④ + H$_2$PtCl$_6$ $\longrightarrow$ (EtO)$_2$Si$\underset{\diagdown \text{O—CH}_2}{\overset{\diagup \text{CH}_2\text{CH}_2}{}}$

⑥ Dokl. **151**, 849 (1963).

Si$_2$C$_{12}$H$_{30}$O$_4$S

① Bis(triethylsilyl) sulfate
   SO$_2$[OSi(C$_2$H$_5$)$_3$]$_2$

② Et$_3$SiOSiEt$_3$ + H$_2$SO$_4$ $\longrightarrow$ 80%

③ (175°/15).

⑥ Bull. soc. chim. France 512 (1963).

Si$_2$C$_{12}$H$_{30}$S

① Bis(3-trimethylsilylpropyl) sulfide
   [(CH$_3$)$_3$SiCH$_2$CH$_2$CH$_2$]$_2$S

② Me$_3$SiCH$_2$CH=CH$_2$ + H$_2$S
   $\longrightarrow$ 19.2%

③ (66°/0.5, 46°/0.05). n_D1.4621 (25°).

⑥ JOC **28**, 3264 (1963).   Brit. 791609
   (1958); CA **52**, 19948 (1958).   Ger.
   1000817 (1957); CA **53**, 13054 (1959).

Si$_2$C$_{12}$H$_{31}$N

① Bis(triethylsilyl)amine
   [(C$_2$H$_5$)$_3$Si]$_2$NH

② Et$_3$SiNH$_2$ + Et$_3$SiCl
   $\overset{160\sim170°}{\longrightarrow}$ (Et$_3$Si)$_2$NH (79~81%)

③ (244~245°). n_D1.4455 (20°). d0.8461
   (20°).

⑥ Izv. OKhN **1958**, 47.   JOC **25**, 2191
   (1960).

Si$_2$C$_{12}$H$_{32}$Sn

① Dimethylbis(3-dimethylsilylpropyl)-
   stannane
   (CH$_3$)$_2$Sn[CH$_2$CH$_2$CH$_2$SiH(CH$_3$)$_2$]$_2$

② Me$_2$Si(H)CH$_2$CH$_2$CH$_2$MgCl
   + Me$_2$SnCl$_2$ $\longrightarrow$

③ (146°/25). n_D1.4730 (25°). d1.052
   (25°).

⑥ US 3043858 (1963); CA **58**, 1489 (1963).
   Brit. 891087 (1962); CA **89**, 11560
   (1963).

Si$_2$C$_{13}$H$_{23}$Cl

① 1-Trimethylsilyl-3-methylphenyl-

chlorosilylpropane
(CH$_3$)$_3$SiCH$_2$CH$_2$CH$_2$SiCl(CH$_3$)C$_6$H$_5$
② Me$_3$SiCH$_2$CH=CH$_2$ + PhSiHClMe
    + H$_2$PtCl$_6$ $\longrightarrow$ 69.3%
③ (140~145°/2).
⑥ Izv. OKhN **1963**, 654.

Si$_2$C$_{13}$H$_{23}$NO
① Trimethylsiloxytrimethylsilylimino-
    phenylmethane
    C$_6$H$_5$C[OSi(CH$_3$)$_3$]=NSi(CH$_3$)$_3$
② (Me$_3$Si)$_2$NNa + PhCOOMe $\longrightarrow$
③ (67~68°/3). n_D1.485 (23°). d0.9278
    (24°/4°).
    IR: 3020, 2940, 2890, 1695, 1605, 1588,
    1493, 1460, 1408, 1255, 1248, 1175,
    1120, 1070, 1025, 970, 931, 840, 793,
    756, 698, 667 cm^{-1}.
⑥ Ber. **96**, 2138 (1963).

Si$_2$C$_{13}$H$_{24}$
① Phenylbis(trimethysilyl)methane
    C$_6$H$_5$CH[Si(CH$_3$)$_3$]$_2$
② Mg + PhCCl$_3$ + THF + Me$_3$SiCl $\longrightarrow$
③ (166°/99). n_D1.4992 (25°).
⑥ JACS **85**, 2243 (1963).

Si$_2$C$_{13}$H$_{24}$N$_2$O
① N-Phenyl-N', N'-bis(trimethylsilyl)-
    carbamide
    [(CH$_3$)$_3$Si]$_2$NCONHC$_6$H$_5$
② Me$_3$SiNHSiMe$_3$ + PhNCO $\longrightarrow$ 96%
③ Solid. [69~70°]. (100°/1 sublimes).
⑥ Z. anorg. allg. Chem. **321**, 208 (1963).

Si$_2$C$_{13}$H$_{31}$Cl
① 1-Triethylsilyl-3-diethylchlorosilyl-
    propane
    (C$_2$H$_5$)$_3$SiCH$_2$CH$_2$CH$_2$Si(C$_2$H$_5$)$_2$Cl
② Et$_3$SiCH$_2$CH=CH$_2$ + H$_2$PtCl$_6$
    + Et$_2$SiHCl $\longrightarrow$ 14.7%
③ (139~144°/2).
⑥ Izv. OKhN **1963**, 654.

Si$_2$C$_{13}$H$_{31}$Cl
① 1-Triethylsilyl-2-methyl-n-butyl-
    chlorosilylethane
    (C$_2$H$_5$)$_3$SiCH$_2$CH$_2$Si(CH$_3$)Cl(n-C$_4$H$_9$)
② H$_2$PtCl$_6$ + Et$_3$SiCH=CH$_2$
    + MeSi(H)(Cl)Bu-n $\longrightarrow$
③ (117°/2). n_D1.4605 (20°). d0.9012
    (20°/4°).
④ + BrMgOCMe$_2$C≡CMgBr $\longrightarrow$
    Et$_3$Si(CH$_2$)$_2$SiMeBu-nC≡CCMe$_2$OH
⑥ Zhur. **33**, 2281 (1963).

Si$_2$C$_{13}$H$_{31}$Cl
① 1-Diethylchlorosilyl-2-methyldi-n-
    propylethane
    (C$_2$H$_5$)$_2$Si(Cl)CH$_2$CH$_2$Si(n-C$_3$H$_7$)$_2$CH$_3$
② H$_2$PtCl$_6$ + Et$_2$Si(Cl)CH=CH$_2$
    + n-Pr$_2$SiHMe $\longrightarrow$
③ (118°/2). n_D1.4551 (20°). d0.8802
    (20°/4°).
⑥ Zhur. **33**, 2281 (1963).

Si$_2$C$_{13}$H$_{32}$
① Hexaethyldisilylmethane
    (C$_2$H$_5$)$_3$SiCH$_2$Si(C$_2$H$_5$)$_3$
② (Cl$_3$Si)$_2$CH$_2$ + EtMgI $\longrightarrow$
③ (243~245°). n_D1.4578 (20°). d0.8218
    (20°).
⑥ Dokl. **99**, 551 (1954); **86**, 559 (1952).

Si$_2$C$_{14}$H$_{16}$Cl$_2$O
① 1,3-Diphenyl-1,3-dimethyl-1,3-di-
    chlorodisiloxane
    [C$_6$H$_5$Si(Cl)CH$_3$]$_2$O
② PhSi(Cl)$_2$Me + H$_2$O $\longrightarrow$
③ (162~163°/4). n_D1.5318 (20°), 1.5317
    (25°). d1.153 (20°).
④ + Ac$_2$O $\longrightarrow$ (AcOSiMePh)$_2$O
⑥ Izv. OKhN **1963**, 651.   JACS **74**, 386
    (1952).

Si$_2$C$_{14}$H$_{18}$O$_3$

① 1,2-Diphenyl-1,2-dimethyl-1,2-di-
   hydoxydisiloxane
   HO-[Si(CH$_3$)(C$_6$H$_5$)O]$_2$-H

② H$_2$O + MeSiCl$_2$Ph $\longrightarrow$

③ [99～101°].

④ + Ti(OBu-n)$_4$
   $\longrightarrow$ Ti[O(SiMePhO)$_2$-H]$_4$

⑥ Izv. SKh **1963**, 1672.

Si$_2$C$_{14}$H$_{22}$F$_{12}$O

① 1,3-Dimethyltetrakis(3,3,3-trifluoro-
   propyl)disiloxane
   [CH$_3$Si(CH$_2$CH$_2$CF$_3$)$_2$]$_2$O

② (CF$_3$CH$_2$CH$_2$)$_2$Si(Me)OEt + EtOH
   + HOH + HCl $\longrightarrow$

③ (132.9～133.0°/7). n_D1.3668 (20°).
   d1.2852 (20°/4°).

⑥ Zhur. **33**, 704 (1963).

Si$_2$C$_{14}$H$_{26}$

① p-Bis(diethylsilyl)benzene
   p-C$_6$H$_4$[SiH(C$_2$H$_5$)$_2$]$_2$

② p-C$_6$H$_4$(MgBr)$_2$ + Et$_2$SiHCl $\longrightarrow$

③ (120～122°/2). n_D1.5074 (25°). d0.8480
   (20°).

⑥ CA **58**, 11392 (1963).

Si$_2$C$_{14}$H$_{26}$

① p-Bis(trimethylsilylmethyl)-
   benzene
   p-C$_6$H$_4$[CH$_2$Si(CH$_3$)$_3$]$_2$

② p-C$_6$H$_4$(CH$_2$MgCl)$_2$ + Me$_3$SiCl $\longrightarrow$

③ (102°/3, 125°/4).

⑥ Izv. OKhN **1963**, 822.

Si$_2$C$_{14}$H$_{26}$O$_2$

① p-Bis(ethoxydimethylsilyl)benzene
   p-C$_6$H$_4$[Si(CH$_3$)$_2$OC$_2$H$_5$]$_2$

② Mg + Me$_2$Si(OEt)$_2$
   + p-C$_6$H$_4$Cl$_2$ $\longrightarrow$
   p-C$_6$H$_4$(MgBr)$_2$ + Me$_2$Si(OEt)$_2$
   $\longrightarrow$ 37%

③ (90～93°/0.05). n_D1.4756 (25°). d0.9370
   (25°/4°).

④ + AcOH $\longrightarrow$ p-C$_6$H$_4$(SiMe$_2$OH)$_2$

⑥ US 3053872 (1962) ; CA **58**, 3457
   (1963).

Si$_2$C$_{14}$H$_{26}$O$_2$S

① Bis(1-trimethylsilylethynylethyl)-
   sulfone
   [(CH$_3$)$_3$SiC≡CCH(CH$_3$)]$_2$SO$_2$

② HOOH + (Me$_3$SiC≡CCHMe)$_2$S
   $\longrightarrow$ 80.2%

③ Solid. [60～61°].

⑥ Izv. OkhN **1963**, 90.

Si$_2$C$_{14}$H$_{26}$S

① Bis(1-trimethylsilylethynylethyl)
   sulfide
   [(CH$_3$)$_3$SiC≡CCH(CH$_3$)]$_2$S

② Me$_3$SiC≡CCH(Cl)Me + NaSH
   $\longrightarrow$ 48%
   EtMgBr + Me$_3$SiC≡CCH(Me)SCN
   $\longrightarrow$ 65%

③ (115～116°/8). n_D1.4945 (20°). d0.892
   (20°/4°).

⑥ Izv. OKhN **1963**, 90.

Si$_2$C$_{14}$H$_{28}$O$_6$Sn

① Bis(trimethylsiloxy)tin dimethacry-
   late
   [CH$_2$=C(CH$_3$)COO]$_2$Sn[OSi(CH$_3$)$_3$]$_2$

② Sn(OSiMe$_3$)$_4$ + CH$_2$=C(Me)COOH $\longrightarrow$

③ Solid. [67～69°].

⑥ Vysokomol. Soed. **5**, 217 (1963).

Si$_2$C$_{14}$H$_{30}$

① 2,5,5-Trimethyl-3-triethylsilyl-5-sila-
   hexadiene-1,3
   (CH$_3$)$_3$SiCH=C[Si(C$_2$H$_5$)$_3$]C(CH$_3$)=CH$_2$

② H$_2$PtCl$_6$ + Et$_3$SiH +
   Me$_3$SiC≡CCHC(Me)=CH$_2$ $\longrightarrow$
   Me$_3$SiCH=C(SiCl$_2$Et)C(Me)=CH$_2$
   + EtMgBr $\longrightarrow$

③ (94～96°/5, 79～80°/3). n_D1.4692 (20°).

d0.8400 (20°/4°).

⑥ Zhur. **33**, 2868 (1963).

Si₂C₁₄H₃₂

① Hexaethyldisilyl-1,2-ethylene
   $(C_2H_5)_3SiCH=CHSi(C_2H_5)_3$

② $Cl_3SiCH=CHSiCl_3 + C_2H_5MgBr$
   ⟶ 76.6%

③ Colorless liquid. (264°). n_D1.4615(20°).
   d0.8226 (20°).
   Sol. in org. solvents; insol. in
   water.

⑥ Dokl. **105**, 865 (1955); CA **50**, 11234
   (1956).

Si₂C₁₄H₃₂O₂

① 1,2-Di-*n*-propyl-1,2-bis(trimethylsiloxy)ethene
   $(n\text{-}C_3H_7)[(CH_3)_3SiO]C=$
   $C[OSi(CH_3)_3](C_3H_7\text{-}n)$

② $n\text{-}PrCOOEt + Na + Me_3SiCl$
   ⟶ 92.3%
   $n\text{-}PrCOCl + Na + Me_3SiCl$ ⟶

③ (106~108°/12). n_D1.4317. d0.8569
   (20°/4°).

⑥ Ber. **96**, 2780 (1963).   J. prakt. Chem.
   12, 18 (1960).

Si₂C₁₄H₃₂O₆

① 1,1,6,6-Tetraethoxy-1,6-disila-2,7-
   dioxacyclodecane

   $$(C_2H_5O)_2Si\underset{\text{OCH}_2\text{CH}_2\text{CH}_2}{\overset{\text{CH}_2\text{CH}_2\text{CH}_2O}{<\qquad>}}Si(OC_2H_5)_2$$

② $H_2PtCl_6 + Me_2Si(OCH_2CH=CH_2)_2$
   $+ Me_2Si[OCH_2CH_2CH_2Si(OEt)_3]_2$
   ⟶

③ (88~91°/1). n_D1.412 (20°). d0.9749
   (20°/4°).

⑥ Dokl. **151**, 849 (1963).

Si₂C₁₄H₃₄

① 1,2-Bis(triethylsilyl)ethane

$(C_2H_5)_3SiCH_2CH_2Si(C_2H_5)_3$

② $EtMgBr + Cl_3SiCH_2CH_2SiCl_3$ ⟶

③ (90~92°/2). [−38°]. n_D1.4575 (20°).
   d0.8236 (20°).

⑥ Dokl. **86**, 551 (1952); **99**, 551 (1954);
   CA **49**, 5271 (1955).   Dokl. **86**, 559
   (1952); CA **47**, 12223 (1953).

Si₂C₁₄H₃₄O

① 3,3,5,5,9,9-Hexamethyl-4-oxa-3,9-
   disilaundecane
   $C_2H_5Si(CH_3)_2CH_2CH_2CH_2C(CH_3)_2OSi\text{-}$
   $(CH_3)_2C_2H_5$

② $EtSi(Me)_2CH_2CH_2CH_2C(Me)CH_2$
   $\underset{\qquad\text{O}\qquad}{\lfloor\qquad\qquad\rfloor}$
   $+ EtSiHMe_2$ ⟶

③ (141~142°/0.5). n_D1.4540(20°). d0.8503
   (20°).

⑥ CA **59**, 2847 (1963).

Si₂C₁₄H₃₄O

① 1,3-Dimethyltetrapropyldisiloxane
   $CH_3Si(C_3H_7)_2OSi(C_3H_7)_2CH_3$

② $H_2O + HCl + PrSiMe_2OMe$ ⟶

③ (115~116°/12, 99°/4). n_D1.4291 (25°),
   1.485 (20°). d0.8354 (25°/4°), 0.8249
   (20°).

⑥ Dokl. **125**, 817 (1959); CA **55**, 19849
   (1961).   Acta Chim. Scand. **9**, 947
   (1955).   JACS **84**, 4730 (1962).

Si₂C₁₄H₃₆

① Decamethyl-2,4,6-trisilaheptane
   $(CH_3)_2Si[C(CH_3)_2Si(CH_3)_3]_2$

② $MeMgBr + Me_2Si(CMe_2SiMe_2F)_2$
   ⟶ 66%

③ (149°/13). n_D1.4870 (20°). d0.8733
   (20°/4°).

⑥ JOM **2**, 136 (1964).

Si$_2$C$_{14}$H$_{36}$Sn

① Di-*n*-butylbis(dimethylsilylmethyl)-
stannane
[(CH$_3$)$_2$Si(H)CH$_2$]$_2$Sn(*n*-C$_4$H$_9$)$_2$

② Bu$_2$SnCl$_2$ + Me$_2$Si(H)CH$_2$MgCl $\longrightarrow$

③ (130°/5). n_D1.4810 (25°). d1.043
(25°/4°).

④ + Na + EtOH
$\longrightarrow$ [Me$_2$Si(OEt)CH$_2$]$_2$Sn(Bu-*n*)$_2$

⑥ JACS **81**, 975 (1959). US 3043858
(1962); CA **58**, 1489 (1963). Brit.
891087 (1962); CA **59**, 11560 (1963).

Si$_2$C$_{15}$H$_{25}$N$_2$

① 2-Chloro-2-cyclohexyl-3-trimethyl-
silyl-2-sila-1,3-dinitrahydrindene

Si(CH$_3$)$_3$

Si(Cl)C$_6$H$_{11}$

② C$_6$H$_{11}$SiCl$_3$ + *o*-C$_6$H$_4$(NHSiMe$_3$)$_2$ $\longrightarrow$

③ Solid. [187~189° decomp.].

⑥ Angew. **2**, 152 (1963).

Si$_2$C$_{15}$H$_{26}$O$_3$

① 2,3-Bis(trimethylsilyl)-1-methyl-
cyclohexene-4,5-dicarboxylic acid
anhydride

②

Me$_3$SiCH=C(SiMe$_3$)C(Me)=CH$_2$ $\longrightarrow$

③ [135~137°].

⑥ Zhur. **33**, 2868 (1963).

Si$_2$C$_{15}$H$_{27}$Cl

① 1-Triethylsilyl-2-methylphenyl-
chlorosilylethane
(C$_2$H$_5$)$_3$SiCH$_2$CH$_2$Si(CH$_3$)(Cl)C$_6$H$_5$

② H$_2$PtCl$_6$ + Et$_3$SiCH=CH$_2$
+ MeSi(H)(Cl)Ph $\longrightarrow$

③ (145°/4). n_D1.5070 (20°). d0.9833
(20°/4°).

④ + BrMgOC(Me)$_2$C≡CMgBr $\longrightarrow$
Et$_3$Si(CH$_2$)$_2$SiMePhC≡CCMe$_2$OH

⑥ Zhur. **33**, 2281 (1963).

Si$_2$C$_{15}$H$_{35}$Cl

① 1-Tri-*n*-propylsilyl-2-methyl-
n-propylchlorosilylethane
(*n*-C$_3$H$_7$)$_3$SiCH$_2$CH$_2$Si(CH$_3$)(*n*-C$_3$H$_7$)Cl

② H$_2$PtCl$_6$ + *n*-Pr$_3$SiCH=CH$_2$
+ MeSiHClPr-*n* $\longrightarrow$

③ (135~137°/5). n_D1.4598 (20°). d0.8898
(20°/4°).

⑥ Zhur. **33**, 2123 (1963).

Si$_2$C$_{15}$H$_{36}$O$_4$

① 1-Triethylsiloxy-3-triethoxysilyl-
propane
(C$_2$H$_5$)$_3$SiOCH$_2$CH$_2$CH$_2$Si(OC$_2$H$_5$)$_3$

② H$_2$PtCl$_6$ + Et$_3$SiOCH$_2$CH=CH$_2$ +
HSi(OEt)$_3$ $\longrightarrow$

③ (118~123°/1). n_D1.426 (20°). d0.9205
(20°/4°).

⑥ Dokl. **151**, 849 (1963).

Si$_2$C$_{16}$H$_{18}$O$_3$

① 1,3-Divinyl-1,3-dihydroxy-1,3-di-
phenyldisiloxane
(CH$_2$=CH)(C$_6$H$_5$)Si(OH)OSi(OH)-
(C$_6$H$_5$)(CH=CH$_2$)

②

③ [107°].

⑥ US 2678938 (1954). JACS **74**, 4584 (1952).

$Si_2C_{16}H_{20}O$

① 1,4-Dimethyl-1,4-diphenyl-1,4-disila-5-oxacyclopentane

$C_6H_5Si(CH_3)CH_2CH_2Si(CH_3)C_6H_5$

$\underset{\qquad}{|\qquad\qquad O\qquad\qquad|}$

② PhSiMe(Cl)CH$_2$CH$_2$SiMePhCl
                (I)

+ LiOH + H$_2$O $\longrightarrow$

(I) + H$_2$O $\longrightarrow$

③ (182°/10). n_D.15492   (25°). d1.047 (25°/4°).

④
$$+ \text{PhSiMeSiMe}_2 + \text{KO-(SiMe}_2\text{O)}_{45}\text{-K}$$
with $\underset{O}{\overset{CH_2-CH_2}{|\quad\quad|}}$

$\longrightarrow$ copolymers

⑥ JACS **82**, 1883 (1960).   US 3041362 (1962); CA **58**, 1558 (1963).

$Si_2C_{16}H_{20}O$

① 1,1-Dimethyl-4,4-diphenyl-1,4-disila-5-oxacyclopentane

$(CH_3)_2SiCH_2-CH_2Si(C_6H_5)_2$

$\underset{\qquad}{|\qquad O\qquad|}$

② HOH +
Ph$_2$Si(Cl)CH$_2$CH$_2$SiMe$_2$Cl $\longrightarrow$

LiOH + HOH
+ Ph$_2$Si(Cl)CH$_2$CH$_2$SiMe$_2$Cl $\longrightarrow$

③ (181°/11). n_D1.5492   (25°). d1.044 (25°/4°).

④
$$+ \underset{Ph_2Si\underset{O}{\diagdown}SiPh_2}{\overset{CH_2-CH_2}{\overset{|\quad\quad|}{}}} +$$

KO-(SiMe$_2$O)$_{45}$-K $\longrightarrow$

copolymers

⑥ JACS **82**, 1883 (1960).   US 3041362 (1962); CA **58**, 1558 (1963).

$Si_2C_{16}H_{22}N_2$

① 1,1-Diphenyltetramethylcyclo-disilazane

$$(CH_3)_2Si\underset{N(CH_3)}{\overset{N(CH_3)}{\diagup\diagdown}}Si(C_6H_5)_2$$

② Ph$_2$SiCl$_2$ + Me$_2$Si(NLiMe)$_2$ $\longrightarrow$

③ (143~144°/4).

⑥ Angew. **75**, 638 (1963).

$Si_2C_{16}H_{24}Cl_2$

① Dimethylferrocenyl(γ-methyldi-chlorosilyl)propylsilane

$C_5H_5FeC_5H_4Si(CH_3)_2CH_2CH_2CH_2Si$-$Cl_2CH_3$

② H$_2$PtCl$_6$ +
$C_5H_5FeC_5H_4Si(Me)_2CH_2CH=CH_2$
+ MeSiHCl$_2$ $\longrightarrow$ 98.5%

③ n_D1.5389 (20°). d1.2046 (20°/4°).

⑥ Dokl. **152**, 1118 (1963).

$Si_2C_{16}H_{26}Fe$

① 1,1'-Bis(trimethylsilyl)ferrocene

$Fe[C_5H_4Si(CH_3)_3]_2$

② C$_5$H$_5$SiMe$_3$ + BuLi + C$_6$H$_6$, under N$_2$, then FeCl$_2$ $\longrightarrow$ 50%

③ (104°/0.15). n_D1.5437 (25°).

⑥ US 3060215 (1962); CA **58**, 6865 (1963).

$Si_2C_{16}H_{30}O_2S$

① Bis(1-dimethylethylsilylethynylethyl) sulfone

$[C_2H_5Si(CH_3)_2C\equiv CC(CH_3)-]_2SO_2$

② (EtSiMe$_2$C≡CCHMe-)$_2$S
+ HOOH $\longrightarrow$

③ Solid. [79°].

⑥ Izv. OKhN **1963**, 90.

$Si_2C_{16}H_{30}S$

① Bis (1-ethyldimethylsilylethynylethyl) sulfide

$[C_2H_5Si(CH_3)_2C\equiv CCH(CH_3)-]_2S$

② NaSH + EtSiMe$_2$C≡CCHClMe $\longrightarrow$

③ (113°/2). n_D1.5085 (25°). d1.9187

(20°/4°).
④ + HOOH ⟶ sulfone
⑥ Izv. OKhN **1963**, 90.

Si$_2$C$_{16}$H$_{32}$
① 4-*t*-Butyl-3,6-bis(trimethylsilyl)-
   cyclohexadiene-1,4

$$\text{(CH}_3)_3\text{SiCH} \overset{\text{CH}}{\diagdown} \text{CH}$$
$$t\text{-C}_4\text{H}_9\text{C} \diagup_{\text{CH}} \diagdown \text{CHSi(CH}_3)_3$$

② Me$_3$SiCl + Li + THF
   + PhBu-*t* ⟶
③ (96°/1.5). n_D1.4732 (25°).
⑥ Fr. 1327544 (1963); CA **59**, 12843
   (1963).

Si$_2$C$_{16}$H$_{32}$O$_4$
① Bis(triethylsilyl) maleate
   [HCCOOSi(C$_2$H$_5$)$_3$]$_2$
② MeCOOSiEt$_3$ + (HCCOOH)$_2$
   ⟶ 65.0%
③ (144.5~145.0°/3). n_D1.4564 (20°).
   d0.9682 (20°/4°).
⑥ Zhur. **33**, 1934 (1963).

Si$_2$C$_{16}$H$_{34}$O$_4$
① Bis(triethylsilyl) succinate
   [CH$_2$COOSi(C$_2$H$_5$)$_3$]$_2$
② (CH$_2$COOH)$_2$ + Et$_3$SiH + Ni (colloidal)
   ⟶ 60.0%
   (CH$_2$COOH)$_2$ + Et$_3$SiH + NiCl$_2$
   ⟶ 58.9%
③ (161.5°/2). n_D1.4455 (20°). d0.9568
   (20°/4°).
⑥ Zhur. **33**, 1934 (1963); **32**, 2561 (1962).

Si$_2$C$_{16}$H$_{36}$O$_2$
① 1,2-Di-*n*-butyl-1,2-bis(trimethylsiloxy)ethene
   [*n*-C$_4$H$_9$COSi(CH$_3$)$_3$]$_2$
② *n*-BuCOCl + Na + Me$_3$SiCl ⟶
   Na + Me$_3$SiCl + *n*-BuCOOEt

⟶ 76%
③ (127.0~129.5°/12~13). n_D1.4359 (20°).
   d0.8565 (20°/4°).
⑥ Ber. **96**, 2780 (1963). J. prakt. Chem.
   12, 18 (1960).

Si$_2$C$_{16}$H$_{36}$O$_2$
① 1,2-Diisobutyl-1,2-bis(trimethoxy-
   silyl)ethene
   [*i*-C$_4$H$_9$COSi(CH$_3$)$_3$]$_2$
② Na + Me$_3$SiCl + *i*-BuCOOEt
   ⟶ 72.9%
③ (116~118°/12~13). n_D1.4364 (20°).
   d0.8583 (20°/4°).
⑥ Ber. **96**, 2780 (1963).

Si$_2$C$_{16}$H$_{38}$O$_2$
① 1,10-Bis(trimethylsiloxy)decane
   (CH$_3$)$_3$SiO(CH$_2$)$_{10}$OSi(CH$_3$)$_3$
② Me$_3$SiCl + HO−(CH$_2$)$_{10}$−OH
   ⟶ 70%
③ (116~118°/0.7). n_D1.4307 (18°).
⑥ CA **59**, 10105 (1963).

Si$_2$C$_{17}$H$_{31}$Cl
① 1-Triethylsilyl-3-ethylphenylchloro-
   silylpropane
   (C$_2$H$_5$)$_3$SiCH$_2$CH$_2$CH$_2$SiClC$_2$H$_5$C$_6$H$_5$
② Et$_3$SiCH$_2$CH=CH$_2$ + PhSiHClEt
   ⟶ 62.8%
③ (168~170°/2).
⑥ Izv. OKhN **1963**, 654.

Si$_2$C$_{18}$H$_{20}$Cl$_2$O$_3$
① 1,3-Diphenyltetramethyldisiloxane-*p*,
   p′-dicarboxylic acid chloride
   O[Si(CH$_3$)$_2$C$_6$H$_4$COCl-*p*]$_2$
② O(SiMe$_2$C$_6$H$_4$COOH-*p*)$_2$ + SOCl$_2$ ⟶
③ Solid. [54~55°].
⑥ Plasticheskie Massy (No.11) 19
   (1962).

Si₂C₁₈H₂₂O₅

① 1,3-Diacetoxy-1,3-dimethyl-1,3-di-
   phenyldisiloxane
   [CH₃CO₂Si(CH₃)(C₆H₅)]₂O
② (PhSiMeCl)₂O + Ac₂O ⟶ 75.5%
③ (194.0∼195.5°/6). n_D 1.5082 (20°).
   d 1.1273 (20°/4°).
⑥ Izv. OKhN, 1963, 651.

Si₂C₁₈H₂₄F₁₈O

① Hexa(3,3,3-trifluoropropyl) disiloxane
   [(CF₃CH₂CH₂)₃Si]₂O
② (CF₃CH₂CH₂)₃SiOEt + EtOH + H₂O
   + HCl ⟶ 88.5%
③ Solid. [143.0∼143.5°].
⑥ Zhur. 33, 704 (1963).

Si₂C₁₈H₂₆O₂

① *o,o′*-Bis(trimethylsiloxy)biphenyl
   [*o*-(CH₃)₃SiOC₆H₄]₂
② (*o*-NaOC₆H₄)₂
   + (CH₃)₃SiNHSiMe₃ ⟶
   (CH₃)₃SiCl + (*o*-HOC₆H₄)₂ ⟶
③ (116∼118°/0.55). n_D 1.5178 (20°).
⑥ Z. Naturf. 18B, 582 (1963). Brit.
   857153 (1960); CA 55, 18684 (1961).

Si₂C₁₈H₂₆O₃

① 1,3-Di-*n*-propoxy-1,3-diphenyldisilo-
   xane
   n-C₃H₇OSiH(C₆H₅)OSiH(C₆H₅)OC₃H₇-*n*
② PhSiH₃ + *n*-PrOH + Cu (powder)
   ⟶ 8.4%
③ (105∼110°/3). n_D 1.4847 (20°).
⑥ Zhur. 33, 2617 (1963).

Si₂C₁₈H₂₈N₂

① *p*-Bis(3-cyanopropyldimethylsilyl)-
   benzene
   p-C₆H₄[Si(CH₃)₂CH₂CH₂CH₂CN]₂
② CH₂=CHCH₂CN + *p*-C₆H₄(SiHMe₂)₂
   + H₂PtCl₆ ⟶ 51.5%
③ (205∼209°/0.1). n_D 1.5187 (25°).

d 0.9816 (25°/4°).
⑥ Mem. Fac. Eng. Osaka City Univ. 4,
   177 (1962).

Si₂C₁₈H₃₁NO₆

① Hexaallyloxydisilazane
   [(CH₂=CHCH₂O)₃Si]₂NH
② SiCl₄ + NH₃ + CH₂=CHCH₂OH ⟶
③ (139°/1∼2). n_D 1.4526 (25°). d 1.0252
   (25°/4°).
⑥ Z. anorg. allg. Chem. 419, 244 (1963).

Si₂C₁₈H₃₄

① *p*-Bis(di-*n*-propylsilyl)benzene
   p-C₆H₄[SiH(C₃H₇)₂]₂
② Pr₂SiHCl + *p*-C₆H₄(MgBr)₂ ⟶ 34%
③ (160∼162°/3). n_D 1.5022 (20°). d 0.8845
   (20°).
⑥ CA 58, 11392 (1963).

Si₂C₁₈H₃₅OP

① Bis(γ-trimethylsilylpropyl)phenyl-
   phosphine oxide
   C₆H₅P(O)[CH₂CH₂CH₂Si(CH₃)₃]₂
② Me₃SiCH₂CH₂CH₂MgCl
   + C₆H₅POCl₂ ⟶
③ (152∼154°/0.1).
④ + H₂SO₄ ⟶
   PhP(O)(CH₂CH₂CH₂SiMe₂OH)₂
⑥ Fr. 1318080 (1963); CA 59, 10132
   (1963).

Si₂C₁₈H₃₆N₂

① *p*-Bis(4-aminobutyldimethylsilyl)-
   benzene
   p-C₆H₄[Si(CH₃)₂CH₂CH₂CH₂CH₂NH₂]₂
② LiAlH₄ +
   p-C₆H₄(SiMe₂CH₂CH₂CH₂CN)₂ ⟶
③ (182∼184°/1). n_D 1.5221 (25°). d 0.9369
   (20°/4°).
⑥ Mem. Fac. Eng. Osaka City Univ. 4,
   177 (1962).

Si$_2$C$_{18}$H$_{38}$

① Bis(trimethylsilyl)cyclododecene
   cyclo-C$_{12}$H$_{20}$[Si(CH$_3$)$_3$]$_2$
② MeMgCl + C$_{12}$H$_{20}$(SiCl$_3$)$_2$ ⟶
③ (132~133°/1). n_D1.4894 (20°). d0.8818
   (25°/3°).
⑥ JOC **28**, 3353 (1963).

Si$_2$C$_{18}$H$_{40}$O$_2$

① 1,2-Isoamyl-1,2-bis(trimethylsilyl)
   ethene
   [*i*-C$_4$H$_9$CH$_2$COSi(CH$_3$)$_3$]$_2$
② Na + Me$_3$SiCl + *i*-BuCH$_2$COOEt
   ⟶ 71.9%
③ (149~151°/13~14). n_D1.4360 (20°).
   d0.852 (20°/4°).
⑥ Ber. **96**, 2780 (1963).

Si$_2$C$_{18}$H$_{41}$Cl

① 1-Tripropylsilyl-3-dipropylchloro-
   silylpropane
   (C$_3$H$_7$)$_3$SiCH$_2$CH$_2$CH$_2$Si(C$_3$H$_7$)$_2$Cl
② Pr$_3$SiCH$_2$CH=CH$_2$ + Pr$_2$SiHCl
   + H$_2$PtCl$_6$ ⟶ 61%
③ (160~162°/2).
⑥ Izv. OKhN **1963**, 654.

Si$_2$C$_{18}$H$_{42}$

① Hexa-*n*-propyldisilane
   (C$_3$H$_7$)$_3$SiSi(C$_3$H$_7$)$_3$
② Pr$_3$SiI + Na (molten) ⟶ 68.3%
③ (128.5~129°/1.5). n_D1.4721 (20°).
   d0.8291 (20°).
⑥ CA **50**, 13729 (1956).   JACS **61**, 363
   (1939).

Si$_2$C$_{18}$H$_{42}$NNaO$_3$

① Bis(triisopropoxysilyl)sodioamine
   (*i*-C$_3$H$_7$O)$_3$SiN(Na)Si(OC$_3$H$_7$-*i*)$_3$
② NaNH$_2$ +
   (*i*-PrO)$_3$Si$-$NH$-$Si(OPr-*i*)$_3$ ⟶
③ Solid. [204~206°].
⑥ Angew. **75**, 95 (1963).

Si$_2$C$_{18}$H$_{44}$O$_2$Sn

① Di-*n*-butylbis(ethoxydimethyl-
   silylmethyl)tin
   (C$_4$H$_9$)$_2$Sn[CH$_2$Si(CH$_3$)$_2$OC$_2$H$_5$]$_2$
② EtONa + *n*-Bu$_2$Sn(CH$_2$SiHMe$_2$)$_2$ ⟶
③ (186°/15). n_D1.4655 (25°). d1.056(25°).
⑥ US 3043858 (1962); CA **58**, 1489
   (1963).   Brit. 891087 (1962); CA **59**,
   11560 (1963).

Si$_2$C$_{18}$H$_{45}$NSn

① Bis(trimethylsilyl)tri-*n*-butyl-
   stannylamine
   [(CH$_3$)$_3$Si]$_2$NSn(C$_4$H$_9$-*n*)$_3$
② Me$_3$SiN(Na)SiMe$_3$
   + *n*-Bu$_3$SnCl ⟶
③ (140~145°/1).
⑥ Angew. Int'l. Ed. **2**, 478 (1963).
   Angew. **75**, 642 (1963).

Si$_2$C$_{19}$H$_{28}$

① Diphenylbis(trimethylsilyl)methane
   (C$_6$H$_5$)$_2$C[Si(CH$_3$)$_3$]$_2$
② Ph$_2$CCl$_2$ + Mg + Me$_3$SiCl ⟶
③ [103°].
⑥ JACS **85**, 2243 (1963).

Si$_2$C$_{19}$H$_{28}$NO

① *N*,*N*'-Bis(phenyldimethylsilylmethyl)carbamide
   CO[NHCH$_2$Si(CH$_3$)$_2$C$_6$H$_5$]$_2$
② COS + PhSiMe$_2$CH$_2$NH$_2$ ⟶
③ Solid. [131~132°].
⑥ US 3049559 (1962); CA **57**, 16412
   (1962).

Si$_2$C$_{19}$H$_{43}$Cl

① 1-Tri-*n*-butylsilyl-2-*n*-butylmethyl-
   chlorosilylethane
   (*n*-C$_4$H$_9$)$_3$SiCH$_2$CH$_2$Si(CH$_3$)(C$_4$H$_9$-*n*)Cl
② H$_2$PtCl$_6$ + *n*-Bu$_3$SiCH=CH$_2$
   + *n*-BuSi(H)(Cl)Me ⟶
③ (173°/4). n_D1.4622 (20°). d0.8915

$(20°/4°)$.

④ + $Me_2C(OMgBr)C\equiv CMgBr$

    $\longrightarrow$ n-$Bu_3SiCH_2CH_2Si(Me)$-

                $(Bu$-$n)C\equiv CCMe_2OH$

⑥ Zhur. **33**, 2281 (1963).

$Si_2C_{20}H_{20}Cl_2$

① p-Bis(methylphenylchlorosilyl)-

   benzene

   p-$C_6H_4[Si(CH_3)(C_6H_5)Cl]_2$

② $MeSi(H)(Ph)Cl + p$-$C_6H_4Cl_2$

   $\overset{650°}{\longrightarrow}$ 29%

③ $(260{\sim}274°/12)$. $n_D 1.6072$ $(20°)$. $d 1.1815$

   $(20°)$.

⑥ Zhur. **32**, 557 (1962).

$Si_2C_{20}H_{22}$

① p-Bis(methylphenylsilyl)benzene

   p-$C_6H_4[SiH(CH_3)C_6H_5]_2$

② p-$C_6H_4(MgBr)_2 + MeSiHClPh$

   $\longrightarrow$ 52%

③ $(205{\sim}207°/3)$. $[42°]$

⑥ Neftekhimiya 2, 632 (1962).

$Si_2C_{20}H_{25}N$

① 2,2,4,4-Tetraphenyl-2,4-disila-

   pyrrolidine

$$(C_6H_5)_2Si\overset{\displaystyle CH_2-CH_2}{\underset{\displaystyle NH}{\diagup\quad\diagdown}}Si(C_6H_5)_2$$

② $(Ph_2SiClCH_2)_2 + NH_3 \longrightarrow$

③ $[150°]$.

⑥ JCS **1963**, 4758.

$Si_2C_{20}H_{28}N_3$

① 1,1-Bis(trimethylsilyl)-3,5-diphenyl-

   -1,2,4-triazole

$$C_6H_5C\underset{\displaystyle N=CC_6H_5}{\overset{\displaystyle N-N[Si(CH_3)_3]_2}{\diagup\diagdown\vert}}$$

② Pyrolysis of $PhC{=}N$

$$\underset{N=N}{\overset{\vert}{\quad}}{\Big\rangle}N(SiMe_3)_2$$

$\longrightarrow$ 95%

$$PhC\underset{\displaystyle N=N}{\overset{\displaystyle N-N}{\diagup\quad\diagdown}}CPh + Me_3SiNHSiMe_3$$

   $\longrightarrow$ 60%

③ $(175{\sim}180°/0.1)$. $[98°]$.

④ Undergoes hydrolysis in acid.

⑥ Ber. **96**, 2750 (1963).

$Si_2C_{20}H_{30}$

① 1,2-Diphenyltetraethyldisilane

   $C_6H_5Si(C_2H_5)_2Si(C_2H_5)_2C_6H_5$

② $Na + PhSiEt_2Cl \longrightarrow 23\%$

③ $(190{\sim}192°/3.5)$. $n_D 1.5563$ $(20°)$.

   $d 0.9629$ $(20°/4°)$.

⑥ Izv. OKhN **1963**, 660.

$Si_2C_{20}H_{34}Fe$

① Dimethylferrocenyl(γ-methyldiethyl-

   silyl)propylsilane

   $C_5H_5FeC_5H_4Si(CH_3)_2CH_2CH_2CH_2Si$-

   $(C_2H_5)_2CH_3$

② $C_5H_5FeC_5H_4Si(Me)_2CH_2CH{=}CH_2 +$

   $H_2PtCl_6 + MeSiHEt_2 \longrightarrow 56\%$

③ $n_D 1.5387$ $(20°)$. $d 1.0558$ $(20°/4°)$.

⑥ Dokl. **152**, 1118 (1963)

$Si_2C_{20}H_{40}O_6Sn_4$

① Bis(triethylsiloxy)stannic

   metharcylate

   $[CH_2{=}C(CH_3)COO]_2Sn[OSi(C_2H_5)_3]_2$

② $Sn(OSiEt_3)_4$

   $+ [CH_2{=}C(Me)COO]_4Sn \rightleftharpoons$

③ Solid. $[85{\sim}87°]$.

④ Polymerized with $(PhCOO)_2$.

⑥ Vysokomol. Soed. **5**, 217 (1963).

$Si_2C_{20}H_{44}$

① Bis(triethylsilyl)cyclooctane

   $cyclo$-$C_8H_{14}[Si(C_2H_5)_3]_2$

② $EtMgBr + C_8H_{14}(SiCl_3)_2 \longrightarrow$

③ $(125{\sim}130°/0.2)$. $n_D 1.4876$ $(25°)$.

⑥ JCS **1963**, 2831.

Si₂C₂₁H₂₂Cl₂
① 1-Diphenylsilyl-2-phenylmethyl-
   chlorosilylethane
   $(C_6H_5)_2SiClCH_2CH_2Si(C_6H_5)(CH_3)Cl$
③ (256°/8).

④ Hydrolyzes to

$$Ph_2Si\underset{O}{\overset{CH_2-CH_2}{\diagdown\diagup}}Si(Me)Ph$$

⑥ US 3041362 (1962) ; CA **58**, 1558 (1963).

Si₂C₂₁H₂₂O
① 1,4,4-Triphenyl-1-methyl-1,4-disila-
   5-oxacyclopentane

$$(C_6H_5)_2Si\underset{O}{\overset{CH_2-CH_2}{\diagdown\diagup}}Si(CH_3)C_6H_5$$

② HOH +
   $Ph_2SiClCH_2CH_2Si(Ph)(Me)Cl \longrightarrow$
③ (241°/11). $n_D1.5860$ (25°). $d1.092$
   (25°).
⑥ US 3041362 (1962) ; CA **58**, 1558 (1963).

Si₂C₂₁H₂₄
① 1,1,1-Trimethyl-2,2,2-triphenyl-
   disilane
   $(CH_3)_3SiSi(C_6H_5)_3$
② $Ph_3SiSi(Me)_2SiPh_3 + THF$
   $+ Li$, then $Me_3SiCl \longrightarrow 65.1\%$
③ Solid. [106~108°].
⑥ JOC **28**, 1651 (1963).

Si₂C₂₁H₂₄O
① 1,1,1-Trimethyl-3,3,3-triphenyl-
   disiloxane
   $(CH_3)_3SiOSi(C_6H_5)_3$
② $SO_2(OSiMe_3)_2 + Ph_3SiH \longrightarrow$
   $Me_3SiONa + Ph_3SiCl \longrightarrow$
③ Solid. (232°/7). [51°]. $n_D1.5587$ (20°).
   $d1.032$ (20°/4°).
⑥ Bull. soc. chim. France 512 (1963).

JACS **74**, 386 (1952).   Ber. **96**, 2132
(1963).

Si₂C₂₁H₃₆Fe
① Dimethylferrocenyl(3-triethylsilyl)-
   propylsilane
   $C_5H_5FeC_5H_4Si(CH_3)_2CH_2CH_2CH_2Si$
   $(C_2H_5)_3$
② $C_5H_5FeC_5H_4Si(Me)_2CH_2CH=CH_2$
   $+ Et_3SiH + H_2PtCl_6 \longrightarrow 57.5\%$
③ $n_D1.5402$ (20°). $d1.0512$ (20°/4°).
⑥ Dokl. **152**, 1118 (1963).

Si₂C₂₂H₂₅Cl
① Methyldiphenylsilylmethyl-
   phenylchloromethylsilylmethane
   $(C_6H_5)_2Si(CH_3)CH_2SiCl(CH_3)C_6H_5$
② $PhSiCl(Me)CH_2Cl$
   $+ Ph_2Si(Me)CH_2Li \longrightarrow$
③ (185°/1).
⑥ Z. anorg. allg. Chem. **322**, 34 (1963).

Si₂C₂₂H₂₆
① p-Bis(ethylphenylsilyl)benzene
   $p\text{-}C_6H_4[SiH(C_2H_5)C_6H_5]_2$
② $PhSi(H)EtCl + p\text{-}C_6H_4(MgBr)_2 \longrightarrow$
③ (210~213°/3). $n_D1.5850$ (20°). $d1.0177$
   (20°).
④ $+ Me_3SiCH=CH_2 + H_2PtCl_6 \longrightarrow$
   $p\text{-}C_6H_4[Si(Et)(Ph)CH_2CH_2SiMe_3]_2$
   (64%)
⑥ Neftekhimiya **2**, 632 (1962) ; CA **58**,
   11342 (1962).

Si₂C₂₂H₃₄
① 1,2-Bis(p-trimethylsilylmethyl-
   phenyl)ethane
   $p\text{-}(CH_3)_3SiCH_2C_6H_4CH_2CH_2C_6H_4CH_2Si$
   $(CH_3)_3\text{-}p$
② $Me_3SiCl + p\text{-}C_6H_4(CH_2MgCl)_2 \longrightarrow$
   $Mg + p\text{-}Me_3SiCH_2C_6H_4CH_2Cl \longrightarrow$
③ Solid. (179~180°/2). [69.5~71.0°].
⑥ Izv. OKhN **1963**, 822.   Zhur. **31**, 1303
   (1961).

$Si_2C_{22}H_{46}O_4$

① Bis(triethylsilyl) suberate
  $[CH_2CH_2CH_2CH_2COOSi(C_2H_5)_3]_2$

③ (213°/2). $n_D 1.4504$ (20°). $d 0.933$
  (20°/4°).

⑥ Izv. OKhN **1963**, 97.

$Si_2C_{22}H_{48}O_6$

① 1,1,6,6-Tetrabutoxy-1,6-disila-5,10-
  dioxacyclodecane

$$(n-C_4H_9O)_2Si \overset{\displaystyle CH_2CH_2CH_2O}{\underset{\displaystyle OCH_2CH_2CH_2}{|\qquad\qquad|}} Si(OC_4H_9\text{-}n)_2$$

② H_2PtCl_6 + $Me_3Si(OCH_2CH=CH_2)_2$
  + $HSi(OBu\text{-}n)_3$ $\longrightarrow$

③ (141~146°/1). $n_D 1.4282$ (20°). $d 0.934$
  (20°/4°).

⑥ Dokl. **151**. 849 (1963).

$Si_2C_{22}H_{49}O_2$

① 1,2-Di-n-heptyl-1,2-bis(trimethylsiloxy)ethene
  $[C_7H_{15}COSi(CH_3)_3]_2$

② Na + Me_3SiCl + $C_7H_{15}COOEt$
  $\longrightarrow$ 79.8%

③ (138~142°/0.2~0.3). $n_D 1.4437$ (20°).
  $d 0.8554$ (20°/4°).

⑥ Ber. **96**, 2780 (1963).

$Si_2C_{23}H_{40}FeO$

① 1-Bis(3-trimethylsilylpropyl)-
  hydroxymethylferrocene
  $C_5H_5FeC_5H_4C[CH_2CH_2CH_2Si(CH_3)_3]_2OH$

② $C_5H_5FeC_5H_4COOMe$
  + $Me_3SiCH_2CH_2CH_2MgCl$ $\longrightarrow$ 90%

③ Solid. [60~62°].

⑥ Dokl. **148**, 598 (1963).

$Si_2C_{24}H_{30}N_2O_4Ti$

① Bis(8-hydroxyquinolinyl)bis-
  (trimethylsiloxy)titanium

②

$\longrightarrow$ 78%

③ Solid. [143~144°].

⑥ Izv. OKhN **1962**, 2138.

$Si_2C_{24}H_{42}Fe$

① Dimethylferrocenyl(γ-methyldi-n-
  butylsilyl)propylsilane
  $C_5H_5FeC_5H_4Si(CH_3)_2CH_2CH_2Si$-
  $(n-C_4H_9)_2CH_3$

② H_2PtCl_6 + n-Bu_2SiHMe
  + $C_5H_5FeC_5H_4SiMe_2CH_2CH=CH_2$
  $\longrightarrow$ 67.7%

③ $n_D 1.5173$ (20°). $d 0.985$ (20°/4°).

⑥ Dokl. **152**, 1118 (1963).

$Si_2C_{24}H_{43}Cl_3O_2$

① Bis(1-t-butyl-1-trimethylsilyl-
  ethynylethyl)acetal of chloral
  $CCl_3CH[OC(CH_3)(C_4H_9\text{-}t)$-
  $C\equiv CSi(CH_3)_2]_2$

② CCl_3CHO +
  t-$BuCMe(OH)C\equiv CSiMe_3$ $\longrightarrow$

③ Liq. (92~94°/0.5). $n_D 1.4656$ (20°).
  $d 1.077$ (20°/4°).

⑥ Zhur. **32**, 3630 (1962).

$Si_2C_{24}H_{46}N_2O_4$

① p-Phenylenebis-4-aminobutyl-
  dimethylsilane adipic acid salt

$$COONH_3CH_2CH_2CH_2CH_2Si(CH_3)_2$$
$$(CH_2)_4 \qquad\qquad\qquad C_6H_4\text{-}p$$
$$COONH_3CH_2CH_2CH_2CH_2Si(CH_3)_2$$

② acid + base $\longrightarrow$

③ Solid. [55~60°].

④ Undergoes dehydration with heat, forming polymers. Mp 74~78°. These are probably polyamides.

⑥ Mem. Fac. Eng. Osaka City Univ. **4**, 177 (1962).

Si₂C₂₄H₄₆O₄

① 1-(*o*-Trimethylsiloxyphenyl)-3-(tri-butoxysilyl)propane

o-$(CH_3)_3SiOC_6H_4CH_2CH_2CH_2Si(OC_4H_9)_3$

② HSi(OBu)₃ +

o-CH_2=$CHCH_2C_6H_4OSiMe_3$ ⟶ 50%

③ (202~204°/1~2). $n_D'1.4954$ (20°). $d\,0.9442$ (20°/4°).

④ + KOH + BuOH ⟶

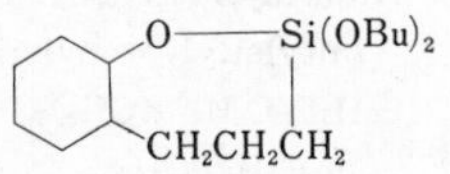

$$\text{cyclohexane ring}\quad O\!-\!\!-\!\!-Si(OBu)_2$$
$$CH_2CH_2CH_2$$

(143~145°/3~4). $n_D1.4812$ (20°). $d\,1.0044$ (20°/4°).

⑥ Izv. OKhN **1962**, 2039.

Si₂C₂₅H₂₈O₃

① Triphenylsiloxydimethylsilylmethyl methacrylate

CH_2=$C(CH_3)COOCH_2Si(CH_3)_2OSi(C_6H_5)_3$

② AcOSiPh₃ +

CH_2=$CMeCOOCH_2SiMe_2OEt$ ⟶ 20%

③ (167°/0.03).

⑥ Izv. OKhN **1962**, 1572.

Si₂C₂₅H₄₈N₂O₄

① *p*-Phenylenebis-4-aminobutyl-dimethylsilane pimelic acid salt

$COONH_3CH_2CH_2CH_2CH_2Si(CH_3)_2$
$(CH_2)_5 \qquad\qquad C_6H_4$-$p$
$COONH_3CH_2CH_2CH_2CH_2Si(CH_3)_2$

② acid + base ⟶

③ [ca. 30°].

④ By heat treatment forms polymers, probably by dehydration to the polyamide. Mol. wt. 9000. Mp 108~

110°.

⑥ Mem. Fac. Eng. Osaka City Univ. **4**, 177 (1962).

Si₂C₂₆H₂₄Cl₂

① 1,2-Bis(diphenylchlorosilyl)ethane

$(C_6H_5)_2SiClCH_2CH_2Si(C_6H_5)_2Cl$

② Ph₂SiHCl + H₂PtCl₆ +

Ph₂SiClCH=CH₂ ⟶

③ Solid. (301°/8). [98°].

⑥ JACS **82**, 1883 (1960).

Si₂C₂₆H₂₄O

① 2,2,4,4-Tetraphenyl-2,4-disila-1-oxacyclopentane

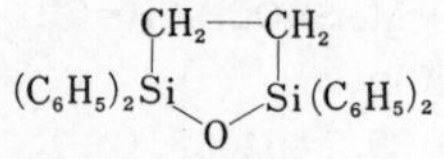

$$CH_2\!-\!\!-\!CH_2$$
$$(C_6H_5)_2Si\qquad Si(C_6H_5)_2$$
$$O$$

② H₂O +

Ph₂SiClCH₂CH₂SiPh₂Cl ⟶

LiOH +

Ph₂SiClCH₂CH₂SiPh₂Cl ⟶

③ Solid. [80~81°]. $n_D1.612$ (25°).

⑥ US 3041362 (1962) ; CA **58**, 1558 (1963). JACS **82**, 1883 (1960).

Si₂C₂₆H₄₂N₂O₄

① *p*-Phenylenebis-4-aminobutyldi-methylsilane terephthalic acid salt

$COONH_3CH_2CH_2CH_2CH_2Si(CH_3)_2$
C_6H_4-$p \qquad\qquad C_6H_4$-p
$COONH_3CH_2CH_2CH_2CH_2Si(CH_3)_2$

② acid + base ⟶

③ Solid. [210~213°].

④ Forms polymers on heat treatment, probably with formation of the polyamide.

⑥ Mem. Fac. Eng. Osaka City Univ. **4**, 177 (1962).

Si₂C₂₆H₅₈O₅

① 1,3-Diamoxy-1,3-di-*t*-amoxy-1,3-diethyldisiloxane

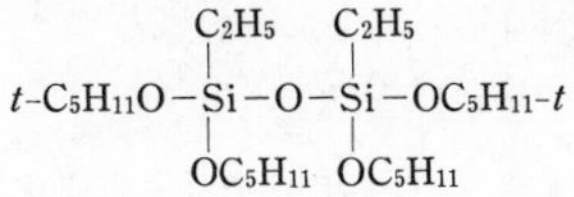

$$\begin{array}{cc} C_2H_5 & C_2H_5 \\ | & | \end{array}$$
$$t\text{-}C_5H_{11}O-Si-O-Si-OC_5H_{11}\text{-}t$$
$$\begin{array}{cc} | & | \\ OC_5H_{11} & OC_5H_{11} \end{array}$$

③ (150~162°).

Resistant to hydrolysis.

⑥ US 2995591 (1958); CA **56**, 3356 (1962).

Si₂C₂₈H₂₈F₆Fe

① 1,1'-Bis(dimethyl-p-trifluorophenyl-silyl)ferrocene

Fe[C₅H₄Si(CH₃)₂C₆H₄CF₃-p]₂

② Me₂SiClC₆H₄CF₃-p + Fe(C₅H₅)₂
+ n-BuLi ⟶

③ [70~71°].

⑥ Dokl. **151**, 1319 (1963).

Si₂C₂₈H₃₀O₃

① 1,1,3,3-Tetramethylbis(p-methoxy-phenyl)disiloxane

[p-C₆H₅OC₆H₄Si(CH₃)₂]₂O

② p-PhOC₆H₄SiMe₂Cl + HOH
+ Na₂CO₃ ⟶
p-PhOC₆H₄SiMe₂ONa
+ p-PhC₆H₄SiMe₂Cl ⟶ 82%

③ (290~292°/8). [−20°]. n_D 1.5652 (20°).
d 1.1032 (20°).

Viscosity: 36.0cs (37.5°).

⑤ Useful as damping or hydraulic fluid.

⑥ Fr. 1321436 (1963); CA **59**, 11561 (1963).
Izv. OKhN **1959**, 1341.

Si₂C₂₈H₅₀Fe

① 1,1'-Bis-(tri-n-propylsilyl)-ferrocene
Fe[C₅H₄Si(C₃H₇-n)₃]₂

② n-Pr₃SiBr + Fe(C₅H₅)₂
+ n-BuLi ⟶

③ (227~233°/1). n_D 1.5213 (20°). d 1.0214
(20°/4°).

⑥ Dokl. **151**, 1319 (1963).

Si₂C₂₈H₅₄N₂O₄

① p-Phenylenebis-4-aminobutyldi-methylsilane sebacic acid salt

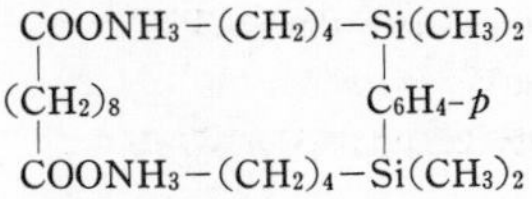

COONH₃−(CH₂)₄−Si(CH₃)₂
|
(CH₂)₈   C₆H₄-p
|
COONH₃−(CH₂)₄−Si(CH₃)₂

② acid + amine ⟶

③ Solid. [160~163°].

④ Polymers are formed by heat treat-ment.

⑥ Mem. Fac. Eng. Osaka City Univ. **4**, 177 (1962).

Si₂C₃₀H₄₂N₂O₄Ti

① Bis(8-hydroxyquinolinyl)bis(tri-ethylsiloxy)titanium
(C₉H₆NO)₂Ti[OSi(C₂H₅)₃]₂

② Et₃SiOH + (C₉H₆NO)₂Ti(OBu)₂ ⟶

③ [162~164°].

⑥ Izv. OKhN **1962**, 2132.

Si₂C₃₀H₅₂O₂Sn

① Bis(isobutylmethylphenylsiloxy)-diisobutyltin
[i-C₄H₉Si(CH₃)(C₆H₅)O]₂Sn(i-C₄H₉)₂

② (i-Bu₃Sn)₂O + i-BuSiMePhOH ⟶

③ (210~212°/2.5). n_D 1.5112   (20°).
d 1.0912 (20°).

IR: Mostly between 700 and 800 cm⁻¹,
some about 480~500 cm⁻¹.

⑥ Zhur. **32**, 4007 (1962).

Si₂C₃₂H₃₀

① 1-Triphenylsilyl-2-diphenylsilyl-ethane
(C₆H₅)₃SiCH₂CH₂SiH(C₆H₅)₂

② Ph₂SiH₂ + Ph₃SiCH=CH₂ ⟶ 70%

③ Solid. [125~126°].

⑥ JCS **1963**, 797.

Si₂C₃₂H₃₂

① 1,1,4,4-Tetramethyl-2,3,5,6-tetra-phenyl-1,4-disilahexadiene-2,5

C(C₆H₅)=C(C₆H₅)
(CH₃)₂Si⟨   ⟩Si(CH₃)₂
C(C₆H₅)=C(C₆H₅)

② Na + Me₂SiCl₂ + PhC≡CPh ⟶
③ (329～330°).
⑥ JACS **85**, 2871 (1963).

Si₂C₃₃H₃₂

① 1-Triphenylsilyl-2-methyldiphenyl-
   silylethane
   (C₆H₅)SiCH₂CH₂Si(C₆H₅)₂CH₃
② Ph₂SiHMe + Ph₃SiCH=CH₂ $\xrightarrow{\gamma\text{-ray}}$ 6%
③ Solid. [135～136°].
⑥ JCS **1963**, 797.

Si₂C₃₄H₃₀O

① 1,3-Dimethyl-1,3-diphenyl-1,3-di-α-
   naphthyldisiloxane
   [C₆H₅Si(CH₃)C₁₀H₇-]₂O
② PhSiMe(C₁₀H₇-1)Cl
   + PhSiMe(C₁₀H₇-1)OK ⟶
③ Solid. [88～89°].
⑥ JACS **82**, 3796 (1960).

Si₂C₃₄H₃₀O

① D-1,3-Di-1-naphthyl-1,3-dimethyl-
   1,3-diphenyldisiloxane
   D-[1-C₁₀H₇Si(CH₃)C₆H₅]₂O
② D-[1-C₁₀H₇Si(Me)PhOK]
   + D-[1-C₁₀H₇Si(Me)(Ph)Cl] ⟶
③ (225～230°/0.09). [87～88°]. [α]_D +9°.
⑥ US 3024262 (1962); CA **57**, 2254 (1962).

Si₂C₃₄H₃₄N₂O₄Ti

① Bis(dimethylphenylsiloxy)bis-
   (8-oxyquinolinyl)titanium

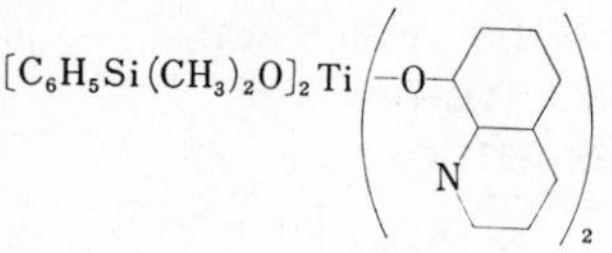

[C₆H₅Si(CH₃)₂O]₂Ti⟨-O—[quinolinyl]⟩₂

② 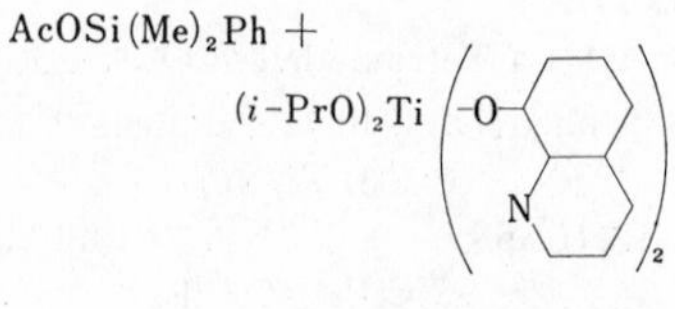 AcOSi(Me)₂Ph +
   (i-PrO)₂Ti⟨-O—[quinolinyl]⟩₂

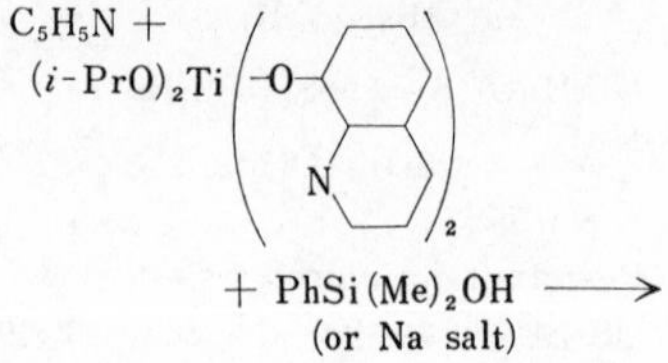

C₅H₅N +
(i-PrO)₂Ti⟨-O—[quinolinyl]⟩₂
+ PhSi(Me)₂OH ⟶
(or Na salt)
③ Cryst. [139～140°].
Sol. in C₆H₁₂.
IR: 906 cm⁻¹.
⑥ JOC **27**, 257 (1962).

Si₂C₃₄H₃₄O

① Dimethyltrimethylsilyltriphenyl-
   siloxymethane
   (C₆H₅)₃SiOC(C₆H₅)₂Si(CH₃)₃
② Ph₃SiOCPh₂K + Me₃SiCl ⟶
③ Cryst. [170～172]°.
Sol. in C₆H₆-MeOH.
IR: 9.7, 10.0, 6.9, 8.0, 11.9, 9.5 μ.
⑥ JACS **82**, 2439 (1960).

Si₂C₃₄H₁₄O₅

① 1,3-Dipentyltetrakis(2-ethyl-
   butoxy)-disiloxane
   {[(C₂H₅)₂CHCH₂O]₂SiC₅H₁₁}₂O
② AmSiCl₃ + Et₂CHCH₂OH
   + picoline, then H₂O ⟶
③ (190～193°/1).
⑥ Brit. 853368 (1959); CA **55**, 12296
   (1961).

Si₂C₃₆H₂₆O₂

① 10,10'-Diphenyl-10,10'-bisphenoxasilin

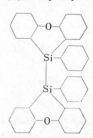

② Na +

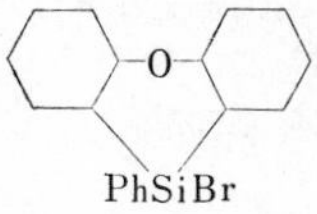

PhSiBr

③ Solid. [231~235°].
⑥ JOC **27**, 1418 (1962).

Si₂C₃₆H₂₆O₃
① 10,10′-Oxybis(10-phenylphenoxa-silin)

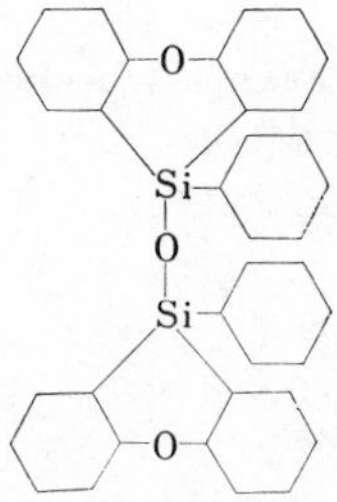

② HCOOH +

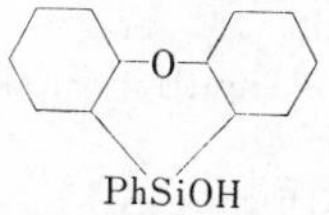

PhSiOH

③ Solid. [189.5~191.0°].
⑥ JOC **27**, 1418 (1962).

Si₂C₃₆H₂₈
① 5,5,10,10-Tetraphenyl-5,10-dihydro-silaanthrene

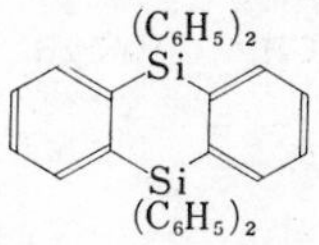

② o-C₆H₄Li₂ + Ph₂SiCl₂ ⟶ 10.4%
Na + o-ClC₆H₄SiHPh₂ ⟶
③ Solid. (ca. 540°). [234~246°].
⑤ Possible high temperature stability.
⑥ JOC **27**, 1836 (1962).   Chem. & Ind.
120 (1960).   JACS **82**, 3605 (1560).

Si₂C₃₆H₃₀
① Hexaphenyldisilane

(C₆H₅)₃SiSi(C₆H₅)₃
② Me₃SiCl + Ph₃SiCl + Na ⟶
Ph₃SiLi + OP(OBu)₃ + THF ⟶
Ph₃SiLi + Ph₃SiCl ⟶
③ Solid. [366~370°].
④ + H(Ni) ⟶ (C₆H₁₁)₃SiSi(C₆H₁₁)₃
⑥ JACS **82**, 6129 (1960) ; **84**, 383 (1962).
JOC **26**, 2471 (1961).   BCSJ **35**, 1840
(1962).

Si₂C₃₆H₃₀
① 1-Triphenylsilyl-2-diphenylsilyl-benzene
(C₆H₅)₃SiC₆H₄SiH(C₆H₅)₂-o
② o-ClC₆H₄SiHPh₂ + Na ⟶
③ Solid. [213~215°].
⑤ Possible stability at high tempera-tures.
⑥ JOC **27**, 1836 (1962).

Si₂C₃₆H₃₀CrO₄
① Bis-(triphenylsilyl) chromate
[(C₆H₅)₃SiO]₂CrO₂
② CrO₂Cl₂ + Ph₃SiONa ⟶
③ Solid. [138~140°].
⑥ U. S. Dpt. of Commerce, OTS, PB
Report 152086 (1960).

Si₂C₃₆H₃₀O
① Hexaphenyldisiloxane
(C₆H₅)₃SiOSi(C₆H₅)₃
② Ph₃SiCl + EtONa ⟶
KOH in EtOH + p-Ph₃SiC₆H₄CHO ⟶
NaK + Ph₃SiCH₂OH ⟶
③ Solid. (494°/740~760). [224°].
④ + H(Ni) ⟶ (C₆H₁₁)₃SiOSi(C₆H₁₁)₃
⑥ Izv. OKhN **1962**, 662.   JOC **25**, 2251
(1960).   Rec. trav. chim. **81**, 88
(1962).   JACS **83**, 827 (1961).

Si₂C₃₆H₃₀O₄S
① Bis(triphenylsilyl) sulfate
SO₂[OSi(C₆H₅)₂]₂
② Ph₃SiOH + SO₂(OSiMe₃)₂ ⟶

Ph₃SiCl + H₂SO₄ ⟶
③ Solid. [134~136°].
④ + H₂O ⟶ Ph₃SiOSiPh₃
⑥ Bull. soc. chim. France 1963, 512.

Si₂C₃₆H₃₁N

① Bis(triphenylsilyl)amine
   (C₆H₅)₃SiNHSi(C₆H₅)₃
② Na + NH₃ + Ph₃SiSiPh₃ ⟶
   Li + NH₃ + Ph₃SiF ⟶
③ [175°].
⑥ JCS 1963, 4758.   JOC 23, 913 (1958).
   Zhur. 24, 868 (1954): English page
   817.

Si₂C₃₆H₃₂N₄

① 1,1,2,4,4,5-Hexaphenyl-1,4-disila-
   2,3,5,6-tetranitracyclohexane
   [(C₆H₅)₂SiN(C₆H₅)NH]₂
② Et₂O + PhNHNH₂ + PhLi + Ph₂SiCl₂
   ⟶ 55%
① Solid. [254~257°].
   Insol. in pet. ether, Et₂O, C₆H₆(cold).
   Turns yellow in air, resistant to
   H₂O and H⁺, and hydrolyzes faster
   in organic solvents.
⑥ Z. anorg. allg. Chem. 311, 270 (1961).

Si₂C₃₆H₃₄N₄O

① 1,2-(2-Phenylhydrazino)-tetraphenyl-
   disiloxane
   C₆H₅NHNHSi(C₆H₅)₂OSi(C₆H₅)₂-
   NHNHC₆H₅
② Et₂O + H₂O + Ph₂Si(NHNHPh)₂ ⟶
③ Solid. [157~158°].
   Slowly turns yellow in air, in benzene or petr. ether more quickly
   going to red-brown.
⑥ Angew. 70, 745 (1958).   Z. anorg.
   allg. Chem. 311, 270 (1961).

Si₂C₃₆H₆₆

① Hexacyclohexyldisilane
   (C₆H₁₁)₃SiSi(C₆H₁₁)₃

② (C₆H₅)₃SiSi(C₆H₅)₃ + H(Ni) ⟶
③ Solid. [249.0~251.5°].
⑥ BCSJ 35, 1840 (1962).

Si₂C₃₆H₆₆O

① Hexacyclohexyldisiloxane
   (C₆H₁₁)₃SiOSi(C₆H₁₁)₃
② Ph₃SiOSiPh₃ + H(Ni) ⟶
③ Solid. [305~308°].
⑥ BCSJ 35, 1840 (1962).

Si₂C₃₇H₃₂O

① Triphenylsiloxytriphenylsilylmethane
   (C₆H₅)₃SiOCH₂Si(C₆H₅)₃
② Ph₃SiCH₂OH + NaK + Et₂O
   ⟶ 10~20%
③ Solid. [131.0~131.5°].
   Sol. in EtOH.
⑥ JACS 83, 827 (1961).

Si₂C₃₇H₃₃O₃P

① Bis(triphenylsilyl) methylphos-
   phonate
   CH₃P(O)[OSi(C₆H₅)₃]₂
② Ph₃SiOEt + MePOOH ⟶ 71.0%
③ Solid. [196°].
⑥ Zhur. 32, 608 (1962).

Si₂C₃₈H₃₀

① Hexaphenyldisilylacetylene
   (C₆H₅)₃SiC≡CSi(C₆H₅)₃
② (C₆H₅)₃SiF + CH≡CH + C₂H₅MgBr
   ⟶ 13%
③ White solid. [156°].
   Sol. in org. solvents.
⑥ Z. anorg. allg. Chem. 276, 20 (1954).
   Zhur. 25, 1128 (1955); CA 50, 3275
   (1954).

Si₂C₃₈H₃₁Cl₃

① 1-Triphenylsilyl-2-tris(*p*-chloro-
   phenyl)silylethane
   (C₆H₅)₃SiCH₂CH₂Si(C₆H₄Cl-*p*)₃
② HSi(C₆H₄Cl-*p*)₃ +

Ph₃SiCH=CH₂ $\xrightarrow{\gamma\text{-ray}}$

③ Solid. [136~138°].

⑥ JCS **1963**, 797.

Si₂C₃₈H₃₄

① 1,2-Bis(triphenylsilyl)ethane
   (C₆H₅)₃SiCH₂CH₂Si(C₆H₅)₃

② Ph₃SiH + Ph₃SiCH=CH₂ ⟶ 41%

③ Solid. [216~217°].
   Sol. in C₆H₆ and light pet. ether.

⑥ JCS **1963**, 797.

Si₂C₃₈H₃₄

① 1,3-Di-*p*-tolyltetraphenyldisilane
   p-(CH₃)C₆H₄Si(C₆H₅)₂Si(C₆H₅)₂-
   C₆H₄(CH₃)-*p*

② Ph₂SiHSiHPh₂ + *p*-MeC₆H₄Li
   ⟶ 66%
   Ph₂SiClSiClPh₂ + *p*-MeC₆H₄Li
   ⟶ 70%

③ Solid. [248~249°].

⑥ JACS **82**, 6129 (1960).   JOC **26**, 1265
   (1961).

Si₂C₃₈H₃₄O₃

① 1,3-Bis(*p*-phenoxyphenyl)-1,3-dime-
   thyl-1,3-diphenyldisiloxane
   [*p*-C₆H₅OC₆H₄Si(CH₃)C₆H₅]₂O

② NaOH + *p*-PhOC₆H₄SiClMePh ⟶

③ (335~350°/25). n_D1.6499 (30°).

⑤ Useful as damping or hydraulic
   fluids.

⑥ Fr. 1321436 (1963) ; CA **59**, 11561 (1963).

Si₂C₃₈H₃₆N₄

① 1,4-Dimethylhexaphenyl-1,4-disila-
   tetranitracyclohexane
   [C₆H₅SiCH₃-NC₆H₅-NC₆H₅-]₂

② PhSiCl₂Me + PhNLiNLiPh
   ⟶ 59.6%

③ Solid. [240~243°].

⑥ JACS **81**, 361 (1959).   Z. anorg. allg.
   Chem. **311**, 270 (1961).

Si₂C₃₈H₈₂O₆

① 1,2-Bis(tri-2-ethylbutoxysilyl)-
   ethane
   [(C₂H₅)₂CHCH₂O]₃SiCH₂CH₂Si-
   [OCH₂CH(C₂H₅)₂]₃

② Et₂CHCH₂OH
   + Cl₃SiCH₂CH₂SiCl₃ ⟶

③ Liquid. (213°/0.1). n_D1.4414 (20°).
   Viscosity : 2367 at −53° to 3.62 at 96°.

⑥ J. Chem. Eng. Data **6**, 437 (1961).

Si₂C₄₀H₃₆

① 1,4-Bis(triphenylsilyl)butene-1
   (C₆H₅)₃SiCH=CHCH₂CH₂Si(C₆H₅)₃

② Ph₃SiCH=CH₂ + Al(Bu-*i*)₃ $\xrightarrow{195°}$ 64%

③ Solid. [240°].

④ Continued treatment gives
   Ph₃SiCH₂CH₂CH₂CH₂SiPh₃.

⑥ JOC **26**, 4092 (1961).

Si₂C₄₀H₃₈

① 1,4-Bis(triphenylsilyl)butane
   (C₆H₅)₃SiCH₂CH₂CH₂CH₂Si(C₆H₅)₃

② Ph₃SiCH=CH₂ + Li ⟶
   (CH₂CH₂Li)₂ + Ph₃SiCl ⟶
   (CH₂CH₂Br)₂ + Ph₃SiLi ⟶
   (CH₂CH₂Cl)₂ + Ph₃SiLi ⟶ 64%

③ [214~215°].

⑥ JOC **28**, 2876 (1963) ; **26**, 4092 (1961).
   JACS **80**, 2677 (1958).

Si₂C₄₀H₃₈

① 1,4-Bis(triphenylsilyl)-2-methyl-
   propane
   (C₆H₅)₃SiCH(CH₃)CH₂CH₂Si(C₆H₅)₃

② Ph₃SiCHMeCH₂CH₂Cl + Ph₃SiLi
   ⟶ 67%

③ Solid. [163~164°].

⑥ JOC **26**, 4092 (1961).

Si₂C₄₀H₃₈N₂

① 1,4-Bis(triphenylsilyl)-1,4-dinitra-
   cyclohexane

$$(C_6H_5)_3SiN \begin{array}{c} CH_2CH_2 \\ \diagdown \\ CH_2CH_2 \end{array} NSi(C_6H_5)_3$$

② $Ph_3SiCl + HN \begin{array}{c} CH_2CH_2 \\ \diagdown \\ CH_2CH_2 \end{array} NH$

$\longrightarrow$ 93%

③ Solid. [287~288°].
Sol. in xylene.
⑤ Possible high temperature resistance.
⑥ JACS **82**, 3319 (1960).

$Si_2C_{41}H_{40}$

① 1,5-Bis(triphenylsilyl)pentane
$(C_6H_5)_3Si(CH_2)_5Si(C_6H_5)_3$
② $CH_2(CH_2CH_2Li)_2 + Ph_3SiCl \longrightarrow$
③ Solid. [145~146°].
⑤ High temperature stability.
⑥ JOC **27**, 1023 (1962).   JACS **80**, 2677 (1958).

$Si_2C_{42}H_{28}Cl_6$

① p-Bis(tri-p-chlorophenylsilyl)benzene
p-$C_6H_4[Si(C_6H_4Cl-p)_3]_2$
② p-$C_6H_4Cl_2 \longrightarrow HSi(C_6H_4Cl-p)_3$
$\longrightarrow$ 20%
p-$C_6H_4(SiCl_3)_2 + Na + p\cdot BrC_6H_4Cl$
$\longrightarrow$ 32%
③ Solid. [268~270°].
⑥ Zhur. **32**, 698(1962); English page 697.
Izv. OKhN **1962**, 168; English page
152. J. prakt. Chem. **21**, 149 (1963).

$Si_2C_{42}H_{30}Cl_4$

① p-Bis(phenyldi-p-chlorophenylsilyl)
benzene
$p\cdot C_6H_4[Si(C_6H_4Cl-p)_2C_6H_5]_2$
② $p\cdot C_6H_4(SiCl_2Ph)_2 + Na + BrC_6H_4Cl-p$
$\longrightarrow$ 34%

$PhCl + (p\text{-}ClC_6H_4)_3SiH \xrightarrow{630°}$
③ Solid. [264°].
⑥ Izv. OKhN **1962**, 168; English page
152. J. prakt. Chem. **21**, 149 (1963).

$Si_2C_{42}H_{34}$

① o-Bis(triphenylsilyl)benzene
o-$C_6H_4[Si(C_6H_5)_3]_2$
② o-$C_6H_4Li_2 + Ph_3SiCl \longrightarrow$
③ Solid. [257.5~259.0°].
⑤ High temperature stability.
⑥ JACS **82**, 3605 (1960).

$Si_2C_{42}H_{34}$

① p-Bis(triphenylsilyl)benzene
p-$C_6H_4[Si(C_6H_5)_3]_2$
② p-$C_6H_4(SiCl_3)_2 + PhCl + Na$
$\longrightarrow$ 8.6%, 44%
p-$Ph_3SiC_6H_4Cl + Ph_3SiCl + Na$
$\longrightarrow$ 33%
p-$C_6H_4(SiCl_3)_2 + Na + PhBr$
$\longrightarrow$ 64%
③ Solid. (350~351°/3). [314~316°].
④ Sol. in DMF.
⑥ Zhur. **32**, 24 (1962).   Rec. trav. chim.
81, 565 (1962).   Izv. OKhN **1962**,
168; English page 152.   J. prakt.
Chem. **21**, 149 (1963).

$Si_2C_{42}H_{34}O_6$

① p-Bis(triphenoxysilyl)benzene
p-$C_6H_4[Si(OC_6H_5)_3]_2$
② $PhOH + p$-$C_6H_4(SiCl_3)_2 \longrightarrow$
③ Liq. (435°).
⑤ Heat transfer agent.
⑥ US 2934502 (1960); CA **54**, 17328 (1960).

$Si_2C_{42}H_{35}AsO_2$

① Bis(triphenylsilyl) phenylarsonate
$C_6H_5As[OSi(C_6H_5)_3]_2$
② $Ph_3SiONa + PhAsI_2 \longrightarrow$ 78%
③ Solid. [119~120°].
Sol. in Et_2O, C_6H_6, Me_2CO and
MeOH; insol. in pet. ether.
IR: 1429, 1114, 1105, 877, 744~737
cm^{-1}.
⑥ JACS **83**, 549 (1961).

Si₂C₄₂H₃₅BO₂

① Bis(triphenylsilyl) phenylboronate
   C₆H₅B[OSi(C₆H₅)₃]₂

② Ph₃SiOH + PhB(OH)₂ ——→ 71%

③ Solid. [132~133°].

⑥ US 2915543 (1959) ; CA **54**, 6649 (1960).

Si₂C₄₂H₄₀

① 2-Methylene-1,5-bis(triphenylsilyl)-
   pentane
   (C₆H₅)₃SiCH₂C(=CH₂)CH₂CH₂CH₂-
   Si(C₆H₅)₃

② Ph₃SiCH₂CH=CH₂ + Al(Bu-*i*)₃
   $\xrightarrow{200°}$ 36%

③ Solid. (109~110°/22°). [99~101°].
   *n*D 1.4439 (25°).

④ + Al(Bu-*i*)₃ ——→
   Ph₃SiCH₂CHMeCH₂CH₂CH₂SiPh₃

⑥ JOC **26**, 4092 (1961).

Si₂C₄₂H₄₂

① Hexa-*p*-tolyldisilane
   (*p*-CH₃C₆H₄)₃SiSi(C₆H₄CH₃-*p*)₃

② (*p*-CH₃C₆H₄)₃SiCl + Na
   $\xrightarrow{\text{reflux in xylene}}$ 58%

③ White solid. [350~353°].
   Very slightly sol. in org. solvents ;
   insol. in H₂O.

④ + K−Na $\xrightarrow{CO_2}$ (*p*-CH₃C₆H₄)₃SiCOOH

⑥ JACS **79**, 971 (1957).

Si₂C₄₂H₄₂

① 2-Methyl-1,5-bis(triphenylsilyl)-
   pentane
   (C₆H₅)₃SiCH₂CH(CH₃)CH₂CH₂CH₂
   Si(C₆H₅)₃

② CH₂ClCHMeCH₂CH₂CH₂Cl
   + Ph₃SiLi ——→ 63%
   Al(Bu-*i*)₃ + Ph₃SiCH₂C-
   (=CH₂)(CH₂)₃SiPh₃ ——→ 10%

③ Solid. [126~127°].

⑥ JOC **26**, 4092 (1961).

Si₂C₄₂H₄₂O

① Hexabenzyldisiloxane
   (C₆H₅CH₂)₃SiOSi(CH₂C₆H₅)₃

② HSi(CH₂Ph)₃ + Et₂NOH $\xrightarrow{\text{reflux}}$
   (PhCH₂)₃SiCl + Me₃SiOEt + H₂O ——→

③ White crystals. (536~548°). [203~
   205°].
   Sol. in org. solvents ; insol. in H₂O.

⑥ JOC **15**, 552(1950). US 2449940(1948) ;
   CA **43**, 667 (1949).

Si₂C₄₂H₄₃N

① Hexa-*p*-tolyldisilylamine
   (*p*-CH₃C₆H₄)₃SiNHSi(C₆H₄CH₃-*p*)₃

② (*p*-CH₃C₆H₄)₃SiF + Li + NH₃
   ——→ 23%

③ Solid. [223~224°].
   Very slightly sol. in org. solvents.

⑥ Zhur. **24**, 868 (1954) ; CA **49**, 8163
   (1955).

Si₂C₄₄H₄₄O₂

① 4,5-Bis(triphenylsiloxy)octene-4
   (C₆H₅)₃SiOC(C₃H₇)=C(C₃H₇)OSi(C₆H₅)₃

② Ph₃SiCl + PrC(ONa)=C(ONa)Pr
   ——→ 45%

③ (280~290°/2).

④ + HOH and (OH)⁻ ——→ Ph₃SiOSiPh₃
   + Br₂ ——→ Ph₃SiBr

⑥ J. prakt. Chem. (4) **12**, 18 (1960).

Si₂C₄₄H₄₆

① 1,2-Bis(tribenzylsilyl)ethane
   (C₆H₅CH₂)₃SiCH₂CH₂Si(CH₂C₆H₅)₃

② PhCH₂MgCl + Cl₃SiCH₂CH₂SiCl₃
   ——→ 81%

③ Solid. [136~137°].

⑤ High temperature stability.

⑥ JOC **27**, 1023 (1962).

Si₂C₄₆H₄₀O₂Ti

① Dicyclopentadienylbis(triphenylsiloxy)titanium
   (Ph₃SiO)₂Ti(C₅H₅)₂

② (C₅H₅)₂TiCl₂ + Ph₃SiONa $\xrightarrow{PhMe}$ 63%

③ (208~210°).

⑥ Rec. trav. chim. **81**, 39 (1962).   US
   3030394 (1962); CA **57**, 3589 (1962).

Si₂C₄₈H₃₈

① 3,3'-Bis(triphenylsilyl)biphenyl
   m-(C₆H₅)₃SiC₆H₄C₆H₄Si(C₆H₅)₃-m

② Ph₃SiCl + BuLi + m-BrC₆H₄C₆H₄Br-m
   $\longrightarrow$ 69%

③ Crystalline. [221~223°].

⑥ JOC **27**, 1023 (1962).

Si₂C₄₈H₄₀N₄

① Octaphenyl-1,2,4,5-tetranitra-3,6-
   disilacyclohexane

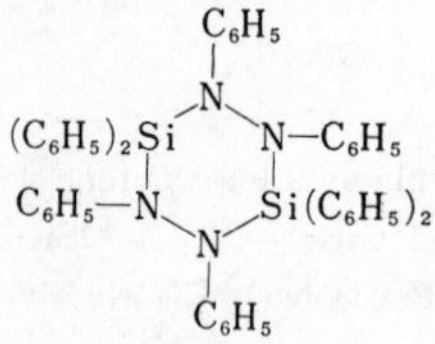

$$(C_6H_5)_2Si \begin{array}{c} C_6H_5 \\ N \\ \\ N \end{array} \begin{array}{c} N-C_6H_5 \\ \\ Si(C_6H_5)_2 \\ C_6H_5 \end{array}$$

② Ph₂SiCl₂ + PhN(Li)N(Li)Ph $\longrightarrow$

③ [348~350°].
   Not affected by air or moisture.

⑥ Z. anorg. allg. Chem. **311**, 270 (1961).

Si₂C₄₈H₄₆

① m-Bis(tribenzylsilyl)benzene
   m-C₆H₄[Si(CH₂C₆H₅)₃]₂

② m-C₆H₄(SiCl₃)₂ + Ph₂CH₂MgCl
   $\longrightarrow$ 16%

③ Solid. [155~157°].

⑤ For high temperature stability.

⑥ JOC **27**, 1023 (1962).

Si₂C₄₈H₄₆

① p-Bis(tribenzylsilyl)benzene

p-(C₆H₅CH₂)₃SiC₆H₄Si(CH₂C₆H₅)₃

② (PhCH₂)₃SiH + p-(PhCH₂)₃SiC₆H₄Li
   $\longrightarrow$ 15%

③ Solid. (520°). [155~157°].

⑤ High temperature stability.

⑥ JOC **25**, 1194 (1960).

Si₂C₅₀H₄₀O₃

① Triphenylsilyl triphenylsiloxy-
   diphenylacetate
   (C₆H₅)₃SiOC(C₆H₅)₂COOSi(C₆H₅)₃

② Ph₃SiOCPh₂K + CO₂ $\xrightarrow{-70°}$

③ [215~216°].

⑥ JACS **82**, 2439 (1960).

Si₂C₅₀H₄₁NO₂S

① 3,7-Bis(triphenylsilyl)-10-ethyl-
   phenothiazine-5,5-dioxide

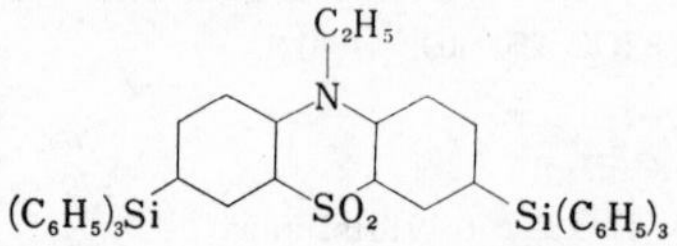

$$(C_6H_5)_3Si \begin{array}{c} C_2H_5 \\ N \\ SO_2 \end{array} Si(C_6H_5)_3$$

② Ph₃SiLi +

$$Br \begin{array}{c} NEt \\ SO_2 \end{array} Br$$

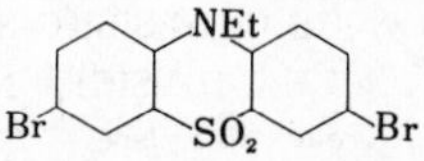

$\longrightarrow$ 19% (17% from the dichloride)

Ph₃SiCl +

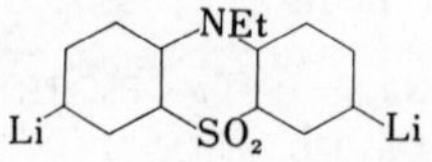

$$Li \begin{array}{c} NEt \\ SO_2 \end{array} Li \longrightarrow$$

③ Solid. [271.0~276.5°].

⑥ JOC **26**, 2938 (1961).

Si₂C₅₀H₅₀O₂

① 1,4-Di-t-butyl-2,5-bis(triphenylsiloxy)benzene
   (t-C₄H₉)₂C₆H₂[OSi(C₆H₅)₃]₂ (1,4,2,5)

② Ph₃SiCl +
   (t-Bu)₂C₆H₂(OH)₂(1,4,2,5) $\longrightarrow$

③ [280.5~281.2°].

⑥ Ric. Sci. Rend. Sez. **A3**, 329 (1963).

CA **59**, 10105 (1963).

$Si_2C_{50}H_{105}$

① 1,2-Bis(trioctylsilyl)ethane
$(C_8H_{17})_3SiCH_2CH_2Si(C_8H_{17})_3$

② $C_8H_{17}MgBr + Cl_3SiCH_2CH_2SiCl_3$
$\longrightarrow$ 44.3%

③ (299~301°/3). n_D1.4703 (20°). d0.8426 (20°).

⑥ Dokl. **116**, 248 (1957). CA **58**, 6852 (1963).

$Si_2C_{50}H_{105}$

① 1,2-Bis(tri-2-ethylhexylsilyl)ethane
$\{[C_4H_9CH(C_2H_5)CH_2]_3SiCH_2\}_2$

② $(CH_2SiCl_3)_2 + BuCHEtCH_2Li$
$\longrightarrow$ 54%

③ Liq. (215~220°/0.04).

⑤ High temperature stability.

⑥ JOC **27**, 1023 (1962).

$Si_2C_{54}H_{42}N_2O_4Ti$

① Bis(8-quinolinoyl)bis(triphenyl-siloxy)titanium

②

$\xrightarrow{C_6H_6}$ 99%

$\xrightarrow{C_6H_6}$ 97%

③ Solid. [190~191°].
IR: 915, 1433 cm^{-1}.

⑥ JOC **27**, 257 (1962).

$Si_2C_{54}H_{42}O_2$

① 1,4-Diphenyl-2,5-bis(triphenyl-siloxy)benzene
$(C_6H_5)_2C_6H_2[OSi(C_6H_5)_3]_2(1,4,2,5)$

② $Ph_3SiCl + Ph_2C_6H_2(OK)_2(1,4,2,5)$ $\longrightarrow$

③ [215.8~216.0°].

⑥ Ric. Sci. Rend. Sez. **A3**, 329 (1963); CA **59**, 10105 (1963).

$Si_2C_{66}H_{52}O_6Ti$

① Bis(1-oxy-1-propene-1,3-diphenyl-3-on)bis(triphenylsiloxy)titanium
$[(C_6H_5)_3SiO]_2Ti(OC(C_6H_5)=CH\text{-}COC_6H_5)_2$

② $(i\text{-}PrO)_2Ti(OCPh=CHCOPh)_2$
$+ Ph_3SiOH \xrightarrow{3.5\,hr.\ in\ C_6H_6}$

③ Solid. [233~238°].

⑥ JOC **27**, 257 (1962).

$Si_2C_{66}H_{114}$

① 1,1,1-Triphenyl-2,2,2-trihexa-decyldisilane
$(C_6H_5)_3SiSi(C_{16}H_{33})_3$

② $Ph_3SiLi + (C_{16}H_{33})_3SiCl$ $\longrightarrow$ 78%

③ (320~325°/0.001). n_D1.5142 (20°).
d0.9081 (20°/4°).

⑥ JOC **24**, 219 (1959).

$Si_2C_{66}H_{130}$

① *m*-Bis(tridecylsilyl)benzene
$m\text{-}C_6H_4[Si(C_{10}H_{21})_3]_2$

② $m\text{-}C_6H_4(SiCl_3)_2 + C_{10}H_{21}Li$ $\longrightarrow$ 58%

③ (285~288°/0.03).

⑥ JOC **27**, 1023 (1962).

$Si_2C_{66}H_{130}$

① *p*-Bis(tridecylsilyl)benzene
$p\text{-}C_6H_4[Si(C_{10}H_{21})_3]_2$

② $p\text{-}C_6H_4(SiCl_3)_2 + C_{10}H_{21}Li$ $\longrightarrow$ 20%

③ (290~294°/0.03).

⑥ JOC **27**, 1023 (1962).

Si₂C₇₈H₅₈

① *p*-Bis(tri-*p*-xenylsilyl)benzene
   p-C₆H₄[Si(C₆H₄C₆H₅-*p*)₃]₂

② *p*-C₆H₄(SiCl₃)₂ + *p*-BrC₆H₄Ph + Na
   $\longrightarrow$ 22%

③ [450°].

⑥ J. prakt. Chem. **21**, 149 (1963).

Si₂C₈₂H₁₅₈Fe

① Bis(tridodecylsilyl)ferrocene
   Fe[C₅H₄Si(C₁₂H₂₅)₃]₂

② Na + (C₁₂H₂₅)₃SiC₅H₅, then FeCl₂ $\longrightarrow$

③ (290~304°/0.004). n_D 1.4916~1.4931
   (20°).

⑥ JOC **27**, 616 (1962).

Si₂C₉₈H₂₀₂

① 1,2-Bis(trihexadecylsilyl)ethane
   (C₁₆H₃₃)₃SiCH₂CH₂Si(C₁₆H₃₃)₃

② C₁₆H₃₃Li + Cl₃SiCH₂CH₂SiCl₃
   $\longrightarrow$ 75%

⑤ High temperature lubricant.

⑥ JOC **27**, 1023 (1962).

Si₃C₃H₆Cl₆

① Cyclohexachlorotrisilylmethylene
   (Cl₂SiCH₂)₃

② CH₂Cl₂ + Si−Cu $\xrightarrow{300°}$
   MeSiCl₃ $\xrightarrow{\text{thermal decompn.}}$

③ [82°].

④ + LiH $\xrightarrow{\text{autoclave}}$

   $\overline{\text{H}_2\text{SiCH}_2\text{SiH}_2\text{CH}_2\text{SiH}_2\text{CH}_2}$

⑥ Dokl. **90**, 387 (1953); CA **48**, 5080 (1954).
   Z. anorg. allg. Chem. **302**, 60 (1959)
   CA **54**, 5686 (1960).

Si₃C₃H₁₂O₃

① Cyclotrimethyltrisiloxane
   (HCH₃SiO)₃

② H(CH₃)SiCl₂ + H₂O $\longrightarrow$

③ (93.8°). n_D 1.3770 (20°). d 0.9677 (20°).

⑥ BCSJ **30**, 608 (1957).   JACS **68**, 962
   (1946).

Si₃C₅H₁₅ClO₃

① Pentamethylchlorocyclotrisiloxane

   $O\underset{\text{Si(CH}_3)_2\text{O}}{\overset{\text{Si(CH}_3)_2\text{O}}{<}}\hspace{-0.5em}>Si(Cl)CH_3$

② MeSiCl₃ + NaO[Si(Me)₂O]₂Na
   $\longrightarrow$ 2.6%

③ (47~50°/5). n_D 1.4050 (20°). d 1.0265
   (20°/4°).

⑥ Izv. OKhN, **1963**, 294.

Si₃C₅H₁₈O₂

① 1,3,5-Trihydropentamethyl-
   trisiloxane
   H(CH₃)₂SiOSi(H)(CH₃)OSi(CH₃)₂H

② H(CH₃)₂SiCl + (CH₃)HSiCl₂ $\xrightarrow{\text{H}_2\text{O}}$

③ (117°). n_D 1.3774 (20°). d 0.8245 (20°).

⑥ BCSJ **29**, 236 (1956).

Si₃C₆H₁₅Cl₃O₃

① Methylchloromethylcyclotrisiloxane
   [CH₃Si(CH₂Cl)O]₃

② MeSiCl₂CH₂Cl + H₂O $\longrightarrow$ 3.5%
   Cl[SiMe(CH₂Cl)O]₂ −
   SiMe(Cl)CH₂Cl + H₂O $\longrightarrow$

③ (129~134°/6.5).

⑥ Rocz. Chem. **36**, 1459 (1962); CA **59**,
   6218 (1963).

Si₃C₆H₁₅Cl₅O₂

① 1,5-Dichloro-1,3,5-trimethyl-1,3,5-
   tris(chloromethyl)trisiloxane
   Cl[Si(CH₃)(CH₂Cl)O]₂−
   Si(CH₃)ClCH₂Cl

② MeSiCl₂CH₂Cl + H₂O $\longrightarrow$ 25.5%

③ (108°/0.3). n_D 1.4632 (20°). d 1.2932
   (20°).

④ + H₂O $\longrightarrow$ [MeSi(CH₂Cl)O]₃ +
   HO[Si(Me)(CH₂Cl)O]₂ −

SiMe(OH)CH₂Cl

⑥ Rocz. Chem. **36**, 1459 (1962) ; CA **59**, 6218 (1963).

Si₃C₆H₁₈Cl₂

① 1,3-Dichlorohexamethyltrisilane
   $(CH_3)_2SiClSi(CH_3)_2Si(CH_3)_2Cl$

② $H_2SO_4 + NH_4Cl$
   $+ Me_3SiSiMe_2SiMe_3 \longrightarrow$

③ (94~95°/18). n_D1.4852 (20°). d0.9865 (20°/4°).

④ $+ (BzO_2) + SO_2Cl$
   $\longrightarrow Me_2SiClSiMe_2Cl$
   $+ Me_2SiCl-SiMe(CH_2Cl)-SiMe_2Cl$

⑥ "Studies in Organosilicon Compounds" Vol. 1, Chap. 5, 7 (1963).

Si₃C₆H₁₈Cl₂O₂

① 1,5-Dichlorohexamethyltrisiloxane
   $(CH_3)_2SiCl[OSi(CH_3)_2]_2Cl$

② $Me_3SiOSiMe_3 + Me_2SiCl_2 \longrightarrow$

③ (44~46°/4).

⑥ Izv. OKhN **1962**, 2133.

Si₃C₆H₁₈O₃

① Hexamethylcyclotrisiloxane
   $[(CH_3)_2SiO]_3$

② $Me_2SiCl_2 + H_2O \longrightarrow \overset{\text{thermal decompn.}}{\longrightarrow}$

③ (130~133°). [64.9°].

④ $+ MeSiCl_3 \longrightarrow$ oil
   $+ CH_2=CHSiCl_3 \longrightarrow$ oil
   $+ EtSiCl_3 \longrightarrow$ oil
   $+ PhSiCl_3 \longrightarrow$ oil

⑥ Izv. OKhN **1963**, 282 ; **1961**, 1275 ; English page 1185. JACS **76**, 5190 (1954).

Si₃C₆H₁₈O₃

① Cyclo-1,3,5-triethyltrisiloxane
   $(C_2H_5SiHO)_3$

② $C_2H_5(H)SiCl_2 + H_2O \longrightarrow$

③ Colorless liq. (67°/20). n_D1.4078 (20°). d0.9673 (20°).
   Sol. in org. solvents.

⑥ BCSJ **30**, 608 (1957).

Si₃C₆H₁₈Se₃

① Hexamethylcyclotrisilselenane
   $[(CH_3)_2SiSe]_3$

② $Me_2SiCl_2 + Na_2Se \longrightarrow$

③ [17~18°].

⑥ Z. anorg. allg. Chem. **321**, 270 (1963).

Si₃C₆H₂₀O₂

① 1,1,3,3,5,5-Hexamethyltrisiloxane
   $(CH_3)_2Si(H)OSi(CH_3)_2OSiH(CH_3)_2$

② $LiAlH_4 + Me_2SiClOSiMe_2OSiMe_2Cl$
   $\longrightarrow 77\%$

③ (128~130°, 124°/50). n_D1.3902 (20°). d0.8818 (20°).

⑥ Ger. 1085875 (1960) ; CA **57**, 27057 (1961). Ger. 1140348 (1962) ; CA **58**, 12600 (1963). Kogyo Kagaku Zasshi, **60**, 1398 (1957).

Si₃C₆H₂₀O₄

① 1,5-Dihydroxyhexamethyltrisiloxane
   $HO[Si(CH_3)_2O_3]H$

③ (79~82°/2, 89~91°/3.0). [5~7°].
   n_D1.4089 (20°), 1.4063, 1.4067 (25°).
   d0.999 (20°/4°).

④ $+ Me_2Si(NEt_2)_2 \longrightarrow$ polymers
   $+ Me_3SiNEt_2 \longrightarrow$ polymers

⑥ Izv. OKhN **1962**, 2243. J. Polymer Sci. **50**, 151 (1961).

Si₃C₆H₂₁N₃

① 1,1,3,3,5,5-Hexamethylcyclotrisilazane
   $[(CH_3)_2SiNH]_3$

② $Me_2SiCl_2 + NH_3 \longrightarrow$

③ (72~74°/11). n_D1.4445 (20°). d0.9258 (20°/4°).

④ $+ PhNH_2 \longrightarrow (Me_2SiNPh)_3$

$+ PhNHC_6H_{11}$

$\longrightarrow (Me_2SiNH)_2(Me_2SiNC_6H_{11})$

$+ NH_4Cl \longrightarrow (Me_2SiNH)_4$

$+ (Et_3NMe)I \dashrightarrow (Me_2SiNH)_4$

$+ KOH \longrightarrow (Me_2SiNH)_4$

⑥ Plasticheskie Massy (No. 8) 18 (1962); CA **58**, 7693 (1963). Zhur. **32**, 1993 (1962). Dokl. **145**, 1049 (1962), English page 709. Zhur. **33**, 252 (1963).

Si₃C₇H₂₁ClO₂

① Heptamethyl-1-chlorotrisiloxane
$(CH_3)_3SiOSi(CH_3)_2OSi(CH_3)_2Cl$

② $MeLi + Me_2SiClSiMe_2OSiMe_2Cl \longrightarrow$

③ $(65°/20)$.

⑥ Ger. 1136336 (1962); CA **58**, 6861 (1963).

Si₃C₇H₂₁Cl₂NO₄

① Bis(dimethoxymethylsilyl)methyl-dichlorosilylamine
$[CH_3Si(OCH_3)_2]_2NSiCl_2CH_3$

② $MeSiCl_3 +$
$MeSi(OMe)_2N(Na)Si(OMe)_2Me \longrightarrow$

③ $(79°/2)$.

⑥ Angew. **75**, 95 (1963).

Si₃C₇H₂₁N

① *N*-Trimethylsilyltetramethylcyclo-disilanimine

$(CH_3)_2Si$
$\qquad\Big|\!\!\searrow NSi(CH_3)_3$
$(CH_3)_2Si$

② $(Me_3Si)N$ derivatives $\xrightarrow{\text{pyrolysis}}$

③ $(172.7°)$. $[-37°]$. $n_D 1.4375$ $(20°)$. $d\,0.827$ $(18°/4°)$.

   IR : 2950, 1400, 2880, 1360, 1250, 1045, 925, 856, 807, 758, 680 cm⁻¹.

⑥ Helv. Chim. Acta **46**, 720 (1963).

Si₃C₇H₂₁N₃

① Vinylpentamethylcyclotrisilazane

$Si(CH_3)_2HN$
$HN\!\!\diagup\qquad\diagdown\!\!Si(CH_3)_2$
$Si(CH_3)HN$
$\quad\big|$
$CH\!=\!CH_2$

② $Me_2SiCl_2 + NH_3 +$
$MeSiCl_2CH\!=\!CH_2 \longrightarrow$

③ $(54\!\sim\!56°/3)$. $n_D 1.4613$ $(20°)$. $d\,0.9414$ $(20°/4°)$.

⑥ Izv. OKhN **1963**, 948.   Dokl. **150**, 93 (1963). Zhur. **33**, 2638 (1963).

Si₃C₇H₂₂O₂

① 1,1,1,3,5,5,5-Heptamethyltrisiloxane
$(CH_3)_3SiOSiH(CH_3)OSi(CH_3)_3$

② $2(CH_3)_3SiCl + (CH_3)HSiCl_2 \xrightarrow{H_2O}$

③ $(141.5°)$. $n_D 1.3818$ $(20°)$. $d\,0.8194$ $(20°)$.

⑥ BCSJ **29**, 547 (1956). JACS **68**, 962 (1946).

Si₃C₇H₂₃NO₂

① Methyldihydroxybis(trimethylsilyl) aminosilane
$CH_3Si(OH)_2N[Si(CH_3)_3]_2$

② $HOH + MeSiCl_2N(SiMe_3)_2 \longrightarrow$

③ $n_D 1.4580$ $(20°)$.

⑥ Angew. **75**, 165 (1963).

Si₃C₇H₂₅N₃

① Methyldiaminobis(trimethylsilyl)-aminosilane
$CH_3Si(NH_2)_2N[Si(CH_3)_3]_2$

② $NH_3 + MeSiCl_2N(SiMe_3)_2 \longrightarrow 70\%$

③ $(101°/17)$. $[50\!\sim\!53°]$. $n_D 1.4354$ $(20°)$.

④ $\xrightarrow{200°} MeSi(NH_2)(NHSiMe_3)_2$
$+ HOH \longrightarrow MeSi(OH)_2N(SiMe_3)_2$

⑥ Angew. **75**, 165 (1963).

Si₃C₈H₁₈N₂O₄

① 1,3-Diisocyanatohexamethyltri-
siloxane
(CH₃)₂Si(NCO)OSi(CH₃)₂O-
Si(CH₃)₂NCO

② Me₂SiClOSiMe₂OSiMe₂Cl
+ AgNCO (or Pb(NCO)₂) ⟶

③ (94°/10). n_D1.4165 (20°). d1.015 (20°).
IR: 3003, 2941, 2381, 2273, 1972, 1445,
1414, 1266, 1010~1149 cm⁻¹.

⑥ Kogyo Kagaku Zasshi **61**, 214 (1958).
Mitsubishi Denki Lab. Reports **4**,
139 (1963).

Si₃C₈H₂₂Cl₂O₂

① 1,3-Bis(chloromethyl)-1,1,2,2,3,3-
hexamethyltrisiloxane
(CH₃)₂Si(CH₂Cl)OSi(CH₃)₂O-
Si(CH₃)₂CH₂Cl

② Me₂SiClCH₂Cl + Me₂SiCl₂ + HOH
+ NaHCO₃ ⟶ 21%
Me₂Si(OH)CH₂Cl + Et₃N
+ Me₂SiCl₂ ⟶ 100%

③ (136~138°/40°, 109°/10). n_D1.4309,
1.4275 (20°). d1.023 (20°).

④ + Na₂S₄ ⟶
(CH₂SiMe₂OSiMe₂OSiMe₂S₄)₄ 74.4%
Inherent viscosity: 0.13.

⑥ JOC **24**, 489, 492 (1959). Angew.
74, 903 (1963).

Si₃C₈H₂₄

① Octamethyltrisilane
(CH₃)₃SiSi(CH₃)₂Si(CH₃)₃

② Na + Me₃SiCl + Me₃SiSiMe₂Cl ⟶
NaK + Me₃SiCl + Me₃SiSiMe₂Cl
⟶ 95%

③ (175~176°). [−52°]. n_D1.4610 (20°).
d0.7717 (20°/4°).

⑥ JOC **26**, 557 (1961). Ber. **96**, 2798
(1963). Angew. **74**, 698 (1962).
JOM 1, 153 (1963).

Si₃C₈H₂₄O₂

① Octamethyltrisiloxane
(CH₃)₃SiO[Si(CH₃)₂O]Si(CH₃)₃

② [(CH₃)₃SiO]₄ + [(CH₃)₃Si₂]O $\xrightarrow{\text{H}_2\text{SO}_4\ \text{H}_2\text{O}}$

③ (153°). n_D1.3848 (20°). d0.8200 (20°).

⑥ JACS **68**, 358 (1946).

Si₃C₈H₂₆N₂

① 1,1,1,3,3,5,5,5-Octamethyltrisilazane
[(CH₃)₃SiNH]₂Si(CH₃)₂

② Me₂SiCl₂ +
Me₃SiN(Li)SiMe₂NHSiMe₃ ⟶
(Me₃Si)₂NSiPr₃ $\xrightarrow{200°}$

③ (72°/10). n_D1.4278 (20°). d0.8318 (22°).

④ + BuLi ⟶
Me₃SiN(Li)SiMe₂NHSiMe₃

⑥ Z. anorg. allg. Chem. **308**, 337(1961).
Ber. **96**, 1071 (1963).

Si₃C₉H₁₈O₃

① 1,3,5-Trimethyl-1,3,5-trivinylcyclo-
trisiloxane
[(CH₂=CH)(CH₃)SiO]₃

② (CH₂=CH)MeSi(OEt)₂ $\xrightarrow{\text{aq. HCl}}$

③ (79.5~80°/20). n_D1.4215 (25°). d0.9669
(25°).

⑥ Nippon Kagaku Zasshi **78**, 1324 (1957).

Si₃C₉H₂₁N₃

① Trimethyltrivinylcyclotrisilazane
[CH₃Si(CH=CH₂)NH]₃

② MeSiCl₂CH=CH₂ + NH₄OH + C₆H₆
⟶ 67%
MeSiCl₂CH=CH₂ + NH₃ ⟶

③ (64.5~65.0°/1, 100°/7). n_D1.4820,
1.4830, 1.4810(20°). d0.9662, 0.9683,
0.9673 (20°/4°).

IR: 3043, 3000, 2955, 2900, 1592, 1406,
1256, 1360~1370, 1009, 920~930, 840,
788, 762~768, 728, 670~680, 615,
525, 420 cm⁻¹.

⑥ Zhur. **33**, 1293, 2638 (1963).   Dokl.
  150, 93 (1963).   Izv. OKhN **1963**,
  948.

Si₃C₉H₂₄

① Cyclohexamethyltrisilylmethylene
  [(CH₃)₂SiCH₂]₃
② (ClCH₂)₂SiMe₂ + (Me₂ClSi)CH₂
  $\xrightarrow{\text{Na in PhMe}}$ 22%
③ (201°). n_D1.4606 (25°). d0.846 (25°).
⑥ US 2607791 (1952).   Brit. 667435.
  Angew. **70**, 701 (1958).   Z. anorg.
  allg. Chem. **299**, 232 (1959).

Si₃C₉H₂₄O₂

① Bis(trimethylsiloxy)methylvinyl-
  silane
  CH₃Si[OSi(CH₃)₃]₂CH=CH₂
② C₂H₂ + Pd–Al₂O₃
  + Me₃SiOSiHMeOSiMe₃ ⟶
③ (46~48°/8.8). n_D1.3941~1.3942 (25°).
⑥ Ger. 1115929 (1961); CA **59**, 3957
  (1963).

Si₃C₉H₂₇AlO₃

① Tris(trimethylsiloxy)aluminum
  Al[OSi(CH₃)₃]₃
② AlCl₃ + Me₃SiONa ⟶ 81%
③ (155°/1). [238°].
⑥ Ber. **96**, 2696 (1963).   Angew. **74**, 328
  (1962).

Si₃C₉H₂₇BO₃

① Tris(trimethylsiloxy)boron
  [(CH₃)₃SiO]₃B
② (Me₃Si)₂O + B₂O₃ $\xrightarrow{350° \text{ in autoclave}}$
  Me₃SiCl + H₃BO₃ ⟶
③ (184.5°). n_D1.4225 (20°). d0.8285 (20°).
⑥ Zhur. **27**, 1476 (1957).

Si₃C₉H₂₇GaO₃

① Tris(trimethylsiloxy)gallium

Ga[OSi(CH₃)₃]₃
② GaCl₃ + Me₃SiONa ⟶ 77%
③ [208°]. Sublimes at 135°.
⑥ Ber. **96**, 2696 (1963).   Angew. **74**, 328
  (1962).

Si₃C₉H₂₇ClO₃Ti

① Tris(trimethylsiloxy)chlorotitanium
  [(CH₃)₃SiO]₃TiCl
② (CH₃)₃SiONa + TiCl₄ ⟶ 53.4%
③ Needles. (103~105°/10). [33°].
  Solv. in org. solvents. Decomp. in
  water.
④ + C₄H₉OH + C₅H₅N
  ⟶ C₄H₉OTi[OSi(CH₃)₃]₃ (46%)
⑥ Izv. OKhN **1958**, 644; CA **52**, 19910
  (1958).

Si₃C₉H₂₇N₃

① Cyclononamethyltrisilazane
  [(CH₃)₂SiNCH₃]₂
② Me₂SiCl₂ + MeN(SiMe₂NLiMe)₂ ⟶
③ (91°/12). [36°].
⑥ Angew. **75**, 368 (1963).

Si₃C₉H₂₇O₄P

① Tris(trimethylsiloxy)phosphine oxide
  [(CH₃)₃SiO]₃PO
② [(CH₃)₃Si]₂O + P₂O₅ (or H₂PO₄) ⟶
  (CH₃)₃SiCl + H₃PO₄ ⟶
③ (86°/4°). n_D1.4090 (20°). d0.9591 (20°).
④ Hydrolyzed by water, org. acids or
  bases. Also cleaved by NaBr.
⑥ Zhur. **25**, 437 (1955).   JACS **66**, 1707
  (1944); **82**, 2710 (1960).

Si₃C₁₀H₂₄O₅

① 1,5-Diacetoxyhexamethyltrisiloxane
  CH₃COO[Si(CH₃)₂O]₃COCH₃
② Ac₂O + Me₂SiCl(OSiMe₂)Cl ⟶ 86%
  Ac₂O + (Me₂SiO)₃ ⟶ 23.7%
③ (92.5°/2, 106~107°/9.5, 140~142°/50,
  212°). n_D1.4029, 1.4030, 1.4008
  (20°). d1.118, 1.0131 (20°/4°).

④ $+ Me_2SiO$

$$\begin{array}{c} Me_2SiO \\ \quad \diagdown O \diagup Si(Me)OBu\text{-}n \\ Me_2SiO \end{array} \longrightarrow$$

$$\left[\begin{array}{c} Me_2SiO \\ \quad \diagdown O \diagup SiMeOSiMe_2O- \\ Me_2SiO \end{array} \right]_2 SiMe_2$$

$+ CH_2=CMeCOOCH_2SiMe_2OEt$

$\longrightarrow (CH_2=CMeCOOCH_2SiMe_2$-
$OSiMe_2O)_2SiMe_2$

⑥ Izv. OKhN **1963**, 1986 ; **1959**, 1767,
English page 1693.   US 2910496
(1959).   Ger. 1039516 (1958) ; CA
54, 17269 (1960).

$Si_3C_{10}H_{25}N_3$

① 1,1-Diethyl-3,5-dimethyl-3,5-αivinyl-
cyclotrisilazane
$[(C_2H_5)_2SiNH][CH_3Si(CH=CH_2)NH]_2$

② $MeSi(CH=CH_2)Cl_2 + NH_3$
$+ Et_2SiCl_2 \longrightarrow$

③ (84~96°/1). $n_D 1.4842$ (20°). $d 0.9515$
(20°/4°).

⑥ Izv. OKhN **1963**. 948.

$Si_3C_{10}H_{26}N_2O_4$

① 1,1,3,3,5,5-Hexamethyl-1,3-di-
acetoxytrisilazane
$[CH_3COOSi(CH_3)_2NH]_2Si(CH_3)_2$

② $(Me_2SiNH)_3 + AcOH \longrightarrow 80\%$

③ (138~140°/15). $n_D 1.4370$ (20°). $d 1.0156$
(20°/4°).

⑥ Zhur. **33**, 3269 (1963).

$Si_3C_{10}H_{26}O_2$

① 2-Allylheptamethyltrisiloxane
$CH_2=CHCH_2Si[OSi(CH_3)_3]_2CH_3$

② $CH_2=CHCH_2SiCl_2Me + Me_3SiCl$
$+NaHCO_3 \longrightarrow 50\%$

③ (103.0~103.5°/59). $n_D 1.4013$ (25°).
$d 0.8342$ (25°/4°).

④ $+ CCl_2 \longrightarrow$

$$\begin{array}{c} CH_2-CHCH_2Si(OSiMe_3)_2Me \\ \diagdown \diagup \\ CCl_2 \end{array}$$

⑥ Coll. Czech. Chem. Comm. **28**, 3808

(1963).

$Si_3C_{10}H_{26}O_3$

① 4,6,6-Trimethyl-4-trimethylsiloxy-4-
sila-5-oxaheptanal
$[(CH_3)_3SiO]_2Si(CH_3)CH_2CH_2CHO$

② $(Me_3SiO)_2SiMeCH_2CH_2CH(OEt)_2$
$+ HOH + HCl \longrightarrow$

③ (58~60°/0.5). $n_D 1.4085$ (25°).

⑥ Ger. 1115929 (1961) ; CA **59**, 3957
(1963).   US 2920092 (1959).

$Si_3C_{10}H_{28}$

① Tris(trimethylsilyl)methane
$CH[Si(CH_3)_3]_3$

② $THF + Mg + Me_3SiCl + CHBr_3$
$\longrightarrow 24.2\%$

③ (101°/20, 195~196°). $n_D 1.4605$, 1.4418
(20°). $d 0.7892$ (20°).

⑥ JACS **85**, 2243 (1963). Izv. OKhN **1960**,
231.

$Si_3C_{10}H_{28}N_2$

① 1,1-Dimethyl-2,5-bis(trimethylsilyl)-1-sila-2,5-dinitracyclo-
pentane

$$\begin{array}{c} CH_2\text{---}CH_2 \\ (CH_3)_3 SiN \qquad NSi(CH_3)_3 \\ \diagdown Si(CH_3)_2 \diagup \end{array}$$

② $Me_3SiN(Li)CH_2CH_2N(Li)SiMe_3$
$\qquad\qquad Me_2SiCl_2 + \longrightarrow$

③ (47°/1, 63~64°/4). $n_D 1.4438$ (20°).

⑥ Z. anorg. allg. Chem. **321**, 31 (1963).

$Si_3C_{10}H_{28}O_3$

① Tris(methoxydimethylsilyl)-
methane
$CH[Si(CH_3)_2OCH_3]_3$

② $C(SiMe_2OMe)_4 + MeOH + MeONa$
$\longrightarrow 67.1\%$
$C(SiHMe_2)_4 + MeOH + MeONa$
$\longrightarrow 52.5\%$

③ (130°/40). n_D1.4385 (25°). d0.932
(25°/4°).

④ + MeOH + MeONa
—→ CH₂(SiMe₂OMe)₂ 43.1%

⑥ JOC. **28**, 2717 (1963)

Si₃C₁₀H₂₉N₃O

① N,N'-Bis(trimethylsilyl)-N-tri-
methylsilylaminocarbamide
(CH₃)₃SiNCON[Si(CH₃)₃]NHSi(CH₃)₃

② Me₃SiNHNHSiMe₃ + Me₃SiNCO —→

③ [110°].
Sublimes at 90°.

⑥ Monatsh. **94**, 63 (1963).

Si₃C₁₀H₃₀N₂O₂

① Hexamethyl-1,5-bis(ethylamino)tri-
siloxane
C₂H₅NHSi(CH₃)₂OSi(CH₃)₂OSi(CH₃)₂-
NHC₂H₅

② EtNH₂ + Et₂SiClOSiMe₂OSiMe₂Cl —→

③ (204~206°). n_D0.8834 (20°). d1.4100
(20°/4°).

⑥ Izv. OKhN **1963**, 1847.

Si₃C₁₁H₂₃N₃

① Phenylpentamethylcyclotrisilazane

$$\begin{array}{c} C_6H_5 \quad CH_3 \\ \diagdown Si \diagup \\ NH \qquad NH \\ (CH_3)_2Si \qquad Si(CH_3)_2 \\ \diagdown NH \diagup \end{array}$$

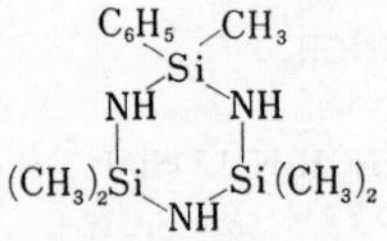

② Me₂SiCl₂ + MeSiCl₂Ph + NH₃ —→

③ (111~112°/3).

⑥ Zhur. **33**, 290 (1963).

Si₃C₁₁H₂₄N

① 1,1-Bis(trimethylsilyl)-2-trimethyl-
silyliminoethene
[(CH₃)₃Si]₂C=C=NSi(CH₃)₃

② Me₃SiCl + Na₂C=C=NNa —→

③ (214~216°). n_D1.4566 (20°). d0.8269
(23°).

IR : 2020 cm⁻¹.

⑥ Angew. **75**, 793 (1963).

Si₃C₁₁H₂₉N₃

① 1-Methyl-1-vinyl-3,3,5,5-tetraethyl-
cyclotrisilazane

$$\begin{array}{c} (C_2H_5)_2 \\ Si \\ NH \qquad NH \\ CH_2=CH(CH_3)Si \qquad Si(C_2H_5)_2 \\ NH \end{array}$$

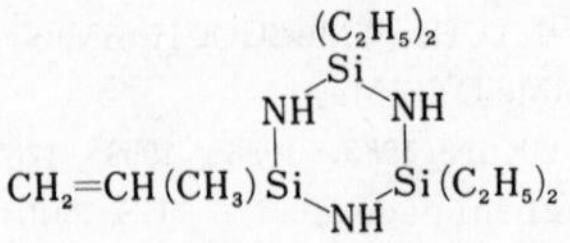

② Et₂SiCl₂ + NH₃ +
MeSiCl₂CH=CH₂ —→

③ (105~107°/1). n_D1.4706 (20°). d0.9423
(20°/4°).

⑥ Izv. OKhN **1963**, 948.

Si₃C₁₁H₃₀

① 1,1,1-Tris(trimethylsilyl)ethane
CH₃C[Si(CH₃)₃]₃

② THF + Mg + Me₃SiCl + MeCCl₃ —→

③ [118°].

⑥ JACS **85**, 2243 (1963).

Si₃C₁₁H₃₂N₂

① N,N,N'-Tris(trimethylsilyl)-
ethylendiamine
[(CH₃)₃Si]₂NCH₂CH₂NHSi(CH₃)₃

② Me₃SiCl
+ Me₃SiNHCH₂CH₂NHSiMe₃ —→

③ (79~80°/3, 237~239°). n_D1.4437 (20°).

⑥ Z. anorg. allg. Chem. **321**, 21 (1963).

Si₃C₁₂H₂₃Cl₂N

① Phenyldichloro[bis(trimethylsilyl)-
amino]silane
C₆H₅SiCl₂N[Si(CH₃)₃]₂

② PhSiCl₃ + (Me₃Si)₂NH —→

③ (115°/1). [38~40°].

④ + NH₃ —→ PhSiCl(NH₂)N(SiMe₃)₂
+ HOH + Et₃N
—→ PhSi(OH)₂N(SiMe₃)₂

⑥ Angew. **75**, 165 (1963).

$Si_3C_{12}H_{24}O_3$

① Tricyclotetramethylenecyclotri-
siloxane

$$\left(\begin{array}{c} CH_2CH_2 \\ | \\ CH_2CH_2 \end{array}\!\!\!>SiO\right)_3$$

② $SiCl_4 + (CH_2CH_2MgBr)_2 \longrightarrow$

$$\begin{array}{c} CH_2CH_2 \\ | \\ CH_2CH_2 \end{array}\!\!\!>SiCl_2 \xrightarrow{H_2O}$$

③ Solid. [199~201°].
IR (strong): 2940, 2865, 1408, 1074,
1034, 1010 cm^{-1}.

⑥ JOC **28**, 1941 (1963).

$Si_3C_{12}H_{25}ClN_2$

① Bis(trimethylsilylamino)phenyl-
chlorosilane
$C_6H_5SiCl[NHSi(CH_3)_3]_2$

② $PhSiCl(NH_2)N(SiMe_3)_2 \xrightarrow{heat}$

③ (123°/0.5). $n_D 1.4930$ (20°).

⑥ Angew. **75**, 165 (1963).

$Si_3C_{12}H_{27}N_3$

① Diaminophenyl[bis(trimethylsilyl)-
amino]silane
$C_6H_5Si(NH_2)_2N[Si(CH_3)_3]_2$

② $PhSiCl(NH_2)N(SiMe_3)_2 \xrightarrow{heat}$

③ (105°/1). $n_D 1.5084$ (20°).

④ At 200° $\longrightarrow PhSi(NH_2)(NHSiMe_3)_2$

⑥ Angew. **75**, 165 (1963).

$Si_3C_{12}H_{27}N_3$

① Methylallylcyclotrisilazane
$[CH_3Si(CH_2CH=CH_2)NH]_3$

② $NH_3 + MeSiCl_2CH_2CH=CH_2 \longrightarrow$

③ (94.0~94.5°/1). $n_D 1.487$ (20°). $d 0.9528$
(20°/4°).

⑥ Zhur. **33**, 1293, 2638 (1963).

$Si_3C_{12}H_{27}N_3$

① Bis(trimethylsilylamino)phenyl-
aminosilane
$C_6H_5Si[NHSi(CH_3)_3]_2NH_2$

② $PhSi(NH_2)_2Si(SiMe_3)_2 \xrightarrow{200°}$

③ (101°/0.5). $n_D 1.4889$ (20°).

⑥ Angew. **75**, 165 (1963).

$Si_3C_{12}H_{28}$

① 1,3-Bis(1-methylvinyl)hexamethyl-
trisilane
$CH_2=C(CH_3)[Si(CH_3)_2]_3C(CH_3)=CH_2$

② $CH_2=CMeMgBr + Cl(SiMe_2)_3Cl$
$\longrightarrow$ 85.5%

③ (110°/15). $n_D 1.4983$ (20°). $d 0.8340$
(20°/4°).

④ + $H_2SO_4 + NH_4HF_2$
$\longrightarrow Me_2Si(OCMe_2SiMe_2F)_2$

⑥ JOM **2**, 136 (1964).

$Si_3C_{12}H_{30}N_2O_4$

① 1,5-Bis(propionoxy)hexamethyl-
trisilazane
$[C_2H_5COOSi(CH_3)_2NH]_2Si(CH_3)_2$

② $(Me_2SiNH)_3 + EtCOOH \longrightarrow$ 56%

③ (124~125°/10). $n_D 1.4370$ (20°). $d 0.9962$
(20°/4°).

⑥ Zhur. **33**, 3269 (1963).

$Si_3C_{12}H_{30}O_3$

① Hexaethylcyclotrisiloxane
$[(C_2H_5)_2SiO]_3$

② $(C_2H_5)_2SiCl_2 + H_2O \xrightarrow{aq.\ NaOH}$ 41%

③ (117°/10). [14°]. $n_D 1.4308$ (20°).
$d 0.9555$ (20°).

⑥ Sci. & Ind. (Japan) **27**, 200 (1953).
Zhur. **27**, 491 (1957).   JACS **70**,
3888 (1948); **63**, 1194 (1941).

$Si_3C_{12}H_{33}N_3$

① Hexaethylcyclotrisilazane

[(C₂H₅)₂SiNH]₃

② NH₃ + Et₂SiCl₂ ⟶

③ (122~127°/1, 128~129°/1). n_D 1.4600, 1.468 (20°). d 0.9324 (20°/4°).

⑥ Zhur. **32**, 2652 (1962); **33**, 252 (1963). CA **58**, 7693 (1963).

Si₃C₁₃H₂₂O₂

① 1,5-Bis(vinylethynyl)-1,1,3,5,5-pentamethyltrisiloxane
[CH₂=CHC≡CSi(CH₃)₂O-]₂SiHCH₃

③ (80°/1.5). n_D 1.4629 (20°). d 0.910 (20°/4°).

⑥ Izv. OKhN **1963**, 97.

Si₃C₁₃H₂₆N₂

① 1,3-Bis(trimethylsilyl)-2-methyl-1,3-dinitra-2-silahydrindene

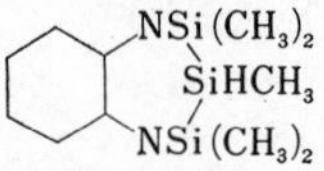

NSi(CH₃)₂
SiHCH₃
NSi(CH₃)₂

② o-C₆H₄(NHSiMe₃)₂ + Et₃N + MeSiHCl₂ ⟶

③ (85~86°/1). n_D 1.5278 (20°).

⑥ Angew. **2**, 152 (1963).

Si₃C₁₄H₃₆O₂

① 1,5-Dibutylhexamethyltrisiloxane
C₄H₉Si(CH₃)₂OSi(CH₃)₂OSi(CH₃)₂C₄H₉

② BuLi + Me₂SiClOSiMe₂OSiMe₂Cl ⟶ 49.5%

③ (133°/20).

⑥ Makromol. Chem. **39**, 167 (1960). Ger. 1136336 (1962); CA **58**, 6861 (1963).

Si₃C₁₄H₃₆O₈

① Dimethylbis(3-trimethoxysilylpropoxy)silane
(CH₃)₂Si[OCH₂CH₂CH₂Si(OCH₃)₃]₂

② H₂PtCl₆ + Me₂Si(OCH₂CH=CH₂)₂ + HSi(OMe)₃ ⟶

③ (127~129°/2). n_D 1.4240 (20°). d 1.039

(20°/4°).

⑥ Dokl. **151**, 849 (1963).

Si₃C₁₅H₃₀O₃

① Cyclopentamethylenecyclotrisiloxane

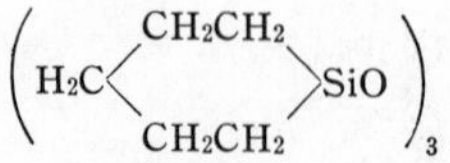

$$\left(H_2C \Big\langle {}^{CH_2CH_2}_{CH_2CH_2} \Big\rangle SiO \right)_3$$

②

$$H_2C \Big\langle {}^{CH_2CH_2}_{CH_2CH_2} \Big\rangle SiCl_2 + HOH \longrightarrow$$

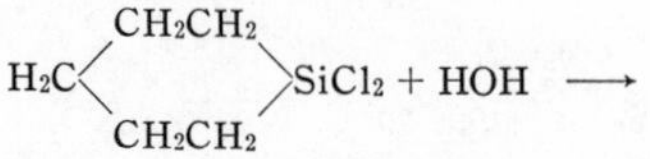

③ Solid. [92~94°].
IR (strong): 2910, 2850, 1016, 1000, 784 cm⁻¹.

⑥ JOC **28**, 1941 (1963).

Si₃C₁₅H₃₈O₂

① Bis(trimethylsiloxy)methyloctylsilane
C₈H₁₇Si[OSi(CH₃)₃]₂CH₃

② C₆H₁₃CH=CH₂ + Pd−Al₂O₃ + Me₃SiOSi(H)MeOSiMe₃ ⟶

③ (84~88°/0.3). n_D 1.4128 (25°).

⑥ Ger. 1115929 (1961); CA **59**, 3957 (1963).

Si₃C₁₆H₂₅N₃

① 1,3-Diphenyltetramethylcyclotrisilazane

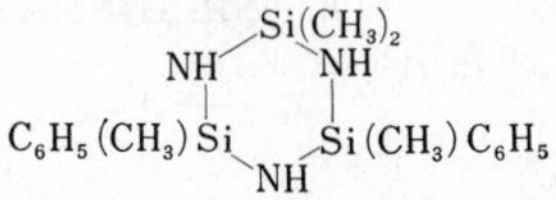

Si(CH₃)₂
NH   NH
C₆H₅(CH₃)Si   Si(CH₃)C₆H₅
NH

② Me₂SiCl₂ + NH₃ + PhSiCl₂Me

③ (170~172°/2).

⑥ Zhur. **33**, 290 (1963).

Si₃C₁₆H₃₂

① Phenyltris(trimethylsilyl)methane
C₆H₅C[Si(CH₃)₃]₃

② Mg + PhCCl₃ + Me₃SiCl + THF ⟶

③ [158～160°].
⑥ JACS **85**, 2243 (1962).

Si₃C₁₆H₄₀O₆

① Bis(3-ethyldimethoxysilylpropoxy)-
dimethylsilane
(CH₃)₂Si[OCH₂CH₂CH₂Si(OCH₃)₂C₂H₅]₂
② Me₂Si(OCH₂CH=CH₂)₂ + H₂PtCl₆
+ EtSiH(OMe)₂ ⟶ 42%
③ (134～135°/1). n_D 1.4320 (20°). d 0.9808
(20°/4°).
⑥ Dokl. **151**, 849 (1963).

Si₃C₁₆H₄₀O₈

① Diethylbis(3-trimethoxysilyl-
propoxy)silane
(C₂H₅)₂Si[OCH₂CH₂CH₂Si(OCH₃)₃]₂
② Et₂Si(OCH₂CH=CH₂)₂
+ HSi(OMe)₃ ⟶
③ (152～153°/1～2). n_D 1.427 (20°).
d 1.0288 (20°/4°).
⑥ Dokl. **151**, 849 (1963).

Si₃C₁₈H₁₈O₃

① 1,3,5-Triphenylcyclotrisiloxane
[H(C₆H₅)SiO]₃
② H(C₆H₅)SiBr₂ + H₂O ⟶ 8%
③ (140～150°/0.07). n_D 1.566 (25°).
⑥ JACS **79**, 1437 (1957).

Si₃C₁₈H₂₄F₁₈O₃

① Hexa(3,3,3-trifluoropropyl)cyclo-
trisiloxane
[(CF₃CH₂CH₂)₂SiO]₃
② tetramer + KOH ⟶ᵈⁱˢᵗⁱˡˡ
③ (155°/1.6). [86.5～87.0°].
⑥ US 3070617 (1962); CA **58**, 12600 (1963).
Brit. 835523 (1960); CA **55**, 1445
(1961).

Si₃C₁₈H₂₆Cl₂

① Bis(p-dimethylchlorosilylphenyl)-

dimethylsilane
(CH₃)₂Si[C₆H₄Si(CH₃)₂Cl-p]₂
② p-C₆H₄Br₂ + Mg + Me₂SiCl₂ ⟶
p-C₆H₄(MgBr)₂ + Me₂SiCl₂ ⟶
③ Solid. (180°/1). [75～80°].
④ + Me₂SiCl₂ ⟶ p-C₆H₄(SiMe₂Cl)₂
⑥ US 3067230 (1962); CA **58**, 10238
(1963). Fr. 1323431 (1963); CA **59**,
10120 (1963).

Si₃C₁₈H₂₈O₂

① 1,5-Diphenylhexamethyltrisiloxane
C₆H₅Si(CH₃)₂OSi(CH₃)₂OSi(CH₃)₂C₆H₅
② Me₂SiClOSiMe₂OSi(Me)₂Cl + PhLi
⟶ 46%
③ (132°/0.02). n_D 1.4913 (20°). d 0.974
(20°/4°).
⑥ JACS **74**, 386 (1952). Ger. 1136336
(1962); CA **58**, 6861 (1963).

Si₃C₁₈H₄₂N₂O₄

① Bis(hexoyloxydimethylsilylamino)-
dimethylsilane
[C₅H₁₁COOSi(CH₃)₂NH]₂Si(CH₃)₂
② (Me₂SiNH)₃ + n-AmCOOH ⟶
51.6%
③ (163～165°/10). n_D 1.4393 (20°). d 0.9564
(20°/4°).
⑥ Zhur. **33**, 3269 (1963).

Si₃C₁₈H₄₄O₆

① Bis(3-methyldiethoxysilylpropoxy)-
dimethylsilane
(CH₃)₂Si[OCH₂CH₂CH₂Si(OC₂H₅)₂CH₃]₂
② H₂PtCl₆ + Me₂Si(OCH₂CH=CH₂)₂
+ MeSiH(OEt)₂ ⟶
③ (142～143°/1). n_D 1.4252 (20°). d 0.9558
(20°/4°).
⑥ Dokl. **151**, 849 (1963).

Si₃C₁₈H₄₅AlO₃

① Tris(triethylsiloxy)aluminum
[(C₂H₅)₃SiO]₃Al

② Al + $(C_2H_5)_3SiOH$ $\xrightarrow{HgCl_2}$

③ Colorless crystals. [159°].
   Sol. in org. solvents. Decomp. in
   water.

⑥ Izv. OKhN **1956**, 74; CA **50**, 13782
   (1956).

$Si_3C_{18}H_{45}BO_3$

① Tris(triethylsiloxy)boron
   $[(C_2H_5)_3SiO]_3B$

② $(C_2H_5)_3SiOCH_3 + H_3BO_3$ $\longrightarrow$ 70%

③ $(310\sim312°, 178\sim179°/13)$. $n_D 1.4379$
   (20°). $d 0.8918$ (20°).

⑥ Zhur. **27**, 1476 (1957).

$Si_3C_{18}H_{45}OP$

① Tris(3-trimethylsilylpropyl)-
   phosphine oxide
   $OP[CH_2CH_2CH_2Si(CH_3)_3]_3$

② $POCl_3 + Me_3SiCH_2CH_2CH_2MgCl$ $\longrightarrow$

③ $(154\sim156°/<0.1)$.

④ $+ H_2SO_4$ $\longrightarrow$
   $OP(CH_2CH_2CH_2SiMe_2OH)_3$

⑥ Fr. 1318080 (1963); CA **59**, 10123(1963).

$Si_3C_{19}H_{31}N_3$

① 1,1-Diphenylheptamethylcyclotri-
   silazane

   $CH_3N\begin{array}{c}\diagup Si(CH_3)_2N(CH_3)\diagdown\\ \diagdown Si(CH_3)_2N(CH_3)\diagup\end{array}Si(C_6H_5)_2$

② $Ph_2SiCl_2 + MeN(SiMe_2NLiMe)_2$ $\longrightarrow$

③ $(151\sim152°/3)$. [62~64°].

⑥ Angew. **75**, 638 (1963).

$Si_3C_{19}H_{46}O_9$

① Tris(triethoxysilyl)methane
   $CH[Si(OC_2H_5)_3]_3$

② $EtOH + C_5H_5N + C_2Si_6Cl_{16}$ [1,1,3,3-
   tetrachloro-2,2,4,4-tetrakis(trichlorosilyl)-1,3-disilacyclobutane]
   $\longrightarrow$

③ $(142\sim144°/4)$. $n_D 1.4180$ (20°).

⑥ Ber. **96**, 2894 (1963).

$Si_3C_{20}H_{48}O_8$

① Bis(γ-triethoxysilylpropoxy)-
   dimethylsilane
   $(CH_3)_2Si[OCH_2CH_2CH_2Si(C_2H_5)_3]_2$

② $Me_2Si(OCH_2CH=CH_2)_2 + H_2PtCl_6$
   $+ HSi(OEt)_3$ $\longrightarrow$ 49%

③ $(154\sim155°/1)$. $n_D 1.4208$ (20°). $d 0.9776$
   (20°/4°).

⑥ Dokl. **151**, 849 (1963).

$Si_3C_{21}H_{24}Cl_2O_2$

① 1,5-Dichloro-1,3,5-triphenyl-1,3,5-
   trimethyltrisiloxane
   $C_6H_5Si(CH_3)ClOSi(CH_3)(C_6H_5)$-
   $OSiCl(CH_3)C_6H_5$

② $PhSiCl_2Me + H_2O$ $\longrightarrow$

③ $(190\sim193°/1)$. $n_D 1.5373$ (25°). $d 1.153$
   (20°/4°).

④ $+ Ac_2O$ $\longrightarrow$
   $(AcOSiMePh)_2SiMePh$

⑤ JACS **74**, 386 (1952).   Izv. OKhN
   1962, 1392; **1963**, 651.

$Si_3C_{21}H_{24}O_3$

① Trimethyltriphenylcyclotrisiloxane
   $[C_6H_5Si(CH_3)O]_3$

② $PhSiCl_2Me + H_2O$ $\longrightarrow$
   (some cleavage of Ph)

③ $(58°/5)$. [99.5° *cis*], [39.5° *trans*].
   $n_D 1.4221$ (20°). $d 1.102$ (25°/25°).
   Viscosity: 203 cs (20°), 187 cs (20°).
   IR: 1060 cm^{-1}.

④ $+ Me_2SiCl_2$ $\longrightarrow$ polymers

⑥ Dokl. **146**, 601 (1962).   Chem. Listy
   49, 894 (1955).   JACS **70**, 1115, 3758
   (1948).

$Si_3C_{21}H_{26}O_4$

① 1,3,5-Triphenyl-1,3,5-trimethyl-1,5-
   dihydroxytrisiloxane
   $HO[Si(CH_3)(C_6H_5)O]_3H$

② MeSiCl₂Ph + H₂O ⟶

③ n_D 1.5383 (20°). d 1.118 (20°/4°).
Brittle pt. −38°

④ + Ti(OBu-n)₄
⟶ Ti[O(SiMePhO)₃H]₄

⑥ Izv. SKh 1963, 1672.

Si₃C₂₁H₂₇N₃

① Triphenyltrimethylcyclotrisilazane
[C₆H₅Si(CH₃)NH]₃

② NH₃ + PhSiCl₂Me ⟶

③ Solid. (240°). [113~114°]. n_D 1.5807
(20°).

⑥ JCSJ 59, 1445 (1956).   Zhur. 33, 290
(1963).

Si₃C₂₂H₃₈N₂O₂

① 3,3-Diethyl-1,5-bis(phenylamino-
methyl)tetramethyltrisiloxane
C₆H₅NHCH₂Si(CH₃)₂OSi(C₂H₅)₂O-
Si(CH₃)₂CH₂NHC₆H₅

② Et₂Si(OH)₂
+ PhNHCH₂SiMe₂OEt ⟶

③ (173~175°/0.5). n_D 1.5218 (20°). d 1.023
(20°/4°).
IR: 2800, 2876, 2910, 2940, 2960, 3016,
3051, 3085, 3422, 1608, 1500, 1452,
1422, 1370 cm⁻¹.

⑥ Izv. OKhN 1961, 2003; 1962, 1958.

Si₃C₂₃H₃₀F₆O₂

① 1-(m-Ethoxydimethylsilylphenyl)-3-
(p-ethoxydimethylsilylphenyl)-
hexafluoropropane
p-C₂H₅OSi(CH₃)₂C₆H₄CF₂CF₂CF₂C₆H₄
Si(CH₃)₂OC₂H₅-m

② p-BrMgC₆H₄CF₂CF₂CF₂C₆H₄MgBr-m
+ Me₂Si(OEt)₂ ⟶ 49%

③ [154.5~155.0°].

④ ⟶heat⟶ gum + 12%

⑥ Chem. & Ind. 1963, 1591.

Si₃C₂₄H₃₂O₄

① 1,3,5-Triphenyl-1,5-di-n-propoxytri-
siloxane
n-C₃H₇OSiH(C₆H₅)OSiH(C₆H₅)O-
SiH(C₆H₅)OC₃H₇-n

② PhSiH₃ + n-PrOH + Cu (powder)
⟶ 10.4%

③ (138°/3). n_D 1.5012 (20°).

⑥ Zhur. 33, 2617 (1963).

Si₃C₂₄H₃₃NO₂

① 1,1,3,5,5-Pentamethyl-1,5-diphenyl-
3-phenylaminomethyltrisiloxane

$$C_6H_5Si(CH_3)_2-O-\underset{\underset{CH_2NHC_6H_5}{|}}{\overset{\overset{CH_3}{|}}{Si}}-O-Si(CH_3)_2C_6H_5$$

② PhSiMe₂OH
+ PhNHCH₂Si(OEt)₂Me ⟶

③ (187~195°/1). n_D 1.5381 (20°). d 1.0534
(20°/4°).
IR: 800, 1050, 1500, 1510 cm⁻¹.

⑥ Izv. OKhN 1962, 1958, 2003.

Si₃C₂₄H₃₃N₃

① Hexamethyl-N,N',N''-triphenyl-
cyclotrisilazane
[(CH₃)₂SiNC₆H₅]₃

② PhNH₂ + (Me₂SiNH)₄ ⟶300°
NH₃ + PhNH₂ + (Me₂SiNH)₄ ⟶
PhNH₂ + (Me₂SiNH)₃ ⟶
Me₂SiCl₂ + PhNH₂ ⟶

③ [243~247°].

④ Undergoes hydrolysis easily.

⑥ Zhur. 32, 1993 (1962); 33, 290 (1963).
Dokl. 145, 1049 (1962).

Si₃C₂₄H₅₀O₇

① Tris(triethylsilyl) citrate

CH₂COOSi(C₂H₅)₃
|
C(OH)COOSi(C₂H₅)₃
|
CH₂COOSi(C₂H₅)₃

② NiCl₂ + Et₃SiH + H₂O

    CH₂COOH
    |
+ C(OH)COOH ⟶
    |
    CH₂COOH

③ (210～211°/2). n_D1.4605 (20°). d1.0113 (20°/4°).

⑥ Zhur. 32, 2561 (1962).

Si₃C₂₇H₃₆B₃Cl₆N₃

① *N,N′,N″*-Triphenyltris(2-methyl-dichlorosilylethyl)triborazane
[CH₃SiCl₂CH₂CH₂BNC₆H₅]₃

② MeSiHCl₂ + (CH₂=CHBNPh)₃ ⟶

③ [170～172°].

④ + H₂O + NaHCO₃ ⟶
[MeSi(OH)₂CH₂CH₂BNPh]₃ (59%)

⑥ Inorg. Chem. 2, 731 (1963).

Si₃C₂₈H₃₆FeO

① 1-Phenyldimethylsilyl-1′-[(phenyl-dimethylsiloxy)dimethylsilyl]-ferrocene
C₆H₅Si(CH₃)₂C₅H₄FeC₅H₄Si(CH₃)₂O-Si(CH₃)₂C₆H₅

② PhSiMe₂C₅H₄FeC₅H₄SiMe₂OLi + PhSiMe₂Cl ⟶

③ (200～208°/0.03). n_D1.5740 (25°).

⑥ US 3036015 (1962); CA **57**, 16656 (1962).   JOC **26**, 4038 (1961).

Si₃C₃₀H₄₅B₃Cl₃N₃

① *N,N′,N″*-Triphenyl-*B,B′,B″*-tris-(2-dimethylchlorosilylethyl)-borazane
[(CH₃)₂SiClCH₂CH₂BNC₆H₅]₃

② Me₂SiHCl + (CH₂=CHBNPh)₃ ⟶ 81%

③ [164～166°].

④ + MeMgBr ⟶ (Me₃SiCH₂CH₂BNPh)₃ (73.6%)

H₂O ⟶
[Me₂Si(OH)CH₂CH₂BNPh]₃ (76%)
Me₃SiOLi ⟶
(Me₃SiOSiMe₂CH₂CH₂BNPh)₃

⑥ Inorg. Chem. 2, 731 (1963).

Si₃C₃₀H₄₈B₃N₃O₃

① *N,N′,N″*-Triphenyl-*B,B′,B″*-tris-[(2-dimethylhydroxysilyl)]ethyl-borazane
[(CH₃)₂Si(OH)CH₂CH₂BNC₆H₅]₃

② H₂O + [Me₂SiClCH₂CH₂BNPh]₃ ⟶ 76%

③ [137°].
IR: 1257, 1377, 3400 cm⁻¹.

⑥ Inorg. Chem. 2, 731 (1963).

Si₃C₃₃H₅₄B₃N₃

① *N,N′,N″*-Triphenyltris(2-trimethyl-silylethyl)borazane
[(CH₃)₃SiCH₂CH₂BNC₆H₅]₃

② MeMgBr + [Me₂SiClCH₂CH₂BNPh]₃ ⟶ 76.3%

③ [157～159°].
IR: 1260, 1250, 840, 750 cm⁻¹.

④ + HOOH ⟶ Me₃SiCH₂CH₂OH

⑥ Inorg. Chem. 2, 731 (1963).

Si₃C₃₆H₃₀O₃

① Hexaphenylcyclotrisiloxane
[(C₆H₅)₂SiO]₃

② (AcO)₂SiPh₂ + NaOH ⟶
Ph₂SiCl₂ + H₂O + Me₂CO ⟶
Ph₂SiCl₂ + ZnO ⟶

③ Crystals. (290～300°/1). [189°]. d1.23 (25°).

⑥ JOC **23**, 1216 (1958); **24**, 861 (1959); **25**, 310 (1960); **26**, 414 (1961).

Si₃C₃₆H₃₀As₂O₆

① Tris(diphenylsilanedioxy)diarsenous anhydride

$$\begin{array}{c} OSi(C_6H_5)_2O \\ \diagup \qquad\qquad \diagdown \\ As-OSi(C_6H_5)_2O-As \\ \diagdown \qquad\qquad \diagup \\ OSi(C_6H_5)_2O \end{array}$$

② $AsCl_3 + NH_4OH + Ph_2SiCl_2 \longrightarrow 40\%$

$AsCl_3 + Ph_2Si(OH)_2 + Et_3N \longrightarrow 42\%$

$AsCl_3 + NH_3(gas) + Ph_2Si(OH)_2$
$\longrightarrow 30\%$

③ Solid. [194°].

Sol. in C_6H_6 and $CHCl_3$.

IR: 1430, 1122, 1113, 1008, 998, 887, 740, 717, 695 cm⁻¹

④ Hydrolyzes very slightly in H_2O even after 300 hrs.

⑥ JACS **82**, 4542 (1960); **83**, 549 (1961).

Si₃C₃₆H₃₂LiN₃

① N-Lithio-Si-hexaphenylcyclotrisilazane

$$\begin{array}{c} \qquad\quad Si(C_6H_5)_2 \\ LiN \qquad NH \\ (C_6H_5)_2Si \qquad Si(C_6H_5)_2 \\ \qquad\quad N \\ \qquad\quad H \end{array}$$

② $(Ph_2SiNH)_3 + BuLi \longrightarrow$

③ Solid. [205~206°].

⑥ Helv. Chim. Acta **45**, 1081 (1962).

Si₃C₃₆H₃₃N₃

① Hexaphenylcyclotrisilazane
[$(C_6H_5)_2SiNH$]₃

② $(C_6H_5)_2SiCl_2 + NH_3$
$\xrightarrow[\text{5 hrs in toluene}]{}$ good yield

③ [235~236°].

④ [$(C_6H_5)_2SiNH$]₃ + aniline $\xrightarrow[]{\text{reflux, 18 hrs}}$
diphenyldianilinosilane

⑥ JACS **75**, 995 (1953).

Si₃C₃₈H₃₆

① 2,2-Dimethylhexaphenyltrisilane
$(C_6H_5)_3SiSi(CH_3)_2Si(C_6H_5)_3$

② $Me_2SiCl_2 + Li + Ph_3SiLi \longrightarrow$

③ Solid. [222~225°].

④ + Li, then $Me_3SiCl \longrightarrow Me_3SiSiPh_3$

⑥ JOC **28**, 1651 (1963).

Si₃C₃₈H₈₄

① Dibutylbis(3-tributylsilylpropyl)-silane
$(C_4H_9)_2Si[CH_2CH_2CH_2Si(C_4H_9)_3]_2$

② $Li + BuBr + Bu_2Si(CH_2CH_2CH_2SiCl_3)_2$
$\longrightarrow 57\%$

③ (273~75°/5). n_D1.4702 (20°). d0.8450 (20°/4°).
IR: 1050, 1080, 1190 cm⁻¹.

⑥ Zhur. **30**, 2594, 2600 (1960).

Si₃C₃₉H₃₉BO₃

① Tris(diphenylmethylsilyl) borate
$B[OSi(C_6H_5)_2CH_3]_3$

② $AcOSiPh_2Me + B(OH)_3 \longrightarrow 77\%$

③ (295~300°/1). n_D1.5840 (20°). d1.120 (20°/4°).
IR: 166, 256, 312, 373, 522, 590, 620, 678, 744, 807, 971, 1003, 1105, 1186, 1234, 1412, 1462, 2886, 2914, 2943, 2969 cm⁻¹.

⑥ Latvijas PSR, Zinatnu, Akademijas, Vestis, Kimijas Serija (No.1) 93 (1961).   Izv. OKhN **1960**, 1607.

Si₃C₄₂H₃₆

① 1-Hydroheptaphenyltrisilane
$(C_6H_5)_3Si-Si(C_6H_5)_2-SiH(C_6H_5)_2$

② $Li + Ph_3Si-SiPh_2-SiPh_2-SiPh_3 \longrightarrow$
$THF + Ph_3SiLi$
$+ Ph_2SiClSiPh_2Cl \xrightarrow[]{LiAlH_4}$

③ Solid. (157.5~158°).

⑥ JACS **81**, 4812 (1959).   JOC **27**, 254 (1962).

Si₃C₄₂H₃₆O

① Heptaphenyl-1-hydroxytrisilane
$(C_6H_5)_3Si-Si(C_6H_5)_2-Si(C_6H_5)_2OH$

② $Ph_3SiLi + Ph_2SiClSiPh_2Cl$

$\xrightarrow{\text{LiAlH}_4}$ (as by-product)

③ Solid. [165~166°].

⑤ High temperature resistance.

⑥ JOC **27**, 254 (1962).

Si₃C₄₂H₄₂O₃

① Hexabenzylcyclotrisiloxane
   [(C₆H₅CH₂)₂SiO]₃

② (C₆H₅CH₂)₂SiCl₂ + HgO ⟶

③ White solid. [98°].
   Sol. in org. solvents ; insol. in water.

⑥ JCS **93**, 439 (1908) ; **125**, 2616 (1924).

Si₃C₄₄H₄₈

① Dimethylbis(3-triphenylsilylpropyl)-
   silane
   (CH₃)₂Si[CH₂CH₂CH₂Si(C₆H₅)₃]₂

② Me₂Si(CH₂CH₂CH₂SiCl₃)₂ + PhLi ⟶

③ Solid. [91~93°].
   IR : 830, 865, 1250~1260, 740, 1104,
   1180, 1490, 1570, 1590, 3000 cm⁻¹

⑥ Zhur. **30**, 2594, 2600 (1960).

Si₃C₄₆H₁₀₀O₈

① Diethylbis[tri(2-methylhexoxy)-
   siloxy]silane
   (C₂H₅)₂Si{OSi[OCH(CH₃)C₅H₁₁]₃}₂

② Et₂SiCl₂ + C₅H₅N
   + ClSi(OCHMeAm)₃ ⟶

③ Liq. (252~255°/0.1). n_D1.4345 (20°).
   d0.9152 (20°/4°).
   Viscosity : 2765 at −53°, 3.44 at 96°.

⑥ US 2780636 (1957) ; CA **51**, 8776 (1957).
   J. Chem. Eng. Data **6**, 437 (1961).

Si₃C₄₈H₄₀

① Octaphenyltrisilane
   (C₆H₅)₃SiSi(C₆H₅)₂Si(C₆H₅)₃

② Ph₃SiK + Ph₂SiCl₂ ⟶ 29%

③ Crystals. [260~262°].
   Sol. in C₆H₆−EtOH.

⑥ JACS **74**, 561 (1952). **81**, 4812 (1959).

JOC **18**, 753 (1963).

Si₃C₄₉H₅₀

① Bis(3-triphenylsilylpropyl)methyl-
   phenylsilane
   C₆H₅Si[CH₂CH₂CH₂Si(C₆H₅)₃]₂CH₃

② PhLi + PhSi(CH₂CH₂CH₂SiCl₃)₂Me

③ (103~104°).
   IR : 2900, 1430, 1100, 700 cm⁻¹.

⑥ Zhur. **30**, 2594, 2600 (1960).

Si₃C₅₀H₄₄O₂

① Diphenylbis(triphenylsilylmethoxy)-
   silane
   (C₆H₅)₂Si[OCH₂Si(C₆H₅)₃]₂

② Ph₃SiCH₂OH + Ph₂SiCl₂ ⟶ 15%

③ [202.0~203.5°].

④ C₅H₅ + 2% KOH in EtOH
   ⟶ Ph₂Si(OH)₂ + Ph₃SiCH₂OH

⑥ JACS **83**, 827 (1961).

Si₃C₅₄H₄₅AsO₄

① Tris(triphenylsilyl) arsenate
   OAs[OSi(C₆H₅)₃]₃

② Ph₃SiCl + KHAsO₄ ⟶ 87%
   Ph₃SiCl + Ag₃AsO₄ ⟶ 26%
   (6days, room temp.)
   AsCl₃ + Ph₃SiOH. then NH₃
   ⟶ 91%
   AsCl₃ + Ph₃SiONa ⟶ 76%
   AsCl₃ + Ph₃SiCl + NH₄OH ⟶ 50%

③ [237~240°].

⑥ JACS **82**, 4542 (1960) ; **83**, 549 (1961).

Si₃C₅₄H₄₅O₃SV

① Tris(triphenylsilyl) thiovanadate
   SV[OSi(C₆H₅)₃]₃

② VCl₄ + S + Ph₃SiONa $\xrightarrow{\text{in C}_6\text{H}_6,\text{ under N}_2}$

③ Solid. [200~202°].

⑥ JOC **27**, 3321 (1962).

Si₃C₅₄H₄₅O₄V

① Tris(triphenylsilyl) vanadate
    OV[OSi(C₆H₅)₃]₃

② Ph₃SiOH + VOCl₃, then NH₃ gas
    ⟶ 95%

③ Solid. [225°].

⑥ JOC **27**, 3321 (1962).

Si₃C₅₄H₄₅O₄P

① Tris(triphenylsilyl) phosphate
    OP[OSi(C₆H₅)₃]₃

② Ph₃SiOH + H₃PO₄ ⟶

③ [244°].

⑥ Zhur. **30**, 2223 (1960).

Si₃C₅₄H₄₈B₃N₃O₃

① *B, B′, B″*-tris(triphenylsiloxy)-
    borazine
    [(C₆H₅)₃SiOBNH]₃

② Ph₃SiONa + (ClBNH)₃ ⟶

③ [164~167°].
    Unstable in moist air.

⑥ Monatsh. **94**, 183 (1963).

Si₃C₅₄H₅₂

① 1,1,1,5,5,9,9,9-Octaphenyl-1,5,9-
    trisilanonane
    (C₆H₅)₂Si[CH₂CH₂CH₂Si(C₆H₅)₃]₂

② PhLi + Ph₂Si(CH₂CH₂CH₂SiCl₃)₂ ⟶
    Ph₃SiH + Ph₂Si(CH₂CH=CH₂)₂
    with peroxides ⟶ 25%

③ [115~117°].
    IR : ca. 700, 1100, 1420, 3080 cm⁻¹.

⑥ JOC **22**, 684 (1957).   Zhur. **30**, 2594.
    2600 (1960).

Si₃C₅₇H₅₄B₃N₃

① *B*-Tris(triphenylsilyl)-*N*-trimethyl-
    borazine
    [CH₃NBSi(C₆H₅)₃]₃

② Ph₃SiLi + (MeNBCl)₃ ⟶ 55%

③ White crystals. [248~251° decomp.].
    Sol. in C₆H₆, CHCl₃, and CH₂Cl₂.

Decomp. in CCl₄.
    IR : 1339, 1434, 1425, 1377, 1359 cm⁻¹.

④ $\xrightarrow{\text{heat}}$ glassy solid

⑥ JINC **15**, 99 (1960).

Si₃C₆₀H₄₈

① Diphenylbis(*p*-triphenylsilyl-
    phenyl)silane
    (C₆H₅)₂Si[C₆H₄Si(C₆H₅)₃-*p*]₂

② Ph₃SiC₆H₄Cl-*p* + Na + Ph₂SiCl₂
    ⟶ 45%

③ Crystals. [365~368°].

⑥ Rec. trav. chim. **81**, 565 (1962).

Si₃C₆₆H₆₀

① Diphenylbis(*p*-tribenzylsilylphenyl)-
    silane
    (C₆H₅)₂Si[C₆H₄Si(CH₂C₆H₅)₃-*p*]₂

② *p*-LiC₆H₄Si(CH₂Ph)₃ + Ph₂SiCl₂
    ⟶ 43.4%

③ Solid. [142.0~143.5°].

⑥ JOC **25**, 1194 (1960).

Si₃C₇₂H₆₀BN

① Tris(triphenylsilyl) boron-triphenyl-
    amine
    (C₆H₅)₃N→B[Si(C₆H₅)₃]₃

② Ph₃NBCl₃ + Ph₃SiK ⟶

③ [55~58°].
    IR : 14.4, 7.0, 3.5 μ.

⑥ JACS **82**, 501 (1960).

Si₃C₇₂H₆₀B₃N₃O₃

① Tris(triphenylsiloxy)-*N, N′, N″*-
    triphenylborazine
    [(C₆H₅)₃SiOBNC₆H₅]₃

② Ph₃SiONa + (ClBNPh)₃ ⟶

③ [234~235°].

⑥ Monatsh. **94**, 183 (1963).

Si₄C₄H₁₆O₄

① Tetramethylcyclotetrasiloxane

$(CH_3SiHO)_4$

② $H_2O + MeSiHCl_2 \longrightarrow$

③ $(134.5°)$. $n_D 1.3890$ $(20°)$. $d 0.9912$
   $(20°/4°)$.

⑥ Coll. Czech. Chem. Comm. **28**, 1384
   (1963). Vysokomol. Soed. **4**, 30
   (1962). Zhur. **29**, 258 (1959).

$Si_4C_8H_{12}Br_{12}O_4$

① Tetramethyltetrakis(tribromo-
   methyl)cyclotetrasiloxane
   $[CH_3SiO(CBr_3)]_4$

② $(Me_2SiO)_4 + Br_2 + Cl_2 \longrightarrow$ 6.3%

③ $(170\sim175°/9)$. $n_D 1.4813$ $(20°)$. $d 1.5558$
   $(20°/4°)$.

⑥ Zhur. **32**, 4022 (1962).

$Si_4C_8H_{16}Br_8O_4$

① 1,3,5,7-Tetramethyltetra(dibromo-
   methyl)cyclotetrasiloxane
   $[CH_3SiO(CHBr_2)]_4$

② $Br_2 + Cl_2 + (Me_2SiO)_4 \longrightarrow$ 23.1%

③ $(129\sim131°/8)$. $n_D 1.4452$ $(20°)$. $d 1.351$
   $(20°/4°)$.

⑥ Zhur. **32**, 4022 (1962).

$Si_4C_8H_{20}Br_4O_4$

① Tetramethyltetra(bromomethyl)-
   cyclotetrasiloxane
   $[CH_3SiO(CH_2Br)]_4$

② $(Me_2SiO)_4 + Br_2 + Cl_2 \longrightarrow$ 45%

③ $(105\sim106°/10)$. $n_D 1.4271$ $(20°)$. $d 1.153$
   $(20°/4°)$.

⑥ Zhur. **32**, 4022 (1962).

$Si_4C_8H_{20}Cl_4O_4$

① Methylchloromethylcyclotetra-
   siloxane
   $[CH_3Si(CH_2Cl)O]_4$

② $Cl-[SiMe(CH_2Cl)O]_3-SiMeClCH_2Cl$
   $+ H_2O \longrightarrow$

③ $(150.5°/0.3)$. $n_D 1.4502$ $(20°)$. $d 1.279$
   $(20°)$.

⑥ CA **59**, 6218 (1963).

$Si_4C_8H_{20}Cl_6O_3$

① 1,7-Dichloro-1,3,5,7-tetramethyl-
   1,3,5,7-tetrachloromethyltetra-
   siloxane
   $Cl-[Si(CH_3)(CH_2Cl)O]_3-Si(CH_3)Cl$
   CH_2Cl

② $H_2O + MeSiCl_2CH_2Cl \longrightarrow$ 10.7%

③ $(153°/0.3)$. $n_D 1.4641$ $(20°)$. $d 1.2957$
   $(20°)$.

④ $+ H_2O \longrightarrow$ $[MeSi(CH_2Cl)O]_4$
   $+ HO-[SiMe(CH_2Cl)O]_3-SiMe-$
   $(OH)CH_2Cl$

⑥ CA **59**, 5218 (1963).

$Si_4C_8H_{21}Cl_3O_3$

① 1-Vinyl-1,1,7-trichlorohexamethyl-
   trisiloxane
   $CH_2=CHSiCl_2-[OSi(CH_3)_2]_3-Cl$

② $FeCl_3 + (Me_2SiO)_3 + Me_2SiCl_2 \longrightarrow$

③ $(75\sim76°/3)$.

⑥ Izv. OKhN **1963**, 282.

$Si_4C_8H_{24}Cl_2N_2$

① 3,3-Dimethyl-2,4-bis(trimethylsilyl-
   1,1-dichloro-1,3-disila-2,4-dinitra-
   cyclobutane
$$(CH_3)_3SiN\diagdown^{\textstyle Si(CH_3)_2}_{\textstyle Si(CH_3)_2}\diagup NSi(CH_3)_3$$

② $SiCl_4 + Me_3Si-NLi-SiMe_2-NLi-$
   $SiMe_3 \longrightarrow$

③ $(118°/21)$. $[28\sim29°]$. $n_D 1.4360$ $(20°)$.

⑥ Ber. **96**, 1071 (1963).

$Si_4C_8H_{24}Cl_2O_3$

① 1,7-Dichlorooctamethyltetrasiloxane
   $(CH_3)_2SiCl-[OSi(CH_3)_2]_3-Cl$

② $(Me_2SiO)_3 + Me_2SiCl_2 \longrightarrow$
   $Me_2SiClOSiMe_2Cl + Me_2SiCl_2 \longrightarrow$
   $FeCl_3 + (Me_2SiO)_4 + Me_2SiCl_2 \longrightarrow$

③ $(77\sim78°/4)$. $n_D 1.4027$ $(20°)$. $d 1.011$

(20°).

④ + $CH_2=CHMgCl$ ⟶
   $CH_2=CHSiMe_2-(OSiMe_2)_3-CH=CH_2$

⑥ Izv. OKhN **1962**, 2133; **1961**, 1261,
   1456.   Ger. 1118199 (1961); CA **56**,
   11803 (1962).

$Si_4C_8H_{24}O_2$

① Octamethyl-1,2,4,5-tetrasiladioxane
   $(CH_3)_2Si-Si(CH_3)_2$

   $\quad\quad\;\; O \;\; O$

   $(CH_3)_2Si-Si(CH_3)_2$

② HOH + EtOEt
   + $Me_2SiBrSiMe_2Br$ ⟶
   HOH + $EtOSiMe_2SiMe_2OEt$ ⟶

③ [45.5~46.5°].

⑥ Kogyo Kagaku Zasshi **66**, 637 (1963).
   JOC **21**, 1264 (1956).

$Si_4C_8H_{24}O_2S_2$

① Octamethy-2,6-dithiacyclotetra-
   siloxane

   $(CH_3)_2Si-O-Si(CH_3)_2$

   $\quad\quad\;\; S \;\;\quad S$

   $(CH_3)_2Si-O-Si(CH_3)_2$

② $O(SiMe_2Cl)_2 + HSH + C_5H_5N$ ⟶

③ (116~122°/2). [38~42°].

⑥ Zhur. **32**, 3447 (1962).

$Si_4C_8H_{24}O_3$

① Octamethyl-1,3,5,7-tetrasila-2,4,6-
   trioxacycloheptane

   $(CH_3)_2Si-O-Si(CH_3)_2$

   $\quad\quad\;\; O \;\;\quad O$

   $(CH_3)_2Si$——$Si(CH_3)_2$

② $Me_2Si(OEt)_2 + HCl + Et_2O$
   + $EtOSiMe_2SiMe_2OEt$ ⟶

③ (67°/10). $n_D 1.4254$ (30°). $d 0.9284$
   (30°/4°).

⑥ Kogyo Kagaku Zasshi **66**, 637 (1963).

$Si_4C_8H_{24}O_4$

① Octamethylcyclotetrasiloxane
   $[(CH_3)_2SiO]_4$

② $C(SiHMe_2)_4 + MeOH + MeONa$ ⟶

③ $n_D 1.3943$ (25°). $d 0.952$ (25°/4°).

⑥ JOC **28**, 2717 (1963).

$Si_4C_8H_{24}O_4$

① 1,3,5,7-Tetraethylcyclotetrasiloxane
   $[H(C_2H_5)SiO]_4$

② $H(C_2H_5)SiCl_2 + H_2O$ ⟶

③ (208°). $n_D 1.4141$ (20°). $d 0.9808$ (20°).

⑥ JACS **77**, 862 (1955).   BCSJ **30**, 608
   (1957).

$Si_4C_8H_{26}N_2O_{10}$

① 1,1,3,3,5,5,7,7-Octamethoxy-1,3,5,7-
   tetrasila-4,8-dinitra-2,6-dioxa-
   cyclooctane

   $(CH_3O)_2Si-O-Si(OCH_3)_2$

   $\quad\quad\;\; NH \;\;\quad NH$

   $(CH_3O)_2Si-O-Si(OCH_3)_2$

② $NH_3 + (MeO)_2SiClOSi(OMe)_2Cl$ ⟶

③ (173~175°/0.05).

④ + KNH_2 ⟶
   $(MeO)_2Si(NHK)OSi(OMe)_2K$

⑥ Z. anorg. allg. Chem. **319**, 362
   (1963).

$Si_4C_8H_{26}O_3$

① 3,5-Dihydrooctamethylsiloxane
   $(CH_3)_3SiOSiH(CH_3)OSi(H)(CH_3)OSi$
   $(CH_3)_3$

② $Me_3SiCl + MeHSiCl_2 \xrightarrow{H_2O}$

③ (81°/28). $n_D 1.3854$ (20°). $d 0.8559$ (20°).

⑥ BCSJ **29**, 547 (1956).   JACS **68**, 962
   (1946).

$Si_4C_8H_{26}O_3$

① 1,1,3,3,5,5,7,7-Octamethyltetrasiloxane

$(CH_3)_2SiH-[(OSiCH_3)_2]_3-H$

② $Me_2Si(H)SiHMe_2 + (Me_2SiO)_4 + H_2SO_4$

　　$\longrightarrow$　14%

$Me_2SiCl-(OSiMe_2)_3-Cl$

　$+ LiAlH_4 \longrightarrow$

$Me_2SiHCl + Me_2SiCl_2 + H_2O \longrightarrow$

③ $(105\sim108°/100)$. $n_D 1.3870 (20°)$. $d 0.8602$
$(20°)$.

⑥ Ger. 1140348 (1962); CA **58**, 12600
(1963).　Ger. 1085875 (1960); CA
56, 27057 (1961).　Zhur. **29**, 248
(1959).　BCSJ **29**, 547 (1956).

Si₄C₈H₂₆O₅

① 1,7-Dihydroxyoctamethyl-
tetrasiloxane

$HO-[Si(CH_3)_2O]_4-H$

② $Me_2SiClOSiMe_2OSiMe_2OSiMe_2Cl$
　$+ NaOH \longrightarrow$　77%

③ $(137\sim140°)$. $n_D 1.4054 (20°)$. $d 0.9886$
$(20°/4°)$.

④ $+ (AcOSiMePh)_2O \longrightarrow$

$HO-[(SiMe_2O)_4(SiMePhO)_2]_xAc$

⑥ Izv. OKhN **1963**, 651; **1962**, 2243.

Si₄C₈H₂₈N₄

① Octamethylcyclotetrasilazane

$[(CH_3)_2SiNH]_4$

② $(Me_2SiNH)_3 + KOH \xrightarrow{160°}$

$(Me_2SiNH)_3 + (Et_3NMe)^+I^- \xrightarrow{300°}$

$Me_3SiCl + NH_3 + (Me_2SiNH)_3 \xrightarrow{20\sim40°}$

$(Me_2SiNH)_3 + NH_4Cl \xrightarrow{220°\sim250°}$

$NH_3 + Me_2SiCl_2 \longrightarrow$

③ $(56\sim57°/1)$. $[97°]$.

④ $+ PhNH_2\ 300° \longrightarrow (Me_2SiNPh)_3$
$+ NH_4Cl\ 300° \longrightarrow (Me_2SiNH)_3$
$+ p-H_2NC_6H_4C_6H_4NH_2-p \longrightarrow$
$(Me_2SiNHSiMe_2NHC_6H_4C_6H_5NH)_x$

⑥ Zhur. **32**, 2652 (1962); **33**, 1294 (1963).

Dokl. **145**, 1049 (1962).　JCS **1963**,
4758.

Si₄C₉H₂₇ClO₃

① Nonamethyl-1-chlorotetrasiloxane

$CH_3-[Si(CH_3)_2O]_3-Si(CH_3)_2Cl$

② $MeLi + (Me_2SiClOSiMe_2)_2O$

　$\longrightarrow$　42%

$Me_3SiOH +$

$Cl(SiMe_2O)_2SiMe_2Cl \longrightarrow$

③ $(96\sim100°/20)$.

⑥ Ger. 1136336(1962); CA **58**, 6861(1963).
Makromol. **55**, 87 (1962); **39**, 167
(1960).

Si₄C₉H₂₉N₃

① *N*-Trimethylsilylhexamethylcyclo-
trisilazane

$(CH_3)_3Si-NH$

$(CH_3)_3SiN\quad Si(CH_3)_2$

$(CH_3)_2Si-NH$

② $(Me_2SiNH)_3 + Na + Me_3SiCl$

　$\longrightarrow$　55$\sim$69%

③ $(112\sim113°/10)$. $n_D 1.4596 (20°)$. $d 0.931$
$(20°)$.

⑥ Inorg. Chem. **2**, 1069 (1963).

Si₄C₁₀H₂₄N₂O₅

① 1,7-Diisocyanatooctamethyltetra-
siloxane

$(CH_3)_2Si(NCO)-[OSi(CH_3)_2]_2-$
$OSi(CH_3)_2NCO$

② $Me_2SiCl-(OSiMe_2)_2-OSiMe_2Cl$
　$+ AgNCO$ (or $Pb(NCO)_2$) $\longrightarrow$

③ $(92\sim93°/3)$. $n_D 1.4147 (20°)$. $d 1.007$
$(20°)$.

IR: 3003, 2941, 2381, 2273, 1972, 1445,
1414, 1261, 1042$\sim$1087 cm^{-1}.

⑥ Kogyo Kagaku Zasshi **61**, 214 (1958).

Si₄C₁₀H₂₇N

① Nonamethyl-1-cyanotetrasilane

CH₃-Si[(CH₃)₂]₄-CN

② Me₃SiSiMe₂CN $\xrightarrow{\text{heat}}$

③ (65~75°/0.4).

⑥ JACS **85**, 3372 (1963).

Si₄C₁₀H₂₈

① 1,1,3,3,4,4,6,6-Hexamethyl-1,3,4,6-
tetrasilacyclohexane

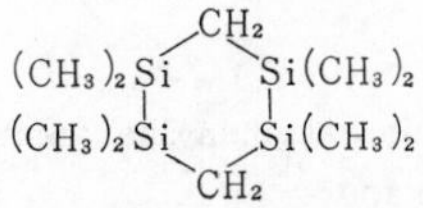

$$(CH_3)_2Si \overset{CH_2}{\underset{CH_2}{\diagup \diagdown}} Si(CH_3)_2$$
$$(CH_3)_2Si \diagdown \diagup Si(CH_3)_2$$

② Mg + Me₃SiFSiMe₂CH₂Cl $\longrightarrow$

③ (108~109°/15). [51~53°].

⑥ Unpublished work.

Si₄C₁₀H₂₈N₄

① Si-Divinyl-Si-hexamethylcyclotetra-
silazane

[CH₃Si(CH=CH₂)NH]₂[(CH₃)₂SiNH]₂

② MeSiCl₂CH=CH₂ + NH₃
+ MeSiCl₂ $\longrightarrow$

③ [63~64°].

⑥ Izv. OKhN **1963**, 948.

Si₄C₁₀H₃₀

① Decamethyltetrasilane

CH₃[Si(CH₃)₂]₄CH₃

② KNa + Me₃SiSi(Me)₂Cl
$\longrightarrow$ 71%, 27%

Na + Me₃SiSiMe₂Cl $\longrightarrow$

MeₓSi₂Cl₆₋ₓ + AgCN, then

MeMgBr $\longrightarrow$

③ (102~103°/13). [-12°]. n_D 1.4871 (20°).
d 0.8073 (20°/4°).

⑥ JOM 1, 153 (1963).   Angew. **74**, 696
(1962). Ber. **96**, 2798 (1963). JACS
85, 3372 (1963).

Si₄C₁₀H₃₀NNa

① Sodiobis(pentamethyldisilanyl)amine

[(CH₃)₃SiSi(CH₃)₂]₂NNa

② NaNH₂ + (Me₃SiSiMe₂)₂NH $\longrightarrow$

③ [58~62°].

⑥ Angew. **75**, 345 (1963).

Si₄C₁₀H₃₀N₂

① N, N′-Bis(trimethylsilyl)tetramethyl-
disilazane

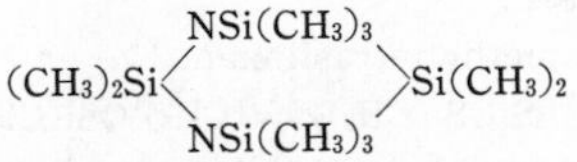

$$(CH_3)_2Si \overset{NSi(CH_3)_3}{\underset{NSi(CH_3)_3}{\diagup \diagdown}} Si(CH_3)_2$$

② Me₃SiN(Li)SiMe₂N(Li)SiMe₃
+ Me₂SiCl₂ $\longrightarrow$

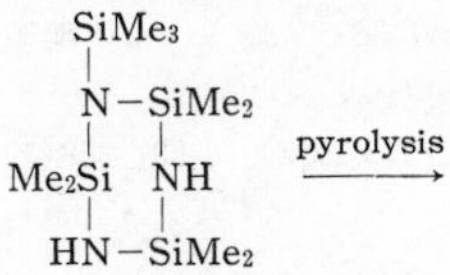

$$\begin{array}{c} SiMe_3 \\ | \\ N-SiMe_2 \\ | \quad | \\ Me_2Si \quad NH \\ | \quad | \\ HN-SiMe_2 \end{array} \xrightarrow{\text{pyrolysis}}$$

③ (85°/7). [38~39°]. n_D 1.4237 (20°).
d 0.998 (20°/4°).

⑥ Angew. **73**, 736 (1962). JCS **1962**, 1721.
Ber. **96**, 1071 (1963).

Si₄C₁₀H₃₀O

① Tetramethyl-1,3-bis(trimethylsilyl)-
disiloxane

[(CH₃)₃SiSi(CH₃)₂]₂O

② HOH + Me₃SiSiMe₂Cl $\longrightarrow$ 89%
EtONa + Me₃SiSiMe₂Cl $\longrightarrow$

③ (89~90°/15). n_D 1.4400 (20°). d 0.8153
(20°/4°).

⑥ Kogyo Kagaku Zasshi **66**, 637 (1963).
JCS **1962**, 548.   Izv. OKhN **1963**,
660.

Si₄C₁₀H₃₀O₂

① Tetramethyl-1,2-bis(trimethylsiloxy)disilane

(CH₃)₃SiOSi(CH₃)₂Si(CH₃)₂OSi(CH₃)₃

② H₂SO₄ + Me₃SiOSiMe₃

$$\text{H}_2\text{SO}_4 + \begin{array}{c} \text{Me}_2\text{Si}-\text{SiMe}_2 \\ | \quad\quad | \\ + \quad \text{O} \quad \text{O} \\ | \quad\quad | \\ \text{Me}_2\text{Si}-\text{SiMe}_2 \end{array} \longrightarrow$$

$$\text{H}_2\text{SO}_4 + \begin{array}{c} \text{Me}_2\text{Si}-\text{SiMe}_2 \\ | \quad\quad | \\ \text{Me}_2\text{Si}-\text{SiMe}_2 \end{array} \longrightarrow$$

HOH + Me₃SiClMe₂SiClSiMe₂Cl ⟶

③ (98~100°/34). n_D 1.4180 (30°). d 0.8220
   (30°/4°).

⑥ Kogyo Kagaku Zasshi **66**, 637 (1963).

Si₄C₁₀H₃₀O₃

① Decamethyltetrasiloxane
   (CH₃)₃SiOSi(CH₃)₂OSi(CH₃)₂OSi(CH₃)₃

② [(CH₃)₃SiO]₄ + [(CH₃)₃Si]₂O

$$\xrightarrow{\text{H}_2\text{SO}_4,\ \text{H}_2\text{O}}$$

③ (194°). n_D 1.3895 (20°). d 0.8536
   (20°).

⑥ JACS **47**, 2739 (1925).   **68**, 358 (1946).

Si₄C₁₁H₃₀O₃

① Vinyltris(trimethylsiloxy)silane
   CH₂=CHSi[OSi(CH₃)₃]₃

② CH₂=CHSiCl₃ + Me₃SiCl + NaHCO₃
   ⟶ 55.4%

③ (86.5~87.5°/15). n_D 1.3948 (25°).
   d 0.8560 (25°/4°).

④ + CCl₂ ⟶ CH₂–CHSi(OSiMe₃)₃
                  \\ /
                  CCl₂

⑥ Coll. Czech. Chem. Comm. **28**, 3088
   (1963).

Si₄C₁₀H₃₁N

① Tetramethyl-1,3-bis(trimethylsilyl)-
   disilazane
   [(CH₃)₃SiSi(CH₃)₂]₂NH

② NH₃ + Me₃SiSiMe₂Cl ⟶ 68.5%

③ (132.5~134.0°/40.5). n_D 1.4609 (20°).
   d 0.8159 (20°).

④ + NaNH₂ ⟶ (Me₃SiSiMe₂)₂NNa

⑥ JCS **1963**, 1091. Angew. **75**, 345 (1963).
   Angew. Int'l. Ed. **2**, 263 (1963).

Si₄C₁₁H₃₂N₂

① 2,2,3,4,4,5,5,6,7,7-Decamethyl-2,4,
   5,7-tetrasila-3,6-dinitracyclo-
   heptane

$$\text{H}_2\text{C}\!\!\begin{array}{c} \diagup \text{Si(CH}_3)_2\text{N(CH}_3)\text{Si(CH}_3)_2 \\ \quad\quad\quad\quad\quad\quad\quad\quad | \\ \diagdown \text{Si(CH}_3)_2\text{N(CH}_3)\text{Si(CH}_3)_2 \end{array}$$

② CH₂(SiMe₂Br)₂ + MeNH₂ ⟶
   CH₂(SiMe₂NHMe)₂ (refluxed) ⟶

③ (97°/3). [44~45°].

⑥ Angew. **75**, 980 (1963).

Si₄C₁₂H₂₃Cl₃O₃

① 1,1,7-Trichloro-1-phenylhexamethyl-
   tetrasiloxane
   C₆H₅SiCl₂–[OSi(CH₃)₂]₃–Cl

② PhSiCl₃ + FeCl₃ + (Me₂SiO)₄ ⟶

③ (102°/2).

⑥ Izv. OKhN **1963**, 282.

Si₄C₁₂H₂₄O₄

① 1,3,5,7-Tetramethyl-1,3,5,7-tetra-
   vinylcyclotetrasiloxane
   [(CH₂=CH)(CH₃)SiO]₄

② (CH₂=CH)(CH₃)Si(OC₂H₅)₂ $\xrightarrow{\text{aq. HCl}}$

③ (111~112°/12).   [−43.5°]. n_D 1.4342
   (20°). d 0.9875 (20°).

⑥ JACS **77**, 1685 (1955). Nippon Kagaku
   Zasshi **78**, 1324 (1957).

Si₄C₁₂H₂₈N₄

① Tetramethyltetravinylcyclotetra-
   silazane
   [CH₃Si(CH=CH₂)NH]₄

② MeSiCl₂CH=CH₂ + NH₃
   ⟶ 11.7%

③ (103~105°/1). n_D 1.4980 (20°). d 0.9979
   (20°/4°) .

⑥ Izv. OKhN **1963**, 948.

Si₄C₁₂H₃₀Cl₂O₃

① 2,2-Dichlorocyclopropyltris(trimethylsiloxy)silane

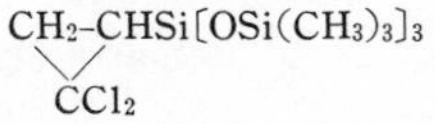

CH₂–CHSi[OSi(CH₃)₃]₃
  \ /
  CCl₂

② CCl₂ + CH₂=CHSi(OSiMe₃)₃
   ⟶ 0.14%

③ (278°). n_D1.4212 (25°). d0.9921(25°/4°).

⑥ Coll. Czech. Chem. Comm. **28**, 3088
   (1963).

Si₄C₁₂H₃₀O₇

① 1,7-Diacetoxyoctamethyltetra-
   siloxane
   CH₃COO-[Si(CH₃)₂O]₄-COCH₃

② Ac₂O + Me₂SiCl-(OSiMe₂)₃-Cl
   ⟶ 84%

③ (108°/2). n_D1.4029 (20°). d1.0081
   (20°/4°).

④ + (Me₂SiO)₂[MeSiO(OBu-*n*)] ⟶

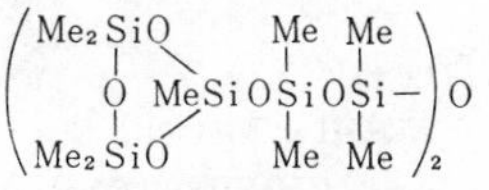

$$\left(\begin{matrix} Me_2SiO & & Me\ Me \\ & O\ MeSiOSiSi- \\ Me_2SiO & & Me\ Me \end{matrix}\right)_2 O$$

+ (Me₂SiO)₃[MeSiO(OBu-*n*)] ⟶

$$\left(\begin{matrix} Me_2SiO & & \\ & O & Me\ Me \\ Me_2Si\ \ MeSiOSiSi- \\ & O & Me\ Me \\ Me_2SiO & & \end{matrix}\right)_2 O$$

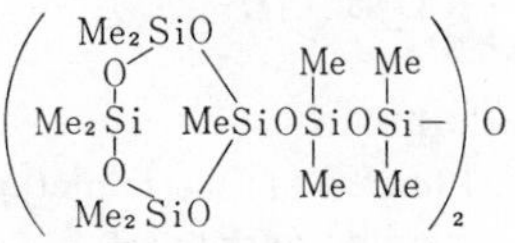

⑥ Izv. OKhN **1963**, 1986.

Si₄C₁₂H₃₂

① Cyclooctamethyltetrasilylmethylene
   [(CH₃)₂SiCH₂]₄

② (ClCH₂)₂SiMe₂ + Na
                    in PhMe
   + (Me₂ClSi)₂CH₂ ⟶

③ (75°/1). n_D1.4690 (25°). d0.8674 (25°).

⑥ US 2607791 (1952). Z. Naturf. **11b**,
   57 (1956).

Si₄C₁₂H₃₂O₃

① Allyltris(trimethylsiloxy)silane
   CH₂=CHCH₂Si[OSi(CH₃)₃]₃

② Me₃SiOLi + CH₂=CHCH₂SiCl₃
   ⟶ 82%

③ (105~106°/1.7). n_D1.4009 (25°).

⑥ Inorg. Chem. **2**, 418 (1963).

Si₄C₁₂H₃₃ClO₃

① Tris(trimethylsiloxy)-3-chloropropyl-
   silane
   [(CH₃)₃SiO]₃SiCH₂CH₂CH₂Cl

② Me₃SiCl + Cl₃SiCH₂CH₂CH₂Cl
   + *i*-PrOH ⟶
   Me₃SiCl + Cl₃SiCH₂CH₂CH₂Cl
   + HOH ⟶

③ (181°/100). n_D1.4108 (25°). d0.9223
   (25°/4°).

④ + (CH₂NH₂)₂ ⟶ (Me₃SiO)₃-
   SiCH₂CH₂CH₂NHCH₂CH₂NH₂

⑥ Brit. 914460 (1963); CA **58**, 10239
   (1963). JACS **82**, 3601 (1960).

Si₄C₁₂H₃₄N₂O₂

① 1,1,3,3,5,5,7,7-Octamethyl-4,8-di-
   ethylcyclo-1,3,5,7-tetrasila-4,8-di-
   aza-2,6-dioxaoctane
       Si(CH₃)₂OSi(CH₃)₂
       | |
   C₂H₅N   NC₂H₅
       | |
       Si(CH₃)₂OSi(CH₃)₂

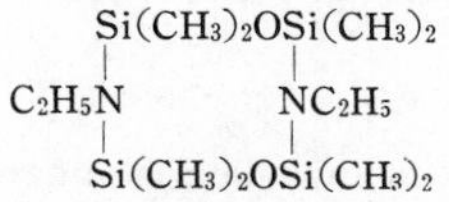

② Me₂SiClOSiMe₂Cl + EtNH₂ ⟶

③ (95~96°/1~2). n_D1.4410 (20°). d0.9470
   (20°/4°).

⑥ Izv. SKh **1963**, 1847.

Si₄C₁₂H₃₄N₂O₂

① *N*, *N*′-Bis(trimethylsilyl)-*Si*-
   dimethyl-*Si*′-diethoxycyclodisilazane
   (CH₃)₂Si−NSi(CH₃)₃
       | |
   (CH₃)₃SiN−Si(OC₂H₅)₂

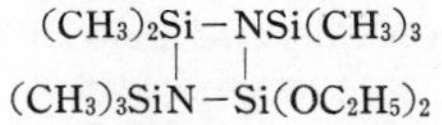

② (EtO)₂SiCl₂ +
   Me₃SiNLiSiMe₂NLiSiMe₃ ⟶

③ (79.5°/1.5). n_D1.4312 (20°).

⑥ Ber. **96**, 1071 (1963).

Si₄C₁₂H₃₄O

① 1,3-Bis(trimethylsilylmethyl)

tetramethyldisiloxane
$[(CH_3)_3SiCH_2Si(CH_3)_2]_2O$

② $Me_3SiSiMe_2CH_2Cl$ + EtONa
+ EtOH $\longrightarrow$

③ $(233\sim234°)$. $[-115°/3]$. $n_D 1.4329$ $(20°)$.
$d 0.8352$ $(20°/4°)$.

④ + $(Me_2SiO)_4$ + SO_3 $\longrightarrow$ lubricating
oil

⑥ "Studies in Organosilicon Compounds" Vol. 1, Chap. 4 (1963).
Brit. 632563 (1949); CA **44**, 6425
(1950). US 2511056 (1950). Japan
4891 (1957); CA **52**, 6779 (1958).

$Si_4C_{12}H_{36}N_2O_3$

① 1,7-Bis(ethylamino)octamethyltetra-
siloxane
$C_2H_5NH-Si(CH_3)_2-[OSi(CH_3)_2]_3-$
NHC_2H_5

② $EtNH_2$ +
$Me_2SiCl-(OSiMe_2)_3-Cl$ $\longrightarrow$

③ $(110\sim113°/1\sim2)$. $n_D 1.4115$ $(20°)$.
$d 0.9100$ $(20°/4°)$.

⑥ Izv. SKh **1963**, 1847 (1963).

$Si_4C_{12}H_{36}O_4Sn$

① Tetrakis(trimethylsiloxy)stannane
$Sn[OSi(CH_3)_3]_4$

② Me_3SiONa + $SnCl_4$ $\longrightarrow$

③ $(83\sim85°/1)$. $[47\sim49°]$.

④ + $CH_2=CMeCOOH$ $\longrightarrow$
$CH_2=CMeCOOSn(OSiMe_3)_3$
+ $(CH_2=CMeCOO)_2Sn(OSiMe_3)_2$
+ Me_3SiOH
+ $(CH_2=CMeCOO)_2Sn$
$\longrightarrow$ $[CH_2=C(Me)COO]_2Sn(OSiMe_3)_2$

⑥ Vysokomol. Soed. **5**, 217 (1963).

$Si_4C_{12}H_{36}O_4Ti$

① Tetrakis(trimethylsiloxy)titanium
$[(CH_3)_3SiO]_4Ti$

② Me_3SiOH + $Ti(OPr-i)_4$ $\longrightarrow$

③ $(60°/1)$. $n_D 1.4292$ $(20°)$.

⑥ JACS **80**, 2585 (1958). Izv. OKhN

1958, 644.   JACS **77**, 170 (1955).

$Si_4C_{13}H_{32}Cl_2O_3$

① 2,2-Dichlorocyclopropylmethyltris-
(trimethylsiloxy)silane
$CH_2-CHCH_2Si[OSi(CH_3)_3]_3$
$\overset{\smile}{C}Cl_2$

② CCl_2 + $CH_2=CHCH_2Si(OSiMe_3)_3$
$\longrightarrow$ 4.8%

③ $(299°)$. $n_D 1.4240$ $(25°)$. $d 0.9887$
$(25°/4°)$.

⑥ Coll. Czech. Chem. Comm. **28**, 3088
(1963).

$Si_4C_{13}H_{36}O_4$

① Tetrakis(methoxydimethylsilyl)-
methane
$C[Si(CH_3)_2OCH_3]_4$

② MeOH + H_2PtCl_6 + $C(SiHMe_2)_4$
$\longrightarrow$ 68.3%

③ $[114\sim115°]$.

④ + MeOH + MeONa
$\longrightarrow$ $CH(SiMe_2OMe)_3$ 67.1%
$CH_2(SiMe_2OMe)_2$ 16.7%

⑥ JOC **28**, 2717 (1963).

$Si_4C_{14}H_{42}GeN_2$

① Dimethylbis[bis(trimethylsilyl)-
amino]germane
$\{[(CH_3)_3Si]_2N\}_2Ge(CH_3)_2$

② Me_2GeCl_2 + $Me_3SiN(Na)SiMe_3$
$\longrightarrow$ 30%~40%

③ $(135°/1)$.

⑥ Angew. **2**, 478 (1963).

$Si_4C_{15}H_{32}O_3$

① Phenyltris(trimethsiloxy)silane
$C_6H_5Si[OSi(CH_3)_3]_3$

② $C_6H_5Si(ONa)_3$ + $(CH_3)_3SiCl$ $\longrightarrow$

③ $(105\sim110°/13)$.

⑥ US 2567110; CA **45**, 10676 (1951).

$Si_4C_{16}H_{32}O_4$

① Tetra(cyclotetramethylene)cyclotetrasiloxane

② SiCl$_4$ + (CH$_2$CH$_2$MgBr)$_2$, then
   HOH ⟶

$$\left(\begin{array}{c}CH_2CH_2 \\ | \\ CH_2CH_2\end{array}\!\!\!>SiCl_2\right) + HOH \longrightarrow$$

③ Solid. [114~116°].
   IR (strong): 2950, 2875, 1076, 1065
   cm^{-1}.
⑥ JOC **28**, 1941 (1963).

Si$_4$C$_{16}$H$_{40}$O$_4$
① Octaethylcyclotetrasiloxane
   [(C$_2$H$_5$)$_2$SiO]$_4$
② (C$_2$H$_5$)$_2$SiCl$_2$ $\xrightarrow{\text{aq. NaOH}}$ 31%
③ (158~159°/10). [−50°]. n_D1.4340 (20°).
   d0.9594 (20°).
⑥ Zhur. **27**, 491 (1957).   JACS **63**, 1194
   (1941); **70**, 3888 (1948).

Si$_4$C$_{16}$H$_{44}$N$_4$
① Octaethylcyclotetrasilazane
   [(C$_2$H$_5$)$_2$SiNH]$_4$
② Et$_2$SiCl$_2$ + NH$_3$ ⟶ along with a
   large amount of trimer
③ (190~192°/10). [16°]. n_D1.4769 (20°).
   d0.9521 (20°/4°).
   Sol. in org. solvents.
⑥ JACS **70**, 3888 (1948).

Si$_4$C$_{17}$H$_{33}$ClO$_3$
① 1-*p*-Vinylphenyl-7-chloromethyl-
   octamethyltetrasiloxane
   p-CH$_2$=CHC$_6$H$_4$Si(CH$_3$)$_2$[OSi(CH$_3$)$_2$]$_3$-
   CH$_2$Cl
② *p*-CH$_2$=CHC$_6$H$_4$SiMe$_2$OH
   + Me$_2$SiClCH$_2$Cl ⟶ 40%
③ (118°/5×10^{-3}). n_D1.4703 (20°). d1.0176
   (20°/4°).
④ Copolymerizes with styrene.

⑥ Makromol. Chem. **67**, 98 (1963).

Si$_4$C$_{20}$H$_{34}$O
① 1,3-Bis(*p*-dimethylsilylphenyl)-
   tetramethyldisiloxane
   O[Si(CH$_3$)$_2$C$_6$H$_4$SiH(CH$_3$)$_2$-*p*]$_2$
② LiAlH$_4$ +
   O(SiMe$_2$C$_6$H$_4$SiMe$_2$Cl-*p*)$_2$ ⟶
③ (167°/5). n_D1.5408(20°). d0.9540 (20°).
⑥ Zhur. Vses. Khim. Obhsch. imeni D. I.
   Mendeleeva **7**, 594 (1962).

Si$_4$C$_{20}$H$_{38}$FeO$_2$
① Bis(1,1′-dimethyltrimethylsiloxy-
   silyl)ferrocene
   Fe[C$_5$H$_4$Si(CH$_3$)$_2$OSi(CH$_3$)$_3$]$_2$
② FeCl$_2$ + LiC$_5$H$_4$SiMe$_2$OSiMe$_3$ ⟶
③ (107~110°/0.01). n_D1.4940 (25°).
   d1.0308 (25°).
⑥ JOC **25**, 1986 (1960).   US 3010982
   (1961).

Si$_4$C$_{20}$H$_{40}$O$_4$
① Tetracyclopentamethylenecyclo-
   tetrasiloxane

$$\left(\begin{array}{c}\;\;CH_2CH_2 \\ H_2C<\!\!\!\!>SiO \\ \;\;CH_2CH_2\end{array}\right)_4$$

② SiCl$_4$ + CH$_2$(CH$_2$CH$_2$MgBr)$_2$, then
   HOH ⟶
③ Solid. [71~73°].
   IR(strong): 2910, 2855, 1068, 783
   cm^{-1}.
⑥ JOC **28**, 1941 (1963).

Si$_4$C$_{20}$H$_{50}$
① Decaethyltetrasilane
   (C$_2$H$_5$)$_3$SiSi(C$_2$H$_5$)$_2$Si(C$_2$H$_5$)$_2$-
   Si(C$_2$H$_5$)$_3$
② Na + Et$_3$SiSiEt$_2$Br ⟶ 20.2%
③ (164~178°). n_D1.5160 (20°).
⑥ Zhur. **33**, 613 (1963).

Si₄C₂₃H₃₀Cl₁₂

① 1,1,3,5,7-Pentamethyl-3,5,7-tri-
   phenyl-1,7-dichlorotetrasiloxane
   (CH₃)₂SiCl[OSi(CH₃)C₆H₅]₃Cl

② Me₂SiCl₂ + [PhSiMeO]₃ ⟶

③ (198~200°/4). n_D 1.5118 (20°). d 1.1276
   (20°/4°).

④ Undergoes hydrolysis at 10° to form
   1,1,3,5,7-pentamethyl-3,5,7-triphe-
   nylcyclotetrasiloxane.

⑥ Dokl. **146**, 601 (1962).   Izv. OKhN
   1962, 1237.

Si₄C₂₄H₃₂F₂₄O₄

① Octa(3,3,3-trifluoropropyl)cyclo-
   tetrasiloxane
   [(CF₃CH₂CH₂)₂SiO]₄

② (CF₃CH₂CH₂)₂Si(OEt)₂ + HOH
   $\overset{90°}{\longrightarrow}$ KOH 200~·220°

③ [141.5~142.0°].

⑥ US 3070617(1962) ； CA **58**, 12600(1963).

Si₄C₂₄H₅₈

① 1,2-Bis(pentaethyldisilanyl)cyclo-
   butane
   CH₂−CH₂
   │   │
   CH − CHSi(C₂H₅)₂Si(C₂H₅)₃
   │
   Si(C₂H₅)₂Si(C₂H₅)₃

② Et₃SiSiEt₃ + (PhCOO)₂ ⟶
   Et₃SiSiEt₃ + (t-BuO)₂ ⟶

③ (183~190°/2). n_D 1.5040 (20°).

⑥ Izv. OKhN **1962**, 2008.

Si₄C₂₄H₆₀O₄Sn

① Tetrakis(triethylsiloxy)stannane
   [(C₂H₅)₃SiO]₄Sn

② (C₂H₅)₃SiONa + SnCl₄ ⟶ 53.7%

③ Colorless liq. (200~202°/4).
   Sol. in org. solvents. Decomp. with
   H₂O.

⑥ Izv. OKhN **1958**, 779 ； CA **52**, 19916
   (1957).

Si₄C₂₄H₆₀O₄Ti

① Tetrakis(triethylsiloxy)titanium
   [(C₂H₅)₃SiO]₄Ti

② (C₂H₅)₃SiOH + TiCl₄ $\overset{pyridine}{\longrightarrow}$

③ (227~239°/7). [95~97°]. n_D 1.4689(20°).
   d 0.9408 (20°).

⑥ Izv. OKhN **1958**, 779. Dokl. **126**, 1261
   (1959).   Chem. & Ind. **1958**, 1231.

Si₄C₂₆H₄₆O

① Bis(1,5,5-trimethyl-1-phenyl-1,5-
   disila)hexyl ether
   [(CH₃)₂SiCH₂CH₂CH₂Si(CH₃)(C₆H₅)]₂O

② HOH + Me₃SiCH₂CH₂CH₂SiMePhCl
   ⟶ 14%

③ (220~225°/2). n_D 1.5000 (20°). d 0.9292
   (20°/4°).

⑥ Izv. OKhN **1963**, 654.

Si₄C₂₆H₄₆S

① Bis(1,5,5-trimethyl-1-phenyl-1,5-
   disilahexyl) sulfide
   [(CH₃)₃SiCH₂CH₂CH₂Si(CH₃)(C₆H₅)]₂S

② C₅H₅N + HSH +
   Me₃SiCH₂CH₂CH₂SiMePhCl ⟶

③ (275~280°/2). n_D 1.5165 (20°). d 0.942
   (20°/4°).

⑥ Izv. OKhN **1963**, 654.

Si₄C₂₆H₄₇N

① Bis(1,5,5-trimethyl-1-phenyl-1,5-
   disilahexyl)amine
   ([(CH₃)₃SiCH₂CH₂CH₂Si(CH₃)(C₆H₅)]₂-
   NH

② NH₄OH +
   Me₃SiCH₂CH₂CH₂SiMePhCl ⟶

③ (220°/2). n_D 1.5121 (20°). d 0.9304
   (20°/4°).

⑥ Izv. OKhN **1963**, 654.

Si₄C₂₆H₆₂O

① Bis(1,1,5,5-tetraethyl-1,7-disila-

heptyl) ether
[(C_2H_5)_3SiCH_2CH_2CH_2Si(C_2H_5)_2]_2O
② HOH + Et_3SiCH_2CH_2CH_2SiEt_2Cl
  ⟶ 44.5%
③ Liq. (200~205°/2). n_D1.4638 (20°).
  d0.8751 (20°/4°).
⑥ Izv. OKhN 1963, 654.

$Si_4C_{26}H_{63}N_2$

① Bis(1,1,5,5-tetraethyl-1,7-disila-
  heptyl)amine
  [(C_2H_5)_3SiCH_2CH_2CH_2Si(C_2H_5)_2]_2NH
② NH_4OH +
  Et_3SiCH_2CH_2CH_2SiEt_2Cl ⟶
③ Liq. (250~252°/2). n_D1.4698 (20°).
  d0.8716 (20°/4°).
⑥ Izv. OKhN, 1963, 654.

$Si_4C_{28}H_{34}O_5$

① 1,7-Dihydroxy-1,3,5,7-tetramethyl-
  1,3,5,7-tetraphenyltetrasiloxane
  HO[Si(CH_3)(C_6H_5)O]_4H
② MeSiCl_2Ph + HOH ⟶
③ n_D1.5366 (20°). d1.111 (20°/4°).
  brittle pt. −35°
④ + Ti(OBu-n)_4
  ⟶ Ti[O(SiMePhO)_4-H]_4
⑥ Izv. SKh 1963, 1672.

$Si_4C_{30}H_{42}FeO_2$

① 1,1'-Bis(dimethylphenylsiloxy-
  dimethylsilyl)ferrocene
  Fe[C_5H_4Si(CH_3)_2OSi(CH_3)_2C_6H_5]_2
② C_5H_5SiMe_2OSiMe_2Ph + FeCl_2
  + BuLi ⟶
③ Solid. (200~205°/0.03). [18.0~19.5°].
⑥ US 3010982(1961) ; CA 57, 2253 (1962).

$Si_4C_{32}H_{38}O_5$

① 1,7-Diacetoxy-1,3,5,7-tetramethyl-
  1,3,5,7-tetraphenyltetrasiloxane
  [CH_3COOSi(CH_3)(C_6H_5)OSi(CH_3)-
  (C_6H_5)-]_2O
② (ClSiMePhOSiMePh-)_2O + Ac_2O

  ⟶ 30%
③ (250~254°/2). n_D1.5320 (25°). d1.144
  (25°/4°).
⑥ Izv. OKhN 1963, 651.

$Si_4C_{32}H_{50}$

① p-Bis(ethylphenyl-2-trimethylsilyl-
  ethylsilyl)benzene
  p-C_6H_4[Si(C_2H_5)(C_6H_5)CH_2CH_2Si-
  (CH_3)_3]_2
② p-C_6H_4(SiHEtPh)_2 +
  Me_3SiCH=CH_2 + H_2PtCl_6 ⟶ 64%
③ (275~278°/2). [25°]. n_D1.5484 (20°).
  d0.9664 (20°).
⑥ Heftekhimiya 2, 632 (1962).

$Si_4C_{34}H_{62}O$

① Bis[ethylphenyl(3-triethylsilylpropyl)
  silyl] ether
  [(C_2H_5)_3SiCH_2CH_2CH_2Si(C_2H_5)C_6H_5]_2O
② HOH + Et_3SiCH_2CH_2CH_2SiEtPhCl
  ⟶ 52%
③ (255~260°/2). n_D1.5035 (20°). d0.9372
  (20°/4°).
⑥ Izv. OKhN 1963, 654.

$Si_4C_{34}H_{62}S$

① Bis[ethylphenyl(3-triethylsilyl-
  propyl)silyl] sulfide
  [(C_2H_5)_3SiCH_2CH_2CH_2Si(C_2H_5)C_6H_5]_2S
② HSH +
  Et_3SiCH_2CH_2CH_2SiEtPhCl ⟶
③ (300°/2).
⑥ Izv. OKhN 1963, 654.

$Si_4C_{34}H_{63}N$

① Bis[ethylphenyl(3-triethylsilyl-
  propyl)silyl]amine
  [(C_2H_5)_3SiCH_2CH_2CH_2Si(C_2H_5)C_6H_5]_2NH
② Et_3SiCH_2CH_2CH_2SiEtPhCl
  + NH_4OH ⟶
③ (270~272°/2). n_D1.5131 (20°). d0.9401
  (20°/4°).

⑥ Izv. OKhN **1963**, 654.

Si₄C₃₆H₃₆N₄O₄

① *sym*-Tetraphenyltetra(2-cyanoethyl)-
cyclotetrasiloxane
[C₆H₅Si(O)CH₂CH₂CN]₄

② PhSi(OH)₂CH₂CH₂CN + C₆H₆ + Na₂CO₃
+ HOH ──→

③ [117°].
IR : 3.42, 4.45, 6.27, 7.00, 7.57, 7.79,
8.88, 9.27, 9.71, 10.01, 11.03,
11.18. 11.34 mμ.

⑥ JOC **26**, 2008 (1961).

Si₄C₃₆H₄₈O₄

① 1,3,5,7-Tetra(2-phenylethyl)-1,3,5,
7-tetramethylcyclotetrasiloxane
[C₆H₅CH₂CH₂Si(CH₃)O]₄

② PhCH₂CH₂SiMeCl₂ + HOH ──→

③ (300~304°/4). n_D 1.5312 (20°). d 1.075
(20°).
IR : 1250, 1090 cm⁻¹.

⑥ Izv. OKhN **1961**, 1615.

Si₄C₃₆H₇₀FeO₂

① 1,1'-[Bis(3-trimethylsilylpropyl)-
hydroxymethyl]ferrocene
Fe{C₅H₄C[CH₂CH₂CH₂Si(CH₃)₃]₂OH}₂

② Fe(C₅H₄COOMe)₂
+ Me₃SiCH₂CH₂CH₂MgCl ──→

③ Solid. [107~108°].

⑥ Dokl. **148**, 598 (1963).

Si₄C₃₆H₈₂O

① Bis[dipropyl(3-tripropylsilylpropyl)
silyl] ether
[(C₃H₇)₃SiCH₂CH₂CH₂Si(C₃H₇)₂]₂O

② HOH + Pr₃SiCH₂CH₂CH₂SiPr₂Cl ──→

③ (230~235°/2). n_D 0.8589 (20°). d 0.8589
(20°/4°).

⑥ Izv. OKhN **1963**, 654.

Si₄C₃₆H₈₃N

① Bis[dipropyl(3-tripropylsilylpropyl)
silyl]amine
[(C₃H₇)₃SiCH₂CH₂CH₂Si(C₃H₇)₂]₂NH

② NH₄OH + Pr₃SiCH₂CH₂CH₂Si(Pr)₂Cl

③ (270~272°/2). n_D 1.4694 (20°). d 0.8582
(20°/4°).

⑥ Izv. OKhN **1963**, 654.

Si₄C₃₈H₉₀Sn₂O

① Bis(1,1,4,4-tetramethyl-6,6-dibutyl-
1,4-disila-6-stannadecyl) ether
[(C₄H₉)₃SnCH₂Si(CH₃)₂CH₂CH₂Si
(CH₃)₂]₂O

② Bu₃SnCH₂SiMe₂CH₂CH₂SiMe₂Cl
+ HOH ──→

③ n_D 1.4850 (25°). d 1.045 (25°/4°).

⑥ JACS **81**, 975 (1959).   US 2920060
(1960).

Si₄C₃₉H₄₁N₃

① 1,1,3,3,5,5-Hexaphenyl-2-trimethyl-
silylcyclotrisilazane

(CH₃)₃SiN─Si(C₆H₅)₂
| |
(C₆H₅)₂Si NH
| |
HN─Si(C₆H₅)₂

② (Ph₂SiNH)₂(Ph₂SiNLi) + Me₂SiCl
$\xrightarrow{C_6H_6}$ 12.5%

③ Solid. (293~300°/1). [80°].

⑥ Helv. Chim. Acta **45**, 1081 (1962).

Si₄C₄₀H₆₀O₄Ti

① Tetrakis(phenyldiethylsiloxy)
titanium
Ti[OSi(C₂H₅)₂C₆H₅]₄

② Ti(OR)₄ + PhSiEt₂OH ──→

③ Liq. (300~305°/5). n_D 1.5454 (20°).
d 1.0459 (20°).

⑥ Khim. i Prakt. Primenenie Kremne-
org. Soedinenii, Trudy Konf. Lenin-
grad (No.1) 161 (1958); CA **54**,
4360 (1960).

Si₄C₄₆H₄₆O₂

① *p*-[Dimethyl(triphenylsiloxy)silyl]-
  benzene
  p-C₆H₄[Si(CH₃)₂OSi(C₆H₅)₃]₂

② Ph₃SiOH + Na + p-C₆H₄(SiMe₂Cl)₂
   $\longrightarrow$ 83%

③ Cryst. (465~475°). [233~238°].

⑥ Izv. OKhN **1960**, 942.

Si₄C₄₈H₄₀

① Octaphenylcyclotetrasilane
  [(C₆H₅)₂Si]₄

② Ph₂SiCl₂ + Na $\longrightarrow$
  Ph₂SiCl₂ + Li $\longrightarrow$

③ Cryst. [321~323°].

④ + PhLi $\longrightarrow$
   Ph₃Si-SiPh₂-SiPh₂-SiPh₂Li
   + Ph₃SiLi $\longrightarrow$ Ph₃Si-(SiPh₂)₄-Li
   + Ph₃SiLi $\longrightarrow$ Ph₃Si-SiPh₂Li
   + Ph₃SiSiPh₂SiPh₂Li $\longrightarrow$
   Ph-(SiPh₂)₆-Li
   + Li $\longrightarrow$ Li-(SiPh₂)₄-Li
   + I₂ $\longrightarrow$ I-(SiPh₂)-I
   + CHCl₂CHCl₂ $\longrightarrow$ Cl-(SiPh₂)₄-Cl

⑥ JACS **82**, 2076 (1960); **83**, 1921 (1961).
  JOC **26**, 1999 (1961).

Si₄C₄₈H₄₀Cl₂

① 1,5-Dichlorooctaphenyltetrasilane
  Cl-[Si(C₆H₅)₂]₄-Cl

② (CHCl₂)₂ + (SiPh₂)₄ $\longrightarrow$ 77%

③ Cryst. [182~183°].

⑥ JACS **83**, 1921 (1961).

Si₄C₄₈H₄₀I₂

① 1,4-Diiodooctaphenyltetrasilane
  I-[Si(C₆H₅)₂]₄-I

② (SiPh₂)₄ + I₂ in C₆H₆ $\longrightarrow$ 55%

③ Cryst. [274~276°].

⑥ JACS **83**, 1921 (1961).

Si₄C₄₈H₄₀O

① Octaphenyl-1-oxa-2,3,4,5-silacyclo-
  pentane
  $$(C₆H₅)₂Si-Si(C₆H₅)₂$$
  $$\begin{array}{c} | \qquad | \\ O \\ | \qquad | \end{array}$$
  $$(C₆H₅)₂Si-Si(C₆H₅)₂$$

② Cl-(SiPh₂)₄-Cl + HOH + t-AmOH
   + PhMe $\longrightarrow$ 32%
   I-(SiPh₂)₄-I + NH₄OH + Me₂CO $\longrightarrow$
   I-(SiPh₂)₄-I + C₆H₅NH₂ + HOH
   + EtOH $\longrightarrow$
   Cl-(SiPh₂)₄-Cl + PhNH₂ + HOH
   + EtOH $\longrightarrow$
   Cl-(SiPh₂)₄-Cl + t-AmOH + HOH
   + PhMe $\longrightarrow$

③ [226~228°].
  IR: 955 cm⁻¹.

⑤ Glue-like.

⑥ Chem. & Ind. **1960**, 1271.   JOC **27**,
  614 (1962).   JCS **119**, 830 (1921).
  JACS **83**, 4089 (1961).

Si₄C₄₈H₄₀O₂

① Octaphenyl-2,5-dioxa-1,3,4,6-tetra-
  silacyclohexane
  $$(C₆H₅)₂Si-Si(C₆H₅)₂$$
  $$\begin{array}{cc} | & | \\ O & O \\ | & | \end{array}$$
  $$(C₆H₅)₂Si-Si(C₆H₅)₂$$

② Ph₂Si(OH)SiPh₂OH + HCOOH $\longrightarrow$
  Ph₂Si(OH)SiPh₂OH + MeC₆H₄SO₂Cl
   + C₅H₅N $\longrightarrow$
  Ph₂Si(OH)SiPh₂OH + (COOH)₂
   + HCONMe₂ $\longrightarrow$
  Ph₂Si(OH)SiPh₂OH + CCl₃CHO
   + MeC₆H₄SO₂Cl $\longrightarrow$

③ Cryst. [219~220°].

⑥ JOC **26**, 1265 (1961); **27**, 614 (1962).

Si₄C₄₈H₄₀O₄

① Octaphenylcyclotetrasiloxane
  [(C₆H₅)₂SiO]₄

② Ph₂Si(OMe)₂ + NaOH $\longrightarrow$

$Ph_2Si(H)Si(H)Ph_2 + HOH$
$+ C_5H_5N \longrightarrow$
$Ph_2Si(OH)_2 + NH_4OH \longrightarrow$
Best catalysts for the hydrolysis are
Me_4NOH, $Me_3N(CH_2Ph)OH$ or "phosphonium silanolates."
③ Solid. [201°].
⑥ JOC 24, 989 (1959); 26, 1265 (1961).
J. Polymer Sci. 40, 35 (1959). JCS
101, 2125 (1912).

$Si_4C_{48}H_{42}$

① 1,1,2,2,3,3,4,4-Octaphenyltetrasilane
$H-[Si(C_6H_5)_2]_4-H$
② $Ph_2SiCl_2 + Na \longrightarrow$
③ [161~162°].
⑥ JOC 27, 254 (1962).

$Si_4C_{48}H_{42}O$

① 1,1,2,2,3,3,4,4-Octaphenyl-1-hydroxy-
tetrasilane
$H-[Si(C_6H_5)_2]_4-OH$
② $CH_2PPh_3 + (SiPh_2)_4 \longrightarrow$
$HO-(SiPh_2)_4-OH$ eluted in
Alumina column. $\longrightarrow$
③ Solid. [182~184°].
⑤ High temperature stability.
⑥ JOC 27, 3647 (1962); 28, 2146 (1963).

$Si_4C_{48}H_{42}O_2$

① 1,4-Dihydroxyoctaphenyltetrasilane
$HO-[Si(C_6H_5)_2]_4-OH$
② $Cl-(SiPh_2)_4-Cl + HOH \longrightarrow 70\%$
③ [212~213°].
⑥ JOC 28, 2146 (1963).

$Si_4C_{48}H_{50}O_5$

① 1-Butoxy-1,3,5,7-tetramethyl-1,3,5,7-
1-naphthyl-7-hydroxytetrasiloxane
$C_4H_9O-[Si(CH_3)(C_{10}H_7-1)O]_4-H$
② $BuOH + HO-[SiMe(C_{10}H_7-1)O]_x-H$
$+ 1-C_{10}H_7Si(OH)_2Me \longrightarrow$
③ (334~344°/1.5~2.0). $d1.1448$ (20°).
⑥ Izv. OKhN 1959, 1041.

$Si_4C_{50}H_{46}$

① 1,4-Dimethyloctaphenyltetrasilane
$CH_3-[(C_6H_5)_2Si]_4-CH_3$
② $Me-(Ph_2Si)_3-Br + MeSiPh_2Li \longrightarrow$
$MeSiPh_2Cl + (Ph_2SiCl)_2 \longrightarrow 29\%$
$Li-(Ph_2Si)_4-Li + OP(OMe)_3$
$\longrightarrow 27\%$
$MeLi + Cl-(Ph_2Si)_4-Cl \longrightarrow 63\%$
$MeLi + Br-(Ph_2Si)_4-Br \longrightarrow$
③ Solid. [222~223°].
⑥ JACS 83, 1921, 4089 (1961); 82, 2076
(1960).

$Si_4C_{50}H_{50}FeO_2$

① 1,1'-Bis(triphenylsiloxydimethyl-
silyl)ferrocene
$Fe[C_5H_4Si(CH_3)_2OSi(C_6H_5)_3]_2$
② $C_4H_9Li + PhSiMe_2OSiMe_2C_5H_5$
$+ FeCl_2 \longrightarrow 37\%$
③ Cryst. [148.5~150.0°].
⑥ JOC 25, 1986 (1960). US 3010982
(1961); CA 57, 2253 (1962).

$Si_4C_{52}H_{46}O_4$

① 1,4-Diacetoxyoctaphenyltetrasilane
$CH_3COO-[Si(C_6H_5)_2]_4-OCOCH_3$
② $(AcO)_2Hg + (SiPh_2)_4 \longrightarrow 79\%$
$(AcO)_2Hg + H-(SiPh_2)_4-H$
$\longrightarrow 72\%$
$Ac_2O + Cl-(SiPh_2)_4-Cl \longrightarrow 14\%$
④ $+HOH + HCl \longrightarrow (OSiPh_2)_x$
⑥ JOC 28, 2905 (1963).

$Si_4C_{52}H_{52}O_4Ti$

① Tetrakis(diphenylmethylsiloxy)
titanium
$Ti[OSi(C_6H_5)_2(CH_3)]_4$
② $NH_3 + Me_3SiOTiCl_3$
$+ Ph_2Si(Me)OH \longrightarrow$
$TiCl_4 + Ph_2Si(Me)OH$ (in C_6H_6) $+ NH_3$
$\longrightarrow 35.8\%$
③ Liq. (346~348°/3). $n_D1.5988$ (21°).
$d1.1394$ (20°).

⑥ Izv. OKhN **1960**, 1712.   Dokl. **122**,
   393 (1958).

Si₄C₅₄H₄₆
① Tris(triphenylsilyl)silane
   HSi[Si(C₆H₅)₃]₃
② SiHCl₃ + Ph₃SiLi ⟶
③ [206～209°].
⑥ JACS **81**, 4812 (1959).

Si₄C₅₄H₄₆
① 1,1,1,2,2,3,3,4,4-Nonaphenyl-
      tetrasilane
   C₆H₅[Si(C₆H₅)₂]₄H
② (Ph₂Si)₄ + Ph₃SiLi ⟶ 13.5%
③ Solid. [198～200°].
⑥ JOC **26**, 1999 (1961).

Si₄C₅₄H₄₆O₃
① Tris(triphenylsiloxy)silane
   [(C₆H₅)₃SiO]₃SiH
② [(C₆H₅)₃SiO]₂SiHCl
      + (C₆H₅)₃SiONa ⟶
   (C₆H₅)₃SiONa + SiHCl₃ ⟶ 54%
③ White solid. [211～212°].
   Slightly sol. in org. solvents.
④ + 20% KOH ⟶ [(C₆H₅)₃SiO]₃SiOH
⑥ Zhur. **27**, 494 (1957).   CA **51**, 15441
   (1957).

Si₄C₅₈H₅₄
① *p*-Bis(*p*-triphenylsilylphenyl-
      dimethylsilyl)benzene
   p-C₆H₄[Si(CH₃)₂C₆H₄Si(C₆H₅)₃-*p*]₂
② Na + Ph₃SiC₆H₄Cl-*p*
      + *p*-C₆H₄(SiMe₂Cl)₂ ⟶ 48%
③ Cryst. [220～222°].
⑥ Rec. trav. chim. **81**, 565 (1962).

Si₄C₆₀H₅₀
① Decaphenyltetrasilane
   C₆H₅−[Si(C₆H₅)₂]₄−C₆H₅
② PhLi + Cl−(SiPh₂)₄−Cl ⟶ 44%
   Ph₃SiLi + Ph₂SiClSiPh₂Cl ⟶ 5%

③ Solid. [358～360°, 350～352°].
⑥ JACS **83**, 1921 (1961).   JOC **27**, 254
   (1962).

Si₄C₇₂H₆₀O₄Ti
① Tetrakis(triphenylsiloxy)titanium
   [(C₆H₅)₃SiO]₄Ti
② (C₆H₅)₃SiOH + TiCl₄ $\xrightarrow{\text{pyridine}}$ 96%
③ [501～505°]. *d*1.215 (29°).
⑥ Izv. OKhN **1957**, 1396

Si₄C₇₂H₆₀O₄V
① Tetrakis(triphenylsiloxy)vanadium
   V[OSi(C₆H₅)₃]₄
② Ph₃SiONa + VCl₄
   $\xrightarrow{\text{in } C_6H_6}$ 63% (under N₂)
   ⟶ 86% (under natural gas)
③ Pale blue-green solid. [264～268°].
④ Oxidizes to OV(OSiPh₃)₃.
⑥ JOC **27**, 3321 (1962).

Si₅C₅H₂₀O₅
① 2,4,6,8,10-Pentamethylcyclopenta-
      siloxane
   [CH₃Si(H)O]₅
② CH₃(H)SiCl₂ + H₂O ⟶
③ Colorless liq. (60°/14). [−108°].
   *n*_D 1.3912 (20°). *d* 0.9985 (20°/4°).
   Sol. in org. solvents.
⑥ BCSJ **30**, 608 (1957).   JACS **68**, 926
   (1946).

Si₅C₉H₂₇ClO₅
① Nonamethylchlorocyclopentasiloxane
   (CH₃)₂SiOSi(CH₃)₂O
         |
         O   ⟩Si(CH₃)Cl
         |
   (CH₃)₂SiOSi(CH₃)₂O
② MeSiCl₃ +
      NaO−(SiMe₂O)₄−Na ⟶
③ (129～132°/1). *n*_D 1.4083 (20°). *d* 1.0410
   (20°/4°).
④ + NH₃ ⟶

Me₂SiOSiMe₂O
|
O   >SiMeNH₂ (32.3%)
|
Me₂SiOSiMe₂O

⑥ Izv. OKhN **1963**, 294.

Si₅C₉H₂₉NO₅

① Nonamethylaminocyclopentasiloxane
$(CH_3)_2SiOSi(CH_3)_2O$
|
O   >Si(CH₃)NH₂
|
$(CH_3)_2SiOSi(CH_3)_2O$

②   Me₂SiOSiMe₂O
|
NH₃ +   O   >SiMeCl
|
Me₂SiOSiMe₂O
⟶ 32.3%

③ (134~137°/1). n_D1.4115 (20°). d1.0160
(20°/4°).

⑥ Izv. OKhN **1963**, 294.

Si₅C₁₀H₃₀Cl₂O₄

① 1,9-Dichlorodecamethylpentasiloxane
$(CH_3)_2SiCl-[OSi(CH_3)_2]_4-Cl$

② Me₂SiCl₂ + (Me₂SiO)₃ $\xrightarrow{250°, \ 3hrs}$
Me₂SiCl₂ + (Me₂SiO)₄ + FeCl₃ ⟶
Me₂SiCl₂ + Me₂SiClOSiMe₂Cl ⟶
Me₂SiCl₂ + HOH ⟶

③ (139°/20). n_D1.4032 (20°). d1.0048
(20°).

④ + FeCl₃ + (Me₂SiO)₄ ⟶
high molecular weight products

⑥ Izv. OKhN **1962**, 2133.   Japan 1444
(1957); CA **52**, 4679 (1958). Makromol. Chem. **39**, 167 (1960).   Izv.
OKhN **1961**, 1456.

Si₅C₁₀H₃₀O₅

① Decamethylcyclopentasiloxane
$[(CH_3)_2SiO]_5$

② (CH₃)₂SiCl₂ + H₂O ⟶ 6.7%

③ Colorless liquid.   (204.5~210.0°).
[−38~−44°]. n_D1.3982(20°). d0.9593
(20°/4°).

Sol. in org. solvents; insol. in water.

⑥ US 2415389 (1947).   JACS **68**, 358,

364, 667 (1946).

Si₅C₁₀H₃₀O₅

① 1,3,5,7-Pentaethylcyclopentasiloxane
$[(C_2H_5)HSiO]_5$

② C₂H₅(H)SiCl₂ + H₂O ⟶

③ Colorless liq. (80°/2). n_D1.4187
(20°). d0.9899 (20°).
Sol. in org. solvents.

⑥ BCSJ **30**, 608 (1957).

Si₅C₁₀H₃₂O₄

① 1,9-Dihydrodecamethylpentasiloxane
$HSi(CH_3)_2[OSi(CH_3)_2]_4H$

② Me₂Si(H)Si(H)Me₂ + (Me₂SiO)₄
+ H₂SO₄ ⟶ 12%

③ (124~126°/50).

⑥ Ger. 1140348 (1962); CA **58**, 12 600
(1963).

Si₅C₁₀H₃₂O₆

① 1,9-Dihydroxydecamethylpenta-
siloxane
$HO[Si(CH_3)_2O]_5H$

② Me₂SiClOSiMe₂OSiMe₂Cl
+ NaOH ⟶ 80.5%

③ (104~106°/1.5). n_D1.4086 (20°), 1.4089
(20°). d0.9807 (20°/4°), 0.9914
(20°/4°).

⑥ Izv. OKhN **1962**, 2243.   Zhur. Anal.
Khim. **9**, 208 (1954); CA **48**, 13542
(1954).

Si₅C₁₁H₃₃ClO₄

① 1-Chloroundecamethylpentasiloxane
$CH_3-[Si(CH_3)_2O]_4-Si(CH_3)_2Cl$

② Me₂SiOH +
Cl−(SiMe₂O)₃−SiMe₂Cl ⟶
MeLi +
Me₂SiCl−(OSiMe₂)₄−Cl ⟶

③ (122~125°/20).

⑥ Makromol. Chem. **55**, 87 (1962). Ger.
1136336 (1962); CA **58**, 6861 (1963).

Si$_5$C$_{12}$H$_{33}$N

① Undecamethyl-1-cyanopentasilane
  CH$_3$−[Si(CH$_2$)$_2$]$_5$−CN

② Me$_3$SiSiMe$_2$CN $\xrightarrow{\text{heat}}$

③ (67.5~71.0°/0.2).

⑥ JACS **85**, 3372 (1963).

Si$_5$C$_{12}$H$_{36}$

① Dodecamethylpentasilane
  CH$_3$−[Si(CH$_3$)$_2$]$_5$−CH$_3$

② Me$_x$Si$_2$Cl$_{6-x}$ + AgCN $\xrightarrow{\text{MeMgBr}}$
  Me$_2$SiCl$_2$ + Na + Me$_3$SiSi$_3$Me$_2$Cl
  ⟶ 9%
  NaK + (Me$_3$SiSiMe$_2$)$_2$ ⟶

③ (131°/8). [−34°]. n_D1.5066 (20°).
  d0.8329 (20°/4°).

⑥ JOM 1, 153 (1963). JACS **85**, 3372
  (1963). Z. Naturf. **18 B**, 765 (1963).

Si$_5$C$_{12}$H$_{36}$O$_4$

① Dodecamethylpentasiloxane
  CH$_3$−[Si(CH$_3$)$_2$O]$_4$−Si(CH$_3$)$_3$

② Me$_2$SiCl−(OSiMe$_2$)$_4$−Cl + MeLi
  ⟶ 83%

③ (79°).

⑥ Ger.1136336(1962) ; CA **58**, 6861(1963).

Si$_5$C$_{12}$H$_{37}$N$_3$

① *N*, *N*′-Bis(trimethylsilyl)-*Si*, *Si*′, *Si*″-
  hexamethylcyclotrisilazane
  [(CH$_3$)$_2$SiNH][(CH$_3$)$_2$SiNSi(CH$_3$)$_3$]$_2$

② Na + (Me$_2$SiNH)$_3$ + Me$_3$SiCl ⟶

③ (81.0~81.7°/10). [−74]°. n_D1.4420
  (20°). d0.973 (20°).

⑥ Inorg. Chem. **2**, 1069 (1963). Helv.
  Chim. Acta **45**, 1081 (1962).

Si$_5$C$_{13}$H$_{36}$O$_6$

① Nonamethylbutoxycyclopenta-
  siloxane
  [(CH$_3$)$_2$SiO]$_4$[CH$_3$Si(O)OC$_4$H$_9$]

② MeSiCl$_2$OBu +
  NaO−(SiMe$_2$O)$_3$−Na ⟶ 4.8%

③ (134~137°/1). n_D1.4110 (20°). d0.9797
  (20°/4°).

⑥ Izv. OKhN 1963, 294.

Si$_5$C$_{14}$H$_{29}$Cl$_3$O$_4$

① 1,1,9-Trichloro-1-phenyloctamethyl-
  pentasiloxane
  C$_6$H$_5$SiCl$_2$−[OSi(CH$_3$)$_2$]$_4$−Cl

② FeCl$_3$ + (Me$_2$SiO)$_3$ + PhSiCl$_3$ ⟶

③ (119~121°/2).

⑥ Izv. OKhN 1963, 282.

Si$_5$C$_{14}$H$_{36}$O$_8$

① 1,9-Diacetoxydecamethylpenta-
  siloxane
  CH$_3$COO−[Si(CH$_3$)$_2$O]$_4$−OCOCH$_3$

② Ac$_2$O + Me$_2$SiCl−(SiMe$_2$O)$_4$−Cl
  ⟶ 85%

③ (134°/2). n_D1.4038 (20°). d1.0021
  (20°/4°).

④ + (Me$_2$SiO)$_3$[MeSiO(OBu-*i*)] ⟶

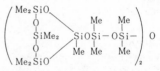

⑥ Izv. SKh 1963, 1986.

Si$_5$C$_{14}$H$_{42}$N$_2$O$_4$

① 1,9-Bis(ethylamino)decamethyl-
  pentasiloxane
  C$_2$H$_5$NHSi(CH$_3$)$_2$[OSi(CH$_3$)$_2$]$_4$−NHC$_2$H$_5$

② EtNH$_2$ +
  Me$_2$SiCl−(OSiMe$_2$)$_4$-Cl ⟶

③ (133~135°/1~2). n_D0.9223 (20°).
  d1.4150 (20°/4°).

⑥ Izv. SKh 1963, 1847.

Si$_5$C$_{20}$H$_{55}$O$_5$Ta

① Penta(dimethylethylsiloxy)tantalum
  Ta[OSi(CH$_3$)$_2$C$_2$H$_5$]$_5$

② Ta(OR)$_5$ + EtSiMe$_2$OH ⟶

③ $(135°/0.1)$.
⑥ JCS **1963**, 204.

$Si_5C_{25}H_{65}O_5Ta$
① Penta(methyldiethylsiloxy)tantalum
Ta[OSi$(C_2H_5)_2CH_3$]$_5$
③ Liq. $(170°/0.1)$.
⑥ JCS **1963**, 204.

$Si_5C_{30}H_{38}Cl_2O_4$
① 1,9-Dichloro-3,5,7,9-tetraphenyl-1,1,
3,5,7,9-hexamethyltetrasiloxane
$(CH_3)_2SiCl - [OSi(CH_3)(C_6H_5)]_4 - Cl$
② Me$_2$SiCl$_2$ + [PhSiMeO]$_4$ $\longrightarrow$
③ $(240\sim242°/4)$. $n_D 1.5201$ $(20°)$. $d 1.1196$
$(20°/4°)$.
④ + HOH $\longrightarrow$ (Me$_2$SiO)(PhSiMeO)$_3$
⑥ Izv. OKhN **1962**, 1237.

$Si_5C_{30}H_{75}O_5Ta$
① Penta(triethylsiloxy)tantalum
Ta[OSi$(C_2H_5)_3$]$_5$
③ $(210°/0.1)$.
⑥ JCS **1963**, 204.

$Si_5C_{30}H_{75}O_5U$
① Penta(triethylsiloxy)uranium
U[OSi$(C_2H_5)_3$]$_5$
② Et$_3$SiOH + U(OEt)$_5$ $\longrightarrow$
③ $(170\sim180°/0.1$ sublimes$)$.
⑥ JCS **1963**, 204.

$Si_5C_{35}H_{70}O_5$
① Methyl-3-glycidylpropyl-
cyclopentasiloxane

$$[CH_3Si(CH_2CH_2CH_2OCH_2\overset{O}{\overset{\triangle}{CHCH_2}})O]_5$$

② Pt + CH$_2$=CHCH$_2$OCH$_2\overset{O}{\overset{\triangle}{CHCH_2}}$
+ (MeSiHO)$_5$ $\longrightarrow$
③ $n_D 1.4660$ $(25°)$. $d 1.120$ $(25°)$.
Viscosity : 160 cs.
⑥ J. Chem. Eng. Data **5**, 59 (1960).

$Si_5C_{35}H_{70}O_{15}$
① Methyl-3-(carboxyethyl)propyl-
cyclopentasiloxane
[OSi$(CH_3)CH_2CH_2CH_2COOC_2H_5$]$_5$
② MeSi(OEt)$_2CH_2CH_2CH_2COOEt$
+ HOH $\longrightarrow$
③ $(230\sim240°/0.3\sim0.4)$. $n_D 1.4500$ $(25°)$.
⑥ Brit. 882095 (1957) ; CA **56**, 8747 (1962).
Brit. 882098 (1961) ; CA **56**, 11620
(1962).

$Si_5C_{36}H_{52}$
① Poly-p-phenylenedimethylsilane,
methyl terminated tetramer
$(CH_3)_3Si - [C_6H_4Si(CH_3)_2 - p]_4 - CH_3$
② Me$_2$SiCl$_2$ + Na +
p-Me$_3$SiC$_6$H$_4$SiMe$_2$C$_6$H$_4$Cl-p $\longrightarrow$
③ Solid. $[170\sim173°]$.
⑥ Rec. trav. chim. **81**, 565 (1962).

$Si_5C_{36}H_{63}N_3O_4$
① 1,1,1,3,5,7,9,9,9-Nonamethyl-3,5,7-
ethylphenylaminomethylpenta-
siloxane

$$(CH_3)_3SiO - \underset{\underset{CH_3}{|}}{\overset{\overset{CH_2N(C_2H_5)C_6H_5}{|}}{(SiO)_3}} - Si(CH_3)_3$$

② NaOH + Me$_3$SiOEt
+ PhNEtSi(OEt)$_2$NH$_2$ $\longrightarrow$
③ $(278\sim284°/1)$. $n_D 1.5487$ $(20°)$. $d 1.083$
$(20°)$.
⑥ Izv. OKhN **1958**, 941.

$Si_5C_{42}H_{56}Fe_2O_2$
① 1,5-Bis(1′-phenyldimethylsilyl-1-
ferrocenyl)hexamethyltrisiloxane
$(CH_3)_2Si[OSi(CH_3)_2C_5H_4FeC_5H_4Si-$
$(CH_3)_2C_6H_5]_2$
② LiOSiMe$_2$C$_5$H$_4$FeC$_5$H$_4$SiMe$_2$Ph
+ Me$_2$SiCl$_2$ $\longrightarrow$ 55%
③ $(283\sim285°/0.03)$. $n_D 1.5791$ $(25°)$.
Pour point $-16°$.

Viscosity : 185 cs (38°).

⑤ Functions as a high temperature
fruid.

⑥ US 3036105 (1962) ; CA **57**, 16656
(1962). JOC **26**, 4038 (1961).

Si₅C₆₀H₅₀

① Decaphenylcyclopentasilane
[(C₆H₅)₃Si]₅

③ (123~126°/0.002). n_D1.6077 (20°).
d1.0270 (20°/20°).

④ + Li ⟶ Li−(Ph₂Si)₅−Li

⑥ Chem. & Ind. **1963**, 954.

Si₅C₆₀H₅₂O₂

① 1,5-Dihydroxydecaphenylpentasilane
HO−[Si(C₆H₅)₂]₅−OH

② Cl−(SiPh₂)₅−Cl + HOH + HCl ⟶

③ [172~174°].

⑥ JOC **28**, 2146 (1963).

Si₅C₆₉H₁₀₆O₇

① 3,5,7-Tris(2-octadecyloxyethyl)-1,
1,1,3,5,7,9,9,9-nonamethylpenta-
siloxane

$$\begin{array}{c} CH_2CH_2OC_{18}H_{37} \\ | \\ (CH_3)_3Si-O-(Si-O-)_3Si(CH_3)_3 \\ | \\ CH_3 \end{array}$$

② CH₂=CHOC₁₈H₃₇ +

$$Me_3Si-O-\left[\begin{array}{c} H \\ | \\ Si-O- \\ | \\ Me \end{array}\right]_3 SiMe_3 \xrightarrow{Pt-C}$$

③ (130~150°/0.33).

⑤ By equilibration, can be introduced
into polysiloxanes.

⑥ US 2913473 (1959).

Si₅C₁₀₈H₁₀₀

① Tetrakis(*p*-tribenzylsilylphenyl)
silane
Si[C₆H₄Si(CH₂C₆H₅)₃-*p*]₄

② SiCl₄ + (PhCH₂)₃SiC₆H₄Li-*p*

⟶ 51%

③ [159~161°].

⑥ JOC **25**, 1194 (1960).

Si₆C₆H₂₄O₆

① 2,4,6,8,10,12-Hexamethylcyclohexa-
siloxane
[(CH₃)HSiO]₆

② CH₃(H)SiCl₂ + H₂O ⟶ 4.4%

③ Colorless liquid. [−79°]. n_D1.3944
(20°). d1.006 (20°/4°).
Sol. in org. solvents ; insol. in
water.

⑥ Zhur. **29**, 248 (1959) ; CA **53**, 21621
(1958). BCSJ **30**, 608 (1957). JACS
68, 962 (1946).

Si₆C₁₂H₃₃Cl₃O₅

① 1,1,11-Trichloro-1-vinyl-decamethyl-
hexasiloxane
CH₂=CHSi(Cl)₂−[OSi(CH₃)₂]₅−Cl

② FeCl₃ + (Me₂SiO)₃ +
CH₂=CHSiCl₃ ⟶

③ (124~126°/3).

⑥ Izv. OKhN **1963**, 282.

Si₆C₁₂H₃₆

① Dodecamethylcyclohexasilane
[(CH₃)₂Si]₆

② Me₂SiCl₂ + Li ⟶ 60%
Me₂SiCl₂ + NaK ⟶ 31%

③ Cryst. [250~252°]. [140°].
Transition point 74.5°. Sublime
point 120°.

④ Sol. in Me₂CO.
+ I₂ ⟶ I−(SiMe₂)₆−I

⑥ JOC **28**, 1651 (1963). Angew. **75**, 206
(1963).

Si₆C₁₂H₃₆I₂

① 1,6-Diiododecamethylhexasilane
I−[Si(CH₃)₂]₆−I

② I₂ + (SiMe₂)₆ ⟶

③ (185°/2).

⑥ Angew. **75**, 206 (1963).

Si$_6$C$_{12}$H$_{37}$O$_5$

① 1-Hydronitradodecamethylcyclohexa-
siloxane

② NH$_3$ + Cl(SiMe$_2$O)$_5$SiMe$_2$Cl
⟶ 38.5%

③ (58~60°/1). n_D1.4122 (20°). d0.9690
(20°/4°).

⑥ Izv. SKh **1963**, 2045.

Si$_6$C$_{12}$H$_{38}$O$_5$

① 1,11-Dihydrododecamethylhexa-
siloxane
(CH$_3$)$_2$Si(H)[OSi(CH$_3$)$_2$]$_5$H

② Me$_2$Si(H)Si(H)Me$_2$ + (Me$_2$SiO)$_4$
+ H$_2$SO$_4$ ⟶ 18%
LiAlH$_4$ + Me$_2$SiCl(OSiMe$_2$)$_x$Cl
⟶ 85%

③ (130°/20). n_D1.3929 (20°). d0.8988
(20°).

⑥ Ger. 1085875 (1960); CA **55**, 27057
(1961). Ger. 1140348 (1962); CA **58**,
12600 (1963).

Si$_6$C$_{12}$H$_{38}$O$_7$

① 1,11-Dihydroxydodecamethylhexa-
.siloxane
HO[Si(CH$_3$)$_2$O]$_6$H

② NaOH +
Me$_2$SiFOSiMe$_2$OSiMe$_2$F ⟶

③ (119~120°/2). n_D1.4099 (20°). d0.9916
(20°/4°).

⑥ Izv. OKhN **1962**, 2243.

Si$_6$C$_{14}$H$_{42}$

① Tetradecamethylhexasilane
CH$_3$[Si(CH$_3$)$_2$]$_6$CH$_3$

② NaK + Me(SiMe$_2$)$_4$Me ⟶
Me$_3$SiSiMe$_2$Cl + Me$_2$SiClSiMe$_2$Cl
+ Na ⟶
Me$_3$SiCl + Me$_2$SiCl$_2$ + Na ⟶

③ (125~128°/1). [28~29°]. n_D1.5155
(20°). d0.8401 (30°/4°).

⑥ Z. Naturf. **18B**, 765 (1963). JOM 1,
153 (1963).

Si$_6$C$_{14}$H$_{42}$O$_2$

① Dodecamethyl-2,3,5,6,8,9-hexasila-4,
7-dioxadecane
CH$_3$-[Si(CH$_3$)$_2$]$_2${O[Si(CH$_3$)$_2$]$_2$}$_2$-CH$_3$

② H$_2$SO$_4$ + (Me$_3$SiSiMe$_2$)$_2$O ⟶

③ (110~111°/3). n_D1.4472 (30°). d0.8458
(30°/4°).

⑥ Kogyo Kagaku Zasshi **66**, 637 (1963).

Si$_6$C$_{14}$H$_{42}$O$_3$

① Dodecamethyl-2,4,5,7,8,10-hexasila-
3,6,9-trioxaundecane
(CH$_3$)$_3$Si-[OSi(CH$_3$)$_2$Si(CH$_3$)$_2$]$_2$
OSi(CH$_3$)$_3$

② H$_2$SO$_4$ + (Me$_2$SiSiMe$_2$O)$_2$ ⟶
Me$_3$SiOSiMe$_3$ + H$_2$SO$_4$

③ (160~161°/34). n_D1.4235 (30°). d0.8524
(30°/4°).

⑥ "Studies in Organosilicon Compounds", Vol 1, Chapter 10 (1963).
Kogyo Kagaku Zasshi **66**, 637(1963).

Si$_6$C$_{14}$H$_{42}$O$_5$

① Quadradecamethylhexasiloxane
CH$_3$[Si(CH$_3$)$_2$O]$_5$Si(CH$_3$)$_3$

② MeLi + Cl(SiMe$_2$O)$_5$SiMe$_2$Cl
⟶ 74%
Me$_3$SiCl + Me$_2$SiCl$_2$ + H$_2$O ⟶

③ (142°). n_D1.4071 (20°). d0.9092 (20°).

⑥ Ger. 1136336(1962); CA **58**, 6861(1963).
Kogyo Kagaku Zasshi **60**, 1398

(1957) ; CA **53**, 17887 (1959).

Si₆C₁₄H₄₇N₅

① Di[bis(trimethylsilylamino)methyl-
   silyl]amine
   {[((CH₃)₃SiNH]₂Si(CH₃)−}₂NH

② MeSi(NH₂)(NHSiMe₃)₂ $\xrightarrow{200°}$

③ (123°/0.3). n_D1.4461 (20°).

⑥ Angew. **75**, 165 (1963).

Si₆C₁₅H₄₂O₇

① Undecamethylbutoxycyclohexa-
   siloxane
   [(CH₃)₂SiO]₅[(CH₃)C₄H₉OSiO]

② MeSiCl₂OBu +
   NaO(SiMe₂O)₃−Na $\longrightarrow$ 54%

③ (200.5~203.5°/1). n_D1.4135 (20°).
   d0.9857 (20°/4°).

⑥ Izv. OKhN **1963**, 294.

Si₆C₁₅H₄₅N₃

① N, N′, N″-Tris(trimethylsilyl)hexa-
   methylcyclotrisilazane
   [(CH₃)₂SiNSi(CH₃)₃]₃

② Na + (Me₂SiNH)₃ + Me₃SiCl $\longrightarrow$
   Me₃SiCl +
   (Me₂SiNH)₂(Me₂SiNLi) $\longrightarrow$
   Me₃SiCl +
   (Me₂SiNH)(Me₂SiNLi)₂ $\longrightarrow$
   Me₃SiCl + (Me₂SiNLi)₃ $\longrightarrow$

③ (143~145°/0.09). [−43°]. n_D1.4823.
   d0.940 (20°).

⑥ Inorg. Chem. **2**, 1069 (1963). Angew.
   73, 467 (1961).

Si₆C₁₆H₃₅Cl₃O₅

① 1-Phenyl-1,1,11-trichlorodecamethyl-
   hexasiloxane
   C₆H₅SiCl₂[OSi(CH₃)₂]₅Cl

② FeCl₃ + (Me₂SiO)₃ + PhSiCl₃ $\longrightarrow$

③ (142~144°/2).

⑥ Izv. OKhN **1963**, 282.

Si₆C₃₄H₅₄FeO₄

① Bis-1,1′-(5-phenylhexamethyltri-
   siloxanyl-1)ferrocene
   Fe{C₅H₄Si(CH₃)₂[OSi(CH₃)₂]₂C₆H₅}₂

② LiC₅H₄SiMe₂OSiMe₂OSiMe₂Ph
   + FeCl₂ $\longrightarrow$ 50%

③ (220~223°/0.15). n_D1.5162 (25°).
   d1.0796 (25°/4°).

⑥ US 3010982 (1961) ; CA **57**, 2253 (1962).
   JOC **25**, 1986 (1960).

Si₆C₃₇H₄₆Cl₂O₅

① 1,1,3,5,7,9,11-Heptamethyl-3,5,7,9,11
   -pentaphenyl-1,11-dichlorohexa-
   siloxane
   (CH₃)₂SiCl[OSi(CH₃)(C₆H₅)]₅Cl

② [PhSiMe(O)]₄ + Me₂SiCl₂ $\longrightarrow$

③ (275~277°/4). n_D1.5289 (20°). d1.1263
   (20°/4°).

⑥ Izv. OKhN **1962**, 1237, English page
   1161.

Si₆C₄₂H₄₈Cl₃N₃

① 1,1,3,3,5,5-Hexaphenyl-2,4,6-tris(dimethylchlorosilyl)cyclotriazine
   [(C₆H₅)₂SiNSi(CH₃)₂Cl]₃

② (Ph₃SiNLi)₃ + Me₂SiCl₂ $\xrightarrow{130~200°}$

③ Solid. (470~480°/720). [90~100°].

④ Resistant to water and acids.

⑥ Angew. **73**, 467 (1961).

Si₆C₄₄H₆₂

① Poly-*p*-phenylenedimethylsilane,
   methyl terminated pentamer

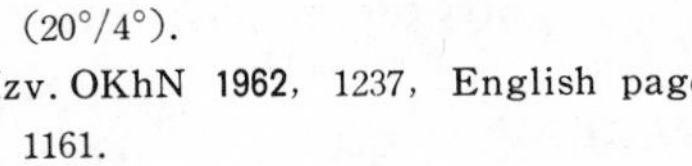

$$(CH_3)_3Si\left(\!\!-\!\!\bigcirc\!\!-\!Si(CH_3)_2\right)_5\!\!-CH_3$$

② Na + Me₂SiCl—◯—SiMe₂Cl

   + Me₃Si—◯—Si(Me)(Me)—◯—Cl

   $\longrightarrow$ 47%

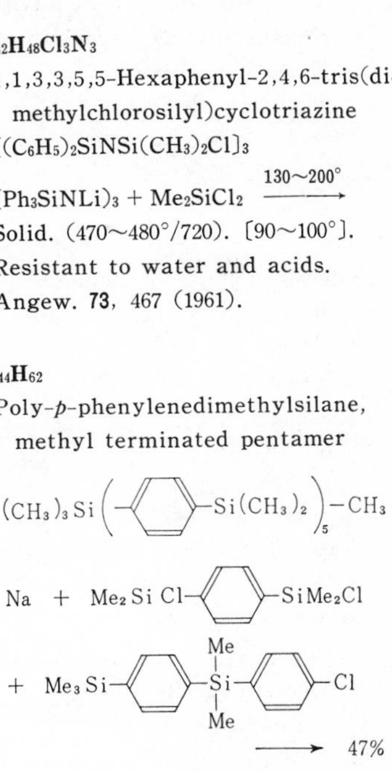

③ Solid. [187~191°].
④ Sol. in PhMe.
⑥ Rec. trav. chim. **81**, 565 (1962).

$Si_6C_{44}H_{62}Fe_2O_3$

① 1,3-Bis(1'-phenyltetramethyl-
 disiloxanyl)ferrocenyltetramethyl-
 disiloxane

$$\left(Fe\left\langle\begin{array}{l}C_5H_4Si(CH_3)_2-\\[4pt]C_5H_4Si(CH_3)_2OSi(CH_3)_2C_6H_5\end{array}\right.\right)_2O$$

② PhLi + MeSiCl₃

$$+ Fe\left\langle\begin{array}{c}C_5H_4SiMe_2\\O\\C_5H_5SiMe_2\end{array}\right. \longrightarrow$$

③ (273~280°/0.06). $n_D 1.5572$ (25°).
 IR: 8.92μ.
⑥ JOC **26**, 4038 (1961). US 3036105
 (1962); CA **57**, 16656 (1962).

$Si_6C_{45}H_{57}N_3$

① 1,1,3,3,5,5-Hexaphenyl-2,4,6-tris-
 (trimethylsilyl)cyclotrisilazane
 $[(C_6H_5)_2SiNSi(CH_3)_3]_3$
② (Ph₂SiNLi)₃ + Me₃SiCl $\longrightarrow$
③ (420~424°/718). [110~120°].
⑥ Angew. **73**, 467 (1961).

$Si_6C_{72}H_{60}$

① Dodecaphenylcyclohexasilane
 $[(C_6H_5)_2Si]_6$
② Li + Ph₂SiCl₂ $\longrightarrow$
 Na + Ph₂SiCl₂ $\longrightarrow$ 5.7%
 PhLi + (Ph₂Si)₄ $\longrightarrow$ 18.5%
③ Solid. [426~430°].
④ + Br₂ $\longrightarrow$ Br(Ph₂Si)₆Br
⑥ JACS **83**, 1921, 4089 (1961). JOC **26**,
 1999 (1961).

$Si_6C_{72}H_{60}Br_2$

① 1,6-Dibromododecaphenylhexasilane
 Br$-$[Si(C₆H₅)₂]₆$-$Br
② Br₂ + (SiPh₂)₆ $\longrightarrow$
③ [204~206°].

⑥ Tetrahedron Letters (No.23) 5 (1960).
 JACS **83**, 4089 (1961).

$Si_6C_{72}H_{62}$

① Dodecaphenyl-1,6-dihydro-hexasilane
 H$-$[Si(C₆H₅)₂]₆$-$H
② Li$-$(SiPh₂)₄$-$Li + Ph₂SiHCl $\longrightarrow$
③ [147~148°].
⑥ JOC **27**, 254 (1962).

$Si_6C_{72}H_{62}O_2$

① Dodecaphenyl-1,6-dihydroxyhexa-
 silane
 HO[Si(C₆H₅)₂]₆OH
② Br$-$(SiPh₂)₆$-$Br + HOH $\longrightarrow$
③ [170~172°].
⑥ JACS **83**, 4089 (1961). JOC **27**, 614
 (1962).

$Si_6C_{74}H_{66}$

① Dodecaphenyl-1,6-dimethylhexa-
 silane
 CH₃[Si(C₆H₅)₂]₆CH₃
② MeLi + Br$-$(SiPh₂)₆$-$Br $\longrightarrow$ 84%
③ [183~184°].
⑥ JACS **83**, 4089 (1961). Tetrahedron
 Latters (No.23) 5 (1960).

$Si_7C_7H_{28}O_7$

① Methylcycloheptasilane
 (CH₃SiHO)₇
③ (84.5°/50). $n_D 1.3945$ (20°). $d 0.966$
 (20°/4°).
⑥ Coll. Czech. Chem. Comm. **28**, 1384
 (1963).

$Si_7C_{14}H_{39}Cl_3O_6$

① 1,1,13-Trichloro-1-vinyldodeca-
 methylheptasiloxane
 CH₂=CHSiCl₂[OSi(CH₃)₂]₆Cl
② FeCl₃ + MeSiCl₃ + (Me₂SiO)₃ $\longrightarrow$
③ (144~146°/3).
⑥ Izv. OKhN **1963**, 282.

Si$_7$C$_{14}$H$_{42}$Cl$_2$O$_6$

① 1,13-Dichlorotetradecamethylhepta-
   siloxane
   Cl[Si(CH$_3$)$_2$O]$_6$Si(CH$_3$)$_2$Cl
② Me$_2$SiCl$_2$ + (Me$_2$SiO)$_3$ $\longrightarrow$
③ (133~135°/4). n_D1.4035 (20°). d0.9996
   (20°).
⑥ Izv. OKhN **1961**, 1456, English page
   1356.   Izv. OKhN **1962**, 2133.

Si$_7$C$_{14}$H$_{44}$O$_8$

① 1,13-Dihydroxytetradecamethyl-
   heptasiloxane
   HO[Si(CH$_3$)$_2$O]$_7$H
② Me$_2$SiClOSiMe$_2$OSiMe$_2$Cl + NaOH
   $\longrightarrow$ 80.5%
③ (130~135°/2). n_D1.4067 (20°). d0.9891
   (20°/4°).
⑥ Izv. OKhN **1962**, 2243.

Si$_7$C$_{14}$H$_{46}$N$_2$O$_6$

① Tetradecamethyl-1, 13-diaminohepta-
   siloxane
   H$_2$N[Si(CH$_3$)$_2$O]$_6$Si(CH$_3$)$_2$NH$_2$
② Cl(SiMe$_2$O)$_6$SiMe$_2$Cl + NH$_3$ $\longrightarrow$ 72%
③ (104~107°/1). n_D1.4059 (20°). d0.9530
   (20°/4°).
⑥ Izv. SKh **1963**, 2045.

Si$_7$C$_{16}$H$_{48}$

① Hexadecamethylheptasilane
   CH$_3$[Si(CH$_3$)$_2$]$_7$CH$_3$
② Na + PhMe + Me$_3$SiSiMe$_2$Cl
   + Me$_2$SiClSiMe$_2$SiMe$_2$Cl $\longrightarrow$ 17%
③ Solid. (194°/16). [19~20°]. n_D1.5264
   (30°). d0.8492 (30°/4°).
⑥ JOM **1**, 153 (1963).

Si$_7$C$_{44}$H$_{54}$Cl$_2$O$_6$

① 1,1,3,5,7,9,11,13-Octamethyl-1,13-di-
   chloro-3,5,7,9,11,13-hexaphenyl-
   heptasiloxane

(CH$_3$)$_2$SiCl[OSi(C$_6$H$_5$)(CH$_3$)]$_6$Cl
② (PhSiMeO)$_3$ + Me$_2$SiCl$_2$ $\longrightarrow$
③ (196~201°/0.01). n_D1.5304 (20°).
   d1.1310 (20°/4°).
⑥ Izv. OKhN **1962**, 1237, English page
   1161.   Dokl. **146**, 601 (1962).

Si$_8$C$_8$H$_{24}$O$_8$

① Tetrameric 1,2-dimethyl-1,2-dioxo-
   disilane
   [CH$_3$Si(O)Si(O)CH$_3$]$_4$
② HCl + EtOEt +
   Me$_2$Si(OEt)$_2$Si(OEt)$_2$Me $\longrightarrow$ 34%
③ (120~160°/11). [315~318°].
⑥ Kogyo Kagaku Zasshi **66**, 637 (1963).

Si$_8$C$_{14}$H$_{42}$O$_9$

① 1,3-Bis(pentamethylcyclotrisiloxy)-
   tetramethyldisiloxane

$$\left[\begin{array}{l}(CH_3)_2SiO\\ \qquad\quad O\\ (CH_3)_2SiO\end{array}\right>Si(CH_3)OSi(CH_3)_2-\right]_2 O$$

② Me$_2$SiO
    $\quad$ O $\;\rangle$SiMe(OBu-n) +
    Me$_2$SiO
    AcO$-$(SiMe$_2$O)$_2-$Ac $\longrightarrow$ 22%
③ (126.5°/2). n_D1.4053 (20°). d1.020
   (20°/4°).
⑥ Izv. SKh **1986** (1963).

Si$_8$C$_{16}$H$_{45}$Cl$_3$O$_7$

① 1,1,15-Trichloro-1-vinylquadradeca-
   methyloctasiloxane
   CH$_2$=CHSiCl$_2$[OSi(CH$_3$)$_2$]$_7$Cl
② CH$_2$=CHSiCl$_3$ + FeCl$_3$
   + (Me$_2$SiO)$_3$ $\longrightarrow$
③ Oil. (174~176°/3).
⑥ Izv. OKhN **1963**, 282.

Si$_8$C$_{16}$H$_{48}$Cl$_2$O$_7$

① 1,15-Dichlorododecamethylocta-
   siloxane
   {(CH$_3$)$_2$SiCl[OSi(CH$_3$)$_3$]$_3-$}$_2$O

② $Me_2SiClOSiMe_2Cl + Me_2SiCl_2$
    $+ HOH \longrightarrow$
③ $(152\sim154°/4)$.
⑥ Izv. OKhN 1962, 2133.

$Si_8C_{16}H_{50}O_9$
① 1,15-Dihydroxyhexadecamethylocta-
    siloxane
    $HO[Si(CH_3)_2O]_8H$
② $NaOH + HO(SiMe_2O)_3H \longrightarrow 79.5\%$
③ $(143\sim145°/2)$. $n_D1.4090$ $(20°)$. $d0.9912$
    $(20°/4°)$.
⑥ Izv. OKhN 1962, 2243.

$Si_8C_{16}H_{52}N_2O_7$
① Hexadecamethyl-1,15-diaminoocta-
    siloxane
    $H_2N[Si(CH_3)_2O]_7Si(CH_3)_2NH_2$
② $Cl(SiMe_2O)_7SiMe_2Cl + NH_3$
    $\longrightarrow 58.6\%$
③ $(121\sim124°/1)$. $n_D1.4055$ $(20°)$. $d0.9542$
    $(20°/4°)$.
⑥ Izv. SKh 1963, 2045.

$Si_8C_{20}H_{47}Cl_3O_7$
① 1-Phenyl-1,1,15-trichloroquadradeca-
    methyloctasiloxane
    $C_6H_5SiCl_2[OSi(CH_3)_2]_7Cl$
② $(Me_2SiO)_3 + PhSiCl_3 + FeCl_3 \longrightarrow$
③ Oil. $(172\sim174°/2)$.
⑥ Izv. OKhN 1963, 282.

$Si_8C_{18}H_{54}$
① Octadecamethyloctasilane
    $CH_3-[Si(CH_3)_2]_8-CH_3$
② $Na + PhMe + AcOEt$
    $+ Me_3SiSiMe_2Cl \longrightarrow$
③ $(194\sim198°/3)$. $[60\sim61°]$.
⑥ "Studies in Organosilicon Com-
    pounds" Vol. 1, Chap. 6 (1963).

$Si_8C_{18}H_{54}O_3$
① Octadecamethyl-2,3,5,6,8,9,11,12-

octasila-4,7,10-trioxatridecane
    $CH_3[Si(CH_3)_2]_2\{O[Si(CH_3)_2]_2\}_3CH_3$
② $H_2SO_4 + (Me_3SiSiMe_2)_2O \longrightarrow$
③ $(156°/3)$. $n_D1.4514$ $(30°)$. $d0.8624$
    $(30°/4°)$.
⑥ Kagyo Kagaku Zasshi 66, 637 (1963).

$Si_8C_{18}H_{54}O_4$
① Hexadecamethyl-2,4,5,7,8,10,11,13-
    octasila-3,6,9,12-tetraoxatetradeca-
    ne
    $(CH_3)_3Si\{O[Si(CH_3)_2]_2\}_3OSi(CH_3)_3$
②

$H_2SO_4 + Me_3SiOSiMe_3$
$+ Me_2Si-SiMe_2 \longrightarrow$
$\quad\quad | \quad\quad |$
$\quad\quad O \quad\quad O$
$\quad\quad | \quad\quad |$
$\quad Me_2Si-SiMe_2$
$H_2SO_4 + (Me_2SiSiMe_2O)_2 \longrightarrow$
$HOH + Me_3SiCl$
$\quad + Me_2SiClSiMe_2Cl \longrightarrow$

③ $(158\sim159°/3)$. $n_D1.4331$ $(30°)$. $d0.8662$
    $(30°/4°)$.
⑥ Kogyo Kagaku Zasshi 66, 637 (1963).

$Si_8C_{38}H_{66}FeO_6$
① Bis-1,1'-(1-phenyloctamethyltetra-
    siloxanyl-1)-ferrocene
    $Fe\{C_5H_4Si(CH_3)_2-[OSi(CH_3)_2]_3-C_6H_5\}_2$
② $BuLi + FeCl_2 +$
    $C_5H_5SiMe_2-(OSiMe_2)_3Ph \longrightarrow$
③ $(245\sim255°/0.04)$. $n_D1.4850$ $(25°)$.
⑥ JOC 25, 1986 (1960).   US 3010982
    (1961);   CA 57, 2253 (1962).

$Si_8C_{48}H_{40}O_{12}$
① Octaphenylcyclooctasiloxane
    $(C_6H_5SiO_{1.5})_8$
② $PhSiCl_3 + HOH \longrightarrow 74\%$
③ Solid. $[343°]$. Decomp. at $500\sim510°$.
⑤ For high temperature stability.
⑥ Arkiv. Kem. 13, 367 (1958); 17, 529
    (1960).

$Si_8C_{48}H_{88}O_{12}$

① Octacyclohexylcyclooctasiloxane
($C_6H_{11}SiO_{1.5})_8$

② $(C_6H_{11}SiO_{1.5})_x$ + OH⁻ ⟶

③ d 1.174.

⑥ JACS **77**, 4248 (1955).

$Si_8C_{51}H_{62}Cl_2O_7$

① 1,5-Dichloro-1,1,3,5,7,9,11,13,15-
nonamethyl-3,5,7,9,11,13,15-hepta-
phenyloctasiloxane
$(CH_3)_2SiCl[OSi(C_6H_5)(CH_3)]_7Cl$

② (PhSiMeO)₃ + Me₂SiCl₂ $\xrightarrow{300°}$

③ (232~235°/0.05). n_D 1.5314 (20°).
d 1.1238 (20°/4°).

⑥ Izv. OKhN **1962**, 1237.

$Si_8C_{60}H_{99}O_7$

① 3,5,7,9,11,13-Hexa(2-phenylethyl)-
dodecylmethyloctasiloxane

$$(CH_3)_3SiO-\overset{\displaystyle CH_2CH_2C_6H_5}{\underset{\displaystyle CH_3}{(SiO)_6}}-Si(CH_3)_3$$

② PhCH₂CH₂SiCl₂Me + Me₃SiCl
+ HOH ⟶

③ (282~300°/4). n_D 1.5079 (20°). d 1.0326
(20°).

⑥ Izv. OKhN **1961**, 1615.

$Si_8C_{66}H_{102}O_7$

① 3,5,7,9,11,13-Hexa(2-*p*-tolylethyl)-
dodecylmethyloctasiloxane

$$(CH_3)_3SiO-\overset{\displaystyle CH_2CH_2C_6H_4CH_3\text{-}p}{\underset{\displaystyle CH_3}{(SiO)_6}}-Si(CH_3)_3$$

② HOH + *p*-MeC₆H₄CH₂CH₂SiCl₂Me
+ Me₃SiOH $\xrightarrow{\text{in PhMe}}$

③ (282~296°/4). n_D 1.5059 (20°). d 1.0189
(20°).

⑥ Izv. OKhN **1961**, 1615, English page

$Si_9C_{16}H_{48}O_{10}$

① 1,5-Bis(pentamethylcyclotrisiloxy)
hexamethyltrisiloxane

$$\left(\begin{array}{c}(CH_3)_2SiO \qquad CH_3 \\ \underset{\displaystyle (CH_3)_2SiO}{O} \Big\rangle SiO\underset{\displaystyle CH_3CH_3}{SiO-} \end{array}\right)_2 Si(CH_3)_2$$

② $$\underset{\displaystyle Me_2SiO}{\overset{\displaystyle Me_2SiO}{O}} \Big\rangle Si(Me)OBu\text{-}n$$
+ AcO(SiMe₂O)₃Ac ⟶ 17.8%

③ (144~146°/1.5). n_D 1.4055 (20°). d 1.022
(20°/4°).

⑥ Izv. SKh **1963**, 1986.

$Si_9C_{18}H_{54}Cl_2O_8$

① 1,17-Dichlorooctadecylmethylnona-
siloxane
$Cl[Si(CH_3)_2O]_8Si(CH_3)_2Cl$

② Me₂SiClOSiMe₂Cl + Me₂SiCl₂ ⟶
(with or without FeCl₃ or (Me₂SiO)₄)
Me₂SiCl₂ + (Me₂SiO)₄ (250°) ⟶

③ (168~170°/4). n_D 1.4042. d 0.9945 (20°).

⑥ Izv. OKhN **1961**, 1456, English page
1356. Izv. OKhN **1962**, 2133.

$Si_9C_{18}H_{56}O_{10}$

① 1,17-Dihydroxyoctadecamethylnona-
siloxane
$HO[Si(CH_3)_2O]_9H$

② NaOH + HO(SiMe₂O)$_x$H ⟶ 83%

③ (158~161°/2). n_D 1.4088 (20°). d 0.9921
(20°/4°).

⑥ Izv. OKhN **1962**, 2243.

$Si_9C_{18}H_{58}N_2O_8$

① Octadecamethyl-1,17-diaminonona-
siloxane
$H_2N[Si(CH_3)_2O]_8Si(CH_3)_2NH_2$

② NH₃ + Cl(SiMe₂O)₈SiMe₂Cl
⟶ 46.4%

③ (128~132°/1). n_D 1.4062 (20°). d 0.9592
(20°/4°).

⑥ Izv. SKh **1963**, 2045.

$Si_9C_{22}H_{53}Cl_3O_8$
① 1-Phenyl-1,1,17-trichlorohexadeca-
  methylnonasiloxane
  $C_6H_5SiCl_2[OSi(CH_3)_2]_8Cl$
② $FeCl_3 + [(CH_3)_2SiO]_3 + PhSiCl_3 \longrightarrow$
③ Oil. (183~185°/2).
⑥ Izv. OKhN **1963**, 282.

$Si_9C_{58}H_{70}Cl_2O_8$
① 1,17-Dichloro-1,1,3,5,7,9,11,13,15,17-
  decamethyl-3,5,7,9,11,13,15,17-
  octaphenylnonasiloxane
  $ClSi(CH_3)_2[OSi(CH_3)C_6H_5]_8Cl$
② $[PhSi(Me)O]_3 + Me_2SiCl_2 \xrightarrow{300°}$
③ (261~264°/0.05). n_D1.5377 (20°).
  d1.1258 (20°/4°).
⑥ Izv. OKhN **1962**, 1237.

$Si_9C_{69}H_{102}O_8$
① Tridecamethyl-3,5,7,9,11,13,15-hep-
  taphenylethylnonasiloxane
  $(CH_3)_3SiO - [Si(CH_3)(CH_2CH_2C_6H_5)O]_7-$
  $-Si(CH_3)_3$
② $Me_3SiCl + HOH$
  $+ PhCH_2CH_2Si(Cl)_2Me \longrightarrow$
③ Oil. n_D1.5179 (20°). d1.0552 (20°).
⑥ Izv. OKhN **1961**, 1615.

$Si_9C_{80}H_{100}Fe_4O_4$
① $\left(Fe\!\!\diagdown\begin{matrix} C_5H_4Si(CH_3)_2C_6H_5 \\ \\ C_5H_4Si(CH_3)_2O- \end{matrix} \right)_4 Si$
② $SiCl_4 + Fe\!\!\diagdown\begin{matrix} C_5H_4SiMe_2Ph \\ \\ C_5H_4SiMe_2OLi \end{matrix}$
  $\longrightarrow 44\%$
③ (286~287°/0.3).
⑥ JOC **26**, 4038 (1961).

$Si_9C_{100}H_{92}$
① 1,1,9,9-Tetramethylhexadecylnona-
  silane
  $C_6H_5Si(CH_3)_2-[Si(C_6H_5)_2]_7-Si(CH_3)_2$
  C_6H_5
② $PhSiMe_2SiPh_2Cl +$
  $Ph_2Si(Li)(SiPh_2)_3SiPh_2Li \longrightarrow 26\%$
③ Solid. (230~232°).
⑤ Possible high temperature material.
⑥ Chem. & Ind. **1963**, 954.

$Si_{10}C_{18}H_{54}O_{11}$
① 1,7-Bis(pentamethylcyclotrisiloxy)-
  octamethyltetrasiloxane
  $\begin{matrix} (CH_3)_2SiO \\ [\quad\quad O \quad\quad \\ (CH_3)_2SiO \end{matrix}\!\!\!>Si(CH_3)OSi(CH_3)_2OSi-$
  $(CH_3)_2-]_2O$
② $\begin{matrix} Me_2SiO \\ \quad\quad O \\ Me_2SiO \end{matrix}\!\!\!>Si(Me)OBu\text{-}n$
  $+ AcO-(SiMe_2O)_4-Ac \longrightarrow 18.3\%$
③ (161~164°/1.5). n_D1.4058 (20°). d1.025
  (20°/4°).
⑥ Izv. SKh **1963**, 1986.

$Si_{10}C_{20}H_{64}N_2O_9$
① 1,19-Diaminoeicosamethyldeca-
  siloxane
  $NH_2[Si(CH_3)_2O]_9Si(CH_3)_2NH_2$
② $NH_3 + Cl(SiMe_2O)_9SiMe_2Cl$
  $\longrightarrow 54.8\%$
③ (151~160°/1). n_D1.4062 (20°). d0.9590
  (20°/4°).
⑥ Izv. SKh **1963**, 2045.

$Si_{10}C_{22}H_{66}$
① Permethyldecasilane
  $CH_3-[Si(CH_3)_2]_{10}-CH_3$
② $Na + Me_3SiSiMe_2Cl + Me_2ClSi-$
  $SiMe_2Cl \xrightarrow{\text{in PhMe and AcOEt}}$
③ Solid. (244°/3). [113~114°].
⑥ Unpublished work.

$Si_{10}C_{22}H_{66}O_4$

① Permethyl-2,3,5,6,8,9,11,12,14,15-
decasila-4,7, 10, 13-tetraoxahexa-
decane
$(CH_3)_3SiSi(CH_3)_2-[OSi(CH_3)_2-$
$Si(CH_3)_2]_4-CH_3$

② $H_2SO_4 +$
$Me_3SiSiMe_2OSiMe_2SiMe_3$ ⟶

③ $(190\sim191°/3)$. $n_D 1.4533$ $(30°)$. $d 0.8743$
$(30°/4°)$.

⑥ "Studies in Organo-silicon Compounds" Vol. 1, Chap. 10 (1963).
Kogyo Kagaku Zasshi **66**, 637(1963).

$Si_{10}C_{22}H_{66}O_5$

① Permethyl-2,4,5,7,8,10,11,13,14,16-
decasila-3,6,9,12,15-pentaoxahepta-
decane
$(CH_3)_3Si-\{O[Si(CH_3)_2]_2\}_4-OSi(CH_3)_3$

② $H_2SO_4 + Me_3SiOSiMe_3$
$+ Me_2Si-SiMe_2$ ⟶
　　　　　| 　|
　　　　　O 　O
　　　　　| 　|
　　　Me_2Si-SiMe_2
$H_2SO_4 + (Me_2SiSiMe_2O)_2$ ⟶

③ $(192\sim196°/2)$. $n_D 1.4400$ $(30°)$. $d 0.8790$
$(30°/4°)$.

⑥ Kogyo Kagaku Zasshi **66**, 637 (1963).

$Si_{10}C_{24}H_{59}Cl_3O_9$

① 1,1,17-Trichloro-1-phenyloctadeca-
methyldecasiloxane
$C_6H_5SiCl_2[OSi(CH_3)_2]_9Cl$

② $(Me_2SiO)_3 + FeCl_3 + PhSiCl_3$ ⟶

③ Oil. $(192\sim194°/2)$.

⑥ Izv. OKhN **1963**, 282.

$Si_{10}C_{36}H_{74}O_9$

① 1,19-Di-p-vinylphenyleicosa-
methyldecasiloxane
p-$CH_2=CHC_6H_4Si(CH_3)_2-[OSi-$
$(CH_3)_2]_9-C_6H_4CH=CH_2$

② p-$CH_2=CHC_6H_4SiMe_2-(OSiMe_2)_x-Cl$

$+ HOH$ ⟶

③ $n_D 1.4641$ $(20°)$. $d 0.965$ $(20°/4°)$.

⑥ Makromol. Chem. **55**, 96 (1962).

$Si_{10}C_{42}H_{74}O_9$

① 3,5,7,9-Tetrakis(trimethylsiloxy)-3,
5,7,9-tetraphenylhexasiloxane
$\{[(CH_3)_3SiO]_2Si(C_6H_5)OSi(C_6H_5)$-
$[OSi(CH_3)_3]\}_2O$

② $Me_3SiCl + PhSiCl_3 + HOH$ ⟶

③ $(255°)$.

⑥ Brit. 848719 (1960); CA **55**, 14382
(1961). Ger. 1046049 (1958); CA
55, 17 580 (1961).

$Si_{10}C_{65}H_{78}Cl_2O_9$

① 1,19-Dichloro-1,1,3,5,7,9,11,13,15,17,
19-undecamethyl-3,5, 7,9, 11,13,15,
17,19-nonaphenyldecasiloxane
$ClSi(CH_3)_2[OSi(CH_3)C_6H_5]_9Cl$

② $(PhSiMeO)_3 + Me_2SiCl_2$ $\xrightarrow{300°}$

③ $(283\sim287°/0.05)$. $n_D 1.5365$ $(20°)$.
$d 1.1239$ $(20°/4°)$.

⑥ Izv. OKhN **1962**, 1237.

$Si_{11}C_{22}H_{70}N_2O_{10}$

① 1,21-Diaminodocosamethylundecasil-
oxane
$H_2N[Si(CH_3)_2O]_{10}Si(CH_3)_2NH_2$

② $NH_3 + Cl(SiMe_2O)_{10}SiMe_2Cl$
⟶ 45.4%

③ $(163\sim166°/1)$. $n_D 1.4065$ $(20°)$. $d 0.9626$
$(20°/4°)$.

⑥ Izv. SKh **1963**, 2045.

$Si_{11}C_{24}H_{72}O_{10}$

① 1,1,1,9,9,9-Hexamethylhexa(trimethylsiloxy)pentasiloxane
$[(CH_3)_3SiO_3]Si-O-$
　　　　　　　　　　$OSi(CH_3)_3$
　　　　　　　　　　|
　　　　　　$-Si-O-Si[OSi(CH_3)_3]_3$
　　　　　　　　　　|
　　　　　　　　　　$OSi(CH_3)_3$

② $(EtO)_2Si[OSi(OEt)_3]_2 + AcOSiMe_3$

+ HOH + HCl $\longrightarrow$ 66%

③ (202°/4.7). [138°]. n_D1.3994 (20°).
  d0.930 (20°).

⑥ Izv. OKhN 1962, 1572.   JACS 68, 691
  (1946).

$Si_{12}C_{22}H_{66}O_{13}$

① 1,7-Bis(heptamethylcyclotetra-
  siloxy)octamethyltetrasiloxane

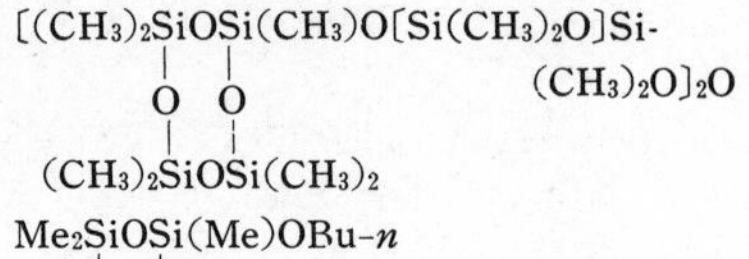

$$[(CH_3)_2SiOSi(CH_3)O[Si(CH_3)_2O]Si-$$
$$\underset{|}{O}\;\underset{|}{O}\qquad\qquad (CH_3)_2O]_2O$$
$$(CH_3)_2SiOSi(CH_3)_2$$

② Me$_2$SiOSi(Me)OBu-n
  $\overset{|}{O}\;\overset{|}{O}$
  Me$_2$SiOSiMe$_2$

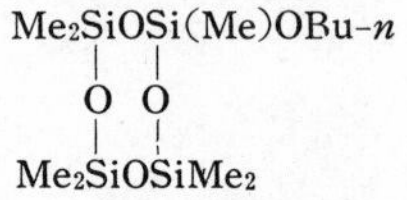

  + AcO$-$(SiMe$_2$O)$_4-$Ac $\longrightarrow$ 29.8%

③ (196~199°/1.5). n_D1.4076 (20°).
  d1.0260 (20°/4°).

⑥ Izv. SKh 1963, 1986.

$Si_{16}C_{36}H_{108}O_{16}Ti$

① Tetrakis[tris(trimethylsiloxy)-
  siloxy]titanium

$Ti\{OSi[OSi(CH_3)_3]_3\}_4$

② (Me$_3$SiO)$_3$SiONa + TiCl$_4$ $\longrightarrow$ 57.3%

③ (223~225°/1.5). n_D1.4201 (20°). d0.9623
  (20°/4°).

⑥ Izv. OKhN 1961, 2169 ; English page
  2028.

$Si_{17}C_{35}H_{105}ClO_{16}$

① 1-Chloropermethylheptadecasiloxane
  $(CH_3)_3Si[OSi(CH_3)_2]_{16}Cl$

② Me$_3$SiCl + (Me$_2$SiO)$_x$ $\longrightarrow$

③ (233~235°/3). n_D1.4035 (20°). d0.9655
  (20°).

⑥ Izv. OKhN 1961, 1960 ; English page
  1502.

$Si_{28}C_{224}H_{280}$

① Poly-p-dimethylsilylphenylene
  $[p-(CH_3)_2SiC_6H_4]_n$ ($\bar{n}$=28)

② Me$_2$Si(C$_6$H$_4$Cl-p)$_2$ + Na
  + Me$_2$SiCl$_2$ $\longrightarrow$

③ Solid. [200~225°].

⑤ High temperature stability.

⑨ Rec. trav. chim. 81, 565 (1962).

7. Organic Compounds of Germanium, Tin, and Lead

(Ge, Sn, Pb)

7.1. Organic Compounds of Germanium

The history of organogermanium compounds started in 1887, when Winkler synthesized tetraethylgermane. Krause cited 26 papers in his book, and Johnson, Quane and Bottei, and Rijkens and van der Kerk have published reviews. There are organohalogenogermanes, R_xGeX_{4-x}, hydrides, esters, ethers, etc. Nomenclature for these compounds is similar to those of organosilicon compounds.

Methods of preparation, as shown below, are similar to those of silicon.

(1) Direct reaction

$$Ge + RX \longrightarrow R_xGeX_{4-x}$$

(2) GeI_2 and RI

$$GeI_2 + 2RI \longrightarrow RGeI_3$$

(3) Wurtz Reaction

$$GeCl_4 + 4C_6H_5Br + Na \longrightarrow (C_6H_5)_4Ge$$

(4) Reactions of GeX_4 with other metal alkyls [$Zn(C_2H_5)_2$, $Hg(C_6H_5)_2$, RMgX, RLi, etc.].

Organogermanium compounds can be divided into four groups, R_4Ge, R_3GeX, R_2GeX_2, and $RGeX_3$.

The Ge–C bond is covalent and stable to many nucleophilic and electrophilic reagents. There are linear compounds such as $R_3Ge(GeR_2)_nGeR_3$ and $(GeR_2)_n$. In these compounds, the Ge–Ge bond is cleaved easily by nucleophilic reagents.

7.1.1. Tetraalkyls (R_4Ge)

These are the most stable compounds towards heat and reagents of all the organogermanes. Tetraalkyl compounds are distillable colorless liquids, and tetraaryl compounds are sharp melting solids. They are stable to water, most acids, bases, and oxygen.

7.1.2. Derivatives of Germane (R_3GeH, R_2GeH_2, $RGeH_3$)

These compounds have been obtained by reduction of the corresponding chloride with $LiAlH_4$ or $NaBH_4$. They react with unsaturated compounds.

7.1.3. Organohalogenogermanes and their Analogs

The Ge–Cl bond reacts with many reagents. Water converts them to germoxanes.

$$2R_3GeX + H_2O \longrightarrow R_3GeOGeR_3 + 2HX$$
$$n R_2GeX_2 + n H_2O \longrightarrow (R_2GeO)_n + 2n HX$$
$$2n RGeX_3 + 3n H_2O \longrightarrow [(RGeO)_2O]_n + 6n HX$$

These reactions are reversible. Similar reactions can be carried out with mercaptans in the presence of suitable acid acceptors.   Thus we have obtained the following compounds; $R_3GeSGeR_3$, $(R_2GeS)_n$, and R_3GeSR'.   Compounds with a Ge-N bond and peroxides, $R_{4-n}Ge(OOR')_n$, have been reported.

7.1.4. Alkali Metal Compounds

$(C_2H_5)_3GeLi$ can be prepared from hexaethyldigermane and lithium in ethylamine, but in ammonia $(C_2H_5)_3GeH$ is obtained.

7.2. Organic Compounds of Tin

The Sn-C bond in organotin compounds is covalent but more ionic than the Si-C and Ge-C bonds.   Accordingly the organic groups attached to tin readily undergo redistribution.   Reactions in aqueous solution and complex formations are stronger than those of organosilicons and germaniums.   It has been found that there is the pentacoordinated or hexacoordinated tin in the complexes.   General methods for preparing Sn-C bonds are as follows:

（1） Reaction of metallic tin or tin alloys with alkyl halides

（2） Tin(II) halides and alkyl halides

$$SnI_2 + RI \longrightarrow RSnI_3$$

（3） Wurtz reaction

（4） Alkylation of tin halides with other organometallic compounds （RLi, R_2Hg, R_2Zn, RMgX, R_3Al, etc.）

（5） Reaction of alkyl halides with sodium stannite

$$CH_3I + Na_2SnO_2 \longrightarrow CH_3SnO_2Na + NaI$$

7.2.1. Tetraorganotins (R_4Sn)

These compounds are prepared conveniently by the reaction of Grignard reagent with tin tetrachloride.

7.2.2. Organotin Hydrides

Stannane, SnH_4 is an unstable compound, but successive substitution of alkyl group gives successively stable alkylstannanes.   Reduction of alkyltin halides with $LiAlH_4$ is convenient for the laboratory manipulation.   Addition of these compounds to unsaturated compounds has been reviewed.

7.2.3. Alkyltin Halides

Redistribution reactions between tetraalkyltins and tin tetrachloride have been used to prepare these compounds.

$$R_4Sn + SnX_4 \longrightarrow R_3SnX + R_2SnX_2, \text{ etc.}$$

Cleavage reactions are also useful:

$$R_3SnSnR_3 + X_2 \longrightarrow 2\,R_3SnX$$

$$R_4Sn + HX \longrightarrow R_3SnX + RH$$

Chemical Structure of Organotin Hydroxides, Oxides and Salts.   Structural aspects of these interesting compounds have been reviewed recently.

7.2.4. Organotin Complexes

Bis-oxinates and bis-acetylacetoates, etc., of dialkyltin are known. Stability constants of these complexes are exceptionally small compared to those of transition metals.

7.2.5. Alkali Metal Compounds

These are active intermediates formed in liquid ammonia.

$$R_3SnX + 2Na \longrightarrow R_3SnNa + NaX$$

7.2.6. Organoditin and Organotin(II) Compounds

Organoditin of the R_3SnSnR_3 type has been obtained by the reaction of alkyl iodides with an Sn–Na alloy, or by the reaction of trialkyltin halides with Na in liquid ammonia. Organotin(II) compounds are considered polymeric substances. They are prepared by the reaction of dimethyltin dibromide with Na in liquid ammonia.

7.3. Organic Compounds of Lead

Among these compounds tetraethyllead is most well known. Organolead compounds are prepared by the reaction of Grignard reagents with lead (II) chloride.

$$2\,PbCl_2 + 4\,RMgX \overset{\varDelta}{\longrightarrow} R_4Pb + Pb + 2\,MgX_2 + 2\,MgCl_2$$

The most characteristic reaction of tetraalkyllead is the formation of alkyl radicals by heating. Halides, R_3PbX, R_2PbX_2, and $RPbX_3$, are known.

REFERENCES

Germanium
1) O. H. Johnson, *Chem. Revs.*, **51**, 259 (1951).
2) D. Quane, R. S. Bottei, *Chem. Revs.*, **63**, 403 (1963).
3) F. Rijkens, G. J. M. van der Kerk, "Organogermanium Chemistry", Germanium Research Committee (1964).
4) "Advances in Organometallic Chemistry", Vol. 3, Academic Press (1965).
Tin
1) R. C. Poller, *J. Organometal. Chem.*, **3**, 321 (1965).
2) "Advances in Organometallic Chemistry", Vol. 1 (1964); Vol. 5 (1967), Academic Press.

【Ge】

GeCCl₃F₃
① Perfluoromethylgermanium
   trichloride
   CF₃GeCl₃
② CF₃GeI₃ + AgCl $\xrightarrow{20°, \ 48\,hrs}$
③ Vapor pressure : 90 mm at 20°.
⑥ Proc. Chem. Soc. **1960**, 282.   JACS
   84, 898 (1962).

GeCF₃I₃
① Perfluoromethylgermanium triiodide
   CF₃GeI₃
② CF₃I + GeI₂ $\xrightarrow{130\sim135° \ (10\,days)}$
③ (40~4°/0.001). [8.4°]. n_D1.6571 (20°).
   Stable at least 48 hrs to water at 25°.
④ + Ag₂O $\longrightarrow$ HCF₃ (92%)
    + AgCl $\longrightarrow$ CF₃CGeCl₃
    + AgF $\longrightarrow$ CF₃GeF₃
⑥ Proc. Chem. Soc. **1960**, 282.   JACS
   84, 898 (1962).

GeCF₆
① Perfluoromethylgermanium trifluoride
   CF₃GeF₃
② CF₃GeI₃ + AgF $\xrightarrow{20°, \ 48\,hrs}$
③ $\log P(mm) = 11.94 - \dfrac{2451}{T}$.
   Vapor pressure : 760 mm at −1.7°.
④ + aq. alkali $\longrightarrow$ HCF₃ (94%)
    + KF $\longrightarrow$ K₂(CF₃)GeF₅
⑥ Proc. Chem. Soc. **1960**, 282.   JACS
   84, 898 (1960).

GeCHCl₅
① (Dichloromethyl)germanium trichloride
   Cl₂CHGeCl₃
② MeGeCl₃ + SO₂Cl₂ $\xrightarrow{Bz_2O_2}$ 40%

③ (168~179°/760). n_D1.5100(20°). d1.8166
   (20°/4°).
⑥ Izv. OKhN **1961**, 2095.

GeCH₂Cl₄
① Chloromethylgermanium trichloride
   ClCH₂GeCl₃
② GeCl₄ + Cu + CH₂N₂
   $\xrightarrow{-60°C \ ether}$ 93.7%
③ (149°/759). n1.5003 (20°). d1.8415
   (20°/4°).
⑥ JACS **77**, 907 (1955).   Izv. OKhN
   1957, 994.

GeCH₃F₃
① Methylgermanium trifluoride
   CH₃GeF₃
② Steuart reaction.
③ (96.5°/751). [38°].
⑥ Izv. OKhN **1957**, 994.

GeCH₃Cl₃
① Methylgermanium trichloride
   CH₃GeCl₃
② MeCl + Ge $\xrightarrow{360°, \ 20 \ wt \ \% \ Cu}$
③ Colorless liq. (111°/760). d1.73
   (24.5°/4°).
⑥ JACS **69**, 1729 (1947).   Z. anorg. allg.
   Chem. **211**, 331 (1961).

GeCH₃Br₃
① Methylgermanium trichloride
   CH₃GeBr₃
② CH₃Br + Ge $\xrightarrow{Cu}$ 20.2%
③ (168°/750). n_D1.577 (20°). d2.6337
   (20°/4°).
   IR : Optika i Spektroscopiya **8**, 394
   (1960).
⑥ Izv. OKhN **1957**, 994.

GeCH₆

① Methylgermane
   CH₃GeH₃

② CH₃Br + NaGeH₃ ⟶

③ $(-35.1°/760)$. $[-158°]$.
   NMR: Ge-H $\tau=6.55$ in cyclohexane
   soln.: Izv. OKhN **1961**, 1758.

⑥ JACS **79**, 1843 (1957). Angew. **73**, 114
   (1961). J. Mol. Spectroscopy **12**, 299
   (1964).

GeC₂H₃Cl₃

① Vinylgermanium trichloride
   CH₂=CHGeCl₃

② ClCH₂CH₂GeCl₃ +

   $\xrightarrow{200°, \text{ distilled}}$ 26.6%

③ $(127.5°/745.5)$. $n_D 1.4815$. $d 1.6520$.

④ + dry HBr ⟶ CH₂=CHGeBr₃

⑥ Izv. OKhN **1956**, 1146. JINC **11**, 24
   (1959).

GeC₂H₅Cl₃

① Ethylgermanium trichloride
   C₂H₅GeCl₃

② C₂H₅Cl + Ge $\xrightarrow{317°C}$

③ $(141.5°/761)$. $[<-33°]$. $n_D 1.47450(2°)$.
   $d 1.6091$ $(20°/4°)$.
   Sol. in org. solvents. Decompd. by
   water.

⑥ JACS **74**, 845 (1951).   Dokl. **128**, 302
   (1959).

GeC₂H₅Cl₃
Chloromethylmethyldichlorogerman

① (ClCH₂)CH₃GeCl₃

② CH₃GeCl₃ + CH₂N₂ $\xrightarrow[-60°]{\text{Et}_2\text{O}}$ 78%

③ $(71.74°/40)$. $n_D 1.4890$ $(25°)$. $d 1.642$
   $(25°/4°)$.

⑥ JACS **77**, 907 (1955).   Izv. OKhN
   1957, 994.

GeC₂H₆F₂

① Dimethylgermanium difluoride
   (CH₃)₂GeFe₂

② (CH₃)₂GeBr₂ + SbF₃ ⟶ 100%

③ $(112°/750)$. $n_D 1.3743$ $(20°)$. $d 1.5726$
   $(20°/4°)$.

⑥ Izv. OKhN **1957**, 994.

GeC₂H₆O

① Poly(dimethylgermanium oxide)
   $[(CH_3)_2GeO]_n$

② (CH₃)₂GeS + H₂SO₄ (in water)
   $\xrightarrow{\text{reflux 7 hrs}}$ (CH₃)₂GeSO₄ $\xrightarrow{\text{BeOH}_2}$
   Evaporating aq. [(CH₃)₂GeO]₄ at
   room temp. for 48 hrs.

③ Fibrous solid. $(211°/760)$. $[132\sim133°]$.
   Sol. in alcohol; insol. in C₆H₆, cyclohexane and CCl₄.

④ $\xrightarrow{210\sim220°, \text{ 24 hrs in sealed tube}}$ $[(CH_3)_2GeO]_3$

⑥ JACS **70**, 1801 (1948); **82**, 4166 (1960).

GeC₂H₆Cl₂

① Dimethylgermanium dichloride
   (CH₃)₂GeCl₂

② Ge + CH₃Cl $\xrightarrow{\text{Cu } 360°}$ 50%

③ Colorless liq. $(119/735, 124°/760)$.
   $[-22°]$. $n_D 1.4552(26°)$. $d 1.492$ $(20°)$.
   Sol. in org. solvents. Decempd. by
   H₂O.

⑥ Z. anorg. allg. Chem. **311**, 331 (1961).
   JACS **69**, 1729 (1947).

GeC₂H₆Br₂

① Dimethylgermanium dibromide
   (CH₃)₂GeBr₂

② CH₃Br + Ge−Cu (4:1) $\xrightarrow{450°}$

③ $(153°/746)$. $n_D 1.5268$ $(20°)$. $d 2.1163$
   $(20°/4°)$.

⑥ Izv. OKhN **1957**, 994.

GeC₂H₈

① Ethylgermane
   $(C_2H_5)GeH_3$

② $NaGeH_3 + C_2H_5Br \longrightarrow$

③ $(11.5°/743.5)$.

⑥ JACS **79**, 1843 (1957). Izv. OKhN
   1961, 1758.

GeC₂H₈

① Dimethylgermane
   $(CH_3)_2GeH_2$

② $(CH_3)_2GeS + Zn-Hg \xrightarrow{\text{EtOH}}$

③ $(-0.6°/760)$. $[-149°]$.

⑥ Izv. OKhN **1961**, 1758. Angew. **73**,
   114 (1961). JACS **75**, 6080 (1953).
   Dokl. **122**, 405 (1958).

GeC₃H₅Cl₃

① Allylgermanium trichloride
   $CH_2=CHCH_2GeCl_3$

② $CH_2=CHCH_2Cl + Ge \xrightarrow{340°, \text{ Cu}}$

   $CH_2=CHCH_2Br + Cl_3GeH \xrightarrow{60°, \text{ 2 hrs}}$
   $CH_2=CHCH_2GeCl_3$ (50%)
   $CH_2=CHCH_2GeBr_3$ (7%)

   $CH_2=CHCH_2Cl + Cl_3GeH \xrightarrow{\text{reflux in ether}}$
   $CH_2=CHCH_2GeCl_3$ (2.55%)

③ $(153.8°/743.5)$. $n_D 1.4928 \,(20°)$. $d\,1.5274$
   $(20°/4°)$.

④ $+ \text{dry HBr} \longrightarrow CH_2=CHCH_2GeBr_3$
   90%

⑥ Izv. OKhN **1961**, 2095 ; **1962**, 460 ; **1956**,
   1146.

GeC₃H₇Cl₃

① *n*-Propylgermanium trichloride
   $(n\text{-}C_3H_7)GeCl_3$

② $GeCl_4 + n\text{-}PrMgCl \xrightarrow{\text{ether}}$

   $n\text{-}PrCl + Ge \xrightarrow{330\sim320°}$

③ Colorless viscous oil. $(167°/767)$.
   $n_D 1.4779 \,(20°)$. $d\,1.5146 \,(20°/4°)$.

⑥ JACS **73**, 5486 (1951) ; **80**, 2931 (1958).
   Izv. OKhN **1961**, 1358.

GeC₃H₉Cl

① Trimethylgermanium chloride
   $(CH_3)_3GeCl$

② $(CH_3)_2GeCl_2 + CH_3MgCl \xrightarrow{\text{ether}} 25\%$

   $(CH_3)_2GeCl_2 + CH_3Li \xrightarrow{\text{ether}} 30\sim35\%$

③ Colorless liquid. $(102°/760, \ 96.5\sim$
   $97°/730)$. $[-14°]$. $n_D 1.4283 \,(20°)$.
   $d\,1.2382 \,(21.5°/4°)$.
   Azeotrope (97% $(CH_3)_3GeCl$ and 3%
   ether)

④ $+ AgCO_3 \longrightarrow [(CH_3)_3Ge]_2O + AgCl$
   $+ CO_2$

⑥ Z. anorg. allg. Chem. **311**, 331 (1961).

GeC₄H₆N₂S₂

① Dimethylgermanium di(isothiocyanate)
   $(CH_3)_2Ge(NCS)_2$

② $Me_2GeCl_2 + NCS^- \xrightarrow{H_2O}$ extracted
   with ether

③ White needles. $(266\sim268°/760)$. $[45.5$
   $\sim47°]$.
   Sol. in alc. and C_6H_6.

⑥ JACS **77**, 4489 (1955).

GeC₄H₉Br₃

① *n*-Butylgermanium tribromide
   $(n\text{-}C_4H_9)GeBr_3$

② $[(n\text{-}BuGeO)_2O]_n + 47\%$ HBr
   $\xrightarrow{\text{boil}}$ extracted with CCl_4, 67%

③ $(237°/760)$. $n\,1.5548 \,(20°)$. $d\,2.1480$
   $(20°/4°)$.

④ $+ H_2O \longrightarrow [(n\text{-}BuGeO)_2O]_n$

⑥ Izv. OKhN **1961**, 2095. JACS **82**, 3016
   (1960).

GeC₄H₉N

① Trimethylgermanium cyanide

(CH₃)₃GeCN

② $Me_3GeI + AgCN \xrightarrow{C_6H_6}$ 70%

③ Translucent white needles. (150°).
[38~38.5°].
Soluble in ether, CHCl₃ and acetone.
IR : JOC **25**, 809 (1960)

④ + S ⟶ Me₃GeNCS
+ BF₃Et₂O ⟶ Me₃GeCN·BF₃

GeC₄H₉NS

① Trimethylgermanium isothiocyanate
(CH₃)₃GeNCS

② $Me_3GeCN + S \xrightarrow[N_2]{170°}$ 90.5%

③ Colorless liq. (191.5~193°/760).
n_D 1.4960 (22°).

⑥ JOC **25**, 809 (1960).

GeC₄H₉I₃

① n-Butylgermanium triiodide
(n-C₄H₉)GeI₃

② $n-BuGeH_3 + I_2$ ⟶ 98%

③ Pale yellow liq. (119~121°/1). d 2.647.
Decomp. slightly at bp.

⑥ JACS **82**, 3016 (1960).

GeC₄H₁₀

① Trimethylgermane
(CH₃)₃GeH

② $(CH_3)_3GeCl + LiAlH_4 \xrightarrow{\text{ether or } Bu_2O}$
$(CH_3)_3GeCl + NaBH_4 \xrightarrow{THF}$

③ (26°/755.5). n_D 1.3890 (20°). d 1.0128
(20°/4°).

⑥ Izv. OKhN **1961**, 1758. Ann. chim.
6, 519 (1961). Dokl. **122**, 405 (1958).

GeC₄H₁₀Cl₂

① Diethylgermanium dichloride
(C₂H₅)₂GeCl₂

② $EtCl + Ge-Cu \; 1:1 \; alloy \xrightarrow{320°}$
$EtGeCl_3 + Et_2GeCl_2$

$Et_4Ge + GeCl_4 + AlCl_3 \xrightarrow{\text{refluxed 10 hrs}}$

③ Colorless liq. (175°/760). [−37°].
Sol. in org. solvents. Decompd. by
H₂O and NH₃.

④ + dry HBr ⟶ Et₂GeBr₂

⑥ JACS **69**, 1729 (1947).

GeC₄H₁₀Br₂

① Diethylgermanium dibromide
(C₂H₅)₂GeBr₂

② $(C_2H_5)_2GeCl_2 + dry \, HBr$ ⟶
$(C_2H_5)_4Ge + GeBr_4$
$+ AlBr_3 \xrightarrow{\text{refluxed 16 hrs}}$
$(C_2H_5)_4Ge + 2\% \, AlCl_3 + i\text{-PrBr}$
⟶ 86.6%

③ Liq. (202°/760, 82°/12). n_D 1.5272 (20°).
d 1.8811 (20°/4°).
Sol. in org. solvents. Decompd. by
H₂O.

⑥ Bull. soc. chim. France 1911 (1961) ;
2095 (1961). Izv. OKhN **1961**, 2095.

GeC₄H₁₁Cl

① Trimethylchloromethylgermane
(CH₃)₃GeCH₂Cl

② $CH_3MgBr + (CH_3)(CH_2Cl)GeCl_2$
$\xrightarrow{\text{ether}}$ 79.8%

③ (113~114°/761.5). n_D 1.4389 (25°).
d 1.189 (25°/4°).

⑥ JACS **77**, 907 (1955). Optika i Spekt-
roskopiya **13**, 68 (1962).

GeC₄H₁₂

① Tetramethylgermane
(CH₃)₄Ge

② $GeCl_4 + 2(CH_3)_2Zn \xrightarrow{0°}$ 100%
$GeCl_4 + 4CH_3MgX$ ⟶ 95%

③ Colorless liq. (43.2°/736). [−88°].
n_D 1.3863 (25°). d 0.9661 (20°/4°).
Sol. in ether ; insol. in H₂O.

⑥ Izv. OKhN **1961**, 1976. Spectrochim.
Acta **16**, 595 (1960). J. Res. Natl.

Bur. Standard **47**, 337 (1951); **49**, 235 (1952).

GeC₄H₁₂

① Diethylgermane
   $(C_2H_5)_2GeH_2$

② $(C_2H_5)_2GeBr_2 + LiAlH_4$
   $$\xrightarrow[\text{ether or Bu}_2\text{O}]{} 90\%$$

③ (74°/760). n_D1.4219 (20°). d1.0390 (20°/4°).

⑥ Izv. OKhN **1961**, 1758; **1941**, 1758. Ann. chim. (Paris) **6**, 519 (1961). Compt. rend. **249**, 131 (1959).

GeC₄H₁₂O

① Trimethylgermanium methoxide
   $(CH_3)_3GeOCH_3$

② $(CH_3)_3GeI + CH_3ONa \xrightarrow{\text{CH}_3\text{OH}} 56\%$

③ (87~88°/753, 91.1°/760). [−102.2°]. n_D1.401 (25°). d1.075 (25°/4°).

⑥ JACS **76**, 310 (1954).

GeC₄H₁₂O₂

① Dimethylgermanium dimethoxide
   $(CH_3)_2Ge(OCH_3)_2$

② $(CH_3)_2GeCl_2 + 2 CH_3ONa$
   $$\xrightarrow{\text{MeOH}} 77\%$$

③ (118~118.5°/763). n_D1.4093 (25°). d1.207 (25°/4°).

⑥ JACS **76**, 310 (1954).

GeC₄H₁₂O₃

① Methylgermanium trimethoxide
   $CH_3Ge(OCH_3)_3$

② $CH_3GeCl_3 + 3 CH_3ONa \xrightarrow{\text{CH}_3\text{OH}} 66\%$

③ (136.5~138°/760). n_D1.4053 (25°). d1.264 (25°/4°).

⑥ JACS **96**, 310 (1954)

GeC₄H₁₂O₄

① Tetramethoxygermane
   $(CH_3O)_4Ge$

② $GeCl_4 + 4 CH_3ONa \xrightarrow{\text{CH}_3\text{OH}} 21\%$
   $GeCl_4 + 4 CH_3OH \xrightarrow{\text{NH}_3 \text{ gas in benzene}}$

③ (145.5°/760). [−18], [23.5]. n_D1.3968 (25°). d1.3244 (25°/4°).

⑥ JACS **75**, 718 (1953). Chem. & Ind. (London) **1953**, 746. Z. anorg. allg. Chem. **275**, 193 (1954).

GeC₅H₈O₂

① Ethylgermanium triformate
   $C_2H_5Ge(OCOH)_3$

② $EtGeI_3 + Pb(OCOH)_2$ (powdered)
   $$\xrightarrow{\text{benzene}}$$

③ (118°/9). [13°]. n_D1.452 (20°). d1.617 (20°/4°).

⑥ JACS **74**, 2371 (1952).

GeC₅H₁₄

① Trimethylethylgermane
   $(CH_3)_3Ge(C_2H_5)$

② $C_2H_5GeI_3 + CH_3MgBr \longrightarrow$

③ (79~80°/760). n_D1.4090 (20°). d0.9843 (20°/4°).

⑥ Compt. rend. **246**, 1708 (1958).

GeC₆H₁₅Cl

① Triethylgermanium chloride
   $(C_2H_5)_3GeCl$

② $(Et_3Ge)_2O + Cl_2$ (or HCl) $\longrightarrow$ 100%
   $Et_4Ge + 2\% AlCl_3 + i\text{-}PrCl$
   $$\xrightarrow{\text{reflux}} 60\%$$

③ Colorless liq. (179.5°/760). n_D1.4650 (20°). d1.175 (20°/4°).
   Sol. in org. solvents. Decompd. by H_2O.

④ + dry HBr $\longrightarrow$ $(C_2H_5)_3GeBr$

⑥ JACS **79**, 326 (1957).

GeC₆H₁₀N₂S₂

① Diethylgermanium diisothiocyanate
   $(C_2H_5)_2Ge(NCS)_2$

② $[(C_2H_5)_2GeO]_{3 \text{ or } 4}$ + HNCS $\longrightarrow$ 80%

③ Mobile liq. (298°/760). [16°]. d 1.356 (20°).

   Easily sol. in 95% EtOH, acetone and petr. ether.

⑥ JACS **73**, 5439 (1951).

GeC₆H₁₂O₄

① Dimethylgermanium diacetate
   $(CH_3)_2Ge(OCOCH_3)_2$

② [Me₂GeO]₄ + excess
   $(CH_3CO)_2O$ $\xrightarrow{\text{reflux 1.5 hrs}}$

③ Easily supercooled to 10~15° without stirring. (188°/760, 94~95°/25). [50°].

⑥ JACS **74**, 2371 (1952).

GeC₆H₁₄

① Trimethylallylgermane
   $CH_2=CHCH_2Ge(CH_3)_3$

② $CH_2=CHCH_2GeCl_3 + CH_3MgBr \longrightarrow$ 42.5%

③ (121°/733). n_D 1.4416 (20°). d 0.9908 (20°/4°).

   IR: Optika i Spektroscopiya **13**, 68 (1962).

⑥ Izv. OKhN **1956**, 1146.

GeC₆H₁₄F₂

① Di-*n*-propylgermanium difluoride
   $(n\text{-}C_3H_7)_2GeF_2$

② $[(C_3H_7)_3Ge]_2O$ + 48% HF $\xrightarrow{\text{distillation}}$

③ (182.8°/764). [0.5°]. n 1.4128 (20°). d 1.248 (20°/4°).

⑥ JACS **74**, 2370 (1952).

GeC₆H₁₄F₂

① Diisopropylgermanium difluoride
   $(i\text{-}C_3H_7)_2GeF_2$

   $(i\text{-}C_3H_7)_2GeBr_2 + SbF_3$ $\xrightarrow{\text{heat 1 hr}}$

③ Musty, penetrating, obnoxious odor. Colorless liq. (174°/760). [−24°].

n_D 1.4146 (20°). d 1.222 (20°/4°).

⑥ JACS **75**, 814 (1953).

GeC₆H₁₄Cl₂

① Di-*n*-propylgermanium dichloride
   $(n\text{-}C_3H_7)_2GeCl_2$

② $[(n\text{-}Pr)_2GeO]_3$ + concd. HCl
   $\xrightarrow[\text{boiling}]{\text{heat to}}$ extracted with petr. ether

③ (209.5°/760). [−45°]. n_D 1.4725 (20°). d 1.275 (20°/4°).

⑥ JACS **74**, 2370 (1952).   JOC **17**, 1172 (1952).

GeC₆H₁₄Br₂

① Di-*n*-propylgermanium dibromide
   $(n\text{-}C_3H_7)_2GeBr_2$

② $[(n\text{-}Pr)_2GeO]_3$ + concd. HBr
   $\xrightarrow[\text{boiling}]{\text{heat to}}$ extracted with petr. ether

③ (240.5°/760). [−52°]. n_D 1.5173 (20°). d 1.6891 (20°/4°).

⑥ JACS **74**, 2370 (1952).

GeC₆H₁₄I₂

① Di-*n*-propylgermanium diiodide
   $(n\text{-}C_3H_7)_2GeI_2$

② $[(n\text{-}Pr)_2GeO]_3$ + 48% HI
   $\xrightarrow[\text{overnight}]{70°}$ extracted with petr.
   ether, 90%

③ (276.5°/760). [−53.5°]. d 2.024 (20°/4°).

⑥ JACS **74**, 2370 (1952).

GeC₆H₁₆

① Dimethyldiethylgermane
   $(CH_3)_2Ge(C_2H_5)_2$

② $(C_2H_5)_2GeF_2 + CH_3MgBr \longrightarrow$

③ (108~109°/760). n_D 1.4221(20°). d 0.9885 (20°/4°).

⑥ Compt. rend. **246**, 1708 (1958).

GeC₆H₁₆

① Triethylgermane

   $(C_2H_5)_3GeH$

② $Et_3GeX + LiAlH_4 \longrightarrow$

③ Colorless liq. $(125°/760)$.

   Sol. in org. solvents; insol. in H_2O.

④ Adds to double bond.

   $Et_3GeH + CH_2=CHCN$

   $\longrightarrow Et_3GeCH_2CH_2CN$

   $Et_3GeH + CH_2N_2 \xrightarrow{UV} Et_3GeMe$

⑥ JACS **74**, 2683 (1952). Angew. **74**, 468

   (1962).   Izv. OKhN **1961**, 1758.

GeC₇H₁₅N

① Triethylgermanium cyanide

   $(C_2H_5)_3GeCN$

② $[(C_2H_5)_3Ge]_2O + HCN \longrightarrow$

③ Colorless mobile liq. $(213°/760)$. $[18°]$.

   $n_D1.4509$ $(20°)$. $d1.111$ $(20°/4°)$.

   Easily sol. in 95% EtOH, aceton and

   petr. ether.

   Odor like that of HCN.

④ $+ AgNCS \xrightarrow{reflux} 65\%$ Et_3GeNCS

   $+ 35\%$ Et_3GeCN

⑥ JACS **73**, 5439 (1951).

GeC₇H₁₅NS

① Triethylgermanium isothiocyanate

   $(C_2H_5)_3GeNCS$

② $[Et_3Ge]_2O + HNCS \xrightarrow{ether} 80\%$

③ Mobile liq. $(252°/760)$. $[-46°]$.

   $n_D1.517$ $(20°)$. $d1.184$ $(20°/4°)$.

   Easily sol. in 95% EtOH, aceton and

   petr. ether.

④ $Et_3GeNCS + AgNCO$

   $\xrightarrow{reflux} Et_3GeNCO$ (90%)

⑥ JACS **73**, 5439 (1951).

GeC₇H₁₈

① Triethylmethylgermane

② $(C_2H_5)_3Ge(CH_3)$

$(C_2H_5)_3GeI + CH_3MgBr \longrightarrow$

$(C_2H_5)_3GeH + CH_2N_2 \xrightarrow{UV}$

③ $(135°/760)$. $n_D1.4332$ $(20°)$. $d0.9906$

   $(20°/4°)$.

⑥ Compt. rend. **246**, 1708 (1958).

   Angew. **74**, 468 (1962).

GeC₈H₁₂

① Tetravinylgermane

   $(CH_2=CH)_4Ge$

② $CH_2=CHMgBr + GeCl_4$

   $\xrightarrow{\text{reflux 20hrs in THF}} 35.4\%$

③ $(52{\sim}54°/27)$. $n_D1.4676$ $(25°)$. $d1.040$

   $(25°)$.

⑥ JACS **79**, 2738 (1957) .   Izv. OKhN

   1961, 2132.

GeC₈H₁₄O₆

① Ethylgermanium triacetate

   $C_2H_5Ge(OCOCH_3)_3$

② $EtGeI_3 + 30\%$ excess $Ag(OCOCH_3)$

   $\xrightarrow{\text{reflux 1hr in dry berzene}}$

③ $(249°/760, 99{\sim}101°/1)$. $n_D1.444$ $(20°)$.

   $d1.393$ $(20°/4°)$.

⑥ JACS **74**, 2371 (1952).

GeC₈H₁₆

① Dimethyldiallylgermane

   $(CH_3)_2Ge(CH_2CH=CH_2)_2$

② $(CH_3)_2GeCl_2 + 2CH_2=CHCH_2MgBr$

   $\longrightarrow 42\%$

③ $(149°/737)$. $n_D1.4645$ $(20°)$. $d1.0337$

   $(20°/4°)$.

⑥ Izv. OKhN. **1956**, 1146.   Zhur. **2**, 562

   (1961).

GeC₈H₁₇ClO₂

① Triethylgermanium monochloro-

   acetate

   $(C_2H_5)_3GeOCOCH_2Cl$

② $(Et_3Ge)_2O + ClCH_2COOH \xrightarrow{100°}$

③ Colorless liq. (234°/760). n_D1.4672
(20°). d1.243 (20°/4°).
Sol. in org. solvents.
⑥ JOC **20**, 900 (1955).

GeC₈H₁₈F₂

① Di-*n*-butylgermanium difluoride
(n-C₄H₉)₂GeF₂
② (n-C₄H₉)₂GeBr₂ + SbF₃
$\longrightarrow$ (C₄H₉)₂GeF₂ (99%)
③ (216°/760). [10°]. n_D1.4222 (20°).
d1.183 (20°/4°).
⑥ JACS **83**, 547 (1961).

GeC₈H₂₀

① Tetraethylgermane
(C₂H₅)₄Ge
② 3 GeCl₄ + 4 (C₂H₅)₃Al $\longrightarrow$ 72.9%
③ Colorless. liq. (163.5°/760). [−92.7°].
n_D1.4430 (20°). d0.9932 (20°/4°).
Sol. in ether ; insol. in H₂O.
④ Et₄Ge + GeBr₃ + AlBr₃
$\xrightarrow[\text{refluxed, 16 hrs}]{}$ (C₂H₅)₂GeBr₂
⑤ Catalysts for low-pressure polymn.
of C₂H₄ used with AlBr₃, AlCl₃,
VBr₃ or VCl₄.
⑥ Dokl. **144**, 1299 (1962).

GeC₈H₂₀O₄

① Tetraethoxygermane
(C₂H₅O)₄Ge
② GeCl₄ + 4 C₂H₅ONa $\xrightarrow[]{\text{C}_2\text{H}_5\text{OH}}$ 65%
GeCl₄ + 4 C₂H₅OH $\xrightarrow[]{\text{NH}_3\text{ gas in benzene}}$
③ Liq. (185.5°/760). [−72°]. n_D1.4061
(20°). d1.1288 (25°/4°).
Sol. in org. solvents ; Decompd. in
H₂O.
⑥ JCS **1958**, 3746 ; **1956**, 4916.   Chem. &
Ind. (London) **1953**, 746.   JACS **78**,
718 (1953).

GeC₈H₂₄N₄

① Tetrakis(dimethylamino)germane

[(CH₃)₂N]₄Ge
② GeBr₄ + (CH₃)₂NH in excess
$\xrightarrow[\text{cyclohexane}]{-60°}$ 80%
③ Colorless liq. (203°/760, 87~89°/15).
[14°]. d1.069 (22°/4°).
⑥ JACS **74**, 1421 (1952).

GeC₉H₁₉N

① Triethylcyanoethylgermane
(C₂H₅)₃GeCH₂CH₂CN
② Et₃GeH + CH₂=CH−CN $\xrightarrow[]{\text{reflux}}$
③ (225~227°/760).
⑥ Compt. rend. **247**, 471 (1958).   Ann.
chim. (Paris) **6**, 519 (1961).

GeC₉H₂₀O

① γ-(Triethylgermyl)propionaldehyde
(C₂H₅)₃GeCH₂CH₂CHO
② (C₂H₅)₃GeH + CH₂=CH−CHO
$\xrightarrow[]{\text{Bz}_2\text{O}_2\text{ or Pt}}$ 60%
③ (129~131°/17).
⑥ Compt. rend. **247**, 471 (1958).

GeC₉H₂₁Cl

① Tri-*n*-propylgermanium chloride
(n-C₃H₇)₃GeCl
② (n-Pr₃Ge)₂O + Cl₂ (or HCl)
$\longrightarrow$ 100%
③ (227°/760). [−70°]. n_D1.464 (20°).
d1.100 (20°/4°).
⑥ JACS **73**, 5440 (1951).

GeC₉H₂₂

① Triethyl-*n*-propylgermane
(C₂H₅)₃Ge(n-C₃H₇)
② (C₂H₅)₃GeI + n-C₃H₇MgBr $\longrightarrow$
③ (73~74°/20). n_D1.4660 (20°). d0.9810
(20°/4°).
⑥ Compt. rend. **246**, 1708 (1958).

GeC₉H₂₂

① Tri-*n*-propylgermane
   (*n*-C₃H₇)₃GeH

② GeCl₄ + *n*-PrLi $\xrightarrow{i\text{-Pr}_2\text{O}}$

③ Colorless liq. (183°/742). n_D1.4340
   (20°). d1.0030 (20°/4°).

⑥ JOC **17**, 1172 (1952).   Ann. chim.
   (Paris) **6**, 579 (1961).

GeC₉H₂₂O

① Triethyl(3-hydroxypropyl)germane
   (C₂H₅)₃GeCH₂CH₂CH₂OH

② (C₂H₅)₃GeH + CH₂=CHCH₂OH
   $\xrightarrow[\text{in PrOH}]{\text{H}_2\text{PtCl}_6\cdot6\text{H}_2\text{O}}$ 73%

③ (89~90°/3). n_D1.4695 (20°). d1.0775.

⑥ Dokl. **136**, 1107 (1961).

GeC₁₀H₁₆

① Trimethylbenzylgermane
   (CH₃)₃GeCH₂C₆H₅

② C₆H₅CH₂GeCl₃ + 3 CH₃MgCl ⟶

③ (94~95°/28). n_D1.5140 (20°). d1.1011
   (20°/4°).

⑥ Izv. OKhN **1960**, 2066.

GeC₁₀H₂₀O₄

① Di-*n*-propylgermanium diacetate
   (*n*-C₃H₇)₂Ge(OCOCH₃)₂

② (*n*-Pr₂GeO)₃ + (CH₃CO)₂O in excess
   $\xrightarrow{\text{reflux 3 hrs}}$

③ Colorless liq. (244.6°/760). [35.6°].
   Sol. in org. solvents. Decompd. by
   H₂O.

⑥ JACS **74**, 2370 (1952).

GeC₁₀H₂₁N

① Tri-*n*-propylgermanium cyanide
   (*n*-C₃H₇)₃GeCN

② (*n*-Pr₃Ge)₂O + HCN ⟶

③ Odor of HCN.
   Colorless mobile liq. (253°/760).

[−13]. n_D1.4544 (20°). d1.041
(20°/4°).
Sol. in 95% EtOH, acetone and petr.
ether.

⑥ JACS **73**, 5439 (1951).   JOC **22**, 1009
(1957).   Izv. OKhN **1957**, 124.

GeC₁₀H₂₁NO

① Tri-*n*-propylgermanium isocyanate
   (*n*-C₃H₇)₃GeNCO

② (*n*-Pr)₃GeCl + AgNCO $\xrightarrow{\text{CH}_3\text{NO}_2,\ \text{C}_6\text{H}_6}$

③ Colorless liq. (238°, 247°). [−19°].
   n1.4602(20°). n_D1.4572(20°). d1.097,
   1.055 (20°/4°).
   Sol. in org. solvents.

⑥ JACS **73**, 5440 (1951).   JOC **20**, 536
(1955).

GeC₁₀H₂₁NS

① Tri-*n*-propylgermanium isothiocyanate
   (*n*-C₃H₇)₃GeNCS

② (*n*-Pr₃Ge)₂O + HSCN $\xrightarrow{\text{ether}}$ 80%

③ Mobile liq. (287°/760). [−50°].
   n_D1.5063 (20°). d1.105 (20°/4°).
   Sol. in 95% EtOH, acetone and petr.
   ether.

④ JACS **73**, 5439 (1951).

GeC₁₀H₂₂O₂

① Tri-*n*-propylgermanium formate
   (*n*-C₃H₇)₃GeOCOH

② (*n*-Pr₃Ge)₂O + 90% HCOOH ⟶

③ Penetrating odor.
   Colorless ; liquid. (233°/760). n1.4505
   (20°). d1.094 (20°/4°).

④ Hydrolyzed rapidly in 95% ethanolic
   sodium hydroxide solution.
   + CHCl₂COOH ⟶
   n-Pr₃Ge(OCOCHCl₂)
   + CH₂ClCOOH ⟶
   n-Pr₃Ge(OCOCH₂Cl)

⑥ JACS **73**, 5798 (1951).

GeC$_{10}$H$_{24}$

① Triethyl-*n*-butylgermane
(C$_2$H$_5$)$_3$Ge(*n*-C$_4$H$_9$)

② Et$_3$GeCl + *n*-C$_4$H$_9$Li $\xrightarrow{\text{ether}}$ 56.1%

③ (180~181.5°/760.7). n_D1.4475 (20°).
d0.9777 (20°/4°).

⑥ JOC **24**, 352 (1959).   Compt. rend.
246, 1708 (1958).

GeC$_{11}$H$_{20}$

① Triethylcyclopentadienylgermane
(C$_2$H$_5$)$_3$GeC$_5$H$_5$

② Et$_3$GeBr + C$_5$H$_5$MgBr $\longrightarrow$ 67%

③ (105°/16). n_D1.5029 (20°). d1.0740
(20°/4°).

④ (C$_2$H$_5$)$_3$GeC$_5$H$_5$ + H$_2$
$\xrightarrow{\text{atmospheric pressure}}$ (C$_2$H$_5$)$_3$GeC$_5$H$_5$

+ Br$_2$ $\longrightarrow$

(C$_2$H$_5$)$_3$GeBr + polymeric residue
+ maleic anhydride $\longrightarrow$
Diels–Alder deriv. (mp 49~50°)

⑥ Compt. rend. **255**, 544 (1962).   Izv.
OKhN **1962**, 1387.

GeC$_{11}$H$_{20}$O$_6$

① Ethylgermanium tripropionate
(C$_2$H$_5$)Ge(OCOC$_2$H$_5$)$_3$

② EtGeCl$_3$ + 30% excess AgOCOC$_2$H$_5$
$\xrightarrow{\text{dry benzene, reflux in ether}}$ 95%

③ (256°/760, 114~6°/2). n_D1.4434 (20°).
d1.271 (20°/4°).

⑥ JACS **74**, 2371 (1952).

GeC$_{11}$H$_{24}$O$_2$

① Tri-*n*-propylgermanium acetate
(*n*-C$_3$H$_7$)$_3$GeOCOCH$_3$

② [(*n*-C$_3$H$_7$)$_3$Ge]$_2$O +
glacial CH$_3$COOH $\longrightarrow$

③ Colorless liq. (236°/760). n_D1.4464
(20°). d1.071 (20°/4°).

④ Hydrolyzed rapidly in 95% ethanolic
sodium hydroxide solution.

⑥ JACS **73**, 5798 (1951).

GeC$_{11}$H$_{26}$

① Trimethylamylgermane
(C$_2$H$_5$)$_3$GeC$_5$H$_{11}$

② Et$_3$GeCl + C$_5$H$_{11}$MgBr $\longrightarrow$

③ (104~105°/20). n_D1.4495 (20°). d0.9625
(20°/4°).

⑥ Compt. rend. **246**, 1708 (1958).

GeC$_{12}$H$_{10}$Cl$_2$

① Diphenylgermanium dichloride
(C$_6$H$_5$)$_2$GeCl$_2$

② PhCl + Ge $\xrightarrow{\text{20wt\% Ag 440°}}$
PhGeCl$_3$ + Ph$_2$GeCl$_2$

③ Colorless liq. [9°].
Sol. in org. solvents; Decompd. by
H$_2$O.

⑥ JACS **69**, 1729 (1947).

GeC$_{12}$H$_{10}$O

① Poly(diphenylgemanium oxide)
[(C$_6$H$_5$)$_2$GeO]$_n$

② Ph$_2$GeBr$_2$ $\xrightarrow{\text{OH}^-}$

③ [238~298°].

④ $\underset{\text{OH}^-}{\overset{\text{HBr}}{\rightleftharpoons}}$ (C$_6$H$_5$)$_2$GeBr$_2$
+ AcOH $\longrightarrow$ [(C$_6$H$_5$)$_2$GeO]$_4$

⑥ JACS **82**, 3324 (1960).

GeC$_{12}$H$_{10}$I$_2$

① Diphenylgermanium diiodide
(C$_6$H$_5$)$_2$GeI$_2$

② GeI$_2$ + Ph$_2$Hg $\longrightarrow$
PhGeI$_3$ + Ph$_2$GeI$_2$ + Ph$_3$GeI
(40~70%)

③ [68~69°].

⑥ Izv. OKhN **1962**, 53.

GeC₁₂H₁₂

① Diphenylgermane
   (C₆H₅)₂GeH₂

② Ph₂GeBr₂ + LiAlH₄ $\xrightarrow[\text{ether}]{}$ 55%

③ Colorless liq. (93°/1). n_D 1.5921 (25°).
   Sol. in ether.

④ + CH₂N₂ $\longrightarrow$ Ph₂GeHMe
   + Ph₂GeMe₂

⑥ JACS 72, 5564 (1950).   Angew. 74,
   468 (1962).

GeC₁₂H₁₉Cl

① Triethyl-*p*-chlorophenylgermane
   (C₂H₅)₃Ge(C₆H₄Cl-*p*)

② Et₃GeBr + *p*-Cl-C₆H₄MgBr
   $\xrightarrow[\text{in ether}]{\text{reflux 6 hrs}}$ 60%

③ (130°/6). n_D 1.5287.

⑥ JCS 1960, 3200.

GeC₁₂H₂₂N₂

① Di-*n*-propyl-biscyanoethylgermane
   (*n*-C₃H₇)₂Ge(CH₂CH₂CN)₂

② *n*-Pr₂GeH₂ + CH₂=CHCN
   $\xrightarrow{\text{in sealed tube, 150°}}$

③ (140°/0.4). n_D 1.4802 (20°). d 1.1058
   (20°/4°).

⑥ Compt. rend. 247, 471 (1958).   Ann.
   chim. (Paris) 6, 519 (1961).

GeC₁₂H₂₅N

① Tri-*n*-propylcyanoethylgermane
   (*n*-C₃H₇)₃GeCH₂CH₂CN

② (*n*-C₃H₇)₃GeH + CH₂=CH−CN
   $\xrightarrow{\text{150° in sealed tube, 24 hrs}}$ 42%

③ (152°/11). n_D 1.4645 (20°). d 1.026 (20°).

⑥ Ann. chim. (Paris) 6, 519 (1961).

GeC₁₂H₂₈

① Diethyldi-*n*-butylgermane
   (C₂H₅)₂Ge(*n*-C₄H₉)₂

② (C₂H₅)₂GeI₂ + 2 *n*-C₄H₉MgBr $\longrightarrow$

③ (109~110°/14). n_D 1.4516 (20°). d 0.9547
   (20°).

⑥ Compt. rend. 246, 1708 (1958).

GeC₁₂H₂₈O

① Tri-*n*-propyl-γ-hydroxypropyl
   germane
   (*n*-C₃H₇)₃GeCH₂CH₂CH₂OH

② (*n*-C₃H₇)₃GeH + CH₂=CHCH₂OH
   $\longrightarrow$ 62%

③ (175~180°/20). n 1.4715 (20°). d 1.0327
   (20°/4°).

⑥ Ann. chim. (Paris) 6, 519 (1961).
   Compt. rend. 247, 471 (1958).

GeC₁₃H₂₂

① Triethylbenzylgermane
   (C₂H₅)₃GeCH₂C₆H₅

② (C₂H₅)₃GeCl + C₆H₅CH₂MgBr
   $\xrightarrow[\text{ether}]{}$ 79%

③ (78~80°/11). n_D 1.5178 (20°).

⑥ JOC 24, 352 (1959).

GeC₁₃H₂₂

① Triethyl-*p*-tolylgermane
   (C₂H₅)₃Ge(*p*-CH₃C₆H₄)

② (C₂H₅)₃GeBr + CH₃C₆H₄MgBr
   $\xrightarrow[\text{ether}]{}$ 65%

③ (136°/16). n 1.5134 (20°).

⑥ JCS 1960, 3200.

GeC₁₃H₂₇NO

① Tri-*n*-butylgermanium isocyanate
   (*n*-C₄H₉)₃GeNCO

② (*n*-Bu)₃GeCl + AgNCO $\xrightarrow{\text{CH₃NO₂, C₆H₆}}$

③ Colorless liquid. (283°/760). [−47°].
   n_D 1.4595 (20°). d 1.044 (20°).
   Sol. in org. solvent.

⑥ JACS 73, 5800 (1951).

GeC13H27NS

① Tri-*n*-butylgermanium isothiocyanate
(*n*-C4H9)3GeNCS

② [(*n*-Bu)3Ge]2O + HNCS $\xrightarrow{\text{ether}}$ 80%

③ Mobile liq. (319°/760). n_D1.5039 (20°).
d1.071 (20°).
Easily sol. in 95% EtOH, acetone
and petr. ether.

⑥ JACS **73**, 5439 (1951).

GeC13H28O2

① Tri-*n*-butylgermanium formate
(*n*-C4H9)3GeOCOH
[(*n*-Bu)3Ge]2O + 90% HCOOH $\longrightarrow$

③ Colorless liq. (267°/760). n_D1.4538
(20°). d1.051 (20°).

⑥ JACS **73**, 5800 (1951).

GeC14H30O2

① Tri-*n*-butylgermanium acetate
(*n*-C4H9)3GeOCOCH3

② (*n*-Bu)3GeI + AgOCOCH3 $\xrightarrow{\text{benzene}}$

③ Colorless liquid. (272°/760). n_D1.4514
(20°). d1.027 (20°/4°).

④ + C6H13COOH
$\longrightarrow$ (*n*-Bu)3Ge(OCOC6H13)

⑥ JACS **73**, 5800 (1951).

GeC14H30Br2

① Tri-*n*-butyl-1,2-dibromoethyl-
germane
(*n*-C4H9)3GeCHBrCH2Br

② (*n*-C4H9)3GeCH=CH2 + Br2 $\longrightarrow$

③ (147°/0.5). n_D1.5102 (20°). d1.3619
(20°/4°).

⑥ Compt. rend. **248**, 2018 (1959).

GeC14H35N

① Tri-*n*-butyl-*γ*-aminopropylgermane
(*n*-C4H9)3GeCH2CH2CH2NH2

② (*n*-Bu)3GeH + CH2=CHCH2NH2

$\longrightarrow$ 74%
(C4H9)3GeCH2CH2CN + LiAlH4 $\longrightarrow$

③ (161°/10). n_D1.4700 (20°). d0.9816
(20°).

⑥ Ann. chim. (Paris) **6**, 519 (1961).

GeC15H31N

① Tri-*n*-butylcyanoethylgermane
(*n*-C4H9)3GeCH2CH2CN

② (*n*-Bu)3GeH + CH2=CH−CN $\xrightarrow[\text{refluxed}]{\text{5 hrs}}$

③ (168~9°/11). n_D1.4660 (20°). d0.09947
(20°).

⑥ Ann. chim. (Paris) **6**, 519 (1961).
Compt. rend. **247**, 471 (1958).

GeC16H34O

① Tri-*n*-butyl-*γ*-hydroxypropyl-
germane
(*n*-C4H9)3GeCH2CH2CH2OH

② (*n*-Bu)3GeH + CH2=CHCH2OH
$\xrightarrow[\text{or Pt}]{\text{Bz}_2\text{O}_2}$ 67%

③ (153~155°/3). n_D1.4717 (20°). d0.999
(20°/4°).

⑥ Ann. chim. (Paris), **6**, 519 (1961).
Compt. rend. **247**, 471 (1958).

GeC16H36

① Tetra-*n*-butylgermane
(*n*-C4H9)4Ge

② BuMgX + GeBr4 $\xrightarrow{\text{ether}}$ 74%

③ Colorless liq. (278°/760). n_D1.4571
(20°). d0.934 (20°/4°).
Sol. in org. solvents; insol. in H2O.

④ + GeCl4 $\xrightarrow{\text{AlCl}_3\ 120\sim200°}$ Bu2GeCl2
+ GeBr4 $\xrightarrow{\text{AlBr}_3,\ \text{refluxed 16 hrs}}$
Bu2GeBr2

⑥ JACS **73**, 5800 (1951). Rec. trav.
chim. **81**, 764 (1962).

GeC$_{16}$H$_{40}$N$_4$

① Tetrakis(diethylamino)germane
    [(C$_2$H$_5$)$_2$N]$_4$Ge

② GeBr$_4$ + Et$_2$NH in excess

$$\xrightarrow[\text{cycohexane}]{25°} \quad 45\%$$

③ Colorless liq. (108~110°/2). n_D 1.4726
    (20°). d 1.215 (22°/4°).

⑥ JACS **74**, 142 (1952).

GeC$_{17}$H$_{32}$

① Tri-*n*-butylcyclopentadienylgermane
    (*n*-C$_4$H$_9$)$_3$GeC$_5$H$_5$

② (*n*-C$_4$H$_9$)$_3$GeBr + BrMgC$_5$H$_5$ $\longrightarrow$

③ (109°/0.4). n_D 1.4942 (29°). d 1.0115
    (20°/4°).

⑥ Compt. rend. **255**, 544 (1962).

GeC$_{18}$H$_{15}$I

① Triphenylgermanium iodide
    (C$_6$H$_5$)$_3$GeI

② GeI$_2$ + (C$_6$H$_5$)$_2$Hg $\longrightarrow$ C$_6$H$_5$GeI$_3$
    + (C$_6$H$_5$)$_2$GeI$_2$ + (C$_6$H$_5$)$_3$GeI
    (40~70%)   (37%)

③ [155~157°].

⑥ Izv. OKhN **1962**, 53.

GeC$_{18}$H$_{15}$Na

① Triphenylgermanium sodium
    (C$_6$H$_5$)$_3$GeNa

② Ph$_4$Ge + Na $\xrightarrow{\text{liq. NH}_3}$

   Ph$_3$GeGePh$_3$ + Na $\xrightarrow{\text{liq. NH}_3}$

③ Sol. in liq. NH$_3$; fairly sol. in ether
    and C$_6$H$_6$.

④ + O$_2$ $\longrightarrow$ (C$_6$H$_5$)$_3$GeONa
    + H$_2$O $\longrightarrow$ (C$_6$H$_5$)$_3$GeH
    + (C$_6$H$_5$)$_3$GeF $\longrightarrow$ [(C$_6$H$_5$)$_3$Ge]$_2$
    + *n*-C$_3$H$_7$Br $\longrightarrow$ (C$_6$H$_5$)$_3$GeC$_3$H$_7$
    + NaBr

⑥ JACS **49**, 457 (1927); **55**, 4694 (1933);
    74, 1418 (1952).

GeC$_{18}$H$_{16}$

① Triphenylgermane
    (C$_6$H$_5$)$_3$GeH

② (C$_6$H$_5$)$_3$GeBr + LiAlH$_4$ $\xrightarrow{\text{ether}}$ 79.5%

③ Translucent, flaky crystals. α [47°],
    β [27°].
    Recrystd. from MeOH.
    Sol. in ether.

④ (C$_6$H$_5$)$_3$GeH + C$_6$H$_5$Li $\longrightarrow$
    (C$_6$H$_5$)$_3$GeLi
    (C$_6$H$_5$)$_3$GeH + (C$_6$H$_5$)$_3$GeLi $\longrightarrow$
    (C$_6$H$_5$)$_3$GeGe(C$_6$H$_5$)$_3$
    (C$_6$H$_5$)$_3$GeH + Cl$_2$ $\longrightarrow$ (C$_6$H$_5$)$_3$GeCl

⑥ JACS **72**, 5566 (1950).

GeC$_{18}$H$_{42}$O$_4$S

① Bis(tri-*n*-propylgermanium) sulfate
    [(*n*-C$_3$H$_7$)$_3$Ge]$_2$SO$_4$

② (C$_3$H$_7$)$_3$GeOCOC$_2$H$_5$ + 100% H$_2$SO$_4$ $\longrightarrow$

③ Colorless liq. (370°/760, 180~182°/1),
    d 1.186 (20°/4°).

④ Hydrolyzed rapidly in 95% ethano-
    lic sodium hydroxide soln.

⑥ JACS **73**, 5798 (1951).

GeC$_{19}$H$_{17}$Cl

① Triphenylchloromethylgermane
    (C$_6$H$_5$)$_3$GeCH$_2$Cl

② ClCH$_2$GeCl$_3$ + C$_6$H$_5$MgBr $\xrightarrow{\text{ether}}$ 76%

③ [117.5~118.5°].

⑥ JACS **79**, 342 (1957).

GeC$_{19}$H$_{18}$O

① Triphenylgermanium methoxide
    (C$_6$H$_5$)$_3$GeOCH$_3$

② (C$_6$H$_5$)$_3$GeOCOCH$_3$ $\xrightarrow{250°}$ 73%

   (C$_6$H$_5$)$_3$GeX + NaOCH$_3$ $\xrightarrow{\text{heat}}$ 97%

③ White crystals. [59~62°, 66~67°].
    Slightly sol. in org. solvents.

⑥ JACS **77**, 4827 (1955).

GeC$_{21}$H$_{19}$N

① Triphenyl-2-cyanoethylgermane

(C$_6$H$_5$)$_3$GeCH$_2$CH$_2$CN

(C$_6$H$_5$)$_3$GeH + CH$_2$=CHCN

$\xrightarrow{50\sim60°}$ 83%

③ [126～129°].

⑥ JOC **26**, 2229 (1961).

GeC$_{22}$H$_{22}$O$_2$

① Triphenyl-2-carbomethoxyethyl-germane

(C$_6$H$_5$)$_3$GeCH$_2$CH$_2$COOCH$_3$

② (C$_6$H$_5$)$_3$GeH + CH$_2$=CH$_2$COOCH$_3$

$\xrightarrow{59\sim69°}$ 50%

③ [62～62.5°].

⑥ JOC **26**, 2299 (1961).

GeC$_{23}$H$_{20}$

① Triphenylcyclopentadienylgermane

(C$_6$H$_5$)$_3$GeC$_5$H$_5$

② (C$_6$H$_5$)$_3$GeBr + C$_5$H$_5$MgBr $\longrightarrow$

③ [176～177°].

⑥ Compt. rend. **255**, 544 (1962).

GeC$_{24}$H$_{20}$

① Tetraphenylgermane

(C$_6$H$_5$)$_4$Ge

② GeBr$_4$ + (C$_6$H$_5$)$_2$Zn

$\xrightarrow{\text{boil 16hrs in toluene}}$ 95%

③ Colorless tetragonal crystals.
[235.7°].

Sol. in C$_6$H$_6$, toluene, CHCl$_3$, CCl$_4$,
CS$_2$ and CH$_3$COCH$_3$; slightly sol. in
alc., ether and petr. ether.

IR : J. Mol. Spectroscopy **17**, 427(1961)

④ + N-bromosuccinimide (1 : 1)

$\xrightarrow{\text{CCl}_4}$ [(C$_6$H$_5$)$_3$Ge]$_2$O + C$_6$H$_5$Br +
succinimide + (C$_6$H$_5$)$_4$Ge

+ N-bromosuccinimide (1 : 2)

$\longrightarrow$ succinimide + (C$_6$H$_5$)$_2$GeO

⑤ Catalysts with AlCl$_3$, AlBr$_3$, VBr$_3$ or
VCl$_5$ for low pressure pelymerisa-
tion of C$_2$H$_4$.

⑥ JACS **49**, 4675 (1955) ; **49**, 457 (1927).
J. Mol. Spectroscopy **7**, 427 (1961).
Spectrochim. Acta **18**, 21 (1962).

GeC$_{28}$H$_{26}$N$_2$

① 5,5′-Diethyl-10,10′-spiro(5,10-dihy-
drophenazagermine)

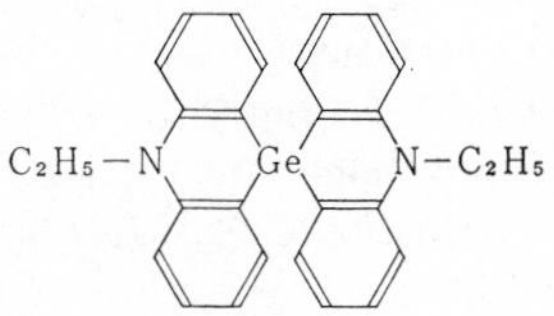

$$C_2H_5-N \quad Ge \quad N-C_2H_5$$

② $C_2H_5-N\begin{matrix}Li\\Li\end{matrix}$ + GeCl$_4$

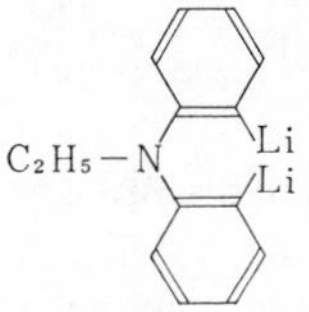

$\xrightarrow{\text{ether}}$ 18.1%

③ Colorless needles. [212～214°].
Recrystd. from ethyl acetate.

⑥ JACS **82**, 2522 (1960).

Ge$_2$C$_6$H$_{18}$

① Hexamethyldigermane

(CH$_3$)$_3$GeGe(CH$_3$)$_3$

② (CH$_3$)$_3$GeBr + K $\xrightarrow{\text{reflux}}$ 74%

③ (138°/758). [−40°]. n_D1.4564 (25°).
IR : JCS **1958**, 2811.

④ (CH$_3$)$_3$GeGe(CH$_3$)$_3$ + K

$\xrightarrow{\text{diglyme}}$ unidentified

⑥ JCS **1960**, 506.   Anal. Chem. **30**,
1689 (1958).

Ge$_2$C$_6$H$_{18}$O

① Hexamethyldigermoxane

[(CH$_3$)$_3$Ge]$_2$O

② 2 (CH$_3$)$_3$GeCl(gaseous) + Ag$_2$CO$_3$

$\longrightarrow$ [(CH₃)₃Ge]₂O (61%)

③ (129°/260). [−61.1°]. n_D 1.4712 (20°).
  IR ; 1236 cm⁻¹(m) δ_{sym}CH₃-(Ge),
  1408 (w), 1332 (vw) δ_{asym}CH₃-(Ge),
  612 (s), 572 (m)ν_{Ge-C}.
  Scectrochim. Acta **16**, 595 (1960).
⑥ Can. J. Chem. **39**, 339 (1961).

GeC₈H₂₀O₈S₂

① Diethylgermanium sulfate
  [(C₂H₅)₂GeSO₄]₂
② Et₂GeO + 100% H₂SO₄ $\longrightarrow$
  extrd. with boiling C₆H₆, 40%
③ White fluffy solid. [115.5〜116.5°].
  Sol. in C₆H₆, 21 g/l(17°), 38 g/l (23°),
  100 g/l (80°).
⑥ JACS **72**, 194 (1950).

Ge₂C₁₂H₂₈O₈S₂

① Di-*n*-propylgermanium sulfate
  [(*n*-C₃H₇)₂GeSO₄]₂
② (*n*-Pr)₂Ge(OCOCH₂Cl)₂ + 100% H₂SO₄
  $\xrightarrow[\text{17 mm}]{}$ 90%
③ Long needle-like crystals. [129°,
  115°].
  Sol. in org. solvents.
⑥ JACS **74**, 2370 (1952).

Ge₂C₁₂H₃₀

① Hexaethyldigermane
  (C₂H₅)₃GeGe(C₂H₅)₃
② EtLi + GeBr₄ $\xrightarrow{\text{Et₂O}}$ Et₃GeGeEt₃ (8%)
  + Et₄Ge (12%)
  Et₃GeBr + Na $\longrightarrow$
③ Colorless mobile liq. (61〜62°/0.007).
  n_D 1.4960 (20°).
  Sol. in ordinary org. solvents.
  Rather pleasant odor
④ (Et₃Ge)₂ + Br₂ $\longrightarrow$ Et₃GeBr
  (Et₃Ge)₂ + 2 Li $\longrightarrow$ Et₃GeLi
⑥ JOC **24**, 352 (1959). JACS **54**, 1635
  (1932).

Ge₂C₂₄H₂₀Br₂

① 1, 2-Dibromotetraphenyldigermane
  (C₆H₅)₂BrGeGeBr(C₆H₅)₂
② Ph₂GeBr₂ + Li−Hg $\longrightarrow$ 60%
③ [167〜169°].
  Recrystallized from C₆H₆.
⑥ JACS **82**, 3321 (1960).

Ge₂C₃₆H₃₀

① Hexaphenyldigermane
  (C₆H₅)₃GeGe(C₆H₅)₃
② (C₆H₅)₃GeBr + Na $\xrightarrow{\text{toluene}}$
③ White solid. [340〜341°].
  Sol. in CHCl₃ ; insol. in ether, org.
  solvents ; recrystd. from C₆H₅ and
  toluene.
  IR : Spectrochim. Acta **18**, 21 (1962).
④ (C₆H₅)₃GeGe(C₆H₅)₃ + Na-K
  $\xrightarrow{\text{THF}}$ (C₆H₅)₃GeNa
  Ph₃GeGePh₃ + Br₂ $\xrightarrow{\text{CCl₄}}$ Ph₃GeBr
  Ph₃GeGePh₃ + Li $\xrightarrow{\text{THF}}$ (C₆H₅)₃GeLi
⑥ JACS **74**, 1418 (1952) ; **72**, 5297 (1950) ;
  78, 5435 (1956) ; **77**, 5509 (1955).
  JOC **23**, 1582 (1958).

Ge₃C₄H₉Cl₃

① *n*-Butylgermanium trichloride
  (*n*-C₄H₉)GeCl₃
② GeCl₄ + *n*-C₄H₉MgCl $\xrightarrow{\text{ether}}$ 30%
③ (184°/760). n_D 1.4750 (20°). d 1.4520
  (20°/4°).
⑥ JACS **82**, 3016 (1960). Dokl. **138**,
  1107 (1961).

Ge₃C₆H₁₈S₃

① Hexamethylcyclotrigermanthiane
  [(CH₃)₂GeS]₃
② CH₃GeCl₂ in 6 N H₂SO₄
  $\xrightarrow{\text{H₂S}}$ precipitate (95%)

③ Waxy white solid. (302°/760). [5.5°].
Sol. in acetone.
⑥ JACS 70, 1801 (1948).

Ge₃C₃₆H₃₀O₃
① Hexaphenylcyclotrigermoxane
   $[(C_6H_5)_2GeO]_3$
② $[(C_6H_5)_2GeO]_n$ $\xrightarrow{\text{HI or NaOH}}$
③ (300°/2). [149°].
④ $[(C_6H_5)_2GeO]_3$ $\xrightarrow{\text{AcOH}}$ $[(C_6H_5)_2GeO]_4$
⑥ JACS 82, 3324 (1960).

Ge₄C₈H₂₄O₄
① Octamethylcyclotetragermoxane
   $[(CH_3)_2GeO]_4$
② $(CH_3)_2GeCl_2 + 2\,NaOH \longrightarrow$
   extracted with petr. ether 67%
③ [91~92°].
   Soluble in benzene.
   IR : 1237 cm⁻¹(m) $\delta_{sym}(CH_3-Ge)$.
④ $\underset{\text{in evacuated tube}}{\xrightarrow{210\sim220°,\ 24\,hrs}}$ $[(CH_3)_2GeO]_3$
⑥ JACS 82, 4166 (1960).   Spectrochim.
   Acta 16, 595 (1960).

Ge₄C₄₈H₄₀O₄
① Octaphenylcyclotetragermoxane
   $[(C_6H_5)_2GeO]_4$
② $[(C_6H_5)_2GeO]_n$ $\xrightarrow{\text{heat}}$
   $[(C_6H_5)_2GeO]_3$ $\xrightarrow{\text{AcOH}}$
③ White prisms. [218°].
   Slightly sol. in org. solvents.
④ $[(C_6H_5)_2GeO]_4 + HBr \longrightarrow$
   $(C_6H_5)_2GeBr_2$ $\underset{\text{AcOH}}{\overset{\text{EtOH(60)}+H_2O(40)}{\rightleftharpoons}}$
   $[(C_6H_5)_2GeO]_n$
⑥ JACS 82, 3324 (1960).

【Sn】

SnCH₃O₃/₂
① Methyltin oxide
   $(CH_3SnO_{3/2})_n$
② $SnCl_2 + CH_3Cl + NaOH \xrightarrow{H_2O} 83\%$
   $HSnOOK + CH_3I \longrightarrow$
③ Insol. in H₂O and most org. solvents.
   IR : Spectrochim. Acta 16, 595
   (1960).
⑥ Chem. Revs. 30, 459 (1960).

SnCH₃S₃/₂
① Methyltin sulfide
   $(CH_3SnS_{3/2})_n$
② $CH_3SnI_3 + H_2S(g)$ in H₂O
   (dil. HCl) $\longrightarrow$
③ Insol. in ether, alcohol, hydrocarbons and H₂O.
⑥ Chem. Revs. 16, 595 (1960)

SnCH₃Br₃
① Methyltin tribromide
   CH_3SnBr_3
② $MeSnO_{3/2} + 3\,HBr \longrightarrow$
③ (211°/760). [53°].
   IR : JACS 82, 3287 (1960).
⑥ Chem. Revs. 60, 459 (1960).

SnCH₃Cl₃
① Methyltin trichloride
   CH_3SnCl_3
② $SnCl_2 + MeCl \longrightarrow$
   $MeSnO_{3/2} + 3\,HCl \longrightarrow$
③ [45~46°, 42~43°].
   IR : JACS 82, 3287 (1960).
⑥ Chem. Revs. 60, 459 (1960).

SnCH₃I₃
① Methyltin triiodide
   CH_3SnI_3
② $Sn + MeI \xrightarrow{Mg} 20\%$

SnI₂ + MeI $\longrightarrow$
KSnCl₃ + MeI $\longrightarrow$
MeSnO₃/₂ + 3 HI $\longrightarrow$

③ (122~125°/5.5). [86.5°].
IR : JACS **82**, 3287 (1960)

⑤ Chem. Revs. **60**, 459 (1960). BCSJ
35, 208 (1962).

SnCH₆

① Methyltin trihydride
CH₃SnH₃

② 4 CH₃SnCl₃ + 3 NaBH₄ $\xrightarrow{H_2O}$

③ Gas. (1.4°/760).
Hydrolyzable.
IR : ν_{Sn-H} 1875 cm⁻¹. NMR : τ 5.86.

⑥ Chem. Revs. **60**, 459 (1960). JACS
85, 1377 (1963).

SnC₂H₃Cl₃

① Vinyltin trichloride
(CH₂=CH)SnCl₃

② (CH₂=CH)₄Sn + 3 SnCl₄ $\longrightarrow$
CH₂=CHMgCl + SnCl₄ $\longrightarrow$ 50%

③ (48~50°/5.2~5.3). (64~65°/15).
n_D 1.5361 (25°).

⑥ Chem. Revs. **60**, 459 (1960).

SnC₂H₅Cl₃

① Ethyltin trichloride
C₂H₅SnCl₃

② Et₄Sn + 3 SnCl₄ $\longrightarrow$

③ (181~184.5°/19), (196~198°/760).
[−10°]. n_D 1.5408 (20°). d 1.965 (20°).

④ + LiAlH₄ $\longrightarrow$ EtSnH₃

⑥ Chem. Revs. **60**, 459 (1960).

SnC₂H₆O

① Dimethyltin oxide
(CH₃)₂SnO

② Me₂SnX₂ + OH⁻(excess) $\longrightarrow$

③ White powder.
Insol. in org. solvents.
Polymer.

④ + HX $\longrightarrow$ Me₂SnX₂(X=Cl, Br, I)

+ PhOH $\longrightarrow$ PhOMe₂SnOSnMe₂OPh
+ Na₂S + 4 H⁺ $\longrightarrow$ Me₂SnS

⑥ Chem. Revs. **60**, 459 (1960).

SnC₂H₆S

① Dimethyltin sulfide
(CH₃)₂SnS

② Me₂SnCl₂ + H₂S(in water) $\longrightarrow$
Me₂SnO + Na₂S
+ H⁺(in water) $\longrightarrow$
Me₂SnO + CS₂ $\xrightarrow{140°,\ 26\,hrs}$ 95%

③ Colorless crystals. [149°].
Sol. in org. solvents.
NMR : Inorg. Chem. **3**, 943 (1964).
Trimer.

⑤ Stabilizer for vinyl resins and elastomers.

⑥ Chem. Revs. **60**, 459 (1960). JOC **26**,
4634 (1961). Inorg. Chem. **1**, 650
(1962).

SnC₂H₆Br₂

① Dimethyltin dibromide
(CH₃)₂SnBr₂

② Me₄Sn + SnBr₄ $\longrightarrow$
Sn + MeBr $\longrightarrow$
Me₂SnO + HBr $\longrightarrow$

③ (209°/760), (90~91°/4.5). [75~77°].
IR : JACS **82**, 3287 (1960)

④ + OH⁻(excess) $\longrightarrow$ Me₂SnO
+ OH⁻ + MeOH
$\longrightarrow$ BrMe₂SnOSnMe₂OMe
$\longrightarrow$ BrMe₂SnOSnMe₂OH
+ NR₃ $\longrightarrow$ Me₂SnBr₂·2 NR₃
+ H₂S $\longrightarrow$ Me₂SnS

⑥ Chem. Revs. **60**, 459 (1960).

SnC₂H₆Cl₂

① Dimethyltin dichloride
(CH₃)₂SnCl₂

② Sn + MeCl $\xrightarrow{Cu\ or\ Mg}$ 90%
Me₄Sn + SnCl₄ $\longrightarrow$
Me₂SnO + HCl $\longrightarrow$

③ (185~190°/760). [108°].

IR: Kogyo Kagaku Zasshi **64**, 541 (1961)

④ + OH⁻ —→ Me₂SnO

+ H₂S or Na₂S —→ Me₂SnS

+ OH⁻ + MeOH —→

ClMe₂SnOSnMe₂OMe,

CMe₂SnOSnMe₂OH

+ HCOOH + HCOONa —→

ClMe₂SnOOCH, Me₂Sn(OOCH)₂

⑥ Chem. Revs. **60** 459 (1960).   JACS **82**, 3287 (1960).

SnC₂H₆I₂

① Dimethyltin diiodide

(CH₃)₂SnI₂

② Me₂SnO + 2 HI —→

Sn + MeI $\xrightarrow{\text{Mg, BuOH}}$

③ (228°/760), (90~93°/6). [44°].

IR: JACS **82**, 3287 (1960).

④ + OH⁻ (excess) —→ Me₂SnO

+ OH⁻ + R'OH

—→ IMe₂SnOSnMe₂OR'

+ NR₃ —→ Me₂SnI₂·2 NR₃

H₂S —→ Me₂SnS

⑥ Chem. Revs. **60**, 459 (1960).   Kogyo Kagaku Zasshi **63**, 114, 1958 (1960).

SnC₂H₆Na₂

① Dimethyltin disodium

(CH₃)₂SnNa₂

② Me₂SnBr₂ + 4 Na(in liq. NH₃) —→

③ Exists in liq. NH₃. (red soln.)

④ + MeI —→ Me₄Sn

⑥ Chem. Revs. **60**, 459 (1960).

SnC₂H₈

① Dimethyltin dihydride

(CH₃)₂SnH₂

② Me₂SnCl₂ + LiAlH₄ $\xrightarrow{\text{dioxane}}$

③ (35°/760). n_D 1.4480 (20°). d 1.4766 (20°/4°).

IR: $\nu_{\text{Sn-H}}$ 1856 cm⁻¹. NMR: $\tau_{\text{Sn-H}}$

5.61.

④ + O₂ —→ Me₂SnO

+ HCl —→ Me₂SnCl₂

⑥ Chem. Revs. **60**, 459 (1960).   JACS **85**, 1377 (1963).   Can. J. Chem. **41**, 3005 (1963).

SnC₃H₇O₂Cl

① Dimethyltin chloride formate

Cl(CH₃)₂SnOOCH

② ClMe₂SnOSnMe₂Cl

+ 2 HCOOH —→

Me₂SnCl₂ + HCOOH

+ HCOONa —→

③ IR: JACS **82**, 3287 (1960).

④ + H₂O —→ ClMe₂SnOSnMe₂Cl

SnC₃H₉Br

① Trimethyltin bromide

(CH₃)₃SnBr

② Me₄Sn + Br₂ —→

③ (165°/760). [27°].

Sol. in org. solvents and H₂O.

IR: JACS **82**, 3287 (1960).

Raman: Z. anorg. allg. Chem. **308**, 212 (1961).

④ + OH⁻ —→ Me₃SnOH

⑥ Chem. Revs. **60**, 459 (1960).

SnC₃H₉Cl

① Trimethyltin chloride

(CH₃)₃SnCl

② Me₄Sn + HCl(g) —→

4 Me₄Sn + Me₂SnCl₂ + SnCl₄ —→ 70%

③ (154~156°/760). [37~32°, 42°].

Sol. in org. solvents and H₂O.

IR: JACS **82**, 3287 (1964).

Raman: Z. anorg. allg. Chem. **308**, 212 (1961).

④ + OH —→ Me₃SnOH

⑥ Chem. Revs. **60**, 459 (1960).

SnC₃H₉F

① Trimethyltin fluoride

(CH₃)₃SnF

② Me₃SnOH + HF $\longrightarrow$

③ Colorless needles.

Sol. in H₂O.

IR: JACS **82**, 3287 (1960). Z.

anorg. allg. Chem. **308**, 212 (1961).

X-ray: JCS **1964**, 2332.

SnC₃H₉I

① Trimethyltin iodide

(CH₃)₃SnI

② Me₄Sn + I₂ $\longrightarrow$

MeI + Sn $\xrightarrow{\text{Mg}}$

③ (67~68°/15). [3.4°]. n_D 1.5724 (20°).

d 1.1216 (28°/4°), 2.1205 (20°/4°).

Electron diffraction: Chem. Revs.

60, 459 (1960).

IR: JACS **82**, 3287 (1960).

⑥ BCSJ **35**, 208 (1962).

SnC₃H₉NO₃

① Trimethyltin nitrate

(CH₃)₃SnNO₃

② Me₃SnBr + AgNO₃ $\xrightarrow{\text{CH₃OH}}$

Me₃SnOH + HNO₃ $\xrightarrow{\text{H₂O}}$

Me₃SnNO₃·H₂O $\xrightarrow{\text{sublimation}}$

③ [140°].

Hygroscopic.

④ + H₂O $\longrightarrow$ Me₃SnNO₃·H₂O

+ 2 NH₃ $\longrightarrow$ Me₃SnNO₃·NH₃

⑥ Proc. Chem. Soc. **1963**, 13. Inorg.

Chem. **2**, 740 (1963). JOM **3**, 76

(1965).

SnC₃H₉N₃

① Trimethyltin azide

(CH₃)₃SnNNN

② Me₃SnCl + NaN₃ $\xrightarrow{\text{H₂O}}$ 61%

③ [120~121°].

Sol. in benzene.

IR, UV: Inorg. Chem. **3**, 889 (1964).

⑥ Chimia **16**, 10 (1962).   Rec. trav.

chim. **81**, 202 (1962).

SnC₃H₉Na

① Trimethyltin sodium

(CH₃)₃SnNa

② Me₃SnCl + 2 Na(in liq. NH₃) $\longrightarrow$

③ Exists in liq. NH₃ (pale yellow).

④ + RX $\longrightarrow$ Me₃SnR

(R=C₆H₅, ClC₆H₄, (C₂H₅)₃Sn,

C₆H₅CH₂ etc.)

⑥ Chem. Revs. **60**, 459 (1960).

SnC₃H₉O₄Cl

① Trimethyltin perchlorate

(CH₃)₃SnClO₄

② Me₃SnBr + AgClO₄ $\xrightarrow{\text{MeOH}}$

③ [125~127°].

Hygroscopic.

IR: Inorg. Chem. **2**, 740 (1963).

Proc. Chem. Soc. **1963**, 13.

④ + 2 NH₃(g) $\longrightarrow$ diammonia adduct

SnC₃H₉AsF₆

① Trimethyltin hexafluoroarsenate

Me₃SnAsF₆

② (CH₃)₃SnBr + AgAsF₆ $\xrightarrow{\text{liq. SO₂}}$

③ White crystals.

IR and ¹⁹F NMR: Inorg. Chem. **2**,

1020 (1963).

⑥ Proc. Chem. Soc. **1963**, 113.

SnC₃H₉BF₄

① Trimethyltin tetrafluoroborate

(CH₃)₃SnBF₄

② Me₃SnBr + AgBF₄ $\xrightarrow{\text{liq. SO₂}}$

Me₄Sn + BF₃ $\longrightarrow$

③ White crystals. [80°].

Hygroscopic.   Sol. in liq. SO₂.

IR and ¹⁹F NMR : Inorg. Chem. 2,
 1020 (1963).
⑥ Proc. Chem. Soc. 1963, 14.

SnC₃H₉F₆Sb
① Trimethyltin hexafluoroantimonate
 $(CH_3)_3SnSbF_6$
② $Me_3SnBr + AgSbF_6$
$$\xrightarrow{liq. SO_2}$$
③ White crystals.
 IR and ¹⁹F NMR : Inorg. Chem. 2,
 1020 (1963).
⑥ Proc. Chem. Soc. 1963, 113.

SnC₃H₁₀
① Trimethyltin hydride
 $(CH_3)_3SnH$
② $4 Me_3SnCl + LiAlH_4 \xrightarrow{dibutylether}$
$Me_3SnNa + NH_3 \xrightarrow{liq. NH_3}$
③ (59°/760).
 Slightly sol. in water.
 IR : ν_{Sn-H} 1380 cm⁻¹.
 NMR : τ_{H-Sn} 5.27.
④ $+ HCl \longrightarrow (CH_3)_3SnCl$
⑥ Chem. Revs. 60, 458 (1960). JACS
 85, 1377 (1963). Z. anorg. allg.
 Chem. 308, 212 (1961).

SnC₃H₁₀O
① Trimethyltin hydroxide

$(CH_3)_3SnOH,$ $\cdots\overset{\overset{\displaystyle CH_3}{|}}{\underset{\underset{\displaystyle CH_3}{|}}{Sn}}\cdots\overset{\displaystyle H}{O}\cdots\overset{\overset{\displaystyle CH_3}{|}}{\underset{\underset{\displaystyle CH_3}{|}}{Sn}}\cdots\overset{\displaystyle H}{O}\cdots$

② $Me_3SnX + OH^- (X=Cl, Br, I) \longrightarrow$
③ [118°]. >80° sublimes.
 Sol. in water and alc.
④ $+ CH_3COOH \longrightarrow Me_3SnOOCCH_3$
⑥ Chem. Revs. 60, 459 (1960). Z. anorg.
 allg. Chem. 315, 283 (1962). JOM
 1, 356 (1964).

SnC₄H₄Cl₄
① *trans*-Bis(2-chlorovinyl)tin-
 dichloride
 $(t\text{-}ClCH=CH)_2SnCl_2$
② $(t\text{-}ClCH=CH)_2Hg + SnCl_2 \longrightarrow 58\%$
③ [77.5~78.5°].
⑥ Chem. Revs. 60, 459 (1960).

SnC₄H₄Cl₄
① *cis*-Bis(2-chlorovinyl)tin dichloride
 $(cis\text{-}ClCH=CH)_2SnCl_2$
② $(cis\text{-}ClCH=CH)_2Hg + SnCl_2$
 $\longrightarrow 58\%$
③ (100~102°/3). n_D 1.5675. d 1.7494
 (20°/4°).
⑥ Chem. Revs. 60, 459 (1960).

SnC₄H₆Cl₂
① Divinyltin dichloride
 $(CH_2=CH)_2SnCl_2$
② $(CH_2=CH)_4 + SnCl_4 \xrightarrow{0\sim10°}$
③ (54~56°/30). [13.2°]. n .5490 (135°).
⑥ Chem. Revs. 60, 459 (1960).

SnC₄H₆N₂S₂
① Dimethyltin diisothiocyanate
 $(CH_3)_2Sn(NCS)_2$
② $Me_2SnCl_2 + 2 NaNCS \xrightarrow{C_2H_5OH} 84\%$
③ [194~196°].
 Sol. in H₂O and polar org. solvents.
④ $+ bipyridine \longrightarrow$
 $(CH_3)_2Sn(NCS)_2\cdot bipy.$ adduct.
⑥ JACS 77, 1302 (1955). JOM 3, 70
 (1965).

SnC₄H₈O₄
① Dimethyltin diformate
 $(CH_3)_2Sn(OOCH)_2$
② $Me_2SnCl_2 + NaOOCH$
 $+ HCOOH \longrightarrow$
③ White needles. [185°].
 IR : JACS 82, 3287 (1960).

⑥ JACS **82**, 3285, 2873 (1960).

SCn₄H₈S₄

① 1,4,6,9-Tetrathio-5-stannaspiro[4,4]-
nonane

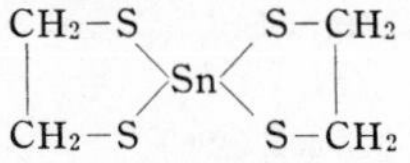

$$\begin{array}{ccc} CH_2-S & & S-CH_2 \\ | & >Sn< & | \\ CH_2-S & & S-CH_2 \end{array}$$

② $SnCl_4 + (CH_2SH)_2 \xrightarrow{H_2O}$

③ Colorless solid. [182~183°].
Sol. in org. solvents.

⑥ JCS **1965**, 1192.   Proc. Chem. Soc.
1963, 312.

SnC₄H₉Cl₃

① *n*-Butyltin trichloride
n-C₄H₉SnCl₃

② n-Bu₄Sn + 3 SnCl₄ ⟶
n-BuMgCl + SnCl₄ ⟶ 13%
Sn + n-BuCl ⟶ n-Bu₄₋ₙSnClₙ

③ (93°/10), (102~103°/12).

④ + Na₂S ⟶ n-BuSnS₃/₂
+ LiAlH₄ ⟶ n-BuSnH₃
+ OH⁻ ⟶ n-BuSnO₃/₂

⑥ Chem. Revs. **60**, 459 (1960).

SnC₄H₉N

① Trimethyltin cyanide
(CH₃)₃SnCN

② Me₃SnI + AgCN $\xrightarrow{benzene}$ 61.5%

③ [184.5~186°].
Sol. in CHCl₃ and acetone.

④ + S ⟶ (CH₃)₃SnNCS

⑥ JOC **25**, 809 (1960).   JACS **82**, 1080
(1960).

SnC₄H₉NS

① Trimethyltin isothiocyanate
(CH₃)₃SnNCS

② Me₃SnCN + S $\xrightarrow{Na, \ 150~160°}$ 51%

Me₃SnCl + NaNCS $\xrightarrow{C_2H_5OH}$ 86%

③ [108.5°].

Sol. in H₂O and org. solvents.

④ + pyridine ⟶ Me₃SnNCS·py
adduct

⑥ JOC **25**, 809 (1960).

SnC₄H₉ClO₂

① Dimethyltin chloride acetate
(CH₃)₂SnCl(OOCCH₃)

② (CH₃)₂SnCl₂ + glacial acetic
acid ⟶
Cl(CH₃)₂SnOSn(CH₃)₂Cl
+ 2 CH₃COOH ⟶

③ [189°].
IR: JACS **82**, 3287 (1960).

④ + H₂O ⟶ Cl(CH₃)₂SnOSn(CH₃)₂Cl

SnC₄H₉S₃/₂

① Butyltin sulfide
(C₄H₉SnS₃/₂)ₙ

② 2 BuSnCl₃ + 3 Na₂S $\xrightarrow{H_2O}$

③ Sol. in benzene.
Tetramer.

⑥ Japan 10640 (1961).

SnC₄H₁₀

① Diethyltin
(C₂H₅)₂Sn

② Et₂SnBr₂ + 2 Na(in liq. NH₃)
⟶ 85%
Et₂SnCl₂ + Et₂SnNa₂
(in liq. NH₃) ⟶
SnCl₂ + Et₂MgBr ⟶

③ d 1.558. Decomp. at 150°.
Moderately sol. in ether, benzene
and ligroin.
Polymer.

④ + Br₂ ⟶ Et₂SnBr₂
+ O₂ ⟶ Et₂SnO
+ HNO₃ ⟶ Et₂Sn(NO₃)₂
+ C₂H₅I ⟶ Et₃SnI

⑥ Chem. Revs. **60**, 459 (1960).

SnC$_4$H$_{10}$Br$_2$

① Diethyltin dibromide
   (C$_2$H$_5$)$_2$SnBr$_2$

② Et$_4$Sn + SnBr$_4$ $\longrightarrow$ 76%

   Sn + EtBr $\xrightarrow{Mg}$ Et$_{4-n}$SnBr$_n$(n=1,2,3)

   Et$_2$Hg + SnBr$_2$ $\longrightarrow$

   Et$_2$SnO + HBr $\longrightarrow$

③ (233°/760). [62~63°].

④ + OH$^-$ $\longrightarrow$ Et$_2$SnO

   + Et$_2$SnO $\longrightarrow$ BrEt$_2$SnOSnEt$_2$Br,
   BrEt$_2$SnOSnEt$_2$OH

⑥ Chem. Revs. **60**, 459 (1960). Kogyo
   Kagaku Zasshi **63**, 1965 (1960).

SnC$_4$H$_{10}$Cl$_2$

① Diethyltin dichloride
   (C$_2$H$_5$)$_2$SnCl$_2$

② Et$_4$Sn + SnCl$_4$ $\longrightarrow$ 85%

   Sn + EtCl $\xrightarrow{Cu, 300°}$

   SnCl$_2$ + EtBr $\xrightarrow{Mg}$

   SnCl$_4$ + AlEt$_3$ $\longrightarrow$

   Et$_2$SnO + HCl $\longrightarrow$

③ [84.5~86°].

④ + OH$^-$(excess) $\longrightarrow$ Et$_2$SnO

   + OH$^-$ $\longrightarrow$ ClEt$_2$SnOSnEt$_2$Cl,
   ClEt$_2$SnOSnEt$_2$OH

   + NR$_3$ $\dashrightarrow$ Et$_2$SnCl$_2$·2 NR$_3$

⑥ Chem. Revs. **60**, 459 (1960).

SnC$_4$H$_{10}$I$_2$

① Diethyltin diiodide
   (C$_2$H$_5$)$_2$SnI$_2$

② Et$_4$Sn + 2 I$_2$ $\longrightarrow$

   Sn + EtI $\xrightarrow{Mg}$ 65%

③ (245~236°/760), (105~107°/3). [44~
   45°].

④ + OH$^-$(excess) $\longrightarrow$ Et$_2$SnO

   + OH$^-$ + R′OH $\longrightarrow$
   IEt$_2$SnOSnEt$_2$OR′, IEt$_2$SnOSnEt$_2$OH

⑥ Chem. Revs. **60**, 459 (1960). Kogyo
   Kagaku Zasshi **63**, 1958 (1960).

SnC$_4$H$_{10}$O

① Diethyltin oxide
   (C$_2$H$_5$)$_2$SnO

② Et$_2$SnX$_2$ + OH$^-$(excess) $\longrightarrow$

③ White powder.
   Insol. in org. solvents.
   Polymer

④ + HX $\longrightarrow$ Et$_2$SnX$_2$(X=Cl, Br)

   + Et$_2$SnX$_2$ $\longrightarrow$ XEt$_2$SnOSnEt$_2$X
   (X=Cl, Br)

   + Na$_2$S + 4 H$^+$ $\longrightarrow$ Et$_2$SnS

⑥ Chem. Revs. **60**, 459 (1960).

SnC$_4$H$_{10}$S

① Diethyltin sulfide
   (C$_2$H$_5$)$_2$SnS

② Et$_2$SnBr$_2$ + Na$_2$S $\xrightarrow{C_2H_5OH}$

③ Heavy liq.(219~221°/8). [24°]. d 1.7264
   (35°/4°).
   Sol. in ether and benzene ; insol. in
   H$_2$O.
   Trimer.

⑥ Chem. Revs. **60**, 459 (1960).

SnC$_4$H$_{10}$S$_2$

① 2, 2-Dimethyl-2-stanna-1.3-dithio-
   cyclopentane

   CH$_2$—S
   | >Sn(CH$_3$)$_2$
   CH$_2$—S

② Me$_2$SnCl$_2$ + (CH$_2$SH)$_2$ $\xrightarrow{OH^-, H_2O}$

③ Needle crystals. [82°].

⑥ JCS **1965**, 1192.

SnC$_4$H$_{11}$I

① Ethyldimethyltin iodide
   (C$_2$H$_5$)(CH$_3$)$_2$SnI

② Me$_3$EtSn + I$_2$ $\longrightarrow$ 87~95%

③ Liq. (77~78°/11). n_D 1.5707 (20°).
   d 2.0264 (20°/20°).

⑥ Chem. Revs. **60**, 459 (1960).

SnC₄H₁₂
① Tetramethyltin
(CH₃)₄Sn
② SnCl₄ + MeMgBr ⟶
③ (78°/760). [−54°]. n_D 1.4386 (25°),
    1.4405 (25°).
④ + SnCl₄ ⟶ Me₃SnCl, Me₂SnCl₂
⑥ Chem. Revs. **60**, 459 (1960).

SnC₄H₁₂
① Butyltin trihydride
C₄H₉SnH₃
② 4 BuSnCl₃ + 3 LiAlH₄ ⟶
    BuSnCl₃ + 3 R'₂AlH ⟶
③ (99~101°/760). n_D 1.4609 (20°).
    IR: ν_{Sn-H} 1855 cm⁻¹. NMR: τ 5.71.
④ + CH₂=CHCOOCH₃
    ⟶ BuSn(CH₂CH₂COOCH₃)₃
    + cyclohexanon ⟶ (BuSn)ₙ
    + H₂ + cyclohexanol
⑥ Chem. Revs. **60**, 459 (1960). Ann.
    653, 164 (1962); **659**, 27 (1962).
    Tetrahedron Letters 143 (1961).

SnC₄H₁₂O
① Trimethyltin methoxide
(CH₃)₃SnOCH₃
③ IR: Optics and Spectrosc. **10**, 421
    (1961).

SnC₄H₁₂O₂
① Dimethyltin dimethoxide
(CH₃)₂Sn(OCH₃)₂
③ IR: Spectrochim. Acta **20**, 51 (1964).

SnC₄H₁₂S
① Methylthiotrimethyltin
(CH₃)₃SnSCH₃
② Me₃SnX + CH₃SH $\xrightarrow{OH^-,\ H_2O}$
③ (163°/760). n_D 1.5303 (20°) d 1.453.
    (20°/4°).
⑥ JCS **1965**, 1192.

SnC₄H₁₂S₂
① Dimethylbis(methylthio)tin
(CH₃)₂Sn(SCH₃)₂
② Me₂SnX₂ + 2 MeSH $\xrightarrow{OH^-,\ H_2O}$
③ (44°/0.05). n_D 1.6003 (20°). d 1.547
    (20°/4°).
⑥ JCS **1965**, 1192.

SnC₅H₁₀
① Trimethyltin acetylide
(CH₃)₃Sn−C≡CH
② Me₃SnCl + NaC≡CH $\xrightarrow{N_2,\ ether}$
③ (92~95°/760).
    Hydrolyse in moist air.
    IR: $\nu_{c≡c}$, 2010 cm⁻¹.
⑥ Inorg. Chem. **1**, 967 (1962).

SnC₅H₁₂
① Trimethylvinyltin
(CH₃)₃(CH₂=CH)Sn
② Me₃SnBr + CH₂=CHMgBr ⟶
③ (99~100°/760). n_D 1.4544 (25°). d 1.265
    (25°/4°).
⑥ Chem. Revs. **60**, 459 (1960).

SnC₅H₁₂O₂
① Trimethyltin acetate
(CH₃)₃SnOOCCH₃
② Me₃SnOH + HOOCCH₃ ⟶
③ [197°].
    IR: ν_{coo} 1574, 1433 cm⁻¹.
    Polymeric in the solid state.
⑥ Chem. Revs. **60**, 459 (1960). JACS
    82, 3287 (1960). Rec. trav. chim.
    82, 90 (1963).

SnC₅H₁₃ClO₃
① Diethyltin chloride formate hydrate
Cl(C₂H₅)₂SnOOCH·H₂O
② ClEt₂SnOSnEt₂Cl
    + 2 HCOOH(excess) ⟶
③ [82°].

⑥ JOM 1, 95 (1963).

SnC₅H₁₄
① Ethyltrimethyltin
   $(CH_3)_3SnC_2H_5$
② $(CH_3)_3SnI + (C_2H_5)_2Zn \longrightarrow$
   $(CH_3)_3SnI + C_2H_5MgBr \longrightarrow$ 81%
   $(CH_3)_3SnBr + Na \longrightarrow (CH_3)_3SnNa$
   $\xrightarrow{C_2H_5Br}$ 80%
③ (108.2°/760). n_D1.4527 (20°).
④ $+ Br_2 \longrightarrow (CH_3)_2(C_2H_5)SnBr$
⑥ Chem. Revs. **60**, 459 (1960).

SnC₅H₁₄S
① Ethylthiotrimetyltin
   $(CH_3)_3SnSC_2H_5$
② $(CH_3)_3SnX + C_2H_5SH \xrightarrow{OH^-, H_2O}$
③ (177°/760). n_D 1.5205 (20°) d 1.394.
   (20°/4°).
⑥ JCS **1965**, 1192.

SnC₅H₁₄S₃
① Ethyltris(methylthio)tin
   $C_2H_5Sn(SCH_3)_3$
② $C_2H_5SnX_3 + 3 CH_3SH$
   $\xrightarrow{O^-, H_2O}$ 30~50%
③ (66°/0.001). n_D1.6232 (20°). d1.548
   (20°/4°).
⑥ JCS **1965**, 1192.

SnC₅H₁₅IS
① Dimethyl(trimethylstannyl)sulfo-
   nium iodide
   $[(CH_3)_3SnS(CH_3)_2]I$
② $(CH_3)_3SnSCH_3 + CH_3I \longrightarrow$
③ White crystals. [223~6° decomp.].
⑥ JCS **1965**, 1192.

SnC₆H₅Br₃
① Phenyltin tribromide
   $PhSnBr_3$
② $Ph_4Sn + 3 SnBr_4 \longrightarrow$

③ (182~183°/29).
⑥ Chem. Revs. **60**, 459 (1960).

SnC₆H₅Cl₃
① Phenyltin trichloride
   $C_6H_5SnCl_3$
② $Ph_4Sn + SnCl_4 \longrightarrow$
③ (142~143°/25), (96°/1.4), (245°/760).
   n_D1.5844 (20°).
⑥ Chem. Revs. **60**, 459 (1960).

SnC₆H₆Cl₄
① *cis*-Tris(2-chlorovinyl)tin chloride
   $(cis\text{-}ClCH=CH)_3SnCl$
② $cis\text{-}ClCH=CHHgCl + Sn \xrightarrow{Na}$
③ (119.5°/1). n_D1.5821 (20°). d1.8058
   (20°/4°).
⑥ Chem. Revs. **60**, 459 (1960).

SnC₆H₆O₂
① Benzenestannonic acid
   C_6H_5SnOOH
② $(C_6H_5)_2SnO + CO_2 \longrightarrow$
③ Sol. in ether, alc., acetone, chloroform, acid and alkali; insol. in
   H_2O and petr. ether.
⑥ Chem. Revs. **60**, 459 (1960).

SnC₆H₈
① Phenyltin trihydride
   $C_6H_5SnH_3$
② $4 C_6H_5SnCl_3 + 3 NaBH_4 \longrightarrow$ 50%
   $C_6H_5SnCl_3 + 3 R'_2AlH \longrightarrow$
③ Heavy oil. n_D1.4370 (20°).
   IR: ν_{Sn-H} 1880 cm^{-1}. NMR: τ 5.07.
⑥ Angew. **73**, 542 (1961). Ann. **653**,
   164 (1962).

SnC₆H₉Cl
① Trivinyltin chloride
   $(CH_2=CH)_3SnCl$
② $3 (CH_2=CH)_4Sn + SnCl_4 \longrightarrow$ 96%
③ (59~60°/6). n_D1.5235.
⑥ Chem. Revs. **60**, 459 (1960).

SnC$_6$H$_{10}$Br$_2$

① Di-1-propenyltin dibromide
(CH$_3$CH=CH)$_2$SnBr$_2$

② 2(CH$_3$CH=CH)Li + SnBr$_4$ $\longrightarrow$
2(CH$_3$CH=CH)MgCl + SnBr$_4$ $\longrightarrow$
(CH$_3$CH=CH)$_2$TlBr + SnBr$_2$
$\longrightarrow$ 75%

③ (121~122°/10). n_D 1.5663. d 1.9360
(20°).

⑥ Chem. Revs. **60**, 459 (1960).

SnC$_6$H$_{13}$ClO$_2$

① Diethyltin chloride acetate
Cl(C$_2$H$_5$)$_2$SnOOCCH$_3$

② Cl(C$_2$H$_5$)$_2$SnOSn(C$_2$H$_5$)$_2$Cl
+ 2 CH$_3$COOH(excess) $\longrightarrow$

③ [94°].

⑥ JOM 1, 95 (1963).

SnC$_6$H$_{14}$Br$_2$

① Di-n-propyltin dibromide
(n-C$_3$H$_7$)$_2$SnBr$_2$

② n-Pr$_4$Sn + SnBr$_4$ $\longrightarrow$

③ (263~265°/760). [49°].

④ + OH$^-$ $\longrightarrow$ n-Pr$_2$SnO
+ n-Pr$_2$SnO
$\longrightarrow$ Br(n-Pr)$_2$SnOSn(n-Pr)$_2$Br,
Br(n-Pr)$_2$SnOSn(n-Pr)$_2$OH

⑥ Chem. Revs. **60**, 459 (1960).

SnC$_6$H$_{14}$Cl$_2$

① Di-n-propyltin dichloride
(n-C$_3$H$_7$)$_2$SnCl$_2$

② Sn + n-PrCl $\xrightarrow{300°,\ Cu}$
n-Pr$_4$Sn + SnCl$_4$ $\longrightarrow$
n-Pr$_2$SnO + HCl $\longrightarrow$

③ [80~81°].

④ + OH$^-$(excess) $\longrightarrow$ n-Pr$_2$SnO
+ OH$^-$ $\longrightarrow$ Cl(n-Pr)$_2$SnOSn(n-Pr)$_2$Cl
+ n-Pr$_2$SnO
$\longrightarrow$ Cl(n-Pr)$_2$SnOSn(n-Pr)$_2$Cl

⑥ Chem. Revs. **60**, 459 (1960).

SnC$_6$H$_{14}$I$_2$

① Di-n-propyltin diiodide
(n-C$_3$H$_7$)$_2$SnI$_2$

② (166~167°/10). n 1.6309 (20°). d 2.2099
(20°/4°).

⑥ Chem. Revs. **60**, 459 (1960). BCSJ **35**,
208 (1962).

SnC$_6$H$_{14}$O

① Di-n-propyltin oxide
(n-C$_3$H$_7$)$_2$SnO

② n-Pr$_2$SnCl$_2$ + OH$^-$(excess) $\longrightarrow$

③ White powder.
Insol. in org. solvents.

④ + HX $\longrightarrow$ n-Pr$_2$SnX$_2$(X=Cl, Br)
+ RCOOH $\longrightarrow$ n-Pr$_2$Sn(OOCR)$_2$
+ n-Pr$_2$SnX$_2$ $\longrightarrow$
X(n-Pr)$_2$SnOSn(n-Pr)$_2$X
(X=Cl, Br, NCS)

⑥ Chem. Revs. **60**, 459 (1960)

SnC$_6$H$_{15}$Br

① Triethyltin bromide
(C$_2$H$_5$)$_3$SnBr

② 3(C$_2$H$_5$)$_4$Sn + SnBr$_4$ $\xrightarrow{210°}$ 70%
Mg$_2$Sn + Hg + C$_2$H$_5$Br $\longrightarrow$
Sn + C$_2$H$_5$Br $\xrightarrow{Mg,\ butanol}$
(C$_2$H$_5$)$_{4-n}$SnBr$_n$(n=1, 2, 3)

③ (97°/13). [−13.5°]. n_D 1.520 (20°).

④ + AgX $\longrightarrow$ (C$_2$H$_5$)$_3$SnX,
(X=F, Cl, OOCCH$_3$, NCO, O$_{1/2}$ etc.)

⑥ Chem. Revs. **60**, 459 (1960). Kogyo
Kagaku Zasshi **63**, 1965 (1960)

SnC$_6$H$_{15}$Cl

① Triethyltin chloride
(C$_2$H$_5$)$_3$SnCl

② 3(C$_2$H$_5$)$_4$Sn + SnCl$_4$ $\xrightarrow{200°}$ 80%
Mg$_2$Sn + C$_2$H$_5$Cl $\longrightarrow$

③ (94°/13). [15.5°]. n_D 1.5055 (20°).
d 1.4288 (23.3°/4°), 1.4396 (20°/4°).

Sol. in org. solvents.

④ $+ OH^-$ ⟶ $(C_2H_5)_3SnOH$

⑥ Chem. Revs. **60**, 459 (1960).   BCSJ
35, 208 (1962).

SnC₆H₁₅F

① Triethyltin fluoride
$(C_2H_5)_3SnF$

② $(C_2H_5)_3SnOH + HF$ ⟶
$(C_2H_5)_3SnX + AgF$ ⟶
$(X = SH, S_{1/2}, I, Br, Cl, etc.)$

③ [302°]. Sublime at 180°.
Sol. in HO_2, alc. and acetic acid.

⑥ Chem. Revs. **60**, 459 (1960).

SnC₆H₁₅I

① Triethyltin iodide
$(C_2H_5)_3SnI$

② $(C_2H_5)_4Sn + I_2$ ⟶ 66%
$(C_2H_5)_3SnSSn(C_2H_5)_3 + AgI \xrightarrow{xylene}$

③ (105.5~106°/16). [−34.5°]. $n_D 1.5653$
(18°), 1.5615 (20°). $d 1.8255$
(17.5°/4°), 1.8232 (20°/4°).
Sol. in organic solvents.

④ $+ NaOC_2H_5$ ⟶ $(C_2H_5)_3SnOC_2H_5$
$+ AgX$ ⟶ $(C_2H_5)_3SnX$
$(X = F, Cl, Br, NCO, NCS, OOCCH_3,$
$O_{1/2})$

⑥ Chem. Revs. **60**, 459 (1960).   BCSJ
35, 208 (1962).

SnC₆H₁₅I

① Ethylmethylpropyltin iodide
$(CH_3)(C_2H_5)(C_3H_7)SnI$

② $(CH_3)_3(C_2H_5)Sn \xrightarrow{I_2}$
$(CH_3)_2(C_2H_5)SnI \xrightarrow{C_3H_7MgBr}$
$(CH_3)_2(C_2H_5)(C_3H_7)Sn \xrightarrow{I_2}$

③ Colorless liq. (108~111°/11). $n_D 1.5548$
(17⁵). $d 1.8182$ (20°/20°).

⑥ Chem. Revs. **60**, 459 (1960).

SnC₆H₁₅I

① Butyldimethyltin iodide
$(C_4H_9)(CH_3)_2SnI$

② $(CH_3)_3(C_4H_9)Sn + I_2$ ⟶ 95%

③ (88~89°/5.4). $n_D 1.5478$ (20°). $d 1.7818$
(20°/4°).

⑥ Chem. Revs. **60**, 459 (1960).

SnC₆H₁₅I

① Isobutyldimethyltin iodide
$(i\text{-}C_4H_9)(CH_3)_2SnI$

② $(i\text{-}C_4H_9)(CH_3)_3Sn + I_2$ ⟶ 91%

③ (95°/15). $n_D 1.5475$ (20°). $d 1.7803$
(20°/4°).

⑥ Chem. Revs. **60**, 459 (1960).

SnC₆H₁₆

① Diethyldimethyltin
$(CH_3)_2(C_2H_5)_2Sn$

② $(C_2H_5)_2SnCl_2 + 2 CH_3MgI$ ⟶ 63%

③ (144~146°/760). $n_D 1.4650$ (19°).

④ $+ 2 HgCl_2$ ⟶ $CH_3HgCl(91\%)$
$+ (C_2H_5)_2SnCl_2$

⑥ Chem. Revs. **60**, 459 (1960).

SnC₆H₁₆

① Triethyltin hydride
$(C_2H_5)_3SnH$

② $4(C_2H_5)_3SnCl + LiAlH_4 \xrightarrow{ether}$
$(C_2H_5)_3SnCl + R'_2AlH$ ⟶

③ (69~70°/47). $n_D 1.4725$ (20°). $d 1.258$
(20°/4°).
IR: ν_{Sn-H} 1809 cm⁻¹. NMR: τ 5.24.

④ $+ H_2C=CHR$
⟶ $(C_2H_5)_3SnCH_2CH_2R$
$+ HgO$ ⟶ $(C_2H_5)_3SnOSn(C_2H_5)_3$
$+ Hg + H_2$
$+ CuBr_2$ ⟶ $(C_2H_5)_3SnBr +$
$CuBr + H_2$

⑥ Chem. Revs. **60**, 459 (1960). Ann.
653, 164 (1962); **659**, 27 (1962).

SnC₆H₁₆

① Dipropyltin dihydride
   (C₃H₇)₂SnH₂

② 2 (C₃H₇)₂SnCl₂ + LiAlH₄ ⟶

③ (39~40.5°/12).
   IR: ν_{Sn-H} 1830 cm⁻¹. NMR: τ 5.42.

④ + CH₂=CHR ⟶
   (C₃H₇)₂Sn(CH₂CH₂R)₂
   (R=C₆H₅, COOCH₃)

⑥ Chem. Revs. **60**, 459 (1960). J. Appl.
   Chem. **9**, 106 (1959).

SnC₆H₁₆O

① Triethyltinhydroxide
   (C₂H₅)₃SnOH

② Et₃SnCl + OH⁻ ⟶ 96%

③ (272°/760). [44~45°], [49~50°].

④ + CH₃COOH ⟶ Et₃SnOOCCH₃
   + PhOH ⟶ Et₃SnOPh
   + H₂SO₄ ⟶ (Et₃Sn)₂SO₄

⑥ Chem. Revs. **60**, 459 (1960).

SnC₆H₁₆O₂

① Diethyltin dimethoxide
   (C₂H₅)₂Sn(OCH₃)₂

③ IR: Optics and Spectrosc. **10**, 421
   (1961).

⑥ Spectrochim. Acta **20**, 51 (1964).

SnC₆H₁₆O₂

① Dimethyltin diethoxide
   (CH₃)₂Sn(OC₂H₅)₂

⑥ Spectrochim. Acta **20**, 51 (1964).

SnC₆H₁₆S₂

① Bis(ethylthio)dimethyltin
   (CH₃)₂Sn(SC₂H₅)₂

② (CH₃)₂SnX₂ + 2 C₂H₅SH $\xrightarrow{OH^-, H_2O}$

③ (58°/0.07). n_D 1.5713 (20°). d 1.440
   (20°/4°).

⑥ JCS **1965**, 1192.

SnC₆H₁₆S₂

① Diethylbis(methylthio)tin
   (C₂H₅)₂Sn(SCH₃)₂

② (C₂H₅)₂SnX₂ + 2 CH₃SH $\xrightarrow{CH^-, H_2O}$

③ (61°/0.1). n_D 1.5793 (20°). d 1.440
   (20°/4°).

⑥ JCS **1965**, 1192.

SnC₇H₈O₂

① *p*-Toluenestannonic acid
   p-CH₃C₆H₄SnOOH

② *p*-CH₃C₆H₄SnCl₃ + KOH + CO₂ ⟶

③ Amorphous powder.
   Sol. in alc., ether, chloroform, ester
   and amine; insol. in H₂O, petr.
   ether and alkali.

⑥ Chem. Revs. **60**, 459 (1960).

SnC₇H₁₅N

① Triethyltin cyanide
   (C₂H₅)₃SnCN

② (C₂H₅)₃SnBr + KCN ⟶ 80%
   (C₂H₅)₃SnX + AgCN ⟶
   (X=SCH₃, S₁/₂, I, Br)

③ [153°].

④ + AgX ⟶ (C₂H₅)₃SnX + AgCN
   (X=F, O₁/₂, OOCCH₃, Cl)

⑥ Chem. Revs. **60**, 459 (1960).

SnC₇H₁₅NO

① Triethyltin isocyanate
   (C₂H₅)₃SnNCO

② (C₂H₅)₃SnX + AgNCO ⟶
   (X=SCH₃, S₁/₂, I, Br)

③ (120~121°/11). [48°].

⑥ JOC **19**, 1300 (1954).

SnC₇H₁₅NS

① Triethyltin isothiocyanate
   (C₂H₅)₃SnNCS

② (C₂H₅)₃SnX + AgNCS ⟶
   (X=SCH₃, S₁/₂, I, Br)

③ (130°/1). [33°].

④ + AgX ⟶ (C$_2$H$_5$)$_3$SnX
    (X=F, OOCCH$_3$)

⑥ JOC 19, 1300, 1766 (1954).

SnC$_7$H$_{16}$O$_2$

① Triethyltin formate
    (C$_2$H$_5$)$_3$SnOOCH

② (C$_2$H$_5$)$_3$SnOH + HCOOH $\xrightarrow{\text{ether}}$

③ Needles. [57~58°]. Sublime below
    the m. p.
    IR : JOM 1, 360 (1964).

SnC$_7$H$_{17}$I

① Isoamyldimethyltin iodide
    (*i*-C$_5$H$_{11}$)(CH$_3$)$_2$SnI

② (CH$_3$)$_3$(*i*-C$_5$H$_{11}$)Sn + I$_2$ ⟶ 86%

③ (115°/15). n_D1.5416 (21°). d1.7027
    (20°/4°).

⑥ Chem. Revs. 60, 459 (1960).

SnC$_7$H$_{18}$

① Butyltrimethyltin
    (CH$_3$)$_3$(C$_4$H$_9$)Sn ⟶

② (CH$_3$)$_3$SnBr + C$_4$H$_9$MgBr ⟶

③ (149~150°/726). n_D1.4560 (21.5°).

⑥ Chem. Revs. 60, 459 (1960).

SnC$_7$H$_{18}$

① Triethylmethyltin
    (CH$_3$)(C$_2$H$_5$)$_3$Sn

② (C$_2$H$_5$)$_3$SnI + CH$_3$MgI ⟶
    3 (C$_2$H$_5$)$_4$Sn + (CH$_3$)$_4$Sn ⟶

③ (162~163°/760). n_D1.4656(20°). d1.2160
    (20°/4°).

⑥ Chem. Revs. 60, 459 (1960).

SnC$_7$H$_{18}$S

① Triethylmethylthiotin
    (C$_2$H$_5$)$_3$SnSCH$_3$

② (C$_2$H$_5$)$_3$SnX + CH$_3$SH $\xrightarrow{\text{OH}^-,\ \text{H}_2\text{O}}$

③ (94°/2). n_D1.5274 (20°). d1.375

(20°/4°).

④ + AgX ⟶ (C$_2$H$_5$)$_3$SnX
    (X=halogens, OOCCH$_3$, O$_{1/2}$)

⑥ JCS 1965, 1192. JOC 19, 1300 (1954).

SnC$_7$H$_{18}$S$_3$

① Tris(ethylthio)methyltin
    CH$_3$Sn(SC$_2$H$_5$)$_3$

② CH$_3$SnX$_3$ + 3 C$_2$H$_5$SH
    $\xrightarrow{\text{OH}^-,\ \text{H}_2\text{O}}$ 30~50%

③ (90°/0.05). n_D1.5972 (20°). d1.469
    (20°/4°).

⑥ JCS 1965, 1192.

SnC$_8$H$_{12}$

① Tetravinyltin
    (CH$_2$=CH)$_4$Sn

② SnCl$_4$ + 4 CH$_2$=CHMgCl $\xrightarrow{\text{THF}}$ 82%

③ (55~57°/17). n_D1.4993 (25°). d1.2651
    (25°/4°).
    IR : $\nu_{\text{C=C}}$ 1908 cm^{-1}.

⑥ Chem. Revs. 60, 459 (1960).

SnC$_8$H$_{14}$ClN

① Trimethyl(pyridine)tin chloride
    (CH$_3$)$_3$SnCl·C$_5$H$_5$N

② (CH$_3$)$_3$SnCl + NC$_5$H$_5$ $\xrightarrow{\text{petr. ether}}$

③ [40~41°].
    X-ray : JCS 1963, 1524.

⑥ JCS 1963, 1519.

SnC$_8$H$_{16}$

① Triethyltin acetylide
    (C$_2$H$_5$)$_3$Sn−C≡CH

② (C$_2$H$_5$)$_3$SnOH + HC≡CH
    $\xrightarrow[\text{15~18 hr}]{\text{100~120°}}$ 22%

③ (100~101°/3). n_D1.4767 (20°). d1.1034
    (20°/4°).

⑥ Dokl. 158, 918 (1964).

SnC₈H₁₈

① Triethylvinyltin

$(C_2H_5)_3(CH_2=CH)Sn$

② $(C_2H_5)_3SnCl + CH_2=CHMgCl \longrightarrow$

③ $(174\sim175°/760)$. $n_D 1.4780(20°)$. $d 1.2133$

$(20°/4°)$.

⑥ Chem. Revs. **60**, 459 (1960).

SnC₈H₁₈

① Di-*tert*-butyltin

$(t-C_4H_9)_2Sn$

② $(t-C_4H_9)_2SnCl_2 + 2 t-C_4H_9MgCl$

$\longrightarrow$ 56%

③ Bright yellow crystls. [205°

decomp.].

Slightly sol. in hot pyridine and hot

butyl ether.

Tetramer.

④ $+ I_2 \xrightarrow{\text{benzene}} I-[(t-C_4H_9)_2Sn]_4-I$

⑥ JOM **1**, 434 (1964).

SnC₈H₁₈Cl₂

① Di-*n*-butyltin dichloride

$(n-C_4H_9)_2SnCl_2$

② $Sn + n\text{-}BuCl \xrightarrow{\text{Cu or Mg}}$

$n\text{-}Bu_4Sn + SnCl_4 \longrightarrow$

③ $(153\sim156°/5)$. [43°].

④ $+ OH^-(\text{excess}) \longrightarrow n\text{-}Bu_2SnO$

$+ H_2O \longrightarrow$

$Cl(n\text{-}Bu)_2SnOSn(n\text{-}Bu)_2Cl$

⑥ Chem. Revs. **60**, 459 (1960).

SnC₈H₁₈O

① Di-*n*-butyltin oxide

$(n-C_4H_9)_2SnO$

② $n\text{-}Bu_2SnX_2 + OH^-(\text{excess}) \longrightarrow$

③ White powder.

Polymer.

④ $+ HX \longrightarrow n\text{-}Bu_2SnX_2$

$+ RCOOH \longrightarrow n\text{-}Bu_2Sn(OOCR)_2$

$+ RSH \longrightarrow n\text{-}Bu_2Sn(SR)_2$

$+ n\text{-}Bu_2SnX_2 \longrightarrow$

$X(n\text{-}Bu)_2SnOSn(n\text{-}Bu)_2X$

⑤ Stabilyzer for polyvinyl chloride.

⑥ Chem. Revs. **60**, 459 (1960).

SnC₈H₁₈O₂

① Triethyltin acetate

$(C_2H_5)_3SnOOCCH_3$

② $(C_2H_5)_3SnOH$ or $(C_2H_5)_3SnOSn(C_2H_5)_3$

$+ CH_3COOH \longrightarrow$ 95%

$(C_2H_5)_3SnSSn(C_2H_5)_3 +$

$2 AgOOCCH_3 \longrightarrow$

③ Needle crystals. $(224°/760)$. [134~

135°].

Sol. in org. solvents.

IR : ν_{coo} 1570, 1420 cm^{-1}.

Bridged polymer by COO group.

⑤ Insecticide.

⑥ Chem. Revs. **60**, 459 (1960).   Rec.

trav. chim. **82**, 90 (1963).

SnC₈H₁₈S

① Dibutyltin sulfide

$(C_4H_9)_2SnS$

② $(C_4H_9)_2SnO + Na_2S \xrightarrow{\text{H}^+, \text{H}_2O}$

$(C_4H_9)_2SnO + CS_2 \xrightarrow{150°, 25\,hr} 99\%$

$(C_4H_9)_4Sn + 2 S \xrightarrow{190°}$

③ [63~69°(?)].

Trimer.

⑤ Stabilizer for rubber, elastmer and

vinylresins.

⑥ Chem. Revs. **60**, 459 (1960).   Ber. **95**,

1428 (1962).   JOC **26**, 4634 (1961).

Inorg. Chem. **1**, 650 (1962).

SnC₈H₁₉Br

① Diethylisobutyltin bromide

$(C_2H_5)_2(i-C_4H_9)SnBr$

② $(C_2H_5)_2(i-C_4H_9)_2Sn + Br_2 \xrightarrow{-34\sim40°}$

③ Liquid. $(122°/17)$. $n_D 1.51586$ $(20°)$.

$d 1.5108$ $(20°/4°)$.

⑥ Chem. Revs. **60**, 459 (1960).

SnC₈H₁₉I
① Butyldiethyltin iodide
   (C₄H₉)(C₂H₅)₂SnI
② (C₄H₉)(C₂H₅)₃Sn + I₂ $\xrightarrow{6\sim10\,hr}$ 86%
③ (134~135°/13). n_D1.5460 (20°). d1.6485
   (20°/4°).
⑥ Chem. Revs. **60**, 459 (1960).

SnC₈H₂₀
① Tetraethyltin
   (C₂H₅)₄Sn
② SnCl₄ + 4 C₂H₅MgBr $\longrightarrow$
   Mg₂Sn + C₂H₅Br(excess) $\longrightarrow$
   Sn−Na−Zn alloy
   + C₂H₅Br(excess) $\longrightarrow$
③ (78°/13). n_D1.4691 (20°).
④ + RCOOH $\longrightarrow$ (C₂H₅)₃SnOOCH
   (R=CHCl₂, CF₃, C₆H₅)
   + X₂(halogen) $\longrightarrow$ (C₂H₅)₃SnX,
   (C₂H₅)₂SnX₂
   + SnCl₄ $\longrightarrow$ (C₂H₅)₂SnCl₂
⑥ Chem. Revs. **60**, 459 (1960).

SnC₈H₂₀
① Dibutyltin dihydride
   (C₄H₉)₂SnH₂
② 2(C₄H₉)₂SnCl₂ + LiAlH₄ $\longrightarrow$
   (C₄H₉)₂SnCl₂ + 2 R′₂AlH $\longrightarrow$
③ (55~59°/5). n_D 1.4703 (20°). d 1.19
   (20°/4°).
   IR: ν_{Sn-H} 1835 cm⁻¹. NMR: τ 5.43.
④ + −C=C− $\longrightarrow$ Sn−$\overset{|}{C}$−$\overset{|}{C}$−H

   + −C≡C− $\longrightarrow$ Sn−$\overset{|}{C}$=C−H
   + CH₃COOH $\longrightarrow$
   CH₃COO(C₄H₉)₂SnSn(C₄H₉)₂OOCCH₃
⑥ Chem. Revs. **60**, 459 (1960). Ann.
   653, 164 (1962). JOC **27**, 837 (1962).

SnC₈H₂₀O
① Ethoxytriethyltin
   (C₂H₅)₃SnOC₂H₅
② (C₂H₅)₃SnCl + C₂H₅ONa $\longrightarrow$
③ (82°/13). n_D1.46553 (23.3°). d1.2394
   (23.3°/4°).
   Easily hydrolized to hydroxide.
⑤ Stabilizer for polyvinyl chloride.
⑥ Chem. Revs. **60**, 459 (1960).

SnC₈H₂₀S
① Triethylethylthiotin
   (C₂H₅)₃SnSC₂H₅
② (C₂H₅)₃SnX + C₂H₅SH $\xrightarrow{OH^-,\,H_2O}$
③ (68°/0.7). n_D 1.5153 (20°). d 1.359
   (20°/4°).
⑥ JCS **1965**, 1192.

SnC₈H₂₀S₂
① Diethylbis(ethylthio)tin
   (C₂H₅)₂Sn(SC₂H₅)₂
② (C₂H₅)₂SnX + 2 C₂H₅SH $\xrightarrow{OH^-,\,H_2O}$
③ (94°/0.05). n1.5572 (20°). d1.319
   (20°/4°).
⑥ JCS **1965**, 1192.

SnC₉H₁₄
① Trimethylphenyltin
   (CH₃)₃(C₆H₅)Sn
② (CH₃)₃SnNa + C₆H₅Br $\longrightarrow$
   (CH₃)₃SnBr + C₆H₅MgBr $\longrightarrow$
③ (203~208°/760).
⑥ Chem. Revs. **60**, 459 (1960).

SnC₉H₁₈O₂
① Triethyltin acrylate
   (C₂H₅)₃SnOOCCH=CH₂
② (C₂H₅)₃SnOSn(C₂H₅)₃ +
   2 CH₂=CHCOOH $\longrightarrow$ 70%
   (C₂H₅)₃SnH + CH₂=CHCOOH
   $\longrightarrow$ 64%
③ [116~117°].

④ $\xrightarrow{\text{heat}}$ $-[-CH_2-CH-]_n-$
  $\quad\quad\quad\quad\quad\quad |$
  $\quad\quad\quad\quad\quad COOSn(C_2H_5)_3$
⑥ Chem. Revs. **60**, 459 (1960).

SnC₉H₂₁Br
① Dibutylmethyltin bromide
  $(C_4H_9)_2(CH_3)SnBr$
② $(C_4H_9)_2(CH_3)_2Sn + Br_2 \longrightarrow 70\%$
③ (102~3°/1). $n_D 1.5083$ (20°). $d 1.447$
  (20°/4°).
⑥ Inorg. Chem. **1**, 647 (1962).

SnC₉H₂₁Br
① Tripropyltin bromide
  $(C_3H_7)_3SnBr$
② $(C_3H_7)_4Sn + Br_2 \longrightarrow$
③ (133°/13). $n_D 1.50655$ (28°). $d 1.4263$
  (25.2°/4°).
⑥ Chem. Revs. **60**, 459 (1960).

SnC₉H₂₁Cl
① Triisopropyltin chloride
  $(i\text{-}C_3H_7)_3SnCl$
⑥ Chem. Revs. **60**, 459 (1960).

SnC₉H₂₁Cl
① Tripopyltin chloride
  $(C_3H_7)_3SnCl$
② $3(C_3H_7)_4Sn + SnCl_4 \xrightarrow{200°} 91\%$
③ (123°/13). $n_D 1.49102$ (28°). $d 1.2678$
  (28°/4°).
⑥ Chem. Revs. **60**, 459 (1960).

SnC₉H₂₁F
① Tripropyltin fluoride
  $(C_3H_7)_3SnF$
② $(C_3H_7)_3SnBr + KF \longrightarrow$
③ [275°].
  Sol. in ethanol.
⑥ Chem. Revs. **60**, 459 (1960).

SnC₉H₂₁I
① Tripropyltin iodide

  $(C_3H_7)_3SnI$
② $(C_3H_7)_4Sn + I_2 \longrightarrow$
③ (140~141°/15). $n_D 1.54082$ (21°). $d 1.5960$
  (30.4°/4°).
⑥ Chem. Revs. **60**, 459 (1960).

SnC₉H₂₂
① Triethylpropyltin
  $(C_2H_5)_3(C_3H_7)Sn$
② $(C_2H_5)_3SnX + C_3H_7MgBr \longrightarrow$
③ (112°/50). $n_D 1.4726$ (20°). $d 1.1710$
  (16.6°/4°).
⑥ Chem. Revs. **60**, 459 (1960).

SnC₉H₂₂
① Tripropyltin hydride
  $(C_3H_7)_3SnH$
② $4(C_3H_7)_3SnCl + LiAlH_4 \xrightarrow{\text{ether}}$
③ (80~81°/12).
  IR: ν_{Sn-H} 1809 cm⁻. NMR: τ 5.23.
④ $+ HC≡CR \longrightarrow$
  $(C_3H_7)_3Sn-CH=CHR$
  $\quad(R=C_6H_5, C_4H_9, CH_2OH)$
  $+ CH_2=CHR \longrightarrow (C_3H_7)_3SnCH_2CH_2R$
  $\quad(R=CN, COOCH_3, CHCONH_2)$
  $+ Br_2 \longrightarrow (C_3H_7)_3SnBr + HBr$
  $+ N_2CHR \longrightarrow (C_3H_7)_3SnCH_2R + N_2$
⑥ Chem. Revs. **60**, 459 (1960). J. Appl.
  Chem. **7**, 356 (1957) ; **9**, 106 (1959).

SnC₁₀H₁₇F₅O₂
① Amyldimethyltin pentafluoropropio-
  nate
  $(C_5H_{11})(CH_3)_2SnOOCC_2F_5$
② $(C_5H_{11})_2(CH_3)_2Sn + C_2F_5COOH$
  $\longrightarrow 30\%$
③ (85~86°/1). $n_D 1.4281$ (20°). $d 1.485$
  (20°/4°).
⑥ Inorg. Chem. **1**, 642 (1962).

SnC₁₀H₁₈N₂S₂
① Dibutyltin diisothiocyanate

$(C_4H_9)_2Sn(NCS)_2$

② $(C_4H_9)_2SnCl_2 + 2\,NaNCS \xrightarrow{C_2H_5OH} 86\%$

③ $[144\sim145°]$.

④ $+$ bipyridine $\longrightarrow$ adduct
$+ (C_4H_9)_2SnO \longrightarrow$
$SCN(C_4H_9)_2SnOSn(C_4H_9)_2NCS$

⑥ Chem. & Ind. (London) 1306 (1960).
JACS 77, 1302 (1955).   JOM 3, 70
(1965).   JCS 1963, 5469.

$SnC_{10}H_{21}BrO_2$

① Dibutyltin bromide acetate
$(C_4H_9)_2SnBr(OOCCH_3)$

② $(C_4H_9)_2SnBr_2 + (C_4H_9)_2Sn(OOCCH_3)_2$
$\xrightarrow{\text{pentane}}$
$CH_3COO(C_4H_9)_2SnSn(C_4H_9)_2OOCCH_3$
$+ Br_2 \longrightarrow$

③ $[66\sim66.5°]$.
Hydrolyzed in air. Sol. in org. solvents.

④ $+ H_2O \longrightarrow$
$Br(C_4H_9)_2SnOSn(C_4H_9)_2Br$

⑥ JACS 82, 5958 (1960).   JCS 1962, 2050.

$SnC_{10}H_{21}Cl$

① Dibutylvinyltin chloride
$(C_4H_9)_2(CH_2{=}CH)SnCl$

② $(C_4H_9)_2SnCl_2 + CH_2{=}CHMgBr$
$\longrightarrow 56\%$
$(C_4H_9)_2(CH_2{=}CH)_2Sn + HCl$
$\longrightarrow 79.3\%$
$(CH_2{=}CH)SnCl_3 + 2\,C_4H_9MgBr \longrightarrow$

③ $(112\sim114°/4)$. $n_D 1.4987\ (20°)$. $d\,1.266$
$(20°/4°)$.

⑥ Chem. Revs. 60, 459 (1960).

$SnC_{10}H_{21}ClO_2$

① Dibutyltin chloride acetate
$Cl(C_4H_9)_2SnOOCCH_3$

② $Cl(C_4H_9)_2SnOSn(C_4H_9)_2Cl$
$+ CH_3COOH(\text{excess}) \longrightarrow$

③ $[61°]$.

⑥ JOM 1, 95 (1963).

$SnC_{10}H_{22}O_2$

① Tripropyltin formate
$(C_3H_7)_3SnOOCH$

② $(C_3H_7)_3SnOSn(C_3H_7)_3 + 2\,HCOOH \longrightarrow$

③ Viscous liq. $(105\sim106°/3)$. $n_D 1.5039$
$(20°)$.
IR: JOM 1, 360 (1964).

$SnC_{10}H_{22}S_2$

① Dibutyltin ethylenedithiolate

$(C_4H_9)_2Sn\!\!\diagup\!\!\!\overset{\displaystyle S}{\underset{\displaystyle S}{}}\!\!\!\diagdown(CH_2)_2$

③ Colorless solid. $(59\sim60°)$.
Sol. in org. solvents.

⑥ Proc. Chem. Soc. 1963, 312.

$SnC_{10}H_{24}$

① Methyltripropyltin
$(CH_3)(C_3H_7)_3Sn$

② $(C_3H_7)_3SnCH_2CH_2CN + CH_3MgI \longrightarrow$

③ $(94\sim96°/11)$.

⑥ Chem. Revs. 60, 459 (1960).

$SnC_{10}H_{24}$

① Triethylisobutyltin
$(C_2H_5)_3(i\text{-}C_4H_9)Sn$

② $3\,(C_2H_5)_4Sn + (i\text{-}C_4H_9)_4Sn \longrightarrow$

③ $(86°/10)$. $n_D 1.47304\ (20.3°)$. $d\,1.1390$
$(20.3°/4°)$.

⑥ Chem. Revs. 60, 459 (1960).

$SnC_{10}H_{24}O_2$

① Dibutyldimethoxytin
$(C_4H_9)_2Sn(OCH_3)_2$

② $(C_4H_9)_2SnCl_2 + 2\,CH_3ONa \longrightarrow 93\%$

③ $(136\sim139°/1.2)$. $n_D 1.4831(20°)$. $d\,1.2862$
$(20°/4°)$.
Tends to polymerize.
IR: Spectrochim. Acta 20, 51 (1964).

⑤ Stabilizer of polyvinyl chloride.

⑥ Chem. Revs. 60, 459 (1960).

SnC₁₁H₁₁Cl₃N₂
① Methyl(2, 2'-bipyridine)tin
   trichloride
   $CH_3SnCl_3 \cdot C_{10}H_8N_2$
② $CH_3SnCl_3 + bipy \xrightarrow{CCl_4}$
③ IR : JCS **1963**, 1519.

SnC₁₁H₂₂
① Tripropyltin acetylide
   $(C_3H_7)_3Sn-C\equiv CH$
② $(C_3H_7)_3SnOH + HC\equiv CH$
   $\xrightarrow[\text{100~120°, 15~18hr}]{} 37\%$
③ (91°/10). n_D 1.4780 (20°). d 1.1555
   (20°/4°).
⑥ Dokl. **158**, 918 (1964).

SnC₁₁H₂₄O₂
① Triproyltin acetate
   $(C_3H_7)_3SnOOCCH_3$
② $(C_3H_7)_3SnOSn(C_3H_7)_3$
   $+ 2\,CH_3COOH \longrightarrow$
   $(C_3H_7)_3SnH + CH_3COOH \longrightarrow 66\%$
③ (81~83°/1). [99~100°].
   Sol. in org. solvents.
   IR : ν_{COO} 1560, 1407 cm⁻¹.
   Polymeric in the solid state.
④ $+ OH^- \longrightarrow (C_3H_7)_3SnOSn(C_3H_7)_3$
   $+ C_6H_5COOH \longrightarrow (C_3H_7)_3SnOOCC_6H_5$
⑥ Chem. Revs. **60**, 459 (1960).

SnC₁₁H₂₄S₂
① Dibutyltin trimethylenedithiolate
   $(C_4H_9)_2Sn\diagup\!\!\!\diagdown(CH_2)_3$ with S atoms
③ Colorless solid. [63~64°].
   Sol. in org. solvents.
⑥ Proc. Chem. Soc. **1963**, 312.

SnC₁₁H₂₅I
① Diamylmethyltin iodide
   $(C_5H_{11})_2(CH_3)SnI$

② $(C_5H_{11})_2(CH_3)_2Sn + I_2 \longrightarrow$
③ (112~114°/1). n_D 1.5295 (20°). d 1.502
   (20°/4°).
⑥ Inorg. Chem. **1**, 647 (1962).

SnC₁₁H₂₆
① Amyltriethytin
   $(C_2H_5)_3(C_5H_{11})Sn$
② $(C_2H_5)_3SnBr + (C_5H_{11})MgBr \longrightarrow$
③ (102°/10). d 1.1258 (20°/4°).
⑥ Chem. Revs. **60**, 459 (1960).

SnC₁₁H₂₆
① Ethyltripropyltin
   $(C_2H_5)(C_3H_7)_3Sn$
③ (101°/10). d 1.1225 (22°/4°).
⑥ Chem. Revs. **60**, 459 (1960).

SnC₁₁H₂₆
① Triethylisoamyltin
   $(C_2H_5)_3(i\text{-}C_5H_{11})Sn$
③ (111°/8.5). n_D 1.47374 (21.8°). d 1.1203
   (20°/4°).
⑥ Chem. Revs. **60**, 459 (1960).

SnC₁₁H₂₉Br₂N
① Tetraethylammonium trimethyltin
   dibromide
   $(C_2H_5)_4N^+ \cdot (CH_3)_3SnBr_2^-$

   $(C_2H_5)_4NBr + (CH_3)_3SnBr \xrightarrow{H_2O}$
③ [150~165° decomp.].
⑥ JACS **83**, 1610 (1961).

SnC₁₂F₁₀Cl₂
① Bis(pentafluorophenyl)tin dichloride
   $Sn(C_6F_5)_2Cl_2$
② $SnCl_4 + 2\,C_6F_5MgBr \longrightarrow$
   $(CH_3)_2Sn(C_6F_5)_2 + SnCl_4 \longrightarrow$
③ (130°/2).
   Hydrolyzes.
④ $+ (CH_3)_4NCl \longrightarrow$
   $[(CH_3)_4N^+]_2SnCl_6^{2-}$
⑥ Proc. Chem. Soc. **1963**, 108.

SnC₁₂H₈Br₂Cl₂

① Bis(*p*-bromophenyl)tin dichloride
   (*p*-BrC₆H₄)₂SnCl₂

② (*p*-BrC₆H₄)₂Hg + SnCl₂ ⟶
   SnCl₄·*p*-BrC₆H₄N₂Cl + 2 Sn ⟶

③ [103°].

⑥ Chem. Revs. **60**, 459 (1960).

SnC₁₂H₈Cl₄

① Bis(*p*-chlorophenyl)tin dichloride
   (*p*-ClC₆H₄)₂SnCl₂

② (*p*-ClC₆H₄)₂Hg + SnCl₂ ⟶
   SnCl₄·2(*p*-ClC₆H₄N₂Cl) + 2 Sn ⟶

③ [86.5°].

⑥ Chem. Revs. **60**, 459 (1960).

SnC₁₂H₉OCl₃

① *o*-Phenoxyphenyltin trichloride
   o-C₆H₅-O-C₆H₄SnCl₃

② (*o*-C₆H₅OC₆H₄)₄Sn + SnCl₄ $\xrightarrow{\text{toluene}}$

③ (184~186°/0.7). [71~72°].

⑥ JCS **1963**, 906.

SnC₁₂H₁₀

① Diphenyltin
   (C₆H₅)₂Sn

② SnCl₂ + 2 LiC₆H₅ $\xrightarrow{-10° \text{ in } Et_2O}$
   (C₆H₅)₂SnCl₂ + 2 Na(in liq. NH₃) ⟶
   (C₆H₅)₂SnH₂ ⟶

③ Yellow powder. [126~130°].
   When monomeric sol. in common org.
   solvents except alcohol and benzene. On standing, polymerizes and
   insol. in org. solvents.
   Hexamer.

④ + O₂ ⟶ (C₆H₅)₂SnO
   + C₆H₅Li ⟶· (C₆H₅)₃SnLi

⑥ Chem. Revs. **60**, 459 (1960). Inorg.
   Chem. **2**, 1310 (1963).

SnC₁₂H₁₀Br₂

① Diphenyltin dibromide

(C₆H₅)₂SnBr₂

② Ph₄Sn + SnBr₄ $\xrightarrow{220°}$
   Ph₂Hg + SnBr₂ ⟶

③ [38°].

⑥ Chem. Revs. **60**, 459 (1960).

SnC₁₂H₁₀Cl₂

① Diphenyltin dichloride
   Ph₂SnCl₂

② Ph₄Sn + SnCl₄ ⟶
   Ph₂Hg + SnCl₂ ⟶

③ [42~44°].

④ + H₂S ⟶ Ph₂SnS
   + OH⁻ ⟶ Ph₂SnO

⑥ Chem. Revs. **60**, 459 (1960).

SnC₁₂H₁₀O

① Diphenyltin oxide
   (C₆H₅)₂SnO

② Ph₂SnX₂ + OH⁻(excess) ⟶

③ White powder. [265° decomp.].
   Insol. in org. solvents.

⑤ Stabilizer for polyvinyl chloride.

⑥ Chem. Revs. **60**, 459 (1960).

SnC₁₂H₁₀S

① Diphenyltin sulfide
   (C₆H₅)₂SnS

② (C₆H₅)₂SnCl₂ + H₂S ⟶ 74%
   (C₆H₅)₂SnO + CS₂ $\xrightarrow{160°, 16hr}$
   (C₆H₅)₂SnO + Na₂S $\xrightarrow{H^+, H_2O}$

③ [183~184°].
   Sol. in org. solvents.
   Trimer.

⑤ Antioxidant for rubber, elastmers.

⑥ Chem. Revs. **60**, 459 (1960). Ber. **95**,
   1428 (1962). JOC **26**, 4634 (1961).
   Inorg. Chem. **1**, 650 (1962).

SnC₁₂H₁₂

① Diphenyltin dihydride
   (C₆H₅)₂SnH₂

② (C₆H₅)₂SnCl₂ + LiAlH₄ $\xrightarrow{\text{ether}}$

$(C_6H_5)_2SnCl_2 + 2 R'_2AlH \longrightarrow$

③ Decomp. above 100° in vacuum.
$n_D 1.5951$ (20°). $d 1.39$ (20°/4°).
IR : ν_{Sn-H} 1855 cm⁻¹.   NMR : τ 3.91.

④ heat $\longrightarrow$ $(C_6H_5)_4Sn + Sn$
$+ (C_6H_5)_2Sn$
$+ CH_2=C(CH_3)COOCH_3 \longrightarrow$
$(C_6H_5)_2Sn[CH_2CH(CH_3)COOCH_3]_2$
$+ CH_3COOH \longrightarrow$
$CH_3COO(C_6H_5)_2SnSn(C_6H_5)_2OOCCH_3$
$+ C_6H_5COCH_3 \longrightarrow C_6H_5CH(OH)CH_3$

⑥ Chem. Revs. **60**, 459 (1960). Ann. **653**,
164 (1962) ; **659**, 27 (1962).   JOC **27**,
837 (1962).

SnC₁₂H₁₄Cl₂N₂

① Dimethyl(2, 2'-bipyridine)tin
   dichloride
   $(CH_3)_2SnCl_2 \cdot C_{10}H_8N_2$

② $(CH_3)_2SnCl_2 + bipy \xrightarrow{\text{benzene}}$
③ [240°].
   Sol. in org. polar solvents.
⑥ JOS **1963**, 1519. JOM **1**, 484 (1964).

SnC₁₂H₁₄CrO₃

① Trimethylstannylbenzenechromium
   tricarbonyl

$(CH_3)_3Sn \longrightarrow$ ⬡
$\quad\quad\quad\quad Cr(CO)_3$

② $Cr(CO)_6 + (CH_3)_3SnC_6H_5$
   $\xrightarrow[\text{155°, 43 hr, diglyme}]{} 34\%$
③ Yellow crystal. [79°].
   Decompd. by air in solution, but
     stable in air in the solid state.
   IR : ν_{CO} 1984, 1908 cm⁻¹.
⑥ Inorg. Chem. **2**, 417 (1963).

SnC₁₂H₁₆N₂Cl₂

① Dimethyldipyridinetin dichloride
   $(CH_3)_2SnCl_2 \cdot 2 C_5H_5N$

② $(CH_3)_2SnCl_2 + 2 Py \xrightarrow{\text{benzene}}$

③ [161°].
⑥ JCS **1963**, 1519.

SnC₁₂H₂₀

① Triethylphenyltin
   $(C_2H_5)_3(C_6H_5)Sn$
② $(C_2H_5)_3SnBr + C_6H_5MgBr \longrightarrow 62\%$
   $(C_2H_5)_3SnSn(C_2H_5)_3 + (C_6H_5)_2Hg$
   $\longrightarrow 30\%$
   $(C_2H_5)_3SnI + C_6H_5Br + Na \longrightarrow$
③ (254°/760). $n_D 1.5653(20°)$. $d 1.2639(0°)$.
⑥ Chem. Revs. **60**, 459 (1960).

SnC₁₂H₂₀O

① Triethyl(o-hydroxyphenyl)tin
   $(C_2H_5)_3Sn(o-C_6H_4OH)$
② $(C_2H_5)_3SnSn(C_2H_5)_3$
   $+ (o-HOC_6H_4)_2Hg \longrightarrow$
   $(C_2H_5)_3SnBr + (o-HOC_6H_4)MgBr$
   $\longrightarrow 54\%$
③ (155~156°/15). $n_D 1.537$ (925°). $d 1.3229$
   (25°/4°).
⑥ Chem. Revs. **60**, 459 (1960).

SnC₁₂H₂₀O

① Triethylphenoxytin
   $(C_2H_5)_3SnOC_6H_5$
② $(C_2H_5)_3SnOSn(C_2H_5)_3 + 2 C_6H_5OH$
   $\longrightarrow 77\%$
   $(C_2H_5)_3SnOH + C_6H_5OH \longrightarrow$
③ (115°/1). $n_D 1.5415(20°)$. $d 1.315(20°/4°)$.
⑥ Chem. Revs. **60**, 459 (1960).

SnC₁₂H₂₀O₄

① Dibutyltin maleate
   $(C_4H_9)_2Sn(OOCCH=CHCOO)$
② $(C_4H_9)_2SnO + maleic anhydride \longrightarrow$
④ Stabilizer for polyvinyl chloride.
⑥ Chem. Revs. **60**, 459 (1960).

SnC₁₂H₂₄

① Dibutyldivinyltin
   $(C_4H_9)_2Sn(CH=CH_2)_2$
② $(C_4H_9)_2SnCl_2 + 2 CH_2=CHMgCl$
   $\longrightarrow 89\%$

$(C_4H_9)_2SnO + 2 CH_2=CHMgCl$
$\longrightarrow$ 85%

③ $(78\sim80°/2)$. $n_D 1.4834$ $(25°)$.

④ $+ AsBr_3 \xrightarrow{95°} (C_4H_9)_2SnBr_2$
$+ (CH_2=CH)_2AsBr$

⑥ Chem. Revs. **60**, 459 (1960).

SnC$_{12}$H$_{24}$O$_4$

① Dibutyltin diacetate
$(C_4H_9)_2Sn(OOCCH_3)_2$

② $(C_4H_9)_2SnCl_2 + 2 CH_3COOK \longrightarrow$
$(C_4H_9)_2SnO + 2 CH_3COOH \longrightarrow$

③ $(142\sim145°/10)$. $n_D 1.4710$ $(20°)$.
Sol. in org. solvents.
IR : ν_{COO} 1616, 1385 cm^{-1}.
The tin atom is hexacoordinated.

④ $+ H_2O \longrightarrow CH_3COO(C_4H_9)_2SnOSn$
$(C_4H_9)_2OOCCH_3$

⑤ Stabilizer for polyvinyl chloride,
antioxidant for rubber, and
catalyzer for polyurethan.

⑥ Chem. Revs. **60**, 459 (1960).

SnC$_{12}$H$_{25}$N

① (2-Cyanoethyl)tripropyltin
$(C_3H_7)_3SnCH_2CH_2CN$

② $(C_3H_7)_3SnH + CH_2=CHCN \longrightarrow$

③ $(157\sim160°/12)$.

④ $+ LiAlH_4 \longrightarrow (C_3H_7)_3SnCH_2CH_2NH_2$

⑥ Chem. Revs. **60**, 459 (1960).

SnC$_{12}$H$_{26}$O

① (3-Hyrdoxy-1-propenyl)tripropyltin
$(C_3H_7)_3SnCH=CH-CH_2OH$

② $(C_3H_7)_3SnH + HC\equiv C-CH_2OH$
$\longrightarrow$ 34%

③ $(120\sim122°/0.006)$.

⑥ Chem. Revs. **60**, 459 (1960).

SnC$_{12}$H$_{27}$Br

① Tributyltin bromide
$(C_4H_9)_3SnBr$

② $(C_4H_9)_4Sn + Br_2 \longrightarrow$

③ $(163°/12)$. $n_D 1.5000$ $(20°)$. d 1.3365

$(20°/4°)$.

⑥ Chem. Revs. **60**, 459 (1960). BCSJ
35, 208 (1962).

SnC$_{12}$H$_{27}$Cl

① Tributyltin chloride
$(C_4H_9)_3SnCl$

② $3 (C_4H_9)_4Sn + SnCl_4 \longrightarrow$ 94.5%
$(C_4H_9)_2SnCl_2 + C_4H_9MgCl \longrightarrow$

③ $(145\sim147°/5)$. $n_D 1.4903(20°)$. d 1.2105,
1.2072 $(20°/4°)$.

④ $+ OH^- \longrightarrow (C_4H_9)_3SnOSn(C_4H_9)_3$

⑥ Chem. Revs. **60**, 459 (1960). BCSJ
35, 208 (1962).

SnC$_{12}$H$_{27}$I

① Triisobutyltin iodide
$(i\text{-}C_4H_9)_3SnI$

③ $(151°/13)$. $n_D 1.52221$ $(22.2°)$. d 1.4378
$(22.2°/4°)$.

⑥ Chem. Revs. **60**, 459 (1960).

SnC$_{12}$H$_{27}$N$_3$

① Tributyltin azide
$(C_4H_9)_3SnNNN$

② $(C_4H_9)_3SnCl(\text{in ether}) + NaN_3$
(in water) $\longrightarrow$ 76%

③ $(118\sim120°/0.18)$. $n_D 1.5097$ $(25°)$.

⑥ Rec. trav. chim. **81**, 202 (1962).

SnC$_{12}$H$_{28}$

① Diamyldimethyltin
$(C_5H_{11})_2(CH_3)_2Sn$

② $(CH_3)_2SnCl_2 + 2 C_5H_{11}MgBr \longrightarrow$ 95%

③ $(68\sim70°/1)$. $n_D 1.4676$ $(20°)$. d 1.098
$(20°/4°)$.

⑥ Inorg. Chem. **1**, 647 (1962).

SnC$_{12}$H$_{28}$

① Tetraisopropyltin
$[(CH_3)_2CH]_4Sn$

② $SnCl_4 + 4 (CH_3)_2CHMgBr \longrightarrow$ 25%

③ $(89°/4)$. $n_D 1.485$ $(20.2°)$.

④ $+ RCOOH \longrightarrow i\text{-}Pr_2Sn(OOCR)_2$

$(R=CH_2Cl, CHCl_2)$
$+ RSH \longrightarrow (C_3H_7)_3SnSR$
$(R=C_6H_5, benzyl, alkyl)$
⑥ Chem. Revs. **60**, 459 (1960).

$SnC_{12}H_{28}$
① Tetrapropyltin
    $(C_3H_7)_4Sn$
② $SnCl_4 + 4 C_3H_7MgBr \longrightarrow$
③ $(110\sim111°/10)$. $n_D 1.4748$ $(20°)$.
④ $+ RCOOH \longrightarrow (C_3H_7)_3SnOOCR$
    $(R=CH_2Cl, CHCl_2)$
    $+ RSH \longrightarrow (C_3H_7)_3SnSR$
    $(R=C_6H_5, CH_3C_6H_4, C_6H_5CH_2, alkyl)$
⑥ Chem. Revs. **60**, 459 (1960).

$SnC_{12}H_{28}$
① Tributyltin hydride
    $(C_4H_9)_3SnH$
② $4 (C_4H_9)_3SnCl + LiAlH_4 \xrightarrow{in\ ether}$
    $2 (C_4H_9)_3SnOSn(C_4H_9)_3$
    $+ LiAlH_4 \xrightarrow{in\ ether}$
③ $(76\sim81°/0.7\sim0.9)$.
    IR : ν_{Sn-H} 1807 cm^{-1}. NMR : τ 5.22.
④ $+ CHR=CHR'$
    $\longrightarrow (C_4H_9)_3SnCHRCH_2R'$
    $+ HC\equiv CH \longrightarrow (C_4H_9)_3SnCH=CH_2$
    $+ C_6H_5CH_2Cl \longrightarrow C_6H_5CH_3$
    $+ (C_4H_9)_3SnCl$
    $+ N_2CHR \longrightarrow (C_4H_9)_3SnCH_2R + N_2$
⑥ Chem. Revs. **60**, 459 (1960).   JOC **28**,
    703 (1963).   JACS **84**, 3584 (1962).
    Ann. **659**, 27 (1962).

$SnC_{13}H_{11}Cl_3N_2$
① Methyl(1, 10-phenanthroline)tin tri-
    chloride
    $CH_3SnCl_3·C_{12}H_8N_2$
② $CH_3SnCl_3 + C_{12}H_8N_2 \xrightarrow{CS_2}$
⑥ JCS **1963**, 1519.

$SnC_{13}H_{20}O_2$
① Triethyltin benzoate

$(C_2H_5)_3Sn(OOCC_6H_5)$
② $(C_2H_5)_3SnOH$ or $(C_2H_5)_3SnOSn(C_2H_5)_3$
    $+ C_6H_5COOH \longrightarrow 64\%$
    $(C_2H_5)_4Sn + C_6H_5COOH \longrightarrow$
③ $(133\sim134°/1)$. $[80°]$.
⑤ Insecticide.
⑥ Chem. Revs. **60**, 459 (1960).

$SnC_{13}H_{25}F_3O_2$
① Diamylmetyltin trifluoroacetate
    $(C_5H_{11})_2(CH_3)SnOOCCF_3$
② $(C_5H_{11})_2(CH_3)_2Sn + CF_3COOH$
    $\xrightarrow{45\sim50°,\ 3hr} 40\%$
③ $(106\sim108°/1)$. $n_D 1.4551$ $(20°)$. $d 1.324$
    $(20°/4°)$.
⑥ Inorg. Chem. **1**, 647 (1962).

$SnC_{13}H_{27}N$
① Tributyltin cyanide
    $(C_4H_9)_3SnCN$
② $(C_4H_9)_3SnCl + KCN \longrightarrow$
③ $[91°]$.
④ $+ S \longrightarrow (C_4H_9)_3SnNCS$
⑥ Australian J. Chem. **17**, 411 (1964).
    J. Appl. Chem. **6**, 49 (1965).

$SnC_{13}H_{27}NS$
① Tributyltin isothiocyanate
    $(C_4H_9)_3SnNCS$
② $(C_4H_9)_3SnCl + MNCS \longrightarrow$
                $(M=Ag, K, NH_4)$
    $(C_4H_9)_3SnCl + thiourea \longrightarrow$
    $(C_4H_9)_3SnOSn(C_4H_9)_3 + thiourea$
    $\longrightarrow 60\sim100\%$
③ $(160\sim162°/0.8)$. $n_D 1.5417$ $(20°)$.
⑥ Aust. J. Chem. **17**, 411 (1964).

$SnC_{13}H_{30}$
① Butyltripropyltin
    $(C_3H_7)_3(C_4H_9)Sn$
② $(C_3H_7)_3SnI + C_4H_9MgBr \longrightarrow$
③ $(137\sim138°/37)$. $n_D 1.4741$ $(20°)$. $d 1.0908$
    $(20°/4°)$.
⑥ Chem. Revs. **60**, 459 (1960).

SnC₁₃H₃₀

① Tributylmethyltin
   $(C_4H_9)_3SnCH_3$

② $(C_4H_9)_3SnCl + CH_3HgBr \longrightarrow$

③ $(121°/10). \ n_D 1.4735 \ (20°). \ d 1.0898$
   $(20°/4°).$

⑥ Chem. Revs. **60**, 459 (1960).

SnC₁₄H₆F₁₀

① Dimethylbis(pentafluorophenyl)tin
   $(CH_3)_2Sn(C_6F_5)_2$

② $(CH_3)_2SnCl_2 + 2 C_6F_5MgBr \longrightarrow$

③ $(94\sim96°/1.7).$

⑥ Proc. Chem. Soc. **1963**, 108.

SnC₁₄H₁₄Br₂

① Di-*p*-tolyltin dibromide
   $(p\text{-}CH_3C_6H_4)_2SnBr_2$

② $(p\text{-}CH_3C_6H_4)_2Hg + SnBr_2 \longrightarrow$

③ [74°].

⑥ Chem. Revs. **60**, 459 (1960).

SnC₁₄H₁₄Cl₂

① Di-*o*-tolyltin dichloride
   $(o\text{-}CH_3C_6H_4)_2SnCl_2$

② $(o\text{-}CH_3C_6H_4)_2Hg + SnCl_2 \longrightarrow$
   $(o\text{-}CH_3C_6H_4)_4Sn + SnCl_4 \longrightarrow$
   $SnCl_4 \cdot 2(o\text{-}CH_3C_6H_4N_2Cl) + 2 Sn$
   $\longrightarrow 20\%$

③ [49~50°].

⑥ Chem. Revs. **60**, 459 (1960).

SnC₁₄H₁₄Cl₂

① Dibenzyltin dichloride
   $(C_6H_5CH_2)_2SnCl_2$

② $C_6H_5CH_2Cl + Sn \longrightarrow$
   $(C_6H_5CH_2)_2Hg + SnCl_2 \longrightarrow$

③ [163~164°].

⑥ Chem. Revs. **60**, 459 (1960).

SnC₁₄H₁₄Cl₂

① Di-*p*-tolyltin dichloride
   $(p\text{-}CH_3C_6H_4)_2SnCl_2$

② $(p\text{-}CH_3C_6H_4)_2Hg + SnCl_2 \longrightarrow$
   $(p\text{-}CH_3C_6H_4)_4Sn + SnCl_4 \longrightarrow$

③ [49~50°].

⑥ Chem. Revs. **60**, 459 (1960).

SnC₁₄H₁₄Cl₂N₂

① Dimethyl(1,10-phenanthroline)tin
   dichloride
   $(CH_3)_2SnCl_2 \cdot C_{12}H_8N_2$

② $(CH_3)_2SnCl_2 + C_{12}H_8N_2 \xrightarrow{\text{benzene}}$

③ [284°] (200°decomp.).

⑥ JCS **1963**, 1519. JOM **1**, 484 (1964).

SnC₁₄H₁₄S₂

① Diphenyltin ethylenedithiolate

$$(C_6H_5)_2Sn \underset{S}{\overset{S}{\big<}} \big> (CH_2)_2$$

② [108~109°].
   Sol. in org. solvents.

⑥ Proc. Chem. Soc. **1963**, 312.

SnC₁₄H₁₈N₂Cl₂

① Diethyl(2,2'-bipyridine)tin
   dichloride
   $(C_2H_5)_2SnCl_2 \cdot C_{10}H_8N_2$

② $(C_2H_5)_2SnCl_2 + (C_5H_4N)_2 \xrightarrow{\text{ether}}$

③ [195~196°].
   Sol. in polar org. solvents.

⑥ JOM **1**, 484 (1964).

SnC₁₄H₂₅F₅O₂

① Diamylmethyltin pentafluoropropio-
   nate
   $(C_5H_{11})_2(CH_3)SnOOCC_2F_5$

② $(C_5H_{11})_2Sn(CH_3)_2 + C_2F_5COOH$
   $\xrightarrow{45\sim50°} 34\%$

③ $(109\sim111°/1). \ n_D 1.4376 \ (20°). \ d 1.360$
   $(20°/4°).$

⑥ Inorg. Chem. **1**, 647 (1962).

SnC₁₄H₂₆O₅

① Dibutylmethoxytin methylmaleate
   $(C_4H_9)_2Sn(OCH_3)OOCCH=CHCOOCH_3$

② $(C_4H_9)_2SnCl_2 + NaOCH_3 +$

HOOCCH=CHCOOCH₃ $\longrightarrow$
③ n_D1.5103 (20°). d1.3740.
⑥ Chem. Revs. **60**, 459 (1960).

SnC₁₄H₃₀
① Tributylvinyltin
   (C₄H₉)₃Sn(CH=CH₂)
② (C₄H₉)₃SnCl + CH₂=CHMgCl $\longrightarrow$
③ (114°/3). n_D1.4761 (25°). d1.081
   (25°/4°).
⑥ Chem. Revs. **60**, 459 (1960).

SnC₁₄H₃₀O₂
① Tributyltin acetate
   (C₄H₉)₃SnOOCCH₃
② (C₄H₉)₃SnOSn(C₄H₉)₃ + 2 CH₃COOH
   $\longrightarrow$ 98%
   (C₄H₉)₃SnX + CH₃COOK $\longrightarrow$
③ Needle crystals. [86~87°].
   Sol. in org. solvents.
   IR : νcoo 1572, 1418 cm⁻¹.
   Polymer bridged by COO group.
④ + OH⁻ $\longrightarrow$ (C₄H₉)₃SnOSn(C₄H₉)₃
⑤ Stabilizer for halogen-contg. resins.
⑥ Chem. Revs. **60**, 459 (1960).   Rec.
   trav. chim. **82**, 901 (1963).

SnC₁₄H₃₂
① Ethyltriisobutyltin
   C₂H₅Sn(*i*-C₄H₉)₃
② (*i*-C₄H₉)₃SnCl + C₂H₅MgBr $\longrightarrow$
③ (115°/10). d1.0779 (21°/4°).
⑥ Chem. Revs. **60**, 459 (1960).

SnC₁₅H₁₄O₂
① (1-Carboxyethyl)diphenyltin
   (C₆H₅)₂Sn⁺−CH(CH₃)COO⁻
② (C₆H₅)₃SnCH(CH₃)(CN) $\xrightarrow{NaOH}$
   (C₆H₅)₃SnCH(CH₃)COONa + HCl
   $\longrightarrow$ 63%
③ White powder. [>320°].
   Insol. in org. solvents.
   Sol. in warm 1 N NaOH.
⑥ Chem. Revs. **60**, 459 (1960).

SnC₁₅H₁₆S₂
① Diphenyltin trimethylenedithiolate

(C₆H₅)₂Sn$\left\langle\begin{smallmatrix}S\\[6pt]S\end{smallmatrix}\right\rangle$(CH₂)₃

③ [103~104°].
   Sol. in org. solvents.
⑥ Proc. Chem. Soc. **1963**, 312.

SnC₁₅H₃₁N
① Tributyl(2-cyanoethyl)tin
   (C₄H₉)₃SnCH₂CH₂CN
② (C₄H₉)₃SnH + CH₂=CHCN $\longrightarrow$
③ (132~138°/0.2).
⑥ Chem. Revs. **60**, 459 (1960).

SnC₁₅H₃₂
① 1-Hexenyltripropyltin
   (C₃H₇)₃SnCH=CHC₄H₉
② (C₃H₇)₃SnH + HC≡CC₄H₉ $\longrightarrow$ 82%
③ (75~80°/0.1).
⑥ Chem. Revs. **60**, 459 (1960).

SnC₁₅H₃₃Br
① Triamyltin bromide
   (C₅H₁₁)₃SnBr
② (C₅H₁₁)₄Sn + Br₂ $\longrightarrow$
③ (189°/13). n_D1.4963 (20°). d1.2678
   (20°/4°).
⑥ Chem. Revs. **60**, 459 (1960).

SnC₁₅H₃₃Cl
① Triisoamyltinchloride
   (*i*-C₅H₁₁)₃SnCl
② (*i*-C₅H₁₁)₃SnBr $\xrightarrow{OH^-}$ (*i*-C₅H₁₁)₃SnOH
   $\xrightarrow{HCl}$
③ (174°/13). [30.2°]. d1.1290 (34.2°/4°).
⑥ Chem. Revs. **60**, 459 (1960).

SnC₁₅H₃₃I
① Triisoamyltin iodide
   (*i*-C₅H₁₁)₃SnI

② $(CH_3)(i-C_5H_{11})_3Sn + I_2 \longrightarrow 87\%$
③ $(178\sim179°/11)$. $[-22°]$. $n_D1.5209(18°)$.
    $d1.3777$ $(26.5°/4°)$.
⑥ Chem. Revs. **60**, 459 (1960).

SnC₁₆H₁₈Cl₂N₂
① Diethyl(1,10-phenanthroline)tin
    dichloride
    $(C_2H_5)_2SnCl_2 \cdot C_{12}H_8N_2$
② $(C_2H_5)_2SnCl_2 + C_{12}H_8N_2 \longrightarrow$
③ $[230\sim231°]$.
⑥ JOM **1**, 484 (1964).

SnC₁₆H₂₀
① Diethyldiphenyltin
    $(C_2H_5)_2(C_6H_5)_2Sn$
② $(C_6H_5)_2SnCl_2 + 2 C_2H_5MgBr$
    $\longrightarrow 78.5\%$
    $(C_2H_5)_2Sn + (C_6H_5)_2Hg \longrightarrow$
③ $(155\sim157°/4)$.
④ $+ h\nu$ in CCl_4, $CHCl_3$ or CH_3OH
    $\longrightarrow (C_6H_5\cdot)$
⑥ Chem. Revs. **60**, 459 (1960).

SnC₁₆H₃₄O₂
① Tributyl(2-carbomethoxyethyl)tin
    $(C_4H_9)_3SnCH_2CH_2COOCH_3$
② $(C_4H_9)_3SnH + CH_2=CHCOOCH_3 \longrightarrow$
③ $(140\sim141°/0.4)$.
⑥ Chem. Revs. **60**, 459 (1960).

SnC₁₆H₃₆
① Tetrabutyltin
    $Sn(C_4H_9)_4$
② $SnCl_4 + 4 C_4H_9MgBr \longrightarrow$
③ $(127°/1.7)$, $(145°/10)$. $n_D1.4730$ $(20°)$.
    $d1.0572$ $(20°/4°)$.
    Sol. in common org. solvents.
④ $+ SnCl_4' \longrightarrow (C_4H_9)_3SnCl$
    $+ (C_4H_9)_2SnCl_2 + C_4H_9SnCl_3$
⑥ Chem. Revs. **60**, 459 (1960).

SnB₁₆H₃₆
① Tetraisobutyltin
    $[(CH_3)_2CHCH_2]_4Sn$

② $SnCl_4 + 4 (CH_3)_2CHCH_2MgBr \longrightarrow$
③ $(130°/10)$. $n_D1.4760$ $(20°)$.
⑥ Chem. Revs. **60**, 459 (1960).

SnC₁₆H₃₆O
① Butoxytributyltin
    $(C_4H_9)_3SnOC_4H_9$
② $(C_4H_9)_3SnX + NaOC_4H_9 \longrightarrow$
③ $(124\sim128°/3)$. $n_D1.4688$ $(20°)$, 1.4726
    $(20°)$.
⑤ Polyvinyl halide stabilizer.
⑥ Chem. Revs. **60**, 459 (1960).

SnC₁₆H₃₆O₂
① Dibutoxydibutyltin
    $(C_4H_9)_2Sn(OC_4H_9)_2$
② $(C_4H_9)_2SnCl_2 + 2 C_4H_9ONa \longrightarrow$
③ $[110\sim115°]$.
    IR: Spectrochim. Acta **20**, 51 (1964).
⑥ Chem. Revs. **60**, 459 (1960).

SnC₁₈H₁₅Br
① Triphenyltin bromide
    $(C_6H_5)_3SnBr$
② $(C_6H_5)_4Sn \xrightarrow{I_2} (C_6H_5)_3SnI \xrightarrow{OH^-}$
    $(C_6H_5)_3SnOH \xrightarrow{HBr}$
    $(C_6H_5)_2Hg + SnBr_2 \longrightarrow$
③ $(249°/13.5)$. $[121\sim122°]$.
⑥ Chem. Revs. **60**, 459 (1960).

SnC₁₈H₁₅Cl
① Triphenyltin chloride
    $(C_6H_5)_3SnCl$
② $3 (C_6H_5)_4Sn + SnCl_4 \longrightarrow 72\%$
    $(C_6H_5)_3SnOH + HCl \longrightarrow$
    $(C_6H_5)_2Hg + SnCl_2 \longrightarrow 75\%$
③ $(249°/13.5)$. $[105\sim107°]$.
④ $+ RMgX \longrightarrow (C_6H_5)_3SnR$
    $+$ ethylene oxide
    $\xrightarrow{Na} (C_6H_5)_3SnCH_2CH_2ONa$
    $+ NaOSiR_3 \longrightarrow (C_6H_5)_3SnOSiR_3$
    $+ OH^- \longrightarrow (C_6H_5)_3SnOH$

⑥ Chem. Revs. **60**, 459 (1960).

$SnC_{18}ClF_{15}$
① Tris(pentafluorophenyl)tin chloride
 $(C_6F_5)_3SnCl$
② $SnCl_4 + 3 C_6F_5MgBr \longrightarrow$
③ [106°].
⑥ Proc. Chem. Soc. **1963**, 108.

$SnC_{18}H_{15}F$
① Triphenyltinfluoride
 $(C_6H_5)_3SnF$
② $(C_6H_5)_3SnCl + KF \longrightarrow$
③ [357° decomp.].
  Sparingly sol. in alc., ether and
   H_2O.
⑥ Chem. Revs. **60**, 459 (1960).

$SnC_{18}H_{15}I$
① Triphenyltin iodide
 $(C_6H_5)_3SnI$
② $(C_6H_5)_4Sn + I_2 \longrightarrow$
③ [121°].
  Sol. in ether and petr. ether.
⑥ Chem. Revs. **60**, 459 (1960).

$SnC_{18}H_{15}Li$
① Triphenyltin lithium
 $(C_6H_5)_3SnLi$
② $SnCl_2 + 3 C_6H_5Li \xrightarrow{-10° \text{ in } Et_2O}$
  $(C_6H_5)_2Sn + C_6H_5Li \longrightarrow$
  $(C_6H_5)_3SnBr + 2 Li \longrightarrow$
  Exists in soln.
④ $+ RX \longrightarrow (C_6H_5)_3SnR$
  $(R=C_6H_5, C_6H_5CH_2, (C_6H_5)_3Sn, \text{ etc. })$
⑥ Chem. Revs. **60**, 459 (1960).

$SnC_{18}H_{15}N_3$
① Triphenyltin azide
 $(C_6H_5)_3SnNNN$
② $(C_6H_5)_3SnCl + NaN_3 \longrightarrow 85\%$
③ [115°].
  IR : ν_{NC} 2093 cm^{-1}.
④ $\xrightarrow{300°} (C_6H_5)_4Sn + N_2 +$ black solid

  $+ SnCl_4 \longrightarrow (C_6H_5)_3SnN_3 \cdot SnCl_4$
⑥ Chimica **16**, 10 (1962). Rec. trav.
  chim. 202 (1962). Inorg. Chem. **3**,
  402, 406 (1964).

$SnC_{18}H_{15}Na$
① Triphenyltin sodium
 $(C_6H_5)_3SnNa$
② $(C_6H_5)_3SnCl + 2 Na(in liq. NH_3) \longrightarrow$
③ Exists in liq. NH_3.
④ $+ (CH_3)_3SnBr$
   $\longrightarrow (C_6H_5)_3SnSn(CH_3)_3$
  $+$ ethylene oxide
   $\xrightarrow{H_2O} (C_6H_5)_3SnCH_2CH_2OH$
  $+ O_2 \longrightarrow (C_6H_5)_3SnOH + (C_6H_5)_4Sn$
   $+ (C_6H_5)_2SnO$
  $+ CH_2Cl_2 \longrightarrow$
   $(C_6H_5)_3SnCH_2Sn(C_6H_5)_3$
⑥ Chem. Revs. **60**, 459 (1960).

$SnC_{18}H_{16}$
① Triphenyltin hydride
 $(C_6H_5)_3SnH$
② $(C_6H_5)_3SnCl + LiAlH_4 \xrightarrow{\text{ether}}$
③ (164~165°/0.3). [26~28°].
  IR : ν_{Sn-H} 1830 cm^{-1}. NMR : τ 3.17.
④ $+ O_2 \longrightarrow (C_6H_5)_3Sn-Sn(C_6H_5)_3$
  $+ HCl \longrightarrow (C_6H_5)_3SnCl$
  $+ \diagup C=C\diagdown \longrightarrow (C_6H_5)_3Sn-\overset{|}{C}-\overset{|}{C}-H$
  $+ R-C_6H_4-X \longrightarrow R-C_6H_5$
   $+ (C_6H_5)_3SnX$
  $+$ cyclohexanone $\longrightarrow$ cyclohexanol
  $+ CCl_4 \longrightarrow CHCl_3 + (C_6H_5)_3SnCl$
⑥ Chem. Revs. **60**, 459 (1960). JOC **27**,
  3370 (1962). Ber. **96**, 3270 (1963).
  JACS **84**, 3584 (1962).

$SnC_{18}H_{16}O$
① Triphenyltin hydroxide
 $(C_6H_5)_3SnOH$
② $Ph_3SnCl + OH^- \longrightarrow$
③ [119~120°].

④ + RCOOH $\longrightarrow$ Ph$_3$SnOOCR
⑤ Stabilizer for polyvinyl chloride.
⑥ Chem. Revs. **60**, 459 (1960).

SnC$_{18}$H$_{26}$Cl$_2$N$_2$
① Dibutyl(2,2′-bipyridine)tin
     dichloride
     (C$_4$H$_9$)$_2$SnCl$_2$·C$_{10}$H$_8$N$_2$
② (C$_4$H$_9$)$_2$SnCl$_2$ + (C$_5$H$_4$N)$_2$ $\xrightarrow{\text{ethanol}}$
③ [180°].
⑥ JCS **1961**, 756. JOM **1**, 484 (1964).

SnC$_{18}$H$_{29}$N
① (1-Cyano-2-phenylethyl)tripropyltin
     (C$_3$H$_7$)$_3$SnCH(CN)CH$_2$C$_6$H$_5$
② (C$_3$H$_7$)$_3$SnH + C$_6$H$_5$CH=CHCN
     $\longrightarrow$ 83%
③ (130~141°/0.0002).
⑥ Chem. Revs. **60**, 459 (1960).

SnC$_{18}$H$_{32}$
① Tributylphenyltin
     (C$_4$H$_9$)$_3$(C$_6$H$_5$)Sn
② (C$_4$H$_9$)$_3$SnLi + C$_6$H$_5$I $\longrightarrow$
     (C$_6$H$_5$)$_4$Sn + 3 (C$_4$H$_9$)$_4$Sn $\longrightarrow$
③ (142°/2.5). n_D1.5155 (20°).
⑥ Chem. Revs. **60**, 459 (1960).

SnC$_{18}$H$_{32}$O$_4$
① 3,3′-(Dibutylstannylene)-
     2,4-pentanedione
     (C$_4$H$_9$)$_2$Sn[CH(COCH$_3$)$_2$]$_2$
② (C$_4$H$_9$)$_2$SnCl$_2$ + 2 NaCH(COCH$_3$)$_2$ $\longrightarrow$
     (C$_4$H$_9$)$_2$Sn(OCH$_3$)$_2$
     + 2 CH$_2$(COCH$_3$)$_2$ $\longrightarrow$
③ (132~133°).
⑤ Stabilizer for halogen-containing
     resinous compds.
⑥ Chem. Revs. **60**, 459 (1960).

SnC$_{18}$H$_{39}$Cl
① Trihexyltin chloride
     (C$_6$H$_{13}$)$_3$SnCl
② 3 (C$_6$H$_{13}$)$_4$Sn + SnCl$_4$ $\xrightarrow{220°}$ 69%

③ (178~180°/1.5). [55.5~56.5°].
⑥ Chem. Revs. **60**, 459 (1960).

SnC$_{19}$H$_{18}$
① Methyltriphenyltin
     (CH$_3$)(C$_6$H$_5$)$_3$Sn
② (C$_6$H$_5$)$_3$SnNa + CH$_3$I $\longrightarrow$
     (C$_6$H$_5$)$_3$SnX + CH$_3$MgBr $\longrightarrow$
③ [60~61°].
⑥ Chem. Revs. **60**, 459 (1960).

SnC$_{20}$H$_{14}$Br$_2$
① Di-1-naphtyltin dibromide
     (1-C$_{10}$H$_7$)$_2$SnBr$_2$
② (1-C$_{10}$H$_7$)$_2$SnCl$_2$ $\xrightarrow{\text{OH}^-}$ (1-C$_{10}$H$_7$)$_2$SnO
     $\xrightarrow{\text{HBr}}$
③ ·[142°].
⑥ Chem. Revs. **60**, 459 (1960).

SnC$_{20}$H$_{14}$Cl$_2$
① Di-1-naphtyltin dichloride
     (1-C$_{10}$H$_7$)$_2$SnCl$_2$
② (1-C$_{10}$H$_7$)$_2$Hg + SnCl$_2$ $\longrightarrow$
     2(1-C$_{10}$H$_7$)MgBr + SnCl$_4$ $\longrightarrow$
③ [137~137.5°].
⑥ Chem. Revs. **60**, 459 (1960).

SnC$_{20}$H$_{18}$
① Triphenylvinyltin
     (C$_6$H$_5$)$_3$(CH$_2$=CH)Sn
② (C$_6$H$_5$)$_3$SnX + CH$_2$=CHMgBr $\longrightarrow$
③ [45.2~45.4°].
⑥ Chem. Revs. **60**, 459 (1960).

SnC$_{20}$H$_{18}$N$_2$O$_2$
① Dimethyltin dioxinate
     (CH$_3$)$_2$Sn(C$_9$H$_6$NO)$_2$
② (CH$_3$)$_2$SnCl$_2$ + 2 C$_9$H$_6$NOH $\xrightarrow[\text{OH}^-]{\text{ethanol}}$
③ [231~233°].
     Sol. in org. solvents; insol. in H$_2$O.
⑥ JOM **1**, 484 (1964).

SnC₂₀H₁₈O₂
① Triphenyltin acetate
  $(C_6H_5)_3SnOOCCH_3$
② $(C_6H_5)_3SnOH + HOOCCH_3 \longrightarrow$ 62%
③ [122~123°].
⑥ Chem. Revs. **60**, 459 (1960).

SnC₂₀H₂₀
① Ethyltriphenyltin
  $(C_2H_5)(C_6H_5)_3Sn$
② $(C_6H_5)_3SnLi + C_2H_5X \longrightarrow$
  $(C_6H_5)_3SnCl + C_2H_5Li$
  or $C_2H_5MgX \longrightarrow$
③ [56~58°]. d1.2953 (62°/4°),
  Sol. in alc. and benzene.
⑥ Chem. Revs. **60**, 459 (1960).

SnC₂₀H₂₀O
① (2-Hydroxyethyl)triphenyltin
  $(C_6H_5)_3SnCH_2CH_2OH$
② $(C_6H_5)_3SnNa \xrightarrow{C_2H_4O}$

  $(C_6H_5)_3SnCH_2CH_2ONa \xrightarrow{H_2O}$ 59%
③ [66~67°].
⑥ Chem. Revs. **60**, 459 (1960).

SnC₂₀H₂₄O₄
① Bis(2-carbomethoxyethyl)diphenyl-
  tin
  $(C_6H_5)_2Sn(CH_2CH_2COOCH_3)_2$
② $(C_6H_5)_2SnH_2 + 2 CH_2=CHCOOCH_3$
  $\longrightarrow$ 34%
③ (191~194°/0.003).
⑥ Chem. Revs. **60**, 459 (1960).

SnC₂₀H₂₈
① Dibutyldiphenyltin
  $(C_4H_9)_2(C_6H_5)_2Sn$
② $(C_6H_5)_4Sn + (C_4H_9)_4Sn \longrightarrow$
  $(C_6H_5)(C_4H_9)_3Sn + (C_6H_5)_3(C_4H_9)Sn$
  $\longrightarrow$ 90%
③ (84~85°/40). n_D1.4662 (25°).
⑥ Chem. Revs. **60**, 459 (1960).

SnC₂₀H₂₈O₂
① Dibutyltin diphenoxide
  $(C_4H_9)_2Sn(OC_6H_5)_2$
② $(C_4H_9)_2SnCl_2 + 2 C_6H_5ONa \xrightarrow{heptane}$
④ $+ H_2O \longrightarrow$
  $C_6H_5O(C_4H_9)_2SnOSn(C_4H_9)_2OC_6H_5$
  $+ (C_4H_9)_2SnO \longrightarrow$
  $C_6H_5O(C_4H_9)_2SnOSn(C_4H_9)_2OC_6H_5$
⑥ JOC **28**, 221 (1963).

SnC₂₂H₃₂
① Bis(2-phenylethyl)dipropyltin
  $(C_3H_7)_2Sn(CH_2CH_2C_6H_5)_2$
② $(C_3H_7)_2SnH_2 + 2 CH_2=CHC_6H_5 \longrightarrow$
③ (172°/0.015).
⑥ Chem. Revs. **60**, 459 (1960).

SnC₂₀H₄₄
① Tetraamyltin
  $(C_5H_{11})_4Sn$
② $NaSn(20\% Zn) + C_5H_{11}Cl \longrightarrow$
  $SnCl_4 + 4 C_5H_{11}MgBr \longrightarrow$
③ (181°/10). n_D1.4720(20°). d1.0206(20°).
⑥ Chem. Revs. **60**, 459 (1960).

SnC₂₀H₄₄
① Tetraisoamyltin
  $[(CH_3)_2CHCH_2CH_2]_4Sn$
② $SnCl_4 + (CH_3)_2CHCH_2CH_2MgBr \longrightarrow$
③ (170°/11). 1.4791(20°).
⑥ Chem. Revs. **60**, 459 (1960).

SnC₂₁H₁₉N
① (2-Cyanoethyl)triphenyltin
  $(C_6H_5)_3SnCH_2CH_2CN$
② $(C_6H_5)_3SnH + CH_2=CHCN \longrightarrow$ 85%
③ [93~94°].
④ $+ NaOH \longrightarrow C_6H_5SnCH_2CH_2COONa$
⑥ Chem. Revs. **60**, 459 (1960).

SnC₂₁H₂₁Cl
① Tribenzyltin chloride
  $(C_6H_5CH_2)_3SnCl$

② Sn + C₆H₅CH₂Cl $\xrightarrow{\text{H}_2\text{O}}$

SnCl₄ + 3 C₆H₅CH₂Cl $\xrightarrow{\text{Mg}}$ 60%

③ [148°].

Sol. in acetone, benzene and chloroform.

Insol. in water.

④ + OH⁻ ⟶ (C₆H₅CH₂)₃SnOH

+ CH₃COONa ⟶

(C₆H₅CH₂)₃SnOOCCH₃

⑥ Chem. Revs. **60**, 459 (1960).

SnC₂₂H₂₁N

① (3-Cyanopropyl)triphenyltin

(C₆H₅)₃SnCH₂CH₂CH₂CN

② (C₆H₅)₃SnH + CH₂=CHCH₂CN

⟶ 73%

③ [80~81°].

⑥ Chem. Revs. **60**, 459 (1960).

SnC₂₂H₂₁N

① (2-Cyano-1-methylethyl)triphenyl-

tin

(C₆H₅)₃SnCH(CH₃)CH₂CN

② (C₆H₅)₃SnH + CH₃CH=CHCN

⟶ 89%

③ [103~104°].

⑥ Chem. Revs. **60**, 459 (1960).

SnC₂₂H₂₄

① Butyltriphenyltin

(C₆H₅)₃(C₄H₉)Sn

② Ph₃SnI + BuMgBr ⟶

BuSnCl₃ + PhCl $\xrightarrow{\text{Na}}$

③ Colorless needles. (222°/3). [61~62°].

Sol. in petr. ether, ethyl acetate and

benzene.

⑥ Chem. Revs. **60**, 459 (1960).

SnC₂₂H₂₈O₂

① (2-Carbomethoxyethyl)triphenyltin

(C₆H₅)₃(CH₃OCOCH₂CH₂)Sn

② (C₆H₅)₃SnH + CH₂=CHCOOCH₃

⟶ 63%

③ [46.5~47°].

④ + NaOH ⟶ C₆H₅SnCH₂CH₂COONa

+ Br₂ ⟶

C₆H₅SnBr₂(CH₂CH₂COOCH₃)

⑥ Chem. Revs. **60**, 459 (1960).

SnC₂₄F₂₀

① Tetrakis(pentafluorophenyl)tin

Sn(C₆F₅)₄

② SnCl₄ + 4 C₆F₅MgBr ⟶

③ [221°].

⑥ Proc. Chem. Soc. **1963**, 108.

SnC₂₄H₅F₁₅

① Phenyltris(pentafluorophenyl)tin

C₆H₅Sn(C₆F₅)₃

② C₆H₅SnCl₃ + 3 C₆F₅MgBr ⟶

③ [100~102°].

⑥ Proc. Chem. Soc. **1963**, 108.

SnC₂₄H₁₆Cl₄

① Tetrakis(*p*-chlorophenyl)tin

(*p*-ClC₆H₄)₄Sn

② SnCl₄ + 4 *p*-ClC₆H₄MgBr $\xrightarrow{\text{dry benzene}}$

③ [199°].

⑥ Chem. Revs. **60**, 459 (1960).

SnC₂₄H₁₈Cl₂O₂

① Di-*o*-phenoxyphenyltin dichloride

(*o*-C₆H₅OC₆H₄)₂SnCl₂

② (*o*-C₆H₅OC₆H₄)₄Sn + SnCl₄ $\xrightarrow{\text{xylene}}$

③ [98~99°].

④ + 2 OH⁻ ⟶ (*o*-C₆H₅OC₆H₄)₂Sn(OH)₂

⑥ JCS **1963**, 706.

SnC₂₄H₁₉Br

① (*p*-Bromophenyl)triphenyltin

p-BrC₆H₄Sn(C₆H₅)₃

② (C₆H₅)₃SnX + BrC₆H₄MgBr ⟶ 69%

(X=Cl, Br)

③ [133~135°].

⑥ Chem. Revs. **60**, 459 (1960).

SnC₂₄H₁₉Cl

① (*p*-Chlorophenyl)triphenyltin

  (*p*-ClC₆H₄)Sn(C₆H₅)₃

② Ph₃SnCl + *p*-ClC₆H₄MgBr $\longrightarrow$ 88%

③ [141°].

④ + PhLi $\longrightarrow$ Ph₄Sn

⑥ Chem. Revs. **60**, 459 (1960).

SnC₂₄H₂₀

① Tetraphenyltin

  (C₆H₅)₄Sn

② SnCl₄ + 4 C₆H₅MgBr $\xrightarrow{\text{ether}}$

  (C₆H₅)₃SnLi + C₆H₅I $\xrightarrow{\text{ether}}$

③ [229°].

④ + SnCl₄ $\longrightarrow$ (C₆H₅)₃SnCl,

  (C₆H₅)₂SnCl₂

⑥ Chem. Revs. **60**, 459 (1960).

SnC₂₄H₅₁Cl

① Trioctyltin chloride

  (C₈H₁₇)₃SnCl

② (C₈H₁₇)₄Sn + HCl(g) $\longrightarrow$ 73%

③ (163～166°/0.008).

⑥ Chem. Revs. **60**, 459 (1960).

SnC₂₄H₅₂

① Tetrahexyltin

  (C₆H₁₃)₄Sn

② SnCl₄ + 4 C₆H₁₃MgBr $\longrightarrow$

③ (209°/10). n_D1.4706 (20°). d0.9959

  (20°/4°).

⑥ Chem. Revs. **60**, 459 (1960).

SnC₂₅H₂₀O₂

① (*p*-Carboxyphenyl)triphenyltin

  (C₆H₅)₃Sn(*p*-C₆H₄COOH)

② Ph₃Sn(C₆H₄CH₂OH) + KMnO₄ $\longrightarrow$

  Ph₃Sn(C₆H₄COOK) $\xrightarrow{H^+}$

③ [166～168° decomp.].

⑥ Chem. Revs. **60**, 459 (1960).

SnC₂₅H₃₀O₂

① 3-(Triphenylstannyl)propanal

  diethylacetal

  (C₆H₅)₃SnCH₂CH₂CH(OC₂H₅)₂

② (C₆H₅)₃SnH +

  CH₂=CHCH(OC₂H₅)₂ $\longrightarrow$

③ [35.5～37.5°].

⑥ Chem. Revs. **60**, 459 (1960).

SnC₂₅H₅₄O

① Methoxytrioctyltin

  (C₈H₁₇)₃SnOCH₃

② (C₈H₁₇)₃SnCl + CH₃ONa $\longrightarrow$

③ n_D1.4781 (20°).

  Sol. in petr. ether.

⑤ Stabilizer for polyvinyl chloride.

⑥ Chem. Revs. **60**, 459 (1960).

SnC₂₆H₂₄

① Triphenyl(phenylethyl)tin

  (C₆H₅)₃SnCH₂CH₂C₆H₅

② (C₆H₅)₃SnH + C₆H₅CH=CH₂ $\longrightarrow$

③ [127～127.5°].

⑥ Chem. Revs. **60**, 459 (1960).

SnC₂₆H₃₂

① Octyltriphenyltin

  (C₆H₅)₃Sn(C₈H₁₇)

② (C₆H₅)₃SnCl + C₈H₁₇MgBr $\longrightarrow$

  (C₆H₅)₃SnH + CH₂=CH−C₆H₁₃ $\longrightarrow$

③ [54～55°].

⑥ Chem. Revs. **60**, 459 (1960).

SnC₂₇H₂₁NO

① Triphenyltin oxinate

  (C₆H₅)₃Sn(C₉H₆NO)

② (C₆H₅)₃SnCl + 8-hydroxyquinoline

  $\xrightarrow{\text{ethanol, OH}^-}$

③ Yellow crystals. [145～146.5°].

  Sol. in org. solvents.

⑥ JOM 1, 427 (1964); **4**, 159 (1965).

SnC₂₈H₂₆O₃

① *m*-Triphenylstannylphenoxyacetic

  acid ethylester

  (C₆H₅)₃Sn(*m*-C₆H₄OCH₂COOC₂H₅)

③ [97~98°].
⑥ Chem. Revs. **60**, 459 (1960).

SnC$_{28}$H$_{28}$
① Tetrabenzyltin
   Sn(CH$_2$C$_6$H$_5$)$_4$
② SnCl$_4$ + 4 C$_6$H$_5$CH$_2$Cl $\xrightarrow{\text{Mg, ether}}$
③ [42~43°].
   Sol. in common org. solvents except
   petr. ether.
   Slowly undergoes atmospheric oxidation.
⑥ Chem. Revs. **6**, 459 (1960).

SnC$_{28}$H$_{28}$O$_4$
① Tetrakis(p-methoxyphenyl)tin
   (p-CH$_3$OC$_6$H$_4$)$_4$Sn
⑥ Chem. Revs. **60**, 459 (1960).

SnC$_{28}$H$_{60}$
① Tetraheptyltin
   (C$_7$H$_{15}$)$_4$Sn
③ (219~221°/2). n_D1.4698 (20°). d0.9748
   (20°/4°).
⑥ Chem. Revs. **60**, 459 (1960).

SnC$_{30}$H$_{22}$N$_2$O$_2$
① Diphenyltin dioxinate
   (C$_6$H$_5$)$_2$Sn(C$_9$H$_6$NO)$_2$
② (C$_6$H$_5$)$_2$SnX$_2$ + 2(8-hydroxyquinoline)
   $\xrightarrow{\text{ethanol, +OH}^-}$
③ Yellow crystals. [231~233°], [251~
   252°].
   Sol. in org. solvents.
⑥ JCS **1961**, 756. JOM **1**, 484 (1964).

SnC$_{30}$H$_{56}$O$_8$
① (Dibutylstannylene)dimalonicacid
   tetrabutylester
   (C$_4$H$_9$)$_2$Sn[CH(CO$_2$C$_4$H$_9$)$_2$]$_2$
② (C$_4$H$_9$)$_2$SnCl$_2$
      + 2 NaCH(CO$_2$C$_4$H$_9$)$_2$ $\longrightarrow$
   (C$_4$H$_9$)$_2$Sn(OCH$_3$)$_2$

   $+ 2\,CH_2(CO_2C_4H_9)_2 \xrightarrow{90°}$
③ n_D1.4544. d1.1055 (20°/4°).
⑤ Stabilizer for vinyl halide resins.
⑥ Chem. Revs. **60**, 459 (1960).

SnC$_{32}$H$_{64}$O$_4$
① Dibutyltin dilaurate
   (C$_4$H$_9$)$_2$Sn[OOC(CH$_2$)$_{10}$CH$_3$]$_2$
② (C$_4$H$_9$)$_2$SnCl$_2$ + 2 sodium laurate $\longrightarrow$
⑤ Stabilizer for polyvinyl chloride,
   antioxidant for rubber, and
   catalyzer for polyester.
⑥ Chem. Revs. **60**, 459 (1960).

SnC$_{32}$H$_{68}$
① Tetraoctyltin
   (C$_8$H$_{17}$)$_4$Sn
② SnCl$_4$ + 4 C$_8$H$_{17}$MgBr $\longrightarrow$ 37%
③ (268°/10). n_D1.4691 (20°). d0.9605
   (20°/4°).
⑥ Chem. Revs. **60**, 459 (1960).

SnC$_{32}$H$_{68}$S$_2$
① Dibutylbis(dodecylthio)tin
   (C$_4$H$_9$)$_2$Sn(SC$_{12}$H$_{25}$)$_2$
② (C$_4$H$_9$)$_2$SnO + 2 C$_{12}$H$_{25}$SH $\longrightarrow$
③ (160°/0.0001). n_D1.5011 (20°).
⑤ Vinylhalide stabilizer.
⑥ Chem. Revs. **60**, 459 (1960).

SnC$_{36}$H$_{60}$S$_2$
① Bis(dodecylthio)diphenyltin
   (C$_6$H$_5$)$_2$Sn(SC$_{12}$H$_{25}$)$_2$
② (C$_6$H$_5$)$_2$SnO + 2 C$_{12}$H$_{25}$SH $\longrightarrow$
⑤ Polyvinyl halide stabilizer.
⑥ Chem. Revs. **60**, 459 (1960).

SnC$_{40}$H$_{28}$
① Tetra-1-naphthyltin
   (C$_{10}$H$_7$)$_4$Sn
② SnCl$_4$ + 4 LiC$_{10}$H$_7$ $\longrightarrow$
③ [310~320° decomp.].
⑥ Chem. Revs. **60**, 459 (1960).

SnC₄₈H₃₆O₄

① Tetra-*o*-phenoxyphenyltin
   (*o*-C₆H₅OC₆H₄)₄Sn
   C₆H₅OC₆H₅ + C₄H₉Li + SnCl₄ $\longrightarrow$
③ [234~235°].
④ + SnCl₄ $\longrightarrow$ (*o*-C₆H₅OC₆H₄)₂SnCl₂
   + I₂ $\longrightarrow$ (*o*-C₆H₅OC₆H₄)₂SnI₂
⑥ JCS **1963**, 706.

Sn₂C₄H₁₂OCl₂

① Tetramethyl-1,3-dichlorodistanno-
   xane
   Cl(CH₃)₂SnOSn(CH₃)₂Cl
② (CH₃)₂SnCl(OOCCH₃) + H₂O $\xrightarrow{\text{alc.}}$
   (CH₃)₂SnO + HCl $\xrightarrow{\text{boiling methanol}}$
   (CH₃)₂SnCl₂ + H₂O + pyridine $\longrightarrow$
③ [390°].
   Sparingly sol. in H₂O and benzene.
   IR: Spectrochim. Acta **16**, 595 (1960).
④ + H₂O + pyridine + CH₃OH $\longrightarrow$
   Cl(CH₃)₂SnOSn(CH₃)₂OCH₃ $\xrightarrow{\text{in air}}$
   Cl(CH₃)₂SnOSn(CH₃)₂OH
   + HCOOH $\longrightarrow$ Cl(CH₃)₂SnOOCH
⑥ JACS **82**, 3285 (1960). JOM **1**, 81(1963).

Sn₂C₄H₁₃O₂Br

① Tetramethyl-1-bromo-3-hydroxy-
   distannoxane
   Br(CH₃)₂SnOSn(CH₃)₂OH
② (CH₃)₂SnBr₂ + H₂O + pyridine $\xrightarrow{\text{CH₃OH}}$
   Br(CH₃)₂SnOSn(CH₃)₂OCH₃ $\xrightarrow{\text{in air}}$
③ [>220°].
   Insol. in nonpolar org. solvents.
⑥ JOM **1**, 81 (1963).

Sn₂C₄H₁₃O₂Cl

① Tetramethyl-1-chloro-3-hydroxy-
   distannoxane
   Cl(CH₃)₂SnOSn(CH₃)₂OH
② Cl(CH₃)₂SnOSn(CH₃)₂Cl + CH₃OH
   (excess) + pyridine $\longrightarrow$

Cl(CH₃)₂SnOSn(CH₃)₂OCH₃ $\xrightarrow{\text{in air}}$
③ [>220°].
⑥ JOM **1**, 81 (1963).

Sn₂C₄H₁₃O₇I

① Tetramethyl-1-iodo-3-hydroxy-
   distannoxane
   I(CH₃)₂SnOSn(CH₃)₂OH
② (CH₃)₂SnI₂ + H₂O + pyridine $\xrightarrow{\text{CH₃OH}}$
   I(CH₃)₂SnOSn(CH₃)₂OCH₃ $\xrightarrow{\text{in air}}$
③ [>220°].
⑥ JOM **1**, 81 (1963).

Sn₂C₆H₁₈

① Hexamethylditin
   (CH₃)₃SnSn(CH₃)₃
② (CH₃)₃SnOH or (CH₃)₃SnBr + Na
   $\xrightarrow[\text{liq. NH₃}]{}$ 71%
③ (182°/756), (85~88°/45). [23°]. *d*1.570
   (25°/4°).
④ + I₂ $\longrightarrow$ (CH₃)₃SnI
   + O₂ $\longrightarrow$ (CH₃)₃SnOSn(CH₃)₃
   + Na(in liq. NH₃) $\longrightarrow$ (CH₃)₃SnNa
   + CCl₄ $\longrightarrow$ (CH₃)₃SnCl
   + (CH₃)₃SnCCl₃
⑥ Chem. Revs. **60**, 459 (1960).

Sn₂C₆H₁₈O

① Bis(trimethyltin) oxide,
   Hexamethyldistannoxane
   (CH₃)₃SnOSn(CH₃)₃
② (CH₃)₃SnOH + Na $\xrightarrow{\text{benzene}}$
③ (86°/24).
   IR: Z. anorg. allg. Chem. **315**, 283
   (1962).
④ + H₂O $\longrightarrow$ CH₂SnOH
⑥ Chem. Revs. **60**, 459 (1960).

Sn₂C₆H₁₈O₄S

① Bis(trimethyltin) sulfate
   [(CH₃)₃Sn]₂SO₄

⑥ Chem. Revs. **60**, 459 (1960).

Sn₂C₆H₁₈S

① Bis(trimethyltin) sulfide
(CH₃)₃SnSSn(CH₃)₃

② 2 (CH₃)₃SnI + Na₂S $\xrightarrow{C_2H_5OH}$

(CH₃)₃SnSCH₃ + S $\xrightarrow{120°,\ 24\,hr}$

③ Oily liq. (118°/18). [7°]. n_D1.5600
(20°). d1.6392 (35°/4°).
Sol. in ether and benzene; insol. in
H₂O.

⑥ Chem. Revs. **60**, 459 (1960).   JCS
1965, 1192.

Sn₂C₈H₁₈

① Bis(trimethyltin) acetylide
(CH₃)₃Sn−C≡C−Sn(CH₃)₃

② 2 (CH₃)₃SnCl(in ether) + NaC≡CNa
$\xrightarrow[\text{in liq. NH}_3]{}$ 81%

③ [59~60°].

④ + diene ⟶ Diels Alder reaction
product.

⑥ JOM **2**, 417 (1964).

Sn₂C₈H₁₈O₅

① Tetramethyl-1,3-diacetoxydistanno-
xane
CH₃COO(CH₃)₂SnOSn(CH₃)₂OOCCH₃

② (CH₃)₂SnO + acetic acid ⟶

③ [240°].
IR: JACS **82**, 3287 (1960).

⑥ JACS **82**, 3285 (1960).

Sn₂C₈H₂₀Br₂O

① Tetraethyl-1,3-dibromodistannoxane
Br(C₂H₅)₂SnOSn(C₂H₅)₂Br

② (C₂H₅)₂SnBr₂ + H₂O $\xrightarrow{\text{ethanol}}$

(C₂H₅)₂SnO + HBr $\xrightarrow{\text{ligroin}}$

③ [172~3°].
Sol. in org. solvents.

④ + pyridine + H₂O ⟶

Br(C₂H₅)₂SnOSn(C₂H₅)OH

⑥ JOM **1**, 81 (1963).

Sn₂C₈H₂₀Cl₂O

① Tetraethyl-1,3-dichlorodistannoxane
Cl(C₂H₅)₂SnOSn(C₂H₅)₂Cl

② (C₂H₅)₂SnCl₂ + H₂O
+ pyridine $\xrightarrow{\text{ethanol}}$
(C₂H₅)₂SnCl₂ + (C₂H₅)₂SnO ⟶

③ [175.5~6.5°].
Sol. in org. solvents.

④ + OH⁻ ⟶
Cl(C₂H₅)₂SnOSn(C₂H₅)₂OH
+ CH₃COOH
⟶ Cl(C₂H₅)₂SnOOCCH₃

⑥ JOM **1**, 81, 95 (1963).

Sn₂C₈H₂₁ClO₂

① Tetraethyl-1-chloro-3-hydroxy-
distannoxane
Cl(C₂H₅)₂SnOSn(C₂H₅)₂OH

② (C₂H₅)₂SnCl₂ + 3 (C₂H₅)₂SnO
+ H₂O ⟶
Cl(C₂H₅)₂SnOSn(C₂H₅)₂Cl + OH⁻ ⟶

③ [218° decomp.].
Sol. in alc. and acetone.

⑥ JOM **1**, 81 (1963).

Sn₂C₁₀H₃₀O₃Si₂

① Tetramethyl-1,3-bis(trimethyl
siloxy)distannoxane
(CH₃)₃SiO(CH₃)₂SnOSn(CH₃)₂OSi-
(CH₃)₃

② (CH₃)₂SnCl₂ + (CH₃)₃SiCl(excess)
+ OH⁻(excess) ⟶

③ [167~8°].
Sol. in org. solvents.
NMR: JOM **3**, 308 (1965)

⑥ JACS **83**, 1342 (1961).   JOM **1**, 81
(1963).

Sn₂C₁₂H₂₈Cl₂O

① Tetrapropyl-1,3-dichlorodistanno-

xane
Cl(C₃H₇)₂SnOSn(C₃H₇)₂Cl

② (C₃H₇)₂SnO + (C₃H₇)₂SnCl₂ $\xrightarrow{\text{benzene}}$
   (C₃H₇)₂SnCl₂ + OH⁻ ⟶

③ [121~122°].
   Sol. in org. solvents.
   Dimer.

④ + OH⁻ ⟶
   Cl(C₃H₇)₂SnOSn(C₃H₇)₂OH
   + CH₃COOH
   ⟶ Cl(C₃H₇)₂SnOOCCH₃

⑥ JOM 1, 81, 95 (1963).

Sn₂C₁₂H₂₉ClO₂

① Tetrapropyl-1-chloro-3-hydroxy-
   distannoxane
   Cl(C₃H₇)₂SnOSn(C₃H₇)₂OH

② (C₃H₇)₂SnCl₂ + 3 (C₃H₇)₂SnO
   + H₂O ⟶
   Cl(C₃H₇)₂SnOSn(C₃H₇)₂Cl + OH⁻ ⟶

③ [175~194° decomp.].
   Sol. in acetone.

⑥ JOM 1, 81 (1963).

Sn₂C₁₂H₃₀

① Hexaethylditin
   (C₂H₅)₃SnSn(C₂H₅)₃

② (C₂H₅)₃SnBr + Na
   $\xrightarrow[\text{NH₃ or diethylether}]{}$ 89%

③ (161~162°/23). n_D 1.53738 (17.8°).
   d 1.4115 (0°/4°).
   Sol. in ether, benzene and petr.
   ether; insol. in alcohol and
   acetone.

④ + H₂O ⟶ (C₂H₅)₃SnOH
   + O₂ ⟶ (C₂H₅)₃SnOSn(C₂H₅)₃
   + AgNO₃ -⟶ (C₂H₅)₃SnNO₃
   + I₂ ⟶ (C₂H₅)₃SnI
   + Na ⟶ (C₂H₅)₃SnNa in liq. NH₃

⑥ Chem. Revs. 60, 459 (1960).

Sn₂C₁₂H₃₀O

① Bis(triethyltin) oxide,

Hexaethyldistannoxane
(C₂H₅)₃SnOSn(C₂H₅)₃

② (C₂H₅)₃SnCl + OH⁻ ⟶
   (C₂H₅)₃SnOH ⟶

③ Oily liq. (154°/10), (100°/1), (272°/
   760). n_D 1.4975 (20°), 1.5010 (20°).

④ + H₂O ⟶ (C₂H₅)₃SnOH
   + 2 H₂S ⟶ [(C₂H₅)₃Sn]₂S

⑥ Chem. Revs. 60, 459 (1960).

Sn₂C₁₂H₃₀O₄S

① Bis(triethyltin) sulfate
   [(C₂H₅)₃Sn]₂SO₄

② (C₂H₅)₃SnOH + H₂SO₄ $\xrightarrow{\text{H₂O}}$ 74%

⑥ Chem. Revs. 60, 459 (1960).

Sn₂C₁₂H₃₀S

① Bis(triethyltin) sulfide
   (C₂H₅)₃SnSSn(C₂H₅)₃

② (C₂H₅)₃SnI + Na₂S(in ethanol) ⟶
   (C₂H₅)₃SnOSn(C₂H₅)₃ + H₂S ⟶

③ (167~167.5/12). n_D 1.5468 (20°). d 1.429
   (20°/4°).
   Sol. in org. solvents; insol. in H₂O.

④ + AgX ⟶ (C₂H₅)₃SnX
   (X=halogen, O₁/₂, OOCCH₃)

⑥ Chem. Revs. 60, 459 (1960).

Sn₂C₁₃H₃₀O₃

① Bis(triethyltin) carbonate
   [(C₂H₅)₃Sn]₂CO₃

② 2 (C₂H₅)₃SnOH + CO₂ ⟶
   (C₂H₅)₃SnBr + NaOH + CO₂ ⟶

③ [138~139° decomp.].

⑥ Chem. Revs. 60, 459 (1960).

Sn₂C₁₄H₃₀

① Bis(triethyltin) acetylide
   (C₂H₅)₃Sn−C≡C−Sn(C₂H₅)₃

② (C₂H₅)₃SnOH + NaC≡CNa
   $\xrightarrow[\text{10~12hr}]{\text{ether}}$ 62%

③ (136~137°/5). n_D 1.5089 (20°). d 1.3430

(20°/4°).

⑥ Dokl. **158** (4) 918 (1964). Ger. 1062244 ;
　 CA **55**, 11303 (1961).

$Sn_2C_{16}H_{22}O_3$

① Tetramethyl-1,3-diphenoxydistanno-
　　xane
　 $C_6H_5O(CH_3)_2SnOSn(CH_3)_2OC_6H_5$

② $(CH_3)_2SnO + C_6H_5OH \longrightarrow$

③ [190~197°].
　 Sol. in org. solvents.

⑥ Can. J. Chem. **41**, 1239 (1963).

$Sn_2C_{16}H_{36}Br_2O$

① Tetrabutyl-1,3-dibromodistannoxane
　 $Br(C_4H_9)_2SnOSn(C_4H_9)_2Br$

② $(C_4H_9)_2SnBr_2 + OH_2 \longrightarrow$

　 $(C_4H_9)_2SnBr_2 + (C_4H_9)_2SnO \xrightarrow{\text{benzene}}$

③ [107~108°].
　 Sol. in org. solvents.

④ $+ OH^- \longrightarrow$
　 $Br(C_4H_9)_2SnOSn(C_4H_9)_2OH$

⑥ JOM 1, 81(1963). JOC **26**, 2304(1961).

$Sn_2C_{16}H_{36}Cl_2O$

① Tetrabutyl-1,3-dichlorodistanno-
　　xane
　 $Cl(C_4H_9)_2SnOSn(C_4H_9)_2Cl$

② $(C_4H_9)_2SnO + (C_4H_9)_2SnCl_2 \xrightarrow{\text{benzene}}$

　 $(C_4H_9)_2SnCl_2 + H_2O \xrightarrow{\text{ethanol}}$
　 $Cl(C_4H_9)_2SnSn(C_4H_9)_2Cl + O_2 \longrightarrow$

③ [112.5°].
　 Sol. in org. solvents.
　 Dimer.

④ $+ 2,2'$-bipyridine
　 $\xrightarrow{\text{ether}} (C_4H_9)_2SnCl_2 \cdot bipy$
　 $+ C_4H_9MgBr \longrightarrow (C_4H_9)_4Sn$

⑥ JOM 1, 81 (1963). JCS **1963**, 5469.

$Sn_2C_{16}H_{37}ClO_2$

① Tetrabutyl-1-chloro-3-hydroxy-
　　distannoxane

$Cl(C_4H_9)_2SnOSn(C_4H_9)_2OH$

② $(C_4H_9)_2SnCl_2 + 3 (C_4H_9)_2SnO$
　 $+ OH_2 \xrightarrow{\text{benzene}}$
　 $Cl(C_4H_9)_2SnOSn(C_4H_9)_2Cl + OH^- \longrightarrow$

③ [109~121° decomp.].
　 Sol. in org. solvents.
　 Dimer.

⑥ JOM 1, 81 (1963).

$Sn_2C_{18}H_{36}N_2OS_2$

① Tetrabutyl-1, 3-diisothiocyanato-
　　distannoxane
　 $SCN(C_4H_9)_2SnOSn(C_4H_9)_2NCS$

② $Cl(C_4H_9)_2SnOSn(C_4H_9)_2Cl$
　 $+ 2 NaNCS \longrightarrow$
　 $(C_4H_9)_2Sn(NCS)_2 + (C_4H_9)_2SnO$
　 $\xrightarrow[\text{benzene}]{} 88\%$

③ [84°].
　 Sol. in org. solvents.
　 IR : ν_{NC} 2041, 1961 cm^{-1}.
　 Dimer.

④ $+ H_2O + $ pyridine $\xrightarrow{C_2H_5OH}$
　 $SCN(C_4H_9)_2SnOSn(C_4H_9)_2OH$

⑥ JCS **1963**, 5469. JOM **3**, 70 (1965).

$Sn_2C_{18}H_{42}O$

① Bis(tri-*n*-propyltin) oxide,
　　Hexa-*n*-propyldistannoxane
　 $(n$-$C_3H_7)_3SnOSn(n$-$C_3H_7)_3$

② $(n$-$C_3H_7)_3SnX + OH^- \longrightarrow$
　 (X＝Cl, Br or OOCCH_3)

③ Oily liq. (142~144°/1), (195~198°/21).
　 $n_D 1.4927$ (20°).

④ $+ RCOOH \longrightarrow (n$-$C_3H_7)_3SnOOCR$
　 $+ C_6H_5OH \longrightarrow (n$-$C_3H_7)_3SnOC_6H_5$
　 $+ RSH \longrightarrow (n$-$C_3H_7)_3SnSR$

⑥ Chem. Revs. **60**, 459 (1960).　 JOM
　 1, 81 (1963).

$Sn_2C_{24}H_{54}O$

① Bis(tri-*n*-butyltin) oxide,
　　Hexa-*n*-butyldistannoxane

$(n-C_4H_9)_3SnOSn(n-C_4H_9)_3$

② $(n-C_4H_9)_3SnX + OH^-(excess) \longrightarrow$
   (X=Cl, Br, or OOCCH₃)

③ $(220\sim230°/10)$. $n_D 1.4872$ $(20°)$.

④ $+ HX \longrightarrow (n-C_4H_9)_3SnX$
   (X=Cl, OOCCH₃)
   $+ CO_2 \longrightarrow [(n-C_4H_9)_3Sn]_2CO_3$

⑥ Chem. Revs. **60**, 459 (1960).   JOM
   1, 81 (1963).

$Sn_2C_{24}H_{54}S$

① Bis(tributyltin) sulfide
   $(C_4H_9)_3SnSSn(C_4H_9)_3$

② $(C_4H_9)_3SnOSn(C_4H_9)_3 + CS_2(excess)$
   $\longrightarrow$ 99%
   $(C_4H_9)_3SnOSn(C_4H_9)_3 + thiourea$
   $\longrightarrow$ 70%

③ $(185\sim188°/0.6)$. $n_D 1.5176(20°)$. $d\,1.1930$
   $(20°/4°)$.

⑥ Inorg. Chem. **1**, 651(1962).   Australian
   J. Chem. **17**, 411 (1964).

$Sn_2C_{28}H_{46}O_3$

① Tetrabutyl-1,3-diphenoxydistanno-
   xane
   $C_6H_5O(C_4H_9)_2SnOSn(C_4H_9)_2OC_6H_5$

② $(C_4H_9)_2SnO + C_6H_5OH \xrightarrow{\text{toluene}}$
   $(C_4H_9)_2SnO + (C_4H_9)_2Sn(OC_6H_5)_2 \longrightarrow$
   $(C_4H_9)_2Sn(OC_6H_5)_2 + H_2O \longrightarrow$

③ $[137\sim139°]$.
   Sol. in org. solvents.

⑥ Can. J. Chem. **41**, 1239 (1963).

$Sn_2C_{36}H_{30}$

① Hexaphenylditin
   $(C_6H_5)_3SnSn(C_6H_5)_3$

② $(C_6H_5)_3SnLi + (C_6H_5)_3SnCl \longrightarrow$ 53%
   $(C_6H_5)_3SnCl + Na(in\ liq.\ NH_3)$
   $\longrightarrow$ 50%
   $C_6H_5HgCl + Na_2Sn \longrightarrow$
   $(C_6H_5)_3SnH + (C_6H_5)_3SnNH_2 \longrightarrow$

③ $[229\sim231°]$.
   Sol. in CHCl₃ and benzene.

④ $+ I_2 \longrightarrow (C_6H_5)_3SnI$

⑥ Chem. Revs. **60**, 459 (1960).

$Sn_2C_{36}H_{30}O$

① Bis(triphenyltin) oxide,
   Hexaphenyldistannoxane
   $(C_6H_5)_3SnOSn(C_6H_5)_3$

② $(C_6H_5)_3SnCl + OH^- \longrightarrow$

③ $[124°]$.

⑥ Chem. Revs. **60**, 459 (1960).

$Sn_2C_{36}H_{30}S$

① Bis(triphenyltin) sulfide
   $(C_6H_5)_3SnSSn(C_6H_5)_3$

② $(C_6H_5)_3SnOSn(C_6H_5)_3 + Na_2S \longrightarrow$
   $(C_6H_5)_3SnOSn(C_6H_5)_3 + CS_2(excess)$
   $\xrightarrow[18\ hr]{95°}$ 99%

③ $[145.5\sim147°]$.

⑥ JOC **26**, 4634 (1961).   Inorg. Chem. **1**,
   651 (1962),

$Sn_2C_{42}H_{42}O$

① Bis(3-triphenylstannylpropyl) ether
   $[(C_6H_5)_3SnCH_2CH_2CH_2]_2O$

② $2(C_6H_5)_3SnH + diallyl\ ether$
   $\longrightarrow$ 33%

③ $[105\sim108°]$.

⑥ Chem. Revs. **60**, 459 (1960).

$Sn_2C_{44}H_{38}$

① 1-Phenyl-1,2-bis(triphenylstannyl)
   ethane
   $(C_6H_5)_3SnCH(C_6H_5)CH_2Sn(C_6H_5)_3$

② $2(C_6H_5)_3SnH + C_6H_5-C\equiv CH$
   $\longrightarrow$ 49%

③ $[139\sim140°]$.

⑥ Chem. Revs. **60**, 459 (1960).

$Sn_2C_{44}H_{42}O_4$

① Ethyleneglycol bis(3-triphenylstan-
   nylpropionate)
   $[(C_6H_5)_3SnCH_2CH_2CO_2CH_2]_2$

② $2(C_6H_5)_3SnH$
   $+ ethyleneglycol\ diacrylate$

$\longrightarrow$ 91%

③ [93~96°].

⑥ Chem. Revs. 60, 459 (1960).

Sn₂C₄₆H₄₂

① 1, 4-Bis[2-(triphenylstannyl)ethyl]-benzene

p-[(C₆H₅)₃SnCH₂CH₂]₂C₆H₄

② 2 (C₆H₅)₃SnH + p-divinylbenzene

$\xrightarrow{100°}$ 40%

③ [136~142°].

⑥ Chem. Revs. 60, 459 (1960).

【Pb】

PbC₂H₆Br₂

① Dimethyllead dibromide

(CH₃)₂PbBr₂

② (CH₃)₄Pb $\xrightarrow{2\,Br_2}$

CH₃MgCl + PbCl₂ $\xrightarrow{\text{in ether+MeI}}$

(CH₃)₄Pb $\xrightarrow{\text{Br}_2 \text{ in ether}}$ 70%

③ White crystals. [50° decomp.]

Slightly sol. in polar org. solvents.

⑥ Ber. 49, 1415 (1916).   JACS 76, 1760 (1950).

PbC₂H₆Cl₂

① Dimethyllead dichloride

(CH₃)₂PbCl₂

② (CH₃)₄Pb $\xrightarrow{2\,Cl_2 \text{ in CH}_3\text{COOR, } -75°}$

③ White crystals. [155~230° decomp].

Sol. in H₂O; slightly sol. in polar org. solvents; insol. in org. solvents.

⑥ Ber. 49, 1415 (1916).   CA 53, 9901 (1959); 55, 14159, 14175(1961); 50, 7728 (1956).

PbC₂H₈

① Dimethylead dihydride

(CH₃)₂PbH₂

② 2 Pb(CH₃)₃X

+ LiAlH₄ $\xrightarrow{\text{ether, } -90\sim-110°}$
(X=Cl orBr)

③ Liq. compd.

Decomp. at −50°.

ΔH_{vap}=6.095 kcal/mol.

④ $\xrightarrow{\text{r. t.}}$ Pb(CH₃)₄ + PbH₄

PbH₄ $\longrightarrow$ Pb + 2 H₂

+ C₂H₄N₂ $\longrightarrow$ Me₄Pb(83%)

+ Me₃PbEt(12%) + Me₂PbEt₂(5%)

⑥ Angew. 72, 494 (1960).   JACS 82, 6264 (1960).

PbC₂H₁₄B₂

① Dimethyllead bis(borohydride)

(CH₃)₂Pb(BH₄)₂

② 2 Al(BH₄)₃ + (CH₃)₄Pb

$\xrightarrow{-19\sim-60° \text{ in vacuum}}$

③ White solid.

Decomp. at −30~−20°.

⑥ JINC 6, 134 (1958).

PbC₃H₈Cl₂

① Ethylmethyllead dichloride

(C₂H₅)(CH₃)PbCl₂

② (CH₃)₃(C₂H₅)Pb $\xrightarrow{-75°}$

(CH₃)₂(C₂H₅)PbCl $\longrightarrow$

③ Solid.

Slightly sol. in org. solvents.

④ $\left.\begin{array}{l} + \text{H}_2\text{S} \\ (\text{NH}_4)_2\text{S} \end{array}\right\}$ $\xrightarrow{\text{in weak alkali soln.}}$

(C₂H₅)(CH₃)PbS

+ KI $\longrightarrow$ (C₂H₅)(CH₃)PbI₂

⑥ Ber. 50, 202 (1917).

PbC₃H₉Cl

① Trimethyllead chloride

(CH₃)₃PbCl

② (CH₃)₄Pb $\xrightarrow{Cl_2, -60°}$

(CH₃)₄Pb $\xrightarrow{\text{HCl in hexane, 20 min.}}$ 60%

(CH₃)₄Pb $\xrightarrow{\text{HCl in dry ether}}$

③ White solid. (187° sublimes).   [190°
   decomp.)].
   Sol. in hot polar org. solvents; insol.
   in H_2O.
④ + $(C_2H_5)_3PbCl$ $\longrightarrow$
   redistribution reaction
   + KBH_4 $\xrightarrow{\text{in } NH_3}$ $(CH_3)_3PbH$
⑥ Ber. **49**, 1415 (1916).   JCS **1958**, 3485.
   CA **53**, 12757 (1959).   Ricerca sci.
   30, 1963 (1960); CA **55**, 14159 (1961).
   Ricerca sci. **30**, 1671 (1960); CA **55**,
   14175 (1961).

PbC₃H₉F

① Trimethyllead fluoride
   $(CH_3)_3PbF$
② $(CH_3)_4Pb$ $\xrightarrow{\text{Br}_2 \text{ in ether, } -74°, \text{ Ag}_2O \text{ r.t.}}$
   $(CH_3)_3PbOH$ $\xrightarrow{\text{HF in EtOH}}$
③ White plates. [305° decomp.]. d 3.53
   (16°/4°).
   Sol. in polar org. solvents; insol.
   ιn org. solvents.
⑥ Ber. **55**, 1282 (1922).

PbC₃H₉NO₃

① Trimethyllead nitrate
   $(CH_3)_3PbNO_3$
② $(CH_3)_4Pb$ + $AgNO_3$ $\xrightarrow{-70°}$ 82.7%
③ Solid.
   Slightly sol. in H_2O, polar org. solvents.
⑥ JACS **65**, 435 (1943).

PbC₃H₁₀

① Trimethyllead hydride
   $(CH_3)_3PbH$
② $Pb(CH_3)_3Cl$ + KBH_4 $\xrightarrow{\text{in liq. } NH_3}$ 75%
   $Pb(CH_3)_3Cl$ + $LiAlH_4$
   $\xrightarrow{\text{ether, } -90\sim-110°}$ 95%
③ Colorless compound. (−5°). [−106°].
   Pb−H bond is rather ιonιc.

ΔH_{vap}=7.425 kcal/mole.
Decomp. slowly above −100° to a red
   solid.
IR : ν(Pb−H)1709 cm⁻¹.
NMR : τ(Pb−H)2.32, (Pb−CH₃)9.15.
   J(²⁰⁷Pb−H)2379, J(²⁰⁷Pb−CH₃)66.7,
   J(¹³C−H)36 cps.
④ + $C_2H_4N_2$ $\longrightarrow$ Me_4Pb 89%
   + Me_3EtPb(11%)
   + HCl $\longrightarrow$ Me_3PbCl + H_2
   + Me_3PbCl $\xrightarrow{\text{liq. } NH_3}$ $Me_3Pb-PbMe_3$
   + C_2H_4 $\longrightarrow$ $EtPbMe_3$ (92%)
   + NH_3 $\rightleftharpoons$ $[PbMe_3]^-NH_4^+$
⑥ Proc. Chem. Soc. **1959**, 124. JCS **1961**,
   1679; **1962**, 1144. Angew. **72**, 494
   (1960).   JACS **82**, 6264 (1960); **85**,
   1377 (1963).

PbC₃H₁₀O

① Trimethyllead hydroxide
   $(CH_3)_3PbOH$
② Me_3PbCl + KOH $\longrightarrow$
③ White needles. Infusible.
   Sol. in H_2O. Decomp. by alkali.
④ + Al or electrolysis $\longrightarrow$ $Me_3Pb \cdot$
⑥ Ber. **71**, 2381 (1938); **55**, 1282 (1922).

PbC₄H₄Cl₄

① Bis(2-chlorovinyl)lead dichloride
   $(CHCl=CH)_2PbCl_2$
② $(CHCl=CH)_2Hg$ + $Pb(OAc)_4$
   $\xrightarrow{\text{in CHCl}_3}$ $(CHCl=CH)HgOAc$
   + $(CHCl=CH)_2Pb(OAc)_2$
   $(CHCl=CH)_2Pb(OAc)_2$ + HCl $\xrightarrow{\text{in EtOH}}$
③ Crystals. [163~167° decomp.].
   Sol. in org. solvents.
④ + Hg $\xrightarrow{\text{MeOH}}$ *trans*-(CHCl=CH)HgCl
   + $SnCl_2$ $\longrightarrow$ $(ClCH=CH)_2SnCl_2$
   + $PbCl_2$
⑥ Izv. OKhN **1949**, 127; CA **43**, 560
   (1949).

PbC$_4$H$_9$MnO$_5$

① Trimethyllead-manganesepenta-
carbonyl
(CH$_3$)$_3$Pb·Mn(CO)$_5$

② NaMn(CO)$_5$ + (CH$_3$)$_3$PbCl
$\xrightarrow[\text{r. t., 3 hrs in THF}]{}$ 47%

③ Purified by distillation at a reduced
pressure.
Yellow solid. (60~62°/0.3). [30~31°].
Fairly stable in air. Sol. in CH$_2$Cl$_2$,
ether, acetone and THF; fairly
sol. in C$_2$H$_5$OH and C$_6$H$_6$; slightly
sol. in n-hexane.

④ + P(C$_6$H$_5$)$_3$ $\xrightarrow{\text{heat or catalytically in N}_2}$
(CH$_3$)$_3$Pb·Mn(CO)$_4$·P(C$_6$H$_5$)$_3$

⑥ JACS **84**, 2486 (1962).

PbC$_4$H$_{10}$Cl$_2$

① Diethyllead dichloride
(C$_2$H$_5$)$_2$PbCl$_2$

② (C$_2$H$_5$)$_4$Pb $\xrightarrow{\text{SO}_3}$ (C$_2$H$_5$)$_2$PbSO$_3$ $\xrightarrow{\text{HCl}}$
(C$_2$H$_5$)$_2$Pb $\xrightarrow{\text{Cl}_2, -60° \text{ in ether}}$
(C$_2$H$_5$)$_4$Pb $\xrightarrow{\text{2 HCl, 90° in ether or toluene}}$

③ White needles. [207~220°, decomp.].
Sol. in H$_2$O and polar org. solvents;
insol. in org. solvent.

④ + (C$_2$H$_5$)$_4$Pb
$\xrightarrow[\text{in butanol}]{\text{8 hr. reflux}}$ 2(C$_2$H$_5$)$_3$PbCl
$\longrightarrow$ (C$_2$H$_5$)PbCl + PbCl$_2$ + (C$_2$H$_5$)$_2$Pb
$\longrightarrow$ PbCl$_2$ + C$_4$H$_{10}$.
+ AgOCOCH$_2$Cl $\longrightarrow$
(C$_2$H$_5$)$_3$PbOCOCH$_2$Cl

⑥ JACS **54**, 3287 (1932); **70**, 3902 (1948);
52, 1975(1930). Ber. **49**, 1415(1916).
JCS **1951**, 658. CA **53**, 9901 (1959);
54, 3725 (1960).

PbC$_4$H$_{10}$O$_2$

① Trimethyllead formate
(CH$_3$)$_3$PbOCOH

② (CH$_3$)$_4$Pb + HCOOH $\xrightarrow{\text{silica gel}}$

③ White crystals. [113°]
Sol. in org. solvents.

⑥ JINC **16**, 204 (1961). JCS **1949**, 2983.

PbC$_4$H$_{10}$O$_3$S

① Diethyllead sulfite
(C$_2$H$_5$)$_2$Pb·SO$_3$

② (C$_2$H$_5$)$_4$Pb + SO$_3$ $\xrightarrow{\text{in ether}}$

③ Solid.
Slightly sol. in H$_2$O; insol. in alc.
and ether; sol. in dil. acid with
evolution of SO$_2$.

④ + dil. HCl $\longrightarrow$ (C$_2$H$_5$)$_2$PbCl$_2$
(pure crystals)

⑥ JCS **1951**, 658. Nature **159**, 491 (1947).

PbC$_4$H$_{12}$Se

① Trimethylmethylselenolead
(CH$_3$)$_3$PbSeCH$_3$

② CH$_3$MgBr + Se $\longrightarrow$ CH$_3$SeMgBr
CH$_3$SeMgBr + (CH$_3$)$_3$PbCl $\longrightarrow$ 50%

③ (75°/3, slightly decomp.). d2.42
(20°/4°).

⑤ Gasoline additives.

⑥ US 3010980; CA **56**, 11620 (1962).

PbC$_5$H$_9$Cl$_3$O$_2$

① Trimethyllead trichloroacetate
(CH$_3$)$_3$PbOCOCCl$_3$

② CCl$_3$COOH + (CH$_3$)$_4$Pb $\xrightarrow{\text{warm}}$

③ White solid. [169°].
Slightly sol. in polar org. solvents.
Darkens when heated to 180°, and
does not melt at 220°.

⑥ JCS, **1949**, 2983.

PbC$_5$H$_9$F$_5$

① Perfluoroethyltrimethyllead
C$_2$F$_5$Pb(CH$_3$)$_3$

② (CH$_3$)$_4$Pb + C$_2$F$_5$I
$\xrightarrow[\text{Zn-Hg, 8 hrs, 150°}]{}$ 28%

③ $\log P\text{mm} = B - AT^{-1}$ ($B = 7.843$, $A =$ 2040) $\Delta H_{vap} = 9.34$ kcal/mol.
(138°, by extrapolation of vapor pressure).
IR: 1070, 1085, 1198, 1318, 927±10, 784, 733 cm^{-1} (methyl rocking).
④ + KOH(aq) $\longrightarrow$ C_2F_5H ↑ (>90%)
⑥ JACS **82**, 6228 (1960). Chem. & Ind. **1959**, 1409.

$PbC_5H_{12}O_2$

① Trimethyllead acetate
$(CH_3)_3PbOCOCH_3$
② $(CH_3)_4Pb + CH_3COOH \xrightarrow{\text{N}_2}$ 84%
③ White solid. [183~184°].
Sol. in polar org. solvents. Recrystd. from H_2O.
IR: JINC **16**, 204 (1961).
⑤ Antifungal and antibacterial activity.
⑥ JACS **67**, 190 (1945).   JCS **1949**, 2983. J. Microbiol. Serol. **28**, 436 (1962); CA **58**, 7308 (1963).

PbC_5H_{14}

① Ethyltrimethyllead
$(CH_3)_3Pb(C_2H_5)$
② $(CH_3)_3PbX + C_2H_5MgBr \longrightarrow$ 85% (X=Cl, Br)
$(CH_3)_4Pb + (C_2H_5)_4Pb \xrightarrow{\text{cat.}}$ partially
$(CH_3)_2Hg + (C_2H_5)_4Pb \xrightarrow{\text{cat.}}$ partially
③ Colorless liquid. (27~28°/11), (128~130°/751). $n_D 1.5154(20°)$. d 1.8824 (15°/4°).
Sol. in org. solvents; insol. in H_2O.
⑥ Ber. **49**, 1125 (1916).   JACS **61**, 2748 (1939); **63**, 947 (1941).

$PbC_6H_6O_2$

① Phenylplumbonic acid
$C_6H_5Pb(O)OH$
② $C_6H_5Pb(OCOCH_3)_3 + NH_4OH \longrightarrow$
$C_6H_5Pb(OCOC_3H_7-i)_3 + NH_4OH$

in EtOH
$\xrightarrow{\hspace{1cm}}$ 85%
③ Yellow solid.
Insol. in H_2O, EtOH and ether.
④ + i-$C_3H_7COOH \longrightarrow$
$C_6H_5Pb(OCOC_3H_7-i)_3$
⑥ Dokl. **85**, 1037 (1952).   CA **47**, 6365 (1953); **50**, 7075 (1956).   Izv. OKhN **1955**, 711.

PbC_6H_9Cl

① Trivinyllead chloride
$(CH_2=CH)_3PbCl$
② $(CH_2=CH)_4Pb \xrightarrow{\text{dry HCl in hexane}}$ 30%
③ [119~121°].
⑥ JACS **81**, 3578 (1959).

PbC_6H_{14}

① Diisopropyllead
$(i$-$C_3H_7)_2Pb$
② $(CH_3)_2CO +$
$20\% H_2SO_4(\text{aq.}) \xrightarrow[\text{Pb electrode}]{\text{electrolysis}}$
mixt. with $(i$-$C_3H_7)_4Pb$
③ Decomp. in air. Decomp. at about 150°. Decomp. gradually at room temp. Highly effensive order.
Sol. in org. solvents; insol. in H_2O.
④ + $h\nu \longrightarrow$ $(i$-$C_3H_7)_4Pb + Pb$
+ O $\longrightarrow$ variable composition of lead and residual oil
residual oil + $CH_3COOH + KBr$
$\xrightarrow{\text{in H}_2\text{O}}$ $(i$-$C_3H_7)_2PbBr_2$
residual oil + $CH_3COOH + HCl$
$\xrightarrow{\text{in H}_2\text{O}}$ $(i$-$C_3H_7)_3PbCl$.
⑥ Ber. **44**, 323 (1911). Helv. Chim. Acta **14**, 1205, 1436 (1931).

$PbC_6H_{14}Cl_2$

① Diethyldichloromethyllead
$(C_2H_5)_2Pb(CH_2Cl)_2$
② $(C_2H_5)_2PbCl_2 + 2CH_2N_2$

Cu-bronze 10~15° in abs. ether
⟶

③ Liq. (96°/2). d1.9890(20°/4°).
Sol. in org. solvents.
⑥ CA **47**, 9257 (1953).

PbC$_6$H$_{15}$Na
① Triethylleadsodium
  (C$_2$H$_5$)$_3$Pb·Na
② (C$_2$H$_5$)$_3$PbPb(C$_2$H$_5$)$_3$
  $\xrightarrow{\text{in liq. NH}_3}$
  + 2 Na
  (C$_2$H$_5$)$_3$PbCl + 2 Na $\xrightarrow{\text{in liq. NH}_3}$
  (C$_2$H$_5$)$_4$Pb + 2 Na + NH$_3$ ⟶
③ Solution in liq. NH$_3$.
④ + n- or sec-C$_4$H$_9$Br ⟶
  (C$_2$H$_5$)$_3$Pb(C$_4$H$_9$-n or -sec) + NaBr
  + C$_6$H$_5$Cl ⟶ (C$_2$H$_5$)$_3$PbC$_6$H$_5$
  + (C$_2$H$_5$)$_4$Pb + etc.
⑥ JOC **18**, 1675 (1953). JACS **57**, 885
  (1935). Australian J.Chem. **14**, 555
  (1961).

PbC$_6$H$_{16}$
① Diethyldimethyllead
  (C$_2$H$_5$)$_2$Pb(CH$_3$)$_2$
② (CH$_3$)$_6$Pb$_2$ + (C$_2$H$_5$)$_6$Pb$_2$ ⟶ 23 mol%
  (CH$_3$)$_4$Pb + (C$_2$H$_5$)$_2$Hg
  $\xrightarrow{\text{cat.}}$ 29.1 mol%
  (C$_2$H$_5$)$_4$Pb + (CH$_3$)$_2$Hg
  $\xrightarrow{\text{cat.}}$ 27.5 mol%
  (CH$_3$)$_4$Pb + (C$_2$H$_5$)$_2$Pb $\xrightarrow{\text{cat.}}$
  (C$_2$H$_5$)$_2$PbCl$_2$ + CH$_3$MgI $\xrightarrow{\text{ether}}$
③ Liq. (51°/13), (52~53°/14). n_D1.5177
  (20°). d1.7906(20°/4°).
⑥ Ber. **49**, 2441 (1916). JACS **61**, 947,
  2748 (1939); **62**, 1542 (1940); **64**, 462
  (1942).

PbC$_6$H$_{16}$
① n-Propyltrimethyllead
  n-C$_3$H$_7$Pb(CH$_3$)$_3$

② n-C$_3$H$_7$MgCl + (CH$_3$)$_3$PbCl $\xrightarrow{\text{ether}}$ 90%
③ Colorless liq. (48~49°/16). n_D1.5082
  (21.0°). d1.7595 (23°/4°).
  Sol. in org. solvents.
⑥ Ber. **49**, 1125 (1916).

PbC$_6$H$_{16}$
① Triethyllead hydride
  (C$_2$H$_5$)$_3$PbH
② (C$_2$H$_5$)$_3$PbX + LiAlH$_4$ $\xrightarrow{\text{in ether}}$ 20%
③ Colorless compd. [−145°]. Decomp.
  at above 0°.
  Unstable.
④ + CH$_2$N$_2$ ⟶ CH$_3$Pb(C$_2$H$_5$)$_3$ (30%)
  + (C$_2$H$_5$)$_4$Pb (69%)
  + HCl ⟶ (C$_2$H$_5$)$_3$PbCl + H$_2$
⑥ JACS **82**, 6264 (1960). JCS **1962**, 1144.

PbC$_6$H$_{18}$OSi
① Hexamethylplumbosiloxane
  (CH$_3$)$_3$PbOSi(CH$_3$)$_3$
② (CH$_3$)$_3$SiONa + (CH$_3$)$_3$PbBr ⟶
③ Colorless liq. (172°). [−1°].
  Stable against dry air and light, and
    very sensitive to water. Unexpec-
    ted thermal stability.
  High vapor pressure.
④ + moisture in the air
  ⟶ hydrolysis
  + O$_2$ $\xrightarrow{>150°}$ Pb(explosion)
⑥ JACS **83**, 2963 (1961).

PbC$_6$H$_{18}$O$_8$N$_2$
① Di-n-propyllead dinitrate dihydrate
  (n-C$_3$H$_7$)$_2$Pb(NO$_3$)$_2$·2 H$_2$O
② (n-C$_3$H$_7$)$_4$Pb + 2 HNO$_3$ $\xrightarrow{\text{ether}}$
③ Colorless crystals. [87~89°].
  Sol. in H$_2$O, polar org. solvents.
⑥ JCS **1935**, 39.

PbC$_7$H$_{14}$O$_2$
① Trimethyllead methacryrate

$(CH_3)_3PbOCOC(CH_3)=CH_2$

② $CH_2=C(CH_3)COOK$

$+ (CH_3)_3PbBr \xrightarrow{\text{in } C_6H_6}$

③ Sol. in polar org. solvents.

⑥ CA **35**, 8151 (1941).

PbC₇H₁₅N

① Triethyllead cyanide
$(C_2H_5)_3PbCN$

② $(C_2H_5)_3PbCl + KCN$

$\xrightarrow{1\frac{1}{4}\text{hrs. reflux in alc., } 80°}$

③ Solid. [189°].
Slightly sol. in polar org. solvents.

⑥ JACS **67**, 190 (1945).　JCS **1949**, 2983.
J. prakt. Chem. **81**, 287 (1860).

PbC₇H₁₅NS

① Triethyllead isothiocyanide
$(C_2H_5)_3PbNCS$

② $(C_2H_5)_3PbCl$

$+ KNCS \xrightarrow{1\frac{1}{2}\text{hrs. reflux in alc.}}$

③ Crystals. [35°].
Sol. in polar org. solvents; insol. in
water.

⑥ JOS **18**, 1341 (1953).　JCS **1949**, 2983.
J. prakt. Chem. **81**, 287 (1860).

PbC₇H₁₈

① n-Butyltrimethyllead
$n\text{-}C_4H_9Pb(CH_3)_3$

② $(CH_3)_3PbBr + n\text{-}C_4H_9MgBr \longrightarrow 80\%$

③ Liq. (64.5°/14). $n_D 1.5035(22.5°)$.
$d 1.6740(24°/4°)$.
Sol. in org. solvents.

⑥ Ber. **49**, 1125 (1916).

PbC₇H₁₈

① Isobutyltrimethyllead
$i\text{-}C_4H_9Pb(CH_3)_3$

② $(CH_3)_3PbCl + i\text{-}C_4H_9MgCl \longrightarrow 90\%$

③ Liq. (58~59°/15), (165~166°/769). n_D
1.5021 (21.2°). $d 1.6684$ (23.5°/4°).

Sol. in org. solvents.

⑥ Ber. **49**, 1125 (1916).

PbC₇H₁₈

① Methyltriethyllead
$CH_3Pb(C_2H_5)_3$

② $(C_2H_5)_3PbCl + CH_3MgCl \xrightarrow{\text{ether}} 90\%$

$(CH_3)_4Pb + (C_2H_5)_4Pb$

$\xrightarrow{BF_3, AlCl_3}$ fractional distillation

$(CH_3)_4Sn + (C_2H_5)_4Pb$

$\xrightarrow{\text{cat.}}$ fractional distillation

③ Liq. (0~70.5°/16). $n_D 1.5158$ (24.3°).
$d 1.7124(23.2°/4°)$.
Sol. in org. solvents.

④ $+ TlCl_3 \longrightarrow (C_2H_5)_3PbCl$
$+ TlCl + CH_3Cl$

⑥ Ber. **49**, 1125 (1916).　JCS **121**, 482
(1922).　JACS **61**, 2748 (1939).

PbC₇H₁₈

① n-Propylethyldimethyllead
$(CH_3)_2Pb(C_2H_5)(n\text{-}C_3H_7)$

② $(CH_3)_3Pb(C_2H_5) + Br_2$

$\xrightarrow{\text{ether}, -75°} (CH_3)_2Pb(C_2H_5)Br$

$(CH_3)_2Pb(C_2H_5)Br + n\text{-}C_3H_7MgCl$
$\longrightarrow 90\%$

③ Liq.(65°/15). $n_D 1.5110(21.8°)$. $d 1.6943$
(23°).
Sol. in org. solvents.

⑥ Ber. **50**, 202 (1917).

PbC₇H₁₈O

① Triethyllead methoxide
$(C_2H_5)_3PbOCH_3$

② $[(C_2H_5)_3Pb]_2O + CH_3OH \longrightarrow$

③ Creamy crystals. [60~70° decomp.].
Sol. in org. solvents. Fumed in air.
Unstable compd.

⑥ Dokl. **136**, 89 (1961).　CA **55**, 27023,
27027 (1961).　Tr. po Khim. i Khim.
Tekhnol. **3**, 381 (1960).

PbC₇H₁₉O₂NS

① Triethyllead methylsulfonamide
   $(C_2H_5)_3PbNHSO_2CH_3$

② $CH_3SO_2NH_2 + (C_2H_5)_3PbOH$
   $\xrightarrow{\text{reflux (30 mins) in hot } C_6H_6}$

③ Crystals. [197° decomp.].

⑥ JCS **1950**, 684.

PbC₈F₁₂

① Tetraperfluorovinyllead
   $(CF_2=CF)_4Pb$

② $CF_2=CFMgI + PbCl_2 \xrightarrow{\text{in ether or in THF}}$

③ $\mu=1.63$ D.
   Liquid. (51~52°/8). $n_D 1.4193(18°)$.
   $d\,2.4020(18°)$.
   IR: $\nu(C=C)$ 1720~1730 cm⁻¹.

⑥ CA **55**, 15336 (1961).

PbC₈H₁₀Cl₂O₄

① Bis(2-chlorovinyl)lead diacetate
   $(CHCl=CH)_2Pb(OCOCH_3)_2$

② $(CHCl=CH)_2Hg + Pb(OCOCH_3)_4$
   $\longrightarrow$ 72%

③ [>115° decomp.]
   Sol. in CHCl₃; moderately sol. in
   C₂H₅OH; poorly sol. in C₆H₆; insol.
   in ether and CCl₄.

④ $+ NH_4OCOCH_3 \longrightarrow (CHCl=CH)_2-$
   $Pb(OCOCH_3)_2 \cdot NH_4OCOCH_3$
   $+ HCl \longrightarrow (CHCl=CH)_2PbCl_2$
   $+ C_6H_5OH \longrightarrow$
   $(CHCl=CH)_2Pb(OC_6H_5)_2$
   $+ H_2SO_4 \longrightarrow (CHCl=CH)_2PbSO_4$

⑥ Dokl. **60**, 67 (1948). CA **43**, 560, 1716
   (1949). Izv. OKhN **1948**, 127.

PbC₈H₁₀Cl₆O₄

① Diethyllead bistrichloroacetate
   $(C_2H_5)_2Pb(OCOCCl_3)_2$

② $(C_2H_5)_2PbSO_3 + Cl_3CCOOH \longrightarrow$

③ Colorless needles. [151° decomp.].

④ $+ H_2S \xrightarrow{\text{in } H_2O}$ clean cream colored

ppt.

⑥ JCS **1951**, 658.

PbC₈H₁₀FeO₄

① Diethyllead-iron tetracarbonyl
   $(C_2H_5)_2Pb \cdot Fe(CO)_4$

② $Ca \cdot H \cdot Fe(CO)_4$
   $+ (C_2H_5)_3PbOH \xrightarrow{\text{in ether}}$

③ Red crystals.
   Sol. in alc., (CH₃)₂CO, ether and
   hexane. Become dull-brown in air
   and light, and less sol. in org.
   solvents.

④ $\xrightarrow{180°}$ yellow vapor + oily drops.
   $+$ hot concd. HNO₃
   $\longrightarrow$ decomp. product.

⑤ Metal plating.

⑥ Z. anorg. allg. Chem. **248**, 84 (1941).
   US 3018194; CA **56**, 8402 (1962).

PbC₈H₁₂

① Tetravinyllead
   $(CH_2=CH)_4Pb$

② $PbCl_2 + CH_2=CHMgBr \xrightarrow{\text{THF}}$ 61%
   $Pb(OCOCH_3)_2 + CH_2=CHMgBr$
   $\xrightarrow{\text{THF}}$ 48.1%
   $(NH_4)_2PbCl_6 + 4MgBrCH=CH_2 \xrightarrow{\text{THF}}$
   $PbCl_4 + 4MgBrCH=CH_2 \xrightarrow{\text{THF}}$

③ (30~40°/1~2), (74~77°/12). $n_D 1.5408$
   (27.5°).
   Sol. in hexane. Decomp. at room
   temp.
   IR: 1860 cm⁻¹ (medium).

④ $+ CH_3COOH$
   $\xrightarrow{\text{silica gel}} (CH_2=CH)PbOCOCH_3$
   (81%)
   $+ HCl(gas)$
   $\xrightarrow{\text{hexane}} (CH_2=CH)_3PbCl$ (31%)
   $+ Cl_3CCOOH$
   $\xrightarrow{\text{silica gel}} (CH_2=CH)_3PbOCOCCl_3$

(74%)

$$+ Cl_2 \xrightarrow{CH_3COOH} (CH_2=CH)_2PbCl_2$$

(72%)

$+ C_6H_5Li \longrightarrow Pb(C_6H_5)_4 +$

$4 LiCH=CH_2$ (91.2%)

$+ Li \longrightarrow 4 LiCH=CH_2 + Pb$ (90%)

$+ PX_3 \longrightarrow (CH_2=CH)_2PbX_2$

$+ P(CH=CH_2)_2X$ (X=Cl, Br)

⑥ JACS **81**, 3578 (1959).   Angew. **71**, 161 (1959).   JOC **26**, 563 (1961). Z. Naturforsh. **14 b**, 809 (1959).

PbC₈H₁₂O₂

② Trivinylleadacetate
   $(CH_2=CH)_3PbOCOCH_3$

② $CH_2=CHMgBr + PbCl_2$

   $\longrightarrow (CH_2=CH)_4Pb \xrightarrow{CH_3COOH} 84\%$

③ (100°/1 sublimes). [169~170°].
   Recrystd. from C₆H₆.

⑥ JACS **81**, 3578 (1959).   CA **59**, 11560 (1963).

PbC₈H₁₆

① Divinyldiethyllead
   $(CH_2=CH)_2Pb(C_2H_5)_2$

② $(C_2H_5)_2PbCl_2 + CH_2=CHMgBr \xrightarrow{THF}$

③ Liq. (30°/2).
   IR : 1860 cm⁻¹(medium), 1915 cm⁻¹, 1970 cm⁻¹(weak).

⑥ Z. Naturforsch. **14 b**, 350 (1959).

PbC₈H₁₆O₄

① Diethyllead diacetate
   $(C_2H_5)_2Pb(OCOCH_3)_2$

② $(C_2H_5)_2Hg + Pb(OCOCH_3)_4$

   $\xrightarrow{3\ months} 91.9\%$ mp (200~201°).

   $(C_2H_5)_2PbOCOCH_3 + Hg(OCOCH_3)_2$

   $\longrightarrow$ mp 130°

③ [200~201°].
   Recrystd. from C₂H₅OH.

④ $\xrightarrow{heat} (C_2H_5)_3PbOCOCH_3 +$
   $C_2H_5Pb(OCOCH_3)_3$

⑥ Dokl. **85**, 1037 (1952) ; CA **47**, 6365 (1953) ; **56**, 493 (1962) ; **37**, 3068 (1943).

PbC₈H₁₇BrO₂

② Triethyllead bromoacetate
   $(C_2H_5)_3PbOCOCH_2Br$

② $(C_2H_5)_3PbOH + CH_2BrCOOH \longrightarrow$

③ Long colorless needles. [121°].
   Recrystd. from C₆H₆.

⑥ JCS **1949**, 2983.

PbC₈H₁₈O₂

① Triethyllead acetate
   $(C_2H_5)_3PbOCOCH_3$

② $(C_2H_5)_4Pb + CH_3COOH \longrightarrow$
   $(C_2H_5)_4Pb + Pb(OCOCH_3)_4 \longrightarrow$
   $(C_2H_5)_3PbOH + CH_3COOH \longrightarrow$

③ White needles. [160~164° decomp.]
   Recrystd. from C₆H₆. Must be kept in the dark.

④ $\xrightarrow{heat} Pb(OCOCH_3)_2 + C_2H_5OCOCH_3$

⑤ Antifungal and antibacterial activity.

⑥ Izv. OKhN **1950**, 203.   CA **44**, 9342 (1950) ; **56**, 493(1962) ; **58**, 7308(1963). JACS **49**, 830 (1927).   JCS **1949**, 919.

PbC₈H₁₈O₂

① Trimethyllead n-valerate
   $(CH_3)_3PbOCOC_4H_9\text{-}n$

② $(CH_3)_4Pb + C_4H_9COOH \xrightarrow{silica\ gel}$

③ [160°].

⑥ JCS **1949**, 2983.

PbC₈H₁₈OS

① Triethyllead thioacetate
   $(C_2H_5)_3PbSCOCH_3$

② $CH_3COSH + (C_2H_5)_3PbOH \longrightarrow$

③ White needles. [45°].
   Recrystd. from dioxane.

⑥ JCS **1951**, 658.

PbC₈H₂₀

① Tetraethyllead
    $(C_2H_5)_4Pb$

② $Pb + 4 C_2H_4 + 2 H_2 \longrightarrow$ 0.15%
    Na−Pb alloy + $C_2H_5Cl \longrightarrow$ 76%
    $4 C_2H_5Li + 2 PbCl_2 \longrightarrow$

③ Colorless liquid. (198~202°/760),
    (78°/10). [−135°]. $n_D 1.5218(18°)$,
    1.5195(20°). $d 1.6528(20°/4°)$.
    Insol. in H_2O and dil. alkali; sol. in
    alc., ether and org. solvents.
    Decomp. in conc. acids.

④ $+ AuCl_3 \xrightarrow{\text{at r. t.}} (C_2H_5)_3PbCl +$
    $(C_2H_5)_2PbCl_2 + PbCl_2 + Au + C_2H_5Cl$
    $+ AgNO_3 \longrightarrow$
    $C_2H_5Ag + (C_2H_5)_3PbNO_3$
    $+ Cu^{++} \longrightarrow$
    $Cu^+ + Pb(C_2H_5)_3^+ + C_2H_5·$
    $+ Hg_2(NO_3)_2 \longrightarrow (C_2H_5)_2Hg,$
    $(C_2H_5)_3Pb^+$, $(C_2H_5)_2Pb^{2+}$ and Hg
    $+ CH_3COOH \longrightarrow$
    $C_2H_6 + (C_2H_5)_3PbOCOCH_3$
    $+ (C_2H_5)_4Pb + (C_6H_5)_2O_2 \longrightarrow C_2H_6,$
    $C_2H_4, C_4H_{10}, (C_2H_5)_3PbOCOCH_3$

⑤ Antiknock agent.

⑥ JACS **72**, 1760 (1950). CA **58**, 5723,
    (1963). Izv.OKhN **26**, 1285(1962);
    CA **58**, 7517 (1963). Dokl. **137**, 618
    (1961); CA **55**, 20925 (1961). JOC
    28, 843 (1963).

PbC₈H₂₀

① Isoamyltrimethyllead
    $(CH_3)_3Pb(i\text{-}C_5H_{11})$

② $(CH_3)_3PbCl + i\text{-}C_5H_{11}MgBr \xrightarrow{\text{ether}}$ 80%

③ Liq. (70°/13). $n_D 1.4926 (20.3°)$. $d 1.524$
    $(21.4°/4°)$.
    Sol. in org. solvents.

⑥ Ber. **49**, 1125 (1916).

PbC₈H₂₀

① Isobuthylethyldimethyllead
    $(i\text{-}C_4H_9)Pb(C_2H_5)(CH_3)_2$

② $(CH_3)_2(C_2H_5)PbBr + i\text{-}C_4HgMgCl$
    $\longrightarrow$ 75%

③ Liq. (74°/13). $n_D 1.50783$ (20.7°).
    $d 1.6234(20.7°/4°)$.
    Sol. in org. solvents.

⑥ Ber. **50**, 202 (1917).

PbC₈H₂₀

① n-Propyldietylmethyllead
    $(C_2H_5)_2Pb(CH_3)(n\text{-}C_3H_7)$

② $(C_2H_5)_2Pb(n\text{-}C_3H_7)Br + CH_3HgCl$
    $\xrightarrow{\text{ether}}$ 95%

③ Liq. (80.8°/15). $n_D 1.51412$ (22.1°).
    $d 1.6403(22.1°/4°)$.
    Sol. in org. solvents.

⑥ Ber. **50**, 202 (1917).

PbC₈H₂₀O

① Triethyllead ethoxide
    $(C_2H_5)_3PbOC_2H_5$

② $[(C_2H_5)_3Pb]_2O + C_2H_5OH \longrightarrow$

③ Colorless crystals. [20°].
    Sol. in org. solvents. Fumes in air.
    Unstable compd.

⑥ Dokl. **136**, 89 (1961); CA **55**, 27027
    (1961). Tr. po Khim. i Khim.
    Tekhnol. **3**, 381(1960); CA **55**, 27023
    (1961).

PbC₈H₂₀S

① Triethylethylthiolead
    $(C_2H_5)_3PbSC_2H_5$

② $(C_2H_5)_3PbOH + C_2H_5SH \xrightarrow{\text{in ether}}$

③ Colorless liq. (76~78°/0.075).
    Unstable liq. Sol. in org. solvents.
    Slowly hydrolyzed by water; slow-
    ly decompd. by light.

④ $+ HCl \longrightarrow (C_2H_5)_3PbCl + C_2H_5SH$

⑥ JCS **1949**, 2983. Nature **159**, 491
    (1947).

PbC₉H₁₄

① Trimethylphenyllead
    $(CH_3)_2PbC_6H_5$

② (CH₃)₃PbBr + C₆H₅MgBr $\xrightarrow{\text{ether}}$

③ Colorless liq. (77~78°/3), (104°/13).
n_D 1.5816(24°). d 1.7342(24°/4°).
Sol. in org. solvents ; Insol. in H₂O.
UV : λ_{max} 206 mμ(ε 27000), 256 mμ
(ε 1300) and 264 mμ(ε 1800).

⑥ Ber. **52**, 1293 (1918).   JCS **1952**, 1068.

PbC₉H₁₄Se

① Trimethylphenylselenolead
(CH₃)₃PbSeC₆H₅

② C₆H₅MgBr + Se $\xrightarrow{\text{in ether}}$ C₆H₅SeMgBr
C₆H₅SeMgBr + (CH₃)₃PbCl $\longrightarrow$
60%

③ Orange oil. d 2.60(20°/4°).

⑤ Gasoline additives.

⑥ US 3010980 ; CA **56**, 11620 (1962).

PbC₉H₁₈O₂

① Triethyllead acryrate
(C₂H₅)₃PbOCOCH=CH₂

② (C₂H₅)₃PbOH + CH₂=CHCOOH
$\longrightarrow$ 98.5%

③ Colorless needles. [120° decomp.].
Sol. in C₆H₆, C₂H₅OH ; very slightly
sol. in H₂O ; recrystd. from C₆H₆

⑥ JCS **1949**, 2983.

PbC₉H₂₀

① Diethylcyclopentamethylenelead
(C₂H₅)₂Pb−(CH₂)₅−|‾

② BrMg(CH₂)₅MgBr
+ (C₂H₅)₂PbCl₂ $\xrightarrow{\text{ether}}$

③ Colorless oil. (111°/13.5). n_D 1.5484
(20°). d 1.6866(20°/4°).
Oxydized in air. Sol. in org. solvents ;
insol in H₂O.

④ + AgNO₃ $\longrightarrow$ Ag
+ Br₂ $\xrightarrow{75°}$ (C₂H₅)₂Pb−(CH₂)₅Br
                                |
                                Br
+ Cl₂ $\xrightarrow{-75° \text{ in } C_2H_5OCOCH_3}$

(C₂H₅)PbCl₂·(CH₂)₅Cl

⑥ Ber. **45**, 2666 (1916).

PbC₉H₂₀O₂

① Triethyllead propionate
(C₂H₅)₃Pb·OCOC₂H₅

② (C₂H₅)₄Pb + C₂H₅COOH
$\xrightarrow{\text{silica gel, 1 hr reflux}}$

③ [141° decomp.].

⑥ JCS **1949**, 2983.

PbC₉H₂₁Cl

① Tri-n-propyllead chloride
(n-C₃H₇)₃PbCl

② C₃H₇I + Mg $\xrightarrow{\text{in ether}}$
C₃H₇MgI $\xrightarrow{\text{PbCl₂ 2hrs heat}}$
(C₃H₇)₄Pb $\xrightarrow{\text{Cl₂ in CH₃COOR}}$

③ White crystals. [133~137°].
Slightly sol. in org. solvent and H₂O.

④ + Ag₂O $\longrightarrow$ [(C₃H₇)₃Pb]₂O + 2 AgCl

⑥ Ber. **49**, 1415, 2445 (1916).   CA **56**,
5069 (1962) ; **57**, 15496 (1962).

PbC₉H₂₂

① Isoamylethyldimethyllead
(i-C₅H₁₁)Pb(C₂H₅)(CH₃)₂

② (CH₃)₂(C₂H₅)PbBr + (i-C₅H₁₁)MgCl
$\xrightarrow{\text{ether}}$ 70%

③ Liq. (92°/14). n_D 1.50524 (21.7°).
d 1.5579(21.7°/4°).
Sol. in org. solvents.

⑥ Ber. **50**. 202 (1917).

PbC₉H₂₂

① Isobutyldiethylmethyllead
(i-C₄H₉)Pb(C₂H₅)₂(CH₃)

② (C₂H₅)₂Pb(i-C₄H₉)Br + CH₃MgCl $\longrightarrow$

③ Liq. (87°/13). n_D 1.5120(19.5°). d 1.5805
(20.8°/4°).
Sol. in org. solvents.

⑥ Ber. **50**, 202 (1917).

PbC₉H₂₂

① Triethyl-*n*-propyllead
$(C_2H_5)_3Pb(n\text{-}C_3H_7)$

② $n\text{-}C_3H_7MgCl + (C_2H_5)_3PbCl \longrightarrow$ 95%

③ Liq. (99.5°/16), (97°/12∼13). n_D 1.5175
(19.7°). d 1.5948(22.5°/4°).
Sol. in org. solvents.

⑥ Ber. **49**, 1125 (1916).

PbC₁₀H₈O₂

① 1-Naphthylplumbonic acid
$1\text{-}C_{10}H_7Pb(O)OH$

② $1\text{-}C_{10}H_7Pb(OCOCH_3)_3 + NH_4OH$
$\xrightarrow[\text{in } CH_3OH \text{ overnight}]{}$ 62.6%

③ Yellow amorphous solid.
Insol. in 50% KOH or conc. HCl.

④ $+ CH_3COOH \longrightarrow$
$1\text{-}C_{10}H_7Pb(OCOCH_3)_3$
$+ i\text{-}PrCOOH$
$\longrightarrow 1\text{-}C_{10}H_7Pb(OCOPr\text{-}i)_3$

⑥ Izv. OKhN 1957, 1484; CA **52**, 7245
(1958).

PbC₁₀H₁₀

① Dicyclopentadienyllead
$(C_5H_5)_2Pb$

② $Pb(NO_3)_2$ in $(CH_3)_2NCHO$
$+ NaC_5H_5 \longrightarrow$

③ Yellow crystals.　No definite mp.
Sol. in org. solvents; insol. in H₂O.
UV: 335 mμ, ε_{max} 7600 in THF, 345 mμ,
ε_{max} 7460 in 2,4-trimethyl pentane.

⑥ Z. anorg. allg. Chem. **286**, 237(1956);
287, 236(1955). Ber. **92**, 780(1959);
93, 1971 (1960). JCS **1959**, 3684;
1961, 547. Z. Electrochem. **64**, 945
(1960); CA **52**, 2929 (1958).

PbC₁₀H₁₆

① Benzyltrimethyllead
$C_6H_5CH_2Pb(CH_3)_3$

② $(CH_3)_3PbBr + C_6H_5CH_2MgBr \longrightarrow$

③ Liquid. (124°/13 decomp.).
Sol. in org. solvents; insol. in H₂O.

⑥ Ber. **52**, 1293 (1918).

PbC₁₀H₁₆

① *p*-Tolyltrimethyllead
$p\text{-}CH_3C_6H_4Pb(CH_3)_3$

② $(CH_3)_3PbBr + p\text{-}CH_3C_6H_5MgBr \xrightarrow{\text{ether}}$

③ Colorless liq. (118∼119°/13).
n_D 1.5732 (20°). d 1.6826 (20°/4°).
Sol. in org. solvents; insol. in H₂O.

⑥ Ber. **52**, 1293 (1918).

PbC₁₀H₁₆O₃S

① Trimethyllead *p*-tolylsulfonate
$(CH_3)_3PbOSO_2C_6H_4CH_3$

② $(CH_3)_4Pb + HO_3SC_6H_4CH_3 \xrightarrow{\text{silica gel}}$

③ Solid. [>220°].

⑥ JCS **1949**, 2983.

PbC₁₀H₂₀O₂

① Triethyllead crotonate
$(C_2H_5)_3PbOCOCH=CHCH_3$

② $(C_2H_5)_3PbOH +$
$CH_3CH=CHCOOH \longrightarrow$

③ Short reedles. [135∼136°].
Very sol. in C₂H₅OH; recrystd. from
C₆H₆.

⑥ JCS **1949**, 2983.

PbC₁₀H₂₄

① *n*-Butyl-*n*-propylethylmethyllead
$(n\text{-}C_4H_9)(n\text{-}C_3H_7)Pb(C_2H_5)(CH_3)$

② $(CH_3)_3Pb(C_2H_5) + Br_2$
$\xrightarrow[\text{ether}, -75°]{} (CH_3)_2Pb(C_2H_5)Br$
$(CH_3)_2Pb(C_2H_5)Br + n\text{-}C_3H_7MgCl$
$\xrightarrow{\text{ether}} (CH_3)_2Pb(C_2H_5)(n\text{-}C_3H_7)$
$(CH_3)_2Pb(C_2H_5)(n\text{-}C_3H_7) + Br_2$
$\xrightarrow[\text{ether}, -75°]{} (CH_3)(C_2H_5)Pb(n\text{-}C_3H_7)Br$
$(CH_3)(C_2H_5)Pb(n\text{-}C_3H_7)Br$
$+ n\text{-}C_4H_9MgBr \xrightarrow{\text{ether}}$

③ Liq. (103°/13). n_D 1.5083. d 1.5185
　(20°/4°).
　Sol. in org. solvents ; insol. in H_2O.
⑥ Ber. **50**, 202 (1917). Ann. **415**, 338
　(1918).

PbC10H24

① Di-n-butyldimethyllead
　$(n-C_4H_9)_2Pb(CH_3)_2$
② $(n-C_4H_9)_2PbCl_2 + CH_3MgBr \longrightarrow$
③ Colorless liq. (108°/10), (96.5°/5).
　n_D 1.5049 (20°). d 1.5210 (20°/4°).
　Sol. in org. solvents ; insol. in H_2O.
⑥ JCS **1935**, 39.

PbC10H24

① Diethyldi-n-propyllead
　$(C_2H_5)_2Pb(n-C_3H_7)_2$
② $BrMg(n-C_3H_7)$
$$+ (C_2H_5)_2PbCl_2 \xrightarrow{\text{ether, 3 hrs}}$$
③ Colorless liq. (99°/10), (70~72°/4).
　n_D 1.5149 (20°). d 1.5331 (20°/4°).
　Sol. in org. solvents ; insol. in H_2O.
④ $+ HCl \longrightarrow (n-C_3H_7)Pb(C_2H_5)Cl$
　$+ EtCOOH \longrightarrow$
　$(C_2H_5)_2Pb(n-C_3H_7)OCOC_2H_5$
⑥ Ber. **49**. 1546 (1916). JCS **1951**, 658 ;
　1935, 39.

PbC10H24

① Methyltri-n-propyllead
　$CH_3Pb(n-C_3H_7)_3$
② $(CH_3)_4Pb + (n-C_3H_7)_4Pb$
$$\xrightarrow{\text{AlCl}_3 \text{ in C}_6\text{H}_{14}, 80°, 5\text{hrs}} 23 \text{ mol\%}$$
③ Colorless liq. (106°/13). n_D 1.5101
　(20°). d 1.5241 (20°/4°).
　Sol. in org. solvents ; insol. in H_2O.
⑥ JACS **62**, 1099 (1940).

PbC11H16

① Trimethyl-p-styryllead
　$p-CH_2=CHC_6H_4Pb(CH_3)_3$
② $(CH_3)_3PbBr +$

$$p-CH_2=CHC_6H_4MgCl \xrightarrow{>30°C, THF}$$
③ Liq. (60~61°/0.0015). n_D 1.6070 (20°).
　d 1.7278 (20°/4°).
④ $\xrightarrow{70°, 1.5\text{hrs}}$ polymerized 40%
⑥ CA **55**, 7332 (1961).

PbC11H26

① Isoamyl-n-propylethylmethyllead
　$(i-C_5H_{11})(n-C_3H_7)Pb(C_2H_5)(CH_3)$
② $(C_2H_5)_2(n-C_3H_7)Pb(i-C_5H_{11})$
$$+ Br_2 \xrightarrow{-75°, \text{ether}}$$
　$(C_2H_5)(n-C_3H_7)Pb(i-C_5H_{11})Br$
$$+ CH_3MgCl \xrightarrow{\text{ether}} 85\%$$
③ Liq. (115°/15). n_D 1.50189 (21°).
　d 1.4792 (20°/4°).
　Sol. in org. solvents.
⑥ Ber. **50**, 202 (1917).

PbC11H28Sn

① 1-Trimethylstannyl-5-trimethyl-
　plumbyl-n-pentane
　$(CH_3)_3Sn(CH_2)_5Pb(CH_3)_3$
② $(CH_3)_3Sn(CH_2)_5Br$
$$+ (CH_3)_3PbBr \xrightarrow{\text{in ether}}$$
③ Colorless viscous oil. (162°/17.5).
　n_D 1.52282(23.2°). d 1.6482 (23.2°/4°).
　Sol. in org. solvents ; insol. in H_2O.
⑥ Ber. **50**, 1549 (1917).

PbC12H6MnO10

① Dimethyllead-bis(manganesepenta-
　carbonyl)
　$(CH_3)_2Pb[Mn(CO)_5]_2$
② $2 NaMn(CO)_5 + (CH_3)_2PbCl_2$
$$\xrightarrow{\text{in THF}} 86\%$$
③ Pale yellow solid. [102~104°].
　Fairly stable in air. Sol. in CH_2Cl_2,
　ether, acetone and THF ; fairly
　sol. in C_2H_5OH and C_6H_6 ; insol. in
　n-hexane.
⑥ JACS **84**, 2486 (1962).

PbC₁₂H₁₀Br₂

① Diphenyllead dibromide

$(C_6H_5)_2PbBr_2$

② $(C_6H_5)_2PbI_2 + AgBr \xrightarrow{\text{in } CH_3OH} 95\%$

$(C_6H_5)_2Pb(NO_3)_2 + 2\,KBr \longrightarrow$

$(C_6H_5)_4Pb \xrightarrow{\text{2Br}_2 \text{ in } CH_3Cl \text{ or } CS_2}$

$(C_6H_5)_2Pb(NO_3)_2 + 2\,NaBr$

$\xrightarrow{\text{in boiling water} + HNO_3} 98\%$

③ Solid. [284~286° decomp.].

⑥ Ber. **60**, 1617 (1927); **49**, 2441 (1916); **20**, 716, 3331 (1887). JACS **61**, 1609 (1939). CA **50**, 7728 (1956).

PbC₁₂H₁₀Cl₂

① Diphenyllead dichloride

$(C_6H_5)_2PbCl_2$

② $\left.\begin{matrix}(C_6H_5)_2PbI_2\\(C_6H_5)_2PbBr_2\end{matrix}\right\} \xrightarrow{AgCl} \left\{\begin{matrix}95\%\\92\%\end{matrix}\right.$

$(C_6H_5)_4Pb + HgCl_2 \xrightarrow{C_2H_5OH,\ 3\,hrs}$

$(C_6H_5)_4Pb \xrightarrow{\text{excess HCl in } c_6H_6} 98.5\%$

③ Solid. [284~286° decomp.].

④ $+ (C_6H_5)_2Hg \xrightarrow{\text{pyridine}} (C_6H_5)_3PbCl$
$+ C_6H_5HgCl$

$+ (C_6H_5)_4Pb \xrightarrow{\text{butanol, 8 hrs reflux}}$
$2\,(C_6H_5)_3PbCl$

⑥ J. Gen. Chem. USSR **4**, 1102 (1934); **6**, 172 (1936). Ann. (Rome) **48**, 940 (1958); CA **53**, 9901 (1959).

PbC₁₂H₁₀O

① Diphenyllead oxide

$(C_6H_5)_2PbO$

② $(C_6H_5)_2Pb(NO_3)_2 + H_2O \xrightarrow{\text{with alkali}}$

③ White solid. Polymeric.

④ $+ Na_2S \xrightarrow{+H^+} (C_6H_5)_2PbS$

⑥ Ber. **68**, 1877 (1935); **20**, 3331 (1887); **60**, 1617(1927). JOC **26**, 4634(1961).

PbC₁₂H₁₀S

① Diphenyllead sulfide

$(C_6H_5)_2PbS$

② $(C_6H_5)_2PbO + Na_2S \xrightarrow{\text{in } H_2O}$

$(C_6H_5)_2Pb(OCOCH_3)_2 + H_2S$
$\xrightarrow{\text{in } CH_3COOH}$

③ Light yellow crystals. [112~115°], [130°].

Unstable in boiling C_6H_6. Sol. in C_6H_6.

⑥ JCS **1950**, 617. Ber. **20**, 3331 (1887). JOC **26**, 4634 (1961).

PbC₁₂H₁₁NO₄

① Diphenyllead hydroxide nitrate

$(C_6H_5)_2Pb(OH)NO_3$

② $(C_6H_5)_2Pb(NO_3)_2 + NH_4OH \longrightarrow$

③ White solid.

Decomp. without melting.

⑥ Ber. **20**, 716 (1887).

PbC₁₂H₁₄O₆

① Phenyllead triacetate

$C_6H_5Pb(OCOCH_3)_3$

② $(C_6H_5)_2Pb(OCOCH_3)_2 + Hg(OCOCH_3)_2$
$\longrightarrow 79\%$

$(C_6H_5)_2Hg + Pb(OCOCH_3)_4 \longrightarrow$

③ White crystals. [103~105°].

Sol. in org. solvents except hydrocarbons.

④ $+ NaOH \xrightarrow{\text{boil}}$ cleavage of the OCOCH₃

$+ (C_6H_5)_2Hg \longrightarrow C_6H_5Hg(OCOCH_3)$

$+ (C_6H_5)_2Pb(OCOCH_3)_2 \xrightarrow{\text{decomp.}}$

$C_6H_5COOCH_3 + Pb(OCOCH_3)_2$

⑥ Izv. OKhN **1955**, 711. CA **50**, 7075 (1956); **51**, 95126 (1957). Dokl. **111**, 1042 (1956). Ber. **90**, 1337 (1957).

PbC₁₂H₂₀O

① Triethyllead phenoxide

$(C_2H_5)_3PbOC_6H_5$

② $(C_2H_5)_4Pb + C_6H_5OH$
$\xrightarrow{\text{150°C, silica gel}}$

③ $(75°/0.5)$.

⑥ US 2008003 (1935); CA **29**, 5862 (1935).

PbC₁₂H₂₀S

① Triethylphenylthiolead
$(C_2H_5)_3PbSC_6H_5$

② $(C_2H_5)_3PbOH + C_6H_5SH \xrightarrow{\text{ether}}$

③ Pale yellow oil. $(125°/0.3)$.
Sol. in org. solvents.

④ $+ HCl \longrightarrow (C_2H_5)_3PbCl + C_6H_5SH$

⑥ JCS **1949**, 2983.

PbC₁₂H₂₂Cl₂

① Dicyclohexyllead dichloride
$(C_6H_{11})_2PbCl_2$

② $(C_6H_{11})_4Pb \xrightarrow{\text{dry HCl gas in CH}_3\text{Cl, 5}\sim10°}$

③ Solid. [180° decomp.].

⑥ Ber. **47**, 3257 (1914).

PbC₁₂H₂₅ClO₂

① Tri-n-propyllead-2-chloropropionate
$(n\text{-}C_3H_7)_3PbOCOCH_2CH_2Cl$

② $(n\text{-}C_3H_7)_3PbOH$
$+ ClCH_2CH_2COOH \longrightarrow$

③ $[99\sim100°]$.

⑥ JCS **1949**, 919.

PbC₁₂H₂₈

① Di-n-butyldiethyllead
$(n\text{-}C_4H_9)_2Pb(C_2H_5)_2$

② $(n\text{-}C_4H_9)_2PbCl_2 + C_2H_5MgBr \longrightarrow$

③ Colorless liquid. $(90°/1)$. n_D 1.5093
$(20°)$. d 1.4580 $(20°/4°)$.
Sol. in org. solvents; insol. in H_2O.

⑥ JCS **1935**, 39.

PbC₁₂H₂₈

① Tetra-isopropyllead
$(i\text{-}C_3H_7)_4Pb$

② $PbMg_2 + i\text{-}C_3H_7Br$
$\xrightarrow{\text{80}\sim\text{120°, 2}\sim\text{12hrs at the pressure of}}$
several hundred psi
$PbCl_2 + i\text{-}C_3H_7MgCl \xrightarrow{\text{ether}}$
Pb$-$Na(alloy)
$+ CH_3COOCH_3$ in dil. $H_2SO_4 \longrightarrow$

③ Colorless liquid. $(120°/14)$. $[-53.5°]$.
n_D 1.5223 $(20°)$.
Sol. in org. solvents; insol. in H_2O.
Decomposed by acids.

⑥ CA **45**, 3865(1951); **26**, 360, 1236(1932).
Ber. **50**, 574 (1917).

PbC₁₂H₃₃ClSi₃

① Tris(trimethylsilylmethyl)lead
chloride
$[(\overset{.}{C}H_3)_3SiCH_2]_3PbCl$

② $(CH_3)_3SiCH_2 \cdot MgCl + PbCl_2 \xrightarrow{\text{in THF}} \cdots\cdots$
$\longrightarrow [(CH_3)_3SiCH_2]_4Pb$
$[(CH_3)_3SiCH_2]_4Pb + PCl_3$
$\xrightarrow{\text{reflux for 6 hrs.}}$

③ Sublime at 1 mmHg(bath temp. 225°).
White solid. $[214\sim216°]$.

⑥ JOC **26**, 2604 (1961).

PbC₁₃H₁₉BrO₂

① Triethyllead p-bromobenzoate
$(C_2H_5)_3PbOCOC_6H_4Br$-p

② $(C_2H_5)_3PbOH + p$-BrC_6H_4COOH
$\longrightarrow 45\%$

③ $[127\sim128°]$.

⑥ JOC **18**, 1341 (1953).

PbC₁₃H₁₉F

① p-Trifluoromethylbenzyltriethyllead
p-$CF_3C_6H_4Pb(C_2H_5)_3$

② $CF_3\text{—}\langle\rangle\text{—}Br + (C_2H_5)_4Pb$
$\xrightarrow{\text{Na, liq. NH}_3} 32\%$

③ $(80°/0.06)$.

④ $+ AgNO_3 \xrightarrow{\text{C}_2\text{H}_5\text{OH, }-78°}$ no reaction

$+ AgNO_3 \xrightarrow{\text{C}_2\text{H}_5\text{OH, r. t.}}$

yellow polymer + Ag

⑥ JCS **1959**, 3001.

PbC₁₃H₁₉NO₄

① Triethyllead *m*-nitrobenzoate

$(C_2H_5)_3PbOCOC_6H_4NO_2\text{-}m$

② $m\text{-}NO_2C_6H_4COOH + (C_2H_5)_4Pb$

$\longrightarrow 97\%$

$m\text{-}NO_2C_6H_4COOH + (C_2H_5)_3PbOH \longrightarrow$

③ Solid. [172~173° decomp.].

⑥ JOC **18**, 1341 (1953).

PbC₁₃H₂₀O₂

① Triethyllead benzoate

$(C_2H_5)_3PbOCOC_6H_5$

② $(C_2H_5)_3PbOH + C_6H_5COOH \longrightarrow$

$(C_2H_5)_6Pb_2 + (C_6H_5)_2O_2 \longrightarrow$

③ Colorless crystals. [127°].

Very sol. in cold alc., acetone and benzene; recrystd. from light petroleum.

⑥ JCS **1951**, 658 ; CA **54**, 7608 (1960).

PbC₁₃H₂₀O₃

① Triethyllead salicylate

$(C_2H_5)_3PbOCOC_6H_4OH\text{-}m$

② $(C_2H_5)_3PbOH + HOC_6H_4COOH$

$\longrightarrow 52\%$

③ Solid. [93°], [74.5°].

Sol. in polar org. solvents ; recrystd. from alcohol-water.

⑥ JOC **18**, 1341 (1953).   JCS **1949**, 2983.

PbC₁₃H₂₁NO₂

① Triethyllead anthranilate

$(C_2H_5)_3PbOCOC_6H_4NH_2\text{-}o$

② $(C_2H_5)_3PbOH$

$+ o\text{-}NH_2C_6H_5COOH \longrightarrow$

⑥ Solid. [96°].

Sol. in polar org. solvents.

⑥ JCS **1949**, 919.

PbC₁₃H₂₂O₃S

① Triethyllead *p*-tolylsulfonate

$(C_2H_5)_3PbOSO_2C_6H_4CH_3\text{-}p$

② $(C_2H_5)_4Pb + HOSO_2C_6H_4CH_3\text{-}p$

$\xrightarrow{\text{reflux with silica gel}}$

③ Solid. [170°].

⑥ JCS **1949**, 2983. Rec. trav. chim. **49**, 766 (1930). JOC **18**, 1341 (1953).

PbC₁₃H₂₃NO₂S

① Triethyllead methylsulfoanilide

$(C_2H_5)_3PbN(C_6H_5)SO_2CH_3$

② $(CH_3)SO_2NH(C_6H_5)$

$+ (C_2H_5)_3PbOH \xrightarrow{\text{alc.}}$

③ Solid. [115.5°].

Sol. in polar org. solvents.

⑥ JCS **1950**, 684.

PbC₁₃H₂₈O₂

① Tri-*n*-propyllead *n*-butylate

$(n\text{-}C_3H_7)_3Pb(OCOC_3H_7\text{-}n)$

② $(n\text{-}C_3H_7)_3PbOH + C_3H_7COOH \longrightarrow$

③ Solid. [105~106°].

Sol. in polar org. solvents.

⑥ JCS **1949**, 919.

PbC₁₄H₁₀MnO₁₀

① Diethyllead-bis(manganese pentacarbonyl)

$(C_2H_5)_2Pb[Mn(CO)_5]_2$

② $2 NaMn(CO)_5 + (C_2H_5)_2PbCl_2$

$\xrightarrow{\text{in THF}} 66\%$

③ Orange solid. [77~79°].

Fairly stable in air. Sol. in CH₂Cl₂, ether, acetone and THF; fairly sol. in C₂H₅OH and C₆H₆ ; insol. in *n*-hexane.

⑥ JACS **84**, 2486 (1962).

PbC₁₄H₁₀N₂

① Diphenyllead dicyanide

$(C_6H_5)_2Pb(CN)_2$

② (C$_6$H$_5$)$_2$PbI$_2$ + AgCN $\xrightarrow{\text{CH}_3\text{OH}}$ 35%

(C$_2$H$_5$)$_2$PbBr$_2$ + AgCN $\xrightarrow{\text{CH}_3\text{OH}}$ 42%

③ Solid. [245~255° decomp.].

Insol. in alc., C$_6$H$_6$ and CHCl$_3$.

⑥ Ber. 60, 1617 (1927).

PbC$_{14}$H$_{14}$Cl$_2$

① Di-*p*-tolyllead dichloride

(*p*-CH$_3$C$_6$H$_4$)$_2$PbCl$_2$

② (*p*-CH$_3$C$_6$H$_4$)$_4$Pb $\xrightarrow{\text{dry Cl}_2 \text{ gas in CS}_2}$

③ Solid.

④ + 2 AgNO$_3$ ⟶

(*p*-CH$_3$C$_6$H$_4$)$_2$Pb(NO$_3$)$_2$ + 2 AgCl

⑥ Ber. 21, 3424 (1888). JACS 53, 3514

(1931); 54, 3287 (1932).

PbC$_{14}$H$_{14}$O$_5$

① Diphenyllead diformate

(C$_6$H$_5$)$_2$Pb(OCOH)$_2$·H$_2$O

② (C$_6$H$_5$)$_4$Pb + HCOOH

$\xrightarrow{\text{50}°, \text{3hrs. in sealed ampoule}}$

(C$_6$H$_5$)$_4$Pb + HCOOH $\xrightarrow{\text{heat}}$

③ White solid.

Sol. in polar org. solvents; slightly

sol. in H$_2$O.

⑥ CA 34, 5049 (1940). Ber. 20, 3331

(1887).

PbC$_{14}$H$_{16}$AsClO$_2$

① Diphenylchlorolead dimethylarsinate

Cl(C$_6$H$_5$)$_2$PbOAs(O)(CH$_3$)$_2$

② (CH$_3$)$_2$As(O)ONa

+ (C$_6$H$_5$)$_2$PbCl$_2$ $\xrightarrow{\text{reflux for 8hrs. in DMF}}$

③ White solid. [>260°]

Insol. in DMF and other common

org. solvents.

④ + glacial CH$_3$COOH

$\xrightarrow{\text{reflux}}$ Cl(C$_6$H$_5$)$_2$PbOOCCH$_3$

(quantitatively)

⑥ Inorg. Chem. 1, 917 (1962).

PbC$_{14}$H$_{16}$O$_7$

① Diphenyllead dioxalate

(C$_6$H$_5$)$_2$Pb(OOC)$_2$·3 H$_2$O

③ White cryst. powder. [293~295°

decomp.].

Slightly sol. in acetone, pyridine and

dil. H$_2$SO$_4$; insol. in other org.

solvents.

⑥ JCS 1922, 978.

PbC$_{14}$H$_{19}$NO$_2$

① Triethyllead phthalimide.

(C$_2$H$_5$)$_3$PbN(CO)$_2$C$_6$H$_4$.

② (C$_2$H$_5$)$_3$PbOH

+ C$_6$H$_4$(CO)$_2$NH $\xrightarrow{\text{in C}_2\text{H}_5\text{OH}}$

③ Crystals. [131°].

Sol. in C$_6$H$_6$ and ether.

④ + dry HCl $\xrightarrow{\text{in ether}}$ C$_6$H$_4$(CO)$_2$NH

⑥ JCS 1949, 2983.

PbC$_{14}$H$_{20}$N$_2$O$_9$

① Di-*p*-tolyllead dinitrate trihydrate

(*p*-CH$_3$C$_6$H$_4$)$_2$Pb(NO$_3$)$_2$·3 H$_2$O

② (*p*-CH$_3$C$_6$H$_4$)$_4$Pb + 2 HNO$_3$ ⟶

③ Solid.

⑥ Ber. 21, 3424 (1888). CA 47, 6365

(1953).

PbC$_{14}$H$_{22}$

① Triethyl-α-styryllead

(C$_2$H$_5$)$_3$PbCH=CHC$_6$H$_5$

② C$_6$H$_5$CH=CHBr + (C$_2$H$_5$)$_4$Pb

$\xrightarrow{\text{Na in liquid NH}_3}$ 40%

③ Viscous yellow liquid. (94°/0.01).

Decomp. even at −78° with separa-

tion of white solid.

+ AgNO$_3$ $\xrightarrow{\text{C}_2\text{H}_5\text{OH, } -78°}$

AgCH=CHPb (deep red ppt.)

⑥ JCS 1959, 300.

PbC$_{14}$H$_{23}$NO$_2$S

① Triethyllead ethylenesulfonanilide
(C$_2$H$_5$)$_3$PbN(C$_6$H$_5$)SO$_2$CH=CH$_2$

② (C$_2$H$_5$)$_3$PbCl +

NaN(C$_6$H$_5$)SO$_2$CH=CH$_2$ $\xrightarrow[\text{r. t.}]{\text{alc., 15 hrs}}$

③ Solid. [100~120°].

④ $\xrightarrow{\text{heat}}$ decomp. with a mild explosion

⑥ Nature **159**, 491 (1947).   JCS **1950**,
684.

PbC$_{14}$H$_{32}$

① Isoamyl-*n*-butyl-*n*-propylethyllead
(*i*-C$_5$H$_{11}$)(*n*-C$_4$H$_9$)Pb(*n*-C$_3$H$_7$)(C$_2$H$_5$)

② (CH$_3$)(C$_2$H$_5$)Pb(*n*-C$_3$H$_7$)(*n*-C$_4$H$_9$)

+ Br$_2$ $\xrightarrow{\text{ether, }-75°}$

(C$_2$H$_5$)Pb(*n*-C$_3$H$_7$)(*n*-C$_4$H$_9$)Br

(C$_2$H$_5$)Pb(*n*-C$_3$H$_7$)(*n*-C$_4$H$_9$)Br

+ *i*-C$_5$H$_{11}$MgCl $\xrightarrow{\text{ether}}$

③ Liq. (144°/14). n_D 1.5035(20°). d 1.3730
(20°/4°).

Sol. in org. solvents ; insol. in H$_2$O.

⑥ Ber. **50**, 202 (1917).

PbC$_{15}$H$_{28}$Si

① 1-Triethylsilyl-4-trimethylplumbyl-
benzene
(C$_2$H$_5$)$_3$SiC$_6$H$_4$Pb(CH$_3$)$_3$

② (C$_2$H$_5$)$_3$SiC$_6$H$_4$Br + (CH$_3$)$_3$PbBr $\xrightarrow{\text{in ether}}$

③ Colorless viscous oil. (191°/17).
n_D 1.54937 (23.8°). d 1.4032 (20°/4°).
Sol. in org. solvents.

⑥ Ber. **50**, 1559 (1917).

PbC$_{16}$H$_{10}$Cl$_6$O$_4$

① Diphenyllead bistrichloroacetate
(C$_6$H$_5$)$_2$Pb(OCOCCl$_3$)$_2$

② (C$_6$H$_5$)$_4$Pb + Cl$_3$CCOOH $\longrightarrow$

③ White solid. [210° decomp.].
Sol. in org. solvents except CCl$_4$ and
light petroleum.

⑥ JCS **1922**, 978.

PbC$_{16}$H$_{12}$O$_4$

① Tetra-2-furyllead
(OC$_4$H$_3$)$_4$Pb

② —MgBr + PbCl$_2$ $\xrightarrow{\text{Et}_2\text{O}}$

③ Crystals. [52~53°].
Sol. in org. solvents.

④ Decompose vigorously by conc. H$_2$SO$_4$.

⑥ Rec. trav. chim. **51**, 1054 (1932) ; CA
27, 502 (1933).

PbC$_{16}$H$_{12}$S$_4$

① Tetrakis(2-thienyl)lead
(SC$_4$H$_3$)$_4$Pb

② —MgI + PbCl$_2$ $\xrightarrow{\text{Et}_2\text{O}}$

③ Pale yellow crystals. [154.5°].

⑥ Ber. **60**, 1582 (1927) ; **65**, 777 (1932).
CA **54**, 17238 (1960).

PbC$_{16}$H$_{16}$

① Diphenyldivinyllead
(C$_6$H$_5$)$_2$Pb(CH=CH$_2$)$_2$

② (C$_6$H$_5$)$_2$PbCl$_2$ + CH$_2$=CHMgBr
$\xrightarrow{\text{THF}}$ 50.1%

③ Pale yellow liq.
Sol. in petr. ether.

④ + Li $\xrightarrow{70° \text{ 2hrs}}$ CH$_2$=CHLi + C$_6$H$_5$Li

⑥ JACS **81**, 3578 (1959).   CA **58**, 11398
(1963).

PbC$_{16}$H$_{16}$O$_4$

① Diphenyllead diacetate
(C$_6$H$_5$)$_2$Pb(OCOCH$_3$)$_2$

② (C$_6$H$_5$)$_4$Pb + Pb(OCOCH$_3$)$_4$ $\longrightarrow$ 46%
(C$_6$H$_5$)$_4$Pb + Hg(OCOCH$_3$)$_2$ $\longrightarrow$

③ White solid. [200~201°].
Recrystd. from C$_6$H$_6$ and one drop of
CH$_3$COOH.

$(C_6H_5)_2Pb(OCOCH_3)_2 \cdot 1$ (or 2)H_2O (mp 194~195°).

④ $+ Hg(OCOCH_3)_2 + CH_3COOH \longrightarrow$
$C_6H_5HgOCOCH_3 + C_6H_5Pb(OCOCH_3)_3$

⑥ CA **44**, 9342 (1950) ; **50**, 3271, 7728, 7075(1956) ; **34**, 5046 (1940).

PbC₁₆H₂₀

① Diphenyldiethyllead
$(C_2H_5)_2Pb(C_6H_5)_2$

② $(C_6H_5)_2PbBr_2 + C_2H_5MgBr \xrightarrow{\text{ether}}$

③ Colorless liq. (176°/8). n_D 1.5939(18°).
d 1.6435 (20°/4°).
Sol. in org. solvents.

④ $+ HCl \longrightarrow Cl_2Pb(C_2H_5)_2$
$+ HBr \longrightarrow Br_2Pb(C_2H_5)_2$
$+ Br_2 \xrightarrow{\text{in CHCl}_3} Br_2Pb(C_2H_5)_2$

⑥ Ber. **49**, 2441 (1916).

PbC₁₆H₂₂O₃S

① Triethyllead-2-naphthyl sulfonate
$(C_2H_5)_3PbOSO_2C_{10}H_7-\alpha$

② $HOSO_2C_{10}H_7 + (C_2H_5)_4Pb$
$\xrightarrow{\text{silica gel, }\frac{1}{2}\text{hr}} (C_2H_5)_3PbOSO_2C_{10}H_7$

③ Solid. [152°].

⑥ JCS **1949**, 2983.

PbC₁₆H₃₆

① Tetra-n-butyllead
$(n-C_4H_9)_4Pb$

② $PbCl_2 + n-C_4H_9MgBr \xrightarrow{\text{ether}}$
$PbMg + C_4H_9I \xrightarrow{\text{Et}_2\text{O, }100\sim120°}$
$PbO + (C_4H_9)_3Al \longrightarrow$
$PbS + (C_4H_9)_2Zn \longrightarrow$
$Pb + Li + C_4H_9X \longrightarrow$

③ Colorless liq. (140°/1), (157°/5).
n_D 1.5119 (20°). d 1.3238 (20°/4°).
Sol. in org. solvents ; insol. in H_2O.

④ $+ HOCOCH_3 \longrightarrow$
$(n-C_4H_9)_3PbOCOCH_3$
$k_1 \times 10^5 = 4.3 \text{ sec}^{-1}.$ $\Delta H = 21.2 \text{ kcal/mol}.$

$+ HClO_4 \longrightarrow (n-C_4H_9)_3PbClO_4$
$+ HCl \longrightarrow (n-C_4H_9)_3PbCl$

⑥ JCS **1935**, 39 ; **1949**, 919.   CA **45**, 3865 (1951) ; **55**, 11362, 23345 (1961) ; **53**, 9149 (1959).   JOC **28**, 843 (1963).

PbC₁₆H₄₄Si₄

① Tetrakis(trimethylsilylmethyl)lead
$[(CH_3)_3SiCH_2]_4Pb$

② $(CH_3)_3SiCH_2MgCl$
$+ PbCl_2 \xrightarrow{\text{THF, }-10°,\text{ reflux. 5 hrs.}}$

③ Colorless liq. (104~105°/0.01).

④ $+ PCl_3 \xrightarrow{\text{reflux 16 hrs.}}$
$[(CH_3)_3SiCH_2]_3PbCl$
$+ (CH_3)_3SiCH_2PCl_2$

⑥ JOC **26**, 2604 (1961).

PbC₁₇H₂₀

① Cyclopentamethylenediphenyllead
$(C_6H_5)_2Pb(CH_2)_5$

② $(C_6H_5)_2PbCl_2 + CH_2(CH_2CH_2Li)_2 \longrightarrow$

③ On standing and exposure to light and air, the compound rapidly colored.
IR : 2650, 965, 909 cm⁻¹.

⑥ JOC **27**, 1422 (1962).

PbC₁₈H₁₅F

① Triphenyllead fluoride
$(C_6H_5)_3PbF$

② $(C_6H_5)_4Pb \xrightarrow[\text{HF in EtOH}]{\text{in ether, KOH}} (C_6H_5)_4PbOH$

③ White microcrystals. [318°, decomp.].
d 1.46 (17°/4°).
Insol. in org. solvents ; very slightly sol. in polar org. solvents.

⑥ Ber. **55**, 1282 (1922).

PbC₁₈H₁₅Ge₄

① Tetrakis(triphenylgermyl)lead
$[(C_6H_5)_3Ge]_4Pb$

② 4 (C₆H₅)₃GeLi + 2 PbCl₂

$$\xrightarrow{\text{in ether under N}_2} 2 [(C_6H_5)_3Ge]_2Pb$$

$$\longrightarrow [(C_6H_5)_3Ge]_2Pb + Pb \quad (23\%)$$

③ Yellow solid.

High stability. Recrystd. from C₆H₆.

⑥ JOM **2**, 260 (1964).

PbC₁₈H₁₅I

① Triphenyllead iodide

(C₆H₅)₃PbI

② $(C_6H_5)_4Pb + I_2 \xrightarrow{\text{CHCl}_3}$

③ White flakes. [138～139°].

Sol. in polar org. solvents.

UV : Proc. Chem. Soc. **1962**, 300.

⑥ JACS **61**, 1685 (1939).　Proc. Chem.
Soc. **1962**, 300.

PbC₁₈H₁₅Li

① Triphenyllead lithium

(C₆H₅)₃PbLi

② $3 C_6H_5Li + PbCl_2 \xrightarrow{-10°C, \text{ in ether}}$

$(C_6H_5)_4Pb + 2 Li \xrightarrow{\text{in THF}}$

$(C_6H_5)_3PbPb(C_6H_5)_3 + 2 Li \xrightarrow{\text{in THF}}$

③ Sol. in ether and THF.

④ + C₆H₅CH₂Cl

$\longrightarrow (C_6H_5)_3PbCH_2C_6H_5 \ (69\%)$

+ *n*-C₃H₇Br

$\longrightarrow (C_6H_5)_3PbC_3H_7\text{-}n \ (58\%)$

+ C₂H₅I $\longrightarrow (C_6H_5)_3PbC_2H_5 \ (45\%)$

$(C_6H_5)_3PbCl + 2 Li \xrightarrow{\text{in THF}}$

$(C_6H_5)_3PbLi \ \xrightarrow{\ \ \times\ } \ C_6H_5COOH$

$3 C_6H_5Li + PbCl_2 \xrightarrow{\text{in ether}}$

$(C_6H_5)_3PbLi \xrightarrow{+CO_2} C_6H_5COOH$

$\xrightarrow[\text{equilibrium in ether}]{\ \ \rightleftharpoons\ \ } (C_6H_5)_2Pb$

+ C₆H₅·Li

⑥ JOC **17**, 630 (1952) ; **27**, 619, 1260, 4232
(1962).　JCS **1961**,4405.　Naturwiss.
39, 450 (1952).

PbC₁₈H₁₅NO₃

① Triphenyllead nitrate

(C₆H₅)₃PbNO₃

② $(C_6H_5)_4Pb + AgNO_3 \xrightarrow{\text{EtOH}}$

③ Solid. [220° decomp.].

Slightly sol. in H₂O.

⑥ JACS **65**, 435 (1943).　JOC **16**, 466
(1951).

PbC₁₈H₁₅Na

① Triphenyllead sodium

(C₆H₅)₃PbNa

② $(C_6H_5)_3Pb \cdot Pb(C_6H_5)_3 + 2 Na \xrightarrow{\text{in liq. NH}_3}$

$(C_6H_5)_3PbCl + 2 Na \xrightarrow{\text{in liq. NH}_3}$

$(C_6H_5)_4Pb + 2 Na + NH_3 \longrightarrow$

③ Solution in liq. NH₃.

⑥ JACS **61**, 731, 1685 (1939).

PbC₁₈H₁₅Sn₄

① Tetrakis(triphenylstannyl)lead

[(C₆H₅)₃Sn]₄Pb

② 4 (C₆H₅)₃SnLi + 2 PbCl₂

$\longrightarrow 2 [(C_6H_5)_3Sn]_2Pb$

$\longrightarrow [(C_6H_5)_3Sn]_4Pb + Pb \ (16\%)$

③ Yellow solid. [200° decomp.].

Recrystd. from CHCl₃-petr. ether.

UV : λ_{max} 298 mμ (ε_{max} 59500) (CHCl₃).

⑥ JOM **2**, 260, 265 (1964).

PbC₁₈H₁₆O

① Triphenyllead hydroxide

(C₆H₅)₃PbOH

② Ph₃PbCl + KOH

$$\xrightarrow{\text{reflux 3 hrs. in EtOH}} 100\%$$

③ White solid. [300～310°, decomp. without melting].

Sol. in hot EtOH.

④ + C₆H₅OH $\xrightarrow{\text{immediately}}$

(C₆H₅)₃PbOC₆H₅ + H₂O

⑥ Ber. **51**, 1298 (1918); **55**, 1282 (1922);
58, 427 (1925).   JPC **64**, 822 (1960).
JACS **82**, 6269 (1960).

PbC₁₈H₁₈Cl₂O₄

① Diethyllead di-*p*-chlorobenzoate
$(C_2H_5)_2Pb(OCOC_6H_4Cl-p)_2$

② $(C_2H_5)_3PbOH + p-Cl-C_6H_4COOH$
$\longrightarrow$ 24%

③ Solid. [185° decomp.].

⑥ JOC **18**, 1341 (1953).

PbC₁₈H₂₀O₄

① Diphenyllead dipropionate
$(C_6H_5)_2Pb(OCOC_2H_5)_2$

② $(C_6H_5)_4Pb + C_2H_5COOH \longrightarrow$ 55%

③ Solid. [183.5∼184.5°].
Sol. in polar org. solvents.

⑥ CA **50**, 3271 (1956).

PbC₁₈H₂₄O₆S₂

① Diethyllead di-*o*-toluenesulfonate
$(C_2H_5)_2Pb(OSO_2C_6H_4CH_3-o)_2$

② $(C_2H_5)_2PbSO_3 + HOSO_2C_6H_4CH_3 \longrightarrow$

③ Solid. [165° decomp.].
Sol. in polar org. solvents; slightly
sol. in cold water.

⑥ JCS **1951**, 658.

PbC₁₈H₂₆O₆

① Phenyllead tri-*n*-butylate
$C_6H_5Pb(OCOC_3H_7-n)_3$

② $(C_6H_5)_2Pb(OCOC_3H_7)_2 + Hg(OCOC_3H_7)_2$
in C_3H_7COOH
$\longrightarrow$ 50%

③ White crystals. [65°].
Sol. in polar olg. solvents.

⑥ CA **47**, 6365 (1953).

PbC₁₈H₃₃F

① Tricyclohexyllead fluoride
$(C_6H_{11})_3PbF$

② $(C_6H_{11})_3PbI \xrightarrow{KF}$

$(C_6H_{11})_3PbOH \xrightarrow{HF}$

③ White microcrystals. [198° decomp.].
d 1.79 (17°/4°).
Sol. in polar org. solvents.

⑥ Ber. **55**, 1282 (1922).

PbC₁₉H₁₈S

① Triphenylmethylthiolead
$(C_6H_5)_3PbSCH_3$

② $2(C_6H_5)_3PbCl + Pb(SCH_3)_2 \longrightarrow$ 100%
$2(C_6H_5)_3PbSNa + MeI \longrightarrow$

③ White crystals. [108∼109°].
Sol. in C_6H_6, *n*-C_6H_{14}, EtOH, CHCl₃ and
most common org. solvents.
Decomp. above melting point.

④ $+ CH_3I \longrightarrow (C_6H_5)_3PbI + (CH_3)_2S$
(quantitatively)
$+ HCl \longrightarrow$
$(C_6H_5)_3PbCl + (C_6H_5)_2PbCl_2 + PbCl_2$

⑥ JOC **28**, 225 (1963).

PbC₁₉H₂₇NO₂S

① Triethyllead *p*-tolylsulfonanilide
$(C_2H_5)_3PbN(C_6H_5)SO_2C_6H_4CH_3-p$

② $CH_3C_6H_4SO_2(C_6H_5)NH$
$(C_2H_5)_3PbOH \xrightarrow{alc.}$

③ Solid. [134°].
Sol. in polar org. solvents.

⑥ JCS **1950**, 684.

PbC₂₀H₁₆O₂

① Di-2-furyldiphenyllead
$(OC_4H_3)_2Pb(C_6H_5)_2$

② $(C_6H_5)_2PbX_2 +$ ⟨furyl⟩$-MgI \xrightarrow{Et_2O}$

③ Solid. [118°].
Sol. in polar org. solvents.

④ $+ HCl \xrightarrow{in\ CHCl_3} (C_6H_5)_2PbCl_2$

⑥ Rec. trav. chim. **51**, 1054 (1932).   CA
27, 502 (1933).

PbC$_{20}$H$_{16}$S$_2$

① Di-2-thienyldiphenyllead
   (SC$_4$H$_3$)$_2$Pb(C$_6$H$_5$)$_2$

② SC$_4$H$_3$MgX + X$_2$Pb(C$_6$H$_5$)$_2$ $\xrightarrow{\text{THF}}$

③ Solid. [185°].
   Slightly sol. in polar org. solvents.

⑥ CA **54**, 17238 (1960).

PbC$_{20}$H$_{18}$

① Triphenylvinyllead
   (C$_6$H$_5$)$_3$Pb(CH=CH$_2$)

② ClPb(C$_6$H$_5$)$_3$ + (CH$_2$=CH)MgBr
   $\xrightarrow{\text{THF}}$ 23.6%

③ White crystals. [33~34°],

④ + Na $\xrightarrow{\text{3hrs, 70°}}$ CH$_2$=CHNa + C$_6$H$_5$Na

⑥ JACS **81**, 3578 (1959).   CA **58**, 11398 (1963).

PbC$_{20}$H$_{18}$OS

① Triphenyllead thioacetate
   (C$_6$H$_5$)$_3$PbSCOCH$_3$

② (C$_6$H$_5$)$_4$Pb + CH$_3$COSH $\longrightarrow$ 12%

③ [94~95°].
   Recrystd. from EtOH.
   IR : JOC **28**, 225 (1963).

⑥ JOC **28**, 1911 (1963).

PbC$_{20}$H$_{20}$O$_4$

① Diphenyllead dimethylmethacryrate
   (C$_6$H$_5$)$_2$Pb[OCOC(CH$_3$)=CH$_2$]$_2$

② Ph$_4$Pb + CH$_2$=C(CH$_3$)COOH
   $\xrightarrow{\text{heat}}$ 72~84%
   Ph$_2$PbO + CH$_2$=C(CH$_3$)COOH
   $\longrightarrow$ 69%

③ Solid. [204~205°].

④ $\xrightarrow{\text{Bz}_2\text{O}_2 \text{ or ABN in C}_6\text{H}_6}$ polymer

⑥ Dokl. **85**, 1037 (1952); CA **47**, 6365 (1953); **58**, 9111(1963); **59**, 1155(1963).
   Zhur. **32**, 3057 (1962); **33**, 1945 (1963).

PbC$_{20}$H$_{21}$AsO$_2$

① Triphenyllead dimethylarsinate
   (C$_6$H$_5$)$_3$PbOAs(O)(CH$_3$)$_2$

② (CH$_3$)$_3$As(O)ONa + (C$_6$H$_5$)$_3$PbCl
   $\xrightarrow{\text{reflux for 8hrs in CH}_3\text{OH}}$ 73%

③ White crystals. [>260°]
   Sol. in CH$_3$OH.

④ + glacial CH$_3$COOH
   $\longrightarrow$ (C$_6$H$_5$)$_2$Pb(OOCCH$_3$)$_2$
   (quantitatively)

⑥ Inorg. Chem. **1**, 917 (1962).

PbC$_{20}$H$_{24}$O$_4$

① Diethyllead di-*p*-toluate
   (C$_2$H$_5$)$_2$Pb(OCOC$_6$H$_4$CH$_3$-*p*)$_2$

② (C$_2$H$_5$)$_3$PbOH + *p*-CH$_3$C$_6$H$_4$COOH
   $\xrightarrow{\text{alcohol}}$ 30%

③ Solid. [186° decomp.].
   Recrystd. from ether.

⑥ JOC **18**, 1341 (1953).

PbC$_{20}$H$_{26}$O$_2$

① Triethyllead diphenylacetate
   (C$_2$H$_5$)$_3$PbOCOCH(C$_6$H$_5$)$_2$

② (C$_2$H$_5$)$_3$PbOH
   + (C$_6$H$_5$)$_2$CHCOOH $\xrightarrow{\text{in alcohol}}$

③ White solid. [164~165°].
   Sol. in polar org. solvents.

⑥ JOC **18**, 1341 (1953).

PbC$_{20}$H$_{28}$

① Di-*n*-butyldiphenyllead
   (*n*-C$_4$H$_9$)$_2$Pb(C$_6$H$_5$)$_2$

③ Yelow oil.
   Unstable. Insol. in gasoline.

⑤ Antinock effect is 0.33 compared with Et$_4$Pb.

⑥ CA **23**, 4201 (1929).

PbC$_{20}$H$_{44}$

① Tetra-*n*-amyllead
   (*n*-C$_5$H$_{11}$)$_4$Pb

② PbS + n-C$_5$H$_{11}$Na $\xrightarrow{\text{90~100° in C}_6\text{H}_6}$

PbCl$_2$ + (n-C$_5$H$_{11}$)$_2$Ba $\longrightarrow$

PbCl$_2$ + n-C$_5$H$_{11}$MgBr $\longrightarrow$

③ Colorless liq. (170~171°). n_D 1.4966
   (20°). d 1.2457 (20°/4°).
   Sol. in org. solvents ; insol. in H$_2$O.
⑥ CA **55**, 11303, 23345 (1961) ; **53**, 9149
   (1959).   JCS **1935**, 39.

PbC$_{21}$H$_{21}$Br

① Tribenzyllead bromide
   (C$_6$H$_5$CH$_2$)$_3$PbBr
② (C$_6$H$_5$CH$_2$)$_4$Pb $\xrightarrow{\text{Br}_2\text{ in pyridine}}$
③ Solid. [150° decomp.].
   Sol. in polar org. solvents ; a soln.
   decomp. rapidly in direct sunlight.
⑥ Ber. **63**, 1381 (1930).

PbC$_{22}$H$_{15}$CoO$_4$

① Triphenyllead-cobalt tetracarbonyl
   (C$_6$H$_5$)$_3$Pb·Co(CO)$_4$
② Na[Co(CO)$_4$] + (C$_6$H$_5$)$_3$PbOH $\longrightarrow$
③ Yellow solid. [98° decomp.].
   Sol. in petr. ether.
⑥ Naturwiss. **44**, 34 (1957).

PbC$_{22}$H$_{18}$O$_4$

① Triphenyllead hydrogenmaleate
   (C$_6$H$_5$)$_3$PbOCOCH=CHCOOH
② (C$_6$H$_5$)$_3$PbOH + HOOCCH=CHCOOH
   $\xrightarrow{\text{in EtOH}}$ solid $\xrightarrow{\text{KOH in EtOH}}$ 90%
③ Solid. [207°].
   Slightly sol. in org. solvents.
⑥ JOC **16**, 466 (1951).

PbC$_{22}$H$_{24}$

① Isobutyltriphenyllead
   i-C$_4$H$_9$Pb(C$_6$H$_5$)$_3$
② i-C$_4$H$_9$MgBr + (C$_6$H$_5$)$_3$PbBr
   $\longrightarrow$ 80.6%
③ Fine needles. [68.0~68.5°].

Sol. in org. solvents.
⑥ CA **23**, 1888 (1929).

PbC$_{23}$H$_{15}$MnO$_5$

① Triphenyllead-manganese pentacarbonyl
   (C$_6$H$_5$)$_3$Pb·Mn(CO)$_5$
② NaMn(CO)$_5$ + (C$_6$H$_5$)$_3$PbCl
   $\xrightarrow{\text{in THF}}$ 79%
③ Purify by recrystallization.
   Yellow solid. [146~148°].
   Fairly stable in air. Sol. in CH$_2$Cl$_2$,
   ether, acetone and THF ; fairly
   sol. in C$_2$H$_5$OH and C$_6$H$_6$; slightly
   sol. in n-hexane.
④ . + P(C$_6$H$_5$)$_3$
   $\xrightarrow{\text{in N}_2\text{ gas}}$ (C$_6$H$_5$)$_3$Pb·M(CO)$_4$·P(C$_6$H$_5$)$_3$
⑥ JACS **84**, 2486 (1962).

PbC$_{23}$H$_{19}$N

① 2-Pyridyltriphenyllead
   (2-C$_5$H$_4$N)Pb(C$_6$H$_5$)$_3$
② 2-C$_5$H$_4$NLi + MgBr$_2$
   $\xrightarrow{\text{ether}}$ 2-C$_5$H$_4$NMgBr
   2-C$_5$H$_4$NMgBr + (C$_6$H$_5$)$_2$PbI$_2$
   $\xrightarrow{\text{ether} + \text{C}_6\text{H}_6}$ (C$_6$H$_5$)$_2$Pb(2-C$_5$H$_4$N)I
   (C$_6$H$_5$)$_2$Pb(2-C$_5$H$_4$N)I + (C$_6$H$_5$)MgBr
   $\xrightarrow{\text{Et}_2\text{O}}$ 67.1%
③ Crystals.
   Sol. in CHCl$_3$ and CH$_3$OH.
⑥ JOC **16**, 1788 (1951).

PbC$_{24}$H$_{18}$

① 1,1-Diphenyldibenzoplumbol

② (C$_6$H$_5$)$_3$PbCl $\xrightarrow{\text{heat}}$ 30%
③ Colorless crystals. [136~137.5°].
   UV : 215 mμ(ε_{max} 67600),   280 mμ(ε_{max}

11250) in 95% EtOH.

④ + HCl $\longrightarrow$ Ph₂PbCl₂ + Ph–Ph

⑥ Angew. **72**, 322 (1960).

PbC₂₄H₂₀

① Tetraphenyllead
    (C₆H₅)₄Pb

② Li₄Pb + 4 C₆H₅X $\longrightarrow$

3 C₆H₅Li + PbCl₂ + C₆H₅I $\longrightarrow$

C₆H₅MgCl + PbCl₂ $\xrightarrow{\text{THF}}$

C₆H₅Na + PbO $\xrightarrow{\text{C₆H₆}}$

Al(C₆H₅)₄Na + Pb(electrode) $\xrightarrow{e^-}$

③ White crystals. [223~225°]
    Slightly sol. in aromatics; insol. in
    H₂O and polar org. solvents.
    UV: λ_{max} 250, 257, 267, 268 mμ.

④ + HCl $\xrightarrow{\text{C₆H₆ + CH₃OH}}$
    (C₆H₅)₃PbCl + C₆H₆

    + AgNO₃ $\xrightarrow{\text{C₆H₆ + C₂H₅OH}}$ Ag ↓
    + (C₆H₅)₃PbNO₃ + C₆H₅·

    + ICl₃ $\xrightarrow{\text{CHCl₃}}$ (C₆H₅)₂PbCl₂
    + (C₆H₅)₃PbCl

    + H₂ $\xrightarrow{\text{60 atm, 200°}}$ Pb ↓ + C₆H₆

    + Pb(OCOCH₃)₄ $\longrightarrow$
    (C₆H₅)₂Pb(OCOCH₃)₂

    + Bz₂O₂ $\xrightarrow{\text{CCl₄, 50 hrs}}$ (C₆H₅)₂PbCl₂(60.8%)
    + C₆H₅Cl + (C₆H₅)₂Pb(OBz)₂

    + C₆H₅(C¹⁴-labelled)
    $\xrightarrow[h\nu]{}$ exchange of C₆H₅ group

⑥ Chem. Revs. **54**, 101 (1954). "Organo-
    lead chemistry" International Lead
    Zinc Research Organization 292,
    Madison Avene, New York.

PbC₂₄H₂₀O₄

① Dinaphtyllead diacetate
    (C₁₀H₇)₂Pb(OCOCH₃)₂

② Pb(OCOCH₃)₄ + (2-C₁₀H₇)₂Hg $\longrightarrow$

③ Solid. [235~236°].

Slightly sol. in polar org. solvents.

⑥ Zhur. **29**, 2253 (1959); CA **54**, 10967
    (1960).

PbC₂₄H₂₀S

① Triphenylphenylthiolead
    (C₆H₅)₃PbSC₆H₅

② 2 (C₆H₅)₃PbCl + Pb(SC₆H₅)₂ $\longrightarrow$ 94%

    (C₆H₅)₄Pb + C₆H₅SH $\xrightarrow{\text{reflux in CHCl₃}}$
    2%

③ White crystals. [106~107°].
    Sol. in C₆H₆, n-C₆H₁₄, EtOH, CHCl₃
    and other org. solvents. Decomp.
    above melting point.

⑥ JOC **28**, 225 (1963).

PbC₂₄H₂₁N

① p-Aminophenyltriphenyllead
    p-NH₂C₆H₄Pb(C₆H₅)₃

② p-BrC₆H₄NH₂ + n-C₄H₉Li
    $\longrightarrow$ p-LiC₆H₄NH₂

    p-LiC₆H₄NH₂ + MgBr₂
    $\longrightarrow$ p-BrMgC₆H₄NH₂

    (C₆H₅)₃PbCl + p-BrMgC₆H₄NH₂
    $\xrightarrow{\text{2 hrs at r. t.}}$ 66%

③ White solid. [172°].
    Slightly sol. in org. solvents.

④ $\xrightarrow[\text{with β-naphthol}]{\text{diazo and coupled}}$
    (C₆H₅)₃Pb(p-C₆H₄NN-C₁₀H₆OH)

⑥ JACS. **64**, 1007 (1942); **72**, 4553 (1950).

PbC₂₄H₂₂As₂O₆

① Diphenyllead bis(phenylarsonate)
    (C₆H₅)₂Pb[OAs(O)(OH)C₆H₅]₂

② (C₆H₅)₃PbCl + 2 C₆H₅As(O)(OH)₂
    $\xrightarrow{\text{80° for 18 hrs. in C₅H₅N}}$ 33%

③ White crystals. [>260°]
    Insol. in common org. solvents.
    IR: $\nu_{Pb-O-As}$ 853 cm⁻¹.

⑥ Inorg. Chem. **1**, 917 (1962).

PbC$_{24}$H$_{24}$
① Diethyldi-1-naphthyllead
   (C$_2$H$_5$)$_2$Pb(C$_{10}$H$_7$-1)$_2$
② (C$_2$H$_5$)$_2$PbCl$_2$ + 1-C$_{10}$H$_7$MgBr ⟶
③ White crystals. [116°].
   Sol. in org. solvents ; recrystd. from
   alc.
⑥ Ber. **52**, 2150 (1919).

PbC$_{24}$H$_{32}$
① Dicyclohexyldiphenyllead
   (C$_6$H$_{11}$)$_2$Pb(C$_6$H$_5$)$_2$
② C$_6$H$_{11}$MgBr + (C$_6$H$_5$)$_2$Pb $\xrightarrow{\text{in ether}}$

   C$_6$H$_5$MgBr + (C$_6$H$_{11}$)$_2$PbCl$_2$ $\xrightarrow{\text{in ether}}$
③ Pale yellow needle crystals. [178∼
   180° decomp.].
   Sol. in org. solvents. Colored in light
   into brown. Solubility in 100 g solvents. EtOH 324 g, C$_6$H$_6$ 2298 g, CCl$_4$
   845 g, AcOEt 231 g.
④ $\xrightarrow{\text{X}}$ (C$_6$H$_{11}$)$_2$PbX$_2$ (X=Br, I)

   $\xrightarrow{\text{HX}}$ (C$_6$H$_{11}$)$_2$PbX$_2$ (X=Cl, Br)
⑥ Ber. **46**, 3257 (1914).

PbC$_{24}$H$_{44}$
① Tetracyclohexyllead
   (C$_6$H$_{11}$)$_4$Pb
② C$_6$H$_{11}$MgBr + PbCl$_2$ $\xrightarrow{\text{ether}}$
③ Canary-yellow glittering foil. Color-
   less crystals. [220° decomp.], [130°
   become yellow].
   Sol. in org. solvents.
④ + HCl gas $\xrightarrow[5\sim-10°C]{\text{in CHCl}_3}$ (C$_6$H$_{11}$)$_2$PbCl$_2$

   + Br$_2$ $\xrightarrow[5°]{\text{in CCl}_4}$ (C$_6$H$_{11}$)$_4$PbBr$_2$

   + I$_2$ $\xrightarrow[40°C]{\text{in CCl}_4}$ (C$_6$H$_{11}$)$_4$PbI$_2$
⑥ Ber. **47**, 3257 (1914) ; **54**, 2061 (1921).

PbC$_{25}$H$_{22}$
① Triphenyl-p-tolyllead
   (C$_6$H$_5$)$_3$PbC$_6$H$_4$CH$_3$-p
② (C$_6$H$_5$)$_3$PbBr + p-CH$_3$C$_6$H$_4$MgBr $\xrightarrow{\text{ether}}$

   (C$_6$H$_5$)$_3$PbCl + p-CH$_3$C$_6$H$_4$Li $\xrightarrow{\text{C}_6\text{H}_6}$

   (C$_6$H$_5$)$_3$PbNa + p-IC$_6$H$_4$CH$_3$ ⟶
③ Solid. [125.5°].
   Stable up to 255°. Sol. in org. solvents ; insol. in H$_2$O.
⑥ Ber. **52**, 2150 (1919).   JACS **54**, 3726
   (1932).   JOC **18**, 1675 (1953).

PbC$_{25}$H$_{40}$
① Benzyltricyclohexyllead
   C$_6$H$_5$CH$_2$Pb(C$_6$H$_{11}$)$_3$
② PbCl$_2$ + C$_6$H$_{11}$MgBr ⟶ Pb(C$_6$H$_{11}$)$_3$
   $\xrightarrow{\text{MgI}_2}$ (C$_6$H$_{11}$)$_3$PbI $\xrightarrow{\text{Na}}$ (C$_6$H$_{11}$)$_3$PbNa
   $\xrightarrow{\text{C}_6\text{H}_5\text{CH}_2\text{Cl}}$ 39%
③ Crystals. [228°].
   Very slightly sol. in aromatic hydrocarbons.
⑥ JACS **61**, 731 (1939).

PbC$_{26}$H$_{20}$O$_4$
① Diphenyllead dibenzoate
   (C$_6$H$_5$)$_2$Pb(OCOC$_6$H$_5$)$_2$
② Ph$_4$Pb + C$_6$H$_5$COOH ⟶
③ White crystals. [240°].
⑥ J. Gen. Chem. USSR **11**, 376 (1941).
   CA **35**, 5870 (1941) ; **47**, 6365 (1953) ;
   50, 3271 (1956).   Dokl. **85**, 1037
   (1952).   Zhur. **25**, 489 (1955).

PbC$_{26}$H$_{23}$N
① 5-Ethyl-10, 10-dihydro-10, 10-diphenyl
   -5 H-phenazyllead

② C$_6$H$_5$PbBr$_2$ + C$_2$H$_5$—N⟨Li,Li⟩

$\xrightarrow{\text{ether, 16hrs}}$

③ Colorless crystals. [121.5~123°].
   Sol. in petr. ether.
⑥ JACS **82**, 2522 (1960).

PbC$_{26}$H$_{24}$

① Diphenyldi-*o*-tolyllead
   (C$_6$H$_5$)$_2$Pb(C$_6$H$_4$CH$_3$-*o*)$_2$

② *o*-CH$_3$C$_6$H$_4$MgBr + (C$_6$H$_5$)$_2$PbI$_2$ $\xrightarrow{\text{ether}}$

③ Crystals. [134~135°].
   Sol. in org. solvents.
⑥ Ber. **49**, 349 (1916).

PbC$_{26}$H$_{24}$

① Triphenyl-2-styryllead
   (C$_6$H$_5$)$_3$PbCH=CHC$_6$H$_5$

② (C$_6$H$_5$)$_3$PbCl + C$_6$H$_5$CH=CHMgBr
   $\xrightarrow{\text{ether}}$ 77%

③ Solid. [107~109°].
   Sol. in org. solvents.
④ + HCl $\longrightarrow$ (C$_6$H$_5$)$_3$PbCl +
   C$_6$H$_5$CH=CH$_2$
⑥ JACS **55**, 4689 (1933).

PbC$_{26}$H$_{25}$N

① *p*-Dimethylaminophenyltriphenyl-
   lead
   p-(CH$_3$)$_2$NC$_6$H$_4$Pb(C$_6$H$_5$)$_3$

② (C$_6$H$_5$)$_3$PbCl
   + *p*-(CH$_3$)$_2$NC$_6$H$_4$Li $\xrightarrow[\text{reflux}]{\text{C}_6\text{H}_6 \text{ and ether}}$

③ Solid. [124~125°].
   Sol. in org. solvents.
④ + CH$_3$COOH $\xrightarrow{\text{petr. ether}}$
   (C$_6$H$_5$)$_3$PbOCOCH$_3$
⑥ JACS **54**, 3726 (1932).

PbC$_{26}$H$_{26}$As$_2$O$_6$

① Diphenyllead bis(benzylarsonate)
   (C$_6$H$_5$)$_2$Pb[OAs(O)(OH)CH$_2$C$_6$H$_5$]$_2$

② (C$_6$H$_5$)$_3$PbCl + 2 C$_6$H$_5$CH$_2$·As(O)(OH)$_2$
   $\xrightarrow{\text{reflux for 16 hrs. in CH}_3\text{OH}}$ 35%

③ White solid. [>260°].
   Insol. in common org. solvents.
   IR: $\nu_{\text{Pb-O-As}}$ 875 cm^{-1}, 855 cm^{-1}.
④ + glacial CH$_3$COOH
   $\longrightarrow$ (C$_6$H$_5$)$_2$Pb(OOCCH$_3$)$_2$
⑥ Inorg. Chem. **1**, 917 (1962).

PbC$_{27}$H$_{20}$O$_6$

① Phenyllead tribenzoate
   C$_6$H$_5$Pb(OCOC$_6$H$_5$)$_3$

② (C$_6$H$_5$)$_4$Pb + *i*-PrCOOH $\longrightarrow$
   (C$_6$H$_5$)$_2$Pb[OCOCH(CH$_3$)$_2$]$_2$ $\xrightarrow{\text{NaOH}}$
   C$_6$H$_5$Pb[OCOCH(CH$_3$)$_2$]$_3$ $\xrightarrow{\text{C}_6\text{H}_5\text{CH}_2\text{OH}}$
   C$_6$H$_5$Pb(OCH$_2$C$_6$H$_5$)$_3$ (41.5%)

③ White crystals. [149.5~151°].
   Sol. in org. solvents; insol. in hydrocarbons; recrystd. from C$_6$H$_6$.
⑥ Izv. OKhN **1955**, 711. Dokl. **85**, 1037
   (1952). CA **50**, 7075(1956); **47**, 6365
   (1953).

PbC$_{27}$H$_{33}$Br

① Trimesityllead bromide
   [2,4,6-(CH$_3$)$_3$C$_6$H$_2$]$_3$PbBr

② 2,4,6-(CH$_3$)$_3$C$_6$H$_2$MgBr + PbBr
   $\xrightarrow[\text{filtrate}]{\text{in THF}}$ $\xrightarrow{\text{cool to } -50°}$
   $\xrightarrow{\text{Br}_2 \text{ in CH}_2\text{Cl}_2}$ yellow soln.
   $\xrightarrow{\text{shake with NaHCO}_3, \text{ wash. dry.}}$
   crude [2,4,6-(CH$_3$)$_3$C$_6$H$_2$]$_3$PbBr
⑥ JCS **1961**, 4405.

PbC$_{28}$H$_{22}$

① 1-Naphtyltriphenyllead
   1-C$_{10}$H$_7$Pb(C$_6$H$_5$)$_3$

② (C$_6$H$_5$)$_3$PbCl + 1-C$_{10}$H$_7$MgBr

528 PbC$_{28}$H$_{28}$

→ 66%

③ White crystals. [101°], [131°].
   Sol. in ether, C$_6$H$_6$ and CHCl$_3$;
      slightly sol. in hot alcohol; insol.
      in cold alc.
⑥ Ber. **52**, 2150 (1919). JACS **55**, 4689
   (1933).

PbC$_{28}$H$_{28}$

① Tetrabenzyllead
   (C$_6$H$_5$CH$_2$)$_4$Pb
② C$_6$H$_5$CH$_2$Na + PbO ⟶
   C$_6$H$_5$CH$_2$Na + PbBr$_2$ ⟶
   (C$_6$H$_5$CH$_2$)$_4$AlLi + PbCl$_2$ ⟶
   C$_6$H$_5$CH$_2$MgBr + PbO ⟶
③ Yellow platelets. [65.5°].
   Sol. in org. solvents. Decomp. by
      air.
⑥ Ber. **88**, 542 (1955).   CA **53**, 9149
   (1959); **55**, 23345 (1961).   Z. Chem.
   3, 89 (1963).

PbC$_{28}$H$_{28}$

① Tetra-*p*-tolyllead
   (*p*-CH$_3$C$_6$H$_4$)$_4$Pb
② *p*-CH$_3$C$_6$H$_4$MgCl + PbCl$_2$ ⟶
   Pb–Na alloy
      + (*p*-CH$_3$C$_6$H$_4$)$_2$SO$_4$ ⟶
③ White crystals. [>321° decomp.].
   [240°].
   Sol. in aromatic hydrocarbons;
      insol. in H$_2$O. Decomp. by acids.

④ $\xrightarrow{\text{heat}}$ CH$_3$—⟨ ⟩—⟨ ⟩—CH$_3$

   + *n*-C$_4$H$_9$Li ⟶ (*n*-C$_4$H$_9$)$_4$Pb
      + 4 CH$_3$C$_6$H$_4$Li
⑥ JACS **62**, 1099 (1940); **61**, 731 (1939).
   CA **49**, 14797 (1955); **54**, 17238 (1960).

PbC$_{28}$H$_{28}$O$_4$

① Tetra-*o*-methoxyphenyllead
   (*p*-CH$_3$OC$_6$H$_4$)$_4$Pb
⊘ (*p*-CH$_3$OC$_6$H$_4$)$_3$Pb + Mg + MgI$_2$

→ 58%

③ Crystals. [145°].
   Sol. in org. solvents; insol. in H$_2$O.
⑥ JACS **61**, 739 (1939).

PbC$_{28}$H$_{30}$N$_2$

① Di-*p*-dimethylaminophenyldiphenyl-
   lead
   [*p*-(CH$_3$)$_2$N·C$_6$H$_4$]$_2$Pb(C$_6$H$_5$)$_2$
② (C$_6$H$_5$)$_2$PbCl$_2$ + 2 *p*-(CH$_3$)$_2$NC$_6$H$_4$Li
   ⟶ 16%
③ White solid. [134~135°].
   Sol. in polar org. solvents.
⑥ JACS **54**, 3726 (1932).

PbC$_{32}$H$_{24}$

① Di-1-naphtyldiphenyllead
   (1-C$_{10}$H$_7$)$_2$Pb(C$_6$H$_5$)$_2$
② (C$_6$H$_5$)$_2$PbCl$_2$ + (1-C$_{10}$H$_7$)MgBr
   ⟶ 81.2%
③ Solid. [137°].
   Sol. in aromatic hydrocarbons.
④ + HCl ⟶ (C$_6$H$_5$)$_2$PbCl$_2$ + C$_{10}$H$_8$
⑥ JACS **55**, 4689 (1933).

PbC$_{36}$H$_{30}$SSn

① Triphenyl(triphenylstannthio)lead.
   (C$_6$H$_5$)$_3$Pb·S·Sn(C$_6$H$_5$)$_3$
② (C$_6$H$_5$)$_3$SnLi $\xrightarrow{+\text{S}}$

   (C$_6$H$_5$)$_3$SnSLi $\xrightarrow{+(\text{C}_6\text{H}_5)_3\text{PbCl}}$
③ [138°].
⑥ Angew. **75**, 138 (1963).

PbC$_{36}$H$_{44}$

① Tetramesityllead
   [2,4,6-(CH$_3$)$_3$C$_6$H$_2$]$_4$Pb
② 2,4,6-(CH$_3$)$_3$C$_6$H$_2$MgBr + PbCl$_2$
   $\xrightarrow{\text{THF, }-25\sim30°\text{ hydrolyzed with water}}$
③ Yellow solid. [242° decomp.].
   Sol. in CCl$_4$.
⑥ JCS **1961**, 4405.

$PbC_{38}H_{30}$

① Bis-triphenyllead acetylide

   $(C_6H_5)_3PbC \equiv CPb(C_6H_5)_3$

② $NaC \equiv CH + (C_6H_5)_3PbX \xrightarrow{\text{liq. } NH_3}$

③ [138.5°].

   Sol. in org. solvents and liq. NH_3.

   Thermally unstable.

④ $+ Ag^+ \longrightarrow Ag_2C_2$

   $+ I_2 \longrightarrow$ cleavage of Pb−C bond.

⑥ CA **49**, 6087 (1955).

$PbC_{44}H_{38}Sn$

① 4-Triphenylplumbyl-2-triphenyl-

   stannylethylbenzene

   $(C_6H_5)_3PbC_6H_4CH_2CH_2Sn(C_6H_5)_3\text{-}p$

② $(C_6H_5)_3SnH + (C_6H_5)_3PbC_6H_4CH=CH_2\text{-}p$

   $\xrightarrow[\text{90°, 3hrs in } C_6H_6]{} 85\%$

③ [177~179°].

⑥ Rec. trav. chim. **80**, 623 (1961); CA

   56, 3500 (1962).

$PbC_{48}H_{80}O_4$

① Diphenyllead distearate

   $(C_6H_5)_2Pb(OCOC_{17}H_{35})_2$

② $(i\text{-}C_3H_7OCO)_2Pb(C_6H_5)_2 + C_{17}H_{35}COOH$

   $\xrightarrow[\text{in EtOH, 35°}]{} 64.1\%$

③ White crystals. [100~101°].

   Sol. in org. solvents.

⑥ Zhur. **25**, 489 (1955).   CA **50**, 3271

   (1956); **47**, 6365 (1953).

$PbC_{64}H_{56}Sn$

① Bis(p-triphenylplumbylphenylethyl)-

   diphenyltin

   $[(C_6H_5)_3PbC_6H_4CH_2CH_2\text{-}p]_2Sn(C_6H_5)_2$

② $(C_6H_5)_2SnH_2 +$

   $2(C_6H_5)_3PbC_6H_4CH=CH_2\text{-}p$

   $\xrightarrow[\text{75°, 2hrs. in } n\text{-hexane}]{} 81\%$

③ Amorph. [71°].

⑥ Rec. trav. chim. **80**, 623 (1961); CA

   56, 3500 (1962).

$PbC_{64}H_{56}Sn_2$

① Bis(p-β-triphenylstannylethyl-

   phenyl)diphenyllead

   $(C_6H_5)_2Pb[C_6H_4CH_2CH_2Sn(C_6H_5)_3\text{-}p]_2$

② $2(C_6H_5)_3SnH + (C_6H_5)_2Pb$

   $(C_6H_4CH=CH_2\text{-}p)_2 \longrightarrow 89\%$

③ [180~182°].

⑥ Rec. trav. chim. **80**, 623 (1961); CA

   56, 3500 (1962).

$Pb_2C_6H_{18}$

① Hexamethyldilead

   $(CH_3)_3Pb \cdot Pb(CH_3)_3$

② $3(CH_3)_3PbOH + Al \longrightarrow$

   $2(CH_3)_3PbOH + Zn \longrightarrow$

   $(CH_3)_3PbOH \xrightarrow{\text{electrolysis}}$

③ Colorless crystals. (238° decomp.).

   [37~38°].

   Sol. in common org. solvents.

④ $\xrightarrow[\text{100° in } N_2 \text{ gas}]{} 3(CH_3)_4Pb + Pb$

⑥ Ber. **71**, 2381(1938).   JOC **2**, 535(1938).

   Trans. Faraday Soc. **36**, 1209(1940).

   JACS **64**, 462 (1942).   Z. anorg.

   allg. Chem. **251**, 125 (1943).

$Pb_2C_{12}H_{30}$

① Hexaethyldilead

   $(C_2H_5)_3Pb \cdot Pb(C_2H_5)_3$

② $(C_2H_5)_3PbCl + Na \xrightarrow{\text{in liq. } NH_3}$

   $3(C_2H_5)_3PbOH + Al \longrightarrow$

   $2(C_2C_5)_3PbOH + Zn \longrightarrow$

   $(C_2H_5)_3PbOH \xrightarrow{\text{electrolysis in } C_2H_5OH}$

③ Clear yellow liq. (100°/2). [<−80°].

   d 1.94.

   Decomp. even in sealed container

   after standing a few days.

④ $+ O_2 \longrightarrow$ a pale yellow solid.

   $\xrightarrow[\text{100° in } N_2]{} 3(C_2H_5)_4Pb + Pb$

   $+ AlCl_3(1~1.5\%)$

   $\xrightarrow[\text{r. t., 2~3hrs}]{} (C_2H_5)_4Pb + Pb$

$$+ 2 (C_2H_5)_3PbBr \xrightarrow{70°, 2hrs} (C_2H_5)_4Pb$$
$$+ PbBr_2$$
$$+ (C_2H_5)_2PbBr_2 \longrightarrow Pb + PbBr_2$$
$$+ (C_2H_5)_3PbBr + (C_2H_5)_4Pb$$
$$+ (CH_2Br)_2$$
$$\xrightarrow{70°, 2.5hrs} (C_2H_5)_4Pb(66\%) + C_2H_6$$
$$+ C_2H_4 + C_4H_{10} + (C_2H_5)_3PbBr + Pb$$
$$+ PbBr_2 + (C_2H_5)_2PbBr_2$$

⑥ Ber. **71** B, 2381 (1938).   JACS **61**, 731 (1939) ; **64**, 462(1942).   Zhur. **31**, 998 (1961).   CA **55**, 23321 (1961) ; **54**, 20937 (1960).   Dokl. **132**, 364 (1960).

$Pb_2C_{12}H_{30}CrO_4$

① Bis(triethyllead) chromate
   $[(C_2H_5)_3Pb]_2CrO_4$
② $(C_2H_5)_3PbOCOCH_3 + K_2CrO_4$
   $\longrightarrow$ 80%
③ Bright yellow crystals. [190°, explode].
   Insol. in org. solvents.
④ $\xrightarrow{sunlight}$ dark products
⑥ JACS **49**, 830 (1927).

$Pb_2C_{12}H_{30}O$

① Bis(triethyllead) oxide
   $[(C_2H_5)_3Pb]_2O$
② $(C_2H_5)_6Pb_2 + O_2 \xrightarrow{60°, 300atm.}$
   $(C_2H_5)_3PbOH$
   $+ Na(powder) \xrightarrow{in\ nonane-C_6H_6}$
③ Yellow green liq. [100° decomp.].
   Sol. in org. solvents.
   Decomp. slowly even at room temp.
   IR : $\nu_{Pb-C} \sim 440\ cm^{-1}$, $\nu_{asym.\ Pb-O-Pb}$
   630 cm^{-1}.
④ $+ H_2O$(in the air) $\longrightarrow$ $(C_2H_5)_3PbOH$
   $+ ROH$ or tertiary hydroperoxide
   $\longrightarrow$ $(C_2H_5)_3PbOH$, $(C_2H_5)_3PbOR$,
   $(C_2H_5)_3PbOOR$
   $+ (CH_3)_2CO \xrightarrow{in\ hexane} (C_2H_5)_3PbOH$
⑥ Dokl. **136**, 89 (1961).   Opt. i Spektro-

skopiya **10**, 79 (1961).   Izv. SFi **26**, 1285 (1962).   CA **58**, 4059, 7517 (1963) ; **55**, 27027 (1961).

$Pb_2C_{12}H_{30}O_4S$

① Bis(triethyllead) sulfate
   $[(C_2H_5)_3Pb]_2SO_4$
② $[(C_2H_5)_3Pb_2]S + Air$
   $\xrightarrow[ether\ in\ a\ dark\ room]{bubble\ for\ 40hrs.\ in}$ 55%
③ White solid.
   5.5% Sol. in H_2O at room temp.
   Recrystd. from H_2O.
⑥ JACS **67**, 190 (1945).

$Pb_2C_{12}H_{30}S$

① Bis(triethyllead) sulfide
   $[(C_2H_5)_3Pb]_2S$
② $(C_2H_5)_3PbCl + Na_2S \xrightarrow{in\ H_2O}$ 86%
③ Yellow green liq. [$-45.1°$]. n_D 1.6249 (20°). d 2.05 (20°/4°).
   Photosensitive.
⑥ JACS **67**, 190 (1945).

$Pb_2C_{14}H_{30}$

① Bis(triethylplumbyl)acetylene
   $[(C_2H_5)_3PbC\equiv]_2$
② $(\equiv CMgBr)_2$
   $+ (C_2H_5)_3PbX \xrightarrow{in\ ether\ or\ CHCl_3}$
   $NaC\equiv CH + (C_2H_5)_3PbX \xrightarrow{in\ liq.\ NH_3}$
   $(X=Cl, Br)$
③ Liq. (135~140°/0.05). n_D 1.567 (20.5°). d 1.904 (20.5°).
   Sensitive to H_2O.
⑥ Z. anorg. allg. Chem. **276**, 20 (1954).

$Pb_2C_{18}H_{34}O_2$

① Bis(triethyllead) resorcinolate
   $[(C_2H_5)_3Pb]_2O_2C_6H_4$
② $(C_2H_5)_4Pb + C_6H_4(OH)_2$
   $\xrightarrow{150°, SiO_2\ gel}$
③ Crystals.

Sol. in org. solvents.

⑤ Disinfectants, insecticides, fungicides and antioxidants for vanishes, liquers, paints, etc.

⑥ US 2008003 ; CA **29**, 5862 (1935).

Pb₂C₃₆H₃₀

① Hexaphenyldilead
$(C_6H_5)_3Pb \cdot Pb(C_6H_5)_3$

② $3\,PbCl_2 + 6\,C_6H_5MgBr \xrightarrow{\text{in ether}}$

$(C_6H_5)_3PbI + Na \xrightarrow{\text{in liq. NH}_3}$

③ Colorless crystals. [155° decomp.], [175° decomp.].

Sol. in CCl₄. CHCl₃. C₆H₆ and acetone ; slight. sol. in liq. NH₃, alc., ether and petr. ether ; insol. in H₂O.

IR : λ_{max} 245 mμ(sh) (ε 33900),   293 mμ (ε 35000).

④ $+ 2\,Li \xrightarrow{\text{in THF or liq. NH}_3}$
$2\,(C_6H_5)_3PbLi$

$+ 2\,CH_3COOH \xrightarrow{\text{in C}_7H_{16} \text{ or C}_6H_6}$
C_6H_6 (90%) $+ Pb(OOCCH_3)_2$ (41%)
$+ Pb(C_6H_5)_4$ (25%)
$+ (C_6H_5)_3Pb(OCOCH_3)_3$ (18%)
$+ (C_6H_5)_3PbPb(C_6H_5)_3$ (3%)

$+ \frac{1}{2}O_2 \longrightarrow [(C_6H_5)_3Pb]_2O$

$+ S \xrightarrow{\text{in C}_6H_6} [(C_6H_5)_3Pb]_2S$

⑥ Ber. **51**, 1301 (1918). JOC **4**, 162 (1939) ; **17**, 630 (1952) ; **18**, 1675 (1953) ; **28**, 1911 (1963). JACS **62**, 2765(1940). Spectrochim. Acta **18**, 21 (1962).

Pb₂C₃₆H₃₀S

① Bis(triphenyllead) sulfide
$[(C_6H_5)_3Pb]_2S$

② $(C_6H_5)_3PbCl + H_2S \xrightarrow{\text{in ROH}}$

③ Yellow solid.
Sol. in org. solvents.

⑥ Ber. **51**, 1298 (1918).

Pb₂C₃₆H₆₆

① Hexacyclohexyldilead
$(C_6H_{11})_3Pb \cdot Pb(C_6H_{11})_3$

② $3\,PbCl_2 + 6\,C_6H_{11}MgBr \xrightarrow{\text{in ether}} 50\%$

③ Almost white crystals. [196° decomp.].

Sol. in C₆H₆ and CHCl₃ ; insol. in C₂H₅OH. Turn to yellow material by light or heat.

④ $+ I_2 \xrightarrow{\text{in C}_6H_6} (C_6H_{11})_3PbI$

$+ Br_2 \longrightarrow (C_6H_{11})_2PbBr_2$

$+ Na \xrightarrow{\text{in ether}}$

$(C_6H_{11})_3PbNa \xrightarrow{+I_2} (C_6H_{11})_3PbI$
$\xrightarrow{+HOH} (C_6H_{11})_3PbH$

$+ catalyzer \longrightarrow (C_6H_{11})_4Pb$
$+ (C_6H_{11})_2Pb$

⑥ Ber. **54**, 2060 (1921) ; **75**, 1744 (1942). JACS **61**, 731 (1939) ; **63**, 2509 (1941). Z. anorg. allg. Chem. **250**, 277(1943) ; **251**, 125 (1943).

Pb₂C₃₈H₃₀

① Bis(triphenylplumbyl)acetylene
$[(C_6H_5)_3PbC{\equiv}]_2$

② $({\equiv}CMgBr)_2$
$+ (C_6H_5)_3PbX \xrightarrow{\text{in ether or CHCl}_3}$

$NaC{\equiv}CH + (C_6H_5)_3PbX \xrightarrow{\text{in liq. NH}_3}$

$NaC{\equiv}CH + (C_6H_5)_3PbX \xrightarrow{200°}$

$C_2I_2 + (C_6H_5)_3PbNa \xrightarrow{\text{in liq. NH}_3}$

③ Solid. [138.5°].
Sol. in common org. solvents.
Stable toward H₂O.

④ $+$ alkali solutions $\longrightarrow C_2H_2$
$+ (C_6H_5)_3PbOH$

⑤ Antiknock agents and pesticides.

⑥ Z. anorg. allg. Chem. **276**, 20 (1954).
Ger. 1062244 ; CA **55**, 11303 (1961).

Pb$_2$C$_{38}$H$_{66}$

① Bis(tricyclohexylplumbyl)acetylene
[(C$_6$H$_{11}$)$_3$PbC≡]$_2$

② NaC≡CH + (C$_6$H$_{11}$)$_3$PbI $\xrightarrow{\text{in liq. NH}_3}$

③ Solid. [136°].
Sensitive to light.

⑤ Gasoline additives, catalysts or stabilizers for polymer and insecticides.

⑥ Naturwiss. **46**, 321 (1959). Ger.
1061322 ; CA **55**, 6500 (1961).

Pb$_2$C$_{39}$H$_{36}$

① 1,3-Bis(triphenylplumbyl)propane
[(C$_6$H$_5$)$_3$PbCH$_2$]$_2$CH$_2$′

② 3 C$_6$H$_5$Li + PbCl$_2$ $\xrightarrow{\text{in (CH}_3)_2\text{O}}$
(C$_6$H$_5$)$_3$PbLi $\xrightarrow{\text{X(CH}_2)_3\text{X}}$ 58%

③ White crystals. [94~95°].
Sol. in org. solvents.

⑥ Iowa State Coll. J. Sci. **26**, 292 (1952) ; CA **47**, 8673 (1953).

Pb$_2$C$_{40}$H$_{30}$

① 1,4-Bis(triphenylplumbyl)butadiyne
[(C$_6$H$_5$)$_3$PbC≡C−]$_2$

② [NaC≡C−]$_2$
+ 2 (C$_6$H$_5$)$_3$PbBr $\xrightarrow{\text{in liq. NH}_3}$.

③ Crystals. [187° decomp.].
Stable in air and humidity.

⑥ Naturwiss. **48**, 570 (1961).

Pb$_2$C$_{40}$H$_{34}$O$_4$

① Bis(triphenyllead)maleate
(C$_6$H$_5$)$_3$PbOCOCH=CHCOOPb(C$_6$H$_5$)$_3$

② [(C$_6$H$_5$)$_3$Pb]$_2$ + (=CH·CO)$_2$O
$\xrightarrow[\text{or } 53° < \varDelta \ll 160°]{\text{in the dark for 5 months}}$ 81%

③ Greyish white crystals. [>300°].
Insol. in common org. solvents ; slightly sol. in boiling H$_2$O ; sol. in CH$_3$COOH.

④ $\xrightarrow{265\sim270°}$ brown products.

⑥ JOC **16**, 466 (1951).

Pb$_2$C$_{40}$H$_{36}$FeO$_4$

① Bis(triphenyllead)-iron tetracarbonyl.
(C$_6$H$_5$)$_3$Pb·Pb(C$_6$H$_5$)$_3$·Fe(CO)$_4$

② CaHFe(CO)$_4$ + (C$_6$H$_5$)$_3$PbOH ⟶
CaHFe(CO)$_4$ + (C$_6$H$_5$)$_3$PbX ⟶
(X=Br, I)

③ Solid.

④ + HgX$_2$ $\xrightarrow{\text{in ether or (CH}_3)_2\text{CO}}$
HgFe(CO)$_4$ + (C$_6$H$_5$)$_3$PbX
(X=Cl, Br)

⑥ Z. anorg. allg. Chem. **254**, 138 (1947) ;
259, 183 (1949).

Pb$_2$C$_{40}$H$_{38}$

① 1,4-Bis(triphenylplumbyl)butane
[(C$_6$H$_5$)$_3$PbCH$_2$CH$_2$−]$_2$

② 3 C$_6$H$_5$Li + PbCl$_2$ $\xrightarrow{\text{in (CH}_3)_2\text{O}}$
(C$_6$H$_5$)$_3$PbLi $\xrightarrow{\text{X(CH}_2)_4\text{X}}$ 46%

③ White crystals. [134~136°].
Sol. in org. solvents.

⑥ Iowa State Coll. J. Sci. **26**, 292 (1952) ;
CA **47**, 8673 (1953).

Pb$_2$C$_{42}$H$_{42}$

① Hexa-o-tolyldilead
(CH$_3$C$_6$H$_4$)$_3$Pb·Pb(C$_6$H$_4$CH$_3$)$_3$

② 3 PbCl$_2$ + 8 o-CH$_3$C$_6$H$_4$·MgBr
$\xrightarrow{\text{reflux for 5.5 hrs. in C}_6\text{H}_6}$ 51%

③ Solid. [240° decomp.].
Sol. in C$_6$H$_6$ and CHCl$_3$; insol. in C$_2$H$_5$OH.
Darkening, associated with a deposition of Pb, takes place at 238~242°.

④ $\xrightarrow{\text{reflux in xylene}}$ (o-CH$_3$C$_6$H$_4$)$_4$Pb
(37%)

+ KMnO$_4$ $\xrightarrow{\text{in acetone}}$

oil $\xrightarrow[+HBr]{+HCl}$ $(o\text{-}CH_3C_6H_4)_3PbCl$

$\searrow$ $(o\text{-}CH_3C_6H_4)_3PbBr$

⑥ Ber. **55**, 888 (1922).   JACS **53**, 1548, 3514 (1931) ; **61**, 731 (1939).   JOC **4**, 162 (1939).

Pb₂C₄₂H₄₂

① Hexa-*p*-tolyldilead
$(CH_3C_6H_4)_3PbPb(C_6H_4CH_3)_3$

② $3 PbCl_2 + 8\, p\text{-}CH_3C_6H_4MgBr$

$\xrightarrow[\text{in } C_6H_6]{}$ 45%

③ Solid. [193° decomp.].
Sol. in C_6H_6 and $CHCl_3$; insol. in CH_3OH.

④ $\xrightarrow{193°}$ $(CH_3C_6H_4)_4Pb + Pb$

$\xrightarrow[\text{in xylene}]{\text{reflux}}$ $(p\text{-}CH_3C_6H_4)_4Pb$ (90%)

$+ n\text{-}C_4H_9Li$ $\underset{}{\overset{\text{in ether}}{\rightleftharpoons}}$

$(n\text{-}C_4H_9)_3PbPb(C_4H_9\text{-}n)_3 + 3 C_6H_5Li$

⑥ Ber. **55**, 888 (1922).   JACS **53**, 3514 (1931) ; **61**, 731 (1939) ; **62**, 3206 (1940).

Pb₂C₄₄H₄₂

① Bis(tri-*o*-tolylplumbyl)acetylene
$[(o\text{-}CH_3C_6H_4)_3PbC\equiv]_2$

② $NaC\equiv CH$

$(o\text{-}CH_3C_6H_4)_3PbBr$ $\xrightarrow{\text{in liq. NH}_3}$

③ [121°].

④ + alkali $\longrightarrow$ $(o\text{-}CH_3C_6H_4)_3PbOH$

⑤ Gasoline additives, catalysts or stabilizer for polymer and insecticides.

⑥ Naturwiss. **46**, 321 (1959).   Ger. 1061322 ; CA **54**, 358 (1960).

Pb₂C₄₄H₄₂

① Bis(tri-*p*-tolylplumbyl)acetylene
$[(p\text{-}CH_3\cdot C_6H_4)_3PbC\equiv]_2$

② $NaC\equiv CH$

$+ (p\text{-}CH_3C_6H_4)_3PbBr$ $\xrightarrow{\text{in liq. NH}_3}$

③ [130°].

④ + alkali $\longrightarrow$ $(p\text{-}CH_3C_6H_4)_3PbOH$

⑥ Naturwiss. **46**, 321 (1959).   Ger. 1061322 ; CA **54**, 358 (1960).

Pb₂C₄₈H₅₄

① Hexa-2,5-xylyldilead
$[(CH_3)_2C_6H_3]_3Pb\cdot Pb[C_6H_3(CH_3)_2]_3$

② $3 PbCl_2 + 6 (CH_3)_2C_6H_3MgBr$

$\longrightarrow$ 50%

③ White crystals.
Sol. in hot C_6H_6 and $CHCl_3$; almost insol. in CH_3OH and C_2H_5OH.

⑥ Ber. **52**, 2165 (1919).   Z. anorg. allg. Chem. **251**, 125 (1943).

Pb₂C₅₀H₅₄

① Bis(tri-2-phenylethylplumbyl)acetylene
$[(C_6H_5CH_2CH_2)_3PbC\equiv]_2$

② $NaC\equiv CH$

$+ C_6H_5CH_2CH_2PbBr$ $\xrightarrow{\text{in liq. NH}_3}$

③ [62°].
Sensitive to light.

④ + alkali $\longrightarrow$ $(C_6H_5CH_2CH_2)_3PbOH$

⑥ Naturwiss. **46**, 321 (1959).   Ger. 1061322 ; CA **54**, 358 (1960).

Pb₃C₂₄H₄₅N₆Fe

① Tris(triethyllead) ferricyanide
$[(C_2H_5)_3Pb]_3Fe(CN)_6$

② $(C_2H_5)_3PbOCOCH_3 + K_3Fe(CN)_6$ $\longrightarrow$

③ Brick-red solid.

⑥ JACS **49**, 830 (1927).

Pb₄C₁₈H₁₅Ge

① Tetrakis(triphenylplumbyl) germanium.
$[(C_6H_5)_3Pb]_4Ge$

② $4 (C_6H_5)_3PbLi + GeCl_4$ $\longrightarrow$ 23%

③ Yellow solid. [210° decomp.].
High stability. Recrystd. from

CHCl₃-petr. ether.

UV : λ_{max} 328 mμ(ε_{max} 63000) in CHCl₃.

⑥ JOM **2**, 260, 265 (1964).

Pb₄C₁₈H₁₅Sn

① Tetraks(triphenylplumbyl)tin
   [(C₆H₅)₃Pb]₄Sn

② 4 (C₆H₅)₃PbLi + SnCl₄

$$\xrightarrow[\text{in ether or THF}]{} 54\%$$

③ Yellow solid. [160° decomp.].
   High stability. Recrystd. from CHCl₃.
   UV : λ_{max} 319 mμ (ε_{max} 67000) in C₆H₆.

⑥ JOM **2**, 260, 265 (1964).

Pb₅C₁₈H₁₅

① Tetrakis(triphenylplumbyl)lead

[(C₆H₅)₃Pb]₄Pb.

② (C₆H₅)₃PbLi $\xrightarrow[]{\text{ice-salt, H₂O₂}}$ 30%

$$C_6H_5MgBr + PbCl_2 \xrightarrow{\text{in ether under N}_2}$$

(C₆H₅)₂Pb $\xrightarrow[]{\text{ice-salt, H₂O₂}}$ 10%

③ Red crystals.
   Insol. in alc. and petr. ether ; sol. in
   CHCl₃ and C₆H₆.
   UV : λ_{max} 444 mμ (ε_{max} 29000), λ_{max}
   358 mμ (ε_{max} 56000) in C₆H₆.

④ + 6 I $\xrightarrow{\text{in CHCl}_3}$ 4 (C₆H₅)₃PbI (92%)
   + PbI₂ (93%)

⑥ JOM **2**, 271 (1964).

8. Organic Compounds of Phosphorus
(P)

8.1. Introduction

The similarity of the electronic structures of nitrogen ($1s^2$, $2s^2$, $2p^3$) and phosphorus ($1s^2$, $2s^2$, $2p^6$, $3s^2$, $3p^3$) may lead to expectation of close resemblance between the organic compounds of these elements. However, this is not the case. We have never known phosphorus analogs of important classes of nitrogen compounds such as nitro-compounds, azo-compounds or aromatic nitrogen-heterocycles (pyridine, quinoline, etc.). There are considerable differences in chemical reactions between analogous compounds of the two elements, such as primary phosphines and primary amines, or phosphine oxides and amine oxides.

These dissimilarities are principally due to the following: first, phosphorus has a lower electronegativity than nitrogen, which gives rise to a strong bonding of phosphorus to oxygen and halogens; second, phosphorus has a more reactive lone pair of electrons (larger polarizability) than the nitrogen atom; and third, only phosphorus has vacant $3d$ orbitals for chemical bonding. The last two features may lead to a strong tendency for phosphorus to make pentavalent phosphorus compounds.

8.2. Classification and Nomenclature

The problem of giving suitable, unambiguous, names for organophosphorus compounds presented considerable difficulty. Recently, a new system of nomenclature for compounds containing one phosphorus atom has been widely adopted which was presented in 1952 by the Chemical Society and the American Chemical Society.

This system uses, as parent structures, a number of phosphorus hydrides and acids, some of which exist only hypothetically. In naming compounds, groups which are bonded by C–P bonds are considered as replacing hydrogen in the appropriate parent structure and are prefixed to its name, whereas negative groups are considered as replacing hydroxyl or oxygen (either doubly bonded to phosphorus or in a hydroxyl group) and are indicated either as a separate word (for example, chloride of amide) replacing the word acid or, if the compound is itself an acid or an ester, by a suitable affix (for example, -chlorid- or -amid-) immediately preceding the valency suffix (-ic acid, -ate, -ous acid, or -ite). Ester groups precede the name as a separate word or words, as in normal usage, and in cases of ambiguity (as in acids in which some, but not all, of the oxygen atoms of the parent structure have been replaced by sulfur atoms, or in substituted amides) the symbols O-, S-, N-, P-, etc., may be used.

The parent structures most frequently used are

H_3P	phosphine
$P(OH)_3$	phosphorus acid
$HP(OH)_2$	phosphonous acid
$H_2P(OH)$	phosphinous acid
$H_3P(O)$	phosphine oxide
$P(O)(OH)_3$	phosphoric acid
$HP(O)(OH)_2$	phosphonic acid
$H_2P(O)(OH)$	phosphinic acid
H_5P	phosphorane.

Examples of this system of nomenclature are shown along with the description of types of compounds containing carbon–phosphorus bonds.

a. Trivalent Phosphorus Compounds.   These are considered as compounds arising from replacement of hydrogens bound to the parent structure of trivalent phosphorus by organic groups, while hydroxyl groups by negative groups:

RPH_2, R_2PH, R_3P: primary, secondary, and tertiary phosphines

$RPCl_2$: CH_3PCl_2 metylphosponous dichloride

$RP(OR')_2$: $C_6H_5P(OC_2H_5)_2$ diethyl phenylphosphonite

R_2PCl: $(CH_3)_2PCl$ dimethylphosphinous chloride

$R_2P(OR')$: $(C_6H_5)_2POC_2H_5$ ethyl diphenylphosphinite

$R_2PNR'_2$: $(CH_3)_2PN(C_2H_5)_2$ N, N-diethyldimethylphosphinous amide.

b. Pentavalent Phosphorus Compounds.   Many more compounds belong to this type, as compared with trivalent phosphorus compounds.   Almost all pentavalent organophosphorus compounds contain four atoms attached to phosporus by covalent bonds, which consist of three single bonds to phosphorus and one semipolar bond between phosphorus and oxygen (or other bivalent atoms or groups such as $=S$, $=NR$, and $=CR_2$).

$RP(O)(OH)_2$: $CH_3P(O)(OH)_2$ methylphosphonic acid

$RP(O)Cl_2$: $C_6H_5P(O)Cl_2$ phenylphosphonic dichloride

$RP(S)(OR')_2$: $CH_3P(S)(OC_2H_5)_2$ diethyl methylphosphonothioate

$RP(O)(OR')Cl$: $CH_3P(O)(OC_2H_5)Cl$ ethyl methylphosphonochloridate

$RP(O)(NR'_2)Cl$: $CH_3P(O)(NHC_2H_5)Cl$ N-ethylmethylphosphonamidic chloride

$R_2P(O)(OR')$: $(CH_3)_2P(O)(OC_2H_5)$ ethyl dimethylphosphinate

$R_2P(S)(OR')$: $(CH_3)_2P(S)(OC_2H_5)$ O-ethyldimethylphosphinothioate.

$R_3P(O)$: $(C_2H_5)(CH_3)(C_6H_5)P(O)$ ethylmethylphenylphosphine oxide

$R_3P=CR'_2$: $(C_6H_5)_3P=CH_2$ methylenetriphenylphosphorane

In addition, there are quaternary phosphonium salts, $[R_4P^+]X^-$, and a few phosphoranes, R_5P, in which five groups are attached covalently to a phosphorus atom.

c. Polyphosphines and Related Cyclic Compounds.   Some representative examples of polyphosphines with the catenations of phosphorus atoms in a molecule, and of rather special cyclic compounds which contain the phosporus atoms in the ring structure, are given:

$(C_6H_5)_2P-P(C_6H_5)_2$ tetraphenyldiphosphine

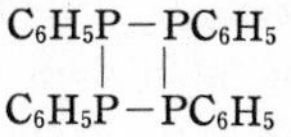

$$C_6H_5P-PC_6H_5$$
$$C_6H_5P-PC_6H_5$$

tetraphenylcyclotetraphosphine [often called "phoshobenzene"]

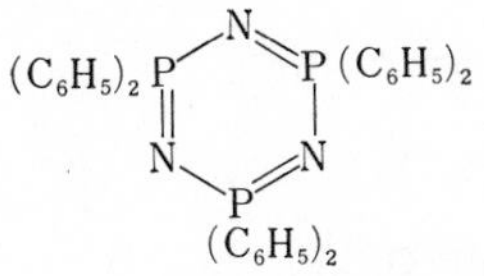

2,2,4,6,6-hexaphenylphosphazatriene ["phosphazene"]

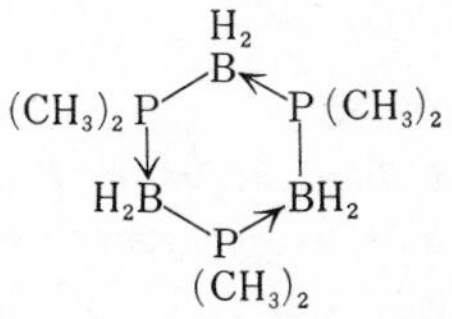

2,2,4,4,6,6-hexamethyl-1,1,3,3,5,5-hexahydrophosphinoborin.

8.3. Methods of Synthesis

Various inorganic phosphorus compounds, such as phosphine, phosphorus tri-halides, phosphorus oxyhalides, alkyl phosphites, and even elemental phosphorus, are used as starting materials for preparing the organophosphorus compounds (formation of C–P bonds). The preparation of phosphine and phosphites will be described in Section 8.5.

a. Reaction of Phosphorus with Alkyl Halides. Heating alkyl halides with red phosphorus and copper powder results in the formation of the mixture R_nPX_{3-n} ($n=0$, 1, 2, 3). However, this is of little use for practical purposes.

$$RX + P \xrightarrow[350°]{\text{Cu powder}} R_2PX + RPX_2 + PX_3$$

$$(R=Me, Et, X=Cl, Br, I)$$

b. Reaction of Organometallic Compounds with Phosphorus Trihalides. This affords the most convenient method for the synthesis of tertiary phosphines. In general, use of Grignard reagents or organolithium compounds only gives rise to complete substitution of all three halogens on phosphorus.

$$PCl_3 + 3\,RM \longrightarrow R_3P + 3\,MCl \ (M=MgX, Li)$$

However, partial alkylation can successfully be effected if less reactive organo-metallic compounds are employed.

$$PCl_3 + R_2Hg \xrightarrow[230\sim250°]{\text{sealed tube}} RPCl_2 + RHgCl \ (\ RHgCl \text{ is decomposed})$$

$$2\,PCl_3 + R_2Cd \xrightarrow[-20°]{} 2\,RPCl_2 + CdCl_2 \ (R=alkyl)$$

$$PCl_3 + RZnBr \longrightarrow RPCl_2 + ZnBrCl$$

$$3\,PCl_3 + Et_4Pb \longrightarrow 3\,EtPCl_2 + PbCl_2 + EtCl$$

$$PBr_3 + Et_4Sn \longrightarrow EtPBr_2 + Et_3SnBr$$

$$3\,PCl_3 + R_3Al(Et_2O,\ C_5H_5N\ complex) \longrightarrow 3\,RPCl_2 + AlCl_3$$

c. Reaction of Phosphorus Trihalides with Alkyl Chlorides.   Addition of alkyl chlorides to a mixture of phosphorus trichloride and aluminum chloride readily forms crystalline complexes (Perren–Kinnear complex). Reduction or hydrolysis of these complexes gives various products.

$$RCl + PCl_3 + AlCl_3 \xrightarrow{\hspace{3cm}} [RP^+Cl_3 \cdot AlCl_4^-]$$

$$\xrightarrow{Al\ (or\ P) + KCl} RPCl_2$$

$$\xrightarrow{H_2O} RP(O)Cl_2$$

$$\xrightarrow{R'OH} RP(O)(OR')_2$$

$$\xrightarrow{S + KCl} RP(S)Cl_2$$

d. Reaction of Halides, Oxides, or Sulfides of Phosphorus with Aromatic Hydrocarbons.   Friedel–Crafts reactions of aromatic hydrocarbons with phosphorus trichloride in the presence of aluminum chloride, followed by decomposition of the resulting complex compounds by phosphorus oxychloride or pyridine, provide a method of preparing arylphosphonous dichlorides. An alternative procedure of decomposing the complex is chlorination followed by ethanolysis, leading to diethyl arylphosphonates.

$$ArH + PCl_3 + AlCl_3 \xrightarrow{\hspace{3cm}} [ArPCl_2 \cdot AlCl_3]$$

$$\xrightarrow{POCl_3\ (or\ C_5H_5N)} ArPCl_2$$

$$\xrightarrow{Cl_2\ then\ EtOH} ArP(O)(OEt)_2$$

Formation of C–P bonds takes place in the reaction of phosphorus pentasulfide and phosphorus pentoxide with aromatic compounds. Diphenylphosphinodithioic acid is obtained from phosphorus pentasulfide and excess benzene in the presence of aluminum chloride.

$$ArH + P_4S_{10} \xrightarrow{AlCl_3} Ph_2P(S)SH$$

The formation of arylphosphonic acids *via* free-radical processes is also known.

$$ArH + P_4H_{10} \xrightarrow[2.\ H_2O]{1.\ 250\sim325°} ArP(O)(OH)_2$$

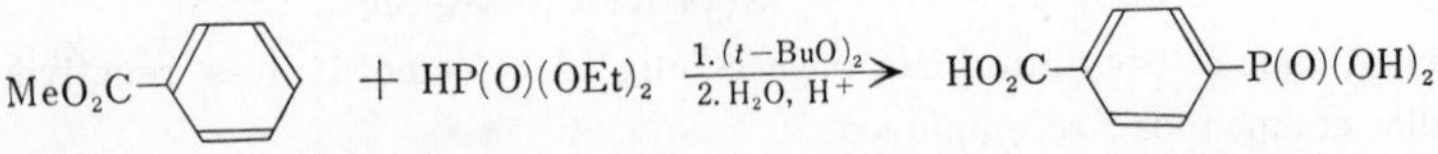

$$MeO_2C\!-\!\langle\ \rangle + HP(O)(OEt)_2 \xrightarrow[2.\ H_2O,\ H^+]{1.\ (t-BuO)_2} HO_2C\!-\!\langle\ \rangle\!-\!P(O)(OH)_2$$

e. Addition of Phosphorus Pentachloride to Olefins and Acetylenes.   Phosphorus pentachloride adds to olefins and acetylenes. Hydrolysis of the resulting alkyl- or alkenyl-tetrachlorophosphorane yields derivatives of alkenylphosphonic acids.

$$PCl_5 + RCH=CH_2 \longrightarrow RCHClCH_2PCl_4 \xrightarrow{H_2O} RCH=CHP(O)(OH)_2$$

$$PCl_5 + R-C\equiv CH \longrightarrow R-CCl=CHPCl_4 \xrightarrow{H_2O} RCCl=CHP(O)(OH)_2$$

f. Addition of P-H Compounds to Activated Double Bonds.   Addition of phosphine and phenylphospine to acrylonitrile in alkaline solution affords the corresponding β-cyanoethylphosphines in good yield.

$$PH_3 + CH_2=CHCN \xrightarrow{\text{aq. KOH, MeCN}} (NCCH_2CH_2)_nPH_{3-n}$$
$$(n=1, 2, 3)$$

$$PhPH_2 + CH_2=CHCN \xrightarrow[25°]{\text{10 N KOH}} PhP(CH_2CH_2CN)_2$$

Dialkyl phosphites are also able to add to carbon–carbon double bonds activated by an electron-withdrawing groups.

$$HP(O)(OR)_2 + R'CH=CHCOR \xrightarrow{\text{NaOEt-EtOH}} R'CH(CH_2COR)P(O)(OR)_2$$

These base-catalyzed additions may be considered as involving attack of an intermediate phophorus anion on an unsaturated β-carbon atom and are analogous to Michael reactions.

g. Free-radical Addition of Phosphorus Compounds to Olefinic Bonds.
Addition of phosphorus compounds with P-H bonds to olefinic double bonds (butene-1, cyclohexene, allyl alcohol, etc.) may occur *via* free-radical mechanisms initiated by peroxides or other compounds, or by ultraviolet irradiation.

$$PhPH_2 + 2 CH_2=CHCH_2OH \xrightarrow{\text{azobisisobutyronitrile}} PhP(CH_2CH_2CH_2OH)_2$$

$$H_2P(O)(ONa) + RCH=CH_2 \xrightarrow{(t\text{-}BuO)_2} RCH_2CH_2PH(O)(ONa)$$

$$HP(O)(OEt)_2 + MeCO_2CH=CH_2 \xrightarrow{\text{dibenzoyl peroxide}} MeCO_2CH_2CH_2P(O)(OEt)_2$$

It should be noted that the additon in the last example occurs in the opposite direction in the presence of a basic catalyst.

$$HP(O)(OEt)_2 + MeCO_2CH=CH_2 \xrightarrow{\text{NaOEt}} MeCO_2CHMeP(O)(OEt)_2$$

h. Addition of P-H Compounds to Carbonyl and Imino Groups.   Reaction of phosphine with aliphatic aldehydes in the presence of hydrogen chloride results in tetra(α-hydroxyalkyl)phosphonium chlorides, whereas addition to ketones gives mainly primary phosphine oxides.

$$H_3P + 4 PCHO + HCl \longrightarrow [RCH(OH)]_4P^+Cl^-$$

$$H_3P + Me_2CO \xrightarrow{H^+} Me_2CHP(O)H_2 + Me_2CHP(O)H\cdot C(OH)Me_2$$

Analogous rearrangement of oxygen occurs in the case of aromatic aldehydes, leading to phosphine oxides.

$$H_3P + PhCHO \xrightarrow{H^+} PhCH_2P(O)[CH(OH)Ph]_2$$

Phosphorous acid and a dialkyl phosphite also undergo similar reactions with aldehydes and ketones to give α-hydroxyalkylphosphonic acids and dialkyl α-

hydroxyalkylphosphonates, respectively.

$$HP(O)(OR)_2 + R'R''CO \xrightarrow{\text{NaOMe-MeOH}} R'R''C(OH)P(O)(OR)_2$$

Thus the reactions of phosphorous acid, and of dialkyl phosphites, with carbonyl groups are similar to the acid- or base-catalyzed aldol condensation.

Additions of P–H compounds to the C=N bond of Schiff's bases are also catalyzed by acid or base.

$$H_2P(O)(OH) + R'R''C=NR \longrightarrow R'R''C(NHR)PH(O)(OH)$$

i.   The Michaelis Reaction.   Alkali-metal derivatives of dialkyl phosphites react with alkyl halides to give dialkyl alkylphosphonates.

$$(RO)_2P(O)Na + R'X \longrightarrow R'P(O)(OR)_2 + NaX$$

In this Michaelis reaction, dibutyl phosphite is conveniently used because of the high solubility of its sodium salt in hydrocarbons.   Trimethylchlorosilane or –stannane may be used as the R'X component, leading to compounds which contain P–M (M=Si or Sn) bonds.

j.   The Arbuzov Reaction.   One of the most widely used methods for forming C–P bonds is the Arbuzov reaction.   Originally, this reaction is concerned with the production of dialkyl alkylphosphonate from a trialkyl phosphite and an alkyl halide.

$$(RO)_3P + R'X \longrightarrow R'P(O)(OR)_2 + RX$$

The resulting alkyl halide, RX, may compete with the starting alkyl halide unless removed from the reaction mixture.   The reaction proceeds in two stages involving nucleophilic attack of the phosphite on alkyl halide to form a quasiphosphonium compound, followed by its decomposition to form a new alkyl halide and a phosphonate.

$$(RO)_2P{\overset{OR}{\diagup}} + R'X \longrightarrow \left((RO)_2\overset{+}{P}{\underset{R' \,:X^-}{\overset{O{-}R}{\diagup}}} \right) \longrightarrow (RO)_2P(O)R' + RX$$

The Arbuzov reaction may be written more generally

$$\underset{B}{\overset{A}{>}}P{:}\overset{OR}{\diagup} + R'X \longrightarrow \underset{B}{\overset{A}{>}}P\overset{O}{\underset{R'}{\diagdown}} + RX$$

where A and B may be primary or secondary alkoxy, aryloxy, alkyl, aryl, or dialkylamino groups.

The Arbuzov reactions of trialkylphosphite may take place with various halogen compounds other than alkyl halides, leading to such pentavalent-phosphorus compounds as derivatives of phosphoric acid and thiophosphoric acid.

Arbuzov reactions involving carbon tetrachloride have been shown to proceed by a free-radical mechanism, being accelerated by peroxides or ultraviolet irradiation.

$$(RO)_3P + CCl_4 \longrightarrow (RO)_2P(O)CCl_3 + RCl$$

k. Reaction of Diazonium Salts with Phosphorus Trihalides.   Reaction of aryldiazonium fluoroborates with phosphorus trichloride in the presence of cuprous chloride, followed by hydrolysis of the products, leads to arylphosphonic acids.

$$PCl_3 + ArN_2^+BF_4^- \xrightarrow[EtOAc]{CuCl} N_2 + ArP^+Cl_3 \cdot BF_4^- \xrightarrow{H_2O} ArP(O)(OH)_2$$

The reaction mechanism presumably involves formation of an aryltrichlorophosphonium salt, which may occur by nucleophilic attack of phosporus trichloride on aryl cations formed by decomposition of the diazonium salt.   However, a free-radical mechanism cannot be ruled out.

In many cases the diarylphosphinic acids are also formed.   Their formation presumably arises from the arylation of arylphosphonous dichlorides, which are formed by exchange reactions of the phosphonium salts with phosphorus trichloride.

l. Oxidative Phosphonation.   When oxygen is passed through mixtures of phosphorus trichloride and saturated hydrocarbons, alkylphosphonic dichlorides are formed.

$$PCl_3 + RH + \frac{1}{2}O_2 \longrightarrow RP(O)Cl_2 + HCl$$

The initial stage probably involves a peroxide-like diradical $Cl_3\overset{\cdot}{P}$-O-O·, which then reacts with hydrocarbons and phosphorus trichloride to give phosphorus oxychloride as a byproduct.

Olefins and acetylenes also undergo the reaction.   Here, the overall reaction may be regarded as addition of phosphorus oxychloride to unsaturated bonds.

$$PCl_3 + RCH{=}CH_2 + 1/2\,O_2 \longrightarrow RCHClCH_2P(O)Cl_2$$
$$PCl_3 + RC{\equiv}CH + 1/2\,O_2 \longrightarrow RCCl{=}CHP(O)Cl_2$$

m. Free-Radical Addition of Phosphorus Trichloride to Olefins.   Phosphorus trichloride undergoes peroxide-induced addition to olefins, for example, 1-octene.

$$PCl_3 + C_6H_{13}CH{=}CH_2 \longrightarrow C_6H_{13}CHClCH_2PCl_2$$

Under similar conditions, copolymers of phosphorus trichloride with dienes such as *p*-xylylene are obtained.

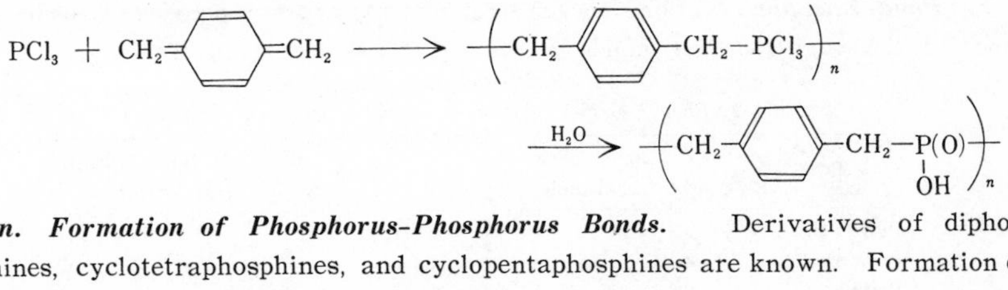

n. Formation of Phosphorus-Phosphorus Bonds.   Derivatives of diphosphines, cyclotetraphosphines, and cyclopentaphosphines are known.   Formation of P-P bonds can be effected by means of:

(i) Heating a mixture of a phosphine and a phosphinous or phosphonous chloride in appropriate solvents

$$Ph_2PH + ClPPh_2 \longrightarrow Ph_2P-PPh_2 + HCl$$

$$2\,RPCl_2 + 2\,RPH_2 \longrightarrow \begin{matrix} RP-PR \\ |\quad | \\ RP-PR \end{matrix} + 4\,HCl \ (R=Ph,\ Et,\ C_6H_{11})$$

(ii) Heating a mixture of a phosphine and phosphinous or phosphonous amide

$$Me_2PH + Me_2NPMe_2 \longrightarrow Me_2P-PMe_2 + HNMe_2$$

$$2\,PhPH_2 + 2\,(Me_2N)_2PPh \longrightarrow \begin{matrix} PhP-PPh \\ |\quad | \\ PhP-PPh \end{matrix} + 4\,HNMe_2$$

(iii) Reduction of a phosphinous or phosphonous halide by a metal or a metal hydride.

$$2\,(CF_3)_2PI + Hg \longrightarrow (CF_3)_2P-P(CF_3)_2 + HgI_2$$

$$RPCl_2 \xrightarrow{\ \text{Mg or Li}\ } [RP]_4$$

In addition to these reactions, cyclotetra- and cyclopentaphosphines are also produced by pyrolysis of $[(CF_3)_2P]_2$ at 350°.

8.4. General Properties

8.4.1. Physical Properties

As mentioned in previous sections, the fact that trivalent phosphorus compounds, such as phosphines, are more nucleophilic than the corresponding nitrogen compounds may be ascribed principally to the lower electronegativity and thus the larger polarizability of a lone pair of electrons on phosphorus.   The trivalent phosphorus also shows a strong tendency to fall into the pentavalent state by forming the P=O bond.   These two features are reflected in preparations and reactions of organophosphorus compounds.

In this connection it should be of particular interest to refer to the bond energies, infrared spectra, and nuclear magnetic resonance spectra of organophosphorus compounds.

a. Bond Energies.   Bond energies for various types of bonds to phosphorus, and for the corresponding bonds to nitrogen, are listed in Table 8.1.

Table 8.1. Bond Energies in Phosphorus and Nitrogen Compounds.

Bond	Bond Energy kcal/mole	Bond	Bond Energy kcal/mole
P−H(PH₃)	77	N−H(NH₃)	93.4
P−C(Me₃P)	65	N−C	72.8
P−O	86~92	N−O	~50
P=O	130~150	N=O(RONO)	145
P−Cl(PCl₃)	76	N−Cl(NCl₃)	46
P−P(P₄)	50	N−N(H₂N−NH₂)	30

Some important points are noted from the data in Table 8.1 as follows:

(i) The phosphorus-hydrogen bond is substantially weaker than the nitrogen-hydrogen bond, which seems consistent with the fact P-H bonds can be readily cleaved in both polar and free-radical processes.

(ii) The phosphorus-oxygen single bond is a fairly strong bond compared to the carbon-oxygen bond (80.9 kcal/mole), while the P=O or phosphoryl double bond (semipolar bond) is about 45 kcal stronger than the P-O single bond.

(iii) The phosphorus-chlorine bond is appreciably stronger than the nitrogen-chlorine bond, and as strong as the carbon-chlorine bond (77.9 kcal/mole). However, the P-Cl bond is much more reactive than the C-Cl bond.

(iv) The phosphorus-carbon bond is comparable in strength to the carbon-carbon bond, and reactions involving its cleavage are not common, except for nucleophilic decomposition of quaternary phosphonium salts.

b. Infrared Spectra. The stretching vibrations of the phosphoryl group (P=O) and the bond dissociation energies for various types of phosphorus compounds are given in Table 8.2. The phosphoryl group (P=O) may be formulated as a hybrid of a double bond and a dipolar bond ($P=O \leftrightarrow \overset{+}{P}-\overset{-}{O}$). This double bond

Table 8.2. *Bond Dissociation Energies and Stretching Vibrations of Phosphoryl Groups.*

Compound	Bond Dissociation Energy $\bar{D}$ (kcal/mole)	Stretching Vibration $\nu_{P=O}$ (cm^{-1})	Force Constant f (md/A)
P_4O_{10}	138	1400	11.0
$F_3P(O)$	130	1415	11.4
$Cl_3P(O)$	128	1292	10.0
$Me_3P(O)$	139	1170	8.2
$Ph_3P(O)$	128	1195	—
$(EtO)_3P(O)$	151	1272	—
$(Me_2N)_3P(O)$	139	1206	—

arises from the ability of phosphorus to accommodate ten electrons in its outer shell by utilizing its empty $3d$ orbitals ($p_\pi - d_\pi$ bonding). Evidence for the double bond character of the P=O group is afforded by its bond length, which is shorter than that calculated for the dipolar form in phosphine oxides $R_3\overset{+}{P} \rightarrow \overset{-}{O}$.

However, it is obvious from Table 8.2 that the stretching frequencies of the phosphoryl group change considerably with the electron-repelling power of various substituents on the phosphorus atom. This means changes in force constant, and hence changes in bond order of the phosphoryl groups.

Thus, it may be said that the dipolar character of the phosphoryl group arises from strong electron-donating substituents, while the double bond character arises from elctron-withdrawing substituents on the phosphorus atom.

c. Nuclear Magnetic Resonance Spectra. The only naturally stable isotope of phosphorus, ^{31}P, has a spin number $I=1/2$, and the resonance frequency for this nucleus is much lower than ^1H for an external magnetic field strength of 14092 gauss (24.3 *vs.* 60 Mc sec^{-1}). This nucleus gives rise to chemical shifts extending over a range of ~500 ppm. Fine structure on the ^{31}P resonance absorption bands arising from indirect spin-spin interaction with other nuclei in the molecule can usually be measured more satisfactorily in the spectrum of the interacting nucleus, but coupling constants of 5 cycles sec^{-1} can also be measured from the ^{31}P spectra.

Chemical shifts for ^{31}P nuclei are usually measured with respect to the single sharp absorption in 85% orthophosphoric acid as an external reference. Trivalent phosphorus nuclei are usually less shielded and show a much larger spread of chemical shifts (~500 ppm) than do pentavalent phosphorus nuclei (~100 ppm). The lower shielding of phosphorus in the trivalent state arises from there being fewer valence electrons to shield the ^{31}P nucleus than in the case of pentavalent phosphorus.

Since, for triply connected phosphorus compounds, the substituents sometimes contribute the same amount to the sielding of the phosphorus nucleus regardless of the other substituents in the molecule, it is possible in this case to calculate, roughly, ^{31}P chemical shifts.

However, this is not the case with quadruply connected phosphorus compounds, and little is known in the case of pentacovalent phosphoranes.

One of the most important features of ^{31}P nuclear magnetic resonance is the fact that the coupling constants of ^{31}P-^{1}H are very large (200~700 cycles sec^{-1}). Application of this coupling to structure determination is of great use. For example, the equilibrium of the primary and secondary esters of phosphorus acid or dialkylphosphinous acids has long been discussed in connection with their structure.

$$(RO)_2P(O)H \; \rightleftharpoons \; (RO)_2POH$$
$$R_2P(O)H \; \rightleftharpoons \; R_2POH$$

^{31}P NMR measurements have shown that more than 95% of the molecules are in the form in which hydrogen is directly attached to the phosphorus atom, since the $J_{\text{P-H}}$ coupling constant observed (~600 cycles sec^{-1}) is that expected for the two nuclei when directly bonded.

8.4.2. Chemical Properties

a. Trivalent Phosphorus Compounds. An outstanding property of the trivalent phosphorus compounds is their strong tendency to become pentavalent ones. The lower alkylphosphines are quite susceptible to oxidation. In general, a hydroxyl group on a trivalent phosphorus is unstable, the stable structure being HP(O)<.

$$RPH_2 \; \xrightarrow{\;[O]\;} \; RP(O)(OH)_2$$
$$R_2PH \; \xrightarrow{\;[O]\;} \; R_2P(O)(OH)$$

Hydrolysis of a phosphinous dichloride gives the secondary phosphine oxide.

$$R_2PCl \xrightarrow{H_3^+O} [R_2POH] \longrightarrow R_2P(O)H$$

In reactions involving its conversion to the pentavalent state, trivalent phosphorus displays strong nucleophilic properties.

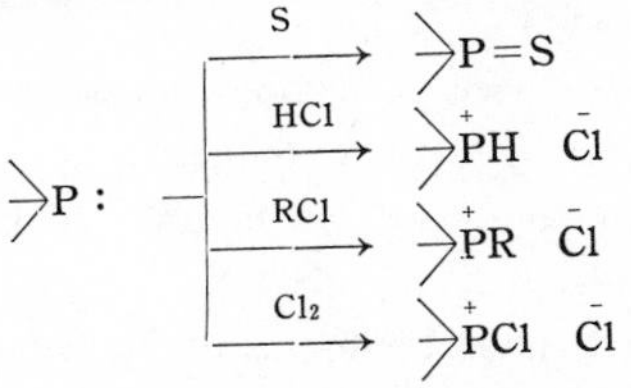

b. Pentavalent Phosphorus Compounds. Organophosphorus compounds in the pentavalent state are relatively stable, and a number of important reactions to form P-C bonds are associated with them. Compounds with P-Cl, P-OR, and P-NR$_2$ groups undergo displacement reactions involving nucleophilic attack on phosphorus. P-H bonds are fairly readily oxidized to P-OH.

The phosphoryl group (P=O) is polarized to show an electron-withdrawing effect, to a similar extent as the carbonyl or nitro group. Thus, when bonded to a benzene ring the phosphoryl group diminishes in reactivity toward electrophilic aromatic substitutions. In aliphatic compounds the phosphoryl group activates hydrogen atoms on the adjacent carbon.

C-P bonds in organophosphorus compounds are very stable and are, in general, cleaved only under drastic conditions. However some alkyl groups substituted by electronegative atoms or groups fairly readily undergo cleavage of their C-P bond.

The cleavage of the P-aryl bond takes place under quite different circumstances; it proceeds by a mechanism involving the usual electrophilic aromatic substitution.

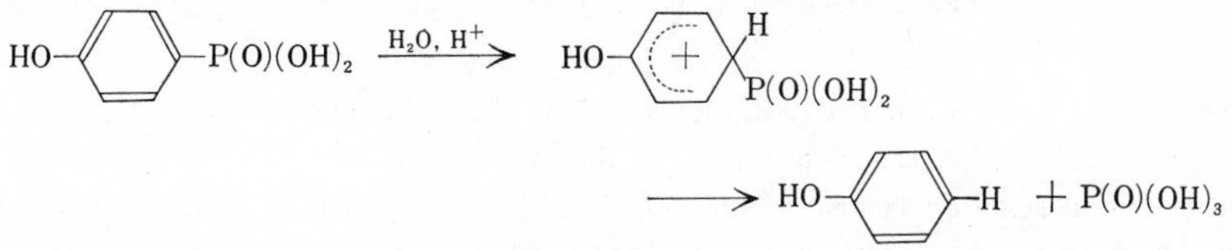

The decomposition of quaternary phosphonium salts by nucleophiles is one of the most interesting reactions involving cleavage of C-P bonds. Some important information on the path of this reaction may be obtained by using optically active phosphonium salts.

c. Stereochemistry of Organophosphorus Compounds. Phosphonium salts with four different substituents bonded to the phosphorus atom are expected to be optically active. In fact, for example, benzylethylmethylphenylphosphonium iodide is successfully resolved *via* silver hydrogen $d(-)$-dibenzoyltartarate. This shows that these compounds resemble tetravalent carbon compounds and quaternary ammonium salts in their stereochemistry.

An electrolytic reduction of some optically active phosphonium salts gives optically active tertiary phosphines.

$$[MePhPr(PhCH_2)P]^+Br^- \xrightarrow[-PhMe]{[H]} MePhPrP$$

$$[\alpha]_D^{20}+35.7° \qquad\qquad\qquad [\alpha]_D^{20}-13.5°$$

The optical stability of these phosphines makes a marked contrast with the behavior of the corresponding tertiary amines, and complete racemization occurs only on heating in boiling toluene for 3 hours.   This stability is similar to the behavior of sulfonium salts.

When an optically active phosphonium salt is treated with hydroxide ion, a phosphine oxide is produced which has a completely inverted configuration. This reaction has been found to be third order, first in the substrate and second in hydroxide ion.   A mechanism involving the pentavalent phosphorus intermediate has been suggested.

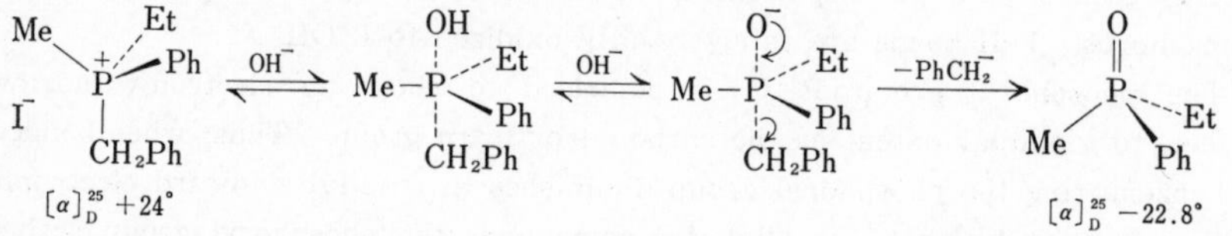

$$[\alpha]_D^{25}+24° \qquad\qquad\qquad\qquad\qquad\qquad\qquad\qquad [\alpha]_D^{25}-22.8°$$

With sodium *n*-butoxide in butanol, however, the same optically active phosphonium salt gives completely racemic phosphine oxide.   It has been suggested that this racemization is caused by interchange of butoxide ions involving a stable phosphonium intermediate:

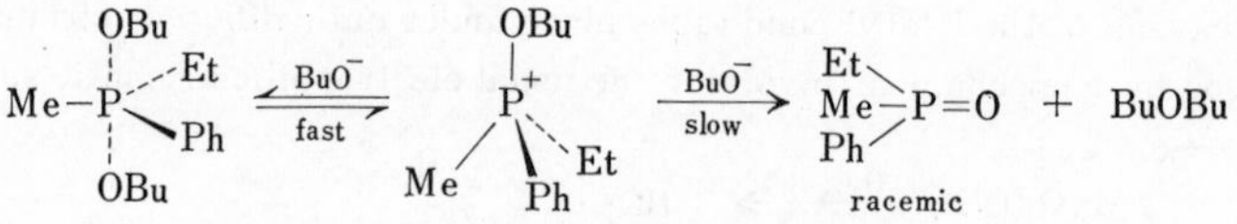

The preparation of alkenes from the reactions of alkylidenetriphenylphosphoranes with aldehydes and ketones is known as the Wittig reaction.   The stereochemical course of the reaction is also of interest.   The Wittig reaction appears to involve initial formation of a zwitterion.   In such a dipolar intermediate the negatively charged oxygen can attack the positively charged phosphorus to result in simaltaneous cleavage of phosphorus-carbon and carbon-oxygen bonds in a four-center-type transition state.

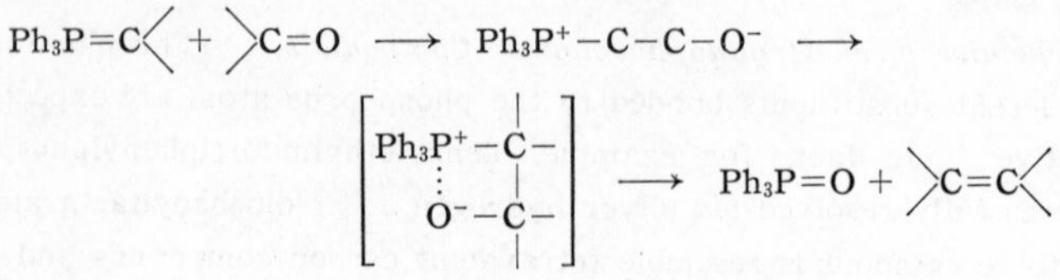

It is concluded that the reaction is stereospecific with respect to the asymmetric phosphorus atom, because the optically active phosphonium salt has been found to give the optically active phosphine oxide without accompanying racemization throughout the reaction with phenyllithium followed by benzaldehyde.

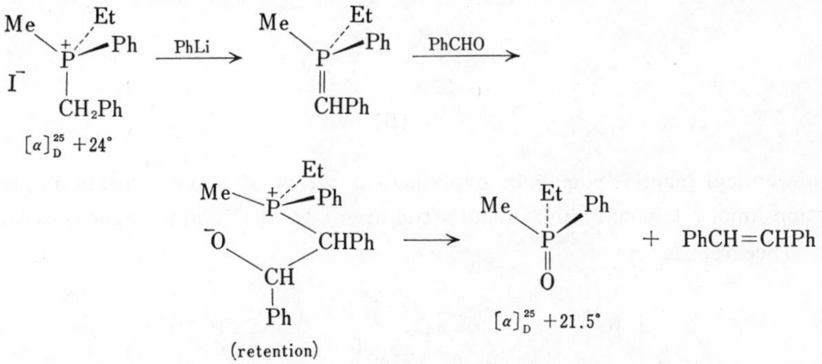

The optical activity due to an asymmetric phosphorus atom can generally be observed with various types of organophosphorus compounds such as phosphonic and phosphinic acids and their derivatives in addition to phosphonium salts, phosphines and phosphine oxides which have already been described.

Recent studies of their optical stability and the stereochemical course of their reactions indicate that most of the nucleophilic substitutions at an asymmetric phosphorus atom proceed with inversion of configuration.

Some organophosphorus compounds with octahedral covalent structure may have a molecular asymmetry. In fact, tris(biphenylene)phosphates such as (I) and their derivatives have successfully been resolved recently. However, bis(biphenylene)biphenylylphosphorane (II) which is produced by acid cleavage of the phosphate shows no optical activity.

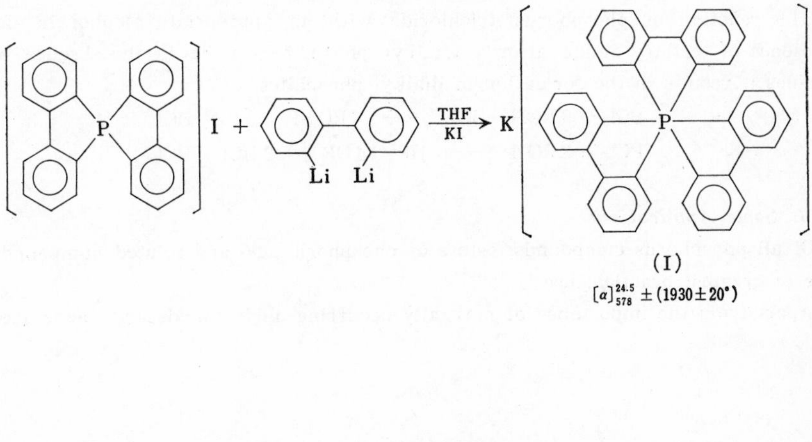

(I)

$[\alpha]_{578}^{24.5} \pm (1930 \pm 20°)$

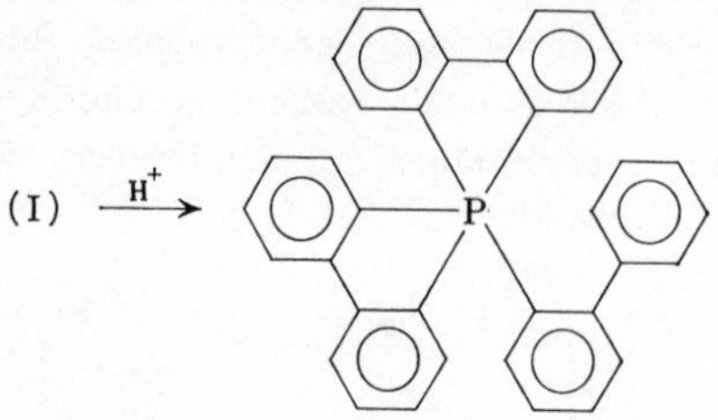

(I) $\xrightarrow{\text{H}^+}$

(II)

This optical inactivity may be explained in terms of rapid process of pseudo rotation among trigonal bipyramidal structures (IIa, IIb) and tetragonal pyramidal (III). (See ref. 12)

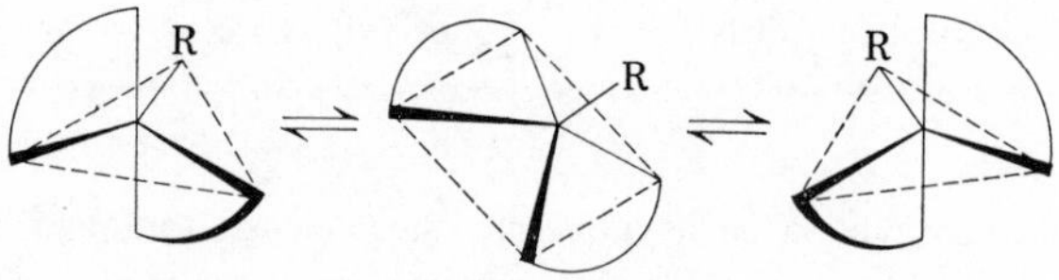

(IIa)   (III)   (IIb)

8.5. Related Compounds

Although phosphine and various phosphites are the most useful starting materials for preparing organophosphorus compounds, these inorganic chemicals are not always available commercially.

Phosphine is prepared by heating phosphorus with caustic alkali in the absence of oxygen, or by heating phosphonium iodide with aqueous potassium hydroxide solution

$$4\,P + 3\,KOH + 3\,H_2O \longrightarrow H_3P + 3\,KH_2PO_2$$
$$PH_4I + OH^- \longrightarrow H_3P + H_2O + I^-$$

The reaction of phosphorus trichloride with an appropriate alcohol in the presence of tertiary amine affords trialkyl phosphites, while in the absence of amines it results in the formation of dialkyl phosphites.

$$PCl_3 + 3\,ROH + R_3N \longrightarrow (RO)_3P + 3\,R_3N \cdot HCl$$
$$PCl_3 + 3\,ROH \longrightarrow HP(O)(OR)_2 + 2\,HCl + RCl$$

8.6. Some Applications

Of all phosphorus compounds, esters of phosphoric acid and related compounds are of greatest practical use.

Apart from the importance of naturally occurring nucleic acids and co-enzymes which are derivatives of phosphates, phosphates are widely used as plasticizers or stabilizers (antioxidants) for synthetic resins, and in insecticides, fungicides, and antistatic agents.

It should be noted that the dehydration reaction by means of esters of phosphoric acid and selective phosphorylation by means of haloacid amides and trialkyl phosphites are important, not only in organic syntheses but also in connection with biochemical procedures.

Some organophosphorus compounds, especially those containing the phenylphosphorus linkages such as $PhPCl_2$, $PhP(O)Cl_2$, $PhP(O)(OH)_2$, and $PhP(O)H(OH)$ have also been used in the preparation of plasticizers, paint additives, etc. Chloromethylphosphorus compounds, for example, $ClCH_2P(O)Cl_2$ and $ClCH_2P(O)(OR)_2$ (R=allyl, propyl, octyl, etc.), are useful for preparing heat-resistant resins, ion-exchange resins, and various additives for resins.

Catalytic actions of a few organophosphorus compounds are known to be important for some organic reactions. Thus, tetrabutylphosphonium hydroxide, prepared from phosphonium iodide and butyl iodide, catalyzes ring-opening polymerization of cyclic dimethylsiloxanes to "silicone rubber". Since the catalyst readily decomposes at higher temperatures, it has no adverse effect on the properties of the silicone rubber.

$$PH_4I + n\text{-}BuI \longrightarrow [n\text{-}Bu_4P]^+I^- \xrightarrow{Ag_2O} [n\text{-}Bu_4P]^+OH^-$$

$$[n\text{-}Bu_4P]^+OH^- \xrightarrow{130\sim170°} n\text{-}C_4H_{10} + n\text{-}Bu_3P(O)$$

Phospholene P-oxide, obtained from the addition of $RPCl_2$ to isoprene, is an efficient catalyst for preparing carbodiimides.

$$2R'\text{-}N=C=O \xrightarrow[\text{(R=Ph,Et)}]{} R'\text{-}N=C=N\text{-}R' + CO_2$$

The mechanism of the catalysis may be considered as the following:

$$R'_3P \rightarrow O + R\text{-}N=C=O \longrightarrow R'_3P=NR + CO_2$$

$$R'_3P=NR + R\text{-}N=C=O \longrightarrow R\text{-}N=C=N\text{-}R + R'_3P \rightarrow O$$

Triphenylphosphine is the most stable ligand in transition metal complexes, and because of this character $Ni(CO)_2(PPh_3)_2$ or $Ni(PPh_3)_2$ shows a selective catalysis for cyclization of acetylenes or butadienes.

Finally, it should be mentioned briefly that macromolecular compounds containing phosphorus atom are of interest. When dimethylphosphine is allowed to react with diborane, the adduct $Me_2PH \cdot BH_3$ is produced. This is converted on heating into a cyclic trimer with elimination of hydrogen. However, if 10 mole % of triethylamine is present, the initial adduct is transformed into a linear polymer, instead of into phosphinoborin, upon heating.

$$2 Me_2PH + B_2H_6 \longrightarrow (Me_2PH \cdot BH_3) \xrightarrow[Et_3N]{} \begin{array}{l} \longrightarrow [Me_2P \cdot BH_2]_3 \\ \longrightarrow [Me_2P \cdot BH_2]_n \end{array}$$

Thermal decomposition of phosphonitrilic compounds may afford some polymers.

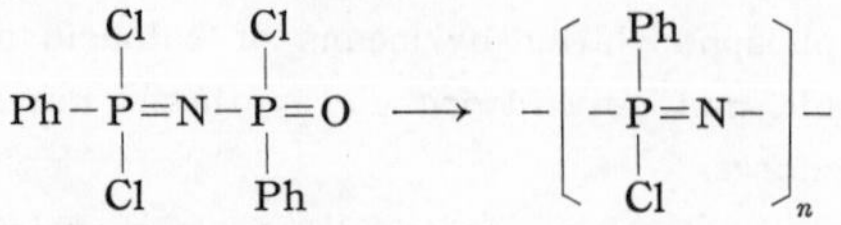

Some chelate polymers of transition metals have also been prepared. The following gives an example.

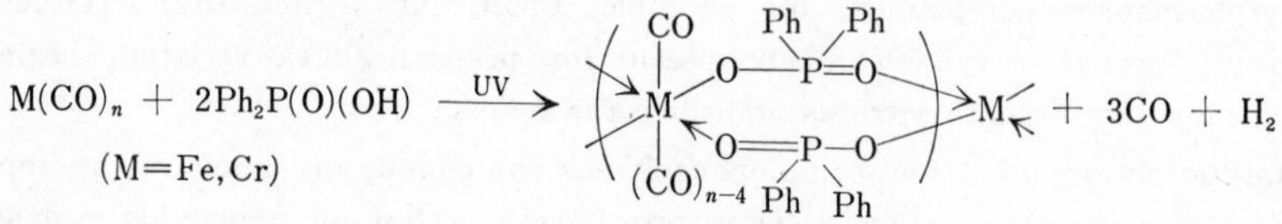

$$M(CO)_n + 2Ph_2P(O)(OH) \xrightarrow{UV} \cdots + 3CO + H_2$$

$$(M=Fe, Cr)$$

REFERENCES

1) G. M. Kosolapoff, "Organophosphorus Compounds", 2nd ed., John Wiley (1958).
2) L. D. Freedman, G. O. Doak, *Chem. Revs.*, **57**, 479~523 (1957).
3) P. C. Crofts, *Quart. Revs.*, **12**, 341~366 (1958).
4) K. D. Berlin, G. B. Butler, *Chem. Revs.*, **60**, 243~260 (1960).
5) G. O. Doak, L. D. Freedman, *Chem. Revs.*, **61**, 31~44 (1961).
6) A. W. Frank, *Chem. Revs.*, **61**, 389~424 (1961).
7) R. F. Hudson, M. Green, *Angew. Chem.*, **75**, 47~56 (1963).
8) S. B. Hartley, W. S. Holmes, J. K. Jacques, M. F. Mole, J. C. McCoubery, *Quart. Revs.*, **17**, 204~223 (1963).
9) L. Maier, in "Progress in Inorganic Chemistry" (Ed. F. A. Cotton), Vol. 5, pp. 27~210, Interscience (1963).
10) "Topics in Phosphrus Chemistry" (Ed. M. Grayson, E. J. Griffith), in 3 vols., Interscience (1964~1965).
11) R. F. Hudson, "Structure and Mechanism in Organo-Phosphorus Chemistry", Academic Press (1965).
12) D. Hellwinkel, *Chem. Ber.*, **99**, 3628~3671 (1966).

【P】

PCBr$_2$Cl$_3$

① Trichloromethylphosphonous dibromide

(CCl$_3$)PBr$_2$

② CCl$_3$PCl$_2$ + red. P + Br$_2$ $\longrightarrow$

③ (98~99°/14).

⑥ Z. Naturf. **17 b**, 703 (1962).

PCBr$_2$F$_3$

① Trifluoromethylphosphonous dibromide

(CF$_3$)PBr$_2$

② CF$_3$PI$_2$ + AgBr $\longrightarrow$ 92.5%

③ (86.7°) estimated.

$\log P(\text{mm}) = 3.8579 - 0.00206\,T + 1.75$
$\log T - 169.47/T$.

⑥ JACS **82**, 3514 (1960).

PCBr$_4$F$_3$

① Tetrabromotrifluoromethyl-phosphorane

(CF$_3$)PBr$_4$

② CF$_3$PBr$_2$ + Br$_2$ $\xrightarrow{0°}$

④ $\xrightarrow{90°}$ CF$_3$Br + PBr$_3$

⑥ JACS **82**, 3514 (1960).

PCCl$_2$F$_3$

① Trifluoromethylphosphonous dichloride

(CF$_3$)PCl$_2$

② CF$_3$PCl$_4$ $\xrightarrow{\text{Hg}}$ CF$_3$PCl$_2$

CF$_3$PI$_2$ + AgCl $\longrightarrow$

③ (0°/157).

④ + H$_2$O $\longrightarrow$ CHF$_3$ + H$_3$PO$_3$

⑥ JACS **80**, 6161 (1958).

PCCl$_3$F$_4$

① Tetrafluorotrichloromethyl phosphorane

(CCl$_3$)PF$_4$

② CCl$_3$PCl$_4 \cdot$ AlCl$_3$ $\xrightarrow{\text{HF}}$ 63%

③ (68~69°/762). d 1.7112 (20°)

④ + P$_2$S$_5$ $\longrightarrow$ (CCl$_3$)P(S)F$_2$

⑥ Zhur. **32**, 301 (1962).

PCCl$_4$F$_3$

① Tetrachlorotrifluoromethyl-phosphorane

(CF$_3$)PCl$_4$

② [(CF$_3$)P]$_4$ + Cl$_2$ $\longrightarrow$

③ (104°) estimated. [−52°].

$\log P\text{mm} = 8.187 - 2106/T$

④ $\xrightarrow{\text{Hg}}$ CF$_3$PCl$_2$

⑥ JACS **80**, 6161 (1958).

PCCl$_5$

① Trichloromethylphosphonous dichloride

(CCl$_3$)PCl$_2$

② White P + CCl$_4$ $\xrightarrow{140°}$

CCl$_3$PCl$_4$ + PI$_3$ + yellow P $\xrightarrow{\text{CCl}_4}$

CCl$_3$PCl$_4$ + CH$_3$OPCl$_2$ $\xrightarrow{35°}$

③ (69~70°/23), (171~172°). [47°].

Easily oxidized in air.

④ + H$_2$O $\longrightarrow$ CHCl$_3$ + H$_3$PO$_3$

⑥ Z. Naturf. **176**, 703 (1962).   Zhur. **28**, 728 (1958).   JOC **23**, 1693 (1958).

PCCl$_7$

① Tetrachlorotrichloromethyl-·phosphorane

(CCl$_3$)PCl$_4$

② CH$_3$PCl$_2$ + Cl$_2$ $\xrightarrow{\text{C}_6\text{H}_5\text{P(O)Cl}_2,\ 60°}$

③ [125~126° decomp].

⑥ Kaufman 974.   JOC **23**, 1693 (1958).

PCF$_3$I$_2$

① Trifluoromethylphosphonous diiodide

(CF₃)PI₂

② $(CF_3P)_4 + I_2 \xrightarrow{110°}$

$P + CF_3I \xrightarrow{280°, \text{ Cu}}$

③ (20°/2).

IR : Can. J. Chem. **40**, 393 (1962),
NMR : JACS **80**, 6161 (1958).

④ $CF_3PI_2 + Hg \longrightarrow$
[(CF₃)P]₄ (60%) + [(CF₃)P]₅ (40%)

⑥ Helv. Chim. Acta **46**, 2026 (1963).

PCF₅

① Trifluoromethylphosphonous
difluoride
(CF₃)PF₂

② $CF_3PI_2 + SbF_3 \longrightarrow 64\%$

③ (−43~−40°).

⑥ Zhur. **29**, 3957 (1959).

PCF₇

① Tetrafluorotrifluoromethyl-
phosphorane
(CF₃)PF₄

② $CF_3PCl_4 + SbF_3 \dashrightarrow$

$(CF_3)_3PF_2 + PF_5 \xrightarrow{100°}$

③ (−35°). [−117].
IR : Inorg. Chem. **2**, 230 (1963).
NMR : Inorg. Chem. **2**, 613 (1963).

④ $\xrightarrow{5\%/\text{month}} (CF_3)_3PF_2 + (CF_3)_2PF_3$
$+ PF_5$

⑥ J. Chem. Phys. **33**, 636 (1960).

PCH₂ClF₄

① Chloromethyltetrafluoro-
phosphorane
(ClCH₂)PF₄

② $(ClCH_2)PCl_2 + SbF_5 \longrightarrow$

③ (47°).
NMR : Inorg. Chem. **2**, 613 (1963).

⑥ Chem. Ind. (London) **1962**, 1868.

PCH₂Cl₃

① Chloromethylphosphonous dichloride
ClCH₂PCl₂

② $ClCH_2P(S)Cl_2 + C_6H_5PCl_2 \xrightarrow{N_2}$
ClCH₂PCl₂ + C₆H₅P(S)Cl₂

③ (128~132°). n_D 1.5282 (25°). d 1.5209
(20°/20°).
Rapidly oxidized and hydrolyzed in
air.
NMR : J. Chem. Eng. Data **7**, 307
(1962).

④ $+ H_2O \xrightarrow{\text{conc. HCl}} ClCH_2P(O)(H)OH$
$+ S \xrightarrow{AlCl_3} ClCH_2P(S)Cl_2$
$3\,ClCH_2PCl_2 + 2\,SbF_3 \longrightarrow$
$3\,ClCH_2PF_2 + 2\,SbCl_3$
$+ SbF_5 \longrightarrow ClCH_2PF_4$

⑥ JACS **83**, 2299 (1961).   Adv. Chem.
Ser. **37**, 150 (1963) ;   CA **58**, 12152
(1963).   Chem. Ind. (London) **1962**,
1868.

PCH₂Cl₃O

① Chloromethylphosphonic dichloride
ClCH₂P(O)Cl₂

② $ClCH_2P(O)(OH)_2 + PCl_5 \longrightarrow$

③ (77~78°/10). n_D 1.4976 (24.8°).
³⁵Cl NQR : JCS **1961**, 2459.

④ $+ NaF \xrightarrow[60\sim230°]{TMS} ClCH_2P(O)F_2 \ (76\%)$
$+ PSCl_3 \xrightarrow{230°} ClCH_2P(S)Cl_2 \ (75\%)$

⑥ Kaufman 971.   JOC **25**, 2016 (1960).
JACS **83**, 1811 (1931).

PCH₂F₃

① Trifluoromethylphosphine
CF₃PH₂

② $CF_3PI_2 + LiAlH_4 \longrightarrow 8\%$
$CF_3PI_2 + H_2O \longrightarrow$
$(CF_3P)_4 + H_2O \xrightarrow{120°}$

③ Colorless gas. (−25.5°).
Spont. inflam.

④ $+ HNO_3 \text{ aq.} \longrightarrow CF_3P(O)(OH)_2$

⑥ JCS **1954**, 3896.   JACS **80**, 6161(1958).

PCH₂F₃O₂

① Trifluoromethylphosphonic acid
   $CF_3P(O)(OH)_2$

② $CF_3PI_2 \xrightarrow{H_2O-H_2O_2}$ 83%

   $(CF_3)_2PI \xrightarrow{H_2O-H_2O_2}$ 88%

   $CF_3PCl_2 \xrightarrow{H_2O-H_2O_2}$ 82%

   $(CF_3)_2PCl \xrightarrow{H_2O-H_2O_2}$ 80%

③ White crystals. [81~82°].
   Sol. in H_2O, hygroscopic. Sublim. at
   85°/10⁻³ mmHg.

④ + Na $\xrightarrow{600°}$ decomp.
   + NaOH $\longrightarrow$ $CF_3P(O)(ONa)_2$
   + $CF_3P(O)(ONa)(OH)$
   + NH₃ aq. $\longrightarrow$ $CF_3P(O)(ONH_4)_2$
   + Ba(OH)₂ $\longrightarrow$ Ba salt (hydrate)

⑥ JCS **1954**, 3598.

PCH₃Br₂

① Methylphosphonous dibromide
   CH_3PBr_2

② red P + CH₃Br $\longrightarrow$

③ (138.5°/720). [−58°]. n_D 1.6104 (20°).
   d 2.186 (20°).
   NMR : J. Chem. Eng. Data **7**, 307
   (1962).

⑥ Helv. Chim. Acta **46**, 2026 (1963).

PCH₃Cl₂

① Methylphosphonous dichloride
   CH_3PCl_2

② $CH_3P(S)Cl_2 + C_6H_5PCl_2 \xrightarrow{350°}$
   $CH_3PCl_2 + C_6H_5P(S)Cl_2$ (>95%)
   [$PCl_3 + CH_3Cl + AlCl_3$]
   $\xrightarrow{\text{diethyl phthalate}}$
   $CH_3Cl + P-Cu \xrightarrow{350°}$ "direct method"

③ (77~79°), (80~81°/729). n_D 1.4960
   (25°). d 1.3039 (20°).
   Solid complex $CH_3Cl_2P\cdot N(CH_3)_3$

³⁵Cl NQR : JCS **1961**, 2459.
NMR : J. Chem. Eng. Data **7**, 307
(1962).

④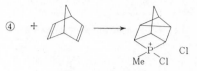

⑥ Helv. Chim. Acta **46**, 2026 (1963).
   Kaufman 972. Proc. Chem. Soc.
   1963, 177. JCS **1963**, 3320.

PCH₃Cl₂O

① Methylphosphonic dichloride
   $CH_3P(O)Cl_2$

② $CH_3PCl_2 + (C_6H_5)_2NCl \longrightarrow$
   $CH_3P(O)Cl_2 + CH_3P(O)[N(C_6H_5)_2]Cl$

③ (163°), (53~54°/10). [33°]. n_D 1.4526
   (40°). d 1.4382 (40°/4).
   NMR : J. Chem. Eng. Data **7**, 307
   (1962).

⑥ Kaufman 971.   Compt. rend. **257**,
   898. (1963).   Zhur. **31**, 1366 (1961).

PCH₃Cl₂S

① Methylphosphonothioic dichloride
   $CH_3P(S)Cl_2$

② $CH_3P(O)Cl_2 + P_4S_{10} \longrightarrow$
   $CH_3PCl_2 + S \xrightarrow{AlCl_3, 70°}$
   $CH_3PCl_4\cdot AlCl_3 + Sb_2S_5(or\ S) \xrightarrow{KCl}$
   64%

③ (142~143), (69.5~70.5°/50), (154°),
   (45~48°/9.5). [−25.8°]. n_D 1.5499
   (20°). d 1.4220. (20°)
   IR : JCS **1961**, 238
   NMR : Helv. Chim. Acta **46**, 2026
   (1963).

④ + NaOR $\longrightarrow$ $CH_3P(S)(OR)_2$

⑥ Zhur. **28**, 2960 (1958).   Bull. soc.
   chim. France **1961**, 735.

PCH₃Cl₂Se

① Methylphosphonoselenoic dichloride

CH₃P(Se)Cl₂

② CH₃PCl₂ + Se $\xrightarrow{AlCl_3}$ 40%

③ (20~21°/0.1). n_D 1.5896 (20°). d
1.7872 (20°).
IR: Bull. soc. chim. France 1961,
739.
NMR: Compt. rend. 253, 644 (1961).

⑥ Bull. soc. chim. France 1960, 1794.

PCH₃Cl₄

① Tetrachloromethylphosphorane
(CH₃)PCl₄

② CH₃PCl₂ + Cl₂ $\xrightarrow{CS_2, \ 0°}$

[(CH₃)₂P(S)]₂ + Cl₂ $\xrightarrow{CCl_4, \ hr}$

③ [198~199°].
Decompd. in air, with H₂O.

④ + AsF₃ ⟶ CH₃PF₄

+ S $\xrightarrow[170°]{KCl}$ CH₃P(S)Cl₂ (61%)

⑥ Zhur. 32, 301 (1962); 28, 2960 (1958).
Ber. 90, 1656 (1957).

PCH₃F₄

① Tetrafluoromethylphosphorane
(CH₃)PF₄

② 3CH₃PCl₂ + 4SbF₃ ⟶
CH₃PCl₄ + AsF₃ ⟶ 70%

CH₃PCl₄·AlCl₃ $\xrightarrow{HF}$ 95%

③ (12.5°/756). [−50°]. d 1.4537. (10°)
NMR: Inorg. Chem. 2, 613 (1963).

④ + P₂S₅ $\xrightarrow{160-170°}$ CH₃P(S)F₂ (81%)

⑥ Chem. Ind (London) 1962, 1868.
Zhur. 32, 301 (1962).

PC₁H₅

① Methylphosphine
CH₃PH₂

② Ca(PH₂)₂ + CH₃Cl ⟶
CH₃PBr₂ + LiAlH₄ ⟶

PH₃ + Na + CH₃Cl $\xrightarrow{liq. NH_3}$
CH₄ + phosphorus vapor ⟶

③ Colorless gas. (−17.1°).
Sol. in ether. Decomp. with H₂O,
alcohol. Spont. inflam.
IR: Spectrochim. Acta 1959, 146.
Microwave spect.: J. Chem. Phys.
35, 2139 (1961).

④ + (CH₂O)ₙ $\xrightarrow{82-85°, \ in \ autoclave}$
CH₃P(CH₂OH)₂

⑥ JACS 73, 5088 (1951); 75, 3869 (1953).
Angew. 71, 574 (1959).

PCH₅O₂

① Methylphosphonous acid
CH₃PO₂H₂

② (CH₃)PH₂ + O₂ $\xrightarrow{H_2O}$

③ Hygroscopic crystals. [104°].

⑥ Kosolapoff 146.

PCH₅O₃

① Methylphosphonic acid
CH₃P(O)(OH)₂

② CH₃P(O)(OC₄H₉)₂ $\xrightarrow{HCl}$ 63%
CH₃P(O)Cl₂ + H₂O ⟶
ClCH₂P(O)(OH)H + NaOH aq. ⟶
29%

③ White crystals. [105°].
Hygroscopic.
NMR: J. Chem. Eng. Data 7, 307
(1962).

⑥ JCS 1963, 3320.   Bull. soc. chim.
France 1962, 1645.   JACS 75, 3379
(1953); 83, 2299 (1961).

PCH₅O₄

① Hydroxymethylphosphonic acid
HOCH₂P(O)(OH)₂

② (C₂H₅O)₂P(O)CH₂OH + 18% HCl aq.
⟶ 27.7%

③ White crystals. [87~88°].
Hygroscopic.
NMR: J. Chem. Eng. Data 7, 307
(1962).

④ ⟶ Al salt

⑤ Hardener for resins.

⑥ Zhur. **6**, 283 (1936).   Can. J. Chem.
   31, 976 (1953).   Plasticheskie
   Massy **1961**, 62.   JOC **25**, 1000
   (1960).

PC₂BrF₆

① Bis(trifluoromethyl)phosphinous
   bromide
   $(CF_3)_2PBr$

② $(CF_3)_4P_2 + Br_2 \xrightarrow{90°}$
   $(CF_3)_2PI + AgBr \longrightarrow 97.8\%$

③ (41.8°) estimated.
   $\log P(mm) = -1510/T + 7.68$
   IR and NMR: JCS **1963**, 960.   JACS
   84, 3442 (1962).

⑥ JACS **82**, 3514 (1960).

PC₂BrF₆O

① Bis(trifluoromethyl)phosphinic
   bromide
   $(CF_3)_2P(O)Br$

② $(CF_3)_2P(O)C_4H_9 + Br_2 \xrightarrow{100°\sim130°}$
   51.7%

③ (78.3°) estimated. [−35.5°].
   $\log Pmm = 5.0476 + 1.75 \log T$
   $\qquad\qquad -0.003833\, T - 1854/T$

⑥ JACS **84**, 3442 (1962).

PC₂Br₃F₆

① Tribromobis(trifluoromethyl)
   phosphorane
   $(CF_3)_2PBr_3$

② $(CF_3)_4P_2 + Br_2 \longrightarrow$
   $(CF_3)_2PBr + Br_2 \longrightarrow$

③ [6.0∼9.4°].
   Non volatile at 0°.

④ $\xrightarrow{90°} CF_3Br + PBr_3 + (CF_3)_2PBr$

⑥ JACS **82**, 3514 (1960).

PC₂ClF₆

① Bis(trifluoromethyl)phosphinous

chloride
$(CF_3)_2PCl$

② $(CF_3)_2PI + AgCl \longrightarrow$

③ (21°).
   Hydrolyzed by alkali.
   IR: JACS **84**, 3442 (1962).
   NMR: JCS **1963**, 960.

④ $+ 2NH_3 \longrightarrow (CF_3)_2PNH_2$ (96%)

⑥ Proc. Chem. Soc. **1957**, 118.   JCS **1953**,
   1565.

PC₂ClF₆O

① Bis(trifluoromethyl)phosphinic
   chloride
   $(CF_3)_2P(O)Cl$

② $[(CF_3)_2P]_2O + Cl_2 \longrightarrow$ (quantitative)

③ (52.6°) estimated.
   $\log Pmm = 6.8433 + 1.75 \log T$
   $\qquad\qquad -0.00700\, T - 1980/T$
   IR: JACS **84**, 3442 (1962).

④ $\xrightarrow{1\% \text{ NaOH, } 100°} CHF_3$

PC₂Cl₂F₃

① Trifluorovinylphosphonous
   dichloride
   $(CF_2=CF)PCl_2$

② $(CF_2=CF)P[N(C_2H_5)_2]_2 + HCl \xrightarrow{(C_2H_5)_2O}$
   66%

③ (81.5∼82.0°). n_D 1.4412 (19°). d 1.574
   (19°).

④ $+ SbF_3 \longrightarrow (CF_2=CF)PF_2$ (64%)

⑥ Khim. Nauka i Prom. **4**, 810 (1959);
   CA **54**, 10838 (1959). Izv. OKhN.
   1960, 1991.

PC₂Cl₃F₆

① Trichlorobis(trifluoromethyl)phos-
   phorane
   $(CF_3)_2PCl_3$

② $(CF_3)_2PCl + Cl_2 \longrightarrow$

③ (48∼49°/100), (82°/355). [−26.0∼−
   25.0°]. d 1.85 (25°).
   IR: JCS **1959**, 1494.

NMR: JCS 1963, 960.

④ + SbF₃ ⟶ (CF₃)₂PF₃

+ H₂O $\xrightarrow{\text{Ag}_2\text{O, H}_2\text{SO}_4}$

(CF₃)₂P(O)(OH)(95%)

⑥ Kaufman 980.   Inorg. Chem. 2, 230 (1963).

PC₂F₆I

① Bis(trifluoromethyl)phosphinous iodide

(CF₃)₂PI

② $\text{AgCO}_2\text{CF}_3 + \text{P} + \text{I}_2 \xrightarrow{195°}$

$\text{CF}_3\text{I} + \text{P} \xrightarrow{220°}$

(CF₃)₃P + (CF₃)₂PI + (CF₃)PI₂
84%   15%   1%

③ (72~73°). n_D 1.403 (15°).

IR: JACS 84, 3442 (1962).

NMR: JCS 1963, 960.

④ $\xrightarrow{\text{Ag}_2\text{CO}_3}$ (CF₃)₂POP(CF₃)₂

+ SbF₃ $\xrightarrow{40°}$ (CF₃)₂PF (37%)

$\xrightarrow{\text{Hg/dry HCl}}$ (CF₃)₂PH (35%)

$\xrightarrow{205°}$ (CF₃)₃P + (CF₃)PI₂

⑥ JCS 1953, 1565.   Zhur. 29, 3957 (1959).   JACS 79, 247 (1957).

PC₂F₇

① Bis(trifluoromethyl)phosphinous fluoride

(CF₃)₂PF

② (CF₃)₂PI + SbF₃ $\xrightarrow{60°}$ (quantitative)

③ (−11~−8°).

Ignites in air.

NMR: JCS 1963, 960.

⑥ Zhur. 29, 3957 (1959).   JACS 86, 3198 (1958).

PC₂F₉

① Trifluorobis(trifluoromethyl)phosphorane

(CF₃)₂PF₃

② (CF₃)₂PCl₃ + SbF₃ ⟶

(CF₃)₂PI + SF₄ ⟶

③ (−5°). [−74°].

IR: Inorg. Chem. 2, 230 (1963).

NMR: Inorg. Chem. 2, 613 (1963).

④ $\xrightarrow{25°}$ (CF₃)₃PF₂ + (CF₃)PF₄

PC₂HF₆

① Bis(trifluoromethyl)phosphine

(CF₃)₂PH

② (CF₃)₂PI + Ni + H₂ $\xrightarrow{110°}$ 65%

(CF₃)₂PI + H₂ $\xrightarrow{\text{UV}}$ low yield

(CF₃)₂P−P(CF₃)₂ + H₂ ⟶ 28%

(CF₃)₂P−P(CF₃)₂ + HCl ⟶

③ Colorless gas. (1°). [−137°].

Sol. in polar solvents. Thermally stable, spont. inflam.

④ + I₂ $\xrightarrow{280°}$ CHF₃ + CF₃I

+ excess HgO ⟶ (CF₃)₂P(O)OH

+ B₂H₆ ⟶ [(CF₃)₂PBH₂]₃

⑥ JCS 1954, 3896.   JACS 80, 3198 (1958); 79, 4242 (1957).

PC₂HF₆O

① Bis(trifluoromethyl)phosphine oxide

(CF₃)₂PH(O)

② (CF₃)₂PH $\xrightarrow{\text{HgO, }-45°}$

④ (CF₃)₂PH(O) ⟶ (CF₃)₂P(OH) was observed on oxidn. of (CF₃)₂PH.

⑥ Proc. Chem. Soc. 1961, 12

PC₂HF₆O

① Bis(trifluoromethyl)phosphinous acid

(CF₃)₂POH

② (CF₃)₂POP(CF₃)₂ + HCl $\xrightarrow{100°}$ 86%

③ (61.4°). [−20.8°].

IR: JACS 84, 3442 (1962).

④ + (CH₃)₃N ⟶ (CH₃)₃N·(CF₃)₂POH

⑥ JACS 82, 1507 (1962).

PC₂HF₆O₂

① Bis(trifluoromethyl)phosphinic acid
   (CF₃)₂P(O)(OH)

② (CF₃)₂PCl₃ + H₂O +`Ag₂O $\xrightarrow{\text{H}_2\text{SO}_4}$ 95%
   (CF₃)₂PH + HgO $\longrightarrow$

③ Colorless liq. (182°).
   Sol. in polar org. solvents.
   IR: JACS **84**, 3442 (1962).

④ + C₆H₅NH₂ $\longrightarrow$
   (CF₃)₂P(O)OH·C₆H₅NH₂

⑥ JCS **1955**, 563.

PC₂H₃Cl₂O

① Vinylphosphonic dichloride
   CH₂=CHP(O)Cl₂

② ClCH₂CH₂P(O)Cl₂ $\xrightarrow{330\sim340°,\ \text{BaCl}_2}$
   85.6%

③ (67~69°/21). n_D 1.4808 (20°). d 1.4092
   (20°).

④ Vinylphosphonic dichloride undergoes radical polymerization and
   copolymerizes with MMA, styrene
   and vinyl alcohol.
   + C₂H₅OH $\xrightarrow{-4°,\ \text{C}_5\text{H}_5\text{N}/(\text{C}_2\text{H}_5)_2\text{O}}$
   CH₂=CHP(O)(OC₂H₅)₂ (45%)

⑥ Zhur. **32**, 3255 (1962). Vysokomol.
   Soed. **3**, 459 (1958). Zhur. OKhN
   1959, 2142.

PC₂H₃Cl₆

① Tetrachloro-1,1-dichloroethyl-
   phosphorane (PCl₅ complex)
   (CH₃CCl₂)PCl₄

② PCl₅ + C₂H₅P(O)Cl₂ $\xrightarrow{\text{C}_6\text{H}_6,\ -\text{HCl}}$
   CH₃CCl₂PCl₃⁺·PCl₆⁻ 70%

④ + SO₂ $\longrightarrow$ CH₃CCl₂P(O)Cl₂ (74%)

⑥ Zhur. **31**, 594 (1961)

PC₂H₃F₄

① 1,1,2,2-Tetrafluoroethylphosphine

HCF₂CF₂PH₂

② CF₂=CF₂ + PH₃ $\xrightarrow{150°}$ 53%

③ Colorless liq. (20~22°).
   Spont. inflam. Extremely vile oder.

④ + CH₃I $\xrightarrow{100°}$ [HCF₂CF₂P⁺(CH₃)₃]I⁻

⑥ JACS **81**, 4801 (1959).

PC₂H₄Cl₃

① Bis(chloromethyl)phosphinous
   chloride
   (ClCH₂)₂PCl

② ClCH₂PCl₂ + CH₂Cl₂ $\xrightarrow{\text{AlCl}_3}$
   $\xrightarrow{\text{Sb, diethyl phthalate}}$ 22%

③ (76°/22).

⑥ Nature **189**, 916 (1961).

PC₂H₄Cl₃O

① 2-Chloroethylphosphonic dichloride
   ClCH₂CH₂P(O)Cl₂

② ClCH₂CH₂P(O)(OH)₂ + PCl₅ $\longrightarrow$ 80%
   [ClCH₂CH₂Cl + PCl₃ + AlCl₃]
   $\xrightarrow{\text{SO}_2,\ \text{diethyl phthalate}}$ 62%

③ (68°/2), (213~217°). n_D 1.4977 (16°).
   d 1.5430 (16°/4°).
   NMR: J. Chem. Eng. Data **7**, 307
   (1962).

⑥ Kosolapoff 73. Australian J. Chem.
   16, 596 (1963). Angew. **74**, 970
   (1962).

PC₂H₅Br₄

① Tetrabromoethylphosphorane
   C₂H₅PBr₄

② C₂H₅PBr₂ + Br₂ $\longrightarrow$

③ [188~190°].

⑥ Z. Naturf. **15** b, 267 (1960).

PC₂H₅Cl₂

① Ethylphosphonous dichloride
   C₂H₅PCl₂

② PCl₃ + Cd(C₂H₅)₂ $\xrightarrow{\text{Et}_2\text{O}}$ 26%

$[C_2H_5Cl + PCl_3 + AlCl_3]$ $\xrightarrow{\text{Sb, diethyl}}$
phthalate

$C_2H_5Cl + P-Cu \xrightarrow{440°} C_2H_5PCl_2 +$
$(C_2H_5)_2PCl$

③ $(114\sim117°)$, $(26°/25)$. n_D 1.4938 $(20°)$.
d 1.2563 $(20°)$.
NMR: J. Chem. Eng. Data 7, 307
(1962).

④ $C_2H_5PCl_2 + RN_2BF_4 \xrightarrow{CuBr} C_2H_5RP$
$(O)OH$

⑥ Kosolapoff 53. Kaufman 977. Can.
J. Chem. 41, 2299 (1963). Helv.
Chim. Acta 46, 2026 (1963).

PC₂H₅Cl₂

① Chloromethylmethylphosphinous
chloride
$(ClCH_2)(CH_3)PCl$

② $ClCH_2PCl_2 + CH_3Cl \xrightarrow{AlCl_3, 100°}$
$\xrightarrow{\text{Sb, 80}\sim85°} 73\%$

③ $(67°/98)$. n_D 1.5140 $(25°)$.

⑥ Can. J. Chem. 39, 842 (1961). Nature
189, 916 (1961).

PC₂H₅Cl₂O

① Chloromethylmethylphosphinic
chloride
$(CH_2Cl)(CH_3)P(O)Cl$

② $CH_3PCl_2 + CH_2O \xrightarrow{80\sim100°} 70\%$

③ $(250°$ decomp.$)$.
NMR: JACS 83, 1811 (1961)

④ $PSCl_3 \xrightarrow[130\sim140°]{PCl_3\text{-}AlCl_3} CH_3(CH_2Cl)P(S)Cl$
(39%)

⑥ Dokl. 1953, 862.

PC₂H₅Cl₂O

① Ethylphosphonic dichloride
$C_2H_5P(O)Cl_2$

② $C_2H_5P(O)(OH)_2 + SOCl_2 \xrightarrow{20°} 62.5\%$

③ $(175°)$, $(75\sim78°/50)$. n_D 1.4661 $(20°)$.

d 1.3678 $(20°)$.

④ $+ C_6H_5OH \xrightarrow{(C_2H_5)_2O, C_5H_5N, 20°}$
$(C_6H_5O)_2P(O)C_2H_5$

$+ PCl_5 \longrightarrow CH_3CCl_2PCl_3 \cdot PCl_6 \xrightarrow{SO_2}$
$CH_3CCl_2P(O)Cl_2$

⑥ Kosolapoff 73. JOC 25, 2006 (1960).
JCS 1961, 2459

PC₂H₅Cl₂S

① Ethylphosphonothioic dichloride
$C_2H_5P(S)Cl_2$

② $C_2H_5PCl_4 \cdot AlCl_3 + S \xrightarrow[170°]{KCl} 60.5\%$

③ $(68\sim69°/20)$, $(82.5°/48.5)$. n_D 1.5435
$(20°)$. d 1.3532 $(20°)$.
IR: Zhur. 29, 1998 (1959).

⑥ JINC 24, 1073 (1962). Zhur. 28, 2960
(1958). Kaufman 976.

PC₂H₅Cl₂Se

① Ethylphosphonoselenoic dichloride
$C_2H_5P(Se)Cl_2$

② $C_2H_5PCl_2 + Se \xrightarrow{AlCl_3} 63\%$

③ $(38\sim39°/1.5)$. n_D 1.5894 $(20°)$. d 1.6987
$(20°)$.

④ $+ C_5H_6NH_2 \xrightarrow{(C_2H_5)_3N/(C_2H_5)_2O}$
$C_2H_5P(Se)(NHC_6H_5)_2$

⑥ Bull. soc. chim. France 1960, 1794;
1961, 739

PC₂H₅Cl₄

① Tetrachloroethylphosphorane
$C_2H_5PCl_4$

② $C_2H_5PCl_2 + Cl_2 \xrightarrow{C_6H_5CH_3}$

③ $[170°]$.

⑥ Kosolapoff 72. Zhur. 33, 2149 (1963).

PC₂H₅F₄

① Ethyltetrafluorophosphorane
$C_2H_5PF_4$

② $3 C_2H_5PCl_2 + 4 SbF_3 \longrightarrow 70\%$

$C_2H_5PCl_4 \cdot AlCl_3 \xrightarrow{HF} 58\%$

③ $(34\sim34.5°/749)$. d 1.3074 $(20°)$.

NMR: Inorg. Chem. 2, 613 (1963).

④ $+ Al_2S_3 \xrightarrow{160°} C_2H_5P(S)F_2$ (90%)

⑥ Chem. Ind. (London) 1962, 1868.

Zhur. 32, 301 (1962).

PC₂H₅I₄

① Ethyltetraiodophosphorane

$C_2H_5PI_4$

② $C_2H_5PI_2 + I \longrightarrow$

③ $[112\sim116°]$.

④ $+ H_2O \longrightarrow HI + C_2H_5P(O)(OH)_2$

⑥ Z. Naturf. 15 b, 267 (1960).

PC₂H₅O₄

① Acetylphosphonic acid

$CH_3COP(O)(OH)_2$

② $P(OH)_3 + CH_3COCl \longrightarrow 83\%$

$CH_3COP(O)(OC_2H_5)_2 + HBr$

$\xrightarrow{3.5\,hr,\,95°} 93.2\%$

③ Glassy solid. $[110\sim114°]$.

Highly hygroscopic.

IR: JCS 1960, 1948.

④ $\longrightarrow$ Ba salt

$+ C_2H_4N_2 + KOH \longrightarrow$

$CH_3COP(O)(OC_2H_5)_2$

⑥ Chem. Ind. (London) 1953, 351.

PC₂H₅O₅

① Phosphonoacetic acid

$HOOCCH_2P(O)(OH)_2$

② $C_2H_5OOCH_2P(O)(OC_2H_5)_2 + HCl \longrightarrow$

③ Crystals. $[142\sim143°]$.

Hygroscopic

Sol. in H_2O, C_2H_5OH and acetone;

insol. in ether, C_6H_6 and $CHCl_3$.

⑥ J. Russ. Phys. Chem. Soc. 59, 239

(1927); 61, 619 (1929). Ber. 57,

1023 (1924). Chem. Ind. (London)

1962, 2085. JOC 24, 434 (1959).

PC₂H₆Br

① Dimethylphosphinous bromide

$(CH_3)_2PBr$

② red P + CH₃Br $\xrightarrow{350°}$

$CH_3PBr_2 + (CH_3)_4Pb \longrightarrow$

③ $[94\sim95°]$.

NMR: J. Chem. Eng. Data 7, 307

(1962).

④ $+ S \xrightarrow{C_6H_5CH_3} (CH_3)_2P(S)Br$

⑥ Helv. Chim. Acta 46, 2026 (1963).

PC₂H₆Cl

① Dimethylphosphinous chloride

$(CH_3)_2PCl$

② $CH_3PCl_2 + CH_3Cl \xrightarrow{AlCl_3}$

$\xrightarrow{Sb,\ diethyl\ phthalate} 45\%$

$(CH_3)_2P(S)Cl + (C_4H_9)_3P \longrightarrow$

③ $(70°/690)$. $[ca.\ 0°]$. d 1.2281 $(23°)$.

⑥ Can. J. Chem. 39, 842 (1961). Nature

189, 916 (1961). JINC 24, 1073

(1962); 20, 82 (1961). Helv. Chim.

Acta 46, 2026 (1963).

PC₂H₆ClO

① Dimethylphosphinic chloride

$(CH_3)_2P(O)Cl$

② $(CH_3)_2P(O)(OH) + PCl_5 \longrightarrow 80\%$

$[(CH_3)_2P(S)]_2 + SOCl_2 \xrightarrow{CCl_4} 90\%$

③ $(204°)$. $[68°]$.

NMR: J. Chem. Eng. Data 7, 307

(1962).

④ $+ NaBH_4 \xrightarrow{diglyme} (CH_3PBH_2)_3$

$+ (CH_2)_x(MgX)_2 \longrightarrow$

$[(CH_3)_2P(O)]_2[CH_2]_x$ $(x=4\sim6)$

$+ NaOCH_3 \xrightarrow{C_6H_6} (CH_3)_2P(O)(OCH_3)$

$+ CH_2\!-\!CH_2 \xrightarrow{AlCl_4}$

$\underset{O}{\diagdown\diagup}$

$(CH_3)_2P(O)(OCH_2CH_2Cl)$

⑥ JACS **82**, 2145 (1960).   Kaufman 977.
   JOC **27**, 4444 (1962).   Ber. **94**, 3056.
   (1961).

PC₂H₆ClO₂

① Chloromethylmethylphosphinic acid
   $(ClCH_2)(CH_3)P(O)(OH)$

② $CH_3PCl_2 + (CH_2O)_n \longrightarrow$
   $CH_3(CH_2Cl)P(O)OP(O)(CH_2Cl)CH_3$
   $\xrightarrow{H_2O}$

③ NMR : J. Chem. Eng. Data **7**, 305
   (1962).   JACS **83**, 4381 (1961).

PC₂H₆ClO₃

① 2-Chloroethylphosphonic acid
   $ClCH_2CH_2P(O)(OH)_2$

② $ClCH_2CH_2POCl_2 \xrightarrow{hydrolysis}$

③ Needles. [74~75°].
   Highly hygroscopic.

⑥ Izv. OKhN **1945**, 597.   Australian
   J. Chem. **16**, 596 (1963).   JINC **22**,
   297 (1961).

PC₂H₆ClS

① Dimethylphosphinothioic chloride
   $(CH_3)_2P(S)Cl$

② $[(CH_3)_2P(S)]_2 + SO_2Cl_2 \xrightarrow{C_6H_6} 77.2\%$

③ (72~75°/12). n_D 1.5451 (20°).

⑥ Ber. **94**, 3051 (1961).

PC₂H₆F₃

① Trifluorodimethylphosphorane
   $(CH_3)_2PF_3$

② $3(CH_3)_2PCl + 6SbF_3 \longrightarrow 56.4\%$
   $(CH_3)_2PCl \cdot AlCl_3 \xrightarrow{HF} 15.8\%$

③ (60~61°/745). n_D 1.3230 (20°). d 1.2155
   (20°).
   NMR : Inorg. Chem. **2**, 613 (1963).

⑥ Chem. Ind. (London) **1962**, 1868.
   Zhur. **32**, 301 (1962).

PC₂H₆Li

① Lithium dimethylphosphide
   $LiP(CH_3)_2 \cdot 1/2(C_2H_5)_2O$

② $(CH_3)_2PH + C_6H_5Li \xrightarrow{ether} 88.6\%$

③ Insol. in ether, C_6H_6 and dioxane.
   Air sensitive.

⑤ Intermediate in prepn. of org. P
   compds.

⑥ Ber. **93**, 1852 (1960).

PC₂H₆Na

① Sodium dimethylphosphide
   $NaP(CH_3)_2$. 1/2 dioxane

② $(CH_3)_2P-P(CH_3)_2 + Na \longrightarrow 43.5\%$

⑤ Intermediate in prepn. of org. P
   compds.

⑥ Ber. ·**93**, 1852 (1960).

PC₂H₇

① Dimethylphosphine
   $(CH_3)_2PH$

② $(CH_3)_2P-P(CH_3)_2 + Na \xrightarrow{H_2O} 88\%$
   $PH_3 + Na + CH_3Cl \xrightarrow{liq. NH_3} 30\%$
   $(CH_3)_2P(S)-P(S)(CH_3)_2 + LiAlH_4$
   $\longrightarrow 66.1\%$

③ Colorless liq. (25°).
   Sol. in org. solvents.   Spont. inflam.,
   decomp. in air.
   NMR : J. Chem. Eng. Data **7**, 307
   (1962).

④ $+ NaNH_2 + NH_4Br \xrightarrow{liq. NH_3}$
   $(CH_3)_2P(NH)P(CH_3)_2$
   $+ C_6H_5Li \longrightarrow (CH_3)_2PLi$
   $+ (HCHO)_3 \longrightarrow (CH_3)_2P(CH_2OH)$

⑥ JACS **83**, 2226 (1961) ; **82**, 2145
   (1960) ; **75**, 3869 (1953) ; Ber. **93**,
   1852 (1960) ; **65**, 64 (1962).

PC₂H₇

① Ethylphosphine
   $C_2H_5PH_2$

② $C_2H_5P(O)(OC_2H_5)_2$ + LiAlH$_4$ $\xrightarrow{\text{diglyme}}$

    C_2H_5Br + LiPH$_2$ $\longrightarrow$ 65%

③ Colorless gas. (25°/748).

    Decomp. in air. Sol. in org.

    solvents.

④ + COCl$_2$ $\longrightarrow$ $C_2H_5PH_2 \cdot COCl_2$

⑥ Ber. **76**, 23 (1943) ;   **87**, 919 (1954).

    Inorg. Chem. 1, 470 (1962).

PC_2H_7O

① 2-Hydroxyethylphosphine

    $HOCH_2CH_2PH_2$

② $PH_3 + CH_2-CH_2$ $\longrightarrow$

          O

③ Colorless liq. (139~140°). n_D 1.4950

    (20°). d 1.0040 (20°/4°).

    Inflam. Sol. in H$_2$O and pyridine,

    slightly sol. in ether and C$_6$H$_6$.

④ + 30% H$_2$O$_2$ $\longrightarrow$

    $HOCH_2CH_2P(O)(OH)_2$

⑥ Compt. rend. **56**, 49 (1947).

$PC_2H_7OS_2$

① Ethylphosphonodithioic acid

    $C_2H_5P(S)(OH)SH$

② $C_2H_5MgBr + P_2S_5$ $\xrightarrow{\text{NiSO}_4}$

    $Ni[SSP(OH)C_2H_5]_2$ $\xrightarrow[\text{acidification}]{(NH_4)_2S}$

③ Oil.

    Unstable.

④ $\longrightarrow$ Ni salt

⑥ Gazz. chim. ital. **76**, 167 (1946).

$PC_2H_7OS_2$

① Methylphosphonodithioic acid

    O-methyl ester

    $CH_3P(S)(OCH_3)SH$

② $(CH_3PS_2)_2 + CH_3OH$ $\longrightarrow$

    quantitative

③ (28°/0.01). n_D 1.5659 (22.5°).

④ $\longrightarrow$ Na salt

⑥ JOC **27**, 3832 (1962).   Zhur. **31**, 140

(1961).

$PC_2H_7O_2$

① Dimethylphosphinic acid

    $(CH_3)_2P(O)(OH)$

② $(CH_3)_2(S)PP(S)(CH_3)_2 + 3 H_2O_2$ $\longrightarrow$

    95%

    $(CH_3)_2P(O)OP(O)(CH_3)_2$ $\xrightarrow{H_2O}$

③ Hygroscopic crystals. [88.5~90.5°].

    Sol. in H$_2$O and organic solvents.

    NMR : JACS **83**, 4381 (1961).

④ + PCl$_5$ $\longrightarrow$ $(CH_3)_2POCl$

    + 3 Cl$_2$ $\longrightarrow$ $(CH_3)(CCl_3)P(O)(OH)$

    + 3 HCl

⑥ JCS **1959**, 3950.   Ber. **90**, 1656 (1957).

    JACS **73**, 5466 (1951).

$PC_2H_7O_2$

① Ethylphosphonous acid

    $C_2H_5PO_2H_2$

② $(C_2H_5)_3P + O_2$ $\xrightarrow{H_2O}$

    $C_2H_5PCl_2 + H_2O$ $\longrightarrow$

    $CH_2=CHCH_2OPCl_2 + C_2H_5MgX$ $\xrightarrow{H_2O}$

③ Liq. d 1.2952 (19°).

⑥ Kosolapoff 146.

$PC_2H_7O_2S$

① Methylphosphonothioic acid

    O-methyl ester

    $CH_3P(S)(OCH_3)OH$

② $CH_3PSCl_2 + CH_3OH + KOH$ $\longrightarrow$ 71%

    $CH_3P(S)(OCH_3)_2 + KOH$ $\xrightarrow{\text{reflux}}$

    38.5%

③ (75~83°/0.3~0.5). n_D 1.5005 (25°).

    d 1.3015 (25°/4°).

④ + $(C_6H_{11})_2NH$ $\longrightarrow$ $CH_3P(O)(OCH_3)$

    $SNH_2(C_6H_{11})_2$

⑥ JCS **1962**, 3824.   JACS **81**, 148 (1959).

$PC_2H_7O_3$

① Ethylphosphonic acid

C$_2$H$_5$P(O)(OH)$_2$

② C$_2$H$_5$P(O)(OC$_2$H$_5$)$_2$ $\xrightarrow{\text{HCl hydrolysis}}$

C$_2$H$_5$P(O)(OC$_4$H$_9$)$_2$ $\xrightarrow{\text{heat}}$ 99%

C$_2$H$_5$P(O)Cl$_2$ $\xrightarrow{\text{H}_2\text{O}}$

③ Crystals. (330~340/8). [61~62°].
Hygroscopic.
Sol. in H$_2$O and polar organic
solvents.

⑥ JACS **67**, 1180 (1945); **76**, 4172(1954);
57, 3379 (1953).   JCS **1962**, 331.

PC$_2$H$_7$O$_3$

① Methylphosphonic acid methyl ester
CH$_3$P(O)(OCH$_3$)OH

② [CH$_3$P(O)OH]$_2$O + CH$_3$OH $\longrightarrow$ 40%
CH$_3$P(O)(OCH$_3$)$_2$ + aq. Ba(OH)$_2$
$\longrightarrow$ 75%

③ (104~105°/0.1). n_D1.4245 (20°).

④ excess SOCl$_2$ $\longrightarrow$ (CH$_3$PO$_2$)$_n$
+ CH$_3$POCl$_2$ + CH$_3$PO(OCH$_3$)Cl

⑥ Men. Poudres **44**, 119 (1962); CA **62**,
11850 (1965).

PC$_2$H$_7$O$_4$

① 2-Hydroxyethylphosphonic acid
HOCH$_2$CH$_2$P(O)(OH)$_2$

② (C$_2$H$_5$O)$_2$PONa + CH$_2$—CH$_2$ $\xrightarrow{\text{CH}_3\text{COOH}}$
$\underset{\text{O}}{\diagdown\diagup}$

③ Oil. (120~130°/9 decomp.).

⑥ Dokl. **56**, 49 (1947).   J. Gen. Chem.
USSR **16**, 1481 (1946).

PC$_2$H$_7$S$_2$

① Dimethylphosphinodithioic acid
(CH$_3$)$_2$P(S)SH

② (CH$_3$)$_2$PSCl + CH$_3$ONa + H$_2$S $\longrightarrow$
as (CH$_3$)$_2$P(S)SNa (22.4%)
ammonium salt $\longrightarrow$ 5%

③ Crystals. [47~50°].
Unstable in air. Sol. in alkali.

④ $\longrightarrow$ Ni salt

$\longrightarrow$ ammonium salt

⑥ Gazz. chim. ital. **77**, 509 (1947).
Zhur. **32**, 3579 (1962).

PC$_2$H$_8$NO$_3$

① 2-Aminoethylphosphonic acid
H$_2$NCH$_2$CH$_2$P(O)(OH)$_2$

② (C$_2$H$_5$O)$_2$P(O)CH$_2$CH$_2$CONH$_2$ + KOH
+ Br$_2$ $\xrightarrow{\text{48% HBr}}$ 71%

C$_6$H$_4$$\diagup\diagdown$$\overset{\text{CO}}{\underset{\text{CO}}{}}$N(CH$_2$)$_2$Br

+ NaPO(OC$_4$H$_9$)$_2$ $\xrightarrow{\text{HCl}}$
NaPO(OC$_4$H$_9$)$_2$ + BrCH$_2$CH$_2$NH$_2$·HBr
$\xrightarrow{\text{HCl}}$

③ Colorless crystals. [281~282°].
Sol. in H$_2$O, insol. in EtOH. Stable to
warm aq. HCl.
Highly hygroscopic.

④ $\longrightarrow$ Ag salt
$\longrightarrow$ Zn salt

⑥ JACS **69**, 2112 (1947); **68**, 2397 (1964).
Compt. rend. **224**, 406 (1947); **224**,
919 (1947).   Nature **184**, 901 (1959).

PC$_3$Br$_2$F$_9$

① Dibromotris(trifluoromethyl)
phosphorane
(CF$_3$)$_3$PBr$_2$

② P(CF$_3$)$_3$ + Br$_2$ $\xrightarrow{\text{CH}_3\text{CN}}$

④ $\longrightarrow$ CF$_3$Br + CF$_3$PBr$_2$ + (CF$_3$)$_2$PBr
+ (CF$_3$)$_3$P + PBr$_3$

⑥ JACS **82**, 3514 (1960).   JCS **1959**,
1494.

PC$_3$Cl$_2$F$_9$

① Dichlorotris(trifluoromethyl)
phosphorane
(CF$_3$)$_3$PCl$_2$

② (CF$_3$)$_3$P + Cl$_2$ $\xrightarrow{-45°}$

③ (107°) estimated. [24.0~25.5°].

Explodes when distd. at 760 mmHg.
IR: JCS **1959**, 1494.
⑥ Kaufman 987.   JCS **1953**, 1565.

PC_3F_9

① Tris(trifluoromethyl)phosphine
   $(CF_3)_3P$
② CF_3I + white P $\xrightarrow[\text{}]{230° \text{ in autoclave}}$ 70%
   CF_3I + red phosphorus
   $\xrightarrow[260° \text{ in sealed tube}]{}$ 54%
③ Liq. (17.3°).
   Stable to air-free H_2O at room temp.,
   inflam. in air.
   IR: Can. J. Chem. **40**, 393 (1962).
   $+ I_2 \xrightarrow{180°} CF_3I + PI_3 + CF_3PI_2$
   $+ (CF_3)_2PI$
   $+ Cl_2 \longrightarrow (CF_3)_3PCl_2$
⑥ JCS **1953**, 1565.

PC_3F_9O

① Tris(trifluoromethyl)phosphine
   oxide
   $(CF_3)_3PO$
③ (23.6°).
   Decomp. with H_2O.
   NMR: JCS **1963**, 960.
⑥ Kaufman 986.

$PC_3H_3F_6$

① Methylbis(trifluoromethyl)phos-
   phine
   $CH_3(CF_3)_2P$
② $(CF_3)_3P + CH_3I \xrightarrow{240°}$ 54%
③ Colorless liq. (35.2°).
④ The compound gives no indication
   of complex formation with carbon
   disulfide or silver iodide.
⑥ JCS **1957**, 3880.

$PC_3H_3F_6O$

① Bis(trifluoromethyl)phosphinous

acid methyl ester
$(CF_3)_2P(OCH_3)$
② $(CF_3)_2P-P(CF_3)_2 + CH_3OH \longrightarrow$
③ [−78.5].
   IR: JACS **84**, 3442 (1962).

$PC_3H_3F_6O$

① Methylbis(trifluoromethyl)phos-
   phine oxide
   $(CF_3)_2P(O)CH_3$
② $CH_3P(CF_3)_2 \xrightarrow{HgO, 80°}$ 97.5%
   $(CF_3)_2POCH_3 \xrightarrow{CH_3I, 130°}$
   $(CF_3)_2P(O)CH_3$ (3.8%)
③ (129.7°). [−27.0~−26.8°].
   $\log P mm = 8.7837 + 1.75 \log T - 0.00836 T$
   $-2858/T$
   IR: JACS **84**, 3442 (1962).
④ cf. $\begin{cases} (CF_3)_2PH \xrightarrow{HgO} (CF_3)_2PH(O) \\ (CF_3)_2PH(O) \longrightarrow (CF_3)_2PH \\ \quad + (CF_3)_2P(O)OH \\ (CF_3)_2PH(O) \longrightarrow (CF_3)_2P(OH) \\ \text{(anti Arbuzov rearrangement)} \end{cases}$
   $(CF_3)_2P(O)CH_3 \longrightarrow$
   $(CF_3)_2P(OCH_3)CH_3$

$PC_3H_4NO_3$

① (2-Cyanovinyl)phosphonic acid
   $NCCH=CHP(O)(OH)_2$
② $NCCH=CHP(O)[OSi(CH_3)_3]_2$
   $\xrightarrow{H_2O \text{ or } CH_3OH \text{ hydrolysis}}$ 30%
④ $+ (C_6H_{11})_2NH \longrightarrow$ dicyclohexyl
   amine salt
⑥ JOC **28**, 2975 (1963).

$PC_3H_6Cl_3O$

① Tris(chloromethyl)phosphine oxide
   $(ClCH_2)_3PO$
② $(ClCH_2)_3P \xrightarrow{40\% HNO_3}$
③ [78°].
   NMR: J. Chem. Eng. Data **7**, 307

(1962).

⑥ Kosolapoff 113.   J. Appl. Chem. **12**, 397 (1962).

PC$_3$H$_6$Cl$_3$OS$_2$

① Methylphosphonodithioic acid
   O-2,2,2-trichloroethyl ester
   CH$_3$P(S)(OCH$_2$CCl$_3$)SH

② (CH$_3$PS$_2$)$_2$ + Cl$_3$CCH$_2$OH $\longrightarrow$
   quantitative

③ [42~43°].

④ + SO$_2$Cl$_2$ $\longrightarrow$ CH$_3$P(S)(OCH$_2$CCl$_3$)Cl

⑥ JOC **27**, 3832 (1962).

PC$_3$H$_6$Cl$_3$O$_3$

① Trichloromethylphosphonic acid
   dimethyl ester
   Cl$_3$CP(O)(OCH$_3$)$_2$

② (CH$_3$O)$_3$P + CCl$_4$ $\longrightarrow$

   Cl$_3$CP(O)(OH)$_2$ + CH$_2$N$_2$ $\xrightarrow{\text{(C}_2\text{H}_5)_2\text{O}}$

③ White solid. (121~122°/12). [37°].
   n_D 1.4615 (50°). d 1.4810 (50°/0°).
   Sol. in org. solvents.

⑥ Zhur. **24**, 1465 (1954). J. Gen. Chem.
   USSR **16**, 1521(1946). Compt. rend.
   acad. Sci. URSS **55**, 219 (1949).

PC$_3$H$_6$F$_3$

① Dimetyltrifluoromethyl phosphine
   (CH$_3$)$_2$CF$_3$P

② (CH$_3$)$_3$P + CF$_3$I $\longrightarrow$ 50%

③ Colorless liq. (46.8°).

④ + CH$_3$I $\longrightarrow$ [(CH$_3$)$_3$(CF$_3$)P$^+$]I$^-$
   + NiCl$_2$ $\longrightarrow$ [(CH$_3$)$_2$PCF$_3$]$_2$NiCl$_2$

⑥ JCS **1956**, 3631. Can. J. Chem. **39**, 595
   (1961).

PC$_3$H$_6$N

① Cyanoethylphosphine
   NCCH$_2$CH$_2$PH$_2$

② CH$_2$=CHCN + PH$_3$ $\longrightarrow$ 6%

③ (54~55°/9). n_D 1.4831 (25°).

④ + $\xrightarrow{\text{di-}t\text{-butylperoxide}}$

   NCCH$_2$CH$_2$PH (*cyclo*-C$_6$H$_{11}$)
   + NCCH$_2$CH$_2$P (*cyclo*-C$_6$H$_{11}$)$_2$

) + HC≡C(CH$_2$)$_4$CH$_3$ $\longrightarrow$
   NCCH$_2$CH$_2$P[CH=CH(CH$_2$)$_4$CH$_3$]$_2$

⑥ JACS **80**, 6690 (1958); **81**, 1103 (1959).
   JOC **26**, 5138 (1961).

PC$_3$H$_7$Cl$_2$

① Propylphosphonous dichloride
   C$_3$H$_7$PCl$_2$

② PCl$_3$ + Cd(C$_3$H$_7$)$_2$ $\xrightarrow{\text{(C}_2\text{H}_5)_2\text{O, } -20\sim35°}$
   44%

③ (140~142°), (43°/15). n_D 1.4842 (20°).
   d 1.1664 (20°/0°).
   Obnoxious odor.

⑥ Trudy Kazan. Khim. Tekhnol. Inst.
   in S. M. Kirova **23**, 138 (1957);
   CA **52**, 9946 c (1958).   Kosolapoff
   53.

PC$_3$H$_7$Cl$_2$O

① Propylphosphonic dichloride
   C$_3$H$_7$P(O)Cl$_2$

② C$_3$H$_7$P(O)(OC$_4$H$_9$)$_2$ + PCl$_5$ $\xrightarrow{150°}$

③ (88~90°/50), (78°/14). n_D 1.4621(20°).
   d 1.286.
   NMR: J. Phys. Radium **24**, 108 (1963)

④ + PCl$_5$ $\longrightarrow$ C$_2$H$_5$CCl$_2$P$^+$Cl$_3$·PCl$_6$$^-$
   $\xrightarrow{\text{SO}_2}$ C$_2$H$_5$CCl$_2$P(O)Cl$_2$

⑥ Ber. **93**, 765 (1960). Dopovidi Akad.
   Nauk. Ukr. RSR **1960**, 1086; CA **56**,
   15142 (1962). Kosolapoff. 73.

PC$_3$H$_7$Cl$_2$O

① Bis(chloromethyl)methylphosphine
   oxide
   (ClCH$_2$)$_2$P(O)CH$_3$

② (ClCH$_2$)$_3$P $\xrightarrow{\text{HCl}}$ 80%

③ (116~117°/1.5). [49~50°].
   IR: Dokl. **143**, 592 (1962).

PC$_3$H$_7$O$_5$

① 3-Phosphonopropionic acid
   HOOCCH$_2$CH$_2$P(O)(OH)$_2$

② (C$_4$H$_9$O)$_2$P(O)CH$_2$CH$_2$CN $\xrightarrow{\text{HCl}}$ 97%

   (C$_2$H$_5$O)$_2$P(S)CH$_2$CH$_2$CO$_2$CH$_3$ $\xrightarrow{\text{HCl}}$

③ Plates. [178~180°].
   Sol. in H$_2$O.

⑥ Izv. OKhN **1946**, 179 ; **1954**, 636. Ber.
   59, 1119 (1926). JACS **82**, 593(1960).

PC$_3$H$_8$BrO$_3$

① (3-Bromopropyl)phosphonic acid
   Br(CH$_2$)$_3$P(O)(OH)$_2$

② (C$_2$H$_5$O)$_2$P(O)(CH$_2$)$_3$Br $\xrightarrow{\text{HBr}}$ 80~90%

③ Colorless plates. [107~108°].
   Sol. in H$_2$O, almost insol. in C$_6$H$_6$.

④ + C$_6$H$_5$NH$_2$ $\longrightarrow$
   C$_6$H$_5$NH(CH$_2$)$_3$P(O)(OH)$_2$

⑥ JACS **66**, 1511 (1944).   Ann. **655**, 59
   (1962).

PC$_3$H$_8$Cl

① Ethylmethylphosphinous chloride
   (C$_2$H$_5$)(CH$_3$)PCl

② (C$_2$H$_5$)(CH$_3$)PCl$_3$·AlCl$_3$ $\xrightarrow{\text{Al/KCl}}$ 68.3%

③ (49~51°/15), (157~160°). n_D 1.474
   (20°).
   d 1.0467 (20°).
   NMR : J. Chem. Eng. Data **7**, 307
   (1962).

④ + S $\xrightarrow{45~50°}$ (CH$_3$)(C$_2$H$_5$)P(S)Cl
   (83.7%)

⑥ Kosolapoff 54. JINC **24**, 1073 (1962).
   Zhur. **28**, 2963 (1958).

PC$_3$H$_8$ClO

① Ethylmethylphosphinic chloride
   (C$_2$H$_5$)(CH$_3$)P(O)Cl

② [(C$_2$H$_5$)(CH$_3$)P(S)]$_2$ + SOCl$_2$ $\xrightarrow{\text{CCl}_4}$ 88%

③ (99~102°/15). n_D 1.4702 (20°).

⑥ Ber. **94**, 3056 (1961).

PC$_3$H$_8$ClO

① 3-Chloropropylphosphonic acid
   ClCH$_2$CH$_2$CH$_2$P(O)(OH)$_2$

② ClCH$_2$CH$_2$CH$_2$P(O)(OC$_4$H$_9$)$_2$ $\xrightarrow{\text{HCl}}$

③ Crystals. [101~103°].

⑥ Ann. **655**, 59 (1962).

PC$_3$H$_8$ClOS$_2$

① Methylphosphonodithioic acid
   O-2-chloroethyl ester
   CH$_3$P(S)(OCH$_2$CH$_2$Cl)SH

② (CH$_3$PS$_2$)$_2$ + ClCH$_2$CH$_2$OH $\longrightarrow$
   quantitative

③ (58°/0.007).

④ + SO$_2$Cl$_2$ $\longrightarrow$
   CH$_3$P(S)(OCH$_2$CH$_2$Cl)Cl

⑥ JOC **27**, 3832 (1962).

PC$_3$H$_8$ClO$_2$

① Methylphosphonochloridic acid ethyl
   ester
   CH$_3$P(O)(OC$_2$H$_5$)Cl

② PCl$_3$ + CH$_3$Cl + AlCl$_3$ $\xrightarrow{\text{C}_2\text{H}_5\text{OH}}$ 47.5%

   CH$_3$P(O)Cl$_2$ + C$_2$H$_5$OH $\xrightarrow{(\text{C}_2\text{H}_5)_3\text{N}}$ 63%

   CH$_3$P(S)(OC$_2$H$_5$)$_2$ + COCl$_2$ $\longrightarrow$

   CH$_3$P(O)(OH)OC$_2$H$_5$ + SO$_2$Cl$_2$ $\longrightarrow$

③ Colorless liq. (33°/0.9). n_D 1.4320
   (25°).
   Sol. in org. solvents.

④ + R$_1$R$_2$NH $\longrightarrow$
   CH$_3$P(O)(OC$_2$H$_5$)NR$_1$R$_2$
   $\begin{pmatrix} \text{R}_1, \text{R}_2=\text{C}_2\text{H}_5, \ s\text{-C}_4\text{H}_9, \ n\text{-C}_4\text{H}_9 \\ \text{R}_1=\text{H} \quad \text{R}_2=n\text{-C}_4\text{H}_9,, \ s\text{-C}_4\text{H}_9, \\ t\text{-C}_4\text{H}_9, \ \text{C}_6\text{H}_5 \end{pmatrix}$
   + NO$_2$C$_6$H$_4$ONa $\longrightarrow$
   CH$_3$P(O)(OC$_2$H$_5$)(OC$_6$H$_4$NO$_2$)
   + C$_2$H$_5$SH $\xrightarrow{(\text{C}_2\text{H}_5)_3\text{N}}$
   CH$_3$P(O)(OC$_2$H$_5$)SC$_2$H$_5$

⑥ JOC **28**, 329 (1963).   JCS **1956**, 2463 ;
   1961, 238, 3067. JACS **79**, 3570 (1957).

PC₃H₈ClS

① Ethylmethylphosphinothioic
   chloride
   $(C_2H_5)(CH_3)P(S)Cl$

② $[(C_2H_5)(CH_3)PS]_2 + SO_2Cl_2 \xrightarrow{C_6H_6}$
   (82%)

   $(C_2H_5)(CH_3)PCl + S \xrightarrow{45\sim50°} 83.7\%$

③ (90~91°/11). n_D 1.531 (20°). d 1.1815
   (20°).

⑥ Ber. **94**, 3051 (1961).   Zhur. **28**, 2963
   (1958).

PC₃H₈F₃

① Ethyltrifluoromethylphosphorane
   $(C_2H_5)(CH_3)PF_3$

② $(CH_3)(C_2H_5)PCl + SbF_3 \longrightarrow 59.9\%$

③ (81~82°/760). n_D 1.3470 (20°).
   d 1.1875. (20°).

⑥ Zhur. **32**, 301 (1962).

PC₃H₈IO₃

① (Iodomethyl) phosphonic acid
   ethyl ester
   $ICH_2P(O)(OH)(OC_2H_5)$

② $(C_2H_5O)_3P + CH_2I_2 \longrightarrow$

③ White crystals. [46~49°].

④ $+ HCl + C_5H_{11}NH_2 \longrightarrow$
   $ICH_2P(O)(OH)_2 \cdot 2\,C_5H_{11}NH_2$

⑥ JCS **1955**, 1756.

PC₃H₉

① Isopropylphosphine
   $i\text{-}C_3H_7PH_2$

② $i\text{-}C_3H_7I + PH_4I + ZnO \longrightarrow$

③ Colorless liq. (41°).
   Sol. in org. solvents. Decomp. in air.

⑥ Ber. **6**, 292 (1873).

PC₃H₉

① Ethylmethylphosphine
   $(CH_3)(C_2H_5)PH$

② $(CH_3)(C_2H_5)P(S)-P(S)(CH_3)(C_2H_5)$

   $+ LiAlH_4 \longrightarrow 44\%$

③ Colorless liq. (54.5°). [−160°].
   Sol. in org. solvents.
   NMR: Ber. **94**, 3056 (1961). J. Chem.
   Eng. Data **7**, 307 (1962).

PC₃H₉

① Trimethylphosphine
   $(CH_3)_3P$

② $CH_3MgI + PCl_3 \longrightarrow$

   $CH_3Li + PCl_3 \xrightarrow{-20\sim-10°}$

③ Colorless liq. (38.4). [−85.9°].
   NMR: J. Chem. Eng. Data **7**, 307
   (1962).

④ $+ (CH_3)_2AsI \longrightarrow$
   $[(CH_3)_2AsP^+(CH_3)_3]I^-$
   $+ CS_2 \longrightarrow (CH_3)_3PCS_2$
   $+ M(CO)_6 \xrightarrow{70°} (CH_3)_3PM(CO)_5,$
   $\qquad\qquad\qquad M=Mo, W$
   $+ BX_3 \xrightarrow{0°} BX_3 \cdot P(CH_3)_3, X=Cl, Br$

⑥ JACS **62**, 1622 (1940).   Z. anorg.
   allg. Chem. **277**, 271 (1954).   Can.
   J. Chem. **40**, 393 (1962).   JOC **27**,
   2573 (1962).

PC₃H₉

① n-Propylphosphine
   $n\text{-}C_3H_7PH_2$

② $n\text{-}C_3H_7Br + LiPH_2 \longrightarrow 69\%$

③ Colorless liq. (54°/750).
   Sol. in org. solvents.

④ $+ HCHO + HCl \longrightarrow$
   $[n\text{-}C_3H_7P(CH_2OH)_3]Cl$
   $+ CH_3COC_6H_5 + HCl \longrightarrow$
   $n\text{-}C_3H_7P[C(CH_3)(OH)C_6H_5]_2$

⑥ Ber. **87**, 919 (1954).   Zhur. **31**, 2729
   (1961).

PC₃H₉Br₂

① Dibromotrimethylphosphorane
   $(CH_3)_3PBr_2$

② $(CH_3)_3P(O) + PBr_5 \xrightarrow{CHCl_3} 93\%$

③ [277~278°].
⑥ Z. Elektrochem. **64**, 598 (1960).

PC₃H₉ClNO

① Trimethylphosphonamidic chloride
$CH_3P(O)(Cl)N(CH_3)_2$
② $CH_3POCl_2 + (CH_3)_2NH \longrightarrow$ 74%
③ (74~75°/1.5). n_D 1.4698 (20°).
d 1.2152 (20°).

④ + $HOCH_2CH_2N(CH_3)_2 \xrightarrow{(C_2H_5)_3N}$
$CH_3P(O)[OCH_2CH_2N(CH_3)_2]N(CH_3)_2$
+ $HOCH_2CH_2N(C_2H_5)_2 \xrightarrow{(C_2H_5)_3N}$
$CH_3P(O)[OCH_2CH_2N(C_2H_5)_2]N(CH_3)_2$
+ $HSCH_2CH_2N(C_2H_5)_2 \xrightarrow{(C_2H_5)_3N}$
$CH_3P(O)[SCH_2CH_2N(C_2H_5)_2]N(CH_3)_2$

⑥ Ann. chim. **50**, 1819 (1960). Zhur. **31**, 1628 (1961).

PC₃H₉Cl₂

① Dichlorotrimethylphosphorane
$(CH_3)_3PCl_2$
② $(CH_3)_3P(O) + SOCl_2 \xrightarrow{CHCl_3}$ 95%
③ [267~268°].
⑥ Z. Elektrochem. **64**, 598 (1960).

PC₃H₉I₂

① Diiodotrimethylphosphorane
$(CH_3)_3PI_2$
② $(CH_3)_3P + I_2 \xrightarrow{C_6H_6}$ 89%
③ [279~280°(decomp.)].
⑥ Z. Elektrochem. **64**, 598 (1960).

PC₃H₉O

① 3-Hydroxypropylphosphine
$HOCH_2CH_2CH_2PH_2$
② $CH_2=CHCH_2OH + PH_3 \longrightarrow$ 26%
③ Colorless liq. (139~140°). n_D 1.4950 (20°). d 1.004 (20°/4°).
④ + 96% $HNO_3 \longrightarrow$
$HOOCCH_2CH_2P(O)(OH)_2$
+ 30% $H_2O_2 \longrightarrow$

$HOCH_2CH_2CH_2P(O)(OH)_2$
⑥ Compt. rend. **56**, 49 (1947). JACS **74**, 3282 (1952).

PC₃H₉O

① Trimethylphosphine oxide
$(CH_3)_3PO$
② $3 CH_3MgBr + POCl_3 \longrightarrow$
③ [140~141°].
⑥ Acta. Chem. Scand. **13**, 1753 (1959).
Kaufman 985. Zhur. **30**, 1976(1960).
Anal. Chem. **34**, 873 (1962).

PC₃H₉O

① Dimethylhydroxymethylphosphine
$(CH_3)_2(HOCH_2)P$
② $(CH_3)_2PH + (HCHO)_3 \xrightarrow{65~67°}$ 80.7%
③ (50~51°/10). n_D 1.5011 (20°). d 0.9931 (20°).
⑥ Dokl. **139**, 1359 (1961); CA **56**, 1475 (1962).

PC₃H₉OS

① Ethylmethylphosphinothioic acid
$C_2H_5(CH_3)P(S)OH$
② $C_2H_5(CH_3)POCl + NaHS \xrightarrow{acidification}$
$C_2H_5(CH_3)POCl + P_2S_2 \xrightarrow{hydrolysis}$
$C_2H_5(CH_3)POMgX + S \xrightarrow{acidification}$
$C_2H_5MgBr + CH_3P(S)Br_2 \longrightarrow$
③ (73~79°/0.06). n_D 1.5117 (20°).
⑥ Roczniki. Chem. **36**, 175 (1962). Ber. **94**, 3043 (1961).

PC₃H₉OS₂

① Isopropylphosphonodithioic acid
i-$C_3H_7P(S)(OH)SH$
② i-$C_3H_7MgBr + P_2S_5 \xrightarrow{NiCl_2}$
$[i$-$C_3H_7P(OH)SS]_2Ni$
$\xrightarrow{(NH_4)_2S, \text{ acidification}}$
③ Oil.
Unstable.

④ ⟶ Ni salt.

⑥ Gazz. chim. ital. **76**, 167 (1946).

PC₃H₉OS₂

① Methylphosphonodithioic acid
   O-ethyl ester
   $CH_3P(S)(OC_2H_5)SH$

② $(CH_3PS_2)_2 + C_2H_5OH \longrightarrow$
   quantitative

③ $(32°/0.05)$. n_D 1.5440 (22.5°).

④ + anhyd. $NH_3 \longrightarrow$
   $CH_3P(S)(OC_2H_5)SNH_4$

⑥ JOC **27**, 3832 (1962).

PC₃H₉O₂

① Bis(hydroxymethyl)methylphos-
   phine
   $(HOCH_2)_2CH_3P$

② $CH_3PH_2 + (HCHO)_n \xrightarrow[82\sim85°]{\text{in steel bomb}} 83\%$

③ $(89\sim91°/3)$. n_D 1.5325 (20°). d 1.157
   (20°).

④ + 6% $H_2O_2 \longrightarrow CH_3P(O)(CH_2OH)_2$

⑥ Dokl. **139**, 1359 (1961). CA **56**, 1457 g
   (1962).

PC₃H₉O₂

① Dimethylphosphinic acid methyl
   ester
   $(CH_3)_2P(O)OCH_3$

② $(CH_3)_2POCl + NaOCH_3 \xrightarrow{C_6H_6} 78\%$

③ Colorless liq. (78.5~79.5°). n_D 1.4299
   (22°).
   Sol. in org. solvents.

⑥ Ber. **90**, 1656 (1957).

PC₃H₉O₂

① Ethylmethylphosphinic acid
   $(CH_3)(C_2H_5)P(O)(OH)$

② $(CH_3)_2N(C_2H_5)P(O)Cl + CH_3MgCl$
   $\xrightarrow{\text{ether}} 15\%$
   $CH_3(C_2H_5)P(S)P(S)(CH_3)C_2H_5 + HgO$
   $+ H_2O \longrightarrow 81\%$

③ $(170\sim172°/11)$. $[7\sim8°]$. n_D 1.4505
   (20°).

⑥ JCS **1958**, 2995.   Ber. **94**, 3051 (1961).

PC₃H₉O₂

① Methylphosphonous acid ethyl ester
   $CH_3P(O)(H)OC_2H_5$

② $CH_3PCl_2 + C_2H_5OH \xrightarrow[(C_2H_5)_2O]{(C_2H_5)_3N}$
   $CH_3P(OC_2H_5)N(C_2H_5)_2 \xrightarrow{H_2O} 32\%$

③ Colorless liq. (70°/15). n_D 1.4221(20°).
   d 1.0511 (20°).
   Stable in dry atm.

④ + C_4H_9OH + Na (small amt.) $\longrightarrow$
   $CH_3P(O)(H)OC_4H_9$
   + $HOCH_2CH_2OH$ + Na (small amt.)
   $\longrightarrow [CH_3P(O)(H)O]_2(CH_2)_2$
   + S $\xrightarrow{\text{dioxane}} CH_3P(S)(OC_2H_5)OH$
   + $CH_2[N(C_2H_5)_2]_2 \longrightarrow$
   $CH_3P(O(C_2H_5))CH_2N(C_2H_5)_2$

⑥ Zhur. **31**, 179 (1961); **32**, 1974
   (1962).

PC₃H₉O₂S

① Methylphosphonothioic acid
   O-ethyl ester
   $CH_3P(OC_2H_5)OSH$

② $CH_3(H)P(O)(OC_2H_5) + S \longrightarrow 85\%$
   $CH_3PSCl_2 + C_2H_5OH + KOH \longrightarrow$
   83%
   $CH_3P(S)(OC_2H_5)_2 + KOH \longrightarrow 87\%$
   $CH_3P(S)(OC_2H_5)Cl + NaOHaq \longrightarrow$
   88.5%

③ $(63°/0.22)$. n_D 1.4951 (20°). d 1.1760
   (20°). IR: Nature **192**, 1283 (1961).

④ + $NH(C_6H_{11})_2 \longrightarrow CH_3P(O)(OC_2H_5)$
   $SNH_2(C_6H_{11})_2$

⑥ JCS **1962**, 3824.   JACS **81**, 148 (1959).
Zhur. **31**, 179 (1961); **30**, 2763, (1960).

PC₃H₉O₂S

① Methylphosphonothioic acid
   O, O-dimethyl ester

CH₃P(S)(OCH₃)₂

② CH₃SCl₂ + CH₃OH $\xrightarrow{BF_3\cdot(C_2H_5)_2O}$ 71%

   CH₃PSCl₂ + CH₃OH + Na $\longrightarrow$ 92%

③ (52~52.5°/8). n_D 1.4743 (20°).

   d 1.1435 (20).

   NMR: Compt. rend. 253, 644 (1961).

④ + SO₂Cl₂ $\xrightarrow{reflux}$ CH₃P(O)(OCH₃)Cl

   + COCl₂ $\longrightarrow$ CH₃P(O)(OCH₃)Cl

   + PCl₅ $\longrightarrow$ CH₃POCl₂ + CH₃PSCl₂

   + PCl₃ + POCl₃ + PSCl₃

⑥ JCS 1962, 3824; 1961, 238. Bull. soc.
   chim. France 1961, 1222.

PC₃H₉O₃

① Tris(hydroxymethyl)phosphine
   (HOCH₂)₃P

② PH₃ + (HCHO)₃ $\xrightarrow{100°}$ 94%

   P(CH₂OH)₄Cl $\xrightarrow{N(C_2H_5)_3}$

③ Needle crystals. (111~113°/2.5).
   [52.8°]. n_D 1.5320 (20). d 1.1601 (20°
   /4°).

   Very hygroscopic.

④ + 7% H₂O₂ $\longrightarrow$ (HOCH₂)₃PO

⑥ Dokl. 139, 1359 (1961); CA 56, 1475
   (1962). Zhur. 32, 553 (1962).

PC₃H₉O₃

① Methylphosphonic acid dimethyl
   ester
   CH₃P(O)(OCH₃)₂

② (CH₃O)₃P + CH₃Br $\longrightarrow$

   (CH₃O)₃P + CH₃I $\longrightarrow$

③ Colorless oil. (67°/12). n_D 1.4105
   (20°). d 1.168 (20°/20°).

   Sol. in org. solvents.

   NMR: J. Chem. Eng. Data 7, 307
   (1962).

④ + COCl₂ $\longrightarrow$ CH₃P(O)(OCH₃)Cl

   + C₁₂H₂₅Br $\xrightarrow{200°}$

   CH₃P(O)(OCH₃)OC₁₂H₂₅

   + CH₃P(O)(OC₁₂H₂₅)₂

+ C₁₂H₂₅I $\xrightarrow{160~170°}$

   CH₃P(O)(OCH₃)OC₁₂H₂₅

   + CH₃P(O)(OC₁₂H₂₅)₂

+ CH₃COOC₁₂H₂₅ $\xrightarrow{250°,\ 18\ hr}$

   CH₃P(O)(OCH₃)OC₁₂H₂₅

   + CH₃P(O)(OC₁₂H₂₅)₂

⑥ Izv. OKhN 1947, 459. JCS 1955, 2964;
   1963, 1004.   JOC 27, 1005 (1962).

PC₃H₉O₃

① Isopropylphosphonic acid
   i-C₃H₇P(O)(OH)₂

② i-C₃H₇P(O)(OC₂H₅)₂ $\xrightarrow{HCl}$

   i-C₃H₇P(O)(OC₄H₉)₂ $\xrightarrow{HCl}$

   i-C₃H₇P(O)Cl₂ + H₂O $\longrightarrow$

③ Waxy solid. [74~75°].
   Slightly sol. in H₂O.

⑥ Ber. 6, 292, 301, 303 (1873); 32, 1572
   (1899).   JACS 76, 4172 (1954); 75,
   3379 (1953).

PC₃H₉O₄

① Tris(hydroxymethyl)phosphine
   oxide
   (HOCH₂)₃PO

② (HOCH₂)₄PCl $\xrightarrow{BaCO_3\ aq.\ soln.}$

   (HOCH₂)₄PCl $\xrightarrow{(C_2H_5)_3N\ 60°}$ 100%

   (HOCH₂)₃P $\xrightarrow{H_2O_2}$ 95%

③ [56~58°] (EtOH).
   Very hygroscopic.

⑥ Dokl. 139, 1359 (1961). Kosolapoff
   113.   Khim-Tekhnol. Inst. 1960,
   No. 29, 20; CA 58, 547 (1963).
   Zhur. 32, 553 (1962). Can. J.
   Chem. 41, 821 (1963).

PC₃H₉S

① Trimethylphosphine sulfide
   (CH₃)₃P(S)

② CH₃₂P(S)Br + CH₃MgBr $\xrightarrow{10~25°}$ 90%

③ [155~156°] (cyclohexane).
  IR: J. Phys. Chem. **65**, 1132 (1961);
    66, 2579 (1962).
  UV: Inorg. Chem. **2**, 192 (1963).
  NMR: J. Chem. Eng. Data 7, 307
    (1962).   JOC **27**, 2573 (1962).
⑤ Kosolapoff 117. JOC **28**, 2430 (1963).
  JINC **24**, 1073 (1962).

PC₃H₉Se

① Trimethylphosphine selenide
  $(CH_3)_3PSe$

② $PCl_3 + 3 CH_3MgBr \xrightarrow{\quad} \xrightarrow{Se}$
③ [140°].
  IR: Inorg. Chem. **2**, 192 (1963).
⑥ Kosolapoff 118.   J. Chem. Eng. Data
  8, 226 (1963).

PC₃H₁₀NO₃

① (3-Aminopropyl)phosphonic acid
  $H_2NCH_2CH_2CH_2P(O)(OH)_2$

② $(C_4H_9O)_2P(O)CH_2CH_2CN \xrightarrow{Pd-BaSO_4 \; HCl}$
  18%
  $BrCH_2CH_2CH_2P(O)(OH)_2 + NH_4OH$
    $\longrightarrow$ 36.5%
③ Colorless needles. [274°].
⑥ JACS **69**, 2112 (1947).

PC₃H₁₁ClN

① *P*-(Trimethyl)aminophosphonium
  chloride
  $[H_2NP(CH_3)_3]Cl$
② $(CH_3)_3P + NH_2Cl \longrightarrow$ 24%
③ [122°].
⑥ Ber. **93**, 405 (1960).

PC₃F₁₁

① Difluorotris(trifloromethyl)phos-
  phorane
  $(CF_3)_3PF_2$

② $(CF_3)_3P + SF_4 \xrightarrow{25°}$
③ (20°). [−102°].

IR: Inorg. Chem. **2**, 230 (1963).
NMR: Inorg. Chem. **2**, 613 (1963).
④ $+ PF_5 \xrightarrow{100°} (CF_3)_3PF_4$
  $+ I \xrightarrow{120°} CF_2I_2$ (30%)

PC₄H₃Cl₂F₆

① Bis(2-chloro-1,1,2-trifluoroethyl)
  phosphine
  $(HCFClCF_2)_2PH$
② $CFCl=CF_2 + PH_3 \longrightarrow$ 6%
③ Colorless liq. (138~142°).
  Spont. inflam.
⑥ JACS **81**, 4801 (1959).

PC₄H₃F₈

① Bis(1,1,2,2-tetrafluoroethyl)phos-
  phine
  $(HCF_2CF_2)_2PH$
② $CF_2=CF_2 + PH_3 \longrightarrow$ 7%
③ Colorless liq. (91~92°).
  Spont. inflam.
⑥ JACS **81**, 4801 (1959).

PC₄H₅F₆O

① Bis(trifluoromethyl)phosphinous
  acid ethyl ester
  $(F_3C)_2P(OC_2H_5)$
② $P_2(CF_3)_4 + C_2H_5OH \longrightarrow$ 98.5%
  $(CF_3)_2PCl + C_2H_5OH \longrightarrow$
③ Unstable.
  IR: JACS **84**, 3442 (1962).
  NMR: JCS 1963, 960.
⑥ JCS **1959**, 375; JCS **1963**, 960.

PC₄H₇Cl₂O₂

① Vinylphosphonochloridic acid 2-
  chloroethyl ester
  $CH_2=CHP(O)(OCH_2CH_2Cl)Cl$
② $CH_2=CHP(O)(OCH_2CH_2Cl)_2 + PCl_5$
    $\longrightarrow$ 62%
③ (94~100°/1).

④ + CH$_3$OH $\xrightarrow{\text{(C}_2\text{H}_5\text{)}_3\text{N}}$

   CH$_2$=CHP(O)(OCH$_2$CH$_2$Cl)(OCH$_3$)

   + (CH$_3$)$_2$NH $\xrightarrow{\text{(C}_2\text{H}_5\text{)}_3\text{N}}$

   CH$_2$=CHP(O)(OCH$_2$CH$_2$Cl)N(CH$_3$)$_2$

⑥ JOC **26**, 3270 (1961).

PC$_4$H$_7$O$_2$

① Divinylphosphinic acid
   (CH$_2$=CH)$_2$P(O)(OH)

② (CH$_2$=CH)$_2$P(O)Cl + H$_2$O ⟶ 62.5%

③ (130~132°/0.002). n_D 1.4880 (20°).
   d 1.1874 (20°).
   Very hygroscopic.

⑥ Zhur. **33**, 382 (1963).

PC$_4$H$_8$Cl$_3$O$_2$

① 1,1-Dichloroethylphosphonochloridic
   acid ethyl ester
   CH$_3$CCl$_2$P(O)(OC$_2$H$_5$)Cl

② CH$_3$CCl$_2$P(O)Cl$_2$ + C$_2$H$_5$OH $\xrightarrow{\text{C}_5\text{H}_5\text{N}}$
   61%

③ (82~83°/4). n_D 1.4698 (20°). d 1.3850
   (20°).

⑥ Dopovidi Akad. Nauk. Ukr. RSR **1960**,
   1086.   Zhur. **31**, 594 (1961).

PC$_4$H$_8$Cl$_5$

① Tetrakis(chloromethyl)phospho-
   nium chloride
   [(ClCH$_2$)$_4$P]Cl

② (HOCH$_2$)$_4$PCl + PCl$_5$ $\xrightarrow{\text{CCl}_4}$
   [(ClCH$_2$)$_3$PCH$_2$OH]Cl $\xrightarrow{\text{SOCl}_2}$ 50~60%

③ [192~193°].
   Picrate [113~114°].

⑥ Kosolapoff 87.   Zhur. **32**, 588 (1962).
   Ann. **659**, 49 (1692).   Ber. **96**, 2109
   (1963).

PC$_4$H$_9$

① Pholpholane,
   Cyclotetramethylenephosphine

CH$_2$—CH$_2$
            P—H
CH$_2$—CH$_2$

② (CH$_3$)$_2$NP(CH$_2$)$_4$BH$_3$ $\xrightarrow{\text{heating}}$ 30%

③ (105.4°). [−88°].
   IR: JACS **82**, 2148 (1960).

PC$_4$H$_9$

① Dimethylvinylphosphine
   (CH$_3$)$_2$(CH$_2$=CH)P

② CH$_2$=CHPCl$_2$ + CH$_3$MgCl ⟶ 35%

③ (67.9°).

⑥ JOC **24**, 635 (1959)

PC$_4$H$_9$ClNO

① N-Allyl-P-methylphosphonamidic
   chloride
   CH$_3$P(O)(Cl)NHCH$_2$CH=CH$_2$

② CH$_3$P(O)Cl$_2$ + NH$_2$CH$_2$CH=CH$_2$
   $\xrightarrow{\text{(C}_2\text{H}_5\text{)}_3\text{N}}$ 73.7%

③ (60~70°/0.0001). [23~24°].

⑥ Zhur. **32**, 915 (1962).

PC$_4$H$_9$Cl$_2$

① Butylphosphonous dichloride
   C$_4$H$_9$PCl$_2$

② PCl$_3$ + Cd(C$_4$H$_9$)$_2$ $\xrightarrow{\text{(C}_2\text{H}_5\text{)}_2\text{O}, \ -20\sim-35°}$
   47%
   [PCl$_3$ + AlCl$_3$ + C$_4$H$_9$Cl]
   $\xrightarrow{\text{Sb, diethyl phthalate}}$

③ (157~160°), (74°/33). n_D 1.4880 (20°),
   n_D 1.4838 (20°). d 1.1670 (20°),
   d 1.1341 (20°/0°).

⑥ Kaufman 993.   Can. J. Chem. **41**,
   2299 (1963).   Izv. OKhN **1962**, 2002.

PC$_4$H$_9$Cl$_2$

① Bis(chloromethyl)ethylphosphine
   (ClCH$_2$)$_2$C$_2$H$_5$P

② [C$_2$H$_5$P(CH$_2$Cl)$_3$]BF$_4$ $\xrightarrow{\text{base}}$ 71.6%
   [C$_2$H$_5$P(CH$_2$Cl)$_3$]Cl $\xrightarrow{\text{NaOH}}$

③ (55~57°/5).

Unstable.

⑥ Tetrahedron Letters **1961**, 724.

Angew. **72**, 211 (1960).

PC₄H₉F₂

① 1,1-Difluoro-2-methylpropyl-
phosphine

$(CH_3)_2CHCF_2PH_2$

② $(CH_3)_2C=CF_2 + PH_3 \longrightarrow$ 67%

③ Colorless liq. (75~77°).

Spont. inflam.

⑥ JACS **81**, 4801 (1959).

PC₄H₉F₄

① Butyltetrafluorophosphorane

$C_4H_9PF_4$

② $3\,C_4H_9PCl_2 + 4\,SbF_3 \longrightarrow$

③ (85~86°).

NMR: Inorg. Chem. **2**, 613 (1963).

⑥ Chem. Ind. (London) **1962**, 1868.

PC₄H₉O₄

① Acethylphosphonic acid dimethylester

$CH_3COP(O)(OCH_3)_2$

② $(CH_3O)_3P + CH_3COCl \xrightarrow{0°}$ 80%

$(CH_3O)_2POH + CH_2CO \xrightarrow[\text{in CCl}_4]{C_5H_5N}$ 5%

③ Oil. (83~85/6.5, 76~78/5, 93~95/6).

n_D 1.4210 (20°). d 1.2109 (20°/4°).

④ $+ NaHSO_3 \longrightarrow$

$CH_3C(OH)(SO_3Na)P(O)(OCH_3)_2$

$+ CH_3OH \xrightarrow{HCl} CH_3COOCH_3$

$+ HP(O)(OCH_3)_2$

$+ C_3H_7OH \xrightarrow{HCl} CH_3COOC_3H_7$

$+ HP(O)(OCH_3)_2$

⑥ Izv. OKhN **1945**, 364; **1947**, 163.

Zhur. **29**, 1219 (1959).

PC₄H₁₀Br₃

① Tribromodiethylphosphorane

$(C_2H_5)_2PBr_3$

② $[(C_2H_5)_2P(S)]_2 + Br_2 \xrightarrow{CCl_4}$ 78%

③ [103.5°].

⑥ Ann. **652**, 28 (1962).   Angew. **74**, 27
(1962).

PC₄H₁₀Cl

① Diethylphosphinous chloride

$(C_2H_5)_2PCl$

② $P-Cu + C_2H_5Cl \xrightarrow[\text{23 hr}]{440°} C_2H_5PCl_2 +$

$(C_2H_5)_2PCl$

$(C_2H_5)_2PCl_3 \cdot AlCl_3 \xrightarrow{Al/KCl}$ 66%

③ (60~70°/15), (61~62°/72). n_D 1.472
(20°). d 1.0233 (20°).

NMR: J. Chem. Eng. Data **7**, 307
(1962).

⑥ Zhur. **28**, 2963 (1958).   JINC **24**, 1073
(1962).   Helv. Chim. Acta **46**, 2026
(1963).

PC₄H₁₀ClO

① Methylpropylphosphinic chloride

$(C_3H_7)(CH_3)P(O)Cl$

② $[C_3H_7CH_3P(S)]_2 + SOCl_2 \xrightarrow{CCl_4}$ 81%

③ (113~116°/12). n_D 1.4686 (20°).

⑥ Ber. **94**, 3056 (1961).

PC₄H₁₀ClO

① Diethylphosphinic chloride

$(C_2H_5)_2P(O)Cl$

② $(C_2H_5)_2P(O)(OH) + PCl_5 \longrightarrow$ 86%

$[(C_2H_5)_2P(S)]_2 + SOCl_2 \longrightarrow$

③ (79~81°/15), (108~109.5°/16). n_D
1.4647 (20°). d 1.1394 (20°).

NMR: J. Chem. Eng. Data **7**, 307
(1962).

④ $[CH_2]_4(MgX)_2 \longrightarrow$

$(C_2H_5)_2P(O)(CH_2)_4P(O)(C_2H_5)_2$

⑥ Kaufman 993.   JCS **1959**, 3950.   JOC
27, 4444 (1962).

PC₄H₁₀ClO

① Ethylphosphinous acid chloride

ethyl ester
$C_2H_5P(OC_2H_5)Cl$
② $C_2H_5P(OC_2H_5)_2 + C_2H_5PCl_2 \longrightarrow$ 77%
③ (35~36°/18). n_D 1.4554 (20°).
④ $+ C_4H_9MgCl \longrightarrow (C_2H_5)(C_4H_9)P$
(OC_2H_5)
⑥ Ber. **95**, 2993 (1962)

PC₄H₁₀ClO₂

① Methylphosphonochloridic acid
isopropyl ester
$CH_3P(O)(OC_3H_7-i)Cl$
② $CH_3P(O)(OC_3H_7-i)SH + NaOCH_3$
$+ COCl_2 \longrightarrow$ 44%
③ Colorless liq. (37°/1.2). n_D 1.4332(25°).
Sol. in org. solvents.
④ $+ NH_2C_6H_5 \longrightarrow$
$CH_3P(O)(OC_3H_7-i)NHC_6H_5$
$+ Na + C_3H_7SH \longrightarrow$
$CH_3P(O)(OC_3H_7-i)SC_3H_7$
$+ C_2H_5ONa + H_2S$
$+ (C_6H_{11})_2NH \longrightarrow$
$CH_3P(O)(OC_3H_7-i)SNH_2(C_6H_{11})_2$
$+ C_2H_5ONa + C_2H_5OH \longrightarrow$
$CH_3P(O)(OC_3H_7-i)(OC_2H_5)$
⑥ JACS **84**, 617 (1962); **79**, 3570 (1957).
JCS **1960**, 1553.

PC₄H₁₀ClO₂

① Ethylphosphonochloridic acid ethyl
ester
$C_2H_5P(O)(OC_2H_5)Cl$
② $C_2H_5P(O)(OC_2H_5)SH + COCl_2 \longrightarrow$
75%
$C_2H_5P(O)(OC_2H_5)SH + NaOCH_3$
$+ COCl_2 \longrightarrow$
$PCl_3 + C_2H_5Cl + AlCl_3 \xrightarrow{C_2H_5OH}$ 62%
③ Colorless liq. (49~50°/3). n_D 1.4345
(25°).
Sol. in org. solvents.
⑥ JACS **84**, 617 (1962); **79**, 3570 (1957).
Chem. Ind. (London) **1960**, 1241.

PC₄H₁₀ClO₂

① Methylphosphonochloridic acid
propyl ester
$CH_3P(O)(OC_3H_7)Cl$
② $CH_3P(S)(OC_3H_7)_2 + COCl_2 \longrightarrow$
$PCl_3 + CH_3Cl + AlCl_3 \xrightarrow{C_3H_7OH}$ 32.5%
③ (46°/1.0). n_D 1.4350 (20°).
④ $+ C_6H_5NH_2 \longrightarrow$
$CH_3P(O)(OC_3H_7)NHC_6H_5$
⑥ JCS **1961**, 3067.

PC₄H₁₀ClS

① Diethylphosphinothioic chloride
$(C_2H_5)_2P(S)Cl$
② $(C_2H_5)_2PCl + S \longrightarrow$ 84.6%
③ (117~120°/15), (90~90.5°/8). n_D
1.5294. (20°). d 1.1438 (20°).
⑥ J. Chem. Eng. Data **7**, 307 (1962).
Kaufman 996. Zhur. **28**, 2963
(1958).

PC₄H₁₀Cl₃

① Trichlorodiethylphosphorane
$(C_2H_5)_2PCl_3$
② $[(C_2H_5)_2P(S)]_2 + Cl_2 \xrightarrow{CCl_4}$
③ [~65°(decomp.)].
⑥ Angew. **74**, 27 (1962).

PC₄H₁₀F₃

① Diethyltrifluorophosphorane
$(C_2H_5)_2PF_3$
② $3(C_2H_5)_2PCl + 3SbF_3 \longrightarrow$ 62.8%
③ (50°/100), (104~105°/763). n_D 1.3650
(20°). d 1.1486 (20°).
NMR: Inorg. Chem. **2**, 613 (1963).
④ $+ Sb_2S_5 \xrightarrow{160~170°} (C_2H_5)_2P(S)F$ (73%)
⑥ Chem. Ind. (London) **1962**, 1868.
Zhur. **32**, 301 (1962).

PC₄H₁₀K

① Potassium diethylphosphide
$(C_2H_5)_2PK$

② $(C_2H_5)_2PP(C_2H_5)_2 + K \xrightarrow{\text{decalin}}$

③ Yellow.

Air-sensitive.

⑤ Intermediate in prepn. of org. P compds.

⑥ Ber. **95**, 64 (1962).

PC₄H₁₀Li

① Lithium diethylphosphide

$(C_2H_5)_2PLi$

② $(C_2H_5)_2PH + LiC_6H_5 \xrightarrow{\text{ether}} 93\%$

$(C_2H_5)_2PP(C_2H_5)_2 + Li \xrightarrow{\text{THF}}$

$(C_2H_5)_2PCl + \text{excess Li} \xrightarrow{\text{THF}}$

③ Sensitive in air and moisture. Sol. in ether and dioxane, insol. in C_6H_6.

④ $+ COCl_2 \longrightarrow (C_2H_5)_2P-P(C_2H_5)_2$

$+ CH_3I \longrightarrow [(CH_3)_2(C_2H_5)_2P^+]I^-$

$+ ClCH_2CH_2Cl \longrightarrow$

$(C_2H_5)_2PCH_2CH_2P(C_2H_5)_2$

$+ CH_2\!-\!CH_2 \longrightarrow (C_2H_5)_2PCH_2CH_2OH$
$\diagdown\!\diagup$
O

⑤ Intermediate in prepn. of org. P compds.

⑥ Ber. **94**, 102 (1961); **92**, 1118, 3183 (1959). JCS **1962**, 1490.

PC₄H₁₀Na

① Sodium diethylphosphide

$NaP(C_2H_5)_2$

② $(C_2H_5)_2PP(C_2H_5)_2 + Na \longrightarrow$

⑤ Intermediate in prepn. of org. P compds.

⑥ Angew. **69**, 307 (1957).

PC₄H₁₁

① Methyl-*n*-propylphosphine

$CH_3(n\text{-}C_3H_7)PH$

② $[(CH_3)(n\text{-}C_3H_7)P(S)]_2 + LiAlH_4$
$\longrightarrow 62.8\%$

③ (78.2°). [−129.5°].

NMR: Ber. **94**, 3056 (1961). J. Chem. Eng. Data **7**, 307 (1962).

PC₄H₁₁

① Diethylphosphine

$(C_2H_5)_2PH$

② $(C_2H_5)_2PCl + K \longrightarrow 91\%$

$(C_2H_5)_2PP(C_2H_5)_2 + Li \xrightarrow{H_2O} 40\%(92\%)$

$[(C_2H_5)_2P(S)]_2 + LiAlH_4$
$\longrightarrow 70\%$

$(C_2H_5)_2POCl + LiAlH_4 \longrightarrow 20\%$

③ Colorless liq. (85°).

Sol. in org. solvents.

NMR: J. Chem. Eng. Data **7**, 307 (1962).

④ $+ CH_3COBr \xrightarrow{BaCO_3}$
$(C_2H_5)_2PCOCH_3$

$+ HI \longrightarrow [(C_2H_5)_2\overset{+}{P}H_2]\overset{-}{I}$

$+ C_6H_5Li \longrightarrow (C_2H_5)_2PLi$

$+ MX_2 \xrightarrow{C_6H_6 \text{ or } C_2H_5OH}$
$\{M[((C_2H_5)_2PH]_4X_2\}$
$M=Co, Ni, X=Cl, Br$

⑥ Ber. **85**, 239 (1952); **91**, 1583 (1958); **92**, 704 (1959); **95**, 64 (1962). JCS **1962**, 1490.

PC₄H₁₁

① *t*-Butylphosphine

$t\text{-}C_4H_9PH_2$

② $H_3P \cdot AlCl_3 + t\text{-}C_4H_9Cl \longrightarrow 50\%$

③ (54°). n_D 1.4252 (20°). d 0.7360 (20°/4°).

IR: Monatsh. **92**, 868 (1962).

⑥ Monatsh. **93**, 230 (1962).

PC₄H₁₁

① Isobutylphosphine

$i\text{-}C_4H_9PH_2$

② $PH_3 + CH_3C(CH_3)\!=\!CH_2 \xrightarrow{AIBN} 34\%$

$LiPH_2 + i\text{-}C_4H_9Br \longrightarrow 71\%$

③ Colorless liq. (78~79.6°). n_D 1.4308

(25°). d 0.693 (20°/4°).

Sol. in org. solvents.

IR: Monatsh. **92**, 868 (1961).

④ + 96% HNO_3 ⟶ $i-C_4H_9P(O)(OH)_2$

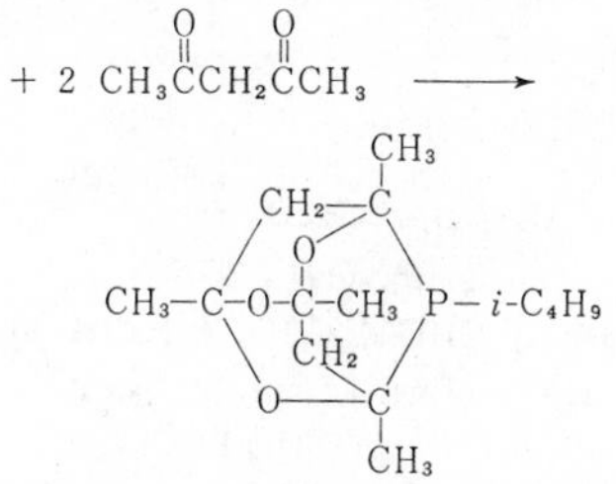

$$+ 2\ CH_3\overset{O}{\overset{\|}{C}}CH_2\overset{O}{\overset{\|}{C}}CH_3 \longrightarrow$$

⑥ Ber. **87**, 919 (1954).   JOC **26**, 5138 (1961).   JACS **74**, 3282 (1952).

PC₄H₁₁

① n-Butylphosphine
$n-C_4H_9PH_2$

② $PH_3 \cdot AlCl_3 + n-C_4H_9Cl$ ⟶ 37%
$CH_2=CHCH_2CH_2 + PH_3$ ⟶ 38%

③ (86.2~87.8°). n_D 1.4477 (20°). d 0.7693 (20°).

IR: Monatsh. **92**, 868 (1961).

④ + 96% HNO_3 ⟶ n-BuP(O)(OH)₂
+ Na + $n-C_4H_9Cl$ ⟶ $(n-C_4H_9)_2PH$

⑥ Monatsh. **93**, 2C0 (1962).   JACS **74**, 3282 (1952).

PC₄H₁₁

① Dimethylethylphosphine
$(CH_3)_2(C_2H_5)P$

② $C_2H_5PCl_2 + CH_3MgCl$ ⟶ 78%

③ (71.2°).

⑥ JOC **24**, 635 (1959).

PC₄H₁₁O

① Ethyldimethylphosphine oxide
$C_2H_5P(O)(CH_3)_2$

② $(CH_3)(C_2H_5)P[OC(CH_3)_2C_4H_9] + CH_3I$
$\overset{100°C}{\longrightarrow}$ 56%

③ (223~225°). [76~77°].

④ $\overset{heat}{\longrightarrow}$ $(CH_3)_2PH(O) + CH_2=CH_2$

⑥ Kosolapoff 115. Zhur. **31**, 3085(1961).
JOC **27**, 4404 (1962).

PC₄H₁₁O

① Diethylphosphine oxide
$(C_2H_5)_2PH(O)$

② $(C_2H_5)_2POC_4H_9$ $\xrightarrow{2\%\ H_2SO_4/dioxane,\ 20°}$ 80%

③ (52~53°/1.15). n_D 1.4549 (20°). d 0.9698 (20°).

⑥ Izv. OKhN **1963**, 1227.

PC₄H₁₁O

① Ethylmethylphosphinous acid
methyl ester
$CH_3(C_2H_5)P(OCH_3)$

② $CH_3(C_2H_5)P(OR) + CH_3OH$ + small amt. Na ⟶ 68%

③ (87.5~88.5°/7). n_D 1.4485 (20°). d 1.0043 (20°).

⑥ Zhur. **31**, 2899 (1961).

PC₄H₁₁OS

① Methylphosphinothioic acid
O-Propyl ester
$CH_3P(S)(H)OC_3H_7$

② $CH_3P(OC_3H_7)N(C_2H_5)_2 + H_2S$ ⟶ 60%

③ (69~71°/6). n_D 1.4840 (20°). d 1.0348 (20°).

⑥ Zhur. **32**, 3062 (1962).

PC₄H₁₁OS

① Diethylphosphinothioic acid
$(C_2H_5)_2P(S)OH$

② $[(C_2H_5)_2P(S)]_2S$ $\xrightarrow{hydrolysis}$

$[(C_2H_5)_2P(S)]_2O$ $\xrightarrow{hydrolysis}$

$C_2H_5MgBr + PSCl_3$ ⟶

③ Plates. [76°].

⑥ Ber. **49**, 63 (1916); **95**, 1703 (1962).

PC$_4$H$_{11}$OS$_2$

① Methylphosphonodithioic acid
   O-propyl ester
   CH$_3$P(S)(OC$_3$H$_7$)SH

② (CH$_3$PS$_2$)$_2$ + C$_3$H$_7$OH $\longrightarrow$
   quantitative

③ (50°/0.02). n_D 1.5356 (22.5°).

④ + SO$_2$Cl$_2$ $\longrightarrow$ CH$_3$P(S)(OC$_3$H$_7$)Cl

⑥ Z. Chem. 1, 289 (1961).   JOC 27, 3832
   (1962).   Zhur. 30, 2763 (1960).

PC$_4$H$_{11}$OS$_2$

① Ethylphosphonodithioic acid O-ethyl
   ester
   C$_2$H$_5$P(S)(OC$_2$H$_5$)SH

② (C$_2$H$_5$PS$_2$)$_2$ + C$_2$H$_5$OH $\longrightarrow$
   quantitative
   C$_2$H$_5$PS(SH)Cl + C$_2$H$_5$OH $\longrightarrow$

③ (38°/0.01). n_D 1.5389 (22.5°).

④ + Cl$_2$ $\longrightarrow$ C$_2$H$_5$P(S)(OC$_2$H$_5$)Cl

⑥ JOC 27, 3832 (1962).   JCS 1952, 3437.

PC$_4$H$_{11}$O$_2$

① Ethylphosphonous acid dimethyl
   ester
   C$_2$H$_5$P(OCH$_3$)$_2$

② C$_2$H$_5$PCl$_2$ + CH$_3$OH $\xrightarrow[\text{(C$_2H_5$)$_2$O}]{\text{(C$_2H_5$)$_3$N}}$ 30%

③ Mobile liq. (73.5~74.5°/225). n_D 1.4210
   (20°). d 0.9515 (20°).
   Inflame on exposure to air.

④ + CuI $\longrightarrow$ C$_2$H$_5$P(OCH$_3$)$_2$·CuI
   + CCl$_4$ $\longrightarrow$ Cl$_3$CP(CH$_3$)(O)OCH$_3$

⑥ Izv. OKhN 1952, 854.

PC$_4$H$_{11}$O$_2$

① Methylphosphonous acid propyl
   ester
   CH$_3$P(O)(H)OC$_3$H$_7$

② CH$_3$PCl$_2$ + C$_3$H$_7$OH $\xrightarrow{\text{(C$_2H_5$)$_3$N}}$

③ Colorless liq. (84°/15). n_D 1.4265(20°).
   d 1.0305 (20°).
   Stable in a dry atm.

⑥ Zhur. 31, 179 (1961).

PC$_4$H$_{11}$O$_2$

① Diethylphosphinic acid
   (C$_2$H$_5$)$_2$P(O)(OH)

② (C$_2$H$_5$)$_2$(C$_6$H$_5$)PO + NaH
   $\xrightarrow[\text{2) HCl}]{\text{1) H$_2$O$_2$}}$ 61.5%
   (C$_2$H$_5$O)$_2$P(O)H + C$_2$H$_5$MgX $\longrightarrow$ 22%
   [(C$_2$H$_5$)$_2$PS]$_2$ + HgO $\xrightarrow{\text{moist C$_6$H$_6$}}$ 76%

③ Colorless liq. (197°/22).
   Sol. in CHCl$_3$, C$_6$H$_5$, C$_2$H$_5$OH and
   H$_2$O ; slightly sol. in ligroin.

④ + PCl$_5$ $\longrightarrow$ (C$_2$H$_5$)$_2$POCl

⑥ Ber. 94, 1317 (1961) ; 95, 1703 (1962).
   JCS 1959, 3950.

PC$_4$H$_{11}$O$_2$S

① Ethylphosphonothioic acid O-ethyl
   ester
   C$_2$H$_5$P(S)(OC$_2$H$_5$)OH

② C$_2$H$_5$P(S)(OC$_2$H$_5$)$_2$ + KOH $\xrightarrow{\text{reflux}}$ 74%
   C$_2$H$_5$P(S)(OC$_2$H$_5$)Cl + NaOH aq. $\longrightarrow$
   80%
   C$_2$H$_5$P(S)(OC$_2$H$_5$)$_2$ + NaOHaq. $\xrightarrow{\text{HCl}}$

③ Liq. (84.5~85.5°/2). n_D 1.4916 (20°).
   d 1.1337 (20°).

④ + HN(C$_6$H$_{11}$)$_2$ $\longrightarrow$
   C$_2$H$_5$P(O)(OC$_2$H$_5$)SNH$_2$(C$_6$H$_{11}$)$_2$
   + NaOCH$_3$ + COCl$_2$ $\longrightarrow$
   C$_2$H$_5$P(O)(OC$_2$H$_5$)Cl
   + COCl$_2$ $\longrightarrow$ C$_2$H$_5$P(O)(OC$_2$H$_5$)Cl

⑥ JACS 81, 148 (1959).   84, 617 (1962).
   Dokl. 104, 861 (1955).   Chem. Ind.
   (Lordon) 539 (1959).

PC$_4$H$_{11}$O$_2$S

① Methylphosphonothioic acid
   O-isopropyl ester
   CH$_3$P(S)(OC$_3$H$_7$-i)OH

② CH$_3$PSCl$_2$ + i-C$_3$H$_7$OH + KOH $\longrightarrow$
   44%
   CH$_3$P(S)(OC$_3$H$_7$-i)$_2$ + KOH $\longrightarrow$
   78.2%

CH$_3$P(S)(OC$_3$H$_7$-i)Cl + NaOHaq. $\longrightarrow$
65%
CH$_3$P(O)(OC$_3$H$_7$-i)Cl + C$_2$H$_5$ONa
+ H$_2$S $\longrightarrow$

③ (84~85°/0.6). n_D 1.4810 (25°). d 1.1130
(25°/4°).

④ + NH(C$_6$H$_{11}$)$_2$ $\longrightarrow$
CH$_3$P(O)(OC$_3$H$_7$-i)SNH$_2$(C$_6$H$_{11}$)$_2$
$\overset{Na}{\longrightarrow}$ Na salt $\overset{CH_3I}{\longrightarrow}$
CH$_3$P(O)(OC$_3$H$_7$-i)SCH$_3$
+ Na + COCl$_2$ $\longrightarrow$
CH$_3$P(O)(OC$_3$H$_7$-i)Cl

⑥ JCS 1962, 3824. JACS 81, 148 (1959);
84, 617 (1962).

PC$_4$H$_{11}$O$_2$S

① Methylphosphonothioic acid O-
propyl ester
CH$_3$P(S)(OC$_3$H$_7$)OH

② CH$_3$PSCl$_2$ + C$_3$H$_7$OH + KOH $\longrightarrow$
65%

CH$_3$P(S)(OC$_3$H$_7$)$_2$ + KOH $\overset{reflux}{\longrightarrow}$
56.5%
CH$_3$P(S)(OC$_3$H$_7$)Cl + NaOH aq. $\longrightarrow$
74.5%

③ (74°/0.35). n_D 14820 (25°). d 1.124
(25°/4°).

④ + NH(C$_6$H$_{11}$)$_2$ $\longrightarrow$ CH$_3$(PO)(OC$_3$H$_7$)
SNH$_2$(C$_6$H$_{11}$)$_2$

⑥ JCS 1962, 3824. JACS 81, 148 (1959).

PC$_4$H$_{11}$O$_3$

① Methylphosphonic acid ethylmethyl
ester
CH$_3$P(O)(OCH$_3$)(OC$_2$H$_5$)

② (C$_2$H$_5$O)(CH$_3$O)$_2$P + CH$_3$I $\overset{reflux\ 1\,hr}{\longrightarrow}$
98%

③ Colorless liq. (74~75°/15).
Sol. in org. solvents.

⑥ JCS 1953, 2224; 1960, 1859.

PC$_4$H$_{11}$O$_3$

① Isobutylphosphonic acid

i-C$_4$H$_9$P(O)(OH)$_2$

② i-C$_4$H$_9$P(O)(OC$_2$H$_5$)$_2$ $\overset{HCl\ hydrolysis}{\longrightarrow}$

i-C$_4$H$_9$P(O)(OC$_4$H$_9$)$_2$ $\overset{hydrolysis}{\longrightarrow}$

③ Scales. [125~126°].
i-C$_4$H$_9$P(O)(OH)$_2$·H$_2$O

⑥ Ber. 6, 292, 301, 303 (1873); 32, 1572
(1899). J. Russ. Phys. Chem. Soc.
45, 690 (1913). Chem. Ind. (London)
1960, 999.

PC$_4$H$_{11}$O$_3$

① Butylphosphonic acid
C$_4$H$_9$P(O)(OH)$_2$

② C$_4$H$_9$P(O)(OC$_4$H$_9$)$_2$ $\overset{HCl\ hydrolysis}{\longrightarrow}$

③ Scales. [105~106°].
Sol. in aqueous media.

⑥ J. Russ. Phys. Chem. Soc. 62, 1533
(1930). JACS 67, 1180 (1945); 76,
4172 (1954); 75, 3379 (1953). JOC
25, 1447. (1960).

PC$_4$H$_{11}$S$_2$

① Diethylphosphinodithioic acid
(C$_2$H$_5$)$_2$P(S)SH

② [(C$_2$H$_5$)$_2$P(S)]$_2$S $\overset{hydrolysis}{\longrightarrow}$
(C$_2$H$_5$)$_2$PSCl + CH$_3$ONa + H$_2$S $\overset{HCl}{\longrightarrow}$
[(C$_2$H$_5$)$_2$PSS]$_2$Ni + NaOH $\longrightarrow$

③ Oil. (68.5~69°/2.5). n_D 1.5858 (20°).
d 1.1306 (20°).
Decomposed gradually and evolved
H$_2$S.

④ $\longrightarrow$ Na salt
$\longrightarrow$ Ni salt

⑥ Gazz. chim. ital. 77, 509 (1947). Ber.
95, 1703 (1962). Zhur. 13, 140,
507 (1961).

PC$_4$H$_{12}$Cl

① Tetramethylphosphonium chloride
[(CH$_3$)$_4$P]Cl

② (CH$_3$)$_4$P·picrate + conc. HCl $\longrightarrow$
quantitative

③ [396~397°].

Very hygroscopic. Easily sol. in water, insol. in acetone, CHCl$_3$ C$_6$H$_6$ and ether.

Forms a double salt with HgCl.

IR: Compt. rend. **253**, 644 (1961),

NMR: Bull. soc. chim. France **1961**, 2408.

⑥ Kosolapoff 86.

PC$_4$H$_{12}$ClO$_4$

① Tetrakis(hydroxymethyl)phosphonium chloride

[(HOCH$_2$)$_4$P]Cl

② P(CH$_2$OH)$_3$ + CH$_2$O + HCl ⟶ 70%

PH$_3$ + CH$_2$O + HCl ⟶

③ [147~150°](CH$_3$COOH).

NMR: Nature **187**, 602 (1960).

⑥ Ann. **659**, 49 (1962); **646**, 65 (1961).

Kaufman 1000.

PC$_4$H$_{12}$I

① Tetramethylphosphonium iodide

[(CH$_3$)$_4$P]I

② (CH$_3$)$_3$P + CH$_3$I ⟶

(CH$_3$)$_2$PNa·1/2 dioxane + (CH$_3$)I ⟶

③ [312~322°(decomp.)].

Forms a double salt with 2 HgCl$_2$.

IR: JCS **1961**, 5127.

UV: Ber. **96**, 2109 (1963).

⑥ Kaufman 1000. Ber. **93**, 1852 (1960).

Australian J. Chem. **15**, 555 (1962).

PC$_5$H$_{10}$Cl$_3$O$_3$

① Trichloromethylphosphonic acid diethyl ester

Cl$_3$CP(O)(OC$_2$H$_5$)$_2$

② (C$_2$H$_5$O)$_3$P + CCl$_4$ $\xrightarrow{(t\text{-}C_4H_9O)_2,\ \text{reflux 18 hr}}$

(C$_2$H$_5$O)$_3$P + CCl$_4$ $\xrightarrow{\text{UV}}$ 70%

③ Colorless liq. (128°/14). n_D 1.4620 (20°). d 1.3670 (14°/0°).

Decomposed in alcohols, sol. in org.

solvents.

IR: Chem. Ind. (London) **1960**, 1058.

⑥ Zhur. **24**, 1465 (1954). JOC **20**, 1356 (1955). JACS **77**, 1156 (1955). JCS **1961**, 3071.

PC$_5$H$_{10}$N

① 2-Cyanoethyldimethylphosphine

(CH$_3$)$_2$(NCCH$_2$CH$_2$)P

② [(CH$_3$)$_2$(NCCH$_2$CH$_2$)$_2$$\overset{+}{P}$]I$^-$ + NaOC$_2$H$_5$ ⟶ 45%

③ (34~35°/0.1). n_D 1.4800 (25°).

⑥ JACS **81**, 4803 (1959)

PC$_5$H$_{11}$Cl$_2$O

① Bis(chloromethyl)propylphosphine oxide

(ClCH$_2$)$_2$P(O)C$_3$H$_7$

② C$_3$H$_7$P(O)(CH$_2$OH)$_2$ + SOCl$_2$ $\xrightarrow{C_6H_6}$

③ (73~75°/5).

⑥ Zhur. **31**, 3421 (1961)

PC$_5$H$_{11}$Cl$_2$O$_3$

① Dichloromethylphosphonic acid diethyl ester

Cl$_2$CHP(O)(OC$_2$H$_5$)$_2$

② PCl$_3$ + CHCl$_3$ + AlCl$_3$ ⟶ complex $\xrightarrow{C_2H_5OH}$ 23%

③ Colorless liq. (82°/0.2). n_D 1.4513 (25°).

IR: Chem. Ind. (London) **1960**, 1058.

⑥ Acta Chem. Scand. **17**, 1262 (1963). JCS **1962**, 2953.

PC$_5$H$_{11}$O$_2$

① Dimethylphosphinic acid allyl ester

(CH$_3$)$_2$P(O)(OCH$_2$CH=CH$_2$)

② (CH$_3$)$_2$POCl + NaOCH$_2$CH=CH$_2$ ⟶ 65%

③ Colorless liq. (97.5~98.5°). n_D 1.4456 (22°).

⑥ Ber. **90**, 1656 (1957).

PC₅H₁₁O₃

① Allylphosphonic acid dimethyl ester
CH₂=CHCH₂P(O)(OCH₃)₂

② CH₂=CHCH₂P(O)Cl₂ + CH₃OH
$\xrightarrow{(C_2H_5)_3N}$ 53%

③ Colorless oil. (85~86°/12).

④ persulfate/bisulfite + C₄H₉Li $\longrightarrow$
polymer

⑥ J. Appl. Chem. **11**, 352 (1961).

PC₅H₁₁O₄

① Acetonylphosphonic acid dimethyl
ester
CH₃COCH₂P(O)(OCH₃)₂

② (CH₃O)₃P + CH₃COCH₂I $\longrightarrow$ 66%
(CH₃O)₃P + CH₃COCH₂Cl $\longrightarrow$

③ Colorless liq. (121~123/11). n_D 1.4337
(20°). d 1.1748 (20°).
Sol. in org. solvents. Discolour in the
light.
IR: Zhur. **26**, 1426 (1956).

⑥ Dokl. **105**, 735 (1955).   JACS **85**,
2394 (1963).

PC₅H₁₁O₅

① 2-Phosphonopropionic acid C-ethyl
ester
C₂H₅OOCCH₂CH₂P(O)(OH)₂

② HOOCCH₂CH₂P(O)(OH)₂ + C₂H₅OH
$\xrightarrow{HCl}$

③ Palates. [64.5~66°].
Sol. in org. solvents.
Highly hygroscopic.

④ + NaOH aq. $\longrightarrow$ Na salt
$\longrightarrow$ Ba salt
$\longrightarrow$ Ca salt
$\longrightarrow$ Zn salt
$\longrightarrow$ Mn salt
$\longrightarrow$ Pb salt

⑥ Ber. **59**, 1119 (1926).

PC₅H₁₂ClOS₂

① Isopropylphosphonodithioic acid
O-2-chloroethyl ester
i-C₃H₇P(S)(OCH₂CH₂Cl)SH

② (i-C₃H₇PS₂)₂ + ClCH₂CH₂OH $\longrightarrow$
quantitative

③ (57°/0.002). n_D 1.5499 (22.5°).

④ SO₂Cl₂ $\longrightarrow$
i-C₃H₇P(S)(OCH₂CH₂Cl)Cl

⑥ JOC **27**, 3832 (1962).

PC₅H₁₂ClO₂

① Isopropylphosphonochloridic acid
ethyl ester
i-C₃H₇P(O)(OC₂H₅)Cl

② PCl₃ + i-C₃H₇Cl + AlCl₃ $\xrightarrow{C_2H_5OH}$ 79%

③ Colorless liq. (53°/1.9). n_D 1.4357
(25°).
Sol. in org. solvents. Decomposed
in H₂O.

⑥ JACS **79**, 3570 (1957)

PC₅H₁₂ClO₃

① Chloromethylphosphonic acid
diethyl ester
ClCH₂P(O)(OC₂H₅)₂

② ClCH₂P(O)Cl₂ + C₂H₅OH $\longrightarrow$ 91.5%

③ (109~110°/10). n_D 1.4424 (20°).
d 1.1997 (20°).
IR: Chem. Ind. (London) **1960**, 1058.

④ + (C₂H₅O)₂PONa $\longrightarrow$
CH₂[PO(OC₂H₅)₂]

⑥ JINC **22**, 297 (1961).   Zhur. **30**, 1602
(1960).   JACS **83**, 1811 (1961).

PC₅H₁₃

① n-Pentylphosphine
n-C₅H₁₁PH₂

② n-C₅H₁₁P(O)(OC₄H₉)₂ + LiAlH₄ $\longrightarrow$
40%
n-C₅H₁₁Cl + H₃P·AlCl₃ $\longrightarrow$ 48%

③ (104°). n_D 1.4431 (20°). d 0.7796 (20°/
4°).

⑥ Monatsh. **90**, 148 (1959); **93**, 230 (1962).

PC₅H₁₃

① *n*-Butylmethylphosphine
  $CH_3(n-C_4H_9)PH$

② $[(CH_3)(n-C_4H_9)P(S)]_2 + LiAlH_4 \longrightarrow$
  79.8%

③ (112.7°). [−107°].
  NMR: Ber. **94**, 3056 (1961). J. Chem. Eng. Data. **7**, 307 (1962).

PC₅H₁₃ClNO

① *N*, *N*-Diethyl-*P*-methylphosphon-amidic chloride
  $CH_3P(O)(Cl)N(C_2H_5)_2$

② $(C_2H_5)_2NH + CH_3P(O)Cl_2 \longrightarrow$ 70%
  $CH_3PCl_2 + (C_2H_5)_2NCl \xrightarrow{\text{in } SO_2}$

③ Oil. (80~82°/0.5). n_D 1.4708 (20°).
  Sol. in org. solvents.

④ $+ HOCH_2CH_2NR_2 \xrightarrow{(C_2H_5)_3N}$
  $CH_3P(O)(OCH_2CH_2NR_2)N(C_2H_5)_2$
  $(R=CH_3, C_2H_5)$
  $+ HSCH_2CH_2N(C_2H_5)_2 \longrightarrow$
  $CH_3P(O)[SCH_2CH_2N(C_2H_5)_2]N$
  $(C_2H_5)_2$

⑥ JCS **1962**, 3591; **1961**, 2459. Ann. Chim. **50**, 1819 (1960). Zhur. **31**, 1366 (1961).

PC₅H₁₃O

① Ethylmethylphosphinous acid ethyl ester
  $(CH_3)(C_2H_5)POC_2H_5$

② $CH_3(C_2H_5)PCl + C_2H_5OH \xrightarrow{C_2H_5NC_6H_5}$
  28%

③ Liq. (67~70°/15). n_D 1.4275 (20°).
  d 0.8755 (20°).
  Fumes in air.

④ ROH + small amt. Na $\longrightarrow$
  $CH_3(C_2H_5)POR$

⑥ Zhur. **31**, 3085 (1961).

PC₅H₁₃OS

① Methylphosphonothious acid *O*-butyl ester
  $CH_3P(S)(H)OC_4H_9$

② $CH_3P(OC_4H_9)N(C_2H_5)_2 + H_2S \longrightarrow$
  80%

③ (92~93°/10). n_D 1.4840 (20°). *d* 0.9932 (20°).

④ $+ Na + (C_4H_9)_2S_2 \longrightarrow$
  $CH_3P(S)(OC_4H_9)SC_4H_9$

⑥ Zhur. **32**, 3062 (1962).

PC₅H₁₃OS₂

① Methylphosphonodithioic acid *O*-butyl ester
  $CH_3P(S)(OC_4H_9)SH$

② $(CH_3PS_2)_2 + C_4H_9OH \longrightarrow$
  quantitative

③ (47°/0.005). n_D 1.5280 (22.5°).

④ $+ SO_2Cl_2 \longrightarrow CH_3P(S)(OC_4H_9)Cl$

⑥ Z. Chem. **1**, 289 (1961). JOC **27**, 3832 (1962).

PC₅H₁₃OS₂

① Methylphosphonodithioic acid *O-sec*-butyl ester
  $CH_3P(S)(OC_4H_9-s)SH$

② $(CH_3PS_2)_2 + s-C_4H_9OH \longrightarrow$
  quantitative

③ (37°/0.003). n_D 1.5232 (22.5).

④ $+ SO_2Cl_2 \longrightarrow CH_3P(S)(OC_4H_9-s)Cl$

⑥ JOC **27**, 3832 (1962).

PC₅H₁₃OS₂

① Methylphosphonothioic acid *S*, *S*-diethyl ester
  $CH_3P(O)(SC_2H_5)_2$

② $CH_3POCl_2 + (C_2H_5)_2S_2 + Na \longrightarrow$
  41.4%
  $CH_3P(SC_2H_5)_2 + NO_2 \longrightarrow$

③ (135~138°/16). n_D 1.4523 (20°).
  d 1.1412 (20°).

Insol. in H$_2$O.

④ + ROH + Na $\xrightarrow{\text{heat}}$ CH$_3$P(O)(OR)$_2$
    R=C$_4$H$_9$, C$_6$H$_{13}$, C$_8$H$_{17}$, s-C$_8$H$_{17}$
    + (CH$_2$OH)$_2$ $\longrightarrow$ undistillable
    product (evidently a polyester)

⑥ Zhur. **31**, 3174 (1961).

PC$_5$H$_{13}$O$_2$

① Bis(hydroxymethyl)-n-propyl phos-
    phine
    (HOCH$_2$)$_2$(n-C$_3$H$_7$)P

② (n-C$_3$H$_7$)$\overset{+}{\text{P}}$(CH$_2$OH)$_3\overset{-}{\text{Br}}$ $\xrightarrow{\text{N(C}_2\text{H}_3)_3}$
    61.4%

③ (84°/1). n_D 1.5061 (20°). d 1.0690
    (20°).

④ + n-C$_3$H$_7$Cl $\longrightarrow$
    (n-C$_3$H$_7$)$_2\overset{+}{\text{P}}$(CH$_2$OH)$_2\overset{-}{\text{Cl}}$ $\xrightarrow{\text{N(C}_2\text{H}_5)_3}$
    (n-C$_3$H$_7$)$_2$P(CH$_2$OH)

⑥ Zhur. **31**, 3421 (1961) ; **32**, 553 (1962).

PC$_5$H$_{13}$O$_2$

① n-Buthylmethylphosphinic acid
    CH$_3$(n-C$_4$H$_9$)P(O)(OH)

② [CH$_3$(n-C$_4$H$_9$)PS]$_2$ + HgO + C$_6$H$_6$
    $\xrightarrow{\text{reflux 1 hr}}$ 89.1%

③ (142°/0.01). [36~37°]. n_D 1.4439 (40°).

⑥ Ber. **94**, 3051 (1961).

PC$_5$H$_{13}$O$_2$

① Methylphosphonous acid diethyl
    ester
    CH$_3$P(OC$_2$H$_5$)$_2$

② CH$_3$PCl$_2$ + C$_2$H$_5$OH $\xrightarrow{\text{(C}_5\text{H}_5)_3\text{N}}$ 82%

③ n_D 1.4168 (25°).

④ + C$_2$H$_5$SCH$_2$CH$_2$OH $\xrightarrow{\text{heat}}$
    CH$_3$P(OC$_2$H$_5$)(OCH$_2$CH$_2$SC$_2$H$_5$)

⑥ JACS **80**, 1150 (1958).

PC$_5$H$_{13}$O$_2$

① Diethylphosphinic acid methyl ester
    (C$_2$H$_5$)$_2$P(O)(OCH$_3$)

② (C$_2$H$_5$)$_2$POCl + CH$_3$ONa $\xrightarrow{\text{CH}_3\text{OH}}$ 65%

③ Colorless liq. (86°/12). n_D 1.4392
    (20°). d 1.0261 (20°/0°).

⑥ Dokl. **91**, 271 (1953).

PC$_5$H$_{13}$O$_2$

① Methylphosphonous acid butyl ester
    CH$_3$P(O)(H)OC$_4$H$_9$

② CH$_3$P(O)(H)OC$_2$H$_5$ + C$_4$H$_9$OH
    + Na (small amt.) $\longrightarrow$ 72%
    CH$_3$PCl$_2$ + C$_4$H$_9$OH $\xrightarrow[\text{(C}_2\text{H}_5)_2\text{N}]{\text{(C}_2\text{H}_5)_3\text{N}}$

③ Colorless liq. (101~103°/18). n_D 1.4263
    d 0.9978 (20°).
    Stable in a dry atm.

④ + S $\xrightarrow{\text{dioxane}}$ CH$_3$P(S)(OC$_4$H$_9$)OH

⑥ Zhur. **31**, 179, 2367 (1961).

PC$_5$H$_{13}$O$_2$S

① Methylphosphonothioic acid
    O, S-diethyl ester
      CH$_3$P(O)(OC$_2$H$_5$)(SC$_2$H$_5$)

② CH$_3$P(S)(OC$_2$H$_5$)$_2$ + C$_2$H$_5$Br $\longrightarrow$ 31%
    CH$_3$P(O)(OC$_2$H$_5$)Cl + C$_2$H$_5$SH
    $\xrightarrow{\text{N(C}_2\text{H}_5)_3}$
    C$_2$H$_5$SNR$_2$ + CH$_3$P(O)(OC$_2$H$_5$)H $\longrightarrow$
    CH$_3$P(S)(OC$_2$H$_5$)OH + C$_2$H$_5$ONa
    + C$_2$H$_5$Br $\longrightarrow$ 57%

③ Colorless liq. (90°/12). n_D 1.4743
    (20°). d 1.0940 (20°).
    Sol. in org. solvents.

④ + COCl$_2$ $\longrightarrow$ CH$_3$P(O)(SC$_2$H$_5$)Cl

⑥ JCS 1961, 3067. Izv. OKhN 193
    (1956). Dokl. **104**, 861 (1955).
    Zhur. **31**, 176 (1961).

PC$_5$H$_{13}$O$_2$S

① Ethylphosphonothioic acid O-ethyl
    O-methyl ester
    C$_2$H$_5$P(S)(OCH$_3$)(OC$_2$H$_5$)

② C$_2$H$_5$PS(OC$_2$H$_5$)OH + CH$_2$N$_2$ $\longrightarrow$

③ Straw liq. (74~75°/9.5). n_D 1.4665

(20°). *d* 1.0647 (20°).

Sol. in org. solvents.

⑥ Dokl. 104, 861 (1955).

PC₅H₁₃O₂S

① Propylphosphonothioic acid *O*-ethyl ester

C₃H₇P(S)(OC₂H₅)OH

② C₃H₇P(S)(OC₂H₅)₂ + NaOH $\xrightarrow{HCl}$

③ (101~102°). *n*D 1.4875 (20°). *d* 1.0974 (20°).

⑥ Dokl. 104, 861 (1955)

PC₅H₁₃O₂S

① Ethylphosphonothioic acid *O*-ethyl-*S*-methyl ester

C₂H₅P(O)(SCH₃)OC₂H₅

② C₂H₅PS(OC₂H₅)OH + CH₂N₂ ⟶

③ Colorless liq. (93.2°/9). *n*D 1.4790 (20°). *d* 1.1058 (20°).

Sol. in org. solvents.   Decomp. in H₂O.

⑥ Dokl. 104, 861 (1955).

PC₅H₁₃O₂S

① Methylphosphonothioic acid *O*-isopropyl-*S*-methyl ester

CH₃P(O)(OC₃H₇-*i*)SCH₃

② CH₃P(OC₃H₇-*i*)OSH + NaOCH₃ + CH₃I ⟶

③ (73~75°/4). *n*D 1.4712 (25°).

⑥ JACS 84, 617 (1962).

PC₅H₁₃O₂S

① Methylphosphonothioic acid *O, O*-diethyl ester

CH₃P(S)(OC₂H₅)₂

② CH₃PSCl₂ + C₂H₅OH $\xrightarrow[\text{reflux}]{\text{BF}_3 \cdot \text{ether}}$ 80%

CH₃PSCl₂ + C₂H₅ONa $\xrightarrow{\text{C}_2\text{H}_7\text{ONa}}$ 90%

(C₂H₅O)₂PSH + C₂H₅ONa + CH₃X ⟶

③ Colorless liq. (76.5~78°/13). *n*D

1.4610 (20°). *d* 1.0553 (20°).

Sol. in organic solvents.

NMR : Compt. rend. 253, 644 (1961) ; J. Phys. Chem. 65, 562 (1961).

④ + C₃H₇I ⟶ CH₃P(O)(OC₂H₅)SC₃H₇

+ COCl₂ ⟶ CH₃P(O)(OC₂H₅)Cl

+ SO₂Cl₂ ⟶ CH₃P(O)(OC₂H₅)Cl

⑥ JCS 1961, 5532.   JACS 80, 3945 (1958).

Izv. OKhN 193 (1956).

PC₅H₁₃O₂S

① Ethylphosphonothioic acid *O*-isopropyl ester

C₂H₅P(S)(OC₃H₇-*i*)OH

② C₂H₅P(S)(OC₃H₇-*i*)₂ + KOH $\xrightarrow{\text{reflux}}$ 44%

③ (79°/0.3). *n*D 1.4776 (25°). *d* 1.0811 (25°/4°).

④ +(C₆H₁₁)₂NH ⟶ C₂H₅P(O)(OC₃H₇-*i*) + SNH₂(C₆H₁₁)₂

⑥ JACS 81, 148 (1959).

PC₅H₁₃O₂S

① Methylphosphonothioic acid *O-sec*-butyl ester

CH₃P(S)(OC₄H₉-*s*)OH

② CH₃PSCl₂ + *s*-C₄H₉OH + KOH ⟶ 30%.

③ (99~100°/0.6~0.7). *n*D 1.4770 (28°).

④ ⟶ CH₃P(O)(OC₄H₉-*s*)SNH₂(C₆H₁₁)₂

⑥ JCS 1962, 3824

PC₅H₁₃O₂S

① Methylphosphonothioic acid *O*-butyl ester

CH₃P(S)(OC₄H₉)OH

② CH₃PSCl₂ + C₄H₉OH + KOH ⟶ 58%

CH₃P(S)(OC₄H₉)Cl + NaOHaq. ⟶ CH₃(H)P(O)(OC₄H₉) + S ⟶ 82.5%

③ (83~84°/0.1). *n*D 1.4829 (25°). *d* 1.0922 (25°/4°).

④ +(C₆H₁₁)₂NH ⟶

CH₃P(O)(OC₄H₉)SNH₂(C₆H₁₁)₂
⑥ JCS **1962**, 3824.   JACS **81**, 148(1959).
Zhur. **31**, 179 (1961).

PC₅H₁₃O₃

① Methylphosphonic acid diethyl
ester
CH₃P(O)(OC₂H₅)₂

② CH₃POCl₂ + C₂H₅OH $\xrightarrow{\text{Na}}$ 80%
P(OC₂H₅)₃ + CH₃I $\longrightarrow$ 95%

③ Oil. (90°/10). n_D 1.4119 (25°). d 1.0508
(25°/0°).
Sol. in org. solvents.
NMR: JACS **84**, 1876 (1962)

④ + (i-C₃H₇O)₃Al $\xrightarrow{115\sim155°,\ 4\,\text{hrs}}$
i-C₃H₇OC₂H₅

⑥ JCS **1947**, 1465.   Zhur. **17**, 2149 (1947).
JACS **79**, 3570 (1957).   Bull. soc.
chim. France **1961**, 1222

PC₅H₁₃O₂

① Hydroxymethylphosphonic acid
diethyl ester
HOCH₂P(O)(OC₂H₅)₂

② (C₂H₅O)₂POH + H₂CO $\longrightarrow$ 30%
ICH₂P(O)(OC₂H₅)₂ + (C₂H₅)₂POK $\longrightarrow$

③ Oil. (72°/5). n_D 1.4342 (20°). d 1.0726
(0°/0°).
IR: Chem. Ind. (London) **1960**, 1058
Dimeric

④ + 18% HCl $\longrightarrow$ (CH₂OH)P(O)(OH)₂

⑥ Zhur. **6**, 283 (1936).   JOC **25**, 1000
(1960).

PC₅H₁₃S

① Diethylmethylphosphine sulfide
(C₂H₅)₂(CH₃)P(S)

② CH₃P(S)Br₂ + C₂H₅MgBr $\longrightarrow$
[(C₂H₅)(CH₃)P(S)]₂ + (C₂H₅)₂(CH₃)
P(S) + (C₂H₅)(CH₃)P(S)OH

③ [66°].
NMR: J. Chem. Eng. Data **7**, 307
(1962).

⑥ Ber. **94**, 3043 (1961).

PC₆Cl₃F₁₄

① Trichlorobis(heptafluoropropyl)
phosphorane
(C₃F₇)₂PCl₃

② (C₃F₇)₂PCl + Cl₂ $\xrightarrow{\text{sealed tube}}$

③ (184±2°).

④ + H₂O₂ $\xrightarrow{\text{H₂O}}$ (C₃F₇)P(O)(OH)₂·2 H₂O

⑥ JCS **1959**, 375.

PC₆H₅Br₂Cl₂

① Dibromodichlorophenylphosphorane
(C₆H₅)PCl₂Br₂

② C₆H₅PCl₂ + Br₂ $\longrightarrow$

③ [208°].
Forms C₆H₅PCl₂Br₄ (mp. 209°) with
excess bromine.

⑥ Kosolapoff 72.

PC₆H₅Br₄

① Tetrabromophenylphosphorane
C₆H₅PBr₄

② C₆H₅PBr₂ + Br₂ $\longrightarrow$

③ Forms C₆H₅PBr₆ (subl. at 110°) with
excess bromine.

⑥ Kosolapoff 72.

PC₆H₅ClF₃

① Chlorotrifluorophenylphosphorane
C₆H₅PClF₃

② C₆H₅PHF₃ + Cl₂ $\longrightarrow$

③ Forms adduct with excess chlorine.

④ + NR₂ $\longrightarrow$ C₆H₅PF₃NR₂

⑥ Zhur. **32**, 2592 (1962).

PC₆H₅Cl₂

① Phenylphosphonous dichloride
C₆H₅PCl₂

② C₆H₆ + PCl₃ $\xrightarrow{\text{AlCl₃}}$ 45.9%
C₆H₅PH(O)OH + PCl₃ $\xrightarrow{\text{C₆H₆}}$ 71%

③ (221∼222°), (140∼142°/57). n_D 1.5960

(20°). d 1.319 (20°).

④ + LiI $\xrightarrow{C_6H_6}$ C₆H₅PI₂

+ LiI $\xrightarrow{(C_2H_5)_2O}$ (C₆H₅PI)₂

+ C₅H₁₁N $\xrightarrow[20°]{C_6H_6}$ C₆H₅P(NC₅H₁₀)₂

$\xrightarrow[180\sim250°]{AlCl_3}$ PCl₃ + (C₆H₅)₂PCl

⑥ Kaufman 1012. Zhur. **31**, 1399 (1961). JOC **26**, 850 (1961). Ber. **94**, 2122 (1961).

PC₆H₅Cl₂O

① Phenylphosphonic dichloride
(C₆H₅)P(O)Cl₂

② C₆H₅PCl₂ + P₂O₅ $\xrightarrow{HCl\ 150°}$

PCl₃ + (C₆H₅CO)₂ $\xrightarrow{C_6H_5}$ C₆H₅COCl + C₆H₅P(O)Cl₂ + (C₆H₅)₂P(O)Cl + CO₂

C₆H₅PCl₂ + SO₃ $\longrightarrow$ C₆H₅P(O)Cl₂ + SO₂(quant. yield)

③ (258°), (137~138°/15). n_D 1.5581 (25°).
d 1.1970 (25°/4°).

⑥ Kaufman 1011 Australian J. Chem.
11, 336 (1958)

PC₆H₅Cl₂S

① Phenylphosphonothioic dichloride
C₆H₅P(S)Cl₂

② C₆H₅PCl₂ + S $\xrightarrow{AlCl_3}$

③ (122~123°/10), (205°/125), (150°/26).
n_D 1.6230 (20°). d 1.4050 (20/4°).

④ + NaF $\xrightarrow{TMS}$ C₆H₅P(S)F₂ (73%)

⑥ Ber. **95**, 199 (1962). JOC **25**, 2016 (1960). Kaufman 1012. JINC **24**, 1073 (1962).

PC₆H₅Cl₄

① Tetrachlorophenylphosphorane
C₆H₅PCl₄

② C₆H₅PCl₂+Cl₂ $\longrightarrow$

③ [73°].

④ + C₂H₅OCH=CH₂ $\xrightarrow{C_6H_6}$

C₂H₅OCH=CHP(C₆H₅)Cl₃ (83%)
+ SbF₃ $\longrightarrow$ C₆H₅PF₄ (66%)

⑥ Izv. OKhN **1962**, 444. Zhur. **29**, 3766 (1959). Kosolapoff 72.

PC₆H₅F₂O

① Phenylphosphonic difluoride
C₆H₅P(O)F₂

② C₆H₅P(O)Cl₂ + ZnF₂ $\longrightarrow$ 90%

C₆H₅P(O)Cl₂ + NaF $\xrightarrow[100°]{TMS}$ 65%

3 C₆H₅P(O)Cl₂ + Na₂SiF₆ $\longrightarrow$ 75%

③ (186~187°), (44°/2.5). d 1.2982 (20°),
d 1.3052 (20°).

⑥ Zhur. **29**, 3766 (1959). JACS **82**, 6176 (1960). Monatsh. **92**, 196 (1961). JOC **25**, 2016 (1960).

PC₆H₅F₄

① Tetrafluorophenylphosphorane
(C₆H₅)PF₄

② C₆H₅P(O)(OH)₂ + SF₄ $\longrightarrow$ 58%
C₆H₅P(O)F₂ + SF₄ $\longrightarrow$ 62%
3 C₆H₅PCl₂ + 4 SbF₃ $\longrightarrow$ 66.7%

③ (134.5~136°). n_D 1.4245 (20°).
d 1.3888 (15°).
NMR: Inorg. Chem. **2**, 613 (1963).

⑥ JACS **82**, 6176 (1960). Chem. Ind.
(London) **1962**, 1868. Zhur. **32**, 301 (1962) ; **29**, 3766(1959).

PC₆H₅Li₂

① Dilithium phenylphosphide
C₆H₅PLi₂

② C₆H₅Li + C₆H₅PH₂ $\xrightarrow{ether}$ 96%

C₆H₅PCl₂ + 4 Li $\xrightarrow{THF}$

③ Slightly sol. in dioxane, THF;
insol. in ether and C₆H₆.
Easily decomp. with air and moist air.

④ + CH₃I $\longrightarrow$ C₆H₅P(CH₃)₂

+ CH₃I $\longrightarrow$ [(CH₃)₃C₆H₅P⁺]I⁻

$+ C_6H_5Br \longrightarrow (C_6H_5)_3P$

⑤ Intermediate in prepn. of phenyl
   substituted P compds.

⑥ Ber. **92**, 1118 (1959).   Chem. Ind.
   (London) **1959**, 541.

$PC_6H_6F_3$

① Trifluorophenylphosphorane
   $(C_6H_5)PHF_3$

② $C_6H_5PCl_2 + KFH_2 \xrightarrow{50\sim60°} 84\%$

③ $(57\sim58°/20)$.

④ $+ H_2O \longrightarrow C_6H_5PO_2H_2$

⑥ Zhur. **31**, 3991 (1961).

PC_6H_6K

① Potassium phenylphosphide
   $C_6H_5 \cdot HPK$

② $C_6H_5PH_2 + K \longrightarrow$

③ Air-sensitive.
   Insol. in organic solvents.

④ $+ BrCH_2CH_2CH_2Br \longrightarrow$
   $C_6H_5HP(CH_2)_3PHC_6H_5$

⑤ Intermediate in prepn. of org. P
   compds.

⑥ Ber. **94**, 107 (1961).

PC_6H_7

① Phenylphosphine
   $C_6H_5PH_2$

② $C_6H_5PCl_2 + LiAlH_4 \xrightarrow{erher} 25.4\%$
   $C_6H_5PCl_2 \xrightarrow{Na} C_6H_5PNa \xrightarrow{H_2O}$
   71.5%
   $C_6H_5P(O)Cl_2 + LiAlH_4 \longrightarrow 55\%$

③ Colorless liq. (160°/760). n_D 1.5796
   (20°). d 1.001 (15°).
   Sol. in org. solvents; slightly sol. in
   H_2O.
   IR: Chem. Ind. (London) **1959**, 541.

④ $+ CF_2=CF_2 \longrightarrow C_6H_5PHCF_2CF_2H$
   $+ C_6H_5P(CF_2CF_2H)_2$
   $+ 2RMgX \longrightarrow C_6H_5P(MgX)_2 + 2RH$
   $+ C_6H_5N=S=O \longrightarrow$

$C_6H_5P(S)(OH)NHC_6H_5$
   or $C_6H_5P(O)(SH)NHC_6H_5$

$+ 2COCl_2 \longrightarrow C_6H_5PCl_2 + 2CO + 2$
   HCl

$+ SO_2Cl_2 \longrightarrow C_6H_5PSCl_2 + H_2O$

$+ 2(C_6H_5)_2PN(CH_3)_2 \longrightarrow$
   $(C_6H_5)_2P - P(C_6H_5) - P(C_6H_5)_2$
   $+ 2HN(CH_3)_2$

$+ Na + C_6H_5Cl \longrightarrow (C_6H_5)_2PH$

$+ K \longrightarrow C_6H_5HPK$

⑥ JACS **74**, 562, 3414 (1952).   Ber. **92**,
   2088 (1959).   Monatsh. **92**, 868
   (1961).

$PC_6H_7OS_2$

① Phenylphosphonodithioic acid
   $C_6H_5P(S)(OH)SH$

② $[C_6H_5P(OH)SS]_2Ni \xrightarrow[\text{acidify}]{(NH_4)_2S}$
   $[C_6H_5P(S)SH]_2S + H_2O \longrightarrow$

③ Solid.
   Unstable.

④ $\longrightarrow$ Ni salt
   $\longrightarrow$ Na salt

⑥ J. Russ. Phys. Chem. Soc. **61**, 2037
   (1929).   Gazz. chim. ital. **76**, 167
   (1946).

$PC_6H_7O_2$

① Phenylphosphonous acid
   $C_6H_5PO_2H_2$

② $C_6H_5PI_2 + H_2O \longrightarrow 91\%$
   $(C_6H_5PI)_2 + H_2O \xrightarrow{heat} 80.6\%$

③ Plate crystals. [82~84°].
   Sol. in polar org. solvents.
   NMR: JACS **78**, 5715 (1956).

④ $+ C_4H_9OH \xrightarrow{C_6H_6} C_6H_5P(OH)OC_4H_9$

⑥ Ber. **94**, 186 (1961)   Helv. Chim. Acta
   36, 1314 (1953)

$PC_6H_7O_3$

① Phenylphosphonic acid

$C_6H_5P(O)(OH)_2$

② $C_6H_5P(O)(OC_2H_5)_2 \xrightarrow[\text{hydrolysis}]{\text{HCl}}$

$p\text{-}ClC_6H_4P(O)(OH)_2 \xrightarrow{H_2(Pd)}$

$[C_6H_5P(O)O\text{-}]_n + nH_2O \longrightarrow$

$(C_6H_5P)_4 + O_2 + H_2O \longrightarrow$

③ White crystals. [165~166].
   Sol. in polar solvents.
   NMR: J. Chem. Eng. Data **7**, 307
   (1962).

⑥ JACS **70**, 186 (1948); **69**, 2020 (1947);
   76, 1045 (1954). Ber. **91**, 2296 (1658).

PC₆H₉

① Trivinylphosphine
   $(CH_2{=}CH)_3P$

② $CH_2{=}CHMgCl + PCl_3 \longrightarrow 55\%$

③ (116.6°).

④ $+ BF_3 \longrightarrow (CH_2{=}CH)_3P \cdot BF_3$
   $+ CS_2 \longrightarrow (CH_2{=}CH)_3PCS_2$
   $+ RX \longrightarrow R(CH_2{=}CH)_3P^+X^-$
   $R = CH_3, C_2H_5, CH_2{=}CH,$
   $X = Br, I$

⑥ JOC **24**, 635 (1959). JACS **79**, 5884
   (1957).

PC₆H₉N₂

① Bis(2-cyanoethyl)phosphine
   $(NCCH_2CH_2)_2PH$

② $PH_3 + CH_2{=}CHCN \longrightarrow 56\%$

③ (157~159°/0.3). n^D 1.5070 (25°).

④ $+ p\text{-}CH_3C_6H_4SO_2Cl \xrightarrow{\text{pyridine}}$
   $(p\text{-}CH_3C_6H_4S)_2$

   $+ p\text{-}CH_3C_6H_4SO_2Cl \xrightarrow{\text{dioxane}}$
   $(NCCH_2CH_2)_2P(O)SC_6H_4CH_3\text{-}p$

   $+ R\text{-}CH{=}CH_2 \xrightarrow{\text{AIBN or }(t\text{-}C_4H_9O)_2}$
   $(NCCH_2CH_2)_2PCH_2CH_2R$

   $+ O_2(\text{air}) \xrightarrow{70°} (NCCH_2CH_2)_2P(O)H$

   $+ HC{\equiv}C(CH_2)_nCH_3 \xrightarrow{\text{AIBN}}$
   $(NCCH_2CH_2)_2PCH{=}CH(CH_2)_nCH_3$
   $n{=}4 \text{ and } 5$

⑥ JACS **81**, 1103 (1959). JOC **26**, 5138
   (1961).

PC₆H₉N₂O₂

① Bis(2-cyanoethyl)phosphinic acid
   $(NCCH_2CH_2)_2P(O)(OH)$

② $(NCCH_2CH_2)_2PH + 34\% \ H_2O_2$
   $\xrightarrow{CH_3COOH} 48\%$

③ [124~125°].

④ $+ H_2S + (C_2H_5)_3N \xrightarrow{\text{pyridine}}$
   $\overset{\displaystyle S}{\underset{\displaystyle \|}{(H_2NCCH_2CH_2)_2P(O)(OH)}}$

⑥ JOC **26**, 5135 (1961).

PC₆H₉N₂S₂

① Bis(2-cyanoethyl)phosphinodithioic
   acid
   $(NCCH_2CH_2)_2P(S)SH$

② $HP(CH_2CH_2CN)_2 + S \xrightarrow{\text{liq. NH}_3 \text{ in CH}_3CN}$
   as NH_4 salt (47%)

   $HP(CH_2CH_2CN)_2 + S \xrightarrow{(C_6H_{11})_2NH_2}$
   as cyclohexylamine salt (47%)

   $HP(CH_2CH_2CN)_2 + S \xrightarrow{C_5H_5N}$
   as pyridinium salt (95%)

⑥ JOC **27**, 2198 (1962); **26**, 5135 (1961).

PC₆H₁₁

① Diethylethynylphosphine
   $HC{\equiv}CP(C_2H_5)_2$

② $(C_2H_5)_2PCl + CH{\equiv}CMgBr \xrightarrow{\text{THF}} 49\%$

③ Colorless liq. (66~67°/77). n_D 1.4808
   (20°).
   IR: Rec. trav. chim. **81**, 993 (1962).

PC₆H₁₁Cl₂O₂

① Vinylphosphonous acid bis(2-chloro-
   ethyl) ester
   $CH_2{=}CHP(OCH_2CH_2Cl)_2$

② $(ClCH_2CH_2O)_2PCl + CH_2{=}CHMgBr$

$\xrightarrow{\text{THF}}$ 60%

③ (93°/22). n_D 1.4945 (20°). d 1.2308 (20°).

④ + HOC₆H₄OH $\xrightarrow{\text{in autoclave}}$

$\underset{|}{\text{CH}_2\text{CH}_2\text{Cl}}$

$(\text{CH}_2=\text{CH})\text{P(O)(OCH}_2\text{CH}_2\text{Cl})$

$\xrightarrow{\text{PCl}_5}$ CH₂=CHP(CH₂CH₂Cl)(O)Cl

$\xrightarrow{\text{Et}_2\text{N}}$ (CH₂=CH)₂POCl

⑥ Zhur. **32**, 3351 (1962).

PC₆H₁₁Cl₂O₂

① 2-Chloroethylvinylphosphinic acid
   2-chloroethyl ester

$\underset{|}{\text{CH}_2\text{CH}_2\text{Cl}}$

$(\text{CH}_2=\text{CH})\text{P(O)(OCH}_2\text{CH}_2\text{Cl})$

② (CH₂=CH)P(OCH₂CH₂Cl)₂

$\xrightarrow[]{190° \text{ in autoclave}}$ 69%

③ (120~122°/1). n_D 1.4930 (20°). d 1.2260 (20°).

④ + PCl₅ $\xrightarrow{\text{C}_6\text{H}_6}$ $(\text{CH}_2=\text{CH})\underset{|}{\overset{\text{CH}_2\text{CH}_2\text{Cl}}{\text{P}}}(\text{O})\text{Cl}$

$\xrightarrow{(\text{C}_2\text{H}_5)_3\text{N}}$ (CH₂=CH)₂P(O)Cl

⑥ Zhur. **33**, 382 (1963).

PC₆H₁₁Cl₂O₃

① Vinylphosphonic acid bis(2-chloro-
   ethyl) ester
   CH₂=CHP(O)(OCH₂CH₂Cl)₂

② ClCH₂CH₂P(O)(OCH₂CH₂Cl)₂

   + anhyd. NaOOCCH₃ $\xrightarrow[5 \text{ hr}]{105~110°}$

   ClCH₂CH₂P(O)(OCH₂CH₂Cl)₂
   + anhyd. Na₂CO₃ ⟶

③ Oil. (137~139°/4). n_D 1.4772 (20°). d 1.3183 (20°/4°). d 1.3212 (20°/20°).

④ $\xrightarrow{\text{BPO}}$ polymer

⑥ JOC **27**, 3851 (1962). Izv. OKhN **1947**, 233 Plasticheskie Massy

1962, 49 ; 1960, 9, 10.

PC₆H₁₁Li₂

① Dilithium cyclohexylphosphide
   (*cyclo*-C₆H₁₁)PLi₂

② C₆H₅Li + *cyclo*-C₆H₁₁PH₂ ⟶ 94%

③ Slightly sol. in dioxane and THF,
   insol. in ether and C₆H₆. Easily
   decomp. with air and moisture.

④ + exess CH₃I ⟶
   [((CH₃)₃C₆H₁₁P⁺]I⁻

⑤ Intermediate in prepn. of cyclohexyl
   substituted P compds.

⑥ Ber. **92**, 1118 (1959).

PC₆H₁₁O₂

① Ethynylphosphonous acid butyl ester
   HC≡CP(O)(OC₄H₉-*n*)H

② HC≡CP(OC₄H₉-*n*)₂ + H₂O

   $\xrightarrow[\text{dioxane}]{\text{H}_2\text{SO}_4}$ 78%

③ (65~66°/1.5). n_D 1.4492 (20°). d 1.0322 (20°).

⑥ Zhur. **32**, 3351 (1962).

PC₆H₁₂Br₃O₃

① 2-Bromoethylphosphonic acid bis-
   (2-bromoethyl) ester
   BrCH₂CH₂P(O)(OCH₂CH₂Br)₂

② PBr₃ + $\underset{\diagdown\,\diagup}{\overset{\text{CH}_2-\text{CH}_2}{\text{O}}}$ ⟶

   (BrCH₂CH₂O)₃P $\xrightarrow{120~130°}$

③ Crystals. (190~191°/2.5). [48~49°].

④ + PCl₅ $\xrightarrow{\text{heat, }140~145°, \text{ 4 hr}}$
   ClCH₂CH₂Br + BrCH₂CH₂P(O)Cl₂

⑥ Izv. OKhN **1947**, 389.

PC₆H₁₂ClO₂

① Vinylphosphonochloridic acid butyl
   ester
   CH₂=CHP(O)(OC₄H₉)Cl

② CH₂=CHP(OC₄H₉)₂ $\xrightarrow{\text{chlorination}}$

47.4%

③ (57°/1.5). n_D 1.4521 (20°). d 1.1166
   (20°).

⑥ Zhur. **32**, 3351 (1962).

PC₆H₁₂Cl₃O₃

① 2-Chloroethylphosphonic acid bis-2-
   chloroethyl ester
   $ClCH_2CH_2P(O)(OCH_2CH_2Cl)_2$

② $P(OCH_2CH_2Cl)_3 \xrightarrow{150\sim160°\ 4hr}$

   $PCl_3 + CH_2-CH_2 \longrightarrow$ 40%
                    \   /
                     O

③ Crystals. (170~172°/5, 169~171°/14).
   [36.8~37.6°]. n_D 1.4828 (26°). d
   1.3906 (26°/0°), d 1.3892 (26°/4°).
   Sol. in org. solvents, insol. in H_2O.
   NMR: J. Chem. Eng. Data 7, 307
   (1962)

④ + H_2O $\longrightarrow\!\!\!\!\times\!\!\!\!\longrightarrow$

   + KOHaq. $\longrightarrow\!\!\!\!\times\!\!\!\!\longrightarrow$

   + HCl $\xrightarrow{heat}$ $ClCH_2CH_2P(O)(OH)_2$

   + PCl_5 $\xrightarrow{heat}$ $ClCH_2CH_2POCl_2$

⑥ Izv. OKhN **1946**, 403. Plasticheskie
   Massy **1960**, 54.

PC₆H₁₂K

① Potassium cyclohexylphosphide
              $cyclo$-$C_6H_{11}PHK$

② $C_6H_{11}PH_2 + K \xrightarrow{n\text{-heptane}}$ 98%

③ Colorless.
   Air-sensitive. Insol. in org. solvents.

④ + $X(CH_2)_nX \longrightarrow$
      $(cyclo$-$C_6H_{11})PH(CH_2)_n$
      $PH(cyclo$-$C_6H_{11})n$=3, 4, 5, 6,
      X=Cl, Br
   + $ClCH_2CH_2Cl \longrightarrow$
      $[(cyclo$-$C_6H_{11})PHCH_2]_2$

⑤ Intermediate in prepn. of org. P
   compds.

⑥ Ber. **94**, 2664 (1961).

PC₆H₁₂N

① Methylethyl 2-cyanoethylphosphine
   $(CH_3)(C_2H_5)(NCCH_2CH_2)P$

② $[(CH_3)(C_2H_5)(NCCH_2CH_2)_2P^+]I^-$
   $+ NaOC_2H_5 \longrightarrow$ 56%

③ (68~70°/1.8). n_D 1.4805 (25°).

⑥ JACS **81**, 4803 (1959).

PC₆H₁₂NO₃

① Cyanomethylphosphonic acid diethyl
   ester
   $NCCH_2P(O)(OC_2H_5)_2$

② $(C_2H_5O)_3P + BrCH_2CN \longrightarrow$

④ + $C_6H_5CHO \xrightarrow{NaNH_2} C_6H_5CH=CHCN$

   + $(C_6H_5)_2CO \xrightarrow{NaNH_2} (C_6H_5)_2C=CHCN$

⑥ BCSJ **35**, 1498 (1962).

PC₆H₁₂NaO₂S

① Carboxymethyldiethylphosphine
   sulfide, sodium salt
   $(NaO_2CCH_2)(C_2H_5)_2P(S)$

② $(C_2H_5)_2PCH_2CO_2Na + S \longrightarrow$

③ [277~280°(decomp.)] (C_2H_5OH).

⑥ Ber. **94**, 2244 (1961); **93**, 803 (1960).

PC₆H₁₃

① 1-Ethylcyclotetramethylene-
   phosphine
   CH_2-CH_2
   | $>P-C_2H_5$
   CH_2-CH_2

② $C_2H_5PLi_2 + Cl(CH_2)_4Cl \longrightarrow$ 21.7%

③ Colorless liq. (145°).
   Oxidized in air.

④ + $CH_3I \longrightarrow$
   $\begin{bmatrix} CH_2-CH_2 \\ |\quad\quad\ >P^+(CH_3)(C_2H_5) \\ CH_2-CH_2 \end{bmatrix} I^-$
   mp 289~291°

⑥ Ber. **94**, 113 (1961).

PC₆H₁₃

① Cyclohexylphosphine
   $C_6H_{11}PH_2$

② PH$_3$ + C$_6$H$_{10}$ $\xrightarrow{\text{AIBN}}$ 49%

C$_6$H$_{11}$POCl$_2$ + LiAlH$_4$ $\longrightarrow$ 47.5%

PH$_3$·AlCl$_3$ + C$_6$H$_{11}$X $\longrightarrow$
          (X=halogen)

③ Colorless liq. (138°). n_D 1.4860 (20°).
   d 0.8750 (20°/4°).
   Sol. in org. solvents.
   IR : Monatsh. **92**, 868 (1961).

④ + 96% HNO$_3$ $\longrightarrow$
   C$_6$H$_{11}$P(O)(OH)$_2$

   + K $\xrightarrow{n\text{-heptane}}$ (C$_6$H$_{11}$)PH·K

   + Na + n-C$_3$H$_7$Cl $\xrightarrow{\text{xylene}}$
   (n-C$_3$H$_7$)(C$_6$H$_{11}$)PH

⑥ Ber. **91**, 1583 (1958). Monatsh. **90**,
   148 (1959) ; **93**, 230 (1962). JOC **26**,
   5138 (1961).

PC$_6$H$_{13}$Br$_2$O$_3$

① 1,2-Dibromoethylphosphonic acid
   diethyl ester
   BrCH$_2$CHBrP(O)(OC$_2$H$_5$)$_2$

② CH$_2$=CHP(O)(OC$_2$H$_5$)$_2$ + Br$_2$ $\xrightarrow{\text{in CH}_3\text{Cl}}$

③ Oil. (129~131.5°/4). n_D 1.4939 (20°).
   d 1.6595 (20°).

⑥ Izv. OKhN 1947, 233 ; **1959**, 21.

PC$_6$H$_{13}$O

① Diethylvinylphosphine oxide
      (C$_2$H$_5$)$_2$P(O)CH=CH$_2$

② (C$_2$H$_5$)$_2$PCl + CH$_2$–CH$_2$ $\xrightarrow{-20°C}$
                    \ /
                     O

   (C$_2$H$_5$)$_2$POCH$_2$CH$_2$Cl (37%)
   $\xrightarrow[\text{(C}_2\text{H}_5)_3\text{N, 120°}]{}$ 50%

③ (62~63°/2). [35~36°].
   IR : Dokl. **135**, 849 (1960).

④ Polymerized by X-ray at 70° *in
   vacuo.* Dose rate 4.5×10^{16} eV/ml.
   sec. gave a polymer of MW 33000.
   Sol. in H$_2$O, C$_2$H$_5$OH and C$_6$H$_6$.

⑥ Vysokomol. Soed. **3**, 1117 (1961).

PC$_6$H$_{13}$O

① Acetyldiethylphosphine
      (C$_2$H$_5$)$_2$(CH$_3$CO)P

② (C$_2$H$_5$)$_2$PH + CH$_3$COBr $\longrightarrow$
   (C$_2$H$_5$)$_2$PLi + CH$_3$COCl $\longrightarrow$ 70.5%

③ Yellow liq. (165~170°).
   Oxidized in air. Sol. in org. solvents.

④ + CH$_3$I $\longrightarrow$ [CH$_3$COP$^+$CH$_3$(C$_2$H$_5$)$_2$]I$^-$

⑥ Ber. **92**, 3183 (1959) ; **85**, 239 (1952).

PC$_6$H$_{13}$OS$_2$

① Cyclohexylphosphonodithioic acid
   C$_6$H$_{11}$P(S)(OH)SH

② C$_6$H$_{11}$MgBr + P$_2$S$_5$ $\longrightarrow$
   [C$_6$H$_{11}$P(OH)SS]$_2$Ni $\xrightarrow{\text{Na}_2\text{S acidification}}$

③ Oil.
   Unstable.

⑥ Gazz. chim. ital. **77**, 509 (1947).

PC$_6$H$_{13}$O$_2$

① Vinylphosphonous acid butyl ester
   CH$_2$=CHP(O)(OC$_4$H$_9$-n)H

② CH$_2$=CHP(OC$_4$H$_9$-n)$_2$ + H$_2$O
   $\xrightarrow[\text{H}_2\text{SO}_4 \text{ in dioxane}]{}$ 92%

③ (50~51°/2). n_D 1.4479 (20°). d 1.C040
   (20°).

④ + C$_2$H$_5$SH $\xrightarrow{\text{(C}_2\text{H}_5)_3\text{N, 100°}}$
   C$_2$H$_5$SCH$_2$CH$_2$P(O)(OC$_4$H$_9$)H
   $\xrightarrow{\text{C}_4\text{H}_9\text{ONa, 110}\sim135°}$ polymer
                              (MW 14300)
   $\xrightarrow{\text{AIBN 100}\sim150°}$ rigid glassy polymer

⑥ Zhur. **32**, 3351 (1962).

PC$_6$H$_{13}$O$_3$

① Cyclohexylphosphonic acid
   C$_6$H$_{11}$P(O)(OH)$_2$

② C$_6$H$_{11}$P(O)(OC$_2$H$_5$)$_2$
   $\xrightarrow{\text{1 : 1 HCl sealed tube, 150°}}$

$HP(O)(OH)_2 + C_6H_{10}$

$\xrightarrow[\text{BPO (or UV)}]{}$ $20\sim26\%$

③ Needles. [166~167°].

Sol. in org. solvents.

⑥ JACS **77**, 4262 (1955).   JOC **24**, 2049
(1959); **25**, 665 (1960).   Zhur. **29**,
3342 (1959).

$PC_6H_{13}O_3$

① Vinylphosphonic acid diethyl ester
$CH_2=CHP(O)(OC_2H_5)_2$

② $(C_2H_5O)_3P + BrCH_2CH_2Br \longrightarrow$
$(C_2H_5O)_3P + BrCH_2CH_2P(O)(OC_2H_5)_2$
$\longrightarrow$ 25.8%

$BrCH_2CH_2P(O)(OC_2H_5)_2 \xrightarrow[\text{C}_2\text{H}_5\text{OH}]{\text{KOH}} 95\%$

③ Colorless liq. (63°/2.5). n_D 1.4300
(20°). d 1.0526 (20°).
Sol. in org. solvents.
IR: JOC **24**, 532 (1959).   Chem. Ind.
(London) **1960**, 1058.

④ $\xrightarrow{\text{BPO}}$ polymer

⑥ Izv. OKhN **1947**, 233.   JACS **70**,
1971 (1948).   JCS **1947**, 1465.

$PC_6H_{13}O_4$

① Acetylphosphonic acid diethyl ester
$CH_3COP(O)(OC_2H_5)_2$

② $(C_2H_5O)_3P + CH_3COCl \xrightarrow{15°} 50\%$

③ Colorles oil. (70~73°/2). n_D 1.4200
(20°). d 1.0991 (20°/4°).
Sol. in org. solvents. Decomp. in
H_2O.

④ $+ NaHSO_3 \longrightarrow$
$CH_3C(OH)(SO_3Na)P(O)(OC_2H_5)_2$

⑥ Izv. OKhN **1945**, 364, **1963**, 675.
Dokl. **102**, 238 (1955).   Zhur. **32**,
467 (1963).

$PC_6H_{14}BrO_3$

① Ethylphosphonic acid ethyl-2-bromo-
ethyl ester

$C_2H_5P(O)(OC_2H_5)(OCH_2CH_2Br)$

② $\overline{}$
$CH_2CH_2OP(OC_2H_5)O + C_2H_5Br \longrightarrow$

③ Oil. (129~130°/11). n_D 1.4610 (20°).
d 1.3860 (20°).

⑥ Izv. OKhN **1948**, 208.   Zhur. **31**,
2052 (1961).

$PC_6H_{14}BrO_3$

① 2-Bromoethylphosphonic acid
diethyl ester
$BrCH_2CH_2P(O)(OC_2H_5)_2$

② $(C_2H_5O)_3P + BrCH_2CH_2Br \longrightarrow 66\%$

③ Oil. (86~87°/2). n_D 1.4550 (25°).
NMR: J. Chem. Eng. Data **7**, 307
(1962).

④ $+ KOH + C_2H_5OH \longrightarrow$
$CH_2=CHP(O)(OC_2H_5)_2$

⑥ JCS **1947**, 1465.   JACS **70**. 1971 (1948).
J. Polymer Sci. **44**, 531 (1960).

$PC_6H_{14}ClO$

① Diethylphosphinous acid 2-chloro-
ethyl ester
$(C_2H_5)_2POCH_2CH_2Cl$

② $(C_2H_5)_2PCl + CH_2-CH_2 \xrightarrow{(C_2H_5)_2O} 37\%$
$\diagdown_{}\diagup$
O

$ClCH_2CH_2OPCl_2 + C_2H_5MgBr \xrightarrow{\text{pyridine}}$
42%

③ (29~30°/2). n_D 1.4670 (20°). d 1.0144
(20°).

④ $\xrightarrow{\text{C}_6\text{H}_5\text{CH}_3} (C_2H_5)_2P(O)CH_2CH_2Cl$
$+ (C_2H_5)_3N \longrightarrow$
$(C_2H_5)_2P(O)CH=CH_2$

⑥ Dokl. **135**, 323, 849 (1960).

$PC_6H_{14}ClO$

① Dipropylphosphinic chloride
$(C_3H_7)_2P(O)Cl$

② $(C_3H_7)_2P(O)(OH) + PCl_5 \longrightarrow 61\%$
$(C_3H_7)_2P(O)(OC_4H_9) + PCl_5 \longrightarrow 81\%$

③ (112~114°/15), (110.5~112°/8).

n_D 1.4638 (20°). d 1.0692.

④ $+ P_2S_5 \xrightarrow{130\sim150°} (C_3H_7)_2P(S)Cl$

   (59%)

⑥ Kaufman 1029. Zhur. **29**, 1450
   (1959).

PC₆H₁₄ClO

① β-Chloroethyldiethylphosphine
   oxide
   $ClCH_2CH_2P(O)(C_2H_5)_2$

② $(C_2H_5)_2PCl + CH_2{-}CH_2 \xrightarrow[37\%]{-20°}$

                         \\O/

   $(C_2H_5)_2POCH_2CH_2Cl \xrightarrow{C_6H_5CH_3} 70\%$

③ (100~101°/1.0). [33~34°]. n_D 1.4855
   (20°), d 1.1154 (20°).

⑥ Dokl. **135**, 849 (1960).

PC₆H₁₄ClO₂

① Propylphosphonochloridic acid
   isopropylester
   $C_3H_7P(O)(OC_3H_7\text{-}i)Cl$

② $C_3H_7P(O)(OC_3H_7\text{-}i)_2 + COCl_2 \longrightarrow$
   80%

③ n_D 1.4310 (23°).

⑥ JCS **1961**, 3067.

PC₆H₁₄ClO₂S

① Ethylphosphonothioic acid O-ethyl-
   S-2-chloroethylester
   $C_2H_5P(O)(OC_2H_5)SCH_2CH_2Cl$

② $C_2H_5P(O)(OC_2H_5)SCl + CH_2{=}CH_2$
   $\longrightarrow$ 60~70%

   $C_2H_5P(O)(OC_2H_5)SK$
     $+ ClCH_2CH_2Cl \longrightarrow$

③ (64~66°/0.05). n_D 1.4921 (25°).

④ $\xrightarrow{SO_2Cl_2} C_2H_5P(O)(OC_2H_5)Cl$

⑥ Chem. Ind. **1960**, 1241 ; **1959**, 539.

PC₆H₁₄ClO₃

① 2-Chloroethylphosphonic acid
   diethylester

   $ClCH_2CH_2P(O)(OC_2H_5)_2$

② $ClCH_2CH_2OPCl_2 + C_2H_5OH \xrightarrow{C_5H_5N}$

   $(C_2H_5O)_2POCH_2CH_2Cl \xrightarrow{heat}$

   $ClCH_2CH_2POCl_2 + C_2H_5OH \xrightarrow{C_5H_5N}$

③ Colorless oil. (103~110°/7), (92~94°/
   4). n_D 1.4390 (20°). n_D 1.4281 (20°).
   d 1.1558 (20°/4°). d 1.1565 (20°/0°).
   NMR : J. Chem. Eng. Data **7**, 307
   (1962).

④ $+ KOH \xrightarrow{in\ C_2H_5OH}$
   $CH_2{=}CHP(O)(OC_2H_5)_2$

⑥ Izv. OKhN **1947**, 97. JACS **75**, 1763
   (1953). JINC **22**, 297 (1961).

PC₆H₁₄FO₃

① 2-Fluoroethylphosphonic acid
   diethylester
   $FCH_2CH_2P(O)(OC_2H_5)_2$

② $(C_2H_5O)_2POH + CH_3ONa$
   $+ BrCH_2CH_2F \longrightarrow$
   $(C_2H_5O)_3P + BrCH_2CH_2F \longrightarrow 17\%$

③ Oil. (74~75°/11).

⑥ JCS **1948**, 699.

PC₆H₁₄NO₂

① N, N-dimethyl-P-vinylphosphon-
   amidic acid ethylester
   $CH_2{=}CHP(O)(OC_2H_5)N(CH_3)_2$

② $CH_2{=}CHP(O)(OC_2H_5)Cl + (CH_3)_2NH$
   $\longrightarrow 64\%$

③ (107~108°). n_D 1.4499 (20°). d 1.0341
   (20°/4°).

④ $+$ styrene $\longrightarrow$ copolymer
   $+$ methyl methacrylate $\longrightarrow$
   copolymer
   $+$ acylonitrile $\longrightarrow$ copolymer
   $+$ vinylacetate $\longrightarrow$ copolymer
   $\longrightarrow$ polymer

⑥ Vysokomol. Soed. **4**, 1385 (1962).

PC₆H₁₅

① _n_-Butyldimethylphosphine
   $(CH_3)_2(n\text{-}C_4H_9)P$

② $[(CH_3)_3C_4H_9\overset{+}{P}]\overset{-}{Br}$ $\xrightarrow{\text{electrolysis}}$ 40%
   $CH_3MgBr + n\text{-}C_4H_9PCl_2 \longrightarrow$ 44.4%

③ (69~70°/100). n_D 1.4458 (20°). d 0.8455
   (20°).

④ $+ C_6H_5CH_2Cl \longrightarrow$
   $(CH_3)_2(C_4H_9)(C_6H_5CH_2)\overset{+}{P}\overset{-}{Cl}$

⑥ Zhur. **26**, 3426 (1956); CA **51**, 9512 h
   (1957).   Ann. **646**, 65 (1961).

PC₆H₁₅

① Di-_n_-propylphosphine
   $(n\text{-}C_3H_7)_2PH$

② $(n\text{-}C_3H_7)_2P - P(n\text{-}C_3H_7)_2 + Na(\text{or K})$
   $\xrightarrow[\text{CH}_3\text{OH or H}_2\text{O}]{\text{decalin, 120~150°}}$ $(n\text{-}C_3H_7)_2PNa$

③ (131~133°).

⑥ Angew. **72**, 210 (1960).   Ber. **95**, 64
   (1962).

PC₆H₁₅

① Diisopropylphosphine
   $(i\text{-}C_3H_7)_2PH$

② $i\text{-}C_3H_7I + PH_4I + ZnO \longrightarrow$

③ Colorless liq. (118°).
   Sol. in organic solvents.

⑥ Ber. **6**, 292 (1873).

PC₆H₁₅

① Triethylphosphine
   $(C_2H_5)_3P$

② $C_2H_5MgCl + PCl_3 \longrightarrow$
   $C_2H_5Li + PCl_3 \xrightarrow{-40°}$

③ (127.5°).
   NMR: JACS **83**, 3192 (1961); JCS
   1961, 3468.

④ $+ (CH_3)_2AsI \longrightarrow$
   $[(CH_3)_2AsP(C_2H_5)_3]I$
   $+ PdCl_2 \longrightarrow [(C_2H_5)_3P]_2PdCl_2$
   $+ CS_2 \longrightarrow (C_2H_5)_3PCS_2$

$+ (C_2H_5)_3N \cdot BH_3 \longrightarrow (C_2H_5)_3PBH_3$

$+ M(CO)_6 \xrightarrow{70°} (C_2H_5)_3PM(CO)_5$
   (M=Mo, W)

$+ BX_3 \xrightarrow{0°} BX_3 \cdot P(C_2H_5)_3$ (X=Cl,Br)

⑥ JOC **24**, 635 (1959); **27**, 2573 (1962).
   JCS **1935**, 1549.   Z. anorg. allg.
   Chem. **277**, 271 (1954).

PC₆H₁₅Br₂

① Dibromotriethylphosphorane
   $(C_2H_5)_3PBr_2$

② $(C_2H_5)_3P + Br_2 \xrightarrow{(C_2H_5)_2O-C_6H_6}$ 86.5%

③ [253° decomp.]
   Insol. in non-polar solvents; sol. in
   CH_3CN and $C_6H_5NO_2$.

⑥ Naturwiss. **46**, 85 (1959).   Z. anorg.
   allg. Chem. **288**, 201 (1956).

PC₆H₁₅Cl₂

① Dichlorotriethylphosphorane
   $(C_2H_5)_3PCl_2$

② $(C_2H_5)_3PO + PCl_5 \longrightarrow$

③ [240~250° decomp.].

⑥ Kosolapoff 73.

PC₆H₁₅I₂

① Diiodotriethylphosphorane
   $(C_2H_5)_3PI_2$

② $(C_2H_5)_3P + I_2 \xrightarrow{(C_2H_5)_2O-C_6H_6}$ 79.8%

③ [140° decomp.].

⑥ Z. anorg. allg. Chem. **288**, 201 (1956).

PC₆H₁₅O

① Dipropylphosphine oxide
   $(C_3H_7)_2PH(O)$

② $(C_3H_7)_2POC_4H_9 \xrightarrow[95\%]{2\% \text{ H}_2\text{SO}_4/\text{dioxane, } 20°}$

③ (71~72°/1.5). [48~50°].

⑥ Izv. OKhN **1963**, 1227.

PC$_6$H$_{15}$O

① Triethylphosphine oxide
   $(C_2H_5)_3PO$

② $3 C_2H_5MgBr + POCl_3 \longrightarrow$

③ Needles. (242.9°, 84~85°/3). [52.9°].
   Deliquescent.

⑥ Kaufman 1033. Z. anorg. allg. Chem.
   314, 113 (1962).   Acta. Chem.
   Scand. **14**, 1485 (1960); **15**, 1337
   (1961).

PC$_6$H$_{15}$O

① Diethyl-2-hydroxyethylphosphine
   $(C_2H_5)_2(HOCH_2CH_2)P$

② $(C_2H_5)_2PLi + CH_2-CH_2 \xrightarrow{\text{ether}} 26\%$
   $\underset{O}{\diagdown\diagup}$

③ Colorless liq. (106~109°/24).
   Air-sensitive. Sol. in org. solvents;
   insol. in water.

④ $+ S \xrightarrow{C_6H_6} (C_2H_5)_2(HOCH_2CH_2)P(S)$
   $+ CS_2 \xrightarrow{\text{ether}}$
   $(C_2H_5)_2(HOCH_2CH_2)PCS_2$
   $+ CH_3I \longrightarrow$
   $[CH_3(C_2H_5)_2(HOCH_2CH_2)\overset{+}{P}]\overset{-}{I}$
   $+ C_2H_5I \longrightarrow$
   $[(C_2H_5)_3(HOCH_2CH_2)\overset{+}{P}]\overset{-}{I}$

⑥ Ber. **94**, 102 (1961).

PC$_6$H$_{15}$O

① Diethylphosphinous acid ethylester
   $(C_2H_5)_2POC_2H_5$

② $(C_2H_5O)PCl_2 + C_2H_5MgX \longrightarrow 31\%$
   $(C_2H_5)_2PCl + C_2H_5OH \xrightarrow{(C_2H_5)_3N}$

③ Colorless liq. (84~85°/15). n_D 1.4328
   (20°). d 0.9964 (20°).
   Decomp. in air. Sol. in organic
   solvents.

⑥ Dokl. **89**, 291 (1953).   Ber. **93**, 1220
   (1960).

PC$_6$H$_{15}$OS$_2$

① Ethylphosphonodithioic acid O-butyl-
   ester
   $C_2H_5P(S)(OC_4H_9)SH$

② $(C_2H_5PS_2)_2 + C_4H_9OH \longrightarrow$
   quantitative

③ (50°/0.006). n_D 1.5237 (22.5°).

④ $+ SO_2Cl_2 \longrightarrow C_2H_5P(S)(OC_4H_9)Cl$

⑥ JOC **27**, 3832 (1962).

PC$_6$H$_{15}$O$_2$

① Ethylphosphonous acid diethylester
   $C_2H_5P(OC_2H_5)_2$

② $(C_2H_5O)_3P + C_2H_5MgCl \longrightarrow 37\%$
   $C_2H_5PCl_2 + C_2H_5OH \xrightarrow{\text{pyridine}} 64.3\%$
   $(C_2H_5O)_2PCl + C_2H_5MgBr \longrightarrow 47\%$

③ Colorless liq. (137~139°). n_D 1.4222
   (20°). d 0.9024 (20°/0°).
   Oxidized violently in air.

④ $+ ROH \xrightarrow{\text{heat}} C_2H_5P(OC_2H_5)OR +$
   C_2H_5OH
   $+ S \xrightarrow{C_6H_6 \text{ in } CO_2 \text{ atm.}}$
   $C_2H_5P(S)(OC_2H_5)_2$
   $+ CH_2=CHCO_2H \longrightarrow$
   $C_2H_5P(O)(OC_2H_5)CH_2CH_2CO_2C_2H_5$
   $+ CuI \longrightarrow C_2H_5P(OC_2H_5)_2 \cdot CuI$
   $+ C_2H_5I \longrightarrow (C_2H_5)_2P(O)OC_2H_5$
   $+ C_4H_9Br \longrightarrow$
   $C_2H_5(C_4H_9)P(O)OC_2H_5$
   $+ CH_3COCH_2Cl \longrightarrow$
   $C_2H_5P(O)(OC_2H_5)OC(CH_3)=CH_2$
   $+ CH_3COCH_2Br \longrightarrow$
   $C_2H_5P(O)(OC_2H_5)CH_2COCH_3$

⑥ Izv. OKhN **1955**, 1021; **1952**, 854.
   Ber. **93**, 1220 (1960).

PC$_6$H$_{15}$O$_2$

① Di-*n*-propylphosphinic acid
   $(n-C_3H_7)_2P(O)(OH)$

② $(C_2H_5O)_2POH + n-C_3H_7MgCl \xrightarrow{H_2O}$
   55%
   $[(C_3H_7)_2PS]_2 + HgO \xrightarrow{\text{moist } C_6H_6} 72\%$

$(C_3H_7)_2P(S)SH + H_2O + 3\% H_2O_2 \longrightarrow$

③ Colorless crystals. [59.5°].

Sol. in H_2O, C_2H_5OH and C_6H_6.

④ $+ PCl_5 \longrightarrow (n\text{-}C_3H_7)_2POCl$

$+ FeCl_3 \cdot 6 H_2O \longrightarrow$

$Fe[(C_3H_7)_2P(O)O]_3$

$+ SnCl_4 \cdot 4 H_2O \longrightarrow$

$Sn[(C_3H_7)_2P(O)O]_4$

$+ CoCO_3 \longrightarrow Co[(C_3H_7)_2P(O)O]_2$

⑥ JACS **73**, 4101 (1951). Ber. **95**, 1703

(1962); **96**, 1733 (1963).

PC₆H₁₅O₂

① Diethylphosphinic acid ethylester

$(C_2H_5)_2P(O)(OC_2H_5)$

② $(C_2H_5)P(OC_2H_5)_2 + C_2H_5I \longrightarrow 65\%$

③ Colorless liq. (91~92°/14). n_D 1.4337

(20°). d 0.9964 (20°/0°).

Sol. in org. solvents.

⑥ Dokl. **91**, 271 (1953).

PC₆H₁₅O₂S

① Butylphosphonothioic acid O-ethyl-

ester

$C_4H_9P(S)(OC_2H_5)OH$

② $C_4H_9P(S)(OC_2H_5)_2 + NaOH \xrightarrow{HCl}$

③ Colorless liq. (64.5~65°/1.5×10⁻³). n_D

1.4831 (20°). d 1.0721 (20°).

Sol. in org. solvents.

⑥ Dokl. **104**, 861 (1955).

PC₆H₁₅O₂S

① Methylphosphonothioic acid O-ethyl-

S-propylester

$CH_3P(O)(OC_2H_5)SC_3H_7$

② $CH_3P(O)(OC_2H_5)SC_2H_5 + C_3H_7I \longrightarrow$

84%

③ (106°/10). n_D 1.4718 (25°).

④ $+ COCl_2 \longrightarrow CH_3P(O)(SC_3H_7)Cl$

⑥ JCS **1961**, 5532, 3067.

PC₆H₁₅O₂S

① Ethylphosphonothioic acid O-butyl-

ester

$C_2H_5P(S)(OC_4H_9)OH$

② $C_2H_5P(S)(OC_4H_9)Cl + NaOH$ aq. $\longrightarrow$

60.5%

③ (95~98°/0.2). n_D 1.4790 (25°). d 1.0679

(25°/4°).

④ $+ (C_6H_{11})_2NH$

$\longrightarrow C_2H_5P(O)(OC_4H_9)SNH_2(C_6H_{11})_2$

⑥ JACS **81**, 148 (1959).

PC₆H₁₅O₂S

① Ethylphosphonothioic acid O, S-

diethylester

$C_2H_5P(O)(OC_2H_5)(SC_2H_5)$

② $C_2H_5P(S)(OC_2H_5)OH + CH_3CHN_2 \longrightarrow$

$C_2H_5P(O)(OC_2H_5)SNa + C_2H_5Br \longrightarrow$

$C_2H_5P(O)(OC_2H_5)Cl + C_2H_5SNa \longrightarrow$

$C_2H_5P(S)(OC_2H_5)_2 + C_2H_5Br \longrightarrow$

33%

③ Liq. (66.5~68°/2.5). n_D 1.4747 (20°).

d 1.0670 (20°).

Sol. in org. solvents.

④ $+ SO_2Cl_2 \longrightarrow C_2H_5P(O)(OC_2H_5)Cl$

$+ NaF + AgNO_3 \longrightarrow$

$C_2H_5P(O)(OC_2H_5)F$

$+ AgNO_3 \xrightarrow{H_2O} C_2H_5P(O)(OC_2H_5)OH$

⑥ Izv. OKhN **1956**, 193. Dokl. **104**,

861 (1955). JCS **1961**, 4624. Chem.

Ind. **1960**, 1241.

PC₆H₁₅O₂S

① Ethylphosphonothioic acid O, O-

diethylester

$C_2H_5P(S)(OC_2H_5)_2$

② $(C_2H_5O)_2PSH + Na + C_2H_5I \longrightarrow 50\%$

$C_2H_5P(S)(OC_2H_5)OH + CH_3CHN_2 \longrightarrow$

③ Liq. (78~78.5°/8). n_D 1.4576 (20°).

d 1.0349 (20°).

Sol. in org. solvents.

④ $+ C_2H_5Br \longrightarrow C_2H_5P(O)(OC_2H_5)SC_2H_5$

$+ 1:1 HCl \xrightarrow{heat} C_2H_5PO_3H_2$

$+ C_2H_5I \xrightarrow{heat} C_2H_5P(O)(OC_2H_5)SC_2H_5$

⑥ Zhur. **24**, 307 (1954). Dokl. **104**, 861

(1955).   Trudy Kagan Khim.
Technol. Inst. No.17, 151 (1953).
Izv. OKhN **1953**, 163.

PC$_6$H$_{15}$O$_3$

① Ethylphosphonic acid diethylester
   C$_2$H$_5$P(O)(OC$_2$H$_5$)$_2$

② (C$_2$H$_5$O)$_3$P + C$_2$H$_5$Br ⟶ 95%
   PCl$_3$ + AlCl$_3$ + C$_2$H$_5$Cl ⟶
   [C$_2$H$_5$PCl$_3$][AlCl$_4$] $\xrightarrow{\text{C}_2\text{H}_5\text{OH}}$ 80%

③ Oil. (82°/10). n_D 1.4168 (20°). d 1.0259
   (20°/4°).
   Sol. in org. solvents.
   IR : JACS **80**, 2999 (1958).   Chem.
   Ind. **1960**, 6058.
   NMR : JACS **79**, 3570 (1957).

④ + HBr ⟶ C$_2$H$_5$P(O)(OH)$_2$

⑥ JCS **1947**, 1465 ; **1955**, 1978.

PC$_6$H$_{15}$O$_3$

① Butylphosphonic acid ethylester
   C$_4$H$_9$P(O)(OC$_2$H$_5$)(OH)

② C$_4$H$_9$P(O)(OH)$_2$ + C$_2$H$_5$OH
   + (C$_6$H$_{11}$N=)$_2$C $\xrightarrow{\text{heat in THF}}$ 60%

③ Colorless liq. (147~149°/1).
   Sol. in org. solvents.

⑥ JACS **79**, 3575 (1957).

PC$_6$H$_{15}$O$_4$

① (Methoxymethyl)phosphonic acid
   diethylester
   CH$_3$OCH$_2$P(O)(OC$_2$H$_5$)$_2$

② (C$_2$H$_5$O)$_3$P + CH$_3$OCH$_2$Cl ⟶ 85%

③ (65~67°/0.1, 120°/20). n_D 1.4230.
   (20°). d 1.088 (20°/20°).
   IR : JCS **1963**, 1324.

⑥ Zhur. **30**, 3979 (1960).

PC$_6$H$_{15}$S

① Triethylphosphine sulfide
   (C$_2$H$_5$)$_3$PS

② 4 C$_2$H$_5$MgBr + PSCl$_3$ ⟶

((C$_2$H$_5$)$_2$PS)$_2$ + (C$_2$H$_5$)$_3$PS

③ [94.5~95.5°] (petr. ether).
   Hygroscopic. Distillable with steam.
   IR : Inorg. Chem. **2**, 192 (1963).

⑥ Kosolapoff 117.   Rec. trav. chim.
   78, 161 (1959).   JOC **27**, 2573 (1962).
   Acta Cryst. **12**, 1053 (1959).

PC$_6$H$_{15}$S$_2$

① Diisopropylphosphinodithioic acid
   (i-C$_3$H$_7$)$_2$P(S)SH

② (i-C$_3$H$_7$)$_2$PSCl + CH$_3$ONa + H$_2$S $\xrightarrow{\text{HCl}}$
   i-C$_3$H$_7$MgX + PSCl$_3$ ⟶

③ (76~76.5°/3). n_D 1.5745 (20°). d 1.0877
   (20°).
   Decomp. gradually and evolved H$_2$S.

④ ⟶ Ni salt
   ⟶ Na salt
   + CH$_2$=CHCN ⟶
      (i-C$_3$H$_7$)$_2$P(S)SCH$_2$CH$_2$CN
   + NaOH + XCH$_2$CH$_2$SC$_2$H$_5$ ⟶
      (i-C$_3$H$_7$)$_2$P(S)SCH$_2$CH$_2$SC$_2$H$_5$

⑥ Gazz. chim. ital. **76**, 167 (1946).
   Zhur. **31**, 140, 507 (1961).   Rec.
   trav. chim. **78**, 161 (1959).

PC$_6$H$_{15}$S$_2$

① Dipropylphosphinodithioic acid
   (C$_3$H$_7$)$_2$P(S)SH

② [(C$_3$H$_7$)$_2$P(S)]$_2$S $\xrightarrow{\text{hydrolysis}}$
   (C$_3$H$_7$)$_2$PSCl + CH$_3$ONa + H$_2$S $\xrightarrow{\text{HCl}}$

③ (91~91.5°/2). n_D 1.5632 (20°). d 1.0691
   (20°).

④ ⟶ Na salt
   ⟶ Ni salt
   + NaOH + XCH$_2$CH$_2$SC$_2$H$_5$ ⟶
      (C$_3$H$_7$)$_2$P(S)SCH$_2$CH$_2$SC$_2$H$_5$

⑥ Ber. **95**, 1703 (1962).   Zhur. **31**, 140,
   507 (1961).

PC₆H₁₅Se

① Triethylphosphine selenide
   $(C_2H_5)_3PSe$

② $PCl_3 + C_2H_5MgBr \xrightarrow{\ \ } \xrightarrow{Se}$

③ [112°].
   IR: Inorg. Chem. **2**, 192 (1963).

⑥ Kosolapoff 118.

PC₆H₁₆BrO₃

① Tris(hydroxymethyl)propylphos-
   phonium bromide
   $[(HOCH_2)_3PC_3H_7]Br$

② $(HOCH_2)_3P + C_3H_7Br \xrightarrow{60°} 78\%$

③ Oil. $n_D 1.5458$ (20°).

⑥ Zhur. **32**, 553 (1962); **31**, 2729 (1961).

PC₆H₁₆I

① Diethyldimethylphosphonium iodide
   $[(CH_3)_2(C_2H_5)_2P]I$

② $(C_2H_5)_2PNa + CH_3I \longrightarrow$
   $(C_2H_5)_2PLi \cdot dioxane + CH_3I \longrightarrow$
   78%

③ [319~321°].
   Hygroscopic. Very easily sol. in
   C_2H_5OH and H_2O; insol. in dioxane
   and ether.

⑥ Kosorapoff 93. Ber. **93**, 1852 (1960);
   92, 1118 (1959).

PC₇H₅Cl₆

① Trichlorotrichloromethylphenyl-
   phosphorane, PCl₅ complex
   $(C_6H_5)(CCl_3)PCl_3$

② $C_6H_5(CCl_3)PCl + Cl_2 \longrightarrow$

   $C_6H_5(CCl_3)P(O)Cl + 2 PCl_5 \xrightarrow{150~160°}$
   57.4%

③ PCl₅ complex melts at 202°.

④ $+ H_2O \longrightarrow C_6H_5(CCl_3)P(O)Cl$
   (93.5%)
   $C_6H_5(CCl_3)PCl_3 \cdot PCl_5 + CH_3P(O)Cl_2$
   $\xrightarrow{100°} C_6H_5(CCl_3)PCl$ (78.4%)

⑥ Zhur. **30**, 1294 (1960).

PC₇H₆Cl₄NO

① P-(Trichloromethyl)-N-phenylphos-
   phonamidic chloride
   $Cl_3CP(O)(Cl)NHC_6H_5$

② $CCl_3POCl_2 + C_6H_5NH_2 \longrightarrow$

③ Solid. [113~113.5°].

⑥ Zhur. **24**, 1465 (1954).

PC₇H₇Cl₂

① Benzylphosphonous dichloride
   $C_6H_5CH_2PCl_2$

② $C_6H_5CH_2Cl + white P \xrightarrow{300°}$

③ (118~119°/12). $n_D 1.586$ (20°). d 1.300
   (20°).

④ $+ NO \xrightarrow{CCl_4} C_6H_5CH_2P(O)Cl_2$

⑥ Kaufman 1045. Zhur. **31**, 3027 (1961).

PC₇H₇Cl₂O₂

① Chloromethylphosphonochloridic
   acid phenylester
   $ClCH_2P(O)(OC_6H_5)Cl$

② $ClCH_2POCl_2 + C_6H_5OH \longrightarrow 50\%$

③ (123~124°/1). $n_D 1.5354$ (20°). d
   1.3989 (20°).

④ $+ C_2H_5OH \longrightarrow$
   $ClCH_2P(O)(OC_6H_5)(OC_2H_5)$

⑥ Zhur. **31**, 3316 (1961).

PC₇H₇F₄

① Benzyltetrafluorophosphorane
   $(C_6H_5CH_2)PF_4$

② $3 C_6H_5CH_2PCl_2 + 4 SbF_3 \longrightarrow$

③ (53°/15).

⑥ Chem. Ind. (London) **1962**, 1868.

PC₇H₈ClO

① Methylphenylphosphinic chloride
   $(CH_3)(C_6H_5)P(O)Cl$

② $(C_6H_5)(CH_3)P(O)CH_2C_6H_5 + COCl_2$
   $\longrightarrow (C_6H_5)(CH_3)P(O)Cl$

   $[(C_6H_5)(CH_3)PS]_2 + SOCl_2 \xrightarrow{CCl_4} 89\%$

③ (167°/22), (124~128°/0.6). [36~38°].
  n_D 1.5602 (20°).
  NMR: J. Chem. Eng. Data **7**, 307
  (1962).
⑥ Kosolapoff 74. Ber. **94**, 3056 (1961).
  JCS **1963**, 1004.

PC₇H₈ClO₂

① Methylphosphonochloridic acid
  phenylester
  $CH_3P(O)(OC_6H_5)Cl$
② $CH_3POCl_2 + C_6H_5OH \longrightarrow$ 53%
③ (114°/2). n_D 1.5223 (20°). d 1.2829
  (20°).
④ $+ CH_2\overset{}{-}CH_2 + AlCl_3 \longrightarrow$
    $\diagdown O \diagup$

  $CH_3P(O)(OC_6H_5)OCH_2CH_2Cl$
  $+ o\text{-cresol} \xrightarrow{\text{heat}}$
  $CH_3P(O)(OC_6H_5)OC_6H_4CH_3\text{-}o$
  $+ p\text{-cresol} \longrightarrow$
  $CH_3P(O)(OC_6H_5)OC_6H_4CH_3\text{-}p$
  $+ \text{methyl salicylate} \xrightarrow{C_5H_5N}$
  $CH_3P(O)(OC_6H_5)OC_6H_4COOCH_3\text{-}o$
⑥ Zhur. **31**, 228, 1705, 3316 (1961).

PC₇H₈ClS

① Methylphenylphosphinothioic
  chloride
  $(CH_3)(C_6H_5)P(S)Cl$
② $[(CH_3)(C_6H_5)P(S)]_2 + SO_2Cl_2 \xrightarrow{C_6H_6}$
  88.5%
③ (91~94°/0.01), (140~150°/15). n 1.6117
  (20°).
⑥ Ber. **94**, 3051 (1961). Kosolapoff 75.

PC₇H₉

① Benzylphosphine
  $C_6H_5CH_2PH_2$
② $LiPH_2 + C_6H_5CH_2Cl \longrightarrow$ 75%
  $C_6H_5CH_2P(O)(OC_2H_5)_2 + LiAlH_4 \longrightarrow$
  48%

③ Colorless liq. (180°).
  Sol. in org. solvents.
⑥ Ber. **91**, 1583 (1958); **87**, 919 (1954).

PC₇H₉

① Methylphenylphosphine
  $CH_3(C_6H_5)PH$
② $(CH_3)(C_6H_5)P(S)-P(S)(CH_3)(C_6H_5)$
  $+ LiAlH_4 \longrightarrow$ 62.5%
  $C_6H_5PH_2 + Na + CH_3X \longrightarrow$ 65%
  $(CH_3)(C_6H_5)PO(OCH_3) + LiAlH_4 \longrightarrow$
  53%
③ Colorless liq. (59~60°/10). n_D 1.5695
  (20°).
  Sol. in org. solvents.
  NMR: Ber. **94**, 3056 (1961). J. Chem.
  Eng. Data **7**, 307 (1962).
④ $+ C_6H_5CH_2Br \xrightarrow{\text{benzene}}$
  $[CH_3(C_6H_5)(C_6H_5CH_2)H\overset{+}{P}]\overset{-}{B}r$
⑥ Ber. **91**, 1583 (1958). Monatsh. **90**,
  792 (1959). JCS **1961**, 2813.

PC₇H₉OS

① Methylphenylphosphinothioic acid
  $CH_3(C_6H_5)POSH$
② $CH_3(C_6H_5)POCl + NaSH \xrightarrow{\text{acidification}}$
  $CH_3(C_6H_5)POCl + P_2S_2 \xrightarrow{\text{alk. hydrolysis}}$
  $CH_3(C_6H_5)POMgX + S \xrightarrow{\text{acidification}}$
③ (82~85°/0.05). n_D 1.5708 (23°).
⑥ Roczniki Chem. **36**, 175 (1962).

PC₇H₉OS₂

① Methylphosphonodithioic acid
  O-phenylester
  $CH_3P(S)(OC_6H_5)SH$
② $(CH_3PS_2)_2 + C_6H_5OH \longrightarrow$ 100%
④ $+ SO_2Cl_2 \longrightarrow CH_3P(S)(OC_6H_5)Cl$
  $+ \text{anhyd. } NH_3 \longrightarrow$
  $CH_3P(S)(OC_6H_5)SNH_4$
⑥ JOC **27**, 3832 (1962).

PC$_7$H$_9$OS$_2$

① Phenylphosphonodithioic acid
   O-methyl ester
   C$_6$H$_5$P(S)(OCH$_3$)SH

② C$_6$H$_5$PCl$_2$ + S + KSH + CH$_3$OH ⟶

④ ⟶ Ni salt

⑥ Chimica e industria **27**, 6 (1945).

PC$_7$H$_9$O$_2$

① Methylphenylphosphinic acid
   (CH$_3$)(C$_6$H$_5$)P(O)(OH)

② (CH$_3$)(C$_6$H$_5$)P(O)(OCH$_3$) + 3% NaOH
   $\xrightarrow{\text{HCl}}$ 77%
   [(CH$_3$)(C$_6$H$_5$)PS]$_2$ + HgO + moist C$_6$H$_6$
   ⟶ 79.5%
   CH$_3$(C$_6$H$_5$)$_2$PO + NaH ⟶
   [CH$_3$(C$_6$H$_5$)$_2$HPONa] $\xrightarrow[\text{2) HCl}]{\text{1) H}_2\text{O}_2}$ 69%
   CH$_3$(C$_6$H$_5$)P(O)OP(O)(C$_6$H$_5$)CH$_3$ $\xrightarrow{\text{H}_2\text{O}}$
   CH$_3$(C$_6$H$_5$)$_2$PO + NaOH $\xrightarrow[\text{2) HCl}]{\text{1) 200}\sim\text{300°}}$
   80%

③ Needle crystals. [133~134°].
   Sol. in org. solvents.
   NMR: JACS **83**, 4381 (1961).

⑥ JACS **82**, 423 (1960). Ber. **94**, 1317,
   3051 (1961); **91**, 64 (1958).

PC$_7$H$_9$O$_3$

① Benzylphosphonic acid
   C$_6$H$_5$CH$_2$P(O)(OH)$_2$

② C$_6$H$_5$CH$_2$PCl$_2$ $\xrightarrow{\text{heat with H}_2\text{O}}$
   C$_6$H$_5$CH$_2$P(O)(OC$_4$H$_9$)$_2$ $\xrightarrow[\text{HCl}]{\text{hydrolysis}}$

③ Prisms. [173~175°].
   Sol. in H$_2$O and polar solvents.

⑥ Zhur. **25**, 2173 (1955); **31**, 3027
   (1961).   JACS **67**, 2259 (1945); **81**,
   3026 (1959). Ber. **92**, 952 (1959).

PC$_7$H$_9$S$_2$

① Methylphenylphosphinodithioic acid

CH$_3$(C$_6$H$_5$)P(S)SH

② (CH$_3$PS$_2$)$_2$ + C$_6$H$_6$ $\xrightarrow{\text{AlCl}_3}$ 75%

③ Light green liq. n_D 1.6787 (22°).
   Decomp. on attempted distillation;
   slowly decomp. on standing at
   room temperature.
   NMR: JOC **27**, 3829 (1962).

④ + NH$_3$ ⟶ CH$_3$(C$_6$H$_5$)P(S)SNH$_4$

⑥ JOC **27**, 3829 (1962).

PC$_7$H$_{10}$Cl$_3$O$_3$

① Trichloromethylphosphonic acid
   diallylester
   Cl$_3$CP(O)(OCH$_2$CH=CH$_2$)$_2$

② (CH$_2$=CHCH$_2$O)$_3$P + CCl$_4$ ⟶ 90%

③ Colorless liq. (118°/0.5). n_D 1.4715
   (20°). d 1.2371 (20°/0°).

④ $\xrightarrow{\text{BPO}}$ polymer
   + NaOH ⟶
   (CH$_2$=CHCH$_2$O)$_2$P(O)(ONa) + CHCl$_3$

⑥ Dokl. **89**, 309 (1953).   J. Appl. Chem.
   8, 459 (1958).

PC$_7$H$_{11}$N$_2$

① Bis(2-cyanoethyl)methylphosphine
   CH$_3$(NCCH$_2$CH$_2$)$_2$P

② [CH$_3$(NCCH$_2$CH$_2$)$_3$P$^+$]I$^-$ + NaOC$_2$H$_5$
   ⟶ 57%

③ (159~160°/0.35). n_D 1.5030 (25°).

⑥ JACS **81**, 4803 (1959).

PC$_7$H$_{12}$NO$_3$

① (2-Cyanovinyl)phosphonic acid
   diethylester
   NCCH=CHP(O)(OC$_2$H$_5$)$_2$

② (C$_2$H$_5$O)$_3$P + CH$_2$=CClCN
   $\xrightarrow{\text{2 hrs. (C}_2\text{H}_5)_3\text{N}}$

③ (94°/0.4, 88°/0.15). n_D 1.4519, 1.4513
   (20°).

⑥ Ann. **657**, 19 (1962).

PC₇H₁₃O

① 3-Methyl-1-ethyl-3-phospholene-1-
   oxide

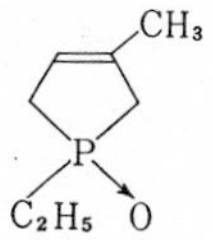

②
$$CH_2=CH-\overset{\overset{\displaystyle CH_3}{|}}{C}=CH_2 + C_2H_5PCl_2$$

$$\xrightarrow{(C_{17}H_{35}CO_2)_2Cu \quad H_2O} \longrightarrow 51\%$$

③ (115~119°/1.2). n_D 1.5050 (25°).

⑥ JACS **84**, 3673 (1962).   US 2663737;
   CA **49**, 760 (1954).

PC₇H₁₃O₃

① Methylphosphonic acid diallylester
   CH₃P(O)(OCH₂CH=CH₂)₂

② (CH₂=CHCH₂O)₃P + CH₃Br ⟶

③ Colorless liq. (102~104°/11). n_D
   1.4466 (20°). d 1.0650 (20°/0°).
   Sol. in org. solvents.

④ + CH₂=C(CH₃)COOCH₃ $\xrightarrow{\text{BPO}}$
   copolymer
   $\xrightarrow{\text{BPO}}$ polymer

⑥ Dokl. **89**, 309 (1953).

PC₇H₁₄Cl₃O₃

① Trichloromethylphosphonic acid
   diisopropylester
   Cl₃CP(O)(OC₃H₇-i)₂

② (i-C₃H₇O)₃P + CCl₄ ⟶

③ Colorless liq. (127~130°/12). n_D
   1.4478 (20°). d 1.2206 (20°/0°).

④ + amine ⟶ diisopropylalkyl-
   aminophosphonate
   + 15% HCl $\xrightarrow{150°}$ i-C₃H₇Cl + H₃PO₃
   + CO₂

⑥ Dokl. **55**, 219 (1947).   Zhur. **16**, 1521
   (1946).

PC₇H₁₅

① Cyclohexylmethylphosphine
   CH₃($cyclo$-C₆H₁₁)PH

② ($cyclo$-C₆H₁₁)PHK + CH₂Cl₂ ⟶   48%

③ (30~31°/3).
   Sol. in ether, C₂H₅OH, C₆H₆ and
   acetone.

④ + CH₃I ⟶
   [(CH₃)₂($cyclo$-C₆H₁₁)P̟H]İ

⑥ Ber. **94**, 2664 (1961).

PC₇H₁₅

① 1-Ethylpentamethylenephosphine

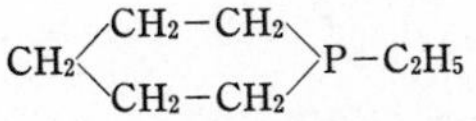

$$CH_2\Big\langle\begin{matrix}CH_2-CH_2\\CH_2-CH_2\end{matrix}\Big\rangle P-C_2H_5$$

② C₂H₅PLi₂ + Br(CH₂)₅Br ⟶   19.7%

③ Colorless liq. (170°).
   Oxidized in air.

④ + S $\xrightarrow{\text{benzene}}$

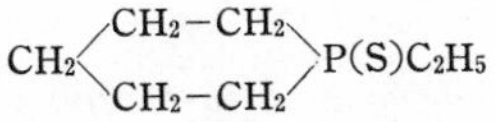

$$CH_2\Big\langle\begin{matrix}CH_2-CH_2\\CH_2-CH_2\end{matrix}\Big\rangle P(S)C_2H_5$$
        mp 97°

   + CH₃I ⟶

$$\Big[CH_2\Big\langle\begin{matrix}CH_2-CH_2\\CH_2-CH_2\end{matrix}\Big\rangle \overset{+}{P}(CH_3)(C_2H_5)\Big]\bar{I}$$
        mp 293~296°

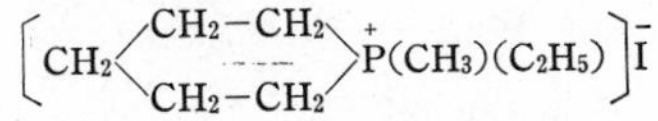

⑥ Ber. **94**, 113 (1961).

PC₇H₁₅O₂

① Allylphosphinic acid butylester
   CH₂=CHCH₂P(O)(OC₄H₉-n)H

② CH₂=CHCH₂P(OC₄H₉-n)₂ + H₂O
   $\xrightarrow{\text{H₂SO₄ in dioxane}}$ 87%

③ (68~68.5°/1.5). n_D 1.4495 (20°).
   d 0.9862 (20°).

⑥ Zhur. **32**, 3351 (1962).

PC₇H₁₅O₂

① Vinylmethylphosphinic acid n-
   butylester
   (CH₃)(CH₂=CH)P(O)(OC₄H₉-n)

② CH₂=CHP(OC₄H₉-n)₂ + CH₃I

hydroquinone 100~110°, in autoclave
———————→

84%

③ (64~64.2°/2). n_D 1.4452 (20°). d 0.9862 (20°).

Raman, UV: Zhur. **32**, 3255, 3351 (1962).

⑥ Dokl. **131**, 1344 (1960).

PC₇H₁₅O₂

① Diethylethoxycarbonylphosphine
$(C_2H_5)_2(C_2H_5OCO)P$

② $(C_2H_5)_2PLi + ClCOOC_2H_5 \longrightarrow 80\%$

③ (53°/3).

Readily oxidized in air.

④ $\xrightarrow[\text{2) 65\% HI}]{\text{1) 2 N-NaOH}} [(C_2H_5)_2\overset{+}{P}H_2]I^-$
$+ NiBr_2 \longrightarrow$
$[CO(OC_2H_5)P(C_2H_5)_2]_2NiBr_2$

⑥ Z. Naturf. **16** b, 837 (1961).

PC₇H₁₅O₃

① Allylphosphonic acid diethylester
$CH_2=CHCH_2P(O)(OC_2H_5)_2$

② $CH_2=CHCH_2Br + (C_2H_5O)_2PONa$
$\xrightarrow[\text{in C₆H₆, 0.5 hr, 20°}]{} 73\%$

③ Colorless oil. (63°/2.5). n_D 1.4350 (20°). d 1.0356 (20°).

IR: Chem. Ind. (London) **1960**, 1058.

④ $+ C_2H_5ONa + C_2H_5OH \xrightarrow{\text{5 hrs}}$
$CH_3CH=CHP(O)(OC_2H_5)_2$
$+ MA \longrightarrow$ copolymer
$+$ poly (1,3-butylene fumarate)
$\longrightarrow$ copolymer

⑥ JACS **80**, 2999 (1958). Zhur. **33**, 432 (1963); **30**, 1608 (1960); **29**, 3947 (1959).

PC₇H₁₅O₄

① (1,2-Epoxy-1-methylethyl) phosphonic acid diethylester
$CH_2-C(CH_3)P(O)(OC_2H_5)_2$
$\underset{O}{\diagdown\diagup}$

② $CH_3COP(O)(OC_2H_5)_2 + CH_2N_2$

in$(C_2H_5)_2O$
$\xrightarrow{\text{3 days}}$
$CH_2=C(CH_3)P(O)(OC_2H_5)_2$
$+ CH_3COOOH \longrightarrow$

③ (75.5~77°/1.5). n_D 1.4294 (20°), d 1.1055 (20°/0°).

⑥ Izv. OKhN **1963**, 675.

PC₇H₁₅O₄

① Acetonylphosphonic acid diethyl-ester
$CH_3COCH_2P(O)(OC_2H_5)_2$

② $CH_3COOC(CH_3)ClCH_2POCl_2 + C_2H_5OH$
$\longrightarrow 60\%$
$(C_2H_5O)_3P + CH_3COCH_2I \longrightarrow 30\%$
$CH_3COCH_2POCl_2 + C_2H_5OH \xrightarrow{C_5H_5N}$
76.6%

③ Colorless liq. (101~102°/2.5, 83~84°/0.4). n_D 1.4370 (20°). d 1.1143 (20°).

Slowly colored in the light.

IR: JACS **85**, 2394 (1963). Chem. Ind. (London) **1960**, 1058.

UV, NMR: JACS **85**, 2394 (1963).

④ $+ Na \longrightarrow$
$[(C_2H_5)_2P(O)CHCOCH_3]Na$

⑥ Dokl. **132**, 842 (1960). JACS **79**, 2608 (1957).

PC₇H₁₅O₅

① Phosphonoformic acid triethylester
$C_2H_5OOCP(O)(OC_2H_5)_2$

② $(C_2H_5O)_3P + ClCOOC_2H_5 \longrightarrow$
$(C_2H_5O)_2POH + Na + ClCOOC_2H_5 \longrightarrow$
$50~60\%$

③ Colorless liq. (135.3°/12). n_D 1.4229 (20°). d 1.0450 (20°/0°).

④ $+ NH_3 \longrightarrow H_2NCOP(O)(OC_2H_5)_2$
$+ H_2O \longrightarrow H_3PO_3 + CO_2$
$+ 0.3\% H_2SO_4 \longrightarrow H_3PO_3 + CO_2$
$+ NaOH$ aq.
$\underset{}{\overset{}{{}}} \begin{cases} \longrightarrow H_3PO_3 + CO_2 \\ \longrightarrow NaOOCP(O)(ONa)_2 \end{cases}$

⑥ J. Russ. Phys. Chem. Soc. **59**, 239
  (1927); Zhur. **17**, 2149 (1947); **26**,
  120 (1956). Ber. **57**, 1023 (1924); **59**,
  1119 (1926).

PC$_7$H$_{15}$O$_5$

① Phosphonoacetic acid *P*-diethyl-
  methyl ester
  CH$_3$OOCCH$_2$P(O)(OC$_2$H$_5$)$_2$

② (C$_2$H$_5$O)$_2$POH + Na
  + ClCH$_2$COOCH$_3$ ⟶

③ Liq. (131.5~132°/9). n_D 1.4355 (20°).
  d 1.1232 (20°/0°).
  Sol. in org. solvents.

④ + NaOH ⟶
  NaOOCCH$_2$P(O)(ONa)(OC$_2$H$_5$)

⑥ Ber. **57**, 1023 (1924). Dokl. **99**, 85
  (1954).

PC$_7$H$_{16}$ClO$_3$

① (3-Chloropropyl) phosphinic acid
  diethyl ester
  ClCH$_2$CH$_2$CH$_2$P(O)(OC$_2$H$_5$)$_2$

② (C$_2$H$_5$O)$_2$PONa + Cl(CH$_2$)$_3$Br ⟶
  68%

③ (90~91°/1). n_D 1.4468 (20°). d 1.1399
  (20°).

④ + PCl$_5$ ⟶ Cl(CH$_2$)$_3$P(O)(OC$_2$H$_5$)Cl

⑥ Zhur. **33**, 1335 (1963).

PC$_7$H$_{17}$O

① Methyldipropylphosphine oxide
  CH$_3$P(O)(C$_3$H$_7$)$_2$

② (C$_3$H$_7$)$_2$POC$_3$H$_7$ + CH$_3$I ⟶ 90%

③ (91~93°/1.0). [39~39.5°].
  Sparingly sol. in H$_2$O and petr.
  ether.

⑥ Zhur. **31**, 2889 (1961).

PC$_7$H$_{17}$O

① Di-*n*-propylhydroxymethylphos-
  phine
  (HOCH$_2$)(*n*-C$_3$H$_7$)$_2$P

② (*n*-C$_3$H$_7$)$_2$P(CH$_2$OH)$_2$Br $\xrightarrow{\text{N(C}_2\text{H}_5)_3}$
  54.3%

③ (73~76°/3). n_D 1.4835 (20°). d 0.9956
  (20°).

④ + *n*-C$_3$H$_7$Br ⟶
  (*n*-C$_3$H$_7$)$_3$P$^+$(CH$_2$OH)Br$^-$
  $\xrightarrow{\text{N(C}_2\text{H}_5)_3}$ (*n*-C$_3$H$_7$)$_3$P

⑥ Zhur. **32**, 553 (1962).

PC$_7$H$_{17}$OS

① Diethylphosphinothioic acid
  O-isopropyl ester
  (C$_2$H$_5$)$_2$P(S)(OC$_3$H$_7$-*i*)

② (C$_2$H$_5$)$_2$PSCl + *i*-C$_3$H$_7$OH ⟶ 86%

③ (96.5~97°/11).

⑥ Ann. **652**, 28 (1962)

PC$_7$H$_{17}$OS

① Dipropylphosphinothioic acid
  O-methyl ester
  (C$_3$H$_7$)$_2$P(S)OCH$_3$

② (C$_3$H$_7$)$_2$PSCl + CH$_3$OH ⟶ 60.5%

③ (118~119°/12).

⑥ Ann. **652**, 28 (1962).

PC$_7$H$_{17}$OS$_2$

① Butylphosphonodithioic acid *O*-
  propyl ester
  C$_4$H$_9$P(S)(OC$_3$H$_7$)SH

② (C$_4$H$_9$PS$_2$)$_2$ + C$_3$H$_7$OH ⟶
  quantitative

③ (60°/0.003). n_D 1.5189 (22.5°).

④ + SO$_2$Cl$_2$ ⟶ C$_4$H$_9$P(S)(OC$_3$H$_7$)Cl

⑥ JOC **27**, 3832 (1962).

PC$_7$H$_{17}$O$_2$

① Methylphosphonous acid di-*n*-propyl
  ester
  CH$_3$P(OC$_3$H$_7$-*n*)$_2$

② CH$_3$PCl$_2$ + *n*-C$_3$H$_7$OH $\xrightarrow{\text{(C}_2\text{H}_5)_3\text{N}}$ 78%

③ n_D 1.4243 (25°).

④ + C$_2$H$_5$SCH$_2$CH$_2$OH $\xrightarrow{\text{heat}}$

CH₃P(OC₃H₇-n)(OCH₂CH₂SC₂H₅)

⑥ JACS **80**, 1150 (1958).

PC₇H₁₇O₂

① Diethylphosphinic acid n-propyl
　　ester
　　(C₂H₅)₂P(O)(OC₃H₇-n)

② (C₂H₅)₂P(O)Cl + n-C₃H₇ONa $\xrightarrow{C_3H_7OH}$
　　50%

③ Colorless liq. (103~104°/13). n_D 1.4356
　　(20°). d 0.9916 (20°/0°).
　　Sol. in org. solvents.

⑥ Dokl. **91**, 271 (1953).

PC₇H₁₇O₂

① Methylphosphonous acid diisopropyl
　　ester
　　CH₃P(OC₃H₇-i)₂

② CH₃PCl₂ + (C₂H₅)₃N + i-C₃H₇OH ⟶
　　79.7%

③ n_D 1.4157 (25°).

④ + C₂H₅SCH₂CH₂OH $\xrightarrow{heat}$
　　CH₃P(OC₃H₇-i)(OCH₂CH₂SC₂H₅)

⑥ JACS **80**, 1150 (1958).

PC₇H₁₇O₂S

① Propylphosphonothioic acid
　　O, S-diethyl ester
　　C₃H₇P(O)(OC₂H₅)SC₂H₅

② C₃H₇P(S)(OC₂H₅)₂ + C₂H₅Br ⟶ 52%

③ Liq. (85~86.5°/3). n_D 1.4733 (20°). d
　　1.0447 (20°).
　　Sol. in org. solvents.

⑥ Izv. OKhN **1956**, 193.

PC₇H₁₇O₂S

① Methylphosphonothioic acid
　　O, O-dipropyl ester
　　CH₃P(S)(OC₃H₇)₂

② CH₃PSCl₂ + C₃H₇OH $\xrightarrow{BF_3 \cdot ether\ reflux}$
　　70%

CH₃PSCl₂ + C₃H₇OH + Na ⟶ 71%

CH₃POCl₂ + C₃H₇OH + (C₂H₅)₃N $\xrightarrow{S}$

③ (95~96°/8). n_D 1.4626 (20°). d 1.0170
　　(20°).

NMR : Compt. rend. **253**, 644 (1961).

④ + SO₂Cl₂ ⟶ CH₃P(O)(OC₃H₇)Cl
　　+ COCl₂ ⟶ CH₃P(O)(OC₃H₇)Cl

⑥ JCS **1962**, 3824 ; **1961**, 238, 3067. Bull.
　　soc. chim. France **1961**, 1222.

PC₇H₁₇O₂S

① Methylphosphonothioic acid
　　O,O-diisopropyl ester
　　CH₃P(S)(OC₃H₇-i)₂

② CH₃PSCl₂ + i-C₃H₇OH $\xrightarrow[reflux]{BF_3 \cdot ether}$ 39%

CH₃PSCl₂ + i-C₃H₇OH + Na ⟶ 71%

CH₃POCl₂ + i-C₃H₇OH + (C₂H₅)₃N
　　$\xrightarrow{S}$ 71%

③ (42~44°/0.25). n_D 1.4508(20°). d 0.9926
　　(20°).

④ + SO₂Cl₂ $\xrightarrow{reflux}$ CH₃P(O)(OC₃H₇-i)Cl
　　+ COCl₂ ⟶ CH₃P(O)(OC₃H₇-i)Cl

⑥ JCS **1962**, 3824 ; **1961**, 238. Bull. soc.
　　chim. France **1961**, 1222.

PC₇H₁₇O₂S

① Methylphosphonothioic acid O-iso-
　　propyl-S-propyl ester
　　CH₃P(O)(OC₃H₇-i)SC₃H₇

② CH₃P(OC₃H₇-i)OSH
　　　+ NaOCH₃ + C₃H₇I ⟶
　　CH₃P(O)(OC₃H₇-i)Cl
　　　+C₃H₇SH + Na ⟶

③ (80°/2). n_D 1.4661 (25°).

⑥ JACS **84**, 617 (1962).

PC₇H₁₇O₂S

① Methylphosphonothioic acid O-ethyl-
　　S-butyl ester
　　CH₃P(O)(OC₂H₅)SC₄H₉

② $CH_3P(S)(OC_2H_5)OH + C_2H_5ONa$
  $+ C_4H_9Br \longrightarrow 56\%$

③ $(112 \sim 114°/9)$. $n_D 1.4815$ $(20°)$. $d 1.0454$
  $(20°)$.

⑥ Zhur. **31**, 179 (1961).

PC₇H₁₇O₂S

① Propylphosphonothioic acid
  O, O-diethyl ester
  $C_3H_7P(S)(OC_2H_5)_2$

② $(C_2H_5O)_2PSH + C_2H_5ONa + C_3H_7Br$
  $\longrightarrow 24\%$

③ Liq. $(63.5 \sim 65.5°/2)$. $n_D 1.4596$ $(20°)$.
  $d 1.0158$ $(20°)$.
  Sol. in org. solvents.

④ $+ C_2H_5Br \longrightarrow$
  $C_3H_7P(O)(OC_2H_5)SC_2H_5$

⑥ Izv. OKhN **1956**, 193.

PC₇H₁₇O₃

① Methylphosphonic acid dipropyl
  ester
  $CH_3P(O)(OC_3H_7)_2$

② $(C_3H_7O)_3P + BrCH(CO_2C_2H_5)_2 \longrightarrow$
  $(C_3H_7O)_2P(O)CH(CO_2C_2H_5)_2 \xrightarrow{\text{Na. } CH_3I}$

③ Oil. $(105 \sim 106°/12, 68 \sim 70°/3)$. $n_D 1.4082$
  $(18°)$. $d 1.0683$ $(0°/0°)$.

⑥ Zhur. **17**, 2149 (1947).

PC₇H₁₇O₃

① Methylphosphonic acid diisopropyl
  ester
  $CH_3P(O)(OC_3H_7-i)_2$

② $CH_3POCl_2 + i\text{-}C_3H_7OH \xrightarrow{\text{Na}} 50\%$

③ Oil. $(78 \sim 79°/10°)$. $n_D 1.4158$ $(20°)$.
  $d 0.9849$ $(20°)$.
  Sol. in org. solvents.
  NMR: J. Phys. Radium. **24**, 108
  (1963).

④ $+ COCl_2 \longrightarrow CH_3P(O)(OC_3H_7-i)Cl$
  $+ i\text{-}C_3H_7Cl$

⑥ JCS **1947**, 1465   JCS **1953**, 2224
  Anal. Chem. **35**, 1179 (1963).

JCS **1963**, 1004

PC₇H₁₇O₃

① Isopropylphosphonic acid diethyl
  ester
  $i\text{-}C_3H_7P(O)(OC_2H_5)_2$

② $PCl_3 + i\text{-}C_3H_7Cl + AlCl_3 \longrightarrow$
  $[i\text{-}C_3H_7PCl_3][AlCl_4] \xrightarrow{C_2H_5OH} 80\%$

③ Colorless liq. $(56 \sim 58°/18)$. $n_D 1.4150$
  $(25°)$. $n_D 1.4154$ $(20°)$. $d 0.9951$
  $(20°)$.
  Sol. in org. solvents.

⑥ JACS **76**, 4172 (1954); **79**, 3570
  (1957); **80**, 5240 (1958). Dokl. **147**,
  612 (1962).

PC₇H₁₈IO

① Triethyl hydroxymethylphospho-
  nium iodide
  $[(C_2H_5)_3P(CH_2OH)]I$

② $(C_2H_5)_3P + CH_2O + HI \longrightarrow$ ca. 60%

③ $[199 \sim 201°]$.

④ $\xrightarrow{\text{NaOH}} (C_2H_5)_3P$ (100%)

⑥ Ann. **659**, 49 (1962).

PC₇H₁₈IO

① Diethyl-2-hydroxyethylmethylphos-
  phonium iodide
  $[(C_2H_5)_2(HOCH_2CH_2)PCH_3]I$

② $(C_2H_5)_2P(CH_2CH_2OH) + CH_3I \xrightarrow{(C_2H_5)_2O}$
  72%

③ $[253 \sim 255°]$.
  Sol. in C_2H_5OH and H_2O; insol. in
  $(C_2H_5)_2O$.

⑥ Ber. **94**, 102 (1961).

PC₇H₁₈NOS

① *N, N*-Diethyl-*P*-methylphosphon-
  amidothioic acid *S*-ethyl ester
  $CH_3P(O)(SC_2H_5)N(C_2H_5)_2$

② $CH_3PCl_2 + (C_2H_5)_2NSC_2H_5 \xrightarrow{\text{in } SO_2} 31\%$

③ (90~91°/4). n_D 1.5032 (20°). d_{20} 1.1996.
⑥ Zhur. 31, 1361 (1961).

PC$_7$H$_{18}$NOS

① N, N-Diethyl-P-methylphosphon-
   amidothioic acid O-ethyl ester
   CH$_3$P(S)(OC$_2$H$_5$)N(C$_2$H$_5$)$_2$
② C$_4$H$_9$SH + (C$_2$H$_5$)$_2$NP(OC$_2$H$_5$)CH$_3$ ⟶
   62.2%
   CH$_3$P(OC$_2$H$_5$)N(C$_2$H$_5$)$_2$ + S ⟶ 64%
③ (98~101°/10). n_D 1.4828 (20°). d 1.0103
   (20°).
⑥ Zhur. 32, 1974, 3070 (1962).

PC$_7$H$_{18}$NOS

① Triethylphosphonamidothioic acid
   O-methyl ester
   C$_2$H$_5$P(S)(OCH$_3$)N(C$_2$H$_5$)$_2$
② C$_2$H$_5$P(OCH$_3$)N(C$_2$H$_5$)$_2$ + S ⟶ 69%
③ Colorless liq. (112~113°/10). n_D 1.4882
   (20°). d 1.0287 (20°).
   Sol. in org. solvents.
⑥ Izv. OKhN 1955, 1021.

PC$_7$H$_{18}$NO$_2$

① N, N-Diethyl-P-methylphosphon-
   amidic acid ethyl ester
   CH$_3$P(O)(OC$_2$H$_5$)N(C$_2$H$_5$)$_2$
② CH$_3$P(O)(OC$_2$H$_5$)Cl + (C$_2$H$_5$)$_2$NH ⟶
   64%
③ (110~114°/22).
⑥ JOC 28, 329 (1963).

PC$_8$H$_5$Br$_2$F$_6$

① Dibromobis(trifluoromethyl)phenyl-
   phosphorane
   (C$_6$H$_5$)(CF$_3$)$_2$PBr$_2$
② C$_6$H$_5$(CF$_3$)$_2$P + Br$_2$ $\xrightarrow{CCl_4}$
④ + H$_2$O ⟶ C$_6$H$_5$(CF$_3$)P(O)OH
   + (CHF$_3$ + HBr)
⑥ Can. J. Chem. 39, 595 (1961).

PC$_8$H$_5$Cl$_6$O

① Phenylbis(trichloromethyl)phos-
   phine oxide
   (C$_6$H$_5$)P(O)(CCl$_3$)$_2$
② C$_6$H$_5$P(O)(CH$_2$Cl)$_2$ $\xrightarrow{Cl_2,\ 150\sim215°}$ 64.5%
③ [133~134°] (C$_2$H$_5$OH).
⑥ Zhur. 30, 1294 (1960).

PC$_8$H$_5$F$_6$

① Bis(trifluoromethyl)phenylphos-
   phine
   (CF$_3$)$_2$C$_6$H$_5$P
② (C$_6$H$_5$P)$_4$ + CF$_3$I $\xrightarrow{heat\ or\ UV}$
③ (62~65°/20).
④ + aq. NaOH (20%) $\xrightarrow{80°}$
   CHF$_3$ + C$_6$H$_5$PO$_2$HNa
   + I$_2$ $\xrightarrow{185°}$ CHF$_3$ + CF$_3$CH$_2$I + PI$_3$
   + Br$_2$ $\xrightarrow{in\ CCl_4}$ C$_6$H$_5$(CF$_3$)$_2$PBr$_2$
⑥ Can. J. Chem. 39, 564 (1961).

PC$_8$H$_6$Cl$_4$NO$_2$

① N-Trichloroacetyl-P-phenylphos-
   phonamidic chloride
   C$_6$H$_5$P(O)(Cl)NHCOCCl$_3$
② C$_6$H$_5$P(NHCOCCl$_3$)Cl$_2$ + 100% HCOOH
③ [135~137°].
⑥ Zhur. 32, 166 (1962).

PC$_8$H$_7$Cl$_4$

① Tetrachlorostyrylphosphorane,
   PCl$_5$ complex
   (C$_6$H$_5$CH=CH)PCl$_4$
② C$_6$H$_5$CH=CH$_2$ + 2 PCl$_5$ $\xrightarrow[C_6H_6]{0°}$
   C$_6$H$_5$CH=CHPCl$_3$$\overset{+}{}P\overset{-}{}Cl_6$ (62%)
   C$_6$H$_5$CH=CH$_2$ + PCl$_5$ ⟶ 90%
③ [65~68°].
   Sol. in non-polar solvents.
   Very hygroscopic.
④ C$_6$H$_5$CH=CHPCl$_3$·$\overset{+}{P}$Cl$_6$

$+ \text{C}_6\text{H}_5\text{CH}=\text{CH}_2 \xrightarrow{70°}$

$2\,\text{C}_6\text{H}_5\text{CH}=\text{CHPCl}_4$

$+ \text{SO}_2 \longrightarrow \text{C}_6\text{H}_5\text{CH}=\text{CHP(O)Cl}_2$

(84%)

⑥ Akad. Nauk. Ukr. RSR **1960**, 801 ;
   CA **55**, 430 (1961).   Zhur. **30**, 4044
   (1960).

PC$_8$H$_7$F$_4$

① Tetrafluorostyrylphosphorane
   $\text{C}_6\text{H}_5\text{CH}=\text{CHPF}_4$

② $3\,\text{C}_6\text{H}_5\text{CH}=\text{CHPCl}_2 + 4\,\text{AsF}_3 \longrightarrow$

③ (97.5~98°/23).
   NMR : Inorg. Chem. **2**, 613 (1963).

⑥ Chem. Ind. (London) **1962**, 1868.

PC$_8$H$_7$O$_3$

① Phenylacetylenephosphonic acid
   $\text{C}_6\text{H}_5\text{C}\equiv\text{CP(O)(OH)}_2$

② $\text{C}_6\text{H}_5\text{CCl}=\text{CHP(O)(OH)}_2 + \text{KOH} \longrightarrow$

③ Crystals. [142°].

④ $\xrightarrow{\text{hydrogenation}} \text{C}_6\text{H}_5\text{CH}_2\text{CH}_2\text{P(O)(OH)}_2$

⑥ Ber. **66**, 278 (1933).

PC$_8$H$_9$ClNO$_2$

① N-Acetyl-P-phenylphosphonamidic
   chloride
   $\text{C}_6\text{H}_5\text{P(O)(Cl)NHCOCH}_3$

② $\text{CH}_3\text{CON}=\text{PC}_6\text{H}_5\text{Cl}_2 + 100\%\ \text{HCOOH}$
   $\longrightarrow$

③ [68~70°].

⑥ Zhur. **32**, 1874 (1962).

PC$_8$H$_9$Cl$_2$O

① Phenylphosphonochloridous acid
   2-chloroethyl ester
   $\text{C}_6\text{H}_5\text{P(OCH}_2\text{CH}_2\text{Cl)Cl}$

② $\text{C}_6\text{H}_5\text{PCl}_2 + \text{CH}_2-\text{CH}_2 \longrightarrow 68\%$
   $\qquad\qquad\qquad\ \ \backslash\underset{\text{O}}{\diagup}$

③ (99~100°/1). n_D 1.5645 (20°). d 1.2896
   (20°).

④ $+ \text{C}_2\text{H}_5\text{MgBr} \xrightarrow{\text{C}_5\text{H}_5\text{N}}$

$\text{C}_6\text{H}_5(\text{C}_2\text{H}_5)\text{POCH}_2\text{CH}_2\text{Cl}$

⑥ Dokl. **135**, 849 (1960).

PC$_8$H$_9$Cl$_2$O$_2$

① 2-Chloroethylphosphonochloridic
   acid phenyl ester
   $\text{ClCH}_2\text{CH}_2\text{P(O)(OC}_6\text{H}_5)\text{Cl}$

② $\text{ClCH}_2\text{CH}_2\text{POCl}_2 + \text{C}_6\text{H}_5\text{OH} \longrightarrow 50\%$

③ (130~132°/1). n_D 1.5329 (20°). d
   1.3528 (20°).

④ $+ \text{C}_2\text{H}_5\text{OH} \longrightarrow$
   $\text{ClCH}_2\text{CH}_2\text{P(O)(OC}_6\text{H}_5)(\text{OC}_2\text{H}_5)$

⑥ Zhur. **31**, 3316 (1961).

PC$_8$H$_9$Cl$_2$O$_2$

① Phenylphosphonochloridic acid
   2-chloroethylester
   $\text{C}_6\text{H}_5\text{P(O)(OCH}_2\text{CH}_2\text{Cl)Cl}$

② $\text{C}_6\text{H}_5\text{P(O)(OCH}_2\text{CH}_2\text{Cl)}_2 + \text{PCl}_5 \longrightarrow$
   71%
   $\text{C}_6\text{H}_5\text{P(OCH}_2\text{CH}_2\text{Cl)}_2 + (\text{Cl}) \dashrightarrow 40\%$
   $\text{C}_6\text{H}_5\text{P(OCH}_2\text{CH}_2\text{Cl)}_2 + \text{HCl} \xrightarrow{(\text{Cl})} 94\%$

③ (155~158°/2). n_D 1.5632 (20°). d 1.3400
   (20°).
   Hydrolyze slowly in H$_2$O.

④ $+ \text{PCl}_5 \longrightarrow \text{C}_6\text{H}_5\text{POCl}_2$
   $+ \text{CH}_2-\text{CH}_2 + \text{AlCl}_3 \longrightarrow$
   $\qquad\ \backslash\underset{\text{O}}{\diagup}$
   $\text{C}_6\text{H}_5\text{P(O)(OCH}_2\text{CH}_2\text{Cl)}_2$
   $+ \text{ROH} \longrightarrow$
   $\text{C}_6\text{H}_5\text{P(O)(OCH}_2\text{CH}_2\text{Cl)(OR)}$
   (R=CH$_3$, C$_2$H$_5$, C$_4$H$_9$, CH$_2$=CHCH$_2$)

⑥ Zhur. **32**, 964 (1962).

PC$_8$H$_9$O$_3$

① Styrylphosphonic acid
   $\text{C}_6\text{H}_5\text{CH}=\text{CHP(O)(OH)}_2$

② $\text{C}_6\text{H}_5\text{CH}=\text{CH}_2 + \text{PCl}_3 + \text{Cl}_2 \longrightarrow 35.7\%$
   $\text{C}_6\text{H}_5\text{CH}=\text{CH}_2 + \text{PCl}_5 \dashrightarrow$

③ Colorless plates. [154.5~155°].

⑥ Ber. **63**, 1158 (1930).   JACS **68**, 2540
   (1946).   Dokl. **127**, 1239 (1959).

PC$_8$H$_9$O$_3$S

① Carboxymethylphenylphosphino-
   thioic acid
   (HOOCCH$_2$)C$_6$H$_5$P(S)OH
② C$_6$H$_5$P(S)(SC$_4$H$_9$)$_2$ + BrCH$_2$COOH ⟶
③ Oil.
④ ⟶ Na salt
⑥ J. Russ. Phys. Chem. Soc. **61**, 2037
   (1929).

PC$_8$H$_{10}$Cl

① Ethylphenylphosphinous chloride
   (C$_2$H$_5$)(C$_6$H$_5$)PCl
② C$_6$H$_5$PCl$_2$ + (C$_2$H$_5$)$_4$Pb $\xrightarrow{120°}$ 73%
③ (180~190°/15), (76°/2). n_D 1.5707(20°).
   d 1.1156 (20°).
   NMR : J. Chem. Eng. Data **7**, 307
   (1962).
④ + S $\xrightarrow{AlCl_3}$ C$_6$H$_5$(C$_2$H$_5$)P(S)Cl
   + CH$_3$MgI ⟶ C$_6$H$_5$(C$_2$H$_5$)PCH$_3$
⑥ Kosolapoff 35. Proc. Chem. Soc.
   1961, 145. Zhur. **32**, 2848 (1962).

PC$_8$H$_{10}$ClO

① Phenylphosphonochloridous acid
   ethyl ester
   C$_6$H$_5$P(OC$_2$H$_5$)Cl
② C$_6$H$_5$PCl$_2$ + C$_6$H$_5$P(OC$_2$H$_5$)$_2$ ⟶ 74%
   C$_6$H$_5$P(S)Cl$_2$ + C$_2$H$_5$OH + (C$_2$H$_5$)$_3$N
   ⟶ 50%
③ (74~75°/0.2). n_D 1.5664 (20°). d 1.2434
   (20°).
④ + C$_2$H$_5$SH $\xrightarrow{C_5H_5N}$ C$_6$H$_5$P(OC$_2$H$_5$)SC$_2$H$_5$
   + (C$_2$H$_5$)$_2$NH ⟶
   C$_6$H$_5$P(OC$_2$H$_5$)N(C$_2$H$_5$)$_2$
⑥ Ber. **95**, 2993 (1962). Zhur. Vsesoyuz
   Khim. Obshchestva im. D. I. Mendeleeva **6**, No.1, 119 (1961) ; CA
   55, 15835 (1961).

PC$_8$H$_{10}$ClO$_2$

① Phenylphosphonochloridic acid ethyl
   ester
   C$_6$H$_5$P(O)(OC$_2$H$_5$)Cl
② C$_6$H$_5$POCl$_2$ + C$_2$H$_5$OH ⟶
③ Colorless liq. (120°/2). n_D 1.5372
   (20°).
   Sol. in org. solvents. Decomp. in
   H$_2$O.
⑥ JACS **75**, 1763 (1953).

PC$_8$H$_{10}$K

① Potassium ethylphenylphosphide
   KP(C$_2$H$_5$)(C$_6$H$_5$)·1 dioxane
② (C$_2$H$_5$)$_2$(C$_6$H$_5$)P + K $\xrightarrow{dioxane}$ 41%
   (C$_2$H$_5$)(C$_6$H$_5$)$_2$P + K $\xrightarrow{dioxane}$ 47.5%
③ Lemon-yellow needles.
④ + C$_2$H$_5$Br $\xrightarrow{dioxane}$
   [(C$_2$H$_5$)$_3$(C$_6$H$_5$)P]Br$^-$
   + H$_2$O ⟶ (C$_2$H$_5$)(C$_6$H$_5$)PH
   + 30% H$_2$O$_2$ + NaOH $\xrightarrow{H_2O}$
   (C$_2$H$_5$)(C$_6$H$_5$)P(O)OH
⑤ Intermediate in prepn. of org. P
   compds.
⑥ Ber. **94**, 392 (1961).

PC$_8$H$_{10}$Na

① Sodium ethylphenylphosphide
   NaP(C$_2$H$_5$)(C$_6$H$_5$)·1 dioxane
② (C$_2$H$_5$)$_2$(C$_6$H$_5$)P + Na $\xrightarrow{dioxane}$ 6.7%
③ Light yellow crystals.
⑥ Ber. **94**, 392 (1961).

PC$_8$H$_{11}$

① Ethylphenylphosphine
   C$_2$H$_5$(C$_6$H$_5$)PH
② C$_2$H$_5$(C$_6$H$_5$)PK·1 dioxane + H$_2$O ⟶
   64.3%
   (C$_6$H$_5$)P(H)CH$_2$CH$_2$P(H)(C$_6$H$_5$)
   $\xrightarrow{pyrolysis}$ 25%
③ Colorless liq. (122~125°).
   Sol. in org. solvents.

④ + CH$_3$I ⟶ [CH$_3$(C$_2$H$_5$)(C$_6$H$_5$)$\overset{+}{P}$H]$\bar{I}$

⑥ Ber. **94**, 392 (1961).   **96**, 279 (1963).

PC$_8$H$_{11}$O

① Dimethylphenylphosphine oxide
    (CH$_3$)$_2$P(O)C$_6$H$_5$

② (C$_6$H$_5$P)$_4$ + CH$_3$I $\xrightarrow{\text{C}_6\text{H}_6,\ 80°}$

    (CH$_3$)$_3$P$^+$(C$_6$H$_5$)I$^-$ $\xrightarrow{\text{NaOH}}$ 86.4%

③ (300~308°). [107~109°].

④ + HgCl$_2$ ⟶ adduct [162~164°
    decomp.]

⑥ Kosolapoff 115. Ber. **94**, 186 (1961);
    93, 405 (1960).

PC$_8$H$_{11}$OS

① Ethylphenylphosphinothioic acid
    C$_2$H$_5$(C$_6$H$_5$)PSOH

② C$_2$H$_5$(C$_6$H$_5$)POMgX + S $\xrightarrow{\text{acidification}}$

    C$_2$H$_5$(C$_6$H$_5$)POCl + NaHS $\xrightarrow{\text{acidification}}$

    C$_2$H$_5$(C$_6$H$_5$)POCl + P$_2$S$_5$ $\xrightarrow{\text{hydrolysis}}$

    C$_2$H$_5$(C$_6$H$_5$)P(S)Cl + NaOH aq. ⟶

③ Oil. (111~112°/0.06). n_D 1.5972 (23°).
    Decomp. on attempted distillation.

④ ⟶ Na salt
    ⟶ cyclohexylamine salt

⑥ J. Russ. Phys. Chem. Soc. **61**, 2037
    (1929).   Roczniki Chem. **36**, 175
    (1962).   JCS **1962**, 540.

PC$_8$H$_{11}$OS$_2$

① Phenylphosphonodithioic acid
    O-ethyl ester
    C$_6$H$_5$P(S)(OC$_2$H$_5$)SH

② (C$_6$H$_5$PS$_2$)$_2$ + C$_2$H$_5$OH ⟶ 99%
    C$_6$H$_5$PSCl$_2$ + KSH + C$_2$H$_5$OH ⟶

④ + anhydrous NH$_3$ ⟶
    C$_6$H$_5$P(S)(OC$_2$H$_5$)SNH$_4$
    ⟶ Ni salt

⑥ JOC **27**, 3832 (1962).   Chim. e ind.
    27, 6 (1945).

PC$_8$H$_{11}$O$_2$

① Methylphenylphosphinic acid
    methyl ester
    (CH$_3$)(C$_6$H$_5$)P(O)(OCH$_3$)

② C$_6$H$_5$P(OCH$_3$)$_2$ + CH$_3$I ⟶ 92%
    CH$_3$(C$_6$H$_5$)PO$_2$H + SOCl$_2$ ⟶
    CH$_3$(C$_6$H$_5$)POCl
    $\xrightarrow{\text{CH}_3\text{OH in pyridine}}$ 25%

③ Colorless liq. (83~85°/0.1). n_D 1.5220
    (21°). d 1.1436 (25°/0°).

④ + COCl$_2$ $\xrightarrow{\text{in CCl}_4}$ C$_6$H$_5$(CH$_3$)POCl
    + 3% NaOH $\xrightarrow{\text{HCl}}$ C$_6$H$_5$(CH$_3$)P(O)OH

⑥ Zhur. **31**, 1517 (1961).   JCS **1958**,
    3129; **1963**, 1004. JACS **82**, 423
    (1960).

PC$_8$H$_{11}$O$_2$

① Ethylphenylphosphinic acid
    (C$_2$H$_5$)(C$_6$H$_5$)P(O)(OH)

② KP(C$_2$H$_5$)(C$_6$H$_5$)·1 dioxane + H$_2$O $\xrightarrow{\text{H}_2\text{O}_2}$

    C$_2$H$_5$(C$_6$H$_5$)$_2$PO + NaOH $\xrightarrow[\text{2) HCl}]{\text{1) 200~300°}}$

    94%
    (CH$_2$=CH)(C$_6$H$_5$)P(O)OH + H$_2$
    $\xrightarrow{\text{C}_2\text{H}_5\text{OH(Pd)}}$ 75%

③ Plate crystals. [79~80°](etherate).

⑥ Ber. **24**, 392 (1961); **91**, 64(1958).
    Roczniki Chem. **34**, 1161 (1960).

PC$_8$H$_{11}$O$_2$

① Phenylphosphonous acid dimethyl
    ester
    C$_6$H$_5$P(OCH$_3$)$_2$

② C$_6$H$_5$PCl$_2$ + CH$_3$OH $\xrightarrow[\text{hexane}]{\text{pyridine}}$ 68%

    C$_6$H$_5$PCl$_2$ + CH$_3$OH $\xrightarrow[\text{(C}_2\text{H}_5)_2\text{O}]{\text{(C}_6\text{H}_5)\text{N(CH}_3)_2}$

    70.5%

③ (98°/17). n_D 1.5261 (25°). d 1.0732 (24°/

0°).

④ $+CH_3I \longrightarrow CH_3(C_6H_5)P(O)OCH_3$
$+ BrCH_2CH_2OOCCH_3 \longrightarrow$
$(CH_3)(C_6H_5)P(O)(OCH_2CH_2OOCCH_3)$
$+ BrCH_2CH_2Br \longrightarrow$
$[CH_2OP(O)(CH_3)(C_6H_5)]_2$

⑥ JACS 82, 423 (1960). Bull. acad. sci.
URSS, Classe sci. chim. 1945, 167.

$PC_8H_{11}O_2$

① Phenyldihydroxymethylphosphine
$(HOCH_2)_2C_6H_5P$

② $C_6H_5PH_2 + 30\%$ HCHO $+$ HCl $\longrightarrow$
$C_6H_5P(CH_2OH)_3Cl \xrightarrow{\text{heat in } (C_2H_5)_3N}$

④ $+ N{\to}O \longrightarrow C_6H_5P(O)(CH_2OH)_2$

⑥ Zhur. 31, 3411 (1961).   CA 57, 4692
(1962).

$PC_8H_{11}O_3$

① Phenylphosphonic acid ethyl ester
$C_6H_5P(O)(OC_2H_5)(OH)$

② $C_6H_5P(O)(OH)_2 + C_2H_5OH \xrightarrow{C_5H_5N}$
74.6% as Ba salt
$(C_6H_5PO_2)_n + C_2H_5OH \xrightarrow{\text{heat}} 84\%$ as
Ba salt

③ Unstable oil.
Very stable in neutral solutions
(pH 3~9).

④ $\xrightarrow[\text{hydrolysis}]{\text{HCl or NaOH}} C_6H_5P(O)(OH)_2$
$\xrightarrow{Ca(OH)_2} Ca$ salt
$\xrightarrow{Ba(OH)_2} Ba$ salt
$\longrightarrow Ag$ salt

⑥ Ann. 181, 265 (1876).   Helv. Chim.
Acta 44, 1817, 1820 (1961).   Ber.
94, 996 (1961).

$PC_8H_{11}O_3$

① Methylphosphonic acid methylphenyl ester

$CH_3P(O)(OCH_3)(OC_6H_5)$

② $C_6H_5OP(OCH_3)_2 + CH_3I$
$\xrightarrow{\text{heat in sealed tube}} 98.5\%$

③ Colorless liq. n_D 1.5054 (20°). d 1.1914
(20°).
Sol. in org. solvents.

⑥ Izv. OKhN 1954, 427.   Dokl. 92, 57
(1953).

$PC_8H_{11}S$

① Dimethylphenylphosphine sulfide
$(CH_3)_2P(S)C_6H_5$

② $(CH_3)_2P(S)Br + C_6H_5MgBr$
$\xrightarrow{(C_2H_5)_2O, \, 0\sim10°} 88\%$

$C_6H_5PCl_2 + CH_3MgBr \longrightarrow \xrightarrow{S} 78\%$

③ $[47.0\sim47.7°]$ $(C_6H_6$-hexane).

⑥ JOC 28, 3430 (1963).   J. Chem. Eng.
News 8, 226 (1963).

$PC_8H_{11}S_2$

① Ethylphenylphosphinodithioic acid
$C_2H_5(C_6H_5)P(S)SH$

② $(C_2H_5PS_2)_2 + C_6H_6 \xrightarrow{AlCl_3} 79\%$

③ $[64.5°]$.
Slowly decomp. on standing at
room temperature.
NMR: JOC 27, 3829 (1962).

④ $+ NH_3 \longrightarrow C_2H_5(C_6H_5)P(S)SNH_4$

$PC_8H_{11}Se$

① Dimethylphenylphosphine selenide
$(CH_3)_2P(Se)C_6H_5$

② $C_6H_5PCl_2 + CH_3MgBr \longrightarrow \xrightarrow{S} 62\%$

③ $(129°/0.90)$. n_D 1.6272 (27°).

⑥ J. Chem. Eng. Data 8, 226 (1963).

$PC_8H_{12}NO_2$

① P-Phenylphosphonamidic acid ethyl
ester

$C_6H_5P(O)(OC_2H_5)NH_2$

② $C_6H_5PO(NH_2)_2 + C_2H_5OH \longrightarrow 90.1\%$

③ Colorless solid. [127°].

Sol. in hot abs. ethanol, hot water, chloroform, acetone, hot xylene; moderately soluble in cold ethanol; only slightly soluble in diethylether, cold water and petroleum ether.

⑥ JOC **22**, 265 (1957).

PC₈H₁₂NO₂

① *P*-Methyl-*N*-phenylphosphonamidic acid methyl ester
$CH_3P(O)(OCH_3)NHC_6H_5$

② $(CH_3O)_2PNHC_6H_5 + CH_3I \longrightarrow 19\%$

③ Solid. [76.5~77.5°].
Sol. in org. solvents.

⑥ Dokl. **96**, 991 (1954).

PC₈H₁₃N₂

① Bis(2-cyanoethyl)ethylphosphine
$C_2H_5(NCCH_2CH_2)_2P$

② $[C_2H_5(NCCH_2CH_2)_3\overset{+}{P}]\overset{-}{I} + NaOC_2H_5$
$\longrightarrow 43.5\%$

$[C_2H_5(NCCH_2CH_2)_3\overset{+}{P}]\overset{-}{I} \xrightarrow{\text{electrolysis}}$
50~70%

③ (153~155°/0.55, 178~180°/3~4). n_D
1.5040 (25°).

⑥ JACS **81**, 4803 (1959). Ann. **646**, 65 (1961).

PC₈H₁₃O₃

① Vinylphosphonic acid diallyl ester
$CH_2=CHP(O)(OCH_2CH=CH_2)_2$

② $ClCH_2CH_2P(O)(OCH_2CH=CH_2)_2$

$+ (C_2H_5)_3N \xrightarrow[50~60° \ 3hrs]{\text{in } C_5H_5N} 66.5\%$

③ (86~88°/1). n_D 1.4555 (20°). d 1.1222
(20°).

④ + 2,2′-dichloroethyl divinylphosphinate $\longrightarrow$ copolymer

⑥ Plasticheskie Massy **1962**, 10; **1961**, 38.

PC₈H₁₅

① Ethynyl-dipropylphosphine
$HC\equiv CP(C_3H_7)_2$

② $(C_3H_7)_2PCl + CH\equiv CMgBr \longrightarrow 60\%$

③ Colorless liq. (55°/11).
IR: Rec. trav. chim. **81**, 993 (1962).

PC₈H₁₅O₃

① Ethylphosphonic acid diallyl ester
$C_2H_5P(O)(OCH_2CH=CH_2)_2$

② $C_2H_5P(O)Cl_2 + CH_2=CHCH_2OH$

$\xrightarrow{C_5H_5N} 65.8\%$

③ Colorless liq. (73~78°/0.5). n_D 1.4470
(25°). d 0.9963 (25°/25°).

Sol. in org. solvents.

④ $\xrightarrow{\text{BPO}}$ polymer

⑥ JACS **76**, 2191 (1954).

PC₈H₁₇

① Di-*n*-propylvinyphosphine
$(CH_2=CH)(n-C_3H_7)_2P$

② $(n-C_3H_7)_2POC_4H_9 + CH_2=CHMgBr$
$\xrightarrow{\text{THF}} 68\%$

③ (68~69°/23). n_D 1.4680 (20°). d 0.8144
(20°).

④ + active MnO₂ $\longrightarrow$
$(n-C_3H_7)_2P(O)CH=CH_2$

⑥ Dokl. **135**, 603 (1960); CA **55**, 12272
(1961).

PC₈H₁₇O

① Dipropylvinylphosphine oxide
$(C_3H_7)_2P(O)CH=CH_2$

② $(C_3H_7)_2POCH_2CH_2Cl \xrightarrow{(C_2H_5)_3N, \ 120°}$
46%

$(C_3H_7)_2POC_4H_9 + CH_2=CHMgBr \xrightarrow{\text{THF}}$
$(C_3H_7)_2PCH=CH_2$

$\xrightarrow{MnO_2/\text{petr. ether, } 40°} 97\%$

③ $(77\sim78°/1.0, 89\sim89.5°/2)$. $[36\sim37°]$.
⑥ Dokl. **135**, 603, 849 (1960).

$PC_8H_{17}O_2$

① Ethylvinylphosphinic acid *n*-butyl
   ester
   $(C_2H_5)(CH_2=CH)P(O)(OC_4H_9-n)$

② $(CH_2=CH)P(OC_4H_9)_2 + C_2H_5I \xrightarrow{10\,hr}$
   37.5%

③ $(68.5\sim69°/2)$. $n_D 1.4470 (20°)$. $d 0.9724$
   $(20°)$.

⑥ Zhur. **32**, 3351 (1962).

$PC_8H_{17}O_2$

① Ethoxycarbonyl methyl diethyl
   phosphine
   $(C_2H_5)_2PCH_2CO_2C_2H_5$

② $(C_2H_5)_2PH + BrCH_2CO_2C_2H_5 \xrightarrow{NaOC_2H_5}$
   53%

③ Colorless liq. $(90\sim91°/12)$.
   Air-sensitive.

④ $+C_2H_5I \longrightarrow [(C_2H_5)_3\overset{+}{P}CH_2CO_2C_2H_5]I^-$

⑥ Ber. **94**, 2244 (1961).

$PC_8H_{17}O_5$

① Phosphonoacetic acid triethyl ester
   $C_2H_5OOCCH_2P(O)(OC_2H_5)_2$

② $(C_2H_5O)_2POH + C_2H_5ONa$
   $ClCH_2COOC_2H_5 \longrightarrow 58\%$

③ Colorless liq. $(152\sim153°/20)$. n_D
   $1.4305 (20°)$. $d 1.1215 (20°)$.
   Sol. in org. solvents.

④ $+ C_6H_5CHO \xrightarrow{piperidine}$
   $C_6H_5CH=CCOOC_2H_5$
           $|$
           $P(O)(OC_2H_5)_2$
   $+ C_6H_5CH\begin{bmatrix}CHCOOC_2H_5 \\ | \\ P(O)(OC_2H_5)_2\end{bmatrix}_2$
   $+ C_6H_5CHO \xrightarrow{piperidine\ hydrolysis}$
   $C_6H_5CH=CHCOOH$

⑥ J. Russ. Phys. Chem. Soc. **46**, 295
   (1914). JACS **68**, 1103 (1946). JOC
   25, 1232 (1960). Izv. OKhN **1963**,
   749 ; **1962**, 1876.

$PC_8H_{18}Cl$

① Dibutylphosphinous chloride
   $(C_4H_9)_2PCl$

② $(C_4H_9)_2PH + COCl_2 \xrightarrow{CH_2Cl_2,\ -30°} 89\%$
   $(C_2H_5)_2NP(C_4H_9)_2 + HCl \xrightarrow{petr.\ ether}$

③ $(91\sim92°/12)$. $(77\sim81°/1.0)$.
   Hygroscopic liq.

⑥ Kosolapoff 55. JOC **26**, 4770 (1961).
   Ber. **92**, 2681 (1959).

$PC_8H_{18}ClO$

① Dibutylphosphinic chloride
   $(C_4H_9)_2P(O)Cl$

② $(C_4H_9)_2P(O)H + PCl_5 \longrightarrow 80.5\%$
   $[(C_4H_9)_2P(S)]_2 + SOCl_2 \longrightarrow$

③ $(156\sim157°/28), (142\sim144/11)$. $n_D 1.4643$
   $(20°)$. $d 1.0296 (20°)$.

④ $+ C_4H_9OH \longrightarrow (C_4H_9)_2P(O)C_4H_9$
   (83%).

⑥ Kaufman 1080. JOC **27**, 4444 (1962).
   Chem. Prumysl. **13**, 191 (1963) ; CA
   59, 15305 (1963).

$PC_8H_{18}ClO$

① Di-*n*-propylphosphinous acid
   2-chloroethyl ester
   $(n\text{-}C_3H_7)_2POCH_2CH_2Cl$

② $ClCH_2CH_2OPCl_2 + CH_3MgBr \xrightarrow{C_5H_5N}$
   40%

③ $(49\sim50°/2)$. $n_D 1.4675 (20°)$. $d 0.9825$
   $(20°)$.

④ $+ (C_2H_5)_3N \xrightarrow{120°}$
   $(C_3H_7)_2P(O)CH=CH_2$

⑥ Dokl. **135**, 849 (1960).

PC₈H₁₉

① Methylethyl(*n*-pentyl)phosphine
CH₃(C₂H₅)(*n*-C₅H₁₁)P

② *n*-C₅H₁₁PCl₂ + C₆H₅CH₂MgX $\xrightarrow{CH_3I}$
[(*n*-C₅H₁₁)(CH₃)(C₆H₅CH₂)₂P]⁺I⁻

$\xrightarrow[2)C_2H_5I]{1)\ LiAlH_4}$ $\left[\begin{array}{c} CH_3 \\ | \\ n\text{-}C_5H_{11}PCH_2C_6H_5 \\ | \\ C_2H_5 \end{array} \right]^+$ I⁻

$\xrightarrow{LiAlH_4}$ 50%

③ (74~74.5°/22). *n*_D 1.4574 (20°).

④ +CH₃I ⟶
[(CH₃)₂(C₂H₅)(*n*-C₅H₁₁)P]⁺I⁻
+ O₂ ⟶ (CH₃)(C₂H₅)(*n*-C₅H₁₁)PO
+ HgCl₂ ⟶
(CH₃)(C₂H₅)(*n*-C₅H₁₁)P·HgCl₂

⑥ JOC **25**, 1996 (1960).

PC₈H₁₉

① Di-*n*-butylphosphine
(*n*-C₄H₉)₂PH

② (*n*-C₄H₉)₂P(S)−P(S)(*n*-C₄H₉)₂
+ LiAlH₄ ⟶ 86%

(*n*-C₄H₉)PH₂ + Na(xylene) $\xrightarrow{n\text{-}C_4H_9Cl}$
82%

(*n*-C₄H₉)₂POH + LiAlH₄ ⟶ 52%
CH₂=CHCH₂CH₃ + PH₃ ⟶ 10%

③ Colorless liq. (184~186°). *n*_D 1.4568
(20°). *d* 0.8078 (20°/4°).
Sol. in organic solvents.
NMR : J. Chem. Eng. Data **7**, 307
(1962).
IR : Monatsh. Chem. **92**, 868 (1961).

④ + 96% HNO₃ ⟶ (*n*-C₄H₉)₂P(O)(OH)
+ *p*-CH₃C₆H₄SO₂Cl $\xrightarrow{pyridine}$
p-CH₃C₆H₄SH + (*n*-C₄H₉)₂P(O)(OH)
+ *p*-CH₃C₆H₄SO₂Cl $\xrightarrow{dioxane}$
(*p*-CH₃C₆H₄S-)₂ + *p*-CH₃C₆H₄SH
+ O₂(air) $\xrightarrow{70°}$ (*n*-C₄H₉)₂P(O)H
+ CH₂=CH−CH=CH₂ $\xrightarrow{AIBN}$

(*n*-C₄H₉)₂PCH₂−CH=CHCH₃
+ Na + *n*-C₄H₉Cl $\xrightarrow{in\ xylene}$
(*n*-C₄H₉)₃P

⑥ Ber. **91**, 1583 (1958) ; **92**, 704 (1959).
Monatsh. **90**, 792 (1959).   JACS **74**,
3282 (1952).

PC₈H₁₉

① Diisobutylphosphine
(*i*-C₄H₉)₂PH

② (CH₃)₂C=CH₂ + PH₃ $\xrightarrow{AIBN}$ 52%

③ Colorless liq. (169~171.8°). [−70°].
*n*_D 1.4487 (20°).
Sol. in org. solvents.

④ + 96% HNO₃ ⟶ (*i*-C₄H₉)₂P(O)(OH)

⑥ JOC **26**, 5138 (1961).   JACS **74**, 3282
(1952).

PC₈H₁₉

① *n*-Butyldiethylphosphine
(C₂H₅)₂(*n*-C₄H₉)P

② *n*-C₄H₉PCl₂ + C₂H₅MgBr ⟶ 72%

(C₂H₅)₂PLi + *n*-C₄H₉Cl $\xrightarrow{ether}$ 60%

③ (110~111°/100). *n*_D 1.4596 (20°). *d* 0.8094
(20°).

④ + C₆H₅CH₂Cl ⟶
[(C₂H₅)₂(C₄H₉)(C₆H₅CH₂)P]⁺Cl⁻

⑥ Zhur. **26**, 3426 (1956) ; CA **51**, 9512
(1957).   Dokl. **132**, 1095 (1960).

PC₈H₁₉O

① Dibutylphosphine oxide
(C₄H₉)₂PH(O)

② (C₄H₉)₂POC₂H₅ $\xrightarrow{1\ N\ H_2SO_4}$ 84%

(C₄H₉)₂PH $\xrightarrow{air/i\text{-}C_3H_7OH,\ 45~50°}$ 47%

③ (74~75°/2, 153°/18). [66°].

④ + CCl₃CHO·H₂O ⟶ adduct
(mp 132~133°)

⑥ Izv. OKhN **1963**, 1227.   JOC **26**, 4626
(1961).   Ber. **93**, 1220 (1960).

PC₈H₁₉O

① Di-*n*-propylphosphinous acid ethyl
   ester
   $(n\text{-}C_3H_7)_2POC_2H_5$

② $(n\text{-}C_3H_7)_2PCl + C_2H_5OH \xrightarrow{\text{pyridine}}$

③ Liq. $(97\sim103°/15)$.

⑥ Kosolapoff 171.

PC₈H₁₉O

① Ethylmethylpentylphosphine oxide
   $(C_2H_5)(CH_3)(C_5H_{11})P(O)$

② $[(CH_3)_2(C_2H_5)(C_5H_{11})P]I \xrightarrow{\text{heat}}$

③ $(76\sim76.5°/0.4)$. $[8\sim9°]$. $n_D\,1.4591$
   $(20°)$.
   Very hygroscopic.

⑥ JOC **27**, 4404 (1962); **25**, 1996 (1960).

PC₈H₁₉O

① Butylethylphosphinous acid ethyl
   ester
   $(C_4H_9)(C_2H_5)P(OC_2H_5)$

② $C_2H_5P(OC_2H_5)Cl + C_4H_9MgCl \xrightarrow{\text{ether}}$
   47%

③ $(63\sim64°/15)$. $n_D\,1.4428$ $(20°)$.

⑥ Ber. **95**, 2993 (1962).

PC₈H₁₉O

① Diethylphosphinous acid butyl ester
   $(C_2H_5)_2POC_4H_9\text{-}n$

② $(C_2H_5)_2PCl + n\text{-}C_4H_9OH \xrightarrow[\;(C_2H_5)_2O\;]{(C_2H_5)_3N}$

③ $(54\sim55°/10)$. $n_D\,1.4410$ $(20°)$. $d\,0.8516$
   $(20°)$.
   Readily oxidize in air.

④ $+ S \longrightarrow (C_2H_5)P(S)OC_4H_9$
   $+ C_4H_9I \longrightarrow (C_2H_5)_2(C_4H_9)PO$
   $+ BrCH_2CO_2C_2H_5 \longrightarrow$
   $(C_2H_5)_2P(O)CH_2CO_2C_2H_5$

⑥ Dokl. **89**, 291 (1953).

PC₈H₁₉OS

① Dibutylphosphinothioic acid
   $(C_4H_9)_2P(S)OH$

② $(C_4H_9)_2P(S)Cl \longrightarrow 85\%$
   $(C_4H_9)_2P(S)H + I_2 \xrightarrow{\text{H}_2\text{O}}$

③ Yellow oil.

④ $+ \text{aniline} \longrightarrow \text{anilinium salt}$

⑥ JOC **27**, 2198 (1962).

PC₈H₁₉OS

① Diethylphosphinothioic acid *O*-butyl
   ester
   $(C_2H_5)_2P(S)OC_4H_9$

② $(C_2H_5)_2POC_4H_9 + S \longrightarrow$

③ Colorless liq. $(74\sim74.5°/1)$.
   $n_D\,1.4833$ $(20°)$. $d\,0.9779$ $(20°)$.
   Sol. in org. solvents.

⑥ Dokl. **89**, 291 (1953).

PC₈H₁₉O₂

① Di-*n*-butylphosphinic acid
   $(n\text{-}C_4H_9)_2P(O)(OH)$

② $[(n\text{-}C_4H_9)_2PS]_2 + HgO \xrightarrow{\text{moist C}_6\text{H}_6}$
   71.5%
   $(n\text{-}C_4H_9)_2PH + H_2O_2 \longrightarrow$
   $(C_2H_5O)_2P(O)H + n\text{-}C_4H_9MgCl$
   $\xrightarrow[\text{2) H}_2\text{O}_2]{\text{1) aq. HCl}} 66\%$
   $(C_2H_5O)_2P(O)H + n\text{-}C_4H_9MgBr \xrightarrow{\text{H}_2\text{O}}$
   72%
   $(n\text{-}C_4H_9)_2P(OC_2H_5) + H_2O_2 \longrightarrow$

③ Colorless needle crystals. $(208\sim210°/$
   $3)$. $[71°]$.

④ $+ PCl_5 \longrightarrow (n\text{-}C_4H_9)_2POCl$
   $+ (n\text{-}C_4H_9)_2POCl \longrightarrow$
   $(n\text{-}C_4H_9)_2P(O)OP(O)(C_4H_9\text{-}n)_2$

⑥ Ber. **95**, 1703 (1962); **93**, 1220 (1960).
   JCS **1959**, 3950.   JACS **73**, 4101
   (1951).   Izv. OKhN **1963**, 1373.

PC₈H₁₉O₂

① Di-*n*-propylphosphinic acid ethyl

ester
$(n-C_3H_7)_2P(O)OC_2H_5$

② $(n-C_3H_7)_2POCl + NaOC_2H_5 \xrightarrow{C_6H_6} 80\%$

③ Colorless liq. $(110\sim112°/14)$. $n_D 1.4369$
   $(21°)$. $d\,0.9567\,(21°/4°)$.

④ $+ (n-C_3H_7)_2POCl \longrightarrow$
   $(n-C_3H_7)_2P(O)OP(O)(C_3H_7-n)_2$

⑥ JACS **73**, 4101 (1951).

PC₈H₁₉O₂

① *n*-Butylphosphonous acid diethyl
   ester
   $n-C_4H_9P(OC_2H_5)_2$

② $(C_2H_5O)_2PCl + n-C_4H_9MgBr \xrightarrow{ether}$
   61%
   $(C_2H_5O)_2PCl + n-C_4H_9MgCl \longrightarrow 63\%$
   $(C_2H_5O)_2PCl + (n-C_4H_9)_2Cd \longrightarrow 40\%$

③ $(78°/20)$. $n_D 1.4310\,(20°)$.

④ $+ C_6H_5CH_2Cl \longrightarrow$
   $n-C_4H_9(C_6H_5CH_2)P(O)(OC_2H_5)$

⑥ Ber. **93**, 1220 (1960).

PC₈H₁₉O₂

① Diethylphosphinic acid *n*-butyl ester
   $(C_2H_5)_2P(O)(OC_4H_9-n)$

② $C_2H_5P(O)(H)(OC_4H_9-n) + Na + C_2H_5I$
   $\longrightarrow 62\%$

   $C_2H_5P(O)Cl + n-C_4H_9ONa \xrightarrow{C_4H_9OH}$
   63%

③ Colorless liq. $(80\sim81°/0.5)$. $n_D 1.4375$
   $(20°)$. $d\,0.9596\,(20°)$.
   Sol. in org. solvents.

⑥ Dokl. **91**, 271 (1953). Izv. OKhN
   1955, 253.

PC₈H₁₉O₂S

① Butylphosphonothioic acid *O, O-*
   diethyl ester
   $C_4H_9P(S)(OC_2H_5)_2$

② $(C_2H_5O)_2PSH + C_2H_5ONa + C_2H_5X$
   $\xrightarrow{heat} 46\%$

③ Liq. $(74.5\sim77.5°/2.5)$. $n_D 1.4600$
   $(20°)$. $d\,1.0004\,(20°)$.
   Sol. in org. solvents.

④ $+ C_2H_5Br \longrightarrow$
   $C_4H_9P(O)(OC_2H_5)SC_2H_5$

⑥ Izv. OKhN **1956**, 193.

PC₈H₁₉O₂S

① Butylphosphonothioic acid *O, S-*
   diethyl ester
   $C_4H_9P(O)(OC_2H_5)SC_2H_5$

② $C_4H_9P(S)(OC_2H_5)_2 + C_2H_5Br$
   $\xrightarrow[\text{in sealed tube}]{} 30\%$

③ Yellow liq $(98.5\sim100°/2.5)$.
   $n_D 1.4728\,(20°)$, $d\,1.0262\,(20°)$.
   Sol. in org. solvents.

⑥ Izv. OKhN **1956**, 193.

PC₈H₁₉O₃

① Ethylphosphonic acid diisopropyl
   ester
   $C_2H_5P(O)(OC_3H_7-i)_2$

② $(i-C_3H_7O)_3P + C_2H_5Br \longrightarrow$

③ Liq. $(90°/19°)$. $n_D 1.4122\,(20°)$.
   Sol. in org. solvents.

④ $+ HBr \longrightarrow C_2H_5P(O)(OC_3H_7-i)(OH)$
   $\longrightarrow$ aq. $C_2H_5P(O)(OH)_2$

⑥ JCS **1955**, 1978.

PC₈H₁₉O₃

① Butylphosphonic acid diethyl ester
   $C_4H_9P(O)(OC_2H_5)_2$

② $(C_2H_5O)_3P + C_4H_9Br \longrightarrow$

③ Oil. $(74°/1)$. $n_D 1.4213\,(25°)$.
   Sol. in org. solvents.
   IR: Chem. Ind. (London) **1960**, 1058.

⑥ JCS **1947**, 1465. JACS **76**, 4172 (1954).
   Chem. Eng. Data Ser. **3**, 310
   (1958).

PC₈H₁₉O₃

① Isobutylphosphonic acid diethyl
   ester

i-C₄H₉P(O)(OC₂H₅)₂

② (C₂H₅O)₂POH + (i-C₄H₉)₂O₂

  + C₆H₅COOCH₃ $\xrightarrow{\text{reflux, 24 hrs}}$ 45%

③ (83°/3).

④ + HCl $\longrightarrow$ i-C₄H₉P(O)(OH)₂

⑥ Chem. Ind. (London) **1960**, 999.

PC₈H₁₉S

① Dibutylphosphine sulfide
  (C₄H₉)₂PH(S)

② (C₄H₉)₂PH $\xrightarrow{\text{C₆H₆ or CCl₄, S}}$ 36%

③ (122~125°/1.5).

④ + (C₄H₉)₂PH(S) + C₆H₅CHO $\longrightarrow$
  (C₄H₉)₂P(S)CH(OH)C₆H₅ (75%)

⑥ JACS **82**, 4751 (1960).

PC₈H₁₉S₂

① Dibutylphosphinodithioic acid
  (C₄H₉)₂P(S)SH

② (C₄H₉)₂P(S)H + S $\longrightarrow$ 79%
  (C₄H₉)₂PH + S + NH₄OH $\longrightarrow$
  as ammonium salt 91%

  (C₄H₉)₂PSCl + CH₃ONa + H₂S $\xrightarrow{\text{HCl}}$

③ (99~99.5°/2). n_D 1.5481 (20°). d 1.0314
  (20°).
  Decomp. gradually and evolved
  H₂S.

④ + SO₂Cl₂ $\longrightarrow$ (C₄H₉)₂P(S)Cl
  $\longrightarrow$ Na salt
  + NaOH + XCH₂CH₂SC₂H₅ $\longrightarrow$
  (C₄H₉)₂P(S)SCH₂CH₂SC₂H₅

⑥ JOC **27**, 2198 (1962) ; **26**, 5133 (1961).
  Zhur. **31**, 140 (1961).

PC₈H₁₉S₂

① Di-*sec*-butylphosphinodithioic acid
  (*sec*-C₄H₉)₂P(S)SH

② *sec*-C₄H₉MgX + PSCl₃ $\longrightarrow$

③ (90°/0.15). n_D 1.5552 (20°).

⑥ Rec. trav. chim. **78**, 161 (1959).

PC₈H₁₉S₂

① Diisobutylphosphinodithioic acid
  (i-C₄H₉)₂P(S)SH

② (i-C₄H₉)₂PH + S $\longrightarrow$ 84%

③ Needles. [39~40°].

④ $\longrightarrow$ Ni salt

⑥ Gazz. chim. ital. **77**, 509 (1947). JOC
  27, 2198 (1962).

PC₈H₂₀BF₄

① Tetraethylphosphonium fluoroborate
  [(C₂H₅)₄$\overset{+}{P}$]$\overset{-}{B}$F₄

② (C₂H₅)₃P + [(C₂H₅)₃O]BF₄ $\xrightarrow{\text{CH₂Cl₂}}$

③ [291°].

⑥ Kaufman 1091. Ber. **91**, 67 (1958).

PC₈H₂₀I

① Tetraethylphosphonium iodide
  [(C₂H₅)₄$\overset{+}{P}$]I

② (C₂H₅)₃P + (C₂H₅)I $\xrightarrow{\text{C₂H₅OH}}$ 77.5%

③ [280~284°].
  IR : Australian J. Chem. **16**, 360
  (1963).

⑥ Kaufman 1091. JACS **82**, 3919
  (1960).

PC₈H₂₀IO

① Triethyl-2-hydroxyethylphospho-
  nium iodide
  [(C₂H₅)₃P⁺(CH₂CH₂OH)]I⁻

② (C₂H₅)₂PCH₂CH₂OH + C₂H₅I $\xrightarrow{\text{(C₂H₅)₂O}}$
  64%

  [(C₂H₅)₃P(CH₂CH₂Cl)]I $\xrightarrow{\text{Ag₂O}}$

③ [168°].

⑥ Ber. **94**, 102 (1961). Kosolapoff 88.

PC₈H₂₀NOS

① Triethylphosphonamidothioic acid
  O-ethyl ester
  C₂H₅P(S)(OC₂H₅)N(C₂H₅)₂

② C₂H₅P(OC₂H₅)N(C₂H₅)₂ + S $\longrightarrow$ 73%

③ Liq. (115~116°/9). n_D 1.4828 (20°).
d 1.0042 (20°).
Sol. in org. solvents.
⑥ Izv. OKhN 1955, 1021.

PC₉H₁₀N
① 2-Cyanoethylphenylphosphine
NCCH₂CH₂(C₆H₅)PH
② C₆H₅PH₂ + CH₂=CHCN $\longrightarrow$ 7.9%
③ (104°/0.5). n_D 1.5649 (20°). d 1.0710
(20°/4°).
⑥ Dokl. 107, 1217 (1959); CA 54, 1377
(1960).

PC₉H₁₁
① Methylvinylphenylphosphine
CH₃(CH₂=CH)(C₆H₅)P
② CH₃(C₆H₅)POC₄H₉ + CH₂=CHMgBr
$\xrightarrow{\text{THF}}$ 59%
③ (90~90.5°/13). n_D 1.5732 (20°). d
0.9714 (20°).
④ + active MnO₂ $\longrightarrow$
CH₃(C₆H₅)P(O)(CH=CH₂)
⑥ Dokl. 135, 603 (1960); CA 55, 12272
(1961).

PC₉H₁₁Cl₄
① Tris(chloromethyl)phenylphos-
phonium chloride
[(ClCH₂)₃PC₆H₅]Cl
② [(ClCH₂)₂P(C₆H₅)CH₂OH]Cl $\xrightarrow{\text{SOCl₂}}$
70%
③ [228~229°].
④ $\xrightarrow{\text{NaOH}}$ C₆H₅P(CH₂Cl)₂
21%
+ C₆H₅P(O)(CH₂Cl)(CH₂CH₂Cl)
51%
⑥ Ann. 659, 49 (1962). Tetrahedron
Letters 1961, 724.

PC₉H₁₁O
① Methylphenylvinylphosphine oxide
(CH₃)(C₆H₅)(CH₂=CH)P(O)

② CH₃(C₆H₅)PCH=CH₂ $\xrightarrow{\text{active MnO₂}}$
88%
③ (127~127.5°/2). [78~79°].
⑥ Dokl. 135, 603 (1960).

PC₉H₁₁O₄
① Benzoylphosphonic acid dimethyl
ester
C₆H₅COP(O)(OCH₃)₂
② (CH₃O)₃P + C₆H₅COCl $\longrightarrow$ 71.6%
③ Yellow oil. (144.5~146°/3.5). n_D
1.5254 (20°). d 1.2400 (20°/4°).
④ + NaHSO₃ $\longrightarrow$
C₆H₅C(OH)(SO₃Na)P(O)(OCH₃)₂
+ NaHSO₃ + KCN $\longrightarrow$
C₆H₅C(OH)(CN)P(O)(OCH₃)₂
⑥ Izv. OKhN 1945, 364, 597; 1947, 163.

PC₉H₁₂N₃
① Tris(cyanoethyl)phosphine
(NCCH₂CH₂)₃P
② (NCCH₂CH₂)₂PH + CH₂=CHCH₂CN
$\xrightarrow{\text{AIBN}}$ 92%
NCCH=CH₂ + PH₃ $\longrightarrow$ 28%
③ White needle crystals. [98~99°].
④ + HCl + 37% aq. CH₂O $\longrightarrow$
[HOCH₂(NCCH₂CH₂)₃P]Cl
+ H₂O₂ $\xrightarrow{\text{CH₃COOH}}$ (NCCH₂CH₂)₃PO
+ S $\xrightarrow{\text{benzene}}$ (NCCH₂CH₂)₃PS
+ H₂O−C₂H₅OH $\xrightarrow{\text{HCl}}$
(C₂H₅O₂CCH₂CH₂)₃P
+ KOH $\xrightarrow{\text{HCl}}$ (HO₂CCH₂CH₂)₃P
+ RX $\longrightarrow$ [(NCCH₂CH₂)₃PR]X̄
R=CH₃, CH₂=CHCH₂, X=Cl, I.
⑥ JACS 81, 1103 (1959). JOC 26, 5138
(1961).

PC₉H₁₃
① Methylethylphenylphosphine
CH₃(C₂H₅)(C₆H₅)P

② $[(CH_3)(C_2H_5)(C_6H_5)(C_6H_5CH_2)\overset{+}{P}]Br^-$

$$\xrightarrow[\text{electrolysis}]{} 77\%$$

$[C_6H_5(CH_3)(C_2H_5)(C_6H_5CH_2)\overset{+}{P}]I^-$

$$\xrightarrow[]{LiAlH_4} 59\%$$

$[(CH_3)(C_2H_5)(C_6H_5)_2\overset{+}{P}]I^- + Na$

$$\xrightarrow[\text{toluene}]{} 50\%$$

③ (82~84°/9, 96~97°/15). n_D 1.5524(25°). d 0.954 (25°).

④ $+ CH_3I \longrightarrow [(CH_3)_2(C_2H_5)(C_6H_5)\overset{+}{P}]I^-$

⑥ JOC 25, 1996 (1960). Ber. 92, 2088 (1959). Ann. 646, 65 (1961). Tetrahedron Letters 1961, 161.

PC₉H₁₃O

① Methylphenylphosphonous acid ethyl ester
$(CH_3)(C_6H_5)POC_2H_5$

② $(CH_3)(C_6H_5)PCl + C_2H_5OH \xrightarrow{\text{pyridine}}$

③ Liq. (125~30°/15).

⑥ Kosolapoff 171.

PC₉H₁₃O

① Ethylmethylphenylphosphine oxide
$(C_2H_5)(CH_3)(C_6H_5)P(O)$

② $[(C_2H_5)(CH_3)(C_6H_5)(C_6H_5CH_2)P^+]I^-$

$$\xrightarrow[\text{NaOH/CH_3OH, 100°}]{} \text{(optical active)}$$

$[(C_2H_5)(CH_3)(C_6H_5)(C_6H_5CH_2)\overset{+}{P}]\overset{-}{O}C_4H_9$

$\longrightarrow$ (racemic)

③ [47~48°]. $[\alpha]_D -22.8\pm1.0°$ (c=2.168 in H_2O, 25°) from d-iodide; $[\alpha]_D$ 22.4±1.0° from l-iodide (25°).

④ $\xrightarrow{\text{heat}} CH_3(C_6H_5)P(O)H + CH_2=CH_2$

⑥ JACS 81, 3805 (1959); 82, 5503 (1960). JOC 28, 2150 (1963); 27, 4404 (1962).

PC₉H₁₃O

① Methylphosphonous acid ethyl-phenyl ester
$CH_3P(OC_2H_5)(OC_6H_5)$

② $C_2H_5OP(CH_3)N(C_2H_5)_2 + C_6H_5OH$

$$\xrightarrow[]{100°} 50\%$$

$C_6H_5OP(CH_3)N(C_2H_5)_2 + C_2H_5OH$

$$\xrightarrow[]{130\sim140} 53\%$$

$CH_3P(OC_2H_5)_2 + C_6H_5OH + $ small amt. of Na $\xrightarrow{\text{heat}}$

③ (91~92°/11). n_D 1.5002 (20°). d 1.0234 (20°).

⑥ Zhur. 32, 1974 (1962).

PC₉H₁₃OS

① Phenylphosphinothioic acid O-propyl ester
$C_6H_5P(S)(H)OC_3H_7$

② $C_6H_5P(OC_3H_7)N(C_2H_5)_2 + H_2S \longrightarrow$ 60%

③ (60°/0.03). n_D 1.5632 (20°). d 1.1082 (20°).

④ $+ CH_2[N(C_2H_5)_2]_2 \longrightarrow$
$C_6H_5P(S)[CH_2N(C_2H_5)_2]OC_3H_7$

⑥ Zhur. 32, 3062 (1962).

PC₉H₁₃O₂

① Benzylbis(hydroxymethyl)phosphine
$(HOCH_2)_2(C_6H_5CH_2)P$

② $[(C_6H_5CH_2)P(CH_2OH)_3]Cl \xrightarrow{N(C_2H_5)_3}$

③ (84~85°/1).

④ $+C_6H_5CH_2Cl \longrightarrow$
$[(C_6H_5CH_2)_2P(CH_2OH)_2]Cl$
$\xrightarrow{N(C_2H_5)_3} (C_6H_5CH_2)_2PCH_2OH$

⑥ Zhur. 32, 553 (1962).

PC₉H₁₃O₂

① Ethylphenylphosphinic acid methyl ester
$(C_2H_5)(C_6H_5)P(O)(OCH_3)$

② $C_2H_5(C_6H_5)POCl + CH_3OH \xrightarrow{(C_2H_5)_3N}$

$C_2H_5(C_6H_5)P(O)SH + NaOCH_3 \xrightarrow{CH_3OH}$ 68%

③ (106~107°/0.8). n_D 1.5218 (23°).

⑥ JCS **1963**, 540. Proc. Chem. Soc. **1962**, 307; **1961**, 145.

PC$_9$H$_{13}$S

① Ethylmethylphenylphosphine sulfide (C$_2$H$_5$)(CH$_3$)(C$_6$H$_5$)P(S)

② C$_2$H$_5$(C$_6$H$_5$)P(S)Cl + CH$_3$MgBr
$$\xrightarrow[\text{(C}_2\text{H}_5\text{)}_2\text{O, } 15\sim35^\circ]{} 84\%$$

③ (103~104°/0.04). [33~34°].

⑥ JOC **28**, 3430 (1963).

PC$_9$H$_{13}$S$_2$

① Isopropylphenylphosphinodithioic acid
    i-C$_3$H$_7$(C$_6$H$_5$)P(S)SH

② (*i*-C$_3$H$_7$PS$_2$)$_2$ + C$_6$H$_6$ $\xrightarrow{\text{AlCl}_3}$ 81%

③ Light green liq. (92°/0.001). n_D 1.6354 (22°).
    Slowly decomp. on standing at room temp.
    NMR: JOC **27**, 3829 (1962).

④ + NH$_3$ $\longrightarrow$ *i*-C$_3$H$_7$(C$_6$H$_5$)P(S)SNH$_4$

PC$_9$H$_{14}$ClO$_3$

① Tris(hydroxymethyl)phenylphosphonium chloride
    [(C$_6$H$_5$)P(CH$_2$OH)$_3$]Cl

② C$_6$H$_5$P(CH$_2$OH)$_2$ + CH$_2$O + HCl $\longrightarrow$ 96%

③ [66~69°].

④ + (CH$_3$CO)$_2$O $\longrightarrow$
    [(C$_6$H$_5$)P(CH$_2$OCOCH$_3$)$_3$]Cl (90%)

⑥ Ann. **659**, 49 (1962).

PC$_9$H$_{14}$I

① Trimethylphenylphosphonium iodide
    [(CH$_3$)$_3$PC$_6$H$_5$]$^+$I$^-$

② (CH$_3$)$_2$PC$_6$H$_5$ + CH$_3$I $\xrightarrow{\text{(CH}_3\text{)}_2\text{O}}$

    C$_6$H$_5$·PLi$_2$ + CH$_3$I $\xrightarrow{\text{(C}_2\text{H}_5\text{)}_2\text{O (or dioxane)}}$ 64%

    (C$_6$H$_5$P)$_4$ + CH$_3$I $\xrightarrow{\text{C}_6\text{H}_6, 80^\circ}$

③ [237~238°].
    Sol. in H$_2$O.
    Picrate. [133~133.5°].

④ $\xrightarrow{\text{Hg/2 e}^-, 70\sim80^\circ}$ (CH$_3$)$_3$P + (47%)

    (CH$_3$)$_2$PC$_6$H$_5$ (40%)

⑥ Kosolapoff 87. Ber. **96**, 279, 2109 (1963); **94**, 186 (1961). Ann. **646**, 65 (1961).

PC$_9$H$_{14}$NOS

① *P*-Methyl-*N*-phenylphosphonamido-thioic acid *O*-ethyl ester
    CH$_3$P(S)(OC$_2$H$_5$)NHC$_6$H$_5$

② CH$_3$P(S)(OC$_2$H$_5$)Cl + C$_6$H$_5$NH$_2$ $\xrightarrow{\text{(C}_2\text{H}_5\text{)}_3\text{N}}$

③ (125°/0.05). n_D 1.5770 (25°).

⑥ JCS **1961**, 5532.

PC$_9$H$_{14}$NOS

① *P*-Methyl-*N*-phenylphosphonamido-thioic acid *S*-ethyl ester
    CH$_3$P(O)(SC$_2$H$_5$)NHC$_6$H$_5$

② CH$_3$P(O)(SC$_2$H$_5$)Cl + C$_6$H$_5$NH$_2$ $\longrightarrow$
    CH$_3$P(S)(OC$_2$H$_5$)NHC$_6$H$_5$ + C$_2$H$_5$I $\longrightarrow$ 72%

③ Needles. [155°].
    IR: JCS **1961**, 3067.

⑥ JCS **1961**, 5532.

PC$_9$H$_{14}$NO$_2$

① *N*-Ethyl-*P*-methylphosphonamidic acid phenyl ester
    CH$_3$P(O)(OC$_6$H$_5$)NHC$_2$H$_5$

② CH$_3$P(O)(OC$_6$H$_5$)Cl + C$_2$H$_5$NH$_2$

③ (142°/0.2). n_D 1.5169 (20°). d 1.1330.

⑥ Zhur. **30**, 4060 (1960).

PC$_9$H$_{14}$NO$_2$

① *P*-Methyl-*N*-phenylphosphonamidic acid ethyl ester
    CH$_3$P(O)(OC$_2$H$_5$)NHC$_6$H$_5$

② CH$_3$P(O)(OC$_2$H$_5$)Cl + C$_6$H$_5$NH$_2$ $\longrightarrow$

52%
③ (160～165°/20).
⑥ JOC **28**, 329 (1963).

PC₉H₁₅O
① Triallylphosphine oxide
  $(CH_2=CHCH_2)_3PO$
② $3 CH_2=CHCH_2MgBr + POCl_3 \xrightarrow{ether}$
③ (78°/0.1).
⑥ J. Appl. Chem. **10**, 395 (1960).

PC₉H₁₅O₃
① Allylphosphonic acid diallyl ester
  $CH_2=CHCH_2P(O)(OCH_2CH=CH_2)_2$
② $(CH_2=CHCH_2O)_3P + CH_2=CHCH_2Br$
  $\longrightarrow$ 91%
③ Liq. (82°/0.5). n_D 1.4600 (20°).
  d 1.0050 (20°/0°).
  Sol. in org. solvents.
④ $\xrightarrow{BPO}$ polymer
⑥ JACS **75**, 3145 (1953). J. Appl. Chem.
  8, 459 (1958).

PC₉H₁₆N
① 2-Cyanoethylcyclohexylphosphine
  $NCCH_2CH_2(cyclo\text{-}C_6H_{11})PH$
② $NCCH_2CH_2PH_2 + \bigcirc \xrightarrow{ABIN}$ 74%
③ (97°/0.3). n_D 1.5088 (25°).
⑥ JOC **26**, 5138 (1961).

PC₉H₁₇O₃
① Propylphosphonic acid diallyl ester
  $C_3H_7P(O)(OCH_2CH=CH_2)_2$
② $C_3H_7P(O)Cl_2 + CH_2=CHCH_2OH \xrightarrow{C_5H_5N}$
  63.3%
③ Liq. (91°/1). n_D 1.4472 (25°). d 1.021
  (25°/25°).
  Sol. in org. solvents.
④ $\xrightarrow{BPO}$ polymer
⑥ JACS **76**, 2191 (1954).

PC₉H₁₈Cl₃O₃
① Trichloromethylphosphonic acid
  dibutyl ester
  $Cl_3CP(O)(OC_4H_9)_2$
② $(C_4H_9O)_3P + CCl_4 \longrightarrow$ 25%
③ Colorless oil. (145～146°/7, 150～155°/
  5). n_D 1.4490 (20°). d 1.1679 (17°/
  0°).
  Decomp. on distillation, darken on
  exposure to light.
④ + amines $\longrightarrow$ dibutyl alkylamino-
  phosphonate
  $+ 15\% HCl \xrightarrow{at\ 150°} H_3PO_3 + CO_2$
  $+ C_4H_9Cl$
⑥ Dokl. **55**, 219 (1947). Zhur. **16**, 1521
  (1964). JACS **69**, 1002 (1947).

PC₉H₂₁
① n-Hexyl-n-propylphosphine
  $n\text{-}C_3H_7(n\text{-}C_6H_{13})PH$
② $n\text{-}C_6H_{13}PH_2 + Na + C_3H_7Cl \longrightarrow$ 61%
③ (194°/760). n_D 1.4579 (20°).
  IR: Monatsh. **92**, 868 (1961).
④ $+ n\text{-}C_9H_{19}X + Na \longrightarrow$
  $C_3H_7(n\text{-}C_9H_{19})(n\text{-}C_6H_{13})P$
⑥ Monatsh. **90**, 792 (1959).

PC₉H₂₁
① Tri-n-propylphosphine
  $(n\text{-}C_3H_7)_3P$
② $[(n\text{-}C_3H_7)_3P(CH_2OH)]Br \xrightarrow{N(C_2H_5)_3}$
  41.2%
  $n\text{-}C_3H_7Li + PCl_3 \xrightarrow{-20\sim-30°}$ 45%
③ (185～186°).
④ $+ (C_2H_5)_3NBH_3 \longrightarrow (n\text{-}C_3H_7)_3PBH_3$
  $+ PdCl_2 \longrightarrow [(n\text{-}C_3H_7)_3P]_2PdCl_2$
  $+ (CH_3)_2AsI \longrightarrow$
  $[(CH_3)_2AsP(n\text{-}C_3H_7)_3]I$
⑥ Zhur. **32**, 553 (1962). JOC **27**, 2573
  (1962).

PC₉H₂₁Br₂

① Dibromotripropylphosphorane
  $(C_3H_7)_3PBr_2$

② $(C_3H_7)_3P + Br_2 \xrightarrow{C_6H_6-(C_2H_5)_2O}$ 86.6%

③ [166°(decomp.)].

⑥ Z. anorg. allg. Chem. **288**, 201 (1956).

PC₉H₂₁O

① Dibutylmethylphosphine oxide
  $(C_4H_9)_2P(O)CH_3$

② $(C_4H_9)_2POC_2H_5 + CH_3I \longrightarrow$ 84%

③ (96~97°/2). [31~33°].

⑥ CA **59**, 5850 (1965).   Dokl. **135**, 323
  (1960).

PC₉H₂₁O

① Tripropylphosphine oxide
  $(C_3H_7)_3PO$

② $(C_3H_7)_3P \xrightarrow{R_3N \to O}$

③ [39°].

⑥ Kosolapoff 113.   Z. anorg. allg.
  Chem. **301**, 188 (1959) ; **314**, 113
  (1962).   Zhur. **32**, 553 (1962).
  Pure Appl. Chem. **2**, 71 (1961).

PC₉H₂₁O

① Dipropylphosphinous acid propyl
  ester
  $(C_3H_7)_2P(OC_3H_7)$

② $(C_3H_7O)PCl_2 + C_3H_7MgBr \longrightarrow$ 46.6%

③ (70~71°/7). n_D 1.4430 (20°). d 0.8473
  (20°).

④ +N-oxide $\longrightarrow$ $(C_3H_7)_2P(O)(OC_3H_7)$
  + S $\longrightarrow$ $(C_3H_7)_2P(S)OC_3H_7$
  + CH₃I $\longrightarrow$ $(C_3H_7)_2(CH_3)P(O)$

⑥ Zhur. **31**, 2889, 3085 (1961).

PC₉H₂₁OS

① Dipropylphosphinothioic acid
  O-propyl ester
  $(C_3H_7)_2P(S)(OC_3H_7)$

② $(C_3H_7)_2POC_3H_7 + S \longrightarrow$ 90%

③ (81~82°/0.5). n_D 1.4778 (20°). d 0.9614
  (20°).

⑥ Zhur. **31**, 2889 (1961).

PC₉H₂₁OS

① Dipropylphosphinothioic acid O-isopropyl ester
  $(C_3H_7)_2P(S)OC_3H_7-i$

② $(C_3H_7)_2PSCl + i-C_3H_7OH \longrightarrow$

③ (125~125.5°/14).

⑥ Ann. **652**, 28 (1962).

PC₉H₂₁OS₂

① Methylphosphonodithioic acid
  O, S-dibutyl ester
  $CH_3P(S)(OC_4H_9)(SC_4H_9)$

② $CH_3P(S)(H)OC_4H_9 + Na + (C_4H_9)_2S_2$
  $\longrightarrow$ 83.5%

③ (115~116°/3). n_D 1.5120 (20°). d 1.0222
  (20°).

⑥ Zhur. **32**, 3062 (1962).

PC₉H₂₁O₂S

① Methylphosphonothioic acid
  O, S-dibutyl ester
  $CH_3P(O)(OC_4H_9)SC_4H_9$

② $CH_3P(S)(OC_4H_9)_2 + C_4H_9Br \longrightarrow$ 22%

③ Liq. (143~146°/13, 92~93°/2). n_D
  1.4681 (20°). d 1.0065 (20°).

⑥ Zhur. **31**, 1361 (1961).   Izv. OKhN
  1956, 193.

PC₉H₂₁O₂S

① Methylphosphonothioic acid
  O, O-dibutyl ester
  $CH_3P(S)(OC_4H_9)_2$

② $CH_3PSCl_2 + C_4H_9OH \xrightarrow{BF_3-ether}$ 81%
  $CH_3PSCl_2 + C_4H_9OH + Na \longrightarrow$ 75%
  $CH_3POCl_2 + C_4H_9OH + (C_2H_5)_3N \xrightarrow{S}$
  $(C_4H_9O)_2PSH + C_4H_9ONa + CH_3X \longrightarrow$
  41%

③ Straw liq. (93~94/0.7). n_D 1.4535

(20°). d 0.9848 (20°).

Sol. in org. solvents.

NMR: Compt. rend. **253**, 644 (1961).

④ + SO$_2$Cl$_2$ $\xrightarrow{\text{reflux}}$ CH$_3$P(S)(OC$_4$H$_9$)Cl

+ COCl$_2$ $\longrightarrow$ CH$_3$P(S)(OC$_4$H$_9$)Cl

+ C$_4$H$_9$Br $\longrightarrow$ CH$_3$P(O)(OC$_4$H$_9$)SC$_4$H$_9$

⑥ JCS **1962**, 3842; **1961**, 238. Bull. soc. chim. France 1222 (1961). Izv. OKhN **1956**, 193.

PC$_9$H$_{21}$O$_2$S

① Methylphosphonothioic acid
   O, O-di-*sec*-butyl ester
   CH$_3$PS(OC$_4$H$_9$-*sec*)$_2$

② CH$_3$PSCl$_2$ + *sec*-C$_4$H$_9$OH
   $\xrightarrow{\text{BF}_3 \text{ ether reflux}}$ 35%

③ (58~60°/0.6). n_D 1.4600 (28°).

⑥ JCS **1962**, 3824.

PC$_9$H$_{21}$O$_3$

① Methylphosphonic acid dibutyl ester
   CH$_3$P(O)(OC$_4$H$_9$)$_2$

② CH$_3$P(O)(SC$_2$H$_5$)$_2$ + Na
   C$_4$H$_9$OH $\xrightarrow{5 \text{ hrs}, 130\sim160°}$
   CH$_3$POCl$_2$ + C$_4$H$_9$OH + Na $\longrightarrow$ 64%

③ (132~135°/15). n_D 1.4246 (20°).
   d 0.9770 (20°/4°).

④ + (*i*-C$_3$H$_7$O)$_3$Al $\xrightarrow{142\sim172°, 190\sim215°}$
   i-C$_3$H$_7$OC$_4$H$_9$
   $\xrightarrow{\text{HCl}}$ CH$_3$P(O)(OH)$_2$

⑤ Extractant.

⑥ Izv. OKhN **1962**, 1753, Zhur. **31**, 3174 (1961). Bull. soc. chim. France **1961**, 1222. Chem. Eng. Data Ser. **3**, 310 (1958). JACS **75**, 3379 (1953).

PC$_9$H$_{21}$O$_3$

① Isopropylphosphonic acid
   diisopropyl ester

i-C$_3$H$_7$P(O)(OC$_3$H$_7$-*i*)$_2$

② *i*-C$_3$H$_7$Cl + PCl$_3$ + AlCl$_3$ $\longrightarrow$
   [*i*-C$_3$H$_7$PCl$_3$][AlCl$_4$]
   $\xrightarrow{i\text{-C}_3\text{H}_7\text{OH(C}_2\text{H}_5\text{OH)}}$ 77%

③ Colorless liq. (61~63°/1, 38.5°/ 0.25, 44°/0.35). n_D 1.4129 (25°).

⑥ JACS **79**, 3570 (1957).

PC$_9$H$_{21}$S

① Tripropylphosphine sulfide
   (C$_3$H$_7$)$_3$PS

② PCl$_3$ + 3 C$_3$H$_7$MgBr $\xrightarrow{\quad}$ $\xrightarrow{\text{S}}$ 61%

③ (112°/1.1). n_D 1.5071 (27°).
   IR: Inorg. Chem. **2**, 192 (1963).

④ Bond dissociation energy D(P=S) is considerably smaller than D(P=O).

⑥ J. Chem. Eng. Data **8**, 226 (1963). Pure Appl. Chem. **2**, 71 (1961).

PC$_9$H$_{21}$Se

① Tripropylphosphine selenide
   (C$_3$H$_7$)$_3$PSe

② PCl$_3$ + 3 C$_3$H$_7$MgBr $\xrightarrow{(C_2H_5)_2O \quad Se}$ $\longrightarrow$ 45%

③ (116°/0.95). [32°].

⑥ J. Chem. Eng. Data **8**, 226 (1963).

PC$_9$H$_{22}$NOS

① N, N-Diethyl-P-methylphosphon-amidothioic acid S-butyl ester
   CH$_3$P(O)(SC$_4$H$_9$)N(C$_2$H$_5$)$_2$

② CH$_3$PCl$_2$ + (C$_2$H$_5$)$_2$NSC$_4$H$_9$ $\xrightarrow{\text{in SO}_2}$ 10%

③ (126~127°/7). n_D 1.5023 (20°).
   d 1.1195 (20°).

⑥ Zhur. **31**, 1361 (1961).

PC$_9$H$_{22}$NOS

① Triethylphosphonamidothioic acid
   O-propyl ester

$C_2H_5P(S)(OC_3H_7)N(C_2H_5)_2$

② $C_2H_5P(OC_3H_7)N(C_2H_5)_2 + S \longrightarrow$ 65%

③ Liq. (84~85°/1). n_D 1.4801 (20°),
　d 0.9892 (20°).
　Soluble in org. solvents.

⑥ Izv. OKhN 1955, 1021.

PC₉H₂₂NOS

① Triethylphosphonamidothioic acid
　O-isopropyl ester
　$C_2H_5P(S)(OC_3H_7-i)N(C_2H_5)_2$

② $C_2H_5P(OC_3H_7-i)N(C_2H_5)_2 + S \longrightarrow$
　67.5%

③ Liq. (118~119.5°/9). n_D 1.4781 (20°).
　d 0.9858 (20°).
　Soluble in org. solvents.

⑥ Izv OKhN 1955, 1021.

PC₁₀H₇Cl₂

① 1-Naphthylphosphonous dichloride
　$1-C_{10}H_7PCl_2$

② $1-C_{10}H_7MgBr \xrightarrow{CdCl_2} (1-C_{10}H_7)_2Cd$
　$\xrightarrow[-30°]{PCl_3}$ 25%

③ (180°/10), (118~120°/0.5). [58~59°].

⑥ Kaufman 1112.　JCS 1958, 3129.

PC₁₀H₇Cl₂O

① 2-Naphthylphosphonic dichloride
　$2-C_{10}H_7P(O)Cl_2$

② $2-C_{10}H_7P(O)(OH)_2 + PCl_5 \xrightarrow{POCl_3, 80°}$

③ (167~168°/2). [45~47°].

⑥ JACS 76, 1045 (1954).

PC₁₀H₇Cl₄

① Tetrachloro-1-naphthyl phosphorane
　$1-C_{10}H_7PCl_4$

② $1-C_{10}H_7PCl_2 + Cl_2 \longrightarrow$

③ [143°].

⑥ Kosolapoff 72.

PC₁₀H₉O₃

① 2-Naphthylphosphonic acid
　$2-C_{10}H_7P(O)(OH)_2$

② $2-C_{10}H_7P(O)(OC_2H_5)_2 \xrightarrow{HCl}$
　$C_{10}H_8 + P_4O_{10} \xrightarrow[\text{in autoclave}]{}$

③ Colorless crystals. [193~194°].
　Very sol. in EtOH, acetone;
　somewhat sol. in ether. Decomp.
　completely when heated at 275°
　24 hrs in a sealed tube.

④ $\xrightarrow[\text{24 hr}]{\text{heat 275°}} C_{10}H_8$
　+ NaOH aq. $\longrightarrow$ hemisodium salt
　+ NH₃ aq. $\longrightarrow$ hemiammonium
　salt
　+ KOH aq $\longrightarrow$ hemipotassium
　salt
　+ o-toluidine $\longrightarrow$ mono-o-toluidine
　salt

⑥ JACS 76, 1045 (1954).　JOC 27, 1402
　(1962).

PC₁₀H₁₁

① Divinylphenylphosphine
　$(CH_2=CH)_2C_6H_5P$

② $C_6H_5PCl_2 + CH_2=CHMgBr \longrightarrow$ 59%

③ Viscous yellow liq. (55°/0.5).

④ + active MnO₂ $\longrightarrow$
　$C_6H_5P(O)(CH=CH_2)_2$

⑥ Dokl. 135, 603 (1960).　CA 55, 12272
　(1961).　JACS 79, 5884 (1957).

PC₁₀H₁₁O

① Phenyldivinylphosphine oxide
　$(C_6H_5)P(O)(CH=CH_2)_2$

② $C_6H_5P(CH=CH_2)_2 \xrightarrow{MnO_2/petr.\ ether}$
　92%

③ (130~130.5°/2). [50~51°].

⑥ Dokl. 135, 603 (1960).

PC₁₀H₁₁O₂

① Phenylphosphonous acid divinylester

C$_6$H$_5$P(OCH=CH$_2$)$_2$

② C$_6$H$_5$PCl$_2$ + (CH$_2$=CHO)$_2$Hg $\xrightarrow{(C_2H_5)_3N}$

   43%

③ (76〜78°/2). n_D 1.5385 (20°). d 1.0633

   (20°).

⑥ Dokl. **132**, 612 (1960).

PC$_{10}$H$_{13}$

① 1-Phenylcyclotetramethylene phos-

   phine

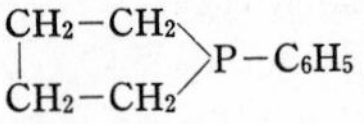

$$\begin{matrix} CH_2-CH_2 \\ | \qquad\qquad \\ CH_2-CH_2 \end{matrix}\!\!\!\Big\rangle P-C_6H_5$$

② C$_6$H$_5$PLi$_2$ + Cl(CH$_2$)$_4$Cl $\longrightarrow$ 29.8%

③ Colorless liq. (132〜133°/17, 97°/3).

   Oxidized in air.

④ $+ S \xrightarrow{benzene}$ $\begin{matrix} CH_2-CH_2 \\ | \qquad\qquad \\ CH_2-CH_2 \end{matrix}\!\!\!\Big\rangle P(S)C_6H_5$

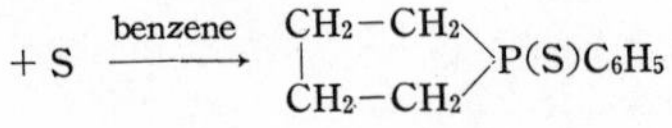

                 mp 77°

   $+ CH_3I$ $\left[\begin{matrix} CH_2-CH_2 \\ | \qquad\qquad \\ CH_2-CH_2 \end{matrix}\!\!\!\Big\rangle\overset{+}{P}(CH_3)(C_6H_5)\right]I^-$

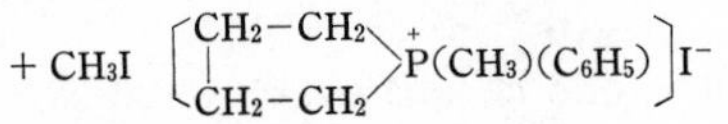

                 mp 130°

⑥ Ber. **49**, 437 (1916); **94**, 113 (1961).

   Ann. **591**, 108 (1955).

PC$_{10}$H$_{13}$

① 1-ethyl-phosphindoline

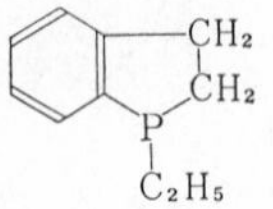

②

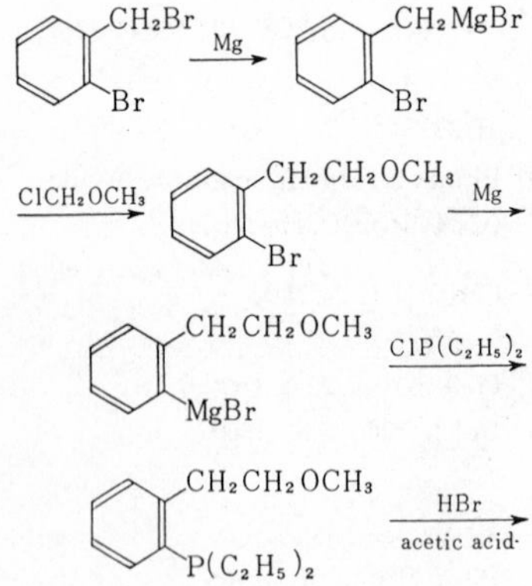

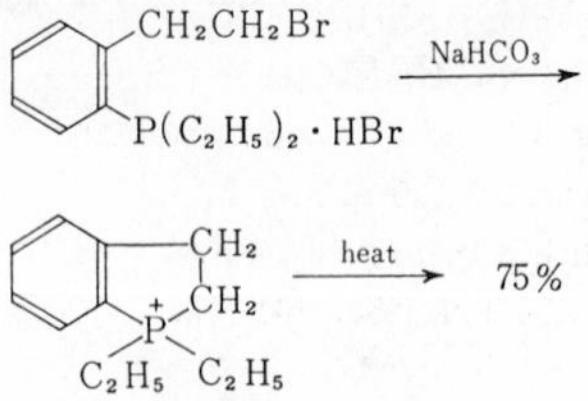

---

③ Colorless oil. (104〜106°/3).

   Readily oxidize in air.

④ $+ C_2H_5I \longrightarrow$

   + potassium palladobromide $\longrightarrow$

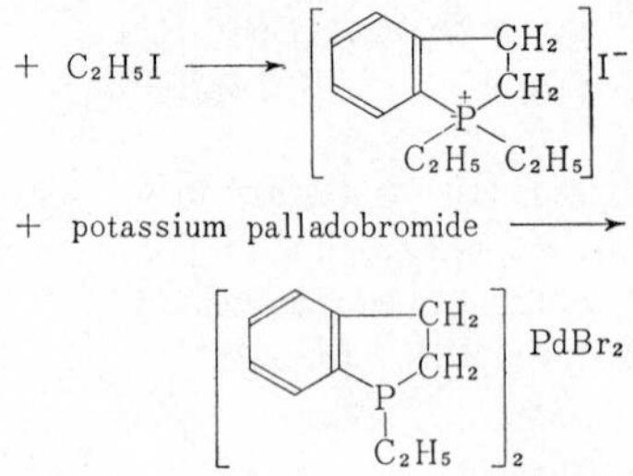

⑥ JCS **1951**, 2205.

PC$_{10}$H$_{13}$Cl$_2$O$_3$

① Phenylphosphonic acid bis(2-chloro-

   ethyl)ester

   C$_6$H$_5$P(O)(OCH$_2$CH$_2$Cl)$_2$

② C$_6$H$_5$P(O)(Cl)(OCH$_2$CH$_2$Cl) + CH$_2$—CH$_2$ $\underset{O}{\diagdown\diagup}$

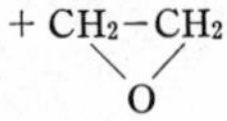

   $+ AlCl_3 \xrightarrow{60°}$

③ (170〜172°/2). n_D 1.5258 (20°).

⑥ Zhur. **32**, 964 (1962).

PC$_{10}$H$_{13}$Cl$_2$O$_2$S

① Phenylphosphonothioic acid

   O,O-bis(2-chloroethylester)

   C$_6$H$_5$P(S)(OCH$_2$CH$_2$Cl)$_2$

② C$_6$H$_5$P(OCH$_2$CH$_2$Cl)$_2$ + S $\xrightarrow{100°,\ 1.5\,hrs}$

③ (158〜160°/1). n_D 1.5629 (20°).

⑥ Zhur. **31**, 947 (1961).

PC$_{10}$H$_{13}$O

① Ethylphenylvinylphosphine oxide

   (C$_2$H$_5$)(C$_6$H$_5$)(CH$_2$=CH)P(O)

② C$_2$H$_5$(C$_6$H$_5$)POCH$_2$CH$_2$Cl $\xrightarrow{\text{(C}_2\text{H}_5)_3\text{N, 120}°}$
   58%

③ (112~113°/1). [43~44°].

⑥ Dokl. **135**, 849 (1960).

PC$_{10}$H$_{14}$Br

① Diethyl(*o*-bromophenyl)phosphine
   (C$_2$H$_5$)$_2$(*o*-BrC$_6$H$_4$)P

② *o*-BrC$_6$H$_4$Br + *n*-C$_4$H$_9$Li + (C$_2$H$_5$)$_2$PCl
   $\xrightarrow[]{-130°}$ 26%

③ (90~91°/0.15).

④ + CH$_3$I $\longrightarrow$
   [CH$_3$(C$_2$H$_5$)$_2$(*o*-BrC$_6$H$_4$)$\overset{+}{\text{P}}$]I$^-$

   + *n*-C$_4$H$_9$Li $\xrightarrow{\text{(C}_2\text{H}_5)_2\text{PCl}}$

   + *n*-C$_4$H$_9$Li $\xrightarrow{\text{(C}_6\text{H}_5)_2\text{PCl}}$

⑥ JCS 1960, 3324.

PC$_{10}$H$_{14}$ClO

① Ethylphenylphosphinous acid
   2-chloroethylester
   C$_2$H$_5$(C$_6$H$_5$)POCH$_2$CH$_2$Cl

② C$_6$H$_5$PCl$_2$ + CH$_2$—CH$_2$ $\longrightarrow$
   \O/

   C$_6$H$_5$P(Cl)OCH$_2$CH$_2$Cl $\xrightarrow{\text{C}_2\text{H}_5\text{MgBr}}$ 56%

③ (81~82°/1). n_D 1.5430 (20°). *d* 1.1111
   (20°).

④ + (C$_2$H$_5$)$_3$N $\xrightarrow{120°}$
   C$_6$H$_5$(C$_2$H$_5$)P(O)CH=CH$_2$

⑥ Dokl. **135**, 849 (1960)

PC$_{10}$H$_{14}$Cl$_3$

① Bis(chloromethyl)ethylphenyl
   phosphonium chloride
   [(ClCH$_2$)$_2$P(C$_2$H$_5$)(C$_6$H$_5$)]Cl

② [(HOCH$_2$)$_2$C$_2$H$_5$C$_6$H$_5$P]Cl $\xrightarrow{\text{SOCl}_2}$ 66%

③ [163~164°].

⑥ Ann. **659**, 49 (1962).   Tetrahedron
   Letters 1961, 724.

PC$_{10}$H$_{15}$

① Benzylydenetrimethylphosphorane
   (CH$_3$)$_3$P=CHC$_6$H$_5$

② [(CH$_3$)$_3$PCH$_2$C$_6$H$_5$]Br $\xrightarrow{\text{C}_4\text{H}_9\text{Li/(C}_2\text{H}_5)_2\text{O}}$

④

   R, R′ (yield %); C$_6$H$_5$, C$_6$H$_5$ (60);
   CH$_3$, C$_6$H$_5$ (53); CH$_3$, CH$_3$ (42)

⑥ JCS 1961, 1266.

PC$_{10}$H$_{15}$

① Methyl(*n*-propyl)phenylphosphine
   CH$_3$(*n*-C$_3$H$_7$)C$_6$H$_5$P

② [CH$_3$(*n*-C$_3$H$_7$)(C$_6$H$_5$)(C$_6$H$_5$CH$_2$)$\overset{+}{\text{P}}$]I$^-$
   $\xrightarrow{\text{cathodic reduction}}$

③ (86~88°/2.5~3).

④ + H$_2$O$_2$ $\longrightarrow$ CH$_3$(*n*-C$_3$H$_7$)(C$_6$H$_5$)P(O)
   + C$_2$H$_5$I $\longrightarrow$
   [CH$_3$(C$_2$H$_5$)(*n*-C$_3$H$_7$)(C$_6$H$_5$)$\overset{+}{\text{P}}$]I$^-$
   + CH$_3$Br $\longrightarrow$
   [(CH$_3$)$_2$(*n*-C$_3$H$_7$)(C$_6$H$_5$)$\overset{+}{\text{P}}$]Br$^-$

⑥ Tetrahedron Letters 1961, 161.

PC$_{10}$H$_{15}$

① *n*-Butylphenylphosphine
   n-C$_4$H$_9$(C$_6$H$_5$)PH

② C$_6$H$_5$PH$_2$ + Na + *n*-C$_4$H$_9$Cl $\longrightarrow$ 86%

③ (102°/9). n_D 1.5400 (20°).

⑥ Monatsh. **90**, 792 (1959).

PC$_{10}$H$_{15}$O

① Methylphenylpropylphosphine
   oxide
   (CH$_3$)(C$_3$H$_7$)(C$_6$H$_5$)PO

② (CH$_3$)(C$_3$H$_7$)(C$_6$H$_5$)P $\xrightarrow{\text{H}_2\text{O}_2}$

③ [158°].
   Monohydrate (180°/13).

⑥ Tetrahedron Letters **1961**, 161.
   Kosolapoff 116.

PC$_{10}$H$_{15}$O

① Ethylphenylphosphinous acid ethylester
   (C$_2$H$_5$)(C$_6$H$_5$)POC$_2$H$_5$

② C$_6$H$_5$P(OC$_2$H$_5$)$_2$ + C$_6$H$_5$PCl$_2$ $\xrightarrow{\text{C}_2\text{H}_5\text{MgCl}}$
   54%

   C$_2$H$_5$P(OC$_2$H$_5$)$_2$ + C$_2$H$_5$PCl$_2$ $\xrightarrow{\text{C}_6\text{H}_5\text{MgCl}}$
   23%

③ Liq. (101~102°/14). n_D 1.5268 (20°).

⑥ Ber. **95**, 2993 (1962)

PC$_{10}$H$_{15}$OS

① Phenylphosphinothioic acid O-butyl-
   ester
   C$_6$H$_5$P(S)(H)OC$_4$H$_9$

② C$_6$H$_5$P(OC$_4$H$_9$)N(C$_2$H$_5$)$_2$ + H$_2$S
   $\longrightarrow$ 76%

③ (75°/0.03). n_D 1.5530 (20°). d 1.0894
   (20°).

⑥ Zhur. **32**, 3062 (1962).

PC$_{10}$H$_{15}$O$_2$

① Phenylphosphonous acid diethylester
   C$_6$H$_5$P(OC$_2$H$_5$)$_2$

② (C$_2$H$_5$O)$_2$PCl + C$_6$H$_5$Li $\longrightarrow$ 56.5%
   C$_6$H$_5$MgCl + (C$_2$H$_5$O)$_3$P $\longrightarrow$ 30%
   C$_6$H$_5$PCl$_2$ + NaOC$_2$H$_5$ $\xrightarrow{\text{EtOH}}$ 73%

③ (63~65°/1). n_D 1.5113 (20°). d 1.0235
   (20°).

NMR : JACS **84**, 3467 (1962).

④ + dil. HCl $\longrightarrow$ C$_6$H$_5$P(OH)(OC$_2$H$_5$)
   + LiAlH$_4$ $\longrightarrow$ C$_6$H$_5$PH$_2$
   + PCl$_3$ $\longrightarrow$ C$_6$H$_5$PCl$_2$
   + C$_2$H$_5$I $\longrightarrow$ C$_2$H$_5$(C$_6$H$_5$)P(O)(OC$_2$H$_5$)
   + RCl $\longrightarrow$ C$_6$H$_5$P(O)(OC$_2$H$_5$)R
   R = (CH$_3$)$_3$SiCH$_2$, C$_2$H$_5$OSi(CH$_3$)$_2$CH$_2$,
   (C$_2$H$_5$O)$_2$Si(CH$_3$)CH$_2$.

⑥ Izv. OKhN **1960**, 133.   JCS **1963**, 540.
   Ber. **93**, 1220 (1960).

PC$_{10}$H$_{15}$O$_2$

① Ethylphenylphosphinic acid ethylester
   (C$_6$H$_5$)(C$_2$H$_5$)P(O)(OC$_2$H$_5$)

② C$_6$H$_5$P(OC$_2$H$_5$)$_2$ + C$_2$H$_5$I $\longrightarrow$ 85%

③ Colorless liq. (100°/0.5).

④ + COCl$_2$ $\longrightarrow$ C$_6$H$_5$(C$_2$H$_5$)POCl

⑥ JCS **1963**, 540.   Proc. Chem. Soc.
   1962, 307.

PC$_{10}$H$_{15}$O$_2$S

① Phenylphosphonothioic acid
   O,O-diethylester
   C$_6$H$_5$P(S)(OC$_2$H$_5$)$_2$

② C$_6$H$_5$P(S)Cl$_2$ + C$_2$H$_5$ONa $\longrightarrow$ 50%

③ Oil. (163°/20, 96°/0.05). n_D 1.5370
   (25°). d 1.12 (15°).

④ + C$_3$H$_7$I $\longrightarrow$ C$_6$H$_5$P(O)(OC$_2$H$_5$)SC$_3$H$_7$

⑥ Chem. Ind. (London) **1961**, 591.   JCS
   1961, 5532.

PC$_{10}$H$_{15}$O$_3$

① Phenylphosphonic acid diethylester
   C$_6$H$_5$P(O)(OC$_2$H$_5$)$_2$

② C$_6$H$_5$POCl$_2$ + C$_2$H$_5$OH $\xrightarrow{\text{C}_5\text{H}_5\text{N}}$
   C$_6$H$_6$ + PCl$_3$ + AlCl$_3$ $\longrightarrow$ complex
   $\xrightarrow{\text{C}_2\text{H}_5\text{OH}}$ 80.4%

③ Colorless liq. (121~123°/2). n_D
   1.4935 (25°).
   Sol. in org. solvents.
   IR : Chem. Ind. (London) **1962**, 1058.
   NMR : J. Chem. Eng. Data **7**, 307

(1962).   JACS **84**, 3467 (1962).

④ + HCl $\longrightarrow$ C$_6$H$_5$P(O)(OH)$_2$

⑥ JACS **69**, 2020 (1947) ; **79**, 3071 (1957).

PC$_{10}$H$_{15}$S

① Diethylphenylphosphine sulfide (C$_2$H$_5$)$_2$C$_6$H$_5$P(S)

② C$_6$H$_5$PCl$_2$ + C$_2$H$_5$MgBr $\xrightarrow{\quad S \quad}$ 73%

③ (127.5°/0.80). n_D 1.5891 (25°).
 UV : Kosolapoff 117.
 NMR : J. Chem. Eng. Data **7**, 307 (1962). JINC **24**, 1073 (1962).

⑥ Inorg. Chem. **2**, 192 (1963). J. Chem. Eng. Data **8**, 226 (1963).

PC$_{10}$H$_{15}$S$_2$

① Ethylphenylphosphinodithioic acid ethylester C$_2$H$_5$(C$_6$H$_5$)P(S)SC$_2$H$_5$

② C$_6$H$_5$P(SC$_2$H$_5$)$_2$ + C$_2$H$_5$I $\longrightarrow$

③ Liq. (169~170°/3.5). d 1.1693 (0°/0°),

④ + C$_2$H$_5$ONa $\longrightarrow$ C$_2$H$_5$(C$_6$H$_5$)P(S)ONa

⑥ J. Russ. Phys. Chem. Soc. **61**, 2037 (1929).

PC$_{10}$H$_{15}$S$_2$

① Diethylphosphinodithioic acid phenylester (C$_2$H$_5$)$_2$P(S)SC$_6$H$_5$

② (C$_2$H$_5$)$_2$P(S)SNa + ClN$_2$C$_6$H$_5$ $\longrightarrow$ 13.6%

③ (128.5~130°/0.02). n_D 1.6211 (20°). d 1.1387 (20°).

⑥ Zhur. Vsesoyuz. Khim. Obshchestva im D. I. Mendeleeva. **6**, No. 1, 119 (1961) ; CA **55**, 15385 (1961).

PC$_{10}$H$_{15}$Se

① Diethylphenylphosphine selenide (C$_2$H$_5$)$_2$P(Se)(C$_6$H$_5$)

② C$_6$H$_5$PCl$_2$ + C$_2$H$_5$MgBr $\xrightarrow{\quad Se \quad}$ 52%

③ (149°/1.7). n_D 1.6086 (27°).

⑥ J. Chem. Eng. Data **8**, 226 (1963).

PC$_{10}$H$_{16}$I

① Ethyldimethylphenylphosphonium iodide [(CH$_3$)$_2$(C$_2$H$_5$)(C$_6$H$_5$)P]I

② KP(C$_2$H$_5$)(C$_6$H$_5$)·dioxane + CH$_3$I $\longrightarrow$ [CH$_3$(C$_6$H$_5$)(C$_2$H$_5$)(C$_6$H$_5$CH$_2$)P]I

$\xrightarrow{\text{LiAlH}_4,\ \text{THF}}$ CH$_3$(C$_6$H$_5$)(C$_2$H$_5$)P

$\xrightarrow{\text{CH}_3\text{I}}$ 94%

(CH$_3$)$_2$(C$_6$H$_5$)P + (C$_2$H$_5$)I $\longrightarrow$

③ [150~151°].

⑥ Kosolapoff 91.   Ber. **94**, 392 (1961).
 JOC **25**, 1996 (1960).   Ann. **646**, 65 (1961).

PC$_{10}$H$_{16}$NOS

① *P*-Methyl-*N*-phenylphosphonamido-thioic acid *S*-propylester CH$_3$P(O)(SC$_3$H$_7$)NHC$_6$H$_5$

② CH$_3$P(O)(SC$_3$H$_7$)Cl + C$_6$H$_5$NH$_2$ $\longrightarrow$ 75%

③ [98~100°].

⑥ JCS 1961, 3067.

PC$_{10}$H$_{16}$NO$_2$

① *P*-Ethyl-*N*-phenylphosphonamidic acid ethylester C$_2$H$_5$P(O)(OC$_2$H$_5$)NHC$_6$H$_5$

② C$_2$H$_5$P(O)(OC$_2$H$_5$)Cl + C$_6$H$_5$NH$_2$ $\longrightarrow$

③ (134°/0.05). [32°].

⑥ JCS 1961, 3076.

PC$_{10}$H$_{16}$NO$_2$

① *P*-Methyl-*N*-phenylphosphonamidic acid propylester CH$_3$P(O)(OC$_3$H$_7$)NHC$_6$H$_5$

② CH$_3$P(O)(OC$_3$H$_7$)Cl + C$_6$H$_5$NH$_2$ $\longrightarrow$

③ (134°/0.05).

⑥ JCS 1961, 3067.

PC$_{10}$H$_{19}$

① 1-Cyclohexyltetramethylene phosphine

$$\begin{array}{c}CH_2-CH_2\\ |\qquad\qquad\rangle P-C_6H_{11}\\ CH_2-CH_2\end{array}$$

② $(cyclo\text{-}C_6H_{11})PLi_2 + Cl(CH_2)_4Cl \longrightarrow$

23.2%

$(cyclo\text{-}C_6H_{11})PH_2 + Br(CH_2)_4Br$

$\xrightarrow{NaOC_2H_5}$ 32%

③ Colorless liq. (94°/3.5).

Oxidized in air.

④ + S $\xrightarrow{benzene}$

$$\begin{array}{c}CH_2-CH_2\\ |\qquad\qquad\rangle P(S)(cyclo\text{-}C_6H_{11})\\ CH_2-CH_2\end{array}$$

mp 153°

+ CH₃I $\longrightarrow$

$$\left[\begin{array}{c}CH_2-CH_2\\ |\qquad\qquad\rangle\overset{+}{P}(CH_3)(cyclo\text{-}C_6H_{11})\\ CH_2-CH_2\end{array}\right]I^-$$

mp 230~232°

⑥ Ber. **94**, 113 (1961); **96**, 2186 (1963).

PC₁₀H₁₉

① Di-*n*-butylethynylphosphine

$HC{\equiv}CP(C_4H_9\text{-}n)_2$

② $(n\text{-}C_4H_9)_2PCl + CH{\equiv}CMgBr \longrightarrow$

70%

③ Colorless liq. (85°/10). n_D 1.4765(20°).

IR: Rec. trav. chim. **81**, 993 (1962).

④ + LiNH₂ $\xrightarrow{\text{in NH}_3}$ $(n\text{-}C_4H_9)_2PC{\equiv}CLi$

$\xrightarrow{\text{CH}_3\text{I or C}_2\text{H}_5\text{I}}$ $(n\text{-}C_4H_9)_2PC{\equiv}CR$;

R=CH₃, C₂H₅

+ C₂H₅SH $\xrightarrow{[(C_2H_5)_2C(CN)Ni]_2}$

$(n\text{-}C_4H_9)_2PCH{=}CHS(C_2H_5)$

PC₁₀H₁₉O₂

① Ethynylphosphonous acid dibutyl-

ester

$HC{\equiv}CP(OC_4H_9\text{-}n)_2$

② $HC{\equiv}CMgBr + (n\text{-}C_4H_9O)_2PCl \longrightarrow$

74%

③ (58.8~60°/2). n_D 1.4520 (20°). d 0.9289

(20°).

④ + H₂O $\xrightarrow{\text{4\% H}_2\text{SO}_4 \text{ in dioxane}}$

$HC{\equiv}CP(O)(H)(OC_4H_9)$

⑥ Dokl. **131**, 1334 (1960).   Zhur. **32**,

3351(1962).

PC₁₀H₁₉O₃

① Butylphosphonic acid diallylester

$C_4H_9P(O)(OCH_2CH{=}CH_2)_2$

② $(CH_2{=}CHCH_2O)_2PONa + C_4H_9Br \longrightarrow$

③ Colorless liq. (75~81°/0.5). n_D 1.4553

(20°). d 1.002 (25°/25°).

④ + *n*-lauryl methacrylate $\xrightarrow{BPO}$

copolymer

$\xrightarrow{BPO}$ polymer

⑥ JACS **76**, 2191 (1954).   J. Polymer

Sci. A 1, 3343, 3357 (1963).

PC₁₀H₂₁

① Di-*n*-butylvinylphosphine

$(n\text{-}C_4H_9)_2(CH_2{=}CH)P$

② $(n\text{-}C_4H_9)_2POC_4H_9 + CH_2{=}CHMgBr$

$\xrightarrow{\text{THF}}$ 82%

③ (48~49°/2). n_D 1.4710 (20°), d 0.8210

(20°),

④ + active MnO₂ $\longrightarrow$

$(n\text{-}C_4H_9)_2P(O)(CH{=}CH_2)$

⑥ Dokl. **135**, 603 (1960).   CA **55**, 12272

(1961).

PC₁₀H₂₁O

① Dibutylvinylphosphineoxide

$(C_4H_9)_2P(O)CH{=}CH_2$

② $(C_4H_9)_2P(OC_4H_9) + CH_2{=}CHMgBr$

$\xrightarrow{\text{THF}}$ $(C_4H_9)_2PCH{=}CH_2$

$\xrightarrow{\text{MnO}_2/\text{petr. ether}}$ 62%

③ (103.5~104.0°/1.5). [37.5~38°].

UV: Zhur. **32**, 3255 (1962).

⑥ Dokl. **135**, 603 (1960).

PC₁₀H₂₁O₂

① Vinylphosphonous acid dibutylester

CH$_2$=CHP(OC$_4$H$_9$-n)$_2$

② (C$_4$H$_9$O)$_2$PCl + CH$_2$=CHMgBr $\xrightarrow{-60°}$
71%

③ (49~51.5°/2). n_D 1.4471 (20°). d 0.9039
(20°).

Raman and UV: Zhur. **32**, 3255
(1962).

④ + S $\xrightarrow{(C_2H_5)_2O}$ CH$_2$=CHP(S)(OC$_4$H$_9$)$_2$

+ CH$_3$I $\longrightarrow$
CH$_2$=CHP(O)(CH$_3$)(OC$_4$H$_9$)

+ H$_2$O $\xrightarrow[\text{dioxane}]{4\% \text{ H}_2\text{SO}_4}$
CH$_2$=CHP(O)(H)OC$_4$H$_9$

+ C$_2$H$_5$I $\longrightarrow$
CH$_2$=CHP(O)(OC$_4$H$_9$)C$_2$H$_5$

+ MnO$_2$ $\longrightarrow$ CH$_2$=CHP(O)(OC$_4$H$_9$)$_2$

+ Cl$_2$ $\xrightarrow{\text{in C}_6\text{H}_5\text{Cl}}$ CH$_2$=CHP(O)
(OC$_4$H$_9$)Cl

⑥ Dokl. **131**, 1334 (1960).   Zhur. **32**,
3351 (1962).

PC$_{10}$H$_{21}$O$_2$S

① Vinylphosphonothioic acid
O, O-dibutylester
CH$_2$=CHP(S)(OC$_4$H$_9$)$_2$

② CH$_2$=CHP(OC$_4$H$_9$)$_2$ + S $\xrightarrow{0° \text{ in (C}_2\text{H}_5)_2\text{O}}$
88%

③ (96.2~96.8°/2.5). n_D 1.4730 (20°).
d 0.9954 (20°).

⑥ Zhur. **32**, 3351 (1962).

PC$_{10}$H$_{21}$O$_3$

① Vinylphosphonic acid dibutylester
CH$_2$=CHP(O)(OC$_4$H$_9$)$_2$

② (C$_4$H$_9$O)$_2$PCl + CH$_2$=CHMgBr $\xrightarrow{-60°}$
CH$_2$=CHP(OC$_4$H$_9$)$_2$ $\xrightarrow{\text{MnO}_2}$ 79%

PCl$_3$ + CH$_2$=CHCl $\xrightarrow{(O)}$ C$_2$H$_3$Cl$_2$POCl$_2$
$\xrightarrow{\text{C}_4\text{H}_9\text{OH}}$ C$_2$H$_3$Cl$_2$P(O)(OC$_4$H$_9$)$_2$
$\xrightarrow{\text{Zn. CuSO}_4}$

③ (89~89.5°/2). n_D 1.4365 (20°). d 0.9812
(20°).

UV and Raman: Zhur. **32**, 3255
(1962).

④ $\longrightarrow$ polymer
+ styrene $\longrightarrow$ copolymer

⑥ Zhur. **32**, 3351 (1962) ; **29**, 3947 (1959).
Vysokomol. soed. **2**, 1432 (1960).

PC$_{10}$H$_{21}$O$_3$

① Cyclohexylphosphonic acid diethylester
C$_6$H$_{11}$P(O)(OC$_2$H$_5$)$_2$

② C$_6$H$_{11}$P(O)Cl$_2$ + C$_2$H$_5$OH
+ C$_2$H$_5$ONa $\longrightarrow$
PCl$_3$ + C$_6$H$_{11}$Cl + AlCl$_3$ $\longrightarrow$ complex
$\xrightarrow{\text{C}_2\text{H}_5\text{OH}}$ 49%

③ Colorless liq. (148°/1.5). n_D 1.4538
(25°).

⑥ JACS **79**, 3570 (1957).   Ber. **85**, 9
(1952).

PC$_{10}$H$_{21}$O$_4$

① Acetylphosphonic acid dibutylester
CH$_3$COP(O)(OC$_4$H$_9$)$_2$

② (C$_4$H$_9$O)$_3$P + CH$_3$COCl $\longrightarrow$ 49.8%

③ Oil. (87~88°/1.5). n_D 1.4301 (20°).
d 1.0199 (20°/4°) .

④ + NaHSO$_3$ $\longrightarrow$
CH$_3$C(OH)(SO$_3$Na)P(O)(OC$_4$H$_9$)$_2$

⑥ Izv. OKhN **1947**, 163. JCS **1960**, 1249.

PC$_{10}$H$_{21}$O$_4$

① Acetylphosphonic acid diisobutyl-
ester
CH$_3$COP(O)(OC$_4$H$_9$-i)$_2$

② (i-C$_4$H$_9$O)$_3$P + (CH$_3$CO)$_2$O $\longrightarrow$ 21.6%

③ Liq. (144~146°). n_D 1.4305 (20°). d
1.0018 (20°).
Sol. in org. solvents.

⑥ Dokl. **102**, 283 (1955).

PC$_{10}$H$_{22}$BrO$_2$

① Carboxymethyltriethylphospho-
nium bromide ethylester

[(C$_2$H$_5$O$_2$CCH$_2$)(C$_2$H$_5$)$_3$P]Br

② (C$_2$H$_5$)$_3$P + BrCH$_2$CO$_2$C$_2$H$_5$ $\longrightarrow$
(C$_2$H$_5$)$_2$PCH$_2$CO$_2$C$_2$H$_5$ + C$_2$H$_5$Br $\longrightarrow$

③ [83.0~83.5°].

⑥ Kosolapoff 89. Ber. **94**, 2244 (1961).

PC$_{10}$H$_{23}$O

① Dibutylphosphinous acid ethylester
(n-C$_4$H$_9$)$_2$P(OC$_2$H$_5$)

② C$_2$H$_5$O$-$PCl$_2$ + n-C$_4$H$_9$MgCl $\xrightarrow{\text{ether}}$
63%
C$_4$H$_9$P(OC$_2$H$_5$)$_2$ + C$_4$H$_9$PCl$_2$ + C$_4$H$_9$PCl$_2$
$\xrightarrow{\text{C}_4\text{H}_9\text{MgCl}}$ 39%

③ Colorless liq. (99~100°/17). n_D 1.4487 (20°).

④ + C$_6$H$_5$CH$_2$Cl $\longrightarrow$
(C$_4$H$_9$)$_2$(C$_6$H$_5$CH$_2$)PO
+ C$_4$H$_9$OH + Na(trace) $\longrightarrow$
(C$_4$H$_9$)$_2$P(OC$_4$H$_9$)
+ LiAlH$_4$ $\longrightarrow$ (C$_4$H$_9$)$_2$PH

⑥ Ber. **93**, 1220 (1960); **95**, 2993 (1962).

PC$_{10}$H$_{23}$O

① Dibutylethylphosphine oxide
(C$_4$H$_9$)$_2$P(O)C$_2$H$_5$

② (C$_4$H$_9$)$_2$POCl + C$_2$H$_5$MgBr $\longrightarrow$ 77%

③ (104°/0.15). n_D 1.4635 (30°). d 0.9218 (20°).

⑥ Proc. Chem. Soc. **1960**, 351.

PC$_{10}$H$_{23}$O$_2$

① Dibuthylphosphinic acid ethylester
(n-C$_4$H$_9$)$_2$P(O)(OC$_2$H$_5$)

② (n-C$_4$H$_9$)$_2$P(O)H + SOCl$_2$ $\xrightarrow[\text{pyridine}]{\text{C}_2\text{H}_5\text{OH}}$
67%
(n-C$_4$H$_9$)$_2$POCl + C$_2$H$_5$Na $\xrightarrow{\text{benzene}}$
74%

③ (96°/1.2). n_D 1.4421 (22°). d 0.9349 (22°/4°).

④ + (n-C$_4$H$_9$)$_2$POCl $\xrightarrow{\text{heat}}$
(n-C$_4$H$_9$)$_2$P(O)OP(O)(C$_4$H$_9$-n)$_2$

+ PCl$_5$ $\longrightarrow$ (n-C$_4$H$_9$)$_2$POCl

⑥ JACS **84**, 3093 (1962); **73**, 4101 (1951).

PC$_{10}$H$_{23}$O$_2$

① Dipropylphosphinic acid butylester
(C$_3$H$_7$)$_2$P(O)(OC$_4$H$_9$-n)

② n-C$_3$H$_7$P(OC$_4$H$_9$)$_2$ + n-C$_3$H$_7$Br
$\xrightarrow{160°}$ 80.8%
C$_3$H$_7$P(O)(OC$_4$H$_9$)H + Na $\xrightarrow{\text{C}_3\text{H}_7\text{Cl}}$ 58.7%

③ (78~79°/1). n_D 1.4389 (20°). d 0.9343 (20°).

④ + PCl$_5$ $\longrightarrow$ (C$_3$H$_7$)$_2$POCl
+ P$_2$S$_5$ $\longrightarrow$ (C$_3$H$_7$)$_2$PSCl

⑥ Dokl. **125**, 1260 (1959). Zhur. **29**, 1450 (1959).

PC$_{10}$H$_{23}$O$_2$

① Ethylphosphonous acid dibutyl
ester
C$_2$H$_5$P(OC$_4$H$_9$-n)$_2$

② C$_2$H$_5$P(OC$_2$H$_5$)$_2$ + C$_2$H$_5$PCl$_2$ $\xrightarrow[\text{pyridine}]{\text{C}_4\text{H}_9\text{OH}}$
11%
C$_2$H$_5$PCl$_2$ + C$_4$H$_9$OH $\xrightarrow{\text{pyridine}}$ 79.4%

③ (94~95°/12). n_D 1.4354 (20°).

⑥ Ber. **95**, 2993 (1962). Izv. OKhN **1952**, 854.

PC$_{10}$H$_{23}$O$_2$S

① Ethylphosphonothioic acid
O, O-dibutyl ester
C$_2$H$_5$P(S)(OC$_4$H$_9$)$_2$

② (C$_4$H$_9$O)$_2$PSH + C$_4$H$_9$ONa + C$_2$H$_5$X
$\longrightarrow$ 65%

③ Liq. (79.5~83°/2, 97~98°/2). n_D
1.4533 (20°). d 0.9775 (20°).
Sol. in org. solvents.

④ + C$_4$H$_9$Br $\xrightarrow{\text{heat}}$
C$_2$H$_5$P(O)(OC$_4$H$_9$)SC$_4$H$_9$

⑥ Dokl. **104**, 861 (1955). Zhur. **24**, 307 (1954). Izv. OKhN **1956**, 185.

PC₁₀H₂₃O₂S

① Ethylphosphonothioic acid
   O, S-dibutyl ester
   $C_2H_5P(O)(OC_4H_9)SC_4H_9$

② $C_2H_5P(S)(OC_4H_9)_2 + C_4H_9Br$

   $\xrightarrow{\text{heat in sealed tube}}$ 14%

③ Liq. (92~94°/2). n_D 1.4660 (20°), d
   0.9951 (20°).
   Sol. in org. solvents.

⑥ Dokl. **104**, 861 (1955).   Izv. OKhN
   1956, 193.

PC₁₀H₂₃O₃

① Ethylphosphonic acid dibutylester
   $C_2H_5P(O)(OC_4H_9)_2$

② $(C_4H_9O)_2POH + Na + C_2H_5Br \longrightarrow$
   $(C_4H_9O)_3P + C_2H_5Br \longrightarrow$ 77%

③ Oil. (137~139°/17, 138~140°/17).
   n_D 1.4282 (20°). d 0.9623 (25°/4°).

④ $+$ HCl $\xrightarrow{\text{reflux over night}}$
   $C_2H_5P(O)(OH)_2$
   $\xrightarrow{\text{heat}}$ $C_2H_5P(O)(OH)_2 + C_4H_9OH$
   $+$ but-1-ene

⑤ Extractant.

⑥ JACS **67**, 1180 (1945).   JCS **1962**, 331.
   Chem. Eng. Data Ser. **3**, 310
   (1958)

PC₁₀H₂₄I

① Methyltripropylphosphonium
   iodide
   $[CH_3(C_3H_7)_3P]I$

② $(C_3H_7)_3P + CH_3I \longrightarrow$

③ [212.5°].

⑥ Kaufman 1136.   JCS **1963**, 1036.

PC₁₀H₂₄NOS

① Triethylphosphonamidothioic acid
   O-butylester
   $C_2H_5P(S)(OC_4H_9)N(C_2H_5)_2$

② $C_2H_5P(OC_4H_9)N(C_2H_5)_2 + S \longrightarrow$ 61%

③ (88~89°/1). n_D 1.4785 (20°). d 0.9789

(20°).

⑥ Izv. OKhN **1955**, 1021.

PC₁₁H₁₃O

① 3-Methyl-1-phenyl-3-phospholene-1-
   oxide

② $CH_2=CHC(CH_3)=CH_2 + C_6H_5PCl_2$
   $\xrightarrow{H_2O}$

③ (106~164°/0.7).

④ $+ 2R-N=C=O \longrightarrow$
   $R-N=C=N-R + CO_2$ (as catalyst)

⑥ JACS **84**, 3673 (1962).   Tetrahedron
   19, 1563 (1963).

PC₁₁H₁₄ClO₃

① Phenylphosphonic acid allyl-
   2-chloroethylester
   $C_6H_5P(O)(OCH_2CH=CH_2)(OCH_2CH_2Cl)$

② $C_6H_5P(O)(OCH_2CH_2Cl)Cl$
   $+ CH_2=CHCH_2OH \xrightarrow{\textit{in vacuo} \ 80~90°}$
   24%

③ (163~165°/1.5). n_D 1.5260 (20°). d
   1.2697 (20°).

⑥ Zhur. **32**, 964 (1962).

PC₁₁H₁₅

① 1-Phenylcyclopentamethylene phosphine

② $C_6H_5PLi_2 + Br(CH_2)_5Br \longrightarrow$ 31.0%

③ Colorless liq. (119°/3).
   Oxidized in air.

④ $+ S \xrightarrow{\text{benzene}}$

   mp 86°

$+ CH_3I \longrightarrow$

$$\left[CH_2 \underset{CH_2-CH_2}{\overset{CH_2-CH_2}{\diagdown}} \overset{+}{P}(CH_3)(C_6H_5) \right] I^-$$

mp 176°

⑥ Ber. **94**, 113 (1961).

PC₁₁H₁₅

① Ethylallylphenylphosphine

$C_2H_5(CH_2=CHCH_2)C_6H_5P$

② $[C_2H_5(CH_2=CHCH_2)(C_6H_5)(C_6H_5CH_2)\overset{+}{P}]$

$Br^- \xrightarrow{\text{electrolysis}} 72\%$

③ (113~115°/15).

④ $+ CH_3I \longrightarrow$

$[CH_3(C_2H_5)(CH_2=CHCH_2)(C_6H_5)\overset{+}{P}]I^-$

⑥ Ann. **646**, 65 (1961).   Tetrahedron Letters 1961, 161.

PC₁₁H₁₅IN

① (2-Cyanoethyl)dimethylphenyl phosphonium iodide

$[(NCCH_2CH_2)P(C_6H_5)(CH_3)_2]I$

② $CH_3(C_6H_5)PH \xrightarrow{\text{1) } CH_2=CHCN, \text{ 2) } CH_3I}$

③ [172~173°].

Picrate [123~125°].

⑥ JCS 1963, 4846.   Ber. **91**, 1583 (1958).

PC₁₁H₁₅O

① Diethylbenzoylphosphine

$(C_2H_5)_2(C_6H_5CO)P$

② $(C_2H_5)_2PLi + C_6H_5COCl \longrightarrow 50\%$

③ Yellow liq. (98~100°/2).

Air-sensitive. Sol. in org. solvents.

④ $+CH_3I \longrightarrow [C_6H_5CO\overset{+}{P}CH_3(C_2H_5)_2]I^-$

$+ C_6H_5NHNH_2 \longrightarrow$

$(C_2H_5)_2PH + C_6H_5CO-NHNHC_6H_5$

$+ NiBr_2 \longrightarrow$

$[C_6H_5COP(C_2H_5)_2]_2NiBr_2$

⑥ Ber. **92**, 3183 (1959).

PC₁₁H₁₅O

① Trimethylphenacylidene phosphorane

$(CH_3)_3P=CHCOC_6H_5$

② $[CH_3PCH_2COC_6H_5]Br \xrightarrow{\text{NaOH/C}_2\text{H}_5\text{OH, 0°}}$

③ [130~131°].

⑥ JCS **1961**, 1266.

PC₁₁H₁₅O₄

① Benzoylphosphonic acid diethyl-ester

$C_6H_5COP(O)(OC_2H_5)_2$

② $(C_2H_5O)_3P + C_6H_5COCl \xrightarrow{\text{heat}} 66.5\%$

③ Light yeilow liq. (141°/2.5). n_D 1.5065 (20°). d 1.1599 (20°/4°).

Insol. in H_2O; sol. in alcohols and ether.

④ $+ NaOH \dashrightarrow$
- → $C_6H_5CHO + Na_3PO_4$ $+ C_2H_5OH$
- → C_6H_5COONa $+ Na_2HPO_3 + C_2H_5OH$

$+ Na-Hg \xrightarrow{\text{in aq. alc., } CH_3COOH}$

$C_6H_5CH(OH)P(O)(OC_2H_5)_2$

⑥ Izv. OKhN **1945**, 364.   JACS **69**, 2112 (1947).

PC₁₁H₁₇

① Ethyl-*n*-propylphenylphosphine

$C_2H_5(n-C_3H_7)(C_6H_5)P$

② $C_6H_5PCl_2 + Pb(C_2H_5)_4$

$\longrightarrow C_2H_5(C_6H_5)PCl \xrightarrow{n-C_3H_7MgX}$

③ (109~111°/9). n_D 1.5360 (20°). d 0.9320 (20°).

④ $+ CH_2=CHCH_2Br \longrightarrow$

$[C_2H_5(CH_2=CHCH_2)(n-C_3H_7)\cdot$

$(C_6H_5)P]^+Br^-$

⑥ Dokl. **143**, 596 (1962).

PC₁₁H₁₇BrN₃

① Tris(2-cyanoethyl)ethylphosphonium bromide

$[(C_2H_5)(NCCH_2CH_2)_3P]Br$

② $(NCCH_2CH_2)_3P + C_2H_5Br \longrightarrow 90\%$

④ $\xrightarrow{\text{Hg/2e, 70~90°}} C_2H_5(NCCH_2CH_2)_2P$

(50~70%)

⑥ Ann. **646**, 65 (1961)

PC₁₁H₁₇O₂

① Benzyl phosphonous acid diethyl
   ester
   $(C_6H_5CH_2)P(OC_2H_5)_2$

② $(C_2H_5O)_3P + C_6H_5CH_2MgCl \longrightarrow 41\%$
   $(C_2H_5O)_2PCl + C_6H_5CH_2MgCl \longrightarrow$
   50%

③ $(88\sim90°/3)$. $n_D 1.5032$ $(20°)$.

⑥ Ber. **93**, 1220 (1960).

PC₁₁H₁₇O₂S

① Phenylphosphonothioic acid *O*-ethyl-
   S-propyl ester
   $C_6H_5P(O)(OC_2H_5)SC_3H_7$

② $C_6H_5P(S)(OC_2H_5)_2 + C_3H_7I$
   $\xrightarrow[\text{reflux, 8 days}]{} 78\%$
   $C_6H_5P(S)(OC_2H_5)_2 + C_3H_7I$
   $\xrightarrow[\text{CH}_3\text{NO}_2, \text{ 96 hrs}]{} 80\%$

③ $(116°/0.01)$.

⑥ JCS **1961**, 5532.

PC₁₁H₁₇O₂S

① Benzylphosphonothioic acid
   O, S-diethyl ester
   $C_6H_5CH_2P(O)(OC_2H_5)SC_2H_5$

② $C_6H_5CH_2P(S)(OC_2H_5)_2 + C_2H_5Br$
   $\xrightarrow[\text{in sealed tube}]{} 42\%$

③ Liq. $(134\sim136/2)$. $n_D 1.5350$ $(20°)$. d
   1.1263 $(20°)$.
   Sol. in org. solvents.

⑥ Izv. OKhN **1956**, 193.

PC₁₁H₁₇O₂S

① Benzylphosphonothioic acid
   O, O-diethyl ester
   $C_6H_5CH_2P(S)(OC_2H_5)_2$

② $(C_2H_5O)_2PSH + C_2H_5ONa$
   $+ C_6H_5CH_2X \longrightarrow$
   $(C_2H_5O)_2PSH + Na + C_6H_5CH_2Cl \longrightarrow$

③ Colorless liq. $(125.5\sim127.5°/3,$ $124\sim$
   $125°/3.5)$. $n_D 1.5305$ $(20°)$. $d 1.0131$
   $(20°)$.

Sol. in org. solvents.

④ $+ C_2H_5Br \longrightarrow$
   $C_6H_5CH_2P(O)(OC_2H_5)SC_2H_5$

⑥ Izv. OKhN **1956**, 193 ; **1953**, 163.

PC₁₁H₁₇O₃

① Benzylphosphonic acid diethyl ester
   $C_6H_5CH_2P(O)(OC_2H_5)_2$

② $C_6H_5CH_2Br + (C_2H_5O)_3P \longrightarrow$
   $(C_2H_5)_2POH + Na + C_6H_5CH_2Cl \longrightarrow$
   45%

③ Colorless liq. $(169\sim167°/25, 155°/14)$.
   $n_D 1.4965$ $(20°)$. $d 1.1200$ $(0°/0)$.
   IR : Chem. Ind. (London) **1960**, 1058.
   NMR : JACS **84**, 3467 (1962).

④ $+ CH_2=CHCN$ or $CH_2=CHCO_2C_2H_5$
   $\longrightarrow$ $C_6H_5CH(CH_2CH_2CO_2H)P(O)-$
   $(OC_2H_5)_2$

⑥ Acta Chem. Scand. **15**, 349 (1961).
   Kogyo Kagaku Zasshi **60**, 21 (1957).
   JCS **1948**, 699.

PC₁₁H₁₈Br

① Dimethylphenylpropylphosphonium
   bromide
   $[(C_6H_5)(C_3H_7)(CH_3)_2P]Br$

② $(C_6H_5)(CH_3)(C_3H_7)P + CH_3Br \longrightarrow$

③ $[118°]$.

⑥ Tetrahedron Letters **1961**, 161.

PC₁₁H₂₁

① 1-Cyclohexylpentamethylene
   phosphine
   $CH_2\underset{CH_2CH_2}{\overset{CH_2CH_2}{<}}P(cyclo\text{-}C_6H_{11})$

② $cyclo\text{-}C_6H_{11}PLi_2 + Br(CH_2)_5Br \longrightarrow$
   20%
   $(cyclo\text{-}C_6H_{11})PH_2 + Br(CH_2)_5Br \longrightarrow$
   57%

③ Colorless liq. $(115°/3)$.
   Oxidize in air.

④ + S $\xrightarrow{\text{benzene}}$

$CH_2\Big\langle{CH_2CH_2\atop CH_2CH_2}\Big\rangle P(S)(cyclo\text{-}C_6H_{11})$

mp 153°

+ CH$_3$I $\longrightarrow$

$\Big[CH_2\Big\langle{CH_2CH_2\atop CH_2CH_2}\Big\rangle P(CH_3)(cyclo\text{-}C_6H_{11})\Big]I$

mp 230~232°

⑥ Ber. **94**, 113 (1961); **96**, 2186 (1963).

PC$_{11}$H$_{22}$NO$_3$

① 2-Cyanoethylphosphonic acid
   dibutyl ester
   $NCCH_2CH_2P(O)(OC_4H_9)_2$

② $(C_4H_9O)_2POH + CH_2=CHCN$
   $\xrightarrow[\text{0.5 hr, steam bath}]{}$ 80%

③ (143~144°/0.8). n_D 1.4420 (23°).

④ + HCl $\xrightarrow{\text{reflux, 6 hr}}$
   $(HO)_2P(O)CH_2CH_2COOH$
   + Pd−BaSO$_4$ + HCl $\longrightarrow$
   $(HO)_2P(O)(CH_2)_3NH_2$
   + H$_2$NOH + 10% HCl $\longrightarrow$
   $(C_4H_9O)_2P(O)CH_2CH_2C(NH_2)$:
   NOH·HCl
   + CH$_3$OH + HCl $\longrightarrow$ iminomethyl
   ester $\longrightarrow$ methyl ester $\longrightarrow$
   $(HO)_2P(O)CH_2CH_2COOH$
   + C$_2$H$_5$OH + HCl $\longrightarrow$
   iminoethyl ester $\xrightarrow{\text{NH}_3}$
   $(C_4H_9O)_2P(O)CH_2CH_2C(NH_2)$:
   NH·HCl

⑥ Arch. Pharm. **295**, 28 (1962).

PC$_{11}$H$_{23}$O$_2$

① Allylphosphonous acid dibutyl ester
   $CH_2=CHCH_2P(OC_4H_9\text{-}n)_2$

② $(n\text{-}C_4H_9O)_2PCl + CH_2=CHCH_2MgBr$
   $\xrightarrow[\text{(C}_2\text{H}_5)_2\text{O}]{}$ 81.5%

③ (59~59.5°/1.5). n_D 1.4500 (20°).
   d 0.8981 (20°).

Raman and UV: Zhur. **32**, 3255
(1962).

④ + CH$_2$=CHCH$_2$Br $\longrightarrow$
   $(CH_2=CHCH_2)_2P(O)OC_4H_9$
   + MnO$_2$ $\longrightarrow$
   $CH_2=CHCH_2P(O)(OC_4H_9)_2$
   + S $\longrightarrow$ $CH_2=CHCH_2P(S)(OC_4H_9)_2$

PC$_{11}$H$_{23}$O$_2$S

① Allylphosphonothioic acid
   O, O-dibutyl ester
   $CH_2=CHCH_2P(S)(OC_4H_9)_2$

② $CH_2=CHCH_2P(OC_4H_9)_2 + S$
   $\xrightarrow[\text{in C}_6\text{H}_6]{}$ 63%
   $(C_4H_9O)_2PSH + Na +$
   $CH_2=CHCH_2Br \xrightarrow{\text{heat}}$

③ Colorless liquid. (88~88.5°/1.5, 120°/
   3). n_D 1.4720 (20°). d 0.9834 (20°).
   Sol. in org. solvents.
   UV and Raman: Zhur. **32**, 3255
   (1962).

⑥ Zhur. **32**, 3351 (1962); **24**, 307 (1954).
   Dokl. **135**, 1150 (1960).

PC$_{11}$H$_{23}$O$_2$

① Allylphosphonic acid dibutyl ester
   $CH_2=CHCH_2P(O)(OC_4H_9)_2$

② $CH_2=CHCH_2P(OC_4H_9)_2 + MnO_2$
   $\longrightarrow$ 83%
   $(C_4H_9O)_3P + CH_2=CHCH_2Br$
   $\xrightarrow[\text{3 hrs, 90~120°}]{}$ 90%

③ (93~94.5°/1.5). n_D 1.4398 (20°).
   d 0.9718 (20°).
   UV and Raman: Zhur. **32**, 3255
   (1962).

⑥ Zhur. **32**, 3351 (1962).

PC$_{11}$H$_{23}$O$_4$

① Acetonylphosphonic acid dibutyl
   ester
   $CH_3COCH_2P(O)(OC_4H_9)_2$

② $CH_3C(OC_4H_9)=CHP(O)(OC_4H_9)_2$

$\xrightarrow{\text{HCl}}$ 53%

③ (126°/1). n_D 1.4400 (20°), d 1.0278 (20°).

⑥ Zhur. **31**, 2028 (1961).

PC$_{11}$H$_{25}$OS

① Dibutylphosphinothioic acid
O-isopropyl ester
(C$_4$H$_9$)$_2$P(S)OC$_3$H$_7$-i

② (C$_4$H$_9$)$_2$P(S)H + i-C$_3$H$_7$OH $\xrightarrow{\text{(C}_2\text{H}_5)_3\text{N}}$
7%

③ (84°/0.1).
Decomp. during distillation.

⑥ JOC **27**, 2198 (1962).

PC$_{11}$H$_{25}$O$_2$

① Propylphosphonous acid dibutylester
C$_3$H$_7$P(OC$_4$H$_9$-n)$_2$

② (n-C$_4$H$_9$O)$_2$PCl + C$_3$H$_7$MgBr $\longrightarrow$ 70%
(n-C$_4$H$_9$O)$_2$PCl + C$_3$H$_7$Li $\longrightarrow$ 60%

③ (93.5~5°/7). n_D 1.4400 (20°). d 0.8844 (20°).

⑥ Zhur. **29**, 1450 (1959). Izv. OKhN **1960**, 133.

PC$_{11}$H$_{25}$O$_2$S

① Propylphosphonothioic acid
O, O-dibutyl ester
C$_3$H$_7$P(S)(OC$_4$H$_9$)$_2$

② (C$_4$H$_9$O)$_2$PSH + Na + C$_3$H$_7$I $\longrightarrow$

③ Liq. (103~104°/2). n_D 1.4580 (20°). d 0.9772 (20°).
Sol. in org. solvents.

⑥ Zhur. **24**, 307 (1954).

PC$_{11}$H$_{25}$O$_3$

① Propylphosphonic acid dibutyl ester
C$_3$H$_7$P(O)(OC$_4$H$_9$)$_2$

② (C$_4$H$_9$O)$_2$POH + Na + C$_3$H$_7$Br $\longrightarrow$
67%

③ (125~127°/6~7).

④ + HCl $\longrightarrow$ C$_3$H$_7$P(O)(OH)$_2$

⑤ Extractant.

⑥ Ber. **93**, 765 (1960),   JACS **75**, 3379 (1953).

PC$_{12}$H$_9$S$_3$

① Tris(1-thienyl)phosphine
(1-C$_4$H$_3$S)$_3$P

② C$_4$H$_3$SMgX + PX$_3$ (X=Cl, Br) $\longrightarrow$

③ (205°/2). [35~36°].

④ $\xrightarrow[\text{in ether}]{\text{oxidation}}$ (C$_4$H$_3$S)$_3$P(O)

+ S $\xrightarrow{\text{CH}_3\text{OH}}$ (C$_4$H$_3$S)$_3$P(S)

+ HgCl$_2$ $\longrightarrow$ 2 [(CH$_3$S)$_3$P]HgCl$_2$

⑥ Z. anorg. allg. Chem. **292**, 245 (1957).

PC$_{12}$H$_{10}$Cl

① Diphenylphosphinous chloride
(C$_6$H$_5$)$_2$PCl

② 2 C$_6$H$_5$PCl$_2$ $\xrightarrow[\text{heat}]{\text{AlCl}_3}$ (C$_6$H$_5$)$_2$PCl + PCl$_3$
70%

③ (316~320°). (170~171°/10). n_D 1.6340 (20°). d 1.1801 (20°/4°).
NMR: J. Chem. Eng. Data **7**, 307 (1962).

⑥ Kosolapoff 55. Chem. Ind. (London) **1961**, 24. Ber. **94**, 2122 (1961).

PC$_{12}$H$_{10}$ClO

① Diphenylphosphinic chloride
(C$_6$H$_5$)$_2$P(O)Cl

② [(C$_6$H$_5$)$_2$P(S)]$_2$ + SOCl$_2$ $\longrightarrow$
(C$_6$H$_5$)$_2$PCl + SO$_3$ $\longrightarrow$
(quantitative)

③ (222°/16), (138~119°/0.15).
NMR: J. Chem. Eng. Data **7**, 307 (1962).

④ + R$_2$NH $\xrightarrow{\text{CCl}_4,\ \text{C}_5\text{H}_5\text{N}}$
(C$_6$H$_5$)$_2$P(O)NR$_2$

⑥ Kosolapoff 74. Monatsh. **93**, 1114
(1962). JOC **27**, 4444 (1962).

PC$_{12}$H$_{10}$Cl$_3$

① Diphenylphosphinothioic chloride
(C$_6$H$_5$)$_2$P(S)Cl

② (C$_6$H$_5$)$_2$PCl + S $\xrightarrow{\text{heat}}$

(C$_6$H$_5$)$_2$P(S)SH + HCl $\xrightarrow{100\sim200°}$
(C$_6$H$_5$)$_2$P(S)SH + PCl$_5$ $\longrightarrow$ 75%

③ (275~280°/15), (155~160°/0.13).
NMR: J. Chem. Eng. Data **7**, 307
(1962)

④ + SOCl$_2$ $\longrightarrow$ (C$_6$H$_5$)$_2$P(O)Cl

⑥ JACS **77**, 1864 (1955). Kosolapoff 75,
JOC **27**, 4444 (1962).

PC$_{12}$H$_{10}$Cl$_3$

① Trichorodiphenylphosphorane
(C$_6$H$_5$)$_2$PCl$_3$

② (C$_6$H$_5$)$_2$PCl + Cl$_2$ $\xrightarrow{\text{CCl}_4, \ -20°\sim25°}$
97%

③ [194~200°].

④

+ NH$_3$ $\longrightarrow$

⑥ Kosolapoff 72. JACS **80**, 2116 (1958).

PC$_{12}$H$_{10}$F$_3$

① Trifluorodiphenylphosphorane
(C$_6$H$_5$)$_2$PF$_3$

② (C$_6$H$_5$)$_2$P(O)(OH) + SF$_4$ $\longrightarrow$ 42%
3 (C$_6$H$_5$)$_2$PCl + AsF$_3$ $\longrightarrow$

③ (91~94°/0.5). (106~107°/2).
NMR: Inorg. Chem. **2**, 613 (1963).

⑥ JACS **82**, 6176 (1960). Chem. Ind.
(London) **1962**, 1868.

PC$_{12}$H$_{10}$I$_3$

① Triiododiphenylphosphorane

(C$_6$H$_5$)$_2$PI$_3$

② [((C$_6$H$_5$)$_2$P]$_2$ + I$_2$ $\longrightarrow$ 95.5%

④ + H$_2$O $\longrightarrow$ (C$_6$H$_5$)$_2$P(O)(OH)
+ C$_6$H$_5$CH$_2$Cl $\longrightarrow$
(C$_6$H$_5$)$_2$(C$_6$H$_5$CH$_2$)P(O) 77%

⑥ Ber. **93**, 861 (1960).

PC$_{12}$H$_{10}$K

① Potassiumdiphenylphosphide
(C$_6$H$_5$)$_2$PK

② (C$_6$H$_5$)$_2$PH + K $\longrightarrow$

(C$_6$H$_5$)$_2$PCl + K $\xrightarrow{\text{dioxane}}$ 73%
(2·dioxane)

(C$_6$H$_5$)$_3$P + K $\xrightarrow{\text{dioxane}}$ 70.1%
(2·dioxane)

③ Orange red crystals.
Sol. in THF and dioxane; insol. in
ether and C$_6$H$_6$.

④ + C$_6$H$_5$Br $\longrightarrow$ (C$_6$H$_5$)$_3$P
+ H$_2$O $\longrightarrow$ (C$_6$H$_5$)$_2$PH

+ CH$_2$—CH$_2$ $\xrightarrow{\text{H}_2\text{O}}$ (C$_6$H$_5$)$_2$PCH$_2$CH$_2$OH
      \   /
       O

⑤ Intermediate in prepn. of org. P
compds.

⑥ Ber. **92**, 227, 1118 (1959); **94**, 102
(1961). Z. Naturf. **14 b**, 349
(1959).

PC$_{12}$H$_{10}$Li

① Lithiumdiphenylphosphide
(C$_6$H$_5$)$_2$PLi·dioxane

② C$_6$H$_5$Li + (C$_6$H$_5$)$_2$PH $\longrightarrow$ 84%
(C$_6$H$_5$)$_3$P + Li $\xrightarrow{\text{THF}}$ 68.5%

③ Sol. in dioxane and THF; insol. in
ether and C$_6$H$_6$. Sensitive with air
and moisture.

④ + CH$_3$I $\longrightarrow$ [(CH$_3$)$_2$(C$_6$H$_5$)$_2$P]I$^-$
+ H$_2$O $\longrightarrow$ (C$_6$H$_5$)$_2$PH

⑤ Intermediate in prepn. of org. P
compds.

⑥ Ber. **92**, 1118 (1959). Z. Naturf. **14 b**,

349 (1959).   JOC **23**, 1063 (1958).

PC$_{12}$H$_{10}$Na

① Sodium diphenylphosphide
   (C$_6$H$_5$)$_2$PNa

② (C$_6$H$_5$)$_2$P−P(C$_6$H$_5$)$_2$ + Na $\xrightarrow{(C_2H_5)_2O}$

(C$_6$H$_5$)$_2$PCl + Na $\xrightarrow{(C_4H_9)_2O}$

(C$_6$H$_5$)$_2$PCl + Na $\xrightarrow{dioxane}$ 52.2%
(1 dioxane)

(C$_6$H$_5$)$_3$P + Na $\xrightarrow{dioxane}$ 25%

(C$_6$H$_5$)$_3$P + Na $\xrightarrow{in\ liq.\ NH_3}$

③ Yellow crystals.

④ + ClCH$_2$CH$_2$Cl $\longrightarrow$
   (C$_6$H$_5$)$_2$P(CH$_2$)$_2$P(C$_6$H$_5$)$_2$
   + RX $\longrightarrow$ R(C$_6$H$_5$)$_2$P
   R=C$_2$H$_5$, C$_3$H$_7$, C$_4$H$_9$.
   + (CH$_3$)$_3$SiCl $\longrightarrow$ (C$_6$H$_5$)$_2$P−Si(CH$_3$)$_3$
   + (C$_2$H$_5$)$_3$SnCl $\longrightarrow$
   (C$_6$H$_5$)$_2$P−Sn(C$_2$H$_5$)$_3$
   + C$_2$H$_5$OH $\xrightarrow{H_2O}$ (C$_6$H$_5$)$_2$PH
   + COCl$_2$ $\longrightarrow$ (C$_6$H$_5$)$_2$PP(C$_6$H$_5$)$_2$
   + CH$_2$Cl$_2$ $\longrightarrow$ (C$_6$H$_5$)$_2$PCH$_2$P(C$_6$H$_5$)$_2$

⑤ Intermediate in prepn. of org. P
   compds.

⑥ Ber. **92**, 227, 1118, 3183 (1959).   JCS
   1962, 1490.   Z. Naturf. **14b**, 349
   (1959).

PC$_{12}$H$_{11}$

① Diphenylphosphine
   (C$_6$H$_5$)$_2$PH

② (C$_6$H$_5$)$_2$P(S)−P(S)(C$_6$H$_5$)$_2$ $\longrightarrow$ 75%
   (C$_6$H$_5$)$_2$PNa + H$_2$O $\longrightarrow$ 72%
   C$_6$H$_5$PH$_2$ + Na + C$_6$H$_5$Cl $\longrightarrow$ 36%
   (C$_6$H$_5$)$_2$PCl$_3$ + LiAlH$_4$ $\longrightarrow$ 30%
   (C$_6$H$_5$)$_2$PCl + Na$_2$CO$_3$ + H$_2$O $\longrightarrow$ 47%
   (C$_6$H$_5$)$_2$POCl + LiAlH$_4$ $\longrightarrow$ 92%

③ Colorless liq. (156∼157°/16). n_D 1.6269
   (20°).

Sol. in org. solvents.
IR : Monatsh. **92**, 868 (1961).
NMR : J. Chem. Eng. Data **7**, 307
   (1962).

④ + excess K $\xrightarrow{ether}$ (C$_6$H$_5$)$_2$PK

   + C$_6$H$_5$Li $\xrightarrow{dioxane}$
   (C$_6$H$_5$)$_2$PLi·(1 dioxane)
   + CH$_2$=CHCN $\longrightarrow$
   (C$_6$H$_5$)$_2$PCH$_2$CH$_2$CN

⑥ JCS **1952**, 4453.   Ber. **92**, 227, 704,
   2088 (1959) ; **91**, 2871 (1958) ; **95**,
   64 (1962).

PC$_{12}$H$_{11}$O

① Diphenylphosphine oxide
   (C$_6$H$_5$)$_2$PH(O)

② (C$_6$H$_5$)$_2$PH $\xrightarrow{air/i\text{-}C_3H_7OH,\ 45\sim50°}$ 85%

   (C$_6$H$_5$)$_2$PCl $\xrightarrow{C_6H_6/H_2O}$

   (C$_6$H$_5$)$_2$POC$_2$H$_5$ $\xrightarrow{1\ N\ H_2SO_4}$ 85%

③ [53∼56°] (C$_2$H$_5$OH).

④ (C$_6$H$_5$)$_2$PH(O) $\longrightarrow$ (C$_6$H$_5$)$_2$P(O)Li,
   (C$_6$H$_5$)$_2$P(O)K

⑥ Izv. OKhN **1962**, 1584.   JOC **24**, 2013
   (1959) ; **26**, 4626 (1961).   Ber. **94**,
   1317, 1323 (1961) ; **93**, 1220 (1960).

PC$_{12}$H$_{11}$OS

① Diphenylphosphinothioic acid
   (C$_6$H$_5$)$_2$P(S)OH

② [(C$_6$H$_5$)$_2$PS]$_2$O $\xrightarrow[hydrolysis]{KOH\ aq.}$

   (C$_6$H$_5$)PSCl + NaOH aq. $\xrightarrow{HCl}$ 95%
   (C$_6$H$_5$)$_2$POCl + NaSH $\longrightarrow$ 67%

③ White needles. [142∼143°].
   Slightly sol. in org. solvents.

④ + HNO$_3$ $\longrightarrow$ (C$_6$H$_5$)$_2$POOH

⑥ Arch. Pharm. **295**, 81 (1962).   JACS
   77, 1864 (1955).

PC$_{12}$H$_{11}$O$_2$

① Diphenylphosphinic acid
(C$_6$H$_5$)$_2$P(O)(OH)

② (C$_2$H$_5$O)$_2$P(O)H + C$_6$H$_5$MgCl

(in heptane) $\xrightarrow[\text{2) H}_2\text{O}_2]{\text{1) aq. HCl}}$ 71%

(C$_2$H$_5$O)$_2$P(O)H + C$_6$H$_5$MgBr

$\xrightarrow[\text{2) Br}_2]{\text{1) aq. HCl}}$ 75%

(C$_6$H$_5$)$_3$PO + NaOH $\xrightarrow[\text{2) HCl}]{\text{1) 200~300°}}$ 100%

(C$_6$H$_5$)$_2$PBr + *N*-oxide $\xrightarrow{\text{CH}_3\text{OH}}$

(C$_6$H$_5$)$_3$P + Li $\xrightarrow{\text{THF}}$ (C$_6$H$_5$)$_2$PH $\xrightarrow{\text{[O]}}$
20%

(C$_6$H$_5$)$_3$PO + LiH $\longrightarrow$

[((C$_6$H$_5$)$_3$HPOCl] $\xrightarrow{\text{H}_2\text{O}_2,\ \text{HCl}}$ 28%

③ Needle crystals. [194~195°].
Sol. in C$_6$H$_6$.
NMR : J. Chem. Eng. Data **7**, 307
(1962).

④ + PCl$_5$ $\xrightarrow{\text{C}_6\text{H}_6}$ Ph$_2$POCl

⑥ Izv. SKh **1964**, 1373. JCS **1959**, 3950.
Zhur. **31**, 3027 (1961). Ber. **91**, 64
(1958).

PC$_{12}$H$_{11}$O$_3$

① Phenylphosphonic acid phenyl ester
C$_6$H$_5$P(O)(OC$_6$H$_5$)(OH)

② C$_6$H$_5$P(O)(OH)$_2$ + C$_6$H$_5$OH

+ (C$_6$H$_{11}$N=)$_2$C $\xrightarrow{\text{in THF heat}}$ 82%

③ White needles. [70~72°].
Sol. in org. solvents.

④ $\longrightarrow$ Ag salt

⑥ Ann. **181**, 265 (1876). Ber. **8**, 1306
(1875). JACS **79**, 3575 (1957).

PC$_{12}$H$_{11}$S

① Diphenylphosphine sulfide
(C$_6$H$_5$)$_2$PH(S)

② (C$_6$H$_5$)$_2$PH $\xrightarrow{\text{C}_6\text{H}_6,\ \text{S}}$ 100%

③ [95~97°] (CH$_3$CN).

⑥ JOC **26**, 5145 (1961). JACS **82**, 4751
(1960).

PC$_{12}$H$_{11}$S$_2$

① Diphenylphosphinodithioic acid
(C$_6$H$_5$)$_2$P(S)SH

② (C$_6$H$_5$)$_2$PH + S $\xrightarrow[\text{in C}_6\text{H}_6]{\text{reflux}}$ 91%

(C$_6$H$_5$PS$_2$)$_2$ + C$_6$H$_6$ $\xrightarrow{\text{AlCl}_3}$ 89%

C$_6$H$_6$ + P$_4$S$_{10}$ $\xrightarrow{\text{AlCl}_3}$ 80%

③ White needles. [55~56°].
Slowly decomp. on standing at room
temperature.
Sol. in org. solvents.
NMR : JOC **27**, 3829 (1962)

④ + Ni salt
+ HCl $\longrightarrow$ (C$_6$H$_5$)$_2$PSCl
+ HNO$_3$ $\longrightarrow$ (C$_6$H$_5$)$_2$POOH

⑥ Gazz. chim. ital. **77**, 518 (1947).
JACS **77**, 1864 (1955). JOC **27**, 3829
(1962). Zhur. **31**, 140 (1961).

PC$_{12}$H$_{13}$N$_2$

① Bis(2-cyanoethyl)phenylphosphine
(NCCH$_2$CH$_2$)$_2$(C$_6$H$_5$)P

② C$_6$H$_5$PH$_2$ + CH$_2$=CHCN $\longrightarrow$ 77%

③ Colorless crystals. (176.5~178°/0.5).
[72~73°]. n_D 1.5672 (25°). *d* 1.1043
(20°).

④ + 30% H$_2$O$_2$ $\xrightarrow{\text{CH}_3\text{COOH}}$
(NCCH$_2$CH$_2$)$_2$C$_6$H$_5$P(O)

+ LiAlH$_4$ $\xrightarrow{\text{ether}}$
C$_6$H$_5$P(CH$_2$CH$_2$CH$_2$NH$_2$)$_2$

+ CH$_3$I $\longrightarrow$
[CH$_3$(C$_6$H$_5$)P⁺(CH$_2$CH$_2$CN)$_2$]I⁻

+ PdBr$_2$ $\longrightarrow$
[((C$_6$H$_5$)P(CH$_2$CH$_2$CN)$_2$]$_2$PdBr$_2$

⑥ Dokl. **127**, 1217 (1959). JCS **1952**,
4453. JACS **81**, 1103 (1959).

PC$_{12}$H$_{15}$O

① Diallylphenylphosphine oxide
   (CH$_2$=CHCH$_2$)$_2$P(O)C$_6$H$_5$

② C$_6$H$_5$P(O)(OC$_6$H$_5$)$_2$ +

   CH$_2$=CHCH$_2$MgBr $\xrightarrow{C_6H_6}$

   cf. C$_6$H$_5$P(O)Cl$_2$ +

   CH$_2$=CHCH$_2$MgBr $\longrightarrow$

③ (169°/1.3). [48~50°].
   Hygroscopic.

④ + lauryl methacrylate $\xrightarrow{\text{radical}}$

   copolymer

   + H$_2$ $\xrightarrow{\text{PtO}_2}$ (C$_3$H$_7$)$_2$P(O)C$_6$H$_5$

⑥ CA **59**, 7555 (1963).   J. Polymer Sci.
   A 1, 3343 (1963).   JACS **82**, 2712
   (1960).

PC$_{12}$H$_{15}$O$_2$

① Phenylphosphonous acid diallyl ester
   C$_6$H$_5$P(OCH$_2$CH=CH$_2$)$_2$

② C$_6$H$_5$PCl$_2$ + CH$_2$=CHCH$_2$OH $\xrightarrow{\text{pyridine}}$
   42.6%

③ Colorless liq. (116~117°/3). n_D 1.5240
   (20°). d 1.0443 (20°/0°).
   Isomerize extensively during distn.
   to derivative of 5-valent P.

④ + CH$_2$=CHCH$_2$Br $\longrightarrow$
   C$_6$H$_5$P(O)(CH$_2$CH=CH$_2$)OCH$_2$CH=CH$_2$
   + RX $\longrightarrow$
   C$_6$H$_5$(R)P(O)OCH$_2$CH=CH$_2$
   R=CH$_3$, C$_2$H$_5$.

⑥ Dokl. **89**, 309 (1953).   Zhur. **25**, 1932
   (1955).

PC$_{12}$H$_{15}$O$_2$S

① Phenylphosphonothioic acid
   O, O-diallyl ester
   C$_6$H$_5$P(S)(OCH$_2$CH=CH$_2$)$_2$

② C$_6$H$_5$P(S)Cl$_2$ + CH$_2$=CHCH$_2$OH $\xrightarrow{C_5H_5N}$
   64.5%

③ Colorless liq. (126~129°/1). n_D 1.5508

   (25°). d 1.115 (25°/25°).
   Soluble in org. solvents.
   NMR: JACS **84**, 3467 (1962).

④ $\longrightarrow$ polymer

⑥ JACS **76**, 2191 (1954).

PC$_{12}$H$_{15}$O$_3$

① Phenylphosphonic acid diallyl ester
   C$_6$H$_5$P(O)(OCH$_2$CH=CH$_2$)$_2$

② C$_6$H$_5$POCl$_2$ + CH$_2$=CHCH$_2$OH
   $\xrightarrow[0~5°]{C_5H_5N}$ 64%

③ Colorless liq. (128°/1). n_D 1.4957
   (25°). d 1.1097 (25°/4°).
   Sol. in org. solvents.

④ + n-lauryl methacrylate $\xrightarrow{\text{BPO}}$
   copolymer
   $\xrightarrow{\text{BPO}}$ polymer

⑥ JACS **70**, 186 (1948); **76**, 2191 (1954).
   J. Polymer Sci. **A 1**, 3343, 3357
   (1963).   Nagoya Kōgyo Gijutsu
   Shikensho Hōkoku **6**, 93 (1957).

PC$_{12}$H$_{16}$K

① Potassium cyclohexylphenyl-
   phosphide
   KP(C$_6$H$_{11}$)(C$_6$H$_5$)·1dioxane

② (C$_6$H$_{11}$)(C$_6$H$_5$)$_2$P + K $\xrightarrow{\text{dioxane}}$ 33%

③ Orange-yellow soln.

④ + 30% H$_2$O$_2$ + NaOH $\xrightarrow[\text{HCl}]{\text{H}_2\text{O}}$
   (C$_6$H$_{11}$)(C$_6$H$_5$)P(O)(OH)

⑥ Ber. **94**, 392 (1961).

PC$_{12}$H$_{17}$O

① Phenylvinylphosphinous acid
   butyl ester
   (C$_6$H$_5$)(CH$_2$=CH)P(OC$_4$H$_9$)

② C$_6$H$_5$P(Cl)(OC$_4$H$_9$) + CH$_2$=CHMgBr
   $\longrightarrow$ 66.5%

③ (76~77°/2). n_D 1.5310 (20°). d 0.9762
   (20°).

④ + MnO₂ ⟶

CH₂=CH(C₆H₅)P(O)OC₄H₉

+ piperidine (aq.) ⟶

C₅H₁₀NCH₂CH₂P(O)C₆H₅

⑥ Dokl. **131**, 1334 (1960). Zhur. **32**,
3351 (1962).

PC₁₂H₁₇O₂

① Phenylvinylphosphinic acid *n*-butyl
ester
$(CH_2=CH)(C_6H_5)P(O)(OC_4H_9-n)$

② CH₂=CHP(OC₄H₉)₂ + C₆H₅I ⟶
77.5%

③ (122~122.5°/2). n_D 1.5180 (20°).
d 1.0605 (20°).

④ + aq. piperidine ⟶
C₅H₁₀NCH₂CH₂P(O)HC₆H₅

⑥ Zhur. **32**, 3351 (1962).

PC₁₂H₁₇O₂

① Cyclohexylphenylphosphinic acid
$(cyclo$-C₆H₁₁)(C₆H₅)P(O)(OH)

② $(cyclo$-C₆H₁₁)(C₆H₅)₂P(O)(OH) + NaOH

$\xrightarrow[\text{2) HCl}]{\text{1) 200~300°}}$ 90%

③ [112~114°].

⑥ Ber. **91**, 64 (1961).

PC₁₂H₁₇O₄

① Phenacylphosphonic acid
diethyl ester
C₆H₅COCH₂P(O)(OC₂H₅)₂

② C₆H₅COP(O)(OC₂H₅)₂ + CH₂N₂ ⟶
92%

P(OC₂H₅)₃ + BrCH₂COC₆H₅ ⟶

③ Oil. (174~176°/2.5, 142~143°/1).
n_D 1.5137 (20°). d 1.1704 (0°/0°).
d 1.1790 (20°).

④ ⟶ Na salt $\xrightarrow{\text{CH}_3\text{I}}$

(C₂H₅O)₂P(O)CH(CH₃)COC₆H₅

+ HCl ⟶ C₆H₅COCH₂P(O)(OH)₂

⑥ Zhur. **4**, 834 (1934) ; **25**, 2173 (1955).

PC₁₂H₁₈Br

① Allylethylmethylphenylphospho-
nium bromide
[(CH₃)(CH₂=CHCH₂)(C₂H₅)(C₆H₅)P]Br

② (C₂H₅)(C₆H₅)(CH₂=CHCH₂)P +
CH₃Br ⟶
(CH₃)(C₂H₅)(C₆H₅)P
+ CH₂=CHCH₂Br ⟶

③ [96~98°].
Very hygroscopic solid.

⑥ Ann. **646**, 65 (1961).

PC₁₂H₁₈I

① Ethyltetramethylenephenyl-
phosphonium iodide
[(C₆H₅)(C₂H₅)PCH₂(CH₂)₂CH₂]I

② C₆H₅PCH₂(CH₂)₂CH₂ + C₂H₅I ⟶

③ [122°].

⑥ Kosolapoff 94.   Z. Naturf. **186**, 84
(1963). Angew. **75**, 669 (1963).

PC₁₂H₁₉

① Ethyl-*n*-butylphenylphosphine
C₂H₅(*n*-C₄H₉)(C₆H₅)P

② C₆H₅PCl₂ + Pb(C₂H₅)₄

⟶ C₂H₅(C₆H₅)PCl $\xrightarrow{n\text{-}C_4H_9MgX}$

③ (121~123°/11). n_D 1.5325 (20°). d
0.9255 (20°).

④ +C₃H₅Br ⟶
[C₂H₅(C₃H₅)(*n*-C₄H₉)(C₆H₅)P]⁺Br⁻

⑥ Dokl. **143**, 596 (1962).

PC₁₂H₁₉N₂

① Bis(2-cyanoethyl)cyclohexyl-
phosphine
(CNCH₂CH₂)₂(*cyclo*-C₆H₁₁)P

② (NCCH₂CH₂)₂PH + ⬡

$\xrightarrow{\text{ABIN}}$ 55%

③ (185~186°/0.4). n_D 1.5241 (25°).

⑥ JOC **26**, 5138 (1961).

PC₁₂H₁₉O
① Ethyl-2-ethoxyethylphenyl-
   phosphine
   $C_2H_5(C_2H_5OCH_2CH_2)C_6H_5P$
② $C_6H_5PH_2 + Na$ (in liq. NH_3)
   $+ C_2H_5Br + C_2H_5OC_2H_4I \longrightarrow 63\%$
③ Colorless liq. (146.5°/18).
④ $+ HBr \xrightarrow{\text{in } CH_3COOH}$
   $[C_2H_5(C_6H_5)\overset{+}{P}H \cdot C_2H_4Br]\overset{-}{Br}$
   $\xrightarrow{NaHCO_3} C_2H_5(C_6H_5)PC_2H_4Br$
⑥ JCS **1958**, 2081.

PC₁₂H₁₉O
① Dipropylphenylphosphone oxide
   $(C_3H_7)_2P(O)C_6H_5$
② $(C_6H_5)P(O)(OC_6H_5)_2 + C_3H_7MgBr \longrightarrow$
③ (121~124°/1.0).
⑥ JACS **82**, 2712 (1960).

PC₁₂H₂₀Br
① Triethylphenylphosphinium
   bromide
   $[(C_2H_5)_3PC_6H_5]Br$
② $(C_2H_5)(C_6H_5)PK \cdot C_4H_8O_2 +$
   $C_2H_5Br \xrightarrow{\text{dioxane}}$
③ [184~186°].
⑥ Ber. **94**, 392 (1961).

PC₁₂H₂₀I
① Triethylphenylphosphonium iodide
   $[(C_2H_5)_3P(C_6H_5)]I$
② $(C_6H_5P)_4 + C_2H_5I \xrightarrow{C_6H_6} 84\%$
③ [137~139°].
⑥ Kosolapoff 89. JCS **1960**, 3324. Ber.
   94, 186 (1961).

PC₁₂H₂₀I
① Ethylmethylphenylpropyl
   phosphonium iodide
   $[(C_2H_5)(CH_3)(C_6H_5)(C_3H_7)P]I$

② $(C_3H_7)(C_2H_5)(C_6H_5)P + CH_3I \longrightarrow$
③ [62°]. $[\alpha]_D$ 4.6°.
⑥ Tetrahedron Letters **1961**, 161.

PC₁₂H₂₁N₂
① Bis(3-aminopropyl)phenyl-
   phosphine
   $(H_2NCH_2CH_2CH_2)_2C_6H_5P$
② $C_6H_5P(CH_2CH_2CN)_2 + LiAlH_4 \longrightarrow$
   48.5%
   $CH_2=CHCH_2NH_2 + C_6H_5PH_2 \xrightarrow{AIBN}$
   78.8%
③ (144°/1, 148.5~149°/1). n_D 1.5728(20°).
   d 1.0292 (20°).
⑥ Dokl. **127**, 1217 (1959); CA **54**, 1377 h
   (1960).   Izv. OKhN **1962**, 290; CA
   57, 15145 (1962).

PC₁₂H₂₁O₃
① Cyclohexylphosphonic acid diallyl
   ester
   $C_6H_{11}P(O)(OCH_2CH=CH_2)_2$
② $C_6H_{11}P(O)Cl_2 + CH_2=CHCH_2OH$
   $\xrightarrow{C_5H_5N} 74.6\%$
③ Colorless liq. (130°/4). n_D 1.4760
   (20°). d 1.0548 (20°/4°).
④ $\xrightarrow{BPO}$ polymer
⑥ JACS **76**, 2191 (1954).   Zhur. **29**,
   2152 (1959).   JACS **72**, 2275 (1950).
   Nagoya Kogyō Gijutsu Shikensho
   Hōkoku **6**, 93 (1951).

PC₁₂H₂₂Li
① Lithium dicyclohexylphosphide
   ($cyclo$-$C_6H_{11})_2PLi$
② ($cyclo$-$C_6H_{11})_2PH + C_6H_5Li \xrightarrow{\text{ether}} 90\%$
③ Slightly sol. in dioxane, insol. in
   ether and C_6H_6.
④ $+ COCl_2 \longrightarrow$
   ($cyclo$-$C_6H_{11})_2P - P(cyclo$-$C_6H_{11})_2$

+ excess CH₃I $\longrightarrow$

$[(CH_3)_2(C_6H_{11})_2P]\overset{+}{I}$

+ CH₂−CH₂ $\longrightarrow$

(over O)

$(cyclo\text{-}C_6H_{11})_2PCH_2CH_2OH$

+ ClCH₂CH₂Cl $\xrightarrow{(C_2H_5)_2O}$

$(cyclo\text{-}C_6H_{11})_2PP(cyclo\text{-}C_6H_{11})_2$

+ ClCH₂CH₂Cl $\xrightarrow{THF}$ $[(cyclo\text{-}C_6H_{11})_2P]_2$

+ $[(cyclo\text{-}C_6H_{11})_2PCH_2]_2$

⑤ Intermediate in prepn. of org. P compds.

⑥ Ber. **92**, 1118, 3183 (1959) ; **94**, 102 (1961).

PC₁₂H₂₃

① Dicyclohexylphosphine
$(cyclo\text{-}C_6H_{11})_2PH$

② $(C_6H_{11})_2POCl + LiAlH_4 \longrightarrow$ 60.2%

PH₃ + ⬡ $\xrightarrow{ABIN}$ 29%

$(cyclo\text{-}C_6H_{11})_2P(S)P(S)(cyclo\text{-}C_6H_{11})_2$

$\xrightarrow{Cu}$ 80%

③ Colorless liq. (129°/8). n_D 1.5142(25°). Sol. in org. solvents.
IR : Monatsh. **92**, 868 (1961).

④ + 96% HNO₃ $\longrightarrow$

$(cyclo\text{-}C_6H_{11})_2P(O)(OH)$

+ HI $\longrightarrow$ $[(C_6H_{11})_2P^+H_2]I^-$

+ NiBr₂ $\longrightarrow$

$[\{(C_6H_{11})_2PH\}_2NiBr_2]$

⑥ Ber. **92**, 704 (1959) ; **95**, 64 (1962). JOC **26**, 5138 (1961).

PC₁₂H₂₃S₂

① Dicyclohexylphosphinodithioic acid
$(C_6H_{11})_2P(S)SH$

② $(C_6H_{11})_2PH + S + NH_4OH \xrightarrow{HCl}$ 90%

③ [103~105°].

④ $\longrightarrow$ Ni salt

$\longrightarrow$ ammonium salt

⑥ Gazz. chim. ital. **77**, 509 (1947).   JOC **26**, 5133 (1961).

PC₁₂H₂₅

① Di-*n*-butylbut-2-enylphosphine
$(n\text{-}C_4H_9)_2(CH_3CH=CHCH_2)P$

② $(n\text{-}C_4H_9)_2PH + CH_2=CH-CH=CH_2$

$\xrightarrow{AIBN}$ 51%

③ (118°/13). n_D 1.4725 (25°).

⑥ JOC **26**, 5138 (1961).

PC₁₂H₂₅

① Di-*n*-pentylvinylphosphine
$(n\text{-}C_5H_{11})_2CH_2=CHP$

② $(n\text{-}C_5H_{11})_2POC_4H_9 + CH_2=CHMgBr$

$\xrightarrow{THF}$ 80%

③ (73~74°/1.5). n_D 1.4708 (20°). d 0.8232 (20°).

④ + active MnO₂ $\longrightarrow$

$(n\text{-}C_5H_{11})_2P(O)(CH=CH_2)$

⑥ Dokl. **135**, 603 (1960).   CA **55**, 12272 (1961).

PC₁₂H₂₅O₅

① Phosphonoacetic acid ethyl *P*-diiso-butyl ester
$C_2H_5OOCCH_2P(O)(OC_4H_9\text{-}i)_2$

② $(i\text{-}C_4H_9O)_2POH + i\text{-}C_4H_9ONa$

$+ ClCH_2COOC_2H_5 \longrightarrow$ 32.5%

③ Liq. (170~171°/10). d 1.0363 (0°/0°).

④ + Na + CH₃I $\longrightarrow$

$(i\text{-}C_4H_9O)_2P(O)CH(CH_3)COOC_2H_5$

⑥ Zhur. **4**, 834 (1934).   Trudy Kazan Khim. Tekhnol. Inst. **8**, 33 (1940).

PC₁₂H₂₇

① Tri-*n*-butylphosphine
$(n\text{-}C_4H_9)_3P$

② $n\text{-}C_4H_9PH_2 + Na + n\text{-}C_4H_9Cl \longrightarrow$ 70%

$n\text{-}C_4H_9PH + Na + n\text{-}C_4H_9Cl \longrightarrow$ 83%

$n\text{-}C_4H_9Li + PCl_3 \xrightarrow{-10°}$ 55%

③ $(240\sim242.2°,\ 109\sim110°/10,\ 135\sim$
  $144°/43)$. $n_D\ 1.4616\ (20°)$.

④ $+ (C_2H_5)_3NBH_3 \longrightarrow (n\text{-}C_4H_9)_3PBH_3$

  $+ PdX_2 \longrightarrow [(n\text{-}C_4H_9)_3P]_2PdX_2$
  $\qquad\qquad\qquad X = Cl,\ Br$

  $+ CS_2 \longrightarrow (n\text{-}C_4H_9)_3P=CS_2Br$

  $+ \text{air} \xrightarrow{\text{hexane}} 42\% \ (C_4H_9)_3PO$

  $\quad + 49\% \ (C_4H_9)_2PO_2C_4H_9$

  $\quad + 6\% \ C_4H_9P(O)(OC_4H_9)_2$

  $\quad + 3\% \ P(O)(OC_4H_9)_3$

  $+ Mn(CO)_5Cl \longrightarrow$
  $\quad [(n\text{-}C_4H_9)_3P]_2Mn(CO)_3Cl$

  $+ GeI_2 \longrightarrow (n\text{-}C_4H_9)_3P\cdot GeI_2$

⑥ Monatsh. **90**, 792 (1959).   JOC **27**,
  2573 (1962).   JACS **84**, 3093 (1962).

$PC_{12}H_{27}$

① Triisobutylphosphine
   $(i\text{-}C_4H_9)_3P$

② $(CH_3)_2C=CH_2 + PH_3 \xrightarrow{\text{AIBN}} 21\%$

③ $(85°/7)$. $n_D\ 1.4530\ (25°)$.

⑥ JOC **26**, 5138 (1961).

$PC_{12}H_{27}Cl_2$

① Tributyldichlorophosphorane
   $(C_4H_9)_3PCl_2$

② $(C_4H_9)_3P + PCl_3 \xrightarrow{C_6H_6}$

   $(C_4H_9)_3P + (C_2H_5)_2PCl \longrightarrow$

③ Sublimes at $120°$/high vacuum. $[134\sim$
   $137°]$ (in sealed tube).

⑥ Inorg. Chem. **3**, 292 (1964).

$PC_{12}H_{27}I_2$

① Tributyldiiodophosphorane
   $(C_4H_9)_3PI_2$

② $(C_4H_9)_3P + I \xrightarrow{(C_2H_5)_2O-C_6H_6} 66.7\%$

③ $[178°\ \text{decomp.}]$.

⑥ Z. anorg. allg. Chem. **288**. 201 (1956).

$PC_{12}H_{27}O$

① Dibutylphosphinous acid butylester

   $(n\text{-}C_4H_9)_2P(OC_4H_9)$

② $(C_4H_9)_2PCl + C_4H_9OH \xrightarrow{\text{pyridine}} 78\%$

   $C_4H_9OPCl_2 + C_4H_9MgCl \longrightarrow 56\%$

   $(C_4H_9)_2P(OC_2H_5) + C_4H_9OH +$
   $\quad Na(\text{trace}) \longrightarrow 70\%$

③ $(116\sim117°/12)$. $n_D\ 1.4495\ (20°)$. d
   $0.8480\ (20°)$.

   Sensitive to atmospheric oxygen and
   moisture.

④ $+ H_2O_2 \longrightarrow (C_4H_9)_2P(O)(OH)$

   $+ C_6H_5CH_2Cl \longrightarrow$
   $\quad (C_4H_9)_2P(O)CH_2C_6H_5 + C_4H_9Cl$

   $+ CH_3I \longrightarrow (C_4H_9)_2(CH_3)PO$

   $+ SO_2Cl_2 \longrightarrow (C_4H_9)_2POCl$

   $+ CH_2=CHCH_2Br \longrightarrow$
   $\quad (C_4H_9)_2P(O)CH_2CH=CH_2$

⑥ Ber. **93**, 1220 (1960).   Izv. OKhN
   1963, 1373.   Dokl. **135**, 323 (1960).

$PC_{12}H_{27}O$

① Tributylphosphine oxide
   $(C_4H_9)_3PO$

② $C_4H_9MgCl + POCl_3 \xrightarrow{i\text{-}C_8H_{18}} 84.4\%$

   $(C_4H_9)_3P \xrightarrow{H_2O_2/C_2H_5OH}$

③ Needles. $(145\sim147°/3)$. $[67\sim69°]$
   (EtOH).
   Deliquescent.

③ $(C_4H_9)_3P \xrightarrow{\text{air 100 ml/min in hexane, 26°}}$
   $(C_4H_9)_3PO\ 42\% + (C_4H_9)_2PO_2C_4H_9$
   $49\% + (C_4H_9)P(O)(OC_4H_9)_2\ 6\% +$
   $OP(OC_4H_9)_3\ 3\%$

⑤ Synergic effect of extractants for
   actinides.

⑥ Izv. OKhN **1962**, 2002.   Zhur. **30**,
   1976 (1960).   JINC **21**, 168 (1961).
   JACS **84**, 3093 (1962).   Kosolapoff
   113.

$PC_{12}H_{27}O_2$

① Dibutylphosphinic acid butylester
   $(n\text{-}C_4H_9)_2P(O)(OC_4H_9\text{-}n)$

② $(n\text{-}C_4H_9)_2P(O)H + SOCl_2$

$\xrightarrow[\text{$n$-C$_4H_9$OH in pyridine}]{}$ 56%

③ $(115°/0.8)$. $n_D\,1.4431\,(22°)$. $d\,0.9212$ $(22°/4°)$.

③ $+ PCl_5 \longrightarrow n\text{-}(C_4H_9)_2POCl$

⑥ JACS **84**, 3093 (1962).

PC₁₂H₂₇O₂

① Butylphosphonous acid dibutylester $n\text{-}C_4H_9P(OC_4H_9\text{-}n)_2$

② $(n\text{-}C_4H_9O)_2PCl + n\text{-}C_4H_9Li \longrightarrow$ 81% $n\text{-}C_4H_9P(OC_2H_5)_2 + n\text{-}C_4H_9OH + Na$ $\longrightarrow$ 78%

③ $(70.5{\sim}71.5°/1.5)$. $n_D\,1.4421\,(20°)$. $d\,0.8814\,(20°)$.

⑥ Ber. **93**, 1220 (1960). JACS **84**, 3093 (1962). Izv. OKhN **1960**, 133.

PC₁₂H₂₇O₂S

① Isobutylphosphonothioic acid O, O-diisobutyl ester $i\text{-}C_4H_9P(S)(OC_4H_9\text{-}i)_2$

② $i\text{-}C_4H_9P(OC_4H_9\text{-}i)_2 + S \longrightarrow$

③ Liq. $n_D\,1.4420\,(20°)$. $d\,0.9639\,(20°/0°)$.

Sol. in org. solvents

⑥ Trudy Kazan Khim. Tekhnol. Inst. **1953**, No. 17, 151.

PC₁₂H₂₇O₂S

① Butylphosphonothioic acid O, O-dibutylester $C_4H_9P(S)(OC_4H_9)_2$

② $(C_4H_9O)_2PSH + Na + C_4H_9Br \longrightarrow$

③ Liq. $(108{\sim}109°/2)$. $n_D\,1.4654\,(20°)$. $d\,0.9780\,(20°)$.

Sol. in org. solvents.

⑥ Zhur. **24**, 307 (1954).

PC₁₂H₂₇O₃

① Butylphosphonic acid dibutylester $C_4H_9P(O)(OC_4H_9)_2$

② $(C_4H_9)_3P \xrightarrow{\text{autoxidation}}$ 6% $(C_4H_9O)_2POH + Na + C_4H_9Br$

$\xrightarrow[\text{or heptane}]{\text{in hexane}}$

③ Oil. $(160{\sim}162°/20)$. $n_D\,1.4323\,(20°)$. $d\,0.9427\,(20°/0°)$.

More stable to hydrolysis than the corresponding ethyl ester.

④ $+ HCl \longrightarrow C_4H_9P(O)(OH)_2$

⑤ Extractant.

⑥ J. Russ. Phys. Chem. Soc. **61**, 1905 (1929). JACS **67**, 1180 (1945); **84**, 3093 (1962). JOC **26**, 846, 1895 (1961).

PC₁₂H₂₇O₃

① Isobutylphosphonic acid diisobutyl-ester $i\text{-}C_4H_9P(O)(OC_4H_9\text{-}i)_2$

② $(i\text{-}C_4H_9O)_3P + i\text{-}C_4H_9I \longrightarrow$

③ Colorless oil. $(133.5{\sim}134°/10)$. $d\,0.9459\,(20°/4°)$.

④ $\xrightarrow{\text{hydrolysis}} i\text{-}C_4H_9P(O)(OH)_2 \cdot H_2O$

⑥ J. Russ. Phys. Chem. Soc. **45**, 690 (1913).

PC₁₂H₂₇S

① Tributylphosphine sulfide $(C_4H_9)_3P(S)$

② $(C_4H_9)_3PBr_2 + H_2S \longrightarrow (C_4H_9)_3P(S) \cdot HBr \longrightarrow$ 25~40%

③ $(137{\sim}138°/1.1)$. $n_D\,1.4945\,(25°)$. $d\,1.0339\,(24°)$.

IR: Izv. Ser. Fiz. **26**, 1278 (1962); UV: Inorg. Chem. **2**, 192 (1963). NMR: J. Chem. Eng. Data **7**, 307 (1962).

⑥ JOC **26**, 5205 (1961).

PC₁₂H₂₇Se

① Tributylphosphine selenide $(C_4H_9)_3P(Se)$

② PCl₃ + 3C₄H₉Li $\xrightarrow{\text{heptane}}$ $\xrightarrow{\text{Se}}$ 51%

③ (150~151°/0.8). n_D 1.5150 (27°).

⑥ J. Chem. Eng. Data **8**, 226 (1963).

PC₁₂H₂₈Br

① Diethyldibutylphosphonium bromide
  [(C₂H₅)₂(C₄H₉)₂P]Br

② (C₂H₅)₂POPC₂H₅(OC₂H₅) +
  C₄H₉Br $\longrightarrow$

③ [146~148°].

⑥ Izv. OKhN 1958, 706.

PC₁₂H₂₉ClN

① *P*-Tributylaminophosphonium
  chloride
  [(C₄H₉)₃PNH₂]Cl

② (C₄H₉)₃P + NH₂Cl $\xrightarrow{5\sim10°}$ 92%

③ [62~65°].

④ + H₂O $\xrightarrow{60°}$ (C₄H₉)₃PO + NH₄Cl
  aq. NaOH $\xrightarrow{\text{r. t.}}$ (C₄H₉)₃PO + NH₃

⑥ JACS **81**, 2982 (1959).

PC₁₂H₂₉O₃Si

① 2-Triethoxysilylethyldiethyl
  phosphine
  (C₂H₅O)₃SiCH₂CH₂P(C₂H₅)₂

② (C₂H₅O)₃SiCH=CH₂ + (C₂H₅)₂PH $\longrightarrow$
  98%

③ Colorless oil. (123~124°/10).

④ + S $\longrightarrow$
  (C₂H₅O)₃SiCH₂CH₂P(S)(C₂H₅)₂

⑥ Makromol. Chem. **52**, 218 (1962).

PC₁₂H₃₃Si₃

① Tris(trimethylsilylmethyl)phos-
  phine
  [(CH₃)₃SiCH₂]₃P

② (CH₃)₃SiCH₂MgCl + PBr₃ $\xrightarrow{\text{THF}-(\text{C}_2\text{H}_5)_2\text{O}}$
  66.5%

③ White crystals. [66~69°].
  Fumes and melts in air.

④ + X₂ $\longrightarrow$ [(CH₃)₃SiCH₂]₃PX₂
  X = Br, I

  + RI $\longrightarrow$ R[(CH₃)₃SiCH₂]₃PI⁻
  R = CH₃, C₂H₅, (CH₃)₃SiCH₂

⑥ JACS **80**, 1336 (1958).

PC₁₂H₃₃OSi₃

① Tris(trimethylsilylmethyl)phos-
  phineoxide
  [(CH₃)₃SiCH₂]₃PO

② POCl₃ + 3BrMgCH₂Si(CH₃)₃ $\xrightarrow{(\text{C}_2\text{H}_5)_2\text{O}}$

③ [182°] (C₂H₅OH).

⑥ JCS 1962, 592; 1959, 3751.

PC₁₃H₁₂ClO

① Chloromethyldiphenylphosphine
  oxide
  (C₆H₅)₂P(O)CH₂Cl

② (C₆H₅)₂P(O)CH₂OH $\xrightarrow{\text{PCl}_5}$ 86%

③ [138~140°].

④ $\xrightarrow{\text{KI}}$ (C₆H₅)₂P(O)CH₂I (83%)

⑥ Tetrahedron Letters 1961, 724.

PC₁₃H₁₃

① Methyldiphenylphosphine
  CH₃(C₆H₅)₂P

② [CH₃(C₆H₅)₃P]I⁻ + Na $\longrightarrow$ 60%
  [CH₃(C₆H₅)₃P]X⁻ + LiAlH₄ $\longrightarrow$
  50~60%, · X = Br, I
  [CH₃(C₆H₅)₃P]Br⁻ $\xrightarrow{\text{electrolysis}}$ 20%

③ (120~122°/0.15, 160°/12),
  NMR: J. Chem. Eng. Data **7**, 307
  (1962).

④ + CH₃I $\longrightarrow$ [(CH₃)₂(C₆H₅)₂P]I⁻
  + C₂H₅I $\longrightarrow$ [CH₃(C₂H₅)(C₆H₅)₂P]I⁻
  + GeI₂ $\longrightarrow$ CH₃(C₆H₅)₂PGeI₂

⑥ JCS 1961, 4263. Ber. **92**, 2088 (1959).
  Ann. **646**, 65 (1961).

PC$_{13}$H$_{13}$O

① Hydroxymethyldiphenylphosphine
   HOCH$_2$(C$_6$H$_5$)$_2$P

② (HOCH$_2$)$_2$(C$_6$H$_5$)$_2$PI$^-$ $\xrightarrow{\text{2 N−NaOH}}$
   C$_6$H$_5$PH$_2$ + HCHO + HCl $\longrightarrow$
   (C$_6$H$_5$)$_2$P(CH$_2$OH)$_2$Cl $\xrightarrow[\text{heat}]{\text{(C}_2\text{H}_5)_3\text{N}}$ 94%

③ (113°/1). n_D 1.6137 (20°). d 0.9316
   (20°).
   Insol. in water.

④ $\xrightarrow{\text{oxidation}}$ HOCH$_2$(C$_6$H$_5$)$_2$P(O)
   + C$_6$H$_5$CH$_2$Br $\longrightarrow$
   [HOCH$_2$(C$_6$H$_5$)$_2$(C$_6$H$_5$CH$_2^+$)P]Br$^-$
   + p-toluenesulfonic acid
   (in CH$_3$COOH) $\xrightarrow{\text{CH}_3\text{I}}$
   [CH$_3$CO$_2$CH$_2$(C$_6$H$_5$)$_2^+$P(CH$_3$)]I$^-$

⑥ Zhur. **31**, 3417 (1961).   CA **57**, 4692
   (1962).   JCS **1961**, 2813.

PC$_{13}$H$_{13}$O

① p-Methoxyphenylphenylphosphine
   C$_6$H$_5$(p-CH$_3$OC$_6$H$_4$)PH

② C$_6$H$_5$(p-CH$_3$OC$_6$H$_4$)P(O)(OH) + LiAlH$_4$
   $\longrightarrow$ 15%

③ (122~130°/0.5). [15~16°].

④ + CH$_2$=CHCO$_2$C$_2$H$_5$ $\longrightarrow$
   C$_6$H$_5$(p-CH$_3$OC$_6$H$_4$)PCH$_2$CH$_2$COOC$_2$H$_5$
   + Na(liq. NH$_3$) $\xrightarrow{\text{CH}_3\text{I}}$
   CH$_3$(C$_6$H$_5$)(p-CH$_3$OC$_6$H$_4$)P

⑥ JCS **1961**, 5454.

PC$_{13}$H$_{13}$O

① m-Methoxyphenyl phenylphosphine
   C$_6$H$_5$(m-CH$_3$OC$_6$H$_4$)PH

② C$_6$H$_5$(m-CH$_3$OC$_6$H$_4$)P(O)OH + LiAlH$_4$
   $\xrightarrow{\text{THF}}$ 17%

③ (135~140°/0.5).
   Sol. in C$_6$H$_6$.

④ + CH$_2$=CHCN $\xrightarrow{\text{in CH}_3\text{COOH}}$
   NCCH$_2$CH$_2$(C$_6$H$_5$)(m-CH$_3$OC$_6$H$_4$)P

   + CH$_2$=CHCOOCH$_3$ $\longrightarrow$
   m-CH$_3$OC$_6$H$_4$P(C$_6$H$_5$)CH$_2$CH$_2$CO$_2$CH$_3$

   + BrCH$_2$CH$_2$CO$_2$C$_2$H$_5$ + Na $\xrightarrow{\text{liq. NH}_3}$
   m-CH$_3$OC$_6$H$_4$P(C$_6$H$_5$)CH$_2$CH$_2$CO$_2$C$_2$H$_5$

⑥ JCS **1961**, 5454.

PC$_{13}$H$_{13}$O

① Diphenylphosphinous acid methylester
   (C$_6$H$_5$)$_2$P(OCH$_3$)

② (C$_6$H$_5$)$_2$PCl + CH$_3$OH $\xrightarrow{\text{pyridine}}$ 51.8%
   (C$_6$H$_5$)$_2$P(OR) + CH$_3$OH + small amt.
   Na $\longrightarrow$ 70%

③ Colorless liq. (151~152°/10). n_D 1.6030
   (20°). d 1.1040 (15°/0°).

④ + CH$_3$I $\longrightarrow$ (C$_6$H$_5$)$_2$P(O)CH$_3$
   + CH$_3$COCl $\longrightarrow$ (C$_6$H$_5$)$_2$P(O)COCH$_3$
   + ClCOOC$_2$H$_5$ $\longrightarrow$
   (C$_6$H$_5$)$_2$P(O)CO$_2$C$_2$H$_5$

⑥ Zhur. **18**, 2008 (1948) ; **31**, 2889
   (1961).

PC$_{13}$H$_{13}$O

① Methyldiphenylphosphine oxide
   CH$_3$P(O)(C$_6$H$_5$)$_2$

② (C$_2$H$_5$O)$_2$P(O)H $\xrightarrow{\text{1) C}_6\text{H}_5\text{MgX, 2) CH}_3\text{Br}}$
   50%
   (C$_6$H$_5$)$_3$P(O) + CH$_3$Li $\longrightarrow$ 83%

③ [112.5~113°] (petr. ether).
   IR: JOC **28**, 123 (1963).
   UV: Monatsh. **94**, 99 (1963).

④
   Ph$_2$P(O)Me + BuLi $\xrightarrow{\text{C}_6\text{H}_{14}, \text{Et}_2\text{O}}{87\%}$
   Ph$_2$P(O)CH$_2$Li $\xrightarrow{\text{CO}_2}$ Ph$_2$P(O)CH$_2$CO$_2$H
   $\xrightarrow{\text{Ph}_2\text{P(O)Cl}}$ (25%) [Ph$_2$P(O)]$_2$CH$_2$
   (40%) BzOEt   R'COR''
   Ph$_2$P(O)CH$_2$C(OH)R'R''
   Ph$_2$P(O)CH$_2$Bz

⑥ Kosolapoff 115.   Ber. **92**. 2088 (1959) ;
   94, 3043, **93**, 405 (1960).   JACS **85**,
   642 (1963).

PC₁₃H₁₃OS

① Phenylbenzylphosphinothioic acid

$C_6H_5(C_6H_5CH_2)P(S)OH$

② $C_6H_5CH_2Cl + C_6H_5P(SC_4H_9)_2$ $\xrightarrow{\text{hydrolysis}}$

③ Crystals. [173~174°].

⑥ J. Russ. Phys. Chem. Soc. **61**, 2037 (1929).

PC₁₃H₁₃O₂

① Methylphosphonous acid diphenyl ester

$CH_3P(OC_6H_5)_2$

② $CH_3P[N(CH_3)_2]_2 + C_6H_5OH \longrightarrow 82\%$

$CH_3P[NHC_6H_5]_2 + C_6H_5OH \longrightarrow 68\%$

$CH_3P[N(C_2H_5)_2]_2 + C_6H_5OH \longrightarrow 56\%$

③ (105~106°/1). n_D 1.5671 (20°). d 1.1420 (20°).

⑥ Zhur. **31**, 2377 (1961); **32**, 3065 (1962).

PC₁₃H₁₃O₃

① Methylphosphonic acid diphenyl ester

$CH_3P(O)(OC_6H_5)_2$

② $(C_6H_5O)_3P + CH_3I \longrightarrow 70\%$

$(C_6H_5O)_2POCH_3 + CH_3I \longrightarrow 88.3\%$

③ Crystals. (201~202°/11). [36~37°]. n_D 1.5518 (20°). d 1.2051 (20°/0°).

④ $+ CH_2C(CH_3)=CH_2MgCl \longrightarrow$

$CH_3P(O)[CH_2C(CH_3)=CH_2]_2$

$+ p\text{-}CH_3C_6H_4MgBr \xrightarrow{\text{in }(C_2H_5)_2O}$

$CH_3P(O)(p\text{-}CH_3C_6H_4)_2$

⑤ Extractant.

⑥ J. Russ. Phys. Chem. Soc. **38**, 687 (1906). Ber. **31**, 1048 (1898). Z. Phys. Chem. **117**, 161 (1925). JOC **25**, 2006 (1960). JACS **74**, 4526 (1952).

PC₁₃H₁₃Se

① Methyldiphenylphosphine selenide

$CH_3P(Se)(C_6H_5)_2$

② $CH_3PCl_2 + C_6H_5MgBr \xrightarrow{\quad} \xrightarrow{Se} 42\%$

③ (200°/1.35). n_D 1.6780 (26°).

⑥ J. Chem. Eng. Data **8**, 226 (1963).

PC₁₃H₂₀I

① Ethylpentamethylenephenylphosphonium iodide

$[(C_6H_5)(C_2H_5)PCH_2(CH_2)_3CH_2]I$

② $C_6H_5PCH_2(CH_2)_3CH_2 + C_2H_5I \longrightarrow$

③ [188°].

⑥ Kosolapoff 94.

PC₁₃H₂₁

① Ethyl-*n*-pentylphenylphosphine

$C_2H_5(n\text{-}C_5H_{11})(C_6H_5)P$

② $C_6H_5PCl_2 + Pb(C_2H_5)_4$

$\longrightarrow C_2H_5(C_6H_5)PCl \xrightarrow{n\text{-}C_5H_{11}MgX}$

③ (129~131°/10). n_D 1.5299 (20°). d 0.9237 (20°).

④ $+ C_3H_5Br \longrightarrow$

$[C_2H_5(C_3H_5)(n\text{-}C_5H_{11})(C_6H_5)P]^+Br^-$

⑥ Dokl. **143**, 596 (1962).

PC₁₃H₂₁

① Ethylbenzyl(*n*-butyl)phosphine

$C_2H_5(n\text{-}C_4H_9)C_6H_5CH_2P$

② $[C_2H_5(n\text{-}C_4H_9)(C_6H_5CH_2)_2P]^+Br^-$

$\xrightarrow{\text{electrolysis}} 86\%$

$[C_2H_5(n\text{-}C_4H_9)(C_6H_5CH_2)_2P]^+Cl^-$

$+$ small amount of

$(C_2H_5)_2(n\text{-}C_4H_9)P \xrightarrow{300°}$

③ (125~129°/6, 137~139°/16). n_D 1.5310 (20°). d 0.9338 (20°).

④ $+ CH_3I \longrightarrow$

$[CH_3(C_2H_5)(n\text{-}C_4H_9)(C_6H_5CH_2)P]^+I^-$

mp 134~136°

$+ CH_2=CHCH_2Br \xrightarrow{\text{ether}}$

$[C_2H_5(n\text{-}C_4H_9)(CH_2=CHCH_2)\text{-}$

$(C_6H_5CH_2)P]^+Br^-$

⑥ Ann. **646**, 65 (1961).   Tetrahedron

Letters **1961**, 161.　Dokl. **92**, 69
(1953); CA **48**, 9945 (1954).　Zhur.
26, 3426 (1956); CA **51**, 9512
(1957).

PC$_{13}$H$_{21}$O$_2$
① Benzylbutylphophinic acid ethyl
　　ester
　　C$_6$H$_5$CH$_2$(C$_4$H$_9$)P(O)OC$_2$H$_5$
② C$_4$H$_9$P(OC$_2$H$_5$)$_2$ + C$_6$H$_5$CH$_2$Cl $\xrightarrow{120\sim160°}$
　　77%
　　C$_4$H$_9$P(O)H(OC$_2$H$_5$) $\xrightarrow{\text{1) Na, 2) C}_6\text{H}_5\text{CH}_2\text{Cl}}$
③ (145°/2). n_D 1.5013 (20°).
④ + HCl $\longrightarrow$ C$_4$H$_9$(C$_6$H$_5$CH$_2$)P(O)(OH)
⑥ Ber. **93**, 779 (1960).　Izv. OKhN **1955**,
　　2523.

PC$_{13}$H$_{25}$O$_2$
① Dicyclohexylphosphinic acid
　　methyl ester
　　(C$_6$H$_{11}$)$_2$P(O)(OCH$_3$)
② C$_6$H$_{11}$MgCl + POCl$_3$ $\longrightarrow$
　　(C$_6$H$_{11}$)$_2$P(O)OH $\xrightarrow{\text{CH}_2\text{N}_2}$
③ [58$\sim$59°].
④ + SOCl$_2$ $\longrightarrow$ (C$_6$H$_{11}$)$_2$POCl
　　+ aq. NaOH $\longrightarrow$ (C$_6$H$_{11}$)$_2$P(O)ONa
⑥ Z. anorg. allg. Chem. **277**, 258 (1954).

PC$_{13}$H$_{25}$O$_2$S
① Methylphosphonothioic acid
　　O, O-dicyclohexyl ester
　　CH$_3$P(S)(OC$_6$H$_{11}$)$_2$
② CH$_3$PSCl$_2$ + C$_6$H$_{11}$OH + Na $\longrightarrow$ 65%
③ (135$\sim$136°/1.5).　n_D 1.5048 (20°).
　　d 1.0709 (20°).
⑥ Bull. soc. chim. France **1961**, 1222.

PC$_{13}$H$_{30}$I
① Tributylmethylphosphonium iodide
　　[(C$_4$H$_9$)$_3$PCH$_3$]I
② (C$_4$H$_9$)$_3$P + CH$_3$I $\longrightarrow$
③ [133.5°].

IR: Spectrochim. Acta **19**, 1905
　　(1963).
⑥ Kosolapoff 90.

PC$_{13}$H$_{30}$I
① Butyltripropylphosphonium iodide
　　[(C$_3$H$_7$)$_3$PC$_4$H$_9$]I
② (C$_3$H$_7$)$_3$P + C$_4$H$_9$I $\longrightarrow$
③ [239$\sim$240°].
⑥ Kosolapoff 90.　JCS **1963**, 1036.

PC$_{14}$H$_{13}$
① 2-Phenylisophosphaindoline

②

③ (182$\sim$186°/15 or 110$\sim$113°/0.2).
④

⑥ JCS **1958**, 2516.

PC$_{14}$H$_{13}$
① Diphenylvinylphosphine
　　CH$_2$=CH(C$_6$H$_5$)$_2$P
② CH$_2$=CHMgCl + (C$_6$H$_5$)$_2$PCl $\xrightarrow{\text{THF}}$
　　56.8%
③ Colorless liq.(117.5$\sim$119°/0.6). n_D
　　1.6260 (24.5°).
　　IR: JOC **26**, 2537 (1961).

④ + 30% H$_2$O$_2$ ⟶

  CH$_2$=CH(C$_6$H$_5$)$_2$P(O)

+ S $\xrightarrow{\text{benzene}}$ CH$_2$=CH(C$_6$H$_5$)$_2$P(S)

+ CH$_3$I ⟶

  [CH$_3$(CH$_2$=CH)(C$_6$H$_5$)$_2$$\overset{+}{P}$]I$^-$

⑥ JOC **26**, 4623 (1961).

PC$_{14}$H$_{13}$O

① Acetyldiphenylphosphine

  CH$_3$CO(C$_6$H$_5$)$_2$P

② (C$_6$H$_5$)$_2$PNa + ClCOCH$_3$ ⟶ 39.8%

③ (143～146°/2.5).

  Sol. in ether, C$_6$H$_6$, C$_2$H$_5$OH ; insol. in petr. ether, H$_2$O.

④

+ O$_2$ $\xrightarrow{\text{CH}_3\text{—}\langle}$ (C$_6$H$_5$)$_2$$\underset{\overset{\|}{O}}{P}$COCH$_3$

⑥ Ber. **94**, 102 (1961).

PC$_{14}$H$_{13}$O

① Diphenylvinylphosphine oxide

  (C$_6$H$_5$)$_2$P(O)CH=CH$_2$

② (CH$_2$=CH)P(C$_6$H$_5$)$_2$ $\xrightarrow{\text{H}_2\text{O}_2/\text{C}_6\text{H}_6}$

  (CH$_2$=CH)P(O)Cl$_2$ + 2 C$_6$H$_5$MgBr ⟶
  15%

  (C$_6$H$_5$)$_2$POC$_2$H$_5$ + (BrCH$_2$)$_2$ ⟶

  (C$_6$H$_5$)$_2$P(O)CH$_2$CH$_2$Br $\xrightarrow{\text{(C}_2\text{H}_5)_3\text{N}}$ 62%

③ [116.5～118°] (heptane–C$_6$H$_5$CH$_3$).

  IR : JOC **26**, 2537 (1961).

④ Polymerized for 50 hrs at 130° *in vacuo*, dose rate 4×10^{15} eV/ml. sec., yielded a polymer, mol. wt. 30000 with glass transition point 180°. Sol. in warm C$_2$H$_5$OH, C$_6$H$_6$ and ppt. from C$_2$H$_5$OH soln. by adding small amt. of H$_2$O.

  (Me$_3$CO)$_2$ (1 wt%) 24 hrs., 140° ⟶
  bulk polymer

  AIBN (1 wt%) in DMF, 120 hrs., 65° ⟶

⑥ Vysokomol. Soed. **3**, 1117 (1961).
  Izv. OKhN **1961**, 2029.   JOC **26**,

4623 (1961).

PC$_{14}$H$_{13}$O$_2$

① Carboxymethyldiphenylphosphine

  HO$_2$CCH$_2$(C$_6$H$_5$)$_2$P

② [(C$_6$H$_5$)$_2$P$^+$(H)CH$_2$CO$_2$C$_2$H$_5$]Br$^-$
  + NaOH ⟶

  (C$_6$H$_5$)$_2$PCH$_2$COOC$_2$H$_5$ + NaOH ⟶
  50～60%

③ Colorless. [120～121°].

  Sol. in org. solvents, stable in air.

④ + S ⟶ (C$_6$H$_5$)$_2$P(S)CH$_2$CO$_2$H

⑥ Ber. **93**, 803 (1960) ; **94**, 2244 (1961).

PC$_{14}$H$_{13}$O$_2$S

① Carboxymethyldiphenylphosphine sulfide

  HO$_2$CCH$_2$P(S)(C$_6$H$_5$)$_2$

② [(C$_6$H$_5$)$_2$P$^+$(H)CH$_2$CO$_2$C$_2$H$_5$]Br$^-$ + S
  $\xrightarrow{\text{NaOH}}$

③ [188～189°] (C$_6$H$_6$).

⑥ Ber. **94**, 2244 (1961) ; **93**, 803 (1960).

PC$_{14}$H$_{13}$S

① Diphenyl vinylphosphine sulfide

  (C$_6$H$_5$)$_2$P(S)CH=CH$_2$

② Ph$_2$PCH=CH$_2$ + S $\xrightarrow{\text{C}_6\text{H}_6, \ 65°}$ 67%

③ [57°] (petr. ether).

  IR : Acta Chem. Scand. **15**, 133 7 (1961).

④ Could not be polymerized in bulk using 1% AIBN one week at 80°, 1% (Me$_3$CO)$_2$ 10 days at 100°, or a total dosage of 30 megarads from an acceterator ; also unsnccessful was SnCl$_4$ in (CH$_2$Cl)$_2$ soln.

⑥ Chem. Ind. **1962**, 139.

PC$_{14}$H$_{14}$ClO

① 2-Chloroethyldiphenylphosphine oxide

  ClCH$_2$CH$_2$P(O)(C$_6$H$_5$)$_2$

② (C$_6$H$_5$)$_2$P(O)CH$_2$CH$_2$OH $\xrightarrow{\text{PCl}_5}$

[(C$_6$H$_5$)$_2$P$^+$(CH$_2$CH$_2$Cl)$_2$]Cl$^-$ $\xrightarrow{OH^-}$

40~48%

③ [125~127°].

⑥ Tetrahedron Letters 1961, 724. Ber. 94, 102 (1961).

PC$_{14}$H$_{14}$Cl$_3$

① Bis(chloromethyl)diphenylphosphonium chloride
[(C$_6$H$_5$)$_2$P(CH$_2$Cl)$_2$]Cl

② [(C$_6$H$_5$)$_2$(CH$_2$Cl)P$^+$(CH$_2$OH)]Cl$^-$ $\xrightarrow{SOCl_2}$
85%

[(C$_6$H$_5$)$_2$P$^+$(CH$_2$OH)$_2$]Cl$^-$ $\xrightarrow{SOCl_2}$

③ [221~225°].

④ $\xrightarrow{2N\ NaOH}$ (C$_6$H$_5$)$_2$P(O)CH$_2$Cl
(40~48%)

$\begin{cases}$ (C$_6$H$_5$)P(O)(CH$_2$Cl)CH$_2$PH (10%)
(C$_6$H$_5$)$_2$PCH$_2$Cl + CH$_2$O (8~10%)
(C$_6$H$_5$)$_2$P(O)CH$_2$Cl + CH$_3$Cl (2~5%) $\end{cases}$

⑥ Tetrahedron Letters 1961, 724.
Ann. 659, 49 (1962). Zhur. 31, 3417 (1961).

PC$_{14}$H$_{14}$K

① Potassium bis-p-tolylphosphide

KP$-\left($ ⟨=⟩ $-$CH$_3\right)_2$ · 1 dioxane

② (p-CH$_3$C$_6$H$_4$)$_3$P + K $\xrightarrow{dioxane}$ 59.6%

③ Yellow-red crystals.
Very sensitive in air. Sol. in org. solvents.

④ + H$_2$O (or ROH) $\longrightarrow$
(p-CH$_3$C$_6$H$_4$)$_2$PH

+ 30% H$_2$O$_2$ + NaOH $\xrightarrow{H_2O}$
(p-CH$_3$C$_6$H$_4$)$_2$P(O)OH

⑤ Intermediate in prepn. of org. P compds.

⑥ Ber. 94, 392 (1961).

PC$_{14}$H$_{15}$

① Methylbenzylphenylphosphine
CH$_3$(C$_6$H$_5$CH$_2$)C$_6$H$_5$P

② [CH$_3$(C$_6$H$_5$)(C$_6$H$_5$CH$_2$)(C$_6$H$_5$)$_2$CHP$^+$]Br$^-$
$\xrightarrow{electrolysis}$ 85%

③ (156~158°/12).

④ + RBr $\longrightarrow$
[CH$_3$(C$_6$H$_5$CH$_2$)(C$_6$H$_5$)PR]$^+$Br$^-$
R=C$_2$H$_5$, n-C$_3$H$_7$, CH$_2$=CHCH$_2$,
(CH$_3$)$_3$C, C$_6$H$_5$CH$_2$, p-O$_2$NC$_6$H$_4$CH$_2$,
CH$_2$CO$_2$H, CH$_2$COC$_2$H$_5$, etc.

⑥ Ann. 646, 65 (1961). Tetrahedron Letters 1961, 161

PC$_{14}$H$_{15}$

① Dibenzylphosphine
(C$_6$H$_5$CH$_2$)$_2$PH

② (C$_6$H$_5$CH$_2$)$_2$P(S)P(S)(CH$_2$C$_6$H$_5$)$_2$ +
LiAlH$_4$ $\longrightarrow$ 45.8%

③ Liq. (115~120°/3).
Sol. in org. solvents.

④ + HI $\longrightarrow$ [(C$_6$H$_5$CH$_2$)$_2$PH$_2$]$^+$I$^-$

⑥ Ber. 92, 704 (1959).

PC$_{14}$H$_{15}$

① Ethyldiphenylphosphine
C$_2$H$_5$(C$_6$H$_5$)$_2$P

② [(C$_2$H$_5$)(C$_6$H$_5$)$_3$P]$^+$I$^-$ + Na $\longrightarrow$ 52%
[C$_2$H$_5$)(C$_6$H$_5$)$_3$P]$^+$Br$^-$ + LiAlH$_4$ $\longrightarrow$
[(C$_2$H$_5$(C$_6$H$_5$)$_3$P]$^+$Br$^-$ $\xrightarrow{electrolysis}$ 59%

③ (129~132°/0.7, 182°/14).
NMR: J. Chem. Eng. Data 7, 307 (1962)

④ + CH$_3$I $\longrightarrow$ [(CH$_3$)(C$_2$H$_5$)(C$_6$H$_5$)$_2$P]$^+$I$^-$
+ GeI$_2$ $\longrightarrow$ C$_2$H$_5$(C$_6$H$_5$)$_2$P·GeI$_2$

⑥ JCS 1961, 4263. Ber. 92, 2088 (1959).
Ann. 646, 65 (1961).

PC$_{14}$H$_{15}$O

① 2-Hydroxyethyldiphenylphosphine
HOCH$_2$CH$_2$(C$_6$H$_5$)$_2$P

② $(C_6H_5)_2PK + CH_2-CH_2 \longrightarrow 56\%$

                             O

$[HOCH_2CH_2(C_6H_5CH_2)(C_6H_5)_2\overset{+}{P}]Cl^-$

$\xrightarrow{\text{electrolysis}}$ 87.5%

③ Colorless liq. (178~184°/18).
Sol. in ether, C$_6$H$_6$, pyridine, THF,
acetone, insol. in H$_2$O.

④ $+ S \xrightarrow{\text{in CS}_2} HOCH_2CH_2(C_6H_5)_2P(S)$

  $+ CH_3I \longrightarrow$

    $[HOCH_2CH_2(CH_3)(C_6H_5)_2\overset{+}{P}]I^-$

  $+ H_2O_2 \longrightarrow HOCH_2CH_2(C_6H_5)_2P(O)$

⑥ Ber. **94**, 102 (1961).   Ann. **646**, 65
(1961).

PC$_{14}$H$_{15}$O

① Methoxymethyldiphenylphosphine
$CH_3OCH_2(C_6H_5)_2P$

② $[CH_3OCH_2(C_6H_5)_3\overset{+}{P}]Cl^- \xrightarrow{\text{1N NaOH}}$

  $CH_3OCH_2(C_6H_5)_2P(O) \xrightarrow{\text{LiAlH}_4}$

③ (138~139°/1).

④ $+ C_6H_5CH_2Br \longrightarrow$

    $[CH_3OCH_2(C_6H_5CH_2)(C_6H_5)_2\overset{+}{P}]Br^-$

  $+ CH_3I \longrightarrow$

    $[CH_3OCH_2(CH_3)(C_6H_5)_2\overset{+}{P}]I^-$

  $+ HBr(\text{in } CH_3COOH) \xrightarrow{CH_3I}$

    $[(CH_3)_2(C_6H_5)_2\overset{+}{P}]I^-$

⑥ JCS **1961**, 2813.

PC$_{14}$H$_{15}$O

① Ethyldiphenylphosphine oxide
$(C_6H_5)_2C_2H_5P(O)$

② $(C_6H_5)_2PH + CH_3CHO + HCl \longrightarrow$
  $(C_6H_5)_2P(O)C_2H_5$

③ [122~123°] (hexane).

④ $(C_6H_5)_2C_2H_5P(O) + (C_6H_5)_2CO$

  $\xrightarrow{\text{PhMe, 130°}} (C_6H_5)_2P(O)OH$ (64%)

  $+ (C_6H_5)_2C=CHCH_3$ (51%)

⑥ JACS **81**, 5519 (1959).   Tetrahedron
18, 1231(1962). Ber. **94**, 1317(1961);
92, 2499 (1959).   Kaufman 1189.

PC$_{14}$H$_{15}$O

① Dibenzylphosphine oxide
$(C_6H_5CH_2)_2PH(O)$

② $(C_6H_5CH_2)_2P(OC_4H_9) \xrightarrow{\text{aq. HCl}}$

③ [108.5~109°].

⑥ Dokl. **135**, 323 (1960).

PC$_{14}$H$_{15}$O

① Diphenylphosphinous acid ethylester
$(C_6H_5)_2POC_2H_5$

② $C_2H_5OPCl_2 + C_6H_5MgBr \longrightarrow 64\%$

  $(C_6H_5)_2PCl + C_2H_5OH \xrightarrow{(C_2H_5)_3N} 87\%$

  $(C_6H_5)_2PN(C_2H_5)_2 + C_2H_5OH \longrightarrow 50\%$

③ Liq. (127~128°/1). n_D 1.5910 (20°).
d 1.0896 (0°).

④ $+ B_{10}H_{14} \longrightarrow B_{10}H_{12}[(C_6H_5)_2POC_2H_5]_2$

  $+ BrCH_2CH_2Br \longrightarrow$

    $(C_6H_5)_2P(O)CH_2CH_2Br$

  $+ n\text{-}C_6H_{13}OH + \text{small amt. Na} \longrightarrow$

    $(C_6H_5)_2POC_6H_{13}\text{-}n$

⑥ JOC **26**, 4623 (1961).   Zhur. **31**, 2377,
2889 (1961).

PC$_{14}$H$_{15}$OS

① Dibenzylphosphinothioic acid
$(C_6H_5CH_2)_2P(S)OH$

② $C_6H_5CH_2MgCl + PSCl_3 \longrightarrow$

③ Plates. [171].
Sol. in NaOH aq.

⑥ Ber. **49**, 63 (1916).

PC$_{14}$H$_{15}$OS

① Methylthiomethyldiphenylphos-
phine oxide
$CH_3SCH_2P(O)(C_6H_5)_2$

② $(C_6H_5)_2P(O)CH_2Cl + CH_3SNa \xrightarrow[\text{EtOH}]{30~90°}$

  87%

③ [139~140°].

④ $CH_3SCH_2P(O)(C_6H_5)_2 \xrightarrow{CH_3CO_2H}$

  $CH_3SO_2CH_2P(O)(C_6H_5)_2$ (85%)

⑥ Tetrahedron Letters **1961**, 724.

PC$_{14}$H$_{15}$OS$_2$

① Phenylphosphonodithioic acid
  O-ethyl-*S*-phenylester
  C$_6$H$_5$P(S)(OC$_2$H$_5$)SC$_6$H$_5$

② C$_6$H$_5$P(S)(OC$_2$H$_5$)SM + ClN$_2$C$_6$H$_5$
  $\longrightarrow$ 11.3% (M=Na, K)

③ (125.5~126.5°/0.25). n_D 1.6305 (20°),
  d 1.1749 (20°).

⑥ Zhur. Vsesoyuz. Khim. Obshchestva
  im. D. I. Mendeleva, **6**, No. 1, 119
  (1961) ; CA **55**, 15385 (1961).

PC$_{14}$H$_{15}$O$_2$

① Methoxymethyldiphenylphosphine
  oxide
  (CH$_3$OCH$_2$)P(O)(C$_6$H$_5$)$_2$

② [(CH$_3$OCH$_2$)P(C$_6$H$_5$)$_3$]Cl $\xrightarrow{\text{1 N NaOH}}$

③ [116~117°] (C$_6$H$_6$-petr. ether).

④ CH$_3$OCH$_2$P(O)(C$_6$H$_5$)$_2$ $\xrightarrow[\text{(C}_4\text{H}_9)_2\text{O}]{\text{LiAlH}_4}$
  (CH$_3$CH$_2$)P(C$_6$H$_5$)$_2$

⑥ JCS **1961**, 2813.   Ber. **94**, 1381 (1961).

PC$_{14}$H$_{15}$O$_2$

① Ethylphosphonous acid diphenylester
  C$_2$H$_5$P(OC$_6$H$_5$)$_2$

② (C$_6$H$_5$O)$_2$PCl + C$_2$H$_5$MgBr
  $\xrightarrow[\text{51%}]{\text{C}_5\text{H}_5\text{N in (C}_2\text{H}_5)_2\text{O}}$

③ (113~115°/1). n_D 1.5623 (20°), 1.1000
  (20°).

④ + S $\longrightarrow$ C$_2$H$_5$P(S)(OC$_6$H$_5$)$_2$

⑥ Zhur. **33**, 899 (1963).

PC$_{14}$H$_{15}$O$_2$

① Diphenylphosphinic acid ethylester
  (C$_6$H$_5$)$_2$P(O)(OC$_2$H$_5$)

② (C$_6$H$_5$)$_2$P(O)OH + CH$_3$CHN$_2$ $\longrightarrow$
  C$_6$H$_5$ + PCl$_3$ + AlCl$_3$ $\xrightarrow{\text{1) Cl}_2, \text{ 2) C}_2\text{H}_5\text{OH}}$

③ (195~198°/0.5).

⑥ Ber. **69**, 2020 (1947) ; **94**, 102 (1961).

PC$_{14}$H$_{15}$O$_2$

① Dibenzylphosphinic acid
  (C$_6$H$_5$CH$_2$)$_2$P(O)(OH)

② (C$_6$H$_5$CH$_2$)$_2$PCl $\xrightarrow{\text{6%H}_2\text{O}_2}$
  (C$_6$H$_5$CH$_2$)$_2$POC$_6$H$_5$ $\xrightarrow{\text{oxidative}}$
  saponification
  $\xrightarrow{}$
  [(C$_6$H$_5$CHOH)$_2$P(O)CH$_2$C$_6$H$_5$]
  reduction
  $\xrightarrow{}$

③ [191~192°].

⑥ Zhur. **31**, 3027 (1961).   Chem.
  Communs. **26**, 1949 (1961).

PC$_{14}$H$_{15}$O$_3$

① Ethylphosphonic acid diphenylester
  C$_2$H$_5$P(O)(OC$_6$H$_5$)$_2$

② (C$_6$H$_5$O)$_3$P + C$_2$H$_5$I $\longrightarrow$
  (C$_6$H$_5$O)$_2$POC$_2$H$_5$ + C$_2$H$_5$I
  $\xrightarrow[\text{80%}]{\text{heat in a sealed tube}}$

③ Liq. (202°/13). n_D 1.5451 (20°).
  d 1.1799 (20°).

⑥ Izv. OKhN **1954**, 427.   Dokl. **92**, 57
  (1953).

PC$_{14}$H$_{15}$S$_2$

① Dibenzylphosphinodithioic acid
  (C$_6$H$_5$CH$_2$)$_2$P(S)SH

② (C$_4$H$_9$O)$_2$PSH + K + C$_6$H$_5$CH$_2$MgCl + S
  $\longrightarrow$ 38.1%
  (C$_6$H$_5$CH$_2$)$_2$PSCl + CH$_3$ONa + H$_2$S $\xrightarrow{\text{HCl}}$

③ [132.5~133.5].
  Decomp. gradually and evolved H$_2$S.

④ + CH$_2$=CHCN $\longrightarrow$
  (C$_6$H$_5$CH$_2$)$_2$P(S)SCH$_2$CH$_2$CN
  + NaOH + C$_6$H$_5$CH$_2$X $\longrightarrow$
  (C$_6$H$_5$CH$_2$)$_2$P(S)SCH$_2$C$_6$H$_5$
  (X=halogen)

⑥ Zhur. **31**, 507 (1961).

PC$_{14}$H$_{15}$Se

① Ethyldiphenylphosphine selenide

$(C_2H_5)P(Se)(C_6H_5)_2$

② $C_2H_5PCl_2 + C_6H_5MgBr \longrightarrow \overset{Se}{\longrightarrow} 67\%$

③ [49°].

⑥ J. Chem. Eng. Data **8**, 226 (1963).

PC₁₄H₁₆Br

① Dimethyldiphenylphosphonium
    bromide
    $[(CH_3)_2\overset{+}{P}(C_6H_5)_2]\overset{-}{Br}$

② $CH_3P(C_6H_5)_2 + CH_3Br \longrightarrow$

③ UV: Ber. **96**, 2109 (1963).
    Picrate [116°].

④ $\overset{Hg/2e^-}{\longrightarrow} (CH_3)_2PC_6H_5 \ (69\%) +$
    $CH_3P(C_6H_5)_2 \ (26\%)$

⑥ Ann. **646**, 65 (1961).

PC₁₄H₁₆ClO₂

① Bis(hydroxymethyl)diphenylphos-
    phonium chloride
    $[(C_6H_5)_2\overset{+}{P}(CH_2OH)_2]\overset{-}{Cl}$

② $(C_6H_5)_2PCH_2OH + CH_2O + HCl \longrightarrow$
    88%

③ [155~157°].

④ $\overset{NaOH}{\longrightarrow} (C_6H_5)_2P(CH_2OH) \ (76\%)$
    $+ (CH_3CO)_2O \longrightarrow$
    $[(C_6H_5)_2P(CH_2OCOCH_3)_2]OCOCH_3$

⑥ Ann. **659**, 49 (1962).

PC₁₄H₁₆I

① Dimethyldiphenylphosphonium
    iodide
    $[(CH_3)_2(C_6H_5)_2\overset{+}{P}]\overset{-}{I}$

② $(C_6H_5)_2PLi\cdot dioxane + CH_3I \overset{dioxane}{\longrightarrow}$
    82%
    $[(C_6H_5)_2P]_2 + CH_3I \overset{THF}{\longrightarrow} 34\%$
    $(C_6H_5)_2PCH_3 + CH_3I \overset{C_6H_6}{\longrightarrow}$

③ [249.5~251°(decomp.)].
    IR: Ber. **92**, 1118 (1919).

⑥ Tetrahedron **18**, 1231 (1962).   Z.
    anorg. allg. Chem. **299**, 58 (1959).
    Tetrahedron Letters **1**, 8 (1959).

Kosolapoff 93.

PC₁₄H₁₇N₂

① Bis(2-cyanoethyl)phenethyl phos-
    phine
    $(NCCH_2CH_2)_2(C_6H_5CH_2CH_2)P$

② $(NCCH_2CH_2)_2PH + C_6H_5CH=CH_2$
    $\overset{DPBP}{\longrightarrow} 47\%$

③ (212°/0.6). n_D 1.5580 (25°).

⑥ JOC **26**, 5138 (1961).

PC₁₄H₁₉O₃

① Phenylphosphonic acid dimethallyl
    ester
    $C_6H_5P(O)[OCH_2C(CH_3)=CH_2]_2$

② $C_6H_5POCl_2 + CH_2=C(CH_3)CH_2OH$
    $\overset{C_5H_5N}{\longrightarrow} 53.5\%$

③ Liq. (140~143°/2~3). n_D 1.5057 (25°).
    d 1.0728 (25°/4°).

⑤ $\longrightarrow$ polymer or copolymer

⑥ JACS **70**, 186 (1948).

PC₁₄H₂₃

① Ethyl(n-hexyl)phenylphosphine
    $C_2H_5(n-C_6H_{13})(C_6H_5)P$

② $C_6H_5PCl_2 + Pb(C_2H_5)_4$
    $\longrightarrow (C_6H_5)_2PCl \overset{n-C_6H_{13}MgX}{\longrightarrow}$

③ (123~125°/5). n_D 1.5255 (20°). d 0.9212
    (20°).

④ $+ C_3H_5Br \longrightarrow$
    $[C_2H_5(C_3H_5)(n-C_6H_{13})(C_6H_5)P]^+Br^-$

⑥ Dokl. **143**, 596 (1962).

PC₁₄H₂₃

① Benzyl$n$-butyl$n$-propylphosphine
    $(n-C_3H_7)(n-C_4H_9)C_6H_5CH_2P$

② $(n-C_3H_7)_2(n-C_4H_9)(C_6H_5CH_2)PCl$
    $\overset{heat \ in \ CO_2}{\longrightarrow}$

③ (113~115°/1). n_D 1.5090 (20°). d 0.9467
    (20°).

⑥ Dokl. **92**, 69 (1953).   Zhur. **26**, 3426
    (1956).

PC₁₄H₂₃O₂

① Bis(2-ethoxyethyl)phenylphosphine
$(C_2H_5OCH_2CH_2)_2C_6H_5P$

② $C_6H_5PH_2 + C_2H_5OCH_2CH_2I + Na$
(liq. NH₃) $\longrightarrow$ 64%

③ Colorless liq. (118～122°/0.5).

④ + PdBr₂ $\longrightarrow$
$[(C_2H_5OCH_2CH_2)_2C_6H_5P]_2PdBr_2$
mp 111～112°

⑥ JCS **1958**, 2081.

PC₁₄H₂₃O₂

① Phenylphosphonous acid dibutyl
ester
$C_6H_5P(OC_4H_9-n)_2$

② $C_6H_5P[N(C_2H_5)_2]_2 + n\text{-}C_4H_9OH$
$\xrightarrow{100°} C_6H_5(n\text{-}C_4H_9O)PN(C_2H_5)_2$
$\xrightarrow[110\sim120°]{n\text{-}C_4H_9OH}$ 57%

③ (116～117°/3). n_D 1.4995 (20°).

④ + B₁₀H₁₄ $\xrightarrow[\text{heat}]{\text{in } C_6H_6}$
$B_{10}H_{12}[C_6H_5P(OC_4H_9)_2]_2$

⑥ Zhur. **32**, 1974 (1962).

PC₁₄H₂₄Br

① Benzylbutylethylmethylphospho-
nium bromide
$[(C_6H_5CH_2)(C_4H_9)(C_2H_5)(CH_3)\overset{+}{P}]\overset{-}{Br}$

② $C_2H_5(C_4H_9)(C_6H_5CH_2)P + CH_3Br \longrightarrow$

③ [134～136°].

⑥ Ann. **646**, 65 (1961).

PC₁₄H₂₄I

① *n*-Butylmethylphenylpropylphos-
phonium iodide
$[(C_4H_9)(CH_3)(C_6H_5)(C_3H_7)\overset{+}{P}]\overset{-}{I}$

② $C_6H_5PH_2 \xrightarrow{CH_2O,\ HCl}$
$[C_6H_5P(CH_2OH)_3]Cl \xrightarrow{1)\ NaOH,\ 2)\ C_3H_7I}$
$[C_6H_5P(CH_2OH)_2(C_3H_7)]I$
$\xrightarrow{1)\ NaOH,\ 2)\ C_4H_9I}$
$[C_6H_5P(CH_2OH)(C_3H_7)(C_4H_9)]I$

$\xrightarrow{1)\ NaOH,\ 2)\ CH_3I}$ 32%

③ [150～152.5°].

⑥ Ann. **659**, 49 (1962).

PC₁₄H₂₅O

① Acetyldicyclohexylphosphine
$CH_3CO(C_6H_{11})_2P$

② $(C_6H_{11})_2PLi + CH_3COCl \longrightarrow$ 85%

③ (122～128°/2).
Air-sensitive. Sol. in org. solvents.

④ + CH₃I $\xrightarrow{\text{ether}}$
$[CH_3\overset{+}{C}OPCH_3(C_6H_{11})_2]I^-$

⑥ Ber. **92**, 3183 (1959).

PC₁₄H₂₇

① Ethyldicyclohexylphosphine
$C_2H_5(C_6H_{11})_2P$

② $(C_6H_{11})_2PCl + C_2H_5MgBr \xrightarrow{CS_2}$
$C_2H_5(C_6H_{11})_2PCS_2(48\%)$
$\xrightarrow[\text{distill}]{C_2H_5OH}$ 87%
$(C_6H_{11})_2PLi + Br(CH_2)_3CO_2C_2H_5 \longrightarrow$
70%

③ Colorless liq. (155～157°/10).

④ + [O] $\longrightarrow$ $C_2H_5(C_6H_{11})_2P(O)$

⑥ Ber. **94**, 102 (1961); **93**, 803 (1960).

PC₁₄H₂₇O

① Dicyclohexyl(2-hydroxyethyl)
phosphine
$(C_6H_{11})_2(HOCH_2CH_2)P$

② $(C_6H_{11})_2PLi + CH_2\text{--}CH_2 \longrightarrow$ 37%
$\underset{O}{\diagdown\diagup}$

③ [110～112°].
Sol. in dioxane, C_2H_5OH and C_6H_6;
insol. in ether.

⑥ Ber. **94**, 102 (1961).

PC₁₄H₂₈I

① Dicyclohexyldimethylphosphonium
iodide
$[(C_6H_{11})_2P(CH_3)_2]I$

② $(C_6H_{11})_2PLi + CH_3I \xrightarrow{\text{dioxane}} 65\%$

$(C_6H_{11})_2PP(C_6H_{11})_2 + CH_3I \longrightarrow 45\%$

③ [217.5~218.5°].

⑥ Ber. **92**, 1118, 2681 (1959).

PC₁₅H₁₄N

① 2-Cyanoethyl diphenylphosphine

NCCH₂CH₂(C₆H₅)₂P

② $(C_6H_5)_2PH + CH_2=CHCN \longrightarrow$

{ no catalyst (71%)

acid catalyst (68%)

base catalyst (42.5%)

③ Colorless crystals. [64~65.4°].

④ $+ NaOC_2H_5$ (or KOH) $\longrightarrow$

(C₆H₅)₂PCH₂CH₂COOH

$+ CH_3I \longrightarrow$

$[CH_3(C_6H_5)_2\overset{+}{P}CH_2CH_2CN]I^-$

$+ PdBr_2 \longrightarrow$

$[((C_6H_5)_2PCH_2CH_2CN)]_2PdBr_2$

⑥ JCS 1961, 5454 ; **1952**, 4453.

PC₁₅H₁₅

① Allyldiphenylphosphine

CH₂=CHCH₂(C₆H₅)₂P

② $(C_6H_5)_2PCl + CH_2=CHCH_2MgCl \longrightarrow$

18%

$[CH_2=CHCH_2(C_6H_5)_3\overset{+}{P}]\overset{-}{Br} + Na \longrightarrow$

52%

③ (194~200°/15).

Easily oxidized in air.

④ $+ NiX_2 \longrightarrow$

$[CH_2=CHCH_2(C_6H_5)_2P]_2NiX_2$

X=Cl, Br, I, SCN

$+ C_6H_5CH_2I \longrightarrow$

$[CH_2=CHCH_2(C_6H_5CH_2)(C_6H_5)_2\overset{+}{P}]I^-$

⑥ JCS **1962**, 693.   Ber. **92**, 2088 (1959).

PC₁₅H₁₆I

① Methyldiphenylvinylphosphonium

iodide

$[(CH_3)(C_6H_5)_2(CH_2=CH)\overset{+}{P}]I^-$

② $(C_6H_5)_2P(CH=CH_2) + CH_3I \longrightarrow 80\%$

③ [119~120°].

⑥ JOC **26**, 4623 (1961).

PC₁₅H₁₇

① Diphenylisopropylphosphine

i-C₃H₇(C₆H₅)₂P

② $[i\text{-}C_3H_7(C_6H_5)_3\overset{+}{P}]Br^- \xrightarrow{\text{electrolysis}}$

25%

$(C_6H_5)_2PNa + i\text{-}C_3H_7Br \longrightarrow 65.5\%$

$[i\text{-}C_3H_7(C_6H_5)_3\overset{+}{P}]I^- \xrightarrow[\text{2) LiAlH}_4]{\text{1) C}_4\text{H}_9\text{Li}} 24\%$

③ Colorless liq. (145~147°/0.5, 165°/13).

④ $+ CH_3I \longrightarrow [CH_3(i\text{-}C_3H_7)(C_6H_5)_2\overset{+}{P}]I^-$

mp 225~226°

$+ GeI_2 \longrightarrow i\text{-}C_3H_7(C_6H_5)_2P \cdot GeI_2$

⑥ JCS 1961, 4263.   Ann. **646**, 65 (1961).

Ber. **92**, 227 (1959).   Angew. **69**,

307 (1957).

PC₁₅H₁₇

① Ethylbenzylphenylphosphine

C₂H₅(C₆H₅CH₂)C₆H₅P

② $[(C_2H_5)(C_6H_5)(C_6H_5CH_2)_2\overset{+}{P}]Br^-$

$\xrightarrow{\text{electrolysis}} 91\%$

$[(C_2H_5)_2(C_6H_5)(C_6H_5CH_2)\overset{+}{P}]Cl^-$

$\xrightarrow{\text{heat in CO}_2}$

③ (165~168°/13). n_D 1.5960 (20°).

d 1.0393 (20°).

④ $+ CH_2=CHCH_2Br \longrightarrow$

$[C_2H_5(CH_2=CHCH_2)(C_6H_5)-$

$(C_6H_5CH_2)\overset{+}{P}]Br^-$

$+ n\text{-}C_4H_9Br \longrightarrow$

$[C_2H_5(n\text{-}C_4H_9)(C_6H_5)(C_6H_5CH_2)\overset{+}{P}]\overset{-}{Br}$

⑥ Ann. **646**, 65 (1961).   Tetrahedron

Letters 1961, 161.   Dokl. **92**, 69

(1953).   CA **48**, 9945 f (1954).

PC₁₅H₁₇BClF₄

① (Chloromethyl)ethyldiphenylphos-

phonium fluoroborate

$[(ClCH_2)(C_2H_5)P(C_6H_5)_2]^+BF_4^-$

② $[(C_6H_5)_2P(C_2H_5)(CH_2OH)]BF_4 \xrightarrow{\text{SOCl}_2}$

63%

$(C_6H_5)_2P(CH_2Cl) + [(C_2H_5)_3O]BF_4$
$\longrightarrow$ ca. 80%

③ $[129\sim130°]$.

⑥ Ann. **659**, 49 (1962).   Tetrahedron Letters **1961**, 724.

PC₁₅H₁₇O

① Ethyl-*m*-methoxyphenylphenyl phosphine
$C_2H_5(m\text{-}CH_3OC_6H_4)PC_6H_5$

② $C_6H_5(m\text{-}CH_3OC_6H_4)PNa + C_2H_5I \longrightarrow$
$C_6H_5(m\text{-}CH_3OC_6H_4)PCH_2CH_2CO_2C_2H_5$
$\xrightarrow{H^+}$

③ AuBr₃ Adduct $[150°]$.

⑥ Proc. Chem. Soc. **1959**, 365.

PC₁₅H₁₇O

① Benzylethylphenylphosphine oxide
$(C_2H_5)(C_6H_5)(C_6H_5CH_2)P(O)$

② $[(CH_3)(C_2H_5)(C_6H_5CH_2)P]OCOCH_3$
$\xrightarrow{\text{AgOCOCH}_3/\text{CH}_3\text{OH, } 40°}$

$(C_2H_5)(C_6H_5)_2P(O) \xrightarrow[\text{2) } C_6H_5CH_2Cl]{\text{1) Na}} 39\%$

③ $[112\sim113°]$.

⑥ JOC **28**, 2150 (1963).   JACS **81**, 5519 (1959).

PC₁₅H₁₇O₂

① Bis(*o*-methoxyphenyl)methylphosphine
$(o\text{-}CH_3OC_6H_4)_2CH_3P$

② $o\text{-}CH_3OC_6H_4MgBr + CH_3PCl_2 \xrightarrow{\text{ether}}$

③ $[128\sim129°]$.

④ $+ H_2O_2 \longrightarrow (o\text{-}CH_3OC_6H_4)_2(CH_3)P(O)$
$+ RI \longrightarrow [(o\text{-}CH_3OC_6H_4)_2(CH_3)\overset{+}{R}P]I^-$
$\qquad R = CH_3, C_2H_5$

⑥ JCS **1956**, 4670.

PC₁₅H₁₇O₂

① Benzylphenylphosphinic acid ethyl-ester
$(C_6H_5)(C_6H_5CH_2)P(O)(OC_2H_5)$

② $C_6H_5P(OC_2H_5)_2 + C_6H_5CH_2Cl \longrightarrow 98\%$

③ $(180\sim182°/0.2)$. $[62.5\sim63.5°]$.

④ $+ KOC(CH_3)_3 \xrightarrow{O_2 \text{ in } C_6H_6}$
$trans\text{-}C_6H_5CH=CHC_6H_5$
$+ C_6H_5CHO + KOC(CH_3)_3 \longrightarrow$
$(C_6H_5)_2C=C(C_6H_5)_2$
$+ C_6H_5COCH_3 + KOC(CH_3)_3 \longrightarrow$
α-methylstilbene

⑥ Ber. **94**, 1987 (1961) ; **95**, 581 (1962).

PC₁₅H₁₈Br

① Ethylmethyldiphenylphosphonium bromide
$[(C_2H_5)(CH_3)(C_6H_5)_2P]Br$

② $CH_3P(C_6H_5)_2 + C_2H_5Br \xrightarrow{CH_3CN, \ 80°}$

③ $[174°]$.

④ $\xrightarrow[60\sim80°]{Hg, \ 2e^-} CH_3(C_2H_5)(C_6H_5)P + \atop (33\%)$
$CH_3P(C_6H_5)_2$
(60.5%)

⑥ Ann. **646**, 65 (1961).

PC₁₅H₁₈I

① Benzyldimethylphenylphosphonium iodide
$[(C_6H_5CH_2)(CH_3)_2(C_6H_5)P]I$

② $(CH_3)_2(C_6H_5)P + C_6H_5CH_2I \xrightarrow{(C_2H_5)_2O}$
83%

③ $[172\sim173°]$.

⑥ Ber. **94**, 186 (1961).

PC₁₅H₁₈IO

① (2-Hydroxyethyl)methyldiphenyl phosphonium iodide
$[(HOCH_2CH_2)(CH_3)\overset{+}{P}(C_6H_5)_2]I$

② $[(HOCH_2CH_2)(C_6H_5CH_2)(C_6H_5)_2P]Br$
$\xrightarrow{Mg/2e^-}$

$(HOCH_2CH_2)(C_6H_5)_2P \xrightarrow{CH_3I} 87.5\%$

$CH_3PPh_2 + HOCH_2CH_2Cl \xrightarrow{KI}$

③ $[185\sim186°]$.

⑥ Ann. **646**, 65 (1961).

PC₁₅H₂₅O

① Benzyldibutylphosphine oxide
(C₄H₉)₂P(O)CH₂C₆H₅

② (C₄H₉)₂POC₂H₅ + C₆H₅CH₂Cl ⟶

③ (215°/5). [63°] (petr. ether).

⑥ Ber. **93**, 1220 (1960).

PC₁₅H₂₅O₃

① Benzylphosphonic acid dibutyl ester
C₆H₅CH₂P(O)(OC₄H₉)₂

② (C₄H₉O)₂PONa + C₆H₅CH₂Cl ⟶

④ + Na $\xrightarrow{\text{C₆H₅CH₃}}$
C₆H₅CH₂P(O)(OC₄H₉)ONa + C₄H₁₀

⑤ Extractant.

⑥ Ekstraktsiya Teoriga. Primenenie
Apparutura, Sb Statei **1962**, (1) 88.
Dept. Com., Office tech. Serv. AD
266675 (1961).

PC₁₅H₂₇O₂

① Dicyclohexylethoxycarbonylphos-
phine
(*cyclo*-C₆H₁₁)₂(C₂H₅OCO)P

② (*cyclo*-C₆H₁₁)₂PLi + C₂H₅OCOCl ⟶
54%

③ Yellow oil. (165~169°/3).
Slowly oxidized in air.

④ + S $\xrightarrow{\text{in CS₂}}$
CO(OC₂H₅)P(S)(*cyclo*-C₆H₁₁)₂
+ CH₃I $\xrightarrow{\text{ether}}$
[CO(OC₂H₅)P⁺(CH₃)(*cyclo*-C₆H₁₁)₂]I⁻
+ NiBr₂ ⟶
[CO(OC₂H₅)P(*cyclo*-C₆H₁₁)₂]₂NiBr₂

⑥ Z. Naturf. **16 b**, 837 (1961).

PC₁₆H₁₇

① Fluoren-9-ylidenetrimethylphospho-
rane

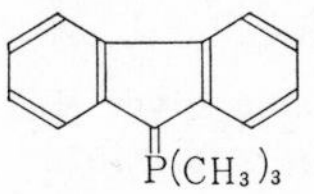

PC₁₆H₁₈Br

② [(CH₃)₃P-C₁₃H₉]Br $\xrightarrow{\text{C₆H₅Li/C₆H₆}}$

④ + C₆H₅CH₃ $\xrightarrow{\text{C₆H₆}}$ C₁₃H₈=CHC₆H₅ (75%)

⑥ Tetrahedron **9**, 130 (1960).

PC₁₆H₁₈Br

① Fluoren-9-yl-trimethylphosphonium
bromide
[(CH₃)₃P-C₁₃H₉]Br

② C₁₃H₉Br + (CH₃)₃P ⟶ 51%

③ [221~223°].
IR: Tetrahedron **9**, 130 (1960).

⑥ Spectrochim. Acta **19**, 1905 (1963).

PC₁₆H₁₈K

① Potassium bis-2,5-dimethylphenyl
phosphide

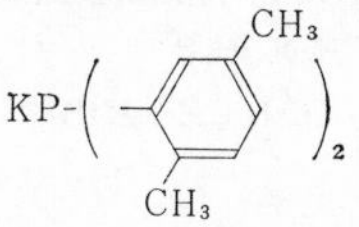

② [2,5-(CH₃)₂C₆H₃]₃P + K $\xrightarrow{\text{dioxane}}$ 20%

③ Orange-yellow soln.

④ + 30% H₂O₂ + NaOH $\xrightarrow{\text{H₂O}}$
[2,5-(CH₃)₂C₆H₃]₂P(O)OH

⑤ Intermediate in prepn. of org. P.
compds.

⑥ Ber. **94**, 392 (1961).

PC₁₆H₁₉

① Dibenzylethylphosphine
(C₆H₅CH₂)₂C₂H₅P

② [C₂H₅(C₆H₅CH₂)₃P⁺]Br⁻ $\xrightarrow{\text{electrolysis}}$
90%

③ (143~145°/1).

④ + CH₃I ⟶
[CH₃(C₂H₅)(C₆H₅CH₂)₂P⁺]I⁻
mp 121°

⑥ Ann. **646**, 65 (1961).

PC₁₆H₁₉

① *n*-Butyldiphenylphosphine
n-C₄H₉(C₆H₅)₂P

② $(C_6H_5)_2PNa + n\text{-}C_4H_9Br \longrightarrow$ 61%

$[n\text{-}C_4H_9(C_6H_5)_3\overset{+}{P}]Br^- \xrightarrow{\text{electrolysis}}$
50%

$[n\text{-}C_4H_9(C_6H_5)_3\overset{+}{P}]Br^- + LiAlH_4 \xrightarrow{\text{THF}}$
54%

③ Colorless liq. (140°/0.45). n_D 1.5931
   (20°).

④ $+ H_2O_2 + NaOH \longrightarrow$
   $(C_6H_5)_2P(O)C_4H_9$

   $+ C_2H_5I \longrightarrow$
   $[(C_6H_5)_2(C_4H_9)(C_2H_5)\overset{+}{P}]I^-$

   $+ GeI_2 \dashrightarrow n\text{-}C_4H_9(C_6H_5)_2P\cdot GeI_2$

⑥ JCS 1961, 4263. Ann. 646, 65 (1961).
   Ber. 92, 227 (1959).

PC₁₆H₁₉

① n-Propylbenzylphenylphosphine
   $(n\text{-}C_3H_7)(C_6H_5CH_2)C_6H_5P$

② $[(n\text{-}C_3H_7)(C_6H_5)(C_6H_5CH_2)_2\overset{+}{P}]Br^-$
   $\xrightarrow{\text{electrolysis}}$ 82%
   $[(n\text{-}C_3H_7)_2(C_6H_5)(C_6H_5CH_2)\overset{+}{P}]Cl^- \longrightarrow$

③ (172~175°/12). n_D 1.5680 (20°).

④ $+ CH_2=CHCH_2Br \longrightarrow$

$$\left[\begin{array}{c} C_3H_7 \\ | \\ (C_6H_5CH_2)\overset{}{P}(CH_2CH=CH_2) \\ | \\ C_6H_5 \end{array} \right]^+ Br^-$$

⑥ Ann. 646, 65 (1961). Tetrahedron
   Letters 1961, 161. Dokl. 92, 69
   (1953). CA 48, 9945 (1954).

PC₁₆H₁₉

① Benzylideneethylmethylphenyl-
   phosphorane
   $(CH_3)(C_2H_5)(C_6H_5)P=CHC_6H_5$

② $[(CH_3)(C_2H_5)(C_6H_5)PCH_2C_6H_5]I$
   $\xrightarrow{C_6H_5Li/(C_2H_5)_2O}$

④ $+ C_6H_5CH-CH_2 \longrightarrow C_6H_5CH-CHC_6H_5$
        $\underset{O}{\diagdown\diagup}$ $\underset{CH_2}{\diagdown\diagup}$

⑥ JACS 84, 677 (1962).

PC₁₆H₁₉O

① Butyldiphenylphosphine oxide

$C_4H_9P(O)(C_6H_5)_2$

② $\{(C_6H_5)_2P[CH(OH)C_3H_7]_2\}Cl$
   $\xrightarrow{\text{1) 2 N NaOH, 2) TOS CH}_3I}$

   $[(C_6H_5)_3PC_4H_9]Br \xrightarrow{OH^-}$

③ [93~94°].

④ $(C_6H_5)_2P(O)C_4H_9 + C_6H_5CH_2C_6H_5$
   $\xrightarrow{C_6H_5CH_3,\ 130°,\ 10\ hrs}$

   $(C_6H_5)_2P(O)OH + (C_6H_5)_2C=CHC_3H_7$
   $\quad\ (55\%) \qquad\qquad\ (43\%)$

⑥ JOC 28, 473 (1963). JCS 1961, 2813.
   Ber. 92, 2499 (1959).

PC₁₆H₁₉O₃

① Butylphosphonic acid diphenyl ester
   $C_4H_9P(O)(OC_6H_5)_2$

② $(C_6H_5O)_2POC_4H_9 + C_4H_9I \longrightarrow$ 52%
   $(C_6H_5O)_3P + C_4H_9I \longrightarrow$

③ Colorless liq. (205~207.5°/11).
   n_D 1.5339 (20°), d 1.1293 (20°).
   Sol. in org. solvents.

⑥ Zhur. 33, 1363 (1963). Compt. rend.
   253, 1573(1961). Dokl. 92, 57(1953).

PC₁₆H₂₀Br

① Benzylethylmethylphenylphosphonium bromide
   $[(C_6H_5CH_2)(C_2H_5)(CH_3)(C_6H_5)P]Br$

② $C_6H_5PH_2 \xrightarrow[HCl]{CH_2O} [C_6H_5P(CH_2OH)_3]Cl$

   $\xrightarrow[\text{2) CH}_3I]{\text{1) NaOH}} [C_6H_5(CH_3)P(CH_2OH)_2]I$

   $\xrightarrow[\text{2) C}_2H_5I]{\text{1) NaOH}}$
   $[(C_6H_5)(CH_3)(C_2H_5)P(CH_2OH)]I$

   $\xrightarrow[\text{2) C}_6H_5CH_2Br]{\text{1) NaOH}}$
   $[(C_6H_5)(CH_3)(C_2H_5)P(CH_2C_6H_5)]Br$

   $(CH_3)(C_6H_5)(C_6H_5CH_2)P + C_2H_5Br$
   $\xrightarrow[70°]{CH_3CN}$

③ [145°].

Resolution by acidic silver-(D)-
dibenzyltartrate.

④ $\xrightarrow[\text{Hg/2e}^-,\ 80\sim90°]{}$ (CH$_3$)(C$_2$H$_5$)(C$_6$H$_5$)P
(77%)

⑥ Tetrahedron Letters **1961**, 161. Ann.
646, 65 (1961).

PC$_{16}$H$_{20}$Br

① Dibenzyldimethylphosphonium
bromide
[(C$_6$H$_5$CH$_2$)$_2$(CH$_3$)$_2$P]Br

② [(C$_6$H$_5$CH$_2$)$_3$PCH$_3$]Br $\xrightarrow[\text{2) CH}_3\text{Br}]{\text{1) NaNH}_2/\text{liq. NH}^3}$

(C$_6$H$_5$CH$_2$)$_2$PCH$_3$ + CH$_3$Br ⟶

③ [141～142°].

④ + LiAlH$_4$ $\xrightarrow{\text{THF}}$ C$_6$H$_5$CH$_2$P(CH$_3$)$_2$

⑥ JACS **79**, 3567 (1957).

PC$_{16}$H$_{20}$I

① Benzylethylmethylphenylphosphonium iodide
[(C$_6$H$_5$CH$_2$)(C$_2$H$_5$)(CH$_3$)(C$_6$H$_5$)P]I

② C$_6$H$_5$PH$_2$ $\xrightarrow{\text{CH}_2\text{O, HCl}}$

[C$_6$H$_5$P(CH$_2$OH)$_3$]Cl $\xrightarrow[\text{2) CH}_3\text{I}]{\text{1) NaOH}}$

[C$_6$H$_5$P(CH$_2$OH)$_2$CH$_3$]I

$\xrightarrow[\text{2) C}_2\text{H}_5\text{I}]{\text{1) NaOH}}$ [C$_6$H$_5$P(CH$_2$OH)CH$_3$C$_2$H$_5$]I

$\xrightarrow[\text{2) C}_6\text{H}_5\text{CH}_2\text{I}]{\text{1) NaOH}}$

[C$_6$H$_5$PCH$_3$C$_2$H$_5$(C$_6$H$_5$CH$_2$)]I (34%)

C$_6$H$_5$PCl$_2$ $\xrightarrow[\text{2) CH}_3\text{I}]{\text{1) C}_6\text{H}_5\text{CH}_2\text{MgCl}}$

[(C$_6$H$_5$)(CH$_3$)(C$_6$H$_5$CH$_2$)$_2$P]I

$\xrightarrow[\text{2) C}_2\text{H}_5\text{I}]{\text{1) LiAlH}_4}$

[(C$_6$H$_5$)(CH$_3$)(C$_2$H$_5$)(C$_6$H$_5$CH$_2$)P]I
(65%)

③ [167～168°]. [α]$_D$ = ±24°.

④ $\xrightarrow[\quad40°\quad]{\text{AgOAc/CH}_3\text{OH}}$

[(C$_6$H$_5$CH$_2$)CH$_3$C$_6$H$_5$C$_2$H$_5$P]OAc

Wittig reaction :

(+)salt $\xrightarrow[\text{(inversion)}]{\text{OH}^-}$ (−)oxide

| Wittig reaction (retention) ↓ | ↑ Wittig reaction (retention) |

(+)oxide $\xleftarrow[\text{(inversion)}]{\text{OH}^-}$ (−)salt

⑥ JOC **25**, 1996 (1960); **28**, 2150 (1963).
Ann. **659**, 49 (1962). JACS **81**, 248
(1959). Kosolapoff 94.

PC$_{16}$H$_{20}$I

① Diethyldiphenylphosphonium iodide
[(C$_2$H$_5$)$_2$(C$_6$H$_5$)$_2$P]I

② (C$_6$H$_5$)$_2$PCl + C$_2$H$_5$I $\xrightarrow{140°}$ 75%

③ [209～210°].

⑥ Ber. **93**, 861 (1960). Kosolapoff 93.

PC$_{16}$H$_{29}$O$_2$

① Ethoxycarbonylmethyldicyclo-
hexylphosphine
(C$_2$H$_5$O$_2$CCH$_2$)(cyclo-C$_6$H$_{11}$)$_2$P

② (cyclo-C$_6$H$_{11}$)$_2$PH + BrCH$_2$CO$_2$C$_2$H$_5$
$\xrightarrow{\text{NaOC}_2\text{H}_5}$ 69%

③ Colorless liq. (147～148°/1).
Air-sensitive.

④ + CH$_3$I ⟶
[CH$_3$(C$_6$H$_{11}$)$_2$PCH$_2$CO$_2$C$_2$H$_5$]I$^-$

⑥ Ber. **94**, 2244 (1961).

PC$_{16}$H$_{31}$O$_2$

① Dicyclohexylphosphinic acid
n-butyl ester
(C$_6$H$_{11}$)$_2$P(O)(OC$_4$H$_9$)

② (cyclo-C$_6$H$_{11}$)$_2$POCl + NaOC$_4$H$_9$
$\xrightarrow{\text{benzene}}$ 80%

③ (134°/0.3). n$_D$ 1.4900 (24°).

⑥ JACS **84**, 3093 (1962).

PC$_{16}$H$_{36}$Br

① Tetrabutylphosphonium bromide
[(C$_4$H$_9$)$_4$P]Br

② (C$_4$H$_9$)$_3$P + C$_4$H$_9$Br $\xrightarrow{\text{(CH}_3)_2\text{CO}}$ 89.5%

③ [99~101°].

IR : Spectrochim Acta **19**, 1905 (1963).

④ Hydroxide is a transient catalyst for silicone polymerization.

⑥ JACS **82**, 3919 (1960). Ind. Eng. Chem. **51**, 515 (1959). J. Polymer Sci. **54**, 375 (1961).

PC₁₇H₂₀Br

① Allylbenzylmethylphenylphosphonium bromide

$$[(C_6H_5CH_2)\overset{\overset{\displaystyle CH_3}{|}}{\underset{\underset{\displaystyle C_6H_5}{|}}{P}}(CH_2CH=CH_2)]^+Br^-$$

② $CH_3C_6H_5(C_6H_5CH_2)P +$

$CH_2=CHCH_2Br \longrightarrow$

③ [142°]. $[\alpha]_D^{20}15.1°$.

④ $\xrightarrow{\text{cathodic, cleavage}}$

$(CH_3)(C_6H_5)P(CH_2C_6H_5) +$

$MePhPCH_2CH=CH_2, [\alpha]_D^{20}\sim10°$

⑥ Tetrahedron Letters **1963**, 965; **1961**, 161. Kaufman 1237.

PC₁₇H₂₁

① *n*-Butylbenzylphenylphosphine

$(n-C_4H_9)(C_6H_5CH_2)C_6H_5P$

② $[(n-C_4H_9)(C_6H_5)(C_6H_5CH_2)_2\overset{+}{P}]Br^-$

$\xrightarrow{\text{electrolysis}} 81\%$

$[(n-C_4H_9)_2(C_6H_5)(C_6H_5CH_2)\overset{+}{P}]Cl^- \xrightarrow{\text{heat}}$

③ (184~190°/11, 151~152°/3). n_D 1.5729 (20°). d 1.0112.

④ $+ CH_3I \longrightarrow$

$[CH_3(n-C_4H_9)(C_6H_5)(C_6H_5CH_2)\overset{+}{P}]I^-$

$+ CH_2=CHCH_2Br \longrightarrow$

$[CH_2=CHCH_2(n-C_4H_9)(C_6H_5)$

$(C_6H_5CH_2)\overset{+}{P}]Br^-$

⑥ Ann. **646**, 65 (1961). Dokl. **92**, 69 (1953); CA **48**, 9945 (1954).

PC₁₇H₂₂

① Trimethylenebis (methylphenylphosphine)

$(CH_3)(C_6H_5)PCH_2CH_2CH_2P(CH_3)(C_6H_5)$

② $[CH_3(C_6H_5)\overset{+}{\underset{\underset{\displaystyle H}{|}}{P}}(CH_2)_3\overset{+}{\underset{\underset{\displaystyle H}{|}}{P}}(C_6H_5)CH_3]\ 2\ I^-$

$\longrightarrow 70\%$

③ (199~201°/4~5).

④ $CH_3(C_6H_5)P(CH_2)_3PCH_3C_6H_5 \xrightarrow[C_6H_6]{S}$

$[CH_3C_6H_5P(CH_2)_3PCH_3C_6H_5]_2S$

mp 126~129°

⑥ Ber. **96**, 2186 (1963).

PC₁₇H₂₂Br

① Benzylmethylphenylpropylphosphonium bromide

$[(C_6H_5CH_2)(CH_3)(C_6H_5)(C_3H_7)P]Br$

② $C_6H_5C_3H_7(C_6H_5CH_2)P + CH_3Br \longrightarrow$

③ [185°]. $[\alpha]_D^{20}35.7°$.

④ $[(C_6H_5CH_2)CH_3\overset{+}{P}(C_6H_5)(C_3H_7)]Br^-$

$\xrightarrow{\text{cathodic, cleavage}}$

$(CH_3)(C_6H_5)(C_3H_7)P + C_6H_5CH_3$

⑥ Tetrahedron Letters **1963**, 965; **1961**, 161.

PC₁₇H₂₂I

① Dibenzylethylmethylphosphonium iodide

$[(C_6H_5CH_2)_2(C_2H_5)(CH_3)P]I$

② $C_2H_5P(CH_2C_6H_5)_2 + CH_3I \longrightarrow$

$CH_3PCl_2 \xrightarrow{\text{1) } C_6H_5CH_2MgCl, \text{ 2) } C_2H_5I} 84\%$

③ [122.5~123°].

④ Redn. of benzyl-contg. phosphonium compds., with LiAlH₄ was used for the synthesis of 2 unsym. tertiary phosphines :

$[CH_3R(CH_2C_6H_5)_2P]I \longrightarrow CH_3RR'P$

$\xrightarrow{\text{1) LiAlH}_4\text{/THF}}_{\text{2) } C_5H_{11}I} [(C_6H_5CH_2)(CH_3)(C_2H_5)-$

$(C_5H_{11})P]I\ (84\%)$

⑥ Ann. **646**, 65 (1961). JOC **25**, 1996 (1960).

PC₁₈F₁₅

① Trispentafluorophenylphosphine

$(C_6F_5)_3P$

② $C_6F_5MgBr + PCl_3 \longrightarrow$ 39.5%

③ White needle crystals. [116~117°].
Thermally stable, resistance to
oxidation.
IR: JACS **82**, 4846 (1960).

④ $\xrightarrow{\text{severe oxidation}}$ $(C_6F_5)_3P(O)$

PC₁₈H₁₅

① Triphenylphosphine
$(C_6H_5)_3P$

② $C_6H_5Li + PCl_3 \longrightarrow$ 61%
$(C_6H_5)_3PS + Na \longrightarrow$ 90%
$C_6H_5MgBr + PCl_3 \longrightarrow$

$[((C_6H_5)_3(C_6H_5CH_2)P]^+Cl^- \xrightarrow{2e^-/Hg}$
89%
$(C_6H_5)_3PO + LiAlH_4 \longrightarrow$ 85%
$(C_6H_5)_3PS + NaH \longrightarrow$ 80%

③ [79°].

④ $+ CS_2 \longrightarrow (C_6H_5)_3P=CS_2$
$+ GeI_2 \longrightarrow (C_6H_5)_3PGeI_2$
$+ NH_2Cl \longrightarrow [(C_6H_5)_3PNH_2]^+Cl^-$
$+ RX \longrightarrow [(C_6H_5)_3PR]^+X^-$
$+ C_4H_9Li \longrightarrow (C_6H_5)_2P-\!\!\!\!<\!\!\!\bigcirc\!\!\!-$
Li
$+ C_4H_{10}$
$+ (C_6H_5)_3SiN_3 \longrightarrow$
$(C_6H_5)_3P=NSi(C_6H_5)_3$

⑥ Dokl. **74**, 501 (1950).   JOC **27**, 2573
(1962).   Z. anorg. allg. Chem. **287**,
208 (1956).   Ber. **91**, 1583 (1958);
92, 2088 (1959).

PC₁₈H₁₅Br₂

① Dibromotriphenylphosphorane
$(C_6H_5)_3PBr_2$

② $(C_6H_5)_3P + Br_2 \xrightarrow{C_6H_6}$

④ $+ CH_3I \xrightarrow{140°, (Na_2SO_3)} (CH_3)(C_6H_5)_3PI$

⑥ Ber. **93**, 861 (1960).   Tetrahedron
Letters **1962**, 583.   Kosolapoff 73.

PC₁₈H₁₅Cl₂

① Dichlorotriphenylphosphorane

$(C_6H_5)_3PCl_2$

② $(C_6H_5)_3P + Cl_2 \longrightarrow$

③ [176°].

⑥ JACS **84**, 1312 (1962).   Monatsh. **93**,
747 (1962).   Kosolapoff 73.

PC₁₈H₁₅F₂

① Difluorotriphenylphosphorane
$(C_6H_5)_3PF_2$

② $(C_6H_5)_3P(O) + SF_4 \xrightarrow[50°]{C_6H_6}$ 67%

$(C_6H_5)_3P + SF_4 \xrightarrow{C_6H_6}$ 69%

③ [136~140°].
Moderately solubles in CHCl₃ and
C₆H₆; insol. in ether.
NMR: Inorg. Chem. **2**, 613 (1963).

⑥ JACS **82**, 1176 (1960).

PC₁₈H₁₅I₂

① Diiodotriphenylphosphorane
$(C_6H_5)_3PI_2$

② $(C_6H_5)_3P + I \xrightarrow{(C_2H_5)_2O-C_6H_6}$ 100%

③ [148° decomp.].

⑥ Z. anorg. allg. Chem. **288**, 201 (1956).
Ber. **93**, 861 (1960).

PC₁₈H₁₅O

① Triphenylphosphine oxide
$(C_6H_5)_3PO$

② $(C_6H_5)_3P \xrightarrow{Br_2 \text{ and } 10\% \text{ NaOH}}$ 75%
$3 C_6H_5MgBr + POCl_3 \longrightarrow$

③ (432°). [156°] $(C_2H_5OH-H_2O)$.
IR: JOC **27**, 2572 (1962); JCS **1962**,
3450.
NMR: J. Chem. Eng. Data **7**, 307
(1962).

④ Autoxidation:
$(C_6H_5)_3P(O) \xrightarrow{0.1 N \text{ NaOH}/C_2H_5OH}$
$(C_6H_5)_2PO_2Na + \text{metaphosphates}$
Titrimetric determination (0.1 N
$HClO_4/(CH_3CO)_2O$ system).

⑥ Anal. Chem. **34**, 873 (1962).   Kosolapoff 114.

PC$_{18}$F$_{15}$O

① Tris(pentafluorophenyl)phosphine
  oxide
  (C$_6$F$_5$)$_2$PO

② C$_6$F$_5$MgBr + PCl$_3$ $\xrightarrow[39.5\%]{}$

  (C$_6$F$_5$)$_3$P $\xrightarrow{Na_2Cr_2O_7, H_2SO_4, CH_3COOH/H_2O}$

③ [169～170°] (petr. ether).
  UV: JACS **82**, 2846 (1960).

PC$_{19}$H$_{15}$O

① Benzoyldiphenylphosphine
  C$_6$H$_5$CO(C$_6$H$_5$)$_2$P

② (C$_6$H$_5$)$_2$PNa + C$_6$H$_5$COCl ⟶ 58.6%

③ Yellow crystals. (199～201°/25). [68～
  81°].
  Sol. in alc., C$_6$H$_6$, slightly sol. in
  ether.

⑥ Ber. **92**, 3183 (1959).

PC$_{18}$H$_{15}$O

① Diphenylphosphonous acid phenyl
  ester
  (C$_6$H$_5$)$_2$POC$_6$H$_5$

② C$_6$H$_5$OPCl$_2$ + C$_6$H$_5$MgCl $\xrightarrow{THF}$ 42%

③ Liq. (265～270°/62). n_D 1.6331 (20°).
  d 1.140 (24°/4°).

④ + PCl$_3$ ⟶ (C$_6$H$_5$)$_2$PCl
  + 1 N H$_2$SO$_4$ ⟶ (C$_6$H$_5$)$_2$P(O)H

⑥ Ber. **93**, 1220 (1960).

PC$_{18}$H$_{15}$O

① *p*-Hydroxyphenyldiphenylphosphine
  HOC$_6$H$_4$(C$_6$H$_5$)$_2$P

② *p*-CH$_3$OC$_6$H$_4$(C$_6$H$_5$)$_2$P + 57% HI ⟶
  90%
  [HOC$_6$H$_4$(C$_6$H$_5$)$_2$PH]Br$^-$ + 3% NaOH
  ⟶ 85%

③ [110～112°].

④ + 10% H$_2$O$_2$ $\xrightarrow{in\ acetone}$
  HOC$_6$H$_4$(C$_6$H$_5$)$_2$P(O)

⑥ Ber. **94**, 2519 (1961).   JOC **25**, 2001
  (1960).

PC$_{18}$H$_{15}$O$_2$

① Bis(*p*-hydroxyphenyl)phenylphos-
  phine
  C$_6$H$_5$(*p*-HOC$_6$H$_4$)$_2$P

② (*p*-CH$_3$OC$_6$H$_4$)$_2$PC$_6$H$_5$ + 57% HI ⟶
  95%
  (*p*-CH$_3$OC$_6$H$_4$)$_2$PC$_6$H$_5$ + 48% HBr
  ⟶ [(*p*-CH$_3$OC$_6$H$_4$)$_2$(C$_6$H$_5$)P$^+$H]Br$^-$
  $\xrightarrow[2)\ CH_3COOH]{1)\ NaOH}$ 85%

③ [159～161°].

④ + H$_2$O$_2$ ⟶ (*p*-HOC$_6$H$_4$)$_2$(C$_6$H$_5$)P(O)

⑥ Ber. **94**, 2519 (1961).   JOC **25**, 2001
  (1960).

PC$_{18}$H$_{15}$S

① Triphenylphosphine sulfide
  (C$_6$H$_5$)$_3$P(S)

② (C$_6$H$_5$)$_3$P·HgCl$_2$ $\xrightarrow{(NH_4)_2S_x/C_2H_5OH}$ 80%

③ [161°] (C$_2$H$_5$OH).
  IR: JOC **27**, 2573 (1962).
  NMR: J. Chem. Eng. Data **7**, 307
  (1962).

⑥ Kosolapoff 117.

PC$_{18}$H$_{15}$Se

① Triphenylphosphine selenide
  (C$_6$H$_5$)$_3$P(Se)

② (C$_6$H$_5$)$_3$P(O) + Se−KH$_2$PO$_4$ $\xrightarrow{330～400°}$
  16%

③ [186～188°] (C$_2$H$_5$OH).

⑥ Kosolapoff 118.   Inorg. Chem. **2**, 192
  (1963).   JOC **27**, 2573 (1962). Chem.
  Ind. **1962**, 359.

PC$_{18}$H$_{16}$N

① *P,P,P*-(Triphenyl)phosphineimide
  HNP(C$_6$H$_5$)$_3$

② (C$_6$H$_5$)$_3$PNSi(CH$_3$)$_3$ $\xrightarrow[H_2SO_4]{i-C_3H_7OH}$ 85%

$[(C_6H_5)_3PNH_2]HSO_4 + NH_3 \longrightarrow$
$[(C_6H_5)_3PNH_2]Cl + NaNH_2 \longrightarrow 83\%$

③ Colorless crystals. [128°].
Sol. in org. solvents without decomp.

④ $+ MX_2 \longrightarrow [(Ph_3PNH)_2 \cdot MX_2$
$M = Co^{II}, Cu^{II}, X = halogen.$
$+ O = C(C_6H_5)_2 \longrightarrow (C_6H_5)_3P(O)$
$+ HN = C(C_6H_5)_2$
$+ C_2H_5I \longrightarrow [(C_6H_5)_3PNH_2]I$
$+ [(C_6H_5)_3PN(C_2H_5)_2]I$
$+ ClSO_2NH_2 \longrightarrow [(C_6H_5)_3PNH_2]Cl$
$+ Br_2 \longrightarrow [(C_6H_5)_3PNH_2]Br$
$+ (C_6H_5)_3PNBr$
$+ H_2O \longrightarrow (C_6H_5)_3PO + NH_3$

⑥ Z. Naturf. **15 b**, 57 (1960). Angew.
71, 626 (1959). Ber. **93**, 405 (1960);
96, 3099 (1963).

PC₁₈H₁₇BrN

① *P*-(Triphenyl) aminophosphonium
bromide
$[H_2NP(C_6H_5)_3]Br$

② $(C_6H_5)_3PNH + Br_2 \longrightarrow$
$(C_6H_5)_3PBr_2 + NH_3 + (C_2H_5)_3N \longrightarrow$
90%

③ [248°].

⑥ Z. anorg. allg. Chem. **311**, 290 (1961).
Ann. **627**, 142 (1959).

PC₁₈H₁₇ClN

① *P*-(Triphenyl) aminophosphonium
chloride
$[H_2NP(C_6H_5)_3]Cl$

② $(C_6H_5)_3P + NH_2Cl \longrightarrow 88\%$
$(C_6H_5)_3PNH + ClSO_2NH_2 \xrightarrow{\text{in benzene}}$

③ [236°].
Sol. in H_2O, CH_3OH, CH_3CN

④ $+ NaNH_2 \longrightarrow (C_6H_5)_3PNH$
$+ boiling\ water \longrightarrow (C_6H_5)_3PO$
$+ NH_4Cl$
$+ KClO_4 \xrightarrow{\text{aq. } C_2H_5OH}$
$[H_2NP(C_6H_5)_3][ClO_4]$

⑥ Ber. **93**, 405 (1960).   JACS **81**, 2982

(1959).   Z. anorg. allg. Chem. **311**,
290 (1961).

PC₁₈H₂₁

① Cyclohexyldiphenylphosphine
$cyclo\text{-}C_6H_{11}(C_6H_5)_2P$

② $C_6H_5MgBr + cyclo\text{-}C_6H_{11}PCl_2 \xrightarrow{\text{ether}}$

③ Colorless crystals. [60~61°].
Sol. in ether, C_6H_6, dioxane, slightly
sol. in alc.

④ $+ H_2O_2 \longrightarrow$
$(C_6H_5)_2(clcyo\text{-}C_6H_{11})_2P(O)$
$+ K \xrightarrow{\text{dioxane}}$
$KP(cyclo\text{-}C_6H_{11})(C_6H_5) \cdot dioxane$

⑥ Ber. **94**, 392 (1961).

PC₁₈H₂₂Br

① Allylbenzylethylphenylphosphonium
bromide
$[(CH_2=CHCH_2)(C_6H_5CH_2)(C_2H_5)\text{-}$
$(C_6H_5)P]Br$

② $(C_2H_5)(C_6H_5)(C_6H_5CH_2)P +$
$CH_2=CHCH_2Br \longrightarrow$

③ [149~152°].

④ $\xrightarrow{\text{Hg/2 e}^-} (C_2H_5)(C_6H_5)(CH_2=CHCH_2)P$
(72%)

⑥ Ann. **646**, 65 (1961).

PC₁₈H₂₃

① Benzylbutyl-*p*-tolylphosphine
$(C_6H_5CH_2)(C_4H_9)(p\text{-}CH_3C_6H_4)P$

② $[(C_4H_9)_2(p\text{-}CH_3C_6H_4)(C_6H_5CH_2)\overset{+}{P}]Cl^-$
$\xrightarrow{\text{heat}}$

③ (196~200°/4). n_D 1.5653 (20°). d 0.9920
(20°).

⑥ Izv. Kazan. Filia Akad. Nauk **1957**,
99;   CA **54**, 6601 (1960).

PC₁₈H₂₃

① Dibenzyl-*n*-butylphosphine
$(C_6H_5CH_2)_2(n\text{-}C_4H_9)P$

② $[(C_6H_5CH_2)(C_2H_5)_2(n\text{-}C_4H_9)P^+]Cl^- \xrightarrow{\text{heat}}$

③ (163~178°/5). n_D 1.5678 (20°).
⑥ Zhur. **26**, 3426 (1956); CA **51**, 9512 (1957).

PC$_{18}$H$_{24}$Br

① Dibenzyldiethylphosphonium bromide
[(C$_6$H$_5$CH$_2$)$_2$(C$_2$H$_5$)$_2$P]Br
② (C$_2$H$_5$)$_2$POPC$_2$H$_5$(OC$_2$H$_5$) + C$_6$H$_5$CH$_2$Br $\longrightarrow$
③ [234~238°].
⑥ Izv. OKhN **1958**, 706.

PC$_{18}$H$_{24}$I

① Butylethyldiphenylphosphonium iodide
[(C$_4$H$_9$)(C$_2$H$_5$)(C$_6$H$_5$)$_2$P]I
② C$_4$H$_9$P(C$_6$H$_5$)$_2$ + C$_2$H$_5$I $\longrightarrow$ 91%
③ [153°].
⑥ Ber. **92**, 227 (1959). Ann. **646**, 65 (1961).

PC$_{18}$H$_{24}$I

① Benzylbutylmethylphenylphosphonium iodide
[(C$_6$H$_5$CH$_2$)(C$_4$H$_9$)(CH$_3$)C$_6$H$_5$)P]I
② (C$_4$H$_9$)(C$_6$H$_5$)(C$_6$H$_5$CH$_2$)P + CH$_3$I $\longrightarrow$
③ [167°].
⑥ Ann. **646**, 65 (1961).

PC$_{18}$H$_{27}$

① Dicyclohexylphenylphosphine
C$_6$H$_5$(cyclo-C$_6$H$_{11}$)$_2$P
② cyclo-C$_6$H$_{11}$MgCl + C$_6$H$_5$PCl$_2$ $\xrightarrow{\text{ether}}$ 50%
③ Colorless crystals. [57~58°].
Sol. in dioxane; slightly sol. in alc. petr. ether. Stable in air.
⑥ Ber. **94**, 392 (1961).

PC$_{18}$H$_{33}$

① Tricyclohexylphosphine
(cyclo-C$_6$H$_{11}$)$_3$P
② cyclo-C$_6$H$_{11}$Li + PCl$_3$ $\xrightarrow{-30°}$ 28%

cyclo-C$_6$H$_{11}$MgX + PX$_3$ $\xrightarrow{\text{CS}_2}$
(X=Cl, Br)

(cyclo-C$_6$H$_{11}$)$_3$P=CS$_2$ $\xrightarrow[\text{(boiling)}]{\text{EtOH}}$

③ [76~78°].
Oxidize in air.
④ + air $\xrightarrow{\text{hexane}}$ 50% (C$_6$H$_{11}$)$_3$PO
+ KMnO$_4$ $\xrightarrow{\text{in acetone}}$
(cyclo-C$_6$H$_{11}$)$_3$P(O)
+ S $\xrightarrow{\text{toluene}}$ (cyclo-C$_6$H$_{11}$)$_3$P(S)
+ X$_2$ $\longrightarrow$ (cyclo-C$_6$H$_{11}$)$_3$PX$_2$
X=Cl, Br
+ FeCl$_3$ $\longrightarrow$ (cyclo-C$_6$H$_{11}$)$_3$PFeCl$_3$
+ CuCl$_2$ $\longrightarrow$ [(cyclo-C$_6$H$_{11}$)$_3$P]$_2$CuCl$_2$
+ Mn$_2$(CO)$_{10}$ $\longrightarrow$
[Mn(CO)$_4$P(cyclo-C$_6$H$_{11}$)$_3$]$_2$
⑥ Z. anorg. allg. Chem. **277**, 258 (1954).
JOC **27**, 2573 (1962).

PC$_{19}$H$_{15}$Cl$_2$

① Dichloromethylenetriphenyl-phosphorane
(C$_6$H$_5$)$_3$P=CCl$_2$
② (C$_6$H$_5$)$_3$P + CHCl$_3$ + t-C$_4$H$_9$OK $\xrightarrow{\text{pentane, 0~5°}}$

(C$_6$H$_5$)$_3$P + CCl$_4$ $\xrightarrow{60°, 2~3 \text{ hr}}$
(C$_6$H$_5$)$_3$PCl$_2$ + (C$_6$H$_5$)$_3$P=CCl$_2$
③ Yellow solid (unisolable).
IR: JACS **84**, 854 (1962).
④ + (C$_6$H$_5$)$_2$CO $\xrightarrow{\text{pentane-Et}_2\text{O}}$
(C$_6$H$_5$)$_2$C=CCl$_2$ (59%)
+ CCl$_4$ + C$_6$H$_5$CH$_3$ $\xrightarrow{\text{excess CCl}_4, 60°}$
(C$_6$H$_5$)$_3$PO + C$_6$H$_5$CHCl$_2$
+ C$_6$H$_5$CH=CCl$_2$
⑥ JACS **82**, 1260 (1960); **84**, 1312 (1962).

PC$_{19}$H$_{16}$Cl

① Chloromethylenetriphenyl-phosphorane
(C$_6$H$_5$)$_3$P=CHCl

② $(C_6H_5)_3P + CH_2Cl_2$

$$\xrightarrow{C_4H_9Li/(C_2H_5)_2O, \ -40\sim-30°}$$

④ $+ (C_6H_5)_3B \xrightarrow{C_6H_6-Et_2O}$

$(C_6H_5)_3PCHClB(C_6H_5)_3$

$+ HBr \longrightarrow [(C_6H_5)_3PCH_2Cl]Br$

$+ CH_3COC_6H_5 \longrightarrow CH_3C_6H_5C=CHCl$
$(cis/trans \doteqdot 1)$ (46%)

$+ (C_6H_5)_2CO \longrightarrow (C_6H_5)_2C=CHCl$
(31%)

⑥ JACS **83**, 1613 (1961); **82**, 1510 (1960); **83**, 1617 (1961). JOC **26**, 4783 (1962). Angew. **72**, 324 (1960).

PC₁₉H₁₇

① Methylenetriphenylphosphorane
$(C_6H_5)_3P=CH_2$

② $[CH_3P(C_6H_5)_3]Br \xrightarrow{C_4H_9Li}$

$[CH_3P(C_6H_5)_3]Br \xrightarrow{C_6H_5Li}$

$[CH_3P(C_6H_5)_3]Br \xrightarrow{CH_3SOCH_2^-Na^+}$

④ $+ HCO_2C_2H_5 \longrightarrow (C_6H_5)_3P=CHCHO$

$+ \langle \rangle =O \longrightarrow \langle \rangle =CH_2$

$+ (C_6H_5)_3PO$

$+ CH_3COCl \longrightarrow$

$[(C_6H_5)_3PCH_2COCH_3]Cl$ (38%)

$+ B_2H_6 \longrightarrow (C_6H_5)_3PCH_2BH_3$ (81%)

⑤ Wittig Reaction (a representative Wittig's reagent.).

⑥ JACS **83**, 367 (1961); 2055 (1961). JCS **1961**, 1266. Tetrahedron Letters **1961**, 811. JOC **28**, 1128 (1963). Org. Syn. **40**, 66 (1960).

PC₁₉H₁₇

① Benzyldiphenylphosphine
$C_6H_5CH_2(C_6H_5)_2P$

② $(C_6H_5)_2PCl + C_6H_5CH_2MgCl \longrightarrow$ 54%

$[(C_6H_5CH_2)(C_6H_5)_3P]Cl + Na \longrightarrow$
53%

$[(C_6H_5CH_2)(C_6H_5)_2HP]Br + NaOH \longrightarrow$

③ (205~208°/1.5, 146~148°/0.15). [142~143°] (decomp.).

④ $+ NiX_2 \longrightarrow [C_6H_5CH_2(C_6H_5)_2P]_2NiX_2$
$X=Cl, Br, I, SCN$

$+ CH_3I \longrightarrow$
$[C_6H_5CH_2(C_6H_5)_2CH_3P^+]I^-$

⑥ JCS **1962**, 693; **1961**, 2813. Ber. **92**, 2088 (1959).

PC₁₉H₁₇

① *p*-Tolyldiphenylphosphine
p-$CH_3C_6H_4(C_6H_5)_2P$

② p-$CH_3C_6H_4PCl_2 + ClC_6H_5 + Na \xrightarrow{ether}$

③ (250°/14).

④ $+ C_{12}H_{25}Br \xrightarrow{100°}$
$[C_{12}H_{25}(p\text{-}CH_3C_6H_4)(C_6H_5)_2P]Br$

⑥ Ber. **83**, 277 (1950).

PC₁₉H₁₇Cl₂

① Chloromethyltriphenylphosphonium chloride
$[(ClCH_2)P(C_6H_5)_3]Cl$

② $[(C_2H_5)_3PCH_2OH]Cl \xrightarrow{SOCl_2}$ 77%

③ [260~261°].

④ $\xrightarrow[OH^-]{}$ $(C_6H_5)_3PO$, $(C_6H_5)_2(C_6H_5CH_2)PO$,
(50~70%)   (10%)
$(C_6H_5)_3P$, CH_2O
(8%)   (4%)

⑥ Ann. **659**, 49 (1962). Tetrahedron Letters **1961**, 724. JACS **82**, 1510, 4215 (1960). Ber. **94**, 1373 (1961).

PC₁₉H₁₇O

① Benzyldiphenylphosphine oxide
$(C_6H_5)_2P(O)CH_2C_6H_5$

② $(C_6H_5)_2PH + C_6H_5CHO \xrightarrow{HCl}$ 85%

$(C_6H_5)_3P + Li \xrightarrow{THF} (C_6H_5)_2PLi$

$\xrightarrow{C_6H_5CH_2Cl, [O]}$

$(C_6H_5)_2PLi + C_6H_5CH_2MgCl \longrightarrow$

③ [192~193°] (C_2H_5OH).

④ $(C_5H_6)_2P(O)CH_2C_6H_5 \xrightarrow{(t\text{-}C_4H_9)_2O_2, \ 210\sim212°}$

$\overset{|}{C}(C_6H_5)[P(O)(C_6H_5)_2]$

$(C_6H_5)_2P(O)CH_2C_6H_5 + C_6H_5CH_2C_6H_5$

$\xrightarrow{C_6H_6, \ 100°}$

$(C_6H_5)_2P(O)OH + (C_6H_5)_2C=CHC_6H_5$
(83%)   (70%)

⑥ Kosolapoff 116. Ber. **92**, 2499 (1959).
Tetrahedron **18**, 1231 (1962). Izv.
OKhN **1962**, 1638. JOC **27**, 619,
1001 (1962).

PC₁₉H₁₇O

① *p*-Tolyldiphenylphosphine oxide
p-CH₃C₆H₄P(O)(C₆H₅)₂

② *p*-CH₃C₆H₄P(C₆H₅)₂ $\xrightarrow{[O]}$

[*p*-CH₃C₆H₄P(C₆H₅)₃]Br + aq. NaOH
⟶ 90%

③ [129~130°].

⑥ Ber. **91**, 52 (1958).

PC₁₉H₁₇O

① *p*-Methoxyphenyldiphenylphosphine
p-CH₃OC₆H₄(C₆H₅)₂P

② *p*-CH₃OC₆H₄PCl₂ + C₆H₅MgBr $\xrightarrow{ether}$
75~80%

p-CH₃OC₆H₄MgBr + (C₆H₅)₂PCl ⟶
70%

③ Colorless crystals. [78~79°].

④ + 57% HI ⟶ *p*-HOC₆H₄P(C₆H₅)₂
+ 48% HBr ⟶
[*p*-HOC₆H₄(C₆H₅)₂P⁺H]Br⁻

⑥ Ber. **94**, 2519 (1961). JOC **25**, 2001
(1960).

PC₁₉H₁₇O₂

① *p*-Methoxyphenyldiphenylphosphine
oxide

② *p*-CH₃OC₆H₄P(C₆H₅)₂ + 10% H₂O₂
$\xrightarrow[\text{acetone}]{}$ 93%

[*p*-CH₃OC₆H₄P(C₆H₅)₃]Br + aq. NaOH
⟶ 87% .

③ [117~118° (C₆H₆-petr. ether)].

④ + 48% HBr ⟶
(C₆H₅)₂P(O)(C₆H₄OH-*p*) (96%)

⑥ Ber. **91**, 52 (1958). JOC **25**, 2001

(1960).

PC₁₉H₁₇S

① Benzyldiphenylphosphine sulfide
(C₆H₅)₂C₆H₅CH₂P(S)

② (C₆H₅)₃P + Li
$\xrightarrow{THF \ (CH_3)_3CCl, \ PSCl_3, \ C_6H_5CH_2Cl}$ 59%

③ [162~163°] (C₂H₅OH).

⑥ Kosolapoff 117. JOC **27**, 1001 (1962).

PC₁₉H₁₈Br

① Methyltriphenylphosphonium
bromide
[(CH₃)P(C₆H₅)₃]Br

② (C₆H₅)₃P + CH₃Br $\xrightarrow{MeCN, \ 60°}$

③ [234~235°].

④ $\xrightarrow{Pb/2e^-}$ (C₆H₅)₂PCH₃ (40%) + (C₆H₅)₃P
(53%)

$\xrightarrow{Mg^-/2e^-}$ (C₆H₅)₂PCH₃(85%) + (C₆H₅)₃P
(5.5%)

⑥ Ann. **646**, 65 (1961). Chem. Ind.
(London) **1961**, 290. Ber. **87**, 1318
(1954).

PC₁₉H₁₈ClO

① Hydroxymethyl(triphenylphosphonium chloride
[(HOCH₂)P(C₆H₅)₃]Cl

② (C₆H₅)₃P + HCHO + HCl ⟶ 90%

③ [190~192°].

④ $\xrightarrow{CH_2N_2, \ -CH_2O}$ [(C₆H₅)₃PCH₃]BF₄

$\xrightarrow{(CH_3CO)_2O}$ [(C₆H₅)₃PCH₂OCOCH₃]Cl

⑥ Ann. **659**, 49 (1962). Angew. **72**, 77
(1960).

PC₁₉H₁₈I

① Methyltriphenylphosphonium iodide
[(C₆H₅)₃PCH₃]I

② (C₆H₅)₃P + CH₃I ⟶

③ [188~189°].

IR : Kosolapoff 90.

⑥ Ber. **93**, 861 (1960). Tetrahedron **18**,
   1023 (1962). JCS **1963**, 1327,
   Australian J. Chem. **16**, 360 (1963).

PC$_{19}$H$_{34}$Cl
① Benzyltributylphosphonium chloride
   [(C$_6$H$_5$CH$_2$)P(C$_4$H$_9$)$_3$]Cl
② (C$_4$H$_9$)$_3$P + C$_6$H$_5$CH$_2$Cl $\longrightarrow$
③ [164.3～164.5°].
   IR : Spectrochim. Acta **19**, 1905(1963).
⑥ Kaufman 1238.

PC$_{20}$H$_{14}$K
① Potassium bis-α-naphthylphosphide

$$KP-\left(\underset{2}{\underset{}{\bigcirc\!\!\bigcirc}}\right)$$

② (C$_{10}$H$_7$)$_3$P + K $\xrightarrow{\text{dioxane}}$
③ Violet soln.
④ + 30% H$_2$O$_2$ + NaOH $\longrightarrow$
   (C$_{10}$H$_7$)$_2$P(O)(OH)
⑤ Intermediate in prepn. of org. P
   compds.
⑥ Ber. **94**, 392 (1961).

PC$_{20}$H$_{15}$
① Phenylethynyldiphenylphosphine
   (C$_6$H$_5$C≡C)(C$_6$H$_5$)$_2$P
② (C$_6$H$_5$)$_2$PLi + ClC≡CC$_6$H$_5$ $\xrightarrow{\text{(C}_2\text{H}_5)_2\text{O}}$ 50%
   (C$_6$H$_5$)$_2$PNa·dioxane + ClC≡CC$_6$H$_5$
   $\longrightarrow$ 50%
③ Colorless crystals. [44°].
   Sol. in C$_6$H$_6$, THF, ether ; insol. in
   H$_2$O.
④ + S $\xrightarrow{\text{C}_6\text{H}_6}$ (C$_6$H$_5$)$_2$P(S)C≡CC$_6$H$_5$
⑥ Ber. **95**, 268 (1962).

PC$_{20}$H$_{16}$BrO
① Bromotriphenylphosphoranylidene
   acetaldehyde
   (C$_6$H$_5$)$_3$P=CBrCHO
② (C$_6$H$_5$)$_3$P=CHCHO + Br$_2$

$\xrightarrow[\substack{10～15° \\ \text{(C}_2\text{H}_5)_3\text{N/CHCl}_3 \\ 10°}]{\text{NaOCOCH}_3/\text{HOCOCH}_3}$ 83%

③ [180～181°].
⑥ Ber. **95**, 2003 (1962).

PC$_{20}$H$_{16}$N
① Triphenylphosphoranylidene aceto-
   nitrile
   (C$_6$H$_5$)$_3$P=CHCN
② [(C$_6$H$_5$)$_3$PCH$_2$CN]Br $\longrightarrow$
③ [190～192°].
④ + Br$_2$ $\longrightarrow$ [(C$_6$H$_5$)$_3$PCHCN]Br (98%)
                |
                Br
   + C$_6$H$_5$CHO $\xrightarrow{\text{C}_6\text{H}_6}$ (C$_6$H$_5$)$_3$PO
   + C$_6$H$_5$CH=CHCN
⑥ Ber. **94**, 578 (1961). JACS **85**, 2790
   (1963). JCS **1961**, 1266.

PC$_{20}$H$_{17}$BrN
① Cyanomethyltriphenylphosphonium
   bromide
   [(NCCH$_2$)P(C$_6$H$_5$)$_3$]Br
② (C$_6$H$_5$)$_3$P + BrCH$_2$CN $\xrightarrow{\text{C}_6\text{H}_6}$ 95%
③ [256～258°].
④ $\xrightarrow{\text{NaOH}}$ [(C$_6$H$_5$)$_3$P(CH$_2$CN)]OH $\longrightarrow$
   [(C$_6$H$_5$)$_3$P=CHCN]
⑥ Ber. **94**, 578 (1961).

PC$_{20}$H$_{17}$O
① Triphenylphosphoranylidene
   acetaldehyde
   (C$_6$H$_5$)$_3$P=CHCHO
② [(C$_6$H$_5$)$_3$PCH$_3$]Br
   $\xrightarrow{\text{1) C}_4\text{H}_9\text{Li, 2) HCO}_2\text{C}_2\text{H}_5}$ 67%
   [(C$_6$H$_5$)$_3$PCH$_2$CHO]Cl + (C$_2$H$_5$)$_3$N
   $\xrightarrow{\text{C}_2\text{H}_5\text{OH}}$

$$\begin{array}{c}\text{N}-\text{CHO} \\ \bigsqcup_{\text{N}} \end{array} + \text{(C}_6\text{H}_5)_3\text{P}=\text{CH}_2 \xrightarrow{\text{C}_6\text{H}_6} 81\%$$

③ [186～187° (decomp.)] [(CH$_3$)$_2$CO].

④ + C$_6$H$_5$CHO $\xrightarrow{C_6H_6}$ C$_6$H$_5$CH=CHCHO
      (60%)
      No reaction with ketones.
⑥ JCS 1961, 1266. Chem. Ind. (London)
      1960, 202. Angew. 74, 294 (1962).
      Yakugaku Zasshi 83, 582 (1963).

PC$_{20}$H$_{18}$NO

① Triphenylphosphoranylidene-
      acetamide
      (C$_6$H$_5$)$_3$P=CHCONH$_2$
④ + C$_6$H$_5$CHO $\longrightarrow$ C$_6$H$_5$CH=CHCN
      + C$_6$H$_5$CH=CHCONH$_2$
⑥ JCS 1961, 1266. Helv. Chim. Acta
      46, 1580 (1963). Gazz. chim. ital.
      93, 668 (1963).

PC$_{20}$H$_{19}$

① Di-m-tolylphenylphosphine
      (m-CH$_3$C$_6$H$_4$)$_2$C$_6$H$_5$P
② m-CH$_3$C$_6$H$_4$MgBr + C$_6$H$_5$PCl$_2$ $\longrightarrow$ 75%
③ (210~220°/0.5). [53~53.5°].
④ + Br$_2$ $\xrightarrow{H_2O}$ (m-CH$_3$C$_6$H$_4$)$_2$(C$_6$H$_5$)P(O)
⑥ JCS 1955, 4107.

PC$_{20}$H$_{19}$

① Di-p-tolylphenylphosphine
      (p-CH$_3$C$_6$H$_4$)$_2$C$_6$H$_5$P
② p-CH$_3$C$_6$H$_4$MgBr + C$_6$H$_5$PCl$_2$ $\longrightarrow$ 40%
③ (140~145°/2). [53~54°].
④ + Br$_2$ $\xrightarrow{aq. NaOH}$
      (p-CH$_3$C$_6$H$_4$)$_2$(C$_6$H$_5$)P(O)
⑥ Izv. OKhN 1958, 783 ; CA 52, 20001
      (1958).

PC$_{20}$H$_{19}$

① Dibenzylphenylphosphine
      (C$_6$H$_5$CH$_2$)$_2$C$_6$H$_5$P
② C$_6$H$_5$PCl$_2$ + C$_6$H$_5$CH$_2$MgCl $\longrightarrow$ 89%
③ (176~177°/0.3). [71~72°].
      Even in a cold ethanolic solution on
      exposure to the air raedily
      oxidized.

④ + NiX$_2$ $\longrightarrow$ [(C$_6$H$_5$CH$_2$)$_2$C$_6$H$_5$P]$_2$NiX$_2$
      X=Cl, Br, I
      + CH$_3$I $\longrightarrow$
      [CH$_3$(C$_6$H$_5$CH$_2$)$_2$(C$_6$H$_5$)$\overset{+}{P}$]I$^-$
      + PdCl$_2$ $\longrightarrow$
      [(C$_6$H$_5$CH$_2$)$_2$(C$_6$H$_5$)P]$_2$PdCl$_2$
⑥ JCS 1962, 693 ; 1959, 2835 ; 1954, 2832.

PC$_{20}$H$_{19}$

① Ethylidenetriphenylphosphorane
      (C$_6$H$_5$)$_3$P=CHCH$_3$
② [(C$_6$H$_5$)$_3$PC$_2$H$_5$]Br $\xrightarrow{C_6H_5Li, (C_2H_5)_2O}$
④ + RCOCl $\longrightarrow$ (C$_6$H$_5$)$_3$P=CCH$_3$COR
      + [(C$_6$H$_5$)$_3$PC$_2$H$_5$]Cl
      + O$_2$ $\longrightarrow$ CH$_3$CH=CHCH$_3$
      (autoxidation)
      + B$_2$H$_6$ $\longrightarrow$ (C$_6$H$_5$)$_3\overset{+}{P}$CHCH$_3\overset{-}{B}$H$_3$ (80%)
      + C$_6$H$_5$CH=NC$_6$H$_5$ $\xrightarrow{130~150°}$
      CH$_2$=C=CHC$_6$H$_5$ (62%)
      + P(C$_6$H$_5$)$_3$ (60%) + C$_6$H$_5$NH$_2$ (56%)
⑥ Ber. 96, 1899 (1963). JACS 83, 367
      (1961). Angew. 75, 475 (1963).

PC$_{20}$H$_{19}$O

① Dibenzylphenylphosphine oxide
      (C$_6$H$_5$CH$_2$)$_2$P(O)C$_6$H$_5$
② (C$_6$H$_5$P)$_4$ + C$_6$H$_5$CH$_2$I $\xrightarrow{C_6H_6}$
      [C$_6$H$_5$P(CH$_2$C$_6$H$_5$)$_3$]I $\xrightarrow{H_2O_2/NaOH}$ 83%
③ [180~181°] (C$_6$H$_6$).
⑥ Kosolapoff 116. Ber. 94, 186 (1961).

PC$_{20}$H$_{19}$O

① Dibenzylphosphinous acid
      phenyl ester
      (C$_6$H$_5$CH$_2$)$_2$P(OC$_6$H$_5$)
② (C$_6$H$_5$O)PCl$_2$ + C$_6$H$_5$CH$_2$MgCl $\longrightarrow$
      15%
③ (200~203°/2.5).
④ + C$_6$H$_5$CH$_2$Cl $\longrightarrow$
      [(C$_6$H$_5$CH$_2$)$_3$P(OC$_6$H$_5$)]Cl +
      (C$_6$H$_5$CH$_2$)$_3$PO
⑥ Ber. 93, 1220 (1960).

PC₂₀H₁₉O₂

① Bis(p-methoxyphenyl)phenylphos-
phine
(p-CH₃OC₆H₄)₂C₆H₅P

② p-CH₃OC₆H₄MgBr + C₆H₅PCl₂ $\xrightarrow{\text{THF}}$
75%

③ Colorless crystals. (89~90°).

④ + 48% HBr $\longrightarrow$
[(p-HOC₆H₄)₂(C₆H₅)$\overset{+}{P}$H]Br⁻

⑥ Ber. **94**, 2519 (1961).   JOC **25**, 2001
(1960).

PC₂₀H₁₉O₂S

① (Methylsulfonyl)methylene-
triphenylphosphorane
(C₆H₅)₃P=CHSO₂CH₃

② (C₆H₅)₃PCH₂SO₂CH₃ $\xrightarrow{\text{aq. NaOH}}$ 65%

③ [201~203°].
Stable to air.

⑥ Tetrahedron Letters **1961**, 724.

PC₂₀H₂₀BF₄

① Ethyltriphenylphosphonium
fluoroborate
[(C₂H₅)(C₆H₅)₃P]BF₄

② (C₆H₅)₃P + [(C₂H₅)₃O]BF₄ $\longrightarrow$

③ [127°].
IR: Australian J. Chem. **16**, 360
(1963).

⑥ Kaufman 1241.

PC₂₀H₂₀Br

① Ethyltriphenylphosphonium bromide
[(C₂H₅)P(C₆H₅)₃]Br

② (C₆H₅)₃P + C₂H₅Br $\xrightarrow{\text{CH₃CN, 100°}}$

③ [205~206°].
IR: JINC **24**, 169 (1962).

④ $\xrightarrow{\text{LiAlH₄/THF}}$ (C₆H₅)₂PC₂H₅
$\xrightarrow{\text{Pb/2 e⁻}}$ (C₆H₅)₃P (91.5%)
$\xrightarrow{\text{Hg/2 e⁻}}$ C₂H₅P(C₆H₅)₂ + (C₆H₅)₃P
(59%)   (35%)

The ligation to P decreased accord-
ing to the following series: CH₃>
C₆H₅>C₂H₅>C₄H₉>i-C₃H₇>t-C₄H₉ ;
HOCH₂CH₂>C₆H₅CH₂

⑥ Australian J. Chem. **16**, 360 (1963).
JCS **1961**, 4263. Ann. **646**, 65 (1961)

PC₂₀H₂₀ClO

① 2-Hydroxyethyltriphenylphospho-
nium chloride
[(HOCH₂CH₂)P(C₆H₅)₃]Cl

② (C₆H₅)₃P + HOCH₂CH₂Cl $\xrightarrow{\text{CH₃CN, 100°}}$

③ [233~236°].

④ $\xrightarrow{\text{Pb/2 e⁻}}$ (C₆H₅)₃P (85%)
$\xrightarrow{\text{NaOH}}$ C₆H₆ + (C₆H₅)₂P(O)H

⑥ Kosolapoff 90.   Ann. **646**, 65 (1961).
Acta. Chem. Scand. **15**, 438 (1961).

PC₂₀H₂₀I

① Ethyltriphenylphosphonium iodide
[(C₆H₅)₃PC₂H₅]I

② (C₆H₅)₃PBr₂ + C₂H₅I $\longrightarrow$ 93%

③ [164~165°].

⑥ Kosolapoff 90.   Ber. **93**, 861 (1960);
95, 58 (1962). Australian J. Chem.
16, 360 (1963).

PC₂₀H₂₀I

① Benzylmethyldiphenylphosphonium
iodide
[(C₆H₅CH₂)(CH₃)(C₆H₅)₂P]I

② (C₆H₅)₂(C₆H₅CH₂)PCl₂ + CH₃I
$\xrightarrow{\text{sealed, 130°}}$ 89%

③ [229~230°].

⑥ Ber. **93**, 861 (1960).

PC₂₀H₂₀N

① N-Ethyl-P, P, P-triphenylphosphine
imide
C₂H₅NP(C₆H₅)₃

② [(C₆H₅)₃PN(C₂H₅)₂]I $\xrightarrow{\text{Pyrolysis}}$
(C₆H₅)₃P + C₂H₅N₃ $\xrightarrow{\text{in light petroleum}}$

③ (198°/2). [96°].

Stable at room temp.

④ + C$_2$H$_5$I $\longrightarrow$ [(C$_6$H$_5$)$_3$PN(C$_2$H$_5$)$_2$]I

⑥ Z. anorg. allg. Chem. **311**, 290 (1961).
JCS **1960**, 3284.   Helv. Chim. Acta
4, 861 (1921).

PC$_{20}$H$_{25}$F$_2$Si

① 1,2-Difluoro-2-triethylsilylvinyl-
diphenylphosphine
(C$_6$H$_5$)$_2$PCF=CFSi(C$_2$H$_5$)$_3$

② (C$_2$H$_5$)$_3$SiCF=CF$_2$ + (C$_6$H$_5$)$_2$PLi $\longrightarrow$
53%

③ Colorless liq. (153~155°/0.35). n_D
1.5619 (25°).

④ + CH$_3$I $\longrightarrow$ [(CH$_3$)$_2$(C$_6$H$_5$)$_2$$\overset{+}{P}$]I$^-$
Quaternization with methyl iodide
result in partial cleavage of the
(C$_2$H$_5$)$_3$SiCF=CF-group.

⑥ Inorg. Chem. **1**, 78 (1962).

PC$_{20}$H$_{27}$

① Dicyclohexylphenylethynylphosphine
(C$_6$H$_5$C≡C)(cyclo-C$_6$H$_{11}$)$_2$P

② (cyclo-C$_6$H$_{11}$)$_2$PLi + ClC≡CC$_6$H$_5$
$\xrightarrow{\text{(C}_2\text{H}_5\text{)}_2\text{O}}$ 35%

③ [74°].

Air-sensitive. Sol. in C$_6$H$_6$, THF,
ether ; insol. in H$_2$O.

④ + S $\xrightarrow{\text{C}_6\text{H}_6}$
(C$_6$H$_5$C≡C)P(S)(cyclo-C$_6$H$_{11}$)$_2$

⑥ Ber. **95**, 268 (1962).

PC$_{20}$H$_{28}$I

① Dibutyldiphenylphosphonium iodide
[(C$_4$H$_9$)$_2$P(C$_6$H$_5$)$_2$]I

② (C$_6$H$_5$)$_2$PC$_4$H$_9$ + C$_4$H$_9$I $\longrightarrow$

③ [154~155°].

IR : Spectrochim. Acta **19**, 1905(1963)

⑥ JCS **1960**, 3324.

PC$_{20}$H$_{28}$I

① Benzyl-n-butylphenyl-n-propyl

phosphonium iodide
[(C$_6$H$_5$CH$_2$)(C$_4$H$_9$)(C$_6$H$_5$)(C$_3$H$_7$)P]I

② C$_6$H$_5$PH$_2$ $\xrightarrow[\text{HCl}]{\text{CH}_2\text{O}}$ [C$_6$H$_5$P(CH$_2$OH)$_3$]Cl

$\xrightarrow[\text{2) C}_3\text{H}_7\text{I}]{\text{1) NaOH}}$ [C$_6$H$_5$P(CH$_2$OH)$_2$C$_3$H$_7$]I

$\xrightarrow[\text{2) C}_4\text{H}_9\text{I}]{\text{1) NaOH}}$ [C$_6$H$_5$P(CH$_2$OH)C$_3$H$_7$C$_4$H$_9$]I

$\xrightarrow[\text{2) C}_6\text{H}_5\text{CH}_2\text{I}]{\text{1) NaOH}}$ 34%

③ [138~141°].

⑥ Ann. **659**, 49 (1962).

PC$_{21}$H$_{15}$O$_3$

① Tribenzoylphosphine
(C$_6$H$_5$CO)$_3$P

② PH$_3$ + C$_6$H$_5$COCl $\xrightarrow{\text{C}_5\text{H}_5\text{N}}$

③ Yellow crystals. [147°].

Stable in H$_2$O and dil. acid soln.,
decomp. in aq. NaOH into PH$_3$ and
C$_6$H$_5$COONa.

④ + C$_2$H$_5$OH $\longrightarrow$ C$_6$H$_5$COC$_2$H$_5$
+ 25% NH$_3$ $\longrightarrow$ C$_6$H$_5$CONH$_2$
+ C$_6$H$_5$NH$_2$ $\longrightarrow$ C$_6$H$_5$CONHC$_6$H$_5$

⑥ Roczniki Chem. **33**, 549 (1959) ; CA
53, 21750 (1959).

PC$_{21}$H$_{15}$N$_2$

① Triphenylphosphoranylidene
malononitrile
(C$_6$H$_5$)$_3$P=C(CN)$_2$

② (C$_6$H$_5$)$_3$PCl$_2$ + H$_2$C(CN)$_2$ $\xrightarrow{\text{(C}_2\text{H}_5\text{)}_3\text{N, C}_6\text{H}_6}$
70%

③ [187~188°].

IR : Ann. **627**, 142 (1959).

UV : Ber. **91**, 437 (1958).

⑥ Kaufman 1245.

PC$_{21}$H$_{18}$BrO$_2$

① Bromo(triphenylphosphoranylidene)
acetic acid methyl ester
(C$_6$H$_5$)$_3$P=CBrCOOCH$_3$

② [(C$_6$H$_5$)$_3$PCH$_2$CO$_2$CH$_3$]Br + KBrO$_3$

15～20°
————→
(C$_6$H$_5$)$_3$P=CHCO$_2$CH$_3$ + Br$_2$

NaOCOCH$_3$ 10～15°
————————————→ 96%
(C$_2$H$_5$)$_3$N/CHCl$_3$, 10°
————————————→

③ [167～168°] (C$_2$H$_5$OH-petr. ether).
UV: JACS **85**, 2790 (1963).

④ + KI $\xrightarrow{\text{CH}_3\text{OH}}$ (C$_6$H$_5$)$_3$P=CICO$_2$CH$_3$

+ CH$_3$CHO $\xrightarrow[70°]{\text{C}_6\text{H}_6}$

trans-CH$_3$CH=CBrCO$_2$H

+ C$_6$H$_5$CH$_3$ $\xrightarrow{\text{C}_6\text{H}_6 \text{ KOH}-\text{CH}_3\text{OH}}$

C$_6$H$_5$C≡CCO$_2$H

⑥ Ber. **94**, 2996 (1961); **95**, 3003 (1962).

PC$_{21}$H$_{18}$O$_3$N$_3$

① Tris(phenylcarbamoyl)phosphine
(C$_6$H$_5$NHCO)$_3$P

② C$_6$H$_5$NCO + PH$_3$ $\xrightarrow[\text{in C}_6\text{H}_6]{(\text{C}_2\text{H}_5)_3\text{N}}$ 13%

[CCl$_3$CH(OH)]$_2$PH + C$_6$H$_5$NCO

$\xrightarrow[\text{in C}_6\text{H}_6]{(\text{C}_2\text{H}_5)_3\text{N}}$ 29%

③ White crystals. [212～213°].
Decomp. suddenly in the range of
245～250°.
IR: JOC **24**, 1460 (1959).

⑥ JACS **83**, 168 (1961).

PC$_{21}$H$_{19}$

① Triphenylvinylmethylenephospho-
rane
(C$_6$H$_5$)$_3$P=CHCH=CH$_2$

② [(C$_6$H$_5$)$_3$PCH$_2$CH=CH$_2$]Br ——→

④ + (C$_6$H$_5$)$_2$PBr $\xrightarrow{\text{NaB(C}_6\text{H}_5)_4}$ [(C$_6$H$_5$)$_3$PCH-
=CHCH$_2$P(C$_6$H$_5$)$_2$]B(C$_6$H$_5$)$_4$

⑥ JACS **83**, 2055 (1961).

PC$_{21}$H$_{19}$NI

① 2-Cyanoethyltriphenylphosphonium
iodide
[(NCCH$_2$CH$_2$)P(C$_6$H$_5$)$_3$]I

② CH$_2$=CHCN + (C$_6$H$_5$)$_3$P + HI ——→
85%

③ [187° decomp.].

④ $\xrightarrow{\text{2 N NaOH}}$ (C$_6$H$_5$)$_3$P (93%)

⑥ Ber. **94**, 1331 (1961).

PC$_{21}$H$_{19}$O

① 1-(Triphenylphosphoranylidene)
propionaldehyde
(C$_6$H$_5$)$_3$P=C(CHO)CH$_3$

② [((C$_6$H$_5$)$_3$PC$_2$H$_5$]I $\xrightarrow{\text{1) C}_4\text{H}_9\text{Li, 2) HCO}_2\text{C}_2\text{H}_5}$

③ [220～222° C$_6$H$_6$-petr. ether)].

④ + HCl ——→ [(C$_6$H$_5$)$_3$PCH(CHO)CH$_3$]Cl

+ C$_6$H$_5$CH$_3$ ——→ C$_6$H$_5$CH=CCH$_3$CHO
(60%)

⑥ JCS **1961**, 1266. Chem. Ind. (London)
1960, 202.

PC$_{21}$H$_{19}$O

① Triphenylphosphoranylidene-2-
propanone
(C$_6$H$_5$)$_3$P=CHCOCH$_3$

② 2 (C$_6$H$_5$)$_3$P=CH$_2$ + CH$_3$COCl $\xrightarrow{\text{C}_6\text{H}_6}$ 51%

(C$_6$H$_5$)$_3$P=CH$_2$ + CH$_3$COSC$_2$H$_5$ $\xrightarrow{\text{C}_6\text{H}_5\text{CH}_3}$
78%

[(C$_6$H$_5$)$_3$PCH$_2$COCH$_3$]Br $\xrightarrow{\text{10% Na}_2\text{CO}_3}$
71%

③ [205～206° (aq. CH$_3$OH)].
IR: Acta Chem. Scand. **15**, 692(1961).

④ + aq. C$_2$H$_5$OH ——→ (CH$_3$)$_2$CO (83%)

+ Br$_2$ $\xrightarrow{(\text{C}_2\text{H}_5)_3\text{N/CHCl}_3}$
(C$_6$H$_5$)$_3$P=CBrCOCH$_3$ (87%)

+ C$_6$H$_5$CH$_3$ ——→ C$_6$H$_5$CH=CHCOCH$_3$
(76%)

⑥ Tetrahedron Letters **1960**, 7. Acta
Chem. Scand. **15**, 692(1961). Ber. **95**,
1513 (1962). BCSJ **35**, 2042 (1962).

PC$_{21}$H$_{19}$O$_2$

① Triphenylphosphoranylideneacetic
acid methyl ester

$(C_6H_5)_3P=CHCOOCH_3$

② $(C_6H_5)_3P=CHCH_3$

$+ [CH_3O_2CCH_2\overset{+}{P}(C_6H_5)_3]Br^- \xrightarrow{C_6H_5CH_3}$

③ [161°].

④ $+ Cl_2 \xrightarrow{C_6H_6, 10°} (C_6H_5)_3P=CClCO_2CH_3$

$+ I_2 \xrightarrow{CH_3OH, 25°} (C_6H_5)_3P=CICO_2CH_3$

(30%)

$+ CH_3I \xrightarrow{CH_3COOC_2H_5}$

$[(C_6H_5)_3PCH_3CO_2CH_3]I$ (75%)

⑥ Ber. **87**, 1318 (1954); **95**, 58, 2921
(1962); **94**, 2996(1961). Proc. Chem.
Soc. **1961**, 454 Tetrahedron Letters
1960, 5.

PC₂₁H₂₀Br

① Allyltriphenylphosphonium bromide
$[(CH_2=CHCH_2)P(C_6H_5)_3]Br$

② $(C_6H_5)_3P + CH_2=CHCH_2Br \xrightarrow{C_6H_6} 92\%$

③ [209~214°].

④ $\xrightarrow{Pb/2e^-} (C_6H_5)_3P$ (67%)

⑥ JOC **23**, 372 (1963).   JACS **82**, 3919
(1960).   Tetrahedron Letters **1961**,
161.

PC₂₁H₂₀BrO

① Acetonyltriphenylphosphonium
bromide
$[CH_3COCH_2P(C_6H_5)_3]Br$

② $(C_6H_5)_3P + BrCH_2COCH_3 \longrightarrow$

③ [226°].
IR: Acta Chem. Scand. **15**, 692(1961).
Treatment with aq. alkali yields the
betaine, [201°].

⑥ Kosolapoff 90.   Gazz. chim. ital. **93**,
668 (1963).   Ber. **88**, 1654 (1955).

PC₂₁H₂₀BrO₂

① (Carbomethoxymethyl)triphenyl

phosphonium bromide
$[(CH_3O_2CCH_2)P(C_6H_5)_3]Br$

② $(C_6H_5)_3P + BrCH_2CO_2CH_3 \xrightarrow{C_6H_6} 89\%$

$\xrightarrow{C_6H_6, 100°} 70\%$

③ [162°].

④ $+ NaNH_2 \longrightarrow (C_6H_5)_3P=CHCO_2CH_3$

$+ NH_3 + NaBr$

⑥ Ber. **94**, 578 (1961); **95**, 2921 (1962);
96, 465 (1963).   Yakugagu Zasshi
82, 1262 (1962).   JOC **27**, 647, 3404
(1962).

PC₂₁H₂₀ClO

① Acetonyltriphenylphosphonium
chloride
$[(CH_3COCH_2)P(C_6H_5)_3]Cl$

② $Ph_3P + ClCH_2COMe \xrightarrow{MeCN}$

③ [237°].
IR: Ann. **646**, 65 (1961).

④ $\xrightarrow{Pb/2e^-} (C_6H_5)_3P$ (94%)

⑥ Kosolapoff 90.

PC₂₁H₂₁

① Triphenyl(isopropylidene)phospho-
rane
$(C_6H_5)_3P=C(CH_3)_2$

② $[(C_6H_5)_3PCH(CH_3)_2]Br + NaNH_2 \longrightarrow$

④ $+ O_2 \longrightarrow (C_6H_5)_3PO + (CH_3)_2CO$

$+ \frac{1}{2}O_2 \longrightarrow (CH_3)_2C=C(CH_3)_2$

$+ (C_6H_5)_2C=C=O \xrightarrow{(C_2H_5)_2O}$

$(C_6H_5)_3\overset{+}{P}-C(CH_3)_2C(O^-)=C(C_6H_5)_2$
(83%)

⑥ Ber. **96**, 1537, 1899 (1963).

PC₂₁H₂₁

① Triphenyl(*n*-propylidene)phospho-
rane
$(C_6H_5)_3P=CHCH_2CH_3$

② $[(C_6H_5)_2PCH_2C_2H_5]Br + NaNH_2 \longrightarrow$

④ $+ O_2 \longrightarrow$

C$_2$H$_5$CH=CHC$_2$H$_5$ + (C$_6$H$_5$)$_3$PO

⑥ Ber. **96**, 1899 (1963).   Izv. OKhN
1963, 1053.

PC$_{21}$H$_{21}$

① Tribenzylphosphine
(C$_6$H$_5$CH$_2$)$_3$P

② C$_6$H$_5$CH$_2$MgCl + PCl$_3$ $\xrightarrow{\text{(C}_2\text{H}_5\text{)}_2\text{O} - \text{C}_6\text{H}_6}$

C$_6$H$_5$CH$_2$Na + PCl$_3$ $\dashrightarrow$ 84.1%

(C$_6$H$_5$CH$_2$)$_3$P(CH$_2$OH)Cl $\xrightarrow{\text{N(C}_2\text{H}_5\text{)}_3}$

③ (208~212/2.5, 203~210/0.5). [92~95°,
185~188°].

Oxidized in air.

④ + NiX$_2$ $\dashrightarrow$ [(C$_6$H$_5$CH$_2$)$_3$P]$_2$NiX$_2$
X=Cl, Br, I or SCN

+ air $\xrightarrow{\text{(C}_2\text{H}_5\text{)}_2\text{O}}$ (C$_6$H$_5$CH$_2$)$_3$PO

+ CH$_3$I $\dashrightarrow$ [(C$_6$H$_5$CH$_2$)$_3$PCH$_3$]$^+$I$^-$

⑥ JCS **1959**, 2835.   Ber. **93**, 1220 (1960).
Zhur. **32**, 553 (1962).

PC$_{21}$H$_{22}$Br

① Triphenylpropylphosphonium
bromide
[(C$_6$H$_5$)$_3$PC$_3$H$_7$]Br

② (C$_6$H$_5$)$_3$P + C$_3$H$_7$Br $\longrightarrow$

③ [229~230°].

⑥ Izv. OKhN **1963**, 1053. Anais. Assoc.
Brasil Quim. **20**, 93 (1961); CA
58, 1487 (1964).

PC$_{21}$H$_{22}$ClO

① Benzyl(2-hydroxyethyl)diphenyl
phosphonium chloride
[(C$_6$H$_5$CH$_2$)(HOCH$_2$CH$_2$)P(C$_6$H$_5$)$_2$]Cl

② (C$_6$H$_5$)$_2$PCH$_2$C$_6$H$_5$ + ClCH$_2$CH$_2$OH $\xrightarrow{105°}$
92%

③ [180~181°].

④ $\xrightarrow{\text{Hg/2 e}^-}$ C$_6$H$_5$CH$_3$ (83%)
+ (HOCH$_2$CH$_2$)P(C$_6$H$_5$)$_2$ (87.5%)

⑥ Ann. **646**, 65 (1961).

PC$_{21}$H$_{22}$I

① Dibenzylmethylphenylphosphonium

iodide
[(C$_6$H$_5$CH$_2$)$_2$(CH$_3$)(C$_6$H$_5$)P]I

② C$_6$H$_5$PCl$_2$ $\xrightarrow{\text{1) C}_6\text{H}_5\text{CH}_2\text{MgCl, 2) CH}_3\text{I}}$ 82%

(C$_6$H$_5$CH$_2$)$_2$PC$_6$H$_5$ + CH$_3$Br $\xrightarrow{\text{KI, 45°}}$

③ [207~208°].

④ $\xrightarrow{\text{1) LiAlH}_4\text{/THF, 2) C}_2\text{H}_5\text{I}}$

[(C$_6$H$_5$CH$_2$)C$_2$H$_5$CH$_3$C$_6$H$_5$P]I (80%)

$\xrightarrow[85\sim90°]{\text{Hg/2 e}^-}$ (C$_6$H$_5$CH$_2$)CH$_3$C$_6$H$_5$P (86%)

⑥ JOC **25**, 1996 (1960).   Ann. **646**, 65
(1961).

PC$_{22}$H$_{17}$

① 1-Naphthyldiphenylphosphine
1-C$_{10}$H$_7$(C$_6$H$_5$)$_2$P

② C$_{10}$H$_7$MgBr + (C$_6$H$_5$)$_2$PCl $\xrightarrow{\text{ether}}$ 33%

③ [122~124°].
Sol. in dioxane, C$_6$H$_6$; slightly insol.
in ether, C$_2$H$_5$OH.

④ + K $\xrightarrow{\text{dioxane}}$
KP(C$_6$H$_5$)(C$_{10}$H$_7$)·2 dioxane

⑥ Ber. **94**, 392 (1961).

PC$_{22}$H$_{18}$NO$_2$

① Triphenylphosphoranylidenecyano-
acetic acid methyl ester
(C$_6$H$_5$)$_3$P=C(CN)COOCH$_3$

② (C$_6$H$_5$)$_3$P + CH$_2$(CN)CO$_2$CH$_3$ $\xrightarrow{\text{Et}_3\text{N, C}_6\text{H}_6}$
83%

③ [212~213°].
IR: Ann. **627**, 142 (1959).
UV: Ber. **91**, 437 (1958).

PC$_{22}$H$_{21}$O$_2$

① Triphenylphosphoranylidene acetic
acid ethylester
(C$_6$H$_5$)$_3$P=CHCOOC$_2$H$_5$

② [(C$_6$H$_5$)$_3$PCH$_2$CO$_2$C$_2$H$_5$]Br
$\xrightarrow{\text{aq. NaOH/C}_6\text{H}_6}$ 76%

[(C$_6$H$_5$)$_3$PCH$_2$CO$_2$C$_2$H$_5$]Cl $\xrightarrow{\text{10% KOH}}$
95%

③ [126~127°].
   IR: Spectrochim. Acta **19**, 1905
   (1963)
④ + RR'C=O ⟶ RR'C=CHCO$_2$C$_2$H$_5$
   + R$\overset{*}{C}$H−CH$_2$ ⟶ R$\overset{*}{C}$H−CHCO$_2$C$_2$H$_5$
      \ /   \ /
       O   CH$_2$

   e.g. C$_6$H$_5$CHO $\overset{k_2}{\longrightarrow}$
   C$_6$H$_5$CH=CHCO$_2$Et (78% trans)
   Kinetics for C$_6$H$_5$CHO
   $k_2=2.6\times10^{-3}$ l/mole·sec. at 20°

   C$_6$H$_5$$\overset{*}{C}$H−CH$_2$ ⟶
            \ /
             O

   C$_6$H$_5$$\overset{*}{C}$H−CHCO$_2C_2H_5$
            \ /
             CH$_2$
   (optically active, trans)
⑤ A representative Wittig's reagent.
⑥ JOC **27**, 998 (1962).   JACS **84**, 3944
   (1962).   Angew. **75**, 85 (1963).
   Ber. **88**, 1654 (1955).

PC$_{22}$H$_{22}$BrO$_2$
① (Carbethoxymethyl)triphenylphos-
   phonium bromide
   [(C$_6$H$_5$)$_3$P(CH$_2$COOC$_2$H$_5$)]Br
② (C$_6$H$_5$)$_3$P + BrCH$_2$CO$_2$C$_2$H$_5$ ⟶
③ [157°].
   IR: Spectrochim. Acta **19**, 1905(1963).
   NMR: JACS **85**, 2790 (1963).
⑥ Kaufman 1251.   Acta Chem. Scand.
   15, 438, 692 (1961).

PC$_{22}$H$_{22}$ClO$_2$
① Carbethoxymethyltriphenylphos-
   phonium chloride
   [(C$_2$H$_5$O$_2$CCH$_2$)P(C$_6$H$_5$)$_3$]Cl
② (C$_6$H$_5$)$_3$P + ClCH$_2$CO$_2$C$_2$H$_5$ $\overset{C_6H_6}{\longrightarrow}$
   [(C$_6$H$_5$)$_3$PCH$_2$CO$_2$C$_2$H$_5$]Cl
③ [144°].
   Dihydrate melts at 87°.
④ $\overset{C_6H_6}{\longrightarrow}$ [(C$_6$H$_5$)$_3$PCH$_3$]Cl + CO$_2$

$\overset{NaOH}{\longrightarrow}$ (C$_6$H$_5$)$_3$P=CHCO$_2$C$_2$H$_5$
$\overset{H^+, H_2O}{\longrightarrow}$ [((C$_6$H$_5$)$_3$PCH$_2$CO$_2$H]Cl
   (decomp.)
⑥ Kosolapoff 90,   J. prakt. Chem. **17**,
   299 (1962).   JOC **27**, 647, 3404 (1962).

PC$_{22}$H$_{23}$
① *sec*-Butylidenetriphenylphosphorane
   (C$_6$H$_5$)$_3$P=C(CH$_3$)CH$_2$CH$_3$
② [(C$_6$H$_5$)$_3$$\overset{+}{P}$CH(CH$_3$)CH$_2CH_3$]$\overset{-}{Br}$ +
   NaNH$_2$ ⟶
④ + O$_2$ ⟶ (C$_6$H$_5$)$_3$PO + CH$_3$COC$_2$H$_5$
⑥ Ber. **96**, 1899 (1963).

PC$_{22}$H$_{23}$
① *n*-Butylidenetriphenylphosphorane
   (C$_6$H$_5$)$_3$P=CHCH$_2$CH$_2$CH$_3$
② [(C$_6$H$_5$)$_3$PCH$_2$C$_3$H$_7$]Br + NaNH$_2$ ⟶
④ + O$_2$ ⟶
   C$_3$H$_7$CH=CHC$_3$H$_7$ + (C$_6$H$_5$)$_3$PO
   + B$_2$H$_6$ ⟶ (C$_6$H$_5$)$_3$$\overset{+}{P}CHC_3H_7$$\overset{-}{B}H_3$
   (85%)
⑥ Ber. **96**, 1899 (1963).   JACS **83**, 367
   (1961).

PC$_{22}$H$_{24}$Br
① Tribenzylmethylphosphonium
   bromide
   [(C$_6$H$_5$CH$_2$)$_3$PCH$_3$]Br
② (C$_6$H$_5$CH$_2$)$_3$P + CH$_3$Br ⟶ 74%
③ [229~229.5°].
④ $\overset{Na\ in\ C_6H_6}{\underset{O_2}{\longrightarrow}}$ (C$_6$H$_5$CH$_2$)$_2$P(O)CH$_3$ (77%)
⑥ Kaufman 1251.   JINC **25**, 801 (1963).

PC$_{22}$H$_{24}$Br
① Butyltriphenylphosphonium bromide
   [(C$_4$H$_9$)(C$_6$H$_5$)$_3$P]Br
② (C$_6$H$_5$)$_3$P + C$_4$H$_9$Br $\overset{CH_3NO_2}{\longrightarrow}$ 80%
   $\overset{C_4H_9OH}{\longrightarrow}$ 90.8%
   $\overset{C_6H_6}{\longrightarrow}$ 55%
③ [249~251°].

④ $\xrightarrow{\text{Pb/2 e}^-}$ (C$_6$H$_5$)$_3$P + (C$_6$H$_5$)$_2$PC$_4$H$_9$
         (77%)   (trace)

$\xrightarrow{\text{Hg/2 e}^-}$ (C$_6$H$_5$)$_3$P + (C$_6$H$_5$)$_2$PC$_4$H$_9$
         (46%)   (50%)

⑥ Kaufman 1251. JACS **82**, 3919 (1960).
   Ber. **96**, 2109 (1963). Spectrochim.
   Acta **19**, 1905 (1963).   Ann. **646**,
   65 (1961).

PC$_{22}$H$_{24}$Br

① Dibenzylethylphenylphosphonium
   bromide
   [(C$_6$H$_5$CH$_2$)$_2$(C$_2$H$_5$)(C$_6$H$_5$)P]Br

② C$_6$H$_5$(C$_6$H$_5$CH$_2$)$_2$P + C$_2$H$_5$Br $\xrightarrow{\text{CH}_3\text{CN, 65}°}$

③ [180~183°].

④ $\xrightarrow{\text{Hg/2 e}^-,\ 80~90°}$ C$_2$H$_5$C$_6$H$_5$PCH$_2$C$_6$H$_5$
                              (91%)

⑥ Ann. **646**, 65 (1961).

PC$_{22}$H$_{24}$ClO

① Dibenzyl-2-hydroxyethylphenyl
   phosphonium chloride
   [(HOCH$_2$CH$_2$)(C$_6$H$_5$)(C$_6$H$_5$CH$_2$)$_2$P]Cl

② C$_6$H$_5$P(CH$_2$C$_6$H$_5$)$_2$ + ClCH$_2$CH$_2$OH $\xrightarrow{100°}$

③ [153~154°].

⑥ Ann. **646**, 65 (1961).

PC$_{22}$H$_{25}$O$_4$S

① (*p*-Methoxyphenyl)dimethylphenyl-
   phosphonium tosylate
   [(*p*-CH$_3$OC$_6$H$_4$)P(CH$_3$)$_2$(C$_6$H$_5$)]-
   SO$_3$C$_6$H$_4$CH$_3$-*p*

② (*p*-CH$_3$OC$_6$H$_4$)PCH$_3$C$_6$H$_5$
   + *p*-CH$_3$C$_6$H$_4$SO$_3$CH$_3$ $\longrightarrow$

③ [132°].

⑥ JCS **1961**, 5454.

PC$_{22}$H$_{26}$BrSi

① Triphenyl (trimethylsilylmethyl)-
   phosphonium bromide
   [(C$_6$H$_5$)$_3$PCH$_2$Si(CH$_3$)$_3$]Br

② (C$_6$H$_5$)$_3$P=CH$_2$ + (CH$_3$)$_3$SiBr $\longrightarrow$

(C$_6$H$_5$)$_3$P + BrCH$_2$Si(CH$_3$)$_3$ $\xrightarrow{\text{C}_6\text{H}_6}$ 27%

③ [175° decomp.].
   Sol. in H$_2$O, CH$_3$COCH$_3$, CH$_3$OH,
   C$_2$H$_5$OH and CH$_2$Cl$_2$.
   Insol. in C$_6$H$_6$, (C$_2$H$_5$)$_2$O and aliphatic
   hydrocarbons.

④ + NaOH $\longrightarrow$ [(C$_6$H$_5$)$_3$PCH$_3$]Br
   + [(CH$_3$)$_3$Si]$_2$O

⑥ Chem. & Ind. (London) **1959**, 849.
   JACS **83**, 1610 (1961).

PC$_{23}$H$_{19}$

① Cyclopentadienylidenetriphenylphos-
   phorane

② Ph$_3$P + $\xrightarrow{\text{CHCl}_3, -40°}$
   $\xrightarrow{\text{1.3N NaOH}}$ 41%

③ [228~231° (CHCl$_3$–C$_2$H$_5$OH)].
   Readily sol. in 5% aq. hydrochloric
   acid.
   IR: Ann. **627**, 142 (1959).
   UV: JACS **79**, 67, 6167 (1957).

④ + $\overset{+}{\text{N}}_2$Ph $\xrightarrow{\text{CH}_2\text{Cl}_2,\text{AcONa}}$ (88%)

⑥ Izv. OKhN **1961**, 140.

PC$_{23}$H$_{26}$Br

① Tribenzylethylphosphonium bromide
   [(C$_6$H$_5$CH$_2$)$_3$PC$_2$H$_5$]Br

② (C$_6$H$_5$CH$_2$)$_3$P + C$_2$H$_5$Br $\xrightarrow{\text{CH}_3\text{CN, 40}°}$

③ [204°].

④ $\xrightarrow{\text{Hg/2 e}^-}$ C$_2$H$_5$P(CH$_2$C$_6$H$_5$)$_2$ (90%)

⑥ Ann. **646**, 65 (1961).

PC$_{24}$H$_{15}$

① Tris(phenylethynyl)phosphine

(C$_6$H$_5$C≡C)$_3$P

② C$_6$H$_5$C≡CMgBr + PCl$_3$ ⟶

   C$_6$H$_5$C≡CNa + PCl$_3$ ⟶

③ [92°].

   X-ray structural investigation: Z.
Krist. **117**. 233 (1962).

④ + weak alkali ⟶ C$_6$H$_5$C≡CH

⑥ Naturwiss. **46**, 321 (1959).

PC$_{24}$H$_{20}$Br

① Tetraphenylphosphonium bromide
[(C$_6$H$_5$)$_4$P]Br

② (C$_6$H$_5$)$_3$P + C$_6$H$_5$N$_2^+$ $\xrightarrow{\text{NaOCOCH}_3,\ \text{HBr}}$

   (C$_6$H$_5$)$_3$P + C$_6$H$_5$Br + C$_6$H$_5$MgBr $\xrightarrow{\text{COCl}_2}$

   (C$_6$H$_5$)$_4$PBr (55%) + (C$_6$H$_5$)$_2$ (85%)

③ [288°].

   NMR: Australian J. Chem. **16**, 360
(1963).

④ + CH$_3$Li ⟶ (C$_6$H$_5$)$_3$P=CH$_2$

   + NaB(C$_6$H$_5$)$_4$ ⟶

   [(C$_6$H$_5$)$_4$P]B(C$_6$H$_5$)$_4$

⑥ Angew. **72**, 416 (1960). Bunseki
Kagaku **10**, 571 (1961). Kosolapoff
87. Ber. **91**, 45 (1958).

PC$_{24}$H$_{20}$I

① Tetraphenylphosphonium iodide
[(C$_6$H$_5$)$_4$P]I

② (C$_6$H$_5$)$_3$P + C$_6$H$_5$I $\xrightarrow{h\nu,\ 65°}$

   (C$_6$H$_5$)$_3$P + C$_6$H$_5$N$_2^+$

   $\xrightarrow{\text{NaOCOCH}_3,\ \text{NaI (buffer soln.)}}$

③ [337°], [323~326°].

   IR: Australian J. Chem. **16**, 360
(1963).

⑥ Kaufman 1255. JOC **27**, 4711 (1962).
Ber. **91**, 45 (1958).

PC$_{24}$H$_{20}$N

① N-Phenyl-P,P,P-triphenylphosphine
imide
C$_6$H$_5$NP(C$_6$H$_5$)$_3$

② (C$_6$H$_5$)$_3$PBr$_2$ + C$_6$H$_5$NH$_2$ $\xrightarrow{(\text{C}_2\text{H}_5)_3\text{N}}$ 70%

(C$_6$H$_5$)$_3$P + C$_6$H$_5$N$_3$ ⟶

③ [128~130°].

④ + R'Br ⟶ [(C$_6$H$_5$)$_3$PNC$_6$H$_5$R']Br

   + CH$_2$C=O ⟶ CH$_2$C=NC$_6$H$_5$

⑥ Ann. **627**, 142 (1959). Helv. Chim.
Acta **2**, 635 (1919).

PC$_{24}$H$_{23}$O$_2$

① 4-Triphenylphosphoranylidene-2-
pentenoic acid methyl ester
(C$_6$H$_5$)$_3$P=C(CH$_3$)CH=CHCOOCH$_3$

② [(C$_6$H$_5$)$_3$PCH(CH$_3$)CH=CHCO$_2$CH$_3$]Br

   $\xrightarrow{\text{aq. NaOH}}$

③ [173°].

④ + all-*trans*-OCHCH=CHCCH$_3$=CHCH
=CHCH=CCH$_3$CH=CHCHO

   ⟶ all-*trans*-methylbixin

⑥ Naturwiss. **46**, 75 (1959).

PC$_{24}$H$_{23}$O$_3$

① Triphenylphosphoranylideneaceto-
acetic acid ethylester
(C$_6$H$_5$)$_3$P=C(COCH$_3$)COOC$_2$H$_5$

② (C$_6$H$_5$)$_3$P + CH$_2$(COCH$_3$)CO$_2$C$_2$H$_5$

   $\xrightarrow{(\text{C}_2\text{H}_5)_3\text{N},\ \text{C}_6\text{H}_6}$ 60%

③ [169~171°].

   UV: Ber. **91**, 437 (1958).

PC$_{24}$H$_{23}$O$_4$

① Triphenylphosphoranylidenesuccinic
acid dimethylester
(C$_6$H$_5$)$_3$P=C(CH$_2$COOCH$_3$)COOCH$_3$

② 2(C$_6$H$_5$)$_3$P=CHCO$_2$CH$_3$ + BrCH$_2$CO$_2$CH$_3$

   $\xrightarrow{\text{CH}_3\text{COOC}_2\text{H}_5,\ 4\ \text{hr}}$ 80%

③ [157~158°].

④ + NaOH + H$_2$O ⟶ (CH$_2$CO$_2$H)$_2$

⑥ Tetrahedron Letters **1960**, 5. Acta
Chem. Scand. **15**, 692 (1961). Ber.
95, 2921 (1962).

PC$_{24}$H$_{25}$

① Cyclohexylidenetriphenylphospho-
rane

$(C_6H_5)_3P=C_6H_{10}$

② $[(C_6H_5)_3PC_6H_{11}]Br + NaNH_2 \longrightarrow$

④ $+ O_2 \longrightarrow$ $=O + (C_6H_5)_3PO$

⑥ Ber. **96**, 1899 (1963).

PC$_{24}$H$_{27}$

① *n*-Hexylidenetriphenylphosphorane
  $(C_6H_5)_3P=CH(CH_2)_4CH_3$

② $[(C_6H_5)_3PCH_2C_5H_{11}]Br + C_6H_5Li$
  $\xrightarrow{(C_2H_5)_2O}$

④ $+ B_2H_6 \longrightarrow (C_6H_5)_3\overset{+}{P}CHC_5H_{11}\overset{-}{B}H_3$
  (92%)

⑥ JACS **83**, 367 (1961).

PC$_{24}$H$_{27}$O$_3$

① Tris(*o*-methoxymethylphenyl)-
  phosphine
  $(o\text{-}CH_3OCH_2C_6H_4)_3P$

② $o\text{-}CH_3OCH_2C_6H_4Br + n\text{-}C_4H_9Li \xrightarrow{PCl_3}$
  58%

③ Colorless crystals. [105~106°].

④ $\xrightarrow{\text{oxidation}} (o\text{-}CH_3OCH_2C_6H_4)_3P(O)$
  $+ CH_3I \longrightarrow$
  $[CH_3(o\text{-}CH_3OCH_2C_6H_4)_3P]\overset{+}{I}{}^-$
  $+ BCl_3 \longrightarrow (o\text{-}ClCH_2C_6H_4)_3P$

⑥ JOC **23**, 1806 (1958).

PC$_{24}$H$_{28}$Br

① Dibenzylbutylphenylphosphonium
  bromide
  $[(C_6H_5CH_2)_2(C_4H_9)(C_6H_5)P]Br$

② $(C_6H_5CH_2)_2PC_6H_5 + C_4H_9Br \xrightarrow{CH_3CN, 100°}$

③ [159°].

④ $\xrightarrow{Hg/2\,e^-} C_4H_9C_6H_5PCH_2C_6H_5$ (81%)

⑥ Ann. **646**, 65 (1961).

PC$_{25}$H$_{20}$NO$_2$

① (*p*-Nitrobenzylidene) triphenylphosphorane
  $(C_6H_5)_3P=CHC_6H_4NO_2\text{-}p$

② $[(C_6H_5)_3PCH_2C_6H_4NO_2\text{-}p]Br$
  $\xrightarrow[-33°, \, 2\,hr]{NaNH_2/NH_3}$

③ [171~172° (ClCH$_2$CH$_2$Cl-petr. ether)].

④ R'OH $\longrightarrow CH_3C_6H_4NO_2\text{-}p$
  $+ (C_6H_5)_3PO + R'_2O$

⑥ JACS **82**, 3919 (1960).   Compt. rend.
  248, 817 (1959).

PC$_{25}$H$_{21}$

① Benzylidenetriphenylphosphorane
  $(C_6H_5)_3P=CHC_6H_5$

② $[(C_6H_5)_3PCH_2C_6H_5]Br \xrightarrow{C_4H_9Li}$
  $[(C_6H_5)_3PCH_2C_6H_5]Br \xrightarrow{NaOC_2H_5, \, C_2H_5OH}$

④ $+ C_6H_5CH_2Cl \longrightarrow$
  $[(C_6H_5)_3PCH(CH_2C_6H_5)C_6H_5]Cl$
  $+ [O] \longrightarrow C_6H_5CH=CHC_6H_5$
  (autoxidation)
  $+ B_2H_6 \longrightarrow [(C_6H_5)_3\overset{+}{P}CHC_6H_5]\overset{-}{B}H_3$
  $+ N_2CHC_6H_5 \xrightarrow{THF}$
  $C_6H_5CH=N-N=CHC_6H_5$ (40%)

⑤ Wittig reaction.

⑥ Tetrahedron **18**, 1023 (1962).   JCS
  1961, 1266.   Ber. **88**, 1654(1955) ; **96**,
  1899 (1963).   JACS **83**, 367 (1961).

PC$_{25}$H$_{22}$Cl

① Benzyltriphenylphosphonium
  chloride
  $[(C_6H_5CH_2)P(C_6H_5)_3]Cl$

② $(C_6H_5)_3P + C_6H_5CH_2Cl \xrightarrow{CH_3CN}$ ca 100%
  $(C_6H_5)_3P + C_6H_5CH_2N_2 \xrightarrow{THF, \, CuCl}$ 10%

③ [287~288°].
  IR : Spectrochim. Acta **17**, 1905(1963).

④ $\xrightarrow{pb/2\,e^-, \, 70~90°} C_6H_5CH_3 + (C_6H_5)_3P$
  (80%)   (85%)

⑥ Kaufman 1260.   Ann. **646**, 65 (1961).
  JOC **27**, 4076 (1962).   Tetrahedron
  18, 1023 (1962).   Ber. **87**, 1318(1954).

PC$_{25}$H$_{25}$O$_4$

① Triphenylphosphoranylidenemalonic

acid diethyl ester

$(C_6H_5)_3P=C(COOC_2H_5)_2$

② $(C_6H_5)_3PCl_2 + CH_2(CO_2C_2H_5)_2$

   $\dfrac{(C_2H_5)_3N,\ C_6H_6}{}$ 81%

③ [106~107°].

IR: Ann. **627**, 142 (1959).

UV: Kaufman 1260.

⑥ Ber. **91**, 437 (1958).

$PC_{25}H_{27}O$

① 4-Triphenylphosphoranylidene-3-heptanone

$(C_6H_5)_3P=C(COC_2H_5)C_3H_7$

② $2(C_6H_5)_3P=CHC_3H_7 + C_2H_5COCl$

   $\dfrac{C_6H_6/(C_2H_5)_2O}{}$

   $(C_6H_5)_3P=C(COC_2H_5)C_3H_7$
   $+ [(C_6H_5)_3PC_4H_9]Cl$

③ [114° (hexane)].

④ $\xrightarrow{\text{pyrolysis}}$ $C_2H_5C\equiv CC_3H_7$

⑥ JCS 1962, 2333.

$PC_{25}H_{35}$

① Tributylfluoren-9-ylidene phosphorane

$(C_4H_9)_3\,P$

② $[(C_4H_9)_3P(C_{13}H_9)]Br \xrightarrow{1\,N\ NaOH} 66\%$

③ [123~124° (($C_6H_5)_2O$)].

Unchanged in soln. of mineral acid.

④ $+ NaOH/CH_3OH \longrightarrow C_{13}H_{10}$ (98%)

   $+ C_6H_5CH_3 \xrightarrow{C_6H_6} C_{13}H_9=CHC_6H_5$ (96%)

⑥ Tetrahedron 9, 130 (1960).

$PC_{25}H_{35}Br_2Sn_2$

① Trimethylstannylmethyltriphenylphosphonium bromide, complex with bromotrimethylstannane

$[(C_6H_5)_3PCH_2Sn(CH_3)_3][(CH_3)_3SnBr_2]$

② $(CH_3)_3SnBr + (C_6H_5)_3P=CH_2 \longrightarrow$

③ [152° decomp.].

⑥ JACS 83, 1610 (1961).

$PC_{25}H_{36}Br$

① Tributylfluoren-9-ylphosphonium bromide

$[(C_4H_9)_3P(C_{13}H_9)]Br$

② $P(C_4H_9)_3 + C_{13}H_9Br \xrightarrow{CH_3COOH} 47\%$

③ [194~195°].

⑥ Tetrahedron 9, 130 (1960).

$PC_{25}H_{39}$

① Benzylidenetricyclohexylphosphorane

$(C_6H_{11})_3P=CHC_6H_5$

② $[(C_6H_{11})_3PCH_2C_6H_5]Cl + NaOC_2H_5$

   $\dfrac{C_2H_5OH}{}$

④ $+ O_2 \longrightarrow trans\text{-}C_6H_5CH=CHC_6H_5$
   $+ (C_6H_{11})_3PO$

⑥ Ber. **96**, 1899 (1963).

$PC_{26}H_{21}O$

① 2-Triphenylphosphoranylidene acetophenone

$(C_6H_5)_3P=CHCOC_6H_5$

② $(C_6H_5)_3P=CH_2 + C_6H_5COCl \xrightarrow{C_6H_6} 71\%$

   $(C_6H_5)_3P=CH_2 + C_6H_5COSC_2H_5 \xrightarrow{C_6H_5CH_3}$

   80%

   $(C_6H_5)_3P=CH_2$

   $+ [(C_6H_5)_3PCH_2C_6H_5CH_2]Br \xrightarrow{C_6H_5CH_3}$

   $[(C_6H_5)_3PCH_2COC_6H_5]Br$

   $\dfrac{10\%\ aq.\ Na_2CO_3}{}$ 58%

③ [178~180° ($C_2H_5OCOCH_3$)].

④ $+ aq.\ C_2H_5OH \longrightarrow CH_3COC_6H_5$
   (93%)

   $+ C_6H_5COCHN_2 \longrightarrow C_{24}H_{18}O$(50~60%)

   $+ C_6H_5CH_3 \longrightarrow C_6H_5CH=CHCOC_6H_5$
   (70%)

⑥ Tetrahedron Letters 1960, 7.   Ber. **95**, 1513 (1962).   Acta Chem. Scand. **15**, 692 (1961). BCSJ **35**, 2042(1962).

PC$_{26}$H$_{21}$O

① Phenyl(triphenylphosphoranylidene)
   acetaldehyde
   (C$_6$H$_5$)$_3$P=C(C$_6$H$_5$)CHO

② 2 (C$_6$H$_5$)$_3$P=CHC$_6$H$_5$ + HCCl$_2$N(CH$_3$)$_2$
   $\longrightarrow$ [(C$_6$H$_5$)$_3$PCC$_6$H$_5$=CHN(CH$_3$)$_2$]Cl
   $\xrightarrow{\text{C}_6\text{H}_5\text{CH}_3}$

   $\xrightarrow[\text{dil. NaOH}]{\text{H}^+}$ [(C$_6$H$_5$)$_3$PCHC$_6$H$_5$CHO]Cl (72%)

③ [124~126° (monohydrate)].

⑥ Tetrahedron Letters, 1962, 1027.

PC$_{26}$H$_{23}$

① α-Methylbenzylidenetriphenylphos-
   phorane
   (C$_6$H$_5$)$_3$P=C(CH$_3$)C$_6$H$_5$

② [(C$_6$H$_5$)$_3$PCHCH$_3$C$_6$H$_5$]Br + NaNH$_2$
   $\longrightarrow$

④ + O$_2$ $\longrightarrow$ C$_6$H$_5$COCH$_3$ + (C$_6$H$_5$)$_3$PO

⑥ Ber. 96, 1899 (1963).

PC$_{26}$H$_{27}$O$_3$

① 3-Oxo-2-(triphenylphosphoranylidene)hexanoic acid ethyl ester
   (C$_6$H$_5$)$_3$P=C(COOC$_2$H$_5$)COC$_3$H$_7$

② 2 (C$_6$H$_5$)$_3$P=CHCO$_2$C$_2$H$_5$ + C$_3$H$_7$COCl
   $\xrightarrow{\text{C}_6\text{H}_6}$ (C$_6$H$_5$)$_3$P=C(CO$_2$C$_2$H$_5$)COC$_3$H$_7$
   + [(C$_6$H$_5$)$_3$PCH$_2$CO$_2$C$_2$H$_5$]Cl

③ [130~131° (aq. C$_2$H$_5$OH)].

④ $\xrightarrow[\text{280/10 mm, 1 hr}]{\text{pyrolysis,}}$ C$_3$H$_7$C≡CCO$_2$C$_2$H$_5$

⑥ JCS 1962, 2333.

PC$_{26}$H$_{27}$O$_4$

① 2-(Triphenylphosphoranylidene)
   succinic acid diethyl ester
   (C$_6$H$_5$)$_3$P=C(COOC$_2$H$_5$)CH$_2$COOC$_2$H$_5$

② [(C$_6$H$_5$)$_3$PCH(CO$_2$C$_2$H$_5$)CH$_2$CO$_2$C$_2$H$_5$]I
   $\xrightarrow{\text{2 N NaOH}}$

③ [104~106°].

⑥ Ber. 94, 1331 (1961).

PC$_{26}$H$_{28}$IO$_4$

① 1,2-Bis(carbethoxy)ethyltriphenyl-
   phosphonium iodide
   [(C$_6$H$_5$)$_3$PCH(CO$_2$C$_2$H$_5$)CH$_2$CO$_2$C$_2$H$_5$]I

② $\underset{\text{CHCO}_2\text{C}_2\text{H}_5}{\overset{\text{CHCO}_2\text{C}_2\text{H}_5}{\|}}$ + (C$_6$H$_5$)$_3$P + HI $\longrightarrow$ 69%

③ [104° decomp.].

④ + aq. NaOH $\longrightarrow$
   (C$_6$H$_5$)$_3$P=CCH$_2$CO$_2$C$_2$H$_5$
   $\quad\quad\quad$ |
   $\quad\quad\quad$ CO$_2$C$_2$H$_5$

⑥ Ber. 94, 1331 (1961).

PC$_{27}$H$_{20}$NO

① Benzoyl(triphenylphosphoranylidene)acetonitrile
   (C$_6$H$_5$)$_3$P=C(COC$_6$H$_5$)CN

② 2 (C$_6$H$_5$)$_3$P=CHCN + C$_6$H$_5$COCl $\xrightarrow{\text{C}_6\text{H}_6}$
   (C$_6$H$_5$)$_3$P=C(COC$_6$H$_5$)CN
   + [(C$_6$H$_5$)$_3$PCH$_2$CN]Cl

③ [208° (aq. C$_2$H$_5$OH)].

④ $\xrightarrow{\text{pyrolysis}}$ C$_6$H$_5$C≡CCN

⑥ JCS 1962, 2333.

PC$_{27}$H$_{23}$

① Cinnamylidenetriphenylphosphorane
   (C$_6$H$_5$)$_3$P=CHCH=CHC$_6$H$_5$

④ + [O] $\longrightarrow$ C$_6$H$_5$(CH=CH)$_3$C$_6$H$_5$

⑥ Angew. 72, 34 (1960).

PC$_{27}$H$_{23}$N$_2$O$_2$

① (Phenylazo)(triphenylphosphoranylidene)acetic acid methyl ester
   (C$_6$H$_5$)$_3$P=C(N$_2$C$_6$H$_5$)COOCH$_3$

② (C$_6$H$_5$)$_3$P=CHCO$_2$CH$_3$ + C$_6$H$_5$N$_2$BF$_4$ $\longrightarrow$
   [(C$_6$H$_5$)$_3$PCH(N$_2$C$_6$H$_5$)CO$_2$CH$_3$]BF$_4$
   $\xrightarrow[>90\%]{\text{base}}$

③ [197~198°].
   Relatively stable to hydrolysis and
   only decompd. on continued boiling in aq. methanol.

⑥ Tetrahedron Letters 1961, 807.

PC$_{27}$H$_{23}$O

① 1-Phenyl-3-(triphenylphosphoranyl-

idene)-2-propanoe
(C$_6$H$_5$)$_3$P=CHCOCH$_2$C$_6$H$_5$

② (C$_6$H$_5$)$_3$P=CH$_2$ + C$_6$H$_5$CH$_2$COSC$_2$H$_5$
$\xrightarrow{\text{C}_6\text{H}_5\text{CH}_3}$ 42%

③ [147~148°](C$_2$H$_5$OCOCH$_3$−petr. ether).

⑥ Ber. **95**, 1513 (1962).

PC$_{27}$H$_{23}$O

① 2-(Triphenylphosphoranylidene)
propiophenone
(C$_6$H$_5$)$_3$P=C(CH$_3$)COC$_6$H$_5$

② (C$_6$H$_5$)$_3$P=CHCH$_3$ + C$_6$H$_5$COCl $\xrightarrow{\text{C}_6\text{H}_6}$
71%
(C$_6$H$_5$)$_3$P=CHCH$_3$ + C$_6$H$_5$COSC$_2$H$_5$
$\xrightarrow{\text{C}_6\text{H}_5\text{CH}_3}$ 93%

③ [170~172° (CH$_3$COOC$_2$H$_5$)].

④ + aq. C$_2$H$_5$OH $\longrightarrow$ C$_2$H$_5$COC$_6$H$_5$
(84%)

⑥ Tetrahedron Letters **1960**, 7; **1961**,
455.   Ber. **95**, 1513 (1962).

PC$_{27}$H$_{23}$O

① 1-Phenyl-1-(triphenylphosphoranylidene)-2-propanone
(C$_6$H$_5$)$_3$P=C(COCH$_3$)C$_6$H$_5$

② [(C$_6$H$_5$)$_3$PCH(C$_6$H$_5$)COCH$_3$]Cl
$\xrightarrow{\text{aq. NaOH in C}_2\text{H}_5\text{OH}}$

(C$_6$H$_5$)$_3$P=CHC$_6$H$_5$ + CH$_3$COCl $\xrightarrow{\text{C}_6\text{H}_6}$
73%
(C$_6$H$_5$)$_3$P=CHC$_6$H$_5$ + CH$_3$COSC$_2$H$_5$
$\xrightarrow{\text{C}_6\text{H}_5\text{CH}_3}$ 68%

③ [167~168° (aq. C$_2$H$_5$OH)].
Stable in H$_2$O and aq. C$_2$H$_5$OH.

④ $\xrightarrow{\text{pyrolysis}}$ C$_6$H$_5$C≡CCH$_3$ (58%)

⑥ JCS **1961**, 1266; **1962**, 2333. Tetrahedron Letters **1960**, 7. Ber. **95**,
1513 (1962).

PC$_{27}$H$_{24}$Cl

① Cinnamyltriphenylphosphonium

chloride
[(C$_6$H$_5$CH=CHCH$_2$)P(C$_6$H$_5$)$_3$]Cl

② C$_6$H$_5$CH=CHCH$_2$Cl + (C$_6$H$_5$)$_3$P $\xrightarrow{\text{xylene}}$
91~93%

③ [224~226°].

⑥ Spectrochim. Acta **19**, 1905 (1963).
JOC **24**, 1969 (1959).

PC$_{27}$H$_{24}$ClO

① α-Phenylacetonyltriphenylphos-
phonium chloride
[(C$_6$H$_5$)$_3$PCH(COCH$_3$)C$_6$H$_5$]Cl

② (C$_6$H$_5$)$_3$P=CHC$_6$H$_5$ + CH$_3$COCl $\xrightarrow{\text{ether}}$
47%

③ [172~173°].

④ + aq. NaOH $\longrightarrow$
(C$_6$H$_5$)$_3$P=C(COCH$_3$)C$_6$H$_5$

⑥ JCS **1961**, 1266.

PC$_{27}$H$_{26}$I

① Tribenzylphenylphosphonium iodide
[(C$_6$H$_5$CH$_2$)$_3$P(C$_6$H$_5$)]I

② (C$_6$H$_5$P)$_4$ + C$_6$H$_5$CH$_2$I $\xrightarrow{\text{C}_6\text{H}_6}$

③ [199~201°].

⑥ Ber. **94**, 186 (1961).

PC$_{27}$H$_{39}$Si$_3$

① Tris(*p*-trimethylsilylphenyl)phos-
phine
[*p*-(CH$_3$)$_3$SiC$_6$H$_4$]$_3$P

② *p*-(CH$_3$)$_3$SiC$_6$H$_4$MgBr + PCl$_3$ $\xrightarrow{\text{Et}_2\text{O}}$
35~45%

③ (112~117°/31). [95~96°](EtOH).

④ Very resistant to oxidation.
p-(CH$_3$)$_3$SiC$_6$H$_4$MgBr + POCl$_3$ $\xrightarrow{\text{Et}_2\text{O}}$
[*p*-(CH$_3$)$_3$SiC$_6$H$_4$]$_3$PO (30%)

⑥ JACS **75**, 4078 (1953).

PC$_{28}$H$_{23}$O$_3$

① Benzoyl(triphenylphosphoranylidene)acetic acid methyl ester
(C$_6$H$_5$)$_3$P=C(COC$_6$H$_5$)COOCH$_3$

② $(C_6H_5)_3P=CHCO_2CH_3 + C_6H_5COCl \xrightarrow{C_6H_6}$
   83%

③ [133~135° $(C_2H_5OCOCH_3)$].

⑥ Ber. **95**, 1513 (1962).

PC$_{28}$H$_{25}$O

① 4-Phenyl-1-(triphenylphosphoranylidene)-2-butanone
   $(C_6H_5)_3P=CHCOCH_2CH_2C_6H_5$

② $(C_6H_5)_3P=CH_2 + C_6H_5CH_2CH_2COSC_2H_5$
   $\xrightarrow{C_6H_5CH_3}$ 80%
   $(C_6H_5)_3P=CH_2 + C_6H_5CH_2CH_2COCl$
   $\xrightarrow{C_6H_6}$ 49%

③ [148~150° $(C_2H_5OCOCH_3)$].

④ + aq. $C_2H_5OH \longrightarrow$
   $C_6H_5CH_2CH_2COC_2H_5$ (78%)

⑥ Tetrahedron Letters 1961, 455. Ber.
   95, 1513 (1962).

PC$_{28}$H$_{25}$O$_2$

① α-(Triphenylphosphoranylidene)-
   hydrocinnamic acid methyl ester
   $(C_6H_5)_3P=C(CH_2C_6H_5)COOCH_3$

② 2 $(C_6H_5)_3P=CHCO_2CH_3 + BrCH_2C_6H_5$
   $\xrightarrow{CH_3COOC_2H_5,\ 5\,hr}$ 75%
   $(+ [(C_6H_5)_3PCH_2CO_2CH_3]Br, 90\%)$

③ [185~187°].

④ + NaOH + $H_2O \longrightarrow$
   $C_6H_5CH_2CH_2CO_2H$ (100%)

⑥ Tetrahedron Letters 1960, 5.   Ber.
   95, 2921 (1962).

PC$_{28}$H$_{28}$I

① Tetrabenzylphosphonium iodide
   $[(C_6H_5CH_2)_4P]I$

② $(C_6H_5CH_2)_3P + C_6H_5CH_2I \longrightarrow$
   $PH_4I + 4 C_6H_5CH_2I \longrightarrow$

③ [191°].

⑥ Kosolapoff 87. Ber. **93**, 1220 (1960).
   CA **54**, 1730 (1960).

PC$_{29}$H$_{25}$O

① 1-Phenyl-4-(triphenylphosphoranyl-

idene)-1-penten-3-one
   $(C_6H_5)_3P=C(CH_3)COCH=CHC_6H_5$

② $(C_6H_5)_3P=CHCH_3 + C_6H_5CH=CHCOCl$
   $\xrightarrow{C_6H_6}$ 73%
   $(C_6H_5)_3P=CHCH_3 +$
   $C_6H_5CH=CHCOSC_2H_5 \xrightarrow{C_6H_5CH_3}$ 70%

③ [205~208 $(C_2H_5OCOCH_3)$].

④ + aq. $C_2H_5OH \longrightarrow$
   $C_6H_5CH=CHCOC_2H_5$ (74%)
   $+ C_6H_5CHO \longrightarrow$
   $C_6H_5CH=CCH_3COCH=CHC_6H_5$ (81%)

⑥ Ber. **95**, 1513 (1962).

PC$_{29}$H$_{25}$O$_3$

① Benzoyl(triphenylphosphoranylidene)acetic acid ethyl ester
   $(C_6H_5)_3P=C(COC_6H_5)COOC_2H_5$

② $(C_6H_5)_3PCl_2 + C_6H_5COCH_2CO_2C_2H_5$
   $\xrightarrow{(C_2H_5)_3N,\ C_6H_6-CCl_4}$ 77%

③ [142~143°] $(C_2H_5OCOCH_3)$.
   UV: JCS 1962, 233.

④ $\xrightarrow{pyrolysis}$ $C_6H_5C≡CCO_2C_2H_5$ (91%)

⑥ JCS 1962, 2333.

PC$_{29}$H$_{27}$O

① 1-Phenyl-4-(triphenylphosphoranylidene)-3-pentanone
   $(C_6H_5)_3P=C(CH_3)COCH_2CH_2C_6H_5$

② $(C_6H_5)_3P=CHCH_3$
   $+ C_6H_5CH_2CH_2COSC_2H_5 \xrightarrow{C_6H_5CH_3}$ 76%
   $(C_6H_5)_3P=CHCH_3 + C_6H_5CH_2CH_2COCl$
   $\xrightarrow{C_6H_6}$ 50%

③ [164~166° $(C_2H_5OCOCH_3)$].

④ $+ C_6H_5CHO \xrightarrow{C_6H_6}$
   $C_6H_5CH=CCH_3COCH_2CH_2C_6H_5$ (64%)

⑥ Tetrahedron Letters 1961, 455. Ber.
   95, 1513 (1962).

PC$_{30}$H$_{25}$

① Pentaphenylphosphorane
   $(C_6H_5)_5P$

② $(C_6H_5)_4PI + {}^{14}C_6H_5Li \longrightarrow$

$(C_6H_5)_4P^{14}C_6H_5 \cdot \frac{1}{2}C_6H_{12}$

$(C_6H_5)_4PI + C_6D_5Li \longrightarrow$

$(C_6H_5)_4PC_6D_5 \cdot \frac{1}{2}C_6H_{12}$

$[(C_6H_5)_3PNCH_3C_6H_5]Br + 2 C_6H_5Li \longrightarrow$

③ [124° (decomp.)] (cyclohexane).

X-ray diffraction and dipole moment measurement in benzene soln.

④ $\xrightarrow{C_6H_6}$ $(C_6H_5)_2$ with 5~6% solvent C_6H_5 groups

⑥ Zhur. **31**, 2350 (1961). Angew. **70**, 506 (1958). Proc. Chem. Soc. **1962**, 251.

PC$_{31}$H$_{23}$

① Fluren-9-ylidenetriphenylphosphorane

$(C_6H_5)_3P=$

② $[(C_6H_5)_3P-C_{13}H_9]Br^- \xrightarrow{1 \text{ N NaOH}} 88\%$

③ [258~260°].

Dipole moment (C_6H_6, 25 °C) 7.09 D.

④ $(C_6H_5)_3P=C_{13}H_8 + RC_6H_4CHO \xrightarrow{C_6H_6}$

$C_{13}H_8 = CHC_6H_4R$

R (yield %); NO$_2$-p (96); Cl-p (93); H (84); CH$_3$O-p (37); (CH$_3$)$_2$N-p (0)

⑥ Tetrahedron **9**, 130 (1960). JOC **24**, 282 (1959).

PC$_{31}$H$_{24}$Br

① Fluoren-9-yl triphenylphosphonium bromide

$[(C_{13}H_9)P(C_6H_5)_3]Br$

② $C_{13}H_9N_2 + (C_6H_5)_3P \xrightarrow{CuBr} 32\%$

③ [307~310°].

⑥ Kosolapoff 90. Tetrahedron **18**, 1023 (1962). Spectrochim. Acta **19**, 1905 (1963).

PC$_{31}$H$_{24}$NO$_2$

① p-Nitro-α-phenylbenzylidenetriphenylphosphorane

$(C_6H_5)_3P=C(C_6H_5)\dot{C}_6H_4NO_2$-$p$

② $[(C_6H_5)_3PCHC_6H_5C_6H_4NO_2$-$p]Br$

$\xrightarrow{C_2H_5ONa - C_2H_5OH}$

③ [230° (decomp.)] (C_6H_6).

Stable to light and H_2O, no change in boling C_2H_5OH, or $CHCl_3$.

UV: Z. Chem. **1**, 93 (1961)

④ No reaction with aldehydes or ketones.

PC$_{31}$H$_{25}$

① Triphenyldiphenylmethylenephosphorane

$(C_6H_5)_3P=C(C_6H_5)_2$

② $[(C_6H_5)_3PCH(C_6H_5)_2]Br + NaNH_2 \longrightarrow$

④ $+ [O] \longrightarrow (C_6H_5)_3PO + (C_6H_5)_2C=O$

⑥ Ber. **96**, 1899 (1963).

PC$_{31}$H$_{25}$O$_2$S

① (p-Phenylsulfonyl)benzylidenetriphenylphosphorane

$(C_6H_5)_3P=CHC_6H_4SO_2C_6H_5$-$p$

② $[(C_6H_5)_3PCH_2C_6H_4SO_2C_6H_5$-$p]Br$

$\xrightarrow{\text{aq. NaOH}}$

③ Relatively stable in H_2O because of its insol. but it hydrolyzes rapidly in the presence of alc.

④ $+ C_6H_5CHO \longrightarrow$

$C_6H_5CH=CHC_6H_4SO_2C_6H_5$-$p$

⑥ Compt. rend. **248**, 817 (1959).

PC$_{31}$H$_{25}$O$_4$S$_2$

① Bis (phenylsulfonyl) methylene triphenylphosphorane

$(C_6H_5)_3P=C(SO_2C_6H_5)_2$

② $(C_6H_5)_3P + CH_2(SO_2C_6H_5)_2 \xrightarrow{(C_2H_5)_3N, \ C_6H_6} 67\%$

③ [267~269°].

IR: Ann. **627**, 142 (1959).

UV: Ber. **91**, 437 (1958).

PC$_{32}$H$_{25}$O

① 2-Phenyl-2-(triphenylphosphoranylidene) acetophenone
   (C$_6$H$_5$)$_3$P=C(C$_6$H$_5$)COC$_6$H$_5$

② [(C$_6$H$_5$)$_3$PCHC$_6$H$_5$COC$_6$H$_5$]Cl $\xrightarrow{\text{NaOH}}$

   (C$_6$H$_5$)$_3$P=CHC$_6$H$_5$ + C$_6$H$_5$COCl $\xrightarrow{\text{C}_6\text{H}_6}$
   64%

   (C$_6$H$_5$)$_3$P=CHC$_6$H$_5$ + C$_6$H$_5$COSC$_2$H$_5$
   $\xrightarrow{\text{C}_6\text{H}_5\text{CH}_3}$ 58%

③ [192~194° (C$_2$H$_5$OCOCH$_3$)].
   Stable in H$_2$O.

⑥ JCS 1961, 1266.   Tetrahedron Letters
   1960, 7.   Ber. 95, 1513 (1962).

PC$_{33}$H$_{27}$O

① (2-Hydroxy-3,3-diphenylallyl) triphenylphosphonium hydroxide,
   inner salt
   (C$_6$H$_5$)$_3$P$^+$−CH$_2$−C=C(C$_6$H$_5$)$_2$
   　　　　　　　　　　|
   　　　　　　　　　O$^-$

② (C$_6$H$_5$)$_3$P=CH$_2$ + (C$_6$H$_5$)$_2$C=C=O
   $\xrightarrow{\text{(C}_2\text{H}_5)_2\text{O}}$ 12%

③ [175.5~177°].

④ $\xrightarrow[\text{(85%)}]{\text{5% HBr}}$ [(C$_6$H$_5$)$_3$P−CH$_2$CCH(C$_6$H$_5$)$_2$]Br
   　　　　　　　　　　　　　　　　||
   　　　　　　　　　　　　　　　O

   $\xrightarrow[\text{(74%)}]{\text{CH}_3\text{I}}$ [(C$_6$H$_5$)$_3$P−CH$_2$CCCH$_3$(C$_6$H$_5$)$_2$]I
   　　　　　　　　　　　　　　　　　　||
   　　　　　　　　　　　　　　　　　O

⑥ Ber. 96, 1535 (1963).

PC$_{34}$H$_{25}$

① 1-Phenylphosphacyclotetraphenyl-
   pentadiene

   C$_6$H$_5$—⌐———┐—C$_6$H$_5$
   C$_6$H$_5$—└—P—┘—C$_6$H$_5$
   　　　　　|
   　　　　C$_6$H$_5$

② C$_6$H$_5$PCl$_2$ + Li−C══C───C══C−Li
   　　　　　　　　|　　|　　|　　|
   　　　　　　　C$_6$H$_5$ C$_6$H$_5$ C$_6$H$_5$ C$_6$H$_5$
   ⟶ 68%

③ Pale yellow, fluorescent needles.

[256~257°].

Quite sensitive to oxidation.

④

⑥ Chem. Ind. 1959, 1250.   JACS 81,
   3163 (1959) ; 82, 5099 (1960).

PC$_{34}$H$_{29}$O

① (2-Hydroxy-1-methyl-3,3-diphenyl
   allyl) triphenylphosphonium
   hydroxide, inner salt
   (C$_6$H$_5$)$_3$P$^+$−CH(CH$_3$)−C=C(C$_6$H$_5$)$_2$
   　　　　　　　　　　　　|
   　　　　　　　　　　　O$^-$

② (C$_6$H$_5$)$_3$P=CHCH$_3$ + (C$_6$H$_5$)$_2$C=C=O
   $\xrightarrow{\text{(C}_2\text{H}_5)_2\text{O}}$ 45%

③ [182~184°].

   $\xrightarrow[\text{(77%)}]{\text{5% HBr}}$

   [(C$_6$H$_5$)$_3$P−CHCH$_3$CCH(C$_6$H$_5$)$_2$]Br
   　　　　　　　　　　　　||
   　　　　　　　　　　　O

⑥ Ber. 96, 1535 (1963).

PC$_{35}$H$_{31}$O

① (2-Hydroxy-1,1-dimethyl-3,3-di-
   phenylallyl) triphenylphosphonium
   hydroxide, inner salt
   (C$_6$H$_5$)$_3$P$^+$−C(CH$_3$)$_2$C=C(C$_6$H$_5$)$_2$
   　　　　　　　　　　　|
   　　　　　　　　　　O$^-$

② (C$_6$H$_5$)$_3$P=C(CH$_3$)$_2$ + (C$_6$H$_5$)$_2$C=C=O
   $\xrightarrow{\text{(C}_2\text{H}_5)_2\text{O}}$ 83%

③ [139~140° (decomp.)] (CH$_2$Cl$_2$
   −C$_2$H$_5$OH).

   Intermediate of allene.

④ $\xrightarrow{5\% \text{ HBr}}$

$[(C_6H_5)_3PC(CH_3)_2C-CH(C_6H_5)_2]Br$
$\qquad\qquad\qquad\quad \underset{O}{\overset{\|}{\;}}$

$\xrightarrow[160°/0.2\,mm]{\text{heat}}$

$(C_6H_5)_3PO + (CH_3)_2C=C=C(C_6H_5)_2$
$\;\;(96\%) \qquad\qquad (64\%)$

⑥ Ber. **96**, 1535 (1963).

$PC_{37}H_{32}BrGe$

① (Triphenylgermylmethyl)triphenyl-
phosphonium bromide
$[(C_6H_5)_3GeCH_2P(C_6H_5)_3]Br$

② $(C_6H_5)_3GeBr + (C_6H_5)_3P=CH_2 \xrightarrow{Et_2O}$

③ [121~122°].
Very sol. in methanol.

⑥ JACS **83**, 1610 (1961).

$PC_{38}H_{37}O$

① (β-Hydroxy-α,α, 2,4,6-pentamethyl-
γ-phenylcinnamyl) triphenylphosphonium hydroxide, inner salt
$(C_6H_5)_3P^+-C(CH_3)_2C=$
$\qquad\qquad\qquad\qquad |$
$\qquad\qquad\qquad\qquad O^-$
$\qquad\qquad C(C_6H_5)[C_6H_2(CH_3)_3-2,4,6]$

② $(C_6H_5)_3P=C(CH_3)_2 +$
$[2,4,6-(CH_3)_3C_6H_2](C_6H_5)C=C=O$
$\xrightarrow[\;\;]{(C_2H_5)_2O} 57\%$
$\quad(C_2H_5)_2O$

③ [145~146° decomp.].
Light-sensitive.

④ $\xrightarrow{10\% \text{ HBr}} \{(C_6H_5)_3PC(CH_3)_2C-$
$\qquad\qquad\qquad\qquad\qquad\underset{O}{\overset{\|}{\;}}$

$CH(C_6H_5)-[C_6H_2(CH_3)_3-2,4,6]\}Br$
$\xrightarrow[160°/0.2\,mm]{\text{heat}} (C_6H_5)_3PO + (CH_3)_2C=$
$C=C(C_6H_5)[C_6H_2(CH_3)_3-2,4,6]$

⑥ Ber. **96**, 1535 (1963).

P_2Cl_5NO

① (Dichlorophosphinyl) phosphorimidic
trichloride
$Cl_3P=N-P(O)Cl_2$

② $[Cl_3P=N-PCl_3]^+[PCl_6]^- + 2SO_2 \longrightarrow$
$3PCl_5 + H_2N-P(O)(OH)_2 \longrightarrow$
$P(O)(NH_2)_3 + 2PCl_5 \longrightarrow$

③ [35°].

④ $+ C_6H_5NH_2 \longrightarrow$

$\qquad\qquad\qquad O$
$\qquad\qquad\qquad \|$
$(C_6H_5NH)_3P=N-P(NHC_6H_5)_2$

⑥ Ber. **94**, 193, 1383, 1388, 1591 (1961).
Z. anorg. allg. Chem. **315**, 181(1962).

$P_2CH_2Cl_4O_2$

① Metylenediphosphonic dichloride
$Cl_2P(O)CH_2P(O)Cl_2$

② $[(HO)_2P(O)]_2CH_2 + PCl_5 \xrightarrow{\text{ligroin}} 60\%$

③ [101~102°].
NMR: J. Chem. Eng. Data **7**, 307
(1962).

④ $+ C_6H_{13}MgBr \xrightarrow{C_6H_6}$
$[(C_6H_{13})_2P(O)]_2CH_2$

⑥ JACS **83**, 1722 (1961).

$P_2CH_6O_6$

① Methylenediphosphonic acid
$(HO)_2P(O)CH_2P(O)(OH)_2$

② $[(C_4H_9O)_2P(O)]_2CH_2 + HCl \longrightarrow$
$[(C_2H_5O)_2P(O)]_2CH_2 + HCl \longrightarrow$

③ [201°].
Insol. in ether and benzene.
IR: JACS **88**, 1722 (1961).
NMR: J. Chem. Eng. Data **7**, 307
(1962); JINC **22**, 297 (1961).

④ $+ PCl_5 \longrightarrow [Cl_2P(O)]_2CH_2 + POCl_3$

⑥ JACS **85**, 3292 (1963). JCS **1959**, 2266.

$P_2C_2H_2F_6$

① Bis(trifluoromethyl)diphosphine
HCF_3P-PCF_3H

② $(CF_3P)_4 + H_2O \xrightarrow{140°}$
$(CF_3P)_5 + H_2O \longrightarrow$

③ (69.5°).
Stable on heating.
IR: JACS **80**, 6161 (1958).

④ $\xrightarrow[+ \text{HCF}_3]{\text{heating in } 225°}$ $CF_3PH_2 + (CF_3)_2PH$

P₂C₂H₈O₆

① Ethylenediphosphonic acid
$(HO)_2P(O)CH_2CH_2P(O)(OH)_2$

② $(CH_2Cl)_2 + (C_2H_5O)_2PONa \xrightarrow{\text{HCl}} 59\%$
$(C_6H_5O)_2P(O)CH_2CH_2P(O)(OC_6H_5)_3$
$\xrightarrow{\text{HCl}} 80\%$

③ Plates. [220~221°]. d 1.4438 (20°).
Sol. in H₂O, C₂H₅OH ; slightly sol. in
(CH₃)₂CO ; insol. in ether, petr.
ether and C₆H₆.
NMR : J. Chem. Eng. Data **7**, 307
(1962).

⑤ Extractant.

⑥ Izv. OKhN **1947**, 631.   JINC **22**, 297
(1961).   Zhur. **30**, 1608 (1960).

P₂C₃H₁₀O₆

① Trimethylenediphosphonic acid
$(HO)_2P(O)(CH_2)_3P(O)(OH)_2$

② $(C_2H_5O)_3P + BrCH_2CH_2CH_2Br \xrightarrow{\text{HBr aq.}}$

③ Crystals. [170.5~172°].
NMR : J. Chem. Eng. Data **7**, 307
(1962).

⑤ Extractant.

⑥ JACS **66**, 1511 (1944).   Ber. **59**, 1119
(1926).   JINC **22**, 297 (1961).

P₂C₄F₁₂

① Tetra(trifluoromethyl)diphosphine
$(CF_3)_2P-P(CF_3)_2$

② $2 (CF_3)_2PI + Hg \longrightarrow 82\%$

③ Colorless liq. (84°).

④ $+ Ni(CO)_4 \longrightarrow$

$$(CO)_3Ni-\overset{\overset{\displaystyle CF_3}{|}}{P}-\overset{\overset{\displaystyle CF_3}{|}}{P}-Ni(CO)_3$$
$$\underset{CF_3}{} \quad \underset{CF_3}{}$$

$+ H_2 \longrightarrow (CF_3)_2PH$

$+ I_2 \xrightarrow{280°} CF_3I$

⑥ JCS **1953**, 1565.   JACS **79**, 4242(1957).

P₂C₄H₁₂

① Tetramethyldiphosphine
$(CH_3)_2P-P(CH_3)_2$

② $(CH_3)_2P(S)P(S)(CH_3)_2 \xrightarrow{\text{reduction}} 90\%$
$(CH_3)_2PH + (CH_3)_2NP(CH_3)_2 \longrightarrow$
85%
$(CH_3)_2PCl + 2 (CH_3)_2PH \longrightarrow 81\%$
$(CH_3)_2NP(CH_3)_2 + (CH_3)_2PH_2Cl \longrightarrow$
96%

③ Colorless liq. (140.2°). [−2.25°].
Air-sensitive.

④ $+ B_2H_6 \longrightarrow (CH_3)_2P-P(CH_3)_2$
$$\underset{BH_3}{\overset{\displaystyle |}{}}$$

$+ 2 HCl \longrightarrow (CH_3)_2PH_2Cl$
$+ (CH_3)_2PCl$

$+ CH_3I \longrightarrow [(CH_3)_5P_2]^+I^-$

$+ K \ (\text{or Na}) \xrightarrow{\text{H}_2\text{O}} (CH_3)_2PH$

$+ CH_2=CH_2 \longrightarrow$
$(CH_3)_2PCH_2CH_2P(CH_3)_2$

⑥ JACS **83**, 2226 (1961).   Ber. **93**, 1852
(1960) ; **95**, 64 (1962).   JINC **24**, 275
(1962) ; **14**, 291 (1960).   Z. Naturf.
15 b, 327 (1960).

P₂C₄F₁₂O

① Bis(trifluoromethyl)phosphinous
acid anhydride
$(CF_3)_2POP(CF_3)_2$

② $(CF_3)_2PI + Ag_2CO_3 \longrightarrow 79\%$

③ (78.4°). [−53.1~−52.6°].
IR : JACS **84**, 3442 (1962).

④ $+ HCl \longrightarrow (CF_3)_2PCl + (CF_3)_2POH$

$+ Cl_2 \longrightarrow (CF_3)_2POCl + (CF_3)_2PCl$

$+ (CH_3)_3N \longrightarrow$
$(CF_3)_2POP(CF_3) \cdot N(CH_3)_3$

⑥ JACS **82**, 1507 (1960).

PC₄H₁₂O₆

① Tetramethylenediphosphonic acid
$(HO)_2P(O)(CH_2)_4P(O)(OH)_2$

② $[(HO)_2P]_2(CH_2)_4 + H_2O_2 \longrightarrow$

③ Red crystals. [190~195°].

NMR : J. Chem. Eng. Data **7**, 307 (1962).

⑥ JINC **22**, 297 (1961). Ber. **95**, 473 (1962).

P$_2$C$_5$H$_{14}$O$_2$

① Bis(dimethylphosphinyl)methane
[(CH$_3$)$_2$P(O)]$_2$CH$_2$

② [Cl$_2$P(O)]$_2$CH$_2$ + CH$_3$MgBr $\longrightarrow$ 10%

③ Needles. [132~134°] (petr. ether).
Hygroscopic.
IR : JACS **83**, 1722 (1961).

P$_2$C$_6$H$_{16}$

① Ethylenebis(dimethylphosphine)
(CH$_3$)$_2$PCH$_2$CH$_2$P(CH$_3$)$_2$

② (CH$_3$)$_2$P−P(CH$_3$)$_2$ + CH$_2$=CH$_2$ $\longrightarrow$
(CH$_3$)$_2$PNa + ClCH$_2$CH$_2$Cl $\xrightarrow{\text{in liq. NH}_3}$
35~40%
(CH$_3$)$_2$P(S)P(S)(CH$_3$)$_2$ + CH$_2$=CH$_2$
$\longrightarrow$ (CH$_3$)$_2$P(S)CH$_2$CH$_2$P(S)(CH$_3$)$_2$
$\xrightarrow{(n\text{-C}_4\text{H}_9)_3\text{P}}$ 78%

③ Colorless liq. (188.1°). [−1~0°]. n_D
1.4887 (25°).

④ + BrCH$_2$CH$_2$Br $\longrightarrow$
[(CH$_3$)$_2$$\overset{+}{\text{P}}$(C$_2H_4$)$_2$$\overset{+}{\text{P}}$(CH$_3$)$_2$]2Br$^-$
+ RuCl$_3$ $\longrightarrow$
trans-[(CH$_3$)$_2$PCH$_2$CH$_2$P(CH$_3$)$_2$]$_2$RuCl$_2$
+ (NH$_4$)$_2$OsCl$_6$ $\longrightarrow$
trans-[(CH$_3$)$_2$PCH$_2$CH$_2$P(CH$_3$)$_2$]$_2$OsCl$_2$

⑥ JACS **83**, 2226 (1961). JCS **1961**, 896
JINC **14**, 291 (1960).

P$_2$C$_6$H$_{16}$

① Ethylenebisethylphosphine
H(C$_2$H$_5$)PCH$_2$CH$_2$P(C$_2$H$_5$)H

② KPH(C$_2$H$_5$) + ClCH$_2$CH$_2$Cl $\xrightarrow{(n\text{-C}_3\text{H}_7)_2\text{O}}$
44%

③ Colorless oil. (90°/18).
Sol. in org. solvents. Air sensitive.

④ $\xrightarrow[\text{(C}_2\text{H}_5)_2\text{O}]{\text{CH}_3\text{I}}$ [H(C$_2$H$_5$)$\overset{+}{\text{P}}$(CH$_3$)CH$_2$CH$_2$$\overset{+}{\text{P}}$H-
(C$_2$H$_5$)(CH$_3$)]2 I$^-$

$\xrightarrow[\text{C}_6\text{H}_6]{\text{S}}$ [H·RP(S)CH$_2$CH$_2$P(S)RH]

⑥ Ber. **96**, 1544 (1963).

P$_2$C$_6$H$_{16}$

① 1,2-Diethyl-1,2-dimethyldiphosphine
(CH$_3$)(C$_2$H$_5$)P−P(C$_2$H$_5$)(CH$_3$)

② (CH$_3$)(C$_2$H$_5$)P(S)−P(S)(C$_2$H$_5$)(CH$_3$)
+ 2 (C$_4$H$_9$)$_3$P $\longrightarrow$
(CH$_3$)(C$_2$H$_5$)P−P(C$_2$H$_5$)(CH$_3$)
+ 2 (C$_4$H$_9$)$_3$PS

③ (188~190°).

④ + S (equivalent) $\longrightarrow$
(CH$_3$)(C$_2$H$_5$)P−P(S)(CH$_3$)(C$_2$H$_5$)
+ [CH$_3$(C$_2$H$_5$)P(S)]$_2$ $\xrightarrow{190°}$
(CH$_3$)(C$_2$H$_5$)P−P(S)(CH$_3$)(C$_2$H$_5$)
+ K (or Na) $\xrightarrow[\text{or CH}_3\text{OH}]{\text{H}_2\text{O}}$ (C$_2$H$_5$)$_2$PH

⑥ JINC **24**, 275 (1962). Helv. Chim.
Acta **45**, 2381 (1962).

P$_2$C$_6$H$_{16}$O$_2$

① Ethylenebis (dimethylphosphine
oxide)
[(CH$_3$)$_2$P(O)]$_2$(CH$_2$)$_2$

② [(*i*-PrO)$_2$P(O)]$_2$(CH$_2$)$_2$ $\xrightarrow{\text{PCl}_5}$
89%
[Cl$_2$P(O)]$_2$(CH$_2$)$_2$ $\xrightarrow{\text{CH}_3\text{MgI}}$

③ [232~233°].
Sublimes at 190°/10.1 mm.

⑥ JCS **1961**, 2423.

P$_2$C$_6$H$_{16}$S$_2$

① Ethylenebis(dimethylphosphine
sulfide)
(CH$_3$)$_2$P(S)CH$_2$CH$_2$P(S)(CH$_3$)$_2$

② (CH$_3$)$_2$P(S)−P(S)(CH$_3$)$_2$
+ CH$_2$=CH$_2$ $\longrightarrow$

⑥ JINC **14**, 291 (1960).

P$_2$C$_6$H$_{16}$S$_2$

① Ethylenebis(ethylphosphine
sulfide)

$[(C_2H_5)P(S)H]_2(CH_2)_2$

② $(C_2H_5PH)_2(CH_2)_2 + S \xrightarrow{C_6H_6}$

③ [109~110°] (aq. CH₃COCH₃).

⑥ Ber. **96**, 1544 (1963).

P₂C₇H₁₈O₂

① Trimethylenebis (dimethylphosphine oxide)

$[(CH_3)_2P(O)]_2(CH_2)_3$

② $(C_2H_5O)_2PHO + CH_3MgI \longrightarrow$

$(CH_3)_2PHO$

$\xrightarrow{(p-CH_3C_6H_4SO_3)_2(CH_2)_3} 23.5\%$

③ [211~212°].

Sublimes in vacuum.

⑥ JCS **1961**, 2423.   JACS **81**, 4803 (1958).

P₂C₈H₁₈

① 1,4-Diethyl-1,4-diphosphacyclo-hexane

$(C_2H_5)PCH_2CH_2P(C_2H_5)CH_2CH_2$

② $C_2H_5(Li)PCH_2CH_2P(Li)C_2H_5$

$+ ClCH_2CH_2Cl \xrightarrow{(C_2H_5)_2O} 58\%$

③ Yellow oil. (135~145°/4).

Oxydized in air.

④ $\xrightarrow[C_6H_6]{S} R-P\underset{\underset{S}{\|}}{\overset{CH_2-CH_2}{\diagup \diagdown}}\underset{CH_2-CH_2}{}P-R$

⑥ Ber. **96**, 1544 (1963).

P₂C₈H₁₈S₂

① 1,4-Diethyl-1,4-diphosphacyclo-hexane 1,4-disulfide

$(C_2H_5)(S)P\underset{CH_2CH_2}{\overset{CH_2CH_2}{\diagup \diagdown}}P(S)(C_2H_5)$

② $EtP\underset{}{\bigcirc}PEt + S \xrightarrow{C_6H_6}$

③ [225~235°].

⑥ Ber. **96**, 1544 (1963).

P₂C₈H₂₀

① Tetraethyldiphosphine

$(C_2H_5)_2P-P(C_2H_5)_2$

② $(C_2H_5)_2PCl + Na \longrightarrow 91\%$

$(C_2H_5)_2PBr + LiP(C_2H_5)_2 \longrightarrow LiBr$

$+ [(C_2H_5)_2P]_2$

$LiP(C_2H_5)_2 + BrCH_2CH_2Br \longrightarrow 81\%$

$LiP(C_2H_5)_2 + CH_2Cl_2 \longrightarrow 76\%$

$(C_2H_5)_2P(S)P(S)(C_2H_5)_2 \xrightarrow{reduction}$

80%

③ Colorless liq. (220~221°).

Air-sensitive.

④ $+ K$ (in decaline) $\xrightarrow{100°} (C_2H_5)_2PK$

$+ K \xrightarrow{H_2O} (C_2H_5)_2PH$

$+ Na \xrightarrow{dioxane} (C_2H_5)_2PNa$

$+ S \xrightarrow{benzene}$

$(C_2H_5)_2P(S)-P(S)(C_2H_5)_2$

$+ C_2H_5I \longrightarrow [(C_2H_5)_5P_2]^+I^-$

⑥ JCS **1957**, 3939; **1962**, 1490. Ber. **92**, 2681 (1959); **93**, 1852 (1960); **95**, 64 (1962).   JINC **24**, 275 (1962).

P₂C₈H₂₀O₂

① Tetramethylenebis(dimethylphosphine oxide)

$[(CH_3)_2P(O)]_2(CH_2)_4$

② $2(CH_3)_2P(O)Cl + BrMg(CH_2)_4MgBr$

$\longrightarrow 36\%$

③ (219~222°/0.35). [203~205°].

Hygroscopic. Forms adduct with C₂H₅OH.

⑥ JCS **1959**, 3950.

P₂C₈H₂₀O₃

① Diethylphosphinic acid anhydride

$(C_2H_5)_2P(O)-O-P(O)(C_2H_5)_2$

② $[(C_2H_5)_2PS]_2 + HgO \xrightarrow{xylene} 72\%$

$(C_2H_5)_2POCl + (C_2H_5)_2P(O)OC_2H_5 \longrightarrow$

73%

③ Colorless liq. (124~125°/0.5). n_D 1.4727 (20°).

Sensitive to moisture.

④ $+ H_2O \longrightarrow (C_2H_5)_2P(O)OH$

⑥ Ber. **95**, 1703 (1962); **96**, 896 (1963).

P₂C₈H₂₀O₄

① Tetramethylenebis(phosphonous acid tetramethyl ester)
$(CH_3O)_2P(CH_2)_4P(OCH_3)_2$

② $ClMg(CH_2)_4MgCl + (CH_3O)_2PCl \longrightarrow$
18.5%
$ClMg(CH_2)_4MgCl + (CH_3O)_3P \longrightarrow$
<10%

③ (87~89°/1). n_D 1.4693 (22°).

④ + 5% aq. HCl $\longrightarrow$
$(CH_3O)(H)(O)P(CH_2)_4P(O)(H)(OCH_3)$

⑥ Ber. **95**, 473 (1962).

P₂C₈H₂₀S₂

① Tetraethyldiphosphine disulfide
$(C_2H_5)_2P(S)-P(S)(C_2H_5)_2$

② $C_2H_5MgBr + PSCl_3 \longrightarrow$ 96%
$C_2H_5MgCl + PSCl_3 \longrightarrow$ 22%

③ Colorless plate crystals. [77~78°].
Sol. in acetone, C_6H_6, CS_2; insol. in H_2O.

④ + Fe $\xrightarrow{\text{reducution}}$ $(C_2H_5)_2P-P(C_2H_5)_2$
+ LiAlH₄ $\longrightarrow$ $(C_2H_5)_2PH$
+ Br₂ $\longrightarrow$ $(C_2H_5)_2P(S)Br$
+ Cl₂ $\longrightarrow$ $(C_2H_5)_2PCl_3$

⑥ Ber. **95**, 64 (1962); **92**, 704 (1959).
Ann. **652**, 28 (1962).

P₂C₉H₂₂O₆

① Methylenediphosphonic acid tetraethyl ester
$(C_2H_5O)_2P(O)CH_2P(O)(OC_2H_5)_2$

② $(C_2H_5O)_3P + CH_2I_2 \longrightarrow$ 18%

③ Colorless oil. (143°/1.5, 135~137°/0.4).
n_D 1.4261 (30°). d 1.1325 (30°).
Sol. in org. solvents.
IR: JACS **88**, 4454 (1962)
UV: NMR: JACS **85**, 2394 (1962);
88, 4454 (1962). J. Chem. Eng. Data
7, 307 (1962).

④ + Na $\longrightarrow$ {[(C₂H₅O)₂PO]₂CH}Na
$\xrightarrow{CH_3I}$ $[(C_2H_5O)_2PO]_2CHCH_3$
+ K + C₄H₉Br $\longrightarrow$

$[(C_2H_5O)_2PO]_2CH_2CH_2CH_2CH_2CH_3$

⑥ JCS **1947**, 1465; **1955**, 3092.

P₂C₁₀H₂₀

① Bis(diethylphosphino)acetylene
$(C_2H_5)_2PC\equiv CP(C_2H_5)_2$

② $(C_2H_5)_2PCl + BrMgC\equiv CMgBr \xrightarrow{\text{THF}}$

③ (54°/0.07). n_D 1.5332 (20°).

④ + H₂ $\xrightarrow{\text{Raney Ni}}$
$(C_2H_5)_2PCH_2CH_2P(C_2H_5)_2$

⑥ JCS **1960**, 1378.

P₂C₁₀H₂₄

① Ethylenebis(diethylphosphine)
$(C_2H_5)_2PCH_2CH_2P(C_2H_5)_2$

② $[(C_2H_5)_2(H)\overset{+}{P}CH_2CH_2\overset{+}{P}(H)(C_2H_5)_2]2\,Br^-$
$\xrightarrow{\text{NaOH}}$

$(C_2H_5)_2PLi + ClCH_2CH_2Cl \xrightarrow{\text{THF}}$ 94%
$PH_3 + Na + C_2H_5Br \xrightarrow{\text{liq. NH}_3}$
$(C_2H_5)_2PCl + BrMgC\equiv CMgBr \xrightarrow{\text{THF}}$
$(C_2H_5)_2PC\equiv CP(C_2H_5)_2 \xrightarrow{\text{H}_2 \text{ (Raney Ni)}}$

③ (124~126°/10). n_D 1.5100 (20°).

④ + Ni(CO)₄ $\longrightarrow$
$[Ni(CO)_2C_2H_4\{P(C_2H_5)_2\}]$
+ RuCl₃ $\longrightarrow$
$trans\text{-}[(C_2H_5)_2PCH_2CH_2P(C_2H_5)_2]_2RuCl_2$
+ (NH₄)₂OsCl₆ $\longrightarrow$
$trans\text{-}[(C_2H_5)_2PCH_2CH_2P(C_2H_5)_2]_2OsCl_2$
+ HI $\longrightarrow$
$[(C_2H_5)_2\overset{+}{P}(H)CH_2CH_2\overset{+}{P}(H)(C_2H_5)_2]2\,I^-$
+ CoX₂ $\longrightarrow$
$[(C_2H_5)_2PCH_2CH_2P(C_2H_5)_2]_2CoX_2$
X=Cl, Br, I
+ CH₃I $\longrightarrow$
$[CH_3(C_2H_5)_2\overset{+}{P}CH_2CH_2\overset{+}{P}(C_2H_5)_2CH_3]2\,I^-$

⑥ JCS **1960**, 1378; **1962**, 1490. JINC **14**, 42 (1960). Ber. **96**, 2186 (1963).

P₂C₁₀H₂₄O₂

① Ethylenebis(diethylphosphine oxide)
$[(C_2H_5)_2P(O)]_2(CH_2)_2$

② $(C_2H_5)_2POCH_2CH_2Cl \xrightarrow{C_6H_5CH_3}$

$[(C_2H_5)_2P(O)]_2(CH_2)_2$
(15%)
$+ (C_2H_5)_2P(O)CH_2CH_2Cl$
(70%)

③ $[122\sim123°]$.

⑥ Dokl. **135**, 849 (1960).

P₂C₁₀H₂₄O₆

① Ethylenediphosphonic acid tetraethyl ester
$(C_2H_5O)_2P(O)CH_2CH_2P(O)(OC_2H_5)_2$

② $(C_2H_5O)_3P + BrCH_2CH_2Br \longrightarrow 61\%$
$(C_2H_5O)_3P +$
$BrCH_2CH_2P(O)(OC_2H_5)_2 \longrightarrow$

③ Colorless liq. (152°/0.5). n_D 1.4410
(20°). d 1.1376 (20°).
Sol. in org. solvents.
NMR : J. Chem. Eng. Data **7**, 307
(1962).

⑥ JCS **1947**, 1465 ; **1955**, 3092. JOC **24**,
532 (1959). JINC **22**, 297 (1961).

P₂C₁₁H₂₆O₆

① Trimethylenediphosphonic acid
tetraethyl ester
$(C_2H_5O)_2P(O)(CH_2)_3P(O)(OC_2H_5)_2$

② $(C_2H_5O)_3P + BrCH_2CH_2CH_2Br \longrightarrow$
75%

③ Colorless liq. (198~199°/8). n_D 1.4422
(30°). d 1.1186 (30°/4°).
NMR : J. Chem. Eng. Data **7**, 307
(1962).

④ $\xrightarrow{\text{hydrolysis}} [(HO)_2P(O)]_2(CH_2)_3$

⑥ JCS **1947**, 1465 ; **1955**, 3092. JACS **66**,
1511 (1944). JINC **22**, 297 (1961).

P₂C₁₂H₁₀Cl₅N

① Phenyldichloro[(phenyldichlorophos-
phoranylidene) amino] phosphorus
chloride
$[C_6H_5P(Cl_2)=N-P(Cl_2)C_6H_5]^+Cl^-$

② $C_6H_5PCl_2 + NH_4Cl + Cl_2 \longrightarrow 60\%$
$C_6H_5PCl_2 + NCl_3 \longrightarrow 20\%$

$[C_6H_5P(Cl_2)NP(Cl_2)C_6H_5]^+PCl_6^- \xrightarrow{\text{heating}}$

③ Crystals. [210°].

④ $+ 4 H_2O$ (or 4 HCOOH)

$$\longrightarrow \overset{O}{\underset{OH}{\overset{\|}{C_6H_5P}}}-N=\overset{OH}{\underset{OH}{PC_6H_5}}$$

⑥ Ber. **96**, 3085 (1963).

P₂C₁₂H₁₂

① Diphenyldiphosphine
$H(C_6H_5)PP(C_6H_5)H$

② $C_6H_5 \cdot HPK + BrCH_2CH_2Br \longrightarrow 57\%$
$C_6H_5 \cdot HPK + CH_2Cl_2 \longrightarrow 50.8\%$

③ $[151\sim152°]$.
Sol. in C_6H_6, dioxane and acetone ;
insol. in H_2O, ether and C_2H_5OH.

④ $+ CH_3I \longrightarrow [(CH_3)_2C_6H_5HP]^+I^-$
$+ C_6H_5Li \longrightarrow C_6H_5(Li)P-P(Li)C_6H_5$

⑥ Ber. **94**, 107 (1961).

P₂C₁₂H₁₃NO₄

① Phenyl[(phenyl-dihydroxyphospho-
ranylidene) amino] phosphonic
acid
$C_6H_5P(O)(OH)-N=P(OH)_2C_6H_5$

② $[C_6H_5P(Cl_2)-N=P(Cl_2)C_6H_5]^+Cl^-$
$+ 4 HCOOH \longrightarrow$

③ Needle crystals. [169°].
Insol. in org. solvents ; slightly sol.
in H_2O ; sol. in $(CH_3)_2SO$ and
CH_3OH.

⑥ Ber. **96**, 3085 (1963).

P₂C₁₂H₂₈

① Tetra-*n*-propyldiphosphine
$(n\text{-}C_3H_7)_2PP(n\text{-}C_3H_7)_2$

② $(n\text{-}C_3H_7)_2P(S)P(S)(n\text{-}C_3H_7)_2 \xrightarrow{Cu} 65\%$
$(n\text{-}C_3H_7)_2P(S)P(S)(n\text{-}C_3H_7)_2 + Na$
$\xrightarrow{\text{dioxane}} 79.6\%$

③ Colorless liq. (112~113°/5).
Air-sensitive.

④ + K (or Na) $\xrightarrow[120\sim150°]{\text{decalin}}$

$(n\text{-}C_3H_7)_2PK$ (or Na)

$\xrightarrow[\text{or } CH_3OH]{H_2O}$ $(n\text{-}C_3H_7)_2PH$

⑥ Ber. **93**, 1852 (1960).   Angew. **71**, 162
(1959).   Ann. **652**, 28 (1962).   Ber.
95, 64 (1962).

$P_2C_{12}H_{28}O_2$

① Tetramethylenebis(diethylphosphine oxide)
$[(C_2H_5)_2P(O)]_2(CH_2)_4$

② 2 $(C_2H_5)_2P(O)Cl + BrMg(CH_2)_4MgBr$
$\longrightarrow$ 41%

③ (181~182°/0.25). [111~112°].

⑥ JCS **1959**, 3950.

$P_2C_{12}H_{28}O_3$

① Di-n-propylphosphinic acid
anhydride
$(n\text{-}C_3H_7)_2P(O)-O-P(O)(C_3H_7\text{-}n)_2$

② $[(C_3H_7)_2PS]_2 + HgO \xrightarrow{\text{xylene}}$ 74%

③ Colorless crystals. (133~134°/0.5).
[28~30°].

④ + H_2O $\longrightarrow$ $(C_3H_7)_2P(O)(OH)$

⑥ Ber. **95**, 1703 (1962).

$P_2C_{12}H_{28}O_4$

① Tetramethylenebis(phosphonous
acid tetraethyl ester)
$(C_2H_5O)_2P(CH_2)_4P(OC_2H_5)_2$

② $ClMg(CH_2)_4MgCl + (C_2H_5O)_2PCl \longrightarrow$
26%
$BrMg(CH_2)_4MgBr + (C_2H_5O)_2PCl \longrightarrow$
<10%

③ (135~137°/2). n_D 1.4604 (20°).

④ + 5% aq. HCl $\longrightarrow$
$[(C_2H_5O)(H)(O)P(CH_2)_2]_2$

+ 5% aq. HCl $\xrightarrow{\text{heat}}$
$(HO)(H)(O)P(CH_2)_4P(O)(H)(OH)$

+ $LiAlH_4$ $\xrightarrow{(C_2H_5)_2O}$ $H_2P(CH_2)_4PH_2$

⑥ Ber. **95**, 473 (1962).

$P_2C_{12}H_{28}O_6$

① Tetramethylenephosphonic acid
tetraethyl ester
$(C_2H_5O)_2P(O)(CH_2)_4P(O)(OC_2H_5)_2$

② $(C_2H_5O)_3P + Br(CH_2)_4Br \longrightarrow$ 61.6%

③ Colorless liq. (169°/0.7). n_D 1.4442
(30°). d 1.1040 (30°/4°).

Sol. in org. solvents.

NMR: J. Chem Eng. Data **7**, 307
(1962).

⑥ JINC **22**, 297 (1961).   Makromol.
Chem. **55**, 191(1962). JCS **1955**, 3092.

$P_2C_{13}H_{30}$

① Pentamethylenebis(diethylphosphine)
$(C_2H_5)_2P(CH_2)_5P(C_2H_5)_2$

② $LiP(C_2H_5)_2 + Br(CH_2)_5Br \longrightarrow$ 65%
$[(C_2H_5)_2(H)P^+(CH_2)_5P^+(H)(C_2H_5)_2]2Br^-$
$\xrightarrow{NaOH}$ 70%

③ Liq. (295~315°, 136~139°/3).

Unstable in air; sol. in ether, C_6H_6,
and C_2H_5OH.

④ + S $\xrightarrow{\text{benzene}}$
$(C_2H_5)_2P(S)(CH_2)_5P(S)(C_2H_5)_2$
mp 111~112°

+ CS_2 $\longrightarrow$
$[(C_2H_5)_2P(CH_2)_5P(C_2H_5)_2]2\,CS_2$
mp 84°

⑥ Ber. **92**, 3175 (1959); **96**, 2186 (1963).

$P_2C_{13}H_{30}S_2$

① Pentamethylenebis-diethylphosphine
disulfide
$(C_2H_5)_2P(S)(CH_2)_5P(S)(C_2H_5)_2$

② $(C_2H_5)_2P(CH_2)_5P(C_2H_5)_2 + S \xrightarrow{\text{benzene}}$
80%

③ [111~112°].

Sol. in acetone, C_6H_6, CH_3OH;
slightly insol. in CS_2.

⑥ Ber. **92**, 3175 (1959).

P₂C₁₄H₁₆

① 1,2-Dimethyl-1,2-diphenyldiphos-
   phine
   $(CH_3)(C_6H_5)PP(C_6H_5)(CH_3)$

② $C_6H_5P(Na)-P(Na)C_6H_5 + 2 CH_3Cl \longrightarrow$
   83%

③ (128～130°/0.5). [75～77°].
   Readily oxidized by air.
   NMR: ³¹P; 38.2, 41.7 ppm.

④ $+ O_2$ (air) $\longrightarrow$ $CH_3(C_6H_5)P(O)(OH)$

⑥ JINC **24**, 275 (1962).   JOC **22**, 385
   (1957).

P₂C₁₄H₁₆

① Ethylene-1,2-bis(phenylphosphine)
   $H(C_6H_5)PCH_2CH_2P(C_6H_5)H$

② $NaPHC_6H_5 + ClCH_2CH_2Cl \longrightarrow$ 85%

③ Colorless liq.
   Sol. in org. solvents, unstable in air.
   This compound does not isolate
   by the vacuum distilation, but can
   be purified by the Al₂O₃ adsorption
   chromatographic method.

④ $+ C_6H_5Li \longrightarrow$
   $(C_6H_5)(Li)PCH_2CH_2P(Li)(C_6H_5)$
   $+ H_2O + Na_2O_2 \xrightarrow{HCl}$
   $[(HO)(C_6H_5)P(O)CH_2-]_2$
   $+ CH_3I \longrightarrow$
   $(CH_3)(C_6H_5)PCH_2CH_2P(C_6H_5)(CH_3)$
   $\xrightarrow{heat}$ $C_6H_5PH_2 + C_2H_5 \cdot C_6H_5PH$
   $+ (C_6H_5P)_4$

⑥ Ber. **96**, 279 (1963).

P₂C₁₄H₁₆O₄

① Ethylenebis(phenylphosphinic acid)
   $[(HO)(C_6H_5)P(O)CH_2-]_2$

② $C_6H_5P(H)CH_2CH_2P(H)C_6H_5$
   $\xrightarrow{1)\ H_2O-Na_2O_2,\ 2)\ HCl}$ 52%

③ [230].
   Slightly sol. in ethanol, methanol,
   and H₂O; insol. in *n*-hexane, C₆H₆
   and THF.

⑥ Ber. **96**, 279 (1963).

P₂C₁₄H₂₈

① Ethylene-1,2-bis(cyclohexylphosphine)
   $[H(cyclo\text{-}C_6H_{11})PCH_2-]_2$

② $2 KPH(cyclo\text{-}C_6H_{11}) + ClCH_2CH_2Cl$
   $\xrightarrow{n\text{-heptane}}$ 83%

③ Colorless liq. (162～168°/4).
   Sol. in org. solvents; insol. in H₂O.
   Air sensitive.

④ $\xrightarrow[(C_2H_5)_2O]{CH_3I}$
   $[H \cdot R\overset{+}{P}(CH_3)CH_2CH_2\overset{+}{P} \cdot R \cdot H(CH_3)]2\ I^-$
   $\xrightarrow[C_6H_6]{S}$ $[H \cdot RP(S)CH_2CH_2P(S)R \cdot H]$

⑥ Ber. **96**, 1544 (1963).

P₂C₁₅H₁₆

① 1,2-Diphenyl-1,2-diphosphacyclo-
   pentane

   $C_6H_5-P\overbrace{\qquad}P-C_6H_5$
   $\quad\ CH_2\quad CH_2$
   $\qquad\ \ \searrow CH_2 \swarrow$

② $C_6H_5LiP(CH_2)_3PLiC_6H_5 + C_2H_4Br_2$
   $\xrightarrow{benzene\text{-}THF}$ 90%

③ (184～190°/4).
   Air-sensitive. Sol. in org. solvents.

④ $+ S \xrightarrow{benzene}$

   $C_6H_5-\overset{\overset{S}{\uparrow}}{P}\overbrace{\qquad}\overset{\overset{S}{\uparrow}}{P}-C_6H_5$
   $\qquad CH_2\quad CH_2$
   $\qquad\ \ \searrow CH_2 \swarrow$

⑥ Ber. **94**, 2656 (1961).

P₂C₁₅H₁₈

① Trimethylenebis(phenylphosphine)
   $H(C_6H_5)PCH_2CH_2CH_2P(C_6H_5)H$

② $C_6H_5 \cdot HPK + BrCH_2CH_2CH_2Br \longrightarrow$
   74%

③ (191～200°/5).
   Sol. in ether, C₆H₆, toluene, THF
   and C₂H₅OH.

Air-sensitive.

④ $+ C_6H_5Li \longrightarrow$
   $C_6H_5P(Li)CH_2CH_2CH_2P(Li)C_6H_5$
   $+ CH_3I \longrightarrow$
   $[CH_3(C_6H_5)(H)\overset{+}{P}CH_2CH_2CH_2\overset{+}{P}-$
   $(H)(C_6H_5)CH_3]2\,I^-$

⑥ Ber. **94**, 107 (1961).

$P_2C_{15}H_{26}$

① 4-Methyl-*o*-phenylenebis(diethylphosphine)

② $3\text{-Br-4-}IC_6H_3CH_3 + 2\,Mg$
   $+ 2\,(C_2H_5)_2PCl \longrightarrow 14\%$

③ $(115°/0.25)$.

④ $+ PdBr_2 \longrightarrow$

   $+ BrCH_2CH_2Br \longrightarrow$

⑥ Chem. Ind. (London) **1956**, 574.

$P_2C_{15}H_{30}$

① Trimethylene-1,3-biscyclohexyl
   phosphine
   $H\cdot C_6H_{11}P(CH_2)_3PC_6H_{11}\cdot H$

② $(cyclo\text{-}C_6H_{11})PHK + Br(CH_2)_3Br \longrightarrow$
   62%

③ $(151°/2)$.
   Sol. in benzene.

④ $+ CH_3I \longrightarrow [CH_3(cyclo\text{-}C_6H_{11})H\overset{+}{P}$
   $(CH_2)_3\overset{+}{P}(cyclo\text{-}C_6H_{11})(CH_3)H]2\,I^-$
   mp 133~135°
   $+ C_6H_5Li \longrightarrow (cyclo\text{-}C_6H_{11})-$
   $P(Li)(CH_2)_3P(Li)(cyclo\text{-}C_6H_{11})$

⑥ Ber. **94**, 2664 (1961).

$P_2C_{16}H_{18}$

① 1,4-Diphenyl-1,4-diphospha-cyclo-

hexane

② $C_6H_5(Li)PCH_2CH_2P(Li)C_6H_5 +$
   $ClCH_2CH_2Cl \xrightarrow{(C_2H_5)_2O} 46\%$

③ Viscous oil. (300~320°/7).
   Sol. in org. solvents, very stable in
   air.

④ $+ S \longrightarrow$

   (*cis* and *trans*)

⑥ Ber. **96**, 279 (1963).

$P_2C_{16}H_{20}$

① Ethylene-1,2-bis(methylphenylphosphine)
   $CH_3(C_6H_5)PCH_2CH_2P(C_6H_5)CH_3$

② $C_6H_5(Li)PCH_2CH_2P(Li)C_6H_5 + 2\,CH_3I$
   $\longrightarrow 53\%$
   $[(CH_3(C_6H_5CH_2)\overset{+}{P}CH_2CH_2\overset{+}{P}(CH_2C_6H_5)-$
   $(C_6H_5)CH_3]2\,Br^-$
   $\xrightarrow{\text{electrolysis}} 83\%$

③ [250~260°].
   Sol. in org. solvents.

④ $+ 2\,CH_3I \longrightarrow$

$$\begin{bmatrix} CH_2-(C_6H_5)\overset{+}{P}(CH_3)_2 \\ CH_2-(C_6H_5)\overset{+}{P}(CH_3)_2 \end{bmatrix}2\,I^-$$
   mp 298° (dec.)

⑥ Ber. **96**, 279 (1963),   Ann. **646**, 65
   (1961).

$P_2C_{16}H_{20}$

① Tetramethylene-1,4-bisphenylphos-
   phine
   $H\cdot C_6H_5PCH_2CH_2CH_2CH_2PC_6H_5\cdot H$

② $(C_6H_5)HPNa + Cl(CH_2)_4Cl \longrightarrow 50.6\%$
   $(C_6H_5)HPK + Br(CH_2)_4Br \longrightarrow 69.5\%$

③ (208~212°/4).
   Air-sensitive. Sol. in ether, C_6H_6,
   C_2H_5OH.

④ $+ C_6H_5Li \longrightarrow$
   $C_6H_5P(Li)(CH_2)_4P(Li)C_6H_5$

+ CH₃I ⟶

[(CH₃(C₆H₅)(H)$\overset{+}{P}$CH₂CH₂−]₂ 2 I⁻

+ S $\xrightarrow{\text{benzene}}$

C₆H₅·H(S)P(CH₂)₄P(S)H·C₆H₅

⑥ Ber. **94**, 107 (1961).

P₂C₁₆H₂₂N₂

① 1,1-Diphenyl-2,2-bis(dimethylamino)
   diphosphine
   (C₆H₅)₂P−P[N(CH₃)₂]₂

② (C₆H₅)₂PNa + ClP[N(CH₃)₂]₂ ⟶
   80.1%

③ Yellow oil. (137～140°/0.001). n_D 1.6221
   (21°).
   Air-sensitive.

④ 2 (C₆H₅)₂P−P[N(CH₃)₂]₂ $\xrightarrow[110°]{\text{heat}}$

   P[N(CH₃)₂]₃
   $+ \dfrac{1}{n}$P[N(CH₃)₂]ₙ + (C₆H₅)₂P−P(C₆H₅)₂

   (C₆H₅)₂P−P[N(CH₃)₂]₂ + (BH₃)₂

   $\xrightarrow[\text{(C₂H₅)₂O}]{}$ $\underset{\text{(C₆H₅)₂P−P[N(CH₃)₂]₂}}{\overset{\text{H₃B BH₃}}{\quad\uparrow\quad\uparrow\quad}}$

   2 (C₆H₅)₂P−P[N(CH₃)₂]₂ + 3 Br₂ ⟶
   2 (C₆H₅)₂PBr + [(CH₃)₂N]₂PBr
   + [(CH₃)₂N]₂PBr₃

⑥ Ber. **96**, 1816 (1963).

P₂C₁₆H₃₀

① 1,4-Dicyclohexyl-1,4-diphospha-
   cyclohexane

   (C₆H₁₁)P$\underset{\text{CH₂CH₂}}{\overset{\text{CH₂CH₂}}{\big\langle}}$P(C₆H₁₁)

② (C₆H₁₁)(Li)PCH₂CH₂P(Li)(C₆H₁₁)
   + ClCH₂CH₂Cl $\xrightarrow{\text{(C₂H₅)₂O}}$ 55%

③ (225～230°/2).
   Sol. in org. solvents; insol. in H₂O.
   Stable in air.

④ $\xrightarrow{\text{C₆H₆}}$ R−P$\underset{\text{CH₂−CH₂}}{\overset{\text{CH₂−CH₂}}{\big\langle}}$P−R
   (two isomer, a-form, mp 325～326;
   b-form, mp 250～255°)

$\xrightarrow{\text{H₂O₂}}$ R−P$\underset{\text{CH₂−CH₂}}{\overset{\text{CH₂−CH₂}}{\big\langle}}$P−R
   ‖   ‖
   O   O

⑥ Ber. **96**, 1544 (1963).

P₂C₁₆H₃₂

① Tetramethylenebis(cyclohexylphosphine)
   H(C₆H₁₁)PCH₂CH₂CH₂CH₂P(C₆H₁₁)H

② (cyclo-C₆H₁₁)PHK + Cl(CH₂)₄Cl ⟶
   65%

③ (165～166°/2). [4°].
   Sol. in C₆H₆.

④ + CH₃I ⟶
   [CH₃(cyclo-C₆H₁₁)H$\overset{+}{P}$CH₂CH₂−]₂ 2 I⁻
   + C₆H₅Li ⟶
   (cyclo-C₆H₁₁)P(Li)CH₂CH₂−]₂
   + S ⟶
   (cyclo-C₆H₁₁)HP(S)CH₂CH₂−]₂

⑥ Ber. **94**, 2664 (1961).

P₂C₁₆H₃₆

① Tetra-n-butylbiphosphine
   (n-C₄H₉)₂PP(n-C₄H₉)₂

② (n-C₄H₉)₂PCl + Na $\xrightarrow{\text{dioxane}}$ 77.8%

   (n-C₄H₉)₂P(S)−P(S)(n-C₄H₉)₂ $\xrightarrow{\text{Cu}}$
   70%

   (n-C₄H₉)₂P(S)−P(S)(n-C₄H₉)₂ + Na
   $\xrightarrow{\text{dioxane}}$ 63%

③ (180～182°/14).
   Air-sensitive.

④ + S $\xrightarrow{\text{benzene}}$
   (n-C₄H₉)₂P(S)−P(S)(n-C₄H₉)₂
   + C₂H₅I ⟶
   [C₂H₅(n-C₄H₉)₄P₂]⁺I⁻
   + K (or Na) $\xrightarrow{\text{decalin}}$
   (n-C₄H₉)₂PK (or Na) $\xrightarrow[\text{or CH₃OH}]{\text{H₂O}}$
   (n-C₄H₉)₂PH

⑥ Ber. **92**, 2681 (1959); **93**, 1852 (1960);

95, 64 (1962).

$P_2C_{16}H_{36}S_2$

① Tetra-*n*-butyldiphosphine disulfide
    $(n-C_4H_9)_2P(S)-P(S)(n-C_4H_9)_2$

② $n-C_4H_9Br + Mg + P(S)Cl_3 \longrightarrow$ 70%

③ Colorless plates. [74.5~75°].
    Sol. in C_2H_5OH, acetone, C_6H_6 and
    ether; insol. in H_2O.

④ $+ Fe \xrightarrow{\text{reduction}}$
    $(n-C_4H_9)_2P-P(n-C_4H_9)_2$
    $+ LiAlH_4 \longrightarrow (n-C_4H_9)_2PH$
    $+ Br_2 \longrightarrow (n-C_4H_9)_2P(S)Br$

⑥ Ber. **95**, 64 (1962); **92**, 704 (1959).
    Ann. **652**, 28 (1962).

$P_2C_{17}H_{22}$

① Pentamethylene-1,5-bis(phenylphos-
    phine)
    $H(C_6H_5)P(CH_2)_5P(C_6H_5)H$

② $C_6H_5 \cdot HPNa + Br(CH_2)_5Br \longrightarrow$ 80%

③ (211~214°/4~5).
    Sol. in ether, C_6H_6, C_2H_5OH and
    THF; insol. in H_2O and petr. ether.
    Air-sensitive.

④ $+ HI \longrightarrow$
    $[H_2(C_6H_5)\overset{+}{P}(CH_2)_5\overset{+}{P}(C_6H_5)H_2]2 I^-$
    $+ C_6H_5Li \longrightarrow$
    $C_6H_5P(Li)(CH_2)_5P(Li)C_6H_5$

⑥ Ber. **94**, 2656 (1961).

$P_2C_{17}H_{34}$

① Pentamethylene-1,5-bis(cyclohexyl-
    phosphine)
    $H(cyclo-C_6H_{11})P(CH_2)_5P(cyclo-C_6H_{11})H$

② $(cyclo-C_6H_{11})PH \cdot K + Br(CH_2)_5Br \longrightarrow$
    64%

③ (177°/2).
    Sol. in C_6H_6; slightly sol. in C_2H_5OH.

④ $+ CH_3I \longrightarrow [(CH_3)(cyclo-C_6H_{11})-$
    $\overset{+}{H}P(CH_2)_5\overset{+}{P}H(cyclo-C_6H_{11})(CH_3)]2 I^-$
    mp 160~162°
    $+ C_6H_5Li \longrightarrow (cyclo-C_6H_{11})P(Li)-$
    $(CH_2)_5P(Li)(cyclo-C_6H_{11})$

⑥ Ber. **94**, 2664 (1961).

$P_2C_{17}H_{38}O_2$

① Bis(dibutylphosphinyl)methane
    $[(C_4H_9)_2PO]_2CH_2$

② $ClCH_2POCl_2 + 2 C_4H_9MgBr$ ⎫
    $\xrightarrow{-5°} ClCH_2PO(C_4H_9)_2$ ⎪ $\longrightarrow$
    $(C_2H_5O)_2PHO + 2 C_4H_9MgBr$ ⎪
    $\longrightarrow (C_4H_9)_2PHO$ ⎭
    $\longrightarrow$ low yield

③ [172~174°] (hexane).

⑥ JOC **28**, 123 (1963).   JCS **1961**, 2423.

$P_2C_{18}H_{24}$

① Ethylenebis(ethylphenylphosphine)
    $C_2H_5(C_6H_5)PCH_2CH_2P(C_6H_5)C_2H_5$

② $C_6H_5PH_2 + C_2H_5Br + BrCH_2CH_2Br$
    $+ Na \xrightarrow{\text{liq } NH_3}$ 36%

③ Colorless crystals. (148~165°/0.4).
    [69~70°].

④ $+ BrC_2H_4Br \longrightarrow$
    $\begin{bmatrix} C_6H_5 \\ C_2H_5 \end{bmatrix} \overset{+}{P} \begin{matrix} CH_2-CH_2 \\ CH_2-CH_2 \end{matrix} \overset{+}{P} \begin{bmatrix} C_6H_5 \\ C_2H_5 \end{bmatrix} 2 Br^-$
    mp 370 (dec.)
    $+ CH_3I \longrightarrow$
    $[CH_3(C_2H_5)(C_6H_5)\overset{+}{P}CH_2]_2 2 Br^-$
    mp 199~200°

⑥ JCS **1958**, 2081.

$P_2C_{18}H_{24}$

① Tetramethylenebis(methylphenyl-
    phosphine)
    $CH_3(C_6H_5)P(CH_2)_4P(C_6H_5)CH_3$

② $CH_3(C_6H_5)(C_6H_5CH_2)P$
    $+ Br(CH_2)_4Br \xrightarrow{\text{in } CH_2=CHCN}$
    $[CH_3(C_6H_5)(C_6H_5CH_2)\overset{+}{P}CH_2CH_2]_2 2Br^-$
    $\xrightarrow{\text{electrolysis}}$ 80%
    $[CH_3(C_6H_5)(H)\overset{+}{P}CH_2CH_2]_2 2I^-$
    $\longrightarrow$ 71%

③ (178~180°/1). [47~48°].

④ $+ CH_3I \longrightarrow$
    $[(CH_3)_2(C_6H_5)\overset{+}{P}CH_2CH_2]_2 2I^-$

$+ S \xrightarrow{C_6H_6} [CH_3(C_6H_5)P(S)CH_2CH_2]_2$

⑥ Ann. **646**, 65 (1961).   Ber. **96**, 2186 (1963).

$P_2C_{18}H_{24}$

① Hexamethylene-1,6-bis(phenylphosphine)

    $H(C_6H_5)P(CH_2)_6P(C_6H_5)H$

② $(C_6H_5)HPNa + Cl(CH_2)_6Cl \longrightarrow 86.5\%$

③ $(207\sim211°/4)$.

    Air-sensitive. Sol. in ether, C_6H_6 and C_2H_5OH; insol. in H_2O and petr. ether.

④ $+ C_6H_5Li \longrightarrow$

    $C_6H_5P(Li)(CH_2)_6P(Li)C_6H_5$

⑥ Ber. **94**, 2656 (1961).

$P_2C_{18}H_{24}O_4$

① Ethylenebis(phenylphosphinic acid ethylester)

    $[(C_2H_5O)(C_6H_5)P(O)CH_2]_2$

② $(C_2H_5O)_2PC_6H_5 + BrCH_2CH_2Br$

    $\xrightarrow{140° \text{ in } CO_2} 50\%$

③ $[68\sim70°]$.

    Sol. in C_6H_6 and C_2H_5OH.

⑥ Roczniki Chem. **33**, 985 (1959).

$P_2C_{18}H_{26}I_2$

① Ethylenebis(dimethylphenylphosphonium iodide)

    $[(CH_3)_2(C_6H_5)PCH_2]_2 \ 2 I$

② $[CH_3(C_6H_5)PCH_2]_2 + CH_3I \longrightarrow 83\%$

③ $[298° \text{ (decomp.)}]$.

    Decompd. in light with the elimination of iodine.

⑥ Ber. **96**, 279 (1963).   Ann. **646**, 65 (1961).

$P_2C_{18}H_{36}$

① Hexamethylene-1,6-bis(cyclohexylphosphine)

    $H(C_6H_{11})P(CH_2)_6P(C_6H_{11})H$

② $(cyclo\text{-}C_6H_{11})PHK + Cl(CH_2)_6Cl \longrightarrow 70\%$

③ $(200\sim201°/2)$. $[13\sim14°]$.

    Sol. in C_6H_6, slightly sol. in C_2H_5OH.

④ $+ CH_3I \longrightarrow$

    $[CH_3(cyclo\text{-}C_6H_{11})\overset{+}{H}PCH_2CH_2CH_2]_2 \ 2 I^-$

    $+ C_6H_5Li \longrightarrow$

    $(cyclo\text{-}C_6H_{11})P(Li)CH_2CH_2CH_2]_2$

    $+ S \longrightarrow$

    $(cyclo\text{-}C_6H_{11})PH(S)CH_2CH_2CH_2]_2$

⑥ Ber. **94**, 2664 (1961).

$P_2C_{18}H_{40}O_2$

① Ethylenebis(dibutylphosphine oxide)

    $[(C_4H_9)_2P(O)CH_2]_2$

② $Bu_2PH +$

    $Bu_2PH(O) + (p\text{-}CH_3C_6H_4SO_3)_2(CH_2)_2$

    $\longrightarrow 40\%$

③ $(222\sim224°/0.8)$. $[174\sim175°]$.

⑥ JOC **27**, 1817 (1962).   JCS **1961**, 2423.

$P_2C_{18}H_{40}O_2$

① Ethylenediphosphonic acid tetrabutyl ester

    $(C_4H_9O)_2P(O)CH_2CH_2P(O)(OC_4H_9)_2$

② $(C_4H_9O)_3P + ICH_2CH_2I \longrightarrow 51\%$

③ $(175\sim178°/5\times10^{-4})$. $n_D \ 1.4484 \ (20°)$, $d \ 1.035 \ (4°)$.

    Hygroscopic.

⑤ Extractants.

⑥ JINC **25** (7), 883 (1963).   BCSJ **34**, 859, 1254 (1961).   JCS **1959**, 2266. JINC **10**, 128 (1959).

$P_2C_{19}H_{42}O_2$

① Trimethylenebis(dibutylphosphine oxide)

    $[(C_4H_9)_2P(O)]_2(CH_2)_3$

② $(C_4H_9)_2PH(O) +$

$(p-CH_3C_6H_4SO_3)_2(CH_2)_3 \longrightarrow 41\%$

③ [128~129°].

⑥ JCS **1961**, 2423.

$P_2C_{20}H_{28}S_2$

① Tetramethylenebis(ethylphenylphosphine sulfide)
   $[(C_2H_5)(C_6H_5)P(S)CH_2CH_2]_2$

② $C_2H_5(C_6H_5)P(CH_2)_4P(C_6H_5)C_2H_5 + S$
   $\xrightarrow{\text{benzene}}$ 15.4%

③ Needle crystals. [179~180°].
   Slightly sol. in CS_2, acetone and
   CH_3OH; sol. in $CHCl_3$, dioxane and
   C_6H_6.

⑥ Ber. **94**, 2656 (1961).

$P_2C_{20}H_{30}I_2$

① Tetramethylenebis(dimethylphenyl
   phosphonium iodide)
   $[(CH_3)_2(C_6H_5)PCH_2CH_2]_2 \cdot 2I$

② $[CH_3(C_6H_5)PCH_2CH_2]_2 + CH_3I \longrightarrow$

③ [217°].

⑥ Ann. **646**, 65 (1961).

$P_2C_{20}H_{44}O_2$

① Tetramethylenebis(dibutylphosphine oxide)
   $[(C_4H_9)_2P(O)CH_2CH_2]_2$

② $2(C_4H_9)_2P(O)Cl + BrMg(CH_2)_4MgBr$
   $\longrightarrow$ 65%

③ (270~271°/2). [116~118°].

⑥ JCS **1859**, 3950.

$P_2C_{24}H_{20}$

① Tetraphenyldiphosphine
   $(C_6H_5)_2P-P(C_6H_5)_2$

② $(C_6H_5)_2PH + ClP(C_6H_5)_2 \longrightarrow$
   $(C_6H_5)_2P(S)-P(S)(C_6H_5)_2 \xrightarrow{\text{Cu}}$ 90%

③ (258~260°/1). [120.5°].
   Thermally stable, undecomp. at its
   boiling point, easily oxidized by
   air.

④ $+ CH_3I \longrightarrow (C_6H_5)_2PI + (C_6H_5)_2PCH_3$

$+ MX_2 \longrightarrow \begin{pmatrix} C_6H_5 & C_6H_5 \\ | & | \\ P\!-\!-\!-\!P \\ | & | \\ C_6H_5 & C_6H_5 \end{pmatrix} MX_2$

$(MX_2 = NiCl_2,\ NiBr_2,\ PdCl_2)$
$+ M(CO)_4 \longrightarrow$

$\begin{array}{c} \quad\quad C_6H_5 \quad C_6H_5 \\ \quad\quad\; | \quad\quad\; | \\ (CO)_3M-P\!-\!-\!-\!P-M(CO)_3 \\ \quad\quad\; | \quad\quad\; | \\ \quad\quad C_6H_5 \quad C_6H_5 \end{array}$

$M = Ni,\ CO$

⑥ Ber. **21**, 1505 (1888); **91**, 2871 (1958);
   95, 64 (1962).

$P_2C_{24}H_{20}Cl_3N$

① Diphenylchloro[(diphenylchloro-
   phosphoranylidene)amino] phosphorus chloride
   $[(C_6H_5)_2P(Cl)=N-P(Cl)(C_6H_5)_2]^+Cl^-$

② $2(C_6H_5)_2PCl + NH_4Cl \longrightarrow$ 90%

③ Colorless crystals.

④ $+ 2HCOOH \longrightarrow$
   $\quad\quad\; OH \quad\; O$
   $\quad\quad\; | \quad\quad\; \|$
   $(C_6H_5)_2P=N-P(C_6H_5)_2 + 2CO$
   $+ 3HCl$

⑥ Ber. **96**, 3091 (1963).

$P_2C_{24}H_{20}S_2$

① Tetraphenyldiphosphine disulfide
   $(C_6H_5)_2P(S)-P(S)(C_6H_5)_2$

② $(C_6H_5)_2P(S)Cl + (C_6H_5)_2P(S)H \longrightarrow$
   79%

③ [168~169°].

④ $+ Cu \longrightarrow (C_6H_5)_2P-P(C_6H_5)_2$
   $+ Cu(H_2) \longrightarrow (C_6H_5)_2PH$

⑥ Ber. **95**, 64 (1962).

$P_2C_{24}H_{21}NO_2$

① Diphenyl[(diphenylhydroxyphos-
   phoranylidene)amino] phosphine
   oxide
   $(C_6H_5)_2P(OH)=N-P(O)(C_6H_5)_2$

② $[(C_6H_5)_2P(Cl)(C_6H_5)_2]^+Cl^-$
   $+ 2HCOOH \longrightarrow$

③ Colorless needle crystals. [266.5°].

Stable to aqueous acidic or basic soln.

④ $+ 2 H_2O \longrightarrow (C_6H_5)_2\overset{\overset{\displaystyle O}{\|}}{P}(ONH_4)$
$+ (C_6H_5)_2P(O)(OH)$

⑥ Ber. **96**, 3091 (1963).

$P_2C_{24}H_{21}NO_2$

① Iminobis(diphenylphosphine oxide)
$(C_6H_5)_2P(O)NHP(O)(C_6H_5)_2$

② $(C_6H_5)_2PCl_3 + NH_4Cl \longrightarrow$

$[Cl_2P(C_6H_5)_2NHP(C_6H_5)_2Cl_2] \overset{H_2O}{\longrightarrow}$

③ [270~272°].

⑥ Vysokomol. Soed. **2**, 377 (1960).

$P_2C_{24}H_{29}I$

① o-Diphenylphosphinophenyltriethyl-
phosphonium iodide
$[o\text{-}(C_6H_5)_2P \cdot C_6H_4 \cdot P(C_2H_5)_3]I$

② $o\text{-}(C_6H_5)_2PC_6H_4P(C_2H_5)_2 + C_2H_5I$
$\overset{C_2H_5OH}{\longrightarrow}$

③ [214°].

⑥ JCS **1960**, 3324.

$P_2C_{24}H_{38}I_2$

① Tetramethylenebis(diethylphenyl-
phosphonium iodide)
$[(C_2H_5)_2(C_6H_5)PCH_2CH_2]_2 \, 2I$

② $(C_2H_5(C_6H_5)PCH_2CH_2)_2 + C_2H_5I$
$\overset{C_2H_5OH}{\longrightarrow} 74.3\%$

③ [210~212°].
Sol. in CH_3OH and C_2H_5OH; insol. in dioxane and $(C_2H_5)_2O$.

⑥ Ber. **94**, 2656 (1961).

$P_2C_{24}H_{44}$

① Tetracyclohexyl diphosphine
$(cyclo\text{-}C_6H_{11})_2PP(cyclo\text{-}C_6H_{11})_2$

② $(cyclo\text{-}C_6H_{11})_2PCl + Na \longrightarrow 67.7\%$
$(cyclo\text{-}C_6H_{11})_2PBr +$
$LiP(cyclo\text{-}C_6H_{11})_2 \longrightarrow$
$LiP(cyclo\text{-}C_6H_{11})_2 + BrCH_2CH_2Br$
$\longrightarrow 84\%$

③ Colorless crystals. [172°].
Sol. in toluene, slightly sol. in dioxane, C_6H_6. Air-sensitive.

④ $+ CH_3I \longrightarrow$
$(cyclo\text{-}C_6H_{11})_2PI + (cyclo\text{-}C_6H_{11})_2PCH_3$
$+ S \overset{in\ CS_2}{\longrightarrow} [(cyclo\text{-}C_6H_{11})_2P(S)-]_2$
$+ O_2 \longrightarrow [(cyclo\text{-}C_6H_{11})_2P(O)-]_2$
$[(cyclo\text{-}C_6H_{11})_2P]_2 + MX_2 \longrightarrow$

$$\begin{matrix} X & \diagdown & P(cyclo\text{-}C_6H_{11})_2 \\ & M & | \\ X & \diagup & P(cyclo\text{-}C_6H_{11})_2 \end{matrix}$$

$MX_2 = NiBr_2$, $NiCl_2$, $PdCl_2$, $CoBr_2$,
$CoCl_2$, CoI_2.

⑥ Ber. **92**, 2681 (1959).

$P_2C_{25}H_{22}$

① Bis(diphenylphosphino)methane
$(C_6H_5)_2PCH_2P(C_6H_5)_2$

② $(C_6H_5)_2PNa + CH_2Cl_2 \longrightarrow 78\%$
$(C_6H_5)_2PCH_2P(O)(C_6H_5)_2$
$+ LiAlH_4 \longrightarrow$

③ White needle crystals. [122°].
Sol. in. C_2H_5OH, dioxane and acetone; insol. in petr. ether.

④ $+ CH_3I \longrightarrow$
$[CH_3(C_6H_5)_2\overset{+}{P}CH_2\overset{+}{P}(C_6H_5)_2CH_3]2\,I^-$
$+ RuCl_3 \longrightarrow$
$trans\text{-}[(C_6H_5)_2PCH_2P(C_6H_5)_2]_2RuCl_2$
$+ (NH_4)_2OsCl_6 \longrightarrow$
$trans\text{-}[(C_6H_5)_2PCH_2P(C_6H_5)_2]_2OsCl_2$

⑥ JCS **1962**, 1490. Pharm. Zentralhalle **99**, 329 (1960). Ber. **92**, 3175 (1959).

$P_2C_{25}H_{22}O_2$

① Bis(diphenylphosphinyl)methane
$[(C_6H_5)_2P(O)]_2CH_2$

② $(C_6H_5)_2P(O)CH_2Cl + (C_6H_5)_2POC_2H_5$
$\longrightarrow 60\%$
$(C_6H_5)_2P(O)CH_2Li + (C_6H_5)_2P(O)Cl$
$\longrightarrow 25\%$

③ [181~182°].
IR: JOC **28**, 123 (1963).
NMR: J. Chem. Eng. Data **7**, 307 (1962).

⑥ Izv. OKhN **1962**, 2103.   Pharm.

Zentralhalle, **99**, 329 (1960).

P₂C₂₆H₂₀

① Bis(diphenylphosphino)acetylene
$(C_6H_5)_2PC\equiv CP(C_6H_5)_2$

② $(C_6H_5)_2PCl + BrMgC\equiv CMgBr \xrightarrow{\text{ether}}$

③ ($198°/3\times10^{-5}$) (decomp.). [$86°$].
Resistant to H_2O, dil. acid and
alkalies.

④ + molten KOH (or alc. KOH) $\xrightarrow{\text{heat}}$
$(C_6H_5)_2POH + HC\equiv CP(C_6H_5)_2$
+ 3% $H_2O_2 \longrightarrow$
$(C_6H_5)_2P(O)C\equiv CP(O)(C_6H_5)_2$
+ S $\xrightarrow{\text{in } CS_2}$
$(C_6H_5)_2P(S)C\equiv CP(S)(C_6H_5)_2$

⑥ Z. anorg. allg. Chem. **287**, 261 (1956).

P₂C₂₆H₂₀O₂

① 1,2-Diphenyl-1,2-dibenzoyldiphos-
phine
$(C_6H_5)(C_6H_5CO)PP(C_6H_5)(COC_6H_5)$

② $C_6H_5P(Na)-P(Na)C_6H_5 + C_6H_5COCl$
$\longrightarrow$ 94%

③ Bright yellow crystals. [$117°$].
Oxidized by air.

④ + Cl₂ $\xrightarrow{H_2O}$ $C_6H_5P(O)(OH)_2$
+ C_6H_5COOH

⑥ JOC **22**, 385 (1957).

P₂C₂₆H₂₄

① Ethylenebis(diphenylphosphine)
$(C_6H_5)_2PCH_2CH_2P(C_6H_5)_2$

② $(C_6H_5)_2PNa + ClCH_2CH_2Cl \longrightarrow$ 75%

③ [$159\sim161°$].
Sol. in EtOH, aceton and C_6H_6.

⑥ JCS **1960**, 1378.   Ber. **92**, 3175 (1959).

P₂C₂₆H₂₄O₂

① Ethylenebis(diphenylphosphine
oxide)
$[(C_6H_5)_2P(O)CH_2]_2$

② $(C_6H_5)_2PCl + (CH_2Br)_2 \xrightarrow{100°,\ H_2O}$
$(p\text{-}CH_3C_6H_4SO_3)_2(CH_2)_2 + (C_6H_5)_2PHO$
$\longrightarrow$ 41%

③ [$276\sim278°$] (C_6H_6).

⑥ Ber. **95**, 581 (1962).   Tetrahedron,
18, 1231 (1962).   JCS **1961**, 2423.
Izv. OKhN **1961**, 2029.

P₂C₂₆H₂₄O₆

① Ethylenediphosphonic acid tetraphenyl ester
$(C_6H_5O)_2P(O)CH_2CH_2P(O)(OC_6H_5)_2$

② $(C_6H_5O)_3P + \begin{matrix}CH_2O\\ | \\ CH_2O\end{matrix}\!\!\!>\!\!C=O \xrightarrow{Cu}$ 40.5%
$(C_6H_5O)_2PCl + CH_2\!-\!CH_2$
            $\underset{O}{\diagdown\diagup}$
$\longrightarrow (C_6H_5O)_2POCH_2CH_2Cl \xrightarrow{\text{heat}}$

③ Needles. [$155\sim155.5°$].
Stable in warm dil. HCl and NaOH.

④ + HCl $\xrightarrow{\text{heat}}$
$(HO)_2P(O)CH_2CH_2P(O)(OH)_2$

⑥ Izv. OKhN **1947**, 631.   JOC **27**, 1817
(1962).

P₂C₂₆H₂₄S₂

① Ethylene-1,2-bis(diphenylphosphine
sulfide)
$(C_6H_5)_2P(S)CH_2CH_2P(S)(C_6H_5)_2$

② $(C_6H_5)_2PCH_2CH_2P(C_6H_5)_2 + S \xrightarrow{\text{benzene}}$
86%

③ [$196\sim198°$].
Sol. in C_6H_6, acetone, dioxane and
$CHCl_3$; insol. in ether and H_2O.

⑥ Ber. **92**, 3175 (1959); **96**, 2186 (1963).

P₂C₂₆H₄₈

① Ethylenebis(dicyclohexylphosphine)
$(cyclo\text{-}C_6H_{11})_2PCH_2CH_2P(cyclo\text{-}C_6H_{11})_2$

② $(cyclo\text{-}C_6H_{11})_2PH + BrCH_2CH_2Br \longrightarrow$
$[(cyclo\text{-}C_6H_{11})_2\overset{+}{P}HCH_2CH_2\overset{+}{P}H$
$(cyclo\text{-}C_6H_{11})_2]2\,Br^- \xrightarrow{NaOH}$ 86%

③ Colorless crystals. [96~97°].

Sol. in org. solvents ; insol. in H_2O.

④ $+ CS_2 \longrightarrow CS_2$-adduct.

$+ S \xrightarrow{C_6H_6} [(cyclo\text{-}C_6H_{11})_2P(S)CH_2]_2$

⑥ Ber. **96**, 2186 (1963).

P₂C₂₇H₂₆

① 2,2-Bis(diphenylphosphino)propane

$(C_6H_5)_2PC(CH_3)_2P(C_6H_5)_2$

② $(C_6H_5)_3P + Na + CH_3CCl_2CH_3$

$\xrightarrow{\text{in liq. NH}_3} 28\%$

③ Needle crystals. [123~123.5°].

Air sensitive.

④ $+ 2\,CH_3I \longrightarrow$

$[(C_6H_5)_2PC(CH_3)_2P(C_6H_5)_2](CH_3I)_2$

$+$ potassium bromopalladite $\longrightarrow$

$[(C_6H_5)_2PC(CH_3)_2P(C_6H_5)_2]PdBr_2$

⑥ JCS **1962**, 1490.

P₂C₂₇H₂₆O₂

① 2,2-Bis(diphenylphosphinyl)propane

$[(C_6H_5)_2P(O)]_2C(CH_3)_2$

② $(C_6H_5)_2PNa + (CH_3)_2CCl_2 \xrightarrow{} \underset{28\%}{}$

$[(C_6H_5)_2P]_2C(CH_3)_2$

$\xrightarrow{\text{1) Br/CHCl}_3,\ 2)\ NaHCO_3}$

③ [270~271°] (C_6H_6).

⑥ JCS **1962**, 1490.

P₂C₂₇H₂₆O₂

① Trimethylenebis(diphenylphosphine oxide)

$[(C_6H_5)_2P(O)]_2(CH_2)_3$

② $(C_6H_5)_2PCl + Br(CH_2)_3Br \longrightarrow \xrightarrow{H_2O}$

$[(C_6H_5)_3P]_2(CH_2)_3 \cdot 2\,Br + NaOH \longrightarrow$

$(C_6H_5)_2P(O)H +$

$(p\text{-}CH_3C_6H_4SO_3)_2(CH_2)_3 \xrightarrow{C_6H_6} 36\%$

③ (295~300°/0.1). [195~196°] $(C_2H_5OH - C_6H_{14})$.

⑥ Ber. **95**, 581 (1962).   JCS **1961**, 2423.

P₂C₂₇H₅₀

① Propylenebis(dicyclohexylphosphine)

$(cyclo\text{-}C_6H_{11})_2P(CH_2)_3P(cyclo\text{-}C_6H_{11})_2$

② $LiP(C_6H_{11})_2 + BrCH_2CH_2CH_2Br \longrightarrow$

③ Oil.

Sol. in ether, dioxane and C_2H_5OH ;

insol. in H_2O.

④ $+ S \longrightarrow$

$(C_6H_{11})_2P(S)(CH_2)_3P(S)(C_6H_{11})_2$

$\underset{\text{mp } 147\sim148°}{}$

$+ CS_2 \longrightarrow$

$(C_6H_{11})_2P(CS_2)(CH_2)_3P(CS_2)(C_6H_{11})_2$

$\underset{\text{mp } 108\sim110°}{}$

⑥ Ber. **92**, 3175 (1959).

P₂C₂₇H₅₀S₂

① Trimethylene-1,3-bis(dicyclohexyl phosphine disulfide)

$(cyclo\text{-}C_6H_{11})_2P(S)(CH_2)_3P(S)\text{-}(C_6H_{11}\text{-}cyclo)_2$

② $(cyclo\text{-}C_6H_{11})_2P(CH_2)_3P(cyclo\text{-}C_6H_{11})_2$

$+ S \xrightarrow{\text{benzene}} 65\%$

③ [147~148].

⑥ Ber. **92**, 3175 (1959).

P₂C₂₈H₂₈

① Tetramethylenebis(diphenylphosphine)

$(C_6H_5)_2P(CH_2)_4P(C_6H_5)_2$

② $[(C_6H_5)_3\overset{+}{P}(CH_2)_4\overset{+}{P}(C_6H_5)_3]2\,Br^-$

$+ LiAlH_4 \xrightarrow{\text{THF}}$

③ [135~136°].

⑥ JCS **1961**, 4263.

P₂C₂₈H₂₈

① Ethylenebis(benzylphenylphosphine)

$[C_6H_5(C_6H_5CH_2)PCH_2]_2$

② $[(C_6H_5CH_2)_2(C_6H_5)\overset{+}{P}CH_2]_2\,2\,Br^-$

$+ LiAlH_4 \xrightarrow{\text{THF}} 95\%$

③ (200°/0.0005). [85~98°].

④ + hot CH₃I ⟶

    $[CH_3(C_6H_5)(C_6H_5CH_2)\overset{+}{P}CH_2]_2$ 2I⁻

    + potassium palladobromide ⟶

⑥ JCS **1959**, 2835.

$P_2C_{28}H_{28}O_2$

① Tetramethylenebis(diphenylphos-
    phine oxide)
    $[(C_6H_5)_2P(O)CH_2CH_2]_2$

② $(C_6H_5)_2PCl + Br(CH_2)_4Br \xrightarrow{160°}\xrightarrow{NaOH}$
    $[(C_6H_5)_3PCH_2CH_2]_2 \cdot 2Br +$
    $NaOC_4H_9 \longrightarrow$
    $2(C_6H_5)_2P(O)Cl + BrMg(CH_2)_4MgBr$
    $\longrightarrow$ 39%
    $(C_6H_5)_3P(O) \xrightarrow{\text{1) Na/glyme, 2) Br(CH}_2)_4Br}$
    66%

③ (290∼291°/1.6). [150∼155°] (C_6H_6).

⑥ Ber. **95**, 581 (1962).   JCS **1959**, 3950.
    JACS **82**, 3919 (1960); **81**, 5519
    (1959).

$P_2C_{28}H_{28}S_2$

① Tetrabenzyldiphosphine disulfide
    $(C_6H_5CH_2)_2P(S)-P(S)(CH_2C_6H_5)_2$

② $C_6H_5CH_2MgCl + PSCl_3 \longrightarrow +25.1\%$

③ [145∼150°].
    Sol. in C_6H_6, $CHCl_3$ and ether; insol.
    in H_2O and petr. ether.

④ + LiAlH₄ ⟶ $(C_6H_5CH_2)_2PH$

⑥ Ber. **92**, 704 (1959).

$P_2C_{28}H_{30}I_2$

① Ethylenebis(methyldiphenylphos-
    phonium iodide)
    $[(CH_3)(C_6H_5)_2PCH_2]_2$ 2I

② $[(C_6H_5)_2PCH_2]_2 + CH_3I \xrightarrow{MeNO_2}$

③ [306∼307°].

⑥ JCS **1960**, 1378.

$P_2C_{28}H_{40}$

① Tetramethylenebis(cyclohexyl-
    phenylphosphine)
    $[(cyclo\text{-}C_6H_{11})C_6H_5PCH_2CH_2]_2$

② $(C_6H_5)P(Li)(CH_2)_4P(Li)(C_6H_5)$
    $+ cyclo\text{-}C_6H_{11}Cl \longrightarrow 60\%$

③ Colorless crystals. [104∼105°].
    Air-sensitive.
    Sol. in org. solvents.

④ + S ⟶
    $[(cyclo\text{-}C_6H_{11})(C_6H_5)P(S)CH_2CH_2]_2$

⑥ Ber. **94**, 2656 (1961).

$P_2C_{28}H_{52}$

① Tetramethylenebis(dicyclohexyl
    phosphine)
    $(cyclo\text{-}C_6H_{11})_2P(CH_2)_4P(cyclo\text{-}C_6H_{11})_2$

② $LiP(cyclo\text{-}C_6H_{11})_2 + Cl(CH_2)_4Cl \longrightarrow$
    62.5%

③ Colorless needle crystals. [98∼100°].

④ + S $\xrightarrow{benzene}$
    $[(cyclo\text{-}C_6H_{11})_2P(S)CH_2CH_2]_2$
    dec. 214∼215°
    $+ CS_2 \longrightarrow$
    $[(cyclo\text{-}C_6H_{11})_2P(CS_2)CH_2CH_2]_2$

⑥ Ber. **92**, 3175 (1959).

$P_2C_{28}H_{52}S_2$

① Tetramethylene-1,4-bis(dicyclo-
    hexylphosphine disulfide)
    $[(cyclo\text{-}C_6H_{11})_2P(S)CH_2CH_2]_2$

② $(cyclo\text{-}C_6H_{11})_2P(CH_2)_4P(cyclo\text{-}C_6H_{11})_2$
    $+ S \xrightarrow{benzene} 80\%$

③ [214∼215°] (decomp.).
    Sol. in C_6H_6, CH_3OH, acetone.

⑥ Ber. **92**, 3175 (1959).

$P_2C_{29}H_{54}$

① Pentamethylenebis(dicyclohexyl
    phosphine)
    $(cyclo\text{-}C_6H_{11})_2P(CH_2)_5P(cyclo\text{-}C_6H_{11})_2$

② LiP(*cyclo*-C₆H₁₁)₂ + Br(CH₂)₅Br

  $\xrightarrow{\text{dioxane}}$

  (*cyclo*-C₆H₁₁)₂PH + Br(CH₂)₅Br $\longrightarrow$
   [(*cyclo*-C₆H₁₁)₂P⁺(H)(CH₂)₅P⁺(H)-
   (*cyclo*-C₆H₁₁)₂]2 Br⁻ $\xrightarrow{\text{NaOH}}$ 71%

③ White crystals. [63~64°].
  Sol. in ether, dioxane, C₂H₅OH and
  C₆H₆; insol. in H₂O; stable in air.

④ + S $\xrightarrow{\text{C₆H₆}}$ (*cyclo*-C₆H₁₁)₂P(S)(CH₂)₅-
   (S)P(*cyclo*-C₆H₁₁)₂
   + CS₂ $\xrightarrow{\text{ether}}$ (*cyclo*-C₆H₁₁)₂P(CS₂)-
   (CH₂)₅(CS₂)P(*cyclo*-C₆H₁₁)₂
   + NiBr₂ $\longrightarrow$ [(*cyclo*-C₆H₁₁)₂P(CH₂)₅-
   P(*cyclo*-C₆H₁₁)₂]NiBr₂

⑥ Ber. **92**, 3175 (1959); **96**, 2186 (1963).

P₂C₃₀H₂₄

① *p*-Phenylenebis(diphenylphosphine)
  (C₆H₅)₂PC₆H₄P(C₆H₅)₂

② 2 (C₆H₅)₂PCl + Li——⟨ ⟩——Li

     $\xrightarrow{\text{hydrocarbon}}$ 19%

③ [166~167°].

④ + CH₃I $\xrightarrow{\text{benzene}}$
   [CH₃(C₆H₅)₂P⁺C₆H₄P⁺(C₆H₅)₂CH₃]₂·2 I⁻
   + C₆H₅N₃ $\xrightarrow{\text{toluene}}$

C₆H₅N=P(C₆H₅)₂——⟨ ⟩——P(C₆H₅)₂=NC₆H₅

   + N₃——⟨ ⟩——N₃ $\longrightarrow$

[—P(C₆H₅)₂——⟨ ⟩——P(C₆H₅)₂=N——⟨ ⟩——N=]ₓ

⑥ JOC **26**, 3998 (1961).

P₂C₃₀H₃₂

① Ethylenebis(dibenzylphosphine)
  (C₆H₅CH₂)₂PCH₂CH₂P(CH₂C₆H₅)₂

② (C₆H₅CH₂)₃P + BrCH₂CH₂Br $\longrightarrow$
   [(C₆H₅CH₂)₃P⁺CH₂CH₂P⁺(CH₂C₆H₅)₃]
   2 Br⁻ $\xrightarrow{\text{LiAlH₄}}$ 76%

③ (180°/0.01).

④ + BrCH₂CH₂Br $\longrightarrow$

[P(C₆H₅CH₂)(CH₂C₆H₅)(CH₂)(CH₂)(CH₂)(CH₂)P(C₆H₅CH₂)(CH₂C₆H₅)] 2 Br⁻

   $\xrightarrow{\text{LiAlH₄}}$ C₆H₅CH₂P⟨ (CH)₄ ⟩PCH₂C₆H₅

⑥ JCS **1959**, 2835.

P₂C₃₀H₃₄Br₂

① Ethylenebis(benzylmethylphenyl-
  phosphonium bromide)
  [(C₆H₅CH₂)(CH₃)(C₆H₅)P]₂(CH₂)₂·2 Br

② CH₃(C₆H₅CH₂)(C₆H₅)P + Br(CH₂)₂Br
   $\xrightarrow{\text{MeCN, 120°}}$ 93.5%

③ [272~273].

④ $\xrightarrow{70\sim90°}$ [CH₃(C₆H₅)PCH₂]₂ (83%)

⑥ Ann. **646**, 65 (1961).

P₂C₃₂H₂₈O₂

① *p*-Phenylenedimethylene(diphenylphosphine oxide)

  (C₆H₅)₂P(O)CH₂——⟨ ⟩——CH₂P(O)(C₆H₅)₂

② (C₆H₅)₂PCl + *p*-C₆H₄(CH₂Br)₂
   $\xrightarrow{\text{CH₃OH, 130°}}$ 50%

③ [322°].

④ $p\text{-}C_6H_4[CH_2P(O)(C_6H_5)_2]_2 + KOBu\text{-}t$

$\xrightarrow{RR'CO,C_6H_5CH_3,130°} (C_6H_5)_2P(O)OH +$

$RR'C=CH-\langle\bigcirc\rangle-CH=CRR'$

(70~90%)

⑥ Ber. **95**, 581 (1962).

$P_2C_{32}H_{30}I_2$

① p-Phenylenebis(methyldiphenyl
   phosphonium iodide)
   $[(C_6H_5)_2(CH_3)PC_6H_4P(CH_3)(C_6H_5)_2]2\,I$

② $[(C_6H_5)_2PC_6H_4P(C_6H_5)_2] + 2\,CH_3I \xrightarrow{C_6H_6}$

③ [334~337° decomp.].

⑥ JOC **26**, 3998 (1961).

$P_2C_{32}H_{38}Br_2$

① Tetramethylenebis(benzylmethyl-
   phenylphosphonium bromide)
   $[(C_6H_5CH_2)(CH_3)(C_6H_5)P(CH_2)_2]_2 \cdot 2\,Br$

② $2\,CH_3(C_6H_5)(C_6H_5CH_2)_4BrP + Br(CH_2)_4$
   $\xrightarrow{CH_3CN,\ 120°}$

⑥ Ann. **646**, 65 (1961).

$P_2C_{37}H_{32}Br_2$

① Methylenebis(triphenylphosphonium
   bromide)
   $[(C_6H_5)_3PCH_2P(C_6H_5)_3] \cdot 2\,Br$

② $(C_6H_5)_3P + CH_2Br_2 \xrightarrow{150°} 40\%$

③ [308~310°].

④ $\xrightarrow{aq.\ Na_2CO_3} [(C_6H_5)_3P=CHP(C_6H_5)_3]Br$
   $\downarrow K/diglyme$
   $[(C_6H_5)_3P=C=P(C_6H_5)_3]$

⑥ JACS **83**, 3539 (1961).

$P_2C_{38}H_{34}Br_2$

① Ethylenebis(triphenylphosphonium
   bromide)
   $[(C_6H_5)_3PCH_2]_2 \cdot 2\,Br$

② $(C_6H_5)_3P + Br(CH_2)_2Br \xrightarrow{140°} 82\%$

③ [308~315° decomp.].

④ $\xrightarrow{NaOH} C_2H_4\ (49\%) + C_6H_{10}\ (46\%)$

⑥ Kosorapoff 90.   Spetrochim. Acta
   19, 1905(1963).   JOC **28**, 2565(1963);
   24, 1969 (1959). Ann. **619**, 10 (1958).

$P_2C_{38}H_{34}Br_6Hg_3$

① (Mercuridimethylene)bis[triphenyl
   phosphonium bromomercurate-
   (II)]
   $[(C_6H_5)_3PCH_2HgCH_2P(C_6H_5)_3](HgBr_3)_2$

② $(C_6H_5)_3P=CH_2 + HgBr_2 \xrightarrow{(C_2H_5)_2O}$

③ [123~126°].
   Not appreciably sol. in H_2O,
   CH_3COCH_3 and EtOH.
   Somewhat sol. in hot CH_3OH.

⑥ JACS **83**, 1610 (1961).

$P_2C_{39}H_{36}Br$

① Trimethylenebis(triphenylphosphonium bromide)
   $[(C_6H_5)_3P]_2(CH_2)_3 \cdot 2\,Br$

② $(C_6H_5)_3P + Br(CH_2)_3Br \xrightarrow{200°} 77\%$

③ [333~335° (decomp.)].

⑥ Ber. **95**, 581 (1962).   Ann. **619**, 10
   (1958).

$P_2C_{40}H_{38}Br_2$

① Tetramethylenebis(triphenylphosphonium bromide)
   $[(C_6H_5)_3PCH_2CH_2]_2 \cdot 2\,Br$

② $(C_6H_5)_3P + Br(CH_2)_4Br \xrightarrow{200~250°}$

③ [292~293°].

④ $\xrightarrow{LiAlH_4,\ THF} (C_6H_5)_2P(CH_2)_4P(C_6H_5)_2$

⑥ JCS **1961**, 4263.   Ber. **95**, 581 (1962).
   JACS **82**, 3919 (1960).   Ann. **619**,
   10 (1958).

$P_2C_{42}H_{42}Br_2$

① Ethylenebis(dibenzylphenylphos-
   phonium bromide)

[$(C_6H_5CH_2)_2(C_6H_5)P]_2(CH_2)_2 \cdot 2\,Br$

② $C_6H_5P(CH_2C_6H_5)_2 + Br(CH_2)_2Br$

$$\xrightarrow[120°]{HCO_2H} 94\%$$

③ [294〜296°].

⑥ Ann. **646**, 65 (1961).

P₂C₄₄H₃₈Br₂

① (o-Phenylenedimethylene)bis(triphenylphosphonium bromide)

$$\left[\begin{array}{c} \text{CH}_2\text{P}(C_6H_5)_3 \\ \text{CH}_2\text{P}(C_6H_5)_3 \end{array} \right] 2\,Br$$

②

$$\text{CH}_2\text{Br} + Ph_3P \xrightarrow{DMF} 89.4\%$$
$$\text{CH}_2\text{Br}$$

③ [295° (decomp.)].

⑥ JOC **28**, 1715 (1963); **27**, 1627 (1962).

P₂C₄₄H₃₈Cl₂

① p-Phenylenedimethylenebis(triphenylphosphonium chloride)
[$(C_6H_5)_3PCH_2C_6H_4CH_2P(C_6H_5)_3$]·2Cl

② $p\text{-ClCH}_2C_6H_4CH_2Cl + P(C_6H_5)_3 \xrightarrow{DMF}$
93〜98%

③ [>400°].

⑥ Spectrochim. Acta **19**, 1905 (1963).
Vysokomol. Soed. **5**, 805 (1963). J.
Chem. Eng. Data **8**, 461 (1963).
JACS **82**, 4669 (1960).

P₂C₅₀H₄₂I₂

① 4,4′-Biphenylenedimethylenebis-
(triphenylphosphonium chloride)
[$(C_6H_5)_3PCH_2C_6H_4]_2 \cdot 2\,Cl$

② $(p\text{-ClCH}_2C_6H_4)_2 + (C_6H_5)_3P$

$$\xrightarrow{(CH_3)_2NCHO} 85\%$$

④ [$(C_6H_5)_3PCH_2C_6H_4]_2Cl_2 + CH_2P$

$$\xrightarrow{LiOC_2H_5/C_2H_5OH}$$

$$\text{CH}_2=\text{CH}-\bigcirc-\bigcirc-\text{CH}=\text{CH}_2$$
(80%)

⑥ Ber. **93**, 998 (1960).

P₂C₅₅H₄₇B

① Diphenylphosphinomethyltriphenyl
phosphoniumtetraphenylborate
[$(C_6H_5)_2PCH_2P(C_6H_5)_3]B(C_6H_5)_4$

② $(C_6H_5)_3P=CH_2 + (C_6H_5)_2PBr \xrightarrow{NaB(C_6H_5)_4}$

③ [185.5〜186.0°].

⑥ JACS **83**, 2055 (1961).

P₂C₉₀H₂₈

① Tetramethylenebis(ethylphenyl
phosphine)
$C_2H_5(C_6H_5)P(CH_2)_4P(C_6H_5)C_2H_5$

② $C_6H_5P(Li)(CH_2)_4P(Li)C_6H_5 + C_2H_5I$
$\longrightarrow$ 62.8%
[$C_2H_5(H)(C_6H_5)\overset{+}{P}CH_2CH_2]_2 \cdot 2\,I^-$
$\longrightarrow$ 61%

③ (225〜230°/4).
Sol. in ether, C_2H_5OH and C_6H_6.

④ + S $\xrightarrow{benzene}$
[$(C_6H_5)(C_2H_5)P(S)CH_2CH_2-]_2$
$\xrightarrow{oxydation}$
[$(C_6H_5)(C_2H_5)P(O)CH_2CH_2-]_2$
+ C_2H_5I $\longrightarrow$
[$(C_2H_5)_2(C_6H_5)\overset{+}{P}CH_2CH_2-]_2 \cdot 2\,I^-$

⑥ Ber. **94**, 2656 (1961); **96**, 2186 (1963).

P₃Br₆N₃

① 1,3,5,2,4,6-Triazatriphosphorine-
2,2,4,4,6,6-hexabromide
(NPBr₂)₃

② $PBr_3 + Br_2 + NH_4Br$

$$\xrightarrow{145\sim155, \text{ in } Cl_2CHCHCl_2}$$

③ [192°].
NMR and IR: JINC **22**, 199 (1961).

⑥ Chem. Ind. (London) **1960**, 1189. Z.
anorg. allg. Chem. **252**, 113 (1943).
JACS **82**, 2647 (1960).

P₃Cl₆N₃

① 1,3,5,2,4,6-Triazatriphosphorine-

2,2,4,4,6,6-hexachloride
($NPCl_2$)₃

② $PCl_5 + NH_4Cl \xrightarrow[\text{in } CH_2CHCHCl_2]{7.5\,hrs}$

③ (256.5°). [114°].
UV: JCS **1960**, 2542.

④ + KF + sulfur dioxide $\longrightarrow$ $N_3P_3F_6$
+ 9 $C_6H_5COONa \longrightarrow$ 3 C_6H_5CN
+ 3 $(C_6H_5CO)_2O$ + $(NaOPO_2)_3$
+ 6 NaCl

+ $AlCl_3$ + $C_6H_6 \longrightarrow$

+ $AlCl_3$ + $C_6H_6 \xrightarrow{\text{drastic condition}}$

⑥ JACS **82**, 2167 (1960); **65**, 1551 (1943);
81, 836 (1959).

P₃Cl₇N₂O

① {Dichloro[(dichlorophosphinyl)
imino]phosphoranyl}phosphor-
imidic trichloride
$Cl_3P=N-PCl_2=N-P(O)Cl_2$

② $[Cl_3P=N-PCl_2=N-PCl_3][PCl_6]$
+ 2 $SO_2 \longrightarrow$

③ [32~33°].

⑥ Z. Naturf. **17 b**, 126(1962). Z. anorg.
allg. Chem. **315**, 191 (1962).

P₃Cl₁₂N

① Trichloro[(trichlorophosphoranyl-
idene) amino] phosphorus hexachlorophosphate
$(Cl_3P=N-P(Cl_3)(PCl_6)$

② $PCl_5 + NH_4Cl + NH_3 \longrightarrow$ 80~90%
$NCl_3 + PCl_3 \longrightarrow$

③ [310~315°] (decomp.).

NMR: Z. Naturf. **17 b**, 126 (1962).

④ + PCl_5 + $NH_4Cl \longrightarrow$ $P_4N_2Cl_{14}$
+ 4 HCl
+ $SO_2 \longrightarrow$ $Cl_3P=N-P(O)Cl_2$
+ $OPCl_3$ + $SOCl_2$

⑥ Ber. **94**, 1591 (1961). Z. anorg. allg.
Chem. **315**, 181, 191 (1962).

P₃F₆N₃

① 1,3,5,2,4,6-Trizatriphosphorine-2,2,
4,4,6,6-hexafluoride
(NPF_2)₃

② $N_3P_3Cl_6 + NaF \xrightarrow[\text{in nitrobenzene}]{\text{heat 2 hrs}}$
65~75%
$N_3P_3Cl_6 + KF$
+ sulfur dioxide $\xrightarrow{120~125°C}$
67 hrs

③ [27.8°]. (50.9°).
IR: JCS **1960**, 3608.

⑥ Chem. Eng. Data Ser. **3**, 323 (1958).
Chem. Ind. (London) **1961**, 347.

P₃C₆H₁₈N₃

① 2,2,4,4,6,6-Hexamethyl-1,3,5,2,4,6-
triazatriphosphorine
$N_3P_3(CH_3)_6$

② $(CH_3)_2PCl_3 + NH_4Cl \longrightarrow$ linear
polymer $\xrightarrow[\text{in } CHCl_3]{(C_2H_5)_3N, \ NH_4Cl}$ 70~75%

③ [195~196°].
Dissolve in cold H_2O without de-
comp.
IR: Proc. Chem. Soc. **1959**, 7.

P₃C₆F₁₈N₃

① 2,2,4,4,6,6-Hexa(trifluoromethyl)-
1,3,5,2,4,6-trizatriphosphorine
$N_3P_3(CF_3)_6$

② $(CF_3)_2PNH_2 + Cl_2 \xrightarrow{(CH_3)_3N \text{ in } CHCl_3}$
12%

③ [64°].
IR: JACS **84**, 549 (1962).

P₃C₆H₂₄B₃

① Dodecahydro-1,1,3,3,5,5-hexa-
methyl-*s*-triphosphatriborin
[(CH₃)₂PBH₂]₃

② (CH₃)₂PCl + NaBH₄ $\xrightarrow{\text{diglyme}}$ 52%

[(CH₃)₂NP(CH₃)₂(BH₃)₂] $\xrightarrow{200°}$ >50%

[(CH₃)₂PS]₂ + LiBH₄ $\xrightarrow{250°}$

③ [87~88°] (CH₃OH).
IR : JCS **1961**, 1822.

④ [(CH₃)₂PBH₂]₃ + C₄H₉Cl $\xrightarrow{\text{AlCl}_4}$
[(CH₃)₂PBCl₂]₃

⑥ JACS **82**, 2145 (1960). Z. Naturf.
15 b, 327 (1960).

P₃C₉H₂₇N₆

① 2,4,6-Trimethyl-2,4,6-dimethyl-
amino-1,3,5,2,4,6-triazatriphos-
phorine
N₃P₃(CH₃)₃[N(CH₃)₂]₃

② N₃P₃Cl₃[N(CH₃)₂]₃ + CH₃MgBr $\longrightarrow$
81%

③ (146~147°/3).
Sol. in ligroin.

④ + HCl $\xrightarrow[\text{reflux}]{\text{xylene}}$ (structure of triazatriphosphorine ring with Me, Cl, N, P substituents)

⑥ Proc. Chem. Soc. **1960**, 404.

P₃C₁₂H₁₀Cl₄N₃

① 2,2-Diphenyl-1,3,5,2,4,6-triazatri-
phosphorine-4,4,6,6-tetrachloride
N₃P₃Cl₄(C₆H₅)₂

② P₃N₃Cl₆ + AlCl₃ + C₆H₆ $\longrightarrow$

④ + Me₂NH $\xrightarrow{\text{in C}_6\text{H}_6}$ (structure of triazatriphosphorine ring with Ph, Ph, P, N, P(NMe₂)₂, NMe₂)₂)

+ H₂O $\longrightarrow$ (C₆H₅)₂PO₂H

+ (C₆H₅)MgBr $\longrightarrow$ N₃P₃(C₆H₅)₆

⑥ Z. anorg. allg. Chem. **304**, 126(1960).
Ber. **75 B**, 215 (1942).

P₃C₁₂H₁₀Cl₁₀N

① Phenyldichloro[(phenyldichloro-
phosphoranylidene) amino]
phosphorushexachlorophosphate
[C₆H₅P(Cl₂)=N−P(Cl₂)C₆H₅]⁺PCl₆⁻

② 2 C₆H₅PCl₂ + NCl₃ + PCl₃ $\longrightarrow$

③ Yellow crystals.

④ $\xrightarrow{\text{heat}}$ PCl₅
+ [C₆H₅−P(Cl₂)=N−P(C₆H₅)Cl₂]⁺Cl⁻

⑥ Ber. **96**, 3085 (1963).

P₃C₁₂H₁₈N₇

① 2,2-Diphenyl-4,4,6,6-tetraamino-
1,3,5,2,4,6-triazatriphosphorine
N₃P₃(C₆H₅)₂(NH₂)₄

② N₃P₃(C₆H₅)₂Cl₄ + NH₃ $\longrightarrow$

③ Amorphous. [106°].
On heating 6 hrs. at 100°, this compound changes to nonhygroscopic
cryst. form ; mp 275°, with identical compn. and infrared spectrum.

⑥ Angew. **70**, 657 (1958). Z. anorg.
allg. Chem. **304**, 126 (1960).

P₃C₁₂H₃₀N₃

① 2,2,4,4,6,6-Hexaethyl-1,3,5,2,4,6-
triazatriphosphorine
N₃P₃(C₂H₅)₆

② (C₂H₅)₂PCl₃ + NH₃ $\xrightarrow[\text{8 hrs}]{-78° \quad 220~250°}$
37%

③ Crystals. [117.5~119°].
Sol. in H₂O, C₆H₆, ligroin, C₂H₅OH.
IR : Z. Naturf. **15 b**, 330 (1960).

P₃C₁₂H₃₆B₃

① 1,1,3,3,5,5-hexaethyldodecahydro-*s*-
triphosphatriborin
[(C₂H₅)₂PBH₂]₃

② $(C_2H_5)_2PCl + NaBH_4 \longrightarrow$ 70%

$[(C_2H_5)_2PS]_2 + LiBH_4 \xrightarrow{280\sim300°}$

$(C_2H_5)_2PCl + LiBH_4 \longrightarrow$

③ $(106\sim108°/0.1, 133\sim134°/1.5)$. $[67\sim68°]$
   (petr. ether). $n_D 1.5312$ (20°).
   IR: JCS 1961, 1822.

④ $C_4H_9Cl \xrightarrow{AlCl_3} [(C_2H_5)_2PBCl_2]_3$

   $C_2H_5I \xrightarrow{I_2} [(C_2H_5)_2PBI_2]_3$

⑥ JACS 82, 2145 (1960).

$P_3C_{12}H_{36}B_3$

See $B_3C_{12}H_{36}P_3$

$P_3C_{17}H_{39}$

① 1,1,1-Tris(diethylphosphinomethyl)
   ethane
   $CH_3C[CH_2P(C_2H_5)_2]_3$

② $CH_3C[CH_2Cl]_3 + (C_2H_5)_2PLi \xrightarrow{THF}$ 41%

③ Colorless oil. (120°/0.1).
   Spont. inflam.

④ $+ C_2H_5I \longrightarrow$
   $CH_3C[CH_2P^+(C_2H_5)_3]_3 \cdot 3\ I^-$

⑥ JCS 1962, 1490.

$P_3C_{24}H_{54}ClN_2O$

① p, p-Dibutyl-N-[dibutyl(dibutyl-
   phosphinylimino) phosphoranyl]
   phosphinimidic chloride
   $Cl-P(n-C_4H_9)_2NP(n-C_4H_9)_2 \cdot$
   $NP(n-C_4H_9)_2O$

② $(C_4H_9)_2PCl_3 + NH_4Cl \longrightarrow$

③ $[171\sim172°]$.

⑥ Vysokomol. Soed. 2, 377 (1960).

$P_3C_{34}H_{33}$

① Bis(diphenylphosphinoethyl)phenyl
   phosphine
   $C_6H_5P[CH_2CH_2P(C_6H_5)_2]_2$

② $C_6H_5P[C_2H_4 \cdot OEt]_2 \xrightarrow[2)\ (C_6H_5)_2PNa]{1)\ HBr}$ 16%

③ $[131\sim132°]$.

Air-sensitive.

④ $+ 3 CH_3I \longrightarrow$
   $C_6H_5P[C_2H_4P(C_6H_5)_2]_2[CH_3I]_3$
   mp 162~163°

⑥ JCS 1962, 1490.

$P_3C_{36}H_{30}N_3$

① 2,2,4,4,6,6-Hexaphenyl-1,3,5,2,4,6-
   triazatriphosphorine
   $N_3P_3(C_6H_5)_6$

② $N_3P_3Cl_4(C_6H_5)_2 + C_6H_5MgBr \longrightarrow$
   $N_3P_3Cl_6 + C_6H_6 + AlCl_3 \longrightarrow$ 20%
   $(C_6H_5)_2PCl_3 + NH_4Cl \xrightarrow[in(CHCl_2)_2]{130\sim135°}$ 4%

③ Colorless needle crystals. $[232\sim233°]$.
   IR: Z. Naturf. 15 b, 330 (1960).

⑥ Chem. Ind. (London) 1960, 839, 1189.
   JACS 80, 2116 (1958).

$P_3C_{36}H_{36}B_3$

① Didecahydro-1,1,3,3,5,5-hexaphenyl-
   s-triphosphatriborin
   $[(C_6H_5)_2PBH_2]_3$

② $(C_6H_5)_2P(O)Cl + NaBH_4 \longrightarrow$
   $(C_6H_5)_2PCl + LiBH_4 \xrightarrow{(C_2H_5)_2O}$

③ $[177°]$ (benzene-C_2H_5OH).
   IR: Trans. Faraday Soc. 59, 806
   (1963).

$P_3C_{41}H_{39}$

① 1,1,1-Tris(diphenylphosphino-
   methyl)ethane
   $CH_3C[CH_2P(C_6H_5)_2]_3$

② $CH_3C[CH_2Cl]_3 + (C_6H_5)_2PNa \xrightarrow{liq.\ NH_3}$
   73%

③ Colorless crystals. $[100\sim101°]$.
   Slowly oxidized in air.

④ $+ 3 CH_3I \longrightarrow$
   $CH_3C[CH_2P(C_6H_5)_2]_3[CH_3I]_3$
   mp 310~311°

⑥ JCS 1962, 1490.

P₄Br₈N₄

① 1,3,5,7,2,4,6,8-Tetrazatetraphospho-
rine-2,2,4,4,6,6,8,8-octabromide
$(NPBr_2)_4$

② $PBr_3 + Br_2 + NH_4Br$
$\xrightarrow{\text{145~155°, in Cl}_2\text{CHCHCl}_2}$

③ [202°].
NMR and IR : JINC **22**, 199 (1961).

⑥ Chem. Ind. (London) **1960**, 1189. Z.
anorg. allg. Chem. **252**, 113 (1943).
Angew. **61**, 438 (1949). JACS **82**,
2647 (1960).

P₄Cl₈N₄

① 1,3,5,7,2,4,6,8-Tetrazatetraphospho-
rine-2,2,4,4,6,6,8,8-octachloride
$(NPCl_2)_4$

② $PCl_5 + NH_4Cl \xrightarrow{\text{7.5 hrs in Cl}_2\text{CHCHCl}_2}$

③ (328.5°). [124°].
UV : JCS **1960**, 2542.

④ $+ HN\underset{CH_2-CH_2}{\overset{CH_2-CH_2}{<}}CH_2 \longrightarrow$

$N_4P_4Cl_4\left(N\underset{CH_2-CH_2}{\overset{CH_2-CH_2}{<}}CH_2\right)_4$

$+ NH_2C_6H_4CH_3\text{-}m \longrightarrow$
$N_4P_4(HNC_6H_4CH_3)_8$

$+ KF + \text{sulfur dioxide} \longrightarrow N_4P_4F_8$

⑥ JACS **83**, 2608 (1961).

P₄Cl₁₄N₂

① Trichloro{dichloro[(trichlorophos-
phoranylidene)amino]phospho-
ranylidene}aminophosphorus
hexachlorophosphate
$[Cl_3P=N-P(Cl_2)N-PCl_3][PCl_6]$

② $PCl_5 + NH_4Cl + NH_3 \longrightarrow$

③ [200~202°].
NMR : Z. Naturf. **17 b**, 126 (1962).

④ $+ NH_4Cl \xrightarrow[\text{in Cl}_2\text{CHCHCl}_2]{\text{150°C}}$

$Cl_2P\underset{N-P}{\overset{N=P}{<}}\overset{Cl_2}{\underset{Cl_2}{>}}N$

$+ SO_2 \longrightarrow$
$Cl_3P=N-PCl_2=N-P(O)Cl_2$

⑥ Z. anorg. allg. Chem. **315**, 181, 191
(1962).

P₄F₈N₄

① 1,3,5,7,2,4,6,8-Tetrazatetraphospho-
rine-2,2,4,4,6,6,8,8-octafluoride
$(NPF_2)_4$

② $N_4P_4Cl_8 + NaF$
$\xrightarrow{\text{heat 24 hrs in nitrobenzene}} 66~74\%$
$N_4P_4Cl_8 + KF + \text{sulfur dioxide}$
$\xrightarrow{\text{120~125°C, 67 hrs}}$

③ (89.7°). [30.5°].
X-ray analysis : JCS **1961**, 4777. Z.
anorg. allg. Chem. **295**, 316 (1958).
IR : JCS **1960**, 3608.

⑥ Chem. Eng. Data Series **3**, 323 (1958).

P₄C₄F₁₂

① Tetrakis(trifluoromethylcyclotetra-
phosphine)
$(CF_3 \cdot P)_4$

② $CF_3PI_2 + Hg \text{ (large excess)} \longrightarrow$
60%
$(CF_3)_4P_2 \xrightarrow{300~350°}$
$(CF_3)_2PH \xrightarrow{350°}$

③ (135°). [66.4°].
Thermally stable up to 300°.

④ $+ I_2 \longrightarrow CF_3PI_2$
$+ Cl_2 \longrightarrow CF_3PCl_2$
$+ HCl, BF_3 \xrightarrow{\hspace{0.3cm}}\times$
$+ H_2O \xrightarrow{140°} H_2 + CF_3PH_2$
$+ (CF_2PH)_2 + HCF_3$

⑥ JACS **79**, 251 (1957); **80**, 6161 (1958).

$P_4C_8F_{24}N_4$

① 2,2,4,4,6,6,8,8-Octa(trifluoromethyl)-1,3,5,7,2,4,6,8-tetrazatetraphosphorine
$N_4P_4(CF_3)_8$

② $(CF_3)_2PNH_2 + Cl_2 \xrightarrow{(CH_3)_3N \text{ in } CHCl_3}$
25%

③ [109°].
IR : JACS 84, 549 (1962).

$P_4C_8H_{20}$

① Tetrakisethylcyclotetraphosphine
$(C_2H_5 \cdot P)_4$

② $KPHC_2H_5 + BrCH_2CH_2Br \longrightarrow$
$2 C_2H_5PCl_2 + 2 C_2H_5PH_2 \longrightarrow$

③ (168~170°).
Oxidize in air.

④ $+ CH_3I \longrightarrow [(C_2H_5P)_4 \cdot CH_3]^+I^-$
$+ X_2 \longrightarrow C_2H_5PX_2$, X=Br, I

⑥ Z. Naturf. 15 b, 267 (1960).

$P_4C_8H_{24}N_4$

① 2,2,4,4,6,6,8,8-Octamethyl-1,3,5,7,2,4,6,8-tetrazatetraphosphorine
$N_4P_4(CH_3)_8$

② $(CH_3)_2PCl_3 + NH_4Cl$
$\xrightarrow{200° \text{ or in refluxing } (CHCl_2)_2}$ linear
polymer $\xrightarrow{(C_2H_5)_3N. NH_4Cl \text{ in } CHCl_3}$

③ [163~164°].
Dissolve in cold H_2O without decomp.
IR : Proc. Chem. Soc. 1959, 7.

$P_4C_{16}H_{40}N_4$

① 2,2,4,4,6,6,8,8-Octaethyl-1,3,5,7,2,4,6,8-tetrazatetraphosphorine
$N_4P_4(C_2H_5)_8$

② $(C_2H_5)_2PCl_3 + NH_3 \xrightarrow{-78°} \xrightarrow{220~250°, \text{ 8 hrs}}$
20%

③ Viscous oil.
Sol. in H_2O, C_6H_6, ligroin, $CHCl_3$,

C_2H_5OH.

⑥ Z. Naturf. 15 b, 330 (1960).

$P_4C_{24}H_{20}$

① Tetrakisphenylcyclotetraphosphine
$(C_6H_5P)_4$

② $C_6H_5P(H)CH_2CH_2P(H)C_6H_5 \xrightarrow{\text{pyrolysis}}$
35%
$2 C_6H_5PCl_2 + 2 C_6H_5PH_2 \longrightarrow$ 84.3%
$C_6H_5PCl_2 + LiAlH_4$ (or LiH, Na, Li)
$\longrightarrow$ 66.5%
$C_6H_5 \cdot HPK + Br_2 \longrightarrow$

③ [150.5°].

④ $+ M \longrightarrow 2 C_6H_5P(M)-P(M)C_6H_5$
(M=Na, Li)
$+ 4 HCl \longrightarrow 2 C_6H_5PH_2 + 2 C_6H_5PCl_2$
$+$ excess $M \longrightarrow 4 C_6H_5PM_2$
M=Na, K, Li
$+ 2 I_2 \longrightarrow \begin{array}{c} C_6H_5-P-I \\ | \\ C_6H_5-P-I \end{array}$

⑥ Ber. 10, 807 (1877); 91, 2296 (1958);
96, 279 (1963). Monatsh. 90, 148
(1959). JOC 22, 385 (1957).

$P_4C_{24}H_{44}$

① Tetrakis(cyclohexyl)cyclotetraphosphine
$(cyclo\text{-}C_6H_{11}P)_4$

② $2 (cyclo\text{-}C_6H_{11})PCl_2$
$+ 2 (cyclo\text{-}C_6H_{11})PH_2 \xrightarrow{\text{toluene}}$

③ [219~220°].

④ $+ X_2 \longrightarrow cyclo\text{-}C_6H_{11}PX_2$
$+$ excess $X_2 \longrightarrow cyclo\text{-}C_6H_{11}X_4$
X=Br, I.

⑥ Z. anorg. allg. Chem. 303, 155 (1960).

$P_4C_{48}H_{40}N_4$

① 2,2,4,4,6,6,8,8-Octaphenyl-1,3,5,7,2,4,6,8-tetrazatetraphosphorine
$N_4P_4(C_6H_5)_8$

② $(C_6H_5)_2PCl_3 + NH_4Cl$
$\xrightarrow{130~135° \text{ in } (CHCl_2)_2}$ 7%

③ Colorless needle crystals. [319.5~
321°].
Sol. in C_6H_6.
⑥ Chem. Ind. (London) **1960**, 839.
JACS **80**, 2116 (1958).   Vysokomol.
Soed. **2**, 377 (1960).   Ber. **76**, 121
(1943).

P₄C₄₈H₄₁N₃O₂
① N-{[(diphenylphosphinylimino)di-
phenylphosphoroanylimino]diphe-
nylphosphoranyl}-P, P-diphenyl-
phosphinimidic acid
$N_3P_4(C_6H_5)_8O_2H$
② $(C_6H_5)_2PCl_3 + NH_4Cl \xrightarrow{H_2O}$
③ [171~171.5°].
⑥ Vysokomol. Soed. **2**, 377 (1960).

P₅Cl₁₀N₅
① 1,3,5,7,9,2,4,6,8,10-Pentazapenta-
phosphorine-2,2,4,4,6,8,8,10,10-
decachloride
② $PCl_5 + NH_4Cl \xrightarrow{7.5\,hrs\ in\ Cl_2CHCHCl_2}$
③ (223~224.3°/13). [41.3°].
UV: JCS **1960**, 2542.
④ + KF + sulfur dioxide ⟶ $N_5P_5F_{10}$

P₅F₁₀N₅
① 1,3,5,7,9,2,4,6,8,10-Pentazapenta-
phosphorine-2,2,4,4,6,6,8,8,10,10-
decafluoride
($NPF_2)_5$
② $N_5P_5Cl_{10} + KF + $ sulfur dioxide ⟶
③ (120.1°). [−50°]. n_D 1.3482 (20°). d
1.8259 (20°/4°).
IR: JCS **1960**, 3608.

P₅C₅F₁₅
① Pentakis(trifluoromethyl)cyclo-
pentaphosphine
($CF_3P)_5$
② $CF_3PI_2 + Hg$ (large excess) ⟶

40%
③ (190). [−33°].
Thermally stable, but undergoes
thermal rearangment at 225°.
④ + I_2 ⟶ CF_3PI_2
+ Cl_2 ⟶ CF_3PCl_2
+ $H_2O \xrightarrow[diglyme]{50°} CF_3PH_2 + (CF_3PH)_2$
+ $H_2(CF_3P)_3$
⑥ JACS **80**, 6161 (1958).

P₆Cl₁₂N₆
① 1,3,5,7,9,11,2,4,6,8,10,12-Hexaza-
hexaphosphorine-2,2,4,4,6,6,8,8,
10,10,12,12-dodecachloride
($NPCl_2)_6$
② $PCl_5 + NH_4Cl \xrightarrow{7.5\,hrs\ in\ Cl_2CHCHCl_2}$
③ (281~282°/26). [92.3°].
UV: JCS **1960**, 2542.
④ + KF + sulfur dioxide ⟶ $N_6P_6F_{12}$

P₇Cl₁₄N₇
① 1,3,5,7,9,11,13,2,4,6,8,10,12,14-Hept-
azaheptaphosphorine-2,2,4,4,6,6,8,
8,10,10,12,12,14,14-tetradecachlo-
ride
($NPCl_2)_7$
② $PCl_5 + NH_4Cl \xrightarrow{7.5\,hrs\ in\ Cl_2CHCHCl_2}$
③ (289~294°/13). [8~12°], d 1.890 (20°/
4°).
UV: JCS **1960**, 2542.
④ + KF + sulfur dioxide ⟶ $N_7P_7F_{14}$

P₇F₁₄N₇
① 1,3,5,7,9,11,13,2,4,6,8,10,12,14-Hept-
azaheptaphosphorine-2, 2,4,4,6,6,8,
8,10,10,12,12-tetradecafluoride
($NPF_2)_7$
② $(NPCl_2)_n + KF + $ sulfur dioxide ⟶
③ (170.7°). [−61°]. n_D 1.3570. d 1.8496
(20°/4°).
⑥ JCS **1960**, 3608.

P$_8$Cl$_{16}$N$_8$

① 1,3,5,7,9,11,13,15,2,4,6,8,10,12,14,16-
Octazaoctaphosphorine-2,2,4,4,6,
6,8,8,10,10,12,12,14,14,16,16-hexa-
decachloride
(NPCl$_2$)$_8$

② PCl$_5$ + NH$_4$Cl $\xrightarrow{\text{7.5 hrs in Cl}_2\text{CHCHCl}_2}$

③ [57~58°].
UV : JCS 1960, 2542.

④ + KF + sulfur dioxide $\longrightarrow$ N$_9$P$_8$F$_{16}$

P$_8$F$_{16}$N$_8$

① 1,3,5,7,9,11,13,15,2,4,6,8,10,12,14,16-
Octazaoctaphosphorine-2,2,4,4,6,
6,8,8,10,10,12,12,14,14,16,16-hexa-
decafluoride
(NPF$_2$)$_8$

② (NPCl$_2$)$_n$ + KF + sulfur dioxide $\longrightarrow$

③ (192.8°). [−16.9°]. n_D 1.3602 (20°).
d 1.8561 (20°/4°).

IR : JCS 1960, 3608.

P$_9$F$_{18}$N$_9$

① 1,3,5,7,9,11,13,15,17,2,4,6,8,10,12,14,
16,18-Nonazanonaphosphorine-
2,2,4,4,6,6,8,8,10,10,12,12,14,14,16,
16,18,18-octadecafluoride
(NPF$_2$)$_9$

② (NPCl$_2$)$_n$ + KF + sulfur dioxide $\longrightarrow$

③ (214.4°). [<−78°]. n_D 1.3622. d 1.8589.
IR : JCS 1960, 3608.

P$_{10}$F$_{20}$N$_{10}$

① 1,3,5,7,9,11,13,15,17,19,2,4,6,8,10,12,
14,16,18,20-Decazadecaphosphorine
-2,2,4,4,6,6,8,8,10,10,12,12,14,14,16,
16,18,18,20,20-eicosafluoride

② (NPCl$_2$)$_n$ + KF + sulfur dioxide $\longrightarrow$

③ (230.8°). [−51°]. n_D 1.3633. d 1.8638
(20°/4°).
IR : JCS 1960, 3608.

9. Organic Compounds of Arsenic, Antimony, and Bismuth

(As, Sb, Bi)

9.1. Organic Compounds of Arsenic

9.1.1. Introduction

Organoarsenic chemistry began in 1837 when R. Bunsen synthesized bis(dimethylarsine)oxide by dry distillation of an equimolar mixture of arsenous acid and potassium acetate. Since then, many organoarsenic compounds have been synthesized, mainly for their pharmacological uses.

Organoarsenic compounds were the most investigated of the organic compounds of group Vb elements, especially from 1910 to 1935. In this period many compounds were first synthesized, for example, arsphenamine, which is well known today as "Salvarsan", and alkyldihalogenoarsine ($RAsX_2$), used largely as a poison gas in World War I. But no active research has been made since 1940, when antibiotics began to draw pharmacological interest away from organoarsenic chemistry. There are many references.

9.1.2. Classification and Nomenclature

Organoarsenic compounds exist in almost every possible form. Trivalent derivatives are named on the basis of arsine (AsH_3), and pentavalent ones on arsenic (As). However, for R_3AsO and R_3AsS, arsine is used as the basis for nomenclature, as they are regarded as coordination compounds of R_3As. Some examples follow:

(1) Trivalent derivatives (arsine)

   Me_2AsCl (dimethylchloroarsine)

   $MeAsH_2$ (methylarsine), etc.

(2) Pentavalent derivatives (arsenic)

   Me_3AsCl_2 (trimethylarsenic dichloride)

   Ph_5As (Pentaphenylarsenic), etc.

"Arsonium" is used for the onium compounds having four M–C bonds, and "arsinic acid" or "arsonic acid" is applied to the hydroxy acid dervatives by analogy by phosphoric compounds.

For example:

(3) Arsonium

   Me_4AsI (tetramethylarsonium iodide)

(4) Arsinic acid

   $Me_2AsO(OH)$ (dimethylarsinic acid)

(5) Arsonic acid

   $MeAsO(OH)_2$ (methylarsonic acid)

9.1.3. Methods of Synthesis

Trialkylarsine or triarylarsine, R_3As, and arsinic acid, $R_2AsO(OH)$, or arsonic acid, $RAsO(OH)_2$, are obtained most easily, and so they are used as the "raw materials" for synthesizing other compounds.   The method of preparing triorgano-arsines and the arsenic acids from inorganic arsenic compounds, such as metallic arsine or trihalogenoarsine, is shown as follows:

a. Synthesis of triorganoarsines (R_3As)

(1)   Heating metallic arsine and methyl iodide in a sealed tube.

$$As + MeI \longrightarrow Me_4AsI + Me_3As$$

(2)   Sodium alloy method

$$Na - As + 3\,RX \longrightarrow R_3As$$

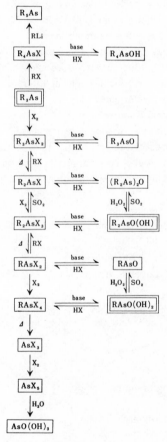

Fig. 9.1.

（3） Organozinc method
$$3 R_2Zn + 2 AsCl_3 \longrightarrow 2 R_3As$$
（4） Metallic sodium method
$$AsX_3 + 3 RX + 6 Na \longrightarrow R_3As$$
（5） Grignard method
$$AsX_3 + 3 RMgX \longrightarrow R_3As$$
（6） Friedel-Crafts method
$$AsX_3 + 3 ArH + AlCl_3 \longrightarrow Ar_3As$$

Of these six methods, the metallic sodium method is the best way to synthesize both alkyl and aryl derivatives.

b. Synthesis of Arsinic Acid and Arsonic Acid.

（1） Using diazonium compounds (Bart method)
$$ArN_2Cl + As(ONa)_3 \longrightarrow ArAsO(OH)_2$$
（2） Heating sodium arsenite with alkyl halide (Meyer method)
$$RX + As(ONa)_3 \longrightarrow RAsO(OH)_2$$
$$2 RX + As(ONa)_3 \longrightarrow R_2AsO(OH)$$

A general systematic synthesis is shown in Fig. 9.1, in which halides are the main materials.

9.1.4. General Properties

a. Structure. In group Vb elements, P, As and Sb are very similar to one another in structure. Arsine has two kinds of derivatives, trivalent and pentavalent. R_3As, a typical type of trivalent derivative, has a trigonal pyramidal structure with As at its apex and three organic radicals at the three corners of its base.

Pentavalent derivatives are of two types. One, represented by R_4AsX, has a tetrahedral structure (R_4As as cation); to this group belong R_3AsO, and R_3AsS. The other has a trigonal bipyramid structure; to this group belongs R_3AsX_2.

b. Physical and Chemical Properties. Many organoarsenic compounds are deadly toxic. Most trivalent derivatives have disagreeable odors, and many of them are volatile liquids. Trivalent derivatives react strongly with O_2 or X_2, and most of them are flammable in air, especially alkyl derivatives having more than two M-C bonds. They have fairly strong donor properties.

9.2. Organic Compounds of Antimony

9.2.1. Introduction

The first organoantimony compounds were obtained around 1850 by C. Löwig *et al.* These compounds were alkyl derivatives of trivalent antimony, which were sensitive to air and spontaneously flammable. For this reason futher progress was very slow until 1880 when air-stable aryl derivatives were synthesized by A. Michaelis *et al.* From 1910 to 1930, a very large number of organoantimony compounds were prepared. Almost all organoantimony compounds known today were synthesized during this period, largely in the hope of finding pharmacologically active substances similar to those of arsenic. In spite of these efforts, remarkable results such as "Salvarsan" in arsenic could not be obtained. However, synthetic methods in organoantimony chemistry underwent great progress during this time.

After this period, as pharmacological interests turned from organometallic compounds to sulfur drugs and further to antibiotics, further progress in organo-antimony chemistry was greatly impeded. In 1938 A. F. Wells determined the molecular structure of $(CH_3)_3SbX_2$ $(X=Cl, Br or I)$ using the technique of X-ray analysis. However, systematic physical and chemical studies have remained limited. Although the physical properties which are associated with synthetic chemistry (mp, bp, d_4^{20}, n_D^{20}) have been recorded for many derivatives, further information, which is eagerly awaited, relates to synthetic studies of other properties such as IR, NMR, dipole moments, thermochemistry, and so on. Some reference books were published at an early stage.

9.2.2. Classification and Nomenclature

The nomenclature of organoantimony compounds is not definitely established, and that of organophosphorus compounds is generally applied. In general, "stibine" is used for trivalent antimony compounds, regarding them as derivatives of stibine (SbH_3). For pentavalent antimony compounds, "antimony" is mainly used as the base. However, for $R_3Sb^{(V)}X$ $(X=VI b elements)$ "stibine" is also applied, regarding them as an additon compound of R_3Sb to X atoms. For the onium compounds having four Sb–C bonds, "stibonium" is used. For the oxy-acid derivatives, stibinic acid or stibonic acid are applied following the example of phosphorus. Examples are shown below:

(1) Stibine
   $(CH_3)_3Sb$ trimethylstibine
   $(CH_3)_2SbCl$ dimethylchlorostibine
   $(CH_3)_3SbS$ trimethylstibine sulfide
(2) Antimony
   $(CH_3)_3SbBr_2$ trimethylantimony dibromide
   $(CH_3)_5Sb$ pentamethylantimony
(3) Stibonium
   $(CH_3)_4SbCl$ tetramethylstibonium chloride
(4) Stibinic acid
   $(C_6H_5)_2Sb(O)OH$ diphenylstibinic acid
(5) Stibonic acid
   $C_6H_5Sb(O)(OH)_2$ phenylstibonic acid

9.2.3. Methods of Synthesis

Preparative methods of organoantimony compounds are a little different for alkyl and for aryl derivatives. But, in both cases, it is convenient in the laboratory to synthesize triorganostibine (R_3Sb) as the first stage. General preparative methods of triorganostibines are shown below.

(1) Grignard method

$$3\,RMgX + SbX_3 \longrightarrow R_3Sb$$

(2) Wurtz-Fittig reaction or potassium-alloy method

$$3\,RX + SbX_3 + 6\,Na \longrightarrow R_3Sb$$

$$3\,RX + K_3Sb \longrightarrow R_3Sb$$

(3) Alkyl or aryl lithium method

$$3\,RLi + SbX_3 \longrightarrow R_3Sb$$

(4) Diazonium salt complex method

$$3\,RN_2X + SbX_3 + Zn \longrightarrow R_3Sb$$

(5) Transalkylaton by organomercury, zinc, aluminum, or tin compounds

$$SbX_3 + 3\,R_3Al \longrightarrow R_3Sb + 3\,R_2AlX$$

$$Sb_2O_3 + 2\,R_3Al \longrightarrow 2\,R_3Sb + Al_2O_3$$

In a laboratory, method (1) is the most convenient for both alkyl and aryl derivatives. Methods (2) and (4) are applied only to the aryl derivatives. The latter (4) is especially convenient for preparing Ar_nSbX_{3-n} ($n=1$, 2 or 3) containing functional groups in aryl radicals. General preparative methods of halogen derivatives are shown below.

a. Alkyl Derivatives. Trialkylstibines, especially low alkyl compounds, are quite sensitive to air. Then, it is more convenient to store R_3SbX_2 as a raw material.

b. Aryl Derivatives. Similar procedures are employed in the preparation of aryl derivatives. However, owing to the succesful application of the the diazonium method to the preparation of Ar_nSb_{3-n} ($n=1$, 2 or 3), and the difficulty of the following two stages, the reaction scheme shown in Fig. 9.3 is generally recommended.

$$Ar_3Sb + ArX \longrightarrow Ar_4SbX$$

$$Ar_2SbX_3 \longrightarrow ArSbX_2$$

9.2.4. General Properties

a. Configuration. Organoantimony compounds have two stable valence states, Sb(III) and Sb(V). A typical compound belonging to the former state is R_3Sb. This has a trigonal pyramidal structure in which an antimony atom and three R groups are at the apicies.

The latter state is roughly classified into three types: tetrahedral, trigonal bipyramidal, and octahedral configurations. The first is represented by R_4SbX, in which the R_4Sb moiety has a charged tetrahedral configuration. The second is the typical configuration of pentavalent antimony compounds, and almost all the compounds represented as R_3SbX_2 are included in this type. The third is not so common, and only a few compounds are reported. $LiSb(C_6H_5)_6$ and $RSbX_3$ (acac) belong to this type.

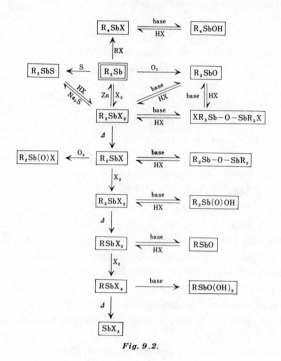

Fig. 9.2.

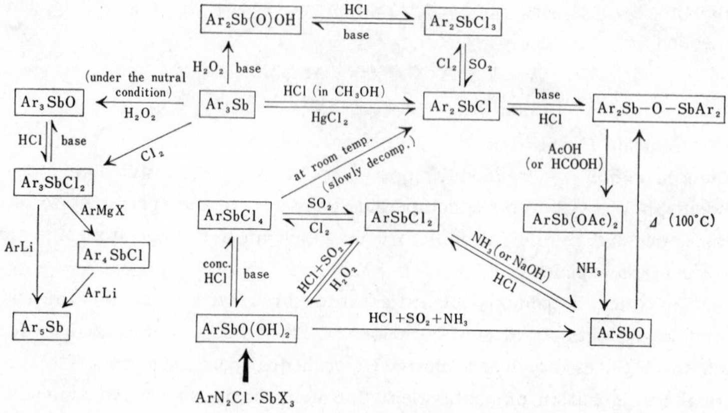

Fig. 9.3.

b. Physical and Chemical Properties.   Many trivalent antimony compounds have an unpleasant odor and are poisonous. As shown in Figs. 9.2 and 9.3, oxidation and reduction of organoantimony compounds occur easily under selected conditions. The reducing property of trivalent antimony compounds is fairly strong, forming pentavalent compounds through reaction with oxygen, sulfur, and so on.

Lower alkyl derivatives of the types R_3Sb and R_2SbX are spontaneously flammable in air. These can also reduce mercury and silver salts, but not HX unless heated in a sealed tube.

The donating ability of trivalent compounds is weak. They can, however, form addition compounds with derivatives of B, Al, Ga, Pt, Pd, Mn, and so on. The general order of the donating power of Vb elements decreases in the order $R_3N >$ $R_3P > R_3As > R_3Sb$. R_3Bi has scarcely any donating ability. The mean dissociation energy of the Sb–C bond in $(CH_3)_3Sb$ is 49.7 kcal/mole.

9.3. Organic Compounds of Bismuth

9.3.1. Introduction and General Properties

The chemistry of organobismuth compounds began in 1850 when Löwig and Schweizer synthesized triethylbismuth. However, the study of organobismuth compounds was limited in many ways because of the flammability of triethylbismuth, until Michaelis and Polis synthesized triphenylbismuth, which is stable in air. In 1913, Challenger and his coworkers began synthesizing organobismuth compounds in order to obtain optically active compounds. They did not the expected compounds, but made a large contribution to the reactions and obtain synthetic methods of organobismuth chemistry.

The investigation of water-soluble compounds, however, was extensive, in expectation of pharmacological effects. The structural chemistry of organobismuth compounds was limited to the most stable triphenylbismuth with a few reports.

Recently, many compounds besides trialkyl and triaryl compounds, which substituted the organic radicals with electronegative groups, have been synthesized. As for aryl compounds, pentavalent compounds and onium salts were prepared.

These compounds, and the literatures up to 1931, were compiled in a review by H. Gilman.

The triaryl compounds are stable in air, but the trialkyl compounds are unstable under heat; and higher homologues decompose explosively when heated under atmospheric pressure. The di- or mono-substituted derivatives of trialkyl- and triarylbismuth are prone to decompose in moisture.

The chemical properties of organobismuth compounds are very different from those of other Vb group compounds.

Trialkyl and triaryl compounds show no donor properties. The mean dissociation energy of the Bi–C bond is about 34 kcal/mole and rather small as compared with that of other Vb group compounds. The reactivities of organobismuth compounds and instability to heat can be attributed to this weak bonding.

Organobismuth compounds show the greatest difference from other Vb compounds in the addition reactions of halogens to trialkyl and triaryl compounds. Halogens add to triarylbismuth easily at low temperature to give fairly stable pentavalent compounds, but the diiodide is very unstable above $-78°C$; on the other hand, trialkylbismuth compounds give di- or monoalkylbismuth halides with elimination of alkyl halides. This is explained by the unstable pentavalent intermediates which decompose to alkyl halides and di- or monosubstituted alkylbismuth derivatives.

Pentaphenylbismuth is prepared by the reaction of triphenylbismuth dihalide and phenyllithium at $-78°C$.

The onium salts cannot be obtained by the reaction of triorganobismuth compounds with alkyl halides or aryl halides. The reaction gives only the starting materials, and at high temperature decomposition occurs. The onium salts are obtained by reaction of pentaphenylbismuth with acids at $-78°C$, or with triphenylboron, or the reaction of triphenylbismuth dichloride with silver perchlorate in absolute ethanol.

9.3.2. Classification and Nomenclature

Organobismuth compounds have three types of derivatives: Trivalent, tetravalent, and pentavalent compounds. The tetra- and pentavalent compounds are known only for the phenyl derivatives.

(i) *Trivalent derivatives*

$(CH_3)_3Bi$ trimethylbismuth

$C_6H_5BiCl_2$ phenylbismuth dichloride

(ii) *Pentavalent derivatives*

$(C_6H_5)_3BiCl_2$ triphenylbismuth dichloride

$(C_6H_5)_5Bi$ pentaphenylbismuth

(iii) *Tetravalent derivatives*

$(C_6H_5)_4BiCl$ tetraphenylbismuthonium chloride

9.3.3. Methods of Synthesis

a. Trialkyl and Triarylbismuth

(i) *Grignard Method*

$$3\,RMgX + BiX_3 \xrightarrow[\text{ether}]{} R_3Bi$$

Widely used for both trialkyl and triaryl compounds. Yield depends upon the solubility of bismuth halides in solvents. This method is used for the mixed organobismuth compounds.

(ii) *Alkylzinc Method*

$$3\,R_2Zn + 2\,BiX_3 \longrightarrow 2\,R_3Bi$$

Used for the preparation of trialkylbismuth compounds; there are no examples for higher alkyl homologs and aryl compounds.

(iii) *Diazonium Salt Complex Method*

$$(ArN_2Cl)_2BiX_3 \xrightarrow{Cu} Ar_2BiX + CuCl + 2N_2$$

$$Ar_2BiX + NH_2NH_2 \longrightarrow Ar_3Bi$$

Used for the aryl compounds, especially with functional groups.

b. Dialkyl- and Diarylbismuth Derivatives

(i) *Redistribution Method*

$$2R_3Bi + BiX_3 \xrightarrow[cool]{} 3R_2BiX$$

Used for both alkyl and aryl derivatives. Triorganobismuth is reacted with bismuth trihalide in a suitable ratio, with cooling.

(ii) *Reaction of Trialkylbismuth with Halogens*

$$R_3Bi + X_2 \xrightarrow[cool]{} R_2BiX + RX$$

Used only for alkylbismuth derivatives.

(iii) *Decomposition of Pentavalent Derivatives*

$$(C_6H_5)_3BiBr_2(or\ I_2) \longrightarrow (C_6H_5)_2BiBr(or\ I)$$

c. Monoalkyl- and Monoarylbismuth Derivatives

$$R_3Bi + 2BiX_3 \xrightarrow[cool]{} 3RBiX_2$$

Used for both alkyl and aryl derivatives and prepared as in b., (i).

d. Pentavalent Compounds

(i) *Dihalide Compounds*

$$Ar_3Bi + Cl_2 \xrightarrow[cool]{} Ar_3BiCl_2$$

(ii) *Pentaphenylbismuth*

$$(C_6H_5)_3BiCl_2 + 2C_6H_5Li \xrightarrow{-78°C} (C_6H_5)_5Bi$$

e. Tetraphenylbismuthonium Compounds

$$(C_6H_5)_5Bi + HX \longrightarrow (C_6H_5)_4BiX$$

$$(C_6H_5)_5Bi + (C_6H_5)_3B \longrightarrow (C_6H_5)_4Bi \cdot (C_6H_5)_4B$$

$$(C_6H_5)_3BiCl_2 + 2AgClO_4 \xrightarrow[abs.\ EtOH]{} (C_6H_5)_4BiClO_4$$

REFERENCES

Arsenic:

W. R. Cullen, "Advances in Organometallic Chemistry", 4, p. 145, Academic Press, New York (1966).

Antimony:

G. E. Coates, "Organometallic Compounds", p. 212, Methuen (1956).

A. F. Wells, "Structural Inorganic Chemistry", 3rd ed., p. 662, Oxford (1962).

P. J. Durrant, B. Durrant, "Introduction to Advanced Inorganic Chemistry", p.

752, Londmans (1962).
Bismuth:
H. Gilman, H. L. Yale, *Chem. Revs.*,   **30**, 281 (1942).

〔As〕

AsCCl₂F₃

① Trifluoromethyldichloroarsine

CF_3AsCl_2

② $(CF_3)_3AsCl_2 \xrightarrow[125°]{20\,hrs.}$

③ Colorless liq. (71°/760). n_D 1.431 (20°).

Sol. in org. solvents ; decompd. by H_2O.

⑥ JCS **1953**, 1552.

AsCF₃I₂

① Trifluoromethyldiiodoarsine

CF_3AsI_2

② $CF_3I + As \xrightarrow[220°]{24\,hrs.} 4\%$

③ Posesses unpleasant odor.

Yellow oil. (100°/48.5), (183°/760).

n_D 1.688 (20°).

Sol. in org. solvents ; decompd. by H_2O.

⑥ Ber. **86**, 275 (1953).   JCS **1953**, 1552.

AsCH₂F₃

① Trifluoromethylarsine

CF_3AsH_2

② $CF_3AsI_2 + LiAlH_4 \longrightarrow 49\%$

$CF_3AsI_2 + Zn-Cu + HCl \longrightarrow 98\%$

③ Gas. (−12.5°/753).

⑥ JCS **1953**, 1552.

AsCH₂F₃O₃

① Trifluoromethylarsonic acid

$CF_3AsO(OH)_2$

② $CF_3AsI_2 + H_2O_2 \xrightarrow{in\ H_2O} 96\%$

③ White powder.

Sol. in H_2O.

④ $\xrightarrow{35°/10^{-2}mmHg} [CF_3AsO(OH)]_2O$

$+ AgO \longrightarrow CF_3AsO(OH)(OAg)$

⑥ JCS **1954**, 881.

AsCH₃Cl₂

① Methyldichloroarsine

CH_3AsCl_2

② $CH_3AsO(ONa)_2 + SO_2 + HCl \longrightarrow$

③ Colorless foaming liq. (129.5~130°/746). [−42.5°]. d 1.8358 (20°/4°).

Posesses very irritating vapor.

④ $\xrightarrow{oxidation} CH_3AsO$

$+ Cl_2 \longrightarrow CH_3AsCl_4$(unstable)

⑥ JACS **69**, 927 (1947).   JCS **1931**, 2518.

AsCH₃Cl₄

① Methylarsenic tetrachloride

CH_3AsCl_4

② $CH_3AsCl_2 + Cl_2 \xrightarrow[-10°]{CS_2}$

③ Colorless crystals.

Sol. in H_2O

⑥ Ann. **107**, 274 (1858).   Proc. Roy. Soc. **A 110**, 523 (1926).

AsCH₃O

① Oxomethylarsine

CH_3AsO

② $CH_3AsCl_2 + K_2CO_3 \longrightarrow$

③ Colorless crystals. [95° decomp.].

④ $+ I_2 \xrightarrow{H_2O} CH_3AsO(OH)_2$

⑥ Ann. **107**, 282 (1858).

AsCH₃S

① Thionomethylarsine

CH_3AsS

② $CH_3AsCl_2 + H_2S \xrightarrow{H_2O}$

③ Colorless crystals. [110°].

Sol. in CS_2 ; slightly sol. in hot EtOH and ether.

Insol. in H_2O.

④ $+ H_2O \longrightarrow As_2S_3$

⑥ Ann. **107**, 279 (1858).

AsCH₅

① Methylarsine
CH₃AsH₂

② $CH_3AsO(ONa)_2 + Zn-Hg + HCl \xrightarrow{alc.}$

③ Colorless liq. (2°/755).
Sol. in org. solvents.
Insol. in H₂O.

④ $+ O_2 \longrightarrow CH_3AsO + H_2O$
$+ 3 O_2 \longrightarrow 2 CH_3AsO(OH)_2$

⑥ Ber. **34**, 3595 (1901).   Am. Chem. J.
33, 117 (1905).

AsCH₅O₃

① Methylarsonic acid
CH₃AsO(OH)₂

② $CH_3AsCl_2 + AgO \longrightarrow$

③ Colorless plates. [159.8°].
Sol. in H₂O and hot EtOH; insol. in
ether.

④ $+ H_3PO_2 \xrightarrow{H_2SO_4} (CH_3As)_x$

⑥ Ann. **107**, 286 (1858).

AsC₂BrF₆

① Bistrifluoromethylbromoarsine
(CF₃)₂AsBr

② $(CF_3)_3As + Br_2 \xrightarrow{-5°} 17\%$

③ Colorless liq. (59.5°/745). n_D 1.398
(20°).
Sol. in org. solvents.

⑥ JCS **1953**, 1552.

AsC₂ClF₆

① Bistrifluoromethylchloroarsine
(CF₃)₂AsCl

② $(CF_3)_3AsCl_2 \xrightarrow[125°]{20\,hrs.}$

③ Colorless oil. (46°). n_D 1.351 (20°).
Sol. in org. solvents.

⑥ JCS **1953**, 1552.

AsC₂F₇

① Bistrifluoromethylfluoroarsine

(CF₃)₂AsF

② $(CF_3)_3As + CoF_3 \xrightarrow{100°}$

$(CF_3)_2AsI + AgF \xrightarrow[20°]{30\,days}$

③ Colorless liq. (25°).
Sol. in org. solvents.

⑥ Ber. **81**, 276 (1953).   JCS **1953**, 1552.

AsC₂HF₆

① Bistrifluoromethylarsine
(CF₃)₂AsH

② $(CF_3)_2AsI + LiAlH_4 \xrightarrow{n-Bu_2O} 16\%$
$(CF_3)_3AsI + Zn-Cu + HCl \longrightarrow 43\%$

③ Colorless liq. (19°/760).
Decomp. slowly at room temp.

⑥ JCS **1953**, 1552.

AsC₂HF₆O₂

① Bistrifluoromethylarsinic acid
(CF₃)₂AsO(OH)

② $(CF_3)_2AsI + H_2O_2 \xrightarrow{sealed\ tube} 86\%$

③ White powder.
Recrystd. from hot CHCl₃.

⑥ JCS **1953**, 1552 ; **1954**, 881.

AsC₂H₂Cl₃

① 2-Chlorovinyldichloroarsine
ClCH=CHAsCl₂

② $HC≡CH + AsCl_3 \xrightarrow[AlCl_3]{}$

③ Colorless liq. (190°/760), (70°/10).
[0.1°]. n_D 1.6153 (10.6°). d 1.8880
(20°/4°).
Sol. in org. solvents.

⑥ JCS **1921**, 448.

AsC₂H₄ClO₃

① 2-Chlorovinylarsonic acid
ClCH=CHAsO(OH)₂

② $ClCH=CHAsH_2 + HNO_3 \longrightarrow$

③ Colorless needles. [130°].
Sol. in H₂O and hot EtOH; insol. in
ether.

⑥ JCS **121**, 1757 (1922).

AsC$_2$H$_4$Cl$_3$

① Bischloromethylchloroarsine
(ClCH$_2$)$_2$AsCl

② AsCl$_3$ + CH$_2$N$_2$ $\longrightarrow$

③ Colorless liq. (86~88°/16). *d* 1.8485
(20°/15°).
Sol. in org. solvents.
Decomp. by H$_2$O or moisture; possesses characteristic odor.

⑥ J. Gen. Chem. USSR **11**, 41 (1941).

AsC$_2$H$_5$Cl$_2$

① Ethyldichloroarsine
C$_2$H$_5$AsCl$_2$

② AsCl$_3$ + (C$_2$H$_5$)$_4$Pb $\xrightarrow[100\sim110°]{N_2}$

③ Colorless liq. (152~155°/740). *d* 1.6595
(20°/4°).
Sol. in org. solvents; very irritating vapor.

⑥ JCS **1931**, 2518.   JACS **69**, 927 (1947).
JOC **14**, 429 (1949).

AsC$_2$H$_5$O

① Oxoethylarsine
C$_2$H$_5$AsO

② C$_2$H$_5$AsCl$_2$ + K$_2$CO$_3$ $\xrightarrow{C_6H_6}$ 57%

③ Crystalizes in the air.
Colorless oil. (158°/10).
Sol. in ether, C$_6$H$_6$ and acetone.

⑥ Ber. **53**, 1014 (1920).

AsC$_2$H$_6$Cl

① Dimethylchloroarsine
(CH$_3$)$_2$AsCl

② [(CH$_3$)$_2$As]$_2$O + HCl $\longrightarrow$

(CH$_3$)$_2$AsO(OH) + H$_3$PO$_2$ $\xrightarrow{HCl}$

③ Pale yellow heavy oil. (106.5~107°).
Sol. in org. solvents.

④ + CH$_3$I $\xrightarrow[\text{sealed tube}]{100°}$ (CH$_3$)$_4$AsI$_3$

⑥ Ann. **37**, 31 (1841). Ber. **54**, 1454 (1921).

AsC$_2$H$_6$Cl$_3$

① Dimethylarsenic trichloride
(CH$_3$)$_2$AsCl$_3$

② (CH$_3$)$_2$AsCl + Cl$_2$ $\xrightarrow{CS_2}$

(CH$_3$)$_2$AsO(OH) + PCl$_5$ $\longrightarrow$

③ Prism–like crystals. [40~50°
decomp.].
Sol. in ether.

⑥ Ann. **107**, 269 (1858).

AsC$_2$H$_6$I

① Dimethyliodoarsine
(CH$_3$)$_2$AsI

② CH$_3$I + As$_2$O$_3$ + NaOH $\xrightarrow[\text{alcohol}]{}$ 46%

[(CH$_3$)$_2$As]$_2$O + HI $\longrightarrow$ 58%
(CH$_3$)$_2$AsO(OH) + H$_3$PO$_2$ $\longrightarrow$

③ Yellow liquid. (154~155°/760).
Sol. in org. solvents; insol. in H$_2$O.

④ + CH$_3$I $\xrightarrow{100°}$ (CH$_3$)$_4$AsI

⑥ Ber. **54**, 1454 (1921). JACS **76**, 4031
(1954).

AsC$_2$H$_7$

① Dimethylarsine
(CH$_3$)$_2$AsH

② (CH$_3$)$_2$AsO(OH) + Zn−Hg + HCl $\longrightarrow$
(CH$_3$)$_2$AsCl + Zn−Pt + HCl $\xrightarrow{}$
        alc.

③ Colorless liq. (35.6°/746). *d* 1.213
(29°/4°).
Sol. in EtOH, ether, CHCl$_3$ and C$_6$H$_6$;
stable in air below 0°; inflammable
in air above 10°.

④ + HBr $\longrightarrow$ (CH$_3$)$_2$AsBr·HBr
(White plate like crystals, stable
in air)
+ (CH$_3$)$_2$AsCl $\longrightarrow$ [(CH$_3$)$_2$As]$_2$

⑥ Am. Chem. J. **33**, 143 (1905). . Chem.
Zentr. **1906** I, 738.

AsC$_2$H$_7$

① Ethylarsine

$C_2H_5AsH_2$

② $C_2H_5AsO(ONa)_2 + Zn-Hg + HCl \longrightarrow$

③ Colorless liquid. (36°). d 1.217(22°/4°).
   Sol. in org. solvents ; inflammable
   in air.

⑥ Am. Chem. J. **33**, 143 (1905).

$AsC_2H_7O_2$

① Dimethylarsinic acid
   $(CH_3)_2AsO(OH)$

② $(CH_3)_2AsCl_3 + H_2O \longrightarrow$

③ Colorless crystals. [200°].
   Sol. in org. solvents.

⑥ Ann. **107**, 263 (1858).

$AsC_2H_7O_3$

① Ethylarsonic acid
   $C_2H_5AsO(OH)_2$

② $C_2H_5Br + As_2O_3 + NaOH \xrightarrow{HCl}$

③ Colorless and odorless needles. [95~
   96°], [99.6°].
   Sol. in H_2O and hot EtOH ; insol. in
   ether ; aq. soln. is very acidic.

④ $+ H_3PO_2 \xrightarrow{\text{dil. } H_2SO_4} (C_2H_5As)_x$

⑥ JACS **44**, 805 (1922).

$AsC_3F_9Cl_2$

① Tristrifluoromethylarsenic
   dichloride
   $(CF_3)_3AsCl_2$

② $(CF_3)_3As + Cl_2 \xrightarrow[\text{r. t.}]{\text{84 hrs}} 34\%$

③ Colorless liq. (98.5°). n_D 1.386 (19°).
   Sol. in org. solvents.

④ $+ Hg \longrightarrow (CF_3)_2Hg$
   $\xrightarrow[125°]{\text{20 hrs}} (CF_3)_2AsCl + CF_3AsCl_2$

⑥ JCS **1953**, 1552.

AsC_3F_9

① Tristrifluoromethylarsine
   $(CF_3)_3As$

② $CF_3I + As \xrightarrow[220°]{\text{24 hrs}} 78\%$

③ Colorless liq. (33.3°).
   Sol. in ether ; stable in air. Posesses irritating odor.

④ $(CF_3)_3As + Cl_2 \xrightarrow[125°]{\text{24 hrs}} CF_3Cl + AsCl_3$

⑥ JCS **1953**, 1552 ; **1952**, 2552.   Ber. **86**,
   272 (1953).

AsC_3F_{11}

① Tristrifluoromethylarsenic difluoride
   $(CF_3)_3AsF_2$

② $(CF_3)_3AsCl_2 + AgF \xrightarrow[20°]{\text{6days}} 52\%$

③ Colorless liq. (57~58°/760).
   Sol. in org. solvents.

⑥ JCS **1953**, 1552.

AsC_3H_6NS

① Dimethylthiocyanoarsine
   $(CH_3)_2AsSCN$

② $(CH_3)_2AsCl + NaSCN \xrightarrow[\text{in acetone}]{}$

③ Colorless oil. (92°/17).
   Sol. in C_6H_6, acetone, EtOH and ether.

⑥ Ber. **54**, 1454 (1921) ; **61**, 676 (1928).

$AsC_3H_7O_3$

① Allylarsonic acid
   $CH_2=CHCH_2AsO(OH)_2$

② $CH_2=CHCH_2Br + As_2O_3$
   $+ NaOH \xrightarrow{HCl}$

③ Colorless needles. [128~129°].
   Recrystd. from H_2O ; sol. in hot
   EtOH.

⑥ JACS **44**, 805 (1922).

AsC_3H_9

① Trimethylarsine
   $(CH_3)_3As$

② $CH_3MgI + AsCl_3 \xrightarrow[\text{ether}]{} 70\%$

③ Colorless liq. (50.1~50.3°). n_D 1.4541

(20°). d 1.310 (20°/0°).

Sol. in org. solvents.

④ + Br$_2$ ⟶ (CH$_3$)$_3$AsBr$_2$

    + excess Br$_2$ ⟶ (CH$_3$)$_3$AsBr$_4$

⑥ Ber. **39**, 160 (1906).   JCS **1954**, 3381.

AsC$_3$H$_9$Br$_2$

① Trimethylarsenic dibromide

    (CH$_3$)$_3$AsBr$_2$

② (CH$_3$)$_3$As + Br$_2$ $\xrightarrow{\text{ether}}$

    (CH$_3$)$_3$AsBr$_2$·Br$_2$ ⟶

    treating with acetone ⟶

③ Colorless liq. [156~160°].

    Sol. in org. solvents.

⑥ Ber. **40**, 1512 (1907).

AsC$_3$H$_9$O

① Trimethylarsine oxide

    (CH$_3$)$_3$AsO

② [(CH$_3$)$_2$As]$_2$O + CH$_3$I + NaOH ⟶

    (CH$_3$)$_3$As $\xrightarrow{\text{oxidation}}$

③ Hygroscopic crystals.

    Sol. in H$_2$O and org. solvents.

⑥ Compt. rend. **137**, 925 (1903).

AsC$_3$H$_9$S

① Trimethylarsine sulfide

    (CH$_3$)$_3$AsS

② (CH$_3$)AsS$_2$ $\xrightarrow{\text{heat}}$

    (CH$_3$)$_3$As + S$_8$

③ Colorless needles. (177.5°).

    Sol. in EtOH, CHCl$_3$ and CS$_2$.

④ + CH$_3$I ⟶ (CH$_3$)$_3$AsS·CH$_3$I

    (colorless needles)

⑥ Am. Chem. J. **33**, 134 (1911).

AsC$_4$F$_{10}$I

① Bispentafluoroethyliodoarsine

    (C$_2$F$_5$)$_2$AsI

② C$_2$F$_5$I + As $\xrightarrow[230°]{40\,\text{hrs}}$

③ Colorless liq. (120°).

Sol. in org. solvents.

⑥ JCS **1954**, 3381.

AsC$_4$H$_5$Cl$_2$O$_2$

① Bis(2-chlorovinyl)arsinic acid

    (ClCH=CH)$_2$AsO(OH)

② (ClCH=CH)$_2$AsCl$_3$ + H$_2$O ⟶

③ Colorless needles. [120°].

    Sol. in H$_2$O.

⑥ JCS **1922**, 1756.

AsC$_4$H$_9$Cl$_2$

① n-Butyldichloroarsine

    n-C$_4$H$_9$AsCl$_2$

② n-C$_4$H$_9$AsO(OH)$_2$ + concd. HCl

    + KI $\xrightarrow{\text{SO}_2}$

③ Colorless oil. (192~194°/760, 120°/60).

    d 1.4664 (20°/4°).

    Sol. in org. solvents ; posesses irri-

    tating vapor.

④ + Cl$_2$ ⟶ n-C$_4$H$_9$AsCl$_4$

    $\xrightarrow{\text{oxidation}}$ n-C$_4$H$_9$AsO

⑥ JACS **44**, 805 (1922).   JCS **1931**, 2518.

AsC$_4$H$_{10}$Cl

① Diethyl-chloroarsine

    (C$_2$H$_5$)$_2$AsCl

② [(C$_2$H$_5$)$_2$As]$_2$O + HCl ⟶

③ Colorless liq. (156°/736).

    Sol. in org. solvents.

⑥ Ber. **54**, 1454 (1921).

AsC$_4$H$_{11}$

① Diethylarsine

    (C$_2$H$_5$)$_2$AsH

② (C$_2$H$_5$)$_2$AsO(OH) + Zn—Hg + HCl ⟶

③ Colorless liq. (105°).

    Sol. in org. solvents ; instan-

    taneously oxidized in air.

⑥ Ann. **437**, 290 (1924).

AsC$_4$H$_{11}$O$_2$

① Diethylarsinic acid

(C$_2$H$_5$)$_2$AsO(OH)

② C$_2$H$_5$Br + C$_2$H$_5$AsCl$_2$ + NaOH $\xrightarrow[\text{acidified}]{\text{HCl}}$

③ Colorless crystals. [190°].
Recrystn. from EtOH ; sol. in H$_2$O.

④ + Zn－Hg + HCl $\longrightarrow$ (C$_2$H$_5$)$_2$AsH

⑥ JACS **44**, 805 (1922) ; **69**, 927 (1922).

AsC$_4$H$_{12}$I

① Tetramethylarsonium iodide
(CH$_3$)$_4$AsI

② (CH$_3$)$_3$As + CH$_3$I $\xrightarrow[\text{sealed tube}]{100°}$

③ Colorless hygroscopic plate. [170～
180°].
Sol. in H$_2$O and hot EtOH ; slightly
sol. in ether ; aq. soln. is very.
acidic.

④ + KOH $\longrightarrow$ (CH$_3$)$_3$As
+ HgI$_2$ $\longrightarrow$ (CH$_3$)$_3$As·HgI$_2$

⑥ Ber. **54**, 1451 (1921).

AsC$_5$H$_7$N$_2$

① n-Propyldicyanoarsine
n-C$_3$H$_7$As(CN)$_2$

② n-C$_3$H$_7$AsCl$_2$ + Hg(CN)$_2$ $\longrightarrow$

③ Colorless crystals. [82～86°].
Sol. in org. solvents ; very poisonous.

⑥ JACS **69**, 927 (1947).   JCS **1921**, 448.

AsC$_6$F$_{15}$

① Trispentafluoroethylarsine
(C$_2$F$_5$)$_3$As

② C$_2$F$_5$I + As $\xrightarrow[230°]{40\,\text{hrs}}$

③ Colorless liq. (96.3°).
Sol. in org. solvents.

⑥ JCS **1954**, 3381.

AsC$_6$H$_4$BrCl$_2$

① p-Bromophenyldichloroarsine
p-BrC$_6$H$_4$AsCl$_2$

② p-BrC$_6$H$_4$AsO(OH)$_2$ + PCl$_3$
$\xrightarrow[\text{CH}_3\text{COOH}]{80\%}$

③ Colorless liq. (90～91°/3).
Sol. in C$_6$H$_6$.

⑥ JACS **76**, 4031 (1954).

AsC$_6$H$_5$Cl$_2$

① Phenyldichloroarsine
C$_6$H$_5$AsCl$_2$

② (C$_6$H$_5$)$_3$As + AsCl$_3$ $\xrightarrow[\text{sealed tube}]{250～260°}$

(C$_6$H$_5$)$_2$Hg + AsCl$_3$ $\longrightarrow$

[((C$_6$H$_5$)$_2$As]$_2$ + HCl $\longrightarrow$

③ Poseses unpleasant odor ; stable in
air.
Colorless liq. (140～143°/40), (254～
258°). n_D 1.6386 (15.3°). d 1.6561
(15.3°/4°).
Sol. in org. solvents ; insol. in H$_2$O.

④ + Na $\xrightarrow[\text{ether}]{\text{N}_2}$ [C$_6$H$_5$As]$_2$

+ HCl $\longrightarrow$ C$_6$H$_6$ + AsCl$_3$

⑥ Ber. **27**, 264 (1894) ; **47**, 2751 (1914).

AsC$_6$H$_5$Cl$_2$O

① Phenyldichloroarsine oxide
C$_6$H$_5$AsOCl$_2$

② C$_6$H$_5$AsCl$_4$ + H$_2$O $\longrightarrow$

③ Colorless crystals. [100°].
Sol. in H$_2$O ; fuming slowly in air.

④ $\xrightarrow{\text{heat}}$ C$_6$H$_5$Cl + AsOCl
+ H$_2$O $\longrightarrow$ C$_6$H$_5$AsO(OH)$_2$

⑥ Ann. **201**, 202 (1880). Ber. **10**, 624
(1877).

AsC$_6$H$_5$Br$_2$

① Phenyldibromoarsine
C$_6$H$_5$AsBr$_2$

② C$_6$H$_5$AsO + HBr $\longrightarrow$

③ Colorless oil. (285° decomp.).
d 2.0983 (15°/4°).
Undecomp. in H$_2$O.

④ + Br$_2$ $\longrightarrow$ C$_6$H$_5$Br + AsBr$_3$

⑥ Ann. **201**, 203 (1880). Ber. **10**, 626
(1877).

AsC₆H₅Cl₄

① Phenylarsenictetrachloride
$C_6H_5AsCl_4$

② $C_6H_5AsCl_2 + Cl_2 \longrightarrow$

③ Yellow needles. [45°].
Sol. in glacial acetic acid.

④ $+ CH_3COOH \longrightarrow C_6H_5AsCl_2$
$+ ClCH_2COOH$

⑥ Ann. **201**, 198 (1880). Ber. **10**, 622 (1877).

AsC₆H₅I₂

① Phenyldiiodoarsine
$C_6H_5AsI_2$

② $C_6H_5AsCl_2 + NaI \xrightarrow[C_2H_5OH]{}$

③ Lemon yellow oil. (190°/12). [15°].
Sol. in org. solvents.

⑥ JCS **117**, 1376 (1920).

AsC₆H₅O

① Oxophenylarsine
C_6H_5AsO

② $C_6H_5AsCl_2 + Na_2CO_3 \xrightarrow{\text{in } H_2O}$

$C_6H_5AsO(OH)_2 + SO_2 \xrightarrow[\text{dil. } H_2SO_4]{KI}$

③ Colorless crystals. [119~120°].
Sol. in hot EtOH and C₆H₆; slightly sol. in cold EtOH; insol. in H₂O.
Possesses characteristic odor.

④ $+ HgO \xrightarrow{\text{alk. soln.}} (C_6H_5)_2Hg$
$+ (C_6H_5)AsO(OH)_2$
$+ HCl \xrightarrow{\text{heat}} C_6H_5AsCl_2$

⑥ Ber. **67**, 322 (1934); **10**, 623 (1877).

AsC₆H₅S

① Thionophenylarsine
C_6H_5AsS

② $[C_6H_5As]_2 + S \longrightarrow$
$C_6H_5AsCl_2 + H_2S \longrightarrow$
$C_6H_5AsO + H_2S \xrightarrow[EtOH]{}$

③ Colorless needles. [152°].
Recrystd. from C₆H₆.
Sol. in hot C₆H₆ and cold CS₂; slightly sol. in cold C₆H₆, EtOH and ether.

④ $+ HNO_3 \longrightarrow C_6H_5AsO(OH)_2$
$+ (C_2H_5)_2Hg \longrightarrow C_6H_5As(C_2H_5)_2$
$+ HgS$

⑥ Ber **15**, 1955 (1882).

AsC₆H₆Br₂Cl₃

① Tris-β-chlorovinylarsenic dibromide
$(ClCH=CH)_3AsBr_2$

② $(ClCH=CH)_3As + Br_2 \xrightarrow[\text{petr. ether}]{}$

③ Colorless needles. [107°].
Sol. in org. solvents.

⑥ JCS **121**, 1757 (1922).

AsC₆H₆Cl₃

① Tris-2-chlorovinylarsine
$(ClCH=CH)_3As$

② $HC\equiv CH + AsCl_3 + AlCl_3 \longrightarrow$

③ Fairly stable in the air.
Colorless oil. (157~158°/28). [3~4°].
Insol. in H₂O and EtOH.

⑥ JCS **1921**, 448.

AsC₆H₇

① Phenylarsine
$C_6H_5AsH_2$

② $C_6H_5AsO(OH)_2 + Zn-Hg + HCl \longrightarrow$

③ Transparent oil. (148°/760). n_D 1.6082 (22°). d 1.349 (25°/15°).
Sol. in EtOH and ether; possesses phenylisonitrile-like odor.

④ $+ O_2 \longrightarrow [C_6H_5As]_2$
$+ $ concd. $HNO_3 \longrightarrow C_6H_5AsO(OH)_2$

⑥ Ber. **34**, 3599 (1901). JACS **44**, 1362 (1922).

AsC₆H₇O₃

① Phenylarsonic acid
$C_6H_5AsO(OH)_2$

② $C_6H_5AsCl_4$ $\xrightarrow{\text{hydrolysis}}$

③ Colorless crystals.

Sol. in H_2O and hot EtOH; insol. in ether; Dehydrated at 158°; stable in hot HNO_3.

④ + H_3PO_2 $\longrightarrow$ $(C_6H_5As)_2$
+ activated H_2 $\longrightarrow$ $C_6H_5AsH_2$
+ SO_2 $\xrightarrow{HCl}$ $C_6H_5AsCl_2$

⑥ Ber. 10, 626 (1877); 27, 265 (1894); 54, 1149 (1921).   Ann. 201, 203 (1880).

AsC₆H₈N

① p-Aminophenylarsine
p-$H_2NC_6H_4AsH_2$

② 4-$H_2NC_6H_4AsO(OH)_2$ + Zn + HCl $\longrightarrow$

③ Colorless oil. (132°/10).
Sol. in org. solvents.

⑥ JCS 1947, 618.

AsC₆H₁₅

① Triethylarsine
$(C_2H_5)_3As$

② C_2H_5MgBr + $AsBr_3$ $\longrightarrow$

③ Colorless liq. (36.5~37°/15.5).
n_D 1.4751 (20°). d 1.0735 (20°/0°).
Sol. in org. solvents; inflammabe in air.

⑥ CA 49, 841 (1955).

AsC₆H₁₅O

① Triethylarsine oxide
$(C_2H_5)_3AsO$

② C_2H_5I + As$-$Na $\longrightarrow$

③ Heavy yellow oil.
Sol. in EtOH and ether; insol. in H_2O.

⑥ Ann. 89, 325 (1854).

AsC₇H₇Cl₂O

① p-Tolyldichloroarsine oxide

4-$CH_3C_6H_4AsOCl_2$

② 4-$CH_3C_6H_4AsCl_4$ + H_2O $\longrightarrow$

③ Colorless crystals. [69°].
Sol. in org. solvents.

⑥ Ann. 201, 253 (1880).

AsC₇H₉

① Benzylarsine
$C_6H_5CH_2AsH_2$

② $C_6H_5CH_2AsO(OH)_2$
+ active hydrogen $\longrightarrow$

③ Pale yellow oil. (140°/262).
Sol. in org. solvents.

⑥ Am. Chem. J. 40, 113 (1908).

AsC₇H₉

① p-Tolylarsine
p-$CH_3C_6H_4AsH_2$

② 4-$CH_3C_6H_4AsO(OH)_2$ + Zn$-$Hg + HCl $\longrightarrow$

③ Colorless oil. (113.5°/44). [20°].
n_D 1.5891 (25°). d 1.295 (25°/25°).
Sol. in org. solvents.

⑥ JACS 44, 1371 (1922).

AsC₇H₁₅BrN

① Triethylarsenic cyanobromide
$(C_2H_5)_3AsCNBr$

② $(C_2H_5)_3As$ + excess CNBr $\xrightarrow{\text{ice cooled}}$

③ Colorless crystals. [67°].
Sol. in org. solvents.

⑥ Ber. 54, 847 (1921).

AsC₉H₁₅

① Triallylarsine
$(CH_2=CH-CH_2)_3As$

② $CH_2=CH-CH_2MgCl$ + $AsCl_3$ $\longrightarrow$

③ Colorless liq. (103.7°/37). n_D 1.5326 (15.5°). d 1.1055 (15.5°/4°).
Sol. in org. solvents.

⑥ Bull. soc. chim. France 41, 1570 (1927).

AsC₉H₂₁

① Tri-n-propylarsine

$(n\text{-}C_3H_7)_3As$

② $n\text{-}C_3H_7MgBr + AsCl_3 \longrightarrow$

③ Colorless liq. (81~82°/16). n_D 1.4763 (20°). d 1.0233 (20°/0°)

Sol. in org. solvents; inflammable in air.

⑥ CA **49**, 841 (1955).

AsC₁₂H₉ClN

① 10-Chloro-5, 10-dihydrophenarsazine

② $C_6H_5AsCl_2 + (C_6H_5)_2NH \xrightarrow{o\text{-}C_6H_4Cl_2}$

$(C_6H_5)_2NH + AsCl_3 \longrightarrow$

③ Yellow needles. [189~190°].

Sol. in org. solvents.

⑥ JCS **1926**, 457.

AsC₁₂H₁₀Cl

① Diphenylchloroarsine

$(C_6H_5)_2AsCl$

② $(C_6H_5)_4Pb + AsCl_3 \xrightarrow[\text{heat}]{\text{toluene}}$

③ Yellow oil. (333°). [38°]. d 1.423 (14°/4°).

Sol. in org. solvents.

⑥ JCS **121**, 104 (1922).

AsC₁₂H₁₀Cl₃

① Diphenylarsenic trichloride

$(C_6H_5)_2AsCl_3$

② $(C_6H_5)_2AsCl + Cl_2 \longrightarrow$

$(C_6H_5)_2AsO(OH) + SOCl_2 \longrightarrow$

③ Yellow crystals. [174°], [191°].

Sol. in org. solvents.

⑥ Ber. **61**, 676 (1928).

AsC₁₂H₁₀F

① Diphenylfluoroarsine

$(C_6H_5)_2AsF$

② $(C_6H_5)_2AsCl + AgF \xrightarrow{C_6H_6}$

③ Colorless liq. (157.5°/8). [17~18°]. d 1.19.

Sol. in org. solvents.

⑥ Ann. **29**, 128 (1928).

AsC₁₂H₁₁

① Diphenylarsine

$(C_6H_5)_2AsH$

② $(C_6H_5)_2AsO(OH) + Zn\text{-}Hg + HCl \longrightarrow$

③ Colorless oil. (174°/25).

Sol. in org. solvents.

⑥ Am. Chem. J. **35**, 45 (1906).

AsC₁₃H₁₀Cl₂N

① Diphenylarsenic cyanodichloride

$(C_6H_5)_2As(CN)Cl_2$

② $(C_6H_5)_2AsCN + Cl_2 \longrightarrow$

③ Colorless crystals. [130~133°].

Sol. in org. solvents.

⑥ JCS **117**, 414 (1920).

AsC₁₃H₁₀N

① Diphenylcyanoarsine

$(C_6H_5)_2AsCN$

② $(C_6H_5)_2AsCl + NaCN \xrightarrow[\text{heat}]{H_2O}$

③ Colorless plates. (204~205°/12). [32~33°].

Sol. in org. solvents.

④ $+ H_2O_2 \longrightarrow (C_6H_5)_2AsCONH_2$

⑥ Bull. soc. chim. France **41**, 1578(1927).

AsC₁₈H₁₅

① Triphenylarsine

$(C_6H_5)_3As$

② $C_6H_5MgX + As(OH)_3 \longrightarrow$

$C_6H_5X + AsCl_3 + Na \longrightarrow$

③ Colorless plates. (232~234°/14). [61°]. d 1.306.

Sol. in ether and C_6H_6; slightly sol. in cold EtOH; insol. in H_2O; sta_ ble in air at room temp.

④ + CH₃I ⟶ (C₆H₅)₃(CH₃)AsI

+ C₂H₅I ⟶ no reaction

+ S₂Cl₂ ⟶ (C₆H₅)₃AsS₂Cl₂
      ether

⑥ Org. Syn. **30**, 95 (1950). Ber. **54**, 2484 (1921) ; **19**, 1032 (1886).

AsC₁₈H₁₅Br₂

① Triphenylarsenic dibromide
(C₆H₅)₃AsBr₂

② (C₆H₅)₃As + Br₂ ⟶

③ Colorless crystals. [215°].
Sol. in C₆H₆ and CHCl₃; insol. in ether and CCl₄; decomp. by moisture.

⑥ Ann. **321**, 162 (1902).

AsC₁₈H₁₅Cl₂

① Triphenylarsenic dichloride
(C₆H₅)₃AsCl₂

② (C₆H₅)₃As + Cl₂ ⟶

③ Colorless plates. [204~205°].
Sol. in hot C₆H₆ and CHCl₃; insol. in ether and CCl₄; decomp. by moisture.

⑥ Ann. **321**, 163 (1902).

AsC₁₈H₁₅O

① Triphenylarsine oxide
(C₆H₅)₃AsO

② (C₆H₅)₃As + H₂O₂ ⟶
                acetone

③ Colorless crystals. [189°].
Sol. in org. solvents.

④ + 2 HCl ⟶ (C₆H₅)₃AsCl₂

⑥ Org. Syn. **30**, 97 (1950).

AsC₁₈H₁₅S

① Triphenylarsine sulfide
(C₆H₅)₃AsS

② (C₆H₅)₃AsCl₂ + H₂S $\xrightarrow[CS_2]{S_2Cl_2}$

③ Bright needles. [162°].

Sol. in org. solvents.

⑥ Ber. **54**, 2485 (1921).

AsC₁₈H₁₆ClO

① Triphenylarsenic hydroxychloride
(C₆H₅)₃As(OH)Cl

② (C₆H₅)₃AsCl₂ + H₂O ⟶

③ Glassy crystals. [171°].
Sol. in org. solvents.

⑥ Ann. **321**, 162 (1902).

AsC₁₈H₁₇O₂

① Triphenylarsenic dihydroxide
(C₆H₅)₃As(OH)₂

② (C₆H₅)₃AsCl₂ + NaOH ⟶

③ Colorless crystals. [115~116°].
Sol. in EtOH

④ + H₂ ⟶ (C₆H₅)₃As
        EtOH
+ H₂S ⟶ (C₆H₅)₃AsS

+ HNO₃ ⟶ (C₆H₅)₃AsOH(NO)₃

⑥ Ann. **201**, 243 (1880). Ber. **19**, 1032 (1886).

AsC₂₁H₂₁

① Tri-p-tolylarsine
(p-CH₃C₆H₄)₃As

② 4-CH₃C₆H₄MgBr + As(OH)₃ ⟶

③ Colorless crystals. [146°].
Sol. in org. solvents.

④ + S₂Cl₂ ⟶ (4-CH₃C₆H₄)₃AsCl₂
+ CH₃I ⟶ (4-CH₃C₆H₄)₃CH₃AsI

⑥ Ann. **321**, 200 (1902).

AsC₂₄H₂₀Br

① Tetraphenylarsonium bromide
(C₆H₅)₄AsBr

② (C₆H₅)₃As + AlCl₃ + C₆H₅Br ⟶

③ Colorless crystals. [314~319°
decomp.].
Sol. in H₂O.

⑥ JCS **1940**, 1192.

AsC$_{24}$H$_{20}$Cl

① Tetraphenylarsonium chloride
   (C$_6$H$_5$)$_4$AsCl
② (C$_6$H$_5$)$_3$As + C$_6$H$_5$Cl + AlCl$_3$ ⟶
③ Colorless crystals. [256~257°].
   Sol. in H$_2$O.
⑥ JACS **57**, 720 (1935). JCS **1940**, 1192.

AsC$_{24}$H$_{20}$I

① Tetraphenylarsonium iodide
   (C$_6$H$_5$)$_4$AsI
② (C$_6$H$_5$)$_3$As + C$_6$H$_5$I + AlCl$_3$ ⟶ 54%
③ White needles. [314~319°].
   Recrystd. from H$_2$O.
⑥ JCS **1940**, 1192.

AsC$_{24}$H$_{20}$I$_3$

① Tetraphenylarsonium triiodide
   (C$_6$H$_5$)$_4$AsI$_3$
② (C$_6$H$_5$)$_4$AsI + I$_2$ ⟶
③ Crystals. [175~176°].
   Sol. in H$_2$O and EtOH; insol. in
   ether and petr. ether.
⑥ JACS **55**, 3056 (1933).   Ann. **577**, 26
   (1952).

AsC$_{30}$H$_{25}$

① Pentaphenylarsine
   (C$_6$H$_5$)$_5$As
② (C$_6$H$_5$)$_4$AsBr + C$_6$H$_5$Li ⟶
③ Colorless crystals. [149~150°].
   Sol. in org. solvents; recrystd. from
   C$_6$H$_{12}$ as (C$_6$H$_5$)$_5$As·½C$_6$H$_{12}$.
⑥ Ann. **577**, 26 (1952).

As$_2$C$_4$F$_{12}$

① Tetrakis(trifluoromethyl)diarsine
   [(CF$_3$)$_2$As]$_2$
② (CF$_3$)$_2$AsI + Hg $\xrightarrow[\text{sealed tube}]{\text{2 days}}$
③ Colorless oil. (106~107°). n_D 1.372
   (19°).
   Sol. in org. solvents.
⑥ JCS **1952**, 2552 ; **1953**, 1552.

As$_2$C$_4$H$_{12}$

① Tetramethyldiarsine
   [(CH$_3$)$_2$As]$_2$
② (CH$_3$)$_2$AsCl + (CH$_3$)$_2$AsH ⟶
③ Colorless oil. (170°). [−6°].
   Sol. in org. solvents ; possesses unpleasant odor ; inflammable in
   air.
⑥ Am. Chem. J. **40**, 123 (1908).

As$_2$C$_4$F$_{12}$O

① Tetrakis(trifluoromethyl)diarsine
   oxide
   [(CF$_3$)$_2$As]$_2$O
② (CF$_3$)$_2$AsI + HgO ⟶
③ Colorless liq. (100°/760). n_D 1.354
   (20°).
   Sol. in org. solvents.
⑥ Ber. **86**, 272 (1953).

As$_2$C$_6$H$_4$Cl$_4$

① o-Phenylenylbisdichloroarsine

② + SOCl$_2$ ⟶

③ Colorless plates. [76~86°].
   Recrystd. from dioxane.
⑥ JCS **1939**, 613.

As$_2$C$_8$H$_{20}$

① Tetraethyldiarsine
   [(C$_2$H$_5$)$_2$As]$_2$
② (C$_2$H$_5$)$_2$AsCl + (C$_2$H$_5$)$_2$AsH ⟶
③ Colorless oil. (185~190°).
   Sol. in org. solvents ; inflammable
   in air.
④ $\xrightarrow[\text{in air}]{}$ (C$_2$H$_5$)$_2$AsO(OH)
⑥ Ann. **89**, 316 (1854) ; **92**, 365 (1854).

As$_2$C$_8$H$_{20}$O

① Bisdiethyldiarsineoxide
[(C$_2$H$_5$)$_2$As]$_2$O

② (C$_2$H$_5$)$_2$AsI + NaOH $\xrightarrow[\text{in H}_2\text{O}]{}$

③ Colorless liq. (90~93.5°/8~9).
d 1.2989 (18.5°/4°).
Sol. in org. solvents.

⑥ Roczniki Chem. **8**, 423 (1928).
Chem. Zentr. **1929**, I, 502.

As$_2$C$_{12}$H$_8$Cl$_2$

① Bis(o-phenylenyl)bis(chloroarsine)

② C$_6$H$_5$AsO(OH)·C$_6$H$_4$·AsO(OH)$_2$ $\xrightarrow[\text{SO}_2]{\text{HCl}}$

③ Colorless crystals. [179~184°].
Recrystd. from CHCl$_3$.

⑥ JCS **1940**, 1193.

As$_2$C$_{12}$H$_{10}$

① Diphenyldiarsine
(C$_6$H$_5$As)$_2$

② C$_6$H$_5$AsO + H$_3$PO$_2$ $\longrightarrow$

(C$_6$H$_5$)AsCl$_2$ + Na $\xrightarrow[\text{ether}]{\text{N}_2}$

③ Colorless needles. [213~214°].
Sol. in C$_6$H$_6$, CHCl$_3$ and CS$_2$; slightly
sol. in EtOH; insol. in ether.

④ + CH$_3$I $\longrightarrow$ (CH$_3$)$_3$(C$_6$H$_5$)AsI
+ C$_6$H$_5$AsI$_2$
+ S $\longrightarrow$ C$_6$H$_5$AsS
$\xrightarrow{\text{oxidation}}$ C$_6$H$_5$AsO + C$_6$H$_5$AsO(OH)$_2$

⑥ Ber. **53**, 427 (1920); **54**, 1453 (1921).

As$_2$C$_{12}$H$_{10}$I$_2$

① Diphenyldiiododiarsine
(C$_6$H$_5$AsI)$_2$

② C$_6$H$_5$AsI$_2$ + H$_3$PO$_2$ $\xrightarrow[\text{alcohol}]{}$

(C$_6$H$_5$As)$_2$ + I$_2$ $\xrightarrow[\text{C}_6\text{H}_6]{}$

4 (C$_6$H$_5$)AsH$_2$ + 2 C$_6$H$_5$AsH$_2$ $\longrightarrow$

③ Yellow needles. [176~177°].
Sol. in org. solvents. Oxidized instantaneously in air.

⑥ JACS **52**, 2937 (1930).

As$_2$C$_{16}$H$_{20}$

① 1,2-Bis(methylphenylarsino)ethane
(C$_6$H$_5$)CH$_3$AsCH$_2$−CH$_2$AsCH$_3$(C$_6$H$_5$)

②

③ Colorless liq. (163~165°/0.2).
Sol. in org. solvents.

⑥ JCS **1955**, 401.

As$_2$C$_{24}$H$_{20}$

① Tetraphenyldiarsine
[(C$_6$H$_5$)$_2$As]$_2$

② (C$_6$H$_5$)$_2$AsI + Hg $\xrightarrow[\text{C}_6\text{H}_6]{}$

[(C$_6$H$_5$)$_2$As]$_2$O + H$_3$PO$_2$ $\xrightarrow[\text{abs. alc.}]{}$

③ Colorless crystals. [135°].
Slightly sol. in EtOH and ether.

④ + Cl$_2$ $\longrightarrow$ (C$_6$H$_5$)$_2$AsCl
+ CH$_3$I $\longrightarrow$ (C$_6$H$_5$)$_2$(CH$_3$)$_2$AsI

⑥ Ber. **54**, 1449 (1921).

As$_2$C$_{24}$H$_{20}$O

① Bis(diphenylarsine)oxide
[(C$_6$H$_5$)$_2$As]$_2$O

② −N$_2$Cl·FeCl$_3$ + AsCl$_3$

$\xrightarrow[\text{acetone}]{\text{Fe}}$ treated with KOH

③ Colorless crystals. [92~93°].
  Sol. in org. solvents.
④ + HCl ⟶ (C₆H₅)₂AsCl
⑥ Zhur. **25**, 2324 (1955).

As₅C₅H₁₅

① Pentamethylpentaarsine
  (CH₃As)₅
② CH₃AsO(OH)₂ + H₃PO₂ $\xrightarrow{H_2SO_4}$
③ Oxidized slowly in air.
  Transparent yellow oil. (190°/5).
  [10°]. *d* 2.159 (15°/4°).
  Sol. in hot glacial acetic acid ; slightly sol. in EtOH and C₆H₆ ; insol. in H₂O.
⑥ JACS **50**, 536 (1928).

〔Sb〕

SbCH₃Br₂

① Methyldibromostibine
  CH₃SbBr₂
② Me₂SbBr₃ $\xrightarrow{heat}$ MeSbBr₂
③ Colorless crystals. [42°].
  Non flamable in air.
④ + Br₂ ⟶ MeSbBr₄
  + KOH ⟶ MeSbO
⑥ Proc. Roy. Soc. **110**, 523 (1926).

SbCH₃Cl₂

① Methyldichlorostibine
  CH₃SbCl₂
② Me₂SbCl₃ $\xrightarrow{heat}$ MeSbCl₂
③ Oily liq. (115~120°/60).
  Non flamable.
④ + Cl₂ ⟶ MeSbCl₄
  + KOH ⟶ MeSbO
⑥ Proc. Roy. Soc. **110**, 523 (1926).

SbCH₃O

① Oxomethylstibine
  CH₃SbO

② MeSbX₂ $\xrightarrow{NaOH}$
③ Polymeric white powder.
⑥ Proc. Roy. Soc. **110**, 523 (1926).

SbCH₅

① Methylstibine
  CH₃SbH₂
② (CH₃)₂SbBr + NaBH₄
  $\dfrac{\text{in } CH_3OCH_2CH_2OCH_3}{}$ ⟶ Me₂SbH
  + MeSbH₂ + Me₂SbBH₂
③ (41°).
  Very unstable ; decomp. above −80°.
⑥ JACS **81**, 1 (1959).

SbC₂H₆Br

① Dimethylbromostibine
  (CH₃)₂SbBr
② Me₃SbBr₂ $\xrightarrow{heat}$ Me₂SbBr
③ Pale yellow crystals. [89°].
  Sol. in org. solvents ; inflammable in air at 40℃.
④ + KOH ⟶ (Me₂Sb)₂O
  + Br₂ ⟶ Me₂SbBr₃
  + O₂ ⟶ Me₂Sb(O)Br
⑥ Proc. Roy. Soc. **110**, 523 (1926).

SbC₂H₆BrO

① Dimethylbromostibine oxide
  (CH₃)₂Sb(O)Br
② Me₂SbBr + O₂ ⟶ Me₂Sb(O)Br
③ White powder.
  Sol. in H₂O ; insol. in acetone.
④ + NaOH ⟶ Me₂Sb(O)OH
  + H₂O ⟶ Me₂Sb(O)OH
⑥ Proc. Roy. Soc. **110**, 523 (1926).

SbC₂H₆Br₃

① Dimethylantimony tribromide
  (CH₃)₂SbBr₃
② Me₂SbBr + Br₂ $\xrightarrow{CS_2}$
③ Unstable even at −15℃.

④ $\xrightarrow{\text{heat}}$ MeSbBr₂ + MeBr

⑥ Proc. Roy. Soc. 110, 523 (1926).

SbC₂H₆Cl

① Dimethylchlorostibine
(CH₃)₂SbCl

② Me₃SbCl₂ $\xrightarrow{\text{heat}}$ Me₂SbCl

③ Colorless liq. (155~60°/750).
Sol. in org. solvents; inflammable
in air at 40°C.

④ + KOH $\longrightarrow$ (Me₂Sb)₂O
+ Cl₂ $\longrightarrow$ Me₂SbCl₃
+ O₂ $\longrightarrow$ Me₂Sb(O)Cl

⑥ Proc. Roy. Soc. 110, 523 (1926).

SbC₂H₆Cl₃

① Dimethylantimony trichloride
(CH₃)₂SbCl₃

② Me₂SbCl + Cl₂ $\xrightarrow{\text{CS}_2}$

③ White crystals. [105~110°
decomp.].
Unstable.

④ $\xrightarrow{\text{heat}}$ MeSbCl₂ + Me₃Cl

⑥ Proc. Roy. Soc. 110, 523 (1926).

SbC₂H₆I

① Dimethyliodostibine
(CH₃)₂SbI

② Me₃SbI₂ $\xrightarrow{\text{heat}}$ Me₂SbI

③ Pale yellow crystals. [86°].
Sol. in org. solvents.

④ + KOH $\longrightarrow$ (Me₂Sb)₂O
+ I₂ $\longrightarrow$ Me₂SbI₃
+ O₂ $\longrightarrow$ Me₂Sb(O)I

⑥ Proc. Roy. Soc. 110, 523 (1926).

SbC₂H₆I₃

① Dimethylantimony triiodide
(CH₃)₂SbI₃

② Me₂SbI + I₂ $\xrightarrow{\text{CS}_2}$

③ Unstable even at −15°C.

④ $\xrightarrow{-\text{CH}_3\text{I}}$ CH₃SbI₂

⑥ Proc. Roy. Soc. 110, 523 (1926).

SbC₂H₇

① Dimethylstibine
(CH₃)₂SbH

② Me₂SbBr + LiBH(OMe)₃
$\longrightarrow$ Me₂SbH

③ (60.7°).
Unstable; slowly decomp. at room
temp.

④ Me₂SbH + HCl $\longrightarrow$ Me₂SbCl + H₂
2 Me₂SbH $\xrightarrow{\text{Hg}}$ Me₂Sb−SbMe₂ + H₂

⑥ JACS 81, 1 (1959).

SbC₃H₉

① Trimethylstibine
(CH₃)₃Sb

② SbCl₃ + 3 MeMgX $\longrightarrow$
SbCl₃ + 3 MeLi $\longrightarrow$
Me₃SbX₂ + Zn $\longrightarrow$ Me₃Sb

③ Colorless liq. (78.5°), (80.6°).
[−87.6°]. d 1.528 (15°).
Sol. in ether; slightly sol. in H₂O;
insol. in EtOH; inflammable in
air.

④ + O₂ $\longrightarrow$ Me₃SbO
+ X₂ $\longrightarrow$ Me₃SbX₂
+ PdCl₂ $\longrightarrow$ (Me₃Sb)₂PdCl₂
+ R−X $\longrightarrow$ Me₄SbX

⑥ JACS 62, 1622 (1940). Trans. Faraday
Soc. 51, 1062 (1955). JCS 1925, 184.

SbC₃H₉Br₂

① Trimethylantimonydibromide
(CH₃)₃SbBr₂

② Me₃Sb + Br₂ $\longrightarrow$

③ Colorless crystals. [170~180°
decomp.]. [198° decomp.].
Sol. in EtOH and acetone, etc.

④ + KOH $\longrightarrow$ Me₃SbO
$\xrightarrow{\text{heat}}$ Me₂SbBr
+ Zn $\longrightarrow$ Me₃Sb

⑥ J. prakt. Chem. [1] **84**, 334 (1861).
　　Proc. Roy. Soc. **110**, 523 (1926).

SbC₃H₉Cl₂

① Trimethylantimony dichloride
　　$(CH_3)_3SbCl_2$
② $Me_3Sb + Cl_2 \longrightarrow$
③ Colorless crystals.
　　Sol. in MeOH and acetone, etc.
④ $\overset{heat}{\longrightarrow} Me_2SbCl$
　　$+ Zn \longrightarrow Me_3Sb$
　　$+ KOH \longrightarrow Me_3SbO$
⑥ J. prakt. Chem. [1] **84**, 334 (1861).
　　Proc. Roy. Soc. **110**, 523 (1926).

SbC₃H₉I₂

① Trimethylantimony diiodide
　　$(CH_3)_3SbI_2$
② $Me_3Sb + I_2 \longrightarrow$
③ Colorless crystals. [107°].
　　Sol. in org. solvents.
④ $+ KOH \longrightarrow Me_3SbO$
　　$\overset{heat}{\longrightarrow} Me_2SbI$
　　$+ Zn \longrightarrow Me_3Sb$
⑥ J. prakt. Chem. [1] **84**, 334 (1861).
　　JCS **1861**, 119.

SbC₃H₉O

① Trimethylstibine oxide
　　$(CH_3)_3SbO$
② $Me_3SbX_2 + KOH \longrightarrow$
③ White crystals.
　　Sol. in H_2O and alc.; insol. in C_6H_6
　　and other hydrocarbon.
④ $+ H_2S \longrightarrow Me_3SbS$
⑥ J. prakt. Chem. [1] **84**, 328 (1861).

SbC₃H₉S

① Trimethylstibine sulfide
　　$(CH_3)_3SbS$
② $Me_3Sb + S \longrightarrow$
　　$Me_3SbO + H_2S \longrightarrow$
③ Colorless crystals.

Sol. in alc. and ether; insol. in cold
H_2O.
⑥ J. prakt. Chem. [1] **84**, 331 (1861).

SbC₄H₇

① Dimethylethynylstibine
　　$(CH_3)_2SbC\equiv CH$
② $Me_2SbBr + NaC\equiv CH \longrightarrow$
③ Colorless liq. (86~88°/388).
⑥ Z. anorg. allg. Chem. **312**, 186 (1961).

SbC₄H₁₀Br

① Diethylbromostibine
　　$(C_2H_5)_2SbBr$
② $Et_3SbBr_2 \overset{heat}{\longrightarrow} Et_2SbBr$
③ Yellowish liquid. (78~80°/15).
　　Sol. in org. solvents.
④ $+ KOH \longrightarrow (Et_2Sb)_2O$
　　$+ Br_2 \longrightarrow Et_2SbBr_3$
⑥ Z. anorg. allg. Chem. **312**, 186 (1961).

SbC₄H₁₂Br

① Tetramethylstibonium bromide
　　$(CH_3)_4SbBr$
② $Me_4SbI + AgBr \longrightarrow$
　　$Me_4SbOH + HBr \dashrightarrow$
③ Colorless crystals.
　　Sol. in H_2O and EtOH; insol. in
　　ether
④ $+ AgNO_3 \longrightarrow Me_4SbNO_3$
⑥ Ann. **78**, 96 (1851); **84**, 50 (1852).
　　Acta Chem. Scand. **7**, 1293 (1953).

SbC₄H₁₂Cl

① Tetramethylstibonium chloride
　　$(CH_3)_4SbCl$
② $Me_4SbI + AgCl \longrightarrow$
　　$Me_4SbOH + HCl \longrightarrow$
③ Colorless crystals.
　　Sol. in EtOH and H_2O.
④ $+ AgNO_3 \longrightarrow Me_4SbNO_3$
⑥ Ann. **78**, 96 (1851); **84**, 50 (1852).
　　Spectrochim. Acta **21**, 263 (1965).
　　Z. anorg. allg. Chem. **273**, 161

(1953).

SbC₄H₁₂I
① Tetramethylstibonium iodide
(CH₃)₄SbI
② (CH₃)₃Sb + CH₃I $\longrightarrow$
③ Colorless crystals. [288~302°
decomp.].
Sol. in EtOH and H₂O.
④ + AgNO₃ $\longrightarrow$ Me₄SbNO₃
⑥ Ann. **78**, 96 (1851); **84**, 50 (1852).
Acta Chem. Scand. **7**, 1293 (1953).

SbC₄H₁₃O
① Tetramethylstibonium hydroxide
(CH₃)₄SbOH
② Me₄SbI + AgO $\cdots\!\longrightarrow$
③ Colorless hygroscopic substance.
Sol. in H₂O.
④ + HX $\longrightarrow$ Me₄SbX
⑥ Ann. **78**, 96 (1851); **84**, 50 (1852).

SbC₅H₁₅
① Pentamethylantimony
(CH₃)₅Sb
② (CH₃)₃SbBr₂ + 2CH₃Li $\longrightarrow$
(CH₃)₄SbBr + CH₃Li $\longrightarrow$
③ Colorless liq. (126~127°). [−18~
−16°].
Sol. in org. solvents; decompd. by
H₂O or air.
④ + (C₆H₅)₃B $\longrightarrow$
[(CH₃)₄Sb][(CH₃)(C₆H₅)₃B]
+ excess CH₃Li $\longrightarrow$ Li[(CH₃)₆Sb]
⑥ Acta Chem. Scand. **7**, 1293 (1953).

SbC₆H₃
① Triethynylstibine
(CH≡C)₃Sb
② HC≡C−MgBr + SbCl₃ $\xrightarrow[-30°]{THF}$
③ Crystal. [71~72°].
Easily sublimes; decompd. by H₂O;
explodes with shock.

⑥ Rec. trav. chim. **83**, 1301 (1964).

SbC₆H₅Cl₂
① Phenyldichlorostibine
C₆H₅SbCl₂
② PhSbO + HCl $\xrightarrow{+CH₃COOH}$
③ Colorless crystals. [62°].
Sol. in org solvents.
④ $\xrightarrow{heat}$ Ph₂SbCl
⑥ Ann. **421**, 219 (1920). Ber. **48**, 1757
(1915). J. Gen. Chem. USSR **25**,
107 (1955).

SbC₆H₅Cl₄
① Phenylantimony tetrachloride
C₆H₅SbCl₄
② C₆H₅Sb(O)(OH)₂ + conc. HCl $\longrightarrow$
C₆H₅SbCl₂ + Cl₂ $\xrightarrow{in\ cold\ ether}$
③ Hygroscopic crystals. [60~65°].
Sol. in hot CHCl₃, C₆H₆, and ether.
④ + H₂O $\longrightarrow$ C₆H₅SbO(OH)₂
⑥ Ann. **421**, 199 (1920).

SbC₆H₅O
① Oxophenylstibine
C₆H₅SbO
② PhSbCl₂ + NaOH $\longrightarrow$
③ Colorless crystals. [150°].
Sol. in acid; insol. in H₂O and
alkaline soln.
④ + H₂S $\longrightarrow$ PhSbS
$\xrightarrow{heat}$ (Ph₂Sb)₂O
⑥ Ber. **31**, 2912 (1898).

SbC₆H₅S
① Thionophenylstibine
C₆H₅SbS
② PhSbO + H₂S $\xrightarrow{alc.}$
PhSbX₂ + H₂S $\xrightarrow{alc.}$
③ Red crystals. [65°].
⑥ Ber. **31**, 2913 (1898).

SbC₆H₇

① Phenylstibine

   C₆H₅SbH₂

② PhSbI₂ + 2 LiBH₄ $\xrightarrow[-50°]{\text{in Et}_2\text{O}}$ PhSbH₂

   + 2 LiI + B₂H₆

③ Decomp. about half an hour at room temp. in ether to give (PhSb)ₙ and H₂.

⑥ Z. Naturf. **12**b, 128 (1957).

SbC₆H₇O₃

① Phenylstibonic acid

   C₆H₅SbO(OH)₂

② PhSbCl₂ + H₂O₂ $\dashrightarrow$

③ White powder.

   Very sol. in NaOH aq. soln. ; decomp. above 25°.

⑥ Ann. **421**, 177, 226 (1920).

SbC₆H₉

① Trivinylstibine

   (CH₂=CH)₃Sb

② SbCl₃ + 3 CH₂=CHMgX $\xrightarrow{\text{in THF}}$

③ Colorless liq. [149.9°].

   Spontaneously inflammable in air; sol. in org. solvents.

④ + MeI $\longrightarrow$ [(C₂H₃)₃MeSb]I

   + SbCl₃ $\longrightarrow$ (CH₂=CH)₂SbCl

   + PtCl₂ $\dashrightarrow$ {(CH₂=CH)₃Sb}₂PtCl₂

⑥ JACS **79**, 5884 (1957).

SbC₆H₁₁

① Diethylethynylstibine

   (C₂H₅)₂SbC≡CH

② Et₂SbBr + NaC≡CH $\dashrightarrow$

③ Colorless liq. (87°/79).

⑥ Z. anorg. allg. Chem. **312**, 186 (1961).

SbC₆H₁₄Br

① Diisopropylbromostibine

   (i-C₃H₇)₂SbBr

② (i-Pr)₃SbBr₂ $\xrightarrow{\text{heat}}$ (i-Pr)₂SbBr

③ Yellowish liq. (93~95°/12).

   Sol. in org. solvents.

④ + KOH $\longrightarrow$ (Pr₂Sb)₂O

⑥ Z. anorg. allg. Chem. **312**, 186 (1961).

SbC₆H₁₅

① Triethylstibine

   (C₂H₅)₃Sb

② SbCl₃ + C₂H₅MgX $\dashrightarrow$

③ Colorless liq. (159.5°). [<−29°].

   d 1.3244 (16°).

   Sol. in EtOH and ether; insol. in H₂O; inflammable in air.

④ + O₂ $\longrightarrow$ (C₂H₅)₃SbO

   + X₂ $\longrightarrow$ (C₂H₅)₃SbX₂

⑥ Dokl. **99**, 543 (1954). JCS **1947**, 1568.

SbC₆H₁₅Br₂

① Triethylantimony dibromide

   (C₂H₅)₃SbBr₂

② Et₃Sb + Br₂ $\longrightarrow$

③ Cololess oilly liq. [−10°].

   Sol. in org. solvents.

④ $\xrightarrow{\text{heat}}$ Et₂SbBr + EtBr

⑥ Ann.**75**, 338 (1830).

SbC₆H₁₅I₂

① Triethylantimony diiodide

   (C₂H₅)₃SbI₂

② Et₃Sb + I₂ $\longrightarrow$

③ Colorless crystals. [70.5°].

   Sol. in org. solvents; stable in air and moisture.

④ $\xrightarrow{\text{heat}}$ Et₂SbI + EtI

⑥ Ann. **75**, 338 (1830).

SbC₆H₁₅O

① Triethylstibine oxide

   (C₂H₅)₃SbO

② (C₂H₅)₃SbBr₂ + KOH ⟶
③ Viscous liq.
   Sol. in H₂O and EtOH; insol. in
   ether.
④ + H₂S ⟶ (C₂H₅)₃SbS
⑥ Ann. **97**, 327, 329 (1856).

SbC₆H₁₅S
① Triethylstibine sulfide
   (C₂H₅)₃SbS
② Et₃SbO + H₂S ⟶
   Et₃Sb + S ⟶
③ Colorless crystals. [118°].
   Sol. in H₂O, alcohol and hot ether;
   insol. in cold ether.
⑥ Ann. **75**, 335 (1850).   JOM **1**, 369
   (1963~4).

SbC₈H₁₈Cl
① Di-*t*-butylchlorostibine
   (*t*-C₄H₉)₂SbCl
② *t*-Bu₃SbCl₂ $\xrightarrow{\text{heat}}$ *t*-Bub₂SCl + *t*-BuCl
③ Yellowish liq. (104°/24).
   Sol. in org. solvents.
④ + KOH ⟶ *t*-Bu₂Sb−O−SbBu-*t*₂
⑥ Z. anorg. allg. Chem. **312**, 186 (1961).

SbC₈H₂₀Cl
① Tetraethylstibonium chloride
   (C₂H₅)₄SbCl
② Et₃Sb + EtCl ⟶
③ Colorless crystals.
   Sol. in H₂O; very hygroscopic.
④ + AgNO₃ ⟶ Et₄SbNO₃
⑥ Ann. **78**, 96 (1851); **84**, 50 (1852).

SbC₉H₂₁
① Tri-*n*-propylstibine
   (*n*-C₃H₇)₃Sb
② SbCl₃ + 3 (*n*-C₃H₇)MgX ⟶
③ Colorless liq. (100°/25). *d* 1.241 (25°).
   Sol. in org. solvents; inflammable
   in air.

④ + O₂ ⟶ (*n*-C₃H₇)₃SbO
   + X₂ ⟶ (*n*-C₃H₇)₃SbX₂
⑥ Ber. **39**, 160 (1906).   JCS **1947**, 1568.

SbC₉H₂₁Br₂
① Tri-*n*-propylantimony dibromide
   (*n*-C₃H₇)₃SbBr₂
② (*n*-Pr)₃Sb + Br₂ ⟶
③ Colorless crystals. [45°].
   Sol. in org. solvents; stable in air
   and H₂O.
④ $\xrightarrow{\text{heat}}$ Pr₂SbBr + PrBr
⑥ JCS **1930**, 1921.

SbC₉H₂₁Cl₂
① Tri-*n*-propylantimony dichloride
   (*n*-C₃H₇)₃SbCl₂
② Pr₃Sb + Cl₂ ⟶
③ Colorless liq.
   Sol. in org. solvents; stable in air
   and H₂O; decomp. by distillation
   to form Pr₂SbCl.
④ $\xrightarrow{\text{heat}}$ Pr₂SbCl + PrCl
⑥ JCS **1930**, 1921.

SbC₉H₂₁O
① Tri-*n*-propylstibine oxide
   (*n*-C₃H₇)₃SbO
② (C₃H₇)₃SbBr₂ + KOH ⟶
③ White jelly like material.
   Sol. in H₂O and EtOH; insol. in
   ether.
④ + H₂S ⟶ (C₃H₇)₃SbS
⑥ JCS **1930**, 1921.

SbC₉H₂₁S
① Tri-*n*-propylstibine sulfide
   (*n*-C₃H₇)₃SbS
② (*n*-Pr)₃SbO + H₂S $\xrightarrow{\text{alcohol}}$
   (*n*-Pr)₃Sb + S ⟶
③ Yellowish crystals. [35°].
   Sol. in alc. and H₂O.

⑥ JCS **1930**, 1921.   JOM **1**, 369
(1963~4).

$SbC_{10}H_7Cl_2$

① α-Naphthyldichlorostibine
α-$C_{10}H_7SbCl_2$

② $(\alpha$-$C_{10}H_7)SbO + 2\,HCl \longrightarrow$

③ [105~106°].

⑥ JACS **55**, 1198 (1933).

$SbC_{11}H_{27}O_2$

① Trimethylantimony di-t-butoxide
$(CH_3)_3Sb(OC_4H_9$-$t)_2$

② $Me_3SbCl_2 + 2\,t$-$BuONa \xrightarrow[35°]{ether}$

③ $(52.5°/1)$. [22°].
Fairly stable.

⑥ Ber. **97**, (2) 449 (1964).

$SbC_{12}H_{10}Br$

① Diphenylbromostibine
$(C_6H_5)_2SbBr$

② $Ph_2SbSbPh_2 + HBr \longrightarrow$

③ [86°].
Sol. in org. solvents ; insol. in H_2O.

④ $+ Br_2 \dashrightarrow Ph_2SbBr_3$

⑥ JACS **53**, 1025 (1931).

$SbC_{12}H_{10}Cl$

① Diphenylchlorostibine
$(C_6H_5)_2SbCl$

② $(PhN_2Cl)_2SbCl_3 + Zn \xrightarrow{CH_3COOEt}$

③ Colorless crystals. [68°].
Sol. in org. solvents ; insol. in H_2O.

④ $+ HCl \longrightarrow (C_6H_5)_2SbCl_3$

⑥ Ann. **421**, 235 (1920).

$SbC_{12}H_{10}Cl_3$

① Diphenylantimony trichloride
$(C_6H_5)_2SbCl_3$

② $Ph_2Sb(O)OH + HCl \longrightarrow$
$Ph_2SbCl + HCl(g) \longrightarrow$

③ Solid. [171~172°].

④ $+ H_2O \longrightarrow Ph_2Sb(O)OH$

⑥ Dokl. **87**, 991 (1952) ; CA **48**, 143
(1954).   Ann. **421**, 236 (1920).   Ber.
44, 2319 (1911).

$SbC_{12}H_{10}I$

① Diphenyliodostibine
$(C_6H_5)_2SbI$

② Ph_2Sb-O-$SbPh_2 + HI \longrightarrow$
Ph_2Sb-$SbPh_2 + HI \longrightarrow$

③ [68~70°].
Sol. in org. solvents ; insol. in H_2O.

⑥ JACS **53**, 1025 (1931).

$SbC_{12}H_{11}$

① Diphenylstibine
$(C_6H_5)_2SbH$

② $Ph_2SbCl + LiBH_4 \longrightarrow Ph_2SbH$

③ Unstable ; readily disproportionates
and lose H_2.

⑥ Z. Naturf. **12 b**, 128 (1957).

$SbC_{12}H_{11}O_2$

① Diphenylstibinic acid
$(C_6H_5)_2Sb(O)OH$

② $PhN_2Cl \cdot SbCl_3 + Fe \xrightarrow{acetone} 5\% \; NH_3$
$\longrightarrow Ph_2Sb(O)OH$

③ White powder. [>285°].

⑥ Dokl. **91**, 1341 (1953) ; **87**, 991 (1952).
CA **49**, 11375 (1954) ; **48**, 143 (1954).

$SbC_{12}H_{27}$

① Tri-n-butylstibine
$(n$-$C_4H_9)_3Sb$

② $SbCl_3 + (n$-$C_4H_9)MgX \longrightarrow$

③ Colorless liq. $(131°/12)$.
Sol. in org. solvents ; insol. in H_2O ;
inflammable in air.

④ $+ O_2 \longrightarrow (n$-$C_4H_9)_3SbO$
$+ X_2 \longrightarrow (n$-$C_4H_9)_3SbX_2$

⑥ JCS **1947**, 1568 ; **1930**, 463.

SbC₁₂H₂₇Br₂
① Triisobutylantimony dibromide
  $(i\text{-}C_4H_9)_3SbBr_2$
② $i\text{-}Bu_3Sb + Br_2 \longrightarrow$
③ Colorless crystals. [88°].
  Sol. in org. solvents; stable in H_2O
  and air.
④ $\xrightarrow{\text{heat}} i\text{-}Bu_2SbBr + i\text{-}BuBr$
⑥ JCS **1932**, 1815.

SbC₁₂H₂₇Cl₂
① Triisobutylantimony dichloride
  $(i\text{-}C_4H_9)_3SbCl_2$
② $(i\text{-}Bu)_3Sb + Cl_2 \longrightarrow$
③ Colorless crystals. [91°].
  Sol. in org. solvents; stable in air
  and H_2O.
④ $\xrightarrow{\text{heat}} i\text{-}Bu_2SbCl + i\text{-}BuCl$
⑥ JCS **1932**, 1815.

SbC₁₂H₂₇I₂
① Triisobutylantimony diiodide
  $(i\text{-}C_4H_9)_3SbI_2$
② $i\text{-}Bu_3Sb + I_2 \longrightarrow$
③ Pale yellow crystals. [70°].
  Sol. in org. solvents; stable in air
  and H_2O.
④ $\xrightarrow{\text{heat}} i\text{-}Bu_2SbI + i\text{-}BuI$
⑥ JCS **1935**, 1815.

SbC₁₄H₁₃O₂
① Diphenylacetoxystibine
  $(C_6H_5)_2SbOCOCH_3$
② $(o\text{-}CH_3C_6H_4)(C_6H_5)_2Sb$
  $+ CH_3COOH \xrightarrow{\text{reflux}}$
③ White solid. [133°].
  Slightly sol. in org. solvents.
⑥ Zhur. **31**, 3757 (1961); CA **57**, 8609
  (1962).

SbC₁₄H₁₄Br
① Di-*p*-tolylbromostibine

$(p\text{-}CH_3C_6H_4)_2SbBr$
② $(p\text{-}CH_3C_6H_4)_3SbBr_2$
  $\xrightarrow{\text{heat}} (p\text{-}CH_3C_6H_4)_2SbBr$
③ Pale yellow crystals. [>290°].
  Sol. in warm org. solvents.
⑥ JCS **1928**, 719.

SbC₁₅H₁₃O₂
① Diphenylacryloxystibine
  $(C_6H_5)_2SbOCOCH=CH_2$
② $[(C_6H_5)_2Sb]_2O + CH_2=CHCOOH \xrightarrow[\text{heat}]{CH_3OH}$
③ Colorless crystals. [115~117°].
  Sol. in toluene.
④ Easily polymerized by AIBN.
⑥ Dokl. **137**, 1368 (1961); CA **55**, 19841
  (1961).

SbC₁₅H₃₃
① Tri-*n*-pentylstibine
  $(n\text{-}C_5H_{11})_3Sb$
② $SbCl_3 + 3 (n\text{-}C_5H_{11})MgBr \longrightarrow$
  $(n\text{-}C_5H_{11})_3SbX_2 + Zn \longrightarrow$
③ Colorless liq. (168°/16). $d\,1.136(18°)$.
  Sol. in org. solvents; insol. in H_2O.
④ $+ Br_2 \longrightarrow (n\text{-}C_5H_{11})_3SbBr_2$
  $+ O_2 \longrightarrow (n\text{-}C_5H_{11})_3SbO$
⑥ JCS **1930**, 463.

SbC₁₆H₁₅O₂
① Diphenylmethacryloxystibine
  $(C_6H_5)_2SbOCOC(CH_3)=CH_2$
② $[(C_6H_5)_2Sb]_2O +$
  $CH_2=C(CH_3)COOH \xrightarrow[\text{heat}]{CH_3OH}$
③ Colorless crystals. [113~115°].
  Sol. in toluene.
④ Easily polymerized by AIBN.
⑥ Dokl. **137**, 1368 (1961); CA **55**, 19841
  (1961).

SbC₁₈H₁₅
① Triphenylstibine

$(C_6H_5)_3Sb$

② $SbCl_3 + 3 (C_6H_5)MgX \longrightarrow$
$3 PhBr + SbCl_3 + 6 Na \longrightarrow$
$3 PhLi + SbCl_3 \longrightarrow$

③ Colorless crystals. ($>360°$). [$50\sim52°$], [$46\sim48°$]. d 1.4343 ($25°$).
Stable in air; sol. in org. solvents; insol. in H_2O.

④ $+ X_2 \longrightarrow Ph_3SbX_2$ (X: halogen)
$+ HNO_3$(concd.)
$\longrightarrow (m\text{-}NO_2C_6H_4)_3Sb(NO_3)_2$
$+ Ph\text{-}X \longrightarrow\!\!\!\!\!| \!\!\!\!\!\longrightarrow Ph_4SbX$
$+ H_2SO_4 \longrightarrow Ph_3SbSO_4$

⑥ JCS **1947**, 1568. J. Gen. Chem. USSR **16**, 777 (1946). Zhur. **25**, 2437 (1955).

SbC₁₈H₁₅Br₂

① Triphenylantimony dibromide $(C_6H_5)_3SbBr_2$

② $Ph_3Sb + Br_2 \xrightarrow[\text{glacial acetic acid}]{}$

③ Colorless crystals. [$216°$].
Sol. in C_6H_6 and EtOH; slightly sol. in aliphatic hydrocarbon.

⑥ Ann. **233**, 50 (1886).

SbC₁₈H₁₅Cl₂

① Triphenylantimony dichloride $(C_6H_5)_3SbCl_2$

② $Ph_3Sb + Cl_2 \longrightarrow$

③ Colorless crystals. [$143°$], [$141.5°$].
Sol. in org. solvents; decomp. by alk.

④ $+ H_2O \longrightarrow Ph_3Sb(OH)Cl$

⑥ Ber. **37**, 4621 (1904). JCS **1910**, 37.

SbC₁₈H₁₅F₂

① Triphenylantimony difluoride $(C_6H_5)_3SbF_2$

② $(C_6H_5)_3SbBr_2 + AgF \longrightarrow$

③ Colorless crystals. [$115°$].
Sol. in org. solvents.

⑥ Sbornik. Statei. Obschei Kh. **2**, 992 (1953).

SbC₁₈H₁₅I₂

① Triphenylantimony diiodide $(C_6H_5)_3SbI_2$

② $(C_6H_5)_3Sb + I_2 \xrightarrow{\text{glacial acetic acid}}$

③ Colorless crystals. [$153°$].
Sol. in org. solvents.

⑥ Ann. **233**, 50 (1886).

SbC₁₈H₁₅S

① Triphenylstibine sulfide $(C_6H_5)_3SbS$

② $Ph_3SbBr_2 + H_2S \xrightarrow{NH_3+MeOH}$

③ Colorless crystals. [$119\sim120°$].
Sol. in C_6H_6 and $CHCl_3$; insol. in alc. and ether.

④ $\xrightarrow{\text{heat}} Ph_3Sb + S$

⑥ Ber. **41**, 2761 (1908).

SbC₁₈H₁₇O₂

① Triphenylantimony dihydroxide $(C_6H_5)_3Sb(OH)_2$

② $Ph_3SbBr_2 + KOH \xrightarrow[\text{EtOH}]{}$

③ [$212°$].
Sol. in acetic acid.

⑥ Ann. **233**, 42 (1886).

SbC₁₈H₁₈N₃

① Tri-*m*-aminophenylstibine $(m\text{-}NH_2C_6H_4)_3Sb$

② $(m\text{-}NO_2C_6H_4)_3Sb + NH_4Cl$
$+ Zn \xrightarrow{\text{boiling alcohol}}$

③ Colorless crystals. [$80°$ decomp.].
Stable in air; sol. in HCl, acetone. EtOH and HCl.

④ $+ X_2 \longrightarrow (NH_2C_6H_4)_3SbX_2$

⑥ JCS **1911**, 2292.

SbC₁₈H₃₉

① Tri-*n*-hexylstibine $(n\text{-}C_6H_{13})_3Sb$

② SbCl$_3$ + (n-C$_6$H$_{13}$)MgBr $\xrightarrow{\text{ether}}$ 67%

(n-C$_6$H$_{13}$)$_3$SbBr$_2$ + Zn $\longrightarrow$

③ Colorless liq. (191~192°/10). n_D 1.4920
(19°). d 1.0860 (10°).
Sol. in org. solvents; insol. in H$_2$O.

④ + Br$_2$ $\longrightarrow$ (n-C$_6$H$_{13}$)$_3$SbBr$_2$
(mp 148°)
+ O$_2$ $\longrightarrow$ (n-C$_6$H$_{13}$)$_3$SbO

⑥ Zhur. **34**, 3462 (1964); CA **62**, 2792
(1965). JCS 1930, 463.

SbC$_{20}$H$_{14}$I

① Di-α-naphthyliodostibine
(α-C$_{10}$H$_7$)$_2$SbI

② (C$_{10}$H$_7$)$_2$SbSb(C$_{10}$H$_7$)$_2$ + HI $\xrightarrow{\text{in AcOH}}$

③ Yellow crystals. [136~137°].
Sol. in org. solvents; insol. in H$_2$O.

⑥ JACS **55**, 1198 (1933).

SbC$_{21}$H$_{21}$

① Tri-p-tolylstibine
(p-CH$_3$C$_6$H$_4$)$_3$Sb

② p-CH$_3$C$_6$H$_4$MgX + SbCl$_3$ $\longrightarrow$

③ Colorless crystals. [64.5°].
Sol. in org. solvents; insol. in H$_2$O.

④ + X$_2$ $\longrightarrow$ (p-CH$_3$C$_6$H$_4$)$_3$SbX$_2$

⑥ Ber. **17**, 925 (1884).

SbC$_{21}$H$_{21}$O

① Tri-p-tolylstibine oxide
(p-CH$_3$C$_6$H$_4$)$_3$SbO

② (MeC$_6$H$_4$)$_3$Sb + H$_2$O$_2$ $\xrightarrow{\text{KOH}}$
(MeC$_6$H$_4$)$_3$SbX$_2$ + KOH $\longrightarrow$

③ Needle like crystals. [223.5°].
Sol. in org. solvents.

⑥ Ber. **17**, 925 (1884).

SbC$_{21}$H$_{45}$

① Tri-n-heptylstibine
(n-C$_7$H$_{15}$)$_3$Sb

② SbCl$_3$ + n-C$_7$H$_{15}$MgBr $\xrightarrow{\text{ether}}$ 58%

③ Colorless liq. (220°/20). n_D 1.4880
(19°). d 1.0610 (10°).
Sol. in org. solvents; insol. in H$_2$O.

④ + Br$_2$ $\longrightarrow$ (C$_7$H$_{15}$)$_3$SbBr$_2$
[136°]

⑥ Zhur. **34**, 3462 (1964); CA **62**, 2792
(1965).

SbC$_{22}$H$_{21}$O$_4$

① Triphenylantimony diacetate
(C$_6$H$_5$)$_3$Sb(OCOCH$_3$)$_2$

② Pb(OCOCH$_3$)$_4$ + Ph$_3$Sb $\xrightarrow[\text{in CHCl}_3]{\text{CH}_3\text{COOH}}$

Ph$_3$Sb(OCOCH$_3$)$_2$ + Pb(OAc)$_2$

Ph$_2$Sb(OCOCH$_3$) + PhN$_2$OCOCH$_3$

$\xrightarrow[\text{acetone}]{\text{in cold}}$ ~6%

Ph$_3$Sb(OH)$_2$ + CH$_3$COOH $\longrightarrow$

③ [215~216° decomp.].

⑥ Zhur. **34**, 946 (1964); CA **60**, 15905
(1964). Dokl. **89**, 877 (1953); CA
48, 5135 (1954). Ber. **97**, 789
(1964).

SbC$_{22}$H$_{25}$O$_2$

① Triphenylantimony diethoxide
(C$_6$H$_5$)$_3$Sb(OC$_2$H$_5$)$_2$

② Ph$_3$SbX$_2$ + 2 EtONa $\longrightarrow$
Ph$_3$SbX$_2$ + 2 EtOH + 2 NH$_3$(gas) $\longrightarrow$

③ Sol. in org. solvents.

④ + H$_2$O$_2$ $\longrightarrow$ [−(C$_6$H$_5$)$_3$Sb−O−O]$_n$

⑥ Ann. **678**, 167 (1964).

SbC$_{24}$H$_{20}$Br

① Tetraphenylstibonium bromide
(C$_6$H$_5$)$_4$SbBr

② Ph$_5$Sb + Br$_2$ $\xrightarrow{\text{CCl}_4}$
Ph$_3$SbBr$_2$ + PhMgBr $\longrightarrow$

③ Colorless crystals. [213~215°].
Sol. in H$_2$O.

⑥ Ann. **577**, 25 (1952). JACS **70**, 737
(1948). JCS 1940, 1195.

SbC$_{24}$H$_{20}$Cl

① Tetraphenylstibonium chloride
   (C$_6$H$_5$)$_4$SbCl

② Ph$_5$Sb + Cl$_2$ $\xrightarrow{\text{CCl}_4}$

   Ph$_3$SbCl$_2$ + PhMgBr $\longrightarrow$

③ Colorless crystals. [204～205°].
   Sol. in H$_2$O.

⑥ Ann. **577**, 25 (1952).   JACS **70**, 737
   (1948).   JCS **1940**, 1195.

SbC$_{24}$H$_{20}$I

① Tetraphenylstibonium iodide
   (C$_6$H$_5$)$_4$SbI

② Ph$_4$SbBr + KI $\xrightarrow[\text{hot H}_2\text{O}]{}$

③ Colorless needle-like crystals. [200°].
   Sol. in H$_2$O.

⑥ JCS **1940**, 1195.

SbC$_{24}$H$_{51}$

① Tri-*n*-octylstibine
   (*n*-C$_8$H$_{17}$)$_3$Sb

② SbCl$_3$ + *n*-C$_8$H$_{17}$MgBr $\xrightarrow[\text{ether}]{}$ 30.4%

③ Colorless liq. (192～193°/6). n_D 1.4740
   (19°). d 1.0140 (10°).
   Sol. in org. solvents; insol. in H$_2$O.

④ + Br$_2$ $\longrightarrow$ (*n*-C$_8$H$_{17}$)$_3$SbBr$_2$
   [129°]

⑥ Zhur. **34**, 3461 (1964); CA **62**, 2792
   (1965).

SbC$_{27}$H$_{57}$

① Tri-*n*-nonylstibine
   (*n*-C$_9$H$_{19}$)$_3$Sb

② SbCl$_3$ + *n*-C$_9$H$_{19}$Br $\xrightarrow{\text{Et}_2\text{O}}$ 33%

③ Colorless liq. (199～200°/6). n_D 1.4768
   (19°). d 0.9975 (10°).
   Sol. in org. solvents; insol. in H$_2$O.

④ + Br$_2$ $\longrightarrow$ (*n*-C$_9$H$_{19}$)$_3$SbBr$_2$
   [125°]

⑥ Zhur. **34**, 3462 (1964); CA **62**, 2792
   (1965).

SbC$_{30}$H$_{21}$

① Tri-*α*-naphthylstibine
   (*α*-C$_{10}$H$_7$)$_3$Sb

② SbCl$_3$ + *α*-C$_{10}$H$_7$MgBr $\xrightarrow[\text{ether}]{}$

③ Crystals. [223～223.5°], [218°].
   Sol. in acetone; slightly sol. in aromatic hydrocarbon; insol. in H$_2$O.

④ + Cl$_2$ $\longrightarrow$ (*α*-C$_{10}$H$_7$)$_3$SbCl$_2$

⑥ Sbornik. Statei Obschei Kh. **2**, 992
   (1953).   JCS **1924**, 869.

SbC$_{30}$H$_{21}$Br$_2$

① Tri-*α*-naphthylantimonydibromide
   (*α*-C$_{10}$H$_7$)$_3$SbBr$_2$

② (*α*-C$_{10}$H$_7$)$_3$Sb + Br$_2$ $\longrightarrow$

③ Pale yellow solid. [229°].
   Sol. in org. solvents.

④ + Zn $\longrightarrow$ (*α*-C$_{10}$H$_7$)$_3$Sb

⑥ JCS **1924**, 869.

SbC$_{30}$H$_{21}$Cl$_2$

① Tri-*α*-naphthylantimony dichloride
   (*α*-C$_{10}$H$_7$)$_3$SbCl$_2$

② (*α*-C$_{10}$H$_7$)$_3$Sb + Cl$_2$ $\longrightarrow$

③ Crystalline solid. [260°].
   Slightly sol. in org. solvents.

④ + Zn $\longrightarrow$ (*α*-C$_{10}$H$_7$)$_3$Sb

⑥ JCS **1924**, 869.

SbC$_{30}$H$_{21}$F$_2$

① Tri-*α*-naphthylantimony difluoride
   (*α*-C$_{10}$H$_7$)$_3$SbF$_2$

② (*α*-C$_{10}$H$_7$)$_3$SbBr$_2$ + AgF $\longrightarrow$

③ Crystalline solid. [279～280°].
   Slightly sol. in org. solvents.

④ + Zn $\longrightarrow$ (*α*-C$_{10}$H$_7$)$_3$Sb

⑥ Sbornik. Statei Obschei Kh. **2**, 992
   (1953).

SbC$_{30}$H$_{25}$

① Pentaphenylantimony
   (C$_6$H$_5$)$_5$Sb

② Ph$_3$SbCl$_2$ + 2 PhLi $\xrightarrow[]{\text{ether}}$

③ White crystals. [168.5~170°].
  Sol. in cyclohexane and other org.
  solvents.
④ $+ I_2 \longrightarrow Ph_4SbI + PhI$
  $+ Ph_3B \longrightarrow [Ph_4Sb]^+[Ph_4B]^-$
⑥ Acta Chem. Scand. **7**, 1293 (1953).
  Ann. **577**, 26 (1952).

SbC₃₀H₆₃

① Tri-*n*-decylstibine
  $(n\text{-}C_{10}H_{21})_3Sb$
② $SbCl_3 + n\text{-}C_{10}H_{21}MgBr \xrightarrow[\text{ether}]{} 38.2\%$
③ Colorless liquid. (203~234°/6).
  $n_D\,1.4615\,(19°)$. $d\,0.9522\,(10°)$.
  Sol. in org. solvents; insol. in H_2O.
④ $+ Br_2 \xrightarrow{CHCl_3} (n\text{-}C_{10}H_{21})_3SbBr_2$
  $[118°]$
⑥ Zhur. **34**, 3462 (1964); CA **62**, 2792
  (1965).

Sb₂C₄H₁₂

① Tetramethyldistibine
  $(CH_3)_2SbSb(CH_3)_2$
② $2\,(CH_3)_2SbBr + 2\,Na \xrightarrow{\text{liq. } NH_3}$
③ Reddish needle like crystals. [17.5°].
  Sol. in C_6H_6, EtOH and ether; spontaneously inflammable in air;
  fairly stable against heating.
  Monomeric in C_6H_6.
④ $+ 2\,CH_3I \longrightarrow Me_2SbI + Me_4SbI$
  $+ X_2 \longrightarrow Me_2SbX$
  $+ O_2 \xrightarrow{\text{in } C_6H_6} Me_2Sb(O)OH$
⑥ Proc. Roy. Soc. **110**, 523 (1926).

Sb₂C₄H₁₂O

① Bis(dimethylstibine) oxide
  $[((CH_3)_2Sb_2]O$
② $Me_2SbX + KOH \longrightarrow$
③ Colorless liq.
  Insol. in H_2O. Inflammable in air.
④ $+ HX \longrightarrow Me_2SbX$
⑥ Proc. Roy. Soc. **110**, 523 (1926).

Sb₂C₆H₁₂

① Bis(dimethylstibino)acetylene
  $(CH_3)_2SbC{\equiv}CSb(CH_3)_2$
② $Me_2SbX + XMgC{\equiv}CMgX \longrightarrow$
③ Colorless liq. (116°/17).
⑥ Z. anorg. allg. Chem. **312**, 186 (1961).

Sb₂C₆H₁₈Br₂O

① Bis(trimethylbromoantimony)oxide
  $[Br(CH_3)_3Sb]_2O$
② $Me_3SbBr_2 + Me_3SbO \xrightarrow{H_2O}$
③ Colorless crystals. [>280°].
  Sol. in H_2O.
⑥ J. prakt. Chem. **84**, 328 (1861). Ber.
  40, 1508 (1907).

Sb₂C₆H₁₈Cl₂O

① Bis(trimethylchloroantimony)oxide
  $[Cl(CH_3)_3Sb]_2O$
② $Me_3SbCl_2 + Me_3SbO \xrightarrow{H_2O}$
③ Colorless crystals.
  Sol. in H_2O, acetone and alc.
⑥ Ber. **40**, 1508 (1907). J. prakt. Chem.
  84, 328 (1861).

Sb₂C₈H₂₀

① Tetraethyldistibine
  $(C_2H_5)_2SbSb(C_2H_5)_2$
② heated Sb(Sb mirror) + $C_2H_5\cdot \longrightarrow$
③ Yellowish oilly liq. [−61°].
  Sol. in org. solvents.
④ $+ O_2 \longrightarrow Et_2Sb(O)OH$
  $+ X_2 \longrightarrow Et_2SbX$
⑥ Trans. Faraday Soc. **30**, 179 (1934).
  JCS **1935**, 366.

Sb₂C₁₀H₂₀

① Bis(diethylstibino)acetylene
  $(C_2H_5)_2SbC{\equiv}CSb(C_2H_5)_2$
② $Et_2SbX + XMgC{\equiv}CMgX \longrightarrow$
③ Colorless liq. [122°/1.5].
⑥ Z. anorg. allg. chem. **312**, 186 (1961).

Sb$_2$C$_{12}$H$_{10}$

① Stibinobenzene

(C$_6$H$_5$SbSbC$_6$H$_5$)$_n$

② PhSbO + NaH$_2$PO$_2$ ⟶

③ Reddish powder.

Inflammable in air ; turn dark above
60° (decomp.).

⑥ Ann. **421**, 221 (1920).

Sb$_2$C$_{24}$H$_{20}$

① Tetraphenyldistibine

(C$_6$H$_5$)$_2$SbSb(C$_6$H$_5$)$_2$

② Ph$_2$SbI + NaH$_2$PO$_2$ ⟶

(Ph$_2$Sb)$_2$O + H$_3$PO$_2$ ⟶

③ Pale yellowish crystals. [121~122°].

Unstable.

④ + I$_2$ ⟶ Ph$_2$SbI

+ O$_2$ ⟶ Ph$_2$SbOOSbPh$_2$

⑥ Ann. **421**, 236 (1920).   JACS **53**, 1025
(1931) ; **55**, 1198 (1933).

Sb$_2$C$_{24}$H$_{20}$O

① Bis(diphenylstibine) oxide

[(C$_6$H$_5$)$_2$Sb]$_2$O

② Ph$_3$Sb + EtOH + HCl

$\xrightarrow{\text{treated with NaOH}}$ (Ph$_2$Sb)$_2$O

③ Colorless crystals. [78°].

④ + H$_2$S ⟶ (Ph$_2$Sb)$_2$S

⑥ Ber. **44**, 2317 (1911).

Sb$_2$C$_{24}$H$_{20}$S

① Bis(diphenylstibine) sulfide

[(C$_6$H$_5$)$_2$Sb]$_2$S

② (Ph$_2$Sb)$_2$O + H$_2$S $\xrightarrow{\text{alcohol}}$

③ Colorless crystals. [69°].

⑥ Ber. **44**, 2318 (1911).

Sb$_2$C$_{36}$H$_{30}$OCl$_2$

① Bis(triphenylchloroantimony) oxide

[Cl(C$_6$H$_5$)$_3$Sb]$_2$O

② Ph$_3$SbCl$_2$ + H$_2$O $\xrightarrow{\text{OH}^-}$

③ Colorless crystals.

⑥ Z. anorg. allg. Chem. **316**, 270 (1962).

【Bi】

BiCH$_3$Br$_2$

① Methylbismuth dibromide

CH$_3$BiBr$_2$

② (CH$_3$)$_3$Bi + 2 BiBr$_3$ $\xrightarrow[\text{ether}]{}$

(CH$_3$)$_2$Zn + 2 BiBr$_3$ $\xrightarrow[\text{ether}]{}$

BiBr$_3$ + CH$_3$MgI ⟶ in small yield

③ Stable in air.

Yellow powder. [214°].

Slightly sol. in alc., glacial acetic
acid and C$_6$H$_6$; insol. in ether.

⑥ Ber. **20**, 1516 (1887).   Bull. soc. chim.
France **31**, 545 (1922).

BiCH$_3$Cl$_2$

① Methylbismuth dichloride

CH$_3$BiCl$_2$

② (CH$_3$)$_3$Bi + 2 BiCl$_3$ $\xrightarrow[\text{glacial acetic acid}]{}$

③ Yellow-white crystals. [242°].

Slightly sol. in alc. and glacial
acetic acid ; insol. in ether.

⑥ Ber. **20**, 1516 (1887).

BiCH$_3$I$_2$

① Methylbismuth diiodide

CH$_3$BiI$_2$

② (CH$_3$)$_3$Bi + 2 CH$_3$I $\xrightarrow{200°}$

③ Becomes dark by light.

Glinting red crystals. [225°
decomp.].

Sol. in alcohol and slightly sol. in
hot glacial acetic acid ; insol. in
ether.

⑥ Ber. **20**, 1516 (1887).

BiC$_2$H$_5$Br$_2$

① Ethylbismuth dibromide

C₂H₅BiBr₂

② (C₂H₅)₃Bi + 2 BiBr₃ $\xrightarrow{\text{ether}}$

C₂H₅BiCl₂ + 2 KBr $\longrightarrow$

③ Yellow-white plate crystals.

⑥ J. prakt. Chem. **61**, 399 (1854). Ber. **20**, 1516 (1887) ; **48**, 1473 (1915).

BiC₂H₅I₂

① Ethylbismuth diiodide
   C₂H₅BiI₂

② C₂H₅BiCl₂ + 2 KI $\longrightarrow$

   (C₂H₅)₃Bi + 2 C₂H₅I $\xrightarrow{\text{heat}}$

③ Glinting red crylstals.

⑥ J. prakt. Chem. **61**, 399 (1854). Ber. **20**, 1516 (1887).

BiC₂H₆Br

① Dimethylbismuth bromide
   (CH₃)₂BiBr

② (CH₃)₃Bi + Br₂ $\xrightarrow{\text{cold ether}}$

③ Stable in air at room temp. ; ignites when heated.
   White powder.
   Sol. in alc. ; insol. in ether.

⑥ Ber. **20**, 1516 (1887).

BiC₂H₆Cl

① Dimethylbismuth chloride
   (CH₃)₂BiCl

② (CH₃)₃Bi + Cl₂ $\xrightarrow{\text{cold ether}}$

③ Stable in air ; ignites when heated.
   White microcrystalline powder.
   [116°].
   Sol. in alc. ; insol. in ether.

⑥ Ber. **20**, 1516 (1887).

BiC₃H₉

① Trimethylbismuth
   (CH₃)₃Bi

② (CH₃)₂Zn + BiBr₃ $\xrightarrow{\text{ether}}$

   Al₄C₃ + BiCl₃ + HCl $\longrightarrow$ 20%

③ Inflammable in air ; upleasant odor ; vapor irritates mucous menbranes.
   Colorless liq. (110°/760). d 2.30 (18°).
   Sol. in org. solvents ; insol. in H₂O.

④ + Cl₂ $\longrightarrow$ (CH₃)₂BiCl
   + Br₂ $\longrightarrow$ (CH₃)₂BiBr
   + CH₃I $\xrightarrow{200°}$ CH₃BiI₂ + 2 C₂H₆

⑥ Ber. **20**, 1516 (1887) ; **46**, 3738 (1913).

BiC₄H₁₀Br

① Diethylbismuth bromide
   (C₂H₅)₂BiBr

② (C₂H₅)₃Bi + Br₂ $\xrightarrow{\text{cold ether}}$

③ Ignites in air.
   Sol. in alc. ; insol. in ether.

⑥ Ber. **20**, 1516 (1887).

BiC₆H₅Br₂

① Phenylbismuth dibromide
   C₆H₅BiBr₂

② (C₆H₅)₂BiBr + Br₂ $\xrightarrow{\text{in CHCl}_3}$

   (C₆H₅)₂BiI + Br₂ $\longrightarrow$

③ Fine yellow needles. [206°].

⑥ JCS **1914**, 2210. Proc. Chem. Soc. **30**, 293 (1914).

BiC₆H₁₅

① Triethylbismuth
   (C₂H₅)₃Bi

② C₂H₅X + BiK₃ $\longrightarrow$

   (C₂H₅)₂Zn + BiBr₃ $\xrightarrow{\text{ether}}$

   (C₂H₅)₂Hg + Bi $\xrightarrow{100°\sim130°}$

③ Disgusting odor ; inflammable in air.
   Volatile liq. (96°/50), (107°/79), (123°/150).
   Sol. in org. solvents.

④ Explodes when heated to 150°.
   + HCl $\longrightarrow$ BiCl₃ + 3 C₂H₆

⑥ Ann. **75**, 355 (1850) ; **82**, 106 (1852).

J. prakt. Chem. **56**, 341 (1852); **61**,
399 (1854). Ber. **20**, 1516 (1887).
JCS **17**, 29 (1864). JACS **59**, 935
(1937).

BiC₁₂H₁₀Br

① Diphenylbismuth bromide
$(C_6H_5)_2BiBr$

② $(C_6H_5)_3Bi + CNBr \longrightarrow$

    $(C_6H_5)_3Bi + IBr \xrightarrow{\text{in dry ether}}$

    $(C_6H_5)_4Pb + BiBr_3 \longrightarrow$

    $2(C_6H_5)_3Bi + BiBr_3 \longrightarrow$

③ Yellow crystals. [158°].

④ $+ Br_2 \xrightarrow{\text{in CHCl}_3} (C_6H_5)BiBr_2 + C_6H_5Br$

⑥ JCS **105**, 2210 (1914); **107**, 16 (1915);
    121, 978 (1922). JACS **63**, 207 (1941).
    Ann. **251**, 323 (1889).

BiC₁₂H₁₀Cl

① Diphenylbismuth chloride
$(C_6H_5)_2BiCl$

② $(C_6H_5)_3Bi + ICl \xrightarrow{\text{dry ether}}$

    $2(C_6H_5)_3Bi + BiCl_3 \xrightarrow{\text{dry ether}}$

    $(C_6H_5)_3Bi + SbCl_3 \longrightarrow$

③ Decomp. by moist solvents.
Colorless crylstals. [185°].
Fairly sol. in dry benzene, toluene
and CHCl₃; less sol. in ether and
light petroleum.

④ $+ 2HCl \longrightarrow BiCl_3 + C_6H_6$

⑥ JCS **107**, 16 (1915); **119**, 913 (1921);
    125, 864 (1924); **121**, 104 (1922).
    JACS **63**, 207 (1941).

BiC₁₂H₁₀I

① Diphenylbismuth iodide
$(C_6H_5)_2BiI$

② $(C_6H_5)_2BiCl + KI \xrightarrow{\text{abs. alc.}}$

③ Yellow powder. [134°].

⑥ JACS **53**, 1025 (1931); **63**, 207 (1941).

JCS **107**, 16 (1915). Ber. **30**, 2843
(1897).

BiC₁₂H₁₀Na

① Diphenylbismus sodium
$(C_6H_5)_2BiNa$

② $Ph_2BiBr + Na \xrightarrow{\text{liq. NH}_3}$

③ Deep red soln.

④ $+ \alpha\text{-}C_{10}H_7I \longrightarrow$ $Ph_2BiI + \alpha\text{-}C_{10}H_7Na$
               $\xrightarrow{\text{NH}_3} C_{10}H_8 + NaNH_2$
                        $+ Ph_3Bi$

         $\longrightarrow Ph_2Bi \cdot C_{10}H_7 + NaI$

    $+ IC_6H_4CO_2H \longrightarrow Ph_2BiC_6H_4CO_2H$

⑥ JACS **63**, 212 (1941).

BiC₁₃H₁₀N

① Diphenylbismuth cyanide
$(C_6H_5)_2BiCN$

② $Ph_3Bi + ICN \xrightarrow[\text{benzene}]{\text{heat}}$

③ Smells of hydrocyanic acid.
Colorless needles like glass wool.
[210° decomp.]
Sparingly sol. in hot alc. and
benzene; less sol. in ether and
light petr.

④ $+ \text{cold HCl} \longrightarrow BiCl_3 + HCN$
    $+ PhCl$

⑥ JCS **107**, 16 (1915); **1926**, 1648; **1922**,
    91.

BiC₁₈H₁₅

① Triphenylbismuth
$(C_6H_5)_3Bi$

② $C_6H_5Br + BiNa_3 \longrightarrow$

    $C_6H_5MgBr + BiCl_3 \xrightarrow{\text{ether}}$

    $(C_6H_5)_2Hg + Bi \xrightarrow{250°}$

③ Pleasant odor, stable in air.
Colorless needles. [78°].
Sol. in org. solvents; insol. in H₂O.

④ $+ HCl \longrightarrow C_6H_6 + BiCl_3$
    $+ ICl \longrightarrow (C_6H_5)_2BiCl$

$+ ICN \longrightarrow (C_6H_5)_2BiCN +$
$BiCl_3 \longrightarrow (C_6H_5)_2BiCl$
$+ AsCl_3 \longrightarrow (C_6H_5)_2BiCl$

⑥ Ber. 20, 54 (1887).   Ann. 251, 323
(1889).

$BiC_{18}H_{15}Br_2$

① Triphenylbismuth dibromide
$(C_6H_5)_3BiBr_2$

② $(C_6H_5)_3Bi + Br_2 \longrightarrow$

③ Does not decomp. by concd. HCl.
Yellow needles. [124°].
Sol. in C_6H_6; insol. in ether and alc.

④ $+ H_2S \longrightarrow (C_6H_5)_3Bi$
$+ 2\,NaOH + CO_2 \xrightarrow[\text{alcohol}]{}$
$(C_6H_5)_3BiCO_3 + 2\,NaBr$

⑥ JCS 105, 2210 (1914); 117, 762 (1920).
Ann. 251, 323 (1889).   Ber. 20, 54
(1887).

$BiC_{18}H_{15}Cl_2$

① Triphenylbismuth dichloride
$(C_6H_5)_3BiCl_2$

② $(C_6H_5)_3Bi + Cl_2 \xrightarrow[\text{ice cold}]{\text{in } CHCl_3}$

③ Does not decomp. by concd. HCl.
White needles. [141.5°].
Insol. in ether and cold alcohol;
sol. in hot alc. and C_6H_6.

④ $+ NH_3 + H_2O \longrightarrow (C_6H_5)_3Bi(OH)Cl$
$+ \text{concd. } H_2SO_4 \longrightarrow (C_6H_5)_3BiSO_4$
$+ 2\,KF \xrightarrow[\text{alcohol+acetone}]{} (C_6H_5)_3BiF_2$

⑥ Ann. 251, 323 (1889).   Ber. 20, 54
(1887).   JCS 117, 762 (1920); 109,
250 (1916); 121, 91 (1922).

$BiC_{18}H_{15}I_2$

① Triphenylbismuth diiodide
$(C_6H_5)_3BiI_2$

② $(C_6H_5)_3Bi + I_2 \xrightarrow[-78°C]{}$

③ Stable at $-78°C$.
Pale orange solid.

⑥ JCS 125, 854 (1924).

$BiC_{18}H_{15}N_6$

① Triphenylbismuth diazide
$(C_6H_5)_3Bi(N_3)_2$

② $Ph_3BiCl_2 + NaN_3 \xrightarrow[\text{8hrs.}]{H_2O}$

③ Explodes violently when suddenly
heated.
Short thick needls. [93°].
Recrystallized from $CHCl_3$–light
petroleum.

⑥ JCS 1934, 405.

$BiC_{18}H_{16}BrO$

① Triphenylbismuth hydroxybromide
$(C_6H_5)_3Bi(OH)Br$

② $(C_6H_5)_3BiBr_2 + NH_3 + H_2O \xrightarrow[\text{in } CHCl_3]{}$

③ Yellow powder. [148°].
Insol. in H_2O, ether and light petroleum; sparingly sol. in boiling
acetone and benzene; sol. in toluene, xylene, alc. and $CHCl_3$.

⑥ JCS 117, 762 (1960).

$BiC_{18}H_{16}ClO$

① Triphenylbismuth hydroxychloride
$(C_6H_5)_3Bi(OH)Cl$

② $(C_6H_5)_3BiCl_2 + NH_3 + H_2O \xrightarrow[\text{CHCl}_3]{}$

③ White solid. [160~161°].
Insol. in H_2O and light petroleum;
sol. in ether, acetone, benzene,
xylene and alc.

④ $+ 2\,CH_3COOH \longrightarrow$
$(C_6H_5)_3Bi(OOCCH_3)_2$

⑥ JCS 117, 762 (1920); 1934, 405.

$BiC_{20}H_{14}Cl$

① Di-α-naphthylbismuth chloride
$(\alpha\text{-}C_{10}H_7)_2BiCl$

② $(\alpha\text{-}C_{10}H_7)_3Bi + ICl \xrightarrow[\text{ether}-CHCl_3]{}$

③ Yellow solids. [168°].
　Decomp. at 240°.
⑥ JCS **1915**, 16 ; **1921**, 913 ; **1922**, 256.

BiC₂₀H₁₅N₂
① Triphenylbismuth dicyanide
　(C₆H₅)₃Bi(CN)₂
② (C₆H₅)₃BiCl₂ + 2 AgCN $\xrightarrow[\text{ether}]{}$
③ Decomp. at 150°.
　Crystalline solids. [129°].
　Sol. in CHCl₃ ; insol. in ether.
④ + 2 HCl $\longrightarrow$ (C₆H₅)₃BiCl₂ + 2 HCN
⑥ JCS **1927**, 209.

BiC₂₂H₁₇
① Diphenyl-α-naphthylbismuth
　(C₆H₅)₂Bi(α-C₁₀H₇)
② α-C₁₀H₇MgBr + (C₆H₅)₂BiBr $\longrightarrow$
　(C₆H₅)₂BiNa + α-C₁₀H₇I $\xrightarrow[\text{liq. NH₃}]{}$
③ White solid. [119°].
　Sol. in CHCl₃, C₆H₆ and toluene ; less
　sol. in alc. and ether.
④ + 3 HCl $\xrightarrow{\text{warm}}$ C₆H₆ + BiCl₃
　+Br₂ $\longrightarrow$ (C₆H₅)₂BiBr + α-C₁₀H₇Br
　+ IBr $\longrightarrow$ (C₆H₅)₂BiBr + α-C₁₀H₇I
⑥ JCS **105**, 2210 (1914) ; **107**, 16 (1915).
　JACS **63**, 212 (1941).

BiC₂₂H₂₁O₄
① Triphenylbismuth diacetate
　(C₆H₅)₃Bi(OOCCH₃)₂
② (C₆H₅)₃BiCO₃ + 2 CH₃COOH $\xrightarrow{\text{heat}}$
③ White powder. [162°].
　Sol. in glacial acetic acid, ethyl
　acetate, CHCl₃, xylene, benzene,
　acetone, CCl₄ and alc. ; insol. in
　H₂O and light petr.
⑥ JCS **117**, 762 (1920).

BiC₂₄H₂₀Br
① Tetraphenylbismuthonium bromide
　(C₆H₅)₄BiBr

② Ph₅Bi + Br₂ $\xrightarrow{-80°}$
③ Very unstable, decomp. at room
　temp.
　Colorless crystals.
⑥ Ann. **578**, 136 (1952).

BiC₃₀H₂₁
① Tri-α-naphthylbismuth
　(α-C₁₀H₇)₃Bi
② α-C₁₀H₇MgBr + BiBr₃ $\longrightarrow$
③ Colorless needles. [235°].
　Fairly sol. in CHCl₃, C₆H₆ and tolu-
　ene ; sparingly sol. in hot alcohol
　and almost insol. in ether and
　light petr. ether.
④ + 3 HCl $\longrightarrow$ BiCl₃ + α-C₁₀H₈
　　　　　　　 quantitatively
⑥ JCS **105**, 2210 (1914).

BiC₃₀H₂₁Br₂
① Tri-α-naphthylbismuth dibromide
　(α-C₁₀H₇)₃BiBr₂
② (α-C₁₀H₇)₃Bi + Br₂ $\xrightarrow[\text{in CHCl₃}]{}$
③ Decomp. at 100° when heated in
　sealed tube.
　Yellow crystals. [119~121° or 110°],
　depending on the rate of heating.
⑥ JCS **105**, 2210 (1914).

BiC₃₀H₂₅
① Pentaphenylbismuth
　(C₆H₅)₅Bi
② Ph₃BiCl₂ + PhLi $\xrightarrow[\text{ether}]{-75°}$
③ Violet crystals. [100~105° decomp.].
④ + Ph₃B $\longrightarrow$ [Ph₄Bi][Ph₄B]
⑥ Ann. **578**, 136 (1952).

10. Organic Compounds of Selenium, Tellurium, and Polonium

(Se, Te, Po)

10.1. Introduction

These three elements are classified as metalloids. Selenium is particularly nonmetallic, closely resembling sulfur. Polonium is a decay product of radon and is itself radioactive. Since its organic chemistry has hardly commenced in a practical sense, it will be omitted in this short description.

The industrial application of organic compounds of selenium and tellurium can be found in a number of patent literatures. Since dialkyl selenide, R_2Se, was found to be a more effective antioxidant for lubricating oil than dialkyl sulfide, R_2S, its practical uses have been extensively studied. It was found that selenium compounds do not form strongly acidic products when oxidized, as sulfur compounds form sulfuric acid as an oxidation products, and therefore selenium compounds form little gum or sludge. Many uses as antioxidants in place of sulfur compounds are claimed in a number of patents.

Alkyl selenols, $RSeH$, having higher alkyls, are claimed to be effective as lubricating oil detergents. Addition of alkyl selenols to the suspension copolymerization of butadiene is said to result in polymers with improved oil resistance and low temperature properties.

10.2. Nomenclature

The nomenclature which is shown in Table 10.1, has long been used in Chemical

Table 10.1.

General Formula	Nomenclature	General Formula	Nomenclature
$RSeH$	alkylselenol	$RTeH$	alkyltellurol
$RSeR$	dialkylselenide	$RTeR$	dialkyltelluride
$RSeX$	alkylselenohalide	$RTeX$	alkyltellurohalide
$RSeX_3$	alkylselenide trihalide	$RTeX_3$	alkyltelluride trihalide
R_2SeX_2	dialkylselenide dihalide	R_2TeX_2	dialkyltelluride dihalide
R_3SeX	trialklyselenonium halide	R_3TeX	trialkyltellurium halide
R_2SeO	dialkylselenoxide	R_2TeO	dialkyltelluroxide
R_2SeO_2	dialkylselenone	R_2TeO_2	dialkyltellurone
$RSeOH$	alkylselenic acid	$RTeOH$	alkyltelluric acid
$RSeO_2H$	alkylseleninic acid	R_2TeOH_2	dialkyltelluride dihydroxide
$RSeO_3H$	alkylselenonic acid	$RTeO_2H$	alkyltellurinic acid
⌷Se	selenophene	⌷Te	tellurophene
$RSeSeR$	dialkyldiselenide	$RTeTeR$	dialkylditelluride

Abstracts. Another systematic nomenclature is based on such parent substances as selenine (SeH_2), selenene (SeH_4), tellurine (TeH_2), and tellurene (TeH_4).

10.3. Methods of Synthesis

a. RMH Compounds. Alkyl selenol is often called selenomercaptan, and its synthesis is similar to that of mercaptans.

$$NaSeH + RX \longrightarrow RSeH + NaX$$

$$NaSeH + RSO_4H \longrightarrow RSeH + NaSO_4H$$

$$Se + RMgX \longrightarrow RSeMgX \overset{H^+}{\longrightarrow} RSeH$$

Alkylselenols are derived from other organoselenium compounds. The following reduction can be carried out, using sodium-alcohol or zinc-acetic acid.

$$Ar_2Se_2, ArSeO_2H, ArSeO_3H \overset{Reduction}{\longrightarrow} ArSeH$$

The synthesis of tellurol is not similar to that of mercaptans, and the following reactions have been used.

$$TeH_2 + RX + NaOC_2H_5 \longrightarrow RTeH + NaX + C_2H_5OH$$

$$Te_3Al_2 + 3 C_2H_5OH \longrightarrow 3 C_2H_5TeH + Al(OC_2H_5)_3$$

b. R₂M Compounds.

$$Se + RI + H_2O + NaOH + HCHO \cdot NaHSO_3 \longrightarrow SeR_2$$

This method gave a yield of 80% when R=methyl, and 50% when R=ethyl or propyl.

$$Se + RMgX \overset{H^+}{\longrightarrow} RSeMgX \overset{NaOH}{\longrightarrow} RSeH \overset{R'X}{\longrightarrow} RSeNa \overset{}{\longrightarrow} RSeR'$$

This method is suitable for the preparation of asymmetric dialkylselenides. These can also be prepared by the following exchange reaction of dialkyl selenide with alkyllithium.

$$RSeR + LiR' \longrightarrow RSeR' + LiR$$

Other synthetic reactions are

$$Na_2Se + 2 RX \longrightarrow R_2Se + 2 NaX$$

$$SeX_4 + 3 HgR_2 \longrightarrow 2 R_2Se + 3 HgX_2 + 2 RX$$

$$2 ArN_2X + Na_2Se \longrightarrow Ar_2Se + N_2 + 2 NaX$$

$$RSeX + R'Li \longrightarrow RSeR' + LiX$$

Dialkyl tellurides are prepared by similar methods. For example,

$$Te + 2 RX \longrightarrow R_2TeX_2 \overset{Na_2SO_3+Na_2CO_3}{\longrightarrow} R_2Te$$

$$Te + RX \overset{NaOH+H_2O}{\longrightarrow} R_2Te$$

$$TeX_2 + RMgX \longrightarrow R_2Te$$

$$Na_2Te + 2 ROSO_3Na \longrightarrow R_2Te + 2 Na_2SO_4$$

c. RMX Compounds. Aliphatic RMX compounds are prepared by the use of potassium selenocyanate.

$$KSeCN + RX \longrightarrow RSeCN + KX$$

Aromatic compounds are usually obtained by the diazonium salt method or from other arylselenium compounds.

$$KSeCN + ArN_2X \longrightarrow ArSeCN + KX$$

$$C_6H_5SeCN + Br_2 \longrightarrow ArSeBr + BrCN$$

$$C_6H_5SeH + Br_2 \longrightarrow C_6H_5SeBr + HBr$$

$$C_6H_5SeSeC_6H_5 + Br_2 \longrightarrow 2\,C_6H_5SeBr$$

d. *RMX₃ Compounds.*

$$RSeX + X_2 \longrightarrow RSeX_3$$

$$(R_2TeO)_x \xrightarrow{HI} RTeO_2H \xrightarrow{HI} RTeI_3$$

e. *R₂MX₂ Compounds.*

$$R_2M + X_2 \longrightarrow R_2MX_2$$

f. *R₃MX Compounds.*

$$R_2Se + R'X \longrightarrow R_2R'SeX \ (R,\ R'=\text{aliphatic or aromatic})$$

$$Se + 3\,RX \longrightarrow R_3SeX$$

$$(C_6H_5)_2SeCl_2 + C_6H_6 + AlCl_3 \longrightarrow (C_6H_5)_3SeCl + HCl$$

$$TeX_4 + 3\,ArMgX \longrightarrow Ar_3TeX + 3\,MgX_2$$

g. *R₂MO Compounds.*   The oxidation of dialkyl selenide to dialkyl selenoxide is conveniently carried out with hydrogen peroxide or peracetic acid, and the oxidation with chromate or permanganate ultimately leads to dialkylselenone.

$$R_2Se \xrightarrow{CrO_4^- \text{ or } MnO_4^-} R_2SeO(+\,R_2SeO_2)$$

$$R_2SeX_2 + H_2O + AgO \ (\text{or NaOH}) \longrightarrow R_2SeO$$

The oxidation of dialkyl telluride is done by nitric acid in some instances.

h. *RMOH Compounds.*   These compounds can be prepared by the following scheme, but their instability to disproportionation led to little research.

$$RSeX + OH^- \longrightarrow RSeOH + X^-$$

i. *R₂MO₂ Compounds.*   The oxidation of diaryl selenide is carried out with strong oxidizing agents such as chromate or permanganate

$$Ar_2Se \xrightarrow{CrO_4^- \text{ or } MnO_4^-} Ar_2SeO_2$$

j. *RMO₂H Compounds.*

$$RSeBr_3 + 2\,H_2O \longrightarrow RSeO_2H + 3\,HBr$$

$$Ar_2Se + H_2O_2 \longrightarrow RSeO_2H + ArH$$

$$(R_2TeO)_n \xrightarrow{KI} R_3TeI + RTeO_2H$$

k. RMO₃H Compounds.

$$RSeX_3 + 3\,H_2O \longrightarrow RSeO_3H + 3\,HX$$

$$RSeO_2H \xrightarrow{\ MnN_4^-\ } RSeO_3H$$

l. Selenophene. Many selenophene derivatives are known. The corresponding tellurophene and its derivatives are not known.

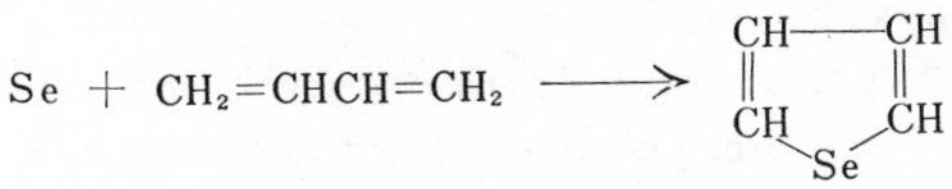

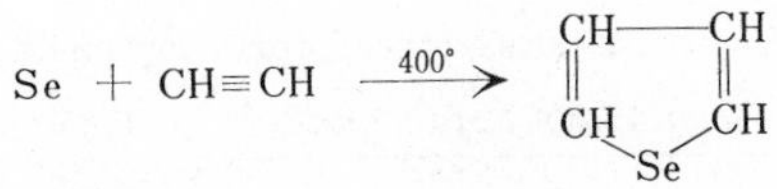

$$Se + CH_2{=}CHCH{=}CH_2 \longrightarrow$$

$$Se + CH{\equiv}CH \xrightarrow{\ 400°\ }$$

m. RMMR Compounds.

$$Na_2Se_2 + 2\,RX \longrightarrow RSeSeR + 2\,NaX$$

$$2\,RSeH + \frac{1}{2}O_2 \longrightarrow RSeSeR + H_2O$$

10.4. General Properties

10.4.1. Physical and Chemical Properties

Electronegativity of the group VI elements decreases from oxygen to sulfur, selenium, and tellurium, and their organic compounds differ from each other in their general properties as follows:

	O S Se Te
Heat stability	high ⟵ low
Heat stability of R₃MX	low ⟶ high
Ionic character of R₃MX	low ⟶ high
Basicity of R₃MOH	low ⟶ high
Heat stability of RMX	low ⟶ high
Heat stability of RMH	high ⟵ low

Volatile compounds have generally an unpleasant odor, as in the case of sulfur compounds. RMH is easily oxidized by air to R_2M_2.

R_2M compounds have lone electron pairs and therefore are likely to form addition compounds with electron acceptors. The formation of these adducts corresponds to the formation of onium and sulfonium compounds from oxygen and sulfur compounds, respectively. For example, alkyl halide reacts with R_2M compounds to give onium halide. Onium hydroxide, which forms on trestment of onium halide with silver oxide, is a strong base in aqueous solution.

$$R_2M + R'X \longrightarrow R_2R'MX$$

R_2M adds oxygen or halogen to yield R_2MO or R_2MX_2, respectively. It can be oxidized with the usual oxidizing agents.   RMX compounds also add halogen to form onium salt RMX_3.

Selenophene has an aromaticity as thiophene does, and is stable against refluxing with water, aqueous alkali, and hydrochloric acid.   It does not change on heating with methyl iodide and is not oxidized by aqueous potassium permanganate.   It decomposes, however, in nitric acid and in concentrated sulfuric acid.

10.4.2. Structures

Two types of R_2TeX_2 compounds, α and β forms, have long been known and identified as *cis* and *trans* isomers.   Colors and melting points of two isomers of dimethyl telluride halide are shown in Table 10.2.   However, these two forms turn out not to be *cis* and *trans* isomers;   the β form is considered to be ionic.

Table 10.2. *Colors and Melting Points* [°C] *of Dimethyl Telluride Halide.*

Isomer ＼ Halide	Cl	Br	I
α	Colorless [92°]	Yellow [92°]	Red [127°]
β	[134°]	Orange [142°]	Greenish black [no mp]

Structural analysis of Ph_2SeX_2 was carried out by the X-ray diffraction method and the compound was found to be bipyramidal, a coordination site being occupied by a lone electron pair (Fig. 10.1).

Fig. 10.1. *Structure of Ph_2SeX_2.*

REFERENCES

1) Nomenclature: T. W. Campbell, H. G. Walker, G. M. Coppinger, *Chem. Revs.*, **50**, 279~349 (1952).

2) E. G. Rochow, D. T. Hurd, R. N. Lewis, "The Chemistry of Organometallic Compounds", John Wiley (1957).

3) N. V. Sidgwick, "The Chemical Elements and Their Compounds", Vol. II, Oxford Univ. Press (1950).

4) C. Kajisaki, K. Sono, "Daiyukikagaku", Vol. 18 (Organometallic Compounds), Asakura, Tokyo (1957).

5) J. H. Harwood, "Industrial Applications of the Organometallic Compounds", Chapman & Hall (1963).

6) Houben-Weyl, "Methoden der Organischer Chemie", Bd. IX (Spezielle Chemische Methoden-Herstellung und Umwandlung von Schwefel-, Selen-, Tellur-Verbindungen), Georg Thieme Verlag (1655).

【Se】

SeCCl$_4$

① Trichloromethylselenide chloride
CCl$_3$SeCl

② CSe$_2$ + Cl$_2$ $\longrightarrow$

③ Colorless liq. (62°/23). n_D 1.5808(21°).
d 2.1140 (21°/21°).
Sol. in org. solvents.

⑥ JCS 1947, 1081.

SeCH$_2$

① Selenoformaldehyde
HCHSe

② SeH$_2$ + HCHO $\longrightarrow$

③ White crystals. [210°].

④ + (NO$_2$)$_2$C$_6$H$_3$NHNH$_2$ $\longrightarrow\!\!\!\times$

⑥ JCS 1938, 415.

SeCH$_2$Cl$_2$

① Monochloromethylselenide chloride
ClCH$_2$SeCl

② ClSeSeCl + CCl$_4$ $\longrightarrow$

③ Dark red liq. (52°/1.5),
Sol. in org. solvents ; insol. in H$_2$O.

④ $\overset{\text{heat}}{\longrightarrow}$ (ClCH$_2$)$_2$Se + SeCl$_4$

⑥ JCS 1950, 1371.

SeCH$_4$

① Methylselenol
CH$_3$SeH

② NaSeH + CH$_3$I $\longrightarrow$

CH$_3$SeSeCH$_3$ + Na $\overset{\text{liq. NH}_3}{\longrightarrow}$
quantitative

③ Colorless liq. (25.5°/760).
Sol. in org. solvents ; insol. in H$_2$O.

④ + Hg(CN)$_2$, AgNO$_3$
$\longrightarrow$ (CH$_3$Se)$_2$Hg, CH$_3$SeAg.
+ I$_2$ $\longrightarrow$ CH$_3$SeSeCH$_3$ + 2 HI

⑥ Atti. accad. Lincei 12, 234 (1930).
JCS 1953, 2839.

SeCH$_4$O$_2$

① Methylseleninic acid
CH$_3$SeO$_2$H

② CH$_3$SeSeCH$_3$ + 2 HNO$_3$ $\longrightarrow$ quant.

③ Crystals. [134° decomp.].
Sol. in polar solvents.

④ $\overset{\text{heat}}{\longrightarrow}$ HCHO + H$_2$O + SeO$_2$

⑥ Rec. trav. chim. 54, 532 (1935).   JOC
5, 587 (1940).

SeC$_2$H$_3$N

① Methyl selenocyanate
CH$_3$SeCN

② KSeCN + CH$_3$X $\longrightarrow$
(X=Br, Cl)

③ Colorless liq. (158°/760),
Sol. in org. solvents ; insol. in H$_2$O.

④ + H$_2$O $\longrightarrow$ CH$_3$SeSeCH$_3$ + CH$_3$SeOH
+ HCN + HCNO

⑥ Ber. 19, 1577 (1886).

SeC$_2$H$_4$

① Selenoacetoaldehyde
CH$_3$CHSe

② HSeMgBr + CH$_3$CHO $\longrightarrow$ 55%

③ [123°].

⑥ J. prakt. Chem. [2] 91, 124 (1915).

SeC$_2$H$_6$

① Dimethylselenide
(CH$_3$)$_2$Se

② Se + CH$_3$I $\longrightarrow$ 88%
P$_2$Se$_5$ + CH$_3$SO$_3$Na $\longrightarrow$ 29.9%

③ Colorless liq. (58.2°/760). n_D 1.4799
(14.6°). d 1.4077 (14.6°/4°).
Sol. in alc. and ether ; insol. in H$_2$O.

④ + H$_2$O$_2$ $\longrightarrow$ CH$_3$SeH + (CH$_3$)$_2$Se(OH)$_2$
+ (CH$_3$)$_2$SeO
+ PtCl$_4$$^{2-}$ $\longrightarrow$ [(CH$_3$)$_2$Se]$_2$PtCl$_2$

⑥ JCS 1942, 570.   Ann. 462, 186 (1928).
JCS 1934, 70.

SeC$_2$H$_6$O

① Dimethylselenoxide

(CH₃)₂SeO

② (CH₃)₂SeBr₂ + H₂O ⟶

③ White crystals. [127°].
Sol. in org. solvents.

⑥ JCS 1942, 572.

SeC₃H₆

① Selenoacetone
CH₃CSeCH₃

② SeH₂ + (CH₃)₂CO ⟶ 50%

③ Red liq. (120°/6~10).

④ + Cl₂ ⟶ SeCl₄

⑥ Ber. 60, 824 (1927).

SeC₃H₉I

① Trimethylselenonium iodide
(CH₃)₃SeI

② Se + CH₃I ⟶ 35%

③ Crystals. [150~151°].
Sol. in polar solvents.

⑥ JACS 77, 509 (1955). JCS 1946, 1128.
Ber. 7, 1278 (1874).

SeC₄H₄

① Selenophene

② CH≡CH + Se $\xrightarrow{400°}$ 15%
CH₂=CH−CH=CH₂ + Se ⟶

③ Colorless liq. (109.9~110.1°/752.1).
n_D 1.568 (15°). d 1.5232 (20°/20°).
Sol. in org. solvents ; insol. in H₂O.

④ ⟶×⟶ picrate

⑥ JCS 1928, 1741. BCSJ 11, 157 (1936).
Dokl. 96, 983 (1954) ; CA 49, 8907
(1955).

SeC₄H₈

① Methylethylselenoketone
(CH₃)(C₂H₅)C=Se

② SeH₂ + (CH₃)(C₂H₅)CO ⟶

③ Red liq.

④ + Cl₂ ⟶ SeCl₄

⑥ Ber. 60, 824 (1927).

SeC₄H₈Cl₂O

① Bis-β-chloroethylselenoxide
(ClCH₂CH₂)₂SeO

② (ClCH₂CH₂)₂SeCl₂ + H₂O ⟶

③ [88° decomp.].
Sol. in org. solvents.

④ + H₂O ⟶ (HOCH₂CH₂)₂SeO

⑥ Finska Kemistsamfundets Medd. 41,
13 (1932) ; CA 26, 5905 (1932).

SeC₄H₈Cl₄

① Bis-β-chloroethylselenide dichloride
(ClCH₂CH₂)₂SeCl₂

② Se₂Cl₂ + C₂H₄ ⟶ 96%

③ Colorless crystals. [122.5°].
Sol. in org. solvents and H₂O.

⑥ JCS 127, 1880 (1925). JACS 44, 395
(1922).

SeC₄H₁₀

① Diethylselenide
(C₂H₅)₂Se

② Se + C₂H₅I ⟶ 60~90%
P₂Se₅ + C₂H₅Br ⟶

③ Colorless liq. (108°/760). n_D 1.4768
(25°). d 1.2300 (20°/4°).
Insol. in H₂O.

⑥ JCS 1942, 570. Ber. 69, 1364 (1936).

SeC₄H₁₀S₂

① Bis(ethylthio)selenide
C₂H₅SSeSC₂H₅

② 4C₂H₅SH + SeOCl₂ ⟶ 51%

③ (94°/13). n_D 1.5791 (12.8°). d 1.4094
(13°/4°).

⑥ Atti. accad. Lincei [6] 9, 1022 (1929) ;
[6] 14, 28(1931) ; CA 24, 306(1930) ;
26, 1896 (1932).

SeC₅H₆

① 2-Methylselenophene

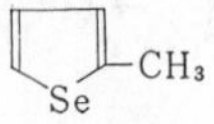

② CH₂=CHCH=CHCH₃ + Se ⟶ 26.5%

③ (131~132°/760). n_D 1.5534(20°). d 1.4242.

⑥ Dokl. **96**, 983 (1954); CA **49**, 8907 (1955).

SeC₅H₈

① 1-Ethylseleno-1-propyne
CH₃C≡CSeC₂H₅

② CH₃C≡CH + C₂H₅Br + Se $\xrightarrow{NaNH_2}$ 75%

③ (46°/11). n_D 1.5245 (20°).

⑥ Rec. trav. chim. **81**, 583 (1962).

SeC₆H₅Cl

① Phenylselenide chloride
C₆H₅SeCl

② C₆H₅SeSeC₆H₅ + 2 SO₂Cl₂ ⟶

③ Red crystals. (92°/5). [64~65°].

⑥ J. pharm. Soc. Japan **55**, 233 (1935). Ber. **66**, 714 (1933).

SeC₆H₅Cl₃

① Phenylselenide trichloride
C₆H₅SeCl₃

② C₆H₅SeCN + 2 Cl₂ ⟶
C₆H₅SeSeC₆H₅ + 3 SO₂Cl₂ ⟶

③ Colorless crystals. [133~134° decomp.].
Sol. in org. solvents.

④ + HI ⟶ C₆H₅SeSeC₆H₅ + HCl + I₂
+ H₂O ⟶ C₆H₅Se(OH)₃

⑥ Ber. **66**, 715 (1933); **72**, 586 (1939).

SeC₆H₅NO₃

① o-Nitrophenylselenic acid
NO₂C₆H₄SeOH

② NO₂C₆H₄SeO₂H + N₂H₄
⟶ 98.5~99.5%

③ Red needles. [164~165° decomp.].
Slightly sol. in org. solvents.

⑥ Bull. soc. chim. France **88**, 666 (1955). Ber. **68**, 1540 (1935).

SeC₆H₅N₃O₄

① Dinitrophenylselenamide
(NO₂)₂C₆H₃SeNH₂

② (NO₂)₂C₆H₃SeBr + NH₃ ⟶ 89%

③ Orange crystals. [140°].
Sol. in org. solvents.

⑥ Acta Chem. Scand. **8**, 1353 (1954).

SeC₆H₆

① Phenylselenol
C₆H₅SeH

② C₆H₅MgBr + Se ⟶
C₆H₅SeSeC₆H₅ + Na ⟶ 70%

③ Colorless liq. (57~59°/8, 183°/760).
d 1.4865 (15°/4°).
Sol. in org. solvents.

④ · + I₂ ⟶ C₆H₅SeSeC₆H₅ + 2 HI

⑥ JACS **50**, 1182 (1928). J. Pharm. Soc. Japan **56**, 600 (1936).

SeC₆H₆

① 2-Vinylselenophene

② β-(2-Selenienyl)acrylic acid
$\xrightarrow{2\text{-}C_{10}H_7NHPh}$ 40%

③ (95~95.5°/81. 69.5~70°/25). n_D 1.6115 (20°). d 1.4460 (20°).

⑥ Zhur. **28**, 3262 (1958). Gazz. chim. ital. **90**, 69 (1960); CA **53**, 14085 (1959); **55**, 7392 (1961).

SeC₆H₆O

① 2-Acetylselenophene

② + Ac₂O $\xrightarrow{ZnCl_2,SnCl_4 \text{ or } H_3PO_4}$ 31.2%

+ AcCl $\xrightarrow{SnCl_4}$ 42%

③ (105~106°/12). n_D 1.5920(20°). d 1.5444

(20°).

④

$$+ \text{alk. KMnO}_4 \longrightarrow \text{[structure]}-\text{COOH}$$

⑥ Uchenye Zapiski Kazau Univ. **113**,
No.8, 115 (1953). Referat. Zhur.
Khim. **1954** No.44652; CA **50**, 938
(1956). BCSJ **14**, 155 (1939).

SeC$_6$H$_6$O$_2$

① Phenylseleninic acid
C$_6$H$_5$Se(O)OH

② C$_6$H$_5$Se(OH)$_3$ $\xrightarrow{\text{heat}}$

③ Crystals. [170°].
Sol. in polar solvents.

⑥ Am. Chem. J. **41**, 336 (1909). Ber.
66, 716 (1933).

SeC$_6$H$_6$O$_3$

① Phenylselenonic acid
C$_6$H$_5$Se(O)$_2$OH

② C$_6$H$_5$SeSeC$_6$H$_5$ + H$_2$O $\longrightarrow$ 26.6%

③ White crystals. (180°/760 explode).
[142°].

⑥ Am. Chem. J. **41**, 329 (1909). Ber.
39, 2200 (1906).

SeC$_6$H$_8$O$_3$

① Phenylseleninic acid hydrate
C$_6$H$_5$Se(OH)$_3$

② C$_6$H$_5$SeSeC$_6$H$_5$ + H$_2$O$_2$ $\longrightarrow$ 84%
Se + Mg + C$_6$H$_5$Br $\longrightarrow$

③ White crystals. (130°/760 decomp.).
[122°].
Sol. in H$_2$O.

⑥ JACS **71**, 674 (1949); **73**, 1076 (1951).
Ber. **88**, 672 (1955).

SeC$_6$H$_{10}$O$_4$

① Biscarboxyethylselenide
Se(COOC$_2$H$_5$)$_2$

② HSeMgBr + Cl(CO)OC$_2$H$_5$
$\longrightarrow$ HSe(CO)OC$_2$H$_5$ $\longrightarrow$

③ (125~127°/760).
⑥ Gazz. chim. ital. **58**, 670 (1928).

SeC$_7$H$_4$N$_2$O$_2$S

① o-Nitrophenyl selenothiocyanate
NO$_2$C$_6$H$_4$SeSCN

② NO$_2$C$_6$H$_4$SeBr + KSCN $\longrightarrow$ 93%

③ Yellowish green crystals. [114°].
Sol. in org. solvents; insol. in H$_2$O.

⑥ Bull. soc. chim. France [5] **17**, 245
(1950). JACS **69**, 2236 (1947).

SeC$_7$H$_4$OS

① Benzoylene selenosulfide

② o-ClSeC$_6$H$_4$COCl + Na$_2$S $\longrightarrow$

③ Yellow crystals. [83~84°].

⑥ Ber. **57**, 1077 (1924).

SeC$_7$H$_5$N

① Phenyl selenocyanate
C$_6$H$_5$SeCN

③ Colorless liq. (127°/17).
Sol. in org. solvents; insol. in H$_2$O.

④ + H$_2$O $\longrightarrow$ C$_6$H$_5$SeSeC$_6$H$_5$
+ C$_6$H$_5$SeOH + HCN + HCNO

⑥ JCS **1928**, 1368. Ber. **65**, 815 (1932).

SeC$_7$H$_7$Cl

① Phenylmonochloromethylselenide
C$_6$H$_5$SeCH$_2$Cl]

② C$_6$H$_5$SeH + HCl + HCHO $\longrightarrow$

③ (63~65°/0.1).

④ + (CH$_3$)$_3$COK $\longrightarrow$ C$_6$H$_5$Se$-\bar{\text{C}}-$H

⑥ Tetrahedron Letters **1963**, 105.

SeC$_7$H$_8$

① Methylphenylselenide
C$_6$H$_5$SeCH$_3$

② PhSeH + (CH$_3$)$_2$SO$_4$ $\longrightarrow$ 80%
PhSeH + CH$_3$X $\longrightarrow$ 70%

③ Colorless liq. (202~203°/743.8, 100°/
10). n_D 1.6060(25°). d 1.3954(25°/4°).
Sol. in org. solvents; insol. in H₂O.
UV: Atti accad. Lincei **14**, 99 (1953).
⑥ JACS **71**, 4062 (1949).

SeC₈H₆N₂O₆

① 2, 4-Dinitrobenzeneselenyl acetate
$(NO_2)_2C_6H_3SeOCOCH_3$
② $(NO_2)_2C_6H_5SeBr + CH_3COOAg \longrightarrow$
③ Yellow crystals. [128~129°].
Sol. in H₂O and org. solvents.
⑥ JACS **73**, 2276 (1951).

SeC₈H₁₀

① Ethylphenylselenide
$C_6H_5SeC_2H_5$
② $C_6H_5SeH + C_2H_5Br \longrightarrow 75\%$
③ Colorless liq. (214~216°/748.4, 120°/8).
n_D 1.5825 (25°). d 1.3167 (25°/4°).
Sol. in org. solvents; insol. in H₂O.
UV: Atti. accad. Lincei **14**, 99(1953).
④ + KMnO₄ + HCl
$\longrightarrow (C_2H_5)(C_6H_5)SeCl_2$
⑥ JACS **50**, 1182 (1928).

SeC₁₂H₈

① Dibenzoselenophene

②

$+ Br_2 \longrightarrow 97\%$

③ White crystals. (136~139°/1.5~2.0).
[73°].
Sol. in org. solvents.
⑥ JACS **72**, 5753 (1950).

SeC₁₂H₉N₃O₄

① 2, 4-Dinitrobenzeneselenyl anilide
$(NO_2)_2C_6H_3SeNHC_6H_5$
② $(NO_2)_2C_6H_3SeBr + C_6H_5NH_2 \longrightarrow 72\%$
③ Red crystals. [144~146.5°].
Sol. in org. solvents.
⑥ JACS **73**, 2276 (1951).

SeC₁₂H₁₀

① Diphenylselenide
$(C_6H_5)_2Se$
② $SeCl_4 + C_6H_5N_2BF_4 \xrightarrow{Zn} 33\%$
$K_2Se_x + C_6H_5N_2Cl \longrightarrow 79~86\%$
③ Colorless liq. (299°/760. 136°/4). [3°].
d 1.3402 (20°).
Sol. in org. solvents.
④ + n-C₄H₉Li $\longrightarrow$ n-C₄H₉SeC₆H₅
+ C₆H₅Li
+ PdCl₂ $\longrightarrow$ 2 $(C_6H_5)_2Se \cdot PdCl_2$
⑥ Izv. OKhN **1960**, 1710; CA **55**, 8335
(1961). Org. Syn. **18**, 27 (1938).

SeC₁₂H₁₀Cl₂

① Diphenylselenide dichloride
$(C_6H_5)_2SeCl_2$
② $(C_6H_5)_2Se \xrightarrow{HNO_3-HCl} 85~87\%$
$SeCl_2 + C_6H_6 \longrightarrow$
③ Colorless needles. [185°].
Sol. in org. solvents.
④ $\xrightarrow{heat} (C_6H_5)_2Se + (C_6H_4Cl)_2Se + 2HCl$
⑥ Org. Syn. **18**, 30 (1938). JACS **50**,
1182 (1928).

SeC₁₂H₁₀O

① Diphenylselenoxide
$(C_6H_5)_2SeO$
② $(C_6H_5)_2SeBr_2 + H_2O \longrightarrow 82\%$
③ Crystals. (230°/760 decomp.). [114°].
Sol. in hot H₂O.
IR: JCS **1928**, 2444.
⑥ Ber. **26**, 2821 (1893).

SeC₁₂H₁₀O₂

① Diphenylselenone
   $(C_6H_5)_2SeO_2$

② $(C_6H_5)_2Se + CH_3COOH \longrightarrow$ 67.3%

③ White crystals. (350°/760 decomp.,
   270°/9.5). [155°].
   Slightly sol. in AcOH.

④ $+ 4HCl \longrightarrow (C_6H_5)_2SeCl_2 + Cl_2$
   $+ 2H_2O$
   $+ S \longrightarrow (C_6H_5)_2Se + SO_2$
   $+ 2PCl_3 \longrightarrow (C_6H_5)_2Se + 2OPCl_3$

⑥ J. prakt. Chem. [2] **131**, 370 (1931).
   JACS **68**, 2672 (1946).

SeC₁₂H₁₀S

① Phenylphenylthioselenide
   $C_6H_5SeSC_6H_5$

② $C_6H_5SeCN + C_6H_5SH \longrightarrow$

③ Yellow crystals. [57~57.7°].
   Sol. in arom. solvents.

⑥ Nippon Kagaku Zasshi **75**, 338 (1954).

SeC₁₂H₁₀S₂

① Bis(phenylthio)selenide
   $C_6H_5SSeSC_6H_5$

② $4C_6H_5SH + SeOCl_2 \longrightarrow$

③ (50~51°). d 1.593 (20°/4°).

⑥ Atti accad. Lincei [6] **11**, 579 (1930).
   CA **24**, 4771 (1930).

SeC₁₈H₁₅Cl

① Triphenylselenonium chloride
   $(C_6H_5)_3SeCl$

② $(C_6H_5)_2SeCl_2 + C_6H_6 \xrightarrow{AlCl_3}$ 67%

③ White crystals. [230° decomp.].
   Sol. in H₂O and CHCl₃; insol. in Et₂O.

⑥ JACS **51**, 3590 (1929); **72**, 4556 (1950).
   Org. Syn. Coll. Vol. II, 240 (1943).

SeC₁₉H₁₇Cl

① Diphenyl-p-tolylselenonium chloride
   $(C_6H_5)_2(p\text{-}CH_3C_6H_4)SeCl$

② $(C_6H_5)_2SeCl_2 + C_6H_5CH_3 \longrightarrow$

③ Brown liq.
   Sol. in polar solvents.

⑥ JACS **53**, 4432 (1931); **55**, 1500 (1933).

SeC₂₄H₅₀O₂

① Di-n-dodecylselenone
   $(n\text{-}C_{12}H_{25})_2SeO_2$

② $(n\text{-}C_{12}H_{25})_2Se$
   $+ (HOOC)C_6H_4COOOH \longrightarrow$

③ [105~106°].
   Slightly sol. in AcOH.

⑥ Ind. Eng. Chem. **41**, 946 (1949).

Se₂C₂H₆

① Dimethyldiselenide
   $CH_3SeSeCH_3$

② $K_2Se_2 + (CH_3)_2SO_4 \longrightarrow$

③ Orange liq. (155~157°/760, 57°/21).

⑥ Rec. trav. chim. **54**, 531 (1935). JCS
   1942, 573.

Se₂C₃H₆

① 1,2-Diselenolane

$$H_2C\!\!\underset{CH_2-Se}{\overset{CH_2-Se}{\Big\langle}}\Big|$$

② $Na_2Se_2 + BrCH_2CH_2CH_2Br \longrightarrow$

③ Colorless liq. (118~119°/779). n_D 1.5612
   (15°). d 1.525 (20°/4°).
   Sol. in org. solvents.

⑥ JCS **1930**, 1497.

Se₃C₄H₁₀

① Diethyltriselenide
   $C_2H_5SeSeSeC_2H_5$

② $C_2H_5SeH + SeOCl_2 \longrightarrow$ 10%
   $C_2H_5SeSeC_2H_5 \longrightarrow$ 6%

③ (100°/26). n_D 1.6092 (12.8°). d 1.7805
   (13°/4°).

⑥ Atti. accad. Lincei [6] **9**, 1021(1929);
   [6] **14**, 28 (1931); CA **24**, 306 (1930);
   26, 1896 (1932).

Se₂C₄H₁₀

① Diethyldiselenide
C₂H₅SeSeC₂H₅

② K₂Se₂ + (C₂H₅)₂SO₄ $\longrightarrow$ 75%

③ Orange liq. (85°/21).

⑥ Rec. trav. chim. **49**, 479 (1930).
JACS **74**, 4742 (1952). JCS **1942**,
573.

Se₂C₄H₁₀S

① Bis(ethylselenyl)sulfide
C₂H₅SeSSeC₂H₅

② C₂H₅SeH + SOCl₂ $\longrightarrow$ 39.4%

③ (98°/26). n_D 1.6024 (12.8°). d 1.7070
(13°/4°).

⑥ Atti accad. Lincei [6] **9**, 1022 (1929);
[6] **14**, 28 (1931); CA **24**, 306 (1930);
26, 1896 (1932).

Se₂C₅H₈

① 2,6-Diselena-spiro-[3.3]-heptane

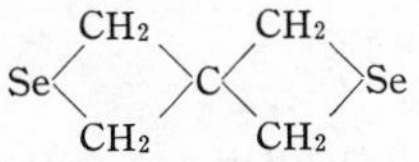

$$Se\underset{CH_2}{\overset{CH_2}{<}}C\underset{CH_2}{\overset{CH_2}{>}}Se$$

② C(CH₂Br)₄ + K₂Se₂ $\longrightarrow$ 75%

③ Red crystals. [67°].

⑥ Rec. trav. chim. **56**, 492 (1937).

Se₂C₁₂H₁₀

① Diphenyldiselenide
C₆H₅SeSeC₆H₅

② C₆H₅SeCN + KOH $\longrightarrow$ 87%

③ Yellow crystals. (203°/11). [62.5°].

⑥ Ber. **65**, 815 (1932). JCS **1926**, 1648.

Se₂C₁₂H₁₀S

① Bis(phenylselenyl)sulfide
C₆H₅SeSSeC₆H₅

② C₆H₅SeH + SOCl₂ $\longrightarrow$

③ [55°].

⑥ Atti accad. Lincei [6] **11**, 579 (1930);
CA **24**, 4771 (1930).

【Te】

TeCH₃I₃

① Methyltelluride triiodide
CH₃TeI₃

② CH₃−TeOH $\overset{KHSO_3}{\longrightarrow}$
     ‖
     O

$$CH_3-Te-O-TeCH_3 \overset{HI}{\longrightarrow}$$
     ‖   ‖
     O   O

③ Crystals resembled pure indigo.
[>100°, decomp.].
Slightly sol. in CHCl₃ and CH₃COOH;
sol. in acetone and ether.
UV: JCS **1929**, 2076.

④ + O₂ $\overset{heat}{\longrightarrow}$ iodine liberation

⑥ JCS **1929**, 560.

TeCH₄

① Methyltellurol,
Methyltelluromercaptane
CH₃TeH

② Al₂Te₃ + CH₃OH $\overset{300\sim350°,\ H_2}{\longrightarrow}$

③ Yellowish liq. (57.0°).
Strong disagreeable odor.

④ + O₂ $\longrightarrow$ telluride

⑥ CA **33**, 163 (1939).

TeC₂H₆

① Dimethyltelluride
(CH₃)₂Te

② (CH₃)₂TeI₂ + H₂O + Na₂SO₃ $\overset{Na_2CO_3}{\longrightarrow}$

CH₃OH + Al₂Te₃ $\overset{320\sim335°}{\longrightarrow}$

③ Pale yellow oil. (94°/770). d>1.
Dissolve slowly in H₂O.
Abominable and persistent odor.

④ + H₂O + O $\longrightarrow$

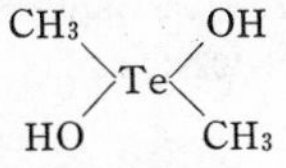

$$\underset{HO}{\overset{CH_3}{>}}Te\underset{CH_3}{\overset{OH}{<}}$$

α-form

+ O₂ $\longrightarrow$ (CH₃)₂TeO₂

$+ H_2O_2 \xrightarrow{\text{alkali}}$ CH_3 $>Te<$ OH / CH_3 OH

β-form

⑥ Ann. **93**, 233 (1855). JCS **117**, 889 (1920). CA **20**, 3273 (1926); **22**, 2150 (1928).

TeC$_2$H$_6$

① Ethyltellurol, Ethyltelluromercaptane C$_2$H$_5$TeH

② Al$_2$Te$_3$ + C$_2$H$_5$OH $\xrightarrow{300\sim350°,\ H_2}$

③ Yellowish liq. (90.0°). Strong disagreeable odor.

④ + O$_2$ $\longrightarrow$ telluride

⑥ CA **33**, 163 (1939).

TeC$_2$H$_6$Br$_2$

① α- or β-Dimethyltelluride dibromide

α-(*trans*) form CH_3 $>Te<$ Br / Br CH_3

β-(*cis*) form CH_3 $>Te<$ Br / CH_3 Br

② CH_3 α $>Te<$ OH / HO CH_3 $\xrightarrow{HBr}$ α-bromide

CH_3 β $>Te<$ OH / CH_3 OH $\xrightarrow{HBr}$ β-bromide

CH_3 $>Te<$ I / I CH_3 $\xrightarrow{AgNO_3}$ CH_3 $>Te<$ NO_3 / NO_3 CH_3

$\xrightarrow{KBr}$ α-bromide

③ α: Yellow leaf crystals. β: Orange leaf crystals. α: [92°]. β: [142°]. Recrystd. from MeOH or EtOH. UV: JCS **1920**, 86.

⑥ JCS **1929**, 2076.

TeC$_2$H$_6$Cl$_2$ (α)

① α-Dimethyltelluride dichloride

CH_3 $>Te<$ Cl / Cl CH_3

② α-dimethyltellurium dichloride $\xrightarrow{HCl}$

③ Colorless monoclinic crystals. [92°]. UV: JCS **117**, 86 (1920). Crystal structure: Acta Cryst. 11, 782 (1958).

TeC$_2$H$_6$Cl$_2$ (β)

① β-Dimethyltelluride dichloride

CH_3 $>Te<$ Cl / CH_3 Cl

② β-dimethyltelluride diiodide $\xrightarrow{HCl}$

③ Light tinged leaf crystals. [134°]. UV: JCS **117**, 86 (1920).

TeC$_2$H$_6$F$_2$

① Dimethyltelluride difluoride (CH$_3$)$_2$TeF$_2$

② (CH$_3$)$_2$TeI$_2$ + AgF$_2$ $\xrightarrow{\text{acetone}}$

③ [84°]. Easily sol. in H$_2$O, EtOH and acetone; insol. in petr. ether; stable in moist air; decomp. at 208°.

④ Aq. soln. is acidic to methyl red.

⑥ JCS **1946**, 1126.

TeC$_2$H$_6$I$_2$ (α)

① α-Dimethyltelluride diiodide

CH_3 $>Te<$ I / I CH_3

② Te + CH$_3$I $\xrightarrow{80°}$ 50%

③ Red monoclinic crystals. [127°]. d 3.34. Sol. in most org. solvents; insol. in H$_2$O. UV: JCS **1928**, 3179. Crystal structure: Acta Cryst. **3**, 319 (1950).

④ + aq. K₂CO₃ ⟶

$$\underset{I}{\overset{CH_3}{>}}Te\underset{H_3C\ CH_3}{\overset{O}{<}}Te\underset{I}{\overset{CH_3}{<}}$$

$$\overset{HNO_3}{\underset{KI}{\longrightarrow}}\ \underset{NO_3}{\overset{CH_3}{>}}Te\underset{CH_3}{\overset{NO_3}{<}}$$

$$\overset{NH_3}{\longrightarrow}\ (CH_3)_2TeI_2\cdot n(NH_3)\qquad n=1\sim6$$

TeC₂H₆I₂ (β)

① β-Dimethyltelluride diiodide

$$\underset{CH_3}{\overset{CH_3}{>}}Te\underset{I}{\overset{I}{<}}$$

② α-iodide $\overset{Ag_2O}{\longrightarrow}$ 2-Me₂Te(OH)₂ $\overset{evapd.}{\longrightarrow}$

β-Me₂Te(OH)₂ $\overset{HI}{\longrightarrow}$ β-iodide

③ Greenish black.
UV: JCS **1929**, 2076.

TeC₂H₆O₂

① Dimethyltellurone
(CH₃)₂TeO₂

② (CH₃)₂Te $\overset{O_2\ or\ peroxide}{\longrightarrow}$

α-(CH₃)₂Te(OH)₂ $\overset{H_2O_2}{\longrightarrow}$

③ White amorph. powder.
Insol. in all solvents; peroxide-like perperties; explosive.

④ Oxidizing properties.
+ HX ⟶ X₂
+ KMnO₄ ⟶ decolorized

⑥ JCS 117, 889 (1920).

TeC₂H₈O₂

① α-Dimethyltelluride dihydroxide
(α-base)

$$\underset{HO}{\overset{CH_3}{>}}Te\underset{CH_3}{\overset{OH}{<}}$$

② α-(CH₃)₂TeI₂ $\underset{HI}{\overset{Ag_2O}{\rightleftharpoons}}$

③ Sol. in H₂O.

④ Weak base.

+ AgNO₃ ⟶ α-(CH₃)₂Te(NO₃)₂

$\overset{heat}{\longrightarrow}$ HOTe(CH₃)₂OTe(CH₃)₂OH ⟶

$$(CH_3)_2Te\underset{O}{\overset{O}{<}\ >}Te(CH_3)_2$$

⟶ (CH₃)₃TeOTe(O)CH₃ (β-base)

⑥ JCS 117, 86, 889 (1920). Ber. **63**, 1590 (1930).

TeC₃H₆

① Telluroacetone

$$CH_3-\underset{\underset{Te}{\|}}{C}-CH_3$$

② TeH₂ + CH₃CCH₃ $\overset{HCl,\ 20\sim25°}{\longrightarrow}$
      ‖
      O

③ Liq. (55∼58°/10∼13). n_D 1.48825 (25°).
d 0.8578 (15°/4°).
Insol. in H₂O; slightly sol. in 95%
EtOH; easily sol. in ether.

⑥ Ber. **64**, 530 (1931).

TeC₃H₈

① n-Propyltellurol,
n-Propyltelluromercaptane
C₃H₇TeH

② TeH₂ + Br(CH₂)₂CH₃ $\overset{C_2H_5ONa,\ 50\sim60°}{\longrightarrow}$

③ Yellowish liq. (121.0°).
Strong disagreeable odor.

④ + O₂ ⟶ telluride

⑥ CA **33**, 163 (1939).

TeC₃H₉I

① Trimethyltellurium iodide
(CH₃)₃TeI

② (CH₃)₃TeO·Te(O)CH₃ (β-base)
$\overset{HI}{\longrightarrow}$ (CH₃)₃TeI + CH₃Te(O)OH

③ Colorless crystals. [240°, decomp.].
Easily sol. in H₂O.

④ (CH₃)₃TeI + CH₃TeI₃
⟶ (CH₃)₃TeI·CH₃TeI₃
      β-diiodide

⑥ JCS 117, 889 (1920); **1929**, 560.

TeC₄H₆O₄

① Tellurodiacetic acid

$$Te \Big\langle \begin{matrix} CH_2COOH \\ CH_2COOH \end{matrix}$$

② $Cl_2Te \Big\langle \begin{matrix} CH_2COOH \\ CH_2COOH \end{matrix}$ $\underset{Cl_2}{\overset{alkali}{\rightleftarrows}}$

③ Yellow needles. [140~141°].
   Sol. in H_2O, alc. and ether; insol. in
   C_6H_6, $CHCl_3$ and light petr. ether.
   Dimorphism.

④ Forms salts with NH_3, Na, Ag or Cu.
   Slowly oxidized in air.

⑥ JCS **127**, 531 (1925).

TeC₄H₁₀

① Diethyltelluride
   $(C_2H_5)_2Te$

② $(C_2H_5)_3Ba(SO_4)_3 + Na_2Te \xrightarrow{H_2O}$

③ Reddish-yellow liq. (137.5°). n_D 1.5182
   (15°). d 1.599 (15°/4°).
   Insol. in H_2O; sol. in alc.; unstable
   in air.
   Disagreeable penetrating odor.

④ + aq. $HNO_3 \longrightarrow (C_2H_5)_2Te(OH)NO_3$
   $H_2O_2 \xrightarrow{alkali} (C_2H_5)_2Te(OH)_2$

⑥ Ann. **79**, 223 (1851); **35**, 111 (1840).
   Ber. **21**, 2045 (1888).   Compt. rend.
   156, 1904 (1913).

TeC₅H₁₀

① Cyclotelluropentane

$Te(CH_2)_5$,

② $Al_2Te_3 + Br(CH_2)_5Br \xrightarrow{heat}$

$TeBr_2 \xrightarrow{alk.}$

③ Lemon-yellow oil. (82~83°/12, 44~

45°/1~2).
Oxidized rapidly in air.
Unpleasant odor.

④ + $H_2O_2 \xrightarrow{CH_3OH}$ H_2O

   + $Br_2 \longrightarrow$

⑥ JCS **1928**, 321.

TeC₆H₅Cl₃

① Phenyltelluride trichloride
   $(C_6H_5)TeCl_3$

② $C_6H_5HgCl + TeCl_4 \xrightarrow{dioxane}$

③ White plate crystals. [215~218°
   decomp.].
   Sparingly sol. in cold non-hydroxylic solvents; easily sol. in acetone
   and EtOH.

④ + $H_2O \xrightarrow{heat}$ acid

⑥ Research **4**, 177 (1951).

TeC₆H₆O₂

① Phenyltellurinic acid

$$C_6H_5Te \Big\langle \begin{matrix} O \\ OH \end{matrix}$$

② $(C_6H_5)_2Te_2 + HNO_3$
   $\longrightarrow C_6H_5Te(O)NO_3 \xrightarrow{KOH}$

③ White powder. [210~211°].
   Insol. in usual org. solvents; sol. in
   acid and base.

⑥ Ber. **48**, 1345 (1915).

TeC₇H₈

① Methylphenyltelluride
   $CH_3TeC_6H_5$

② $Te + I_2 + CH_3I + C_6H_5I + Mg$
   $\xrightarrow{ether\ 3hrs.} 40\%$

③ Yellow oil. (118~122°/22).

④ + HgX₂ ⟶ (CH₃)(C₆H₅)TeHgX₂

X=I, Cl, Br.

⑥ JCS **1939**, 589.

TeC₈H₆S₂

① Di-2-thienyltelluride

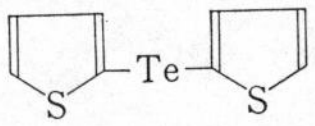

② 4 (thienyl)MgBr + TeCl₂ ⟶

$\xrightarrow{ZnCl_2, 80°C}$

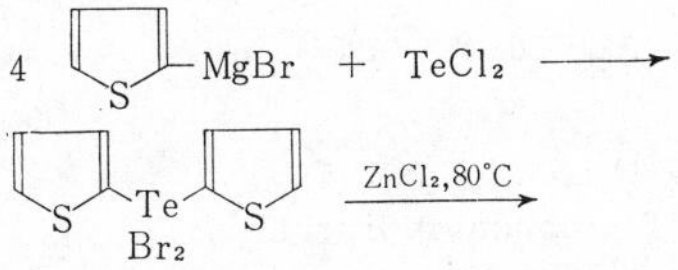

③ Colorless crystals. [50.5°].
Easily sol. in ether, C₆H₆, CHCl₃
and petr. ether ; decomp. at 220°.

④ + CH₃I ⟶

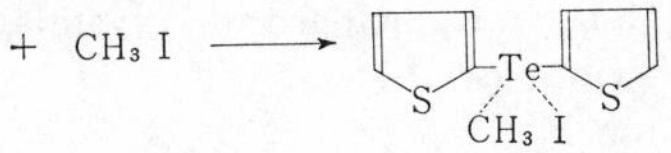

+ H₂O₂ ⟶ white precipitate

+ AgNO₃ $\xrightarrow{alcohol}$ white precipitate

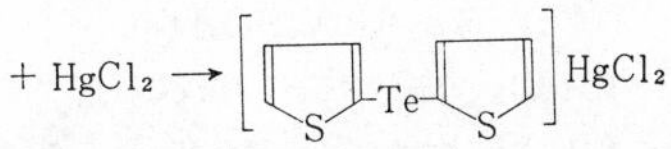

+ HgCl₂ ⟶

⑥ Ber. **65**, 777 (1932) ; **62**, 1710 (1929).

TeC₁₂H₈S

① Thiophenoxytellurine

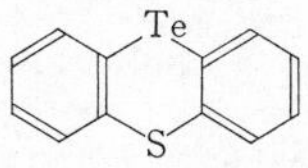

② $\xrightarrow{heat}$

42%

$\xrightarrow{Na_2S \cdot 9H_2O}$ 96%

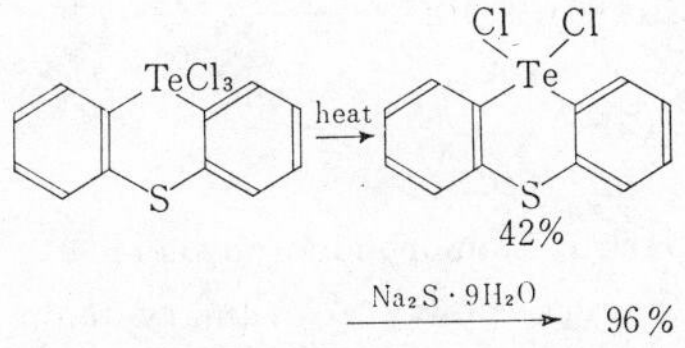

③ Pale yellow needles. [122~123.5°].
⑥ Tetrahedron **11**, 15 (1960).

TeC₁₂H₁₀

① Diphenyltelluride
(C₆H₅)₂Te

② (C₆H₅)₂Hg + 2 Te $\xrightarrow[4\sim5\,hrs.]{220\sim230°}$ 70%

2 C₆H₅MgBr + TeBr₂
$\xrightarrow[reflux\ 2\sim3\,hrs.]{ether}$ 60%

③ Light yellow liq. (145~6°/3.5, 174°/10,
182°/14). [4.2°]. n_D 1.6911 (15°).
d 1.5741 (0°/4°), 1.5558 (15.2°/4°).

④ + 65% HNO₃ ⟶ C₆H₅Te(=O)(NO₃)

+ Br₂ ⟶ (C₆H₅)₂TeBr₂

⑥ Ber. **27**, 1768 (1894) ; **48**, 1345 (1915) ;
34, 570 (1901). Compt. rend. **156**, 1904
(1913).

TeC₁₂H₁₀Cl₂

① Diphenyltelluride dichloride
(C₆H₅)₂TeCl₂

② (C₆H₅)₂Te + HCl $\xrightarrow{ether}$ quantitative
C₆H₅MgBr + TeCl₄
$\xrightarrow{ether, SO_2Cl_2}$ 88.3~91.7%

③ Colorless crystals. [160~611°, 162~
163°].
Easily sol. in CHCl₃ and CH₃OH ;
slightly sol. in C₆H₅ and ligroin.

④ + H₂O ⟶ (C₆H₅)₂Te(OH)(Cl)

[233~235°].

+ NaOH, NH₃, or Ag₂O ⟶
(C₆H₅)₂Te(OH)₂ $\xrightarrow{-H_2O}$ (C₆H₅)₂TeO

⑥ Ann. **391**, 326 (1912). Ber. **89**, 1270
(1956).

TeC₁₂H₁₀O

① Diphenyltelluroxide
(C₆H₅)₂TeO

② $(C_6H_5)_2TeBr_2$ $\xrightarrow{\text{aq. Na}_2\text{CO}_3,\ 50°}$ 90%

③ Colorless crystals. [>185°].

④ $+ HNO_3 \longrightarrow (C_6H_5)_2Te\diagdown\diagup\begin{matrix}NO_3\\NO_3\end{matrix}$

[160°]

⑥ Ber. **27**, 1768 (1894) ; **49**, 1082.

TeC₁₂H₁₂O₂

① Diphenyltelluride dihydroxide
$(C_6H_5)_2Te(OH)_2$

② $(C_6H_5)_2TeO \xrightarrow{\text{H}_2\text{O}}$

$(C_6H_5)_2TeCl_2 \xrightarrow{\text{alkali}}$

③ [192~193°].

⑥ Ann. **391**, 326 (1912).

TeC₁₃H₁₃I

① Methyldiphenyltellurium iodide
$(CH_3)(C_6H_5)_2TeI$

② $(C_6H_5)_2Te + CH_3I \longrightarrow$ quantitative

③ Colorless crystals. [123~124 decomp.].

Sol. in CHCl₃; insol. in ether.

④ $\xrightarrow{\text{AgBr}} (CH_3)(C_6H_5)_2TeBr$ [137~138°]

$\xrightarrow{\text{AgNO}_3} (CH_3)(C_6H_5)_2TeNO_3$

[168~169°]

⑥ Ann. **399**, 262 (1913).

TeC₁₈H₁₆I

① Triphenyltellurium iodide
$(C_6H_5)_3TeI$

② $C_6H_5MgBr + TeCl_4 \xrightarrow{\text{ether}} (C_6H_5)_3TeBr$

$\xrightarrow{\text{KI}}$ 7~11%

③ Colorless needles. [247~249°].

Sol. in CHCl₃; sparingly sol. in alc. ;
insol. in C₆H₅, ligroin and ether.

⑥ Ber. **44**, 2287 (1911).   Compt. rend.
151, 611 (1910).

TeC₂₀H₁₄

① Di-α-naphthyltelluride

$(C_{10}H_7)_2Te$

② $\alpha\text{-}(C_{10}H_7)_2TeBr_2 \xrightarrow{\text{Na}_2\text{SO}_3}$ 62%

$\alpha\text{-}(C_{10}H_7)_2Hg + 2\ Te$

$\xrightarrow[\text{190~198°,\ 8 hrs}]{}$ 53%

③ Brownish yellow leaf crystals.
[126.5°].

Sol. in ether and alc.

④ $+ Br_2 \longrightarrow (C_{10}H_7)_2TeBr_2$

$+ Cl_2 \longrightarrow (C_{10}H_7)_2TeCl_2$

⑥ JACS **30**, 831 (1908).

TeC₂₄H₂₀

① Tetraphenyltelluride
$(C_6H_5)_4Te$

② $(C_6H_5)_3TeCl + C_6H_5Li \xrightarrow{\text{ether}}$ 33.6%

$(C_6H_5)_2TeCl_2 + C_6H_5Li \longrightarrow$ 51.8%

③ Monoclinic holohedral crystals.
[104~106° decomp.].

④ $\xrightarrow{\text{H}_2\text{O}} (C_6H_5)_3TeOH$

$\xrightarrow{\text{KBr}} (C_6H_5)_3TeBr$

$+ B(C_6H_5)_3 \xrightarrow{\text{ether}}$

$[(C_6H_5)_3Te]^+[B(C_6H_5)_4]^-$

$+ CH_2Cl_2 \longrightarrow (C_6H_5)_3TeCl$

$+ C_6H_5Li \rightleftharpoons [(C_6H_5)_5Te]Li$

⑥ Ann. **577**, 39 (1952).

Te₂CH₂

① Ditelluromethane

$CH_2\diagdown\diagup\begin{matrix}Te\\\|\\Te\end{matrix}$

② $Cl_3TeCH_2COOH \xrightarrow{\text{TeCl}_4}$

$CH_2\diagup\diagdown\begin{matrix}TeCl_3\\TeCl_3\end{matrix} \xrightarrow{\text{alkali}}$

③ Dark red amorphous powder.

Changes slowly at ordinary temp. ;
explodes at high temp. in air ;
insol. in H₂O or org. solvents.

④ + Cl$_2$ $\longrightarrow$ CH$_2$$\Big\langle$ $\begin{matrix} TeCl_3 \\ TeCl_3 \end{matrix}$

$\xrightarrow{\text{heat}}$ red or black materials
(CH$_2$Te$_2$)$_x$

⑥ JCS **127**, 531 (1925).

(TeCH$_2$)$_n$

① Poly(telluroformaldehyde),
Polymethylenetelluride
(CH$_2$Te)$_n$

② CH$_2$N$_2$ + Te $\xrightarrow{500°}$

③ Red solid. (Very low vapour pressure).
Insol. in org. solvents.

⑥ JACS **56**, 2381 (1934).   JCS **127**, 531
(1925).

Te$_2$C$_{12}$H$_{10}$

① Diphenylditelluride
(C$_6$H$_5$)$_2$Te$_2$

② (C$_6$H$_5$)$_2$Te + Te $\xrightarrow{\text{pyrolysis}}$
C$_6$H$_5$MgX + TeX$_2$ $\longrightarrow$
C$_6$H$_5$TeCl$_3$ $\xrightarrow{\text{alkali}}$

③ Bright orange fibrous needles. [66~
67°].
Easily sol. in acetone, CHCl$_3$ and
CCl$_4$; moderately sol. in ether;

sparingly sol. in EtOH.
UV: Research. **4**, 177 (1951).

④ + X$_2$ $\longrightarrow$ C$_6$H$_5$TeX$_3$ (X=Cl, Br, I)
+ CH$_3$I $\longrightarrow$ (CH$_3$)$_2$C$_6$H$_5$TeI
+ C$_6$H$_5$(CH$_3$)TeI$_2$
$\xrightarrow{\text{pyrolysis}}$ (C$_6$H$_5$)$_2$Te + Te
$\rightleftharpoons$ C$_6$H$_5$Te. (in soln.)

+ HNO$_3$ $\longrightarrow$ C$_6$H$_5$Te$\Big\langle$ $\begin{matrix} O \\ NO_3 \end{matrix}$

⑥ Ber. **48**, 1345 (1915).

【Po】

PoCO

① Poloniumcarbonyl
Po(CO)

③ Colorless gas.

⑥ Kaufman 1508.

PoC$_2$H$_6$

① Dimethylpolonium
(CH$_3$)$_2$Po

⑥ CA **29**, 3595 (1935).

PoC$_{14}$H$_{14}$

① Dibenzylpolonium
(C$_6$H$_5$CH$_2$)$_2$Po

③ Crystals.

⑥ CA **29**, 3595 (1935).

11. Organic Compounds of Transition Elements (Part 1)

(Cu, Ag, Au)

11.1. Compounds of Univalent Metals

There are three kinds of organometallic compounds. The first is alkyl- and aryl-metals having metel-carbon σ bonds, the second is complex compounds of ethylene and other unsaturated compounds, and the third is salt-like acetylides.

Alkyl- and aryl-metals are generally unstable and their properties are not fully understood. Their stability decreases in the order

$$Cu > Ag > Au$$
$$Aryl > Alkyl$$

Only aryl compounds of copper and silver are isolated in pure states.

Olefins or carbon monoxide form complex compounds. The complexes with Cu (I) and Ag(I) are known to exist only in solutions, and haver neve been isolated. The complex with Au(I) is also known in solution, and is isolated as a complex of the $RAuPR'_3$ type.

Acetylides are known for all the univalent metals, and are highly explosive.

11.2. Compounds of Multivalent Metals

Organic compounds of Cu(II) and Ag(II) are not known, but those of Au(III) were discovered in 1907. Three types of compounds, R_3Au, R_2AuX, and $RAuX_2$, are known and are most stable when complexed with a strong electron donor.

11.3. Uses

Organic compounds of group Ib metals are important as reaction intermediates. Methylcopper, CH_3Cu, was found during the study of the direct synthesis of methylchlorosilanes, which are the starting materials for silicone resins. It has a short lifetime, but is nevertheless important since it is a key intermediate in copper catalysis.

Olefin complexes of copper and silver are also unstable, and are considered to play important roles as intermediates in metal-catalyzed olefin reactions.

11.4. Methods of Synthesis

11.4.1. Alkyl and Aryl Compounds

$$CuX + RMgX \longrightarrow CuR + MgX_2$$
$$CuX + RLi \longrightarrow CuR + LiX$$

When cuprous iodide is allowed to react with methyllithium in ether at $-15°C$, methylcopper forms as a yellow precipitate. It decomposes on warming to copper, methane, and ethane. The same methylcopper is obtained by the reaction of cupric nitrate and tetramethyllead as shown in the equations:

$$Cu^{2+} + Me_4Pb \longrightarrow Me_3Pb^+ + Cu^+ + Me$$

$$Cu^+ + Me_4Pb \longrightarrow Me_3Pb^+ + CuMe$$

Methylcopper is known to form in the reaction of methyl chloride and copper at $350°C$. Its formation was recognized by the movement of a copper film in a stream of methyl chloride, and its half life at $250°C$ was estimated to be 0.002 sec.

Silver nitrate has most frequently been used in the preparation of silver compounds.

$$AgNO_3 + Me_4Pb \xrightarrow[-14 \text{ to } -60°]{\text{in alcohol}} MeAg + Me_3PbNO_3$$

When silver nitrate is used in excess in an alcoholic solution in its reaction with tetramethyllead, there occurs the precipitation of $(MeAg)_2AgNO_3$. Alkyl compounds of tin and bismuth can be used as alkylating agents in place of tetramethyllead. Compounds of Au(I) are usually obtained as complexes with electron donors. Compounds of Au(III) are isolated.

$$AuX + RMgX + R'_3P \longrightarrow RAu \cdot PR'_3$$

$$AuX_3 + 3\,MeLi \xrightarrow[\text{in ether}]{-65°} Me_3Au \xrightarrow{-40°} Au + C_2H_6$$

$$AuCl_3 \cdot Py + MeMgI \xrightarrow{\text{in pyridine}} (Me_2AuI)_2 \quad [\text{mp } 78.5°]$$

11.4.2. Olefin Complexes

Crystals of cuprous chloride absorb ethylene under high pressure to form a complex of $1:1$ composition.

$$Cu_2Cl_2 + C_2H_4 \xrightarrow{\text{high pressure}} C_2H_4 \cdot CuCl$$

The formation of 1:1 complexes of cuprous chloride in aqueous solutions is known with many olefins. Similar complexes of silver are generally less stable than the corresponding copper complexes.

Silver perchlorate forms solid complexes with olefins. For example, when cyclohexene is brought into contact with silver perchlorate, an exothermic reaction takes place which yields a white powdery complex.

11.4.3. Acetylides

When acetylene is passed through an aqueous ammoniacal solution of cuprous chloride or silver nitrate, there forms acetylide as a red-brown (Cu_2C_2) or colorless (Ag_2C_2) precipitate, respectively. When the reaction of potassium acetylide (KC_2H) with cuprous iodide is carried out at low temperature in liquid ammonia, it results in the formation of an orange acetylide (CuC_2H). This compounds is fairly unstable and decomposes above $-45°C$ to Cu_2C_2.

$$CuI + KC_2H \xrightarrow{\text{in NH}_3, \ -78°} CuC_2H \xrightarrow{-45°} Cu_2C_2 + C_2H_2$$

11.5. General Properties

11.5.1. Physical and Chemical Properties

When dried in air at room temperature, methylcopper explodes violently. Ethylcopper is more unstable and cannot be isolated. Phenylcopper, on the other hand, is fairly stable, and decomposes slowly at room temperature and violently at 80°C.

Methylcopper combines with one mole of methyllithium to form a colorless complex compound, which is insoluble in ether and shows a positive Gilman test. It reacts with benzoyl chloride to yield a ketone, and adds to the $C=C-C=O$ system at the 1,4-position.

Stability of organosilver compounds varies widely depending on the nature of the organic group. Phenylsilver is the most stable, decomposing at $-18°$ into silver and biphenyl.

The complex $C_2H_4 \cdot CuCl$, which is obtained from solid cuprous chloride and ethylene gas under high pressure, decomposes slowly at $25°$ and rapidly at $100°$. The complex with butadiene is a little less stable. Olefin complexes of silver perchlorate or of silver nitrate decompose on addition of water.

It is well known that silver perchlorate is soluble in aromatic hydrocarbons; this is due to the formation of complexes of silver percholorate with the aromatic rings.

Copper acetylide, $RC\equiv CCu(I)$, is an important intermediate in the oxidative coupling reactions, where conjugated diynes are obtained from alkyl acetylenes, $RC\equiv CH$.

11.5.2. Structures

The structure of methylcopper has not been clarified, but there is some data on its infrared spectra.

Cyclopentadienylcopper triethylphosphine complex, $C_5H_5CuPEt_3$, forms white needles and is one of the most stable organocopper compounds. It reacts with ferrous chloride to yield ferrocene and decomposes in dilute acid to give cyclopentadiene. These facts, along with spectral data, suggests a δ-bond between the copper and carbon atoms.

The silver-carbon bond in silver-olefin complexes is similar to those in olefin π-complexes of palladium and platinum. But in the former, the $5s$ orbital of silver overlaps with the π-bonding orbital of the olefin and there is a back coordination of silver d-orbital to the π-antibonding orbital of the olefin.

In crystals of the benzene-silver perchlorate complex, the benzene ring and the silver atoms alternately coordinate with each other to form linear arrangement.

Silver atoms are not situated symmetrically above and below the benzene ring, and the benzene ring is distorted.

In crystals of dimethylacetylene-cuprous chloride complex, the unit $(MeC\equiv CMe \cdot CuCl)_4$ forms a molecule, the copper and chlorine atoms forming an eight-membered ring.

In cuprous acetylides of monoalkylacetylene or monoarylacetylene, the copper atom is coordinated by a triple bond through an *sp* hybrid orbital of copper, and this coordination is considered to be the main reason for its insolubility.

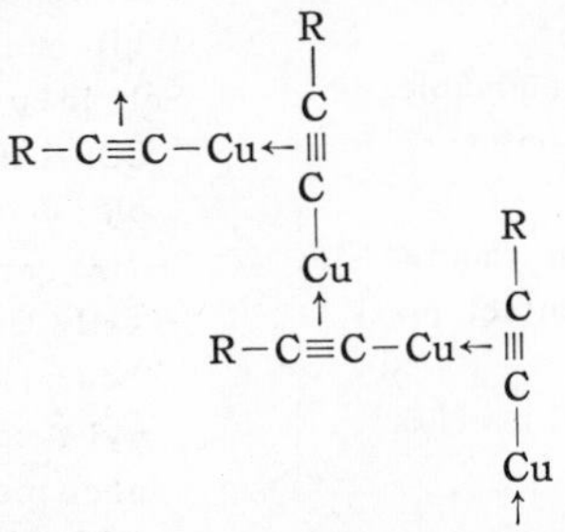

$$
\begin{array}{c}
R \\
| \\
C \\
R-C\equiv C-Cu\leftarrow ||| \\
C \\
| \\
Cu \\
\uparrow
\end{array}
\qquad
\begin{array}{c}
R \\
| \\
C \\
R-C\equiv C-Cu\leftarrow ||| \\
C \\
| \\
Cu \\
\uparrow
\end{array}
$$

Dimethyliodogold, Me$_2$AuI, forms crystals which melt at 78.5°. It dimerizes in benzene solution, the gold atom being four-coordinated.

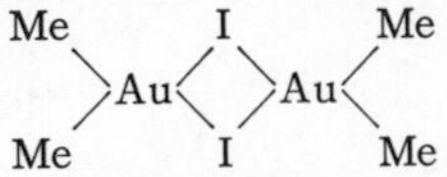

$$
\begin{array}{ccccc}
Me & & I & & Me \\
& \diagdown & & \diagdown & \\
& Au & & Au & \\
& \diagup & & \diagup & \\
Me & & I & & Me
\end{array}
$$

Di-*n*-propylcyanogold, $(n\text{-Pr})_2$AuCN, is tetrameric, the gold atom again being stabilized by four-coordination.

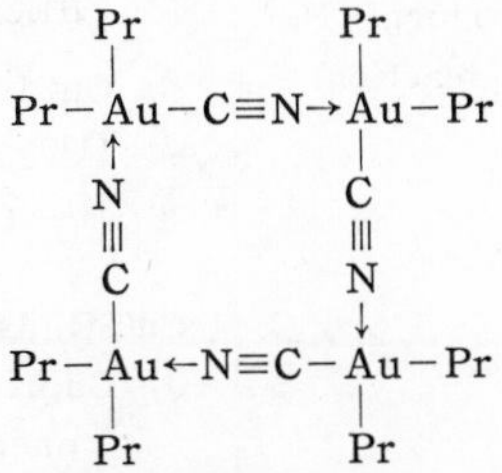

$$
\begin{array}{cc}
Pr & Pr \\
| & | \\
Pr-Au-C\equiv N\rightarrow Au-Pr \\
\uparrow & | \\
N & C \\
||| & ||| \\
C & N \\
| & \downarrow \\
Pr-Au\leftarrow N\equiv C-Au-Pr \\
| & | \\
Pr & Pr
\end{array}
$$

REFERENCES

1) N. V. Sidgwick, "The Chemical Elements and Their Compounds", Vol. I, Oxford Univ. Press (1952).
2) G. E. Coates, "Organometallic Compounds", John Wiley (1960).
3) H. G. Rochow, D. T. Hurd, R. N. Lewis, "The Chemistry of Organometallic Compounds", John Wiley (1957).
4) M. Kumada, "Daiyukikagaku", Vol. 18 (Organometallic Compounds), Asakura, Tokyo (1957).
5) J. H. Harwood, "Industrial Applications of the Organometallic Compounds", Chapman & Hall (1963).

【Cu】

CuCH₃

① Methylcopper
   CH₃Cu

② CuI + CH₃Li $\xrightarrow{-15°}$

   CuNO₃ + (CH₃)₄Pb $\xrightarrow{-70\sim-20°}$

③ Yellow solid
   Sol. in ether. Spont. inflammable.
   Explode in air at room temp.

④ $\longrightarrow$ CH₃· + Cu

⑤ Transient intermediate in the reaction between Cu–Si contact mass and CH₃Cl.

⑥ JACS 67, 963(1945). JOC 17, 1630(1952).

CuC₃H₃ClN

① Cuprous chloride-acrylonitrile adduct
   CuCl·CH₂=CHCN

② CuCl + CH₂=CHCN $\xrightarrow{-78°}$

③ Crystals. (32.5°/22 decomp.).
   Stable in a sealed tube. Decomp. in air.

④ + ArN₂ $\longrightarrow$ Meerwein Product + N₂

⑤ Intermediate of Meerwein reaction.

⑥ Ber. 94, 1891 (1961).

CuC₃O₃

① Copper tricarbonyl
   Cu(CO)₃

② CO + Cu₂O $\longrightarrow$

③ Colorless crystals.
   Sublimes readily.

⑥ Nature 153, 24, 593 (1944).

CuC₆H₃K₂

① Patassium ethynylocuprate
   K₂[Cu(C₂H)₃]

② KC≡CH + Cu₂C₂ $\xrightarrow{\text{in NH}_3}$

   3KC≡CH + CuI $\longrightarrow$

③ Colorless crystals.

④ + CuI $\longrightarrow$ 3K[Cu(C₂H)₂] + KI
   + H₂O $\longrightarrow$ Cu₂C₂ + C₂H₂ + KOH

⑥ Ber. 89, 415 (1956). Z.anorg.allg. Chem. 292, 287 (1957).

CuC₆H₅

① Phenylcopper
   C₆H₅Cu

② C₆H₅MgI + CuI $\longrightarrow$ 86%

③ White solid. [80° decomp.].
   Sol. in pyridine; insol. in CHCl₃, CCl₄, C₆H₆ and C₂H₅Br. Very unstable; decomp. in air and in H₂O.

④ + H₂O $\longrightarrow$ C₆H₆ + Cu(OH)
   + C₆H₅COCl $\longrightarrow$ C₆H₅COC₆H₅
   + benzalacetophenone $\longrightarrow$ β-phenyl-γ-benzoyl-γ-benzhydrylbutyrophenone $\longrightarrow$ C₆H₅·C₆H₅ + Cu₂O
   + BrCH₂CH=CH₂ $\longrightarrow$ C₆H₅CH₂CH=CH₂
   + C₆H₅NCO $\longrightarrow$ C₆H₅CONHC₆H₅

⑥ Compt.rend. 177, 322 (1923). JOC 17, 1630 (1952).

CuC₆H₉

① 1–Hexynylcopper
   C₄H₉C≡CCu

② CuCl + C₄H₉C≡CH $\xrightarrow{\text{EtOH, H}_2\text{O, NH}_3}$

③ [140∼150°].

⑥ JOC 21, 180 (1956).

CuC₈H₁₁AsClO

① Cuprous chloride-methylmethoxyphenylarsine adduct
   C₆H₅(CH₃)As(OCH₃)·CuCl

② C₆H₅(CH₃)As(OCH₃) + Cu₂Cl₂ $\longrightarrow$

③ [70∼72°].

⑥ Zhur. 24, 2044 (1954); CA 49, 14663 (1955).

CuC₁₁H₁₇AsClO

① Cuprous chloride-butylphenylmethoxyarsine adduct
   C₆H₅(C₄H₉)As(OCH₃)·CuCl

② $C_6H_5(C_4H_9)As(OCH_3) + Cu_2Cl_2 \longrightarrow$

③ [40~41°].

⑥ Zhur **24**, 2044 (1954); CA **49**, 14663 (1955).

CuC₁₁H₂₀P

① Cyclopentadienylcopper-triethyl-
phosphine adduct
$C_5H_5Cu \cdot P(C_2H_5)_3$

② $C_5H_6 + Cu_2O + (C_2H_5)_3P \longrightarrow 60\%$

③ White needles (60°/0.001 sublimes).
[127~128°].
Sol. in petr. ether, C_6H_6 and ether;
insol. in H_2O. Stable to H_2O.
Decomp. in air and $CHCl_3$.

④ $+ H^+ \longrightarrow C_5H_6$
$+ CS_2 \longrightarrow$
$+ FeCl_2$ in THF $\longrightarrow$ ferrocene

⑥ JINC **2**, 32 (1956).

Cu₂C₂H₂Cl₂

① Bis(chlorocopper)acetylene
$C_2H_2(CuCl)_2$

② $C_2H_2 + 2CuCl \longrightarrow$

③ Colorless crystals. (25°/434).

⑥ Acta Chem. Scand. **8**, 533 (1954).

Cu₂C₇H₈Br₂

① Norbornadiene-di(cuprous bromide)

$BrCu\text{----}\!/\!\!\!\!/\text{----}CuBr$

② $C_7H_8 + 2CuBr \xrightarrow{\text{in EtOH}} 29\%$

③ White crystals.
Insol. in org. solvents. Decomp. in air.

④ in vacuo $\longrightarrow C_7H_8 + CuBr$
$+ H_2O \longrightarrow C_7H_8 + CuO$

⑥ JCS **1959**, 3178.

Cu₃C₂H₂Cl₃

① Tris(chlorocopper)acetylene
$C_2H_2 \cdot (CuCl)_3$

② $C_2H_2 + 3CuCl \longrightarrow$

③ Colorless crystals. (25°/287).

④ $+ C_2H_2 \longrightarrow C_2H_2(CuCl)_2$

⑨ Acta Chem. Scand. **8**, 533 (1954).

【Ag】

AgCH₃

① Methylsilver
$AgCH_3$

② $AgNO_3 + Pb(CH_3)_4 \xrightarrow{\text{in EtOH, } -78°}$

③ Yellow solid. [−70° decomp.].
Insol. in org. solvents. Very unstable.

④ $\xrightarrow{> -70°, \text{ decomp.}} Ag + CH_3 \cdot$

⑥ Gazz. chim. ital. **86**, 77 (1956). Ber. **74**, 1089 (1941).

AgC₄H₇

① Isobutenylsilver
$(CH_3)_2C=CHAg$

② $(C_2H_5)_3PbCH=C(CH_3)_2 + AgNO_3 \xrightarrow{\text{in EtOH, } -76°}$

③ Orange crystals. [−20° decomp].
Sol. in ether. Very unstable.

④ $\longrightarrow Ag + (CH_3)_2C=CH \cdot$

⑥ JCS **1956**, 3640. Ber. **74**, 1089, 1297 (1941).

AgC₆H₅

① Phenylsilver
AgC_6H_5

② $AgCl + C_6H_5MgBr \longrightarrow$

③ Gray powder. [−18° decomp.].
Sol. in ether and pyridine; insol. in
org. solvents. Very unstable;
explode in air.

④ $\longrightarrow Ag + C_6H_5 \cdot C_6H_5$
$+ C_6H_5NCO \longrightarrow C_6H_5NHCOC_6H_5$
$+ CH_3COCl \longrightarrow C_6H_5COCH_3 + AgCl$
$+ CH_2=CHCH_2Br \longrightarrow$
$C_6H_5CH_2CH=CH_2 + AgBr$

⑥ Ber. **56**, 2064 (1923). Compt. rend. **177**, 322 (1923). Rec. trav. chim. **55**, 821 (1936).

AgC₆H₆ClO₄

① Benzene-silver perchlorate
   $C_6H_6 \cdot AgClO_4$

② $C_6H_6 + AgClO_4 \longrightarrow$

③ Plates.
   Decomp. in air; stable under a
   vapor pressure of C_6H_6.
   Raman: JACS **80**, 5075 (1958).

⑥ Chem. Revs. **54**, 713 (1954).

AgC₈H₈NO₃

① Cycloöctatetraene-silver nitrate

② $AgNO_3 +$ $\longrightarrow$ 29%

③ Pale yellow crystals. [125~126°].
   Slowly decomp. in air.

④ $\xrightarrow{\text{heat}}$ $C_8H_8 + AgNO_3$

   $\xrightarrow{\text{recryst. in AgNO}_3}$ $2C_8H_8 \cdot 3 AgNO_3$

   $\xrightarrow{\text{aq. NH}_3}$ C_8H_8

⑤ Purification of COT

⑥ J. Phys. Chem. **63**, 845 (1959).   JACS
   72, 2515 (1950).

Ag₂C₇H₈N₂O₆

① Norbornadiene-di(silver nitrate)

② norbornadiene + 2 AgNO₃
   $\xrightarrow[\text{in H}_2\text{O}]{}$ 46%

③ White crystals.
   Sol. in MeOH, EtOH, CCl₄, CHCl₃
   and C_6H_6; insol. in Ac₂O, ether and
   ligroin. Decomp. in H₂O and air.

④ $+ H_2O \longrightarrow C_7H_8 + AgNO_3$

⑥ JCS **1959**, 3178.

Ag₃C₁₂H₁₀NO₃

① Bis(phenynsilver)-silver nitrate
   $(C_6H_5Ag)_2AgNO_3$

② $AgNO_3 + (C_6H_5)_3PbC_2H_5 \xrightarrow{\text{in EtOH}}$ 43%

③ Yellow crystals. [70~100° decomp.].
   Sol. in alc. and C_6H_6. React with pyridine, piperidine, dimethylformamide and other N-bases. Slowly
   decomp. at room temp.

④ $+ HNO_3 \longrightarrow$ detonation

⑥ Ber. **52**, 2150 (1919).

【Au】

AuCH₃Br₂

① Methyldibromogold
   CH_3AuBr_2

② $(CH_3)_2AuBr + Br_2 \longrightarrow$

③ Red prism. [80~100° decomp.].
   Sol. in CHCl₃. Sensitive to light.

④ $\xrightarrow{\text{heat}}$ $AuBr + CH_3Br$

⑥ JCS **1939**, 762.

AuC₂H₆Br

① Dimethylbromogold
   $(CH_3)_2AuBr$

② $(CH_3)_2Au(acac) + HBr \longrightarrow$ 66%

③ Colorless needle. [69° decomp.].
   Sol. in ligroin. Can be stored for a
   few days. Sensitive to light.

④ $+ HSC_6H_4COOH \longrightarrow$
   $(CH_3)_2AuSC_6H_4COOH$
   $+ S(CH_2C_6H_5)_2 \longrightarrow$
   $(CH_3)_2BrAu \cdot S(CH_2C_6H_5)_2$
   $+ Br_2 \longrightarrow CH_3AuBr_2$
   $+ AgCN \longrightarrow (CH_3)_2AuCN$

⑥ JCS **1939**, 762.

AuC₃H₉

① Trimethylgold
   $(CH_3)_3Au$

② $AuBr_3 + CH_3Li \xrightarrow{-65°}$

③ Yellow oil. (−35° decomp.). [<−78°].

Very unstable.

④   + $NH_2CH_2CH_2NH_2$ ⟶

   $[(CH_3)_3Au \cdot NH_2CH_2]_2$

   + Et_2O ⟶ $(CH_3)_3Au \cdot OEt_2$

   $2(CH_3)_3Au + AuBr_3$ ⇌

   $3(CH_3)_2AuBr$

   + HCl ⟶ $(CH_3)_2AuCl + CH_4$

   + HSR ⟶ $(CH_3)_2AuSR + CH_4$

⑥   JACS **70**, 550 (1948).

AuC₄H₁₀Cl

①   Diethylchlorogold

   $(C_2H_5)_2AuCl$

② $AuCl_3 + C_2H_5MgCl$ ⟶   15%

③   [48° decomp.].

   Sol. in org. solvents. Insol. in H_2O.

   Decomp. in a few days in solution.

④   + HSC_6H_4COOH ⟶

   $(C_2H_5)_2AuSC_6H_4COOH$

   + AgCN ⟶ $(C_2H_5)_2AuCN$

⑥   JCS **1939**, 762.

AuC₆H₅Cl₂

①   Phenyldichlorogold

   $C_6H_5AuCl_2$

② $AuCl_3 + C_6H_6$ ⟶

   $(C_6H_5)_2AuCl + Cl_2$ ⟶

③   Yellow crystals. [73~75°].

   Slightly sol. in H_2O and ether; insol.

   in org. solvents.

④   + HCl ⟶ $C_6H_5Cl + Au$

   + NaCl ⟶ $Na^+[C_6H_5AuCl_3]^-$

   $\xrightarrow{heat}$ $AuCl + C_6H_5Cl$

   + reducing agent ⟶   Au

⑥   JACS **53**, 2701, 3053 (1931).

AuC₆H₁₄Br

①   Di-*n*-propylbromogold

   $(n\text{-}C_3H_7)_2AuBr$

② $AuBr_3 + 2C_3H_7MgBr$ ⟶   15%

③   Liq. (95° decomp.).

   Sol. in org. solvents; insol. in H_2O.

   Can be stored for a few days.

④   + HSC_6H_4COOH ⟶

$(C_3H_7)_2AuSC_6H_4COOH$

   + Br_2 ⟶ $n\text{-}C_3H_7AuBr_2$

   + AgCN ⟶ $(n\text{-}C_3H_7)_2AuCN$

⑥   JACS **53**, 2701 (1931). JCS **1939**, 762.

AuC₆H₁₄Br

①   Diisopropylbromogold

   $(i\text{-}C_3H_7)_2AuBr$

② $AuBr_3 + i\text{-}C_3H_7MgBr$ ⟶

③   [>100° decomp.].

   Sol. in org. solevnts; insol. in H_2O.

   Can be stored for a few days.

   Light sensitve.

④   + HSC_6H_4COOH ⟶

   $(i\text{-}C_2H_7)_2AuSC_6H_4COOH$

   + Br_2 ⟶ $i\text{-}C_3H_7AuBr_2$

   + AgCN ⟶ $(i\text{-}CH_3H_7)_2AuCN$

⑥   JACS **53**, 2701 (1931). JCS **1939**, 762.

AuC₆H₁₄Cl

①   Di-*n*-propylchlorogold

   $(n\text{-}C_3H_7)_2AuCl$

② $AuCl_3 + 2C_3H_7MgCl$ ⟶   4%

③   Yellow oil. (107° decomp.).

   Sol. in org. solvents; insol. in H_2O.

   Can be stored for a few days.

④   + HSC_6H_4COOH ⟶

   $(C_3H_7)_2AuSC_6H_4COOH$

   + AgCN ⟶ $(C_3H_7)_2AuCl$

⑥   JACS **53**, 2701 (1931). JCS **1939**, 762.

AuC₆H₁₄Cl

①   Diisopropylchlorogold

   $(i\text{-}C_3H_7)_2AuCl$

② $AuCl_3 + 2i\text{-}C_3H_7MgCl$ ⟶

③   [95° decomp.].

   Sol. in org. solvents; insol. in

   EtOH. Can be stored for a few

   days. Light sensitive.

④   + HSC_6H_4COOH ⟶

   $(i\text{-}C_3H_7)_2AuSC_6H_4COOH$

   + AgCN ⟶ $(i\text{-}C_3H_7)_2AuCN$

⑥   JACS **53**, 2701 (1931). JCS **1939**, 762.

AuC₇H₄Cl₃N

① 3-Cyanophenyldichlorogold

  NCC₆H₄AuCl₂

② NCC₆H₅ + AuCl₃ ⟶

③ Yellow soild. [168°].

  Sol.in NO₂Ph ; insol. in H_2O.

  Decomp. in EtOH and acetone.

④ + Br₂ $\xrightarrow{100°}$ NCC₆H₄Br

   + H⁺ ⟶ NCC₆H₅

   + NH₃ ⟶ NCC₆H₅ + AuN₂H₃

   + NaCl ⟶ Na⁺[NCC₆H₄AuCl₃]⁻

   + reducing agent ⟶ Au

⑥ JACS **56**, 2057 (1934).

AuC₇H₇Br₂

① Benzyldibromogold

  C₆H₅CH₂AuBr₂

② (C₆H₅CH₂)₂AuBr + Br₂ ⟶

③ Ruby-red needle. [140° decomp.].

  Sol. in org. solvents ; insol. in H_2O.

  Stable in air. Light sensitive.

⑥ JACS **53**, 2707 (1931).

AuC₇H₇Cl₂

① Tolyldichlorogold

  CH₃C₆H₄AuCl₂

② AuCl₃ + CH₃C₆H₅ ⟶

③ Yellow crystals.

  Sol. in ether, EtOH, and C₆H₆ ; insol.

   in petr. ether, H_2O and CCl₄. Light

   sensitive.

④ + HCl ⟶ CH₃C₆H₄Cl + Au

   + NaCl ⟶ Na⁺[CH₃C₆H₄AuCl₃]⁻

   + reduciug agent ⟶ Au

⑥ JACS **53**, 3057 (1931).

AuC₇H₁₃O₂

① Dimethylacetylacetonylgold

  (CH₃)₂AuO₂C₅H₇

② (CH₃)₂AuI + C₅H₈O₂ ⟶

③ [84°].

  Sol. in org. solvents. Decomp. in

EtOH. Light sensitive. Characteristic odor.

④ + HBr ⟶ (CH₃)₂AuBr

⑥ JCS **1939**, 762.

AuC₇H₁₄N

① Di-*n*-propylcyanogold

  (*n*-C₃H₇)₂AuCN

② (*n*-C₃H₇)₂AuX + AgCN ⟶

③ [95° decomp.].

  Sol. in. org. solvents ; insol in H_2O.

④ + NH₂CH₂CH₂NH₂ ⟶

   [(C₃H₇)₂Au(CN)←NH₂CH₂]₂

   $\xrightarrow{\text{heat}}$ AuCN + C₃H₇·

⑥ JACS **53**, 2701 (1931).

AuC₇H₁₄N

① Diisopropylcyanogold

  (*i*-C₃H₇)₂AuCN

② (*i*-C₃H₇)₂AuX + AgCN ⟶

③ Needles. (121° decomp.). [88∼90°].

  Sol.in ether, CHCl₃. and C₆H₆ ; insol.

   in H_2O.

④ $\xrightarrow{>100°}$ [(*i*-C₃H₇)₂Au(CN)←AuCN]₂

   + 2RR (R=*i*-C₃H₇)

    ⟶ 4AuCN + 2C₃H₇·C₃H₇

   + NH₂CH₂CH₂NH₂ ⟶

   [(C₃H₇)₂Au(CN)←NH₂CH₂]₂

⑥ JACS **53**, 2701 (1931).

AuC₈H₇ClNO

① *p*-Methoxyphenylisocyanato-

  chlorogold

  (*p*-CH₃OC₆H₄NC)AuCl

② HAuCl₄ + *p*-CH₃OC₆H₄NC $\xrightarrow{\text{in EtOH}}$

③ [199°].

  Sol. in alcohol ; insol. in org. solvents.

  Very stable in crystalline state

  but unstable in solution.

⑥ Gazz. chim. ital. **86**, 195 (1956).

AuC₈H₁₈Br

① Diisobutylbromogold

$(i\text{-}C_4H_9)_2AuBr$

② $2i\text{-}C_4H_9MgBr + AuBr_3 \longrightarrow 10\%$

③ Colorless oil.

Sol. in org. solvents; insol. in H_2O.
Can be stored for a few days.
Light sensitive.

④ $+ HSC_6H_4COOH \longrightarrow$
$(i\text{-}C_4H_9)_2AuSC_6H_4COOH$
$+ Br_2 \longrightarrow i\text{-}C_4H_9AuBr_2$
$+ AgCN \longrightarrow (i\text{-}C_4H_9)_2AuCN$

⑥ JACS **53**, 2701 (1931). JCS **1939**, 762.

$AuC_8H_{18}Br$

① Di-n-butylbromogold
$(n\text{-}C_4H_9)_2AuBr$

② $AuBr_3 + 2C_4H_9MgBr \longrightarrow 15\%$

③ Liq. (65° decomp.).

Sol. in org. solvents; insol. in H_2O.
Can be stored for a few days.

④ $+ HSC_6H_4COOH \longrightarrow$
$(n\text{-}C_4H_9)_2AuSC_6H_4COOH$
$+ Br_2 \longrightarrow n\text{-}C_4H_9AuBr_2$
$+ AgCN \longrightarrow (n\text{-}C_4H_9)_2AuCN$

⑥ JACS **53**, 2701 (1931).

$AuC_9H_{18}N$

① Diisobutylcyanogold
$(i\text{-}C_4H_9)_2AuCN$

② $(i\text{-}C_4H_9)_2AuX + AgCN \longrightarrow$

③ (160° decomp.). [112~113°].

Sol. in org. solvents; insol. in H_2O.

④ $+ NH_2CH_2CH_2NH_2 \longrightarrow$
$[(C_4H_9)_2Au(CN)\leftarrow NH_2\text{-}CH_2]_2$
$\overset{heat}{\longrightarrow} AuCN + C_4H_9\cdot$

⑥ JCS **1936**, 324.

$AuC_9H_{18}N$

① Di-n-butylcyanogold
$(n\text{-}C_4H_9)_2AuCN$

② $(n\text{-}C_4H_9)_2AuX + AgCN \longrightarrow$

③ [125° decomp.].

Sol. in org. solvents; insol. in H_2O.

④ $+ NH_2CH_2CH_2NH_2 \longrightarrow$
$[(C_4H_9)_2Au(CN)\leftarrow NH_2CH_2]_2$

$\overset{heat}{\longrightarrow} AuCN + C_4H_9$

⑥ JCS **1939**, 762.

$AuC_{12}H_{22}Br$

① Dicyclohexylbromogold
$(C_6H_{11})_2AuBr$

② $AuBr_3 + C_6H_{11}MgBr \longrightarrow 4\%$

③ [148° decomp.].

Sol. in C_6H_6, ether and $CHCl_3$;
insol. in H_2O. Stable in air.

⑥ JCS **1939**, 762.

$AuC_{12}H_{22}Cl$

① Dicyclohexylchlorogold
$(C_6H_{11})_2AuCl$

② $AuCl_3 + 2C_6H_{11}MgCl \longrightarrow 9\%$

③ [180° decomp.].

Slightly sol. in org. solvents;
insol. in H_2O. Stable in air.

④ $+ HSC_6H_4COOH \longrightarrow$
$(C_6H_{11})_2AuSC_6H_4COOH$
$+ AgCN \longrightarrow (C_6H_{11})_2AuCN$

⑥ JACS **53**, 2701 (1931). JCS **1939**, 762.

$AuC_{13}H_{22}N$

① Dicyclohexylcyanogold
$(C_6H_{11})_2AuCN$

② $(C_6H_{11})_2AuX + AgCN \longrightarrow$

③ [152° decomp.].

Sol. in C_6H_6 and $CHCl_3$; insol. in
EtOH, EtAc and acetone.

④ $\overset{heat}{\longrightarrow} AuCN + C_6H_{11}\cdot$
$+ H_2NCH_2CH_2NH_2 \longrightarrow$
$[(C_6H_{11})_2Au(CN)\leftarrow NH_2CH_2\cdot]_2$

⑥ JACS **53**, 2701 (1931).

$AuC_{14}H_{14}Br$

① Dibenzylbromogold
$(C_6H_5CH_2)_2AuBr$

② $AuBr_3 + 2C_6H_5CH_2MgBr \longrightarrow 23\%$

③ (85° explod). [77° decomp].

Sol. in ether, C_6H_6 and $PhCH_2Cl$;
insol. in H_2O. Can be stored for a

few days.

④ + HSC_6H_4COOH ⟶

$(C_6H_5CH_2)_2AuSC_6H_4COOH$

+ AgCN ⟶ $(C_6H_5CH_2)_2AuCN$

⑥ JACS **53**, 2701 (1931).

$\overset{4}{A}uC_{14}H_{14}Cl$

① Dibenzylchlorogold

$(C_6H_5CH_2)_2AuCl$

② $AuCl_3 + C_6H_5CH_2MgCl$ ⟶ 14%

③ [>70° decomp.].

Sol. in org. solvents ; insol. in H_2O.

Can be stored for a few days.

④ + HSC_6H_4COOH ⟶

$(C_6H_5CH_2)_2AuSC_6H_4COOH$

+ AgCN ⟶ $(C_6H_5CH_2)_2AuCN$

⑥ JACS **53**, 2701 (1931).

$AuC_{15}H_{14}N$

① Dibenzylcyanogold

$(C_6H_5CH_2)_2AuCN$

② $(C_6H_5CH_2)_2AuCl + AgCN$ ⟶

③ [122° decomp.].

Sol. in warm aq. NH_3. Decomp. in

six weeks.

④ + $NH_2CH_2CH_2NH_2$ ⟶

$[(C_6H_5CH_2)_2Au(CN){\leftarrow}NH_2CH_2]_2$

$\overset{heat}{\longrightarrow}$ $AuCN + C_6H_5CH_2\cdot$

⑥ JACS **53**, 2701 (1931).

$Au_2C_8H_{26}N_2$

① Trimethylgold-ethylenediamine

adduct

$2Au(CH_3)_3\cdot NH_2CH_2CH_2NH_2$

② $(CH_3)_2AuI + NH_2CH_2CH_2NH_2$ ⟶

③ White crystals. [94° decomp.].

Sol. in ether.

⑥ JCS **1939**, 762.

12. Organic Compounds of Zinc, Cadmium, and Mercury

(Zn, Cd, Hg)

12.1. Introduction

In 1849, Frankland reported that diethylzinc, the first organozinc compound, was synthesized by the reaction of ethyl iodide with zinc. This discovery is said to be the start of organometallic chemistry, since many other organometallics were derived from this compound. The first synthesis of an organomercury compound was also made by Frankland. In 1850, he reported formation of a gaseous product by a reaction between ethyl iodide and mercury with the aid of light. Two years later, the formation of methylmercuric iodide by the reaction of methyl iodide with mercury was reported by Frankland. In 1843, Hoffmann obtained a compound containing mercury by a reaction of aniline with mercuric chloride. However, this was not a true organomercuric containing a carbon–mercury bond. In 1856, Wanklyn prepared the first organocadmium compound, diethylcadmium, by the reaction between ethyl iodide and cadmium.

The characteristic properties of zinc, cadmium, and mercury are listed in Table 12.1. For comparison, some IIa group elements are included.

Table 12.1. Properties of Group II Metals.

	Zn	Cd	Hg	Mg	Ca	Ba
Atomic number	30	48	80	12	20	56
Electronic structure	$3\,d^{10}4\,s^2$	$4\,d^{10}5\,s^2$	$5\,d^{10}6\,s^2$	$2\,p^6 3\,s^2$	$3\,p^6 4\,s^2$	$5\,p^6 6\,s^2$
Melting point, °C	419	321	−38.9	649	810	830
Boiling point, °C	906	764	357	1100	1439	1737
Atomic radius, Å	1.25	1.41	1.44	1.36	1.74	1.98
Ionic radius (divalent), Å	0.74	0.97	1.10	0.65	0.99	1.35
Ionization energy, kcal/mole						
I_1	216.5	207.3	240	176.2	140.9	120.1
I_2	414.0	389.7	423.2	346.5	273.6	230.6
Electronegativity	1.6	1.7	1.9	1.2	1.0	0.9

For the synthesis of organometallics of group IIb, the following inorganic materials are used most frequently:

Metallic zinc, cadmium, and mercury; halides of zinc, cadmium, and mercury; oxyacid salts of mercury, such as sulfate, nitrate and perchlorate. Some of the physical and chemical properties which appear to be important for organometallic syntheses will be mentioned briefly.

Zinc chloride (mp 275°) forms many kinds of hydrates.

$$\text{Ice} \underset{}{\overset{-62°}{\rightleftharpoons}} 4\,\text{aq.} \overset{-30°}{\rightleftharpoons} 3\,\text{aq.} \overset{+6°}{\rightleftharpoons} 2\tfrac{1}{2}\,\text{aq.} \overset{11.5°}{\rightleftharpoons} 1\tfrac{1}{2}\,\text{aq.} \overset{26°}{\rightleftharpoons} 1\,\text{aq.} \overset{28°}{\rightleftharpoons} 0\,\text{aq.}$$

Because of the strong hygroscopic property, it appears to be difficult to remove the trace of water. Zinc bromide (mp 394°) also forms hydrates.

$$3 \text{ aq.} \rightleftharpoons 2 \text{ aq.} \overset{37°}{\rightleftharpoons} 0 \text{ aq.}$$

The solubilities of zinc halides in water are very large, and that of zinc iodide (mp 446°) is the largest.   The solubility of zinc chloride has been studied in the greatest detail.   Zinc chloride is readily soluble in organic solvents containing oxygen and nitrogen, such as alcohols, esters, ketones, furfural, amines, and nitriles.   Zinc bromide is also readily soluble in alcohols.   Its solubility in ether is smaller than that of zinc chloride.   Except for the iodide (mp 385°), cadmium halides form hydrates.

$$CdCl_2 \text{ (mp 568°)}: \quad Ice \overset{-9°}{\rightleftharpoons} 4 \text{ aq.} \overset{-5°}{\rightleftharpoons} 2\frac{1}{2} \text{ aq.} \overset{34°}{\rightleftharpoons} 1 \text{ aq.} \overset{ca.\ 100°}{\rightleftharpoons} 0 \text{ aq.}$$

$$CdBr_2 \text{ (mp 381°)}: \quad 4 \text{ aq.} \overset{36°}{\rightleftharpoons} 1 \text{ aq.} \overset{ca.\ 100°}{\rightleftharpoons} 0 \text{ aq.}$$

Cadmium halides are readily soluble in water, although the solubilities are smaller than those of the corresponding zinc halides.   The solubilities in organic solvents increase in the order chloride, bromide, and iodide,   For example, the solubilities in ethanol (100 g) at room temperature are 1.52 ($CdCl_2$), 26.5 ($CdBr_2 \cdot 4$ aq.), and 74.3 g (CdI_2).   In ether, chloride is sparingly soluble, and bromide ($CdBr_2 \cdot 4$ aq.) and iodide are more soluble (0.4 and 0.143 g into 100 g of ether respectively).

Aqueous solutions of these cadmium halides show unusual behavior with regard to electrical conductivity. This is due to the formation of $[Cd(hal)_3]^-$ or $[Cd(hal)_4]^{2-}$ by "autocomplex formation" and shows the strong complex-forming ability of cadmium ion.   The fact that organozinc and -cadmium compounds form "ate-complexes" demonstrates the same property in zinc and cadmium.

In contrast with the larger dissociation constants of mercuric nitrate, sulfate, and perchlorate, mercuric halides dissociate only slightly; for example, less than 1% mercuric chloride dissociates in 1/20 N aqueous solution.   Mercuric fluoride is a strong electrolyte.   The dissociation constants of organic acid salts of mercury (II) are roughly the same as those of the acids.   Mercury derivatives which are obtained by the substitution of hydrogen attached to carbon (for example, derivatives of hydrogen cyanide, acetamide, and imide), do not dissociate and form no mercuric oxide precipitate on treatment with aqueous sodium hydroxide. Oxyacid salts of mercury(II) form many kinds of hydrates, for example, $Hg\ (NO_3)_2 \cdot 8$ aq., $Hg(NO_3)_2 \cdot 1$ aq., $Hg(NO_3)_2 \cdot 1/2$ aq., $HgSO_4 \cdot 1$ aq., $Hg(ClO_4)_2 \cdot 6$ aq.

Upon diluting with water mercuric nitrate becomes yellow and turbid due to partial hydrolysis, and sulfate forms $HgSO_4 \cdot 2\,HgO$. However, an aqueous solution of perchlorate remains clear even after dilution.

12.2. Classification and Nomenclature

Group IIb metals form organometallics of R_2M, $RR'M$, and RMX type, where R, R'=alkyl, alkenyl, alkinyl or aryl, and X=inorganic or organic acid radicals.

According to the general rule, organometallics are named by adding the name of the metal to that of the organic radical. For example, the names of the organozinc compounds Et_2Zn, MeZnEt, and MeZnCl are diethylzinc, methylethylzinc, and methylzinc chloride respectively. Organocadmium and -mercury compounds are named similarly. It is possible to express the group containing metal as a prefix. For example, ClHg- is chloromercuri-. In the case of complex cyclic compounds, it is convenient to name them in the following manner. For example, $O\underset{CH_2-CH_2}{\overset{CH_2-CH_2}{\diagup\diagdown}}Hg$ is 1-oxa-4-mercuracyclohexane.

In the case of zinc and cadmium compounds, -ate complexes, $R_2Zn \cdot M'R$ or $R_2Cd \cdot M'R$, are formed by the reaction of dialkylzinc or -cadmium with alkali metal (M').

Alkyl-alkoxyzinc (RZnOR) and alkyl-alkylperoxyzinc (RZnOOR) are also known. The same types of compounds have also been obtained in the cases of cadmium and mercury. In the case of mercury, RHgHgR-type compounds, and those which contain a bond between mercury and other metals, are also obtained. It appears to require further investigation to determine whether $RCdR'$ ($R \neq R'$) can be synthesized or not.

12.3. Methods of Synthesis

Because of limited space, the synthetic methods are demonstrated by chemical equation, using as many examples as possible and a minimum of explanation. The books and reviews listed at the end of this chapter are recommended for details.

12.3.1. Zinc Compounds

(1) $RX + Zn \longrightarrow (RZnX) \longrightarrow R_2Zn$

This reaction was discovered by Frankland and is famous historically. Primary and secondary alkyl iodides and bromides react according to this equation. A copper-zinc couple is often used in place of metallic zinc, and the preparation of a reactive couple suitable for the reaction has been reported. Example: R=Et, n-Pr, i-Pr, $C_2H_5C \equiv CCH_2$-.

(2) $RBr + RI \xrightarrow{\text{Zn-Cu}} R_2Zn$

It is reported that the yields of dialkylzinc are improved by using a mixture of alkyl bromide and iodide. Example: R=Et, n-Pr, i-Pr, n-Bu, i-Bu, sec-Bu.

(3) $R_2Hg + Zn \longrightarrow R_2Zn$

Many examples have been reported. It must be mentioned that the preparation must be done very carefully, because dialkylmercury is extremely toxic.

Example: R=i-Am, p-F-C_6H_4-, p-Cl-C_6H_4-, o-Me-C_6H_4-, p-Me-C_6H_4-, p-MeO-C_6H_4-, p-(Me$_2$N)-C_6H_4-, p-H_2N-C_6H_4-. β-$C_{10}H_9$-, C_6H_5-, $C_6H_5CH_2$-.

(4) $2 RMgX' + ZnX_2 \longrightarrow R_2Zn$

Dialkylzinc thus obtained is usually used for the preparation of ketones without isolation. Dialkylzinc has been isolated by this method. Example: R=CH_2=CH-, cyclopentadienyl.

(5) $RMgX' + R'H + ZnX_2 \longrightarrow RZnR'$

Although this reaction is not generally applicable, unsymmetrical zinc compounds were prepared in the case of cyclopentadiene. Example: R=Et, C_6H_5-, R'= cyclopentadienyl.

(6) $2 R_3Al + ZnX_2 \longrightarrow R_2Zn + 2 R_2AlX$

Example: R= Me, Pr, Bu, C_7H_{15}-, $CH_3CH(C_6H_5)CH_2$-.

(7) $RNa + ZnBr_2 \longrightarrow R_2Zn$

Example: R=methylcyclopentadienyl.

(8) $RMgX + R'ZnI \longrightarrow RZnR'$

For the preparation of unsymmetrical zinc compounds, this reaction is used most widely. Example: R, R'=Et, Et; Et, n-Pr; Et, i-Bu; n-Pr, n-Pr; n-Pr, n-Bu; i-Bu, i-Bu; i-Bu, i-Am; i-Am, i-Am.

(9) $Zn(NH_2)_2 + CH \equiv CH \longrightarrow (CH \equiv C-)_2 Zn \cdot 2 NH_3$

(10) $RX + Zn \longrightarrow RZnX$

Example: R, X=Et, I; i-Pr, I; CH_3CH=$CHCH_2$-, Br; $CH_3O(CH_2)_4$-, I; ICH_2-, I; CH_2=$CHCH_2$-, Br.

(11) $3 Et_2Zn + 2 M \longrightarrow 2 MEt \cdot ZnEt_2 + Zn$

M means alkali metal and the product is an ate complex. The same complex formation is reported as follows:

$$Zn(SCN)_2 \cdot 2 NH_3 + 4 KC \equiv CH \longrightarrow K_2Zn(C \equiv CH)_4$$
$$K_2Zn(CN)_4 + 4 KC \equiv CH \longrightarrow K_2Zn(C \equiv CH)_4$$
$$Me_2Zn + 2 LiMe \xrightarrow{\text{ether}} Li_2ZnMe_4 \cdot OEt_2$$

(12) $Zn + 2 C_2H_4 + H_2 \longrightarrow Et_2Zn$

It is reported that the reaction takes place by electrolysis using $NaF \cdot 2 AlEt_3$ as cathode and aluminum as anode.

12.3.2. Cadmium Compounds

(1) $RX + Cd \longrightarrow R_2Cd$

Although this reaction is important historically, it has no practical use, since the yields are usually low.

(2) $Ph_2Hg + Cd \longrightarrow Ph_2Cd$

(3) $RMgX + CdBr_2 \longrightarrow R_2Cd$

Example: R=Me, Et, n-Pr, i-Pr, n-Bu, i-Bu, i-Am, C_6H_{13}-, C_7H_{15}-, C_8H_{17}-,

$(CH_3)_2CHCH_2\underset{|}{C}=CH_2$, o-MeC$_6H_4$-, p-MeC$_6H_4$-, m-MeOC$_6H_4$-.

(4) $RLi + CdBr_2 \longrightarrow R_2Cd$

Example : R=n-Bu, Ph.

(5) $R_3Al + CdX_2 \longrightarrow R_2Cd + RAlX_2$

Example : R=Et, X=Cl.

(6) $Cd + 2 C_2H_4 + H_2 \longrightarrow Et_2Cd$

Cathode is NaF·2 AlEt$_3$ and anode is aluminum.

12.3.3. Mercury Compounds

(1) $RX + Hg \longrightarrow RHgX$.

This reaction has a long history, but it cannot be recommended as a general preparative method.

Although iodides are reactive to this method, bromides and chlorides are rather inactive. As compared with saturated compounds, allyl and propargyl iodide are more reactive. In the case of polyhalogen compounds, the reaction proceeds readily at 70~80° under irradiation with ultraviolet rays. It is reported that a special type of bromide reacts according to this equation. For example, benzhydryl bromide forms benzhydrylmercuric brmide. However, the yield is low because of the side reaction which forms tetraphenylethane. Example : RX=CCl$_3$Br, CHCl$_2$Br, CHCl$_2$I.

(2) $Li(CH_2)_nLi + Hg \xrightarrow{\text{Argon}} \left[\begin{array}{c}-(CH_2)_n-\\ \hline -Hg-\end{array}\right] + Hg\left[\begin{array}{c}-(CH_2)_n-\\ -(CH_2)_n-\end{array}\right]Hg + \text{polymer}$

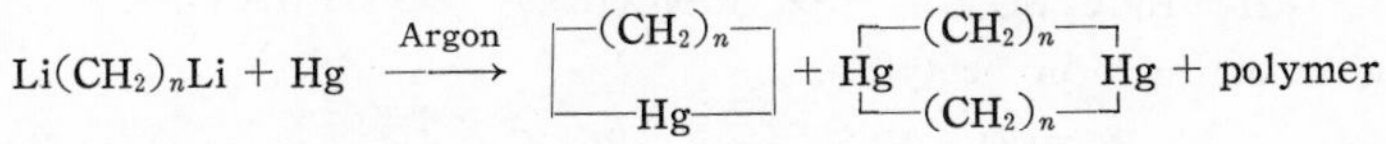

Example : n=4, 5, 6, 10.

(3) $NaF·2 Al(C_2H_5)_3 \xrightarrow[\text{Hg electrode}]{\text{electrolysis}} (C_2H_5)_2Hg$

(4) $2 RX + Ha\text{-}Hg \xrightarrow[\text{benzene, xylene}]{\text{cat. } CH_3CO_2Et} R_2Hg$

This reaction is most widely used for the preparation of R$_2$Hg, and is applied to alkyl halides of C$_1$~C$_8$ (including n-, *sec*- and *tert*-halides) and aralkyl halides. In the case of dihalides, the following results are reported :

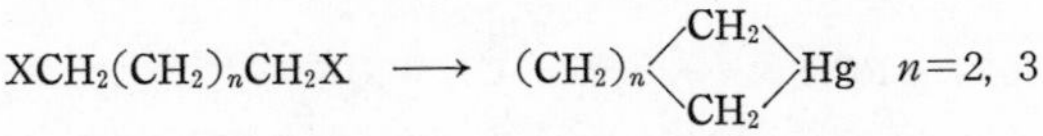

$$XCH_2(CH_2)_nCH_2X \longrightarrow (CH_2)_n\underset{CH_2}{\overset{CH_2}{<}}\!\!\!>Hg \quad n=2,\ 3$$

The formation of ⬡$\underset{-CH_2}{\overset{-CH_2}{<}}$Hg and ⬡$\underset{Hg}{\overset{Hg}{<}}$⬡ by the same reaction is also reported.

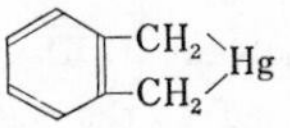

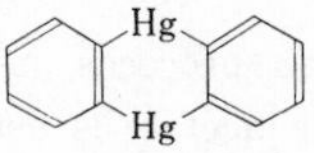

(5) $ArN_2Cl·HgCl_2 + M \longrightarrow ArHgCl + N_2 + MCl_2$

This is one of Nesmeyanov's reactions and M is a divalent or trivalent metal. When Ar=C$_6$H$_5$, and M=Hg, Zn, or Fe, the yields are about 70% in water as solvent.

(6) $ArN_2X + Hg \longrightarrow ArHgX$

This reaction is known as Water's reaction and is analogous to reaction 5.

(7) $[Ar_2I]^{+}Cl^{-} + Hg \longrightarrow ArHgCl$

Example : $Ar = p\text{-}MeC_6H_4\text{-}$ (55% yield), $p\text{-}MeOC_6H_4\text{-}$ (77%), $p\text{-}BrC_6H_4\text{-}$ (75%), $m\text{-}NO_2C_6H_4\text{-}$ (40%), $m\text{-}EtOC_6H_4\text{-}$ (47%).

(8) $RH + HgX_2 \longrightarrow RHgX$

Active methylene and aromatic compounds are substituted by mercury according to the equation.   As the mercurating reagents, mercuric acetate and oxide are used most frequently. The reaction of diethyl malonate, dimethyl methylmalonate, and trinitromethane is reported. In the case of acetylacetone and dibenzoyl-methane, the formation of polymeric products containing mercury is reported. With aromatic compounds, mixtures of $o\text{-}$, $m\text{-}$ and $p\text{-}$substituted isomers are obtained. As a typical example of electrophilic aromatic substitution, detailed studies of the orientation and mechanism are reported.   In the following cases, the substitution takes place on the side chain: $C_6H_5COCH_2\text{-}$, $o\text{-}NO_2C_6H_4CH_2\text{-}$.   With pyridine, pyridin N-oxide, thiophene, and furan, the substitutions take place at the 3, 2, 2, and 2 positions, respectively. The same substitution is observed in ferrocenes. As a special type of mercurating agent $Hg[C(NO_2)_3]_2$ is reported to react by the following equation :

$$RH + Hg[C(NO_2)_3]_2 \longrightarrow RHgC(NO_2)_3 \xrightarrow{Cl^{-}} RHgCl$$

Acetylene reacts to form acetylide.

$$RC \equiv CH + HgX_2 \longrightarrow (RC \equiv C-)_2Hg$$

Example : $CH \equiv CH$, $XC \equiv CH$, $CH_3C \equiv CH$, $C_6H_5C \equiv CH$, $C_{10}H_9C \equiv CH$, $C_4H_3SC \equiv CH$, $p\text{-}MeC_6H_4SC \equiv CH$

The hydrogen of diazomethane is reported to react in the following two ways :

$$CH_2N_2 + HgCl_2 \longrightarrow Hg(CHN_2)_2$$

$$CH_2N_2 + HgCl_2 \longrightarrow ClCH_2HgCl$$

(9) $-C \equiv C- + HgX_2 \longrightarrow -CX = CHgX-$

Nesmeyanov studied the stereochemistry of this reaction.

(10) $\displaystyle >C=C< + HgX_2 + ROH \longrightarrow \begin{array}{c} | \quad | \\ -C-C- \\ | \quad | \\ OR \ HgX \end{array} + HX$

This oxymercuration reaction proceeds in the solvent ROH (water, alcohols, or organic acids), and mercuric acetate is usually used as the mercuric salt.   This reaction is applicable to various kinds of olefins, and mercury adds to the more electronegative carbon.   Many papers on the stereochemistry and mechanism are reported.   In some cases, condensation takes place as follows :

$$C_2H_4 \longrightarrow HOCH_2CH_2HgCl \longrightarrow O(CH_2CH_2HgCl)_2$$

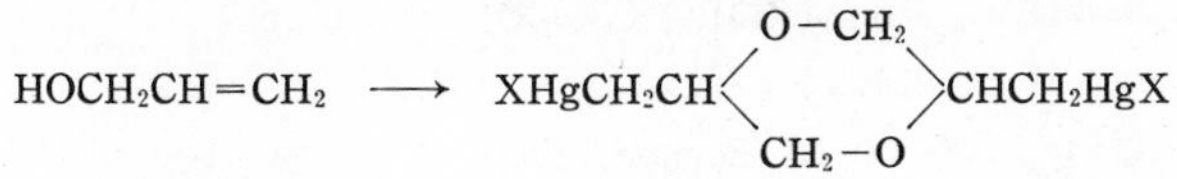

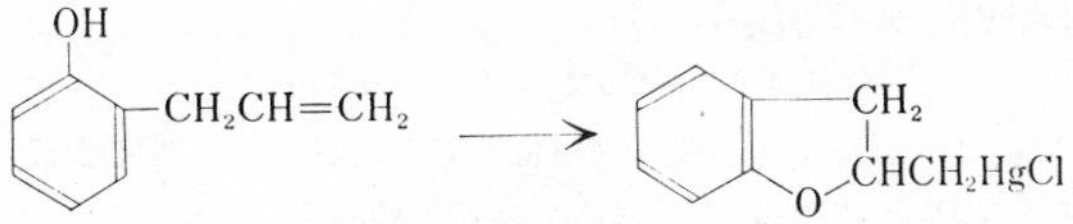

$$HOCH_2CH=CH_2 \longrightarrow XHgCH_2CH\begin{matrix} O-CH_2 \\ \diagdown \\ CH_2-O \end{matrix}CHCH_2HgX$$

In the case of fluorides, unusual reactions are frequently observed, as well as the normal reaction.

$$CF_2=CFCl + HgF_2 \longrightarrow CF_3CFClHgF$$

In the case of tetrafluoroethylene, it is reported that $CF_3(CF_2)_nCF_2HgF$ is formed. $CF_2=CHCF_3$ and $CF_2=CFCF_3$ react to form $(CF_3CHCF_3)_2Hg$ and $(CF_3CFCF_3)_2Hg$. The fact that polyfluoroolefins are oxymercurated is unusual, since normal electrophilic addition reactions do not proceed with these compounds.

As a special example of oxymercuration, the following reaction is reported.

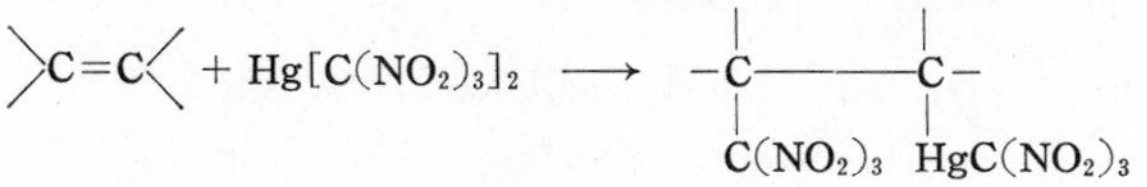

$$>C=C< + Hg[C(NO_2)_3]_2 \longrightarrow \begin{matrix} | & | \\ -C\text{------}C- \\ | & | \\ C(NO_2)_3 & HgC(NO_2)_3 \end{matrix}$$

(11) $CH_2=C\begin{matrix} OEt \\ OEt \end{matrix} + HgX_2 \xrightarrow{Me_2CO} \xrightarrow{KCl} (ClHg)_3CCOOC_2H_5$

$+ HgX_2 \xrightarrow{H_2O} \xrightarrow{KCl} Hg(CHClCOOC_2H_5)_2$

$+ HgX_2 \xrightarrow{Et_2O} \xrightarrow{KCl} (ClHg)_2CClCOOC_2H_5$

The reaction products of ketene acetal depend on the solvent.

(12) 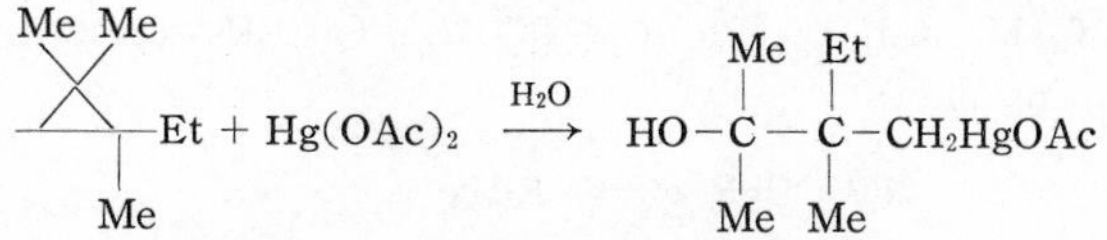 $\begin{matrix} Me \; Me \\ \diagup\kern-0.6em\diagdown \\ \diagup\kern-0.6em\diagdown\text{---Et} \\ | \\ Me \end{matrix} + Hg(OAc)_2 \xrightarrow{H_2O} HO-\overset{\underset{Me}{|}}{\underset{}{C}}\overset{Me}{\underset{}{|}}-\overset{Et}{\underset{Me}{\overset{|}{C}}}-CH_2HgOAc$

The reaction of cyclopropane with mercuric acetate forms an organomercury compound.

(13) $RLi + HgX_2 \longrightarrow RHgX$ or R_2Hg

Example: $R=CH_3CH=CH-, C_6H_5C=CH_2,$ and camphor-4.

$$R_3B + HgX_2 \longrightarrow R_2Hg$$

Example: $R=C_2H_5-, CH_2=CH-.$

$$KBR_4 \text{ (or } NaBR_4) + HgX_2 \longrightarrow RHgX$$

Example: $R=C_6H_5-, p\text{-}MeC_6H_4-, C_2H_5^-.$

$$R_2BX + HgX_2 \longrightarrow R_2Hg$$

Example: $R=CH_2CH-.$

$$RB(OH)_2 + HgX_2 \longrightarrow RHgX$$

Example: R=o-MeC$_6$H$_4$-, m-MeC$_6$H$_4$-, C$_6$H$_5$CH$_2$-, ferrocenyl.

$$RMgX + HgX_2 \longrightarrow RHgX$$

Example: R=C$_n$H$_{2n+1}$- (n=1-10, normal), sec-C$_3$H$_7$-. iso-C$_4$H$_9$-, sec-C$_4$H$_9$. $tert$-C$_4$H$_9$-, $tert$-C$_5$H$_{11}$-. n-C$_{12}$H$_{25}$-, n-C$_{16}$H$_{33}$-.

$$2\,RMgX + HgX_2 \longrightarrow R_2Hg$$

Example: R=Me, sec-Pr, sec-Bu, C$_6$H$_5$-, C$_6$H$_5$CH$_2$-, p-NH$_2$C$_6$H$_4$. p-MeC$_6$H$_4$-, C$_6$H$_5$C(CH$_3$)$_2$CH$_2$-, CH$_2$=CH-, C$_6$H$_5$C≡C-, cyclo-C$_3$H$_5$-, cyclo-C$_6$H$_{11}$-.

$$Et_3Al + HgBr_2 \longrightarrow Et_2Hg$$

$$(CF_3)_3P + HgO \longrightarrow (CF_3)_2Hg$$

$$R_2Zn + HgCl_2 \longrightarrow RHgX \text{ (or } R_2Hg)$$

Example: R=CH$_2$=CHCH$_2$-, C$_6$H$_5$CH$_2$-, C$_6$H$_5$C≡CCH$_2$-, C$_6$H$_5$C=C=CHCH$_3$, Et.

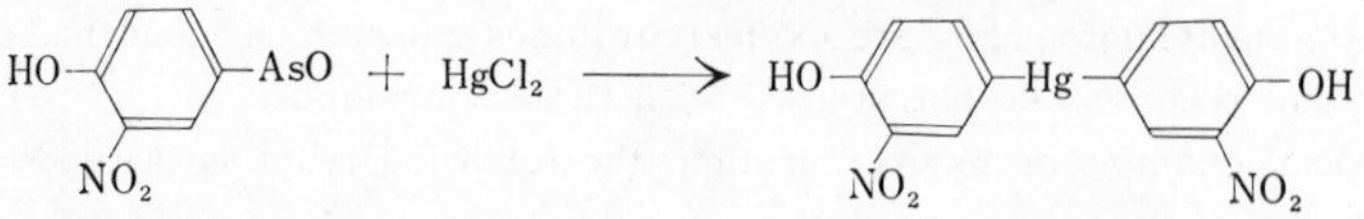

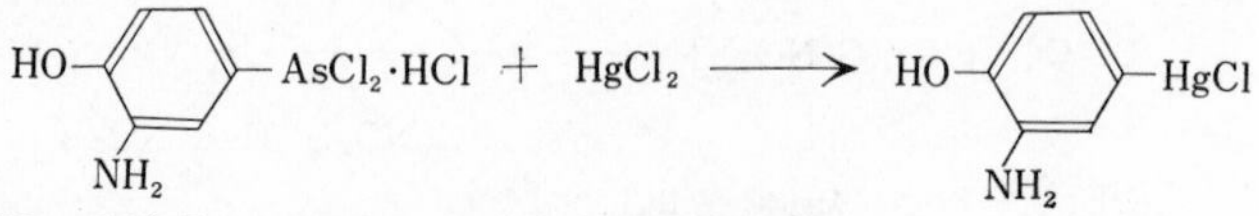

$$(CH_2=CH)_4Sn + HgCl_2 \longrightarrow CH_2=CH-HgCl$$

$$(CH_2=C(CH_3))_2SnBr_2 + HgCl_2 \longrightarrow CH_2=C(CH_3)-HgBr$$

$$(C_6H_5)_3Sb + HgCl_2 \longrightarrow C_6H_5HgCl$$

$$(Et)_4Pb + Hg(PO_4)_2 \longrightarrow C_2H_5HgPO_4$$

(14) RMgX + R'HgX $\longrightarrow$ RHgR'

Example: R, R'=(Me, n-Bu), (Me, Ph), (Ph, cyclo-C$_6$H$_{11}$-), (Ph, naphtyl), (Ph, p-MeC$_6$H$_4$-), (Me, 2,4,6-(Me)$_3$C$_6$H$_2$-), (Ph, o-MeOC$_6$H$_4$-), (p-(CH$_2$=CH)C$_6$H$_4$-, Ph), (cis-2-MeO-cyclo-C$_6$H$_{10}$, neophyl).

(15) (RCOO)$_2$Hg $\xrightarrow{\ \Delta\text{ or }h\nu\ }$ RCOOHgR $\longrightarrow$ R$_2$Hg

Example: R=Me, Et, Ph, 2,4-(NO$_2$)$_2$C$_6$H$_3$-.

$$CCl_3HgCl + Cl_3COONa \longrightarrow (CCl_3)_2Hg$$

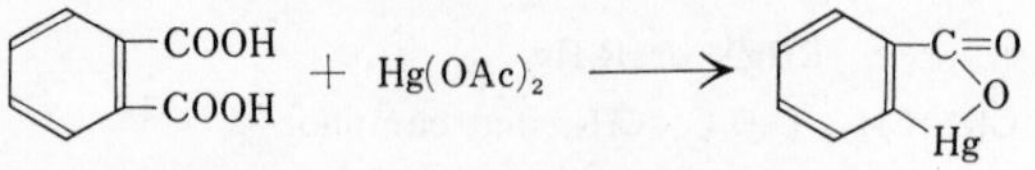

(16) (C$_6$H$_4$NH$_2$)$_2$Hg + AcOH $\longrightarrow$ p-NH$_2$C$_6$H$_4$HgOAc

(17) EtNHNH$_2$ + HgO $\longrightarrow$ Et$_2$Hg

$$PhNHNH_2 + HgO + HgCl_2 \longrightarrow PhHgCl$$

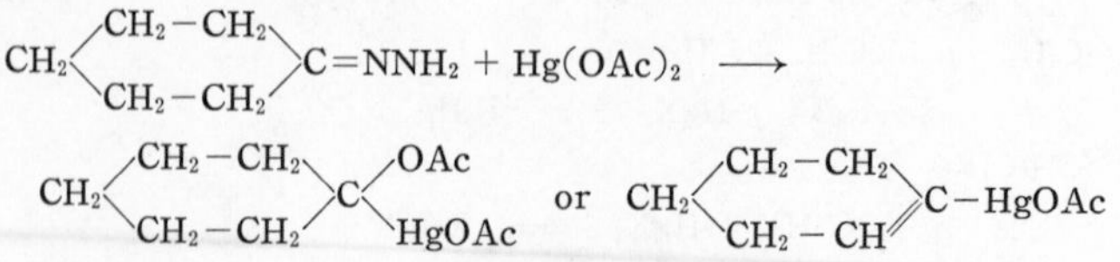

(18) $CO + Hg(OAc)_2 + HOAc \longrightarrow CH_3OCOHgOAc$

(19) $2\,RHgX \longrightarrow R_2Hg + HgX_2$ (symmetrization)

   $RHgX + R'HgX \longrightarrow RR'Hg + HgX_2$ (co-symmetrization)

It is well known that symmetrization proceeds in the presence of various reducing agents such as potassium iodide and sodium thiosulfate.   Kinetics of these reactions have been studied by Reutov and by Jensen.   Jensen synthesized optically active R^*HgR^* in the presence of metallic magnesium.

(20) Denigè's reaction.   This reaction is used conveniently for the qualitative analysis of tertiary alcohol and substituted olefins.   The formula of the resulting yellow precipitate is given as $R\left(\!\!\begin{array}{c}\diagdown \\ \diagup\end{array}\!\!O\!\!\begin{array}{c}\diagup Hg \diagdown \\ \diagdown Hg \diagup\end{array}\!\!SO_4\right)_3.$

(21) $-\overset{|}{\underset{\underset{OAc}{|}}{C}}\!\!-\!\!\overset{|}{\underset{\underset{HgOAc}{|}}{C}}-\ +\ RH\ \xrightarrow{H^+}\ R-\overset{|}{\underset{|}{C}}-\overset{|}{\underset{|}{C}}-HgOAc$

Example: R=aromatics and active methylene compounds such as β–diketone and β–ketoester.

12.4. General Properties

12.4.1. Physical Properties

In the case of R_2M (M=Zn, Cd and Hg), the compounds are generally volatile liquids when R is alkyl, and are solid when R is aryl. For example, when R is methyl, the boiling points of $(CH_3)_2M$ (M=Zn, Cd and Hg) at atmospheric pressure are 46°, 105.5°, and 92° respectively. Trouton constants of dialkylzinc were determined and the vapor is shown to be monomolecular. In benzene solution and at their freezing points, these are also monomolecular. Dielectric constants (for example, 2.55 for diethylzinc), conductivities, atomic refractivities, and dipole moments are reported.

Although the studies on infrared absorption of carbon–metal bonds are not so familiar, it is expected that this field will be explored extensively in the near future as a convenient instrument for low–frequency field is developed.   Several data are reported: 561 and 479 cm^{-1} for ν_{C-Zn} (by IR); 550 and 450 cm^{-1} for ν_{C-Hg} (by IR); 570 cm^{-1} for ν_{C-Hg} (by Raman spectroscopy). In the case of diethyl compounds, Raman spectra are reported for zinc, cadmium, and mercury compounds.

Effects of mercury on the ultraviolet absorptions of other fuctional groups are reported. Studies by nuclear magnetic resonance are currently of interest.

The results of X-ray and electron diffraction and microwave spectroscopy show that the bond angles of C–Hg–C and C–Hg–X are 180° in general. In the presence of oxygen atom, it is reported that deviations from this normal bond angle are observed in several cases. The bond angles of ϕ–Hg–X and ϕ–Hg–ϕ are reported to be 151~165°. In the cases of zinc and cadmium compounds, the angles are 180° in general.

The results of studies by the electron- impact method show that the dissociation energies of C–Hg bond change remarkably depending on the structure. An unusual low bond energy of C–Hg bond can be demonstrated by thermochemical calculations, and it is not surprising that mercury in organomercurics can be replaced by almost any other metal.

The Hg–X bond in RHgX has an ionic nature. For example, CH_3HgClO_4 dissociates completely in aqueous solution, and the existing cation is said to be a hydrated form, $CH_3HgOH_2{}^+$.

12.4.2. Chemical Properties

Thermal stability of cadmium compounds is the lowest among the organometallics of group IIb metals. The only organocadmium which can be stored for a long time is dimethylcadmium; the others decompose even at room temperature and the decomposition is accelerated by the action of light. Organozinc compounds are moderately stable and do not decompose at below about 150°. Organomercurials are much more stable thermally and R_2Hg with higher alkyls can be distilled under reduced pressure.

Although the chemical properties of organozinc and -cadmium compounds resemble each other, those of mercury are considerably different. The former react with air and water, and ignite in some cases, but the latter are stable to oxygen and water. R_2Cd is more stable in air than R_2Zn, and RZnX is less reactive in air than R_2Zn. Since organozinc compounds are stable in carbon dioxide, this atmosphere is used to exclude the effect of air in handling these compounds.

However, it must be added that metylzinc iodide reacts with carbon dioxide readily in pyridine solution.

The reaction with Michler's ketone is used to compare the reactivity of organometallics. The reaction times which are required for the developement of color are reported to be 27.5, 100, and more than 1000hr with diethylzinc, -cadmium, and -mercury respectively, and the reactivity decreases in this order.

It must be noted that organomercurials are very toxic and handling must be very careful to avoid inhalation of the vapor and contact with the skin.

a. Zinc Compounds.

（1） Oxidation by Air.

$$R_2Zn + O_2 \longrightarrow RZnOR \longrightarrow (RO)_2Zn$$

Example: R=Me, Et.

$$R_2Zn + O_2 \longrightarrow RZnOOR \overset{R_2Zn}{\longrightarrow} (RO)_2Zn$$

Example: R=Et, Bu.

$$R_2Zn + O_2 \longrightarrow R-R + ZnO$$

Example: R=Ph.

(2) Exchange of Anion.

$$RZnI + Cu_2X_2 \longrightarrow RZnX$$

Example: R=Et, X=Cl, CN.

(3) Reactions with Inorganic Reagents.

$$R_2Zn + H_2O \longrightarrow RH$$

Example: R=alkyl, vinyl.

$$Et_2Zn + 2\,NH_3(dry) \longrightarrow Zn(NH_2)_2 + 2\,C_2H_6$$

$$2\,PhZnC\equiv CPh + 2\,NH_3(liq.) \longrightarrow Zn(C\equiv CPh)_2 \cdot 2\,NH_3 + Ph_2Zn$$

$$R_2Zn + BX_3 \longrightarrow RBX_2 + RZnX$$

Example: R=vinyl.

$$R_2Zn + I_2 \longrightarrow RZnI$$

Example: R=Ph.

$$R_2Zn + ZnX_2 \longrightarrow RZnX$$

Example: R, X=(p-MeC$_6$H$_4$-, Br), (Et, I), (Ph, I).

$$Ph_2Zn + LiH \xrightarrow{Et_2O} LiPh_2 \cdot ZnH \cdot Et_2O$$

$$2\,EtZnI + 2\,Na \longrightarrow Et_2Zn + Zn + 2\,NaI$$

$$Et_2Zn + 2\,Na \longrightarrow 2\,EtNa + Zn$$

(4) Formation of -Ate Complex.

$$3\,Et_2Zn + 2\,Na \longrightarrow 2\,NaEt_3Zn + Zn$$

(5) Exchange of Organic Radical.

$$R_2Zn + R'H \longrightarrow RZnR' \longrightarrow R'_2Zn$$

Example: R=Ph, R'=PhC≡C-.

(6) Ketone Synthesis.

$$RCOCl + R'ZnI \longrightarrow RCOR' + ZnClI$$

$$RCOX + R_2'Zn \longrightarrow RCOR' + R'ZnX$$

This reaction is the most important synthesis for organozinc compounds.

(7) Reaction with Ketone. Organozinc compounds do not generally react with ketone, and as a result are used for ketone synthesis. However, there are exceptions as follows:

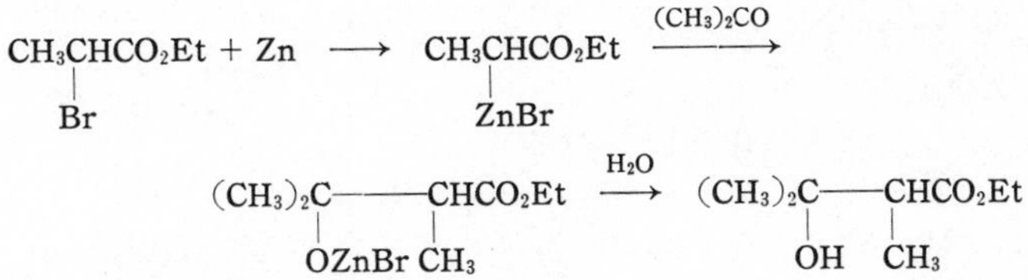

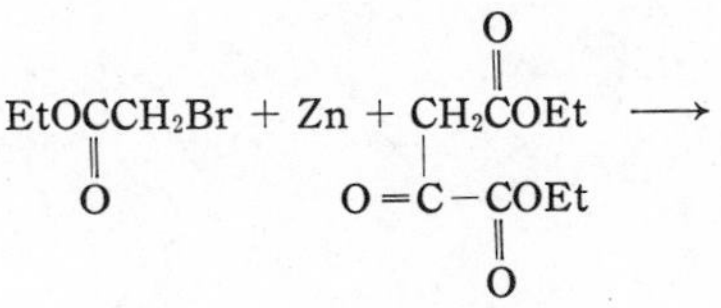

$$CH_3CHCO_2Et + Zn \longrightarrow CH_3CHCO_2Et \xrightarrow{(CH_3)_2CO}$$
$$\quad\quad | \qquad\qquad\qquad\qquad\qquad |$$
$$\quad\quad Br \qquad\qquad\qquad\qquad\quad ZnBr$$

$$(CH_3)_2C\text{———}CHCO_2Et \xrightarrow{H_2O} (CH_3)_2C\text{———}CHCO_2Et$$
$$\qquad\quad | \qquad\qquad | \qquad\qquad\qquad\qquad | \qquad\qquad |$$
$$\qquad OZnBr \quad CH_3 \qquad\qquad\qquad OH \quad\quad CH_3$$

$$\qquad\qquad\qquad\qquad\qquad\qquad O$$
$$\qquad\qquad\qquad\qquad\qquad\qquad \|$$
$$EtOCCH_2Br + Zn + CH_2COEt \longrightarrow$$
$$\quad \| \qquad\qquad\qquad\qquad |$$
$$\quad O \qquad\qquad\qquad\quad O=C-COEt$$
$$\qquad\qquad\qquad\qquad\qquad\qquad\quad \|$$
$$\qquad\qquad\qquad\qquad\qquad\qquad\quad O$$

$$\underset{\substack{| \\ CH_2CO_2Et}}{\overset{\substack{CH_2CO_2Et \\ |}}{BrZnO-C-CO_2Et}} \xrightarrow{H_2O} \underset{\substack{| \\ CH_2CO_2Et}}{\overset{\substack{CH_2CO_2Et \\ |}}{HO-C-CO_2Et}}$$

The mechanism of the Reformatsky reaction, which uses metallic zinc, is similar to those mentioned above.

$$(CH_3)_2CO + BrCH_2CO_2Et \xrightarrow{Zn} \underset{\substack{| \\ OZnBr}}{(CH_3)_2C-CH_2CO_2Et}$$

$$\xrightarrow{H_2O} \underset{\substack{| \\ OH}}{(CH_3)_2CCH_2CO_2Et}$$

Migration of zinc is assumed in some cases to explain the products.

$$CH_3CH=CHCH_2ZnBr \longrightarrow \underset{\substack{| \\ ZnBr}}{CH_3CHCH=CH_2} \xrightarrow{RCOR'}$$

$$\underset{\substack{| \\ R'COZnBr \\ | \\ R}}{CH_3CHCH=CH_2} \longrightarrow \underset{\substack{| \\ OH}}{\overset{\substack{R' \quad CH_3 \\ | \quad |}}{RC-CHCH=CH_2}}$$

(8)   Coupling.

$$2(CH_3)_3CCl + Et_2Zn \longrightarrow 2(CH_3)_3CEt + ZnCl_2$$

(9)   Cyclopropane Formation.

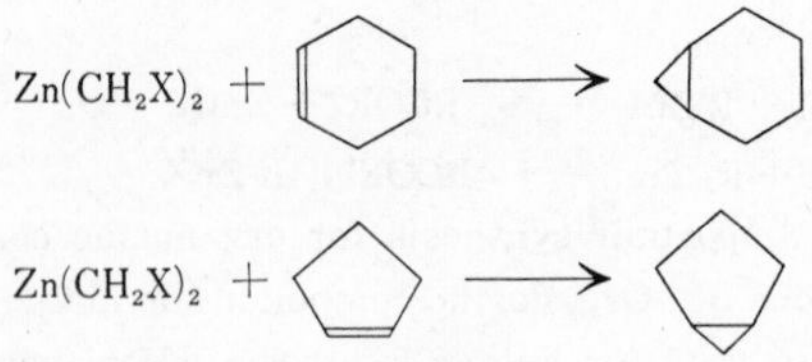

An analogous reaction proceeds as follows:

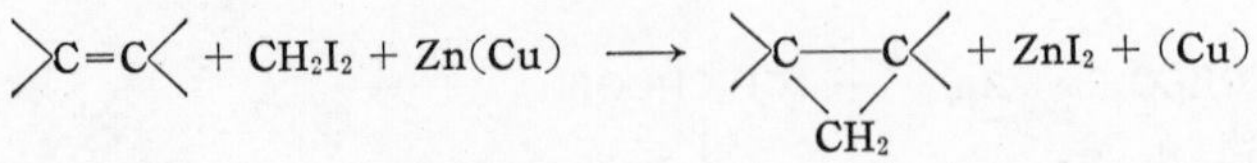

(10)   Reaction with Metal Salts.

$$R_2Zn + MX_n \longrightarrow MR_n$$

Example: R=Me, X=Cl, M=As, Pb, Si, P; R=Et, X=Cl, M=Pb, Sn.

$$R_2Zn + R'_mMX_n \longrightarrow R_nMR'_m$$

Example: R=Me, R'=Et, X=I, M=Sn; R=Me, R'=Me, X=I, M=Hg.

(Methylcyclopentadienyl)$_2$Zn + FeCl$_2$ $\longrightarrow$ Methylferrocene

b. Cadmium Compounds.

(1)   Oxidation.

$$R_2Cd + O_2 \longrightarrow Cd(OOR)_2$$

$$Me_2Cd + R'OOH \longrightarrow MeCdOOR'$$

(2) Ketone Synthesis. This is the most important reaction of organocadmium compounds. In general, the reagents are prepared by the reaction of Grignard reagent with cadmium halogenide and are used without isolation.

$$R_2Cd + R'COX \longrightarrow R'COR + CdX_2$$

An interesting result is reported in that the reaction does not proceed when the cadmium compound is isolated and subjected to the reaction, and that the ketone formation takes place only after $MgBr_2 \cdot OEt_2$ is added. In the presence of lithium bromide, the following reaction takes place:

$$Bu_2Cd + 2\,ClCOCO_2Et \xrightarrow{\ LiBr\ } 2\,BuCOCO_2Et$$

The following abnormal reactions are reported in the ketone synthesis:

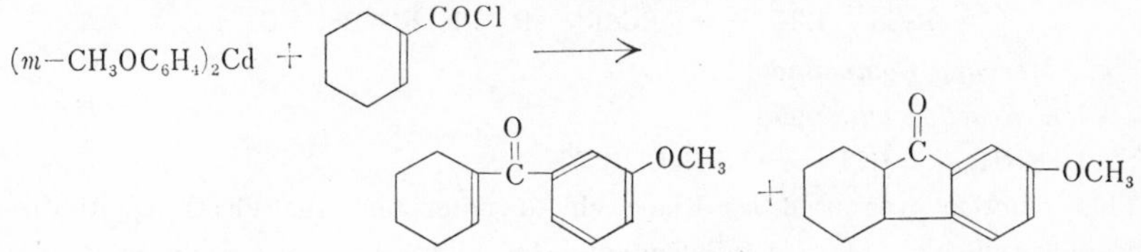

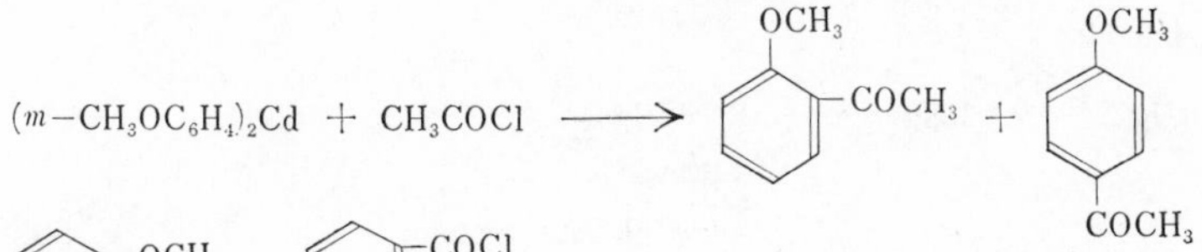

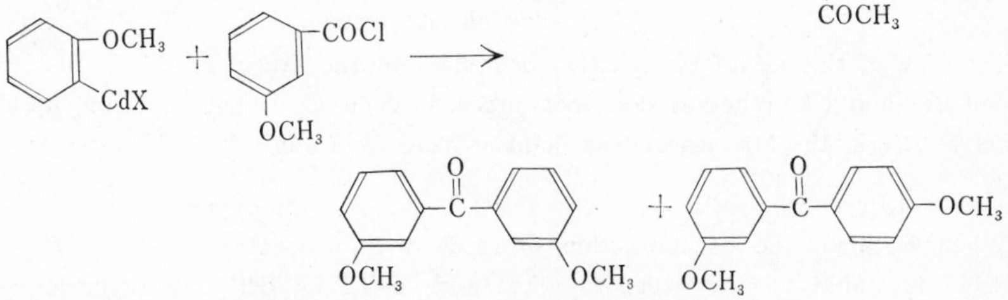

(3) Reaction with Ketone. Although organocadmium compounds do not react with ketone in general, the following exceptions are reported.

$$RCOCO_2Et + R'_2Cd \longrightarrow \xrightarrow{H_2O} R-\underset{\underset{OH}{|}}{\overset{\overset{R'}{|}}{C}}-\underset{\overset{\|}{O}}{C}OEt$$

Example: R=H, alkyl; R'=alkyl.

$$RCHXCOR' + R''_2Cd \longrightarrow \text{ no reaction}$$

$$RCX_2COR' + R''_2Cd \longrightarrow RCX_2\underset{\underset{OH}{|}}{\overset{\overset{R''}{|}}{C}}R' \quad (R'=H, alkyl)$$

$$\underset{CO_2H}{\overset{CO_2H}{|}} \ \text{or} \ \underset{COCl}{\overset{COCl}{|}} + R_2Cd \ \longrightarrow \ \text{oxoalcohol}$$

(4) Cyclopropane Formation.

$$(ICH_2)_2Cd + PhCH=CH_2 \ \longrightarrow \ \underset{\underset{CH_2}{\diagdown \diagup}}{PhCH-CH_2}$$

(5) Reaction with Tertiary Halide.

$$t\text{-}BuCl + (n\text{-}C_8H_{17})_2Cd \ \longrightarrow \ \text{isobutylene}$$

(6) Reaction with Cadmium Halide.

$$R_2Cd + CdX_2 \ \longrightarrow \ RCdX$$

Example: R, X=(Et, Cl), (Et, Br), (Et, I), (Me, I), (Pr, I), (Bu, Cl), (Bu, Br), (Ph, Cl), (o-MeOC$_6$H$_4$-, I).

(7) Reaction with Acetylene.

$$R_2Cd + R'H \ \longrightarrow \ RCdR' \ \ (R=Ph, \ R'=PhC{\equiv}C-)$$

c. Mercury Compounds.

(i) *Reaction with Acid.*

(1) $RHgR' + HCl \ \longrightarrow \ RHgCl + R'H$

This reaction was used by Kharasch to determine the electronegativities of organic radicals. More detailed studies by kinetic measurements have recently been reported.

(2) $RHgZ \ \overset{H^+}{\longrightarrow} \ RHg^+ \ \longrightarrow \ R^+ + Hg$
$$\hspace{4.5cm} \Big| \ HOAc$$
$$\hspace{4.5cm} \longmapsto \ ROAc + \text{olefin}$$

The rate of this solvolytic reaction decreases in the order $Z=ClO_4 > BF_4 > OTs > OBs$, and the reaction does not proceed when Z=halogen. Using optically active RHgZ, the kinetics and mechanism have been studied.

(3) $RHgX \ \overset{HClO_4}{\longrightarrow} \ RH$

When R=aryl, the decomposition proceeds with concentrated acid. Although RHgX is stable to acid when R=alkyl and X=Cl or Br, alkylmercuric iodide decomposes with perchloric acid according to the above equation.

(4) $\underset{\underset{OR \ HgX}{|}}{-\overset{|}{C}-\overset{|}{C}} + HX \ \longrightarrow \ -\overset{|}{C}=\overset{|}{C}- + HgX_2 + HOR$

Deoxymercuration, which is the reverse reaction of oxymercuration, proceeds readily with hydrohalogenic acid and much slower with oxyacid.

(ii) *Reaction with Base.*   Organomercurials, including R$_2$Hg and RHgX, are stable to base. The following exception is reported.

(5) $\underset{\underset{CH_2CH_2HgX}{|}}{RCOCHCOR'} \ \overset{KOH}{\longrightarrow} \ \underset{\underset{CH_2CH_2}{\diagup\diagdown}}{RCO-C-COR'} + Hg$

(iii) *Reaction with Halogen.*

(6) $RHgX + X_2 \longrightarrow RX + HgX_2$

In nonpolar solvents, the reaction proceeds through a radical mechanism. In polar solvents, the reaction is S_E2 and proceeds stereospecifical!y.

(iv) *Reaction with Reducing Reagent.* In general, RHgX reacts with reducing agent to form R_2Hg. In some cases, reduction proceeds further to form metallic mercury. The mercury content of the organomercy compound is determined conveniently by reducing to mercury with zinc dust or stannous chloride.

(v) *Reaction with Metals.*

(7) $RHgX + {}^{203}Hg \longrightarrow R^{203}HgX + Hg$

$\qquad RHgCl + Na \longrightarrow R_2Hg \longrightarrow RNa$

The same kind of metal exchange takes place similarly with Be, Mg. Cd, Al, Bi, Fe, Cu, and Zn.

(vi) *Reaction with Metal Halogenides.*

(8) $(PhCH_2)_2Hg + FeCl_3 \xrightarrow{\text{EtOCH}_2\text{CH}_2\text{OH}} PhCH_2OCH_2CH_2OEt + HgCl_2$

$\qquad\qquad\qquad\qquad \xrightarrow{\text{Dioxane}} PhCH_2HgCl + PhCH_2Cl$

$\qquad + CuCl_2 \xrightarrow{\text{EtOCH}_2\text{CH}_2\text{OH}} PhCH_2OCH_2CH_2OEt + HgCl_2$

$\qquad\qquad\qquad\qquad \xrightarrow{\text{Dioxane}} PhCH_2Cl + HgCl_2$

$\qquad\qquad 2\,R_2Hg + SnCl_4 \longrightarrow 2\,RHgCl + R_2SnCl_2$

Example: $R=C_6H_5-$.

$\qquad\qquad R_2Hg + SbCl_3 \longrightarrow R_3SbCl_3 + RHgCl + Hg$

Example: $R=C_6H_5-$.

$\qquad\qquad R_2Hg + SiCl_4 \longrightarrow RHgCl$

Example: $R=C_6H_5-$.

$\qquad\qquad R_2Hg + BCl_3 \longrightarrow RBCl_2 + HgCl_2$

Example: $R=C_6H_5-$, $p\text{-MeOC}_6H_4-$. $p\text{-EtOC}_6H_4-$, $C_{10}H_9-$.

$\qquad\qquad R_2Hg + PCl_3 \longrightarrow RPCl_2 + HgCl_2$

Example: $R=C_6H_5-$, $o\text{-MeC}_6H_4-$, $p\text{-MeC}_6H_4-$, $2,4\text{-Me}_2C_6H_3-$, $p\text{-MeOC}_6H_4-$, $p\text{-C}_6H_4\text{-}$ $CH_2CH_2C_6H_4-$.

$\qquad\qquad R_2Hg + AsCl_3 \longrightarrow RAsCl_2 + R_2AsCl + R_3As$

Example: $R=n\text{-Pr}$, $\alpha\text{-C}_4H_3S-$, C_6H_5-.

Similar reaction with $TlBr_3$ has been reported recently.

(vii) *Exchange Reaction between Organomercurials.* Exchange reactions according to Equations 9~11 have been studied by using mercurics containing radioactive mercury and optically active alkyls. The mechanism is S_E2 or S_Ei.

(9) $RHgX + Hg^*X_2 \rightleftharpoons RHg^*X + HgX_2$

(10) $R^0Hg^*X + RHgX \rightleftharpoons R^0Hg^*R + HgX_2$

(11) $R^0Hg^*X + R_2Hg \rightleftharpoons R^0Hg^*R + RHgX$

In connection with the above reaction, the mechanism of the following reactions were also studied.

$$(12) \quad R_2Hg + R'_2Mg \longrightarrow R'_2Hg + R_2Mg$$

$$(13) \quad R_2Hg + R'MgX \longrightarrow R'HgR + RMgX$$

In the presence of acid, the products of reaction 9 change as follows:

$$(14) \quad RHgOAc + Hg(OAc)_2 \xrightarrow[\text{HOAc}]{H^+} ROAc + Hg_2(OAc)_2$$

Example: $R=C_6H_5CH_2-$, $p\text{-MeOC}_6H_4CH_2-$.

(viii) *Thermal Decomposition.*

$$(15) \quad RHgOCOR' \longrightarrow ROCOR' + Hg$$

Example: $R=CH_3-$, $CH_2=CH-$, cyclopentenyl, cyclohexenyl; $R'=CH_3-$, $ClCH_2-$, Cl_2CH-, Cl_3C-, C_6H_5-.

$$(CH_2=CH-)_2Hg + ROH \longrightarrow CH_2=CH_2 + ROCH=CH_2 + Hg$$

Example: $R=CH_3CO-$, C_6H_5-.

$$(CH_2=CH-)_2Hg + RSH \longrightarrow CH_2=CH_2 + RSCH=CH_2 + Hg$$

Example: $R=C_{12}H_{25}-$.

(ix) *Miscellaneous.*

$$(16) \quad C_6H_5HgCCl_2Br + {>}C{=}C{<} \longrightarrow C_6H_5HgBr + -\overset{|}{\underset{\diagdown\diagup}{C}}-\overset{|}{\underset{CCl_2}{C}}-$$

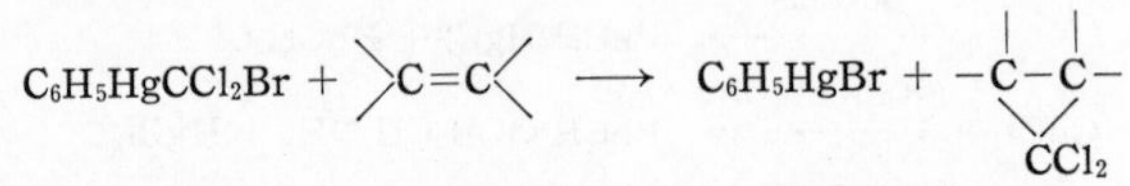

(17) $Hg(CH_2CHO)_2$ is used to introduce $-OCH=CH_2$ or $-CH_2CHO$ into organic compounds.

REFERENCES

1) Ed. by Kinki Society of the Chemical Industry, "Organometallic Chemistry and Its Applications", Asakura, Tokyo (1962).

2) J. Cason, *Chem. Revs.*, **40**, 15 (1957).

3) H. Gilman, "Organic Chemistry. An Advanced Treatise", John Wiley (1953).

4) H. C. Kaufman, "Handbook of Organometallic Compounds", D. van Nostrand (1961).

5) O. A. Reutov, *Angew. Chem.*, **72**, 198 (1960).

6) E. G. Rochov, D. T. Hurd and R. N. Lewis, "Chemistry of Organometallic Compounds", John Wiley (1957).

7) N. V. Sidgwick, "The Chemical Elements and Their Compounds", Oxford (1950).

8) F. C. Whitmore, "Organic Compounds of Mercury", The Chemical Catalog Co. (1921).

9) Ed. by F. G. A. Stone, R. West, "Advances in Orgenometallic Chemistry", Vol. 4, Academic Press (1966).

【Zn】

ZnCH₂I₂

① Iodomethylzinc iodide
ICH₂ZnI

② $CH_2I_2 + Zn-Cu \xrightarrow[\text{in ether, heat}]{} 40\%$

$CH_2N_2 + ZnI_2 \xrightarrow[\text{under N, at r. t.}]{\text{in ether-dioxane,}}$

③ Slowly decomp. at room temp. and
quickly at higher temp.

④ $+I_2 \longrightarrow CH_2I_2 + ZnI_2$

$+H_2O \longrightarrow CH_3I + Zn(OH)_2 + ZnI_2$

$+\text{olefins} \xrightarrow[]{\text{in ether, 35°}}$ cyclopropane

derivatives 10~70%

$+CH_2N_2 \longrightarrow (ICH_2)_2Zn$

⑥ Chemistry of Organometallic Compounds 62 (1959). Compt. rend.
188, 1555 (1929). Ann. **650**, 1
(1961). JACS **81**, 4256 (1959).

ZnC₂H₄Cl₂

① Bis(chloromethyl)zinc
(ClCH₂)₂Zn

② $ZnCl_2 + CH_2N_2 \xrightarrow[]{\text{in ether}}$

③ Sol. in ether.

④ $\xrightarrow[]{\text{heat}}$ cyclopropane, ethylene, ethane

$+ I_2 \longrightarrow (ICH_2)_2Zn$

$+ I_2 \xrightarrow[]{-80°} CH_2I_2(38\%) + CH_2ICl(44\%)$

$+ \text{cyclohexene} \xrightarrow[]{\text{heat}}$ norcaran(57%)

$+ (CH_3)_3N \xrightarrow[]{\text{in abs. ether}}$

$[(CH_3)_3NCH_2ZnCH_2N(CH_3)_3]2Cl$

$+ Ph_3P \xrightarrow[]{\text{in ether}}$

$[Ph_3PCH_2ZnCH_2PPh_3]2Cl$

$+ Ph_3Sb \xrightarrow[]{\text{in abs. ether}} [Ph_3SbCH_3]Cl$

⑥ Ann. **656**, 18 (1962); **650**, 1 (1961).

ZnC₂H₄I₂

① Bis(iodomethyl)zinc

(ICH₂)₂Zn

② $ZnI_2 + CH_2N_2$

$\xrightarrow[\text{under N, in dioxane-ether, r. t.}]{} 80\%$

③ Sol. in dioxane, ether.

④ $+ I_2 \xrightarrow[]{\text{in ether}} CH_2I_2 \ (65\sim85\%)$

$+ \text{cyclohexene} \xrightarrow[]{\text{heat}}$ norcaran (57%)

$+ 5\% HCl \longrightarrow CH_3I$

⑥ Ann. **650**, 1 (1961); **656**, 18 (1962).

ZnC₂H₅Cl

① Ethylzinc chloride
C₂H₅ZnCl

② $EtZnI + Cu_2Cl_2 \xrightarrow[]{\text{in ether}} 80\%$

③ Colorless liq.
Sol. in ether; decomp. in H₂O.

④ $+ 2I \longrightarrow C_2H_5I + ZnICl$

⑥ Bull. soc. chim. France [4] **33**, 1414
(1923).

ZnC₂H₅I

① Ethylzinc iodide
C₂H₅ZnI

② $C_2H_5I + Zn-Cu \text{ pair} \xrightarrow[]{\text{in ether}}$

③ White crystals.
Decomp. in H₂O; stable under CO₂.

④ $\xrightarrow[]{\text{heat}} Et_2Zn + ZnI_2$

$+ H_2O \longrightarrow C_2H_6$

$+ Na \longrightarrow Zn + NaI + Et_2Zn$

⑥ Krause and Grosse. (1937). Bull.
soc. chim. France [4] **33**, 1414 (1923).
Am. Chem. J. **25**, 422 (1901).
Chem. Zentr. **1903**, 339.

ZnC₂H₆

① Dimethylzinc
(CH₃)₂Zn

③ Colorless liq.(46°/760, 0°/124). [−42°].
d 1.386 (10°).
Decomp. in H₂O and alc.; sol. in org.
solvents. Stable in a sealed tube.
Spontaneously inflammable.

Raman: Ann. **130**, 118 (1864).

IR: 615cm^{-1}; J. Chem. Phys. **17**, 128 (1949).

④ + O$_2$ ⟶ CH$_3$ZnOCH$_3$
+ cyclic ethers ⟶ stable adducts

⑥ Ind. J. Phys. **5**, 145 (1930). JACS **76**, 2262 (1954). Z. anorg. allg. Chem. **319**, 183 (1962).

ZnC₂H₆O

① Methylmethoxyzinc
CH$_3$ZnOCH$_3$

② (CH$_3$)$_2$Zn + O$_2$ ⟶
(CH$_3$)$_2$Zn + CH$_3$OH ⟶

③ White crystals.
Sol. in alc. Odor of camphor.

⑥ Chemistry of Organometallic Componds 62 (1959). Chem. Zentr. **1864**, 403. JCS **1946**, 688.

ZnC₃H₅Br

① Allylzinc bromide
H$_2$C=CHCH$_2$Br + Zn $\xrightarrow{\text{in THF}}$ 70%

③ IR: 1610(s), 1640cm^{-1}(sh)

④ ⟶ (H$_2$C=CHCH)$_2$Zn
+ RCOR' ⟶
RR'C(OZnBr)CH$_2$CH=CH$_2$

⑥ Bull. soc. chim. France **1958**, 1475; **1962**, 974; CA **57**, 5939 (1962).

ZnC₃H₇I

① Isopropylzinc iodide
(CH$_3$)$_2$CHZnI

② *i*-PrI + Zn–Cu $\xrightarrow{\text{in ligroin}}$

⑥ Krause, Grosse 62 (1937).

ZnC₄H₆

① Divinylzinc
(CH$_2$=CH)$_2$Zn

② ZnCl$_2$ + 2CH$_2$=CHMgBr $\xrightarrow{\text{THF}}$

③ Liq. (32°/22).

Spontaneously inflammable in air. Easily hydrolyzed. Less stable than Et$_2$Zn.

IR: JOM 92, 138 (1960).

④ + H$_2$O ⟶ CH$_2$=CH$_2$
(quantitatively)
+ BX$_3$ ⟶ CH$_2$=CHZnX +
CH$_2$=CHBX$_2$
decomp. ⟶ ethylene + butadiene
+ black solid

⑥ Z. Naturf. **14b**, 352 (1959).

ZnC₄H₇Br

① Crotylzinc bromide
CH$_3$CH=CHCH$_2$ZnBr

② CH$_3$CH=CHCH$_2$Br + Zn $\xrightarrow{\text{in THF, under N}}$

③ IR: 1610(s), 1640cm^{-1}(w).

④ + RCOR' ⟶

RR'C(OZnBr)CH(CH$_3$)CH=CH$_2$ $\xrightarrow{\text{H}_2\text{O}}$
RR'C(OH)CH(CH$_3$)CH=CH$_2$

⑥ Bull. soc. chim. France **1958**, 1475.

ZnC₄H₁₀

① Diethylzinc
(C$_2$H$_5$)$_2$Zn

② C$_2$H$_5$I + Zn $\xrightarrow{\text{under N, 80~90°,1~2 hrs.}}$ 92%

Et$_3$Al + ZnCl$_2$ $\xrightarrow{\text{in Et}_3\text{Al}_2\text{Cl}_3,\ 100°}$ 92.7%

③ Colorless liq. (116.8°/761, 30°/27). [−33.8°, −35.1°]. n_D 1.4983 (20°). d 1.205 (20°).
Decomp. in H$_2$O and alc.; sol. in org. solvents.
NMR: JACS **82**, 5983 (1960).
IR: 564cm^{-1}; J. Chem. Soc. Japan **66**, 1477 (1963).
Spontaneously inflammable.

④ + O$_2$ ⟶ C$_2$H$_5$ZnOOC$_2$H$_5$ ⟶
Zn(OOEt)$_2$ $\xrightarrow{\text{Et}_2\text{Zn}}$ Zn(OEt)$_2$

$\xrightarrow{\text{H}_2\text{O}}$ EtOH

+ alkyldichloramine $\xrightarrow{\text{petr. ether}}$

RNHC₂H₅ (40~50%)

+ H₂O $\longrightarrow$ EtZnOH + C₂H₆

+ NaH $\xrightarrow{\text{in glycol ether}}$ NaH·2ZnEt₂

⑥ Handbook of Chemistry and Physics (1958). JACS **82**, 5983 (1960) ; **76**, 2262 (1954). Chem. & Ind. **1959**, 750.

ZnC₄H₁₀O₂

① Ethyl(ethylperoxy)zinc
C₂H₅ZnOOC₂H₅

② Et₂Zn + O₂ $\xrightarrow{\text{in ligroim}}$

⑥ Krause, Grosse (1937). Ber. **23**, 396 (1890).

ZnC₄H₁₀O₄

① Bis(ethylperoxy)zinc
(C₂H₅OO)₂Zn

② Et₂Zn + O₂ $\xrightarrow{\text{in anisole, ether}}$

③ White solid.
Non volatile. Insol. in aprotic solvents.

⑥ Chem. & Ind. **1959**, 750.

ZnC₅H₁₂

① Ethylpropylzinc
C₂H₅ZnC₃H₇

② EtZnI + PrMgBr $\longrightarrow$

③ Liq. (27°/10). n_D 1.4891 (17°). $n_{H\alpha}$ 1.4851 (17°). d 1.1558 (18.5°/4°).
Sol. in org. solvents. The rate of disproportionation is rather slow at room temp.

⑥ Krause, Grosse 118 (1937). Ber. **59**, 931 (1926).

ZnC₅H₁₂O

① Ethylisopropyloxyzinc
(CH₃)₂CHOZnC₂H₅

② Et₂Zn + *i*-PrOH $\longrightarrow$

③ Stable in excess of *i*-PrOH.

⑥ Can. J. Chem. **41**, 1368 (1963).

ZnC₆H₅I

① Phenylzinc iodide
C₆H₅ZnI

② (C₆H₅)₂Zn + I₂ $\longrightarrow$

③ Solid. [decomp.].
Sol. in ether ; decomp. in H₂O.

⑥ Chemistry of Organometallic Compounds 62 (1959). Ber. **46**, 1679 (1913).

ZnC₆H₁₃IO₂

① Ethyliodozinc dioxanate
C₂H₅ZnI·C₄H₈O₂

② Et₂Zn + ZnI₂ $\xrightarrow{\text{in dioxane}}$ 80%

EtI + Cu−Zn + dioxane $\xrightarrow{\text{in ether}}$ 81%

③ White crystals.

④ + C₆H₅COCl $\xrightarrow{\text{5°, in toluene}}$
C₆H₅COC₂H₅ (31%)

⑥ Dokl. **124**, 602 (1959).

ZnC₆H₁₄

① Dipropylzinc
(C₃H₇)₂Zn

② Zn−Cu powder + PrBr + PrI
$\xrightarrow{\text{under N, 2~3 hrs.}}$

③ Liq. (160°/760, 48°/10). n_D 1.4845 (18.6°). d 1.1034 (20°/4°).
Decomp. in H₂O. Sol. in org. solvents.
Spontaneously inflammable.

⑥ Handbook of Chemistry and Physics (1958). JACS **76**, 2262 (1954).

ZnC₆H₁₄

① Diisopropylzinc
(*i*-C₃H₇)₂Zn

② Zn−Cu powder + *i*-PrBr + *i*-PrI

under N, 20°
───────→ 85%

③ Colorless liq. (139°/760, 96°/40).
Sol. in org. solvents. Decomp. in
H₂O.

⑥ Krause, Grosse (1937).   JACS **76**,
2263 (1954)；**66**, 893 (1944).

ZnC₆H₁₄

① Ethylisobutylzinc
C₂H₅Zn(*i*-C₄H₉)

② C₂H₅ZnI + *i*-C₄H₉MgBr ──→

③ Liq. (48°/11). n_D 1.4714(16.6°).
d 1.0861(16.6°/4°).
Sol. in org. solvents. About a half
was recovered after two weeks at
room temp.

⑥ Krause, Grosse 118 (1937).   Ber. **59**,
931 (1926).

ZnC₆H₁₅Ce

① Cesium triethylzinc
CeZn(C₂H₅)₃

② Et₂Zn + Ce ──→

③ Solid. [37°].
Sol. in org. solvents. Decomp. in
H₂O.

④ + PhCOPh ──→
Ph₂CEt(OCe) + Et₂Zn

⑥ Krause, Grosse (1937).   Compt.
rend. **223**, 1006 (1946).

ZnC₆H₁₅K

① Potassium triethylzinc
KZn(C₂H₅)₃

② Et₂Zn + K ──→

③ Solid. [68~71°].
Sol. in org. solvents. Decomp. in
H₂O.

⑥ Krause, Grosse (1937).

ZnC₆H₁₅Na

① Sodium triethylzinc
NaZn(C₂H₅)₃

② Et₂Zn + Na ──→

③ Liq. [27°].
Sol. in org. solvents.

⑥ Krause, Grosse (1937).

ZnC₆H₁₅Rb

① Rubidium triethylzinc
RbZn(C₂H₅)₃

② ZnEt₂ + Rb ──60°──→

③ Colorless crystals. [70~75°].
Sol. in org. solvents.

⑥ Krause, Grosse (1937).   Ber. **59**, 2646
(1926).

ZnC₇H₁₀

① Ethylcyclopentadienylzinc
C₅H₅ZnC₂H₅

② EtMgBr + C₅H₆ + ZnCl₂ ──in ether, reflux──→

③ White crystals. [69~70°].
Sensitive to air. Solvolyzed in alcs.
or H₂O. Sol. in ether and hydrocarbons.

④ + FeCl₂ ──in THF──→ ferrocene

⑥ Z. Naturf. **15b** 332 (1960). Z. Elektrochem. **64**, 945 (1960).

ZnC₇H₁₆

① Propylisobutylzinc
C₃H₇Zn(*i*-C₄H₉)

② PrZnI + *i*-BuMgBr ──→

③ Liq. (52°/9). n_D 1.4697 (16°). *d* 1.047
(17°/4°).
Sol. in org. solvents. About a half
was recovered after two weeks at
room temp.

⑥ Krause, Grosse (1937).   Ber. **59**, 931
(1926).

ZnC₈H₄K₂

① Dipotassium tetraacetylenylzinc
K₂[Zn(C≡CH)₄]

② Zn(SCN)₂2NH₃ + 4KC≡CH ──→

60〜70%

$K_2 \cdot Zn(CN)_4 + 4KC \equiv CH \longrightarrow$

③ Insol. in dry C_6H_6, petr. ether,
dimethylformamide, CCl_4.

④ $+ H_2O \longrightarrow K_2[Zn(OH)_4] + C_2H_2$

$+ Br_2 \xrightarrow{\text{under N, 50°}} Br_2C=CHBr$

$+ Br_3CCHBr_2$

⑥ Ber. **91**, 2861 (1958).

ZnC₈H₁₈

① Dibutylzinc
$(C_4H_9)_2Zn$

③ Liq. (195°/760, 81〜82°/9).
Decomp. in H_2O.

④ $+ O_2 \longrightarrow Zn(OOBu)_2 \xrightarrow{Bu_2Zn}$

$(BuO)_2Zn \xrightarrow{H_2O} BuOH$

$Zn(OOBu)_2 + H_2O \longrightarrow BuOOH$

⑥ Handbook of Chemistry and Physics
1958. Chem. & Ind. **1959**, 750.

ZnC₈H₁₈

① Diisobutylzinc
$(i\text{-}C_4H_9)_2Zn$

② $Zn-Cu$ power $+ i\text{-}BuI + i\text{-}BuBr \longrightarrow$

③ Colorless liq. (170°/760, 55°/10).
n_D 1.4603(16°). d 1.0080(16.5°/4°).
Sol. in org. solvents. Decomp. in
H_2O.

⑥ Ber. **59**, 931 (1926).

ZnC₈H₁₈

① Di-*sec*-butylzinc
$(s\text{-}C_4H_9)_2Zn$

② $Zn-Cu$ pair $+ s\text{-}BuBr + s\text{-}BuI$
$\longrightarrow$ 72%

③ (56°/4).

⑥ JACS **66**, 893 (1944).

ZnC₈H₁₈O₄

① Bis(butylperoxy)zinc
$(C_4H_9OO)_2Zn$

② $Bu_2Zn + Et_2O(O_2 \text{ satd.}) \longrightarrow$

④ $+ H_2O \longrightarrow BuOOH + BuOH$
$+ Bu_2Zn \longrightarrow 2Zn(OBu)_2$
$\xrightarrow{H_2O} BuOH$

⑥ Chem. & Ind. **1959**, 750.

ZnC₈H₂₂Li₂O

① Tetramethyl-dilithiozinc etherate
$(C_2H_5)_2O \cdot Li_2Zn(CH_4)_4$

② $(CH_3)_2Zn + LiCH_3 \xrightarrow{\text{in ether}}$

③ Solid.
Not inflammable in air. Decomp.
vigorously in H_2O.

⑥ Chemistry of Organometallic compounds (1959). JOC **13**, 711 (1948).

ZnC₉H₂₀

① Isobutylisoamylzinc
$i\text{-}C_4H_9Zn(i\text{-}C_5H_{11})$

② $i\text{-}BuZnI + i\text{-}AmMgBr \longrightarrow$

③ Liq. (84°/11). n_D 1.4694(16°).
d 1.008(18°).
Sol. in org. solvents. About a half
was recovered after three weeks
at room temp.

⑥ Krause, Grosse (1937). Ber. **59**, 931
(1926).

ZnC₁₀H₁₀

① Dicyclopentadienylzinc
$(C_5H_5)_2Zn$

② $C_5H_5MgBr + ZnCl_2 \xrightarrow{\text{in ether}}$

③ IR: 660(w), 613(s), 345 cm⁻¹(s); Ber.
93, 1171 (1960).

⑥ Z. Naturf. **15 b**, 332 (1960).

ZnC₁₀H₁₄

① Bis(2-pentynyl)zinc.
$(C_2H_5C \equiv CCH_2)_2Zn$

② $C_2H_5C \equiv CCH_2Br + Zn \longrightarrow$

③ IR: Compt. rend. **248**, 1356 (1959).

ZnC₁₀H₁₅IO
① Phenyliodozinc etherate
$C_6H_5ZnI \cdot (C_2H_5)_2O$
② $(C_6H_5)_2Zn + ZnI_2 \xrightarrow{\text{in ether}} 79\%$
④ $+ C_6H_5COCl$
$\xrightarrow[\text{0°, in toluene}]{} C_6H_5COC_6H_5 \ (72\%)$
⑥ Dokl. **124**, 602 (1959).

ZnC₁₀H₂₂
① Diisoamylzinc
$(i\text{-}C_5H_{11})_2Zn$
② $i\text{-}AmZnI + i\text{-}AmMgBr \longrightarrow$
$(i\text{-}Am)_2Hg + Zn \longrightarrow$
③ Colorless liq. (220°/760, 120°/10).
n_D 1.4705(17°). d 0.9939 (19°/4°).
Decomp. in H_2O. Sol. in org. solvents.
⑥ Krause, Grosse 117 (1937). Ber. **59**,
931 (1926). Ann. **130**, 122 (1864).

ZnC₁₁H₁₀
① Phenylcyclopentadienylzinc
$C_5H_5ZnC_6H_5$
② $C_6H_5MgBr + C_5H_6 +$
$ZnCl_2 \xrightarrow{\text{reflux in ether}}$
③ White crystals. [74~76°].
Sensitive to air. Sol. in ether and
hydrocarbons. Decomp. in alcs.
and H_2O.
④ $+ FeCl_2 \longrightarrow$ ferrocene
⑥ Z. Naturf. **15**b 332(1960). Z. Elektrochem. **64**, 945 (1960).

ZnC₁₁H₁₇BrO
① *p*-Tolylbromozinc etherate
$p\text{-}CH_3C_6H_4ZnBr \cdot (C_2H_5)_2O$
② $(p\text{-}CH_3C_6H_4)_2Zn + ZnBr_2 \xrightarrow{\text{in ether}} 73\%$
③ White crystals.
⑥ Dokl. **124**, 602 (1959)

ZnC₁₂H₈Cl₂
① Bis(*p*-chlorophenyl)zinc

$(p\text{-}ClC_6H_4)_2Zn$
② $p\text{-}ClC_6H_4MgCl + ZnCl_2 \xrightarrow{\text{in THF}}$
$(p\text{-}ClC_6H_4)_2Hg + Zn \xrightarrow{\text{in xylene}} 75\%$
③ White needles. [212~214°].
Sol. in hot xylene; less sol. in cold
xylene and petr. ether.
④ $+ SnBr_4 \longrightarrow (p\text{-}ClC_6H_4)_2Sn$
$+ H_2O \longrightarrow ClC_6H_5$
⑥ Krause, Grosse (1937). Ber. **63**, 1138
(1934).

ZnC₁₂H₈F₂
① Bis(*p*-fluorophenyl)zinc
$(p\text{-}FC_6H_4)_2Zn$
② $(p\text{-}FC_6H_4)_2Hg + Zn \xrightarrow{\text{in xylene}} 38\%$
③ White crystals. [135~136°].
Sol. in xylene; slightly sol. in petr.
ether.
⑥ Krause, Grosse 119 (1937). Ber. **67**,
1138 (1934).

ZnC₁₂H₁₀
① Diphenylzinc
$(C_6H_5)_2Zn$
② $(C_6H_5)_2Hg + Zn$ powder $\xrightarrow{\text{under N, heat}}$
$(C_6H_5)_2Hg + Zn \xrightarrow{\text{in boiling xylene}} 70\%$
$ZnBr_2 + Ph_3Al + Ph_2AlCl \longrightarrow$
③ White needles. (280~285°/760). [107°].
Sol. in ether, benzene; slightly sol.
in petr. ether. Decomp. in H_2O;
decomp. but not inflammable in
air.
④ $+$ dry $O_2 \longrightarrow ZnO +$ biphenyl
$+ I_2 \xrightarrow{\text{in benzene}} C_6H_5ZnI \xrightarrow{\text{heat}} ZnI_2$
⑥ Krause, Grosse 119 (1937). Ber **46**,
1679 (1913); **67**, 1138 (1934). US
3080409; CA **59**, 3957 (1963).

ZnC₁₂H₁₂Li
① Lithium diphenylzinc hydride
$Li \cdot ZnH(C_6H_5)_2$

② $Ph_2Zn + LiH$ $\xrightarrow{\text{fusion}}$ 83%

③ Colorless crystals.

Decomp. in air. Evolves hydrogen in H_2O or alcs. Sol. in THF; slightly sol. in ether, benzene; hardly sol. in dioxane.

⑥ Ann. **577**, 11 (1952).

$ZnC_{12}H_{14}$

① Bis(methylcyclopentadienyl)zinc $(CH_3C_5H_4)_2Zn$

② $Na + CH_3C_5H_5$

$\xrightarrow{\text{in ether}}$ Na salt (suspension)

$\xrightarrow{ZnCl_2}$

③ White crystals. [ca. 250° decomp.]. Fairly stable in H_2O and air; slightly sol. in THF. Decomp. in dil. acid.

④ + dil. acid $\longrightarrow$ decomp.

$+ H_2O$ $\longrightarrow$ slowly hydrolyzed

$+ FeCl_2$ $\xrightarrow{\text{heat in THF}}$ methylferrocene

⑥ Z. anorg. allg. Chem. **307**, 120 (1960).

$ZnC_{13}H_{17}N$

① Diethylzinc isoquinolinate $(C_2H_5)_2Zn \cdot C_9H_7N$

② $Et_2Zn + isoquinoline$

$\xrightarrow{\text{under N, in } n\text{-pentane}}$

③ Yellow crystals. (60°/0.2 decomp.). [9~10°].

Sensitive to air and moisture. Electrical conductivity in toluene $1 \times 10^{-4} \mho$.

④ $+ O_2$ $\longrightarrow$ deep red viscous oil (unidentified)

⑥ Angew. **74**, 901 (1962).

$ZnC_{14}H_{10}$

① Phenyl(2-phenylethynyl)zinc $C_6H_5ZnC \equiv CC_6H_5$

② $Ph_2Zn + PhC \equiv CH$ $\xrightarrow{\text{in ether}}$

③ Colorless crystals. [132.5~133.5°].

Sol. in THF, benzene and ether.

Decomp. in H_2O.

④ $+ H_2O$ $\longrightarrow$ $PHC \equiv CH + C_6H_6 + ZnO$

$\underset{\text{in ether}}{\rightleftharpoons}$ $Zn(C \equiv CC_6H_5)_2 + Ph_2Zn$

$+ NH_3$ liq.

$\longrightarrow$ $[Zn(C \equiv CPh)_2 2NH_3] \downarrow + Ph_2Zn$

⑥ Ber. **95**, 2155 (1962).

$ZnC_{14}H_{14}$

① Di-*o*-tolylzinc $(o\text{-}CH_3C_6H_4)_2Zn$

② $(o\text{-}CH_3C_6H_4)_2Hg + Zn$ $\xrightarrow{\text{in xylene}}$ 39%

③ White crystals. [207~210°].

Sol. in org. solvents; less sol. in petr. ether.

⑥ Krause, Grosse 119 (1937). Ber. **67**, 1138 (1934).

$ZnC_{14}H_{30}$

① Diheptylzinc $(C_7H_{15})_2Zn$

② $ZnCl_2 + 2 Al(C_7H_{15})_3$ $\xrightarrow{\text{under N, 15 min.}}$

③ $(121 \sim 123^\circ / 10^{-4})$.

⑥ Brit. 836734; CA **55**, 3435 (1963).

$ZnC_{16}H_{10}$

① Bis(2-phenylethynyl)zinc $(C_6H_5C \equiv C)_2Zn$

② $Ph_2Zn + PhC \equiv CH$ $\xrightarrow{\text{in ether}}$ 80%

③ Colorless crystals. [200°].

Readily sol. in liq. NH_3; insol. in org. solvents. Not explosive.

④ $+ NH_3(liq.)$

$\xrightarrow{-78°}$ $Zn(C \equiv CPh)_2 \cdot 2NH_3 \downarrow$

$\xrightarrow{NH_3 \text{ gas}}$ $[Zn(NH_3)_4][Zn(C \equiv CPh)_4]$

$+ NH_3(gas)$ $\longrightarrow$ $Zn(NH_2)_2$

$+ 2H^+$ $\longrightarrow$ $Zn^{2+} + PhC \equiv CH$

⑥ Ber. **95**, 2155 (1962).

$ZnC_{16}H_{20}N_2$

① Bis(*p*-dimethylaminophenyl)zinc

[*p*-(CH₃)₂NC₆H₄]Zn

② [*p*-(CH₃)₂NC₆H₄]Hg + Zn $\xrightarrow{\text{in xylene}}$
30%

③ Crystals. [135~137°].
Sol. in hot xylene; insol. in petr. ether.

⑥ Krause, Grosse 119 (1937).   Ber. 63, 1138 (1934).

ZnC₁₈H₂₂

① Bis(2-phenylpropyl)zinc
(CH₃CHPhCH₂)₂Zn

② ZnCl₂ + 2 Al(CH₂CHPhCH₃)₃ ⟶

③ (129~131°/0.01).

⑥ Brit. 836734; CA 55, 3435 (1963).

ZnC₂₀H₁₄

① Di-β-naphthylzinc
(C₁₀H₇)₂Zn

② Hg(β-C₁₀H₇)₂ + Zn $\xrightarrow{\text{in boiling xylene}}$
67%

③ White crystals. [184~186°].
Sol. in hot xylene; less sol. in petr. ether.

⑥ Krause, Grosse 119 (1937).   Ber. 63, 1138 (1934).

【Cd】

CdC₂H₆

① Dimethylcadmium
(CH₃)₂Cd

② CH₃Br + Mg $\xrightarrow{\text{ether}}$ CH₃MgBr
$\xrightarrow{\text{CdBr₂, reflux}}$ 85%

③ Colorless liq. (105.5°/758). [−4.5°].
n_D 1.5849(18°). d 1.9846(17.9°/4°).
Sol. in org. solvents.
Musty odor. Spontaneously
inflammable. Decomp. in H₂O.
Raman: Z. Naturf. 2a 454 (1947).

④ + PhCOCl + MgBr₂
$\xrightarrow{\text{40° in ether}}$ PhCOCH₃ (74%)

+ 2 ClCOCOOEt + 2 LiBr

$\xrightarrow{-65° \text{ in THF}}$ 2 CH₃COCOOEt (51%)

⑥ Ber. 50, 1813 (1917).   Nature 188, 140 (1960).

CdC₂H₄I₂

① Bis(iodomethyl)cadmium
(ICH₂)₂Cd

② CdI₂ + CH₂N₂
$\xrightarrow{\text{under N, in THF-ether, r. t.}}$ 80%

③ Sol. in THF and ether.

④ + 5% aq. HCl ⟶ CH₃I(80%)
+ Br₂ $\xrightarrow{\text{in ether, then hydrolyzed}}$
CH₂Br₂ + CH₂BrI + CH₂I₂
1 : 10 : 4
+ I₂ $\xrightarrow{\text{in THF}}$ CH₂I₂ (73%)
+ PhCH=CH₂ ⟶ PhCH–CH₂ (23%)
＼／
CH₂

⑥ Ann. 650, 1 (1961).

CdC₄H₁₀

① Diethylcadmium
(C₂H₅)₂Cd

② C₂H₅Br + Mg $\xrightarrow{\text{ether}}$ C₂H₅MgBr
$\xrightarrow{\text{CdBr₂}}$ 90%

CdCl₂ + Et₃Al + Et₂AlCl ⟶

③ Colorless oil.   (64°/19.5). [−21°].
n_D 1.5680 (18°). d 1.6564 (22°/4°).
Sol. in org. solvents. Fumes in air.
Inflammable at temp. higher than
180°.
Musty odor.

④ + 2 CH₃COCl + 2 MgBr₂
$\xrightarrow{28°, \text{ in benzene}}$ 2 CH₃COC₂H₅ (97%)

+ O₂ $\xrightarrow{\text{r. t.}}$ Cd(OOEt)₂

⑥ Ber. 50, 1813 (1917).   Chem. & Ind. 1958, 1177.   US 3080409; CA 59, 3957 (1963).

CdC₆H₁₄

① Dipropylcadmium

(C₃H₇)₂Cd

② PrCl + Mg $\xrightarrow{\text{ether}}$ PrMgCl $\xrightarrow{CdCl_2}$
   85%

③ Oil. (84°/21.5). [−83°]. n_D 1.5291
   (17.6°). d 1.4184(19.4°/4°)
   Sol. in org. solvents. Decomp. in H_2O.

⑥ Ber. **50**, 1813 (1917).

CdC₆H₁₄

① Diisopropylcadmium
   [(CH₃)₂CH]₂Cd

② i-PrBr + Mg $\xrightarrow{\text{ether}}$ i-PrMgBr $\xrightarrow{CdBr_2, 0°}$

⑥ JOC **25**, 1666 (1960).

CdC₈H₁₈

① Dibutylcadmium
   (C₄H₉)₂Cd

② BuBr + Li $\xrightarrow{-30°, \text{ in ether}}$ BuLi
   $\xrightarrow{CdBr_2, 35°}$ 80%

   BuBr + Mg $\longrightarrow$ BuMgBr $\xrightarrow{CdBr_2}$ 70%

③ Oil. (103.5°/12.5). [−48°]. n_D 1.5155
   (19.5°). d 1.3054 (19.7°/4°).
   Sol. in org. solvents. Decomp. in H_2O.

④ + 2ClCOCOOEt + LiBr
   $\xrightarrow{-65° \text{ in THF}}$ 2 BuCOCOOEt (68%)

⑥ Ber. **50**, 1813 (1917). Nature **188**, 140
   (1960).

CdC₈H₁₈

① Diisobutylcadmium
   (i-C₄H₉)₂Cd

② i-BuBr + Mg $\longrightarrow$ i-BuMgBr
   $\xrightarrow{CdBr_2}$ 75%

③ Oil. (90.5°/20). [−37°]. n_D 1.4997
   (18°). d 1.2674(20°/4°).
   Sol. in org. solvents. Decomp. in H_2O.

⑥ Ber. **50**, 1813 (1917).

CdC₁₀H₂₂

① Diisoamylcadmium

(i-C₅H₁₁)₂Cd

② i-C₅H₁₁Br + Mg $\longrightarrow$ i-C₅HI₁₁MgBr
   $\xrightarrow{CdBr_2}$ 55%

③ Oil. (121.5°/15). [−115°]. n_D 1.5039
   (19°). d 1.2184(22°/4°).
   Sol. in org. solvents. Decomp. in H_2O.

⑥ Ber. **50**, 1813 (1917).

CdC₁₂H₂₆

① Dihexylcadmium
   (C₆H₁₃)₂Cd

② C₆H₁₃Br + Mg $\xrightarrow{\text{in ether}}$
   C₆H₁₃MgBr $\xrightarrow{CdCl_2}$

④ + CH₃COCO₂C₂H₅
   $\xrightarrow{H_2O}$ C₆H₁₃C(OH)CO₂Et (54%)
   |
   CH₃

⑥ Compt. rend. **250**, 145 (1960).

CdC₁₂H₁₀

① Diphenylcadmium
   (C₆H₅)₂Cd

② PhBr + Mg $\xrightarrow{\text{ether}}$ PhMgBr $\xrightarrow{CdBr_2}$

   Ph₂Hg + Cd $\xrightarrow{180°}$

   PhLi + CdBr₂ $\xrightarrow{\text{under N}}$

③ Crystals. [174°].
   Sensitive to air and moisture.
   Dipole moment in C_6H_6, 0.66 D ; in
   dioxane, 1.45D. Decomp. in H_2O,
   alc., amines, NH_3 to form benzene.

④ + HgCl₂ $\longrightarrow$ Ph₂Hg
   + SnCl₄ $\longrightarrow$ Ph₄Sn
   + SbCl₃ $\longrightarrow$ Ph₃Sb
   + PbCl₂ $\xrightarrow{\times}$
   + NO $\longrightarrow$ PhN=NNO₃

⑥ Ber. **46**, 1682 (1913). Z. Elektrochem.
   60, 58 (1956). J. Gen. Chem. USSR
   7, 2649 (1937) ; CA **32**, 2095 (1938).

CdC₁₄H₁₄O₂

① Di-m-anisylcadmium.
   (m-CH₃OC₆H₄)₂Cd

② m-CH₃OC₆H₄Br + Mg $\xrightarrow{\text{ether}}$

m-CH₃OC₆H₄MgBr $\xrightarrow{\text{CdCl}_2 \text{ in benzene}}$

④ +

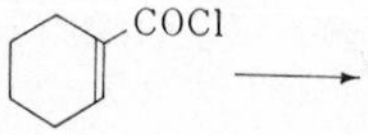

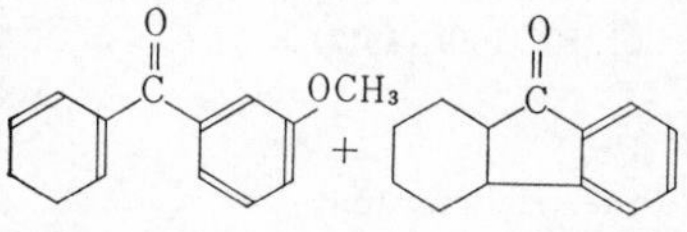

The organocadmium compd. shown above was acylated abnormally— on the carbon atom adjacent to that originally bonded to the halogen atom.

⑥ JACS **81**, 967 (1959)

CdC₁₆H₁₀

① Bis(phenylethynyl)cadmium
(C₆H₅C≡C)₂Cd

② Ph₂Cd + PhC≡CH $\xrightarrow{\text{in ether}}$

③ Crystals.
IR : Z. anorg. allg. Chem. **319**, 320 (1963).
Non pyrophoric.

④ + H₂O or acid $\longrightarrow$ Cd²⁺ + PhC≡CH
+ NH₃(liq.) $\longrightarrow$ Cd(C≡CPh)₂·x NH₃

CdC₂H₅Cl

① Ethylcadmium chloride
C₂H₅CdCl

② Et₂Cd + CdCl₂ $\xrightarrow{\text{r.t.}}$ 60.6%

④ + PhCOCl $\xrightarrow{5°, \text{ in dry toluene}}$ PhCOC₂H₅

⑥ Dokl. **125**, 348 (1958).   CA **53**, 19853 (1959).

CdC₂H₅Br

① Ethylcadmium bromide
C₂H₅CdBr

② Et₂Cd + CdBr₂ $\xrightarrow{\text{room temp., 10 hrs}}$
67.8%

④ + PhCOCl $\xrightarrow{5°, \text{ in dry toluene}}$ EtCOPh

⑥ Dokl. **125**, 348 (1959).   CA **53**, 19853 (1959).

CdC₂H₅I

① Ethylcadmium iodide
C₂H₅CdI

② Et₂Cd + CdI₂ $\xrightarrow{\text{r.t.}}$ 84.3%

④ EtCdI + PhCOCl
$\xrightarrow{5°, \text{ in dry toluene}}$ EtCOPh

⑥ Dokl. **125**, 348 (1959).   CA **53**, 19853 (1959).

CdC₄H₉Br

① Butylcadmium bromide.
C₄H₉CdBr

② Bu₂Cd + CdBr₂
$\xrightarrow{\text{r.t., in abs. ether}}$ 67%

④ + PhCOCl $\xrightarrow{5°, \text{ in dry toluene}}$ PhCOC₄H₉

⑥ Dokl. **125**, 348 (1959) ; CA **53**, 19853 (1959).

CdC₄H₁₀O₄

① Bis(ethylperoxy)cadmium
(C₂H₅OO)₂Cd

② Et₂Cd + O₂ $\xrightarrow{\text{r.t.}}$

③ White solid.

④ + terephthaloyl chloride $\longrightarrow$
diethyl diperoxyterephthalate

⑥ Chem. & Ind. **1958**, 1177.

CdC₇H₇OBr

① m-Anisylcadmium bromide
m-CH₃OC₆H₄CdBr

② m-CH₃OC₆H₄Br + Mg
$\xrightarrow{\text{in ether-benzene}}$ m-CH₃OC₆H₄MgBr
$\xrightarrow{\text{CdCl}_2, \text{ reflux}}$

④ + m-CH₃OC₆H₄COCl $\xrightarrow{\text{in C}_6\text{H}_6, \text{ r. t.}}$
liq. ketone (20%)

$\begin{cases} 3,3'\text{-dimethoxybenzophenone}(35\%) \\ 3,4'\text{-dimethoxybenzophenone}(65\%) \end{cases}$

⑥ JOC **23**, 349 (1958).

CdC₇H₇OI

① *m*-Anisylcadmium iodide
   m-CH₃OC₆H₄CdI

② *m*-CH₃OC₆H₄I + Mg $\xrightarrow{\text{in ether-benzene}}$

   m-CH₃OC₆H₄MgI $\xrightarrow{\text{CdCl}_2,\ \text{reflux}}$

④ + *m*-CH₃OC₆H₄COCl $\xrightarrow{\text{in C}_6\text{H}_6,\ \text{reflux}}$
   liq. ketone (17%)
   $\begin{cases} 3,3'\text{-dimethoxybenzophenone} \\ 3,4'\text{-dimethoxybenzophenone} \end{cases}$

⑥ JOC **23**, 349 (1958).

CdC₈H₄K₂

① Dipotassium tetraethynylcadmium
   K₂[Cd(C≡CH)₄]

② Cd(NH₂)₂ + CH≡CH
   + KC≡CH $\xrightarrow{\text{in liq. NH}_3}$

③ IR : Z. anorg. allg. Chem. **319**, 320
   (1963).
   A stronger electrolyte than
   K₂Zn (C≡CH)₄ in liq. NH₃.

CdC₁₀H₁₄O₂

① Methyl-2-phenyl-2-propylperoxy-
   cadmium
   CH₃CdOOC(CH₃)₂C₆H₅

② (CH₃)₂Cd + 2-phenyl-2-
   propylhydroperoxide ⟶

③ Recrystd. from cyclohexane. Stable
   in solution at room. temp.

④ $\xrightarrow{50°}$ CH₃OCdC(CH₃)₂C₆H₅

⑥ Chem. & Ind. **1958**, 1177.

CdC₁₁H₂₀O₂

① Methyl-decahydro-9-naphthylper-
   oxycadmiuim
   CH₃CdOOC₁₀H₇

② (CH₃)₂Cd + decahydro-9-naphthyl

hydroperoxide ⟶

③ White crystals. [80° decomp.].
   Recrystd. from pentane.

⑥ Chem. & Ind. **1958**, 1177.

CdC₂₄H₅₀S₂

① Didodecylthiocadmium
   Cd(SC₁₂H₂₅)₂

③ White powder.
   Insol. in H₂O. Decomp. in acid.

⑥ Krause, Grosse (1937).   US 2713589
   (1955).

CdC₃₂H₂₀Ba

① Barium tetra(phenylethynyl)-
   cadmium
   BaCd(C≡CC₆H₅)₄

② Cd(SCN)₂ + KC≡CPh
   + Ba(SCN)₂ $\xrightarrow{\text{in liq. NH}_3}$

③ Sensitive to H₂O and acids.
   Non explosive.
   IR : Z. anorg. allg. Chem. **319**, 320
   (1963).

【Hg】

HgCBrCl₃

① Trichloromethylmercuric bromide
   Cl₃CHgBr

② HgBr₂ + CHCl₃ + *t*-C₄H₉OK $\xrightarrow{\text{in C}_6\text{H}_6}$
   HgBr₂ + Cl₃CCOONa
   $\xrightarrow{\text{heat, in monoglyme}}$ 44.5%

③ [160~161°].

⑥ JOC **28**, 1129 (1963).

HgCH₂I₂

① Iodomethylmercuric iodide
   ICH₂HgI

② CH₂I₂ + Hg
   $\xrightarrow{\text{in sunlight(small amounts of I}_2 \text{ or Hg}_2\text{I}_2)}$
   (+ excess of Hg ⟶ CH₂(HgI)₂)

③ [109°].

Sol. only in hot CH_2I_2.

④ $+ HgCl_2 \xrightarrow{\text{in EtOH}} ClCH_2HgI$

$+$ aq. NaOH $\longrightarrow$ Hg

$+$ aq. HCl $\longrightarrow$ CH_3HgI

$+ KI \xrightarrow{\text{in } H_2O} CH_3HgI$

⑥ Whitmore (1921).

HgCH₃Br

① Methylmercuric bromide
CH_3HgBr

② $CH_3MgBr + HgBr_2 \xrightarrow{\text{in ether}} 94\%$

③ White needles. [172°].
Recrystd. from alc. Sol. in alc. and
$CHCl_3$; insol. in H_2O.

⑤ Bactericide.

⑥ "Beilsteins Handbuch der organiesc-
hen Chemie" E4, 1051. J. prakt.
Chem. 120, 249 (1929).

HgCH₃Cl

① Methylmercuric chloride
CH_3HgCl

② $CH_3HgOH + HCl \longrightarrow$
$(CH_3COO)_2 + Hg(OAc)_2$
$\xrightarrow{\text{in HOAc, aq. } CaCl_2} 99\%$

③ White crystals. [170°]. d 4.063(25°/4).
Volatile with steam. Sol. in EtOH,
$CHCl_3$ and C_6H_6; slightly sol. in
H_2O.
Disagreeable odor.

⑤ Fungicides and germicides.

⑥ J. prakt. Chem. 120, 249 (1929). Zhur.
25, 697 (1955).   CA 50, 2451 (1958).

HgCH₃I

① Methylmercuric iodide
CH_3HgI

② $CH_3MgI + HgCl_2 \xrightarrow{\text{in ether}} 85\sim88\%$

$CH_3I + Hg_2(OAc)_2(\text{or } Hg_2SO_4) \xrightarrow{\text{heat}}$

③ Light yellow needles. [144.7~145.0°].
Recystd. from alc. Sparingly sol. in

alc. and $CHCl_3$; insol. in H_2O.

⑥ JACS 44, 153 (1922).   Zhur. Vser.
Khim, Obsch. im., D. I. Mendeleva
7, 594 (1962); CA 58, 5709 (1963).

HgCH₄O

① Methylmercuric hydroxide
CH_3HgOH

② $CH_3HgCl + $ aq. KOH $\xrightarrow{\text{in alc.}}$
$CH_3HgI + Ag_2O$
$\xrightarrow{\text{in MeOH or } CHCl_3} 97.3\%$

③ Crystals. [95°].
Recrystd from MeOH or pyridine.
Sol. in hot H_2O and most org. sol-
vents; sparingly sol. in cold ether.

⑥ Beilsteins Handbuch der organi-
schen Chemie EII4, 1050 (1942).
JACS 45, 1842 (1923).

HgC₂Cl₆

① Bis(trichloromethyl)mercury
$(CCl_3)_2Hg$

② $HgCl_2 + CCl_3COONa$
$\xrightarrow{\text{heat, in monoglyme}} 71.5\%$
$Cl_3CHgCl + CCl_3COONa$
$\xrightarrow{\text{heat, in monoglyme}} 67.5\%$

③ [140~141°].

④ $+ 2RCH = CH_2$
$\longrightarrow 2RCH - CH_2 + HgCl_2$

⑥ JOC 28, 1129 (1963).

HgC₂F₆

① Bis(trifluoromethyl)mercury
$(CF_3)_2Hg$

② $(CF_3)_3P + HgO \longrightarrow 96\%$

⑥ JACS 82, 5759 (1960).

HgC₂N₆O₁₂

① Bis(trinitromethyl)mercury

② HC(NO₂)₃ + HgO $\xrightarrow{\text{in ether}}$ 80%

③ [200~205° decomp.].

④ + PhH $\xrightarrow{\text{in EtOH}}$ PhHgC(NO₂)₃ + Hg[C(NO₂)₃]₂

+ PhNH₂ $\xrightarrow{\text{in EtOH}}$ PhNHHgC(NO₂)₃ + C₄H₄O

$\xrightarrow{\text{in ether ; aq. NaCl}}$ α-C₄H₃OHgCl

(25%)

⑥ Izv. OKhN **1960**, 505 ; CA **54**, 22559 (1960).

HgC₂H₂Cl₂

① (*cis-, trans-*)2-Chlorovinylmercuric chloride

ClCH=CHHgCl

② CH≡CH + HgCl₂ $\xrightarrow{\text{aq. HCl}}$ *trans-*

CH≡CH + HgCl₂(vapor.) $\xrightarrow{120°}$ *cis-*

③ [*trans-* 124° ; *cis-* 79°].

Stable towards acids. Sol. in C₆H₆ and alc.

④ + KCN $\longrightarrow$ HgCl₂·KCN + CH≡CH

+ Na₂S₂O₃ $\longrightarrow$ CH≡CH

+ C₅H₅N $\longrightarrow$ ClCH≡CHHg(C₅H₅N)Cl

+ KI $\longrightarrow$ K₂HgI₄ + CH≡CH

+NH₃ $\longrightarrow$ (ClCH=CH)₂Hg

⑥ The Chemistry of Organometallic Compounds (1959). Bull. Acad. Sci. USSR, Classe Sci. Chim. **1945**, 145, 239.

HgC₂H₂N₄

① Bis(diazomethyl)mercury

Hg(CHN₂)₂

② CH₂N₂ + Hg(OAc)₂ $\longrightarrow$

③ Liq.

⑥ Nature **199**, 903 (1963) ; CA **59**, 11546 (1963).

HgC₂H₃BrO₂

① Bromomercuriacetic acid

BrHg-CH₂COOH

② HOCH₂CH₂HgBr + Br₂ + KOH $\xrightarrow{\text{in H₂O}}$

③ White crystals. [198°].

⑥ Whitmore (1921).

HgC₂H₃ClO

① Chloromercuriacetaldehyde

ClHgCH₂CHO

② Hg(OAc)₂ + CH₂=CHO-*n*-Bu $\xrightarrow{\text{1) in H₂O 2) aq. NaCl}}$ 85%

③ [130~131°].

Recrystd. from hot H₂O.

④ + CH₃COCl $\longrightarrow$ CH₂=CHOCOCH₃ + HgCl₂ ; O-alkylation

+ Ph₃CCl $\longrightarrow$ Ph₃COCH₂CHO + HgCl₂ ; C-alkylation

⑥ Bull. Acad. Sci. USSR, Classe Sci. Chim. **1947**, 63 ; CA **42**, 4148 (1948).

HgC₂H₄O₄

① Ethane hexemercarbide

C₂Hg₆O₂(OH)₂,

$$\left(\begin{array}{c} \text{HO}-\text{Hg} \quad \text{Hg}-\text{OH} \\ \text{Hg}-\text{C}-\text{C}-\text{Hg} \\ \text{O}-\text{Hg} \quad \text{Hg}-\text{O} \end{array} \right)$$

② HgO + aq. KOH + C₂H₅OH $\xrightarrow{\text{heat}}$

③ Yellowish white.

Insol. in most org. solvents.

⑥ Whitemore (1921).

HgC₂H₅Cl

① Ethylmercuric chloride

C₂H₅HgCl

② EtMgCl + HgCl₂ $\xrightarrow{\text{in ether}}$

Et₂Zn + HgCl₂ $\xrightarrow{\text{in ether}}$

③ Silvery iridescent leaflets. [192.5°]. d 3.5.

Sparingly sol. in cold alc. ; readily sol. in hot alc.; slightly sol. in ether ; insol. in H₂O.

Sublimes easily even at 40°. More
toxic than methylmercuric chloride.

⑥ J. prakt. Chem. **120**, 249 (1929). Whitmore (1921).

HgC₂H₅Cl

① 2-Hydroxyethylmercuric chloride
$HOCH_2CH_2HgCl$

② $CH_2=CH_2 + Hg(OAc)_2$

$\xrightarrow[\text{in H}_2\text{O ; aq. NaCl}]{}$ 80%

③ [153~155°].
Insol. in all common solvents.
Light sensitive.
NMR : JACS **80**, 4824 (1958).

⑥ Ber. **33**, 1340 (1900).

HgC₂H₆

① Dimethylmercury
$(CH_3)_2Hg$

② $CH_3I + Na-Hg \xrightarrow[]{\text{in C}_6\text{H}_6, \text{CH}_3\text{OAc}}$

$CH_3HgI + CH_3MgI \xrightarrow[]{\text{in ether}}$

③ Colorless liq. (93~96°/760). n 1.5473
(17°). d 3.0824(20°/4°).
Insol. in H₂O ; sol. in alc. and ether.
Extremely poisonous.
IR : Ber. **90**, 2703 (1957).

⑥ Whitmore (1921).

HgC₃H₃N₃O₇

① Trinitromethylmercuri-
acetaldehyde
$(O_2N)_3CHgCH_2CHO$

② $EtOCH=CH_2 + Hg[C(NO_2)_3]_2$

$\xrightarrow[\text{in H}_2\text{O or alc.}]{}$ 65%

③ [128°].

⑥ Dokl. **124**, 834 (1959) ; CA **53**, 16041
(1959).

HgC₃H₅ClO

① Acetonylmercuric chloride
CH_3COCH_2HgCl

② $C_3H_6 + Hg(OAc)_2$

$\xrightarrow[]{\text{in H}_2\text{O ; KMnO}_4, \text{AcOH ; aq. HCl}}$ 53%

③ [102~102.5°].

④ $+ Ph_2Hg \xrightarrow[]{\text{in CHCl}_3} (CH_3COCH_2)_2Hg$

⑥ Zhur. **29**, 1182 (1959) ; CA **54**, 1273
(1962).

HgC₃H₅I

① Allylmercuric iodide
$CH_2=CHCH_2HgI$

② $CH_2=CHCH_2I + Hg \xrightarrow[]{\text{in EtOH}}$

③ [135°].
Turns to yellow by light and heat.
Insol. in H₂O.

⑥ Whitmore (1921).

HgC₃H₆O₂

① Methylmercuric acetate
$CH_3HgOCOCH_3$

② $CH_3HgI + AgOAc \xrightarrow[]{\text{in alc.}}$

$Hg(OAc)_2 + CH_3COOOH$

$\xrightarrow[\text{in HOAc}]{}$ 93~95%

③ Needles. [101°, 128°].
Recrystd. from MeOH. Easily sol. in
H₂O, AcOH and alc. ; sparingly
sol. in C₆H₆, toluene, CCl₄, CS₂,
pyridine, ether.
Sublimable.

⑥ JACS **44**, 153 (1922). Dokl. Akad.
Belorus SSR **4**, 288 (1960) ; CA **55**,
10377 (1961).

HgC₃H₇Cl

① n-Propylmercuric chloride
n-C_3H_7HgCl

② n-PrMgCl + excess of HgCl₂ $\xrightarrow[]{\text{in ether}}$

③ Cryst. plates. [147°].
Recrystd. from EtOH. Sol. in CHCl₃
and hot EtOH ; hardly sol. in cold
alc. ; insol. in H₂O.

⑥ Whitmore (1921). JACS **47**, 3009
(1925).

HgC₃H₇ClO

① 2-Methoxyethylmercuric chloride
   CH₃OCH₂CH₂HgCl

② CH₂=CH₂

   $$+ Hg(OAc)_2 \xrightarrow{\text{in MeOH r. t. ; aq. NaCl}}$$

③ White powder. [68.0~68.5°].
   Sol. in polar org. solvents.
   NMR : JACS **80**, 4824 (1958).

④ + aq. HCl ⟶ CH₂=CH₂ + HgCl₂
   + CH₃OH

⑥ JACS **80**, 4824 (1958).   Chem. Revs.
   48, 7 (1951).

HgC₄Cl₆

① Bis(trichlorovinyl)mercury
   (CCl₂=CCl)₂Hg

② CHCl=CCl₂ + Hg(CN)₂ $\xrightarrow{\text{in aq. NaOH}}$

③ Colorless shiny plates. [83°].
   Sol. in ether, CHCl₃.

⑥ Whitmore (1921).

HgC₄H₂

① Diethynylmercury
   (CH≡C)₂Hg

② 2CH≡CH + K₂HgI₄ + KOH $\xrightarrow{\text{in H}_2\text{O}}$

   2CH≡CH + 2Hg(CN)₂ $\xrightarrow{\text{in H}_2\text{O}}$

③ [203~204°].

④ + I₂ $\xrightarrow{\text{in aq. KI}}$ CH≡CI
   + addn. products

   + I₂ $\xrightarrow{\text{in liq. NH}_3}$ (IC≡C)₂Hg

⑥ Whitmore (1921). JACS **48**, 469(1926).

HgC₄H₂F₂I₂

① Bis(2-fluoro-2-iodovinyl)mercury
   (CFI=CH)₂Hg

② CF≡CH + K₂HgI₄ $\xrightarrow{\text{aq. KOH}}$

③ Crystals. [99°].

④ + Br₂ $\xrightarrow{\text{in CCl}_4}$ (CFIBr−CHBr)₂Hg

⑥ Zhur. Vses. Khim. Obshchestva im.

D. I. Mendeleeva **8** (2), 231 (1963) ;
CA **59**, 5185 (1963).

HgC₄H₃ClS

① α-Chloromercurithiophene
   α-C₄H₃SHgCl

② C₄H₄S + HgCl₂

   $$+ NaOAc \xrightarrow{\text{in alc.-H}_2\text{O, r. t.}}$$

③ [183°].
   Recrystd. from hot acetone or CHCl₃.
   Slightly volatile and sublimes even
   at 100°. Sol. in aq. alkali.

④ + I₂ ⇸ no reaction

   + Na $\xrightarrow{\text{in xylene}}$ di-α-thienylmercury

⑥ Whitmore (1921).

HgC₄H₆O₂

① Mercuribis(acetaldehyde)
   (CH₂CHO)₂Hg

② HgO + CH₃CH₂CH₂CH(OCH=CH₂)₂
   $\xrightarrow{\text{Hg(OAc)}_2, \text{ in H}_2\text{O−EtOH}}$

   HgO+2i-BuOCH=CH₂
   $\xrightarrow{\text{Hg(OAc)}_2 \text{ in H}_2\text{O−EtOH}}$

③ [93~94°].
   IR : BCSJ **38**, 1841 (1965).

④ + CH₃COCl ⟶ CH₂=CHOCOCH₃
   + HgCl₂
   + Ph₃CCl ⟶ Ph₃CCH₂CHO
   + HgCl₂
   + COCl₂ ⟶ (CH₂=CHO)₂CO
   + 2ClHgCH₂CHO
   + (CH₃)₃SiCl ⟶ (CH₃)₃SiOCH=CH₂
   + ClHgCH₂CHO

⑤ Reagent for introducing vinyloxy
   groups.

⑥ Zhur. **33**, 2079 (1960) ; CA **59**, 10102
   (1963).   Dokl. **102**, 97 (1955) ; CA
   50, 4773 (1956).

HgC₄H₆O₃

① Methyl acetoxymercuriformate
   CH₃CO₂HgCO₂CH₃

② $Hg(OAc)_2 + CO(2 \text{ atm.}) \xrightarrow{\text{in MeOH}} 88\%$

③ Crystals. [110° decomp.].

Sol. in $CHCl_3$, alc., fairly sol. in warm H_2O, ethyl acetate, acetone and C_6H_6; hardly sol. in ether.

④ $\xrightarrow{\text{heat}}$ $CO + Hg_2(OAc)_2$

+ A(unknown; M. W. in $CHCl_3$ is 310)

+ $1N$ HCl $\longrightarrow$ $ClHgCO_2CH_3$

(decomp. with $5N$ HCl)

+ $1N$ NaOH $\longrightarrow$ $Hg + NaHCO_3$

⑥ Ber. **46**, 2869 (1913); **53**, 984 (1920).

HgC₄H₇ClO₂

① 2-Acetoxyethylmercuric chloride
$CH_3COOCH_2CH_2HgCl$

② $Hg(OAc)_2 + CH_2=CH_2 \xrightarrow{\text{in AcOH; aq. KCl}}$

③ Needles. [64~65°].
Recrystd. from ligroin.

⑥ JACS **82**, 3880 (1960).

HgC₄H₉Br

① t-Butylmercuric bromide
$(CH_3)_3CHgBr$

② t-BuMgBr + $HgBr_2$ $\longrightarrow$

③ Needles. [106°].
Decomp. in light and when heated in solvents. Could not be recrystd.

⑥ JACS **45**, 822 (1923).

HgC₄H₉ClO

① 2-Ethoxyethylmercuric chloride
$C_2H_5OCH_2CH_2HgCl$

② $CH_2=CH_2 + Hg(OAc)_2$ $\xrightarrow{\text{in EtOH; aq. NaCl}}$

③ [92°, 87~89°].
Recrystd. from alc.
Sol. in most org. solvents; insol. in H_2O.

⑥ Ber. **46**, 2869 (1913).   JACS **82**, 3880 (1960).

HgC₄H₁₀

① Diethylmercury
$(C_2H_5)_2Hg$

② EtI + Na—Hg $\xrightarrow{\text{CH}_3\text{AcO in C}_6\text{H}_6, \text{ heat}}$
$Et_2Zn + HgCl_2$ $\longrightarrow$
$(C_2H_5)_3B + HgO \xrightarrow{\text{in H}_2\text{O}} 95\%$

③ Colorless liq. (159°, 57°/16). $n_D 1.5476$ (16.9°). d 2.4660(20°/4°).

④ + Bz_2O_2 $\xrightarrow{\text{heat}}$ $EtC_6H_4CO_2H$
+ EtHgOBz

⑥ Whitmore (1921).   JACS **82**, 3051 (1960).   Dokl. **144**, 132 (1962).

HgC₅H₄ClN

① 2-Pyridylmercuric chloride
$2-C_5H_4N-HgCl$

② $2 C_5H_4N-SO_2Cl + HgCl_2$ $\longrightarrow$

③ White solid. [275°].
Recrystd. from MeOH.

⑥ JACS **77**, 4658 (1955).

HgC₅H₄ClN

① 3-Pyridylmercuric chloride.
$3-C_5H_4N-HgCl$

② $C_5H_5N + Hg(OAc)_2$
$\xrightarrow{\text{in H}_2\text{O, heat; aq. NaCl}} 50\%$

$3-C_5H_4N-N_2Cl \cdot HgCl_2$
+ HCl $\xrightarrow{\text{in acetone-H}_2\text{O, Cu-bronze}}$

③ Needles. [265~268° decomp.].
Sol. in H_2O.

⑥ JACS **77**, 4658 (1955).

HgC₅H₈N₆O₁₃

① 2-(Trinitromethyl)-3-(trinitro-methylmercuri)-1-propanol
$(O_2N)_3CHgCH_2CH[C(NO_2)_3]CH_2OH$

② $Hg(C(NO_2)_3)_2 + CH_2=CHCH_2OH$
$\xrightarrow{\text{r. t.}} 54\%$

③ [150°].
Recrystd. from H_2O.

④ + aq. HCl

⟶ ClHgCH₂CH[C(NO₂)₃]CH₂OH
  (mp 89~90°)
  + excess CH₂=CHCH₂OH
  ⟶ Hg{CH₂CH[C(NO₂)₃]CH₂OH}₂
  (80%, 108° decomp., recrystd. from
  xylene)
⑥ Izv. OKhN **1962**, 272 ; CA **57**, 12522
  (1962).

HgC₅H₉IO₂

① 2-(Iodomercurimethyl)dioxane

$$O\begin{array}{c} CH_2-CH \\ \diagdown \\ CH_2-CH_2 \end{array}\begin{array}{c} CH_2HgI \\ \diagup \\ O \end{array}$$

② HOCH₂CH₂OCH₂CH=CH₂
  + Hg(OAc)₂ $\xrightarrow{\text{in } H_2O,\ heat\ ;\ aq.\ NaOH-KI}$
③ [78~80°].
  Rerystd. from MeOH—H₂O.
⑥ JACS **76**, 2701 (1954).

HgC₅H₁₀

① Pentamethylenemercury,
  Mercuracyclohexane

$$CH_2\begin{array}{c} CH_2-CH_2 \\ \diagup\diagdown \\ CH_2-CH_2 \end{array}Hg$$

② Li(CH₂)₅Li + Hg ⟶
  BrHg(CH₂)₅HgBr + Na—Hg
  $\xrightarrow{\text{in alc. or } C_6H_6}$
④ + Br₂(or I₂) $\xrightarrow{\text{in } C_6H_{14}}$ Br(CH₂)₅HgBr
  (or I(CH₂)₅HgI)
  + HgX₂ $\xrightarrow{\text{in } C_6H_6}$ XHg(CH₂)₅HgX
⑥ Compt. rend. **255**, 1930 (1962).
  Whitmore (1921).

HgC₅H₁₂O₃

① 2-Ethoxy-3-hydroxypropylmercuric
  bromide
  HOCH₂CH(OC₂H₅)CH₂HgBr
② Hg(OAc)₂
  + CH₂=CHCH₂OH $\xrightarrow{\text{in EtOH ; aq. KBr}}$
③ Crystals.
  Recrystd. from HOAc. Insol. in H₂O.

⑥ Ger. 446324.

HgC₅H₁₃IO

① 2-Iodomercui-2-(trimethlsilyl)ethyl
  alcohol.
  (CH₃)₃SiCH(HgI)CH₂OH
② Me₃SiCH=CH₂ + Hg(OAc)₂
  + NaOH $\xrightarrow{\text{in } H_2O\ ;\ CO_2\ ;\ aq.\ KI}$
③ [102~104°].
  Recrystd. from ligroin.
⑥ Z. Naturf. **14b**, 137 (1959) ; CA **53**,
  17889 (1958).

HgC₆F₁₄

① Bis(heptafluoroisopropyl)mercury
  (CF₃CFCF₃)₂Hg
② 2CF₃CF=CF₂ + HgF₂ $\xrightarrow{\text{in HF}}$ 65~80%
③ (116.6°/760). [16.2~16.4°]. n_D 1.3271
  (20). d 2.5454 (20°/4°).
  Unchanged by heating at 116° for
  26 days.
  Sol. in org. solvents ; insol. in H₂O.
  Highly toxic.
④ + Na₂S $\xrightarrow{\text{in } H_2O}$ HgS
  + CSCl₂ $\xrightarrow{200°}$ (CF₃)₂CFHgCl
⑥ JACS **85**, 180 (1963). JOC **28**, 184
  (1963).

HgC₆H₃NO₃

① 4-Hydroxymercuri(aci-2-nitro-
  phenol)anhydride

② o-NO₂C₆H₄ONa
  + Hg(OAc)₂ $\xrightarrow{\text{in alc. -H_2O, heat}}$
③ Yellowish powder.
  Insol. in common org. solvents.
④ + (NH₄)₂S ⟶ no reaction
⑥ Ber. **39**, 1105 (1906).

HgC₆H₄ClF

① *p*-Fluorophenylmercuric chloride
   p-FC₆H₄HgCl

② *p*-FC₆H₄NH₂ + HNO₂

   $+ HBF_4 \xrightarrow{\text{in } H_2O \; ; \; HgCl_2 - SnCl_2}$

③ Small glistening plates. [293~294°
   decomp.].
   Sol. in alc., acetone, HOAc; slightly
   sol. in C₆H₆; insol. in H₂O.

⑥ JACS **58**, 2308 (1936); **61**, 3005 (1939).

HgC₆H₄ClNO₂

① *p*-Nitrophenylmercuric chloride
   p-NO₂C₆H₄HgCl

② PhNO₂ + Hg(OAc)₂ $\xrightarrow{150° \; ; \; \text{aq. NaCl}}$

③ [265~266°].
   Sol. in hot ligroin and ether; insol.
   in cold.

⑥ Whitmore (1921). JACS **43**, 611(1921).

HgC₆H₅ClO

① *p*-Chloromercuriphenol
   p-ClHgC₆H₄OH

② PhOH + 2Hg(OAc)₂

   $\xrightarrow{\text{in } H_2O \; ; \; \text{aq. NaCl}}$ *o*-, *p*-mixtures

③ [152.5°].
   Recrystd. from hot H₂O. Sol. in aq.
   NaOH.

④ + PhCOCl ⟶ ClHgC₆H₄OCOC₆H₅
   + HZ(acid) ⟶ HgZ₂ + PhOH

   $+ \text{PhN}_2\text{Cl} \xrightarrow{\text{in aq. NaOH}} \text{PhN=N-}$ [structure: phenol ring with OH and HgCl]

⑥ Whitmore (1921).

HgC₆H₅Cl₂

① *p*-Chlorophenylmercuric chloride
   p-ClC₆H₄HgCl

② *p*-ClC₆H₄N₂Cl + HgCl₂

$\xrightarrow{\text{Cu in acetone}}$ 46%

$(p\text{-ClC}_6\text{H}_4)_2\text{ICl} + \text{Hg} \xrightarrow{\text{in acetone, heat}}$ 77%

③ Crystals. [225~240°].
   Recrystd. from alc.

⑥ Ber. **62**, 1016 (1929).   Dokl. **122**, 825
   (1958); CA **53**, 477 (1959).

HgC₆H₇NO₂

① *N*-Vinylmercurisuccinimide

$$\begin{matrix} CH_2-CO \\ | \qquad\quad \diagdown \\ CH_2-CO \end{matrix} NHgCH=CH_2$$

② (CH₂=CH)₂Hg + $\begin{matrix} CH_2-CO \\ | \qquad\quad \diagdown \\ CH_2-CO \end{matrix}$NBr

   $\xrightarrow{\text{in } CCl_4, \text{ heat}}$ 95%

③ [113~114°].
   Considerably thermally stable

④ + aq. HCl ⟶ CH₂=CHHgCl

   $+ \begin{matrix} CH_2-CO \\ | \qquad\quad \diagdown \\ CH_2-CO \end{matrix}$NH

⑥ Z. Naturf. **17b**, 135 (1962).

HgC₆H₉ClO₂

① *trans*-2-Acetoxy-1-methyl-1-propen-
   ylmercuric chloride
   Me(AcO)C=CMeHgCl

② MeC≡CMe + Hg(AOc)₂

   $\xrightarrow{\text{in HOAc, r.t. ; aq. KCl}}$

   $\begin{cases} trans- & 70\% \\ cis- & \text{relatively small amt.} \end{cases}$

③ [*trans*-: 140°, *sis*-: 95~96°]

⑥ Izv. OKhN **1954**, 1008; CA **50**, 171
   (1956).

HgC₆H₁₀

① Dipropenylmercury
   (*cis*- or *trans*-CH₃CH=CH)₂Hg

② *cis*- or *trans*-CH₃CH=CHHgBr

   $+ \text{Na}_2\text{SnO}_2 \xrightarrow{\text{in } H_2O, \text{ heat}}$

③ (*trans*-: 87°/14.5, *cis*-: 79~80°/14).
   trans-: *n* 1.5622(20°), *cis*-: *n* 1.5628
   (20°). *trans*-: *d* 2.2120 (20°/4°),

cis- : *d* 2.2297(20°/4°).

⑥ Izv. OKhN **1959**, 1216 ; CA **54**, 1272 (1960).

HgC6H10

① Dicyclopropylmercury
   (C3H5)2Hg

② (CH2=CH)2Hg + CH2I2

   + Zn(Cu) $\xrightarrow{\text{in THF, 40°}}$

   (C3H5)Br + Mg $\xrightarrow{\text{heat, in THF}}$

   C3H5MgBr $\xrightarrow{\text{HgCl2, in THF, heat}}$ 64%

③ (92~95°/3,110~112°/18). n_D 1.5937(20°).
   Stable when kept refrigerated.

④ + dry HCl $\xrightarrow{\text{in C6H6 75°}}$ C3H5HgCl
                              (mp 186~187°)

   + AcOH $\longrightarrow$ C3H5HgOAc
                              (mp 80~81°)

⑥ Z. Naturf. **17b**, 135 (1962). JACS **73**, 3176 (1951).

HgC6H10O4

① β-Acetoxyethylmercuric acetate
   AcOCH2CH2HgOAc

② CH2=CH2 + Hg(OAc)2 $\xrightarrow{\text{in HOAc}}$

③ [96~98°].
   Recrystd. from ligroin.

④ + aq. KCNS

   $\xrightarrow{\text{in HOAc, HNO3}}$ AcOCH2CH2HgCNS

⑥ JACS **81**, 5316 (1959).

HgC6H10O5

① Hydroxymercurimethylmalonic
   methylester
   HOHgCMe(CO2Me)2

② CH3CH(CO2Me)2 + HgO

   $\xrightarrow{\text{in H2O}}$ 96.5%

③ Yellowish red. [235° decomp.].

④ + aq. NaOH $\xrightarrow{\text{in H2O, heat}}$

⑤ Stronger infectant.

⑥ Ber. **42**, 777 (1909). Whitmore (1921).

HgC6H11ClO2

① 3, 3-Diacetyl-propylmercuric
   chloride
   (CH3CO)2CHCH2CH2HgCl

② (CH3CO)2CH2 + AcOCH2CH2HgOAc
   in HOAc, HClO4 ; aq. NaCl
   $\longrightarrow$

③ White powder. [132~133°].
   Sol. in alc., C6H6, CHCl3, pyridine,
   and dimethylsulfoxide ; insol. in
   H2O.

④ + aq. NaOH $\longrightarrow$ (CH3CO)2·C$\underset{\diagdown CH_2}{\overset{\diagup CH_2}{<}}$
   + Hg

⑥ JOC **31**, 447 (1966).

HgC6H14

① Di-*n*-propylmercury
   (*n*-C3H7)2Hg

② PrMgBr + PrHgBr $\xrightarrow{\text{in ether}}$

   PrMgBr + HgBr2 $\xrightarrow{\text{in ether}}$

③ Colorless liq. (189~191°/760, 81~84°/
   19). n_D 1.5170 (20°). *d* 2.124 (16°),
   2.0208 (20°/4°).
   Insol. in H2O ; sol. in alc. and ether.

⑥ JACS **44**, 153 (1922). Krause, Grosse
   (1937).

HgC7H4O2

① *o*-Hydroxymercuribenzoic acid
   anhydride

② *o*-C6H4(CO2H)2 + Hg(OAc)2 $\xrightarrow{170°}$

③ White powder.
   Insol. in usual solvents ; sol. in aq.
   NaOH.

⑥ Whitmore (1921).

HgC₇H₅ClO₂

① *p*-Chloromercuribenzoic acid
   p-HO₂CC₆H₄HgCl

② p-CH₃C₆H₄HgCl + KMnO₄ $\xrightarrow{\text{in aq. NaOH}}$

③ [273°].
   Reprecipitated with HCl from aq.
   NaOH solution.

⑥ Org. Syn. Col. Vol. I, p. 159 (1941).

HgC₇H₅Cl₃

① Trichloromethyl-phenylmercury
   PhHgCCl₃

② PhHgBr + CHCl₃ $\xrightarrow{t\text{-C}_4\text{H}_9\text{OK, in C}_6\text{H}_6,\ 0°}$
   51%
   CCl₃CO₂C₂H₅ + PhHgBr
   $\xrightarrow[\text{in C}_6\text{H}_6,\ 0°\ ;\ \text{NaOCH}_3]{}$ 62%

③ White crystals. [116.5~118.0°].
   Recrystd. from *n*-hexane.

④ $+ \;\rangle C=C\langle \xrightarrow{\text{in C}_6\text{H}_6\ \text{heat}}$ PhHgBr

$+ \rangle\overset{\displaystyle CCl_2}{\overset{\displaystyle \wedge}{C-C}}\langle$

⑥ JOC 27, 1491 (1962); 28, 1129 (1963).

HgC₇H₇Cl

① Benzylmercuric chloride
   C₆H₅CH₂HgCl

② PhCH₂MgCl + HgCl₂ $\longrightarrow$
   PhCH₂B(OH)₂ + HgCl₂ $\longrightarrow$

③ [104°].
   Sol. in alc., ether, C₆H₆, CHCl₃ and
   AcOH.

⑥ Whitmore (1921).

HgC₇H₇ClO

① *p*-Anisylmercuric chloride
   p-CH₃OC₆H₄HgCl

② Hg(OAc)₂ + C₆H₅OCH₃
   $\xrightarrow{\text{aq. NaCl}}$ *o*-, *p*- mixtures
   (p-MeOC₆H₆)₂ICl + Hg
   $\xrightarrow{\text{in acetone, heat}}$ 53%

③ Fine needles. [176.5°].
   Recrystd. from alc. ; moderately
   sol. in hot H₂O.

⑥ Whitmore (1921).   Dokl. 122, 825
   (1958); CA 53, 477 (1958).

HgC₇H₈

① Methylphenylmercury
   C₆H₅HgCH₃

② PhMgBr + C₃HgCl $\xrightarrow{\text{in ether, 5°}}$
   CH₃MgBr + PhHgCl $\longrightarrow$

③ Liq.

⑥ "Beilsteins Handbuch der organi-
   schen Chemie," E Ⅱ 16, 664.   JACS
   48, 3141 (1926).

HgC₇H₁₁ClO

① *exo-cis*-3-Hydroxy-2-norbornyl-
   mercuric chloride

② norbornene + HgO
   $\xrightarrow{\text{HClO}_4\ ;\ \text{in H}_2\text{O, 50°}}$ 86%

③ [131.0~131.5°].
   Recrystd. from ethylacetate-heptane.

④ $+ N_2H_4 \xrightarrow{\text{in aq. NaOH}}$ Hg +

⑥ JACS 85, 2746 (1963).

HgC₇H₁₄

① Cyclohexylmethylmercury
   C₆H₁₁HgCH₃

② C₆H₁₁MgCl + CH₃HgCl $\xrightarrow{\text{in ether, 5°}}$

⑥ "Beilsteins Handbuch der organi-
   schen Chemie", E Ⅱ, 664.   JACS
   48, 3141 (1926).

HgC₇H₁₅ClO

① 3-Methyl-3-hydroxy-2-ethyl-butyl-
   mercuric chloride
   Me₂C(OH)CHEtCH₂HgCl

② + Hg(OAc)₂ $\xrightarrow{\text{in H₂O; aq. KCl}}$

③ [62°].
   Recrystd. from petr. ether.

⑥ Vestn. Mosk. Univ. Khim. Ser. II **16**,
   No. 1, 67(1961); CA **56**, 14091(1961).

HgC₈H₄ClMnO₃

① (Chloromercuricyclopentadienyl)
   manganese tricarbonyl

   [structure: cyclopentadienyl–HgCl, Mn(CO)₃]

② [structure: cyclopentadienyl–SO₂Na, Mn(CO)₃] + HgCl₂
   $\xrightarrow{\text{in H₂O−EtOH, heat}}$ 79.5%

③ Yellow crystals. [135~136°].
   Recrystd. from EtOH.

④ + *n* - BuLi $\xrightarrow{\text{in ether}}$

   [structure: Hg bridging two cyclopentadienyl–Mn(CO)₃]

   (mp 178~9°)

   (recrystd. from C₆H₆ and CS₂)

⑥ JACS **82**, 5667 (1960).

HgC₈H₆S₂

① Di(α-thienyl)mercury

   $\left(\text{[thienyl structure with S]} \right)_2$ Hg

② α-C₄H₃SHgCl + NaI $\xrightarrow{\text{in acetone}}$

③ [197°].
   Recrystd. from C₆H₆. Insol. in H₂O;

hardly sol. in cold alc.; fairly sol.
in cold acetone.

⑥ Whitemore (1921).

HgC₈H₇Br

① α-Bromomercuristyrene
   PhC(HgBr)=CH₂

② PhCBr=CH₂ + Li $\xrightarrow{\text{in ether, 8~10°}}$
   PhCLi=CH₂ + HgBr₂
   $\xrightarrow{\text{in ether; 1% aq. HBr}}$ 33%

③ [89.5~90.5°].
   Recrystd. from acetone.

④ + NH₃−gas $\xrightarrow{\text{in C₆H₆}}$ (PhC=CH₂)₂Hg

⑥ Izv. OKhN 1957, 942; CA **52**, 6238
   (1957).

HgC₈H₇Cl

① β-Chloromercuristyrene
   C₆H₅CH=CHHgCl

② PhCH=CHB(OH)₂ + HgCl₂
   $\xrightarrow{\text{in acetone, heat}}$ 95%

③ [216.5~217.5°].

⑥ Zhur. **26**, 1876 (1956); CA **51**, 4980
   (1959).

HgC₈H₇ClO

① Phenacylmercuric chloride
   C₆H₅COCH₂HgCl

② C₆H₅COCH₃ + Hg(OAc)₂ $\xrightarrow{\text{150°; aq. KCl}}$

③ [145~146°].
   Recrystd. from high boiling ligroin
   or acetone.

④ + aq. HCl ⟶ C₆H₅COCH₃

⑥ Whitmore (1921).

HgC₈H₈O₂

① Phenylmercuric acetate
   C₆H₅HgOAc

② C₆H₆ + Hg(OAc)₂ $\xrightarrow{\text{heat}}$

③ White rhombic prisms. [149°].
   Slightly sol. in cold H₂O; more sol.

in hot ; sol. in HOAc, C_6H_6 and alc.
Recrystd. from H_2O or alc.

④ $\xrightarrow{150°}$ decomp.

⑤ Bactericide.

⑥ Whitmore (1921).

HgC₈H₉NO₂

① *p*-Aminophenylmercuric acetate
p-$NH_2C_6H_4HgOAc$

② $PHNH_2 + HgO$

$\xrightarrow{\text{in aq. NaOH}}$ $(PhNH)_2Hg$

$(PhNH)_2Hg$

$+ HOAc(or\ Hg(OAc)_2) \xrightarrow{\text{in H}_2\text{O, heat}}$

$PhNH_2 + Hg(OAc)_2 \xrightarrow{\text{in H}_2\text{O}}$

③ Colorless thick prisms. [167°].
Insol. in H_2O and ether ; hardly sol.
in alc. and $CHCl_3$. Sol. in dil. acids
and dil. bases.

④ $+$ conc. KOH $\longrightarrow$ $C_6H_4NH_2$
$+ HOAc \longrightarrow$
p-$CH_3CONHC_6H_4HgOAc$
Can be diazotized by the usual
method.

⑥ Whitmore (1921).

HgC₈H₁₀

① Di-*n*-butylmercury
$(C_4H_9)_2Hg$

② n-$BuMgBr + HgCl_2 \xrightarrow{\text{in ether}}$ 47%

n-$BuI + Na-Hg \xrightarrow{\text{in AcOH}}$

③ Liq. (223~224°/760, 117~118°/10).
Insol. in H_2O ; sol. in most org.
solvents.

⑥ Whitmore (1921).　JACS **44**, 153
(1922).

HgC₈H₁₄O₃

① *trans*-2-Hydroxycyclohexylmercuric
acetate

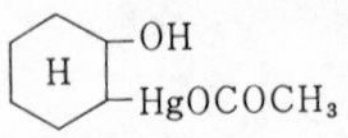

② $+ Hg(OAc)_2 \xrightarrow{\text{in H}_2\text{O, r.t.}}$

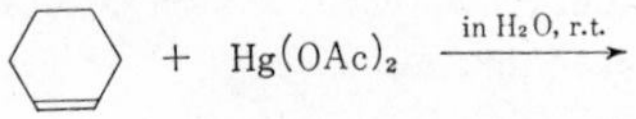

③ [112.5~113.0°].
Recrystd. from HOAc.

④ $+ Ph_2SnCl_2 + NaOH$

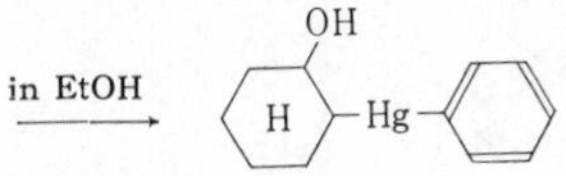

$\xrightarrow{\text{in EtOH}}$

⑥ Ber. **69**, 1631 (1936).

HgC₈H₁₅ClO

① 1-Chloromercurimethyl-1-methoxy-
cyclohexane

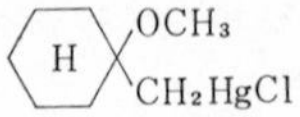

② $=CH_2 + Hg(OAc)_2 \xrightarrow{\text{in MeOH; aq. NaCl}}$

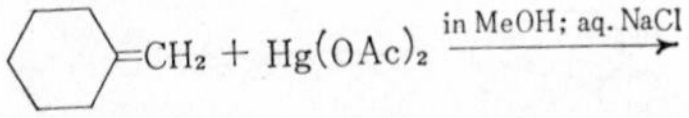

③ [68.3~69.0°].
Recrystd. from hexane.

④ $+ NaBH(OCH_3)_3$

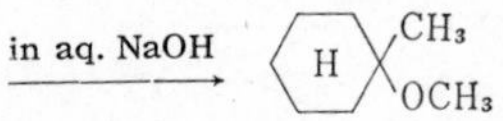

$\xrightarrow{\text{in aq. NaOH}}$

⑥ Can. J. Chem. **38**, 21 (1960).

HgC₈H₁₈

① Di-*s*-butylmercury
$(C_2H_5CHMe)_2Hg$

② s-$BuHgI + SnCl_2 \xrightarrow{\text{in aq. NaOH}}$

s-$BuMgBr + HgCl_2 \xrightarrow{\text{in ether}}$

③ Liq. (95.5~97°/18). n_D 1.5110(25°).

⑥ JACS **77**, 3747 (1955) ; **45**, 820 (1923).

HgC₉H₇Cl

① 3-Phenylpropargylmercuric chloride
$C_6H_5C\equiv CCH_2HgCl$

② Zn + PhC≡CCH₂Br $\xrightarrow{\text{in THF, heat}}$
(PhC≡CCH₂)₂Zn
$\xrightarrow{\text{HgCl}_2 \text{ in THF, heat}}$ 77%
③ [108°].
⑥ Compt. rend. **254**, 1100 (1962).

HgC₉H₉ClO
① 2-Chloromercurimethyl-2, 3,-dihyd-
robenzofurane.

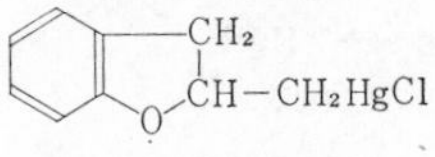

②

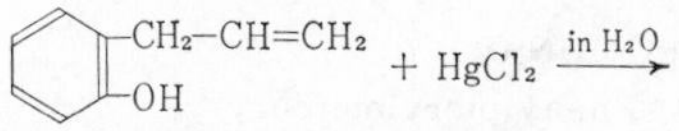

③ [137°].

④ + Na—Hg $\xrightarrow{\text{in C}_6\text{H}_6, \text{ heat}}$

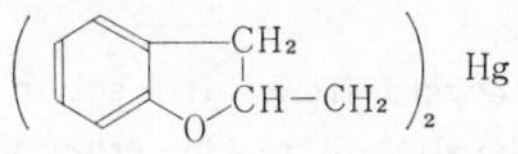

+ H₂S $\xrightarrow{\text{in dil. acid soln.}}$

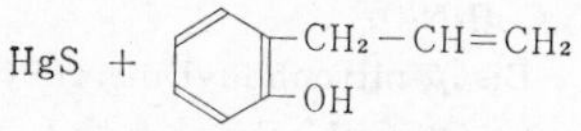

HgS +

⑥ JACS **45**, 1842 (1923).

HgC₉H₉NaO₂S
① Thimerosal,
Sodium o-ethylmercurimercapto-
benzoate
o-C₂H₅HgSC₆H₄COONa

② EtHgOH + [SH / COONa] $\xrightarrow{\text{in EtOH}}$

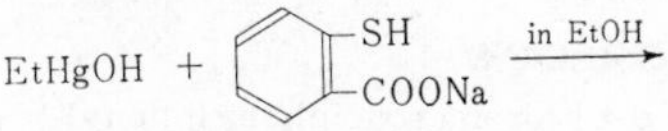

③ Cream-colored crystals.
Stable in air, but not in sunlight ;
Sol. in H₂O and alc. ; insol. in ether
and C₆H₆.
⑤ Fungicide and bactericide.
⑥ US 1589599(1926). JACS **53**, 992(1931).

HgC₉H₁₄O₃
① β-(p-Methoxyphenyl)ethylmercuric
iodide
p-CH₃OC₆H₄CH₂CH₂HgI
② MeOC₆H₅ + AcOCH₂CH₂HgOAc
$\xrightarrow{\text{HClO}_4, \text{ in HOAc ; aq. KI}}$
③ [127~150°].
Recrystd. from EtOH.
⑥ JACS **80**, 6005 (1958).

HgC₁₀H₈N₂
① Di-3-pyridylmercury
(3-C₅H₄N)₂Hg
② 3-AcOHg-C₅H₄N + 2Na₂S₂O₃
$\xrightarrow{\text{in H}_2\text{O}}$ (85%)
(3-C₅H₄Hg)₂NH₂Cl + 3Na₂S₂O₃ $\xrightarrow{\text{in H}_2\text{O}}$
③ [225~226°].
Insol. in cold alc. ; sol. in hot alc. and
hot xylene.
⑥ JACS **77**, 4658 (1955).

HgC₁₀H₉Cl
① 1-Chloromercuri-1-phenyl-1,2-buta-
diene
C₆H₅C(HgCl)=C=CHCH₃
② 2PhCBr=C=CHCH₃ + Zn
$\xrightarrow{\text{in THF, heat}}$ (PhC=C=CHCH₃)₂Zn
+ HgCl₂ $\xrightarrow{\text{in THF, heat}}$ 60%
③ [123°].
⑥ Compt. rend. **254**, 1100 (1962).

HgC₁₀H₉ClFe
① Chloromercuridicyclopentadienyl-
iron

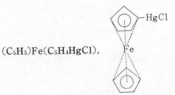

(C₅H₅)Fe(C₅H₄HgCl),

② (C₅H₅)Fe[C₅H₄—B(OH)₂]

$+ \text{HgCl}_2 \xrightarrow{\text{in H}_2\text{O–acetone}}$

③ [192~194° decomp.].
Recrystd. from xylene.
⑥ Ber. **93**, 2717 (1960).

HgC₁₀H₁₆O₄
① 1-Acetoxymercuri-1-acetoxy-
cyclohexane

② $(\text{CH}_2)_5\text{C}=\text{NNH}_2$
$+ \text{Hg(OAc)}_2 \xrightarrow{\text{in C}_6\text{H}_6,\ \text{r. t.}}$
③ Red oil.
Decomp. on standing.

④ $+ \ \text{CaCl}_2 \xrightarrow{\text{in EtOH}}$

$\left(\text{mp } 101\sim3°(\text{Et}_2\text{O}) \right)$

$\xrightarrow{\text{aq. KOH}}$ Hg $+$

⑥ Izv. OKhN **1959**, 50 ; CA **53**, 14965
(1958).

HgC₁₀H₁₇Cl
① Camphor-4-mercuric chloride

②

③ Stable. Sol. in acetone and ethyl
acetate

④ $+ \text{LiAlH}_4 \longrightarrow$

$+ \text{Na}_2\text{Sn(OH)}_4 \longrightarrow$

$+ \text{I}_2 \xrightarrow{\text{in dioxane}}$

⑥ JACS **78**, 2597 (1956)

HgC₁₀H₁₈O₂
① Bis($\alpha,\ \alpha$-dimethylacetonyl)mercury
$(\text{CH}_3\text{COC(CH}_3)_2)_2\text{Hg}$
② $(\text{CH}_3\text{COCMe}_2\text{CO}_2)_2\text{Hg} \xrightarrow{90°,\ in\ vacuo}$
③ Crystals. [120° decomp.].
Recrystd. from toluene or xylene.
Unstable. Sol. in EtOH and
acetone ; hardly sol. in ether.
④ $+ (\text{NH}_4)_2\text{S} \longrightarrow \text{HgS}$
⑥ JACS **45**, 2970 (1923).

HgC₁₂H₇N₃O₆
① Phenylpicrylmercury
$(\text{O}_2\text{N})_3\text{C}_6\text{H}_2\text{HgC}_6\text{H}_5$
② 2,4,6-$(\text{NO}_2)_3\text{C}_6\text{H}_2\text{CO}_2\text{HgPh}$
$\xrightarrow{228°,\ in\ vacuo}$
③ [227.5°].
Recrystd. from C₆H₆ ; sol. in acetone;
hardly sol. in alc., ether and C₆H₆.
⑥ JACS **47**, 1952 (1925).

HgC₁₂H₈N₂O₄
① Bis(p-nitrophenyl)mercury
$(p\text{-O}_2\text{NC}_6\text{H}_4)_2\text{Hg}$
② $p\text{-NO}_2\text{C}_6\text{H}_4\text{N}_2\text{Cl} + \text{HgCl}_2$
$\xrightarrow{\text{Cu–powder in acetone ; aq. NH}_4\text{OH}}$
③ Yellow crystals. [320° decomp.].
Hardly sol. in almost usual solvents.
⑥ Ber. **62**, 1016 (1929). Dokl. **122**, 825
(1958) ; CA **53**, 477 (1958).

HgC₁₂H₉ClO₂S
① o-Chloromercuriphenylphenyl-
sulfone
$o\text{-ClHgC}_6\text{H}_4\text{SO}_2\text{C}_6\text{H}_5$
② $\text{Ph}_2\text{SO}_2 + \text{Hg(OAc)}_2$
$\xrightarrow[\text{aq. NaCl}\ 80\%]{\text{AcOH, heat}}$
③ [247~248° decomp.].
④ $+ \text{Br}_2 \xrightarrow{\text{in AcOH}} o\text{-BrC}_6\text{H}_4\text{SO}_2\text{C}_6\text{H}_5$

⑥ Pharm. Bull. (Japan) **3**, 105 (1955);
CA **50**, 10035 (1955).

HgC₁₂H₉N₂O

① 3-Phenylazo-4-oxyphenylmercuric
chloride
$C_6H_5-N=N-C_6H_3(OH)HgCl$

② $C_6H_5N_2Cl + HOC_6H_4HgCl \xrightarrow[CO_2\,;\,HOAc]{\text{in aq. KOH}\,;}$

③ Needles.
Recrystd. from AcOH. Sol. in alc.
and hot C_6H_6; insol. in ether and
$CHCl_3$.

⑥ Ber. **35**, 2853 (1902).

HgC₁₂H₁₀

① Diphenylmercury
$(C_6H_5)_2Hg$

② $PhBr + Na-Hg \xrightarrow{\text{in xylene, EtOAc}}$

$PhMgBr + HgCl_2 \xrightarrow{\text{in ether}}$

$PhHgOAc + Na_2SnO_2 \xrightarrow{\text{in aq. NaOH}}$

③ White glassy needles. (204°/10.5).
[125~126°].

  • Insol. in H_2O, readily sol. in $CHCl_3$,
CS_2 and C_6H_6; less sol. in ether
and hot alc.
Toxic, very irritating effect on eyes.

⑥ Whitmore (1921). Krause, Grosse
(1937).

HgC₁₂H₁₂N₂

① Bis(*p*-aminophenyl)mercury.
$(p\text{-}NH_2C_6H_4)_2Hg$

② $p\text{-}NH_2C_6H_4HgOAc + $ aq. $Na_2S_2O_3 \longrightarrow$
$p\text{-}NH_2C_6H_4HgOAc + $ aq. KOH
$+ Na_2S \longrightarrow$

③ Colorless needles. [174° decomp.].
Sol. in $CHCl_3$; hardly sol. in EtOH
and C_6H_6; insol. in ether.

⑥ Whitmore (1921).

HgC₁₂H₁₈

① Di-1-cyclohexenylmercury

② $HgCl + SnCl_2 + NaOH \xrightarrow{\text{EtOH-H}_2\text{O}}$

③ (170°/10).
Sol. in ether. Unpleasant odor

⑥ Izv. OKhN 1959, 50; CA **53**, 14965
(1958).

HgC₁₂H₂₂

① Dicyclohexylmercury
$(C_6H_{11})_2Hg$

② $C_6H_{11}Br + Na-Hg \xrightarrow{\text{in AcOH}}$

③ Needles. (170°/10). [139°].
Slightly sol. in ether, C_6H_6; sol. in
alc.; insol. in H_2O. Recrystd.
from EtOH.

④ $+ PhCOCl \xrightarrow{\text{heat}} C_6H_{11}HgCl$
$+ C_6H_{11}COC_6H_5$

⑥ "Beilsteins Handbuch der organis-
chen Chemie", E II **16**, 664. Chem.
Zentb. **92**, 766 (1921).

HgC₁₄H₁₀N₄O₈

① Bis(2,4-dinitrobenzyl)mercury
$[2,4\text{-}(NO_2)_2C_6H_3CH_2]_2Hg$

② $[(NO_2)_2C_6H_3CH_2CO_2]_2Hg \xrightarrow{180°,\ in\ vacuo}$

③ Bright powder.
Insol. in all usual org. solvents
except pyridine.

⑥ JACS **43**, 2238 (1921).

HgC₁₄H₁₄

① Dibezylmercury
$(C_6H_5CH_2)_2Hg$

② $C_6H_5CH_2MgCl + HgCl_2 \xrightarrow{\text{in ether}}$

$C_6H_5MgCl + C_6H_5CH_2HgCl \xrightarrow{\text{in ether}}$

③ Colorless needles.
Easily sol. in alc., ether, $CHCl_3$, CS_2,
AcOH, C_6H_6 and AcOEt; hardly

sol. in ligroin.

④ $\xrightarrow{170°}$ Hg + (C₆H₅CH₂)₂

⑥ Whitmore (1921).

HgC₁₄H₁₄

① Di-*o*-tolylmercury

   (*o*-CH₃C₆H₄)₂Hg

② *o*-BrC₆H₄CH₃ + Na−Hg

   $\xrightarrow[\text{in xylene, EtOAc, heat}]{}$ 33%

③ White tablet crystals. (219°/14).

   [108°].

   Sol. in hot C₆H₆.

⑥ Whitmore (1921).

HgC₁₆H₁₀

① Bis(phenylethynyl)mercury

   (PhC≡C)₂Hg

② 2PhC≡CH + K₂HgI₄ + NaOH $\xrightarrow{\text{in H}_2\text{O}}$

   PhC≡CMgBr + HgCl₂ $\xrightarrow{\text{in ether}}$

③ Glittering white leaflets. (39～40°/14).

   [124.5～125°].

   Moderately sol. in ether and alc. ;

   sol. in CHCl₃, C₆H₆ and hot alc.

⑥ Whitmore (1921). JACS **48**, 469 (1926).

HgC₁₆H₁₄O₄S

① *o*-Carbomethoxyphenylmercuric

   sulfide

   (*o*-CH₃OCOC₆H₄Hg)₂S

② C₆H₅CO₂CH₃ + Hg(OAc)₂

   $\xrightarrow[\text{HOAc ; aq. NaCl}]{}$ *o*-ClHgC₆H₄CO₂CH₃

   o-ClHgC₆H₄CO₂CH₃ + H₂S $\xrightarrow{\text{in MeOH}}$

③ White amorphous powder.

   Slightly sol. in alc., ethyl acetate,

   acetone, ether and low foiling

   ligroin ; easily sol. in CHCl₃, C₆H₆

   and aniline.

⑥ Whitmore (1921).

HgC₁₆H₂₀N₂

① Bis (*p*-dimethylaminophenyl)

mercury

[*p*-(CH₃)₂NC₆H₄]₂Hg

② *p*-BrC₆H₄N(CH₃)₂ + Na−Hg $\xrightarrow{\text{in xylene}}$

   p-(CH₃)₂NC₆H₄HgOH + Na₂S

   $\xrightarrow[\text{in aq. NaOH}]{}$

③ Needles. [169°].

   Slightly sol. in EtOH and ether ;

   readily sol. in CHCl₃.

④ + CH₃I ⟶ [(CH₃)₃NI−C₆H₄−]₂Hg

⑥ Whitmore (1921).

HgC₁₈H₁₄S₂

① Bis(*p*-tolylmercaptoethynyl)

mercury

(p-MeC₆H₄SC≡C)₂Hg

② 2(*p*-NeC₆H₄SC≡CH) + HgI₂ $\xrightarrow{\text{in 95% EtOH}}$

③ Crystals. [145.5～146.5°].

⑥ JACS **78**, 2760 (1956) ; **48**, 469 (1926).

HgC₁₈H₁₆O₅

① 3,5-Dicarboxy-2,6-diphenyl-1-oxa-4-

   mercura-cyclohexane

② PhCH(OMe)CH−C=O + KI $\xrightarrow{\text{in alc.}}$ 10%

$\qquad\qquad\quad$ | |

$\qquad\qquad\;$ Hg−O

③ [200°].

   Insol. in org. solvents ; easily sol.

   in alkali.

④ + acid ⟶ no reaction

   + sulfide ⟶ no reaction

⑥ Whitmore (1921).

HgC₁₈H₁₈O₄

① Bis(ω-methoxycarbonylbenzyl)

   mercury

   (C₆H₅CHCO₂CH₃)₂Hg

② PhCH(HgBr)CO₂Me

   + NH₃ $\xrightarrow{\text{in anhyd. CHCl}_3}$

PhCH(HgBr)CO₂Me + Ph₂Hg

in chloroform
───────→ 85%

③ [140°].
Recrystd. from EtOH.
⑥ Zhur. Fiz. Khim. **33**, 152 (1959); CA
    54, 1378 (1960).   Dokl. Vysshei,
    Khim. i. Khim. Teknol. **1958**, 754.

$HgC_{20}H_8Br_2Na_2O_6$
① Mercurochrome

② dibromofluorescein + $Hg(OAc)_2$
in aq. NaOH
  + HgO ───────→
③ Green crystals.
    Sol. in H_2O; slightly sol. in EtOH
    and acetone; insol. in $CHCl_3$ and
    ether.
⑤ Fungicide and bactericide.
⑥ Commentary of the national formul-
    ary of Japan, Japan (1959).

$HgC_{20}H_{18}$
① Di-1-naphthylmercury
    $(1-C_{10}H_7)_2Hg$
② $2-C_{10}H_7Br$ + Na−Hg paste
in xylene, heat
───────────→
in C_6H_6−EtOAC, heat
───────────→

③ White shiny rhombic prisms. [243°].
    Insol. in H_2O; slightly sol. in hot alc.,
    cold C_6H_6 and ether; readily sol.
    in hot CS_2 and $CHCl_3$
    Odorless.   Inert to air or light.
⑥ Whitmore (1921).

$HgC_{20}H_{26}$
① Dineophylmercury

    $[C_6H_5(CH_3)_2CCH_2]_2Hg$
② $PhCMe_2CH_2MgCl$ + $PhCMe_2CH_2HgCl$
in ether
───────→ 57%
③ White needles. [26.0∼26.5°].
⑥ JACS **77**, 3747 (1955).

$HgC_{28}H_{22}$
① Bis(2,2-diphenylvinyl)mercury
    $[(C_6H_5)_2C=CH]_2Hg$
② $Ph_2C=CHMgBr$ + $HgBr_2$ ──in ether──→
③ Needles. [140°].
    Recrystd. from propylalcohol.
⑥ Ann. **463**, 103 (1928).

$Hg_2C_4H_2Cl_2S$
① 2,5-Bis(chloromercuri)thiophene

② C_4H_4S + $Hg(OAc)_2$
in alc.−H_2O.   aq. NaCl
─────────→ ────→
③ White earthy powder. [275° decomp.].
    Insol. in usual solvents.
④ + concd. HNO_3 ──→ no reaction

+ NaI ───────→

+ C_5H_5N ──→

⑥ Whitmore (1921).

$Hg_2C_4H_8Cl_2O$
① Bis(2-chloromercuriethyl)ether
    $O(CH_2CH_2HgCl)_2$
② HgO + aq. H_2SO_4
aq. NaCl
  + $CH_2=CH_2$ ──── ────→
③ White crystals. [190°].
    Hardly sol. in H_2O, alc. and ether.
⑥ Whitmore (1921).

Hg₂C₅H₁₀Cl₂

① 1,5-Bis(chloromercuri)pentane
   BrHg(CH₂)₅HgBr

② BrMg(CH₂)₅MgBr + 2HgBr₂

   $\xrightarrow{\text{in ether}}$ 89.4%

③ Needle Crystal. [150°].

   Easily sol. in cold pyridine, aniline
   and dimethylaniline.

④ + KI $\xrightarrow{\text{in C}_6\text{H}_6\text{-EtOH}}$ diiodide(needles,
   mp 117°)

   + I₂ $\xrightarrow{\text{in C}_6\text{H}_6}$ I(CH₂)₅I + HgI₂

   + Ag₂O + C₂H₅OH

   $\xrightarrow{\text{in xylene, heat}}$ HOHg(CH₂)₅HgOH
   (80%)

⑥ Ber. **47**, 177 (1914).

Hg₂C₇H₅NO₃

① o-Nitrobenzalmercuric hydroxide
   anhydride

   o-NO₂C₆H₄CH$\diagdown^{\text{Hg}}_{\diagdown\text{Hg}}$O

② HgO + o-NO₂C₆H₄CH₃ $\xrightarrow{\text{in aq. NaOH}}$
   96%

③ Yellow solid. [220° decomp.].
   Insol. in usual solvents; fairly sol.
   in AcOH and less in 20% H₂SO₄;
   sol. in aq. NaHCO₃.

④ + 30% HCl $\longrightarrow$ Hg + anthranil
   + 10% HCl $\longrightarrow$ o-NO₂C₆H₄CH(HgCl)₂
   + HNO₃ $\longrightarrow$ o-NO₂C₆H₄CHO (87%)

⑥ Whitmore (1921).

Hg₂C₇H₁₀

① 3,9-Dimercura-1-cyclononyne

   $\begin{array}{c} \text{CH}_2 \\ \text{CH}_2 \quad\quad \text{CH}_2 \\ \text{CH}_2 \quad\quad \text{CH}_2 \\ \text{Hg-C}\equiv\text{C-Hg} \end{array}$

② O₃NHgCH₂(CH₂)₃CH₂HgNO₃

+ HC≡CH $\xrightarrow{\text{0°C, in alc., NH}_4\text{OH}}$

③ Insol. in all common org. solvents.
   Sensitive to light.

④ + I₂ $\xrightarrow{\text{in C}_6\text{H}_6}$ HgI₂ + I(CH₂)₅I

⑥ Ber. **47**, 177 (1914).

Hg₂C₁₀H₁₀ClN₃

① Bis(3-pyridylmercuri)ammonium
   chloride
   (3-C₅H₄NHg)₂NH₂Cl

② 3-C₅H₄N·HgCl + NH₄OH $\longrightarrow$

③ [170°].

④ + aq. NaOH $\longrightarrow$ no reaction
   + aq. Na₂S₂O₃
   $\longrightarrow$ di-3-pyridylmercury

⑥ JACS **77**, 4685 (1955).

Hg₂C₁₂H₈

① 9,10-Dimercura-9,10-dihydro-
   anthracene

② o-BrC₆H₄Br + Na-Hg $\xrightarrow{\text{in C}_6\text{H}_6\text{, HOAc}}$

③ Solid. [>300°].

④ + HOAc $\xrightarrow{\text{heat}}$ o-C₆H₄(HgOAc)₂
   + I₂ $\xrightarrow{\text{aq, KI}}$ o-C₆H₄I₂

⑥ Ber. **63**, 2275 (1930).

Hg₂C₁₂H₂₂O₆

① 1,4-Diacetoxymercuri-2,3-diethoxy-
   butane
   [AcOHgCH₂CH(OC₂H₅)]₂

② CH₂=CHCH=CH₂ + Hg(OAc)₂

   $\xrightarrow{\text{in EtOH}}$ $\begin{cases} \alpha\text{- meso from (60\%)} \\ \beta\text{- racemic from (33\%)} \end{cases}$

③ Crystals. [153~154°].
   Sparingly sol. in H₂O; sol. in aq.
   alkali.

④ + I₂ + KI $\longrightarrow$
   α- and β-2,3-diethoxy-1,4-

diiodobutanes

⑥ JACS **63**, 131 (1941).

$Hg_3C_3H_9BF_4O$

① Tris(methylmercuri)oxonium tetrafluoroborate
   $(MeHg)_3OBF_4$

② MeHgOH + HBF_4 $\xrightarrow{\text{in MeOH}}$

③ Crystals. [98°].
   Stable in dry atom.

⑥ Croat. Chem. Acta **29**, 425 (1957) ; CA
   53, 1122 (1959).

$Hg_4C_{14}H_{22}O_9$

① $\alpha, \alpha', \beta, \beta'$-Tetrakis (acetoxymercuri)
   diisopropyl ether
   $[AcOHgCH_2CMe(HgOAc)]_2O$

② $Me_2C=NNH_2 + Hg(OAc)_2$
   $\xrightarrow{\text{in aq. } Cu(OAc)_2}$

③ [150° decomp.].

④ + Br_2 $\longrightarrow$ CH_3COCH_2Br

⑥ Dokl. **111**, 835 (1956) ; CA **53**, 6996
   (1958).

$Hg_4C_{20}H_{24}N_2O_{10}$

① 1,1-Diacetoxymercuriphenyl-3,4-
   diacetoxymercuri-2,3-dimethyl-4-
methxoy-5-pyrazolone

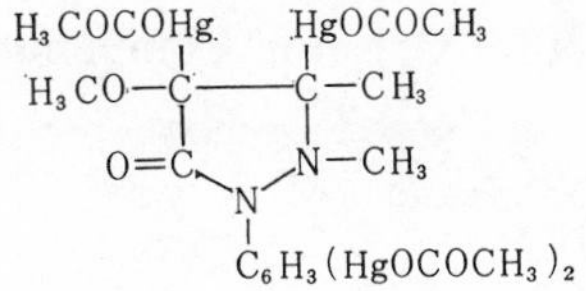

②

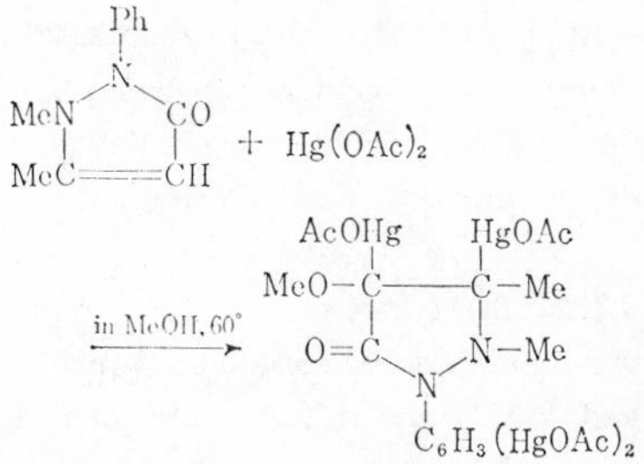

③ Rhombic needles. [200~205°].
   Insol. in most org. solvents ; sol. in
   warm dilute AcOH soln.

④ + dil. aq. HCl $\xrightarrow{\text{r.t.}}$

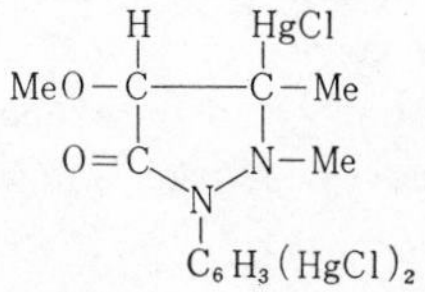

⑥ Ber. **47**, 2736 (1914).

13. Organic Compounds of Transition Metals (Part 2)

In this chapter, the organometallic compounds having at least one transition metal-carbon bond are discussed. The organic derivatives of Cu, Ag, Au, Zn, Cd, and Hg, which are similar to those of nontransition metals, are discussed in other chapters.

13.1. Introduction

Although a few organometallic compounds of transition metals, such as Zeise's salt (1927) and others, have been known for a long time, the synthesis of most compounds of this class has only been achieved comparatively recently. Since the discovery of ferrocene in 1951 by two groups of workers, and the discovery of the coordinated polymerization catalysts by Ziegler and Natta, there has been extensive research into the synthesis, structure. and nature of bonding of various organo-transition metal compounds including, for example, metal carbonyls, metal π-complexes of olefins, diolefins, acetylenes, aromatic nuclei and generally unstable σ-bonded alkyl and aryl transition metals. The reactivities of the organic part attached to the transition metals, and the catalytic activities of these complexes, have also been studied.

13.2. Classification and Nomenclature

The organometallic compounds of transition metals can be classified into five main groups, as shown in Table 13.1. The compounds in [1] are the alkyl or aryl derivatives of transition metals and contain the normal σ-bond between metal and carbon. Very few simple alkyl derivatives are known for transition metals, because they are usually less stable thermally and chemically than those of nontransition metals.

Table 13.1. *Organometallic Compounds of Transition Metals.*

[1] $(CH_3)Cl_3Ti$, $(CH_3)_2Pt(R_3P)_2$
[2] $Cr(CO)_6$, $[Mn(CO)_5]_2$, $Fe(CO)_5$
[3] $(C_5H_5)_2Fe$, $Cr(C_6H_6)_2$
[4] $[Cl_2Pt(CH_2=CH_2)]_2$, $Fe(CO)_3(CH_2=CHCH=CH_2)$, $Co_2(CO)_6(RC\equiv CR)$
[5] $(CH_2=CH=CH_2)Co(CO)_3$, $[(CH_2=CH=CH=CH=CH_2)Fe(CO)_3]^+$

The compounds in [2] are called metal carbonyls, in which some moles of carbon monoxide coordinate to various transition metals. The compounds in [3] are π-complexes in which various aromatic rings, such as the cyclopentadienyl or benzene ring, coordinate to metals. Since the discovery of ferrocene in 1951,

π-cyclopentadienyl derivatives of many other transition metals have been prepared.

The compounds in [4] are also π-complexes, in which the various unsaturated organic species, such as olefins, dienes, or acetylenes, coordinate to metals. Since 1950, many complexes of this class have been synthesized.

The compounds in [5] are complexes which contain various other specific bonds, such as π-allyl- or π-pentadienyl-metal bonds.

The bonds between various organic species and transition metals are usually more complicated than those of nontransition metals, because the d-orbitals of the metals participate in the bonds; the π-component of the metal-carbon bond plays an important role. Some examples are shown in Fig 13.1.

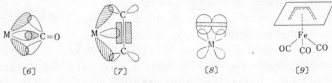

Fig. 13.1.

The bonding in metal carbonyls is shown in [6]. This bond is caused by an overlap of the filled carbon σ-orbital with an empty metal σ-orbital, and another overlap of a filled d_π-orbital with an empty antibonding $p\pi$-orbital of carbon monoxide. The latter is essentially π-bonding and is called back-bonding or back-donation.

The bonding between the metal and ethylene is shown in [7]. Ethylene donates the electron pair of its π-orbital to an empty orbital of the metal (for example, dsp^2 hybrid orbitals in Pt). Then the back-donation of excess negative charge on the metal is caused by overlapping of a filled metal orbital with an antibonding orbital of ethylene.

The bonding between an aromatic ring (for example, a cyclopentadienyl or benzene ring) and a metal is shown in [8]. There is essentially one delocalized covalent bond caused by the overlapping of a singly occupied π-orbital of the ring with a singly occupied dxz or dyz metal orbital. [9] shows the bonding of a metal with a diene, which is similar to the metal-cyclopentadienyl ring bond.

The complexes having the bonding of [7], [8] or [9] are called π-complexes, because the onganic species coordinate to metals, using their π-MO's in these complexes. The same organic group sometimes bonds to the metal in different ways. The designation π-C_5H_5 is made to distinguish π-bonding from σ-bonding, for example, σ-C_5H_5, where there is metal to carbon σ-bonding. The bond formed by overlapping of the π-MO of the olefin with a suitable σ-orbital of the metal is sometimes called a μ-bond.

The nomenclature of the organometallic compounds of transition metals is very complicated, and has no definite rules. The same compound is often named in several different ways. In this chapter, the ligands which are bonded to the metal by a covalent bond are prefixed to the name of the the metal.

The molecular ligands such as R_3P or ethylene, C_2H_4, are written in parentheses ( ). For example, $Cr(CO)_6$, $[Mn(CO)_5]_2$, and $Fe(CO)_5$ are written as hexa-(carbonyl)-chromium, deca(carbonyl)-dimanganese, and penta(carbonyl)-iron, respectively. $(\pi\text{-}C_5H_5)Co(CO)_2$ is named π-cyclopentadienyl-di(carbonyl)-cobalt. The prefix π- or σ-shows the nature of the bond between the ligand and the metal. $(C_5H_5)_2Fe$ is called "ferrocene", and in general the complexes having the "sandwich" structure of two cyclopentadienyl rings are called "metallocene". $(C_6H_6)_2Cr$ is named di(benzene)-chromium, or bis(benzene)-chromium, and complexes of this type are called bis(arene)-metal complexes in general.

The following are some examples of other complexes. $[Cl_2Pt(CH_2=CH_2)]_2$: tetrachloro-bis(ethylene)-diplatinum,   or   dichloro-bis(ethylene)-μ,μ'-dichloro-diplatinum (prefix μ shows a bridging bond). $Fe(CO)_3(CH_2=CHCH=CH_2)$: tri(carbonyl)-(butadiene)-iron. $Co_2(CO)_6(RC\equiv CR)$: hexa(carbonyl)-(dialkyl-acetylene)-dicobalt. $(CH_2=CH=CH_2)Co(CO)_3$: π-allyl-tri(carbonyl)-cobalt. $[(CH_2=CH=CH=CH=CH_2)Fe(CO)_3]^+$: π-pentadienyl-tri(carbonyl)-iron cation.

In rational formulas, molecular ligands are suffixed to the name of the metal, and organic radicals or atomic ligands are prefixed to the name of the metal: for example, $(\pi\text{-}C_5H_5)Mn(CO)_2(C_2H_4)$, $(\pi\text{-}C_5H_5)(Cl)Cr(NO)_2$, $(\pi\text{-}C_5H_5)(\sigma\text{-}C_5H_5)Fe(CO)_2$, and $(\pi\text{-}C_3H_5)(Cl)Ni(PPh_3)$.

These rules of nomenclature and expression of rational formulas are adopted only for this list of compounds. In other cases, the traditional expressions are used.

13.3. *Mothods of Synthesis*

13.3.1. *Alkyl or Aryl Compounds of Transition Metals*

These compounds can be synthesized by the reaction of metal halides with Grignard reagents, alkyllithium, or alkyl aluminum as in the case of nontransition metals. Because most of the simple alkyl or aryl derivatives are stable only at low temperature and are also extremely sensitive to air and moisture, the syntheses of these compounds must be performed at low temperature and under inert atomosphere. CH_3Cl_3Ti and $C_6H_5VOCl_2$ are synthesized by the reactions shown in Eq. (1) and (2).

$$(CH_3)_2AlCl + TiCl_4 \xrightarrow{\;-88°\text{ in hexane}\;} CH_3AlCl_2 + CH_3TiCl_3 \qquad (1)$$

$$(C_6H_5)_2Hg + VOCl_3 \longrightarrow C_6H_5VOCl_2 + C_6H_5HgCl \qquad (2)$$

In the case of relatively electropositive metals such as Ti and V, the metal-carbon σ-bond is considerably ionic and somewhat stable thermally, but these compounds must also be synthesized at low temperature. At room temperature or a little above, $C_6H_5VOCl_2$ decomposes to form biphenyl.

The reaction between phenylmagnesium bromide and chromium chloride in THF, which forms a strong coordinate-covalent bond with chromium, leads to σ-bonded triphenylchromium 3 THF, as shown in Eq. (3). The only really stable simple alkyls of transition metals are the methyl derivatives of Pt(IV), which are synthesized by the reaction shown in Eq. (4).

$$C_6H_5MgBr + CrCl_3 \xrightarrow{\text{in THF}} (C_6H_5)_3Cr(THF)_3 \qquad (3)$$

$$CH_3MgI + PtCl_4 \longrightarrow (CH_3)_4Pt, (CH_3)_3PtI, \text{ etc.} \qquad (4)$$

It is well known that the stability of metal-carbon σ-bonds may be affected by other ligands on the metal. Thus, the transition metals coordinated by phosphins, carbon monoxide, or the cyclopentadienyl group often form stable metal-carbon σ-bonds (Eq. 5 and Eq. 6).

$$(Ph_3P)_2PtCl_2 + CH_3MgI \longrightarrow (CH_3)_2Pt(Ph_3P)_2 \qquad (5)$$

$$NaMn(CO)_5 + CH_3I \longrightarrow CH_3Mn(CO)_5 \qquad (6)$$

The complex acetylides involving essentially normal σ-type bonding between metal and alkynyl group have been reported for several metals. The metal-carbon bonds are stabilyzed by such resonance hybrids as $M-C\equiv CH \leftrightarrow M^+=C=CH^-$, as in the case of metal carbonyls. The general preparation involves the reaction between an alkali acetylide and a metal salt in liquid ammonia as shown in Eq. (7) and Eq. (8).

$$KC\equiv CH + Cr(NH_3)_6(NO_3)_2 \xrightarrow{\text{liq. NH}_3} K_3Cr(C\equiv CH)_6 \qquad (7)$$

$$NaC\equiv CR + Mn(SCN)_2 \xrightarrow{\text{liq. NH}_3} Na_2Mn(C\equiv CR)_4 \qquad (8)$$

13.3.2. Metal Carbonyls

In the case of nickel, iron, and cobalt, the free metals appear to react directly with carbon monoxide to give the carbonyls. By this method Mond discovered nickel carbonyl in 1888. The more useful methods involve reactions of suitable salts or complexes of the metal with carbon monoxide under high pressure, as shown in Eq. (9) and Eq. (10).

$$NiCl_2 \xrightarrow{NH_3} Ni(NH_3)_6Cl_2 \xrightarrow{CO} Ni(CO)_4 \qquad (9)$$

$$CoCO_3 + CO + H_2 \longrightarrow Co_2(CO)_8 \qquad (10)$$

In the case of other metals, the preparation of carbonyls is somewhat difficult. The earlier method used in these preparations involved the reaction of metal salts with Grignard reagents in the presence of CO in an appropriate solvent, for example, Job and Cassal's Grignard method for the preparation of chromium hexacarbonyl (Eq. 11)

$$PhMgBr + CrCl_3 + CO \longrightarrow Cr(CO)_6 \qquad (11)$$

In recent years, many novel methods have been reported. The reaction of chromous or chromic acetylacetonate with CO under high pressure in the presence of powdered magnesium and iodine, with pyridine as solvent, gave $Cr(CO)_6$ (Natta *et al.*).

The carbonylation of chromic chloride takes place in the presence of aluminum chloride, powdered aluminum, and benzene to produce $Cr(CO)_6$ (Fischer *et al.*).

The reaction of chromic chloride with carbon monoxide under pressure in the presence of triethylaluminum, in ether or benzene, gave $Cr(CO)_6$ in good yield. $Mn_2(CO)_{10}$ is also prepared by this method in 80% yield (Podall).

The carbonylation of manganese dichloride in the presence of sodium benzophenone ketyl, with THF as solvent, gave $Mn_2(CO)_{10}$ (Closson *et al.*).

Recently, $V(CO)_6$ was prepared by the reaction of $V(CH_3C_6H_5)_2$ with carbon monoxide, or by the carbonylation of VCl_3 (or $VOCl_3$) in the presence of powdered zinc and magnesium.

13.3.3. Transition Metal–Arene Complexes

a. Metallocene.   Ferrocene, representative of the metallocenes, was simultaneously and independently discovered by two groups of chemists, Kealy and Pauson (1951), and Miller *et al.* (1952).   In an attempt to prepare the unknown compound, fulvalene, Kealy and Pauson hoped to couple cyclopentadienyl magnesium bromide with ferric chloride. (Eq. 12)

Instead of the expected dihydrofulvalene, an orange crystalline compound, ferrocene ($C_{10}H_{10}Fe$) was obtained (Eq. 13).

$$(12)$$

fulvalene

$$\xrightarrow{FeCl_3} \; (C_5H_5)_2Fe \qquad\qquad (13)$$

Miller *et al.* obtained ferrocene by passing cyclopentadiene vapor over hot iron powder(300°). Today metallocene may be synthesized by the following procedures, as shown in Eq. (14), (15), and (16).

$$C_5H_6 + Na \;\longrightarrow\; C_5H_5Na \;\xrightarrow{FeCl_2}\; (\pi\text{--}C_5H_5)_2Fe \qquad\qquad (14)$$

$$2\,C_5H_6 + FeCl_2 + 2\,Et_2NH \;\longrightarrow\; (\pi\text{--}C_5H_5)_2Fe + 2\,Et_2NH\cdot HCl \qquad (15)$$

$$2\,C_5H_6 + FeCl_2 + NaOEt \;\longrightarrow\; (\pi\text{--}C_5H_5)_2Fe \qquad\qquad (16)$$

The procedure shown in Eq. (14) involves preparing the ionic cyclopentadienides of Li, Na, and Mg in a suitable solvent, such as THF or dimethoxyethane, and combining it with the appropriate metal compound, such as ferrous chloride. This method is the most general for synthesizing various cyclopentadienyl-metal compounds.   The procedures shown in Eq. (15) and (16) are simpler for preparing ferrocene.

b. Dibenzene Chromium.   The most practical method for preparing dibenzenechromium is the direct interaction of benzene with anhydrous chromium chloride, in the presence of powdered aluminum and aluminum trichloride (Eq. 17).

$$CrCl_3 + Al + AlCl_3 + C_6H_6 \longrightarrow Cr(C_6H_6)_2^+ \xrightarrow{\text{Na}_2\text{S}_2\text{O}_4} \cdot Cr(C_6H_6)_2 \qquad (17)$$

The reaction mixture is hydrolized to afford the cation $(C_6H_6)_2Cr^+$, and the cation can be reduced to neutral $(C_6H_6)_2Cr$ by reducing agents such as sodium dithionite. Dibenzene derivatives of Mo and V are also prepared by this method.

13.3.4. *Transition Metal–Olefin Complexes*

Zeise's salt, $K[(C_2H_4)PtCl_3]$, is prepared by the reaction between ethylene and potassium chloroplatinate (Eq. 18). When the solution is acidified, the non-ionic complex $[Pt(C_2H_4)Cl_2]_2$ is obtained. Other olefin complexes are prepared by exchange reactions like Eq. 20. The analogous palladium complexes, which are rather less stable than those of platinum, are obtained more conveniently by Kharash's method (Eq. 21).

The rhodium complexes $[Rh(C_2H_4)_2X]_2$ and $(C_5H_5)Rh(C_2H_4)_2$ have the same bond type as that of Zeise's salt.

Recently, as shown in Eq. 22, many metal carbonyl-ethylene complexes have been obtained. Ethylene is coordinated to such intermediate complexes as $(C_5H_5)(CO)_2$-Mn$\cdots$, $[(C_5H_5)(CO)_2Fe^-\cdots]^+$, which are formed under radiation by light or abstraction of halogen anion by aluminum trichloride.

As a special case, a nickel complex coordinated to two molecules of acrylonitrile is obtained through reaction between nickel carbonyl and acrylonitrile. In this complex, acrylonitrile coordinates to nickel through its carbon–carbon double bond. $Fe(CO)_4(CH_2=CHCN)$ is an analogous complex.

$$K_2PtCl_4 + C_2H_4 \longrightarrow K[Pt(C_2H_4)Cl_3] + KCl \qquad (18)$$

$$K[Pt(C_2H_4)Cl_3] + HCl \longrightarrow [Pt(C_2H_4)Cl_2]_2 \qquad (19)$$

$$[Pt(C_2H_4)Cl_2]_2 + 2C_6H_5CH=CH_2 \longrightarrow [Pt(C_6H_5CH=CH_2)Cl_2]_2 + 2C_2H_4 \qquad (20)$$

$$\left.\begin{array}{l} PdCl_2 + 2C_6H_5CN \longrightarrow PdCl_2(C_6H_5CN)_2 \\ 2PdCl_2(C_6H_5CN)_2 + 2C_2H_4 \longrightarrow [Pd(C_2H_4)Cl_2]_2 + 4C_6H_5CN \end{array}\right\} \qquad (21)$$

$$\left.\begin{array}{l} (C_6H_5)Mn(CO)_3 + C_2H_4 \xrightarrow{UV} (C_5H_5)Mn(CO)_2(C_2H_4) \\ (C_5H_5)Fe(CO)_2X + C_2H_4 \xrightarrow{AlX_3} [(C_5H_5)Fe(CO)_2(C_2H_4)]^+AlX_4^- \\ Mn(CO)_5X + C_2H_4 \xrightarrow{AlX_3} [Mn(CO)_5(C_2H_4)]^+AlX_4^- \end{array}\right\} \qquad (22)$$

$$Ni(CO)_4 + 2CH_2=CHCN \longrightarrow Ni(CH_2=CHCN)_2$$
$$\xrightarrow{Ph_3P} Ni(CH_2=CHCN)_2(Ph_3P) \qquad (23)$$

$$PhC\equiv CPh + Co_2(CO)_8 = (PhC\equiv CPh)Co_2(CO)_6 + 2CO \qquad (24)$$

13.3.5. *Transition Metal–Diene Complexes*

Although relatively few olefin-transition metal complexes are clearly isolated, many diene complexes are known. Especially, many analogs of $Fe(CO)_3$(diene) have been obtained.

In 1930, Rheilen and his co-workers studied the reaction of conjugated dienes with $Fe(CO)_5$ and isolated stable organo ion complexes. For example, butadiene forms pale yellow crystals (mp 19°) identified as $Fe(CO)_3(CH_2=CHCH=CH_2)$.

Dienes react easily with iron carbonyls ($Fe(CO)_5$, $Fe_2(CO)_9$ and $Fe_3(CO)_{12}$) on heating or photoreaction to afford complexes. The reaction of $Fe(CO)_5$ requires from several hours to several days at $120\sim160°$ (in a sealed tube, if a low boiling point diene is used.)

In many cases, dienes react more easily with $Fe_3(CO)_{12}$ at $60\sim120°$ and give good results. $(\pi-C_5H_5)Co(CO)_2$ reacts in the same manner as $Fe(CO)_5$ to give $(\pi-C_5H_5)$-Co(diene)-type complexes.

13.3.6. Transition Metal–Acetylene Complexes

Reppe and his co-workers obtained many complexes, whose structures were unknown, from the reaction of acetylenes with iron carbonyls. Recently, structures of some of these complexes have been made clear. The wide variety of structures in these complexes is interesting.

$Co_2(CO)_6(RC\equiv CR)$ is one of the simple complexes. When diphenylacetylene reacts with $Co_2(CO)_8$ in petroleum ether for 2 hours at room temperature, purple crystals of this complex (mp $109.5\sim110°$) are obtained (Eq. 24). The $(\pi-C_5H_5)Ni$ group,

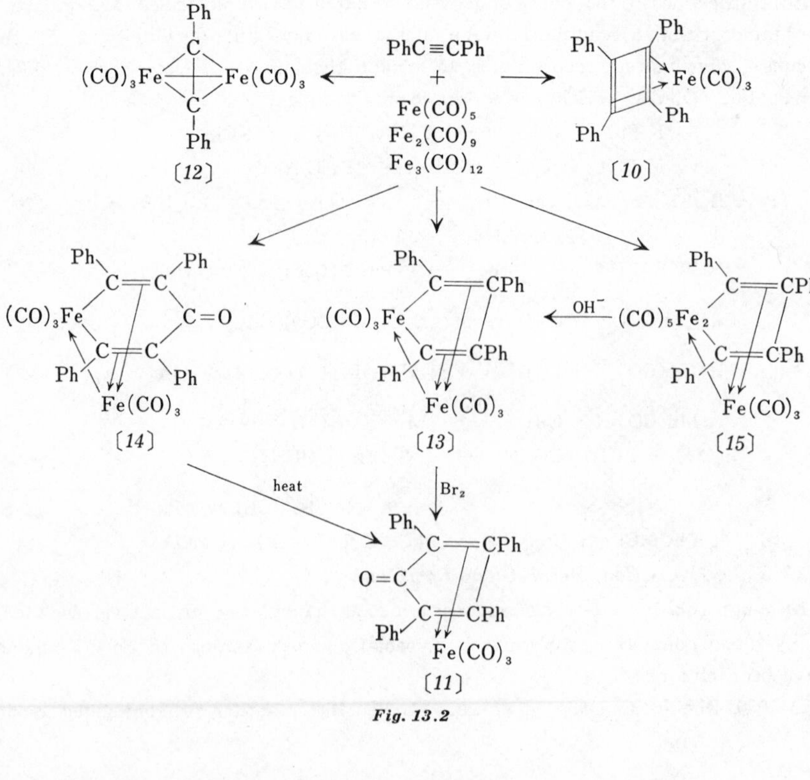

Fig. 13.2

which is isoelectronic with the $Co(CO)_3$ group, forms analogous complexes such as $(\pi\text{-}C_5H_5)_2Ni_2(\text{acetylene})$ by the reaction of $(\pi\text{-}C_5H_5)_2Ni$ with acetylenes. The reaction of iron carbonyls with diphenylacetylene is rather complicated. When diphenylacetylene is heated with $Fe(CO)_5$, $Fe_2(CO)_9$, or $Fe_3(CO)_{12}$ in benzene or petroleum ether, various products are separated by chromatography. These are shown in Table 13.2. Small amounts of hexaphenylbenzene and tetraphenylcyclopentadienone (tetracyclone) are also obtained.

Table 13.2.

Composition	Color	mp (°C)	Amount of product
[10] $Fe(CO)_3(A)_2$	Yellow	234	Small
[11] $Fe(CO)_4(A)_2$	"	Ca. 180	Large
[12] $Fe_2(CO)_6(A)$	Red	150	Small
[13] $Fe_2(CO)_6(A)_2$	Orange	Ca. 200	Large
[14] $Fe_2(CO)_7(A)_2$	Red	Ca. 160	Large at initial stage of reaction
[15] $Fe_2(CO)_8(A)_2$	Black	Ca. 210	Medium

* A: $C_6H_5C\equiv CC_6H_5$

Those Complexes having complicated structures (Fig. 13.2), and other complexes reported recently, will be mentioned in another chapter.

13.3.7. *Transition Metal-π-Allyl Complexes*

Although alkyl halides react with $NaCo(CO)_4$ to give only unstable complexes, $RCo(CO)_4$, which decompose at $0°$, allyl halides react with $NaCo(CO)_4$ to afford stable yellow crystals identified as a π-allyl complex (mp $-33°$), which remain unchanged even at room temperature. A similar complex is obtained by the reaction of $HCo(CO)_4$ with butadiene (Eq. 26).

The π-allyl complex of palladium [16] is prepared by reaction of allyl alcohol with palladium chloride in 50% acetic acid.

$$H_2C=CHCH_2X + NaCo(CO)_4 \longrightarrow (H_2C\cdots CH\cdots CH_2)Co(CO)_3 \qquad (25)$$
$$H_2C=CHCH=CH_2 + HCo(CO)_4 \longrightarrow (CH_3-CH\cdots CH\cdots CH_2)Co(CO)_3 \qquad (26)$$

[16]

13.4. *General Properties*

13.4.1. *Alkyl and Aryl Compounds of Transition Metals*

Transition metal-carbon σ-bonds are known to be unstable in many cases. The reaction of Grignard reagents with transition metal halides frequently results in the formation of a coupling product of alkyl groups without the formation of expected alkyl transition metal compounds (Eq. 27).

$$RMgX + CoCl_2 \longrightarrow R-R \qquad (27)$$

The reasons for the instability of transition metal–carbon σ-bonds are fully discussed by Chatt and Shaw. Transition metals differ from other metals with respect to the presence of unfilled d-orbitals. The d-orbitals in the penultimate shells are on an energy level close to that of the valence s- and p-orbitals. Accordingly, electrons in d-orbitals can easily be promoted into antibonding σ-orbitals of the metal–carbon bond, or, if d-orbitals are empty, electrons in metal-to-carbon bonding orbitals can be promoted into a d-orbital, in either case weakening the metal–carbon bond. According to this hypothesis, the energy difference, $\varDelta E$, between these orbitals must exceed some crucial value for isolation of sufficiently stable alkyl transition metal compounds. In metal complexes in which the energy levels of the non-σ-bonding d-orbitals lie below those of the antibonding σ-levels, an increase in the energy difference is attained by the coordination of suitable ligands, such as carbon monoxide, trialkyl- and triaryl-phosphine, and π-cyclopentadienyl radical, which can lower still further the energy of the non-σ-bonding d-orbital by combining with π-orbitals of low energy. The difference in stability between R_2Ni and $R_2Ni(PR_3)_2$, as one example, can be explained according to this hypothesis, as shown in Fig. 13.3 and 13.4.

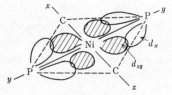

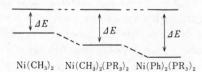

$$Ni(CH_3)_2 \quad Ni(CH_3)_2(PR_3)_2 \quad Ni(Ph)_2(PR_3)_2$$

Fig. 13.3. π-*type bonding in* $NiR_2(PR_3)_2$.

Fig. 13.4. *Energy differences between the highest occupied and the lowest vacant orbitals.*

The stability of σ-bonding is also affected by the nature of the alkyl groups. Generally, phenyl derivatives are more stable than simple alkyl derivatives of transition metals. Antibonding π-orbital of phenyl group overlaps with the non-σ-bonding d-orbitals to add double bond character to the metal–carbon bond. This situation results in an increase in $\varDelta E$ and in an increase in metal–carbon strength itself.   The higher stability of perfluoroalkyl-metal bond to the corresponding alkyl metal bond is attributable to the participation of a C–F anti-bonding σ-orbital, making a partial metal–carbon multiple bond. Electronegativity differences between metal and carbon also affect the thermal stability by an ionic term. Thus, electropositive metal alkyl compounds are thermally more stable than electronegative metal alkyl compounds, as shown by the isolation of simple titanium alkyl compounds $(CH_3)_{4-n}TiCl_n$ and failure to isolate analogous nickel compounds. Another important factor influencing the stability of alkyl metal compounds is a steric one. For example, *ortho*-substituted aryl nickel compounds such as *trans*-$(PR_3)_2Ni(mesityl)X$ have higher stability than the simple phenyl analog. The shielding of the metal by the *ortho*-substituents hinders the approach of reagent molecules to make the carbon-metal bond stabilize chemically.

Reactivities of alkyl transition metal compounds are interesting in connection with the catalysis of transition metals. When alkyl transition metal compounds are heated above their decomposition points, cleavage of metal-carbon bond occurs, giving saturated hydrocarbons or olefins depending on the type of reactions, which may include coupling reactions, disproportionation of generated alkyl radicals, and in some cases, hydrogen abstractions from solvent (Eq. 28).

$$2\ CH_3CH_2-M \longrightarrow \begin{cases} \longrightarrow CH_3CH_2CH_2CH_3 \\ \longrightarrow CH_3CH_3 + CH_2{=}CH_2 \\ \longrightarrow CH_3CH_3 \end{cases} \qquad (28)$$

It is well known that the insertion reaction of olefins into the metal-carbon bond is a propagation step of the metal catalyzed polymerization. For example, in Ziegler polymerization of ethylene by Et_3Al-$TiCl_4$ catalyst, the initial formation of ethyl-titanium bond and the subsequent repeated insertion of ethylene into this polymer was suggested as a mechanism for the polymerization (Eq. 29).

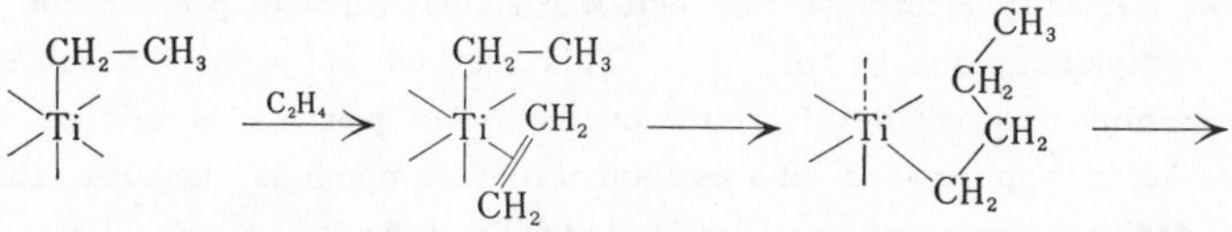

$$(29)$$

Insertion reactions of carbon monoxide into metal-carbon σ-bonds are more common. When methylmanganese pentacarbonyl was treated with pressured carbon monoxide, acetylmanganese pentacarbonyl was formed. On heating the acetylmanganese pentacarbonyl, carbon monoxide was evolved to give the methyl compound (Eq. 30). Insertion and elimination of carbon monoxide proceed reversibly.

$$CH_3Mn(CO)_5 \underset{-CO}{\overset{+CO}{\rightleftharpoons}} CH_3COMn(CO)_5 \qquad (30)$$

This type of reaction commonly occurs in many catalytic reactions in which carbon monoxide is a reactant. Preparation of π-crotyl complex from butadiene and metal hydride is explained as an insertion reaction of butadiene to metal hydrogen bond (Eq. 26). Similar reactions also occur in the case of metal-carbon bonds.

As shown in (Eq. 31), acetyl cobalt carbonyl reacts with butadiene to give a π-allylcobalt complex, and the complex gives 1-acetyl-1,3-butadiene when treated with a base in the presence of carbon monoxide.

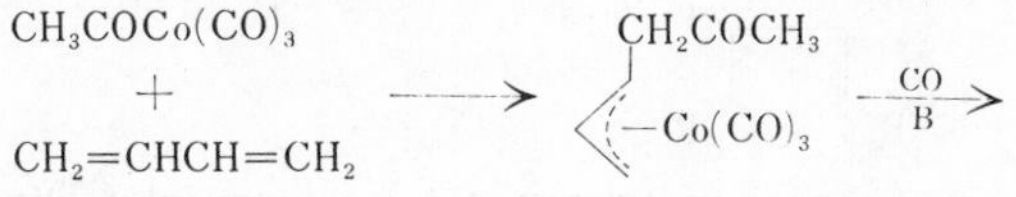

$$CH_3COCH{=}CHCH{=}CH_2 + HB\ Co(CO)_4^- \qquad (31)$$

As was shown in Fig. 13.2 as an example, various kinds of acetylene complexes are formed by the reaction of acetylenes with metal carbonyls such as $Fe(CO)_5$ and $Co_2(CO)_8$.   Compounds [17], [18], and [19] are some of these complexes.

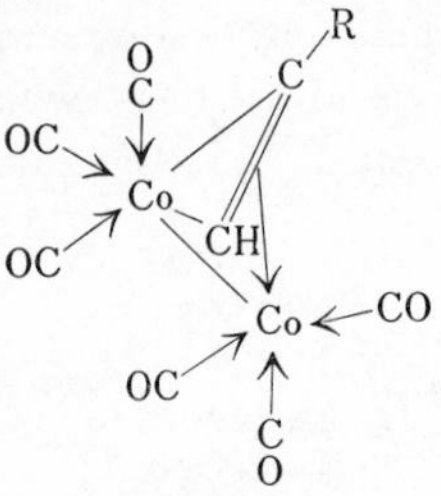

[17] 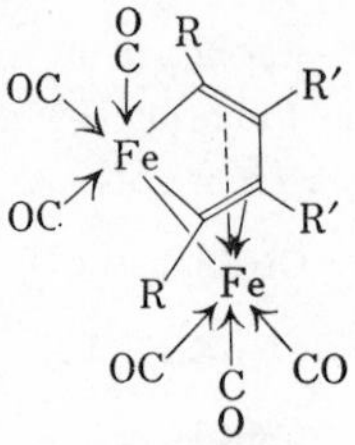   [18] 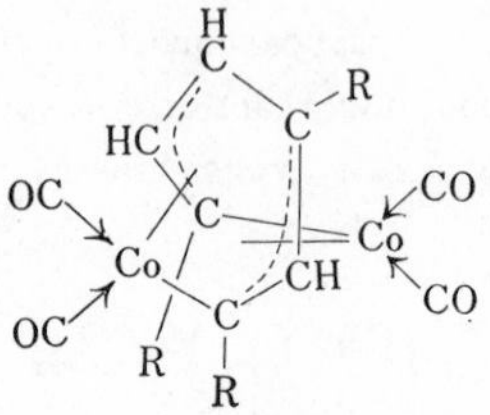   [19] 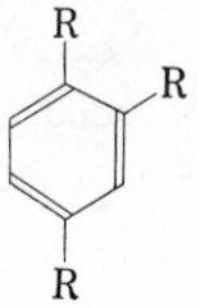   [20]

They are heterocyclic compounds which have transition metal–carbon σ-bond. when compound [19] is thermally decomposed or treated with bromine, a benzene derivative [20] forms upon the elimination of cobalt.   Based on this observation, the reaction was successfully applied to prepare *ortho*-di-*tert*-butyl benzene derivatives from *tert*-butyl acetylene and cobalt carbonyl through preparation of a intermediate complex analogous to [19].   This method of preparing benzene derivatives containing two *tert*-butyl groups in the *ortho* position is one of the interesting synthetic applications of organometallic compounds, because their preparation by ordinary organic reactions is sterically difficult.

Formation of compounds [17], [18], and [19] also suggests a mechanism for the cyclic polymerization of acetylene with metal carbonyl as a catalyst, in which acetylenes are inserted successively into metal–carbon σ-bonds.

When alkyl transition metals are employed for cyclic polymerization of acetylenes, alkyl groups are taken in the product molecule as one component in some cases.   Thus, $Ph_3Cr(THF)_3$, $Me_3Cr(THF)_3$, or $Et_2Ni(THF)_n$ in tetrahydrofurane is treated with disubstituted acetylene to give substituted naphthalene, cyclopentadiene, or cyclohexadiene (Eq. 32).

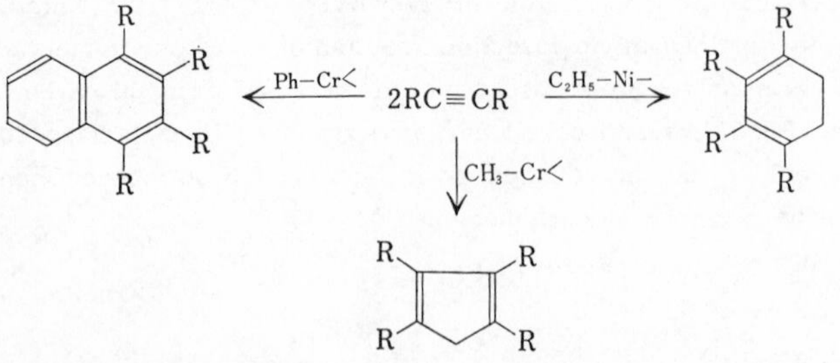

(32)

Mutual transformations between σ- and π-complexes are another interesting reaction of alkyl transition metal compounds.   Equation 33 shows an example of a reaction of this type. Hydride abstraction from ethyl iron complex affords a π-ethylenic complex, and conversely, hydride addition to the π-complex regenerates the original σ-complex.

$$(C_5H_5)(CO)_2Fe-CH_2CH_3 \quad \xrightarrow[+H^+(NaBH_4)]{-H^-(Ph_3C\cdot ClO_4)} \quad \left[(C_5H_5)(CO)_2Fe \leftarrow \begin{matrix} CH_2 \\ \| \\ CH_2 \end{matrix} \right]^+ \tag{33}$$

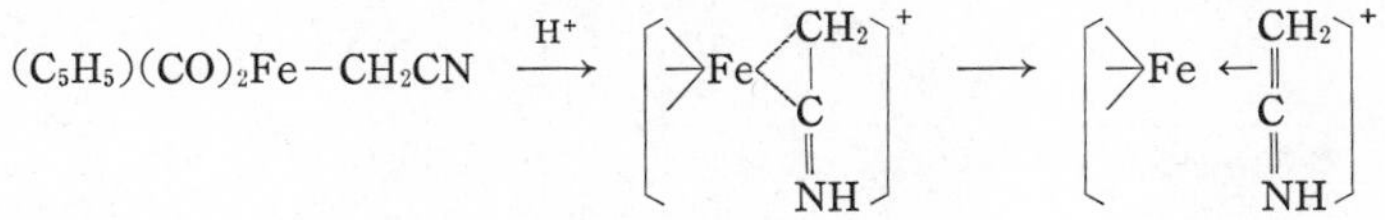

$$(C_5H_5)(CO)_2Fe-CH_2CN \quad \xrightarrow{H^+} \quad \left[\underset{}{>}Fe\underset{\underset{NH}{\overset{\|}{C}}}{\overset{CH_2}{\diagdown}} \right]^+ \longrightarrow \left[>Fe \leftarrow \underset{\underset{NH}{\overset{\|}{C}}}{\overset{CH_2}{\|}} \right]^+ \tag{34}$$

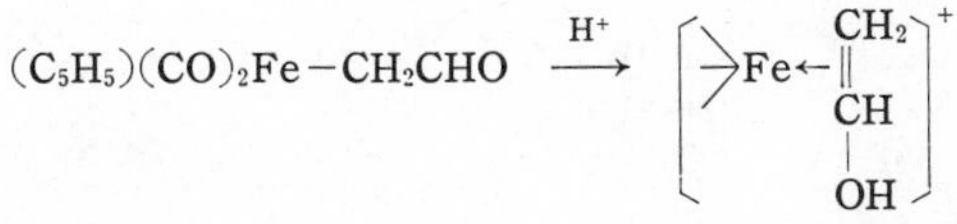

$$(C_5H_5)(CO)_2Fe-CH_2CHO \quad \xrightarrow{H^+} \quad \left[>Fe\leftarrow \underset{\underset{OH}{\overset{\|}{CH}}}{\overset{CH_2}{\|}} \right]^+ \tag{35}$$

$$(C_5H_5(CO)_2Fe-CH_2C\equiv CH \quad \xrightarrow{H^+} \quad \left[>Fe\leftarrow \underset{\underset{CH_2}{\overset{\|}{C}}}{\overset{CH_2}{\|}} \right]^+ \tag{36}$$

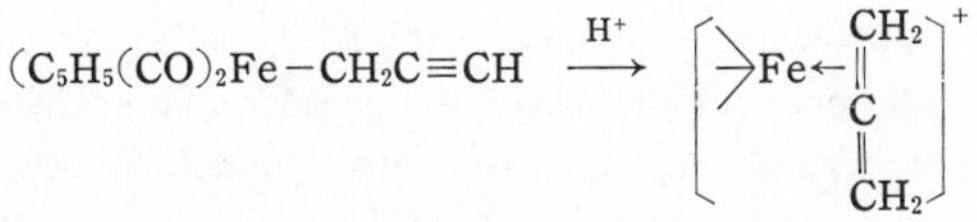

In some cases, protonation of σ-alkyl metal complex affords new olefin complexes as shown in Eq. (34) to (36). This synthetic route for π-complex is very interesting because some of these coordinated olefinic ligands have not been isolated as well definite compounds.

13.4.2. Metal Carbonyls

The metal carbonyls shown in Table 13.3 have the low valent metal, that is, at the valency state of 0 or -1, at the coordination center. CO molecule, represented by a resonance hybrid as shown in Eq. (37), coordinates to the metal using its

$$:\overset{-}{C}\equiv\overset{+}{O}: \quad \longleftrightarrow \quad :C=O: \quad \longleftrightarrow \quad :\overset{+}{C}-\overset{..}{\underset{..}{O}}:^- \tag{37}$$

lone pair on the carbon atom. In the coordination of each CO molecule to the metal, the effective atomic number (EAN) of the metal increases by 2 units. A typical example is described below. The classical valence bond formulation of iron atom (Fe^0) is shown in Fig. 13.5. When CO molecules coordinate to the iron atom, the eight $3d$-electrons are thought to adopt a spin-paired configuration as a result of the strong ligand caused by the CO molecule. Thus, five molecules

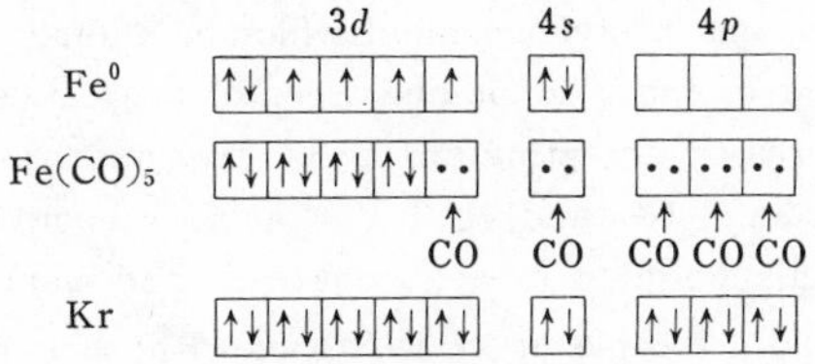

Fig. 13.5.

Table 13.3.

V(CO)$_6$	Cr(CO)$_6$	Mn$_2$(CO)$_{10}$	Fe(CO)$_5$	Co$_2$(CO)$_8$	Ni(CO)$_4$
[V(CO)$_6$]	[Cr(CO)$_5$]$^{2-}$	[Mn(CO)$_5$]$^-$	Fe$_2$(CO)$_9$	Co$_4$(CO)$_{12}$	[Ni$_2$(CO)$_6$]$^{2-}$
	[Cr(CO)$_{10}$]$^{2-}$	[Mn(CO)$_6$]$^+$	Fe$_3$(CO)$_{12}$	[Co(CO)$_4$]$^-$	[Ni$_4$(CO)$_9$]$^{2-}$
			[Fe(CO)$_4$]$^{2-}$		
			[Fe$_2$(CO)$_8$]$^{2-}$		
			[Fe$_3$(CO)$_{11}$]$^{2-}$		
			[Fe$_4$(CO)$_{13}$]$^{2-}$		
			[Fe(CO)$_6$]$^{2+}$		
[Nb(CO)$_6$]$^-$	Mo(CO)$_6$	Tc$_2$(CO)$_{10}$	Ru(CO)$_5$	Rh$_2$(CO)$_3$	
	[Mo(CO)$_5$]$^{2-}$		Ru$_3$(CO)$_{12}$	[Rh(CO)$_3$]$_4$(?)	
	[Mo$_2$(CO)$_{10}$]$^{2-}$			Rh$_6$(CO)$_{16}$	
[Ta(CO)$_6$]$^-$	W(CO)$_6$	Re$_2$(CO)$_{10}$	Os(CO)$_5$	Ir$_2$(CO)$_8$	
	[W(CO)$_5$]$^{2-}$	[Re(CO)$_5$]$^-$	Os(CO)$_{12}$	[Ir(CO)$_3$]$_4$(?)	
	[W$_2$(CO)$_{10}$]$^{2-}$	[Re(CO)$_6$]$^+$	[Os(CO)$_6$]$^{2+}$		

of CO fill the five vacant dsp^3 hybrid orbitals.   This makes the EAN of the iron atom 36, and the electron configuration the same as the next inert gas, Kr. This tendency of the EAN of the metal to adopt formal inert gas configuration determines the coordination number of the metal carbonyls empirically and explains their stability.   However, the nature of the metal–CO bond still remains to be explained.   The donor strength of the carbon lone pair in CO seems not very strong for the stable bond formation, so another type of bonding must be involved.   The molecular orbitals of CO are illustrated in Fig. 13.1, [6].   In the coordination to the metal, the filled orbital, that is, the lone pair of CO, overlaps with the suitable vacant σ-orbital of the metal, and at the same time, the vacant antibonding $\pi*$ orbital of CO overlaps with the suitable, filled metal $d\pi$-orbital forming a π-bond.   In short, CO coordinates to the metal by its lone pair and receives the back donation of electrons from the metal to the vacant CO orbital. The metal–carbon bond, thus, becomes stabilized by the partial double bond character, one by a σ-bond and the other by a π-bond.   The bonding can be illustrated as the resonance hybrid shown below Eq. (38).

$$\overset{-}{M}-\overset{+}{C}{\equiv}O \quad \longleftrightarrow \quad M{=}C{=}O \quad \longleftrightarrow \quad \overset{+}{M}{\equiv}C-\overset{-}{O} \tag{38}$$

As described above, CO is bonded to the metal, simultaneously functioning as a σ-donor and π-acceptor.   The low valence stabilizing ligand is not limited to CO.   Other examples of this type of ligand includes isonitrile, R–NC, phosphine, R$_3$P, thioether, diolefin, and acetylene, all of which have dual (donor and acceptor) properties.   The extent of these donor and acceptor properties varies considerably among ligands.   Whereas π-accepting ability is stronger than σ-donating in CO, σ-donating is stronger in R–NC and in R$_3$P.   Metal carbonyl is in many cases stable even at the valene states 0, -1, and -2, and very often unstable at $+2$.   But the many metal complexes of R–NC and R$_3$P are stable at $+2$.   This stability difference may be indicative of the relative strength of the donor–acceptor properties of these ligands.

The structure of the metal carbonyls is of interest. $Cr(CO)_6$, $Fe(CO)_5$, and $Ni(CO)_4$ have octahedral, trigonal bipyramidal, and tetrahedral structures, respectively. $Mn_2(CO)_{10}$ has a binuclear structure in which two octahedra share each apex. On the other hand, two octahedra share each edge in $Co_2(CO)_8$, and the two axes of each $Co(CO)_4$ plane are at a certain angle, as shown in [21] (a).

(a)   (b)

[21] $CO_2(CO)_8$

Two kinds of CO groups are apparent in this $Co_2(CO)_8$ molecule. One is bonded to one metal only and is called a terminal carbonyl, and the other is bonded to two metals and is called a bridge carbonyl. Identification of these is often made by the infrared stretching frequency of the CO group. Terminal carbonyl absorbs generally above $1900 \, cm^{-1}$, and bridge carbonyl below $1900 \, cm^{-1}$. Table 13.4 shows, $Cr(CO)_6$, $Mn_2(CO)_{10}$, $Fe(CO)_5$, and $Ni(CO)_4$, all of which have terminal carbonyl groups only.

Table 13.4. IR Spectra of Metal Corbonyls (cm^{-1}).

$Cr(CO)_6$	2000			
$Mn_2(CO)_{10}$	2063	2028	1997	
$Fe(CO)_5$	2028	1994		
$Fe_2(CO)_9$	2087	2023	1831	
$Co_2(CO)_8$	2077	2054	2034	1859
$Ni(CO)_4$	2050	2043		

Irradiation of $Fe(CO)_5$ affords $Fe_2(CO)_9$, in which both terminal and bridge carbonyls are found as evidenced by the infrared data in Table 13.4. This method for the identification of carbonyl group cannot be applied to the metal carbonyls having coordinated Lewis bases, as mentioned below. Thus, terminal carbonyl absorbs below $1900 \, cm^{-1}$.

Reactivity of metal carbonyls deserves mentioning. Reaction of various Lewis bases with metal carbonyls can be classified into two categories from the difference in the σ-donor and π-acceptor character of the bases. One class is the substitution reaction in which one or more CO groups are substituted by the bases, as exemplified in Eq. (39). The other is the so-called base reaction, in which metal carbonyl anion is formed as shown in Eq. (40).

Substitution $Ni(CO)_4 + R_3P \longrightarrow Ni(CO)_2(R_3P)_2$ (39)

Base reaction $Mn_2(CO)_{10} + B \longrightarrow [Mn(B)_6]^{++}[Mn(CO)_5]_2^{-}$ (40)

Table 13.5. Sub. (*Substitution*), B.R. (*Base Reaction*).

Metal carbonyl	Base P(OR)₃	PPh₃	RNC	o-Phenanthrolines o, o'-dipyridil	Pyridine
Cr(CO)₆	Sub.	Sub.	Sub.	Sub.	Sub.
Mn₂(CO)₁₀	Sub.	Sub.	B.R.	B.R.	B.R.
Fe(CO)₅	Sub.	Sub.	Sub.	B.R.	B.R.
Co₂(CO)₈	Sub.	B.R.	B.R.	B.R.	B.R.
Ni(CO)₄	Sub.	Sub.	Sub.	B.R.	B.R.

Tabulation of these reactions of metal carbonyls reveals some regularity, as shown in Table 13.5.

The σ-donor strength of the bases increases in the approximate order $(RO)_3P$ < Ph_3P < $R-NC$ < o-phenanthroline < $2,2'$-dipyridyl < pyridine, and the π-accepting ability is in the reverse order. The electronegativity of the metal in these metal carbonyls is in the approximate order Cr < Mn < Fe < Co < Ni. Table 13.5 shows the tendency for more base reaction to occur on an increase in the σ-donor strength of the base. A similar tendency is observed for the base reaction on an increase in the electronegativities of the central metals. On inspection of the infrared spectra ($\nu_{C\equiv O}$) of the substitution product, such as $Ni(CO)_2(R_3P)_2$ as formed by Eq. (39), a relationship between the nature of the Lewis base and the infrared $C\equiv O$ stretching frequency can be readily inferred. When the σ-donation is strong and the π-accepting ability is weak, the metal-carbon bond will contribute more to the hybrid (A) in Eq. (41) and $\nu_{C\equiv O}$ will be in smaller wavenumbers. In the reverse case, it will contribute more to hybrid (B) and $\nu_{C\equiv O}$ will be larger.

$$\overset{+}{B}\rightleftharpoons\overset{-}{M}=C=O \qquad \overset{-}{B}\rightleftharpoons M-\overset{+}{C}\equiv\overset{+}{O} \qquad (41)$$
$$(A) \qquad\qquad (B)$$

The σ-donor strength of the Lewis bases as listed in Table 13.6 increase in the order, PCl_3 < $P(OR)_3$ < PPh_3 < PBu_3 < dipy. The $\nu_{C\equiv O}$ of the complexes formed from these Lewis bases with nickel carbonyl decreases in the same order. The σ-donor strength can also be evaluated by use of the NMR chemical shifts of the ^{31}P nucleus in these complexes.

Table 13.6.

	ν_{C-O} (cm⁻¹)	$\delta^{p-m} - \delta^{p}$ (ppm)
Ni(CO)₂(PCl₃)₂	2090	+32
Ni(CO)₂[P(OR)₃]₂	2050	−21
Ni(CO)₂(PPh₃)₂	2010	−39
Ni(CO)₂(PBu₃)₂	2000	−44
Ni(CO)₂(dipyridil)	1950	
Mo(CO)₃ (diethylenetriamine)	1883 1723	

Now, ^{31}P NMR chemical shift of PX_3 measured by the difference from the ^{31}P NMR signal of orthophosphoric acid, is expressed as δ^p (ppm). The similar shift of $Ni(CO)_2(PX_3)_2$ is represented as δ^{p-m}. The value of $\delta^{p-m} - \delta^p$ is listed in the right hand column of Table 13.6. Stronger σ-donor strengths of PX_2 are expected to further reduce the shielding of the P nucleus coordinated to the nickel and value of $\delta^{p-m} - \delta^p$ is expected to be more negative. The experimental results confirm this, as shown in Table 13.6.

The insertion of CO into the R–M σ-bond in alkyl–metal carbonyls was mentioned in Section 13.4.1. Various metal complexes are formed from the reaction of a wide variety of unsaturated compounds, especially dienes and acetylenes with metal carbonyls. Of these complexes, the synthetic methods were briefly summarized in Section 13.3, and their structure and properties will be discussed in the following sections on diene and acetylene complexes (13.4.5.; 13.4.6.)

13.4.3. *Transition Metal–Arene Complexes.*

a. Metallocene.   The nature of the bonding in ferrocene has been discussed by a number of researchers. Fischer *et al.* suggested that all π-electrons in the cyclopentadienyl ring are donated to the vacant orbitals of iron atom and make up the krypton structure, as shown in Fig. 13.6 (a). Although such a rare gas

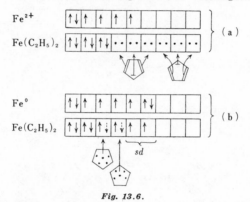

Fig. 13.6.

electron configuration accounts for the diamagnetism and stability, and so forth, of these compounds or metal carbonyls, it also presents difficulties in explaining the aromaticity of ferrocene. Then, Moffitt *et al.* obtained many important conclusions by the application of molecular orbital theory. The bonding between iron atom and cyclopentadienyl ring is intrinsicaly a single covalent bond, as shown in Fig. 13.6 (b). At all events, ferrocene has a sandwich structure in which two

[22]

cyclopentadienyl rings coordinate to the iron atom as shown in [22].

As a result of its easy preparation, stability, and aromaticity, many derivatives have been prepared and the field of ferrocene chemistry has been advanced. As is shown in Fig. 13.7, ferrocene is oxidized by proper oxidants to blue water-soluble ferricinium ion (b).

Friedel-Crafts acylation is one of the most useful reactions of ferrocene and gives a mono-acyl derivative (c) and a hetro-di-acyl derivative (c'), but no homo-

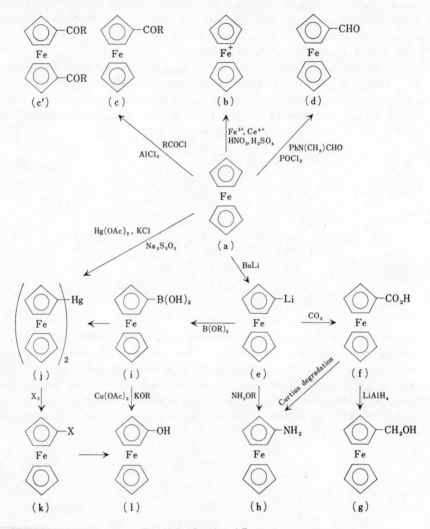

Fig. 13.7. *Reaction of Ferrocene.*

diacyl derivative. This reaction proceeds so easily that only acetylferrocene is produced even in a competition reaction with a tenfold excess of anisole. Vielsmeier reaction gives formylferrocene (d).   Metallation with butyllithium gives lithioferrocene (e) and hetero-dilithioferrocene. This provides preparative methods for carboxylic acids (f), methylol (g), and amino (h) derivatives.   The reaction of (e) with tributyl borate also gives boronic acid (i), which is displaced by anion of cuprous salt so easily that is used in the preparation of ferrocene derivatives. Ferrocene reacts easily with mercuric acetate in benzene to give a $-HgOAc$ derivative which produces a compound (j) on treatment with KCl and sodium thiosulfate. This compound (j) is used in the preparation of haloferrocene (k) etc. The Mannich reaction of ferrocene has proved to be of great synthetic value as shown in Eq. (42).

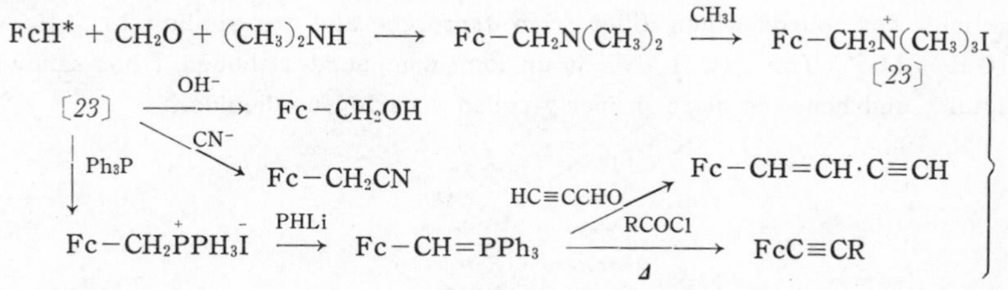

$$FcH^* + CH_2O + (CH_3)_2NH \longrightarrow Fc-CH_2N(CH_3)_2 \xrightarrow{CH_3I} Fc-CH_2\overset{+}{N}(CH_3)_3I$$
$$[23]$$

$$[23] \xrightarrow{OH^-} Fc-CH_2OH$$

$$\xrightarrow{CN^-} Fc-CH_2CN$$

$$\downarrow Ph_3P$$

$$Fc-CH_2\overset{+}{P}PH_3\overset{-}{I} \xrightarrow{PHLi} Fc-CH=PPh_3 \quad \xrightarrow[\varDelta]{HC\equiv CCHO} \quad \begin{array}{l} Fc-CH=CH\cdot C\equiv CH \\ RCOCl \\ FcC\equiv CR \end{array}$$

$$(42)$$

Homo-disubstituted ferrocenes may be optically resolved because of their molecular asymmetry, as shown in Eq. [24] (a) and (b).

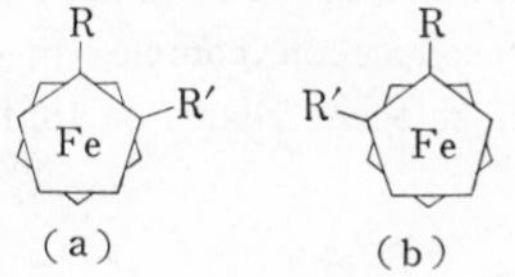

$$[24]$$

Recently, various compounds have been optically resolved. This optical isomer does not racemize, so far as the substituent is not displaced. This asymmetry is sometimes called as "ferrocene asymmetry".

Good methods have not been developed for cleaving iron atom and ligand in ferrocene derivatives. Hence structure elucidation is often achieved by physical methods. Regarding the infrared absorption spectra of ferrocenes, a "9~10 rule" is known and is often used to distinguish homo-substitution from hetero-substitution.

"9~10" means the infrared absorptions at 9μ (1100cm^{-1}) and 10μ (1000cm^{-1})

---

* The symbol Fc means (C$_5$H$_5$)Fe(C$_5$H$_4$), accoordingly, FcH is ferrocene itself. Ferrocene is also

represented sometimes as 〈Fe〉 .

respectively. This absorption is strong in ferrocene itself, considerably weaker in mono- or homo-disubstituted compounds, and disappears entirely when both cyclopentadienyl rings are substituted.

Although various metallocenes besides ferrocene have lately been investigated, only a few examples is described in this chapter. Ruthenocene, $(C_5H_5)_2Ru$, and Osmocene, $(C_5H_5)_2Os$, in the same series with ferrocene are also stable and are less oxidizable than ferrocene. Reactivity with electrophiles decreases from ferrocene to ruthenocene to osmocene. Under identical Friedel–Crafts conditions, ferrocene gave 100% of the diketone, ruthenocene gave 64% of the monoketone and 19% of the diketone, osmocene gave 60% of monoketone only. Although ferrocene is antiprismatic in the solid state, ruthenocene and osmocene are prismatic. Among the cyclopentadienyl derivatives of transition metals, there are some ionic compounds which differ from ferrocene and are similar to $C_5H_5^-Na^+$ or $(C_5H_5^-)_2Mg^{2+}$. Thus, $(C_5H_5)_2Mn$ is an ionic compound although it has sandwich structure, and hence is more properly called a cyclopentadienide.

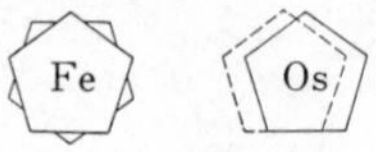

Ferrocene Rutenocene
Osmocene

Many metallocenes other than those of Fe, Ru, and Os are paramagnetic and react with oxygen, so the handling them is often difficult. Their reactivities differ in accordance with their central metals. For example, vanadocene reacts with acetylenedicarboxylic ester to produce the complex in which acetylene coordinates directly to vanadium, while nickelocene reacts so that a cyclopentadienyl ring is attacked by acetylene.

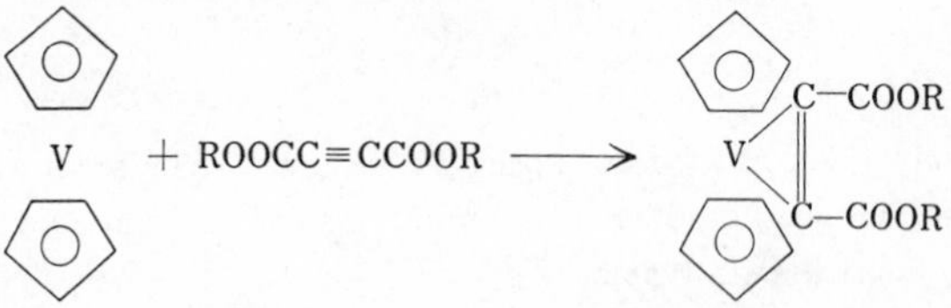

(43)

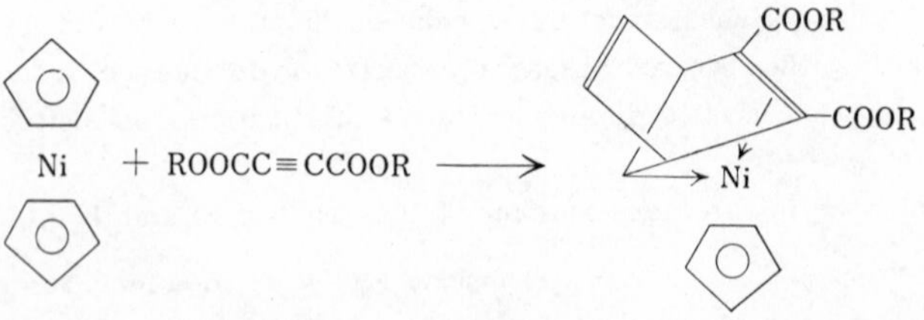

(44)

b. Dibenzenechromium. Dibenzenechromium, in which the two benzene rings coordinate to chromium atom in a sandwich structure, was synthesized for the first time by Fischer *et al.* It is readily oxidized but has remarkable thermal stability.

It has been shown that its crystal is a cubic modification containing 4 moles of dibenzenechromium per unit cell and belonging to the space group Pa_3. It had been decided that the $C-C$ bond distance of the benzene ring is $1.38 \pm 0.05 Å$, assuming the symmetry of the molecule to be D_{6h}. However, a later study by Jellinek concluded that the $C-C$ bond distances of the benzene ring which are $1.436 \pm 0.012 Å$ and $1.366 \pm 0.012 Å$ are alternately different, and that the ring has a considerable extent of strain, though it is planar.

But Cotton *et al.* have recently confirmed from their X-ray analysis that the difference in the $C-C$ bond distances of the benzene ring is small, and that the ring is only a little deviated from six-axial symmetry. Jellinek has recently admitted that the difference in the $C-C$ bond distances of the benzene ring is small.

Dibenzenechromium is readily oxidized by oxygen or air in the presence of water to produce $(C_6H_6)_2Cr^+$, and it reacts with *n*-amylsodium to produce a metalated derivative, which can further react with C_6H_5CHO, CO_2, CH_2O, CH_3CHO, etc., to give various derivatives (Eq. 45).

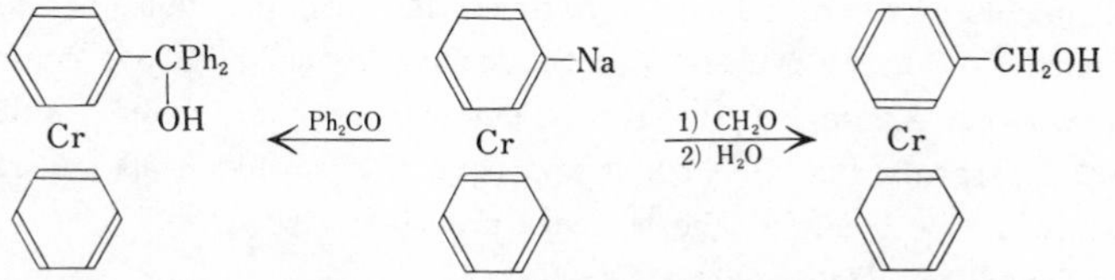

$$(45)$$

Dibenzenevanadium, similar to dibenzenechromium, gives two kinds of crystal modifications, monoclinic and cubic, independent of the condition of recrystallization. Both modifications exhibit virtually identical infrared spectra. Furthermore, both spectra prove the existence of D_{6h} symmetry for the vanadium complexes.

Metal carbonyls react with aromatic compounds to yield complexes such as $(C_6H_6)Cr(CO)_3$. But the manner of the coordination of the ligand to metal differs in accordance with the kind of metal. For example, $(C_{14}H_{10})Cr(CO_3)$, which is produced by the reaction between anthracene and $Cr(CO)_6$, is a complex having an aromatic ring, while $(C_{14}H_{10})Fe(CO)_3$, which is produced by the reaction between $Fe(CO)_5$ and anthracene, is a diene complex.

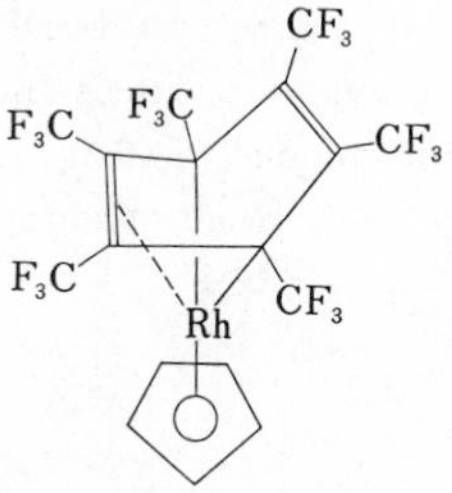

[25] 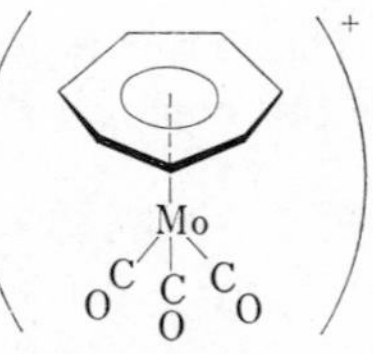   [26]

$(C_5H_5)Rh(CO)_2$ reacts with $CF_3C\equiv CCF_3$ to yield $(C_4H_4)RhC_6(CF_3)_6$ in which 3 moles of acetylene trimerize to form a six-membered ring. But it is concluded by X-ray analysis that this six-membered ring is nonplanar and coordinated to Rh with two σ-bonds and one π-bond by means of localized double bonds, as shown in [25]. It is interesting that even a benzene ring coordinates to metal in the localized double bond system due to its electronegative substituents.

c. *Tropylium Complexes.*   It is well known that tropylium cation $C_7H_7^+$, as well as benzene, is a 6π-electron system and possesses aromaticity. Some complexes coordinated with this tropylium ion have been reported. For example, $[(C_7H_7)Mo(CO)_3^+]BF_4^-$ was obtained by the elimination of H in the reaction of (cycloheptatriene)$Mo(CO)_3$ and Ph_3CBF_4. It has been recognized that in this complex C_7H_7 is coordinated as tropylium ion, a seven-membered aromatic ring shown in [26], because of the facts that its infrared spectrum shows symmetry of C_7H_7 ligand, that its NMR spectrum possesses a single peak at 3.82τ, as well as the evidence of its ultraviolet spectra.

The corresponding complexes of Cr and W also have the same structure, and the central metals of these complexes possess the rare gas configuration. The nonionic complex $(C_7H_7^+)V^{-1}(CO)_3$ is of the same type as the above complexes. It is concluded that although C_7H_7 in this complex is coordinated as tropylium ion at low temperature (ca. $-50°C$), it approaches a seven-membered ring with three localized double bonds as the temperature rises $(160°C)$.

13.4.4. *Transition Metal–Olefin Complexes*

It is wellknown that Ag^+ and Cu^+ form unstable complexes with olefins, while Zeise's salts, $K[Pt(C_2H_4)Cl_3]$ and $[Pt(C_2H_4)Cl_2]_2$, are stable olefin complexes. The analogous palladium complexes, for instance $[Pd(C_2H_4)Cl_2]_2$, are wellknown complexes which seem to play a significant role in the Wacker-Hoechst method, although they are slightly less stable than platinum complexes.

The structure and bonding of these complexes was studied in great detail by Chatt and his co-workers. The infrared spectrum of propylene–platinum complex shows a strong $C=C$ stretching band at $1500\,cm^{-1}$, which is $140\,cm^{-1}$ lower than that for free propylene. Ethylene–platinum complex also shows $C=C$ stretching absorption at $1506\,cm^{-1}$, though it is quite weak. This observation suggests that ethylene should not undergo significant loss of its symmetry through coordination.

These results indicate a structure in which ethylene occupies one of four coordination positions in the square-planer platinum complex, and is perpendicular to the plane involving platinum and other ligands [27]. Such structure is confirmed

[27]

by X-ray diffraction study.

In these complexes, electrons from the π-bonding orbital of ethylene coordinate to one of the dsp^2 orbitals of platinum, and the simultaneously filled d orbital of platinum overlaps the empty antibonding π-orbital of ethylene, as shown in Fig. 13.1 [7]. The latter is called "back donation". Consequently, ethylene-platinum bond has double bond character. This explanation proposed by Chatt and his co-workers is a variation of Dewar's proposal for silver-olefin complexes.

Recently, the rotation of ethylene about the bond linking it to rhodium was reported from NMR studies of $(C_5H_5)Rh(C_2H_4)_2$ at several temperatures.

$[Pt(C_2H_4)Cl_2]_2$ gives a monomeric complex coordinated to NH_3 by treating with NH_3. This also affords a complex coordinated to two molecules of ethylene in the presence of excess ethylene at low temperature, which decomposes at room temperature. probably, by *trans*-effect. $[Pt(C_2H_4)Cl_2]_2$ is decomposed by CN^- and liberates ethylene gas. Hydration gives acetaldehyde and metallic platinum. In the case of the analogous palladium complexes, hydration occurs very easily. It is considered that the palladium complexes take part in the Wacker-Hoechst method, one of the famous methods for olefin oxidation, as intermediates.

$$
\begin{array}{l}
K[Pt(C_2H_4)Cl_3] \xrightarrow[\text{or } C_2H_4]{NH_3} Pt(C_2H_4)(NH_3)Cl_2 \text{ or} \\
\qquad\qquad\qquad\qquad\qquad Pt(C_2H_4)_2Cl_2 \\
\Big\downarrow HCl \\
[Pt(C_2H_4)Cl_2]_2 \xrightarrow{KCN} C_2H_4 + K_2[Pt(CN)_4] + KCl \\
\Big\downarrow PhCH=CH_2 \qquad \Big| H_2O \\
[Pt(PhCH=CH_2)Cl_2]_2 \quad \longmapsto \quad CH_3CHO + Pt + HCl
\end{array}
\qquad (46)
$$

The olefins in platinum-olefin complexes retain their initial configuration. For example, *cis*- and *trans*-2-butene form distinguishable complexes with platinum. So when these are decomposed by aq. KCN, the initial olefins are liberated. This characteristic reaction was used for optical resolution of cyclic olefin by Cope *et al.* From the rigid nature of the eight-membered carbon ring, *trans*-cyclooctene (abbr. *t*-CO) has two optical isomers. Cope and his co-workers prepared *t*-CO-Pt complex from ethylene-platinum complex containing optically active amine (R^*NH_2), namely $(C_2H_4)PtCl_2(NH_2R^*)$. Two isomers of this complex were separated by the difference in their solubilities and then decomposed by aq. KCN. Optically active *trans*-cyclooctene is liberated from the complex (Eq. 47).

$$
\begin{array}{ccc}
H_2C=CH_2 & & t\text{-}C_8H_{14} \\
\downarrow & \xrightarrow{\ t\text{-}C_8H_{14}\ } & \downarrow \\
Cl-Pt-Cl & & Cl-Pt-Cl \\
\downarrow * & & \uparrow * \\
H_2NCHC_6H_5(+) & & H_2NCHC_6H_5(+) \\
| & & | \\
CH_3 & & CH_3
\end{array}
$$

$$\underline{\text{fractional crystallization}} \left[\begin{array}{l} \longrightarrow \quad [\alpha]_D^{21.5} + 67° \quad \xrightarrow{\text{CN}^-} \quad t\text{-}C_8H_{14} \ [\alpha]_D^{25} - 458° \\ \longrightarrow \quad [\alpha]_D^{23} - 25° \quad \xrightarrow{\text{CN}^-} \quad t\text{-}C_8H_{14} \ [\alpha]_D^{25} + 440° \end{array} \right\} \quad (47)$$

Olefins which have no symmetry axis perpendicular to the plane involving the double bond, such as propylene, styrene, and *trans*-2-butene, are expected to give antipodes like (a) and (b) in [28] when they are coordinated to metal. In fact, diastreoisomers of $[PtCl_2(H_2NC^*H(CH_3)C_6H_5)(trans\text{-}2\text{-}butene)]$ are separated by the difference in their solubilities. Molecular asymmetry caused by coordination of olefin is noticed in relation to stereospecific polymerization of olefin.

(a)   (b)

[28]

13.4.5. *Transition Metal–Diene Complexes*

Reihlen, who first synthesized (butadiene)Fe(CO)$_3$, proposed a structure for this complex in which butadiene is linked to Fe with σ-bonds at both ends of butadiene, as shown in [29]. Such a structure consisting of Fe$-$C σ-bond cannot explain both its stability and its diamagnetism, because the Fe atom has 34 electrons in its shell.

[29]   [30]   [31]

After a time, Hallam and Pauson, who discovered ferrocene, proposed, from reactivity and the infrared spectrum of this complex, a structure in which butadiene forms a plane and coordinates to Fe perpendicular to this plane [30]. Green and his co-workers suggested an alternative structure [31] from the NMR spectrum of this complex. The spectrum shows both saturared aliphatic (sp^3) and olefinic (sp^2) protons. They interpreted this result to mean that both terminal CH$_2$ groups link to Fe through a σ-bond and a double bond through a μ-bond. Results of an X-ray diffraction study of Fe(CO)$_3$(CH$_2$=CHCH=CH$_2$) correspond with a π-complex structure, as shown in [30]. That of Fe(CO)$_3$(triphenyltropone) shows an intermediate structure between [30] and [31]. The structure [31] is prefered when diene is substituted by electronegative group like CF$_3$. For example, cyclopentadienone complexes [32] and [25] illustrate this case.

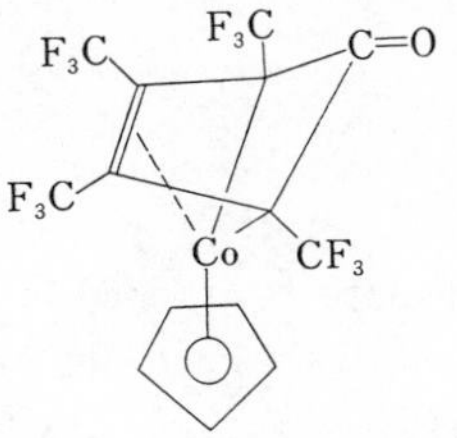

[32]

Although it is difficult to discuss bonding only on the basis of infrared and NMR spectra, these measurements can be of considerable use in assigning a structure. For example, in the infrared spectrum of (diene)Fe(CO)$_3$, there appears a sharp, intense absorption at about 2050 cm^{-1}, and broader bands at 1985 cm^{-1} and 1975 cm^{-1} as ν_{CO}.

In the NMR spectra of acyclic diene complexes, the protons on C^2 and C^3 lie in the region 4.6~4.9τ when saturated substituents are present on a terminal carbon, and in the case of unsaturated substituents, they lower to the region 4.0~4.6τ by deshielding.

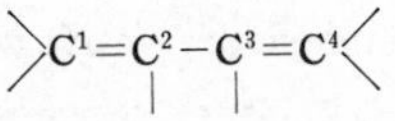

$$\rangle C^1 = C^2 - C^3 = C^4 \langle$$

The anti protons on C^1 and C^4 show absorption at 9.5~9.8τ and the syn protons at 8.2~8.4τ when substituents are absent, and the anti protons 8.9~9.4τ and the syn protons at 7.32τ when saturated substituents are present. In cyclic diene complexes, the protons on C^2 and C^3 lie in th region 4.0~4.6τ, and the syn hydrogens on C^1 and C^4 in the region 6.6~7.3τ. Such values can be of practical use in structural studies of new complexes.

Another problem in the NMR spectra of diene complexes is the valence tautomerism which is observed in such complexes as (C$_8$H$_8$)Fe(CO)$_3$. (C$_8$H$_8$)Fe(CO)$_3$ and (C$_8$H$_8$)Fe$_2$(CO)$_6$, obtained by the reaction of Fe(CO)$_5$ with cyclooctatetraene (COT), have been given the structures shown in [33] and [34] by X-ray studies. But the NMR spectra of [33] show only one peak at 4.7τ, indicating equivalence of all eight protons in the ring. Although the answer is not yet entired agreed upon,

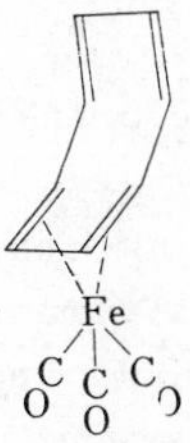

[33]

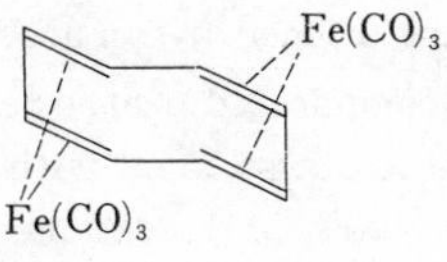

[34]

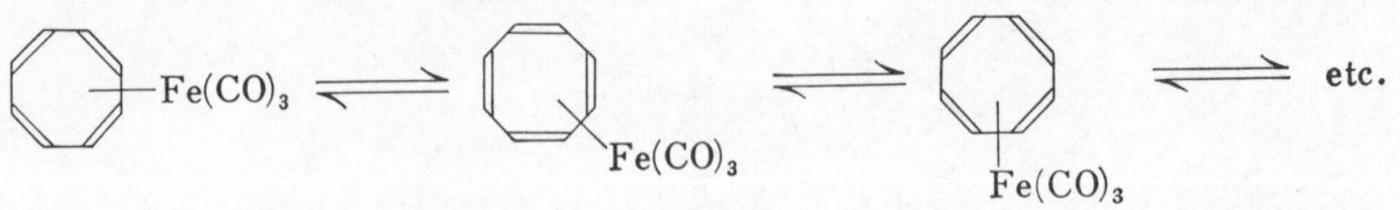

these NMR spectra may be explained by a rapid internal exchange of the $Fe(CO)_3$ group with the other double bond in the ring (Eq. 48). Some nonconjugated dienes such as tricycloheptadiene (norbornadiene) [35] and 1,5-cyclooctadiene have been known to form diene complexes with various metals.

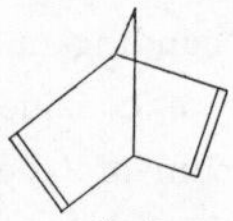

[35]

13.4.6. *Transition Metal–Acetylene Complexes*

Reactions of acetylenes with various organometallic compounds have yielded a wide variety of acetylene transition metal complexes with unusual configurations and types of bonding.

Some examples of simple acetylene complexes are shown in [36], [37], and [38], in which one molecule of acetylene derivative coordinates to metal. Although the complexes [36] are the same type as Zeise's salt, they are unstable and can not be isolated unless at least one substituent R is a *t*-butyl group. The complexes [37] are obtained by the reduction of $(R_3P)_2PtCl_2$ with hydrazine, in the presence

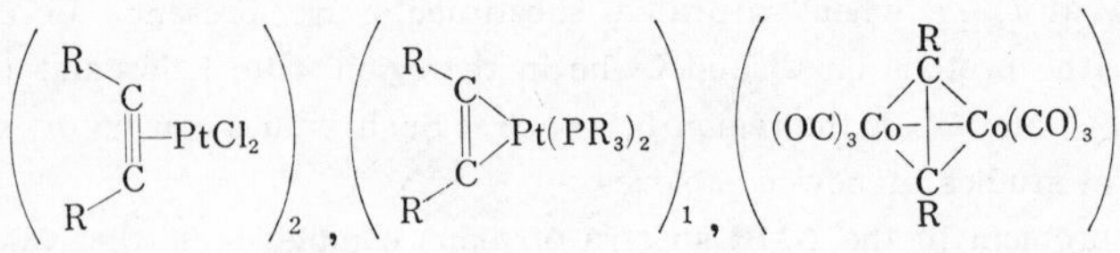

[36]   [37]   [38]

of an acetylene, and have absorptions in the region of $1700\,cm^{-1}$, which is lower by about $400\,cm^{-1}$ than those of uncoordinated acetylenes. This fact indicates that, in these complexes, the bond order of the triple bond is reduced almost to that of a double bond. $(Ph_3P)_2Ni(RC{\equiv}CR)$ or $(\pi{-}C_5H_5)(CO)_2V(RC{\equiv}CH)$ also belongs to this bonding type.

The reactions of acetylenes with $Co_2(CO)_8$ form the complexes [38], in which two cobalt atoms are bridged by an acetylene.

There are many complicated acetylene complexes, in which two or more acetylene molecules become associated with a single metal atom. For example, the complexes [39], [40], and [41], obtained by the reaction of acetylenes with iron carbonyls, have been called the ferracyclopentadiene system, because they have a five-membered heterocyclic structure containing iron atom.   The complexes,

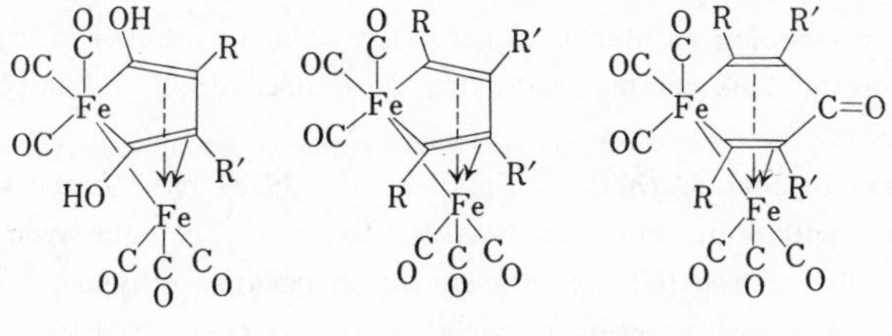

[39]   [40]   [41]

$Co_2(CO)_4(RC\equiv CR)_3$, obtained by further attack of acetylenes to [38], were found by X-ray analysis to be bis-π-allyl complexes [43], although at first their structures had been suggested as seven-membered heterocyclic ring structures [42]. The reaction of $Fe(CO)_5$ with acetylenes affords the complexes [44] and [45]. In these complexes, acetylene and carbon monoxide are bonded together to form a cyclopentadienone ring and a tropon ring.

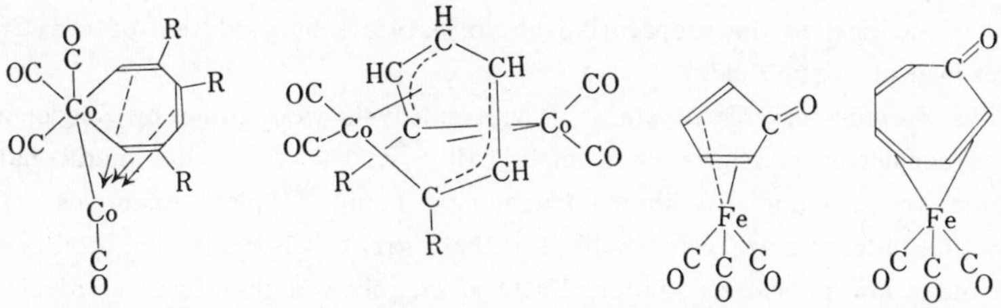

[42]   [43]   [44]   [45]

The complexes in which two molecules of acetylene are linked together to form cyclopentadiene are well known to be as shown in [46], [47], and [48]. X-ray data of [47] confirms that four π-electrons on the ring delocalize to all four carbons.

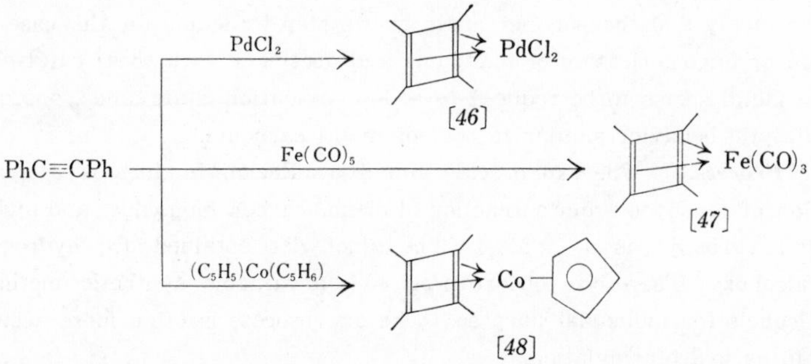

[46]

[47]

[48]

13.4.7. Catalytic Behavior of Organometallic Compounds of Transition Metals

Since the discovery of the Reppe reaction (about 1940), the catalytic behavior of metal carbonyls has been widely investigated. The commercial significance of the discovery of Ziegler–Natta catalysts (about 1950) stimulated studies on the organometallic complex catalysts.   There after a large number of organic synthetic reactions using various complex catalysts were discovered.   Some typical examples will be given.

   a.   Wacker–Hoechst Method.   Smidt *et al.* (1959) have found that ethylene is oxidized with palladium chloride catalyst to form acetoaldehyde.   Today this method is applied to the industrial preparation because ethylene is cheaper than the acetylene used as a starting material in the former method.   This reaction consists of two steps (Eq. (49) and (50)).

$$CH_2=CH_2 + PdCl_2 + H_2O \longrightarrow CH_3CHO + Pd + 2\,HCl \qquad (49)$$

$$Pd + 2\,HCl + 1/2\,O_2 \longrightarrow PdCl_2 + H_2O \qquad (50)$$

Although the step of Eq. (49) is slower than that of Eq. (50), the addition of $CuCl_2$ or $FeCl_3$ as an oxygen carrier can accelerate the former and make the catalytic reaction proceed smoothly.   In the reaction of Eq. 49, a complex of Zeise's salt type, $[Pd(CH_2=CH_2)Cl_3]^-$, has been believed to be a catalytic intermediate.   This method is modified to the preparation of vinylacetate by oxidation of ethylene in the presence of acetic acid.

   b.   The Ziegler-type Catalysts.   These catalysts were found by Ziegler about 1950 and consist of mixtures of a metal alkyl and a transition metal halide, aluminum triethyl and titanium tetrachloride being   typical examples.   These combination catalysts are remarkable for their great polymerization ability with olefins under low pressure.   Later, Natta *et al.* showed that these catalysts give stereospecific polymers of propylene and other olefins.   These catalytic systems are also called Ziegler–Natta catalysts, they marked the beginning of an enormous development in the area of stereospecific polymerizations.   It is thought that, as mentioned on p. 833, in the polymerization of ethylene with AlR_3–$TiCl_4$ or AlR_3–$TiCl_3$, the R–Ti bond is an active center, into which the insertion of ethylene occurs repeatedly and the polymer chain grows step by step.   In the case of the cyclization or oligomerization of butadiene and acetylene with these catalysts, the transition metal seems to be reduced to a low oxidation state and consequently shows catalytic behavior similar to that of metal carbonyl.

   c.   Oxo Process.   The oxo process found by Roelen in 1938 is a synthetic preparation of aldehyde from a reaction of olefin, carbon monoxide, and hydrogen, using cobalt carbonyl as a catalyst.   The aldehydes obtained are hydrogenated to form alcohols.   Therefore the oxo process is a valuable synthetic method for C_8–C_{13} alcohols for industrial purpose.   The oxo process is often more accurately referred to as hydroformylation.

   The following mechanism for this process is proposed.   Cobalt carbonyl reacts with hydrogen to form a hydrocobaltcarbonyl such as $HCo(CO)_4$ or $HCo(CO)_3$, and as shown in Eq. 51 olefin insertion occurs between the H–Co bond, followed by carbon monoxide insertion between the alkylcobalt bond to form an acylcobalt

$$RCH{=}CH_2 + CO + H_2 \xrightarrow{Co_2(CO)_8} RCH_2CH_2CHO \qquad (51)$$

$$HCo(CO)_n \xrightarrow{RCH=CH_2} RCH_2CH_2Co(CO)_n \xrightarrow{CO}$$

$$RCH_2CH_2COCo(CO)_n \xrightarrow{H_2} RCH_2CH_2CHO + HCo(CO)_n \qquad (52)$$

bond. This in turn is cleaved by hydrogen to give aldehyde, simultaneously regenerating hydrocarbonyl catalyst. These reactions suggest that the σ-bond between the transition metal and carbon or hydrogen is very reactive and so olefin, carbon monoxide, and hydrogen easily insert between the bond. Synthetic reactions of organic compounds from carbon monoxide can be almost explained by the conception of the carbon monoxide insertion.

d. Cyclization of Butadiene or Acetylene. Several years ago (1954), Reed reported that $[(PhO)_3P]_2Ni(CO)_2$ catalyzed the cyclic dimerization of butadiene to cyclooctadiene (COD) or vinylcyclohexene. Recently, Wilke *et al.* (1959) have found that Ziegler-type catalysts selectively catalyze the cyclization of butadiene. Thus butadiene is converted to 1,2-polymer with $Ti(OBu)_4$–$AlEt_3$ and to cyclic trimer cyclododecatriene (CDT) with $TiCl_4$–AlR_2Cl or $CrCl_3$–AlR_3. With an NiX_2–AlR_3–donor system (donor means Ph_3P, CO, diene, or acetylene), it is converted to COD or CDT depending on the nature of the donor. Wilke *et al.* have studied the mechanism of this reaction and have isolated the catalytic intermediate. In the proposed structure, shown in Fig. [49], the linear product formed from three molecules of butadiene attaches to Ni atom through two π-allyl bonds at both terminals. Recently, Shaw *et al.* have prepared $[RuCl_2(C_4H_6)_3]$ from the reaction of $RuCl_3$ with butadiene, which has been shown to have the structure [50] based on X-ray analysis. The structure is quite similar to that of [49], and [50] also gives CDT by thermal decomposition.

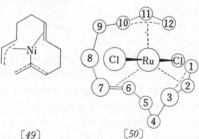

[49]　　　　　　[50]

It is well known that acetylenes also give cyclic oligomers such as benzene derivatives or cyclooctatetraene with various catalysts. In these cyclizations ferracyclo [40], bis-π-allyl [43] and cyclobutadiene [47] complexes described in p. 847 are thought to be catalytic intermediates.

13.5. Related Compounds
13.5.1. Acetylacetonate Complexes

One of the starting materials widely used in the preparation of organotransition metal complexes is acetylacetonate complex. The complex is a salt of acetylacetone and metal. Although the complex does not belong to the class of organometallic complexes, it forms mostly inner salt and is insoluble in water but soluble in organic media. Acetylacetonate complexes of almost all transition metals were prepared, for example, chromium(III) acetylacetonate $Cr(C_5H_7O_2)_3$, cobalt(III) acetylacetonate $Co(C_5H_7O_2)_3$, and nickel(II) acetylacetonate $Ni(C_5H_7O_2)_2$.

13.5.2. Phosphine Complexes

Phoshine derivatives such as PR_3, $P(OR)_3$, and phosphorous trihalide are ligands having both electron donor and acceptor properties like those of carbon monoxide, and so can form low oxidation state metal complexes. A large number of phosphine complexes are known, including $Ni(PF_3)_4$, $Ni(PCl_3)_4$, $Ni[P(OPh)_3]_4$, $Pt(PPh_3)_4$, and $Pt(Ph_2PCH_2CH_2PPh_2)_2$. Although these complexes do not contain direct bonding between carbon and transition metal, they have properties similar to those of carbonyl and isonitrile complexes of transition metals. A large number of complexes such as $Ni(CO)_2(PPh_3)_2$ and $(\pi-C_5H_5)Ni(PPh_3)Cl$, which consist of mixed ligands, are also known.

13.5.3. Cyanide Complexes

Cyanide complexes of transition metals contain metal-carbon bonds, the bond between metal and cyanide group is similar to that between metal and carbon monoxide.   However, they do not generally belong to the class of organometallic compounds. Most cyanide complexes of transition metals have polymeric structures, and many of them are insoluble both in organic solvents and water.   However, on treating with potassium cyanide they form complex salts which dissolve in water. For example, to an aqueous solution of $NiCl_2$, one equivalent of a solution of potassium cyanide was added to give $Ni(CN)_2$ as an insoluble product, to which an excess of potassium cyanide was added to give $K_2Ni(CN)_4$, which is soluble in water.

13.5.4. Transition Metal Hydride Complexes

Hydride derivatives of transition metals are roughly divided into simple hydrides and hydride complexes. The simple hydrides containing metallic hydride (TiH or TiH_2, for example) are obtained by fusing H_2 on to metal at high temperature, and compounds such as CuH, AuH, CaH$_2$, and ZnH$_2$ are obtained from the reaction of transition metal salts with LiAlH$_4$ or NaBH$_4$. These show very different properties from those of organometallic compounds. On the other hand, hydride complexes are organotransition metal complexes, and H may be regarded as the smallest alkyl group. As the transition metal-alkyl bond is stabilized by the coordination of CO, PR$_3$, or cyclopentadienyl group, the transition metal-hydride bond is also stabilized by these ligands. Therefore, a large number of hydride complexes, such as HMn(CO)$_5$, H$_2$W(π-C$_5$H$_5$)$_2$, HCr(π-C$_5$H$_5$)(CO)$_3$, IrHCl$_3$(PR$_3$)$_3$, and OsHCl(CO)(PR$_3$)$_3$, have been prepared.

REFERENCES

The chemistry of organotransition metal compounds has primarily developed since 1950, so there are few earlier references. However, in the last few years many excellent books have appeared. In the Journal of Organometallic Chemistry (Elsevier Publishing Co.), which is published monthly, a large number of reports on organotransition metal complexes appear. In addition, the following journals and books are recommended as references.

1) "Organometallic Chemistry Reviews", Vol. 1 (1966), Vol. 2 (1967), Elsevier Publishing Co.
2) "Annual Surveys of Organometallic Chemistry", (edited by D. Seyferth, R. B. King), Vol. 1 (1965); Vol. 2 (1965), Elsevier Publishing Co.
3) "Organometallic Syntheses" (edited by R. B. King) (transition-metal compounds), Vol. 1, Academic Press (1965).
4) "Advances in Organometallic Chemistry" (edited by F. G. A. Stone, R. West), Vol. 1 (1964), Vol. 2 (1964), Vol. 3 (1965), Vol. 4 (1966), Vol. 5 (1967), Academic Press.
5) "The Chemistry of Organometallic Compounds" (edited by D. Seyferth), M. Rosenblum, "Chemistry of the Iron Group Metallocenes", Part. 1, John Wiley & Sons (1965).
6) "Survey of Progress in Chemistry", Vol. 1, W. F. Little, "Metallocene", Academic Press (1963).
7) "Organometallic Chemistry" (edited by H. Zeiss), Reinhold Publishing Co. (1960).
8) "Organometallic Compounds" (G. E. Coates), Methuen & Co. Ltd., John Wiley & Sons (1960).
9) "Organometallic Chemistry and Its Application" (edited by the Division of Organometallic Chemistry, Kinki Society of the Chemical Industry), Asakura, Tokyo (1962).
10) "Organometallic Chemistry", Kagakudojin, Kyoto (1966).
11) "Advanced Inorganic Chemistry" (2nd Ed., edited by F. A. Cotton, G. Wilkinson), Interscience (1966).
12) "Organometallic Compounds" (edited by M. Dub), Vol. 1 (2nd Ed.), Springer-Verlag (1966).
13) "Transition Metal Chemistry" (edited by R. L. Carlin), Vol. 1 (1965), Vol.

2 (1966), Vol. 3 (1966), Marcel Dekker.

14) "Metal π-Complexes" (E. O. Fischer, H. Werner), Vol. 1, Elsevier (1966).

【Co】

CoC₃NO₄

① Nitrosyl-tri(carbonyl)-cobalt
  Co(NO)(CO)₃

② KCo(CO)₄ + NO + H₂O $\longrightarrow$ 58%
  NaCo(CO)₄ + NaNO₂ + CH₃CO₂Na
  $\longrightarrow$

③ Deep red mobile liq. (48.6°). [−11°].
   d 1.47 (20°).
   Insol. in H₂O ; miscible with most
   org. solvents. Decompd. at 55°.
   IR : ν_{NO}, 1832 cm⁻¹.
   Bond length ; N−O 1.10Å, C−O 1.14
   Å, Co−C 1.83Å.

④ + Br₂ $\longrightarrow$ CoBr₂ + NO + CO

⑥ Inorg. Syn. **2**, 239 (1947).

CoC₄HO₄

① Hydrido-tetra(carbonyl)-cobalt
  (H)Co(CO)₄

② Co₂(CO)₈ + C₅H₅N $\xrightarrow{\text{H}_2\text{SO}_4}$

  NaCo(CO)₄ $\xrightarrow{\text{H}_2\text{SO}_4}$

③ Light yelow liq. Volatile with CO
   stream at room temp. [−26].
   Darkens rapidly above −33°, cannot
   be stored at room temp. without
   high CO pressure.
   IR : $\nu_{C\equiv O}$ 2049, 2066 cm⁻¹ ; ν_{Co-H}∼1934
   cm⁻¹.
   NMR : τ 20.
   Strongly acidic in aq. soln.

④ $\xrightarrow{25°}$ H₂ + Co₂(CO)₈

  + $\rangle$C=C$\langle$ $\longrightarrow$ $\rangle$CH−C$\langle$
                                        |
                                     Co(CO)₄

  * Tetrahedral arrangement of car-
    bonyl groups around cobalt atoms
    has been proposed, but recently 5
    -coordinated trigonal bipyramidal
    structure was proposed.

⑥ Inorg. Syn. **5**, 192 (1957).

CoC₅H₃O₄

① Methyl-tetra(carbonyl)-cobalt
  (CH₃)Co(CO)₄

② NaCo(CO)₄ + CH₃I $\xrightarrow{\text{Et}_2\text{O}}$

③ Light yellow liq. Volatile with
   stream of nitrogen. [−44°].
   Very unstable. Decompd. at −35°
   in nitrogen ; stable in gaseous
   state at room temp.
   IR : ν_{CH} 3013, 2939 cm⁻¹ ; $\nu_{C=O}$ 2111,
   2036, 1996 cm⁻¹.

④ $\xrightarrow{\text{heat}}$ CH₃COCH₃

⑥ Z. Naturf. **13**b, 192 (1958).

CoC₆H₅O₃

① π-Allyl-tri(carbonly)-cobalt

  (π-C₃H₅)Co(CO)₃,

② CH₂=CH−CH₂Br + NaCo(CO)₄ $\xrightarrow{25°, \text{Et}_2\text{O}}$
  CH₂=CH−CH₂Cl + KCo(CO)₄
  $\xrightarrow{\text{MeOH}}$ 66%

③ Reddish yellow liq. (39°/15). [−33∼
   −32°].
   Sol. in org. solvents. Oxidized rapidly
   in air ; no decomp. at room temp.
   under nitrogen.
   IR : $\nu_{C\equiv O}$ 2066, 1984 cm⁻¹.
   NMR : τ 4.91(m), 3.06(d), 2.14(d).

④ + Ph₃P $\longrightarrow$ π-C₃H₅Co(CO)₂PPh₃

⑥ JACS **83**, 1601 (1961).

CoC₇H₅O₂

① π-Cyclopentadienyl-di(carbonyl)
  -cobalt

$(\pi\text{-}C_5H_5)Co(CO)_2,$

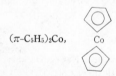

② $Co_2(CO)_8 + C_5H_6 \xrightarrow{\text{r. t.}}$

$(\pi\text{-}C_5H_5)_2Co + CO \xrightarrow{130°, 10\,hr} 25\%$

③ Deep red liq. (37~38.5/2 or 139~40°/
  710). [−22°].
  Easily miscible with most org. sol-
  vents. Unstable in air.
  Dimagnetic.
  IR: $\nu_{C\equiv O}$, 2035, 1965 cm⁻¹.
  UV: λ_{max} 295, 390, 410 mμ.

④ + PhC≡CPh ⟶ π-C₅H₅-Co
  -(tetracyclone)
  + 1,5-cyclooctadiene ⟶
  π-C₅H₅Co(1,5-cyclooctadiene)

⑥ Z. Naturf. **10b**, 355 (1955). Inorg. Syn.
  7, 112 (1963).

CoC₁₀H₁₀

① Di-π-cyclopentadienyl-cobalt

$(\pi\text{-}C_5H_5)_2Co,$

② $NaC_5H_5 + CoCl_2 \longrightarrow$
  $[(\pi\text{-}C_5H_5)_2Co]^+ + LiAlH_4 \longrightarrow$

③ Violet-black crystals. (80°/1 sublime).
  [173~174°].
  Sol. in hydrocarbons. Very sensitive
  to oxygen; not attacked by
  oxygenfree H₂O.
  Paramagnetic, 1.76 BM.

④ + air + H₂O ⟶ $[(\pi\text{-}C_5H_5)_2Co]^+$
  + CO $\xrightarrow{150\,atm., 150°}$ $(\pi\text{-}C_5H_5)Co(CO)_2$

+ CCl₄ ⟶ $[(\pi\text{-}C_5H_5)_2Co]^+$

⑥ Z. Naturf. **8b**, 327(1953). Naturwiss.
  42, 96 (1955).

CoC₁₀H₁₀X

① Di-π-cyclopentadienyl-cobalt tribromide
  $[(\pi\text{-}C_5H_5)_2Co^{III}]X, \quad X=Br_3^-$

② Co^III acetylacetonate
  + C₅H₅MgBr $\xrightarrow{1)\ C_6H_6\ 2)\ Br_2}$

③ Orange powder.
  Stable in air; slowly evolves bro-
  mine. Sol. in THF; sparingly sol.
  in H₂O.
  Tri-iodide, simple halides (X=Cl, Br,
  I) and picrate have been prepared.

④ + 1/2 LiAlH₄ ⟶ $[(\pi\text{-}C_5H_5)_2Co]Br$
  + excess LiAlH₄
  ⟶ π-C₅H₅Co(C₅H₆)

⑥ JACS **74**, 6148 (1952).

CoC₁₀H₁₁

① π-Cyclopentadienyl-
  (cyclopentadiene)-cobalt

$(\pi\text{-}C_5H_5)Co(C_5H_6),$

② $[(\pi\text{-}C_5H_5)_2Co^{III}]^+Br_3^- + LiAlH_4 \longrightarrow$

③ wine-red crystals. (80°/5 sublime).
  [98~99°].
  Sol. in org. solvents.
  Very unstable to air.
  IR: NMR: JCS **1959**, 3753.
  UV: λ_{max} 263.8, 327, 397 mμ.

④ + PhC≡CPh $\xrightarrow{110°}$ π-C₅H₅Co(C₄Ph₄)
  $\xrightarrow{air}$ $[(\pi\text{-}C_5H_5)_2Co^{III}]^+$

$$\xrightarrow{\text{heat}} (\pi\text{-}C_5H_5)_2Co + H_2$$

$CoC_{13}H_{13}$

① π-Cyclopentadienyl-(cyclooctatetraene)-cobalt

$(\pi\text{-}C_5H_5)Co(C_8H_8)$,

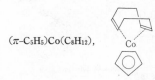

② cyclooctatetraene + π-$C_5H_5Co(CO)_2$
$$\xrightarrow[]{140° \text{ or UV}} 7\%$$

③ Brown crystals. (80°/5 sublime). [81~82°].

Sol. in common org. solvents. Stable in air as solid.

IR : $\nu_{C=C}$ 1637 cm^{-1}.

UV : λ_{max} 245 mμ (log ε 4.32).

NMR : τ 4.5, 5.8, 6.8 (4 : 5 : 4).

④ + H$_2$ $\xrightarrow{\text{Raney Ni}}$
π-C_5H_5Co(1.5-cyclooctadiene)

+ Br$_2$ $\longrightarrow$ decomp.

+ PhC≡CPh $\longrightarrow$ π-$C_5H_5Co(C_4Ph_4)$

⑥ BCSJ **33**, 425 (1960).

$CoC_{13}H_{17}$

① π-Cyclopentadienyl-(1,5-cyclooctadiene)-cobalt

$(\pi\text{-}C_5H_5)Co(C_8H_{12})$,

② 1.5-cyclooctadiene + π-$C_5H_5Co(CO)_2$
$$\xrightarrow[]{140°} 30\%$$

③ Orange crystals. (80°/5 sublime). [102°].

Sol. in petroleum ether and benzene. Stable in air.

UV : λ_{max} 361 mμ(log ε 2.87).

④ + PhC≡CPh $\longrightarrow$

π-$C_5H_5Co(Ph_4C_4)$ 48%

⑥ BCSJ **34**, 452 (1961).

$CoC_{14}H_{27}O$

① π-Cyclopentadienyl-tetra(methylcyclpentadienone)cobalt

$(\pi\text{-}C_5H_5)Co\{(CH_3)_4C_4CO\}$,

(I)

② π-$C_5H_5Co(CO)_2$ + $CH_3C≡CCH_3$ $\longrightarrow$

③ Orange crystals. [178~180°].

Stable in air. Hygroscopic. Very sol. in H$_2$O; sol. in ether.

IR : $\nu_{C=O}$ 1569 cm^{-1}.

X-ray proved its structure as (I), All C=C bond length: 1.43 Å.

④ + HCl $\longrightarrow$
$[\pi\text{-}C_5H_5Co((CH_3)_4C_4COH)]^+Cl^-$

⑥ Chem. & Ind. **1959**, 1381.   JACS **83**, 752 (1961).

$CoC_{18}H_{18}M_4$

① Sodium hexapropynyl-cobaltate
$[(CH_3C≡C-)_6Co]M_4$ M=Na

② NaC≡CCH$_3$ + Co(NH$_3$)$_4$(SCN)$_2$
$$\xrightarrow[]{\text{lig. NH}_3} 40~50\%$$

③ Green crystals.

Insol. in ether and benzen. Readily oxydized in air ; stable under nitrogen for weeks ; burns in air at 120°. Paramagnetic, 1.8 B. M.

④ + O$_2$ $\longrightarrow$ $[(CH_3C≡C-)_6Co]^{3-}Na_3^+$

+ H$_2$O $\longrightarrow$ $CH_3C≡CH$

⑥ Z. anorg. allg. Chem. **282**, 210 (1955).

$CoC_{22}H_{20}O_4P$

① σ-But-3-enoyl-(triphenylphosphine)-tri(carbonyl)-cobalt
$(CH_2=CH-CH_2-CO)Co(CO)_3P(C_6H_5)_3$

② Na[(Co(CO)$_4$] + CH$_2$=CH-CH$_2$-COCl
+ Ph$_3$P $\longrightarrow$
Na[Co(CO)$_4$] + CH$_2$=CH-CH$_2$Br + CO
+ Ph$_3$P $\longrightarrow$

③ Yellow crystals. [82° decomp.].
Decomp. in air.
IR: $\nu_{C\equiv O}$ 2041, 1961 cm^{-1};
$\nu_{C=O}$ 1667 cm^{-1}; $\nu_{C=C}$ 1626 cm^{-1}.

④ $\xrightarrow{\text{heat}}$
$\begin{array}{c} CH_2 \\ \diagup\diagup \\ CH \\ \diagdown\diagdown \\ CH_2 \end{array}$ Co(CO)$_2$PPh$_3$

⑥ JACS **83**, 1097 (1961).

CoC$_{24}$H$_{36}$X

① Bis-(hexamethylbenzene)cobalt
hexafluorophosphate
{Co[(CH$_3$)$_6$C$_6$]$_2$}$^+$X$^-$, X=PF$_6$

② CoCl$_2$ + Al + 3 AlCl$_3$ + 6 (CH$_3$)$_6$C$_6$
$\xrightarrow{\text{NH}_4\text{PF}_6}$ quantitative

③ Deep yellow crystals. [170° decomp.].
Insol. in H$_2$O; very sol. in acetone.
The solution decomp. easily.
IR: JOM **1**, 307 (1964).
Stable in air. Paramegnetic*,
2.95 B. M.

④ + Na $\xrightarrow{\text{liq. NH}_3}$ {[(CH$_3$)$_6$C$_6$]$_2$Co}
* Similar diamagnetic compound,
{Co[(CH$_3$)$_6$C$_6$]$_2$}$^+$(BPh$_4$)$^-$ has been
obtained by different way.

⑥ JACS **83**, 825 (1961).

CoC$_{33}$H$_{45}$

① π-Cyclopentadienyl-(tetraphenylcy-
clobutadiene)-cobalt

(π-C$_5$H$_5$)Co[C$_4$(C$_6$H$_5$)$_4$],

$\begin{array}{c} \text{Ph} \quad\quad \text{Ph} \\ \boxed{} \\ \text{Ph} \diagdown\;\diagup \text{Ph} \\ \text{Co} \\ \langle\bigcirc\rangle \end{array}$

② π-C$_5$H$_5$-Co(cyclooctatetraene) +

PhC≡CPh $\longrightarrow$ 40%
π-C$_5$H$_5$Co(1.5-cyclooctadiene)
+ PhC≡CPh $\longrightarrow$ 48%
(π-C$_5$H$_5$)$_2$Co + PhC≡CPh $\longrightarrow$

③ Yellowish brown crystals. [256°].
Sol. in benzene. Stable in air, therma-
lly stable up to 360° under nitrogen.
UV: λ_{max} 241, 254, 278 mμ.

④ + Na $\xrightarrow{\text{lig. NH}_3}$ PhCH$_2$-CHPh
-CHPh-CH$_2$Ph (mp 181°)
+ Br$_2$ $\longrightarrow$ decomp.

⑥ BCSJ **34**, 452 (1961).

CoC$_{38}$H$_{52}$P$_2$

① Dimesityl-bis-(phenyl diethylphosphine)-cobalt
{(CH$_3$)$_3$C$_6$H$_2$}$_2$Co{P(C$_2$H$_5$)$_2$C$_6$H$_5$}$_2$

② CoBr$_2$(PPhEt$_2$)$_2$
+ mesitylmagnesium bromide $\longrightarrow$

③ Lemon yellow. [127~129°].
Stable at room temp.
Paramagnetic. 2.5~2.7 B. M.

④ Trans planar structure.

⑥ Chem. & Ind. **1959**, 675.

Co$_2$C$_8$O$_8$

① Octa(carbonyl)-dicobalt

Co$_2$(CO)$_8$,
$\begin{array}{ccc} & O & \\ OC & C & CO \\ OC-Co & & Co-CO \\ OC & C & CO \\ & O & \end{array}$

[I]

② Co(CO)$_3$ $\xrightarrow{\text{H}_2,\ \text{CO, 150°}}$
HCo(CO)$_4$ $\xrightarrow{\text{heat}}$

③ Orange brown crystals. (vapor pressure 0.07 mm at 15°). [51° decomp.].
Sol. in benzene. Unstable in air;
stable under CO.
IR $\nu_{C\equiv O}$ 2070, 2043, 2025 cm^{-1};
$\nu_{>C=O}$ 1858 cm^{-1}.
UV: λ_{max} 280, 346 mμ.

The structure was determined as (I)
by X-ray.

④ $\xrightarrow{60°}$ Co$_4$(CO)$_{12}$

$\underrightarrow{\text{H}_2,\ \text{CO 100 atm}}$ HCo(CO)$_4$

+ CH≡CH $\longrightarrow$ (HC≡CH)Co$_2$(CO)$_6$

* The structure in solution involves two isomers.

⑥ Inorg. Syn. **5**, 190 (1957).   Acta
Cryst. **17**, 732 (1964).   Helv. chim.
Acta. **47**, 1064 (1964).

Co$_2$C$_8$HgO$_8$

① Mercury tetra(carbonyl)-cobaltate
Hg[Co(CO)$_4$]$_2$

② Co$_2$(CO)$_8$ + Hg $\longrightarrow$
HgCl$_2$ + Na[Co(CO)$_4$] $\longrightarrow$
Co$_2$(CO)$_8$ + Na−Hg $\longrightarrow$

③ Orange crystals. (80°/5 sublime).
[81~82°].
Stable in air.
Unstable in room lights.

④ + PhC≡CPh $\xrightarrow{90~100°}$
Ph$_6$C$_6$ + Co$_2$(CO)$_6$PhC≡CPh

+ PhC≡CH $\xrightarrow{80~90°}$
Co$_4$Hg$_2$(CO)$_{12}$(PhC≡CH)$_2$

⑥ Inorg. Chem. **1**, 965 (1962).

Co$_2$C$_8$H$_2$O$_6$

① (Acetylene)-hexa(carbonyl)-dicob-
alt
Co$_2$(CH≡CH)(CO)$_6$,

② Co$_2$(CO)$_8$ + C$_2$H$_2$ $\longrightarrow$

③ Dark red liq. (64~66°/3.5~4). [13.0~
13.6°].
Sol. in most org. solvents. Stable in
air in crystalline state.
Diamagentic.
IR : $\nu_{C≡O}$ 2096,   2059,   2033 cm^{-1} (in
MeOH).

④ + CO $\longrightarrow$ Co$_2$(CO)$_9$·C$_2$H$_2$

⑥ JACS **78**, 120 (1956).

Co$_2$C$_{12}$H$_2$N$_{10}$M$_6$·4H$_2$O

① Hexapotassium decacyano-(acetylene)-dicobalt.
[Co$_2$(CN)$_{10}$(C$_2$H$_2$)]M$_6$·4H$_2$O   M=K

② C$_2$H$_2$ + CoCl$_2$ + KCN $\xrightarrow{\text{H}_2\text{O, 0°, air-free}}$

③ Yellow brown crystals.   [~70° in
vacuo].
Readily sol. in H$_2$O. Thermally somewhat unstable, slowly decompd.
by air.
Diamagnetic.
IR : ν_{CH} 2980 cm^{-1} ; ν_{CN} 2140, 2115 cm^{-1},
$\nu_{C=C}$ 1615 cm^{-1}.
NMR : −64 cps (from H$_2$O, 40 Mc.)

⑥ JCS **1959**, 1629.

Co$_2$C$_{12}$H$_{12}$O$_4$

① Di-(butadiene)-tetra(carbonyl)-dico-
balt.
[(C$_4$H$_6$)Co(CO)$_2$]$_2$,

② Co$_2$(CO)$_8$ + butadiene $\xrightarrow{60° \text{ or UV}}$

③ Copper-colored crystals. [118° decomp.].

Unstable in air

IR: $\nu_{C\equiv O}$ 2042, 2020 cm^{-1}; $\nu_{>C=O}$ 1845, 1823 cm^{-1}

UV: λ_{max} 344, 420 mμ.

⑥ Z. Naturf. 16 b 138 (1961).   JCS 1961 602.

Co₂C₁₃H₂O₉

① (Acetylene)-nona(carbonyl)-dicobalt

$Co_2(CO)_9(C_2H_2)$,

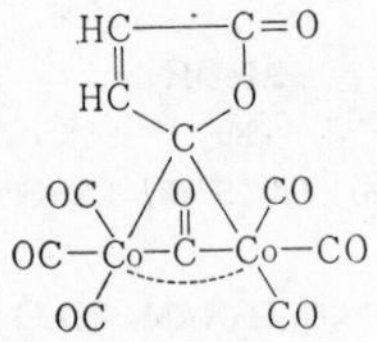

(I)

② $Co_2(CO)_6C_2H_2 \xrightarrow{CO\ 210\ atm.}$ 90%

③ Red crystals. [113~115° decomp].

Sol. in petroleum ether. Stable in air.

IR: $\nu_{C\equiv O}$ 2110, 2070, 2053, 2037 cm^{-1}; $\nu_{>C=O}$ 1845, 1779 cm^{-1}.

X-ray study showed the structure to be (I).

④ + pyridine $\longrightarrow$ Co[Co(CO)₄]₂ + CO

⑥ JACS 81, 2339 (1959).   Proc. Chem. Soc. 1959, 156.

Co₂C₁₈H₁₆O₄

① Bis-(bicyclo[2, 2, 1]heptadiene)-tetra(carbonyl)-dicobalt

[Co(C₇H₈)(CO)₂]₂,

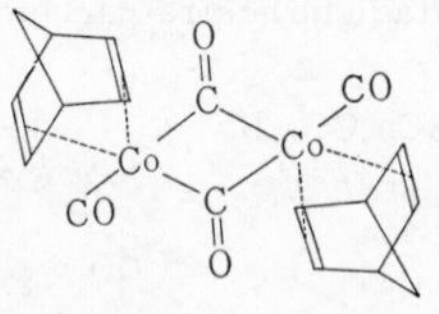

② C₇H₈ + Co₂(CO)₈ $\xrightarrow{60°}$ 70%

③ Red crystals.[147° decomp.].

Unstable in air.

IR: $\nu_{C\equiv O}$ 2021, 1996 cm^{-1}; $\nu_{>C=O}$ 1798

cm^{-1}.

⑥ JCS 1961, 602.

Co₂C₄₂H₃₀O₆P₂

① Bis-(triphenylphosphine)-hexa(carbonyl)-dicobalt

{Co(CO)₃[P(C₆H₅)₃]}₂

② Co₂(CO)₈ + 2 Ph₃P $\xrightarrow{below\ 4°,\ 1\sim2\ days}$

2 Co₄(CO)₁₂ + Ph₃P $\longrightarrow$

③ Dark brown crystals.

Insol. in most org. solvents; slightly sol. in acetone.

IR: $\nu_{C\equiv O}$ 2030, 1960 sh, 1950 cm^{-1}.

Diamagnetic.

⑥ Ber. 91, 1230 (1958).

Co₂C₄₃H₃₀O₇P₂

① Tri(carbonyl)-bis(triphenylphosphine)-cobalt tetra(carbonyl)-cobaltate

[Co^I(CO)₃(PPh₃)₂] [Co(CO)₄]

② Co₂(CO)₈ + 2 PPh₃ $\xrightarrow{30°,\ dioxane}$

③ Dark red crystals.

Sol. in acetone.

Slowly decomp. in air.

Diamagnetic.

④ + [BPh₄]$^-$

$\longrightarrow$ [Co(CO)₃(PPh₃)₂] [BPh₄]

+ [(π-C₅H₅)₂Co^{III}]$^+$

$\longrightarrow$ [(π-C₅H₅)₂Co] [Co(CO)₄]

⑥ Ber. 91, 1230 (1958).

Co₃C₁₇H₇O₉

①

(C₆H₅CH₂C)Co₃(CO)₉.

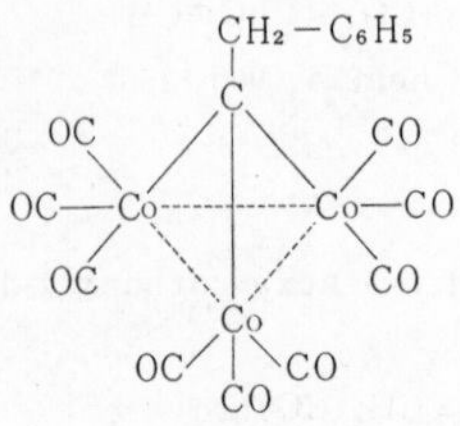

② Co₂(CO)₆(PhC≡CH) + aq. H₂SO₄

heat
$\xrightarrow{\quad}$ 35%

③ Violet needles. [68°].
Readily sol. in org. solvents.
Stable in air.

④ $+ Br_2 \xrightarrow{CCl_4, 0°} CoBr_2 + PhCH_2-CBr_3$
(mp. 48~49°)
$+ H_2O_2 \longrightarrow PhCH_2CO_2H$

⑥ Chem. & Ind. 1960, 1264.

Co₃C₂₀H₁₈O₂X

① Tri-(benzene)-di(carbonyl)-tricobalt
bromide
[Co₃(C₆H₆)₃(CO)₂]⁺X⁻, X=Br

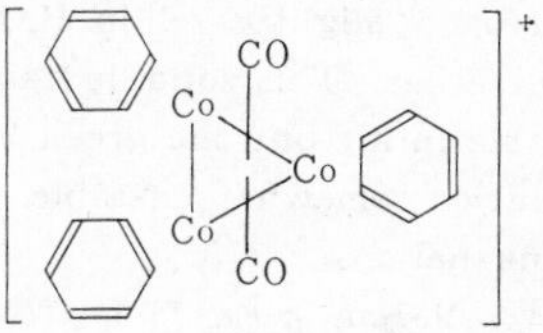

② $Co_2(CO)_8 + AlBr_3 + C_6H_6 \xrightarrow{60°}$
$Hg[Co(CO)_4]_2 + C_6H_6 \xrightarrow{1)\,AlCl_3,\;2)\,NaBPh_4}$
X=BPh₄

③ Brown crystals. [111~116° decomp.]
Sol. in acetone.
Stable in air.
Paramagnetic.
IR: $\nu_{C=O}$ 1612, 1590 cm⁻¹.
UV: λ_{max} 425 mμ (in C₆H₆).

④ + AlBr₃
$\longrightarrow$ [Co₃(C₆H₆)₃(CO)₂][AlBr₄]

⑥ Angew. 70, 744 (1958). Gazz. chim.
ital. 88, 1170 (1959).

Co₃C₃₈H₃₀N₆O₈

① Hexa(pyridine)-cobalt tetra(carbonyl)-cobaltate
[Co^II(C₅H₅N)₆][Co(CO)₄]₂

② $Co_2(CO)_8 + pyridine \xrightarrow{benzene}$

③ Red solid
Sol. in H₂O.

Fairly stable in air.
IR: $\nu_{C=O}$ 1878 cm⁻¹.

④ + aq. H₂SO₄ $\longrightarrow$ HCO(CO)₄

⑥ Inorg. Syn. 5, 192 (1957). JACS
74, 1216 (1952).

Co₄C₁₂O₁₂

① Dodeca(carbonyl)-tetra cobalt

Co₄(CO)₁₂,

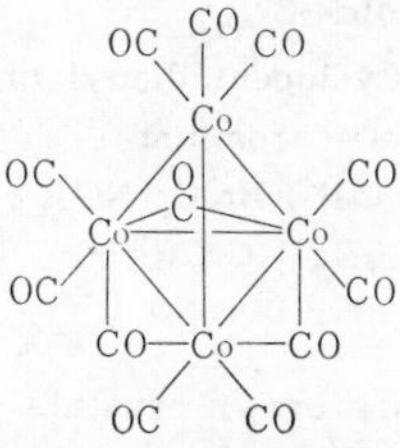

(I)

② $Co_2(CO)_8 \xrightarrow{50°}$
$Co_2(CO)_8 + H_2 + Co^{II} salts \longrightarrow$

③ Black crystals. Not volatile. [60°
decomp.].
Unstable in air.
Sol. in benzene.
IR: $\nu_{C=O}$ 2063, 2055, 2037.5, 2027,
1866.5 cm⁻¹
The structure was proposed as (I)
by X-ray.

④ + PhC≡CPh $\longrightarrow$
Co₄(CO)₁₀PhC≡CPh

⑥ J. Chem. Phys. 31, 1676 (1959). Chim.
e ind. 41, 132 (1959). Inorg. Syn.
2, 243 (1947).

[Cr]

CrC₅H₅ClN₂O₂

① π-Cyclopentadienyl-chloro-di(nitrosyl)-chromium
(π-C₅H₅)(Cl)Cr(NO)₂

② NaC₅H₅
$+ CrCl_3 \xrightarrow{THF,\;1)\,reflux,\,2\,hr.\;2)\,NO}$

③ Greenish-yellow crystals. [~140° de
comp. without melting].

Very sol. in CHCl₃; moderately sol
in benzene; slightly sol. in petr.
ether. The crystals are quite stable in air.

IR: ν_{NO} 1812, 1707 cm⁻¹.

⑥ JINC 2, 38 (1956).   Z. anorg. allg.
Chem. 317, 226 (1962).

CrC₅H₅BrN₂O₂

① π-Cyclopentadienyl bromo-di(nitrosyl)-chromium
$(\pi\text{-}C_5H_5)(Br)Cr(NO)_2$

② $C_5H_5Na + CrCl_3 \longrightarrow (\pi\text{-}C_5H_5)_2Cr$
$$\xrightarrow{\text{ether, HBr, NO}} 65\%$$

③ Dark brown crystals. [140.5~141°].

④ $\xrightarrow{\text{aq. AgNO}_3,\ \text{HI}} \pi\text{-}C_5H_5Cr(NO)_2I$

⑥ JINC 3, 104 (1956).

CrC₆O₆

① Hexa(carbonyl)-chromium
$Cr(CO)_6$

② $CrCl_3 + PhMgBr + CO \xrightarrow{\text{ether}} 45~51\%$

$Cr(acac)_3 + Mg + CO \xrightarrow{\text{Pyridine, I}_2} 82\%$

$CaCl_3 + Ph_2CONa + CO \xrightarrow{\text{THF}} 59\%$

$CrCl_3 + Al + CO \xrightarrow{\text{bezene, AlCl}_3} 88\%$

$CrCl_3 + Na + CO \xrightarrow{\text{diglyme}} 80\%$

③ Coloreess crystals. [151~152°
sublime].

Sol. in ether, CHCl₃ and other
org. solvents; insol. in H₂O and
methanol.

IR: ν_{CO} 2100, 2020, 1985 cm⁻¹.

④ $+ RNC \longrightarrow Cr(CO)_5(CNR)$

$+ Ph_3P$
$\longrightarrow Cr(CO)_5(PPh_3), Cr(CO)_4(PPh_3)_2$

$+ benzene \longrightarrow Cr(CO)_3(C_6H_6)$

$+ pyridine \xrightarrow{\text{reflux}} Cr(CO)_5(py)$

$+ ethylenediamine$
$$\xrightarrow{120°,\ 1\,hr.} Cr(CO)_4(en)$$

⑥ Inorg. Syn. 3, 156 (1950).   JACS 79,
3611 (1957); 80, 6117 (9158); 83,
2057 (1961).   Ber. 92, 3050 (1959).

CrC₆H₅N₂O₃X

① π-Cyclopentadienyl-di(nitrosyl)
-(carbonyl)-chromium hexa-fluorophosphate
$[\pi\text{-}(C_5H_5)Cr(NO)_2(CO)]X, \quad X = PF_6$

② $\pi\text{-}C_5H_5Cr(NO)_2Cl + AlCl_3 + CO$
$$\xrightarrow{\text{benzene, 60°, 17 hr., NH}_4\text{PF}_6} 45\%$$

③ Olive-brown   powder. [143~144°
decomp.].

Insol. in non polar solvents; sol in
acetone; slightly sol. in H₂O, alc.
and ether. The solid is fairly
stable in air but the green brown
solution somewhat unstable.

Diamagnetic.

IR: ν_{CO} 2137 cm⁻¹; ν_{NO} 1873, 1779 cm⁻¹.

⑥ Z. anorg. allg. Chem. 317, 226
(1962).

CrC₆H₈N₂O₂

① π-Cyclopentadienyl-methyl-di(nitrosyl)-chromium
$(CH_3)(\pi\text{-}C_5H_5)Cr(NO)_2$

② $\pi\text{-}C_5H_5Cr(NO)_2Br + CH_3MgI \longrightarrow 60\%$

③ Dark green   crystals. (25~50°/va-
cuum, sublime). [82.8~83.2°].

Readily sol. in petr. ether and indeed
in all common org. solvents.

Slowly decomp. in org. solvents by
air.

Diamagnetic.

IR: ν_{NO} 1779, 1670 cm⁻¹ (in CCl₄).

UV: 4600 Å (ε 1520), 3000 Å (ε 2750).

NMR: 2.6 ppm (C₅H₅), 6.9 ppm (CH₃)
(reference, C₆H₅ in toluene)

⑥ JINC 3, 104 (1956).

CrC₇H₄O₃S

① Tri(carbonyl)-(thiophene)-chromium

Cr(CO)₃(C₄H₄S)

② Cr(CO)₆ + C₄H₄S

$$\xrightarrow[\text{205~210°, 5~7 hr.}]{} 2.6\text{~}3.4\%$$

③ Red. (85~95°/vacuum, sublime). [145° decomp.].

Sol. in benzene, ether and petr. ether. The crystals are stable in air but the solution decomp. in air.

Diamagnetic.

IR : ν_{CO} 1977, 1907, 1889 cm⁻¹.

UV : 318, 410 m μ

Dipole moment : 5.29 D.

⑥ Ber. **91**, 2395 (1958).

CrC₇H₅NO₃

① π-Cyclopentadienyl-(nitrosyl)-di (carbonyl)-chromium

(π-C₅H₅)Cr(CO)₂(NO)

② [π-C₅H₅Cr(CO)₃]₂ + NO

$$\xrightarrow[\text{benzene}]{} \text{nearly quantitative yield}$$

③ Bright orange-red crystals. [67~68°].

Very sol. in org. solvents.

Stable in air.

Diamagnetic.

⑥ Z. Naturf. **10b**, 598 (1955).

CrC₈H₆O₃

① Hydrido-π-cyclopentadienyl-tri(car-bonyl)-chromium

(H)(π-C₅H₅)Cr(CO)₃

② (π-C₅H₅)₂Cr + H₂ + CO $\xrightarrow[\text{70°, 15 hr.}]{}$ 45%

Cr(CO)₆ + KC₅H₅ $\xrightarrow[\text{2 hr, HCl}]{\text{DMF, 130°,}}$ 30~60%

[π-C₅H₅Cr(CO)₃]₂ + H₂ $\xrightarrow{70°}$

③ Golden yellow crystals. sublime. [57~58° decomp.].

Readily sol. in ether, acetone, ben-zene and petr. ether.

Instantaneously oxidized by air.

Diamagnetic.

NMR : τ=4.70 (C₅H₅), 15.52 (Cr−H)

(in C₆H₁₂)

④ $\xrightarrow{\text{heat}}$ [π-C₅H₅Cr(CO)₃]₂ + H₂

⑥ Z. anorg. allg. Chem. **282**. 47 (1955).

JINC **3**, 104 (1956).   Inorg. Syn. **7**, 136 (1959).

CrC₉H₆O₃

① Tri(carbonyl)-(benzene)-chromium

Cr(CO)₃(C₆H₆)

② Cr(C₆H₆)₂ + Cr(CO)₆ $\longrightarrow$ 25%

Cr(CO)₆ + C₆H₆ $\xrightarrow{\text{diglyme, 9 hr.}}$ 35%

③ Yellow crystals. [166°], [162~163°].

Sol. in acetone, benzene, acetic acid, CCl₄, EtOH and MeOH ; slightly sol. in petr. ether. Stable in air.

Diamagnetic.

IR : ν_{CO} 1987, 1917 cm⁻¹(in C₆H₁₂) ; 1981, 1907 cm⁻¹ (in CS₂).

NMR ; τ=4.763.

Dipole moment : 4.92±0.05 D (25°, benzene)

④ + Ph₃P $\longrightarrow$ Cr(CO)₃(PPh₃)₃

+ C₅H₅N $\longrightarrow$ Cr(CO)₃py₃

⑥ Ber. **90**, 2532 (1957) ; **91**, 2763 (1958).

Z. Naturf. **13b**, 458 (1958).   JCS **1959**, 551.

CrC₉H₈O₃

① π-Cyclopentadienyl-methyl-tri(car-bonyl)-chromium

(CH₃)(π-C₅H₅)Cr(CO)₃

② π-C₅H₅Cr(CO)₃Na

+ CH₃I(or (CH₃)₂SO₄) $\longrightarrow$1~3%

③ Yellow.

Quite readily oxidized in air.

Difficult to obtain a pure state.

IR : ν_{CO} 1787, 1685 cm⁻¹ (in CS₂).

NMR : τ 5.24 (C₅H₅), 9.32 (CH₃) (in CCl₄).

⑥ JINC **3**, 104 (1956).   JCS **1963**, 1133.

CrC₁₀H₈O₃

① Tri(carboryl)-(cycloheptatriene)

-chromium

$Cr(CO)_3(C_7H_8)$,

② $C_7H_8 + Cr(CO)_6$ $\xrightarrow{\text{light petr. } 100\sim120°,\ 15hr}$

③ Orange red crystals. Sublime. [128 ~130 decomp.].

Sol. in light petroleum, CHCl₃, benzene, and many other org. solvents. Stable in air and to light. The solution decomp. in air and light.

IR: ν_{CO} 1992, 1930, 1907 cm⁻¹ (C₆H₁₂).

Dipole moment: 4.52±0.05 D (C₆H₆).

⑥ JCS 1958, 4559. Proc. Chem. Soc. 93, (1959).

CrC₁₀H₁₀

① di-π-Cyclopentadienyl-chromium (π-C₅H₅)₂Cr

② $Cr(NH_3)_6(C_5H_5)_3$ $\xrightarrow{\text{thermal decomp.}}$

$Cr(CO)_6 + C_5H_6$ $\xrightarrow{280\sim350°}$ ~30%

$CrCl_2$(or CrCl₃) + C₅H₅Na $\xrightarrow[\text{THF, 1 hr}]{}$ 70%

$CrCl_3 + C_5H_5MgBr$ $\longrightarrow$ 60~70%

③ Fine scarlet needles. (80~100°/vacuum, sublime). [173°].

Sol. in org. solvents.

Air sensitive; thermally stable at least 300°. Paramagnetic.

Dipole moment: 0±0.41 D (25°, C₆H₆).

④ $+ I_2$ $\longrightarrow$ $(\pi$-C₅H₅)₂Cr⁺

⑥ Z. Naturf. 8b, 444 (1953); 9b, 417 (1954). JACS 76, 209 (1954). Angew. 68, 462 (1956).

Cr₂C₁₀H₁₀N₄O₄

① Di-π-cyclopentadienyl-tetra (nitrosyl)-dichromium [(π-C₅H₅)Cr(NO)₂]₂

② π-C₅H₅Cr(NO)₂Cl + NaBH₄ $\xrightarrow{\text{H}_2\text{O, benzene}}$ 5%

$NaC_5H_5 + CrCl_3 + NO$ $\longrightarrow$ 1.9%

③ Red-violet crystals. [158~159° decomp.]

Stable in air.

IR: ν_{NO} 1672 cm⁻¹ (terminal), 1505 cm⁻¹ (bridge).

UV: λ_{max} 271 mμ (ϵ 33700).

NMR: τ 4.32.

④ $+ I_2$ $\xrightarrow{\text{CHCl}_3}$ π-C₅H₅Cr(NO)₂I (23%) [143~147°]

⑥ Inorg. Chem. 3, 791 (1964).

CrC₁₂H₆M₃

① Potassium hexaethynylchromate M₃[(HC≡C)₆Cr]   M=K

② $Cr(NH_3)_6(NO_3)_3 + HC≡CK$ $\xrightarrow{\text{liq. NH}_3}$

③ Orange solid.

Very explosive.

Paramagnetic, 3.9 BM.

④ $+ CN^-$ $\xrightarrow{\text{H}_2\text{O}}$ [Cr(CN)₆]K₃ + C₂H₂ + OH⁻

⑥ Ber. 88, 1723 (1955)

CrC₁₂H₉O₃M₃

① Potassiumtripropionyl-tri(carbonyl) -chromate M₃[(CH₃C≡C)₃Cr(CO)₃]   M=K

② $Cr(CO)_3(NH_3)_3 + KC≡CCH_3$ $\xrightarrow{\text{liq. NH}_3}$ ~59%

③ Yellow green.

Insol. in most water free org. solvents. Not explosive but pyrophoric and highly sensitive to moisture.

IR: $\nu_{C≡C}$ 2180 cm⁻¹; ν_{CO} 2050, 1965, 1840, ~1700, ~160 cm⁻¹.

⑥ Z. anorg. allg. Chem. 320, 135 (1963).

CrC₁₂H₁₂

① Di(benzene)-chromium

Cr(C$_6$H$_6$)$_2$,

② CrCl$_3$ + Al + C$_6$H$_6$
AlCl$_3$, 150°, 15 hr.
$\xrightarrow{\hspace{2cm}}$ 95~98%

③ Brown-black crystals. (~150°/vacuum, sublime). [284~285°].
Somewhat sol. in org. solvents such as benzene ; sparingly sol. in ether and petr. ether ; insol. in H$_2$O.
Fairly rapidly oxidized in air.
IR : 3.0, 3.3~3.35, 6.1~6.2, 7.0, 7.8, 8.9, 10.0, 10.3, 11.2, 12.0, 12.5μ
UV : λ_{max} 517, 413 mμ.
NMR : +2.94 ppm
(reference, benzene).
Diamagnetic.
Dipole moment : 0±0.37 D (25°, C$_6$H$_6$).

④ + H$_2$O + O$_2$ $\longrightarrow$ Cr(C$_6$H$_6$)$_2$OH
$\xrightarrow{\text{KI}}$ Cr(C$_6$H$_6$)$_2$I

⑥ Z. Naturf. **10 b** 655 (1955). Z. anorg. allg. Chem. **286**, 142 (1955). Inorg. Syn. **6**, 132 (1960).

CrC$_{10}$H$_{12}$BrO$_2$

① π-Cyclopentadienyl-bromo-chromium-acetylacetonate

② Cr(acac)$_3$ + C$_5$H$_5$MgBr $\xrightarrow{\text{benzene, 25°}}$ 3%

③ Dark green crystals. (165~170°/1 mm, sublime). [190° decomp.].
Stable in dry nitrogen ; Decomp. by H$_2$O with foramation of bromide ion.

⑥ Chem. & Ind. **1956**, 1388.

CrC$_{11}$H$_{11}$

① π-Cyclopentadienyl-(benzene)-chromium
(π-C$_5$H$_5$)Cr(C$_6$H$_6$)

② CrCl$_3$ + PhMgBr + C$_5$H$_5$MgBr $\xrightarrow{\text{THF}}$

③ Orange rhombic crystals. (80~100°/vacuum, sublime). [227~229° decomp].
Quite sol. in org. solvents such as ether, benzene, THF and petr. ether ; slightly sol. in acetone and methanol. Decomp. by air.
Paramagnetic, 1.70 BM.
IR : "C$_5$H$_5$" 1100, 165 cm^{-1}, "C$_6$H$_6$" 998, 459 cm^{-1}
Dipole moment : 0±0.41 D (25°, benzene)

⑥ Z. Naturf. **13 b**, 197 (1958).

CrC$_{11}$H$_{12}$O$_2$

① Di(carbonyl)-(cyclopentadiene)-(butadiene)-chromiun
Cr(CO)$_2$(C$_5$H$_6$)(C$_4$H$_6$)

② [π-C$_5$H$_5$Cr(CO)$_3$]$_2$ + CH$_2$=CHCH=CH$_2$
n-heptane, Hg, UV, 6 hr.
$\xrightarrow{\hspace{2cm}}$ 12~15%

③ Orange yellow crystals. [118~121°].
Easily sol. in benzene, cyclohexane, pentane, ether, THF, acetone and ethanol. The solid is fairly stable in air but the solution decomps. in air after several time.
IR : ν_{CO} 1983, 1872 cm^{-1} (KBr) ; "C$_4$H$_6$" 1503, 1363 cm^{-1} ; "C$_5$H$_6$" 2890, 1375 cm^{-1}.

⑥ Ber. **93**, 3006 (1960).

CrC$_{11}$H$_{10}$O$_3$

① Tri(carbonyl)-(cyclooctatriene-1, 3, 5)-chromium

Cr(CO)$_3$(C$_8$H$_{10}$),

② Cr(CO)$_6$ + cyclooctatriene

$$\xrightarrow{130°,\ 7\,hr.} 13\%$$

③ Red crystals. [~96° decomp.].
Sol. in most org. solvents.
Air sensitive.
IR: ν_{CO} 1856, 1881, 1977 cm^{-1} (KBr).

⑥ Ber. **92**, 2645 (1959).

CrC$_{12}$H$_{12}$

① π-Cyclopentadienyl-π-cyclohepta-
trienyl-chromium

(π-C$_5$H$_5$)(π-C$_7$H$_7$)Cr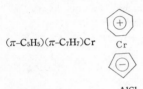

② π-C$_5$H$_5$Cr(C$_6$H$_6$) + C$_7$H$_8$ $\xrightarrow{AlCl_3}$

[π-C$_5$H$_5$-πC$_7$H$_7$Cr]$^+$ (75%) $\xrightarrow{Na_2S_2O_4-KOH}$

CrCl$_3$ + C$_5$H$_6$ + C$_7$H$_8$ + i-C$_3$H$_7$MgBr

$\xrightarrow{-78°}$ 2.2%

③ Blue-green. (80°/vacuum, sublime).
[~230° decomp.].
Diamagnetic.
IR: "C$_5$H$_5$" 1423, 1110, 1014/1004, 822,
808 cm^{-1}; "C$_7$H$_7$" 1244, 970, 860, 863,
808 cm^{-1}.
NMR: τ=6.90, 508 (intensity 5:7)
(C$_6$H$_6$).
Dipole moment: 0.79±0.05 D (C$_6$H$_6$).

⑥ Angew. **75**, 94 (1963).   Inorg. Chem.
3, 785 (1964).

CrC$_{12}$H$_{12}$O$_2$

① π-Cyclopentadienyl-π-cyclopentenyl-
di(carbonyl)-chromium

(π-C$_5$H$_5$)(π-C$_5$H$_7$)Cr(CO)$_2$,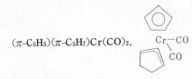

② (π-C$_5$H$_5$)$_2$Cr + H$_2$ + CO

$$\xrightarrow{65\sim68°,\ 14\sim15\,hr} 3.8\%$$

③ Yellow crystals. (50~70°/vacuum,
sublime). [73~74°].
Readily sol. in benzene and cyclohexane; slightly. sol. in pentane and
hexane.
Diamagnetic.
IR: ν_{CO} 1916, 1835 cm^{-1}.
NMR: (40Mc)+116, +118, +139, +222
cps (reference, benzene)
Dipole moment: 3.49±0.06 D (25°,
benzene)

⑥ Z. Naturf. **15b**, 59 (1960).   Ber. **94**,
2413 (1961).

CrC$_{23}$H$_{15}$O$_5$Sb

① Penta(carbonyl)-(triphenylstibine)
-chromium
Cr(CO)$_5$[Sb(C$_6$H$_5$)$_3$]

② Cr(CO)$_6$ + SbPh$_3$ $\xrightarrow{diglyme,\ 160\sim165°}$
83% (crude), 43% (pure)

③ Yellow crystals. [147~149°].
IR: ν_{CO} 2065, 1988, 1943 cm^{-1} (CCl$_4$)

⑥ JACS **83**, 3200 (1961).

CrC$_{23}$H$_{15}$O$_5$P

① Penta(carbonyl)-(triphenylphosphine)-chromium
Cr(CO)$_5$[P(C$_6$H$_5$)$_3$]

② Cr(CO)$_6$ + PPh$_3$ $\xrightarrow{diglyme,\ reflux,\ 4\,hr.}$
84% (crude), 31% (pure)

③ Pale yellow crystals. [127~128°].
IR: ν_{CO}, 2066, 1988, 1942 cm^{-1} (CCl$_4$).

⑥ JACS **83**, 3200 (1961).

CrC$_{23}$H$_{15}$AsO$_5$

① Penta(carbonyl)-tri(phenylarsine)
-chromium
Cr(CO)$_5$[As(C$_6$H$_5$)$_3$]

② Cr(CO)$_6$ + AsPh$_3$ $\xrightarrow{diglyme,\ 160\sim165°}$
96% (crude), 55% (pure)

③ Yellow crystals. [135~135.5°].
IR ν_{CO}, 2066, 1988, 1942 cm^{-1} (CCl$_4$).

⑥ JACS **83**. 3200 (1961).

CrC₄₀H₃₀O₄P₂

① Tetra(carbonyl)-bis-(triphenylphosphine)-chromium
  Cr(CO)₄[P(C₆H₅)₃]₂

② Cr(CO)₆ + 2PPh₃ $\xrightarrow{\text{diglyme, }160\sim165°}$
  36% (crude), 12% (pure)

③ Yellow powder. [250~252°].
  IR: ν_{CO} 2012, 1949, 1897 cm⁻¹ (CCl₄).

⑥ JACS **83**, 3200 (1961).

Cr₂C₁₃H₁₉S₃

① Di-π-cyclopentadienyl-tri-μ-methyl-
  sulfido-dichromium
  (π-C₅H₅)₂Cr₂(SCH₃)₃,

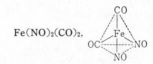

② [π-C₅H₅Cr(CO)₃]₂ + (CH₃)₂S₂
  $\xrightarrow{\text{reflux, 20 hr.}}$ 32%
  [π-C₅H₅Cr(CO)₃]₂Hg + (CH₃)₂S₂ ⟶

③ Purple crystalline.
  Decomp. on storage for several mon-
  ths.
  IR: 3130, 2980, 2900, 1430, 1012, 809 cm⁻¹.

⑥ JACS **85**, 1587 (1963).

Cr₂C₁₆H₁₀O₆

① Di-π-cyclopentadienyl-hexa(carbonyl)-chromium
  [(π-C₅H₅)Cr(CO)₃]₂

② (π-C₅H₅)₂Cr + CO $\xrightarrow{150\sim170°}$
  Cr(CO)₆ + KC₅H₅ ⟶
  [π-C₅H₅Cr(CO)₃]K $\xrightarrow{\text{HCl}}$
  π-C₅H₅Cr(CO)₃H $\xrightarrow{60°}$
  Cr(CO)₆ + NaC₅H₅ $\xrightarrow{\text{diglyme}}$
  [π-C₅H₅Cr(CO)₃]Na $\xrightarrow{\text{C₇H₇Br}}$ 37%

③ Deep-green crystals. (100~120°/0.1
  mm, sublime). [163~168° decomp.].
  Sparingly sol in org. solvents.

④ + H₂ $\xrightarrow{70°}$ π-C₅H₅Cr(CO)₃H

⑥ Z. Naturf. **106**, 140 (1955). Z. anorg.
  allg. Chem. **282**, 47 (1955). Inorg.
  Syn. **7**, 104 (1963).

Cr₂C₁₆H₁₀HgO₆

①
  [(π-C₅H₅)Cr(CO)₃]₂Hg

② C₅H₅Na + Cr(CO)₆ $\xrightarrow{\text{diglyme}}$
  π-C₅H₅Cr(CO)₃Na $\xrightarrow{\text{Hg(CN)₂}}$ 40%

③ Yellow crystalline sold. (130°/0.1mm,
  sublime).
  Fairly sol in org. solvents.
  Remarkably stable thermally.

⑥ Inorg. Syn. **7**, 104 (1963).

【Fe】

FeC₂N₂O₄

① Di-(nitrosyl)-di(carbonyl)-iron

Fe(NO)₂(CO)₂,

② Na[HFe(CO)₄] + NaNO₂
  + CH₃CO₂H ⟶

③ Deep red crystals. volatile. [18.5°].
  Decompd. at 50°. Insol. in H₂O; sol.
  in org. solvents. Rapidly oxidized in
  air.
  Bond lengths: Fe−C 1.84Å, Fe−N
  1.77Å.
  Dipole moment: 0.72D.

⑥ Brauer 1355.

FeC₄Br₂O₄

① Dibromo tetra(carbonyl)-iron
  (Br)₂Fe(CO)₄

② $Fe(CO)_5 + Br_2 \xrightarrow{0°} 75\%$

③ Red-drown solid.
Decompd. in water ; decompd. slowly at room temp. Light sensitive. Insol. in petroleum ether.

④ $\xrightarrow{heat} FeBr_2 + CO$

⑥ Brauer 1350.

FeC₄H₂O₄

① Di-hydrido-tetra(carbonyl)-iron
$(H)_2Fe(CO)_4$

② $K_2Fe(CO)_4 + 2HCl \longrightarrow$
$Fe(CO)_4I_2 + NaBH_4 \longrightarrow$

③ Yellow liq. (vap. press. 11mm at 10°) (extrapolated value). [−70°].
Decomp. below −10°.
Unstable in air.
NMR : $\tau 21.1$.
$pK_1 \sim 4.4$; $pK_2 \sim 14$.
Bond lenght ; Fe−C 1.82Å.

④ $\xrightarrow{-10°} H_2 + H_2Fe_2(CO)_8$

⑥ Inorg. Syn. **2**, 243 (1947).

FeC₅O₅

① Penta(carbonyl)-iron

$Fe(CO)_5$,

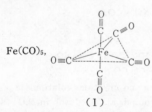

(I)

② iron powder + CO $\xrightarrow{sulfur, 250°}$
Raney iron + CO $\xrightarrow{sulfur, 100°, 100atm.}$

③ Orange liq. (102.6°). [−20°]. d 1.46 (20°/4°).
Miscible with most org. solvents ; not miscible with H_2O. Unstable in the light.
IR : $\nu_{C\equiv O}$ 2028, 1994 cm⁻¹.
UV : 250mμ (shoulder).

Bond lengths : Fe−C 1.79Å, C−C 1.12Å.

④ $+ Ph_3P \xrightarrow{250°} Fe(Ph_3P)(CO)_4$
$+ 2Ph_3P \xrightarrow{250°} Fe(Ph_3P)_2(CO)_3$
$+ Br_2 \xrightarrow{0°} Fe(CO)_4Br_2$
$NaOH \xrightarrow{MeOH} Na[HFe(CO)_4]$
The structure was determined as (I) by X-ray.

⑤ For iron plating ; for preparation of iron metal.

⑥ Brauer 1342.   Acta Cryst. **17**, 663 (1964).

FeC₅F₃IO₄

① Trifluoromethyl-tetra(carbonyl)-iodo-iron
$(CF_3)(I)Fe(CO)_4$

② $Fe(CO)_5 + CF_3I \xrightarrow{70°, 100 hr} 6\%$

③ Orange red crystals. (35°/0.1). [91 ~94°]
Stable in dry air ; decompd. by moisture.
IR : ν_{C-F} 1055 cm⁻¹.

④ $+ CF_2=CF_2 \xrightarrow{100°} \begin{array}{c} CF_2-CF_2 \\ \diagdown\;CF_2\diagup \end{array}$
$+ CH_2=CH_2 \longrightarrow \begin{array}{c} CF_2-CH_2 \\ \diagdown\;CH_2\diagup \end{array}$

⑥ JACS **83**, 3604 (1961).

FeC₆H₄O₄

① (Ethylene)-tetra(carbonyl)-iron
$Fe(CO)_4(C_2H_4)$

② $C_2H_4 + Fe_2(CO)_9 \xrightarrow{r. t., 48hr, 50atm} 34\%$

③ Orange yellow liq. (34°/12). $n_D1.5426$ (25°). d 1.3862 (25°/4°).
Decompd. slowly in air ; even under nitrogen at room temp. ; stable at −78° ~ −30°.
IR : $\nu_{C=C}$ 1551 cm⁻¹ ; $\nu_{C\equiv O}$ 2088, 2007,

2013 sh, 1986 cm⁻¹.

Dipole moment : 1.53 D (in C_6H_6).

④ $\xrightarrow{\text{heat}}$ C_2H_4 + $Fe_3(CO)_{12}$

⑥ Helv. Chim. Acta **46**, 1588 (1963).

FeC₇H₃NO₄

① Tetra(carbonyl)-(acrylonitrile)iron
   $Fe(CO)_4(CH_2=CHCN)$,

(I)

② $CH_2=CHCN + Fe(CO)_5$
   $\xrightarrow{\text{sun light}}$ small yield

   $CH_2=CHCN + Fe_2(CO)_9 \xrightarrow{\text{heat}}$ 2~3%

③ Yellow crystals. (40°/vac., sublime).
   [47~48°].

   Decomp. at 60°; changes to dark
   brown solid in air at room temp. ;
   stable below 0°.

   IR : $\nu_{C\equiv O}$ 2226, 2110 cm⁻¹.

   NMR : τ 7.7, 7.8 (2 : 1).

   Diamagnetic. Strucure was determined as (I) by X-ray.

   Bond lengths : C=C 1.40 Å, Fe···CH₂
   2.10 Å, Fe···CH 2.09 Å.
            |
            CN

⑥ Chem. & Ind. **1960**, 49. Acta Cryst.
   15, 1117 (1962).

FeC₇H₅IO₂

① π-Cyclopentadienyl-di(carbonyl)
   -iodo-iron

   $(\pi\text{-}C_5H_5)(I)Fe(CO)_2$,

② $[\pi\text{-}C_5H_5Fe(CO)_2]_2 + I_2 \longrightarrow$ 65%
   $Fe(CO)_4I_2 + C_5H_5Na \longrightarrow$ 10%

$\pi\text{-}C_5H_5Fe(CO)_2Cl + NaI \xrightarrow{\text{acetone}}$ 65%

③ Black crystals. (90°/0.1 sublime).
   [117~18° decomp.].

   Sparingly sol. in pentane ; sol. in
   polar org. solvents. Stable in air.

   IR : $\nu_{C\equiv O}$ 2042, 1982 cm⁻¹.

④ + $CH_3MgI \longrightarrow (\pi\text{-}C_5H_5)(CH_3)Fe(CO)_2$

⑥ Inorg. Syn. **7**, 110 (1963).

FeC₇H₅BrO₂

① π-Cyclopentadienyl-di(carbonyl)
   -bromo-iron

   $(\pi\text{-}C_5H_5)(Br)Fe(CO)_2$,

② $[\pi\text{-}C_5H_5Fe(CO)_2]_2 + Br_2 \longrightarrow$ 82%
   $[\pi\text{-}C_5H_5Fe(CO)_2]_2 + 34\%$ aq. HBr
   + air $\xrightarrow{\text{EtOH}-\text{CHCl}_3}$ 65%

③ Red brown crystals. [105~107° vac].
   [98~102° decomp.].

   Stable in air.

   IR : $\nu_{C\equiv O}$ 2049, 1995 cm⁻¹.

④ + PhLi or PhC≡CNa
   $\longrightarrow [\pi\text{-}C_5H_5Fe(CO)_2]_2$
   + C_5H_5Na or C_5H_5Li
   $\longrightarrow [\pi\text{-}C_5H_5(\sigma\text{-}C_5H_5)Fe(CO)_2$

⑥ JCS **1956**, 3030.

FeC₇H₆O₃

① Tri(carbonyl)-(butadiene)-iron

   $Fe(CO)_3(C_4H_6)$,

② $C_4H_6 + Fe(CO)_5 \xrightarrow{150°}$

③ Pale yellow crystals. (48°/0.06). [19°]
   Stable in air ; stable in concd. H₂SO₄.

Diamagnetic.

IR : $\nu_{C\equiv O}$ 2051, 1978 cm⁻¹.

UV : λ_{max} 211 mμ.

NMR : τ4.72, 8.32, 9.78 (1 : 1 : 1).

Structure was shown to be (I) by X-ray.

Bond lengths : $\quad$ C$-$C 1.46Å, 1.45Å

$\qquad$ Fe$-$C 2.14Å, 2.06Å.

④ $\quad$ + HCl $\quad\longrightarrow\quad$ π-C₄H₇Fe(CO)₃Cl

$\qquad$ + PhP(OEt)₂

$\qquad\xrightarrow{120\sim140°}$ Fe(C₄H₆)(CO)₂[PhP(OEt)₂]

⑥ $\quad$ Ann. **482**, 161 (1930).$\quad$ JCS **1958**, 642.

FeC₇H₇ClO₃

① $\quad$ π-Butenyl-tri(carbonyl)-chloro-iron

$(\pi$-C₄H₇)Fe(CO)₃Cl,

② $\quad$ Fe(CO)₃(butadiene) + HCl

$\qquad\longrightarrow$ 30~45%

$\quad$ CH₃$-$CH=CH$-$CH₂Cl + Fe₂(CO)₉ $\xrightarrow{40°}$

③ $\quad$ Yellow brown crystals.(room temp./
0.05 sublime). [58~60°, decomp.].
Insol. in H₂O ; sol. in org. solvents.
Relatively stable at room temp.
Diamagnetic.

IR : $\nu_{C\equiv O}$ 2041, 2000, 1961, 1920cm⁻¹.

NMR : τ 5.08, 5.83, 7.10, 7.93 (1 : 2 :
1 : 3)

④ $\xrightarrow{heat}$ CO + mixture of butenes

⑥ $\quad$ JACS **83**, 3726 (1961).$\quad$ Helv. Chim.
Acta **45**, 1927 (1962).

FeC₈F₈O₄

① $\quad$ Perfluorotetramethylene-tetra(carbonyl)-iron

$(CF_2)_4$Fe(CO)₄,

② $\quad$ C₂F₄ + Fe(CO)₅ $\longrightarrow$

③ $\quad$ Colorless crystals. Sublimable *in
vacuo*. [77°].
Decompd. at 193°. Air-stable.

IR : $\nu_{C\equiv O}$ 2160, 2120, 2100 cm⁻¹.

NMR(F) : 70.6, 136.9ppm. (from
CCl₃F).

④ $\quad$ + Br₂ $\xrightarrow{70°}$

$\qquad\longrightarrow$

* $\quad$ Previously formulated as
(C₂F₄)₂Fe(CO)₃.

⑥ $\quad$ Chem. & Ind. **1960**, 1358.$\quad$ JACS **83**,
248 (1961).

FeC₈F₁₀O₄

① $\quad$ Di-perfluoroethyl-tetra (carbonyl)
-iron

$\qquad$ (C₂F₅)₂Fe(CO)₄

② $\quad$ Na₂[Fe(CO)₄] + 2C₂F₅COCl $\longrightarrow$ 13%

③ $\quad$ Very pale yellow crystals. (25°/0.1
sublime). [62~63.5].
Stable in air. Very volatile at room
temp.

IR : $\nu_{C\equiv O}$ 2151 w, 2098 s, 2080 s cm⁻¹.

④ $\quad$ + aq. 20% KOH $\xrightarrow{3\,hr,\,60°}$ trace CF₃CF₂H

$\quad$ + concd. HCl $\xrightarrow{60°,\,12hr}$ 15% CF₃CF₂H

$\xrightarrow{100°}$ CF₃$-$CF=CF$-$CF₃ +
CF₃CF₂CF=CF₂

⑥ $\quad$ JACS **83**, 3604 (1961)

FeC₈H₂O₆

① $\quad$ [Tetra (carbonyl) ferra]-cyclopent-
ene-3-dione-2.5

② $\quad$ C₂H₂ + Fe₂(CO)₉ $\longrightarrow$ small yield

$(C_2H_2)Fe_2(CO)_6(COH)_2 \xrightarrow{\text{oxidation}}$

③ Orange red crystals. [118° decomp.].
Stable in air.
IR : $\nu_{C=O}$ 1670 cm⁻¹.

④ $\xrightarrow{\text{heat}}$ maleic acid

⑥ Proc. Chem. Soc. **1959**, 150.   Chem.
& Ind. **1959**, 703.

FeC₈H₄O₄

① Tri (carbonyl)-(cyclopentadienone)
iron

$Fe(CO)_3(C_5H_4O),$

② $Fe(CO)_5 + 2C_2H_2 \xrightarrow{75\sim80°, \text{ EtOH}-H_2O}$
as hydroquinone adduct.
$Fe(CO)_5 + C_2H_2 \xrightarrow{\text{petr. ether}}$ less soluble
products $\xrightarrow{CO}$ 20%

③ Light yellow crystals. [114~116°].
Very sol. in dilute mineral acids ;
sol. in H₂O. Stable in air.
Diamagnetic.
IR : $\nu_{C=O}$ 1637 cm⁻¹.
Dipolemoment : 4.45 D.

④ $\xrightarrow{\text{heat 114°}}$ $Fe(CO)_2(C_5H_4O)$
+ hydrazine $\longrightarrow$ hydrazone
+ HX $\longrightarrow$ $[Fe(CO)_3(C_5H_4OH)]^+X^-$
X=Cl, Br.
+ hydroquinone
$\longrightarrow$ hydroquinone adduct

⑥ Ber. **95**, 1170 (1962).

FeC₈H₈O₂

① π-cyclopentadienyl-methyl-di(carbonyl)-iron

$(CH_3)(\pi-C_5H_5)Fe(CO)_2,$

② Na[π-C₅H₅Fe(CO)₂] + CH₃I $\xrightarrow{\text{THF}}$ 70%

π-C₅H₅Fe(CO)₂I + CH₃MgI $\xrightarrow{\text{ether}}$ 50%

③ Caramel-like crystals. (sublime in
vacuo). [78~82°].
Sol. in org. solvents. Unstable in air ;
decomp. at 120° under nitrogen.
IR : $\nu_{C\equiv O}$ 2010, 1955 cm⁻¹.
NMR : τ 5.9, 10.1 (5 : 3).
UV : λ_{max} 353 mμ.

④ + PhC≡CPh $\xrightarrow{120°}$
1,2,3,4-tetraphenyl ferrocene
$\xrightarrow{\text{heat}}$ $[(\pi-C_5H_5)Fe(CO)_2]_2$

⑥ JINC **3**, 104 (1956).

FeC₉H₇O₃X

① π-Cyclohexadienyl-tri(carbonyl)-
iron tetrafluoroborate
$[(\pi-C_6H_7)Fe(CO)_3]^+X^-,$ X=BF₄

② (1. 3-cyclohehxadiene)Fe(CO)₃
+ Ph₃C⁺BF₄⁻ $\xrightarrow{CH_2Cl_2}$

③ Pale yellow solid. [190° decomp.].
Sol. in H₂O. DMSO and DMF.
Air-stable, stable in aq. solution
Diamagnetic.

④ + BPh₄⁻ $\longrightarrow$ tetraphenyl borate
+ ClO₄⁻ $\longrightarrow$ perchlorate

⑥ Angew. **72**, 919 (1960).

FeC₉H₉O₂X

① Cyclopentadienyl-di (carbonyl)-
(ethylene)iron hexafluorophosph
-ate
$[(\pi-C_5H_5)Fe(CO)_2(C_2H_4)]X,$ X=PF₆

② π-C₅H₅Fe(CO)₂Br + CH₂=CH₂ + AlBr₃
$\xrightarrow[\text{r. t., (PF}_6)^-]{}$ 88~78%

③ Orange crystals. (not volatile).

Sol. in acetone ; insol. in ether.

IR : $\nu_{C\equiv O}$ 2083, 2049 cm^{-1} ; $\nu_{C=C}$ 1527 cm^{-1}.

Diamagnetic.

⑥ Ber. **94**, 1200 (1961).

FeC₁₀H₆O₄

① Tri(carbonyl)-(tropone)-iron

Fe(CO)₃(C₇H₆O),

② C₂H₂ + Fe₂(CO)₉ $\xrightarrow{20\sim 24\ \text{atm.,}\ 20\sim 25°}$ 28%

   tropone + iron carbonyls $\longrightarrow$

③ Red crystals. Sublime at 40° in vacuo
   [63.5~64.5°], [83~84°]. d 1.65 g/cc.
   Sol. in benzene ; less sol. in petroleum ether, methanol. Somewhat
   light and air sensitive.

   IR : $\nu_{C\equiv O}$ 2066, 2008, 1992 cm^{-1} ;
   $\nu_{C=O\ or\ C=C}$ 1637, 1613 cm^{-1}

   Dipole moment : 4.30 D.

④ + PhNH·NH₂ $\longrightarrow$ phenylhydrazone
   + Ph₃P $\longrightarrow$ Fe(CO)₃(PPh₃)₂
   + (C₇H₆O)Fe(CO)₂·PPh₃
   + FeCl₃ $\longrightarrow$ tropone + FeCl₂

⑥ Ber. **95**, 1179 (1962).

FeC₁₀H₈O₃

① Tri (carbonyl)-(cycloheptatriene)
   -iron

Fe(CO)₃($cyclo$-C₇H₈),

② $cyclo$-C₇H₈ + Fe(CO)₅ $\xrightarrow{\text{heat}}$

③ Orange yellow liq. (70°/0.4). [-2°,
   5°].

   Stable in air.

   IR : $\nu_{C\equiv O}$ 2050, 1995 cm^{-1}.

   Dipole moment : 2.43 D.

* Previously formulated as
   Fe(CO)₂(C₇H₈)

⑥ JCS **1961**, 594.   JACS **83**, 467 (1961).

FeC₁₀H₈O₃

① Tri (carbonyl)-(bicyclo [2,2,1]
   heptadiene)-iron

Fe(CO)₃·($bicyclo$-C₇H₈),

② $bicyclo$-C₇H₈ + Fe(CO)₅
   $\xrightarrow{\text{reflux or U. V.}}$ 30%

③ Orange-red liq. (60.5°/0.2). [~10°].
   Slowly oxidized in air. Sol. in concd.
   H₂SO₄.
   Miscible with org. solvents.
   NMR : τ 6.88, 8.75 (6 : 2).

④ + FeCl₃ $\longrightarrow$ $bicyclo$-C₇H₈

⑥ JACS **81**, 1266 (1959).

FeC₁₀H₉ClHg

① Ferrocenyl-mercuric chloride,
   Ferrocenylchloromercury
   (π-C₅H₅)(π-C₅H₄HgCl)Fe

② ferrocene + Hg(OAC)₂ $\xrightarrow{\text{KCl}}$
   ferrocenyl boronic acid + HgCl₂
   $\longrightarrow$ 26%

③ Golden yellow crystals. [194~196°]
   Stable in air.

④ + Na₂S₂O₃ $\longrightarrow$
   diferrocenyl mercury
   + CH₃COCl $\longrightarrow$ acetyl ferrocene
   + I₂ $\longrightarrow$ iodo ferrocene
   + Br₂ $\longrightarrow$ bromo ferrocene

⑥ Ber. **93**, 2717 (1960).   JOC **22**, 900
   (1957).

FeC₁₀H₉Br

① Bromoferrocene
   (π-C₅H₄Br)(π-C₅H₅)Fe

② ferrocene boronic acid + CuBr₂ ⟶
di-ferrocenyl-mercury + Br₂ ⟶
ferrocenyl mercuric chloride
   + Br₂ ⟶
③ [32~33°].
Stable in air; stable in KOH and
CH₃CO₂K.
④ + Cu(OAc)₂ ⟶ acetoxyferrocene
+ Mg
   ⟶ ferrocenylmagnesium bromide
⑥ Dokl. **100**, 1099 (1955).   JOC **26**, 1034
(1961).

FeC₁₀H₁₀

① Ferrocene,
Dicyclopentadienyl-iron

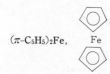

(π-C₅H₅)₂Fe,

② C₅H₅MgBr + FeCl₂ ⟶
C₅H₆ + FeCl₂ + NHEt₂ ⟶ 73~84%
C₅H₆ + FeCl₂ + NaOEt + EtOH
   ⟶ 90%
③ Orange crystals (249°). [173~174°].
Sol. in most org. solvents.
Stable in air; stable up to 470° in
nitrogen. Diamagnetic.
UV: λ_{max} 325, 440 mμ.
Ferrocene ⇌ ferrocene⁺ + e
$E° = +0.3$ v
Polarography: $E_{1/2} = -0.59$.
X-ray analysis proved its antiprismatic sandwich structure.
④ + CH₃COCl + AlCl₃
   ⟶ acetylferrocene
+ Li + EtNH₂ ⟶Fe
+ cyclopentadiene
⑤ High temperature material; antiknock additive.
⑥ Org. Syn. **36**, 31, 34 (1956).   JOC **25**,
1435 (1960).   Angew. **74**, 301, 347

(1962).

FeC₁₀H₁₁N

① Aminoferrocene
(π-C₅H₄-NH₂)(π-C₅H₅)Fe,

② ferrocene carboxylic acid
Curtius rearrangement
   ⟶

ferrocenyllithium + NH₂OCH₃ ⟶
nitro ferrocene + Fe + HCl ⟶
③ Yellow brown crystals. [153~155°].
Unstable in air.
$K_B = 1.55 \times 10^{-9}$
④ + (CH₃CO)₂O
   ⟶ acetylamino ferrocene
+ p-toluenesulfonylchloride
   ⟶ p-toluene sulfonyl amino
ferrocene
⑥ JACS **77**, 6295 (1955).   JOC **24**, 1487
(1959).

FeC₁₁H₈O₃

① Tri (carbonyl)-(cyclooctatetraene)
-iron

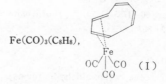

Fe(CO)₃(C₈H₈),   (I)

② Cyclooctatetraene
UV or heat
   + Fe(CO)₅ ⟶
③ Red crystals. (80°/5 sublime). [94°].
Stable in air. Sol. in most org. solv-
ents; sol. and stable in concd.
H₂SO₄.
IR: $\nu_{C\equiv O}$ 2150, 1990 cm⁻¹ (CHCl₃).

NMR : τ4.8(single peak) (C$_6$H$_6$).

The structure was determiend as(I)
by X-ray.

④ + Ph$_3$P $\longrightarrow$ Fe(CO)$_3$(PPh$_3$)$_2$

+ CO $\xrightarrow{80°}$ Fe(CO)$_5$ + C$_8$H$_8$

+ Fe(CO)$_5$ $\xrightarrow{UV}$ Fe$_2$(CO)$_6$(C$_8$H$_8$)

⑥ JACS **82**, 366 (1960). Chem. & Ind.
1959, 975. BCSJ **32**, 880 (1959).
Nippon Kagaku Zasshi, **81**, 1072
(1960).

FeC$_{11}$H$_8$O$_4$

① Tri(carbonyl)-(cyclooctatrienone)
iron

Fe(CO)$_3$(C$_8$H$_8$O),

② cyclooctatrienone + Fe$_3$(CO)$_{12}$ or
Fe$_2$(CO)$_9$ $\longrightarrow$ 50%

③ Yellow crystals. (70~90°/0.25 subli-
ime). [103°].
Sol. in benzene.
Stable in air.
IR : $\nu_{C\equiv O}$ 2054, 1983, 1971 cm^{-1}; $\nu_{>C=O}$
1560, 1635 cm^{-1}.
NMR : τ ~3.8, 4.43, 6.59, 7.10, 7.72
(2 : 2 : 1 : 2 : 1).

⑥ Ber. **96**, 1755 (1963). Inorg. Chem.
2, 807 (1963).

FeC$_{11}$H$_{10}$O

① ferrocene carboxaldehyde, formyl
ferrocene.
(π-C$_5$H$_4$CHO)(π-C$_5$H$_5$)Fe,

② ferrocene + PhNH·CHO $\xrightarrow{POCl_3}$ 78%

ferrocene + Cl$_2$CHOC$_2$H$_5$ $\xrightarrow{AlCl_3}$

ferrocenylcarbinol + MnO$_2$ $\longrightarrow$ 98%

③ Brownish red crystals. [121~22°].
Stable in air. Sol. in petroleum ether.
IR : $\nu_{C=O}$ 1676, 1666 cm^{-1}.
UV : λ_{max} 342, 464 mμ.

④ + PhOCH$_3$ $\longrightarrow$ phenyl
-(β-ferrocenyl vinyl)ketone
+ NaBH$_4$ $\longrightarrow$ ferrocenylcarbinol
+ (CH$_3$)$_2$NH
$\longrightarrow$ (*N,N*-dimethylamino)
-methyl-ferrocene

⑥ JACS **79**, 3416 (1957). JCS **958**, 650.

FeC$_{11}$H$_{10}$O$_2$

① Ferrocene carboxylic acid.
(π-C$_5$H$_4$CO$_2$H)(π-C$_5$H$_5$)Fe,

② acetyl ferrocene + I$_2$ $\xrightarrow{pyridine}$ 50%

ferrocenyl lithium + CO$_2$ $\longrightarrow$ 4.5%

③ Yellow crystals. [225~30°].
Stable in air
UV : λ_{max} 342sh, 445 mμ.
pKa, 6.78 (in 2 : 1 ethanol-water).

④ + H$_2$SO$_4$ $\longrightarrow$ sulfonated products.

+ EtOH $\xrightarrow{C_6H_6, HCl}$ ethyl etter

+ CH$_2$N$_2$ $\xrightarrow{ether}$ methyl ester

+ PCl$_5$ $\longrightarrow$ acid chloride

⑥ JACS **77**, 3009 (1955). Chem. & Ind.
1957, 1388.

FeC$_{11}$H$_{11}$X

① π-Cyclopentadienyl-(benzene)-iron
tribromide

$[(\pi\text{-}C_5H_5)Fe(C_6H_6)]^+X^-, \quad X=Br_3$

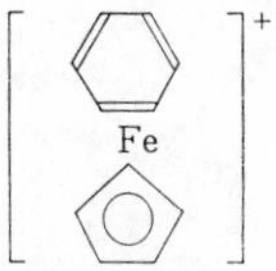

② $\pi\text{-}C_5H_5Fe(CO)_2Cl + AlCl_3 + C_6H_6$

$\xrightarrow[\text{60%}]{\text{1) reflux 2) Br}_2}$

③ Orange crystals. Not volatile.
Sol. in THF and acetone; insol. in
H₂O.

④ + LiAlH₄ ⟶ $(\pi\text{-}C_5H_5)(\pi\text{-}C_6H_7)Fe$
+ concd. HCl
⟶ $[(\pi\text{-}C_5H_5Fe(C_6H_6)]^+ + Br_2$

⑥ JCS **1960**, 989.

FeC₁₁H₁₂

① π-Cyclopentadienyl-π-cyclohexadi-
enyliron

$(\pi\text{-}C_5H_5)(\pi\text{-}C_6H_7)Fe,$

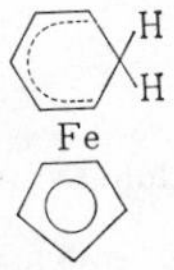

② $[\pi\text{-}C_5H_5Fe(C_6H_6)]^+Br_3^- + LiAlH_4$
⟶ 50%

③ Orange red crystals. (sublimable
in vac). [135~136°].
Sol. in light petroleum.
Fairly stable in air.
IR : JCS **1960**, 989.
NMR : τ4.13, 5.93, 7.4~8.7.
Previously formulated as π-cyclo-
pentadiene-(benzene)iron.

④ $\xrightarrow{\text{aq. HCl}}$ decomposition

⑥ Chem. & Ind. **1961**, 1408.

FeC₁₂H₁₂

① Vinyl ferrocene
$(\pi\text{-}C_5H_4CH=CH_2)(\pi\text{-}C_5H_5)Fe,$

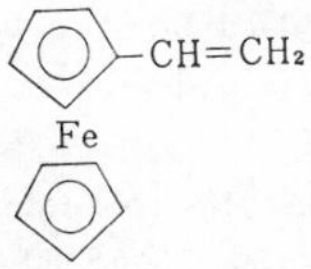

② methyl(ferrocenyl)carbinol $\xrightarrow{\text{heat}}$
21%
methyl-(ferrocenyl)carbinylacetate
$\xrightarrow{\text{heat}}$ 56%

③ Red solid. (80~85°/0.2 sublime).
[48~49°].
Very sol. in ether, petroleum ether
and methanol.
Camphor-like odor.

④ $\xrightarrow{\text{85% H}_3\text{PO}_4 \text{ or azobis (isobutyronitrile)}}$

polymer
+ HCl
⟶ 1-ferrocenyl ethyl chloride
$\xrightarrow{\text{1) Br}_2, \text{2) KOH}}$ ferrocenylacetylene

⑥ JACS **77**, 6295 (1955). Ber. **94**, 219
(1961).

FeC₁₂H₁₂O

① Acetylferrocene
$(\pi\text{-}C_5H_4CO\cdot CH_3)(\pi\text{-}C_5H_5)Fe,$

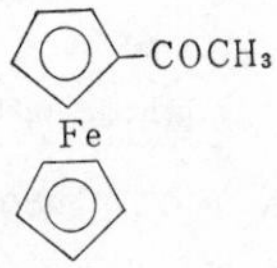

② ferrocene + CH₃COCl $\xrightarrow{\text{AlCl}_3}$ 86%

③ Orange crystals. Sublimes in vacuo
[85~86°].
Stable in air.
Sol. in petroleum ether, methanol
and benzene.
IR : $\nu_{C=O}$ 1672 cm⁻¹.
UV : λ_{max} 337, 456 mμ.

④ + I₂ $\xrightarrow{\text{pyridine}}$ ferrocene carboxylic
acid

$+ LiAlH_4 \longrightarrow$ ferrocenyl
-(methyl)carbinol
$+ Zn-Hg + HCl \longrightarrow$ ethylferrocene
$+ NH_2OH$
$\longrightarrow$ acetylferrocene oxime
⑥ JCS 1958, 650. JACS 80, 5443 (1958).

FeC₁₁H₁₂O
① Ferrocenyl carbinol
$(\pi\text{-}C_5H_4CH_2OH)(\pi\text{-}C_5H_5)Fe$
② ferrocene carboxaldehyde $+ NaBH_4$
$\longrightarrow$ 85%
ferrocenyl methyl-trimethylammom-
ium iodide $+ KOH \longrightarrow$
methyl ferrocene-carboxylate $+$
$LiAlH_4 \longrightarrow$
③ Yellow crystals. [74~76°].
Stable in air.
④ $+ MnO_2$
$\longrightarrow$ ferrocene-carboxaldehyde
⑥ JACS 79, 3416 (1957).

FeC₁₁H₁₂O₃
① Tri(carbonyl)-(cyclooctadiene-1,5)
iron
$Fe(CO)_3(cyclo\text{-}C_8H_{12}\text{-}1,5)$
② cyclooctadiene-1,5 $+ Fe(CO)_5$
$\xrightarrow{UV, r.t.}$ 5%
cyclootadiene-1,5
$+ Fe_3(CO)_{12} \xrightarrow{benzene, reflux}$
③ Orange oil. (90°/5). n_D 1.5765 (20°).
Sol. in org. solvents.
Unstable in air; slowly decompd.
even in nitrogen.
IR : $\nu_{C\equiv O}$ 2049, 1965 cm⁻¹.
④ As catalyst for the isomerization :
cyclooctadiene-1,5
$\longrightarrow$ cyclooctadiene-1,3
⑥ Nippon Kagaku Zasshi, 81, 1072(1960).
JINC 16, 233 (1961).

FeC₁₂H₁₀O₂
① π-Cyclopentadienyl-σ-cyclopentadi-

enyl-di(carbonyl)-iron
$(\pi\text{-}C_5H_5)(\sigma\text{-}C_5H_5)Fe(CO)_2,$

② $\pi\text{-}C_5H_5Fe(CO)_2Br + C_5H_5MgBr \longrightarrow$
$\pi\text{-}C_5H_5Fe(CO)_2I + C_5H_5Na \longrightarrow$ 15%
③ Orange crystals. [46°].
Fairly stable in air.
IR : $\nu_{C\equiv O}$ 2013, 1965 cm⁻¹.
NMR : τ3.5 $(\sigma\text{-}C_5H_5)$, 5.0 $(\pi\text{-}C_5H_5)$.
④ Reacts with maleic anhydride, but
the product was unstable.
⑥ JINC 3, 104 (1956).

FeC₁₂H₁₄
① (Cyclohexadiene-1,3)-(benzene)-iron

$Fe(C_6H_6)(cyclo\text{-}C_6H_8),$

② cyclohexadiene-1,3 $+ FeCl_3$
$+ i\text{-}PrMgBr \xrightarrow{-50°, ether}$ 32~38%
③ Yellow crystals. [102~104°].
Unstable in air.
IR : 2865, 2817, 1253, 1227, 1167, 1062,
1023, 1000, 890, 874, 847 cm⁻¹. due to
C_6H_8. 1842, 1648, 1774 cm⁻¹, due to
C_6H_6.
NMR : τ5.13, 5.42, 7.48, 8.6.
⑥ Z. Naturf. 17b 776 (1962).

FeC₁₃H₁₂O₅
① Tri(carbonyl)-(duroquinone)-iron
$Fe(CO)_3[(CH_3)_4C_6O_2],$

② $2CH_3-C\equiv C-CH_3 + Fe(CO)_5 \xrightarrow{\text{sun light}}$

③ Orange crystals. [∼50° decomp].
Stable in air.
IR: $\nu_{C\equiv O}$ 2066, 2012; $\nu_{>C=O}$ 1639, 1618 cm⁻¹.

④ + air ⟶ duroquinone
+ HCl ⟶ duro-hydroquinone
+ $FeCl_2$

⑥ JACS **80**, 1009 (1958).

FeC₁₃H₁₇N

① *N,N*-Dimethylaminomethyl-ferrocene
{π-$C_5H_4\cdot CH_2\cdot N(CH_3)_2$}($\pi$-$C_5H_5$)Fe

② ferrocene + CH_2O + $NH(CH_3)_2$
$\xrightarrow{H^+}$ 48∼51%

formyl ferrocene + $NH(CH_3)_2$ $\xrightarrow{Ni}$
ferrocene + $(CH_3)_2NCH_2N(CH_3)_2$
⟶ 51%

③ Clear amber liq. (91∼92°/0.45).
n_D 1.5893 (25°).
Sol. in ether.

④ + CH_3I ⟶ ferrocenylmethyl-
trimethyl-ammonium iodide
+ H_2SO_4 ⟶ diferrocenyl ethane

⑥ JOC **22**, 355 (1957); **21**, 382 (1956).

FeC₁₄H₁₈

① [Cycloheptadiene(1,3)]-[cyclohepta-
triene(1,3,5)]-iron
Fe(*cyclo*-C_7H_{10})(*cyclo*-C_7H_8)

② *cyclo*-C_7H_{10} + cyclo-C_7H_8 + *i*-PrMgBr
+ $FeCl_3$ $\xrightarrow{\text{ether}}$ 31%

③ Yellow orange crystals. (55∼60°/
high vac. sublime). [90∼92°].

Very sol. in org. solvents.
Unstable in air, thermally not very
stable. Diamagnetic.
NMR: τ5.18, 5.98, 6.29, 7.71, 8.80.

④ + $FeCl_3$ $\xrightarrow{80\sim100°}$ *cyclo*-C_7H_{10}
+ *cyclo*-C_7H_8

⑥ JOM **1**, 90 (1963).

FeC₁₆H₁₄

① Phenylferrocene
(π-$C_5H_4C_6H_5$)(π-C_5H_5)Fe

② ferrocene + PhN_2^+ ⟶ 17%
diphenyl ferrocene as by-product

③ Yellow crystals. [110∼111°].
Stable in air
UV: λ_{max} 237, 277, 447 mμ.

④ In concd. H_2SO_4. forms green solution.
+ CH_3COCl
$\xrightarrow{AlCl_3}$ various acetylated products

⑥ JACS **77**, 3012 (1955); **81**, 4530 (1959).

FeC₁₈H₁₄

① Di-π-indenyl-iron,
Dibenzoferrocene

(π-C_9H_7)$_2$Fe,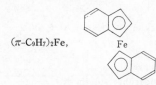

② indenylmagnesium bromide
+ $FeCl_3$ ⟶

③ Purple crystals. Sublimable in
vacuum. [184∼185°]. *d* 1.446 (20°/4).
Readily sol. in benzene; moderately
in acetone, ligroin and ether.
Stable in air. Diamagnetic.
UV: λ_{max} 263 mμ (log ε 4.30), 420 mμ
(log ε 2.78).

IR: JACS **76**, 2024 (1954).

④ + H_2 $\xrightarrow{\text{catalyst}}$

di-(tetrahydroindenyl)iron

⑥ Z. Naturf. **8b** 694 (1953)

FeC₁₈H₁₈M₄

① Sodium hexapropynylferrate
$M_4^+[(CH_3C\equiv C-)_6Fe]^{4-}$, M=Na

② $CH_3C\equiv C-Na + Fe(NH_3)_4(SCN)_2$

$\xrightarrow{\text{liq. NH}_3}$ 20%

③ Yellow crystals.
Very sensitive to hydrolysis.
Decomp. at 100° in dry air.
Diamegnetic.

④ $+ O_2 \longrightarrow$ brown oxidized product
$+ H_2O \longrightarrow CH_3C\equiv CH + Fe(OH)_2$

⑥ Z. anorg. allg. Chem. **287**, 17 (1956).

FeC₁₈H₂₄X₂

① (Dimesitylene)-iron diiodide
$\{[(CH_3)_3C_6H_3]_2Fe\}X_2$, X=I

② mesitylene + FeBr₂ + Al + AlCl₃

$\xrightarrow{\text{KI}}$ 9%

③ Red crystals.
Considerably sol. in H₂O.
Slowly decompd. in air; lightsensi-
tive; stable in acidic aq. solution.
Diamagnetic.

④ tetraphenylborate, Reineacke-ate,
tetrafluoroborate, and perchlorate
have been isolated.

$\xrightarrow{\text{OH}^-}$ Fe(OH)₂ + mesitylene

⑥ Ber. **89**, 2397 (1956).

FeC₂₀H₁₂O₄

① Tri(carbonyl)-(2,5-diphenylcycl-

opentadienone)iron
Fe(CO)₃[(C₆H₅)₂C₅H₂O],

② $PhC\equiv CH + Fe_3(CO)_{12} \xrightarrow{80°}$

$PhC\equiv CH + Fe(CO)_5 \xrightarrow{\text{UV, heat}}$

(2,5-diphenylcyclopentadienone
dimer) + Fe₂(CO)₉ $\longrightarrow$

③ Yellow crystals. (130°/vac. sublime).
[230° decomp.].
Sol. in benzene and acetone, less in
petroleum ether and methanol.
Stable in air.
IR: $\nu_{C\equiv O}$ 2062, 2004, 1988, $\nu_{>C=O}$ 1616
cm⁻¹.

④ $\dfrac{+ PhC\equiv CPh}{} \longrightarrow$ 1,2,3,4-(C₆H₆)₄C₆H₂

No reaction with phenylhydrazine,
hydroxylamine, and sodium borohydride.

⑥ JINC **10**, 250 (1959).

FeC₃₀H₂₀O₃

① Tri(carbonyl)-(tetraphenylallene)
-iron
Fe(CO)₃[(C₆H₅)₂C=C=C(C₆H₅)₂]

② $Ph_2C=C=CPh_2 + Fe(CO)_5$

$\xrightarrow{\text{isooctane, 120°}}$ 29%

③ Red crystals. (180°/5 mm sublime with
decomp.). [102~103°].
Sol. in benzene and EtOH.
Stable in air; decomp. at 230°.
IR: $\nu_{C\equiv O}$ 2060, 1999, 1985 cm⁻¹.
UV: λ_{max} 468 mμ.

④ $+ Ph_3P \xrightarrow{80°}$ Fe(CO)₃(PPh₃)₂
$+ Ph_2C=C=CPh_2$

⑥ BCSJ **37**, 292 (1964).

FeC₃₁H₂₀O₃

① Tri(carbonyl)-(tetraphenylcyclobu-
tadiene)iron

Fe(CO)₃[(C₆H₅)₄C₄],

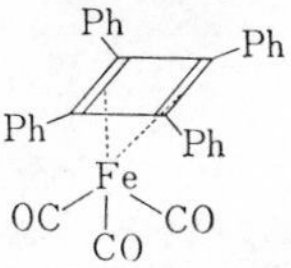

(I)

② PhC≡CPh + Fe(CO)₅ $\xrightarrow{250°}$

PhC≡CPh + Fe₃(CO)₁₂ $\xrightarrow{80°}$ 1.2%

cyclo-(C₈H₈)Fe(CO)₃ + PhC≡CPh ⟶

③ Light yellow crystals. (180°/vac.
sublime). [234°]. d 1.39 g/cc.
Exceptionally stable in air.
No reaction with carbon monoxide.
IR: $\nu_{C\equiv O}$ 2033, 1965, 1931 cm⁻¹.
Monoclinic. The structure was
determined as (I) by X-ray.

④ + LiAlH₄ ⟶
PhCH=CPh−CPh=CHPh

⑥ JINC **10**, 250 (1959).   Nature **186**,
798 (1960).

FeC₃₂H₂₀O₄

① Tri(carbonyl)-(tetraphenyl cyclo
pentadienone)iron

Fe(CO)₃[(C₆H₅)₄C₅O],

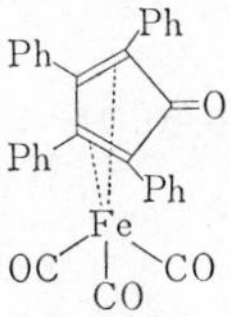

② PhC≡CPh + Fe(CO)₅ $\xrightarrow{140\sim60°}$

tetracyclone + Fe(CO)₅ ⟶

PhC≡CPh + Fe + CO $\xrightarrow{200°}$

③ Yellow crystals. (140°/vac. sublime).
[∼180° decomp.]. d 1.35 g/cc.
Sol. in benzene.
Stable in air.
Triclinic.
IR: $\nu_{C\equiv O}$ 2062, 2012, 1988, 1642 cm⁻¹;
$\nu_{C=O}$ 1642 cm⁻¹.

④ $\xrightarrow{\text{heat}}$ tetracyclone.

⑥ JINC **10**, 250 (1959); **11**, 42 (1959).

FeC₃₉H₃₀O₃P₂

① Tri(carbonyl)-bis(triphenyl phosphine)iron.

Fe(CO)₃[P(C₆H₅)₃]₂,

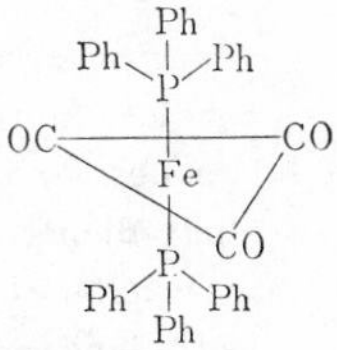

② 2Ph₃P + Fe(CO)₅ $\xrightarrow{250°}$

2Ph₃P + Fe₃(CO)₁₂ $\xrightarrow{\text{THF, reflux}}$

③ Yellow crystals. [272° decomp].
Very stable in air; not attacked by
H₂O, alcoholic KOH and sodium in
liq. NH₃. Stable at 110° for 24 hrs.
IR: $\nu_{C\equiv O}$ 1890 cm⁻¹.

④ $\xrightarrow{\text{H}_2\text{SO}_4}$ protonated compound.

+ I₂ $\xrightarrow{\text{ether}}$ Fe(CO)₂(PPh₃)₂I₅

+ K $\xrightarrow{\text{dioxane, reflux}}$ Ph₂PK

⑥ Inorg. Chem **2**, 151 (1963).

Fe₂C₉O₉

① Nona(carbonyl)-diiron

Fe₂(CO)₉,

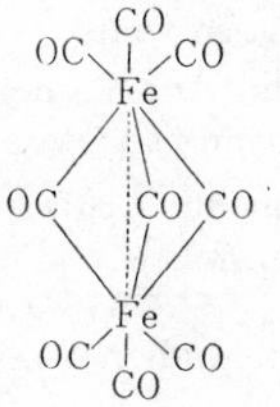

(I)

② Fe(CO)₅ $\xrightarrow{\text{UV, or sunlight in AcOH}}$ 30%

③ Orange crystals. Not volatile. [100°
decomp]. d 2.085 (18°/4°).
Sparingly sol. in methanol and
ethanol; practically insol. in ether,
petroleum ether and benzene.
Fairly stable in air.

IR : $\nu_{C\equiv O}$ 2087, 2023, 1831 cm^{-1}.

The structure was determined as (I) by X-ray.

④ $\xrightarrow{80°}$ Fe(CO)$_5$ + Fe$_3$(CO)$_{12}$

$\xrightarrow{100\sim120°}$ Fe + Fe(CO)$_5$

+ maleic anhydride $\longrightarrow$ Fe(CO)$_4$·

(maleic anhydride)

+ butadiene $\longrightarrow$ Fe(CO)$_4$·

(bntadiene)

+ ethylene $\longrightarrow$ Fe(CO)$_4$·(ethylene)

⑥ Brauer 1343.

$Fe_2C_{10}H_4O_6$

① (Tricarbonyl-ferra-cyclopentadiene)
-tri(carbonyl)-iron

[C$_4$H$_4$Fe(CO)$_3$]Fe(CO)$_3$,

② C$_2$H$_2$ + Fe$_3$(CO)$_{12}$ $\longrightarrow$ 12%

Thiophene + Fe$_3$(CO)$_{12}$ $\longrightarrow$ 5%

③ Orange crystals. (40°/10^{-2} sublime).
[54~55°].

Relatively thermally stable.

Sol. in org. solvents.

Monoclinic, Diamagnetic.

IR : $\nu_{C\equiv O}$ 2079, 2042, 2006, 1998 cm^{-1}.

Dipolemoment : 2.86 D.

④ + CO $\xrightarrow{220°,160atm}$ tri-carbonyl
-(cyclopentadienone)-iron

+ Ph$_3$P

$\longrightarrow$ [C$_4$H$_4$Fe(CO)$_3$]Fe(CO)$_2$PPh$_3$

⑥ Ber 95, 1155 (1962). JCS 1960, 989.

$Fe_2C_{12}H_8O_8$

① (Tricarbonyl ferra-2,5-dihydroxy
-3,4-dimethyl-cyclopentadiene)
tri(carbonyl)-iron

[(CH$_3$)$_2$C$_4$(OH)$_2$Fe(CO)$_3$]Fe(CO)$_3$,

(I)

② CH$_3$C≡CCH$_3$ + Na[HFe(CO)$_4$] $\longrightarrow$

③ Yellow crystals.

Stable in air. Sol. in dil. aq. NaOH.

IR : $\nu_{C\equiv O}$ 1998, 2033, 2073 cm^{-1}.

The structure was determined as (I).

pK_a : 6.30, 9.14.

④ $\xrightarrow{oxidation}$ CH$_3$-C-CO$_2$H
‖
CH$_3$-C-CO$_2$H

+ PhCH$_2$Cl + pyridine dibenzoate
[mp. 156°]

⑥ JACS 78, 6206 (1956). Proc. Chem.
Soc. 1958, 233.

$Fe_2C_{14}H_8O_6$

① Hexa(carbonyl)-(cyclooctatetrane)
-diiron

Fe$_2$(CO)$_6$·(C$_8$H$_8$),

(I)

② Fe(CO)$_3$(C$_8$H$_8$) + Fe(CO)$_5$ $\xrightarrow{UV}$

C$_8$H$_8$ + Fe(CO)$_5$ excess $\xrightarrow{heat\ or\ UV}$

③ Yellow-orange crystals. (120°/5 sublime). [185° decomp.].

Stable in air. Sparingly sol. in benzene.

IR : $\nu_{C\equiv O}$ 2035, 1970 cm^{-1}.

UV : λ_{max} 258 mμ.

NMR : τ4.4, 6.9 (1 : 1)

The structuse was determined as (I) by X-ray.

④ + Br$_2$ $\longrightarrow$ FeBr$_2$ + CO

⑥ JACS 82, 366 (1960). Chem. & Ind.

1959, 957.   BCSJ **33**, 880 (1959).

$Fe_2C_{14}H_{10}O_4$

① Di-π-cyclopentadienyl-tetra(carbonyl)-di-iron
$[(\pi\text{-}C_5H_5)Fe(CO)_2]_2$.

(I)

② $Fe(CO)_5$ + cyclo-C_5H_6 $\xrightarrow{140°}$ ca. 70%
$Fe(CO)_5$ + dicyclopentadiene
$\xrightarrow[38\%]{160\sim70°}$

③ Deep violet crystals. (110°/0.1 sub-
lime with decomp.). [194° decomp].
Sol. in benzene. The solution is
unstable in air.
Stable in air as crystals.
IR : $\nu_{C\equiv O}$ 2005, 1958 ; $\nu_{C=O}$ 1786cm⁻¹.
The structure was determined as
(I) by X-ray.

④ + Na−Hg
$\xrightarrow{r.t.}$ $Na[\pi\text{-}C_5H_5Fe(CO)_2]$
+ Br_2 $\longrightarrow$ $\pi\text{-}C_5H_5\cdot Fe(CO)_2Br$
+ HCl + air $\xrightarrow{CHCl_3}$ $\pi\text{-}C_5H_5Fe(CO)_2Cl$
$\xrightarrow{220°}$ ferrocene

⑥ JCS **1956**, 3030.   Inorg. Syn. **7**, 110
(1963).

$Fe_2C_{15}H_{10}O_5$

① Penta(carbonyl)-(azulene)-diiron
$Fe_2(CO)_5\cdot(C_{10}H_{10})$,

② azulene + $Fe(CO)_5$ $\xrightarrow{100°, 5 days}$ ca. 15%

③ Dark red solid. [~100° decomp.].
Sol. in boiling petroleum ether.

Diamagnetic.
IR : $\nu_{C=O}$ 2046, 1996, 1976cm⁻¹.
UV : λ_{max} 280, 330, 405, 515m μ.
Dipole moment : 3.97D (in benzene).

⑥ JCS **1960**, 4290.

$Fe_2C_{34}H_{20}O_6$

① Hexa(carbonyl)-(tetraphenylbuta-
triene)-diiron
$Fe_2(CO)_6\{(C_6H_5)_2C=C=C=C(C_6H_5)_2\}$

② $Ph_2C=C=C=CPh_2$ + $Fe(CO)_5$
$\xrightarrow[26\%]{140°, 14 hr}$

③ Deep red crystals. [200° decomp].
Sol. in benzene ; slightly sol. in *n*-he-
xane. Very stable in air, also stab-
le in solution. Diamagnetic.
IR : $\nu_{C\equiv O}$ 2072, 2032, 1998, 1988cm⁻¹
UV : No maximum.

④

$\xrightarrow{heat, 250°}$ $Ph_2C=C=C=CPh_2$ +

⑥ BCSJ **37**, 292 (1964).   JOM **3**, 7 (1965).
JCS(A) **1966**, 594.

$Fe_2C_{36}H_{20}O_7$

① (Tricarbonyl-ferra-tetraphenylcy-
clohexadieneone)-tri(carbonyl)
-iron
$[(C_6H_5)_5C_5O\cdot Fe(CO)_3]Fe(CO)_3$,

② $PhC\equiv CPh$ + $Fe_2(CO)_9$ or $Fe_3(CO)_{12}$
$\xrightarrow[3.5\%]{80°}$

$PhC\equiv CPh$ + $Fe(CO)_5$ $\xrightarrow{UV, r.t.}$

③ Deep red crystals. [ca. 160° decomp].
D 1.35.

Sol. in benzene.

Stable in air.

Monoclinic. Diamagnetic.

IR: $\nu_{C\equiv O}$ 2075, 2053, 2016; $\nu_{C=O}$ 1667 cm^{-1}.

④ + LiAlH$_4$ $\xrightarrow{\text{heat}}$ tetraphenylquinone

$\xrightarrow{\text{UV or CO}}$ } $\longrightarrow$ (tetraphenylcyclo-pentadienone)Fe(CO)$_3$

⑥ JINC **10**, 250 (1959).

$Fe_3C_{12}O_{12}$

① Dodeca(carbonyl)-triiron

Fe$_3$(CO)$_{12}$

② Na[HFe(CO)$_4$] + MnO$_2$ $\longrightarrow$

Fe$_2$(CO)$_9$ $\xrightarrow{80°,\ \text{benzene}}$

③ Black crystals.

Deep green as powder. (80°/vac. sublime). [~140° decomp.].

Sparingly sol. in benzene and n-hexane.

The deep green solution is unstable in air.

Unstable in air (very slow air-oxidataion).

IR: $\nu_{C\equiv O}$ 2043, 2020, 1997, 1858, 1826 cm^{-1}.

④ + PPh$_3$ $\xrightarrow{80°}$ Fe(CO)$_4$(PPh$_3$)

$\xrightarrow{\text{heat}}$ Fe mirror

+ Na $\xrightarrow{\text{THF}}$ Na$_2$[Fe(CO)$_4$]

* The structure has not been definitely determined.

(OC)$_3$Fe $\underset{\underset{CO}{\overset{O}{\parallel}C}}{\overset{\overset{O}{\parallel}C}{\diagup\diagdown}}$ Fe $\underset{\underset{CO}{\overset{O}{\parallel}C}}{\overset{O}{\diagup\diagdown}}$ Fe(CO)$_3$ or

$\begin{array}{c} OC \quad CO \\ OC-Fe-CO \\ OC \diagup \qquad \diagdown CO \\ OC-Fe----Fe-CO \\ OC \mid \qquad \mid \diagdown CO \\ \quad CO \quad CO \end{array}$

⑥ Inorg. Syn. **7**, 193 (1963).

【Ir】

[IrC$_2$I$_4$O$_2$]M, M=K

① Potassium tetraiodo-di(carbonyl)-iridium

[I$_4$Ir(CO)$_2$]K

② IrI$_3$ + KI $\xrightarrow{\text{CO, 200 atm, 200°}}$

③ Red crystals.

Sol. in H$_2$O (better if acidified with som hydrogen iodide), diethylether, acetone, and ethylalcohol.

IR: ν_{CO} 2051 cm^{-1} (in nujol).

④ $\xrightarrow{>250°,\ \text{CO}}$ [I$_5$Ir(CO)]K$_2$ + [I$_3$Ir(CO)$_2$]$_2$ + CO

⑥ JCS **1964**, 961.

IrC$_3$O$_3$

① Tri(carbonyl)-iridium

[Ir(CO)$_3$]$_n$

② IrCl$_3$ $\xrightarrow{CO}$ Ir(CO)$_2$Cl$_2$ $\xrightarrow{CO}$ Ir(CO)$_3$Cl $\xrightarrow{CO}$

③ Canary yellow crystals. [210° decomp.].

Insol. in common org. solvents.

Stable in air.

⑥ Z. anorg. allg. Chem. **245**, 321 (1940); **246**, 138 (1941).

IrC$_3$I$_3$O$_3$

① Triiodo-tri(carbonyl)-iridium

I$_3$Ir(CO)$_3$

② IrI$_3$ $\xrightarrow{\text{CO, 250 atm, 100°, 18 hr}}$

③ Red crystals. Sublime.

Sol. in benzene and hexane.

IR: ν_{CO} 2178, 2114 cm^{-1} (in nujol).

⑥ JCS **1964**, 961.

IrC₁₀H₁₅

① π-Cyclopentadienyl-(cyclopentadiene)-iridium.
(π-C₅H₅)Ir(C₅H₆)

② IrCl₃ + KC₅H₅ + C₅H₆ ⟶
0.5~1%

③ Bright yellow crystals. (60°/*in vacuo*
sublime). [130~132°].
Sol. in acetone, petr. ether, benzene
and CH₃OH ; insol. in H₂O.

④ + H⁺

$$\xrightarrow{\text{Na[B(C}_6\text{H}_5\text{)}_4\text{]}}$$ (π-C₅H₅)₂IrB(C₆H₅)₄

⑥ Ber. **92**, 1624 (1959)

IrC₁₃H₃₀Cl₃OP₂

① Trichloro-(carbonyl)-bis(triethylphosphine)-iridium
Cl₃Ir(CO){P(C₂H₅)₃}₂,

② *trans*-Ir{P(C₂H₅)₃}₃Cl₃

$$\overline{\underset{\xrightarrow{\text{CO, reflux 6 hrs}}}{\text{CO 65atm, 55°, 20 hr in acetone}}}$$

H₂IrCl₅ + P(C₂H₅)₃

③ Pale yellow crystals. [159~161°].
IR : ν$_{CO}$ 2031 (in nujol), 2041 (in
C₆H₆) ; 2050 cm⁻¹(in CHCl₃).

⑥ JCS **1964**, 1625.

IrC₂₁H₃₀OP

① Trichloro-(carbonyl)-bis(diethylphenylphosphine)-iridium
Cl₃Ir(CO)[P(C₂H₅)₂(C₆H₅)]₂,

(I)

② H₂IrCl₆ + P(C₂H₅)₂(C₆H₅)

2-methoxy ethanol + HCl,
CO, boiling for 20 min
$\xrightarrow{\hspace{3cm}}$ 64%

reflux for 8hr.

③ Yellow prisms. [175~182°].
IR : ν$_{CO}$ 2081(in nujol), 2105 (in C₆H₆) ;
2109 cm⁻¹ (in CHCl₃).

④ $\xrightarrow{\text{KOH in boiling ethanol}}$

HCl₂Ir(CO)[P(C₂H₅)₂(C₆H₅)]

⑥ JCS **1964**, 1625.

IrC₃₇H₃₀ClOP₂

① Chloro-(carbonyl)-bis(triphenylphosphine)-iridium
(Cl)Ir(CO){P(C₆H₅)₃}₂

② IrCl₃·(H₂O)$_x$ or (NH₄)₂IrCl₆
+ P(C₆H₅)₃, aq. 2-(β-methoxyethoxy)
-ethanol
$\xrightarrow{\hspace{3cm}}$ 86%

③ Yellow crystals. [323~325° decomp.].
Sol. in benzene ; insol. in H₂O and
alcohol.
Stable in benzene.
IR : ν$_{C=O}$ 1944 cm⁻¹.

④ $\xrightarrow{\text{O}_2\text{ in C}_6\text{H}_6}$ O₂ClIr(CO)[P(C₆H₅)₃]₂

$\xrightarrow{\text{H}_2\text{ in C}_6\text{H}_6}$ H₂ClIr(CO)[P(C₆H₅)₃]

$\xrightarrow{\text{Cl}_2}$ Cl₃Ir(CO)[P(C₆H₅)₃]₂

$\xrightarrow{\text{HCl}}$ HCl₂Ir(CO)[P(C₆H₅)₃]₂

⑥ JACS **83**, 2784 (1961) ; **84**, 679 (1962).

Ir₂C₄I₆O₄

① Hexaiodo-tetra(carbonyl)diiridium
[(I)₃Ir(CO)₂]₂

② IrI₃ $\xrightarrow{\text{CO, 250 atm, 18 hr.}}$ I₃Ir(CO)₃

IrI₃ + KI $\xrightarrow{\text{200 atm, 200°}}$ [I₄Ir(CO)₂]K
$\xrightarrow{\text{250°}}$

③ Brown red crystals.

Stable both in the solid state and in solution.

IR : ν_{CO} 2123, 2807 cm⁻¹ (in nujol).

⑥ JCS 1964, 961.

IrC₆H₂₄Cl₂

① Dichloro-dicycloocta-1, 5-diene-diiridium

[ClIr(C₈H₁₂)]₂

② Na₂IrCl₆ + C₈H₁₂ $\xrightarrow{\text{EtOH}-\text{H}_2\text{O, 70}\sim\text{80}°}$

③ Orange red crystals.[>200° decomp.].
Sol. in CHCl₃ and benzene. Stable at room temp. under N₂ in the solid.

④ + P(C₆H₅)₃ ⟶
ClIr(C₈H₁₂)[P(C₆H₅)₃]
+ HCl ⟶ [Cl₂HIr(C₈H₁₂)]₂

⑥ Z. Naturf. **20b**, 602 (1965).

Ir₂C₁₆H₂₆Cl₄

① Dihydrido-dichloro-dicycloocta-1,5-diene diiridium.

[HCl₂Ir(C₈H₁₂)]₂

② H₂IrCl₆ + C₈H₁₂ $\xrightarrow{\text{EtOH, heat, 2 hr}}$ 70%

③ White yellow crystals. [>200° decomp.].
IR : ν_{Ir-H} 2261 cm⁻¹.

④ + (C₂H₅)₂P(C₆H₅)
⟶ HCl₂Ir[P(C₂H₅)₂(C₆H₅)]₃
+ Na₂CO₃ $\xrightarrow{\text{MeOH}}$ [(OCH₃)Ir(C₈H₁₂)]₂
+ NaC₅H₅ ⟶ Ir(C₅H₅)(C₈H₁₂)

⑥ Tetrahedon Letters **1964**, 1301.

【Mn】

MnCH₃I

① Methyl-iodo-manganese
(CH₃)(I)Mn

② MnI₂ + CH₃Li ⟶

⑥ Angew. **71**, 627 (1959).   Z. Naturf. **15b**, 547 (1960).

MnC₂H₆

① Dimethyl-manganese
(CH₃)₂Mn

② MnI₂ + CH₃Li $\xrightarrow{\text{Et}_2\text{O}}$

③ Pyrophoric powder. (light yellow).
[80° decomp.].
Sensitive to shock and air.
Gilman test : positive.

④ + MeLi ⟶ Li[MnMe₃]
+ MnI₂ $\xrightarrow{\text{ether}}$ MeMnI

⑥ Z. Naturf. **15b**, 547 (1960).

MnC₄NO₅

① Tetra(carbonyl)-(nitrosyl)-manganese

Mn(CO)₄(NO)

② HMn(CO)₅
+ p-CH₃C₆H₄SO₂N(NO)CH₃ ⟶

③ Dark red crystals. Deep red liq.
[-1.5~0.0°].
Sensitive to air.
Diamagnetic. Vaper pressure about 8 mm at 25°.
IR : $\nu_{C=O}$ 2095(m), 2019(s), 1972(s) cm⁻¹; $\nu_{N=O}$ 1759(s) cm⁻¹.

④ $\xrightarrow{+\ h\nu}$ Mn₂(CO)₉(NO)₂

⑥ JACS **83**, 2593 (1961).

MnC₅BrO₅

① Bromo-penta(carbonyl)-manganese
(Br)Mn(CO)₅

② Mn₂(CO)₁₀ + Br₂ ⟶

③ Yellow crystals.
Stable at 55°/0.1 mm.
IR : $\nu_{C=O}$ 2064, 2017 cm⁻¹.

④ + CNPh $\xrightarrow{\text{T. H. F}}$ Mn(CO)Br(CNPh)₄
+ MnBr(CNPh)₅
+ CNPh $\xrightarrow{\text{EtOH}}$ Mn(CO)₃Br(CNPh)₂
+ CNPh $\xrightarrow{\text{diglyme}}$ Mn(CO)₂Br(CNPh)₃
$\xrightarrow{\text{heat}}$ [Mn(CO)₄Br]₂ + CO

⑥ CA **53**, 15838 (1959). JCS **1959**, 1501.

MnC₅ClO₅

① Chloro-penta(crbonyl)-manganese
(Cl)Mn(CO)₅

② $Mn_2(CO)_{10} + Cl_2 \xrightarrow{0°}$

③ Pale yellow crystals.
(40°/0.1 sublime)
IR : $\nu_{C=O}$ 2070, 2016 cm⁻¹.

④ $\xrightarrow{heat}$ Mn₂(CO)₈Cl₂ + 2CO
+ 2PPh₃ $\longrightarrow$ ClMn(CO)₃(PPh₃)₂
+ 2C₅H₅N $\longrightarrow$ ClMn(CO)₃(C₅H₅N)₂
+ 2NH₃ $\longrightarrow$ ClMn(CO)₃(NH₃)₂

⑥ CA **53**, 15838 (1959). JCS **1959**, 1501.
JACS **76**, 3831 (1954).

MnC₅HO₅

① Hydrido-penta(carbonyl)-manganese
(H)Mn(CO)₅

② $Mn_2(CO)_{10} + NaBH_4 \longrightarrow$
red brown powder $\xrightarrow{concd. H_3PO_4}$
$Mn_2(CO)_{10} + H_2 \longrightarrow$

③ [about −20°].
Decomp. above 100°.
Sparingly sol. in H₂O ; sol. in org.
solvents.
Dipole moment : 0.70±0.05 D.

④ + CH₂N₂ $\longrightarrow$ CH₃Mn(CO)₅ + N₂

⑥ Z. Naturf. **12 b**, 478 (1957) ; **13 b**, 339
(1958).

MnC₆O₆X

① Hexa(carbonyl)-manganese tetrachloroaluminate
[Mn(CO)₆]⁺AlCl₄⁻

② Mn(CO)₅Cl + AlCl₃ + CO $\longrightarrow$

③ Crystals. [130∼140° decomp.].
Decomp. under N with in a few days
(turn to yellow).

④ + H₂O $\longrightarrow$ Mn₂(CO)₁₀ + CO₂

⑥ Angew. **73**, 581 (1961). CA **56**, 12918
(1962). Ber. **95**, 249 (1962).

MnC₆H₃O₅

① Methyl-penta(carbonyl)-manganese
(CH₃)Mn(CO)₅

② NaMn(CO)₅ + CH₃I $\longrightarrow$
HMn(CO)₅ + CH₂N₂ $\longrightarrow$

③ Colorless crystals. (140∼145°). (30°/
vacuum, sublime). [94.5∼95°].
Vapar pressure : 3 mm at 28.8°.
IR : $\nu_{C=O}$ 2083, 2000, 1960 cm⁻¹.

④ + Br₂ $\longrightarrow$ CH₃Br + BrMn(CO)₅
+ CO $\xrightarrow[500\,psi]{20°}$ CH₃COMn(CO)₅

⑥ JOC **22**, 598 (1957). Ann. **618**, 24
(1958).

MnC₇H₃O₆

① Acetyl-penta(carbonyl)-manganese
(CH₃CO)Mn(CO)₅

② NaMn(CO)₅ + CH₃COCl $\longrightarrow$

③ White crystals. [54.5°].
Volatile.
IR : $\nu_{C=O}$ 2105, 2041, 1992 cm⁻¹.

④ $\xrightarrow[-CO]{\varDelta}$ CH₃Mn(CO)₅
+ Br₂ $\longrightarrow$ BrMn(Co)₅

⑥ JOC **22**, 598 (1957).

MnC₇H₄X

① (Ethylene)-penta(carbonyl)-manga-
nese tetrachloroaluminate
[Mn(CO)₅(C₂H₄)]⁺X⁻, X=AlCl₄

② Mn(CO)₅Cl + AlCl₃ + C₂H₄ $\longrightarrow$

③ Colorless.
Diamagnetic.
IR : $\nu_{C=C}$ 1510 cm⁻¹ ; $\nu_{C=O}$ 2165 (s), 2083
(ss), 2062(ss) cm⁻¹.

④ + H₂O $\longrightarrow$ [Mn(CO)₆]⁺

⑥ Angew. **73**, 581 (1961).

MnC₇H₅O₄

① π-Allyl-tetra(carbonyl)-manganese
(π-C₃H₅)Mn(CO)₄

② Mn₂(CO)₁₀ + Na−Hg $\longrightarrow$
NaMn(CO)₅ + CH₂=CHCH₂Cl

$\longrightarrow$ CH$_2$=CHCH$_2$Mn(CO)$_5$ $\xrightarrow{100°}$

③ Yellow crystals. (60~62°/9). [55~56°].

Relatively stable to oxygen.

IR: $\nu_{C=C}$ 1505 cm^{-1}; $\nu_{C=O}$ 2110, 2060, 2049, 1950 cm^{-1}.

⑥ CA **56**, 1480 (1962). US 2990418. JACS **83**, 1601 (1961).

MnC₇H₅O₅

① Ethyl-penta(carbonyl)-manganese (C$_2$H$_5$)Mn(CO)$_5$

② Mn$_2$(CO)$_{10}$ + Na-Hg $\longrightarrow$
NaMn(CO)$_5$ + C$_2$H$_5$J $\longrightarrow$

③ Colorless needles. [58°].
Stable in air. Sublime in high vacuum at room temp.
Vaper pressure. 3.5 mm. at 45°.

④ + Ph$_3$C·BF$_4$

$\longrightarrow \left[(CO)_5-Mn- \begin{matrix} CH_2 \\ \| \\ CH_2 \end{matrix} \right]^+$

⑥ Ann. **618**, 24 (1958). JOM **1**, 58 (1963).

MnC₇H₆O₃X

① (Benzene)-tri(carbonyl)-manganese perchlorate
[Mn(CO)$_3$(C$_6$H$_6$)]$^+$X$^-$, X=ClO$_4$

② Mn(CO)$_5$Cl + AlCl$_3$ + C$_6$H$_6$ $\longrightarrow$
yellow soln. + HClO$_4$ $\longrightarrow$

③ Pale yellow crystals. [100° decomp.].

④ + NaBH$_4$ $\longrightarrow$ C$_6$H$_7$Mn(CO)$_3$
+ LiAlH$_4$ $\longrightarrow$ C$_6$H$_7$Mn(CO)$_3$

⑥ CA **56**, 3499 (1962).   JCS **1961**, 3807.

MnC₈H₄Na₂

① Sodium tetra-ethynylmanganate
Na$_2$[Mn(C≡CH)$_4$]

② 4Na(C≡CH) + Mn(SCN)$_2$ $\longrightarrow$
Na$_2$[Mn(C≡CH)$_4$] + 2NaSCN

③ Rose.
Stable at low temp.
Dipole moment: 5.89±0.14 D.

④ + Ba(SCN)$_2$ $\longrightarrow$ Ba[Mn(C≡CH)$_4$]

+ 2NaSCN
+ 4H$^+$ $\longrightarrow$ Mn^{2+} + 4HC≡CH + 2Na$^+$

⑥ Ber. **90**, 1315 (1957).

MnC₈H₅O₃

① π-Cyclopentadienyl-tri(carbonyl)-manganese
(π-C$_5$H$_5$)Mn(CO)$_3$

② C$_5$H$_5$Na + MnCl$_2$ + CO $\longrightarrow$

③ Pale yellow crystals. [76.8~77.1°].
Stable to air and light. Decomp. by UV.
Strong camphoraceous odor. Sublime.
IR: $\nu_{C=O}$ 2023, 1939 cm^{-1}

④ + HNO$_3$ $\longrightarrow$ [(π-C$_5$H$_5$)Mn(CO)$_2$NO]$^+$
+ PPh$_3$ $\longrightarrow$ (π-C$_5$H$_5$)Mn(CO)$_2$(PPh$_3$)

⑥ JINC **1**, 163 (1955); CA **56**, 3514 (1962); **53**, 8089, 8100 (1959).

MnC₈H₅O₇

① Carboethoxy-penta(carbonyl)-manganese
(COOC$_2$H$_5$)Mn(CO)$_5$,

$$\begin{matrix} & CO & \\ OC & | & CO \\ & Mn & \\ OC & | & CO_2C_2H_5 \\ & CO & \end{matrix}$$

② [Mn(CO)$_6$]$^+$ + C$_2$H$_5$O$^-$ $\longrightarrow$
Na[Mn(CO)$_5$] + ClCO$_2$C$_2$H$_5$ $\longrightarrow$

③ [59.5°].
Diamagnetic. Octahedral configuration.
IR: $\nu_{C≡O}$ 2128, 2031, 2012, 1953 cm^{-1};
$\nu_{C=O}$ 1644 cm^{-1}.

④ + 2HCl $\longrightarrow$ [Mn(CO)$_6$]Cl·HCl
+ C$_2$H$_5$OH

⑥ Ber. **97**, 1693 (1964).

MnC₉H₇O₃

① π-Methylcyclopentadienyl-tri(carbonyl)-manganese
(π-CH$_3$C$_5$H$_4$)Mn(CO)$_3$

② (π-CH$_3$C$_5$H$_4$)$_2$Mn + CO $\longrightarrow$

③ Yellow crystals. (112°/10). [1.7
～2.0°].

④ $+ Na + CO \xrightarrow{\text{125°, 700 psi}} Mn_2(CO)_{10}$

⑥ CA **56**, 4787 (1962).   JOC **26**, 2587
(1961).   JINC **9**, 86 (1958).

MnC₉H₉O₂

① π-Cyclopentadienyl-(ethylene)
-di(carbonyl)-manganese
$(\pi\text{-}C_5H_5)Mn(CO)_2(C_2H_4)$

② $(\pi\text{-}C_5H_5)Mn(CO)_3 + C_2H_4 \longrightarrow$

③ Orange red crystals. [116～118°,
decomp.].
Decomp. by sunlight.
IR : $\nu_{C\equiv C}$ 1499 cm⁻¹ ; $\nu_{C=O}$ 2024, 1966,
1938, 1923, 1908 cm⁻¹.

⑥ CA **55**, 10415 (1961). Z. Naturf. **15 b**,
676 (1960).

MnC₁₀H₁₀

① Di-π-cyclopentadienyl-manganese
$(\pi\text{-}C_5H_5)_2Mn$

② $MnCl_2 + NaC_5H_5 \longrightarrow$

③ Brown crystals. [172～173°].
Sensitive to air and H₂O. A sharp
color change occurs at 159～160°,
becoming a very pale pink.
Paramagnetic.

④ $+ FeCl_2 \longrightarrow (\pi\text{-}C_5H_5)_2Fe + MnCl_2$
$+ 2H_2O \longrightarrow 2C_5H_6 + Mn(OH)_2$

⑥ JINC **2**, 95 (1956).

MnC₁₁F₅O₅

① Pentefluorphenyl-penta(carbonyl)
-manganese
$(C_6F_5)Mn(CO)_5$

② $Mn(CO)_5Br + C_6F_5MgBr \longrightarrow$

③ Pale yellow crystals. [121～122°].
IR : $\nu_{C=O}$ 4.68, 4.87, 5.00, 5.08 μ (KBr
pellet).
¹⁹F NMR : (in C₆H₆) *ortho* 25.87
(multiplet) *meta* 83.06 (multiplet),
para 79.16 (triplet) [J_F-F=26±2
cps] (unit: ppm).

⑥ Inorg. Chem. **3**, 300 (1964).

MnC₁₁H₅O₅

① Phenyl-penta(carbonyl)-manganese
$(C_6H_5)Mn(CO)_5$

② $Mn(CO)_5Br + C_6H_5Li \longrightarrow$

③ Colourless crystals. [52°].
Volatile.

④ $+ CO \longrightarrow C_6H_5COMn(CO)_5$

⑥ CA **57**, 12530 (1963).   JOC **22**, 598
(1957).

MnC₁₁H₇O₃

① [(1,2-Propenylene)-cyclopentadi-
enyl]-tri(carbonyl)-manganese
$(\pi\text{-}C_8H_7)Mn(CO)_3$

② $C_2H_2 + Mn_2(CO)_{10} \xrightarrow{\text{150°, 43 atm}}$
$C_2H_2 + CH_3Mn(CO)_5 \xrightarrow{\text{150°, 43 atm}}$

③ Yellow oil. (144°/18mm).
NMR : 191, 277, 382 cps from TMS
(area ratio 2 : 3 : 2).
Diamagnetic.

④ $+ H_2 \longrightarrow (C_8H_9)Mn(CO)_3$

⑥ JACS **82**, 1251, 4209 (1960).

MnC₁₁H₉O₃

① [(1,2-Trimethylene)-cyclopentadie-
nyl]-tri(cairbonyl)-manganese
$(\pi\text{-}C_8H_9)Mn(CO)_3$

② $C_8H_8 + Mn_2(CO)_{10} \longrightarrow$
$(\pi\text{-}C_8H_7)Mn(CO)_3 + H_2 \longrightarrow$

③ Yellow crystals. [34.5～35.5°].

⑥ JACS **82**, 1251, 4209 (1960).

MnC₁₂H₅O₆

① Benzoyl-penta(carbonyl)-manganese
$(C_6H_5CO)Mn(CO)_5$

② $NaMn(CO)_5 + C_6H_5COCl \longrightarrow$

③ White crystals. [94～96° decomp.].
IR : $\nu_{C=O}$ 4.7, 4.85, 4.9 μ ; $\nu_{>C=O}$ 6.7 μ

④ $\xrightarrow[-CO]{\Delta} C_6H_5Mn(CO)_5$

⑥ JOC **22**, 598 (1957).

MnC$_{12}$H$_6$K$_3$
① Potassium hexa-ethynylmanganate
   K$_3$[Mn(C≡CH)$_6$]
② 2K$_2$[Mn(C≡CH)$_4$] + 4K(C≡CH) +
   1/2O$_2$ + 2NH$_3$ ⟶
   2K$_3$[Mn(C≡CH)$_6$] + 2KNH$_2$ + H$_2$O
③ Black blue needles.
   Stable at low temp.
⑥ Ber. 90, 1315 (1957).   Z. anorg. allg.
   Chem. 293, 323 (1957).

MnC$_{12}$H$_7$O$_3$
① π-Indenyl-tri(carbonyl)-manganese
   (π-C$_9$H$_7$)Mn(CO)$_3$
② (π-C$_9$H$_7$)$_2$Mn + CO ⟶
③ [50∼51°].
④   CHCO
   + ‖   O ⟶ adduct (mp 226∼
     CHCO
     228°)
⑥ CA 52, 8535 (1958).   Z. Naturf. 16b,
   759 (1961).   US 2818417.

MnC$_{12}$H$_7$O$_5$
① Benzyl-penta(carbonyl)-manganese
   (C$_6$H$_5$CH$_2$)Mn(CO)$_5$
② Mn$_2$(CO)$_{10}$ + Na-Hg ⟶ NaMn(CO)$_5$
   + C$_6$H$_5$CH$_2$X ⟶
③ Pale yellow cryrsals. [37.5∼38.5].
   Sublime in vacuo.
⑥ CA 56, 8744 (1962) ; 51, 16168 (1957).
   JOC 22, 598 (1957).

MnC$_{12}$H$_{10}$
① Diphenyl-manganese
   (C$_6$H$_5$)$_2$Mn
② MnI$_2$ + PhLi ⟶
③ Green.
   Decomp. by acid.
   Gilman test : positive.
⑥ Angew. 71, 627 (1959).   Z. Naturf.
   15b, 547 (1960).

MnC$_{21}$H$_{15}$O$_2$
① π-Cyclopentadienyl-(diphenylacetyl-

ene)-di(carbonyl)-manganese
   (π-C$_5$H$_5$)Mn(CO)$_2$(C$_6$H$_5$C≡CC$_6$H$_5$)
② (π-C$_5$H$_5$)Mn(CO)$_3$ + C$_6$H$_5$C≡CC$_6$H$_5$ ⟶
③ Yellow crystals. [104∼105°].
   Stable in air. Sol. in org. solvents.
   The soln. rapidly decompd. with air.
⑥ CA 56, 5991 (1962).   Z. Naturf. 16b,
   402 (1961).

MnC$_{22}$H$_{17}$O$_2$
① π-Methylcyclopentadienyl-(diphenylacetylene)-di(carbonyl)-manga-
   nese
   (π-CH$_3$C$_5$H$_4$)Mn(CO)$_2$(C$_6$H$_5$C≡CC$_6$H$_5$)
② (π-CH$_3$C$_5$H$_4$)Mn(CO)$_3$ +
   C$_6$H$_5$C≡CC$_6$H$_5$ $\xrightarrow{h\nu}$
③ Red crystals. [70∼72°].
   Easily sol. in petroleum ether,
   benzene, acetone and methanol.
④ + C$_6$H$_5$C≡CC$_6$H$_5$ $\xrightarrow{h\nu}$
   (π-CH$_3$C$_5$H$_4$)Mn(CO)(C$_6$H$_5$C≡CC$_6$H$_5$)$_2$
⑥ CA 56, 14311 (1962).   Ber. 95, 455
   (1962).

Mn$_2$C$_{10}$O$_{10}$
① Deca(carbonyl)-dimanganese
   [Mn(CO$_5$)$_2$]
② Mn(OAc)$_2$ + Al(C$_2$H$_5$)$_3$ + CO $\xrightarrow[200\,atm]{80\sim100°,}$
   MnCl$_2$ + benzophenone Na + CO
   $\xrightarrow{100°,\,200\,atm}$
③ Yellow crystals. [153∼155°].
   IR : $\nu_{C=O}$ 2063, 2028, 1997 cm^{-1}.
④ + Na−Hg ⟶ NaMn(CO)$_5$
   + Cl$_2$ ⟶ Mn(CO)$_5$Cl
   + PPh$_3$ ⟶ Mn(CO)$_4$(PPh$_3$)
   + H$_2$ ⟶ 2HMn(CO)$_5$
⑥ JACS 82, 1325 (1960) ; 80, 6167 (1958).

Mn$_2$C$_{12}$N$_2$O$_4$
① Di-π-cyclopentadienyl-di (carbonyl)-
   di(nitrosyl)-dimanganese

[(π-C₅H₅)Mn(CO)(NO)]₂

② [(π-C₅H₅)Mn(CO)₂(NO)]⁺ +
   NaBH₄ ⟶

③ Violet crystals. [>200° decomp.].
   Unstable in benzene.
   IR : $\nu_{C=O}$ 1956, 1781, 1707 cm⁻¹ ; $\nu_{N=O}$
   1509 cm⁻¹

④ $\xrightarrow{+ h\nu}$ (C₅H₅)₆Mn₆(NO)₈

⑤ Equilibrium mixture of

$$\begin{array}{c} \text{C}_5\text{H}_5 \quad \text{CO} \quad\quad \text{NO} \\ \text{Mn}\!-\!\!-\!\text{Mn} \\ \text{NO} \quad\quad \text{CO} \quad \text{C}_5\text{H}_5 \end{array} \qquad \begin{array}{c} \text{C}_5\text{H}_5 \quad \text{NO} \quad\quad \text{CO} \\ \text{Mn}\!-\!\!-\!\text{Mn} \\ \text{CO} \quad\quad \text{NO} \quad \text{C}_5\text{H}_5 \end{array}$$

$$\begin{array}{c} \text{C}_5\text{H}_5 \quad \text{NO} \quad\quad \text{CO} \\ \text{Mn}\!-\!\!-\!\text{Mn} \\ \text{NO} \quad\quad \text{CO} \quad \text{C}_5\text{H}_5 \end{array}$$

⑥ JACS **85**, 2529 (1963). Inorg. Chem.
   3, 791 (1964).

Mn₂C₃₂H₂₀O₈P₂

① Di-μ-(diphenylphosphido)-octa-
   (carbonyl)-dimanganese
   [Mn(CO)₄{P(C₆H₅)₂}]₂

② Mn₂(CO)₁₀ + P₂(C₆H₄)₄ ⟶

③ Bright yellow crystals. [249~252°
   decomp.].
   IR : $\nu_{C=O}$ 2053 (s), 1992 (vs), 1957 (s)
   cm⁻¹(ClCH₂H₂Cl).

⑥ JACS **86**, 823 (1964).

【Mo】

MoC₆H₆

① Hexa(carbonyl)-molybdenum
   Mo(CO)₆

② MoCl₅ + C₆H₅MgBr $\xrightarrow{\text{CO}}$
   MoCl₅ + Na + CO
   $\xrightarrow[\text{diglyme, }-20°, 4\,\text{hr and }0\sim25°, 16\,\text{hr}]{}$ 65%
   MoCl₅ + Fe(CO)₅ $\xrightarrow{\text{CO, Et}_2\text{O, HCl}}$ 28.5%

③ Colorless solid. Sublime.

Sol. in ether and benzene.
IR : ν_{CO} 2120, 2022, 1990 cm⁻¹.

④ $\xrightarrow{\text{heat}}$ Mo + CO
   + pyridine $\xrightarrow{80\sim85°}$ [Mo(CO)₃py₃]
   + ethylenediamine
   ⟶ [Mo₂(CO)₆en₃]
   + aromatic compound
   ⟶ Mo(CO)₃Ar
   + RCOOH ⟶ [Mo(OCOR)₂]
   + NaBH₄ ⟶ [HMo(CO)₅]
   + C₅H₅Na ⟶ π-C₅H₅Mo(CO)₃Na

⑥ JACS **83**, 2057 (1961).

MoC₇C₅NO₃

① π-Cyclopentadienyl-(nitrosyl)-
   di(carbonyl)-molybdenum
   (π-C₅H₅)Mo(CO)₂(NO)

② (π-C₅H₅)Mo(CO)₃H + *N*-methyl-*N*
   -nitroso-*p*-toluenesulfonamide
   $\xrightarrow[\text{in ether}]{}$ 55%
   (π-C₅H₅)Mo(CO)₃H + NO ⟶

③ Orange crystals. (50°/vacunm sub-
   lime). [85.2~85.7°].
   Readily sol. in org. solvents without
   decomp.
   IR : $\nu_{CO, NO}$ 2015, 1940, 1910, 1678 cm⁻¹
   (CS₂).

⑥ JINC **3**, 104 (1956). Z. Naturf. **10b**,
   598 (1955).

MoC₈H₆O₃

① Hydrido-π-cyclopentadienyl-tri(carbonyl)-molybdenum
   (H)(π-C₅H₅)Mo(CO)₃

② Mo(CO)₆ + NaC₅H₅ ⟶
   π-C₅H₅Mo(CO)₃Na $\xrightarrow[\text{CH}_3\text{COOH}]{\text{THF,}}$ ~90%

③ Bright yellow crystals. (50°/0.1
   sublime). └[50~52° decomp.], [54~
   55°].
   Sol. in ether, acetone, benzene and
   petr. ether. The crystals require
   several minutes for complete de-

compn.

Decomp. at~110° in vacuum.

IR : ν_{CO} 2030, 1949, 1913 cm^{-1} (CS$_2$)

NMR : τ 4.70 (C$_5$H$_5$), 15.52 (Mo−H) (in C$_6$H$_{12}$).

④ + CCl$_4$ ⟶ (π-C$_5$H$_5$)Mo(CO)$_3$Cl

+ CH$_3$I ⟶ (π-C$_5$H$_5$)Mo(CO)$_3$I

heat
⟶ [π-C$_5$H$_5$Mo(CO)$_3$]$_2$ + H$_2$

+ CH$_2$N$_2$ ⟶ (π-C$_5$H$_5$)Mo(CO)$_3$CH$_3$

⑥ Z. anorg. allg. Chem. **282**, 47 (1955). JINC **3**, 104 (1956). Inorg. Syn. hes **7**, 136 (1963).

MoC₉H₆O₃

① Tri(carbonyl)-(benzene)-molybdenum

Mo(CO)$_3$(C$_6$H$_6$)

② C$_6$H$_6$ + Mo(CO)$_6$ $\xrightarrow{200°, 12 hr.}$ 6%

③ Green-yellow crystals. (70~100°/ vacuum. sublime). [120~125° decomp].

Less stable than chromium analogue.

Diamagnetic.

IR : $\nu_{C=O}$ 1991, 1919 cm^{-1}.

⑥ Z. Naturf. **13 b**, 458 (1958). Ber. **91**, 2763 (1958).

MoC₉H₈InO₃

① π-1-Methylpyridine-tri(carbonyl)-molybdenum iodide

② [C$_5$H$_5$NCH$_3$]I + Mo(CO)$_6$ $\xrightarrow{THF, reflux}$

③ Yellow. [120° decomp.].

Sol. in ethanol and H$_2$O ; sparingly sol. in non-polar solvents.

⑥ Proc. Chem. Soc. **1959**, 61.

MoC₉H₈O₃

① Methyl-π-cyclopentadienyl-tri(carbonyl)-molybdenum

(CH$_3$)(π-C$_5$H$_5$)Mo(CO)$_3$

② (π-C$_5$H$_5$)Mo(CO)$_3$Na + CH$_3$I ⟶ 85%

(π-C$_5$H$_5$)Mo(CO)$_3$H + CH$_2$N$_2$

$\xrightarrow{ether, 0°, 24 hr.}$ 4%

③ Yellow crystals. (25~50°/vacuum, sublime). [124° decomp].

Readily sol. in petr. ether and indeed in all common org. solvents. Slowly decomp. in org. solvents in air.

Diamagnetic.

IR : ν_{CO} 2020, 1937 cm^{-1}.

UV : 3.150 Å (ε 1.960)

NMR : τ 4.73 (C$_5$H$_5$), 9.66 (CH$_3$) (in CCl$_4$).

④ + I$_2$ ⟶ (π-C$_5$H$_5$)Mo(CO)$_3$I + CH$_3$I

⑥ JINC **3**, 104 (1956).

MoC₁₀H₇O₃X

① π-Tropenium-tri(carbonyl)-molybdenum fluoroborate

[(π-C$_7$H$_7$)Mo(CO)$_3$]X, X=BF$_4$

② Mo(CO)$_3$(C$_7$H$_8$) + Ph$_3$CBF$_4$

⟶ 98~100%

③ Light orange needles. [>270° decomp.].

Insol. in H$_2$O and pentane ; slightly sol. in CH$_2$Cl$_2$; very sol. in acetone, acetonitril and 96% H$_2$SO$_4$.

Stable in air, but slowly decomp. in org. solvents.

IR : ν_{CO} 2076, 2007, 1959 cm^{-1} (KBr).

UV : λ_{max} 238 (ε 14700), 299 (ε 29000), 380 m μ (ε 1300).

NMR : Single proton resonance band.

⑥ JACS **80**, 5570 (1958).

MoC₁₀H₈O₃

① Tri(carbonyl)-(cycloheptatriene)-molybdenum

Mo(CO)₃(C₇H₈),

② Mo(CO)₆ + cycloheptatriene

    light pter., 100~120°, 7 hr
→

③ Orange-red crystals. Sublime. [100.5
~101.5°].

Sol. in light petr., CHCl₃, C₆H₆, and
many other org. solvents. The soiid
may be stored indefinitely; the
solution decomp. in air and light.
The decomp. is particularly rapid
in acetone or alc.

IR: ν_{CO} 2000, 1929, 1895 cm⁻¹.

UV: λ_{max} 252 (ε=12300), 324 (ε=7450),
383 (ε=4200), 482 m μ (ε=600).

Dipole moment: 6.12 D.

④ + Ph₃P ⟶ Mo(CO)₃(PPh₃)₃
+ Ph₃CBF₄ ⟶ tricarbonyl-π-tropi-
nium-molybdenum fluoroborate

⑥ JCS **1958**, 4559. Z. Naturf. **14 b**, 347
(1959).

MoC₁₀H₉O₃X

① π-Cyclopentadienyl-tri(carbonyl)
-(ethylene)-molydenum hexa-fluorophosphate
[(π-C₅H₅)Mo(CO)₃(C₂H₄)]X, X=PF₆

② π-C₅H₅Mo(CO)₃Cl + C₂H₄

    AlBr₃, benzene, 20°, 16 hr., NH₄PF₆
→ 24%

③ Light yellow powder. [~104°
decomp.].

Slightly light sensitive.

IR: ν_{CO} 2105, 2053, 2006 cm⁻¹;
$\nu_{C=C}$ 1511 cm⁻¹.

⑥ Ber. **94**, 1200 (1961).

MoC₁₀H₁₂

① Dihydrido-di-π-cyclopentadienyl
-molybdenum

(H)₂(π-C₅H₅)₂Mo

② C₅H₅Na + MoCl₅

    THF, NaBH₄
→ ~50%

③ Yellow crystals. (80~130° vacuum
sublime). [183~185°].

Sensitive to air. Sparingly sol. in
light petroleum, moderately sol. in
benzene. React. with halogenated
solvents. Diamagnetic.

IR: ν_{Mo-H} 1847 cm⁻¹.

NMR: τ 18.76 (Mo−H), τ 5.64 (triplet,
J=0.96, C₅H₅).

Dipole moment: 1.96±0.04 D (25°
benzene).

④ + H⁺ ⟶ [(π-C₅H₅)₂MoH₃]⁺

⑥ Z. Naturf. **14 b**, 738 (1959); **15 b**, 135
(1960). JCS **1961**, 4854.

MoC₁₀H₁₂O₂

① Di(carbonyl)-di-(butadiene)-moly-
denum
Mo(CO)₂(C₄H₆)₂

② Mo(CO)₆ + CH₂=CHCH=CH₂

    n-heptane, UV, 5 hr
→ 3~6%

[C₆H₃(CH₃)₃]MO(CO)₃ +
CH₂=CHCH=CH₂

    n-pentane, UV, 8hr
→ 11~15%

③ Amber yellow. (40~45°/vacuum,
sublime). [110° decomp.].

IR(nujol): ν_{CO} 1980, 1938 cm⁻¹.

④ decomp. → Mo(CO)₆

⑥ Ber. **93**, 3006 (1960).

MoC₁₁H₁₀O₃

① σ-Allyl-π-cyclopentadienyl-tri(carbonyl)-molyebdenum
(π-C₅H₅)(σ-C₃H₅)Mo(CO)₃

② Na[(π-C₅H₅)Mo(CO)₃] + CH₂=CH

    THF, 1.5 hr
−CH₂Cl → 40%

③ Pale yellow oil. (40°/10⁻³). [~−5°].

Thermally unstable; readily oxidized
in air. Sol. in common org. solvents.
Characteristic camphoraceous odour.

IR : ν_{CO} 2021, 1911, 1856 cm⁻¹.

NMR : τ 7.73(doublet, J=8cps, CH₂),
6.5 (complex, =CH₂), 4.89 (singlet
π-C₅H₅), 4.0 (complex, =CH−).

④ $\xrightarrow{\text{UV}}$

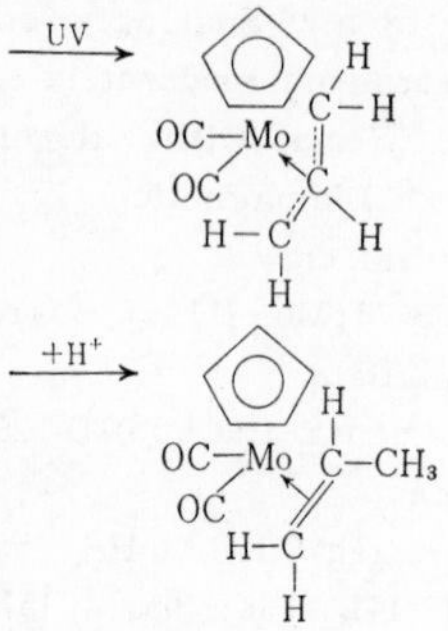

$\xrightarrow{+H^+}$

$\xrightarrow{\text{heat}}$ [(π-C₅H₅)Mo(CO)₃]₂

⑥ JCS **1963**, 889.

MoC₁₁H₁₀O₃

① Tri(carbonyl)-(cycloctatriene)-
  molybdenum

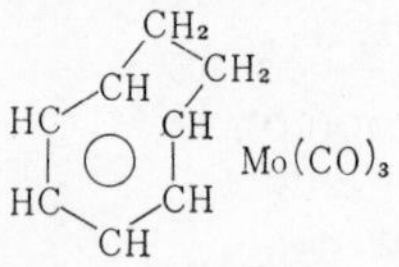

② Mo(CO)₆ + cyclooctatriene
  $\xrightarrow[\text{145°, 6hr}]{}$ 68.7%

③ Orange red. [115~118° decomp.].
  Sensitive to air and light. Sol. in
  petr. ether, benzene, chloroform,
  ether and alcohol. Diamagnetic.
  IR : ν_{CO} 2000, 1936, 1912 cm⁻¹ (in cyclohexane).
  Dipole moment : 4.15 D (25°, cyclohexane)

④ + mesitylene
  $\xrightarrow[\text{130°, 4hr}]{}$ Mo(CO)₃[C₆H₃(CH₃)₃] (88%)

⑥ Ber. **92**, 2645 (1959).

MoC₁₁H₈O₄

① Tetra(carbonyl)-(bicyclohepta-

diene)-molybdenum

Mo(C₇H₈)(CO)₄,

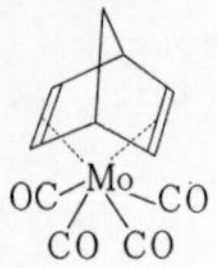

② Mo(CO)₆ + C₇H₈ ⟶

③ Pale yellow plates. [76~77°]
  Stable in air.
  IR : ν_{CO} 4.93, 5.05~5.2, 5.35 μ.

⑥ JACS **81**, 1266 (1959).

MoC₁₁H₁₁

① π-Cyclopentadienyl-(benzene)-
  molybdenum
  (π-C₅H₅)Mo(C₆H₆)

② [(π-C₅H₅)Mo(CO)(benzene)]⁺PF₆⁻
  $\xrightarrow[\text{THF, LiAlH₄, 0°}]{}$

③ Red crystals. (50°/vacuum, sublime).
  [216~218°].
  Sol. in org. solvents.
  Air sensitive.
  Paramagnetic, 1.68 BM.
  IR : "C₅H₅" 1404, 1096, 996, 814, 791 cm⁻¹;
  "C₆H₆" 1404, 977, 950, 838, 761 cm⁻¹.

⑥ Angew. **76**, 98 (1964).

MoC₁₂H₉O₃M₃

① Potassium tri(propionyl)-tri(carbonyl)molybdate
  M₃[(CH₃−C≡C)₃Mo(CO)₃], M=K

② Mo(CO)₃(NH₃)₃ + KC≡CCH₃
  $\xrightarrow[\text{liq. NH₃}]{}$ ~50%

③ Yellow green.
  Insol. in C₂H₅OH, acetone; slightly
  sol. in CH₃OH. Decomp. with H₂O
  or dil. mineral acid. Not explosive
  but air and moisture senstive and
  pyrophoric.
  IR : $\nu_{C≡C}$ 2062 cm⁻¹; ν_{CO} 1875, 1730~
  1600 cm⁻¹.

⑥ Ber. **97**, 207 (1964).

MoC$_{12}$H$_{12}$

① Di(benzene)-molybdenum

Mo(C$_6$H$_6$)$_2$,   Mo

② MoCl$_5$ + Al + C$_6$H$_6$ $\xrightarrow{\text{AlCl}_3, 120°, 15\,\text{hr}}$ 27%

③ Green crystals. (100~105° vacuum, sublime). [~115° decomp.].
   d 1.65.
   Very unstable in air; less stable than di(benzene)-chromium.
   Diamagnetic.
   IR: 362, 424, 773, 811, 877, 962, 1003, 1030, 1107, 1131, 1421, 2916, 3030 cm^{-1}.
   UV: λ_{max} 435, 389 mμ.
   Dipole moment: 0 D.
⑥ Ber. **89**, 1805 (1956); **93**, 2065 (1960).

MoC$_{12}$H$_{11}$OX

① π-Cyclopentadienyl-(carbonyl)-(benzene)-molybdenum hexa-fluorophosphate
   [(π-C$_5$H$_5$)Mo(C$_6$H$_6$)(CO)]X, X=PF$_6$

② (π-C$_5$H$_5$)Mo(CO)$_3$Cl + C$_6$H$_6$
   $\xrightarrow{\text{AlCl}_3, \text{benzene}, \text{NH}_4\text{PF}_6}$ 19.1%

③ Deep red.
   Very sensitive to air and light.
   IR: ν_{CO} 2013 cm^{-1}; "C$_6$H$_6$" 3126, 1445, 1136, 967 cm^{-1}; "C$_5$H$_5$" 3126, 3124, 1424, 1408, 1107, 1071, 1023, 993 cm^{-1}.
   NMR: τ 4.92 and 4.64 (5 : 6).
⑥ Z. Naturf. **18 b**, 504 (1964).

MoC$_{14}$H$_{12}$O$_2$

① π-Cyclopentadienyl-π-cycloheptatrienyl-di(carbonyl)-molybdenum

(π-C$_5$H$_5$)(π-C$_7$H$_7$)Mo(CO)$_2$, OC—Mo—CO

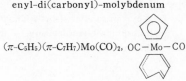

② π-(C$_7$H$_7$)Mo(CO)$_2$I + NaC$_5$H$_5$
   $\xrightarrow[\text{r. t., 18hr}]{}$ ~10%

③ Orange crystals. [111~112°].
   IR: ν_{CO} 1933, 1893 cm^{-1}.
   UV: λ_{max} 306 mμ (ϵ 11600),   758 mμ (ϵ 315).
   NMR: τ 4.93 (C$_7$H$_7$), 5.21 (C$_5$H$_5$).
⑥ Tetrahedron letters 1137 (1963).
   Inorg. Chem. **3**, 785 (1963).

MoC$_{23}$H$_{15}$O$_5$P

① Penta(carbonyl)-tri(phenylphosphine)-molybdenum
   Mo(CO)$_5$[P(C$_6$H$_5$)$_3$]

② Mo(CO)$_6$ + Ph$_3$P $\xrightarrow{\text{diglyme, 160~165°}}$
   91%(crude), 52%(pure).

③ White crystals. [138~139°].
   IR: ν_{CO} 2074, 1988, 1946 cm^{-1} (CCl$_4$).
⑥ JACS **83**, 3200 (1961).

MoC$_{26}$H$_{19}$O$_3$P

① Triphenylphosphoniumcyclopentadienyl-tri(carbonyl)-molybdenum

Ph$_3$P$^+$—⬡   Mo(CO)$_3$

② Ph$_3$P$^+$—C$_5$H$_4^-$ + Mo(CO)$_6$
   $\xrightarrow{\text{CH}_3\text{O}\cdot\text{CH}_2\text{CH}_2\text{O}\cdot\text{CH}_3 \text{ boil}}$ ~60%

③ Yellow crystals.
   Readily sol. in CHCl$_3$; slightly sol. in C$_6$H$_6$; insol. in H$_2$O.
⑥ Chem. & Ind. **1959**, 1067.

MoC$_{57}$H$_{45}$O$_3$P$_3$

① Tri(carbonyl)-tris-(triphenylphosphine)-molybdenum
   Mo(CO)$_3$[P(C$_6$H$_5$)$_3$]$_3$

② C$_7$H$_8$Mo(CO)$_3$ + 3 PPh$_3$ $\xrightarrow{\text{benzene, reflux.}}$

③ Fine yellow crystals. [160° decomp.].
   IR: ν_{CO} 1934, 1835 cm^{-1}.

⑥ JCS **1959**, 2323.

Mo₂C₁₆H₈O₆

① Hexa(carbonyl)-(azulene)-dimolyb-
denum
$Mo_2(CO)_6(C_{10}H_8)$

② $Mo(CO)_6$ + azulene
$\xrightarrow{\text{high boiling petroleum, reflux}}$

③ Black crystals. [>150° decomp.].
Sparingly sol. in common org.
solvents. Somewhat sol. in glacial
acetic acid and CHCl₃.
Parmagnetic. 1.22 BM per molybde-
nun atom.
IR : ν_{CO} 2033, 1960 cm⁻¹.

⑥ Chem. & Ind. **1958**, 1025.

Mo₂C₁₆H₁₀O₃

① Di-π-cyclopentadienyl-hexa(carbonyl)-dimolyblbdenum
$[(\pi\text{-}C_5H_5)Mo(CO)_3]_2$

② $C_5H_5Na + Mo(CO)_6 \longrightarrow$
$Na[(\pi\text{-}C_5H_5)Mo(CO)_3]_2 \xrightarrow{CH_3COOH}$
$H[(\pi\text{-}C_5H_5)Mo(CO)_3] \xrightarrow{THF, O_2} 50\%$
$Mo(CO)_6 + C_5H_6 \xrightarrow{240°} \sim 30\%$
$Mo(CO)_6$ + dicyclopentadine $\longrightarrow 85\%$

③ Dark purple-red crystals. (150~160°/
0.1 sublime), [215~217° decomp]
Readily sol. in CCl₄, C₂H₅OH, CS₂ and
C₆H₆ ; sparingly sol. in ligroin.
Stable in air if pure.
Diamagentic.
IR : ν_{CO} 1960, 1916 cm⁻¹.

⑥ JINC **3**, 104 (1956). Z. anorg. allg.
Chem **282**, 47 (1955). JACS **76**, 209
(1954). Inorg. Syn. **7**, 107 (1963).

Mo₂C₁₆H₁₆O₄S₂

① Di-π-cyclopentadienyl-di-μ-methyl-
sulfido-tetra(carbonyl)-dimoly-
bdenum

② $(\pi\text{-}C_5H_5)Mo(CO)_3H + CH_3SSCH_3$
$\xrightarrow{\text{pentane, 3 days}} 95\%$

③ Black crystals. [130° decomp.].
Stable in air.
IR : ν_{CO} 1965, 1947, 1877, 1869, 1852 cm⁻¹.
NMR : τ 4.53, 4.70, 8.13, 8.18.

⑥ JCS **1963**, 720.

Mo₂C₁₆H₁₇O₄P

① Hydrido-di-π-cyclopentadienyl-μ-di-
methylphosphido-tetra(carbonyl)-
dimolyblbdnem

② $(\pi\text{-}C_5H_5)Mo(CO)_3Na$
$+ (CH_3)_2PCl \longrightarrow$

③ Orange red rods. [215°].
IR : ν_{CO} 1935, 1872 cm⁻¹ (in CS₂) ;
2018, 1930, 1859 cm⁻¹ (in hydrocarbon
mull).
NMR : τ 5.31 (doublet, $J_{HP} \approx 0.3$ cps,
C₅H₅), 8.38 (double doublet, J=9.9
and 0.4 cps, CH₃), 21.73 (doublet, J_{HP}
=36.6 cps, Mo−H).

⑥ Inorg. Chem. **2**, 1031 (1963).

Mo₂C₁₈H₂₂O₄P₂

① Di-π-cyclopentadienyl-bis-μ-dimeth-
ylphosphido-tetra(carbonyl)-dimo-
lyblbdenum

② $[\pi\text{-}C_5H_5Mo(CO)_3]_2 + (CH_3)_4P_2$

$\xrightarrow[\text{toluene, reflux, 16 hr.}]{}$ 31%

③ Orange plates. [210° decomp.].

IR : ν_{CO} 1941, 1929, 1860 cm⁻¹(in CS₂) ;
1938, 1912, 1856, 1844 (in halocarbon
mull).

NMR : τ 4.73 ($J_{HP}=0.8$ cps, C₅H₅), 8.33
($J_{HP}=4.5$ cps, CH₃) (in CDCl₃).

⑥ Inorg. Chem. 2, 1031 (1963).

【Ni】

NiC₄O₄

① Tetra(carbonyl)-nickel
Ni(CO)₄

② Ni + CO ⟶
NiSO₄ + Na₂S₂O₄ + NH₃ + H₂O + CO
⟶85~90%

NiS + CO + NaOH $\xrightarrow{50\sim60°,\ 60\,hr}$ 75%

③ Colorless liq. (42.3°/754). [−25°].
n_D 1.4584 (0°). d 1.356 (0°).

Slowly oxidized in air. Mixture with
air is explosive. Toxic with musty
smell. Sol. in benzene, CHCl₃, Et₂O
and EtOH.

IR : ν_{CO} 2050, 2043 cm⁻¹.

④ $\xrightarrow{heat}$ Ni + C + CO₂

+ O₂ ⟶ NiO + CO₂

+ RNC ⟶ Ni(CO)(CNR)₃,
Ni(CNR)₄

+ Ph₃P ⟶ Ni(CO)₃PPh₃,
Ni(CO)₂(PPh₃)₂

+ phenanthroline
⟶ (phenanthroline)Ni(CO)₂

⑤ Preparation of pure nickel metal.
Catalyst for polymerization of

acetylene.

⑥ Z. anorg. allg. Chem. **269**, 292 (1952).
Inorg. Syn. **2**, 234 (1964).

NiC₄H₁₄N₄

① Di-ethynyl-tetra(amine)-nickel
(HC≡C)₂Ni(NH₃)₄

② Na₂Ni(−C≡CH)₄ + Ni(SCN)₂·6 NH₃

$\xrightarrow{NH_3}$ 80~90%

③ Colorless.

Stable only in NH₃. It loses ammonia in nitrogen atmosphere and
gives very explosive gray product.

⑥ Ber. **90**, 2678 (1957).

NiC₅H₅NO

① π-Cyclopentadienyl-(nitrosyl)-nickel
(π-C₅H₅)Ni(NO)

② (π-C₅H₅)₂Ni + NO

$\xrightarrow[\text{petr. ether, r. t.}]{}$ 45%

③ Dark red oil. (47~48°/15, 144~145°
/715). [−41°].

Miscible with org. solvents. Air
stable.

Diamagnetic.

IR : ν_{NO} 1820 cm⁻¹.

⑥ JINC **1**, 165 (1955).   Z. Naturf. **10b**,
598 (1955).

NiC₆H₅IO

① π-Cyclopentadienyl-iodo-(carbonyl)
-nickel
(π-C₅H₅)(I)Ni(CO)

② $[\pi\text{-}C_5H_5Ni(CO)]_2 + I_2$ ⟶ 28%

③ Black-violett crystals. [>20° decomp.].

Slightly sol. in most org. solvents.

④ + Ph₃P ⟶ π-C₅H₅Ni(PPh₃)I

⑥ Ber. **91**, 1725 (1958).

NiC₆H₆N₂

① Di(acrylonitril)-nickel
Ni(CH₂=CH−CN)₂,

$$\begin{array}{c} C\equiv N \\ H_2C \diagdown CH \\ Ni \\ HC \diagdown CH_2 \\ N\equiv C \end{array}$$

② $Ni(CO)_4 + CH_2=CH-CN \xrightarrow{boil}$

③ Red crystalline solid. [~100° decomp.].
Sparingly sol. in most org. solvents.
Pyrophoric in air.
IR: ν_{CN} 2220 cm^{-1}.

④ $\xrightarrow{heat}$ $CH_2=CH-CN + Ni$
$+ Ph_3P \longrightarrow Ni(CH_2=CH-CN)_2PPh_3$
$+ 2Ph_3P \longrightarrow Ni(CH_2=CH-CN)_2\cdot$
$2PPh_3$

$+ PhC\equiv CPh \longrightarrow NC-\underset{Ph\ Ph}{\overset{Ph}{\bigcirc}}-Ph$

⑤ Catalyst of the preparation of cyclooctatetraene from acetylene and of heptatrienenitril from acetylene and acrylonitril.

⑥ JACS **81**, 5310 (1959) ; **82**, 1008 (1960).

NiC₆H₁₀

① Di-π-allyl-nickel
$(\pi\text{-}C_3H_5)_2Ni$

② $NiBr_2 + CH_2=CH-CH_2-Cl \xrightarrow{ether,-10°}$

③ Yellow-orange crystals. [+1°].
Readily sol. in hydrocarbon.
Flamable in air.

④ $+ H_2 \longrightarrow CH_3CH_2CH_3 + Ni$
$+ CO \longrightarrow Ni(CO)_4$
$+ CH_2=CHCH_2CH_2CH=CH_2$
$+ PEt_3 \longrightarrow Ni(PEt_3)_4$
$+ CH_2=CHCH_2CH_2CH=CH_2$

⑤ Catalyst of the formation of cyclododecatriene from butadiene.

⑥ Angew. **73**, 756 (1961).

NiC₇H₅F₃O

① Trifluoromethyl-π-cyclopentadienyl-(carbonyl)-nickel
$(\pi\text{-}C_5H_5)(CF_3)Ni(CO)$

② $[\pi\text{-}C_5H_5Ni(CO)]_2 + CF_3I \longrightarrow$ 18%

③ Red liq.
Air stable.
IR: ν_{CO} 2078, 2032 cm^{-1}; "other bands" 3125, 1400, 1351, 1069, 1024, 976, 903, 868, 835, 799, 704 cm^{-1}.
NMR: τ 4.64 (relative to hexamethylsiloxane, C_5H_5); δ −5.6 ppm (relative to CCl₃F, CF₃).

⑥ JCS **1964**, 1752. '

NiC₈H₄M₂

① Potassium tetraethynyl-nickelate
$M_2[(HC\equiv C)_4Ni]$, $M=K$

② $Ni(NH_3)_6(SCN)_2 + KC\equiv CH \xrightarrow{liq.\ NH_3}$
$[Ni(CN)_4]K_2 + KC\equiv CH \xrightarrow{liq.\ NH_3}$

③ Yellow crystalline solid.
Explosive.
Diamagnetic.

④ $+ K \xrightarrow{liq.\ NH_3} [(HC\equiv C)_4Ni]K_4$
$+ CN^- + H_2O \longrightarrow [Ni(CN)_4]^{2-}$
$+ C_2H_2 + OH^-$

⑥ Z. anorg. allg. Chem. **279**, 146 (1955) ; **295**, 227 (1958).

NiC₈H₅F₅O

① Pentafluoromethyl-π-cyclopentadienyl-(carbonyl)-nickel
$(C_2F_5)(\pi\text{-}C_5H_5)Ni(CO)$

② $[\pi\text{-}C_5H_5Ni(CO)]_2 + C_2F_5I$
$\xrightarrow{r.\ t.,\ 1hr.}$ 18%

③ Red purple liq.
Air stable.
IR: ν_{CO} 2081, 2034 cm^{-1}; "other bands" 3125, 1600, 1517, 1449, 1401, 1353, 1295, 1272, 1178, 1047, 1026, 976, 910, 834, 801, 729 cm^{-1}.

¹H−NMR: τ 4.53 (relative to hexa-methyl-siloxane, C₅H₅).

¹⁹F−NMR: δ 83.5 ppm (relative to CCl₃F, CF₃).

δ 73.0 ppm (relative to CCl₃F, CF₂).

④ + Ph₃P $\xrightarrow{\text{r.t., 3hr.}}$

(C₂F₅)(π-C₅H₅)Ni(PPh₃) (76%)

⑥ JCS 1964, 1752.

NiC₈H₁₀

① π-Cyclopentadienyl-π-allyl-nickel

(π-C₃H₅)(π-C₅H₅)Ni,

② (π-C₅H₅)₂Ni + CH₂=CH−CH₂MgCl

$\xrightarrow[\text{THF,0°, 2 days}]{}$ ~50%

(π-C₃H₅NiBr)₂ + NaC₅H₅ ⟶ 33%

③ Red violet liq. (~73~75°/12, ~50°/0.45). [7~9°].

Very sol. in common org. solvents.

Very sensitive to air. Characteristic unpleasant smell.

Diamagnetic.

IR: "C₅H₅" 1401, 1124, 999, 845, 789 cm⁻¹.

UV: λ_{max} 550 (ε=112), 378 (ε=8600), 315 (ε=1960), 272 (ε=18600), 240~250 mμ (ε=8600).

NMR: τ 4.21 (C₅H₅); τ 6.30 (central H of π-allyl); τ 6.88, 6.94 (J=3cps); τ 8.02, 8.23 (J=11cps).

Dipole moment: 0.78±0.06D(25°)

⑥ JACS 83, 1601 (1961). Ber. 94, 2409 (1961).

NiC₈H₁₂Cl₂

① Tetramethylcyclobutadiene-nickel -dichloride

Ni[(CH₃)₄C₄]Cl₂.

②

③ Red violet powder. [>210°/12 decomp.].

Slightly sol. in most org. solvents except methylene chloride and chloroform. Dissolves in H₂O giving blood-red solution.

Thermally quite stable.

Diamagnetic.

NMR: Single proton resonance.

④ + NaNO₃ $\xrightarrow{H_2O}$

⑥ Ann. 623, 1 (1959). Ber. 94, 2038 (1961). Helv. Chim. Acta 45, 647 (1962).

NiC₁₀H₁₀

① Di-π-cyclopentadienyl-nickel (π-C₅H₅)₂Ni

② Ni(NH₃)₆(SCN)₂ + KC₅H₅ $\xrightarrow{NH_3}$

Ni(acac)₂ + C₅H₅MgBr ⟶

Ni(NH₃)₆Cl₂ + C₅H₅Na $\xrightarrow{THF}$ 90~96%

③ Dark green crystals. (80~90°/vacuum, sublime). [173~174°].

Slowly decomp. in air.

Paramagnetic, μ_{eff} 2.88 BM.

Dipole moment: 0±0.33 D (25° benzene).

④ $\xrightarrow{\text{oxidation}}$ (π-C₅H₅)₂Ni⁺

+ NO ⟶ π-C₅H₅NiNO

+ Ni(PPh₃)₂Cl₂

⟶ π-C₅H₅Ni(PPh₃)Cl

$$+ \text{H}_2 \xrightarrow{\text{Na}-\text{Hg, EtOH}} (\pi\text{-C}_5\text{H}_5)\text{Ni}(\pi\text{-C}_5\text{H}_7)$$

⑥ Z. Naturf. **8b**, 217 (1953).   JACS **57**,
1011 (1953).   Ber. **95**, 3084 (1962).

NiC₁₀H₁₂

① π-Cyclopentadienyl-π-cyclopentenyl
-nickel
$(\pi\text{-C}_5\text{H}_5)(\pi\text{-C}_5\text{H}_7)\text{Ni}$,

② $\text{Ni(CO)}_4 + \text{C}_5\text{H}_6 \xrightarrow{\;n\text{-hexane}\;} 18\%$

$(\pi\text{-C}_5\text{H}_5)_2\text{Ni} \xrightarrow{\;\text{EtOH, Na}-\text{Hg}\;}$

③ Deep red crystalline solid. Volatile.
[43~44.5°].
Easily sol. in benzene, ether, hexane,
dioxane, CCl₄, CS₂, THF, toluene
and acetonitril. Sensitive to air.
Decomp. at ~160°.
Diamagnetic.
IR : 2851, 2890, 2944, 3052, 3077, 3111,
887, 911, 1107 cm⁻¹.
UV : λ_{max} 570 mμ.
NMR : τ=4.72, 4.87, 6.04, 8.93 (5 : 1 :
2 : 4) (in benzene).
Dipole moment : 1.16±0.07 D (25°,
hexane).

⑥ Ber. **92**, 1423 (1959) ; **95**, 695 (1962).

NiC₁₁H₂₀IP

① π-Cyclopentadienyl-iodo-(triethylphosphine)-nickel
$(\pi\text{-C}_5\text{H}_5)(\text{I})\text{Ni}[\text{P}(\text{C}_2\text{H}_5)_3]$

② $\pi\text{-C}_5\text{H}_5\text{Ni(CO)I} + \text{PEt}_3$

$\xrightarrow{\;\text{benzene, }-15°,\text{ 1hr.}\;} 88\%$

③ Red crystals [59°].
Insol. in n-hexane ; sol. in benzene.
Air stable.

⑥ JINC **24**, 1690 (1962).

NiC₁₂H₁₀F₄

①

② $(\pi\text{-C}_5\text{H}_5)_2\text{Ni} + \text{F}_2\text{C}=\text{CF}_2$

$\xrightarrow{\;\text{THF, 75}\sim80°,\text{ 16hr.}\;} 5.7\%$

③ Red crystals. (50°/vacuum, sublime).
[93~94°].
Moderately air stable.
¹H−NMR : (relative to hexamethyldisiloxane) τ 4.48 (triplet, J=~5
cps), 4.75 (C₅H₅), 6.07 (multiplet),
7.33 (multiplet).
¹⁹F−NMR : δ 116.3 ppm (relative to
CCl₃F).

⑥ JACS **84**, 498 (1962).

NiC₁₂H₁₈

①

② t,t,t-cyclododecatriene + Ni(acac)₂
+ AlR₃

$\xrightarrow{\;-40°,\text{C}_4\text{H}_6\;}$

③ Red brown oil.

④ $+ \text{H}_2 \xrightarrow{\;\text{heat}\;}$ cyclododecane + Ni

$+ \text{H}_2 \xrightarrow{\;20°\;}$ n-dodecane + Ni

$+ \text{CO} \xrightarrow{\;20°\;} \text{Ni(CO)}_4$
+ cyclododecatriene

$+ \text{Ph}_3\text{P} \longrightarrow$ PPh₃

⑤ Catalyst of the polymerization of
butadiene to cyclododecatriene.

⑥ Angew. **73**, 755 (1961).

NiC₁₂H₁₆As₂O₂

① (*o*-Phenylene bis-dimethylarsine)-
di(carbonyl)-nickel
Ni(CO)₂[C₆H₄As₂(CH₃)₄],

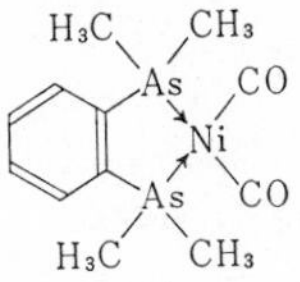

H₃C   CH₃
  As   CO
       Ni
  As   CO
H₃C   CH₃

② Ni(CO)₄ + Diarsine

$\xrightarrow{\text{benzene-light petroleum, reflux}}$

③ Large colorless crystals. [125°].
Readily sol. in non-hydroxylic solvents ; moderately sol. in alc. ;
insol. in H₂O.
Monomeric in freezing benzene. Diamagnetic.
IR : ν_{CO} 1996, 1940 cm⁻¹.

④ + I₂ $\xrightarrow{\text{benzene}}$ Ni(diarsine)I₂

+ Br₂ $\xrightarrow{\text{benzene}}$ Ni(diarsine)Br₂

⑥ JCS **1952**, 2906.

NiC₁₆H₁₆O₄

① π-Cyclopentadienyl-2, 3-di-methoxy-
carbonyl-2π, 5-norbornadienyl-
nickel

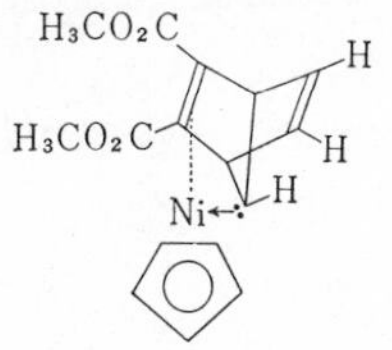

H₃CO₂C
          H
H₃CO₂C
          H
     Ni   H

② (π-C₅H₅)₂Ni + CH₃O₂CC≡CCO₂CH₃

$\xrightarrow[\text{THF, r. t., 65 hr.}]{}$ 68%

③ Orange red solid. [84°].
Stable in air.
Diamagnetic.

NMR : τ 3.45, 4.76, 6.3, 7.82 (1 : 5 :
8 : 1).

④ + H₂ $\xrightarrow{\text{EtOH, Pt catalyst}}$ Ni +
cyclohexane + *endo-cis*-2, 3
-norbornane-dicarboxylate

⑥ JACS **82**, 6193 (1960).   Inorg. Chem.
2, 713 (1963).

NiC₁₆H₂₂N₄

① Di-phenylethynyl-tetra(amine)
-nickel
[(C₆H₅)C≡C]₂Ni(NH₃)₄

② Na₂Ni(−C≡CPh)₄ + Ni(NH₃)₆(SCN)₂

$\xrightarrow{\text{NH}_3}$ 50~80%

Ni(CN)₂ + KC≡CPh $\xrightarrow{\text{NH}_3}$

③ Yellow.
Sol. in benzene and toluene.
Paramagnetic.

④ $\xrightarrow{\text{vacuum}}$ {(PhC≡C)₂Ni}ₙ

+ CO $\longrightarrow$ Ni(CO)₄

⑥ Ber. **90**, 2678 (1957)

NiC₁₆H₂₄

① Di(cyclooctadiene-1, 5)-nickel

Ni(C₈H₁₂)₂,

② Cyclooctadiene-1, 5 + AlR₃ +
Ni(acac)₂ $\longrightarrow$

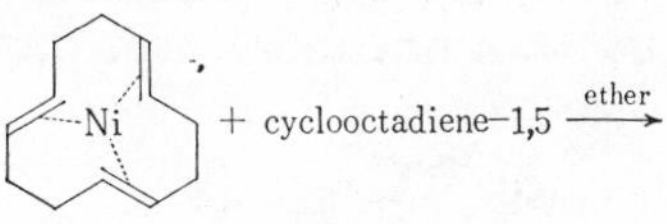

Ni   + cyclooctadiene–1,5 $\xrightarrow{\text{ether}}$

③ Yellow crystals.

④ H₂ $\longrightarrow$ cyclooctane + Ni
+ CO $\longrightarrow$ cyclooctadiene-1, 5
+ Ni(CO)₄

⑥ Angew. **72**, 581 (1960).

NiC₁₆H₃₂P₂

① Diethynyl-bis(triethylphosphine)
   -nickel
   trans-(CH≡C)₂Ni[P(C₂H₅)₃]₂

② *trans*-Ni(PEt₃)₂Cl₂ $\xrightarrow{\text{NH}_3}$ 39%

③ Pale yellow needles. [36~36.5°].
   IR : 3229 cm⁻¹ (H−C≡) ; 1923 cm⁻¹
   (C≡C) (in nujol).

⑥ Chem. & Ind. **1959**, 675.   JCS **1960**,
   1718.

NiC₁₇H₁₄N₂

① π-Cyclopentadienyl-*o*-phenylazophe-
   nyl-nickel

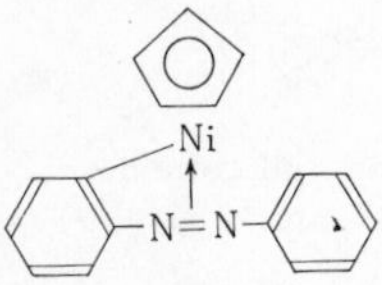

② (π-C₅H₅)₂Ni + C₆H₅N=NC₆H₅ $\xrightarrow{135°,\ 4\text{hr.}}$

③ Purple-blue crystals. (100°/10⁻⁵,
   sublime). [118~119°].
   Sol. in hydrocarbons, ethers, alcohols, CCl₄ and CS₂ ; insol. in H₂O.
   Quite stable to oxidation and can
   be exposed to air without noticea
   ble decomp.
   Diamagnetic.
   NMR : τ 4.67 (singlet), 3.08 (triplet),
   2.07 (quadruplet), 1.85 (doublet).
   UV : λ_{max} 252(ε=14000), 268(ε=13050),
   345 (ε=7550), 585 mμ (ε=6200).

④ + LiAlH₄ $\xrightarrow{\text{Et}_2\text{O}}$ azobenzene
   + LiAlD₄ $\longrightarrow$ orange product
   containing ca. 10% of D (mp 64~
   68°)

⑥ JACS **85**, 1544 (1963).

NiC₁₈H₂₀O₂

① (Cyclooctatetraene)-(duroquinone)

-nickel

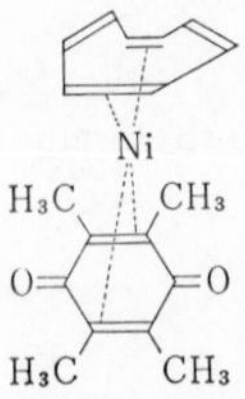

② di-(duroquinone)-nickel
   + cyclooctatetraene
   $\xrightarrow{\text{CH}_2\text{Cl}_2,\ 60\sim80°,\ 6\,\text{hr.}}$ 40%

   Ni(CO)₄ + duroquinone
   + cyclooctatetraene
   $\xrightarrow{\text{CH}_2\text{Cl}_2,\ \text{reflux},\ 4\,\text{hr.}}$ 65%

③ Brown-red crystals. [165° decomp.].
   Sol. in CH₂Cl₂, benzene and alcohol ;
   slightly sol. in H₂O and ether ;
   insol. in petr. ether. Stable in air.
   Diamagnetic.
   NMR(DCCl₃) : τ 7.88 (CH₃),   6.13
   (coordinated olefinic proton) 3.98
   (olefinic proton).
   Dipole moment : 3.47 D.

⑥ Z. Naturf. **16 b**, 353 (1961).

NiC₂₀H₂₄O₄

① Di(duroquinone)-nickel

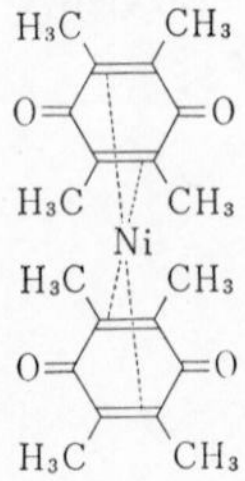

② Ni(CO)₄ + duroquinone $\xrightarrow{\text{benzene, reflux}}$

③ Red crystals. [205° decomp. without
   melting].
   Sparingly sol. in alc. benzene and
   aceton ; moderately sol. in CHCl₃

and CH$_2$Cl$_2$.

Diamagnetic.

IR : νco 1577 cm^{-1}.

NMR : (CH$_2$Cl$_2$) τ 8.40 (CH$_3$).

⑥ JACS **82**, 6420 (1960). Z. Naturf. **16 b**, 353 (1961).

NiC$_{21}$H$_{15}$O$_3$P

① Tri(carbonyl)-(triphenylphosphine)
-nickel
Ni(CO)$_3$[P(C$_6$H$_5$)$_3$]

② Ph$_3$P + Ni(CO)$_4$ $\xrightarrow{20°}$

③ White crystals. [123°].
Sol. in benzene, toluene and pyridine.
Difficulty sol. in alc.
IR : νco 1994, 1933 cm^{-1}.

④ Ni(CO)$_3$(Ph$_3$P) $\xrightarrow{123°}$ Ni(CO)$_2$(Ph$_3$P)$_2$

⑤ Catalyst of the preparation of acrylic acid ester from acetylene, CO and ROH, and of cyclic trimerization of acetylenes.

⑥ Ann. **560**, 104 (1948).

NiC$_{21}$H$_{20}$ClP

① π-Allyl-chloro-(triphenylphosphine)
-nickel
(π-C$_3$H$_5$)(Cl)Ni[P(C$_6$H$_5$)$_3$]

② CH$_2$=CH−CH$_2$Cl +
Ni(CO)$_3$(PPh$_3$) $\xrightarrow{CH_3OH, 40°}$

③ Orange prisms. [140~150°, decomp.].
The solid may be handled for short time in air, but the solution decomp. quickly.
NMR : τ6.85, 5.75, 3.60 (intensity 2 : 2 : 1) ; τ1.6 (Ph).

⑥ Chem. & Ind. **1961**, 986.

NiC$_{22}$H$_{15}$BrO

① Triphenylcyclopropenyl-bromo-
(carbonyl)-nickel

(π-Ph$_3$C$_3$)(Br)Ni(CO),

②

Ph—⟨⟩—Ph + Ni(CO)$_4$ $\xrightarrow{CH_3OH, r.t.1hr}$
Br Ph

③ Brick-red crystals. [~120° decomp.].
Sparingly sol. in THF and methanol.
The solution is oxidized instantly by air. The solid is fairly air stable.
Dimeric structure (Br bridge) is plausible.
IR : νco 2039 cm^{-1}.

⑥ Inorg. Chem. **3**, 604 (1964).

NiC$_{23}$H$_{20}$IP

① π-Cyclopentadienyl-iodo-(triphenylphosphine)-nickel
(π-C$_5$H$_5$)(I)Ni[P(C$_6$H$_5$)$_3$]

② π-C$_5$H$_5$Ni(CO)I + PPh$_3$
$\xrightarrow{benzene, -15°, 1hr.}$ 84%

③ Dark maroon. [130° decomp.].
Air stable.

⑥ JINC **24**, 1690 (1962).

NiC$_{24}$H$_{23}$P

① Methyl-π-cyclopentadienyl-(triphenylphosphine)-nickel
(π-C$_5$H$_5$)(CH$_3$)Ni[P(C$_6$H$_5$)$_3$]

② π-C$_5$H$_5$Ni(PPh$_3$)Cl + CH$_3$MgI $\longrightarrow$ 67%

③ Dark green crystals. [115~118° decomp.].
Stable in air. Sol. in most org. solvents but decomp. in CCl$_4$.
Diamagnetic.
NMR : τ2.56 (C$_6$H$_5$), 4.94 (C$_5$H$_5$), 10.82 (doublet, JPH=6cps, CH$_3$).

⑥ BCSJ **37**, 907 (1964).

NiC₂₄H₄₀P₂

① Di-phenyl-bis(triethylphosphine)
   nickel
   $(C_6H_5)_2Ni[P(C_2H_5)_3]_2$

② $trans[Ni(PEt_3)_2Br_2]$
   $+ PhMgBr \xrightarrow{\text{benzene-ether, } -30°}$

③ Pale yellow needles.   [125~130°
   decomp.].
   Decomp. very rapidly in ethanol.

⑥ JCS **1960**, 1718.

NiC₂₈H₂₄F₅IP₂

① Perfluoroethyl-(1, 2-bisdiphenylphos-
   phinoethane)-nickel

②

$$\xrightarrow{CH_2Cl_2, 70°, 24hr} 70\%$$

③ Reddish-brown needles. [>260° de-
   comp.].
   Reasonably stable in air.
   Diamagnetic.

⑥ JCS **1963**, 723.

NiC₂₈H₄₀P₂

① $trans$-Diphenylethynyl-bis-(triethylphosphine)-nickel
   $trans$-$(PhC\equiv C)_2Ni[P(C_2H_5)_3]_2$

② $trans$-$Ni(PEt_3)_2Cl_2 + NaC\equiv CPh$
   $\xrightarrow{\text{liq. NH}_3} 94\%$

   $trans$-$Ni(PEt_3)_2Br_2 + PhC\equiv CMgBr$
   benzene−ether

③ Yellowish orange. [149~151°].
   Diamagnetic.

⑥ JCS **1960**, 1718.

NiC₃₀H₅₂P₂

① Di-mesityl-bis-(triethylphosphine)-
   nickel
   $[1,3,5-(CH_3)_3C_6H_2]_2Ni[P(C_2H_5)_3]_2$

② $trans[Ni(PEt_3)_2Br_2]$ + mesitylmagnesium bromide $\xrightarrow{\text{THF-benzene}} 65\%$

③ Pale yellow. [148~150°].
   Dipole moment : ~0D.

④ + HCl ⟶
   $[1,3,5-(CH_3)_3C_6H_2]Ni(PEt_3)_2Cl$

⑥ JCS **1960**, 1718.

NiC₃₈H₃₀O₂P₂

① Di(carbonyl)-bis-(triphenylphosphine)-nickel
   $Ni(CO)_2[P(C_6H_5)_3]_2$

② $Ni(CO)_4 + 2Ph_3P \xrightarrow{50°C}$ almost
   quantitative

③ Pale cream-coloured crystalline solid.
   [206~209°], [210~215° decomp.].
   Sol. in benzene, toluene and pyridine ; difficulty sol. in alc.
   IR : ν_{CO} 2063, 1987 cm⁻¹.

⑤ Catalyst of the preparation of acrylic acid esters from acetylene, CO
   and ROH, and of cyclic trimerization of acetylenes, and of oligomerization of butadiene.

⑥ Ann. **560**, 104 (1948).   JCS **1950**, 69.

NiC₃₈H₃₄P₂

① Di(triphenylphosphine)-(ethylene)
   -nickel
   $Ni[P(C_6H_5)_3]_2(CH_2=CH_2)$

② $Ni(acac)_2 + (C_2H_5)_2AlOC_2H_5 + Ph_3P$
   $\xrightarrow{P : Ni=2 : 1, \text{ benzene, } 20°} 75\%$

③ Yellow crystals.

④ + donor ⟶ (Ph₃P)₂Ni·donor
    + C₂H₄
⑥ Angew. **74**, 693 (1962)；**73**, 33 (1961).

Ni₂C₆H₁₀I₂
① Di-π-allyl-diiodo-dinickel
    (π-C₃H₅)₂(I)₂Ni₂
② Ni(CO)₄ + C₃H₅I ⟶ 9.7%
③ Dark red crystals. [118~120°decomp.].
    Sensitive to light and air.
    IR: "C−C" 1449, 1015, 496cm⁻¹; "C−H"
    741, 971cm⁻¹.
    UV: λ_{max} 445 (ε=~1210), 290~300
    (ε=~9000), 275m μ (ε=~12500)
    Dipole moment: 1.62±0.07D (25°,
    benzene).
⑥ Ber. **94**, 2409 (1961).

Ni₂C₁₂H₁₀O₂
① Di-π-cyclopentadienyl-di(carbonyl)
    -dinickel
    (π-C₅H₅)₂Ni₂(CO)₂
② (π-C₅H₅)₂Ni + Ni(CO)₄
       benzene, 70°C
    ──────────── 50%
       benzene, reflux, 3.5 hr.
    ──────────── 74%
③ Purple-red. [139°decomp.]. [146~147°].
    Easily sol. in benzene and CHCl₃;
    sol. in petr. ether, ether and alc.;
    insol. in H₂O. Pure crystals are
    stable in air. Diamagnetic.
    Dipole moment: 0±0.38D (25°, ben-
    zene)
④ + I₂ ⟶ π-C₅H₅Ni(CO)I
⑥ Ber. **91**, 1725 (1958)；**92**, 938 (1959).
    JCS **1961**, 577.

Ni₂C₁₂H₁₂
① Di-π-cyclopentadienyl-(acetylene)
    -dinickel
    (π-C₅H₅)₂Ni₂(HC≡CH)
② (π-C₅H₅)₂Ni + CH≡CH ⟶ 48%

③ Light green lustrous plates. [143~
    144° decomp.].
    Moderately sol. in saturated hydro-
    carbon. Very sol. in all other com-
    mon org. solvents.
    Can be handled readily in air for
    short periords of time.
    Diamagnetic.
⑥ JACS **82**, 502 (1960).

Ni₂C₁₄H₁₀F₆
① Di-π-cyclopentadienyl-(hexafluoro-2
    -butyne)-dinickel
    (π-C₅H₅)₂Ni₂(C₄F₆)
② CF₃C≡CF₃ + [π-C₅H₅Ni(CO)]₂ ⟶
③ Green-black. (40°/vacuum, sublime).
    [91~92°].
⑥ Chem. & Ind. **1960**, 1137.

Ni₂C₂₂H₂₀S₂
① Di-π-cyclopentadienyl-di-μ-phenyl-
    sulfido-nickel
    (π-C₅H₅)₂[(C₆H₅)S]₂Ni₂,

② (π-C₅H₅)₂Ni + 2PhSH
       beznene, r. t., 15 hr.
    ──────────── 95%
    π-C₅H₅NiCOI + PhSH + base ⟶ 85%
③ Black crystals. [125°].
    Easily sol. in common org. solvents.
    Stable to air even in solution.
    Diamagnetic.
⑥ JINC **24**, 1688 (1962).

Ni₂C₂₄H₂₀
① Di-π-cyclopentadienyl-(diphenylace-
    tylene)-dinickel
    (π-C₅H₅)₂Ni₂[(C₆H₅)C≡C(C₆H₅)],

② $[\pi\text{-}C_5H_5Ni(CO)]_2 + PhC\equiv CPh$

$$\xrightarrow{\text{toluene, 30~120 min}} 88\%$$

$(\pi\text{-}C_5H_5)_2Ni + Ni(CO)_4 + PhC\equiv CPh$

$$\xrightarrow{\text{benzene, 6 hr.}} 85\%$$

③ Black crystals. [149~150°].
Stable in air. The solution in non-polar solvents is oxidized slowly by air and the solution in polar solvents such as ethanol or acetic acid is oxidized rapidly.

④ $+ H_2 \xrightarrow{\text{Na, alc, liq. NH}_3}$

PhCH$_2$CH$_2$Ph 89%

$$\xrightarrow{\text{oxidation}} PhC\equiv CPh\ 100\%$$

⑥ JACS **81**, 4757 (1959).   JCS **1961**, 577.

Ni$_2$C$_{24}$H$_{20}$N$_2$

① Di-π-cyclopentadienyl-di-(phenyliso-nitril)-di-nickel
$\{(\pi\text{-}C_5H_5)Ni[CN(C_6H_5)]\}_2$

② $(\pi\text{-}C_5H_5)_2Ni + Ni(CNPh)_4$

$$\xrightarrow{\text{boiling benzene}}$$

③ [91°].
IR: ν_{NC} 2174 cm^{-1}.

⑥ Angew. **74**, 466 (1962).

Ni$_2$C$_{34}$H$_{30}$P$_2$

① Di-π-cyclopentadienyl-bis-μ-(diphe-nylphosphido)-dinickel
$(\pi\text{-}C_5H_5)_2Ni_2[P(C_6H_5)_2]_2$

② $[\pi\text{-}C_5H_5Ni(CO)]_2 + P_2Ph_4$

$$\xrightarrow{\text{toluene, reflux, 16 hr.}} 65\%$$

③ Dark brown needles.   [264~265° decomp.].
NMR: τ2.2 and 2.75 (complex band due to the phenyl protons); τ5.16

(triplet, J_{HP}=0.6 cps, C$_5$H$_5$).

⑥ Inorg. Chem. **2**, 1031 (1963).

Ni$_3$C$_{17}$H$_{15}$O$_2$

① Tri-π-cyclopentadienyl-di(carbonyl)-trinickel
$(\pi\text{-}C_5H_5)_3Ni_3(CO)_2$

② $(\pi\text{-}C_5H_5)_2Ni + Ni(CO)_4 \xrightarrow{105°,\ 60\ hr.} 82\%$

$[\pi\text{-}C_5H_5Ni(CO)]_2 \xrightarrow{\text{sublimation, }>130°}$

$[\pi\text{-}C_5H_5Ni(CO)]_2 \xrightarrow{\text{Na--Hg, CH}_3OH}$

③ Dark green. [~200°, decomp.].
Slightly sol. in org. solvents.
Stable in air.
Paramagnetic, 1.79 BM.
Dipole moment: 0D.

⑥ Ber. **91**, 1725 (1958).

【Os】

OsC$_{10}$H$_{10}$

① Di-π-cyclopentadienyl-osmium (osmocene)
$(\pi\text{-}C_5H_5)_2Os$

② $OsCl_5 + NaC_5H_5 \longrightarrow 22\%$

③ Colorless crystals. [229~230°].
Stable in air.

④ $+ C_6H_5COCl \xrightarrow{AlCl_3}$ monobenzoyl-osmocene

$+ 2Fe^{3+} + H_2O \longrightarrow [(\pi\text{-}C_5H_5)_2OsOH]^+ + 2Fe^{2+} + H^+$

⑥ Chem. & Ind. **1958**, 756.   Ber. **92**, 2302 (1959).   JACS **82**, 76 (1960).

OsC$_{12}$H$_{12}$O

① π-Cyclopentadienyl-π-acetylcyclo-pentadienyl-osmium,
Acetylosmocene
$(\pi\text{-}C_5H_5)(\pi\text{-}C_5H_4COCH_3)Os$,

② (π-C$_5$H$_5$)$_2$Os + CH$_3$COCl

    AlCl$_3$, in CH$_2$Cl$_2$
    ―――――――→   69%

③ Light yellow needles. [126°]
   Stable in air.

⑥ JACS **82**, 76 (1960).

OsC$_{12}$H$_{14}$

① (Benzene)-(cyclohexadiene-1, 3)-os-
   mium

   Os(C$_6$H$_6$)(C$_6$H$_8$),

② OsCl$_3$ + *iso*-C$_3$H$_7$MgBr + cyclohexadi-
            UV
   ene-1,3 ――→ 0.15~0.25%

③ Colorless crystals. Sublime at 60~65°
   in vacuo. [114~116°].
   Decomp. at ca. 170°.

⑥ Ber. **96**, 3217 (1963).

OsC$_{17}$H$_{14}$O

① π-Cyclopentadienyl-π-benzoyl-
   cyclopentadienyl-osmium,
   Benzoylosmocene
   (π-C$_5$H$_5$)(π-C$_5$H$_4$COC$_6$H$_5$)Os,

     ―COC$_6$H$_5$
     Os

② (π-C$_5$H$_5$)$_2$Os + C$_6$H$_5$COCl

    AlCl$_3$, in CH$_2$Cl$_2$
    ―――――――→   62%

③ Light yellow needles. Sublime at 130
   ~140° *in vacuo*. [133.5°].
   Sol. in benzene.
   IR : ν_{CO} 1631 cm^{-1}.

④ + LiAlH$_4$ ―――in ether――→
   (π-C$_5$H$_5$)[π-C$_5$H$_4$CH(OH)C$_6$H$_5$]Os

⑥ Chem. & Ind. **1958**, 756 ; JACS **82**,
   76 (1960) ; **84**, 1845 (1962).

OsC$_{17}$H$_{16}$O

① Osmocenylphenylcarbinol
   (π-C$_5$H$_5$)[π-C$_5$H$_4$CH(OH)C$_6$H$_5$]Os,

     ―CH―C$_6$H$_5$
    Os OH

② (π-C$_5$H$_5$)(π-C$_5$H$_4$COC$_6$H$_5$)Os + LiAlH$_4$

   ―in ether――→ 91%

③ Snow-white needles. [115.7~116°].

④ + HN$_3$ ―in benzene――→ osmocenylphenyl-
   carbinyl azide

⑥ JACS **84**, 1845 (1962).

OsC$_{20}$H$_{49}$ClP$_4$

① *trans*-Hydrido-chloro-di[1, 2-bis-
   (diethylphosphino)-ethane]-
   osmium
   trans-[(H)(Cl)Os{C$_2$H$_4$[(C$_2$H$_5$)$_2$P]$_2$}$_2$]

② *cis*-Os{C$_2$H$_4$[(C$_2$H$_5$)$_2$P]$_2$}$_2$Cl$_2$
   LiAlH$_4$
   ――→ 47%

③ Colorless needles. [170.5~171.5°].
   Decomps. at ca 315° in vacuo.
   IR : ν_{Os-H} 2039 cm^{-1}.
   NMR : τ 36.5 (Os-H).
   Dipole moment : 4.6 D.

⑥ Proc. Chem. Soc. **1959**, 153. JCS **1961**
   2605.

OsC$_{52}$H$_{48}$Cl$_2$P$_4$

① *trans*-Dichloro-di[1,2-bis-(diphenylphosphino)-ethane]osmium
   trans-(Cl$_2$)Os{C$_2$H$_4$[P(C$_6$H$_5$)$_2$]$_2$}$_2$

② (NH$_4$)$_2$OsCl$_6$ + C$_2$H$_4$[P(C$_6$H$_5$)$_2$]$_2$
   ――→ 80%

③ Orange crystals. [293~296° decomp.].
   Efflorescing to yellow crystals.

⑥ JCS **1961**, 897.

$Os_2C_{12}H_8O_6$

① $(C_6H_8)Os_2(CO)_6$,

② $Os_3(CO)_{12}$ + 2,3-dimethylbutadiene
   -1, 3 $\xrightarrow{\text{200°C, in sealed tube}}$

③ Colorless crystals. Sublime at 80° *in vacuo.* [120°].
   Stable in air. Sol. in org. solvents such as benzene and ether.
   IR: ν_{CO} 2088, 2053, 2020, 2000, 1984, 1976 cm^{-1}.
   Os−Os distance: 2.74Å.

⑥ Z. Naturf. **18b**, 83 (1963). Proc. Chem. Soc. **1963**, 380.

$Os_2C_{14}H_{10}O_4$

① Di-π-cyclopentadienyl-tetra(carbonyl)-diosmium
   $[(\pi\text{-}C_5H_5)Os(CO)_2]_2$,

② $Os(CO)_3Cl_2$ + NaC_5H_5 $\xrightarrow{\text{reflux in THF}}$

③ Sublime at 130° *in vacuo.* [197°].
   Sol. in ether and benzene; insol. in H_2O.
   Diamagnetic.

⑥ Z. Naturf. **17b**, 274 (1962).

$Os_2C_{84}H_{90}Cl_4P_6 \cdot 2H_2O$

① Tri-μ-chloro-hexakis(ethyldiphenylphosphine)-diosmiumchloride dihydrate

$\{(Cl)_3Os_2[C_2H_5(C_6H_5)_2P]_6Cl\} 2 \cdot H_2O$

② $(NH_4)_2OsCl_6$ + $C_2H_5(C_6H_5)_2P$ $\longrightarrow$ 95%

③ Yellow-orange plates. [180~182° decomp.].

④ + ditertiary phosphine $\longrightarrow$ *cis*-[Os(ditertiary phosphine)$_2$Cl$_2$]
   + cyclooctadiene-1.5 $\longrightarrow$ [Os(C$_8$H$_{12}$)[C$_2$H$_5$(C$_6$H$_5$)$_2$P]$_2$Cl$_2$]

⑥ JCS **1961**, 897.

$Os_3C_{12}O_{12}$

① Dodeca(carbonyl)-osmium

$Os_3(CO)_{12}$,

(I)

② OsO_4 + CO $\longrightarrow$

③ Yellow crystals. [224°]
   The structure was determined as(I) by X-ray diffraction.
   Average Os−Os distance: 2.88Å.

⑤ Previously formulated as $Os_2(CO)_9$.

⑥ Z. Elektrochem. **49**, 288 (1943). Inorg. Chem. **1**, 521 (1962). Quart. Rev. **17**, 133 (1963)

【Pd】

PdC_5H_5Cl

① π-Cyclopentadienyl-chloro-palladium
   $(\pi\text{-}C_5H_5)(Cl)Pd$

② $PdCl_2$ + C_5H_6 $\longrightarrow$

③ Dark brown solid.
   Insol. in usual org. solvents; sol. in aqueous, alcoholic or liq. ammonia.
   Diamagnetic. Probably polymeric halogen-bridged structure.

④ + NaC₅H₅ $\xrightarrow{\text{in liq. NH}_3}$ no reaction

⑥ Angew. **71**, 651 (1959).

PdC₆H₂MN₂

① Barium dicyano–diethynyl–palladate
   cis-M[(HC≡C)₂Pd(CN)₂] M=Ba

② K₂[Pd(CN)₄] or [Pd(en)(CN)₂]
      + KC≡CH + Ba(SCN)₂ $\longrightarrow$ 80%
           (en=ethylenediamine)

③ Heavy, fine-crystals.
   Decomp. in air. Under N₂ slightly
   sol. in dimethylformamide and dimethylsulfoxide ; insol. in abs.
   acetone, methanol, ethanol, CS₂
   and CCl₄.
   IR : $\nu_{C\equiv N}$ 2140 cm⁻¹, $\nu_{C\equiv C}$ 1968 cm⁻¹.

⑥ Ber. **95**, 1470 (1962).

PdC₈H₈Cl₂

① Dichloro–(cyclooctatetraene-1, 3, 5,
   7)-palladium
           (Cl)₂Pd(C₈H₈)

② Pd(C₆H₅CN)₂Cl₂ + C₈H₈ $\longrightarrow$

③ Orange crystals. [~150° decomp.].
   Very sol. in CHCl₃ ; moderately sol.
   in C₆H₆ ; insol. in petroleum ether·
   IR : $\nu_{C=C}$ 1488 cm⁻¹.

⑥ Ber. **95**, 158 (1962).

PdC₈H₁₀

① π-Allyl-π-cyclopentadienyl-palla-
   dium
   (π-C₃H₅)(π-C₅H₅)Pd,

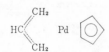

② [(π-C₃H₅)PdCl]₂
      + NaC₅H₅ $\xrightarrow{\text{in benzene + THF}}$

③ Red needles. (40°/30 sublime). [63~
   63.5°].
   Stable in air for a few days at room
   temp.

Diamagnetic.
   Powerful and unpleasant smell.
   Dipole moment : <1.5 D.

⑥ Proc. Chem. Soc. **1960**, 247.   Chem.
   & Ind. **1961**, 517.

PdC₈H₁₂Cl₂

① Dichloro-(cyclooctadiene-1, 5)-palla-
   dium

   (Cl)₂Pd(C₈H₁₂),   ⬡ PdCl₂

② Na₂PdCl₄ + C₈H₁₂ $\xrightarrow{\text{in methanol}}$

③ Pale yellow needles. [205~210° decomp.].
   Most stable olefin-palladium complex. Sparingly sol. in cold alcohol
   and benzene ; slightly sol. in hot
   benzene, chloroform, acetone,
   ethylmethylketone and diethyl
   carbonate.

⑥ JCS **1957**, 3413.

PdC₁₁H₁₄

① π-Cyclopentadienyl-π-cyclohexenyl
   -palladium

   (π-C₅H₅)(π-C₆H₉)Pd,   Pd

② [(C₆H₈)PdCl]₂ + KC₅H₅ $\xrightarrow{\text{in benzene}}$ 60%

③ Red crystals. Sublime at 35~40° in
   vacuo. [69°].
   Stable in air. Easily sol. in org.
   solvents.
   Diamagnetic.
   Dipole moment : 2.1D (in cyclohexane).

④ + (C₆H₅)₃P $\longrightarrow$ Pd[(C₆H₅)₃P]₄

⑥ Ber. **93**, 2075 (1960) ; **95**, 695, 703 (1962).

Chem. & Ind. 1961, 517.   Tetrahedron Letters 1961, 48.

PdC₁₂H₁₆

① π-Cyclopentadienyl-π-cycloheptenyl
-palladium

$(\pi$-$C_5H_5)(\pi$-$C_7H_{11})Pd,$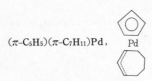

② $[(\pi$-$C_7H_{11})PdCl]_2 + NaC_5H_5 \longrightarrow 26\%$
③ Red-violet crystals.
Sol. in org. solvents. Very unstable.
⑥ Ber. **95**, 695 (1962).

PdC₁₃H₃₃BrP₂

① Methyl-bromo-bis(triethylphosphine)-palladium
$(CH_3)(Br)Pd[(C_2H_5)_3P]_2$
② $Pd[(C_2H_5)_3P]_2Br_2 + CH_3MgBr$
$\longrightarrow 78\%$
③ Colorless solid. [73~74°].
Readily sol. in acetone, ethanol and
hydrocarbons.
Dipole moment: 4.0D
⑥ Chem. & Ind. 1958, 160.   JCS 1960,
2008.

PdC₁₄H₁₀N₂

① Di(phenyl isonitrilo)-palladium
$Pd(C_6H_5NC)_2$
② $Pd(C_6H_5NC)_2I_2 + C_6H_5NC + KOH$
$\xrightarrow{\text{in ethanol}} 50\%$
③ Green-brown crystals. [170~190°
decomp.].
Insol. in all solvents except isonit-
riles, quinoline, pyridine and nitrobenzene.
Diamagnetic $\chi_M = -40 \times 10^{-6}$.
④ $+ I_2 \longrightarrow Pd(C_6H_5NC)_2I_2$
$+ 3(RO)_3P \longrightarrow Pd[(RO)_3P]_3$-

$(C_6H_5NC) + C_6H_5NC$
⑥ JCS 1955, 3924.

PdC₁₄H₃₆P₂

① Dimethyl-bis(triethylphosphine)
-palladium
$(CH_3)_2Pd[(C_2H_5)_3P]_2$
② $Pd[(C_2H_5)_3P]_2Br_2 + CH_3Li \xrightarrow{-35°} 90\%$
③ Sublime at 40~50° *in vacuo*. [47~49°].
Unstable in solution in org. solvents.
Trans-configuration.
④ + aqueous-ethanolic HBr
$\longrightarrow Pd[(C_2H_5)_3P]_2Br_2$
⑥ Chem. & Ind. 1958, 160.   JCS 1960,
2008.

PdC₂₈H₂₀Cl₂

① Dichloro-(tetraphenyl cyclobutadiene)-palladium
$(Cl_2)Pd[C_4(C_6H_5)_4],$

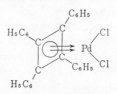

② $PdCl_2 + C_6H_5C\equiv CC_6H_5 \xrightarrow{\text{HCl in ethanol}}$
③ Deep red crystals. [272° decomp.].
Stable in air. Insol. in H₂O and all
org. solvents exeept chloroform
saturated with hydrogen chloride
and dimethylformamide.
④ + LiBr $\xrightarrow{\text{in acetone}} Pd(C_{28}H_{20})Br_2$
+ NaI $\xrightarrow{\text{in acetone}} Pd(C_{28}H_{20})I_2$
$\xrightarrow{\text{heat in vac.}}$ 1,4-dichloro-1,2,3,4-tetra-
phenyl-butadiene-1,3
$\xrightarrow{\text{LiAlH}_4 \text{ or NaBH}_4}$ 1,2,,3,4-tetra-
phenyl-butadiene-1,3
⑥ Angew. **72**, 34 (1960).   JACS **84**, 2329
(1662).   Gazz. chim. ital. **94**, 252
(1964).

PdC₇₂H₆₀P₄

① Tetrakis(triphenylphosphine)
   -palladium
   $$Pd[(C_6H_5)_3P]_4$$

② $Pd[(C_6H_5)_3P]_2Cl_2 + (C_6H_5)_3P + H_2NNH_2$
   in alc.
   $\xrightarrow{\quad\quad}$ 60%
   $Pd(NO_3)_2 + (C_6H_5)_3P \longrightarrow$

③ Yellow crystals. [100~105° decomp.].
   Stable to air for only a short time ;
   on prolonged exposure turns from
   yellow to orange. Sol. in benzene.

⑥ JCS 1957, 1186.   Ber. **95**, 703 (1962).

Pd₂C₄H₈Cl₄

① μ, μ'-Dichloro-bis[chloro-(ethylene)]-di-palladium
   $[(Cl)_2Pd(C_2H_4)]_2,$

② $Pd(C_6H_5CN)_2Cl_2 + C_2H_4 \xrightarrow{\text{in benzene}}$
   $PdCl_2 + C_2H_4 \xrightarrow{\text{90000 p. s. i, in benzene}}$

③ Light canary yellow crystals.
   Slightly sol. in benzene, chloroform
   and ether ; insol. in petr. ether
   and acetic acid.

④ $+ C_6H_5CH=CH_2 \xrightarrow{\text{in benzene}}$
   $[Pd(C_8H_8)Cl_2]_2 + Pd(C_8H_8)_2Cl_2$

⑥ JACS **60**, 882 (1938) ; **77**, 4984 (1955).
   Chem. & Ind. **1960**, 1191.

Pd₂C₆H₁₀Cl₂

① Di-π-allyl-μ, μ'-dichloro-dipalladium
   $[(\pi\text{-}C_3H_5)(Cl)Pd]_2,$

② $CH_2=CH-CH_2OH$

in 50% glacial acetic acid
$+ PdCl_2 \xrightarrow{\quad\quad\quad\quad\quad\quad\quad}$
$CH_2=CH-CH_2Cl + PdCl_2$ or
$Na_2PdCl_4 \longrightarrow$

③ Yellow solid.
   Sol. in acetone, chloroform, ethyla-
   cetate, benzene, hydrohalogenic
   acid aqueous solution etc.
   Diamagnetic.

④ $+ H_2O \longrightarrow CH_2=CHCHO +$
   $CH_3CH=CH_2 + 2HCl + 2Pd$
   $\xrightarrow{145°} CH_2=CHCH_2Cl + Pd$
   $+ NaC_5H_5 \longrightarrow (\pi\text{-}C_5H_5)(\pi\text{-}C_3H_5)Pd$

⑥ Angew. **71**, 284, 456 (1959).   Russ.
   J. Inorg. Chem. **4**, 1218 (1959).

Pd₂C₈H₁₂Cl₄

① $(\pi\text{-}4\text{-Chlorobut-2-enyl})\text{-}\mu, \mu'$-dichloro
   -dipalladium
   $[(\pi\text{-}C_4H_6Cl)(Cl)Pd]_2,$

② $Pd(C_6H_5CN)_2Cl_2 + CH_2=CHCH=CH_2$
   $\xrightarrow{\text{in benzene}}$

③ Light yellow solid.
   Stable in air. Sol. in benzene ; insol.
   in petroleum ether.
   Previously formulated as butadiene-
   palladium dichloride.

④ $+ CH_3OH \longrightarrow$

   $+ NaC_5H_5 \longrightarrow (\pi\text{-}C_5H_5)(\pi\text{-}C_4H_6Cl)Pd$
   $+ acac \longrightarrow (\pi\text{-}C_4H_6Cl)Pd(acac)$
   acac=acetyl acetonate

⑥ JACS **79**, 1277 (1957).   JCS **1936**, 4806.

Pd₂C₁₂H₁₈Cl₂

① Di-π-cyclohexenyl-μ, μ'-dichloro
-dipalladium
[(π-C₆H₉)(Cl)Pd]₂,

② Pd(CO)Cl₂ + C₆H₈ $\xrightarrow{\text{in THF}}$ 65%

Na₂PdCl₄ + C₆H₈ $\xrightarrow{\text{in acetic acid}}$

PdCl₂ + C₆H₈ $\xrightarrow{\text{in THF}}$ 52%

③ Yellow solid. [95~105° decomp.].
Sol. in chloroform, methylene chloride, benzene, toluene, glacial acetic acid, acetone, acetonitril and THF; moderately sol. in ether and ethanol; insol. in hydrocarbon and H₂O.

④ + KC₅H₅
$\xrightarrow{\text{in benzene}}$ (π-C₅H₅)(π-C₆H₉)Pd
+ KC₅H₄CH₃
$\longrightarrow$ (π-C₅H₄CH₃)(π-C₆H₉)Pd

⑥ Ber. **93**, 2075 (1960); **95**, 695 (1962).
Chem. & Ind. **1961**, 517.

Pd₂C₁₄H₂₂Cl₂

① Di-π-cycloheptenyl-μ, μ'-dichloro-
dipalladium
[(π-C₇H₁₁)(Cl)Pd]₂,

② PdCl₂ + cycloheptadiene-1, 3
$\xrightarrow[\text{in THF}]{}$ 51%

③ [140~150 decomp.].

⑥ Ber. **95**, 695 (1962).

Pd₂C₁₆H₁₆Cl₄

① μ, μ'-Dichloro-bis-[chloro-(styrene)]

-dipalladium
[(Cl₂)Pd(C₆H₅C₂H₃)]₂

② Pd(C₆H₅CN)₂Cl₂ + C₆H₅CH=CH₂
[Pd(CH₂=CH₂)₂Cl₂]₂
+ C₆H₅CH=CH₂ $\longrightarrow$

③ Light red-brown solid.
Stable 2~3 days in desicator; decomp. rapidly in acetone or alc.

⑥ JACS **60**, 882 (1938). Chem. & Ind.
1960 (1191).

【Pt】

PtC₂H₄Cl₃M·H₂O

① Potassium trichloro(ethylene)-platinate, Zeise's Salt
[(Cl)₃Pt(C₂H₄)]M(H₂O), M=K

② K₂PtCl₄ $\xrightarrow{\text{4\% HCl-H₂O, C₂H₄}}$

H₂PtCl₆ + C₂H₅OH $\xrightarrow{\text{KCl}}$

H₂PtCl₄ + CH≡CH $\longrightarrow$

③ Yellow crystals. [>200° decomp.].
n_D 1.717. d 2.88.
Sol. in H₂O.

④ + CH₃MgI $\longrightarrow$ (CH₃)₃PtI
+ CO $\longrightarrow$ K[Pt(CO)Cl₃]
+ H₂ $\longrightarrow$ Pt

⑥ Inorg. Syn. **5**, 210 (1957). Ann. **21**,
497 (1831). JCS **1934**, 971.

PtC₃H₉I

① Iodo-trimethyl-platinum
(CH₃)₃(I)Pt

② cis-Pt(C₅H₅N)₂Cl₄ + CH₃MgBr
$\longrightarrow$ 60%
K[Cl₃Pt(C₂H₄)] + CH₃MgI $\longrightarrow$
[Cl₂Pt(C₂H₄)]₂ + CH₃MgI $\longrightarrow$

③ Yellow crystals.

④ + K $\longrightarrow$ (CH₃)₆Pt₂
+ CH₃Na $\longrightarrow$ (CH₃)₄Pt
+ C₅H₅N $\longrightarrow$ (CH₃)₃IPt·2 C₅H₅N

⑤ The parent compound for the preparation of a wide range of methyl platinum derivatives.

⑥ JCS **1951**, 299. JCS **95**, 571 (1909).

PtC₄H₁₂

① Tetramethyl-platinum
$(CH_3)_4Pt$

② $(CH_3)_3PtI + CH_3Na \longrightarrow$ 46%

③ Sol. in benzene, acetone, ether and petroleum ether.

④ + HCl $\longrightarrow$ $(CH_3)_3PtCl$

⑥ JACS **60**, 3086 (1938).

PtC₆H₁₆ClP₂

① *trans*-Hydrido-chloro-bis(triethyl phosphine)-platinum
trans-$(H)(Cl)Pt\{P(C_2H_5)_3\}$

② *cis*-Pt$\{P(C_2H_5)_3\}_2Cl_2$ $\xrightarrow{N_2H_4 \cdot H_2O}$

cis-Pt$\{P(C_2H_5)_3\}_2Cl_2$ $\xrightarrow{C_2H_5OH+KOH}$

cis-Pt$\{P(C_2H_5)_3\}_2Cl_2$ $\xrightarrow{HCOOH}$

cis- or *trans*-Pt$\{P(C_2H_5)_3\}_2Cl_2$ $\xrightarrow{LiAlH_4}$

cis-C₆H₅Pt$\{P(C_2H_5)_3\}_2Cl$ $\xrightarrow{20°, H_2 \ 1atm}$

③ Stable in air.

④ + C_2H_4 $\longrightarrow$ $C_2H_5Pt\{P(C_3H_5)_3\}_2Cl$
+ CCl_4 $\longrightarrow$ $Pt\{P(C_2H_5)_3\}_2Cl_2$

⑥ Proc. Chem. Soc. **1957**, 343.

PtC₇H₈Cl₂

① Dichloro-(norbornadiene)-platinum
$(Cl)_2Pt(C_7H_8)$

② H_2PtCl_4 + norbornadiene
in glacil acetic acid
$\longrightarrow$

③ Fine white crystals. [230~280° decomp.]

Somewhat sol. in acetic acid, chloroform, and acetone ; insol. in H_2O.

⑥ JCS **1959**, 3178.

PtC₇H₁₅Cl₂OP

① *cis*-Dichloro-(carbonyl)(triethylphosphine)-platinum

cis-$(Cl)_2Pt(CO)\{(C_2H_5)_3P\}$

② $(C_2H_5)_3P$ $\diagdown$ Pt $\diagup$ Cl $\diagup$ $\diagdown$ Pt $\diagup$ Cl
Cl Cl $P(C_2H_5)_3$

+ CO $\xrightarrow{\text{in benzene}}$ 90%

③ White prisms. [134~136°].
Sol. in benzene.
IR : $\nu_{C=O}$ 2100 cm⁻¹(in nujol or CHCl₃)

⑥ JCS **1964**, 1662.

PtC₈H₁₀

① π-Cyclopentadienyl-π-allyl-platinum
$(\pi\text{-}C_3H_5)(\pi\text{-}C_5H_5)Pt$

② $CH_3CH=CH_2PtCl_3$ + $CH_2=CH$
$-CH_2MgBr$ + C_5H_5Na $\longrightarrow$

③ Lemon-yellow crystals. [63~64°].
Stable in air.
NMR : τ6.4, 6.43 and 7.97 (allylic protons), 4.25τ (cyclo-pentadienyl protons) (in C₆H₆ at 40Mc).

⑥ Chem. & Ind. **1961**, 517.

PtC₈H₁₁I

① Iodo-methyl-(norbornadiene)-platinum
$(CH_3)(I)Pt(C_7H_8)$

② $Pt(C_7H_8)I_2$ + CH_3MgBr $\longrightarrow$ 45%

③ Orange crystals. [122~124° decomp.].
IR : ν_{Pt-C} 572, 544 cm⁻¹.

⑥ Inorg. Chem. **2**, 1255 (1963).

PtC₈H₁₂Cl₂

① Dichloro-(cycloocta-1,5-diene) -platinum
$(Cl)_2Pt(C_8H_{12})$

② Cycloocta-1, 5-diene + Na_2PtCl_4 $\longrightarrow$

③ White crystals. [220~278° decomp.].
Insol. in most org. solvents except boiling CHCl₃, CH₂Cl₂ and acetic acid.
Monomeric and non-electrolytes in nitrobenzene.

④ + LiBr $\longrightarrow$ $Br_2Pt(C_8H_{12})$
+ LiI $\longrightarrow$ $I_2Pt(C_8H_{12})$

$+ CH_3OH \xrightarrow{Na_2CO_3} [ClPt(C_8H_{12}OCH_3)]_2$

⑥ JCS 1957, 4735.

PtC₈H₁₄

① π-Cyclopentadienyl-trimethyl-platinum

$(CH_3)_3(\pi\text{-}C_5H_5)Pt$

② $(CH_3)_3PtI + C_5H_5Na \xrightarrow{THF}$

③ White prisms. $(25°/10^{-2}$ sublime). [65°].

Very sol. in common org. solvents.

Stable in air.

Monomeric.

NMR : τ9.12 (methylprotons) and 4.39 (cyclopentadienylprotons).

⑥ Z. Naturf. 18b, 507 (1963).

PtC₈H₁₄O₂Cl₃M

① $K^+\{Cl_3Pt[(CH_3)_2(HO)C\cdot C\equiv C\cdot C(OH)\cdot (CH_3)_2]\}^-$

② $(CH_3)_2(HO)CC\equiv CC(OH)(CH_3)_2$

$+ K_2PtCl_4 \xrightarrow{in\ H_2O}$

$(CH_3)_2(HO)C\cdot C\equiv C\cdot C(OH)(CH_3)_2$

$+ K[Cl_4Pt(C_2H_4)] \xrightarrow{in\ acetone}$

③ Yellow crystals.

Sol in H_2O, acetone or C_2H_5OH ; insol. in ether, petr. ether, benzene and $CHCl_3$. Unstable in air.

Diamagnetic.

IR : $\nu_{C\equiv C}$ 2010cm⁻¹.

④ $\xrightarrow{CH_3-C_6H_4-NH_2} trans\text{-}[Cl_2Pt\{(CH_3)_2 (HO)C\cdot C\equiv C\cdot C(OH)(CH_3)_2\}(CH_3 -C_6H_4-NH_2)]$

⑥ Nature 184, 526 (1959). JCS 1963, 5170.

PtC₁₀H₁₄

① Dimethyl-(cyclooctatetraen)-platinum

$(CH_3)_2Pt(C_8H_8)$

② $Pt(C_8H_8)I_2 + CH_3MgBr \longrightarrow 5\%$

③ Yellow crystals. [80~90°].

IR : ν_{Pt-C} 563, 548cm⁻¹.

⑥ Inorg. Chem. 2, 1255 (1963)

PtC₁₀H₁₈

① Dimethyl-(1, 5-cyclooctadiene)-platinum

$(CH_3)_2Pt(C_8H_{12})$

② $Pt(C_8H_{12})I_2 + CH_3MgBr \longrightarrow 71\%$

③ Colorless crystals. [94~95° decomp.].

NMR : τ5.11 (triplet, CH), 7.62 (triplet, CH₂), 9.19 (triplet, CH₃).

⑥ Inorg. Chem. 2, 1255 (1963).

PtC₁₂H₁₆N₂

① Dimethyl-di(pyridine)-platinum

$(CH_3)_2Pt(C_5H_5N)_2$

② $(CH_3)_2Pt(C_8H_{12}) \xrightarrow{+C_5H_5N} 5\%$

③ Yellow crystals. [206~209° decomp.].

⑥ Inorg. Chem. 2, 1255 (1963).

PtC₁₄H₃₃ClO

① Acetyl-chloro-bis(triphenylphosphine)-platinum

$(CH_3CO)(Cl)Pt\{P(C_2H_5)_3\}_2$

② $trans\text{-}[CH_3(Cl)Pt\{P(C_2H_5)_3\}_2] \xrightarrow{CO,\ 150\sim100atm,\ 90°C}$

③ Colorless crystals. [70~71°].

IR : $\nu_{C=O}$ 1629cm⁻¹ (in CCl_4).

⑥ Proc. Chem. Soc. 1961, 67.

PtC₁₄H₃₆P₂

① cis-Dimethyl-bis(triethylphosphine)-platinum

$cis\text{-}(CH_3)_2Pt\{P(C_2H_5)_3\}_2$

② $cis\text{-}Pt\{P(C_2H_5)_3\}_2Cl_2 \xrightarrow{CH_3MgCl\ or\ CH_3Li} 60\%$

③ Colorless prisms. [81~82°].

Sol. in ether. Stable in air.

Dipole moment : 5.65 D.

④ $+ I_2 \longrightarrow trans\text{-}[CH_3Pt\{P(C_2H_5)_3\}_2I] + CH_3I$

$+ HCl \longrightarrow cis\text{-}[CH_3Pt\{P(C_2H_5)_3\}Cl]$

+ CH₄

+ 2 HCl $\longrightarrow$ *cis*-[Pt{P(C₂H₅)₃}Cl₂]

+ 2 CH₄

+ MgI₂ $\dashrightarrow$ *trans*-{Pt[P(C₂H₅)₃]₂I₂}

+ *trans*-[CH₃Pt{P(C₂H₅)₃}₂I]

+ CH₃MgI

⑥ JCS **1959**, 705.

PtC₁₆H₃₂P₂

① *trans*-Diethynyl-bis(triethylphosphine)-platinum
trans-[(HC≡C)₂Pt{P(C₂H₅)₃}₂]

② *cis*-{P(C₂H₅)₃}₂PtCl₂

+ NaC≡CH $\xrightarrow{\text{liq. NH}_3}$

③ White needle crystals. [62～63°].
Stable in air.
IR: $\nu_{C≡C}$ 1958 cm⁻¹.

⑥ JCS **1959**, 705, 4020.

PtC₂₄H₄₀P₂

① *cis*-Diphenyl-bis(triethylphosphine)
-platinum
cis-{(C₆H₅)₂Pt[P(C₂H₅)₃]₂}

② *cis*-{P(C₂H₅)₃}₂Cl₂ + C₆H₅MgBr
$\xrightarrow{20°C}$ 56%

③ White needle crystals. [144～160°,
decomp].

④ + Cl₂ $\xrightarrow{\text{in CCl}_4}$ (C₆H₅)₂PtCl₂P(C₂H₅)₃

+ I₂ $\xrightarrow{\text{in benzene}}$ (C₆H₅)₂PtI₂P(C₂H₅)₃

⑥ JCS **1959**, 4020.

PtC₅₀H₄₀P₂

① (1,2-Diphenylacetylene)-bis(triphenylphosphine)platinum
Pt(C₆H₅C≡CC₆H₅){P(C₆H₅)₃}₂

② *cis*-Cl₂Pt{P(C₆H₅)₃}₂ +
C₆H₅C≡CC₆H₅
$\xrightarrow{\text{N}_2\text{H}_4\cdot\text{H}_2\text{O in C}_2\text{H}_5\text{OH, 60°C}}$

③ Yellow crystals.
Sol. in benzene. Stable in air.

IR: $\nu_{C≡C}$ in the region of 1700 cm⁻¹.

④ + O₂N·C₆H₄-C≡C-C₆H₄·NO₂
$\xrightarrow[\text{in benzene}]{}$ Pt{P(C₆H₅)₃}₂(O₂N-C₆H₄
-C≡C-C₆H₄·NO₂)

⑥ Proc. Chem. Soc. **1957**, 208.

PtC₅₀H₄₂P₂

① (*trans*-Stilben)-bis(triphenylphos-
hine)-platinum
Pt(C₆H₅-CH=CH-C₆H₅){P(C₆H₅)₃}₂

② *cis*-Cl₂Pt{P(C₆H₅)₃}₂ + *trans*-C₆H₅
-CH=CH-C₆H₅ $\xrightarrow{\text{N}_2\text{H}_4\cdot\text{H}_2\text{O in C}_2\text{H}_5\text{OH}}$

③ Colorless crystals. [131～140°
decomp.].

④ + CH≡CH
$\xrightarrow[\text{in benzene}]{}$ Pt(HC≡CH){P(C₆H₅)₃}₂

⑥ JCS **1962**, 3269.

PtC₅₄H₄₅P₃

① Tris(triphenylphosphine)-platinum
Pt{P(C₆H₅)₃}₃

② *cis*-Cl₂Pt{P(C₆H₅)₃}₂
+ P(C₆H₅)₃ $\xrightarrow{\text{N}_2\text{H}_4\cdot\text{H}_2\text{O in C}_2\text{H}_5\text{OH}}$

I₂Pt[P(C₆H₅)₃]₂ $\xrightarrow{\text{N}_2\text{H}_4\cdot\text{H}_2\text{O}}$

③ Yellow crystals. [125～135°].
Sol. in benzene and CH₂Cl₂; slightly
sol. in C₂H₅OH. Moderately stable
in air.

④ $\xrightarrow{\text{CH}_3\text{I}}$ *trans*-CH₃IPt{P(C₆H₅)₃}₂I
+ [CH₃P(C₆H₅)₃]I

⑥ JCS **1958**, 2323.

PtC₅₅H₄₅OP₃

① Mono(carbonyl)-tris(triphenylphosphine)-platinum.
Pt(CO)[P(C₆H₅)₃]

② Pt{P(C₆H₅)₃}₄ $\xrightarrow{\text{CO, 300 atm.}}$
Pt(CO)₂{P(C₆H₅)₃}₂ +
2 P(C₆H₅)₃ $\xrightarrow[\text{in ether}]{}$

③ Orange red crystals. [130°].
Sol. in org. solvents. Moderately
stable in air.
⑥ JCS **1958**, 2323.

PtC₇₂H₆₀P₄

① Tetrakis(triphenylphosphine)
-platinum
Pt{P(C₆H₅)₃}₄

I₂Pt{P(C₆H₅)₃}₂
$$+ 2P(C_6H_5)_3 \xrightarrow{N_2H_4 \cdot H_2O}$$
I₂Pt{P(C₆H₅)₃}₂ + 3P(C₆H₅)₃
$$+ 2KOH \longrightarrow$$
K₂PtCl₄ + 2KOH + 5P(C₆H₅)₃ ⟶

③ Ivory yellow crystals. [118°]
Sol. in benzene or CHCl₃; insol. in
EtOH. Stable in air for many
hours.
④ + 2CO ⟶ Pt(CO)₂{P(C₆H₅)₃}₂
$$+ H_2 \xrightarrow{\text{in benzene}} H_2Pt\{P(C_6H_5)_3\}_2$$
+ I₂ ⟶ I₂Pt{P(C₆H₅)₃}₂
⑥ JCS **1958**, 2323; **1963**, 2080.   Nature
190, 528 (1961).

Pt₂C₂O₂Cl₄

① μ, μ′-Dichloro-dichloro-di(carbonyl)
-di-platinum

(Cl)₄Pt₂(CO)₂,

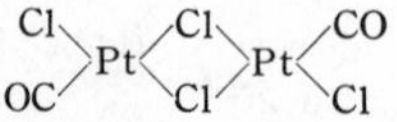

② $$Pt + Cl_2 + CO \xrightarrow{250°}$$
③ Yellow crystals. Sublime. [192°].
Stable in air.
IR : ν_{CO} 2152 cm⁻¹.
④ $$\xrightarrow{NaC_5H_5} [\pi\text{-}C_5H_5\text{-}Pt(CO)]_2$$
$$\xrightarrow{\text{dipy.}} [Pt(CO)(dipy)]^+[Pt(CO)Cl_3]^-$$
$$\xrightarrow{As(CH_3)(C_6H_5)_2}$$
Pt(CO)[As(CH₃)(C₆H₅)₂]Cl
⑥ JCS **1956**, 1860.

[Pt₂C₄H₆Cl₆]M₂

① K₂[Cl₆Pt₂(C₄H₆)], M=K
② $$K_2PtCl_4 + C_4H_6 \xrightarrow{5\% \ HCl-H_2O}$$
③ Orange crystals. [265° decomp.].
Stable in dry air.
⑥ JCS **1953**, 2939.   JACS **79**, 1279 (1957).
Inorg. Syn. **6**, 216 (1960).

Pt₂C₄H₈Cl₄

① μ, μ′-Dichloro-bis(ethylene)-di-
platinum
[(Cl)₂Pt(C₂H₄)]₂
② K₂PtCl₄ + C₂H₄ ⟶
Na₂PtCl₆ + C₂H₅OH ⟶ 75%
③ Rose colored solids. [165° decomp.].
Slightly sol. in most org. solvents;
easily sol. in acetone or ethanol.
④ + 4H₂ ⟶ 2Pt + 2C₂H₆ + 4HCl
+ 8KCN ⟶ 2K₂Pt(CN)₄ + 2C₂H₄
+ 4KCl
+ 2H₂O ⟶ 2Pt + 2H₃CHO + 4HCl
$$+ 2C_2H_4 \xrightarrow{-80°, \text{ acetone}}$$
2[Cl₂Pt(C₂H₄)₂](trans form ?)
$$+ 2C_2H_4 \xrightarrow{\text{r. t., acetone}}$$
2[Cl₂Pt(C₂H₄)₂](cis form ?)
⑥ JCS **1953**, 2939.   Inorg. Syn. **5**, 210
(1957).

Pt₂C₆H₁₈

① Hexamethyl-di-platinum
(CH₃)₆Pt₂
② $$(CH_3)_3PtI + K \xrightarrow{\text{in benzene}} 60\%$$
③ Very sol. in benzene, acetone and
ether ; slightly sol. in cold petroleum ether.
④ + I₂ ⟶ (CH₃)₃PtI
⑥ JACS **60**, 3086 (1938).

Pt₂C₈H₁₂Cl₄

① μ, μ′-Dichloro-2,4-dichloro-1,3-bis
-(butadiene)-di-platinum

CH$_2$=CH–CH=CH$_2$

② Pt$_2$Cl$_4$(C$_2$H$_4$)$_2$ +
   CH$_2$=CHCH=CH$_2$ ⟶
③ Dark brick-red.
   Unstable at room temp.
   Showed a weak absorption at
   1608 cm^{-1} due to the free double
   bond of each butadiene molecule
⑥ JACS **79**, 1277 (1957).

Pt$_2$C$_8$H$_{16}$Cl$_4$

① μ-Dichloro-dichloro-di(*trans*-2-bu-
   tene)-platinum
   [(Cl)$_2$Pt(*trans*-C$_4$H$_8$)]$_2$
② [Cl$_3$Pt(C$_2$H$_4$)] +
   trans-2-butene ⟶
③ Bright yellow. [110~115°].
   Unstable.
④ $\xrightarrow{\text{NaCN}}$ *trans*-CH$_3$CH=CHCH$_3$
⑥ JACS **79**, 1279 (1957).

Pt$_2$C$_{12}$H$_{10}$O$_2$

① Di-π-Cyclopentadienyl-di(carbonyl)
   -di-platinum
   [(π-C$_5$H$_5$)Pt(CO)]$_2$
② Cl$_2$Pt(CO)$_2$ + C$_5$H$_5$Na $\xrightarrow{\text{in benzene}}$ 5.8%
③ Red crystals.
   Sol. in common org. solvents.
   Unstable.
   Diamagnetic. dimereric.
   IR : ν_{CO} 2005 cm^{-1} (in nujol); 2020,
   1996 cm^{-1} (in C$_6$H$_{12}$).
④ + I$_2$ ⟶ C$_5$H$_5$Pt(CO)I
⑥ Ber. **96**, 2008 (1963). Z. Naturf. **18 b**,
   429 (1963).

Pt$_2$C$_{12}$H$_{20}$

① Tetramethyl-μ-(cyclooctatetraene)-
   diplatinum
   (CH$_3$)$_4$Pt$_2$(C$_8$H$_8$),

② I$_2$Pt(C$_8$H$_8$) + CH$_3$MgI
   $\xrightarrow{\text{in benzene}}$ 36%
③ Yellow crystals. [168~171°].
   Moderately sol. in chlorinated hydrocarbons and benzene.
   IR : ν_{Pt-C} 564, 548 cm^{-1}.
   NMR : τ 4.48(CH, 7 bands), 9.22(CH$_3$,
   triplet).
④ + P(C$_6$H$_5$)$_3$ ⟶
   [(CH$_3$)$_2$Pt{P(C$_6$H$_5$)$_3$}$_2$] + C$_8$H$_8$
   + C$_5$H$_5$Na ⟶ (C$_5$H$_5$)$_2$Pt(CH$_3$)$_2$
⑥ JACS **83**, 2768 (1961). Inorg. Chem.
   2, 1255 (1963).

Pt$_2$C$_{18}$H$_{28}$Cl$_2$O$_2$

① μ, μ′-Dichloro-bis(8-methoxycyclooct
   -4-enyl)-di-platinum

② Cl$_2$Pt(C$_8$H$_{12}$) $\xrightarrow{\text{Na}_2\text{CO}_3 \text{ in CH}_3\text{OH}}$
③ White powder. [150~170° decomp.].
   Sol. in org. solvents.
④ + *p*-CH$_3$C$_6$H$_4$NH$_2$ $\xrightarrow{\text{in CHCl}_3}$
   [(C$_8$H$_{12}$OCH$_3$)Pt(*p*-CH$_3$C$_6$H$_4$NH$_2$)Cl]
⑥ JCS **1957**, 2496.

Pt$_2$C$_{20}$H$_{36}$Cl$_4$

① μ-Dichloro-dichloro-di(2, 2, 5, 5-
   tetramethylhex-3-yne)-di-pla-
   tinum
   (Cl)$_4$Pt$_2$(*t*-C$_4$H$_9$·C≡C·C$_4$H$_9$-*t*)$_2$,

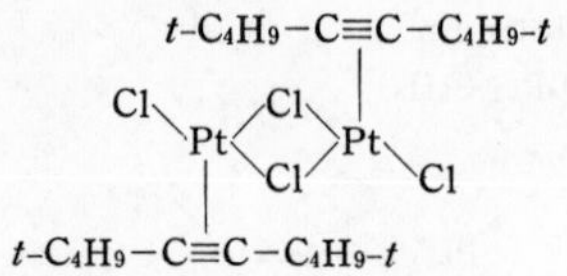

$$t\text{-}C_4H_9-C\equiv C-C_4H_9\text{-}t$$

$$t\text{-}C_4H_9-C\equiv C-C_4H_9\text{-}t$$

② NaPtCl₄ + t-C₄H₉·C≡C·C₄H₉-t

r. t. in C₂H₅OH
$\xrightarrow{}$ 81%

Cl₄Pt₂(C₂H₄)₂ + t-C₄H₉·C≡C·C₄H₉-t

in acetone
$\xrightarrow{}$ 74%

③ Red prisms. [184~187° decomp.].
Moderately sol. in light petroleum;
very sol. in other org. solvents;
insol. in H₂O. Stable in air.
Diamagnetic. Non-electrolytic in
nitrobenzene.
IR: $\nu_{C\equiv C}$ 2023, 2005 cm⁻¹.

④ + 2C₅H₅N $\longrightarrow$ 2·*trans*[Cl₂Pt(C₁₀H₁₈)
(C₅H₅N)]
+ KCl $\longrightarrow$ K[Cl₃Pt(C₁₀H₁₈)]

⑥ JCS 1961, 827.

Pt₂C₂₂H₃₀Cl₂O₂

① μ, μ'-Dichloro-bis(dicyclopentadiene
methoxide)-di-platinum
Cl₂Pt₂(C₁₀H₁₂OCH₃)₂

② Cl₂Pt(dicyclopentadiene) +
CH₃OH $\xrightarrow{\text{CH}_3\text{COONa or NaCO}_3}$

③ White plates. [205~220°].
Stable in air. Sol. in CHCl₃; insol. in
H₂O.
Dimeric. Non-electrolytic in nitro-
benzene.

④ + LiI $\longrightarrow$ I₂Pt₂(C₁₀H₁₂OCH₃)₂
+ NaSCN $\longrightarrow$ (NCS)₂Pt₂
－(C₁₀H₁₂OCH₃)₂
+ C₂H₅SNa $\longrightarrow$ (C₂H₅S)₂Pt₂
－(C₁₀H₁₂OCH₃)₂
+ p-CH₃C₆H₄NH₂ $\longrightarrow$
ClPt(C₁₀H₁₂OCH₃)(p-CH₃C₆H₄·NH₂)

⑥ Ber. 41, 1625 (1908). JCS 1957, 2496.

【Re】

ReC₅HO₅

① Hydrido-penta(carbonyl)-rhenium
(H)Re(CO)₅

② NaRe(CO)₅ or LiRe(CO)₅ $\xrightarrow{\text{H}_3\text{PO}_4}$

③ Colorless liq.
Air sensitive.
Typical unpleasent odor.

④ $\xrightarrow{100°}$ [Re(CO)₅]₂ + H₂

⑥ Quart. Rev. 1, 331 (1947). Z. Naturf.
14 b, 132 (1959).

ReC₆O₆X

① Hexa(carbonyl)-rhenium tetrachloroaluminate
[Re(CO)₆]·X, X＝AlCl₄

② Re(CO)₅Cl + AlCl₃
+ CO $\xrightarrow{300\sim350\,\text{atm., }85\sim95°}$

③ [205° decomp.].
Sol. in H₂O without decomp.
IR: ν_{CO} 2083 cm⁻¹ (KBr).

⑥ Angew. 73, 580 (1961). Quart. Rev.
17, 133 (1963). Ber. 96, 3028 (1963).

ReC₆H₃O₅

① Methyl-penta(carbonyl)-rhenium
(CH₃)Re(CO)₅

② NaRe(CO)₅ + CH₃I $\xrightarrow{\text{THF}}$

③ Colorless crystals. [120°].
Decomp. above ca. 140°.
Volatile

⑥ Z. Naturf. 14 b, 132 (1959).

ReC₈H₅O₃

① π-Cyclopentadienyl-tri(carbonyl)
-rhenium
(π-C₅H₅)Re(CO)₃

② Re(CO)₅Cl + NaC₅H₅
reflux in benzene
$\xrightarrow{}$ 89%

③ Yellow solid. [111~114°]. Sublime at 100° *in vacuo*.

Stable in air. Sol. in org. solvents.

④ + RCOCl $\xrightarrow{\text{AlCl}_3, \text{ in CS}_2}$

(π-RCOC$_5$H$_4$)Re(CO)$_3$ R=CH$_3$, C$_6$H$_5$

⑥ JCS **1958**, 4314.   Chem. & Ind. **1958**, 980.   JOM 1, 191 (1963).

ReC$_{10}$H$_7$O$_4$

① π-Acetylcyclopentadienyl-tri(carbonyl)-rhenium

(π-C$_5$H$_4$COCH$_3$)Re(CO)$_3$

② (π-C$_5$H$_5$)Re(CO)$_3$ + CH$_3$COCl

$\xrightarrow{\text{AlCl}_3, \text{ in CS}_2}$ 43%

③ Colorless crystals. [78°].

Stable in air. Sol. in org. solvents.

IR : ν_{CO} 2033, 1919, 1689 cm^{-1} (KBr).

⑥ JOM 1, 191 (1963).

ReC$_{10}$H$_{11}$

① Hydrodo-di-π-cyclopentadienyl-rhenium

(H)(π-C$_5$H$_5$)$_2$Re

② ReCl$_5$ + NaC$_5$H$_5$ $\xrightarrow{\text{in THF}}$ ~20%

③ Yellow crystals. [161~162°].

Sol. in petroleum ether, benzene and ether. Unstable in air.

IR : ν_{Re-H} 2030 cm^{-1} (in CS$_2$) ; 2037, 2000 cm^{-1} (crystals).

Diamagnetic.

④ + CO $\longrightarrow$ (π-C$_5$H$_5$)Re(CO)$_2$(C$_5$H$_6$)

$\underset{\text{OH}^-}{\overset{\text{H}^+}{\rightleftharpoons}}$ (π-C$_5$H$_5$)$_2$Re$^+$H$_2$

+ HCl $\longrightarrow$ [(π-C$_5$H$_5$)$_2$Re]Cl

⑥ JACS 77, 342 (11955). JCS **1958**, 3916, 4314.

ReC$_{12}$H$_7$O$_3$

① Indenyl-tri(carbonyl)-rhenium

(π-C$_9$H$_7$)Re(CO)$_3$,

② Re(CO)$_5$Cl + NaC$_9$H$_7$

$\xrightarrow[\text{reflux in benzene}]{}$ 80%

③ Colorless. Sublime at 90° *in vacus*. [89°].

Stable in air.

IR : ν_{CO} 2024, 1908 cm^{-1}.

⑥ JOM 1, 191 (1963).

ReC$_{12}$H$_{11}$O$_2$

① π-Cyclopentadienyl-di(carbonyl)-(cyclopentadiene)-rhenium

(π-C$_5$H$_5$)Re(CO)$_2$(C$_5$H$_6$)

② (π-C$_5$H$_5$)ReH + CO $\xrightarrow{250\,\text{atm. }100°}$

③ Pale yellow crystals. [111~112°].

④ + H$_2$ $\longrightarrow$ (π-C$_5$H$_5$)Re(CO)$_2$(C$_5$H$_8$)

⑥ Naturf. **12b**, 737 (1957).   JCS **1958**, 4314 ; **1959**, 3753.

ReC$_{13}$H$_{10}$IN$_2$O$_3$

① Iodo-tri(carbony)-bis(pyridine)-rhenium

(I)Re(CO)$_3$(C$_5$H$_5$N)$_2$

② [Re(CO)$_4$I]$_2$ + C$_5$H$_5$N $\xrightarrow{\text{reflux}}$ 79%

Re(CO)$_5$I + C$_5$H$_5$N $\xrightarrow{\text{reflux}}$ 72%

③ Pale yellow crystals.

IR : ν_{CO} 2041, 1934, 1891 cm^{-1}.

⑥ JCS **1958**, 3149.

ReC$_{15}$H$_9$O$_4$

① π-benzoylcyclopentadienyl-tri(carbonyl)-rhenium

(π-C$_5$H$_4$COC$_6$H$_5$)Re(CO)$_3$

② (π-C$_5$H$_5$)Re(CO)$_3$ + C$_6$H$_5$COCl

$\xrightarrow{\text{AlCl}_3, \text{ in CS}_2}$ 41%

③ Colorless crystals. [101°].

Stable in air. Sol. in org. solvents.

IR : ν_{CO} 2037, 1946, 1916, 1639 cm^{-1}.

⑥ JOM 1, 191 (1963).

$ReC_{16}H_{12}Cl$
① Chloro-bis(phenylacetylene)-rhe-
   nium
   $(Cl)Re(C_6H_5C\equiv CH)_2$
② $ReCl_3 + C_6H_5C\equiv CH \longrightarrow$
③ Very stable.
   Monomeric. Diamagnetic.
   IR : $\nu_{C\equiv C}$ 1700 cm^{-1}.
⑥ Nature 186, 233 (1960).

$ReC_{40}H_{30}O_4 \cdot X$
① Tetra(carbonyl)-bis(triphenylphosphine)-rhenium-tetrachloro
   -aluminate
   $\{Re(CO)_4[P(C_6H_5)_3]_2\} \cdot X$, $X = AlCl_4$
② $Re(CO)_3[P(C_6H_5)_3]_2Cl + AlCl_3 + CO$
   $\xrightarrow[\text{400 atm, 20°C}]{} 70\%$
③ Colorless. [200°].
   Sol. in methanol, acetone and THF ;
   slightly sol. in H_2O ; insol. in
   ether, petroleum ether and benzene.
④ $+ B \xrightarrow{\text{in } CH_3OH-H_2O} \{Re(CO)_4$
   $[P(C_6H_5)_3]_2\} \cdot B$
   $B = [Cr(NH_3)_2(NCS)_2]^-$, $B(C_6H_5)_4^-$,
   ClO_4^-
⑥ Ber. 96, 3035 (1963).

$Re_2C_8Cl_2O_8$
① Di-μ, μ'-Dichloro-octa(carbonyl)
   -dirhenium
   $[(Cl)Re(CO)_4]_2$
② $Re(CO)_5Cl \xrightarrow{\text{reflux in light petroleum}} 86\%$
③ Fine white crystals.
   Decomp. on heating without melting.
   Sparingly sol. in org. solvents.
   IR : ν_{CO} 2043, 2010, 1964 cm^{-1} (in
   $CHCl_3$).
④ $+ CO \xrightarrow{\text{high temp. and pressure}}$
   $Re(CO)_5Cl$

⑥ JCS 1958, 3149.

$Re_2C_{10}O_{10}$
① Deca(carbonyl)-dirhenium
   $[Re(CO)_5]_2$
② Re_2S_7, Re_2O_7 or $KReO_4$
   $+ CO \xrightarrow[\text{200 atm, 250°}]{}$
③ Colorless crystals. [177°].
   Very stable. Resist. to dil. acids,
   bases and concd. HCl ; decomp. by
   hot HNO_3 or H_2SO_4.
   Monoclinic.
   IR : ν_{CO} 2049, 2013, 1983 cm^{-1}.
④ $+ 2M \longrightarrow 2MRe(CO)_5$ M = alkali-
   metal
   $+ X_2 \longrightarrow 2Re(CO)_5X$ X = halogene
   $+ pyridine \xrightarrow[\text{240°, 16 hrs}]{} Re(CO)_3$
   (pyridine)$_2$
   $+ o$-phenanthroline
   $\xrightarrow{\text{120°, in benzene, sealed tube}}$
   $Re(CO)_3(o$-phenanthroline)
⑥ Z. anorg. allg. Chem. 248, 262 (1941).
   Quart. Rev. 1, 331(1947). Z. Naturf.
   14 b, 132 (1959).   Quart. Rev. 17,
   133 (1963).

【Rh】

RhC_4HO_4
① Hydrido-tetra(carbonyl)-rhodium
   $(H)Rh(CO)_4$
② $Rh + CO + H_2 \xrightarrow{200°}$
   $RhCl + CO \xrightarrow{200°}$
③ Pale yellow crystals. Sublime readily.
   $[-10° \sim -12°]$.
   Decompd. readily at room temp. to
   form pure $Rh(CO)_4$.
⑥ Z. anorg. allg. Chem. 251, 96 (1943).

$RhC_7H_5O_2$
① π-Cyclopentadienyl-di(carbonyl)-

rhodium

(π-C$_5$H$_5$)Ph(CO)$_2$

② [(Cl)Ph(CO)$_2$]$_2$ $\xrightarrow{\text{C}_5\text{H}_5\text{Na}}$ 26.8%

③ Deep orange liq. [−11°].

Very sol. in org. solvents. Unstable in air.

Diamagnetic.

IR: ν_{CO} 2051, 1987 cm^{-1}.

⑥ Naturf. **16b**, 225 (1961).

RhC$_9$H$_{13}$

① π-Cyclopentadienyl-di(ethylene)

-rhodium

(π-C$_5$H$_5$)Rh(C$_2$H$_4$)

② C$_5$H$_5$Na + [(C$_2$H$_4$)$_2$RhCl]$_2$ $\longrightarrow$

③ Yellow crystals. Volatile. [72~73°].

Sol. in org. solvents. Stable in air.

NMR: τ 4.92 (sharp, C$_5$H$_5$), 7.25 and 9.00 (broad, C$_2$H$_4$).

⑥ Inorg. Chem. **2**, 528 (1963).

RhC$_{10}$H$_{11}$

① π-Cyclopentadienyl-(cyclopentadiene)-rhodium

(π-C$_5$H$_5$)(C$_5$H$_6$)Rh

② RhCl$_3$ + C$_5$H$_5$Na $\xrightarrow[\text{in THF}]{\quad}$ $\xrightarrow{\text{NaBH}_4}$ 40%

π-(C$_5$H$_5$)$_2$RhCl $\xrightarrow{\text{NaBH}_4}$ 80%

Orange yellow crystals. (50°/*in vacuo*. sublime). [121~122°]

Decomp. in air, but stable in absence of air. Sol. in benzene, light petroleum, and similer org. solvents.

UV: λ_{max} 369 (2840), 297 (3010), 236.5 mμ (19700).

④ + H$^+$ $\longrightarrow$ π-(C$_5$H$_5$)$_2$Rh$^+$ + $\frac{1}{2}$H$_2$

+ H$_2$O$_2$ + H$^+$ $\longrightarrow$ π-(C$_5$H$_5$)Rh$^+$ + H$_2$O

+ CCl$_4$ $\longrightarrow$ π-(C$_5$H$_5$)$_2$Rh$^+$Cl$^-$ + CHCl$_3$

⑥ Ber. **92**, 1624 (1959).　JCS **1959**, 3753.

RhC$_{13}$H$_{17}$

① π-Cyclopentadienyl-(cyclooctadiene)-rhodium

(π-C$_5$H$_5$)Rh(C$_8$H$_{10}$)

② [(Cl)Rh(C$_8$H$_{10}$)]$_2$ + C$_5$H$_5$Na $\xrightarrow{\text{in THF}}$

③ Yellow solid. [108~108.5°].

Very sol. in chloform, dichoromethane and benzene; moderately sol. in alc., light petroleum and ether. Stable in N$_2$.

⑥ JCS **1957**, 4735.　Nature **177**, 853 (1956).

RhC$_{17}$H$_{14}$ClN$_2$O$_3$

① Chloro-(carbonyl)-di(p-methoxy-phenylisonitrile)-rhodium

(Cl)Rh(CO)(p-CH$_3$OC$_6$H$_4$NC)$_2$

② Rh$_2$(CO)$_4$Cl$_2$

+ p-CH$_3$OC$_6$H$_4$NC $\xrightarrow{\text{in benzene}}$

③ [40~50° decomp.].

Stable in solid state; decomp. rapidly in solution.

Diamagnetic. Non conducting in C$_6$H$_5$NO$_2$

④ + p-CH$_3$OC$_6$H$_4$NC

$\xrightarrow{\text{NH}_4\text{PF}_6}$ [Rh(CH$_3$OC$_6$H$_4$NC)$_4$]PF$_6$

+ P(C$_6$H$_5$)$_3$

$\longrightarrow$ Rh(p-CH$_3$OC$_6$H$_4$CN)$_2${P(C$_6$H$_5$)$_3$}

⑥ Gazz. chim. ital. **89**, 1632 (1959).

Rh$_2$C$_4$O$_4$Cl$_2$

① $\mu\mu'$-Dichloro-tetra(carbonyl)-dirhodium

OC　　　Cl　　　CO
　＼Rh＜　＞Rh＜
OC　　　Cl　　　CO

② RhCl$_3$ + CO $\xrightarrow{\text{200 atm., 150°C}}$ 98%

③ Ruby-red needles. [123°].

Insol. in H$_2$O; very sol. in usual org. solvents.

Diamagnetic.

IR: ν_{CO} 2110, 2090, 2082, 2005 cm^{-1} (in CCl$_4$).

④ $\xrightarrow{C_5H_5Na}$ π-$C_5H_5Rh(CO)_2$

$\xrightarrow{Ph_3P}$ $Rh(CO)(Ph_3P)_2Cl$

$\xrightarrow{C_5H_5N}$ $(C_5H_5N)_2(CO)_2Rh\underset{Cl}{\overset{Cl}{<}}>Rh$

$(CO)_2(C_5H_5N)_2$

⑥ Ann **560**, 1, 93, 104 (1948). Z. anorg. allg. Chem. **251**, 96 (1943). Ber. **90**, 2425 (1957).   JACS **83**, 1761 (1961).

$Rh_2C_8O_8$

① Octa(carbonyl)-dirhodium
    $[Rh(CO)_4]_2$

② $RhCl_3 + CO \longrightarrow$
    $Na_3RhCl_6 + H_2 \xrightarrow[CO,\ 200\,atm,\ 200°]{} Rh$

③ Orange-yellow crystals. [76° decomp.].
    Very sensitive to air, H_2O, acids or bases.

⑥ Z. anorg. allg. Chem. **215**, 242 (1933); **251**, 96 (1943).

$Rh_2C_8H_{16}Cl_2$

① $\mu\mu'$-Dichloro-tetra(ethylene)-dirhodium
    $[(Cl)Rh(C_2H_4)_2]_2$

② $RhCl_3 \cdot 3H_2O + C_2H_4 \xrightarrow{aq.\ CH_3OH}$

③ Orange red. [115° decomp.].
    Moderately stable in air.
    Dimeric.

④ $\xrightarrow{C_5H_5Na}$ π-$C_5H_5Rh(C_2H_4)_2$
    $\xrightarrow{C_8H_8}$ $[ClRh(C_8H_8)]_2$

⑥ Inorg. Chem. **1**, 722 (1962).

$Rh_2C_{16}H_{24}Cl_2$

① $\mu\mu'$-Dichloro-di(cycloocta-1,5-diene)-dirhodium
    $[(Cl)Rh(C_8H_{12})]_2$

② $RhCl_3 \cdot 3H_2O + C_8H_{12}$
    $\xrightarrow[\text{boil in } C_2H_5OH]{} 60\%$
    $Cl_2Rh_2(CO)_4 + C_8H_{12} \longrightarrow$

$RhCl_3 \cdot 3H_2O + C_8H_{12} \xrightarrow{NaBH_4,\ r.\ t.}$

③ Orange-Yellow crystals. [256°].
    Sol· in chlorinated solvents; moderately sol. in other org. solvents; insol. in H_2O.
    Dimeric. Diamagnetic. Non-electrolyte in nitrobenzene.
    NMR: $\tau\,5.8$ and $4.3(C_8H_{12}$, suggesting that C_8H_{12} has a "tub" cofiguration).

④ $+ 2L \longrightarrow 2[ClRh(C_8H_{12})L]$
    L = amine or phosphine
    $+ 2HCl \longrightarrow 2H[Cl_2Ph(C_8H_{12})]$
    $+ 2\pi$-$C_5H_5Na \longrightarrow 2\pi$-$C_5H_5Rh(C_8H_{12})$
    $+ LiBr \xrightarrow{\text{in acetone}} [BrRh(C_8H_{12})]_2$
    $+ 2$diamine
    $\longrightarrow 2[Rh(C_8H_{12})(diamine)]Cl$

⑥ JCS **1957**, 4735.

【Ru】

$RuC_2I_2O_2$

① Di-iodo-di(carbonyl)-ruthenium
    $\{(I)_2Ru(CO)_2\}n$

② $RuI_3 \xrightarrow{CO,\ 250°}$

② Reddish-brown. No decomp. below 250°.
    Insol. in the common solvents.
    Iodine-bridged polymer.
    Diamagnetic.
    IR: ν_{CO} 1995, 2050 cm^{-1}.

④ $\xrightarrow{p\text{-toluidine, 100°C}}$
    $[I_2Ru(CH_3C_6H_4NH_2)_2(CO)_2]$
    $\xrightarrow{As(C_6H_5)_2(CH_3)}$
    $\{I_2Ru[As(C_6H_5)_2(CH_3)]_2(CO)_2\}$
    $\xrightarrow{NH_2C_6H_5,\ reflux}$
    $[I_2Ru(C_6H_5NH_2)_2(CO)_3]$

⑥ JCS **1959**, 3178; **1956**, 2879.

RuC_5O_5

① Penta(carbonyl)-ruthenium

Ru(CO)$_5$

② RuCl$_3$ $\xrightarrow{\text{N}_2\text{H}_4\cdot\text{H}_2\text{SO}_4-\text{NaOH}}$ Ru-black

Ag or Cu−coated autoclave,
300°, 400 atm, 14 days
$\xrightarrow{\hspace{3cm}}$

RuI$_3$ $\xrightarrow[\text{Cu−coated autoclave}]{\text{CO, 455 atm, 24 hr, 170°, Ag in}}$

③ Coloress liq. Very volatile. [−22°].
Very sensitive to light.

④ $\xrightarrow{h\nu}$ [Ru(CO)$_4$]$_3$

$\xrightarrow[\hspace{2cm}]{\text{NO gas, 120°, 13 hr}}$ Ru(NO)$_5$

⑥ Z. anorg. allg. Chem. **226**, 385 (1936).

RuC$_7$H$_5$IO$_2$

① π-Cyclopentadienyl-iodo-di(carbonyl)-ruthenium
(π-C$_5$H$_5$)(I)Ru(CO)$_2$

② [(C$_5$H$_5$)Ru(CO)$_2$]$_2$ $\xrightarrow{\text{I}_2 \text{ in CCl}_4}$

③ Orange crystals. (100°/0.1 sublime).
[103∼105°].
IR: ν_{CO} 2055(vs), 2007(vs), 1976(sh),
1840(vw) cm^{-1}.

④ $\xrightarrow{\text{NaBH}_4}$ (C$_5$H$_5$)(H)Ru(CO)$_2$

⑥ JCS **1963**, 1133.

RuC$_7$H$_6$O$_2$

① π-Cyclopentadienyl-hydrido-
di(carbonyl)-ruthenium
(H)(π-C$_5$H$_5$)Ru(CO)$_2$

② (π-C$_5$H$_5$)Ru(CO)$_2$I $\xrightarrow{\text{NaBH}_4}$

③ Colorless liq. Volatile.
Very sensitive to air.
IR: ν_{Ru-H} 1853 cm^{-1} (in CS$_2$).
NMR: τ 20.92 (in C$_6$H$_{12}$).

⑥ JCS **1963**, 1133.

RuC$_7$H$_8$Cl$_2$

① Dichloro-(norbornadiene)-ruthenium
[(Cl)$_2$Ru(C$_7$H$_8$)]$_n$

② RuCl$_3$·H$_2$O + C$_7$H$_8$ $\xrightarrow{\text{C}_2\text{H}_5\text{OH}}$

③ Yellow crystals. [190∼200° decomp.].

Insol. in H$_2$O and all org. solvents.
Diamagnetic.

④ $\xrightarrow{\text{LiBr}}$ C$_7$H$_8$RuBr$_2$

$\xrightarrow{\text{C}_5\text{H}_5\text{N}}$ Ru(C$_5$H$_4$N)$_4$Cl$_2$

p-toluidine
$\xrightarrow{\hspace{2cm}}$

Ru(C$_7$H$_8$)(*p*-CH$_3$C$_6$H$_4$NH$_2$)$_2$Cl$_2$

⑥ JCS **1959**, 3178.

RuC$_8$H$_8$O$_2$

① π-Cyclopentadienyl-methyl-di(carbonyl)-ruthenium
(π-C$_5$H$_5$)(CH$_3$)Ru(CO)$_2$

② [(C$_5$H$_5$)Ru(CO)$_2$]$_2$ $\xrightarrow{\text{1\% Na−Hg}}$

(C$_5$H$_5$)Ru(CO)$_2$Na $\xrightarrow{\text{CH}_3\text{I}}$

③ White volatile solids. (40°/0.1 sub
lime). [39∼40°].
Sol. in org. solvents.
IR: ν_{CO} 1960(vs), 1933(sh), 1845(vw),
1805(vw), 1740(vw) cm^{-1} (in CS$_2$).

⑥ JCS **1963**, 1133.

RuC$_{10}$H$_{10}$

① Di-π-cyclopentadienyl-ruthenium,
Ruthenocene

(π-C$_5$H$_5$)$_2$Ru,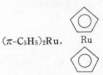

② Ru^{III}(acac)$_3$ + C$_5$H$_5$MgBr $\xrightarrow{20\%}$

RuCl$_3$ + C$_5$H$_5$Na $\xrightarrow{\hspace{1cm}}$ 52%

③ Yellowish white crystals. (120∼130°/
in vacuo, sublime). [195∼196°].
Sol. in org. solvents. Unaffected by
bases, sulfuric acid or HCl in
absence of O$_2$.
UV: λ_{max} 280 (log ε=2.2), 320 mμ (log
ε=2.3).
Diamagnetic.

④ $\xrightarrow[\text{controlled potential anodic oxidation}]{C_2H_5OH-HClO_4}$

$(C_5H_5)_2Ru^+ClO_4^-$

$\xrightarrow{CH_3COCl,\ AlCl_3}$ $(CH_3CO \cdot C_5H_4)(C_5H_5)Ru$

$+ (CH_3CO \cdot C_5H_4)_2Ru$

$\xrightarrow{Hg(OCOCH_3)_2}$ $(C_5H_4 \cdot HgCl)(C_5H_5)Ru$

$\xrightarrow{n-C_4H_9Li}$ $(C_5H_4 \cdot Li)(C_5H_5)Ru$

$+ (C_5H_4Li)_2Ru$

⑥ JACS **74**, 6146 (1952).   Spectrochim. Acta **10**, 307 (1958).   Ber. **92**, 2302 (1959).   Org. Syn. **41**, 96 (1961).

$RuC_{17}H_{14}O$

① π-Cyclopentadienyl-benzoyl cyclopentadienyl-ruthenium,
Benzoylruthenocene
$(C_5H_5)(C_6H_5COC_5H_4)Ru$,

② $(C_5H_5)_2Ru + C_6H_5COCl$ $\xrightarrow{AlCl_3}$ 64%
③ Yellow crystals. [124.5~125°].
Sol. in CH_2Cl_2 and benzene.
IR: ν_{CO} 1631 cm^{-1}.
⑥ JACS **82**, 76 (1960).

$[RuC_{18}H_{24}]^{2+}X_2^{2-}$

① Di(mesitylene)-ruthenium-di-tetraphenylborate
$[Ru\{C_6H_3(CH_3)_3\}_2]^{2+}X_2^-$, $X^-=B(C_6H_5)_4^-$
② $RuCl_3 + AlCl_3 + Al + C_6H_3(CH_3)_3$
$\xrightarrow[130°,\ 8\sim10\,hrs]{Na[B(C_6H_5)_4]}$ 11%
③ Yellow needles.
Sol. in acetone, insol. ether and H_2O.
⑥ Z. anorg. allg. Chem. **291**, 305 (1957).

$RuC_{32}H_{28}Cl_2H_4$

① Dichloro-tetra(p-tolylisocyanide)-ruthenium
$(Cl)_2Ru(p-CH_3C_6H_4NC)_4$
② $RuCl_3 + p-CH_3C_6H_4NC$
in anhyd. C_2H_5OH
③ Light green crystals. [256° decomp.].
Stable in air.
Diamagnetic.
⑥ Gazz. chim. ital. **85**, 1111 (1955).

$RuC_{53}H_{52}P_4$

① cis-Hydrido-methyl-di(1,2-bis-diphenylphosphinoethane) ruthenium
cis-(H)(CH$_3$)Ru
$\{(C_6H_5)_2PCH_2CH_2P(C_6H_5)_2\}_2$
② trans-(Cl$_2$)Ru
$\{(C_6H_5)_2PCH_2CH_2P(C_6H_5)_2\}$
$\xrightarrow[80°,\ \{Al^I(CH_3)_3\}_2]{}$ 70% trans-ClCH$_3$Ru
$\{(C_6H_5)_2P(H_2CH_2P(C_6H_5)_2\}_2$ $\xrightarrow{LiAlH_4}$ 65%
③ Colorless crystals. [247~251.5° decomp.].
Sol. in benzene. Decomp. slowly in air.
IR: ν_{M-H} 1884 cm^{-1}; τ 18.9.
Dipole moment: 3.25 D.
④ $\xrightarrow{HCl}$ trans-$\{(Cl)(Me)Ru-$
$[(C_6H_5)_2P \cdot CH_2CH_2P(C_6H_5)_2]_2\} + H_2$
⑥ JCS **1963**, 6017.

$Ru_2C_{14}H_{10}O_4$

① Di-π-cyclopentadienyl-tetra(carbonyl)-diruthenium
$[(π-C_5H_5)Ru(CO)_2]_2$
② $Ru(CO)_2I_2 + C_5H_5Na$ $\longrightarrow$ 60%
③ Yellow crystals. (140~155° in vacuo sublime). [185° decomp.].
UV: λ_{max} 263, 328, 440 mμ (ε 10083, 6720, 500)
④ 1% Na-Hg $\longrightarrow$ π-$C_5H_5Ru(CO)_2Na$
$\xrightarrow{CH_3I}$ π-$C_5H_5Ru(CO)_2 \cdot CH_3$
⑥ Z. Naturf. **17 b**, 421 (1962).

Ru₃C₁₂O₁₂

① Dodeca(carbonyl)-triruthenium
   [Ru(CO)₄]₃

② Ru(CO)₅ $\xrightarrow{h\nu \text{ or } 50°}$

③ Yellow crytals. [150° decomp.].
   Insol. in H₂O; sol in org solvents
   Stable to air and light
   The structure was determined as
   trinuclear ruthenium carbonyl for
   the widely accepted Ru₂ (CO)₉ by
   X-ray diffraction.

④ $\xrightarrow{I_2}$ RuI₂(CO)₂

⑥ Z. anorg. allg. Chem. **225**, 385 (1936).
   JACS **83**, 2203 (1961).

【Tc】

TcC₈H₅O₃

① Cyclopentadienyl-tri(carbonyl)
   technetium
   (π-C₅H₅)Tc(CO)₃

② Tc(CO)₅Cl + NaC₅H₅ ⟶ 86%
   [(π-C₅H₅)Mo(CO)₃]₂ $\xrightarrow{\text{neutron}}$

③ (120°/vac. sublime). [87.5°].
   UV: λ_{max} 274 mμ (log ε 3.69).

⑥ Naturwiss. **49**, 156, 279 (1962).

TcC₁₀H₁₀

① Dicyclopentadienyl technetium
   [(π-C₅H₅)₂Tc]₂

② NH₄TcO₄ ⟶ TcCl₄ $\xrightarrow{\text{NaC}_5\text{H}_5}$ 8%

③ Golden yellow crystals. [155°].
   Extremely air sensitive.
   Dimeric. Diamagnetic.
   IR: 3100, 1915~1940 (broad), 1410,
     1340, 1257, 1188, 1100, 1050, 1003, 996,
     803, 775 cm⁻¹.
   NMR: τ5.61.

⑥ JACS **83**, 4474 (1961).

TcC₁₂H₁₂F₆P

① Di(benzene)technetium hexafluoro-
   phosphate

[Tc(C₆H₆)₂]PF₆

② TcCl₄ + Al + AlCl₃ + C₆H₆
   $\xrightarrow{135°,\ 2\,\text{days}}$ 7%

③ Pale yellow-green solid. [250°
   decomp.].
   Stable to air, acids and bases.
   UV: λ_{max} 400 mμ (log ε 1.98).
   Diamagnetic.
   IR: 3096, 1443, 1157, 1146, 1022, 978, 916,
     836, 778, 740 cm⁻¹.
   NMR: τ4.64.

⑥ Tetrahedron Letters **1962**, 253.

Tc₂C₁₀O₁₀

① Dodeca(carbonyl)-ditechnetium
   Tc₂(CO)₁₀

② NH₄TcO₄ ⟶ Tc₂O₇
   $\xrightarrow{220°,\ 20\,\text{hr.,\ CO}}$ 7%

③ Colorless crystals. [159~160°].
   Air sensitive.
   IR: ν_{CO} 2064, 2016, 1981 cm⁻¹.
   Diamagnetic.

④ + I₂ $\xrightarrow{100°,\ 30\,\text{hrs.}}$ [Tc(CO)₄I]₂
   + I₂ + CO ⟶ Tc(CO)₅I
   + CCl₄ ⟶ Tc(CO)₅Cl
   + [Tc(CO)₄Cl]₂

⑥ JACS **83**, 2953 (1961). Angew. **73**, 579
   (1961).

【Ti】

TiCH₃Cl₃

① Methyl-trichloro-trtanium
   (CH₃)(Cl)₃Ti

② TiCl₄ + (CH₃)₂AlCl ⟶

③ Violet crystals. Yellow liq. (120°).
   [28~29°].
   Sol. in org. solvents such as hexane,
   benzene and chlorinated hydrocarbons.

④ + ROH ⟶ ROTiCl₃ + CH₄
   + SnCl₄ ⟶ TiCl₄ + Sn(CH₃)₄
   + 1/2 O₂ ⟶ CH₃OTiCl₃

$+ I_2 \longrightarrow CH_3I + TiCl_3I$

⑤ Catalyst for ethylene polymerzation.

⑥ Angew. 71, 618 (1959).

TiC₂H₅Cl₃

① Ethyl-trichloro-titanium
$(C_2H_5)(Cl)_3Ti$

② $TiCl_4 + (C_2H_5)_4Pb \xrightarrow{-80°} 40-50\%$

③ Violet solid.
0.005 M−solution in toluene showed 20% decomp. in 5 hrs. at 60∼70°.

④ $+ 1/2\ O_2 \longrightarrow C_2H_5OTiCl_3$

⑤ The system $C_2H_5TiCl_3-R_4Pb$ is a catalyst for ethylene polymerization.

⑥ Proc. Chem. Soc. 1959, 227.

TiC₂H₆Cl₂

① Dimethyl-dichloro-titanium
$(CH_3)_2(Cl)_2Ti$

② $(CH_3)_3Al + CH_3TiCl_3 \longrightarrow$

③ Brack crystals.
Sol. in hexane forming bright-yellow solution in which $(CH_3)_2(Cl)_2Ti$ decomp. readily.

⑥ Angew.71, 618 (1959).

TiC₅H₅Cl₃

① π-Cyclopentadienyl-trichloro-titanium
$(\pi\text{-}C_5H_5)(Cl)_3Ti$

② $(\pi\text{-}C_5H_5)_2 \cdot TiCl_2 + TiCl_4 \longrightarrow 84\%$
$(\pi\text{-}C_5H_5)_2 \cdot TiCl_2 + Cl_2 \longrightarrow$

③ Yellow prisms. [185° decomp.].
Sol. in ethers, ketones, aromatics, concd. H_2SO_4. Relatively stable in air.
IR: ν_{C-H}: 3.3μ

④ $+ C_5H_5Na \longrightarrow (\pi\text{-}C_5H_5)_2 \cdot TiCl_2$ (85%)
$+Cl_2 \longrightarrow TiCl_4 + C_5H_5Cl_5$

⑥ JACS 80, 4744 (1958); 81, 1364 (1959).

TiC₆H₅Al₂Cl₈

① $[TiAlCl_5C_6H_5]AlCl_3,$
$TiAl_2Cl_8(C_6H_6)$

② $TiCl_4 + AlCl_3 + Al + C_6H_6 \longrightarrow$

③ Violet crystals. [110∼115° decomp.].
Vesy sol. in benzene and toluene; slightly sol. in aliphatic hydrocarbons.

④ $+ O_2 \xrightarrow{\text{moisture}} HCl + C_6H_5OH$
$+ H_2O \longrightarrow C_6H_6$
$+ \text{mesitylene} \longrightarrow C_6H_6$

⑥ Tetrahedron 8, 86 (1960). Ber. 94, 2416 (1961).

TiC₁₀H₁₀

① Di-π-cyclopentadienyl-titanium
$(\pi\text{-}C_5H_5)_2Ti$

② $TiCl_2 + C_5H_5Na \xrightarrow{\text{THF}}$

③ Green crystals. (120∼180°/10⁻³ sublime, decomp.).
Diamagnetic.

④ $+ FeCl_2 \longrightarrow [(C_5H_5)_2Ti^{III}]^+$
(indigo-colored)
↓
$[(C_5H_5)_2Ti^{IV}(OH)]$
(yellow)
$+ THF \longrightarrow$ green paramagnetic tetrahydrofuranate
↓
brown diamagnetic form

⑥ JINC 2, 149 (1956).

TiC₁₀H₁₀Cl₂

① Di-π-cyclopentadienyl-dichloro-titanium
$(\pi\text{-}C_5H_5)_2(Cl)_2Ti$

② $C_5H_5Li + TiCl_4 \longrightarrow 72\%$
$C_5H_5Na + TiCl_4 \longrightarrow 90\%$

③ Dark red crystals. (190°/2 sublime). [289∼291°].
Moderately sol. in toluene, chloroform and alcohols; sparingly sol. in ether, benzene, CS_2, CCl_4, petroleum ether and H_2O.
NMR: τ3.42 (in CCl_3D).
Dipole moment: 5.57±0.05 D.

⑥ JACS 76, 4281 (1954).

TiC$_{12}$H$_{10}$O$_2$

① Di-π-cyclopentadienyl-di(carbonyl)
   -titanium
   (π-C$_5$H$_5$)$_2$Ti(CO)$_2$

② TiCl$_4$ + C$_5$H$_5$Na + CO
   $\xrightarrow[\quad\quad\quad\quad]{100°,\ 110\,atm(r.\ t.\ )}$ 45%

   (C$_5$H$_5$)$_2$TiCl$_2$ + C$_5$H$_5$Na + CO
   $\xrightarrow[\quad\quad\quad\quad]{100°,\ 110\,atm(r.\ t.\ )}$ 18%

   (C$_5$H$_5$)$_2$TiCl$_2$ + BuLi + CO $\xrightarrow{150°,\ 240\,atm}$

③ Red-brown needles. (90°/1 sublime
   with appreciable decomp.) [above
   90° decomp.].
   Readily sol. in common org. solvents.
   Very air sensitive and pyrophoric
   in air; stable in N$_2$.
   IR: ν$_{C-O}$ 5.09, 5.31μ (in C$_6$H$_6$ or
   THF).
   + I$_2$ ⟶ CO

⑥ JACS **83**, 1287 (1961).

TiC$_{12}$H$_{15}$AlCl$_3$

① (C$_2$H$_5$)(π-C$_5$H$_5$)$_2$(Cl)$_3$TiAl,

② (C$_5$H$_5$)$_2$TiCl$_2$ + Al(C$_2$H$_5$)$_2$Cl ⟶
   (C$_5$H$_5$)$_2$TiCl + Al(C$_2$H$_5$)Cl$_2$ ⟶

③ [88~92°].
   Highly sol. in aromatic solvents.
   Paramagnetic, 1.57 B. M.

④ + HCl ⟶ (C$_5$H$_5$)$_2$TiCl$_2$

⑥ Tetrahedron **8**, 81 (1960).

TiC$_{12}$H$_{16}$

① Dimethyl-di-π-cyclopentidienyl
   -titanium
   (CH$_3$)$_2$(π-C$_5$H$_5$)$_2$Ti

② (C$_5$H$_5$)$_2$TiCl$_2$ + CH$_3$MgI ⟶ 1%

③ Orange-Yellow waxy solid. (40°/10^{-4}

sublime). Decompd. above 100°.

IR: ν$_{C-H}$ 3090(w), 2930(m), 2860(m),
2780(w)cm^{-1}.

NMR: (π-C$_5$H$_5$), 1.5 ppm. (CH$_3$), 7.6
ppm (relative to C$_6$H$_5$ protons in
toluene).

⑥ JINC **3**, 104 (1956).

TiC$_{13}$H$_{15}$

① Di-π-cyclopentadienyl-π-allyl-
   titanium
   (π-C$_5$H$_5$)$_2$(π-C$_3$H$_5$)Ti

② (π-C$_5$H$_5$)$_2$·TiCl$_2$
   + CH$_2$=CHCH$_2$MgBr ⟶

③ Violet crystals. [118° decomp.].
   Readily oxydized by air, stable in N$_2$.
   IR: π-C$_5$H$_5$ 1435 cm^{-1}.
   UV: λ$_{max}$ 510 mμ (hexane).

④ + O$_2$ + HCl ⟶ (π-C$_5$H$_5$)$_2$·TiCl$_2$
   + Octanol ⟶ CH$_3$CH=CH$_2$ (80%)

⑥ Angew. **76**, 274 (1964).

TiC$_{14}$H$_{20}$AlCl$_2$

① (C$_2$H$_5$)$_2$(π-C$_5$H$_5$)$_2$(Cl)$_2$TiAl,

② (C$_5$H$_5$)$_2$TiCl$_2$ + Al(C$_2$H$_5$)$_3$ ⟶
   (C$_5$H$_5$)$_2$TiCl + AlCl(C$_2$H$_5$)$_2$ ⟶

③ Blue crystals. [126~130°]
   Highly sol. in aromatic solvents.
   Paramagnetic, 1.70 B. M.

④ + HCl ⟶ (C$_5$H$_5$)$_2$TiCl$_2$

⑤ Catalyst for ethylene polymerization.

⑥ JACS **79**, 2975 (1957).   Tetrahedron
   8, 86 (1960).

TiC$_{15}$H$_{26}$O$_3$

① Tri-isopropoxy-phenyl-titanium

$(i\text{-}C_3H_7O)_3(C_6H_5)Ti$

② $C_6H_5Li + (i\text{-}C_3H_7O)_4Ti$
$\longrightarrow C_6H_5Ti(O\ i\text{-}C_3H_7)_3 \cdot i\text{-}C_3H_7OLi \cdot$
$LiBr \cdot (C_2H_5)_2O \xrightarrow{\quad}$
$\qquad\qquad\qquad\qquad \text{TiCl}_4 \text{ or AlCl}_3$

③ White crystals. [88~90°].
Stable on storage at 10°; rapid decompositon takes place on heating at 100~120°.

④ $+ 1/2\ O_2 \longrightarrow C_6H_5OTi(O\ i\text{-}C_3H_7)_3$
$+ H_2O \longrightarrow C_6H_6 + TiO_2 \cdot (H_2O)_n$
$+ 3\ i\text{-}C_3H_7OH$

⑥ JACS **74**, 2693 (1952); **75**, 3877, 3882 (1953).

$TiC_{16}H_{10}ClF_5$

① Di-π-cyclopentadienyl-perfluorophenyl-chloro-titanium
$(\pi\text{-}C_5H_5)_2(C_6F_5)(Cl)Ti$

② $(C_5H_5)_2TiCl_2 + C_6F_5MgBr \longrightarrow$

③ [187~188°].
NMR: $\tau 3.58$(triplet, J ca. 0.4 cps; through-space coupling between C_5H_5 ring proton with C_6F_5 ortho fluorine atom, (in CCl_3D).

⑥ Inorg. Chem. **3**, 300 (1964).

$TiC_{22}H_{20}$

① Di-π-cyclopentadienyl-diphenyl-titanium
$(\pi\text{-}C_5H_5)_2(C_6H_5)_2Ti$

② $(\pi\text{-}C_5H_5)_2 \cdot TiCl_2 + C_6H_5Li \longrightarrow 55\%$

③ Orange-yellow crystals. [146~148° decomp.].
Stable for some day in a cold chest; gradually decomp. at room temp.
Dipole moment: 2.78 ± 0.02 D.

④ above 105° $\longrightarrow C_6H_6$
$+ C_6H_5Li \rightleftharpoons [(\pi\text{-}C_5H_5)_2 \cdot$
$(C_6H_5)_3Ti]^-Li^+$

⑥ JACS **76**, 2278 (1954); **77**, 3604 (1955).

$Ti_2C_{24}H_{40}Al_2$

①

② $(C_5H_5)_2TiCl + (C_2H_5)_3Al \xrightarrow{80°,\ in\ C_6H_6}$

③ Red crystals. [169~171° decomp.].
Very sol. in aromatic hydrocarbons.
The structure was studied by X-ray on single crystal.

④ $+ HCl + Cl_2 \xrightarrow{in\ ether} (C_5H_5)_2TiCl_2$
$(95~97\%)$

⑤ Benzene solution of this complex to promote ethyene polymerization.

⑥ Tetrahedron **8**, 86 (1960).

【V】

$VC_5H_5Cl_2O$

① π-Cyclopentadienyl-oxy-dichloro-vanadium
$(\pi\text{-}C_5H_5)(O)(Cl)_2V$

② $\pi\text{-}C_5H_5V(CO)_4 + HCl(\text{or } Cl_2) + O_2$
$\longrightarrow 30~48\%$
$\pi\text{-}C_5H_5VCl_3 + O_2 \longrightarrow 73\%$

③ Blue-black crystals. (100~130° *in vacuo* sublime). No const. m. p.
$d\ 1.75\ (21°)$.
Readily sol. in benzene, chloroform, ether and THF, slightly in petroleum ether. Fairly stable in air.
Hydrolyzed with H_2O.
Diamagnetic.
IR: 1455, 1425, 1026, 1005, 967, 947, 823, 785 cm⁻¹.
Dipole moment: 4.93 ± 0.09 D.

④ $+ Br_2 \longrightarrow \pi\text{-}C_5H_5VOBr_2$

⑥ Ber. **91**, 1342 (1958) ; **93**, 701 (1960).

VC$_5$H$_5$Cl$_3$

① π-Cyclopentadienyl-trichloro-vanadium
  $(\pi$-C$_5$H$_5)($Cl$)_3$V

② π-C$_5$H$_5$V(CO)$_4$ + Cl$_2$ $\longrightarrow$ 42%

③ Dark violet crystals from toluene.
  (130~160° *in vacuo* sublime).
  Decompose without melting.
  Sol. in benzene, CHCl$_3$ and CCl$_4$;
  insol. in petroleum ether.
  Very unstable in air. Hydrolyzed
  with H$_2$O.
  Paramagnetic.
  IR : Ber. **93**, 1171 (1960).

④ + Br$_2$ $\longrightarrow$ π-C$_5$H$_5$VBr$_3$
  + O$_2$ $\longrightarrow$ π-C$_5$H$_5$VOCl$_2$

⑥ Ber. **93**, 701 (1960).

VC$_6$O$_6$

① Hexa(carbonnyl)-vanadium
  V(CO)$_6$

② VCl$_3$ + Mg + C$_5$H$_5$N + CO
  $\xrightarrow{\text{Zn}+\text{I}_2,\ 230\,\text{atm.},\ 120°}$

  Mg(C$_5$H$_5$N)$_n$[V(CO)$_6$]$_2$ $\xrightarrow{\text{HCl}}$ 38%

  VCl$_3$ + Na + diglyme + CO $\xrightarrow{230\,\text{atm.},\ 110°}$
  [Na(diglyme)$_2$][V(CO)$_6$]
  $\xrightarrow{\text{H}_3\text{PO}_4}$ 60%

③ Blue crystals, characteristic odor.
  (45~50°/10~20 sublime). [70° decomp.].
  Slightly sol. in aromatic hydrocarbons.
  Very unstable in air.
  Paramagnetic. Monomeric (a=11.97,
  b=11.28, c=6.47Å, N=4, P_{n2_1a}).
  Pyrophoric.
  IR : ν_{co} 1980 cm^{-1} (n-heptane).

④ + I$_2$ $\longrightarrow$ VI$_3$ + 6CO
  + (π-C$_5$H$_5)_2$V + 2CO

$\longrightarrow$ [(π-C$_5$H$_5)_2$V(CO)$_2$][V(CO)$_6$]
+ Ni(o-phenanthroline)$_3$Cl $\longrightarrow$
[Ni(o-phenanthroline)$_3$][V(CO)$_6$]
+ CH$_3$COCH$_3$(or CH$_3$OCH$_3$, CH$_3$OH,
CH$_2$PPh$_3$) $\longrightarrow$ [V(CH$_3$COCH$_3$)$_6$]-
(or [V(CH$_3$OCH$_3$)$_4$]-, [V(CH$_3$OH)$_6$]-,
[V(CH$_2$PPh$_3$)$_4$]-)[V(CO)$_6$]$_2$
+ C$_7$H$_8$ $\longrightarrow$ π-C$_7$H$_7$V(CO)$_3$
+ [π-C$_7$H$_7$VC$_7$H$_8$][V(CO)$_6$]

⑥ Chim. e Ind. **44**, 990 (1962). Chem.
  & Ind. 1961, 144. Ber. **95**, 3070
  (1962). Inorg. Chem. **2**, 721 (1963).

VC$_8$H$_5$O$_2$M$_2$

① Pottasium π-cyclopentadienyl-tri
  (carbonyl)-vanadate
  M$_2$[(π-C$_5$H$_5$)V(CO)$_3$], M=K

② π-C$_5$H$_5$V(CO)$_4$
  $\xrightarrow{\text{Na in liq. NH}_3}$ $\xrightarrow{\text{KI in liq. NH}_3}$ 68%

③ Yellow salt.
  Very unstable in air. Decomp. at
  high temp. *in vacuo.*
  Diamagnetic.
  IR : ν_{co} 1748, 1645 cm^{-1} (M=Cs).

④ + H$_2$O $\longrightarrow$ [π-C$_5$H$_5$HV(CO)$_3$]$^-$ + OH$^-$
  + H$^+$ $\longrightarrow$ [(π-C$_5$H$_5$)V(CO)$_3$]$_2$

⑥ Ber. **91**, 2205 (1958) ; **93**, 165 (1960).

VC$_9$H$_5$O$_4$

① π-Cyclopentadienyl-tetra(carbonyl)
  -vanadium
  $(\pi$-C$_5$H$_5$)V(CO)$_4$

② (π-C$_5$H$_5)_2$V + CO + H$_2$ $\xrightarrow{310\,\text{atm.},\ 140°}$ 97%

③ Orange crystals. (80~100° *in vacuo*
  sublime). [138°].
  Sol. in benzene, CHCl$_3$, CCl$_4$ and THF.
  Fairly stable in air; air sensitive
  in solvents.
  Diamagnetic.

④ + CH$_3$COCl(or(CH$_3$CO)$_2$O)
  $\xrightarrow{\text{AlCl}_3}$ π-CH$_3$COC$_5$H$_4$V(CO)$_4$
  + Cl$_2$ $\longrightarrow$ π-C$_5$H$_5$VCl$_3$

$+ Cl_2(or HCl) + O_2 \longrightarrow \pi\text{-}C_5H_5VOCl_2$

$+ Na \xrightarrow{\text{in liq. } NH_3} [\pi\text{-}C_5H_5V(CO)_3]Na_2$

$+ C_4H_6 \xrightarrow{UV} \pi\text{-}C_5H_5V(C_4H_6)(CO)_2$

$+ C_7H_8 \longrightarrow (\pi\text{-}C_5H_5)(\pi\text{-}C_7H_7)V$

$+ (CH_3)_2S_2 \longrightarrow [\pi\text{-}C_5H_5V(CH_3S)_2]_2$

⑥ Ber. **91**, 2205 (1958) ; **93**, 701, 1001 (1960). Inorg. Chem. **2**, 219 (1963).

$VC_{10}H_7O_3$

① π-Cycloheptatrienyl-tri(carbonyl) vanadium

$(\pi\text{-}C_7H_7)V(CO)_3$

② $V(CO)_6 + C_7H_8 \xrightarrow{65°} \pi\text{-}C_7H_7V(CO)_3$

$+ [\pi\text{-}C_7H_7VC_7H_8][V(CO)_6]$
(21%)

③ Shiny dark crystals form n-hexane. (60°/0.1 sublime). [134~137°].

Readily sol. in MeOH, ether, diglyme, acetone, $CHCl_3$, CCl_4 and petroleum ether ; insol. in H_2O. Stable in air for several hrs. ; unstble in solution.

Diamagnetic.

IR : 1950, 1875, 3375, 1430, 785 cm^{-1} (KBr).

NMR : $\tau 5.2$ (symm. doublet, $\tau 5.1$ and $\tau 5.3$).

⑥ JACS **83**, 2023.   Chim. e Ind. **44**, 1217 (1962).

$VC_{10}H_{10}$

① Di-π-cyclopentadienyl-vanadium

$(\pi\text{-}C_5H_5)_2V$

② $C_5H_5MgBr + VCl_4 \longrightarrow 45\sim55\%$

$C_5H_5Na + VCl_3 (or \ VCl_4)$

$\longrightarrow 50\sim55\% \ (or \ \sim47\%)$

③ Dark-violett crystals. (80~100° *in vacuo* sublime). [167~168°].

Sol. in benzene and THF.

Very unstable in air.

Paramagnetic. Sandwich structure.

IR : Ber. **91**, 2205 (1958).

④ $+ CO \longrightarrow \pi\text{-}C_5H_5V(CO)_4$

$+ HCl \longrightarrow (\pi\text{-}C_5H_5)_2VCl$

$+ (\pi\text{-}C_5H_5)_2VCl_2 \longrightarrow (\pi\text{-}C_5H_5)_2VCl$

⑥ Ber. **92**, 780 (1959) ; **93**, 1171 (1960).

$VC_{10}H_{10}Cl$

① Di-π-cyclopenatenyl-chloro-vanadium

$(\pi\text{-}C_5H_5)_2(Cl)V$

② $C_5H_5Na + VCl_4 \longrightarrow 23.4\%$

$(\pi\text{-}C_5H_5)_2V + HCl \longrightarrow$

$(\pi\text{-}C_5H_5)_2V + (\pi\text{-}C_5H_5)_2VCl_2 \longrightarrow 71\%$

$(\pi\text{-}C_5H_5)_2VCl_2 + PhLi \xrightarrow{-50° \ HCl}$

③ Indigo-blue crystals. (ca. 165°/0.2 sublime). [206~207°].

Sol. in dimethylcellosolve ; moderately in ether and slightly in petroleum ether and cyclohexane. Unstable in air.

Paramgnetic.

UV : λ_{max} (cyclohexane) 242, 338, 740 $m\mu$.

④ $+ HCl + O_2 \longrightarrow (\pi\text{-}C_5H_5)_2VCl_2$

$+ CH_3MgBr \longrightarrow (\pi\text{-}C_5H_5)_2VCH_3$

⑥ Ber. **93**, 701 (1960).   Chem. Ind. **1960**, 119.   Rec. trav. chim. **80**, 831 (1961).

$VC_{10}H_{10}Cl_2$

① Di-π-cyclopentadienyl-dichloro-vanadium

$(\pi\text{-}C_5H_5)_2(Cl)V$

② $C_5H_5MgCl + VCl_4 \longrightarrow$

$C_5H_5Na + VCl_4 \ (or \ VClO_3) \longrightarrow 65\%$

$(\pi\text{-}C_5H_5)_2V + HCl + O_2 \longrightarrow$

③ Pale green crystals. (Difficultly sublime). [ca. 250° decomp.]. $d \ 1.60$ g/c.c.

Sol. in $CHCl_3$, ACOEt, C_2H_5OH and H_2O ; insol. in ligroin and petroleum ether ; sparingly sol. in ether, CCl_4, CS_2, benzene, and toluene.

Paramagnetic.

IR: JACS **76**, 4281 (1954)

④ + (π-C$_5$H$_5$)$_2$V $\longrightarrow$ (π-C$_5$H$_5$)$_2$VCl

$\xrightarrow{\text{H}_2\text{O}}$

+ picric acid $\xrightarrow{}$ picrate, dark
green ppt.

⑥ Ber. **93**, 701 (1960).

VC$_{11}$H$_{11}$O$_2$

① π-Cyclopentadienyl-(butadiene)-di
(carbonyl)-vanadium
(π-C$_5$H$_5$)V(C$_4$H$_6$)(CO)$_2$

② π-C$_5$H$_5$V(CO)$_4$ + C$_4$H$_6$ $\xrightarrow{\text{UV}}$ 27%

③ Red crystals. (60~80° *in vacuo*
sublime). [135~40° decomp.].
Easily sol. in benzene, cyclohexane,
n-pentane, ether, THF, acetone
and ethanol. Unstable in air.
Diamagnetic.
IR: C$_5$H$_5$ 1426, 1116, 1016, 1008 ; C$_4$H$_6$
1483 ; ν_{CO} 1894, 1818 cm^{-1} (KBr).

⑥ Ber. **93**, 3006 (1960).

VC$_{11}$H$_{13}$

① Methyl-di-π-cyclopentadienyl-vana-
dium
(CH$_3$)(π-C$_5$H$_5$)$_2$V

② (π-C$_5$H$_5$)$_2$VCl + CH$_3$MgBr $\xrightarrow{-50°}$ 27%

③ Grey powder. [80~100° decomp.].
Sol. in noupolar and in polar org.
solvents. Very unstable in air.
UV: Rec. trav. chim. **80**, 831 (1961).

VC$_{12}$H$_{10}$O$_2$X

① Di-π-cyclopentadienyl-di (carbonyl)-
vanadium hexa(carbonyl)-vandate
[(π-C$_5$H$_5$)$_2$V(CO)$_2$]X, X=[V(CO)$_6$]

② (π-C$_5$H$_5$)$_2$V + V(CO)$_6$ + CO
$\xrightarrow{15°}$ quantitatively.

③ Orange solid.
Sol. in THF and acetone ; insol. in
H$_2$O, aliph. and aromatic solvents.
Fairly air stable in dry state. Air
sensitive in solns.

Diamagnetic.
IR: 2050, 2010 (CO)$_2$; 1860 (CO)$_6$;
3120 cm^{-1}(ν_{C-H}).

④ + I$_2$ $\longrightarrow$ [(π-C$_5$H$_5$)$_2$V(CO)$_2$]I$_3$
+ NaBPh$_4$
$\longrightarrow$ [(π-C$_5$H$_5$)$_2$V(CO)$_2$][BPh$_4$]

⑥ Inorg. Chem. **2**, 721 (1963).

VC$_{12}$H$_{12}$

① Di(benzene)-venadium
V(C$_6$H$_6$)$_2$

② VCl$_4$ + Al + 2C$_6$H$_6$
$\xrightarrow{\text{AlCl}_3,\,\text{reflux 20 hr.}}$ [V^I(C$_6$H$_6$)$_2$]AlCl$_4$

5V^I(C$_6$H$_6$)$_2$ $\xrightarrow{\text{H}_2\text{O}}$ 4V^0(C$_6$H$_6$)$_2$ + V^{II}
+ 2C$_6$H$_6$ 13~25%

③ Red-brown crystals. (120~150° *in
vacuo* sublime). [277~278°].
Sol. in benzene, ether, pyridine, petroleum ether and acetone ; scares-
ly insol. in carbon tetrachloride ;
highly air-sensitive.
Paramagnetic. Sandwich sturcture.
IR: similar to Cr(C$_6$H$_6$)$_2$

④ 2C$_6$H$_6$(g) + V(g) $\longrightarrow$ V(C$_6$H$_6$)$_2$(g)
−143.4 kcal./mol.

⑥ Ber. **90**, 250 (1957) ; **94**, 2204 (1961).

VC$_{12}$H$_{12}$

① π-Cyclopentadienyl-π-cyclohepta-
trienyl-vanadium
(π-C$_5$H$_5$)(π-C$_7$H$_7$)V

② π-C$_5$H$_5$V(CO)$_4$ + C$_7$H$_8$ $\xrightarrow{120°}$ 40%

③ Purple crystals. (100° *in vacuo*
sublime). [130° decomp.].
Sparingly sol. in org. solvents.
Stable. in air. Air sensitive in solns.
Paramagnetic. Sandwich structure.

⑥ JACS **81**, 5263 (1959).

VC$_{14}$H$_{15}$X

① Tropilium-π-cycloheptatrine-vana-
dum hexa(carbonyl)-vanadate

$[(\pi\text{-}C_7H_7)(C_7H_8)V]X, \; X=[V(CO)_6]$

② $V(CO)_6 + C_7H_8 \; \xrightarrow{50°}$

③ Red-brown microcrystalline solid.
Sol. in acetone; insol. in H_2O and
hydrocarbons.
Paramagnetic.
IR: ν_{CO} 1850 cm^{-1}.

④ $+ \; NaBPh_3 \; \longrightarrow$
$[(\pi\text{-}C_7H_7)(C_7H_8)V]BPh_4$

⑥ Chim. e Ind. **44**, 1217 (1962).

V₂C₁₄H₂₂S₄

① Bis[di-methyl sulfido-π-cyclopen-
tadienyl vanadium]
$[((CH_3S)_2(\pi\text{-}C_5H_5)V]_2$

② $+ \; \pi\text{-}C_5H_5V(CO)_4 + (CH_3)_2S_2 \; \longrightarrow$ 59%
or CH₃SH $\longrightarrow$ 20%

③ Brown-black crystals. (160°/0.1 sublime). [>292°, above 200° decomp.].
Weakly paramagnetic. Binuclear
complex with four thio-bridging
groups is assumed.
IR: 2872, 1294, 1013, 795 (CS₂ soln.),
1435 cm^{-1} (C₂Cl₄ soln.).

⑥ Inorg. Chem. **2**, 219 (1963).

【W】

WC₆O₆

① Hexa(carbonyl)-tungsten
$W(CO)_6$

② $WCl_6 + PhMgBr + CO \; \longrightarrow$
$WCl_6 + Na + CO$
$\xrightarrow{\text{diglyme, } -20, 4\,hr. \text{ and } 0\sim25°, 16\,hr.}$ 75%
$WCl_6 + Al + CO$
$\xrightarrow{Et_2O, 100°, \; 4\sim6hr}$ 68~90%
$WCl_6 + Fe(CO)_5 \; \xrightarrow{Et_2O, \; H_2}$ 81~85%

③ Colorless crystals. (60~70°/vacuum,
sublime).
Sparingly sol. in C₂H₅OH, ether and
benzene.

Decomp. slowly in sunlight; decomp.
rapidly at about 150°.
Diamagnetic.
IR: ν_{CO} 2120, 2015, 1980 cm^{-1}.

④ $\xrightarrow{150°} W + CO$
$+ \; pyridine \; \xrightarrow{reflux} \; W(CO)_5(py)$
$+ \; ethylenediamine$
$\xrightarrow{120°, \; 2\,hr.} \; W(CO)_4(en)$

⑤ Useful for plating tungsten on other metals and ceramic bodies.

⑥ Inorg. Syn. **5**, 135 (1957).   JACS **83**,
2057 (1961).   Zhur. neorg. Khim.
4, 249 (1959); CA **53**, 1907 (1959).

WC₇H₅NO₃

① π-Cyclopentadienyl-(nitrosyl)-
di(carbonyl)-tungsten
$(\pi\text{-}C_5H_5)W(CO)_2(NO)$

② $[\pi\text{-}C_5H_5W(CO)_3]^- + NO \; \xrightarrow{H_2O}$

③ Orange red crysals. (55~60°/vacuum,
sublime). [105~107°].

⑥ Z. Naturf. **10b**, 598 (1955).

WC₈H₆O₃

① Hydrido-π-cyclopentadienyl-tri-
(carbonyl)-tungstun
$(H)(\pi\text{-}C_5H_5)W(CO)_3$

② $W(CO)_6 + NaC_5H_5 \; \longrightarrow$
$\pi\text{-}C_5H_5W(CO)_3Na$
$\xrightarrow{CH_3COOH, \; THF} \; \sim 90\%$

③ Pale yellow. Sublime. [66~67°], [68.5
~69.5°].
Readily sol. in ether, acetone, benzene and petr. ether. Fairly stable
in air and stable up to 180° *in
vacuo*.
IR: ν_{CO} 2020, 1929, 1880 cm^{-1} (CS₂).
NMR: τ 4.65 (C₅H₅), 17.33 (W−H).

④ $\xrightarrow{O_2, \; heat} \; [\pi\text{-}C_5H_5W(CO)_3]_2$

⑥ Z. anorg. allg. Chem. **282**, 47 (1955).
JINC **3**, 104 (1956).   Inorg. Syn.

7, 136 (1963).

WC₉H₆O₃

① Tri(carbonyl)-(benzene)-tungsten
$W(CO)_3(C_6H_6)$

② $C_6H_6 + W(CO)_6 \xrightarrow{215°,\ 20\,hr} 2\%$

③ Lemon yellow. (90~120°/vacuum,
sublime). [140~145° decomp.].
IR: ν_{CO} 1990, 1916 cm⁻¹ (in C_6H_{12}).

⑥ Z. Naturf. **13b**, 458 (1958). Ber. **91**,
2763 (1958).

WC₉H₈O₃

① Methyl-π-cyclopentadienyl-tungsten
$(CH_3)(\pi\text{-}C_5H_5)W(CO)_3$

② $\pi\text{-}C_5H_5W(CO)_3Na + CH_3I \longrightarrow 80\%$
$\pi\text{-}C_5H_5W(CO)_3H + CH_2N_2 \longrightarrow$

③ Lemon yellow.(40°/vacuum, sublime).
[144.7~145.3°].
Sol. in ether and acetone. Quite sta-
ble in air.
Diamagnetic.
IR: ν_{CO} 2020, 1930, 1740 cm⁻¹.
UV: 3.130 Å (ε=2.430).
NMR: τ4.62 (C_5H_5), 9.60 (CH_3).

④ $+ I_2 \longrightarrow \pi\text{-}C_5H_5W(CO)_3I + CH_3I$

⑥ Z. anorg. allg. Chem. **282**, 47 (1955).
JINC **3**, 104 (1956).

WC₁₀H₉O₃X

① π-Cyclopentadienyl-tri(carbonyl)
-(ethylene)-tungsten hexafluoro-
phosphate
$[(\pi\text{-}C_5H_5)W(CO)_3(C_2H_4)]X,\ X=PF_6$

③ Pale yellow crystalline powder.
[120° decomp.].
Slightly sensitive to air and light.
Diamagnetic.
IR: ν_{CO} 2105, 2053, 2004 cm⁻¹; $\nu_{C=C}$
1510 cm⁻¹.

⑥ Ber. **94**, 1200 (1961).

WC₁₀H₁₂

① Dihydrido-di-π-cyclopentadienyl

tungsten
$(H)_2(\pi\text{-}C_5H_5)_2W$

② $C_5H_5Na + WCl_6 \xrightarrow{THF,\ NaBH_4} \sim 65\%$

③ Yellow crystals. Sublime at 80° *in
vacuo.* [193~195°].
Sol. in benzene.
React with halogenated solvents.
Moderately stable in air.
Diamagnetic.
IR: ν_{W-H} 1896 cm⁻¹.
NMR: τ5.76 (triplet, J=0.75, C_5H_5),
22.28 (W–H).
Dipole moment: 1.96±0.04D (25°,
benzene)

④ $+ H^+ \longrightarrow [(\pi\text{-}C_5H_5)_2(H_3)W]^+$
$+ BF_3 \longrightarrow (\pi\text{-}C_5H_5)_2(H_2)W(BF_3)$

⑥ Z. Naturf. **14b**, 738 (1959); **15b**, 135
(1960). JCS **1961**, 4854.

WC₁₁H₁₀O₃

① σ-Allyl-π-cyclopentadienyl-tri(carbonyl)-tungsten
$(\sigma\text{-}C_3H_5)(\pi\text{-}C_5H_5)W(CO)_3$

② $\pi\text{-}C_5H_5W(CO)_3Na + CH_2=CHCH_2Cl$
$\longrightarrow 40\%$

③ Pale Yellow crystals. [24~25°].
The solution decomp. after a few
minutes in air.
IR: ν_{CO} 2019, 1904; $\nu_{C=C}$ 1609 cm⁻¹.
NMR: τ7.68 (doublet, J=8.4cps.
CH_2), 5.47 (complex, $=CH_2$), 4.75
(singlet. C_5H_5), ~4 (complex,
–CH=).

④

$\xrightarrow{+H^-} \pi\text{-}C_5H_5-iso\,C_3H_7W(CO)_3$

⑥ JOM 1, 230 (1963).

$WC_{12}H_9O_3M_3$

① Potassium tripropyionyl-tri(carbon-yl)-tungstate
$M_3[(CH_3-C\equiv C)_3W(CO)_3]$, M=K

② $W(CO)_3(NH_3)_3 + KC\equiv CCH_3$
$\xrightarrow{\text{liq. } NH_3}$ 22%

③ Yellow orange.
Inosl. in acetone, DMF, ether, THF and petr. ether.
Decomp. with H_2O and dil. acid.

⑥ Ber. 97, 207 (1964).

$WC_{12}H_{11}OX$

① π-Cyclopentadienyl-(carbonyl)-(benzene)-tungsten hexafluoro-phosphate
$[(\pi-C_5H_5)W(CO)(C_6H_6)]X$, X=$PF_6$

② $\pi-C_5H_5W(CO)_3Cl + C_6H_6$
$\xrightarrow{AlCl_3, \text{benzene}, NH_4PF_6}$ 6.64%

③ Yellow.
IR: ν_{CO} 2009 cm^{-1}, "C_6H_6" 3126, 1433, 1147, 963, "C_5H_5" 3126, 1425, 1405, 1105, 1078, 1018, 990 cm^{-1}.
NMR: τ 4.54, 4.49 (intensity 6 : 5).

⑥ Z. Naturf. 18 b, 504 (1963).

$WC_{12}H_{12}$

① Di(benzene)-tungsten

$W(C_6H_6)_2$,   W

② $WCl_6 + Al + C_6H_6$
$\xrightarrow{AlCl_3, 140°, 20hr.}$ 1.8%

③ Dark green leaflets. (60°/vacuum, sublime). d 2.42.
Decomp. in air. Somewhat sol. in benzene; sparingly sol. in org. solvents.

Diamagnetic.
IR: 331, 387, 779, 877, 961, 976, 985, 1030, 1107, 1126, 1414, 2898, 3012 cm^{-1}.
UV: 455, 406 mμ.
Dipole moment: 0D.

④ $+ I_2 \longrightarrow [W(C_6H_6)_2]I$

⑥ Ber. 93, 2065 (1960).

$WC_{12}H_{12}O_4$

① Tetra(carbonyl)-(cyclooctadiene-1, 5)-tungsten

$W(CO)_4(C_8H_{12})$,

② cyclooctadiene-1,5 + $W(CO)_6$
$\xrightarrow{4hr. N_2}$ 53%

③ Yellow. [>110° decomp.].
Moderately air sensitive, especially in soln.
IR: ν_{CO} 2041, 1946, 1898 cm^{-1} (in CS_2).

④ + hexamethylbenzene
$\longrightarrow$ $W(CO)_3[C_6(CH_3)_6]$

⑥ Chem. & Ind. 1959, 1349.

$WC_{23}H_{15}O_5P$

① Pentacarbonyl-tri(phenylphosphine)-tungsten
$W(CO)_5[P(C_6H_5)_3]$

② $W(CO)_6 + Ph_3P \xrightarrow{\text{diglyme, } 160\sim165°}$
84% (crude), 42% (pure)

③ Pale yellow crystals. [146~147°].
IR: ν_{CO} 2075, 1980, 1938 cm^{-1} (CCl_4).

④ JACS 83, 3200 (1961).

$W_2C_{16}H_{10}O_6$

① Di-π-cyclopentadienyl-hexa (carbon-yl)-ditungsten
$[(\pi-C_5H_5)W(CO)_3]_2$

② $W(CO)_6 + C_5H_6 \xrightarrow{\sim280°}$

$W(CO)_6 + C_5H_5Na \xrightarrow{DMF}$

$$[\pi\text{-}C_5H_5W(CO)_3]Na \xrightarrow{CH_3COOH}$$

$$\pi\text{-}C_5H_5W(CO)_3H \xrightarrow{O_2}$$

③ Purple-red crystals. [240~242° decomp.].

Readily sol. in CHCl$_3$, but rather less sol. than its molybdenum analog in other org. solvents and insol. in ligroin.

Diamagnetic.

IR: ν_{CO} 1959, 1911 cm^{-1}.

⑥ JACS **76**, 209 (1954).   Inorg. Syn. **7**, 136 (1963).

W$_2$C$_{18}$H$_{22}$O$_4$P$_2$

① Di-π-cyclopentadienyl-bis-μ-dimethylphosphido-tetra(carbonyl)$^-$ditungsten

② $[\pi\text{-}C_5H_5W(CO)_3]_2 + (CH_3)_4P_2$

$$\xrightarrow[\text{ethylcyclohexane, reflux, 24 hr}]{} 20\%$$

③ Orange prisms. [255° decomp.].

IR: ν_{CO} 1933, 1921, 1848 (in CS$_2$); 1930, 1906, 1846, 1831 (in halocarbon mull).

NMR: τ 4.61 (triplet, $J_{HP}=0.4$ cps, C$_5$H$_5$), 8.13 (triplet, $J_{HP}=4.4$ cps, CH$_3$).

⑥ Inorg. Chem. **2**, 1031 (1963).

[Zr]

ZrC$_5$H$_5$Cl$_3$

① Cyclopentadienyl-trichloro-zirconium

(π-C$_5$H$_5$)(Cl)$_3$Zr

② ZrCl$_4$ + (C$_5$H$_5$)$_2$Mg $\xrightarrow{100\sim110°}$ 70%

ZrCl$_3$ + C$_5$H$_6$ $\longrightarrow$ 15%

③ Cream crystals. [237~238° decomp.]. Almost unchanged after brief exposure to air.

IR: JOM **2**, 334 (1964).

NMR: 6.65 ppm (π-C$_5$H$_5$).

ZrC$_{10}$H$_{10}$Cl$_2$

① Di-π-cyclopentadienyl-dichloro-zirconium

(π-C$_5$H$_5$)$_2$(Cl)$_2$Zr

② 2C$_5$H$_5$Li + ZrCl$_4$ $\xrightarrow{THF}$ 75%

2C$_5$H$_6$ + ZrCl$_2$ $\longrightarrow$ 30%

③ Colorless crystals. [248° in sealed tube].

Sol. in benzene and chloroform. Stable in air.

IR: JOM **2**, 334 (1964).

NMR: 6.50 ppm (π-C$_5$H$_5$).

④ + HBr $\xrightarrow{benzene}$ (C$_5$H$_5$)$_2$ZrBr$_2$

+ NaI $\xrightarrow{acetone}$ (C$_5$H$_5$)$_2$ZrI$_2$

+ LiBH$_4$ $\longrightarrow$ (C$_5$H$_5$)$_2$Zr(BH$_4$)$_2$

+ PhNH$_2$ $\xrightarrow{H_2O}$ [(C$_5$H$_5$)$_2$ZrCl]$_2$O

⑥ Compt. Rend. **256**, 443 (1963).

ZrC$_{38}$H$_{30}$

① 1, 1-Bis-π-cyclopentadienyl-2, 3, 4, 5-tetraphenyl-zircona-cyclopentadiene

② (C$_5$H$_5$)ZrCl$_2$ + C$_6$H$_5$(Li)C=C(C$_6$H$_5$)- -C(C$_6$H$_5$)=C(Li)C$_6$H$_5$ $\longrightarrow$ 53%

③ Orange crystals. [140~170° decomp.]. Insol in ether and petr. ether; very sol. in CH$_2$Cl$_2$.

Stable in air. Sensitive to light. Readily hydrolyzed by alcohols and H$_2$O.

⑥ JACS **83**, 4411 (1961).

II.

Short Explanations of Technical Terms

Acetylide: The term "acetylide" is generally given to compounds in which a terminal hydrogen atom of an acetylene is substituted by a metal.   Carbides are also included in this class.   Normally acetylides contain C_2^{2-} ions (or RC_2^{-} ions) and evolve acetylene on hydrolysis, although the acetylides of thorium and the lanthanides evolve ethylene, methane, and hydrogen along with acetylene. Acetylides are generally prepared by passing acetylene into solutions of metals or metal salts (especially liquid ammonia solution).

Acetylides of Li, Na, K, Cs, Cu, Ag and Au possess the empirical formula M_2C_2, that of Al is $M_2(C_2)_3$, and those of Y, La, Ce, Pr, Nd and Sm are MC_2.   Acetylides of heavy metals, such as those of Cu, Ag, and Au are generally explosive.   Many acetylides of transition metals have the structure $M-C \equiv CH$ or $M-C \equiv CR$ and are often called alkynyl derivatives.

Alfin catalyst: Alfin catalyst was developed by A. A. Morton at 1952 as a polymerization catalyst for butadiene.   The name was coined by the discoverer since the catalyst is a particular combination of the salts of **al**cohol and ole**fin**. A typical example is as follows: Amylsodium is prepared in a hydrocarbon solvent from amyl chloride and a sodiun dispersion.   Half an equivalent of isopropyl alcohol is added to the suspension, converting half the amylsodium into sodium isopropoxide.   Propylene is introduced into the mixture to convert the rest of amylsodium into allylsodium.   Therefore the final catalyst mixture consists of allylsodium, sodium isopropoxide, and sodium chloride, and is insoluble in hydrocarbon solvents and colored greenish blue.

The rate of polymerization of butadiene with Alfin catalyst is much higher than with a sodium dispersion, yielding high molecular weight polymer independent of the amount of catalyst.   Each of the three components of the catalyst is indispensable, the catalyst without one component showing very low activity. Alfin catalyst is effective not only for butadiene but also as a anionic catalyst for other vinyl monomers.   Styrene gives an isotactic polymer.

Alfol process: This is a manufacturing process for higher alcohols, which was developed by the Continental Oil Co. (U. S. A.) in 1961 and based upon the discovery of K. Ziegler in 1954.   The name was originated from the fact that the process produces higher alcohols from aluminum alkyl and ethylene (**al**uminum-ole**f**in-alcoh**ol**).   The whole process consists of the following four reaction steps.

(1) Synthesis of triethylaluminum

$$Al + 3/2 H_2 + 2 Al(C_2H_5)_3 \longrightarrow 3 Al(C_2H_5)_2H$$
$$3 Al(C_2H_5)_2H + 3 C_2H_4 \longrightarrow 3 Al(C_2H_5)_3$$

(2) Polymerization

$$Al(C_2H_5)_3 + (l+m+n)\,C_2H_4 \longrightarrow Al{\overset{\displaystyle (C_2H_4)_lC_2H_5}{\underset{\displaystyle (C_2H_4)_nC_2H_5}{-(C_2H_4)_mC_2H_5}}}$$

(3) Oxidation

$$Al{\overset{\displaystyle (C_2H_4)_lC_2H_5}{\underset{\displaystyle (C_2H_4)_nC_2H_5}{-(C_2H_4)_mC_2H_5}}} + 3/2\,O_2 \longrightarrow Al{\overset{\displaystyle O(C_2H_4)_lC_2H_5}{\underset{\displaystyle O(C_2H_4)_nC_2H_5}{-O(C_2H_4)_mC_2H_5}}}$$

(4) Hydrolysis

$$Al{\overset{\displaystyle O(C_2H_4)_lC_2H_5}{\underset{\displaystyle O(C_2H_4)_nC_2H_5}{-O(C_2H_4)_mC_2H_5}}} + 3\,H_2O \longrightarrow Al{\overset{\displaystyle OH}{\underset{\displaystyle OH}{-OH}}} + 3\,C_2H_5(C_2H_4)_{l,m,n}OH$$

Antibonding orbital: The molecular orbitals (MO's) for diatomic molecules are obtained by linear combination of atomic orbitals on the basis of LCAO approximation:

$$\psi = \psi_A \pm \lambda\psi_B$$

For a homonuclear molecule λ is ± 1, but for a heteronuclear molecule this is not so.   The value of λ may range from zero to infinity, and is a measure of the polarity of the orbitals.   The MO's $\psi_A + \lambda\psi_B$ and $\psi_A - \lambda\psi_B$ are called bonding and antibonding orbitals, respectively, the latter being distinguish by an asterisk.   The shapes of two kinds of orbital are quite different (I and II).

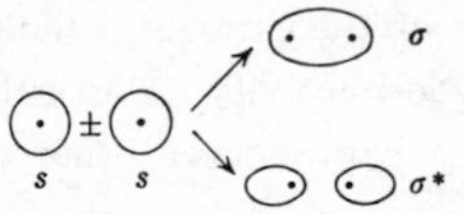

(I) 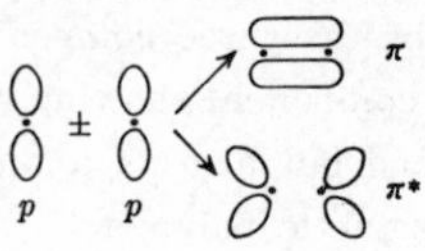   (II) 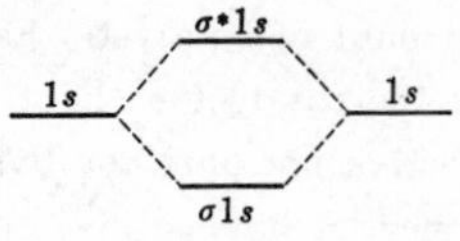   (III)

In hydrogen molecule, two $1s$ atomic orbitals can combine with each other to give a bonding MO ($\sigma 1s$) and an antibonding MO (σ^*1s).   The former is more stable than either isolated $1s$ atomic orbital and the latter less stable (III).   In the ground state the $\sigma 1s$ orbital is filled by two electrons to give stable hydrogen molecule.   However, in the case of He_2 with four electrons, the σ^*1s orbital as well as the $\sigma 1s$ orbital must be doubly occupied.   Then the electronic energy in the $\sigma 1s$ orbital can be compensated by that in the σ^*1s orbital, leading to dissociation to the parent atoms.   Sometimes, the antibonding π^* orbital (II) may be available for back-bonding from metal atom or ion, in which the orbital can overlap with a metal d orbital (See $d_\pi - p_\pi$ bond).

Arbuzov reaction: This reaction is a conversion of a trialkyl phosphite to a dialkyl alkylphosphonate by the action of an organic halide, as indicated by the equation:

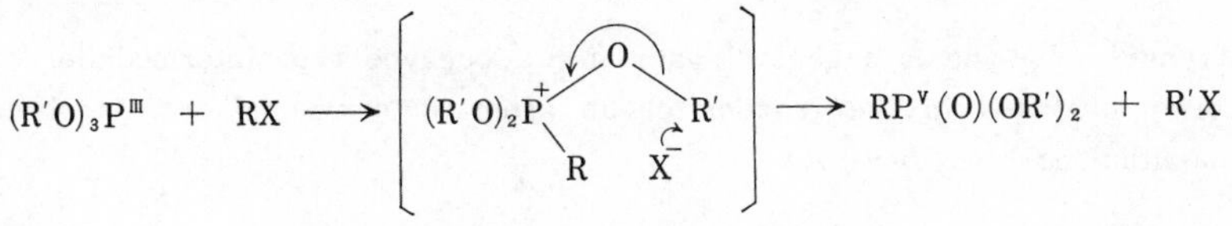

$$(R'O)_3P^{III} + RX \longrightarrow \left[(R'O)_2\overset{+}{P}\diagup\underset{R \quad X}{\overset{O}{\diagdown}}R' \right] \longrightarrow RP^V(O)(OR')_2 + R'X$$

quasi-quaternary
phosphonium salt

As a result of the reaction, the valency of phosphorus is increased from 3 to 5. The Arbuzov reaction is also observed with dialkyl alkylphosphonites, $RP(OR')_2$, which are transformed into alkyl dialkylphosphinates $RR''P(OR')$ upon treatment with $R''X$.   Besides alkyl halides, other compounds containing a halogen, for example, halogen-substituted ethers, carboxylic esters, and so forth, also may be used. For example:

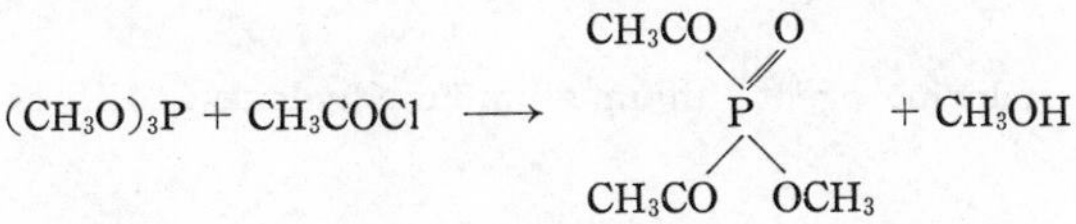

$$(CH_3O)_3P + CH_3COCl \longrightarrow \underset{CH_3CO \quad OCH_3}{\overset{CH_3CO \quad O}{P}} + CH_3OH$$

Arene complexes: These are defined as the π-complexes in which various arene ring such as benzene or naphthalene coordinate to a metal atom using six π-electrons.   Dibenzene-chromium, $(C_6H_6)_2Cr$, and benzene-chromium-tricarbonyl, $(C_6H_6)(CO)_3Cr$, are typical examples. (See, *Ate-complex*)

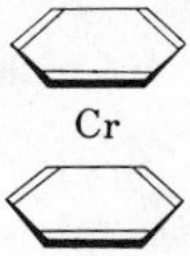

Cr

Argentation: Silver salts (mainly nitrate and perchlorate) react with carbon–carbon double bonds, and sometimes with triple bonds, to form π-complexes (S. Winstein, H. J. Lucus *et al.*, *J. Am. Chem. Soc.*, **60**, 836 (1938)).   A number of crystalline compounds of mono- and di-olefin derivatives has been isolated (M. A. Bennett, *Chem. Revs.*, **62**, 611 (1962)).   Winstein represented the structure by a resonating formula:

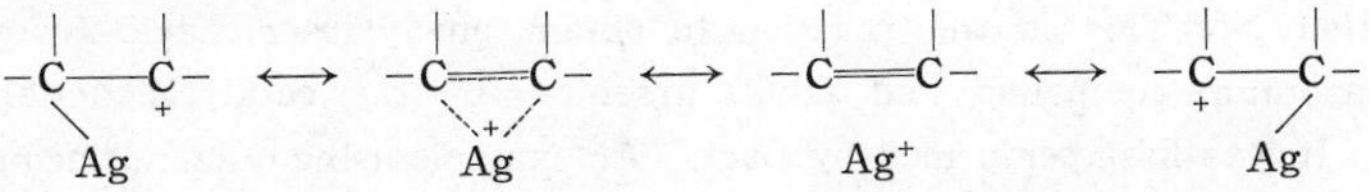

$$-\overset{|}{\underset{Ag}{C}}\overset{|}{\underset{+}{-C}}- \longleftrightarrow -\overset{|}{\underset{Ag}{C}}\overset{|}{\underset{+}{=C}}- \longleftrightarrow -\overset{|}{C}=\overset{|}{\underset{Ag^+}{C}}- \longleftrightarrow -\overset{|}{\underset{+}{C}}\overset{|}{\underset{Ag}{C}}-$$

Dewar (*Bull. soc. chin. France*, **18**, C 79 (1951)) explained the bonding in terms of a μ-bond which is formed between the $5s$ orbital of silver and the π–$2p$ orbital of olefin and the π-bond which is formed by back donation of $4d$ electrons of silver to π^*-$2p$ orbitals. Equilibrium constants (argentation constants) of this addition reaction are reported (T. Fueno *et al.*, *J. Am. Chem. Soc.*, **87**, 170 (1965)).

Aryne: Aryne is a general name for a benzyne type intermediate, which is often observed in the reaction of an aromatic compound such as benzene or naphthalene. (See *Benzyne*)

Ate-complex: This is an organic complex ion from an electron deficient compound such as boron or aluminum alkyl (aryl) or hydride, and an alkyl (aryl) compound or a hydride of an alkali or alkaline earth metal.   Alkyl (aryl) anion from the latter is coordinated to the electron deficient atom of the former.
　　Example:

$$(CH_3)_3B + CH_3Li \xrightarrow[\text{Ether}]{} \left[\begin{array}{c} CH_3 \\ | \\ H_3C-B-CH_3 \\ | \\ CH_3 \end{array} \right]^{-} Li^{+}$$

The well known reducing agent lithium aluminum hydride $LiAlH_4$ is a compound of this type.

Atomic orbital: The wave function describing the state of an electron in an atom is called an atomic orbital. In hydrogen like atoms, the space part of the function is defined by three quantum numbers:
　(1) Principal quantum number, n.
　(2) Azimuthal quantum number, l.
　(3) Magnetic quantum number, m.
The functions with $l=0$, 1, 2 and 3 are called s, p, d and f orbitals, respectively.

Back bonding: See *Back donation*.

Back donation: In a metal-ligand bond, the electron donation from metal orbitals (particularly d orbitals) to vacant ligand orbitals is called back donation. Typical ligands which can accept electrons from metal atom are trialkylphosphines, carbon monoxide in metal carbonyls and unsaturated organic molecules in π-complexes.

Bart reaction: This is the reaction to obtain phenylarsonic acid from an aromatic diazonium compound and alkali arsenite, by the catalytic action of copper salt. It was first performed by Bart. An example using benzenediazonium hydrochloride is shown below.

$$\phi N_2Cl + Na_3AsO_3 \longrightarrow \phi AsO(ONa)_2 + NaCl + N_2$$

By using this phenylarsonic acid as the starting material, the same reaction is repeated in alkali solution, and then the secondary acid called arsinic acid is obtained.

$$\phi As(ONa)_2 + \phi'N_2Cl \longrightarrow \phi\phi'AsO(ONa) + NaCl + N_2$$

The application of this reaction is not limited to arsenite, but also includes bismuthenite.   The reaction is especially useful in adding arsenic, and bismuth in desired positions in aromatic rings.   For example, 4-hydroxy-3-nitrophenyarsonic acid can be prepared with good yield by this method, and the product is a useful intermediate to the medicine "Arsphenamine".

Bechamp reaction :   This is the reaction by which an aryl arsonic acid is prepared by reacting aromatic compounds such as amine or phenol, or their derivatives, with the corresponding syrupy arsenic acid by dehydration under heating.

$$NH_2\!\!-\!\!\langle\bigcirc\rangle + H_3AsO_4 \longrightarrow H_2N\!\!-\!\!\langle\bigcirc\rangle\!\!-\!\!AsO(OH)_2 + H_2O$$

This is a direct substitution reaction of benzene with arsenic acid, and is very similar to the sulfonation reaction except that it is harder than the latter and is possible only with amino or hydroxy derivatives.   For aniline or phenol, *para* substitution is preferred, and from α-naphthylamine, 1-amino-2-naphthalene arsonic acid is obtained, although the reaction with β-naphthylamine does not proceed. The reaction is reversible, and is generally brought to completion by heating at $150\sim160°C$ for $6\sim12$ hours without solvent.   In the case of phenol the reversibility is especially strong, and by removing the water promptly after its generation the yield is greatly improved.   The mechanisum is supposedly based on cationoid substitution by enlarging the electron shell of arsenic atom, and the strong E effect which is needed is produced by introducing hydroxy or amine group.

Benzyne :   Benzyne, which was proposed independently by G. Wittig and J. D. Roberts about 1953, is an unstable cyclic C_6H_4 intermediate, and is sometimes called dehydrobenzene or benzin.   Benzyne can be understood to be a hybrid of the polar and nonpolar resonance forms (Eq. 1).   For example, the reactions shown in Eq. 2 and 3 are known to proceed via a benzyne intermediate. (See *Aryne*)

$$\qquad\qquad\qquad\qquad\qquad\qquad\qquad\qquad (1)$$

$$\qquad\qquad\qquad\qquad\qquad\qquad\qquad\qquad (2)$$

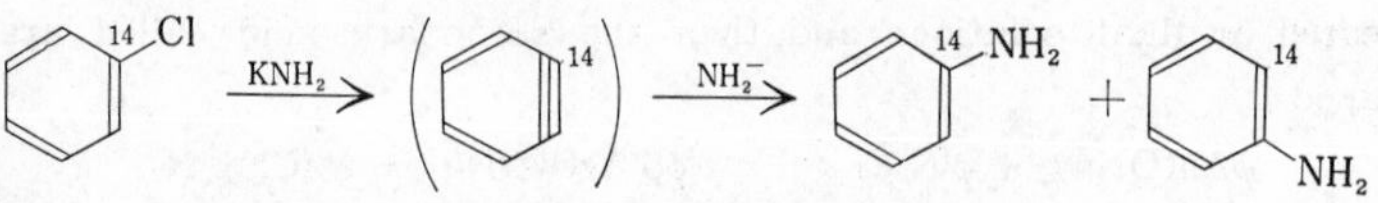

$$\text{[benzene-]}^{14}\text{Cl} \xrightarrow{\text{KNH}_2} \left(\text{[}^{14}\text{]}\right) \xrightarrow{\text{NH}_2^-} \text{[}^{14}\text{]NH}_2 + \text{[}^{14}\text{]}_\text{NH}_2 \qquad (3)$$

Borazole (Borazine):   This is a compound having a six-membered cyclic ring bonded alternatively by B and N. The parent compound is borazine, $B_3N_3H_6$, which was found by Stock in 1926.

Borazine has the same electron distribution as benzene, is properly named as inorganic benzene, and has been investigated considerably. In recent years, the derivatives of this substance have been studied as medicines, heat resistant materials, and neutron absorbent. The borazole ring is fairly stable at high tempeature but is rather susceptible to water, alcohol, and hydrogen halides, with which it forms 1: 3 adducts of cyclohexane type. By using excess reagent, the ring is cleaved and decomposed. A compound having a B–N bond is prone to cyclization and forms borazine ring; many condensation products are prepared from this borazine mother body.

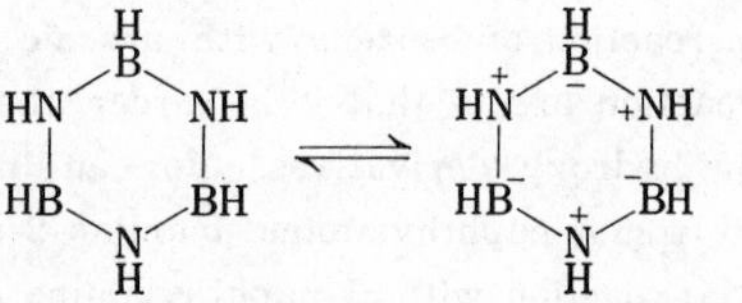

B–N 1.44 ± 0.02 Å

$\angle$NBN $120°$

Borazine has the following physical properties; bp $55°$, mp $-58.0°$, latent heat of evaporation 7034 cal/mole, paracol 207.9, critical temperature $252°$C.

Bridge bond: Bonds connecting two atoms or groups are called bridge bonds. Typical compounds having bridge bond are following:

(1) Electron-deficent compounds such as diborane,

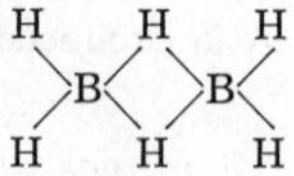

(2) Some aluminum halides and aluminum alkoxides,

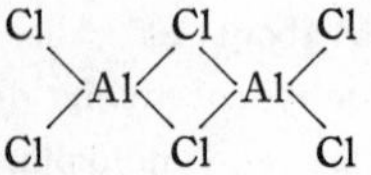

(3) Some polynuclear metal carbonyls,

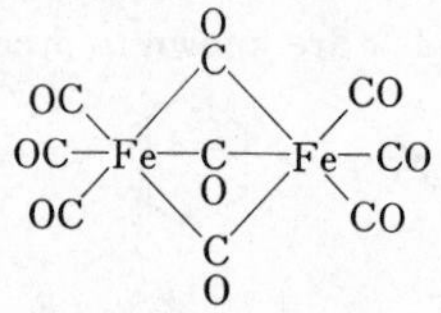

Carbenes: The term "carbene" $(: CY_2)$ named by Doering, refers to an unstable intermediate having a bivalent carbon atom. It can be in two different electronic states: singlet state and triplet state. The singlet state carbene has an electrophilic character and add to double bond stereospecifically. On the other hand, the triplet state carbene has a typical biradical character and does not undergo any insertion reaction. The electronic state of carbene depends upon Y. It is generally known that carbene such as $:CH_2$, $:CHCH_2CH_3$, $:CBr_2$ $:CCl_2$, $:CHCl$, $:CHCOOC_2H_5$, $:CHCOCH_3$ and $:C{\diagup CH_2 \atop \diagdown CH_2}$ are singlet state, and carbene such as $:C(C_6H_5)_2$ and $:CHC{\equiv}CH$ are triplet state. Carbenes adds to double bond to form cyclopropane rings. Insertion reactions, isomerization, substitution reactions, and intramolecular reaction are also well known. Carbenes are prepared by the photochemical decomposition of diazomethane and ketene, and by the elimination of hydrogen halide from haloform or other halogen derivatives in the presence of potassium *tert*-butoxide or alkyllithium. Silene having a bivalent silicon atom is also known as a carbene-like unstable intermediate.

Carbides: The term "carbide" is generally applied to carbides of metals, and indicates calcium carbide in a narrow sense. Carbides are prepared by the reaction of metals, metal oxides or metal salts with carbon, carbon monoxide, methane, acetylene or calcium carbide at high temprature. Carbides are classified into two types by their reactivities; (1) Carbides of the elements of groups Ia and IIa having the formula M_2C_2 or MC_2 form methylacetylene, and Al_4C_3, BeC and Mn_3C form methane. (2) Carbides in which carbon atoms occupy the holes in close-packed array of metal atoms are expressed as interstitial carbides. These are chemically inactive and have very high melting points. TiC, Cr_3C_2, TaC, NbC, Mo_2C, W_2C, VC, and Fe_3C are examples of this class.

Carbonation: The reaction of carbon dioxide with organic compounds of alkali metals and alkaline earth metals gives salt of carboxylic acids. This type of reaction occasionally affords a useful way to synthesize carboxylic acids and is called carbonation. Organic compouns of zinc, mercury, and other metals which are more electronegative, do not react with carbon dioxide. The following are examples.

$$RMgX + CO_2 \longrightarrow R{-}\overset{\overset{\displaystyle O}{\|}}{C}{-}O{-}MgX$$

$$RMgX + R{-}\overset{\overset{\displaystyle O}{\|}}{C}{-}O{-}MgX \longrightarrow R{-}\underset{\underset{\displaystyle R}{|}}{\overset{\overset{\displaystyle OMgX}{|}}{C}}{-}OMgX$$

The second reaction proceeds very slowly so that generally carboxylic acid can be synthesized in satisfactory yield. In practice, carbonation can be effected simply by pouring the Grignard solution onto finely powdered solid carbon dioxide (dry ice) with stirring.

The following are examples applied to heterocyclic compound using alkali metal reagents.

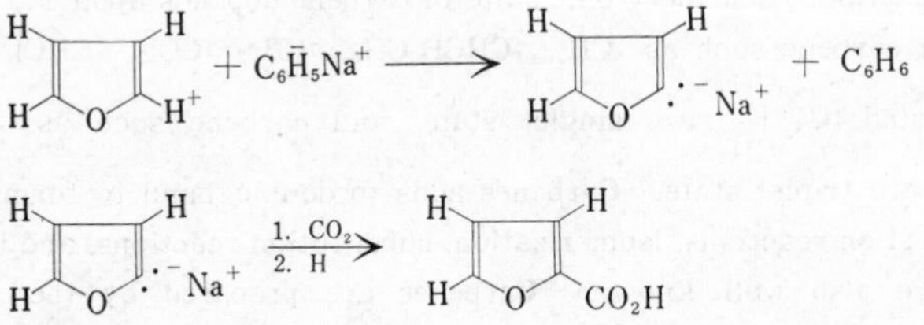

Chelate :   A ligand containing two or more functional groups which can simultaneously occupy positions in the first coordination sphere of the same metal atom or ion is a chelate. Familiar examples are ethylenediamine, $H_2N \cdot CH_2 \cdot CH_2 \cdot NH_2$, and acetylacetonate anion, $[CH_3CO \cdot CH \cdot COCH_3]^-$, each of which can occupy two coordination positions on a metal atom or ion to give a cyclic structure containing the metal. For instance :

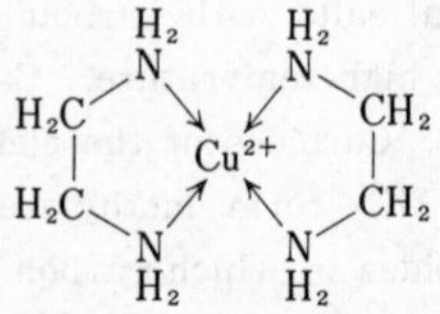

To designate the cyclic structure which arise from the union of metallic atoms with organic or inorganic molecules or ion, the term "chelate" was proposed by Morgan and Drew (1920). The name is derived from the Greek word *chela* which means the claw of a lobster or crab.

Coordination compounds :   A coordinating bond (and, hence, a coordination compound) can be formed between any atom or ion which can donate an unshared pair of electrons (the donor) and any atom or ion which can accept the pair of electrons (the acceptor). The donor is ordinarily nonmetallic; it may be a negative ion, such as Cl^-, CN^-, NO_2^-, or acetylacetonate anion, or a neutral molecule, such as H_2O, NH_3, CO or 2,2'-bipyridine.

Although in a metal complex an acceptor requires several donors, as in the case of $[Co(NH_3)_6]Cl_3$ or $Fe_2(CO)_9$, the term "coordination compound" is also given to an adduct which is formed by one donor and one acceptor, such as $(C_2H_5)_3Al \cdot O(C_2H_5)_2$, or between two or more donors and two or more acceptors.

Cyclopentadienyl metal complexes :   These are defined as complexes in which one or more cyclopentadienyl rings coordinate to metal atoms. In this class, some complexes consist of two cyclopentadienyl rings which coordinate to one metal atom with a sandwich structure like that of ferrocene, and some complexes consist of one cyclopentadienyl ring in combination with other ligands, for example, $(\pi-C_5H_5)Mn(CO)_3$. After the discovery of ferrocene, cyclopentadienyl complexes of almost all transition metals were prepared. The bonding is essentially one delocalized covalent bond formed by the overlapping of a singly occupied π-orbital of the ring with a singly occupied d-orbital of the metal.

Dative bond :   In σ and π bonds the two electrons may come either one from each atom or both from the same atom. The latter case is called a coordinate bond or dative bond. This type of bond is usually formed between a Lewis base and a Lewis acid, for example, $(CH_3)_3N$ and BF_3, which are donor and acceptor molecules, respectively. The name "donor-acceptor bond" is also used. An electron transfer from nitrogen atom to boron atom yields the N^+ and B^- species, which are both isoelectronic with carbon atom. These ions may make an electron pair bond similar to the C-C bond. Thus the coordination bond between $(CH_3)_3N$ and BF_3 is formally assumed to be associated with the electrostatic force as well as with the electron pairing, that is $(CH_3)_3N^+-B^-F_3$, apart from the electron transfer energy. For this reason, the term "semipolar bond" is sometimes used.

Desilylation reaction :   The cleavage of carbon–silicon bond in organosilicon compounds and the break down of the silicon component is called a desilylation reaction. Si–C bond has an 11% ionic nature and is fairly sensitive to attack by ionic reagents. The ease of the cleavage reaction is greatly affected by the structure of the organo group departing from the silicon atom, and also by the remaining organo group. Many examples of this reaction are known; the reaction of phenyl derivatives, which are easily cleaved by a cationic reagent, particularly an acidic reagent, is a representative example. Gilman carried out a study of the cleavage reaction between hydrogen chloride and Me₃Si–Ar in glacial acetic acid as solvent:

$$Me_3Si-Ar + HCl \xrightarrow{\text{AcOH solvent}} Me_3SiCl + ArH$$

He found that the ease of cleavage of the Si–Ar bond is increased by strengthening the electron density of the substituted radical on the aromatic ring, as shown by the following series.

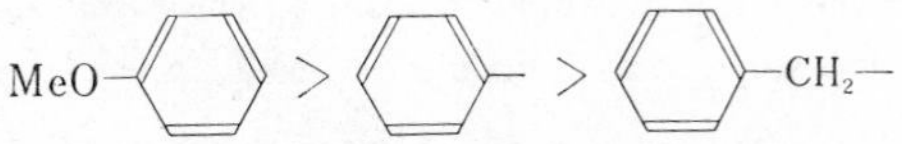

The Si–Ar bond can be cleaved by bromine or iodine by the following reaction:

$$Me_3SiPh + X_2 \longrightarrow Me_3SiX + PhX \quad (X=Br, I)$$

This reaction is often applied to the preparation of bromosilane. The Si–Ar bond is also affected by aluminum trichloride and result in a desilylation reaction. Basic reagent may also attack the carbon–silicon bond, liberating olefin and other compounds as discussed below.

α-Elimination: A compound containing carboxyl or carboalkoxy group bonded to the silicon atom is very unstable to base, and the cleavage of the Si–C bond easily takes place liberating carbon monoxide. For example, $(C_6H_5)_3SiCO_2H$ can be decomposed completely by dilute aqueous NaOH solution or by anhydrous ethanol containing a catalytic amount of sodium ethylate at room temperature.

$$RO^- + (C_6H_5)_3SiCO_2H \longrightarrow (RO-\underset{\underset{O}{\|}}{Si}-C-OH)^-$$

$$\longrightarrow ROSi(C_6H_5)_3 + CO + OH^-$$

β-Elimination: A compound which contains halogen atom at the *β*-position away from the silicon atom, can usually generate olefin easily by cleaving the Si–C by the attack of a basic reagent. The cleavage takes place by merely titrating with the dilute alkali solution.

$$Cl_3SiCH_2CH_2Cl + 4\,NaOH\,aq. \longrightarrow Si(OH)_4 + CH_2{=}CH_2 + 4\,NaCl$$

One of the halogens connected at the *β*-position can be eliminated with the same ease as is the chlorine atom connected to silicon.

$$Cl_3SiCHBrCHClBr + 4\,NaOH_{aq.} \longrightarrow$$
$$Si(OH)_4 + BrCH{=}CHCl + 3\,NaCl + NaBr$$

γ-Elimination: Some of the *γ*-halogenated alkyl silicon compounds are susceptible to the cleavage of Si–C bond by the attack of a nucleophilic reagent forming cyclopropane. For example, *γ*-chloropropyltrichlorosilane is cleaved easily by adding ethanolic potassium at room temperature.

$$Cl_3SiCH_2CH_2CH_2Cl \xrightarrow[\text{room temp.}]{KOH-C_2H_5OH} Si(OH)_4 + \overline{CH_2{-}CH_2{-}CH_2} + Cl^-$$

Diamagnetism: When a substance is placed in a magnetic field of strength H gauss, polarity is induced in atoms or molecules in the substance. If the intensity of this induced magnetism is I, the total magnetic flux is given by $B = H + 4\pi I$. The ratio B/H is called the magnetic permeability of the medium and the quantity $I/H(\chi)$ the molar susceptibility. In a vacuum $B=H$. In any other medium χ is either negative or positive; in the former case the medium is said to be diamagnetic and in the latter paramagnetic. For the discussion of chemical problems, the susceptibility per gram molecule is used; this is given by $\chi_M = (M/\rho)\chi$, where ρ is the density.

Diamagnetism arises from the interaction of the applied magnetic field with the filled electronic orbitals of the atom in the medium. The direction of the magnetic field due to the induced polarity in each atom is opposed to that of the applied field and therefore the magnetic flux is reduced. The diamagnetic susceptibility is invariably small. For most diamagnetics, the susceptibility is practically independent of the temperature over wide ranges, because the induced polarity is the same whatever the orientation of the atoms or molecules with respect to the applied field.

The susceptibility of molecules can be given as the sum of terms for separate atoms, an allowance being necessary in some cases for the different type of bonds. This additivity of diamagnetic susceptibility is expressed in Pascal's law, $\chi_M = \chi_A + \lambda$, where λ is a factor related to the bond type in the molecule.

Dimroth reaction :   Substitution of a hydrogen atom on an aromatic nucleus by the HgX group from a mercuric salt, HgX_2, is the Dimroth reaction, also called "mercuration."

$$ArH + HgX_2 \longrightarrow ArHgX + HX$$

This reaction is usually effected either at low temperature in water, alcohol or acetic acid, or at higher temperature (150°) in the absence of solvent. Mercuric acetate is most frequently used as the mercurating agent, although mercuric oxide is sometimes used. Depending upon the conditions under which the reaction is effected, either a free radical or a polar mechanism may be operative. Thus, the mercuration using ionic mercuric salts, for example, $Hg(NO_3)_2$ and $Hg(ClO_4)_2$, in a strongly acidic solution proceeds by a polar mechanism.

$$NO_2C_6H_5 + Hg^+ClO_4 \longrightarrow m\text{-}NO_2C_6H_4HgClO_4 + H^+$$

On the other hand, the mercuration with mercuric acetate, which is a weak electrolyte, in a nonpolar solvent such as CCl_4 may proceed by a free-radical mechanism, giving rise to the formation of o- and p-isomers as the major products regardless of the nature of substituents on the nucleus.

$$CH_3OOCC_6H_5 + Hg(OCOCH_3)_2 \longrightarrow$$
$$o\text{-}CH_3OOCC_6H_4HgOCOCH_3 + CH_3COOH$$

Furan, thiophene and selenophene readily undergo mercuration at room temperature to give *ortho*-mercurated products. Pyridine is mercurated only at 180°C.

Disproportionation :   Disproportionation is a process in which self-oxidation and self-reduction take place at the same time. In disproportionation an element exists in a higher oxidation state on one hand, and in a lower one on the other, in comparison with its initial oxidation state. The ease of disproportionation is associated with close energy levels of valence electrons in these two oxidation states.

$$\overset{(+5)}{4\,KClO_3} \longrightarrow \overset{(-1)}{KCl} + \overset{(+7)}{3\,KClO}$$

$$\overset{(-2)}{4\,SnO} \longrightarrow \overset{(0)}{Sn} + \overset{(+2,\,+4)}{Sn_3O_4}$$

$$\overset{(+1)}{Hg_2O} \longrightarrow \overset{(0)}{Hg} + \overset{(+2)}{HgO}$$

However, disproportionation does occur with no change in valency of an element.

$$3\,C_6H_{10} \longrightarrow 2\,C_6H_{12} + C_6H_6$$

$$2\,CH_2O + H_2O \longrightarrow CH_3OH + HCOOH$$

Organic free radicals also undergo disproportionation by abstracting a hydrogen atom bonded to a carbon adjacent to that bearing an unpaired electron.

$$2\,C_2H_5\cdot \longrightarrow C_2H_4 + C_2H_6$$

d_π–p_π bond : d_π–p_π bond is defined as a π–bond formed by interaction between a d-orbital of one atom and a p-orbital of another atom.   Some representations of this kind of bond are shown in (I) and (II), in which the overlap of pertinent orbitals is indicated.

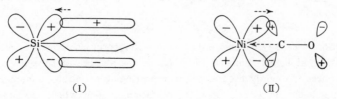

(I)   (II)

(I) shows the contribution of electrons from the occupied π–molecular orbitals of a phenyl group to the vacant d-orbitals of silicon atom.   (II) portrayes a similar but exactly opposite type of bond, in which electrons from filled d-orbitals of nickel atom are contributed to the vacant antibonding molecular orbital of carbon monoxide.   This is typical of the metal carbonyls.   There are good experimental and theoretical reasons for believing that the representative elements in the fourth, fifth and sixth periods make use of the same type of d_π–p_π bonding.

As exceptional ligands, nitric oxide and oxygen molecules have partially filled π orbitals.   In the complexes formed by these molecules the unshared electron may go into a molecular orbital of approximately the same symmetry together with electrons from the metal ion, and hence pair with a metal electron.   This is a rather unusual type of the d_π–p_π bonding.

Dry box :   A dry box is an airtight box equipped with a pair of rubber gloves in order to handle air- or moisture-sensitive substances in an atmosphere of inert gas (nitrogen, helium or argon) or dry air. It is essential that it must be completely airtight, that the air inside the box be replaced with an inert gas quickly and surely, and that handling with rubber gloves inside of the box must be easy. The picture (Fig. a) shows a commercial dry box. In order to make the replacement quickly, the dry box has a device to make the evacuation of the whole apparatus possible followed by the introduction of inert gas. When a reagent is brought in or taken out, the evacuation of the whole apparatus can be replaced by the evacuation of the side chamber.

A handy substitute is a box which is eqipped with a pair of rubber gloves and is attached at the top to a polyethylene bag (Fig. b). The replacement of the inside air can be done by repeatedly deflating and inflating the bag with an inert gas.

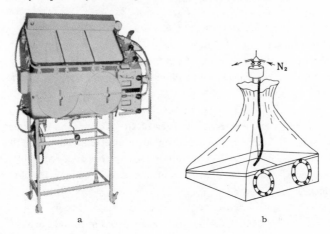

a   b

Electron affinity :   The electron affinity (E. A.) of an atom or ion is the energy released (or needed for the atom having a negative E. A.) when the atom or ion takes an extra electron into the valence shell. Thus for an atom we have the equation :

$$\text{Atom} + \text{Electron} \longrightarrow \text{Uninegative ion} + \text{E. A.}$$

In the case of transition metal element or ions, electrons may be accepted by the d-, s- or p-orbitals so that there are really three relevant E. A.'s. The magnitude of the E. A. depends on the nature of the atomic orbitals into which an electron is accepted.

The ionization potential (I. P.) of an atom is the minimum energy required to completely remove an electron from the atom. This process may be written :

$$\text{Atom} + \text{I. P.} \longrightarrow \text{Unipositive ion} + \text{Electron}$$

The ionization energy required to detach the first electron is called the first I. P. and subsequent ones the second, third, fourth, and so forth, I. P.'s. For a molecule or molecular ion, the E. A. and the I. P. can similarly defined.

Reference :   V. I. Vedeneyev, L. V. Gurvich, V. N. Kondrat'yev, V. A. Medvedev and Ye. L. Frankevich, "Bond Energies, Ionization Potentials and Electron Affinities," English Ed., Edward Arnold (1966).

Electron deficient molecule :   See *Three center bond.*

Electronegativity :   Electronegativity may broadly be defined as the ability of an atom in a molecule to attract electrons from the surroundings to itself. It is a very general result that the bond energy of a heteronuclear diatomic molecule

AB (E_{AB}) is almost always greater than the arithmetic or geometric mean of the bond energies of homonuclear diatomic molecules A_2 and B_2 (E_{AA} and E_{BB}, respectively):

$$E_{AB} = (E_{AA} + E_{BB})/2 + \varDelta_{AB}$$
$$\text{or } E_{AB} = \sqrt{E_{AA} \cdot E_{BB}} + \varDelta_{AB}$$

This extra bond energy $\varDelta_{AB}$ in an AB molecule is presumably due to contributions from the canonical ionic bonds. By noting that the extra bond energy is closely related with the electronegativity difference between the two atoms, Pauling has proposed the equation:

$$\chi_A - \chi_B = 0.208\sqrt{\varDelta_{AB}}$$

where χ_A and χ_B are electronegativities of the atoms A and B, respectively, and the factor 0.208 converts from kcal/mole to electron volt units. The square root of $\varDelta_{AB}$ was used because it gives a more nearly consistent set of electronegativities for the atoms. The ionic character of the A–B bond can be obtained from the equation:

$$\text{Ionic character}(\%) = 16|\chi_A - \chi_B| + 3.5|\chi_A - \chi_B|^2.$$

It should be realized, however, that each different atomic orbitals in a molecule has a different electronegativity and therefore atomic electronegativities vary from molecule to molecule, depending on the valence orbitals under consideration. Furthermore, the electronegativity of an atom in a molecule increases with increasing positive charge on the atom. Thus, the electronegativity may be closely associated with electronic structure in a molecule, and one can estimate the electronegativity from measurements of the physical properties which are more or less related to the electronic structures of the molecules under consideration. For this purpose, the following properties are available; (1) bond energy, (2) electron affinity and ionization potential, (3) dipole moment, (4) vibrational stretching force constant, (5) electrostatic potential, (6) stability ratio, (7) nuclear magnetic resonance, (8) nuclear quadrapole resonance and (9) work function.

Reference: H. O. Pritchard and H. A. Skinner, *Chem. Revs.*, **55**, 745 (1955).

Equilibration :   Equilibration means to set up equilibria between members of a homologous series, ranging from monomers or low molecular weight cyclic oligomers to high molecular weight cyclic or linear polymers. Certain heteroatomic systems are capable of undergoing polymerization-depolymerization under proper conditions to give the oligomer-polymer equilibrium. For example, hexachlorocyclotriphosphazene (1) can be converted to a high polymer (2) when heated to 250°~300°C. If the polymer is heated above 350°C, it depolymerizes to trimer and higher cyclic oligomers.

Similarly, octamethylcyclotetrasiloxane (3) when heated approximately to 200° in the presence of acidic or basic catalysts, is converted to a higher polymer. The polymer depolymerizes to cyclic trimer, tetramer, and oligomers at temperatures near 400°.

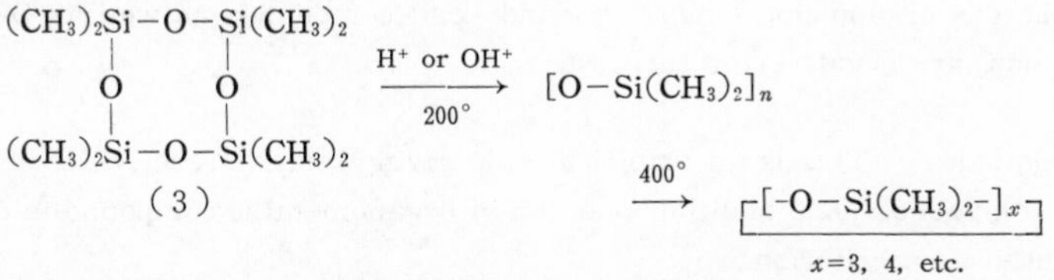

$$(CH_3)_2Si-O-Si(CH_3)_2$$

$$(CH_3)_2Si-O-Si(CH_3)_2 \quad \xrightarrow[200°]{H^+ \text{ or } OH^+} \quad [O-Si(CH_3)_2]_n$$

$$(3) \qquad \xrightarrow{400°} \quad [[-O-Si(CH_3)_2-]_x]$$

$$x=3, 4, \text{ etc.}$$

If a chain stopper, for example, hexamethyldisiloxane ("monofunctional compounds"), is present in the above reaction system, the equilibrium mixture of a homologous series of linear methylpolysiloxanes with trimethylsiloxy end groups are obtained.

Ferricenium ions: Ferrocene is oxidized to blue water-soluble ferricenium ion by the proper oxidizing agents such as Fe^{3+}, Ce^{4+} or HNO_3. Ferricenium ion is reversibly reduced to ferrocene by the proper reducing agents such as $S_2O_3^{2-}$, $S_2O_4^{2-}$ or Sn^{2+}.

$$(\pi\text{-}C_5H_5)_2Fe \rightleftharpoons (\pi\text{-}C_5H_5)_2Fe^+ + e$$

$$E_{1/2}(\text{in } 90\% \text{ EtOH}) = -0.31 \text{ volt}$$

Ferrocene: Ferrocene, $(\pi\text{-}C_5H_5)_2Fe$, was simultaneously and independently discovered by two groups of chemists.   In an attempt to prepare the unknown compound fulvalene, Kealy and Pauson hoped to couple cyclopentadienyl magnesium bromide with ferric chloride.   Instead of the expected dihydrofulvalene, ferrocene $(C_{10}H_{10}Fe)$ was obtained.   Miller *et al.* obtained ferrocene by passing cyclopentadiene vapor over hot iron powder.   Recently, various convenient synthetic methods have been found.

Ferrocene is an orange crystalline compound, mp 173°C, diamagnetic, nonpolar and unaffected by aq. NaOH or conc. HCl.   The bonding between iron atom and cyclopentadienyl ring is intrinsically a single covalent bond.   Ferrocene has been thought to have aromaticity, because the cyclopentadienyl ring in the ferrocene molecule reacts like an aromatic ring and is easily acylated, metalated and mercurated.   These properties prompted the name "ferrocene".   In general, transition metal complexes having similar structure to ferrocene are called metallocene.

Gilman color test: This is a color test for qualitative analysis of organometallic compounds, developed by Henry Gilman for Grignard reagents.   A small volume of the solution to be tested is treated, at room temperature, with an equal volume of a 1% solution of Michler's ketone in dry benzene.   The reaction product is then hydrolyzed by the slow addition of water (about the same volume).   The subsequent addition of several drops of a 0.2% solution of iodine in glacial acetic acid develops a characteristic greenish-blue color when Grignard reagent is present.

Organo-lithium, -sodium, -calcium and -barium compounds exhibit positive color tests, whereas organo-zinc, -mercury, and -lead compounds as well as O–Mg and N–Mg bonds, are negative for the test.

Gilman's rule :   This is an empirical rule giving relative reactivities of organo-metallic compounds.   The addition reaction of organometallic compound to carbonyl bond is used as a criterion.

For nontransition element the reactivity increases with atomic weight of the metal; $Li-R < Na-R < K-R < Rb-R < Cs-R$.   For transition element the order is reversed; $Cu-R > Ag-R > Au-R$.   For element in the same group, the least reactive organometallic compound of a nontransition metal exhibits higher reactivity than the most reactive one of a transition metal; $Li-R > Cu-R$.   In the same period the reactivity decreases with increasing atomic number; $Li-R > Be-R > B-R$.   The decrease in reactivity with one increased group number exceeds the increase in reactivity with one increased period number: $Li-R > Mg-R$.

Glove Box :   A glove box is an airtight box similar to a dry box.   It is equipped with a air-filter and is suitable, for example, for handlings medicines in clean air, radiochemical operations and so on.   The name is often used synonymously with "dry box"

Grignard reagent :   In 1899 Barbier discovered that the reaction of ketones with alkyl halides in the presence of magnesium followed by hydrolysis gave alcohols.

$$RCOCH_3 + CH_3I + Mg \longrightarrow RC(OH)(CH_3)_2$$

Shortly after, Victor Grignard found that alkylmagnesium halides can be prepared separately in ether.

$$CH_3I + Mg \longrightarrow CH_3MgI$$
$$CH_3MgI + R_2CO \longrightarrow R_2C(CH_3)(OMgI)$$
$$R_2C(CH_3)(OMgI) + H_2O \longrightarrow R_2C(CH_3)OH + \frac{1}{2}MgI_2 + \frac{1}{2}Mg(OH)_2$$

The organomagnesium halides, or Grignard reagents, react with ketones to give alcohols after hydrolysis.

There have been numerous applications of Grignard reagents to organic synthesis as well as studies on structures and reaction mechanisms (See Chapter 2).

Victor Grignard received a Nobel Prize in 1912 for his contributions.

Hydroboration :   This is a process in preparative chemistry which was studied and developed by H. C. Brown from 1955 to 1960.   The name is given to the reaction which produces an organoboron compound by adding olefin or acetylene to diborane.

$$RCH=CH_2 + H-B\big\langle \longrightarrow RCH_2CH_2B\big\langle$$

As the diborane source, the immediate product of the reaction $NaBH_4 + BF_3O(C_2H_5)_2$ is used, and addition to the multiply bonded compound is carried out at or below room temperature, using THF or diglyme as solvent. $H-B\big\langle$ adds to double bonds as cis mode from the direction of least steric hindrance, and the direction of addition is characterized as anti-Markownikoff.   This tendency is increased for the dialkylborane R_2BH (for example, $R=(CH_3)_2CHCH(CH)_3-$) having a bulky substituted group.   The intermediate organoboron is usually used directly in the further reaction without separation.   The reaction has many variations, one of which is the oxidation of the adduct with a basic solution of hydrogen peroxide, to produce the corresponding alcohol, and one is the preparation of α-olefin from inner olefin, which is obtained by a series of the isomerizations by heat and replacement.

Hydroformylation :   This reaction consists of the treatment of olefins with hydrogen and carbon monoxide in the presence of cobalt catalyst to produce aldehydes.   The reaction is often called the oxo process.   Cobalt carbonyl is known to be the actual catalyst, but in commercial practice, various cobalt salts (for example, cobalt soaps such as cobalt stearate and naphthenate) are used as catalyst precursors.   Conditions for hydroformylation normally include temperatures from $110°$ to $160°$ and pressures of 200 to 300 atm. of synthesis gas.   The aldehydes obtained by this reaction are hydrogenated to primary alcohols.   Therefore, hydroformylation is a valuable synthetic method for C_8^-, C_9^-, C_{10}^-, C_{13}-alcohols from C_7^-, C_8^-, C_9^-, and C_{12}-olefins for industrial purposes.

Ligand :   The term ligand refers to any ion or molecule which is directly attached to a metal ion and bonded to it.   The ligands can be classified as follows:
  (a) Monoatomic and polyatomic anions
  (b) Neutral polar molecules
  (c) Unsaturated hydrocarbons and their radicals
  (d) Chelating agents
The most common types of ligands are (a) and (b), and the latter almost always have one or more pairs of unshared electrons, for example, H_2O, NH_3, and CO.
In comparison type (c) is more unusual, and includes olefins, acetylene, benzene,

and the cyclopentadienyl radical.   The ligands of type (d) have two or more functional groups so arranged that they can simultaneously occupy positions in the first coordination sphere of the same metal ion.   Familiar examples are ethylenediamine, $NH_2CH_2CH_2NH_2$, and acetylacetonate ion. $(CH_3COCHCOCH_3)^-$, which are bidentate ligands, and ethylenediaminetetraacetate ion $(^-O_2CCH_2)_2NCH_2\text{-}CH_2N(CH_2CO_2^-)_2$, which can probably occupy six coordination positions in an octahedral complex.

Ligand field theory :   When a transition metal ion is surrounded by six negative ions or dipolar molecules so arranged that the negative ends of their dipoles are pointed towards the central ion (I), the five d orbitals no longar have the same energy but are split into two groups, an upper doublet (e_g or d_γ) and a lower triplet (t_{2g} or d_ε).   This splitting is due to the tendency of the electrons of the metal to avoid those regions where the field due to the ligand is greatest.   The e_g orbitals, $d_{x^2-y^2}$ and d_{z^2}, are directed towards the ions and as a result are destabilized, and the t_{2g} orbitals, d_{xy}, d_{xz} and d_{yz}, point along the bisectors of the angle between the bond directions and therefore stabilized (II).   The magnitude of the splitting between the t_{2g} and the e_g orbitals is symbolized Δ or $10Dq$.

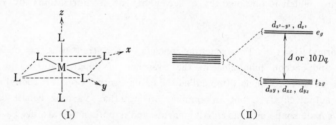

(I)   (II)

The splitting of the d orbitals in complex compounds is also derived from the molecular orbital theory, by which the t_{2g} orbitals are unaffected by σ bonding while the e_g orbitals combine with ligand orbitals to give a doubly degenerate bonding orbital (e_g) and a doubly degenerate antibonding orbital e_g^* (III).

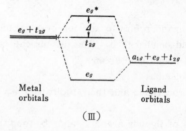

(III)

Provided that the ligand orbitals are more stable than the metal orbitals, the e_g orbital is mainly a ligand orbital and the e_g^* orbital mainly a metal orbital.

Thus a σ bond between the metal and the ligands can cause the splitting of the d orbitals.

Ligands such as phosphines and arsines have empty d_π orbitals, which are stable enough to take part in bonding although they are not stable enough to be occupied. In a regular octahedral complex, the ligand d_π orbitals can interact with the t_{2g} orbitals to increase Δ values by double bonding. On the contrary, when the ligand d_π orbitals are stable and occupied, for example in F^- and H_2O, the t_{2g} orbitals are raised in energy by the interaction. This lead to a decrease in Δ.

Thus the total splitting of the d orbitals in a complex is thought of as the algebraic sum of a number of individual contributions due to electrostatic effects, σ and π bondings, and so forth. Thus the term ligand field theory may be given for a electrostatic crystal field theory which takes into account the covalent character derived from the molecular orbital theory, or a molecular orbital theory in which all important electrostatic interactions are treated in detail.

References: L. E. Orgel, "An Introduction to Transition Metal Chemistry: Ligand Field Theory", 2nd Ed., Methuen (1966); C. J. Ballhausen, "Introduction to Ligand Field Theory", McGraw Hill (1962).

Markownikoff's rule :   This rule governs the direction of hydrogen halide addition to olefin. When hydrogen halide HX adds to an unsymmetrical olefin, halogen generally adds to the carbon having the fewer hydrogen atoms.

$$\overset{\delta+}{H}-\overset{\delta-}{X} + CH_3-CH=CH_2 \longrightarrow CH_3-\underset{\underset{X}{|}}{CH}-CH_3$$

The rule was formulated for hydrogen halide, but it has also been established for mercaptane $(X=-SR)$, alcohol $(X=-OR)$, and other compounds. At high temperature, the rule does not hold because of isomerization. The mechanism is explained by the ion reaction in the direction of polarization of HX, and the reaction directs to stabilization of the carbonium cation intermediate. But for the most metallic hydride $(\overset{\delta+}{M}-\overset{\delta-}{H})$, the direction of polarization is reverse to that in hydrogen halide, and therefore the anti-Markownikoff rule applies.

Mercuration :   There is no strict definition for this term, but mercuration generally means the introduction of mercury into organic compounds. This term is used most frequently for the formation of aromatic mercury compounds by the reaction of mercuric salts (usually acetate) with aromatic substances. Aromatic mercuration is an electrophilic substitution and a number of papers on the mechanism and orientation have been published. Active methylenes can also be mercurated.

Olefins react with mercuric salts in the solvent ROH (R=H, alkyl or acyl):

$$-\overset{|}{C}=\overset{|}{C}- + HgZ_2 + ROH \longrightarrow -\overset{|}{\underset{OR}{C}}-\overset{|}{\underset{HgZ}{C}}- + HZ$$

This reaction is called oxymercuration.

Metalation :   Metalation is the substitution of a metal for a hydrogen on a carbon atom in an organic molecule.   Common metalating agents are (1) free metals, (2) organometallic compounds, and (3) metal salts. Organic compounds with active methyl, methylene, or methine group are easily metalated.

(1) $RH + M \longrightarrow RM + \frac{1}{2}H_2$.

Example : alkali metal with acetylene, cyclopentadiene, or triphenylmethane.

(2)   Example : 9-fluorenyllithium from fluorene and butyllithium.

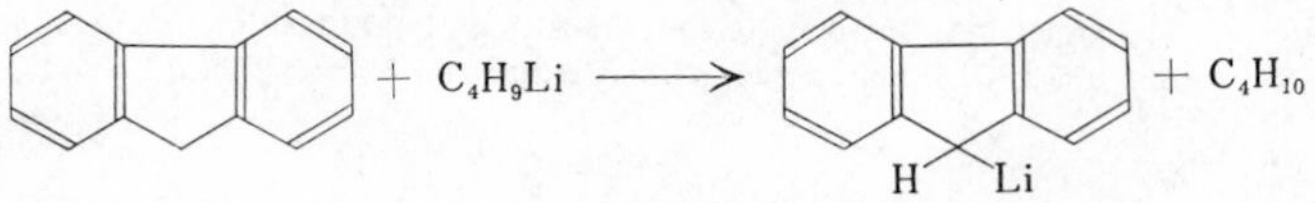

(3)   Aromatic hydrocarbons with metal halide of strong electron acceptability.

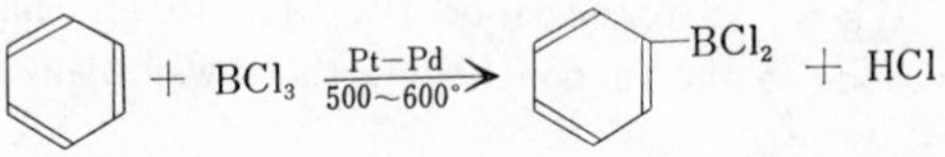

Metal carbonyl :   Compounds of metal having carbon monoxide as a ligand are called metal carbonyls.   Since the discovery of the metal carbonyls $Ni(CO)_4$ and $Fe(CO)_5$ by Mond in 1890, many other metal carbonyls have been prepared. Typical examples in the first transition series are $V(CO)_6$, $Cr(CO)_6$, $Mn_2(CO)_{10}$, $Fe(CO)_5$, $Co_2(CO)_8$, $Ni(CO)_4$, but many other metal carbonyls containing halogen, phosphine, amine, hydrogen, aromatic compounds, and unsaturated compounds other than carbon monoxide, have also been known. Metal carbonyls of iron, cobalt, and nickel are frequently used as catalysts for reactions using carbon monoxide, olefins, and acetylenes as reactant.

Metal hydride :   A metal hydride is a compound with a metal–hydrogen bond. Highly electropositive metals form salt-like hydrides, whereas for less electro-positive metals, a metal–hydrogen bond exhibits covalent nature.   For example, an alkali metal hydride is a typically ionic compound, NaH forming NaCl-type crystals. Silane, SiH_4, on the other hand, is gaseous at ordinary temperatures. Metal hydrides of transition metals are interstitial compounds and resemble metal in appearance as well as in properties. Metal hydride generally behave similarly to metal alkyls. Metal hydrides, especially complex hydrides such as $LiAlH_4$, are powerful and selective reducing agents.

Metallocene :   The term "metallocene" is generally given to those bis-cyclopenta-dienyl metal complexes in which the bonding is recognized as π-bonding, and in which some degree of aromatic character may be expected.   Among the first-row transition metals, $(\pi\text{-}C_5H_5)_2Ti$, $(\pi\text{-}C_5H_5)_2V$, $(\pi\text{-}C_5H_5)_2Cr$, $(\pi\text{-}C_5H_5)_2Fe$, $(\pi\text{-}C_5H_5)_2Co$, and $(\pi\text{-}C_5H_5)_2Ni$ are metallocenes. Ferrocene, $(\pi\text{-}C_5H_5)_2Fe$, is representative and has been most thoroughly investigated.   Among the cyclopentadienyl derivatives of transition metals, there are some ionic compounds which differ from ferrocene and are similar to $C_5H_5^-Na^+$ or $(C_5H_5^-)_2Mg^{2+}$.   Thus, $(C_5H_5)_2Mn$ is an ionic com-pound although it has a sandwich structure, and is more properly called manganese cyclopentadienide.

Meyer reaction :   This is a reaction between an alkali metal arsenite and an alkylating agent in an aqueous or alcoholic solution which produces an alkylarsonic acid (discovered in 1883 by V. Meyer).

$$\begin{array}{l} NaO \\ NaO \!\!\!\!\!\!\!\! \rightarrow As: \\ NaO \end{array} + R-X \longrightarrow \begin{array}{l} NaO \\ \!\!\!\!\!\!\!\! >As-R + NaX \\ NaO \quad \| \\ O \end{array}$$

In this equation RX may be halo derivatives of various organic compounds such as aliphatic saturated hydrocarbons, aliphatic carboxylic acids and their deriva-tives, as well as alcohols, ketones, sulfides and esters.   Aromatic halides in general do not undergo this reaction; however, in a few cases, the expected products may be obtained in low yield under rather drastic conditions.

Mössbauer effect :   This Mössbauer effect is the γ-ray resonance absorption spectrum found by the German physist Mössbauer.   The application of this type of spectroscopy has spread widely to many scientific fields.   In the application of this spectroscopy to chemistry, the electron density and the distortion of the electric field around the metal are detected.   The atoms used in this type of spectro-scopy are mainly tin and iron.   The interaction energy between nucleus and electrons (particularly s electrons) in energy absorbing compounds is, in general, somewhat different from that in energy emitters, if the chemical constitutions and the oxidation states of the absorbers are different from those of the emitter. This energy difference, usually expressed as the relative velocity of the absorber to the emitter, is called isomer shift. Isomer shift is a measure of the s electron density.   If the metal nucleus has a nucler spin $I \geqq 1$ (in excited state both ^{57}Fe and ^{119}Sn have $I=3/2$), the distortion of the electric field around the metal nucleus is detected as quadrapole splitting.   Therefore, the appearance of quadra-pole splitting indicates that the molecule has no cubic symmetry.

Natta catalyst :   Natta catalyst is an improvement over Ziegler catalyst. The improvement minimizes the formation of amorphous atactic polypropylene which accompanies crystalline isotactic polypropylene in the polymerization of propylene. It is a feature of this catalyst that it uses transition elements of low valency.   It is formed by the combination of titanium trichloride and triethylaluminum. Titanium trichloride is an ionic crystalline substance which is insoluble in hydrocarbon solvents, and shows no change in appearence on mixing with triethylaluminum. Propylene polymerizes on the surface of titanium trichloride crystals. The catalyst is effective not only for propylene, but also for α-olefins and usually gives polymers of higher tacticity than Ziegler catalyst.

Nesmeyanov reaction :   This is decomposition of a double salt of an aryldiazonium halide with a metal halide by treatment with a pulverized metal to produce an aromatic organometallic compound, as indicated by the general equation

$$(ArN_2X)_m \cdot MX_n + M' \longrightarrow Ar_mMX_{n-m} + M'X_p + m\,N_2$$

where M stands for a metal to be arylated and M' for a metal (reducing agent) having valence p. This type of reaction was first observed in 1929 by A. N. Nesmeyanov for arylmercuric compounds :

$$ArN_2Cl \cdot HgCl_2 + Cu \longrightarrow ArHgCl + CuCl_2 + N_2$$

Since then it has been extended to synthesis of arylmetallic compounds of Sn, Pb, Tl, Bi, As, Sb, Se and so on. Ketones and esters are used most conveniently as solvents.

Olefin complexes :   These are defined as π-complexes in which various olefinic compounds coordinate to metal atoms by the π-electrons of the C=C double bond. Zeise's salt, $K[(CH_2{=}CH_2)PtCl_3]$ (1827), is a typical example. Despite its early discovery, much of the progress in this field has been achieved since 1950. Recently, many other olefin complexes of low valent transition metal having suitable ligands, such as phosphines or CO, have been prepared. Ethylene complex $(Ph_3P)_2Ni(C_2H_4)$, butadiene complex $(OC)_4Fe(C_4H_6)$, acrylonitrile complex $Ni(CH_2{=}CHCN)_2$, and maleic acid ester complex $(OC)_4Fe(ROOCCH{=}CHCOOR)$ are some examples of these complexes.

Onium compound :   This is coordination compound formed from a compound containing an element with a lone pair (for example, oxygen, sulfur or nitrogen), and a proton or other cationic reagent.

Example : $:NH_3 + H^+Cl^- \longrightarrow [NH_4]^+Cl^-$
                              Ammonium compound

$[R_2OR']^+X^-$: Oxonium compound ; $[R_3PR']^+X^-$: Phosphonium compound ; $[R_2SR']^+X^-$: Sulfonium compound.

Oxonium compound :   An oxonium compound is an onium compound in which oxygen is the coordinating atom. It is therefore, a compound of $[R_2OR']^+X^-$ type.

Example : $CH_3-\overset{..}{\underset{..}{O}}-CH_3 + HCl \longrightarrow [CH_3-\overset{..}{\underset{|}{O}}-CH_3]^+Cl^-$
$$\phantom{CH_3-\overset{..}{\underset{..}{O}}-CH_3 + HCl \longrightarrow [CH_3-\overset{..}{\underset{|}{O}}-}}H$$

Methyl ether hydrochloride is formed by coordination of a lone pair on ether oxygen to acid proton, the resultant trivalent oxygen cation being ionically bonded to the acid anion. Aldehydes, ketones, and esters also form oxonium compounds. Lewis acid may take part instead of protonic acids.

Example : $C_6H_5-\underset{\underset{Cl}{|}}{C}=\overset{..}{\underset{..}{O}} + AlCl_3 \longrightarrow C_6H_5-\underset{\underset{Cl}{|}}{C}=\overset{+}{O} \longrightarrow \overset{-}{A}lCl_3$

Oxo process (oxo reaction, oxo synthesis):   During the studies on Fischer-Tropsch hydrocarbon synthesis in 1938, O. Roelen discovered the oxo process, in which olefins react with hydrogen and carbon monoxide in the presence of cobalt catalyst to yield oxygenated products. (See *Hydroformylation*)

Paramagnetism (See also *Diamagnetism*) :   The atoms or molecules of a paramagnetic substance have permanent magnetic moments and tend therefore to become oriented in an applied field. As a result, paramagnetic substances increase the magnetic flux due to the applied field. Even in a paramagnetic substance the induced polarity which exists in a diamagnetic substances will still be operative. Although the two effects are opposed in the paramagnetic substances, the magnitude of the diamagnetic effect is small compared to the paramagnetic one, leading to a positive value for the susceptibility. The paramagnetic susceptibility is dependent on the temperature, because the orientation of the permanent dipoles in an applied field is opposed by thermal motion. The temperature dependency is expressed by Curie's law, or more exactly by Curie–Weiss's law.

An electron in an orbital, or spinning about an axis, is equivalent to a magnet with a moment $\mu_e = he/4\pi mc$. The atoms, ions, or molecules containing incomplete electron shells with unpaired electrons are paramagnetic, and the magnetic moment is expressed as a multiple of the unit μ_e. This unit is known as the Bohr magneton.

Apart from free radicals there are three main groups of paramagnetic atoms or molecules :

(1) Molecules containing first period elements with unpaired p electron (NO and O_2),

(2) transition elements with unpaired d electrons, and

(3) lanthanides and actinides, with unpaired f electrons.

For ions of the transition elements, the magnetic moment μ (in Bohr magneton) is expressed by $\sqrt{4S(S+1)+L(L+1)}$, where S is the resultant spin and L the resultant angular momentum. The contribution of orbital angular momentum is, however, negligible in the elements of (2). As a result, the magnetic moments are approximately given by the expression $\mu=2\sqrt{S(S+1)}$. For the rare earth elements the magnetic moment cannot be expressed by considering only the resultant spin, because the $4f$ electrons are screened by the $5s$ and $5p$ shells. It is therefore necessary to take into account the orbital angular momentum.

Certain paramagnetic substances exhibit, below a certain critical temperature characteristic of the substance, a type of magnetism called ferromagnetism, of which the susceptibility is very large compared with paramagnetic substances. Ferromagnetism arises from the parallel alignment of the spins of atomic magnets, and can exist in the absence of an external field.

π-Allyl metal complexes : Allyl halogenide reacts with $NaCo(CO)_4$ to afford stable yellow complexes identified as π-allyl complexes instead of σ-allyl compounds (Eq. 1).

$$CH_2=CHCH_2Cl + NaCo(CO)_4 \longrightarrow (CH_2=CH=CH_2)Co(CO)_3 \qquad (1)$$

The term "π-allyl complex" is generally given to those π-complexes on which a delocalized planar allyl radical coordinates to a metal atom as the contributer of three electrons (Eq. 2). A number of compounds containing this type of bonding have been prepared. For example, bis-π-allyl nickel, $(\pi$-$C_3H_5)_2Ni$, has been shown to be a sandwich compound. Tris-π-allyl metal compounds such as $(\pi$-$C_3H_5)_3Co$ are also known. According to the suggestion by Wilke, an intermediate in the trimerization of butadiene to cyclododecatriene with nickel complex catalysts might be a bis-π-allyl complex (Eq. 3).

(2)　　　　　　　　　(3)

π-Complex : Compounds containing unsaturated organic species bonded to metal with their π-type molecular orbital are called π-complexes. $[(CH_2=CH_2)PtCl_3]^-$, $(CH_2=CH-CH=CH_2)Fe(CO)_3$, $(C_6H_6)_2Cr$, and $(\pi$-$C_5H_5)_2Fe$ are some examples of π-complexes.

Radical ion (ion radical) : This is a free radical with an electric charge. An example is formation of naphthalene anion radical by the reaction of naphthalene with sodium in tetrahydrofuran:

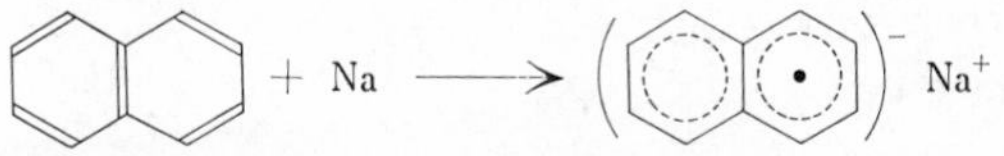

An electron is transferred from sodium to naphthalene, forming naphthalene anion with a delocalized unpaired electron. The ion then shows paramagnetic resonance absorption. The deep green solution exhibits electroconductivity. Aminium salt $[R_3N\cdot]^+ClO_4^-$ is an example of a radical cation.

Redistribution :   This is a chemical reaction in which two or more substituents exchange sites with each other on one or more kinds of polyfunctional central atoms or moieties. The exchange eventually reaches an equilibrium state. Reactions of this type have variously been described in the literature as redistribution, exchange, interchange, scrambling reactions, and also disproportionations, comproportionations, symmetrizations, dissymmetrizations, etc.   In certain cases, the sorting of substituents about the central atom follows the laws of "random" statistics, while in other cases "nonrandom" equilibrated mixtures are produced. For example:

Random:

$$(C_2H_5)_4Si + (C_3H_7)_4Si \overset{AlCl_3}{\rightleftharpoons}$$
$$(C_2H_5)_3Si(C_3H_7) + (C_2H_5)_2Si(C_3H_7)_2 + (C_2H_5)Si(C_3H_7)_3$$

Nonrandom:

$$2\,(CH_3)_3SiCl \overset{AlCl_3}{\rightleftharpoons} (CH_3)_2SiCl_2 + (CH_3)_4Si$$

For pertinent references, see K. Moedritzer, *Organometal. Chem. Revs.*, 1, 179 (1966); J. C. Lockhart, *Chem. Revs.*, **65**, 131 (1965).

Reppe reactions :   These were discovered by W. Reppe and his co-workers just before or during World War II, and relate to a number of reactions of acetylene and carbon monoxide under pressure, exemplified as follows.

(1) Vinylation:

$$HC\equiv CH + ROH \overset{KOH}{\longrightarrow} CH_2=CHOR$$

(2) Ethynylation:

$$CH_2O + HC\equiv CH \xrightarrow{Copper\ acetylide} HOCH_2C\equiv CH + HOCH_2C\equiv CCH_2OH$$

(3) Cyclization reaction:

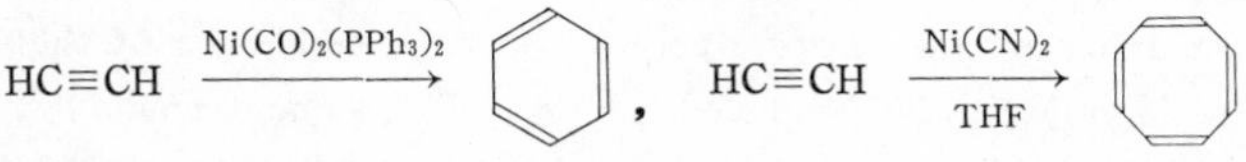

$$HC\equiv CH \xrightarrow{Ni(CO)_2(PPh_3)_2} \bigcirc \quad , \quad HC\equiv CH \xrightarrow[THF]{Ni(CN)_2} \bigcirc$$

(4) Carbonylation:

$$Ni(CO)_4 + C_2H_2 + HCl + ROH \quad \xrightarrow[\text{Ni-catalyst}]{} \quad CH_2{=}CHCOOR$$
$$C_2H_2 + CO + ROH$$

Sandwich structure :   Since 1950, a large number of transition metal complexes have been prepared which have a sandwich structure, in which a metal is located between two planar organic species such as cyclopentadienyl ring or benzene. Ferrocene (1) and dibenzenechromium (2) are representatives of sandwich compounds. Di-π-allylnickel (3) is also confirmed to have a sandwich structure.

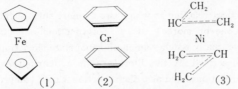

Fe (1)   Cr (2)   Ni (3)

Schlenk tube :   This is a glass vessel, devised by W. Schlenk for the reaction and preservation of air-sensitive organometallics. A Schlenk tube has two side tubes, as shown in the Figure, in order to facilitate the connection to inert gas. When an organometallic compound is preserved or a reaction is carried out for a long time, the side tubes are sealed off as shown in the Figure.

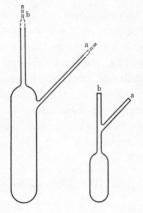

Semipolar bond :   See *Dative bond.*

Silicone :   This name was first proposed by Wohler in 1851, but was often used by Kipping for the description of organosilicon compounds having the experimental formula R_2SiO which were similar to that of the ketone R_2CO. Soon after that time, it was found that the compound having the experimental formula R_2SiO actually corresponded to the polymer consisting of a siloxane (SiOSi) chain, but the term "silicone" has remained in use for the polymer. This is still the popular commercial name for organopolysiloxane. It seems suitable to limit the word to the high molecular weight materials, but actually hexamethyldisiloxane, $Me_3SiO\text{-}SiMe_3$, is also called by this name.

σ bond, π bond and δ bond :   In diatomic molecules, the wave functions with angular momentum, around the axis connecting the two atoms, $|\Lambda|=0,1$, and 2 are called σ, π and δ orbitals, respectively. The bond consisting of the electrons in the σ orbital is called the σ bond and so on. The same terminology is used by extention for nonliner polyatomic molecules. For example, the C–H bonds in ethylene are made of σ bonds and the C=C double bond is made of a σ and the π bond. In ferrocene, the bond made of $d_{\pm 2}$ orbitals in iron and $e_{2g}^{\pm}$ group orbitals constructed from two cyclopentadienyl groups is a δ bond.

Trans effect :   This was proposed by Chernyaev (1926) in order to elucidate ligand replacement reactions in square planar complexes of Pt(II) and Pd(II). The effect refers to the ability by which ligands labilize the group trans to them. An example is the preparation of the isomeric dichlorodiamminoplatinum complexes (Eq. 1 and 2). Since Cl has a stronger trans effect than NH_3, the substi-

$$\underset{Cl}{\overset{Cl}{>}}Pt\underset{Cl}{\overset{Cl}{<}}{}^{2-} \xrightarrow{NH_3} \underset{Cl}{\overset{Cl}{>}}Pt\underset{Cl}{\overset{NH_3}{<}}{}^{-} \xrightarrow{NH_3} \underset{Cl}{\overset{Cl}{>}}Pt\underset{NH_3}{\overset{NH_3}{<}} \tag{1}$$

$$\underset{NH_3}{\overset{NH_3}{>}}Pt\underset{NH_3}{\overset{NH_3}{<}}{}^{2+} \xrightarrow{Cl^-} \underset{NH_3}{\overset{NH_3}{>}}Pt\underset{Cl}{\overset{NH_3}{<}}{}^{+} \xrightarrow{Cl^-} \underset{NH_3}{\overset{Cl}{>}}Pt\underset{Cl}{\overset{NH_3}{<}} \tag{2}$$

tution mostly occurs at the trans position to Cl. The trans effects of a variety of ligand increase in the order : $H_2O <OH^- <NH_3 <RNH_2 <$ pyridine $<Cl^- <Br^-$ $<SCN^-$, I^-, NO_2^-, SO_3H^-, $PR_3 <R_2S$, $SC(NH_2)_2 <NO$, CO, C_2H_4, CN^-. This order is similar to the order of acceptor ability in back-donation from filled metal π-orbital to vacant ligand π-orbital. This effect is now used to prepare Pt(II) square complexes or to predict their kinetic behavior.

Transmetalation :   Transmetalation is the reaction of an organometallic compound, RM, with another metal, M' to form an organometallic compound, RM'.

$$RM + M' \;\rightleftharpoons\; RM' + M$$

It is an important synthetic method for isolating pure organometallic compounds. An example is the preparation of pure dialkylmagnesium from dialkylmercury and magnesium, without any contamination by halogen or ether, and differently from the Grignard method. The reaction proceeds to the formation of an organometallic compound with higher reactivity from an organometallic compound with lower reactivity.

Three center bond :   Atomic orbitals can overlap, leading to bond formation, in various ways. The simplest one is that the maximum overlapping occurs along the line joining the atoms; this is normal σ bond. In addition to the formation of a σ bond there may be p orbitals which can overlap to form a π bond. The third possibility is the overlap of an orbital of one atom with orbitals of two or more atoms, forming a multicentre bond (I). This type of bond is not as common, but it occurs in many organometallic compounds; in diborane a $1s$ atomic orbital of a bridged hydrogen atom can overlap with sp^3 hybrid orbitals of the two boron atoms (II), where two electrons, one from a hydrogen atom and the other from either boron atom, can be used for each B-H-B linkage. This case is defined as a three-center, two-electron bond. This type of bond occurs in the higher boranes, in ethylene complexes of certain metals, and in some metal alkyls such as

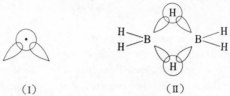

(I)   (II)

$[Al(CH_3)_3]_2$, $[Be(CH_3)_2]_n$, $[In(CH_3)_3]_4$, and $[Pt(CH_3)_3Cl]_4$. They are often called electron-deficient molecules, because they have not enough electrons to make electron-pair bonds.

Wacker–Höchst process :   This is an industrial process for the manufacture of acetaldehyde by direct oxidation of ethylene.   It was developed under the cooperation of Wacker Chemie and Farbwerke Höchst AG, and was put into operation in 1958 in Germany.   In an aqueous solution of cupric chloride and palladium chloride, ethylene is oxidized by oxygen at about 100°C (one step method).   Cupric chloride acts as an oxidizing agent to regenerate palladium chloride for palladium, which is formed as the result of the oxidation of ethylene.   There is also a two-step method, in which ethylene is oxidized by an aqueous mixture of palladium chloride and cupric chloride, and then the oxidizing mixture is regenerated by air. A π-complex of ethylene and palladium chloride is considered to play an important role.

Wittig reaction :   The Wittig reaction is a process leading to the formation of compounds with a carbon–carbon double bond by treatment of an alkylidenetri-phenylphosphorane with an aldehyde or a ketone.   For example, if a methylene-triphenylphosphorane (1) is allowed to react with acetone, a dipolar compound (2) is formed, which is then decomposed, via the cyclic transition state (3), to an olefin and phosphine oxide.

$$(C_6H_5)_3P{=}CRR' + (CH_3)_2CO \longrightarrow (C_6H_5)_3P^+CRR'C(CH_3)_2$$
$$(1) \hspace{6em} (2) \quad \overset{|}{O^-}$$

$$(C_6H_5)_3\overset{+}{P}{-}CRR'$$
$$\overset{\diagdown\ \ \diagup|}{O{-}C(CH_3)_2} \longrightarrow CRR'{=}C(CH_3)_2 + (C_6H_5)_3PO$$
$$(3)$$

The Wittig reaction is stereospecific as far as the asymmetric phosphorus is concerned, because the optically active phosphonium salt (4), the precursor of benzylidenetriphenylphosphorane (5), gives the optically active phosphine oxide (6) with retention of configuration under sequential reaction with phenyllithium and benzaldehyde.

$$
\begin{array}{c}
\underset{\displaystyle CH_2C_6H_5}{\overset{\displaystyle C_6H_5}{CH_3-\overset{|}{\underset{|}{P^+}}-C_6H_5}} \xrightarrow{C_6H_5Li} \underset{\displaystyle CHC_6H_5}{\overset{\displaystyle C_2H_5}{CH_3-\overset{|}{\underset{\|}{P}}-C_6H_5}} \xrightarrow{C_6H_5CHO}
\end{array}
$$

$$
\underset{(4)}{} \qquad \underset{(5)}{}
$$

$$
C_6H_5CH=CHC_6H_5 + \underset{\displaystyle O}{\overset{\displaystyle C_2H_5}{CH_3-\overset{|}{\underset{\|}{P}}-C_6H_5}}
$$

$$
\text{\textit{cis} and \textit{trans}} \qquad (6)
$$

Wurtz–Fittig reaction :   This consists of the following; formation of hydrocarbon from alkyl halide and sodium (Wurtz reaction); introduction of alkyl group into the aryl compound by the action of sodium on aryl halide and alkyl halide (Fittig reaction):

$$
R'X + RX + 2\,Na \longrightarrow RR' + 2\,NaX
$$

The reaction is considered to proceed by an ionic mechanism through an organosodium compound RNa(R'Na) as intermediate.

Ylide and ylene :   A dipolar ion in which a positively charged onium atom (N, P, As, S, etc.) is bonded covalently to a negatively charged carbon atom.   Treatment of a quaternary ammonium or phosphonium salt with an organolithium reagent gives an ylide with the general formula (1).

$$
[(CH_3)_4M]^+Br^- + RLi \longrightarrow (CH_3)_3\overset{+}{M}-\overset{..}{\overset{-}{C}H_2} + RH + LiBr
$$

$$
(1)
$$

This ylide reacts with a ketone to give a compound called "betain" (2).

$$
(CH_3)_3\overset{+}{M}-\overset{-}{C}H + (C_6H_5)_2CO \longrightarrow (CH_3)_3\overset{+}{M}-CH_2-\underset{\displaystyle O^-}{\overset{|}{C}(C_6H_5)_2}
$$

$$
M=N, P, As \qquad\qquad (2)
$$

In the ammonium ylide the ammonium group is capable of stabilizing the adjacent carbanion only by an electrostatic interaction between opposite charges.   In contrast, phosphonium as well as arsonium ylides may use their vacant d-orbitals to exist as the resonance hybrid as follows.

$$
\overset{+}{M}-\overset{..}{\overset{-}{C}} \longrightarrow M=C
$$

$$
(1) \qquad\qquad (3)
$$

The latter structure (3) is called an ylene.   One of the best known reactions of phosphonium ylides is the Wittig reaction.

Zerewitinoff apparatus :   Active organometallics react with compounds having active hydrogen according to the following equations to yield hydrocarbon gases or hydrogen.

$$R\text{-Metal} + R'OH \longrightarrow RH + \text{Metal-}OR'$$
$$H\text{-Metal} + R'OH \longrightarrow H_2 + \text{Metal-}OR'$$

A Zerewitinoff apparatus is a device to measure quantitatively the evolved gas.

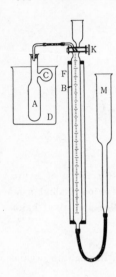

Zerewitinoff originally used his apparatus for the determination of active hydrogen of organic compounds by measuring the evolved methane from the reaction with methylmagnesium iodide. The method can inversely be used for the determination of active metal–alkyl bonds (alkyl must be lower aliphatic or hydrogen). Organometallics include compounds of groups I and II and some of group III in the periodic table. The apparatus consists of a reaction flask and a gas burette. The figure shows the original one used by Zerewitinoff. A: reaction flask, B: gas burette, C: methylmagnesium iodide solution, D, F: water jacket, K: stopcock, M: mercury well.

Ziegler catalyst: The catalyst was discovered by K. Ziegler in 1955 as a polymerization catalyst of ethylene. It consists of a transition metal of groups IV to VIII of the periodic table and an organometallic compound of groups I to III. A typical combination is $TiCl_4$–$AlEt_2Cl$. Polymerization goes smoothly at normal temperature and pressure to yield high molecular weight polyethylene. The polymer has a low degree of branching as compared with the so-called high pressure polyethylene (ICI process). The process is called the "low pressure process" as contrasted to the high pressure process. When titanium tetrachloride is mixed with diethylaluminum chloride in a inert hydrocarbon solvent, the former is alkylated by the latter, and then the decomposition of titanium-alkyl bonds leads to the formation of low valent titanium, resulting in the formation of a brown precipitate. The precipitate is a complexed substance containing titanium, aluminum, chlorine, ethyl group and so on in varying ratios. Polymerization is considered to be carried out on the surface of the complex through an ionic mechanism.

Besides ethylene, many α–olefins are polymerized by Ziegler catalyst to stereoregular polymers. The catalyst is generally ineffective for the stereoregular polymerization of heteroatom monomers containing heteroatoms such as O, N, S, and halogens.

Ziegler catalyst can be modified widely by changing the components or by the addition of a third component, and this type of catalyst is sometimes called a "modified Ziegler catalyst".

INDEX